W9-CHR-460

CONNECT WITH THE WORLD AROUND THEM

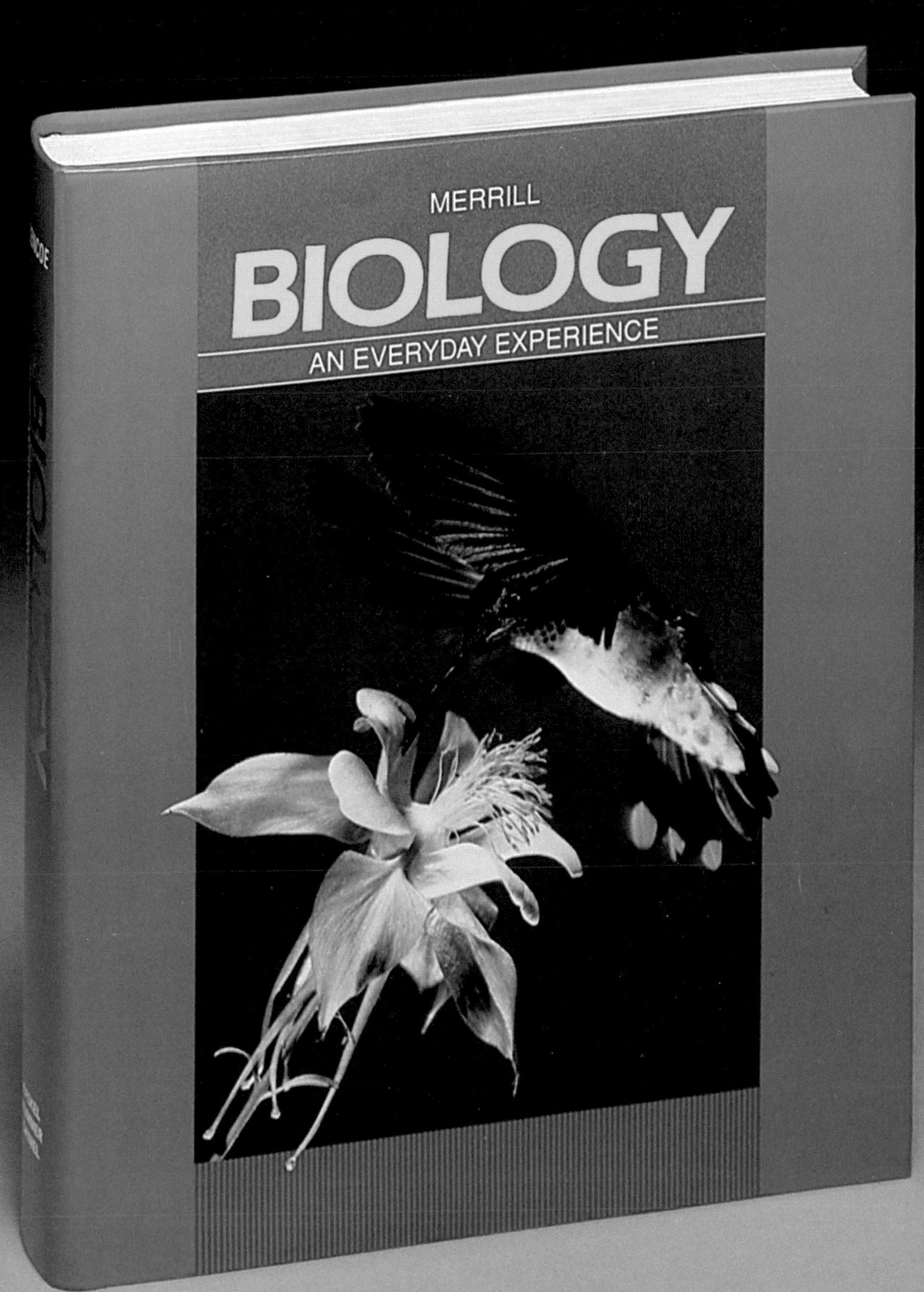

GLENCOE

Macmillan/McGraw-Hill

Biology Is Now Within Your Students' Grasp

Biology: An Everyday Experience was specifically designed to reach those students who have had little success with science in the past. It covers **all** the fundamental high school biology concepts in a format that is easy to understand and comprehend. The text continuously applies the study of biology to your students' everyday world, thereby making it real, relevant, and exciting.

A **Try This** activity at the beginning of each chapter provides the kind of concrete experience that helps students focus on the new concepts presented.

Try This!

How does a squid move? Inflate a balloon and release it. Observe the movement and direction of the balloon. Compare it with the movement of a squid.

Students are introduced to each unit and chapter through the use of photography, supported by thought-provoking scenarios. Both the unit and chapter openers help to stimulate the interest of the students and prepare them for upcoming lessons.

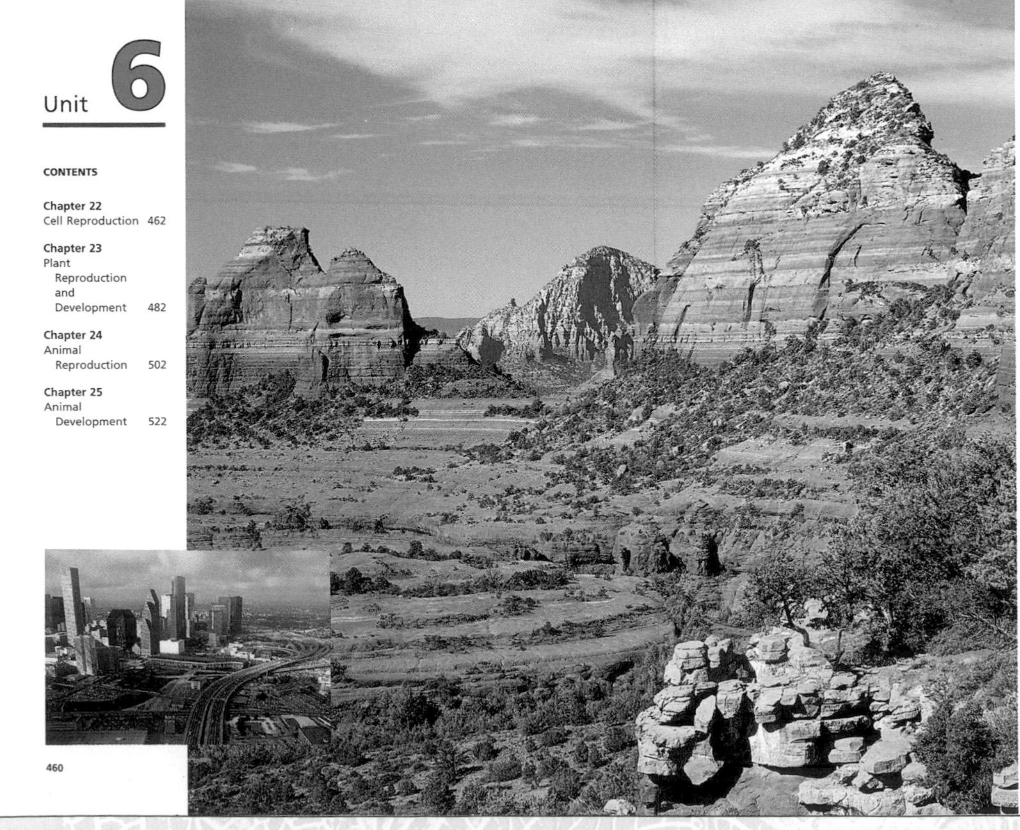

Unit 6

CONTENTS

460

Reproduction and Development

What would happen if...

the present rate of population growth continued? The population of North America would increase to about 487 000 000 by the year 2000.

If a population of 487 000 000 people were spread out evenly over all of North America, there would be about 20 people per square kilometer. But the population is not spread out evenly. Few people live in desert and mountain areas. Most people are in cities along rivers, lakes, or oceans. The population density in cities can be hundreds of people per square kilometer.

The world population was about 5 162 000 000 in 1989. At a growth rate of 1.6%, the world population would be about 6 147 000 000 in the year 2000. That's about 41 people per square kilometer. How might this many people affect life on Earth?

461

Classroom-Tested Concept Development Makes Learning Easier

Common, "everyday" analogies, supported by captivating photographs and illustrations, help to make biology concepts more understandable.

An on-target reading level and controlled vocabulary help students learn and remember important ideas about the world of living things.

An **Idea Map** promotes visual learning and makes studying easier by providing a graphic representation of the main ideas in every lesson.

1:3 Scientific Method

Much of the work of biology is to solve problems. Problems are not solved by flipping a coin or taking a guess as to the outcome. Scientists use a series of steps called a **scientific method** to solve problems. The following steps are often used: recognizing the problem, researching the problem, forming a hypothesis (hi PAHTH uh sus), testing the hypothesis, and drawing conclusions.

Objectives

7. **Explain** the steps of the scientific method.
8. **Compare** the difference between a hypothesis and a theory.
9. **Explain** how technology is used to solve everyday problems.

Key Science Words

scientific method
hypothesis
experiment
variable
control
data
theory
technology

Recognizing and Researching the Problem

Have you ever tried to turn on a light and found that it didn't work? Maybe you have turned the key in a car's ignition and the car didn't start. If you have had problems like those, you probably have used a scientific method to solve them.

A biology class raised guppies for a class project. Paula thought the guppies would have more young if the light in the aquarium was turned off part of the time. Other students thought the light should be left on all the time. But, Paula had observed that her guppies at home had more young than the ones at school. She also knew that she kept her aquarium light turned off part of the time. The class had a problem. What should they do about the aquarium light?

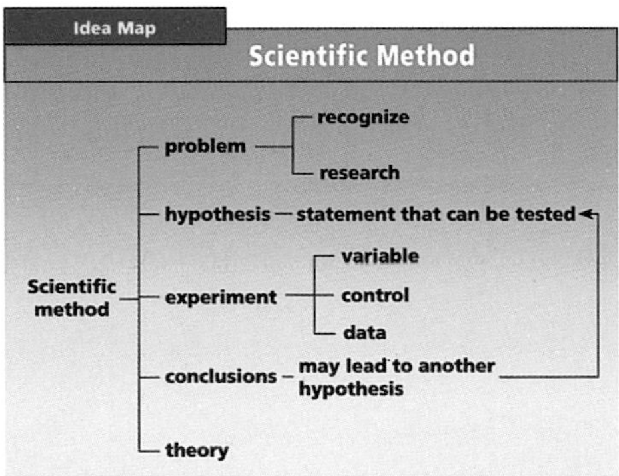

Study Tip: Use this idea map as a study guide to scientific method. Notice that a conclusion may lead to a second hypothesis. The second hypothesis then leads to more experiments and further conclusions.

1:3 Scientific Method 15

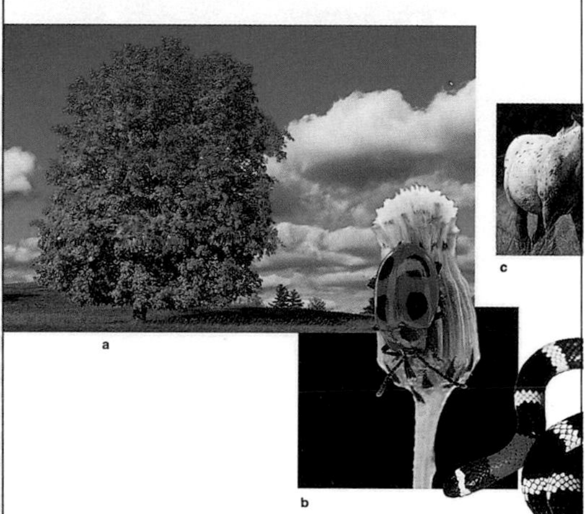

Figure 2-9 The maple tree (a), ladybug (b), horse (c), and coral snake (d) are all made of cells.

Your cells and the cells of every living thing around you are complex structures with many parts. Each part has a function that is important to the life of the cell. All of the living things in Figure 2-9 are made of cells. What other living things can you name that are made of cells?

Check Your Understanding

6. Which cell part is being described?
   (a) helps keep cytoplasm inside
   (b) controls most of the cell's activities
   (c) a liquid-filled space for storage
   (d) green parts of plants that trap energy from the sun
   (e) clear, jellylike material in which most of the cell's chemical reactions take place
7. Name two cell parts found in plant cells that are not found in animal cells.
8. Why are mitochondria called "powerhouses" of the cell?
9. **Critical Thinking:** How do mitochondria and chloroplasts differ?
10. **Biology and Writing:** Write three sentences describing the cell parts that make up a wooden table.

2:2 Cell Parts and Their Jobs 37

Check Your Understanding questions not only review concepts but encourage students to use critical thinking skills and apply reading, writing or math skills to the study of biology.

STUDENT EDITION

Hands-On Activities Motivate Students and Make the Study of Biology Fun

Students will truly enjoy learning about biology because *Biology: An Everyday Experience* offers many hands-on activities and skill exercises that captivate students' attention and keep them interested in learning.

The many labs within the textbook encourage students to make observations, analyze data, and apply what they have learned—important skills needed for the study of biology and for success in the everyday world.

Each chapter contains two full page **Labs** designed to be completed within one class period. Throughout the procedures, students are reminded of the important skills being used.

Lab 6–1 Nonvascular Plants

Problem: What are some traits of a nonvascular plant?

Skills

make and use tables, interpret data, use a microscope, measure in SI, infer

Materials

moss
light microscope
3 microscope slides
coverslip
hand lens or stereomicroscope
forceps
paper towel
metric ruler
dropper

Procedure

1. Copy the data table.
2. Place the moss plant on the paper towel and examine it with the hand lens.
3. **Measure in SI:** Find the hairlike cells that act as roots for the moss. Measure their lengths in millimeters. Complete the table.
4. Observe the stem part with the hand lens. Complete the table for this part.
5. Observe the leaf parts with the hand lens. Complete the table for these parts.
6. Use the forceps to remove one of the leaves. Make a wet mount slide and observe the cells under low power.
7. Find the chloroplasts in the cells. Determine how thick the leaf is by moving the focus up and down.

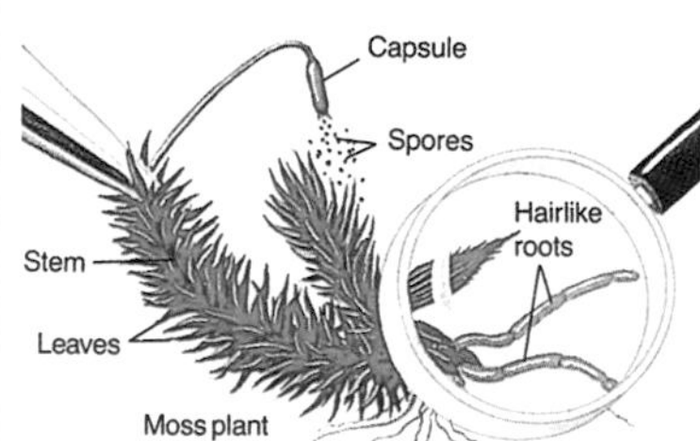

8. Find a spore capsule at the end of a brownish stalk. Observe the spore capsule with the hand lens. Complete the table.
9. Place the spore capsule on a slide. Add two drops of water. Place a second slide on top of the capsule. Press firmly down with your thumb on the top slide so that the capsule is crushed. Carefully remove the top slide. Place a coverslip over the crushed capsule.
10. Examine the released spores under low power. Draw and label the spores.

Data and Observations

1. Which parts of the moss are green?
2. What shapes are moss leaves?

PART	COLOR	SHAPE	LENGTH (mm)
Rootlike hairs			
Stem			
Leaf			
Spore case			

Analyze and Apply

1. **Infer:** How are the green parts used by a moss?
2. Describe the overall size of the plant.
3. How many cell layers are in a moss leaf?
4. **Apply:** Why do moss plants live in moist areas?

Extension

Design an experiment to find out if mosses grow better in wet or dry places.

6:2 Nonvascular Plants 119

Mini Lab

How Can You Catch a Spider Web?

Observe: Find a spider web covered with dew. Catch the web by placing a piece of black paper against it. Sprinkle some flour over the web on the paper and tap off the excess. What do you see? *For more help, refer to the **Skill Handbook,** pages 704-705.*

Mini Labs give you additional hands-on activities to help reinforce the chapter concepts. Ideal for in-class exercises or take-home activities.

Skill Development is Comprehensive and On-Going

Skill Check margin activities use the biology content from the lesson to reinforce important skills.

Skill Check

Calculate: The United States has 1/20 of the world's population, but uses 1/3 of the world's energy resources. If the population of the United States is 250 million, what is the world population? *For more help, refer to the **Skill Handbook**, pages 718-719.*

A two-page, photo-oriented **Problem Solving** feature offers a unique way for students to use critical thinking skills as they apply biology concepts.

PROBLEM SOLVING

FEATURES OF LIVING THINGS

It may be difficult to define the word *life*, but living things are often easy to recognize. You probably recognize the deer and plants as living things and the other objects as nonliving things.

Nonliving things may have some of the same features as living things. Look at photo a. How is the icicle like a living thing? What feature of life does the copier in photo b have?

In photo c you see a hot air balloon. How is it similar to a living thing? What feature of life can you identify in photo d? How is the smoke detector in photo e like a living thing? How is the solar panel in photo f like a living thing?

All of the things shown on these pages have features of living things, and yet they are different from the deer and the plants. How are the deer and the plants different from the other things?

a

b

c

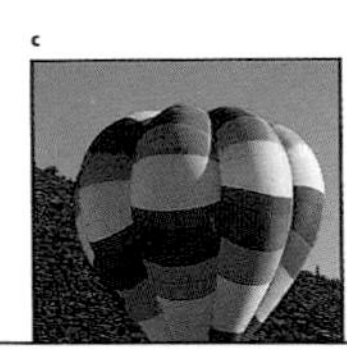

d

42

The **Skill Handbook,** at the back of the text, provides a step-by-step description and illustration of all the skills applied in the Skill Check activities and Mini Labs. The handbook saves valuable reteaching time as it allows students to master skills at their own pace.

SKILL HANDBOOK

5 Using Numbers

Two important methods of science are the comparing of information and the repeating of experiments. All scientists use the skills of measuring volume, length, and mass in SI, and calculating in order to confirm hypotheses, results, and conclusions.

e

Skill: Measuring in SI—Volume

Volume measurements are made in milliliters (mL) or liters (L). 1000 milliliters = 1 liter. The equipment used for measuring volume is a graduated cylinder.

Learning the Skill

1. Locate the units on the graduated cylinder in Figure 1.
2. To read the volume of liquid in a graduated cylinder, do the following:
   (a) Place the cylinder on a flat surface.
   (b) Make sure you read the volume of liquid at eye level.
   (c) The surface of the liquid will form a curve. Find the lowest point of the curve and read the volume.

Troubleshooting

1. Figure 1 shows a correct volume reading.
2. The reading in Figure 2 is incorrect because:
   (a) The cylinder is not on a flat surface.
   (b) The top of the liquid is not at eye level.
   (c) The lowest point of the curve is not being used to read the volume.

Skill: Measuring in SI—Length

Measurements of length, distance, and height are made in millimeters (mm), centimeters (cm), and meters (m). The equipment used for measuring length is a metric ruler.

Learning the Skill

1. First decide which units you want to measure in. The units you choose will depend on the size of the object or distance being measured.
2. Note the divisions on the ruler. Figure 3 shows these divisions. One meter is divided into 100 centimeters. Each centimeter is divided into 10 millimeters.
3. Place one end of the object you are measuring next to the zero mark on the ruler. Note where the other end stops and read the number of units shown there.

Example

1. Measure the length of a leaf.
2. Place one end of the leaf at the zero mark as shown in Figure 2.
3. The leaf in the figure is 35 mm.

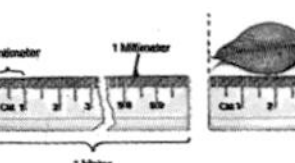

Read level at lowest point (26 mL)

Incorrect reading of 12 mL

1 Centimeter

1 Millimeter

1 Meter

FIGURE 1 FIGURE 2 FIGURE 3 FIGURE 4

Skill: Measuring in SI—Mass

f

Mass measurements are made in grams (g), milligrams (mg), or kilograms (kg). The equipment used is a balance.

Learning the Skill

1. Place the object to be massed onto the pan. Note: liquids must be in a container; powders or solids must be placed on paper. The mass of the container or paper must later be subtracted from the total mass.
2. Slide all the riders to the left and release the locking mechanism.
3. Figure 1 shows that the back beam measures mass in 10 gram units. The middle beam measures mass in 1 gram units. The front beam measures mass in 0.1 and 0.01 gram units.
4. Starting with the rider on the back beam, move the rider to the right until the pointer drops below the zero point. Then move it back one notch. Repeat this process with the rider on the middle beam. Move the front rider until the pointer lines up with the zero point (center line).
5. The mass of the object will be the total of all the numbers indicated by the riders of the three beams.

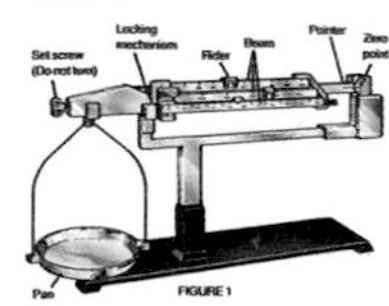

FIGURE 1

Example

The mass of the object measured on the balance in Figure 1 would be 47.52 g.

Skill: Calculating

Calculations may involve averaging numbers, comparing sets of numbers, or calculating area or volume.

Learning the Skill: Averaging

1. Add together the numbers to be averaged.
2. Divide the total by the number of figures used. The resulting number is the average.

Learning the Skill: Comparing Numbers

1. To find out how many times larger something is, *divide the smaller number into the larger.*
2. To find out how many times smaller something is than something else, *divide the larger number into the smaller.*

Learning the Skill: Calculating Area

1. Multiply the length times the width.
2. The result is the area in *square* units, for example, square meters or square centimeters.

Example

1. Calculate the area of the rectangle shown below.

3 cm

5 cm

2. Length = 3 cm
   Width = 5 cm
   Area = length × width = 15 square centimeters
   Square units may be written cm^2, m^2, or mm^2.

Learning the Skill: Calculating Volume

1. Multiply length times width times height.
2. The result is the volume in *cubic* units, such as cubic meters or cubic centimeters.

Example

1. Calculate the volume of the cube shown below.

15 mm

35 mm

15 mm

2. Length = 35 mm
   Width = 15 mm
   Height = 15 mm
   Volume = length × width × height = 7875 cubic millimeters
   Cubic units may be written cm^3, m^3, or mm^3.

STUDENT EDITION

Special Features Capture Students' Interest by Relating Biology to the World Outside the Classroom

All of the special features in the text are designed to show students how biology affects them as individuals and as members of society. They motivate students and make the study of biology more interesting.

Science and Society provides case studies that encourage students to explore different sides of a current issue and develop their own viewpoints.

Science and Society

Are Animal Experiments Needed?

Millions of animals are used each year for research conducted in the United States and for dissections in high school classrooms. In most cases, the animals are treated with great care. In other cases, however, the animals are mistreated and many die. Sometimes the research itself is fatal and the animals die. Rats and mice are the animals used most often, but dogs, cats, pigs, rabbits, and frogs are also used. Monkeys and apes are used to study diseases such as cancer and AIDS because these animals are similar to humans. Many high school students dissect frogs, worms, fish, and even mammals. These animals are purchased from companies that usually raise them for the purpose of scientific study, although some animals are captured f the wild.

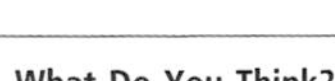

1. Many people in the United States protest the use of animals in experiments and in dissections. These people argue that it is cruel and the animals are made to suffer unnecessarily. They also argue that animals are not enough like humans to give useful results. Should animals be used in laboratory experiments? Should experiments be done if they cause the animals to suffer? Should there be strict laws governing the use of animals in labs?

2. Many people defend the use of animals in lab experiments. Doctors studying living animals say the results of experiments allow many human lives to be saved. Vaccines that protect people from diseases were tested on animals before being given to humans. Animals are used to test the safety of drugs and are being used to develop artificial body parts. Do you think human welfare should be placed over animal welfare? If animals are not used, how should new drugs be tested?

3. Many teachers f biology students dissect animals to lear structure of body syste how they work. These teachers say that stud cannot learn these thi looking at pictures in textbooks. People whc disagree say that this i good reason for killin animals. Do you think dissections are needed teaching biology stud Does it make a differe whether the animals u wild animals captured scientific use or anima for sale to schools?

Conclusion: If animals used in laboratories, v the alternatives?

Animal rights activists

Bio Tip

Consumer: On a farm, it takes 16 kilograms of plants to produce one kilogram of beef, but only five kilograms of plants to produce one kilogram of chicken. Think about this the next time you help with the shopping.

Biotips provide pertinent and interesting information connecting biology to health, consumer information, or leisure time activities.

Career Close-Up

Athletic Trainer

Are you interested in sports? You might want a job working with athletes. You might want to work with students in high school, but you could also train athletes in college. Maybe one day you will be training a professional team. To become an athletic trainer you will need to understand how muscles and bones make up the human body. Take courses in biology, health, human physiology, chemistry, and physics in order to start your career. Other useful courses include nutrition, drugs, first aid, health, and human anatomy.

In a typical day you may be asked to work directly with athletes. As the trainer, you will supervise exercises and you might be required to treat sprains, muscle cramps, or other minor body injuries. Other activities for an athletic trainer include meal planning, repairing of sports equipment, and ordering of training room supplies.

As an athletic trainer, your future is rewarding. With a college degree, the starting salary can be more than $20 000 per year.

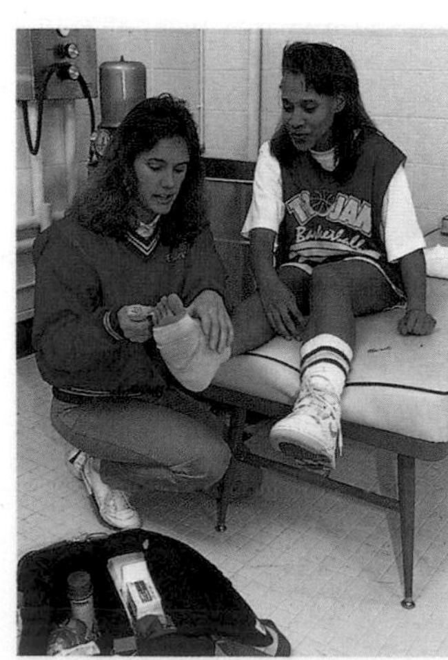

An athletic trainer understands the importance of warm-up exercises to avoid muscle damage.

Career Close-up covers a wide range of interesting, attainable career choices.

CONNECTIONS

Biology in Your World

The Animal World

Classification is used to make sense out of all the many kinds of living things in the world. In this unit, you have seen how organisms are similar. You have also looked at some of the relationships among organisms—from simple, one-celled monerans to complex animals.

LITERATURE

Primate to Primate

Dian Fossey left her home in Kentucky in 1966 to go to Zaire (ZI uhr) and Rwanda (roo AHN duh) in Africa. There, she studied the endangered mountain gorilla in the Virunga (vuh RUN guh) Mountains.

Fossey learned to accept the animals on their own terms. She was able to learn how gorillas form family groups. She saw behaviors that scientists didn't know existed in gorillas.

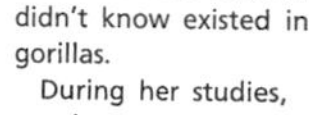

During her studies, poachers were a constant threat. A poacher is a person who hunts or takes plants or animals illegally. Fossey fought a never-ending battle to protect the gorillas and their natural habitat.

Fossey studied gorillas for 13 years. Her experiences are discussed in her book, *Gorillas in the Mist.*

GEOGRAPHY

Coral Reefs

Coral reefs are found in tropical oceans. Coral reefs are built by animals called coral polyps. These creatures are related to jellyfish. They live in colonies and make hard limestone skeletons around their soft bodies. As old colonies die, new ones grow on top of the old skeletons.

The largest coral reef is the Great Barrier Reef off the coast of Australia. It is over 1900 kilometers long.

Divers often see crabs, worms, fish, octopuses, and sponges living within a coral reef. Coastline development, oil spills, and pollution threaten these fragile and beautiful communities.

178

LEISURE

Collecting Fossils

You can have fun searching for fossils of organisms that lived long ago. Fossils are often found in rocks such as shale, clay, sandstone, and limestone that were formed underwater. Since fossils are found in layers, try to find exposed areas such as cliffs, quarries, riverbanks, and road or railway cuts. You will need a shovel, hammer, chisel, notebook, and bags for specimens. You may find fossils of sea lilies, which are related to starfish. Fossil clams, snails, and insects are also common.

Take careful notes, and label and wrap all your specimens. You just might turn up something unusual!

CONSUMER

Tasty Morsels from the Sea

Do you enjoy eating lobster, crab, or shrimp? They are all jointed-leg animals. Scallops, clams, oysters, mussels, and snails are soft-bodied animals. To some people, sea urchins and sea cucumbers, both relatives of the starfish, are delicacies. Fish, such as cod, haddock, and tuna, which are vertebrates, are also enjoyed by many people.

You don't have to live near the ocean or go to a fancy restaurant to enjoy good seafood. Many grocery stores have a seafood department that receives fresh or frozen shipments regularly.

Seafood is best fresh and should be properly cooked. Ask at the store when shipments are received. To be considered fresh, seafood should have been received within the last 24 hours. Keep seafood cold and plan to serve it right away. You can freeze it if it hasn't been previously frozen.

Do you like to help in the kitchen? Try a simple recipe, and surprise your family with a seafood dinner.

179

Connections is a cross-curriculum feature found at the end of each unit. It ties biology to such disciplines as literature and art, and places special emphasis on consumer and leisure activities.

TECHNOLOGY

Eye "Fingerprints"

Blood vessels can be seen clearly in the human eye. These vessels run along the back surface of the eye. That is why a doctor sometimes shines a flashlight into your eyes. The condition of these blood vessels gives the doctor clues about your general health.

The pattern of blood vessels in the eye is different for every person. It's like having a "fingerprint" of your eye.

Using a computer scanner, scientists can identify people based on blood vessel patterns in their eyes. This technology can be used to screen applicants for drivers' licenses. It prevents people who already have licenses from obtaining duplicates. The states of Wisconsin and California are already planning to use this new technology in the issuing of drivers' licenses.

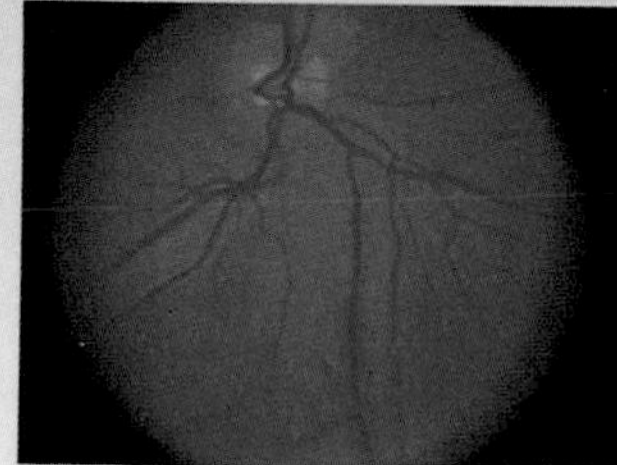

A view of the back of your eye

Technology is a feature that allows students to relate technological advances in biology to real-life applications.

Teacher Wraparound Edition Provides Instant Access to Lesson Plans and Teaching Options

The **Teacher Wraparound Edition,** featuring a four-step teaching cycle, provides everything you need to teach, reteach, check for understanding, and expand upon the key concepts discussed in the textbook.

Cooperative Learning activities, proven effective for students of all ability levels, are presented frequently throughout the margin. These activities give you additional options to reinforce key concepts.

Each lesson plan is broken down into four steps—**Focus, Teach, Apply,** and **Close.** A proven teaching strategy that makes it easy for you to plan your lessons and meet your teaching goals.

TEACH

Independent Practice

Study Guide/*Teacher Resource Package*, p. 59. Use the Study Guide worksheet shown at the bottom of this page for independent practice.

Cooperative Learning: Divide the class into two groups: patients and doctors. Have each patient describe his/her digestive complaint to a doctor. The doctor should then diagnose the problem and suggest treatment.

MOTIVATION/Brainstorming

How many commercials on TV advertise products to cure digestive problems? Have students name the products and then discuss them.

ACTIVITY/Demonstration

Add a few drops of dilute hydrochloric acid to several thicknesses of paper. Have students note how rapidly the paper is destroyed by the acid. This simulates the nature of an

10:2 The Human Digestive System

PREPARATION

Materials Needed

Make copies of the Transparency Master, Application, Enrichment, Reteaching, Skill, and Lab worksheets in the *Teacher Resource Package.*

▶ Photocopy diagrams of the digestive system and gather colored pencils for Lab 10-2.

Key Science Words

saliva	liver
salivary gland	bile
esophagus	gallbladder
stomach	large intestine
hydrochloric acid	appendix
small intestine	villi
pancreas	mucus

Process Skills

In the Mini Labs, students will use numbers and experiment. In Lab 10-2, they will classify and interpret diagrams. In the Skill Check, students will understand science words.

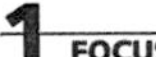

1 FOCUS

▶ The objectives are listed on the student page. Remind students to preview these objectives as a guide to this numbered section.

ACTIVITY/**Brainstorming**

An operation performed on very obese people involves removing a section of the small intestine. Have your students speculate as to why this kind of operation helps with weight loss. Less intestine means less absorption of food.

Objectives

4. **Trace** the path of food from the mouth to body cells.
5. **Compare** the human digestive system with those of other animals.
6. **Identify** the problems of the digestive system.

Key Science Words

saliva
salivary gland
esophagus
stomach
hydrochloric acid
small intestine
pancreas
liver
bile
gallbladder
large intestine
appendix
villi
mucus

10:2 The Human Digestive System

Humans provide a good example of how digestive systems work. If you understand digestion in humans, you should be able to understand it in other animals.

Nutrients Are Digested

Many nutrients must be digested before they can be used, while others are already in a usable form. Table 10-1 shows which nutrients are already usable and which are not.

Water, vitamins, and minerals can move directly from your digestive system into body cells without being changed. Fats, proteins, and carbohydrates must be acted upon by enzymes in your digestive system. There are different kinds of enzymes for each nutrient that must be digested. For example, enzymes that speed up changes in fats cannot change proteins and carbohydrates. Enzymes that speed up changes in proteins cannot help with the breakdown of fats or carbohydrates. The digestive system, therefore, must make different kinds of enzymes for each different nutrient.

TABLE 10–1. NUTRIENTS

Nutrient	Already in Usable Form
Water	yes
Vitamins	yes
Minerals	yes
Fat	no
Protein	no
Carbohydrate	no

A Trip Through the Digestive System

Let's take a trip through the human digestive system to see how it works. To make it a little more interesting, we will look at what happens to a hamburger. Remember that ground meat is mostly protein, mayonnaise is mostly fat, and the bun is mostly carbohydrate. The entire trip of the hamburger through the digestive system takes about 21 hours. Figure 10-3 shows how the entire digestive system looks from one end to the other.

The hamburger enters the system through the mouth. In the mouth, teeth break and grind the food. The breaking and grinding cause the hamburger to change physically. **Saliva** is a liquid that is formed in the mouth and that contains an enzyme. Saliva speeds up chemical changes in the carbohydrates of the bun. It has no chemical effect on proteins or fats. Figure 10-3 shows that saliva is made in the salivary (SAL uh ver ee) glands. **Salivary glands** are three pairs of small glands located under the tongue and behind the jaw. Saliva passes from the glands through small tubes leading to the mouth.

208 Digestion 10:2

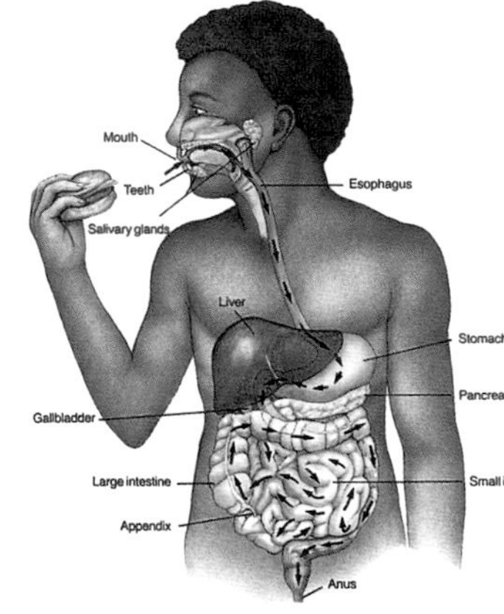

Figure 10-3 Follow the path of a meal through the digestive system.

The broken down hamburger remains in the mouth for about one minute. Swallowing moves it from the mouth into the esophagus (ih SAHF uh gus). The **esophagus** is a tube that connects the mouth to the stomach. Muscles in the esophagus push the food toward the stomach. These events are shown in Figure 10-3. This part of the trip takes less than one minute.

As it leaves the esophagus, the food enters the stomach. The **stomach** is a baglike, muscular organ that mixes and chemically changes protein. It can hold about one liter of liquid and food.

How does food reach your stomach?

2 TEACH

MOTIVATION/Demonstration

Have students observe prepared slides of the intestine (cross section) under the microscope. This will allow students to see the villi. A 35-mm slide projected on the classroom screen would also be an effective way for them to see the extensive surface area of this organ.

Concept Development

▶ The human body may form 250 to 1500 mL of saliva per day.

▶ Point out that the digestive system produces eleven different enzymes. Each enzyme changes a specific nutrient into a usable form.

Guided Practice

Have students write down their answers to the margin question: Muscles in the esophagus move food toward the stomach.

MOTIVATION/Enrichment

Point out that food is prevented from entering the windpipe by the closure of the epiglottis during swallowing. This closure is an example of a reflex action. The muscle contraction called peristalsis is a second example of a reflex. The muscles that line the esophagus contract to push food down into the stomach.

Independent Practice

Study Guide/*Teacher Resource Package*, pp. 56-57. Use the Study Guide worksheets shown at the bottom of this page for independent practice.

OPTIONS

Science Background

Think of the digestive system as a long tube through which food passes. Each organ of the system makes up the tube or is attached to the tube and helps with the digestion of different food types.

STUDY GUIDE 56

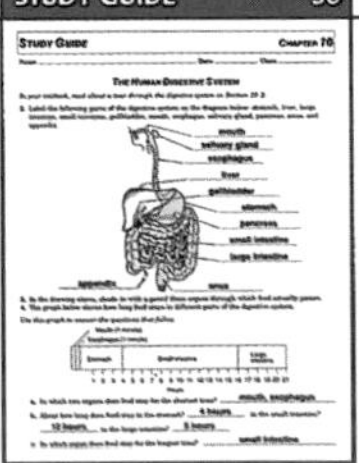

STUDY GUIDE 57

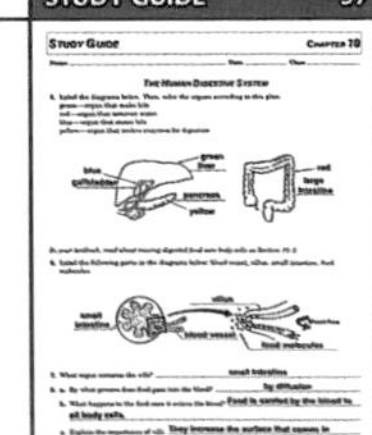

208

209

All of the program resources are referenced within the bottom margin as they apply to the lesson. For extra convenience, many of the teaching masters and student worksheets are actually reproduced on the pages of the teacher edition.

TEACHER EDITION

...als have digestive systems with only one ...ydra is a small, simple animal with only one ...igestive process is simple. The opening serves ...th and an anus as shown in Figure 10-8. Its ...t a hollow sac within the animal's body. What ...you studied in Chapter 7 have one opening to ...system?

...als have no digestive system. Animals such ...are examples. Tapeworms live inside the ...ems of other animals. Digested food passes ...es by diffusion. It may not be a very good ...or the animal in whose body the tapeworm ...rtainly works for the tapeworm.

...of the Digestive System

...ive system, like any body system, may have ...may have heard of ulcers or heartburn. An ...is a sore or hole on the inside of either the ...small intestine. Figure 10-9 shows a ...of the inside of a normal stomach and the ...stomach with an ulcer. The ulcer is caused ...h lining being digested, or "eaten" away. ...t enzymes and stomach acids are found in ...hese enzymes and acids cause the ulcer. ...however, the stomach or intestine does not ...here is usually a chemical covering on the ...vering is called mucus (MYEW kus). **Mucus**

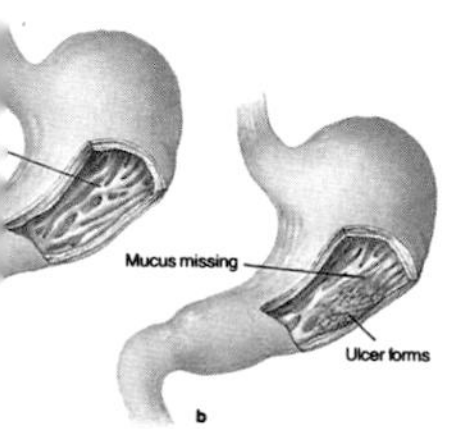

Figure 10-10 Eating too many rich or acidic foods can cause heartburn. Which food is more acidic, a pickle, or a potato?

is a thick, sticky material that protects the stomach and intestinal linings from enzymes and stomach acid. It's the same sticky, thick material that lines your nose.

Heartburn is a problem caused by stomach acids moving into the esophagus. Most of the time, stomach acids stay in the stomach. They then pass into the small intestine. When stomach acids move into the esophagus, they cause a burning feeling. However, nothing is being "burned." The problem also has nothing to do with the heart. The esophagus lies behind the heart. The pain feels like it is coming from the heart, even though it isn't.

Eating too much at one time may result in heartburn, Figure 10-10. The stomach can hold only so much food. If too much is eaten, some may back up into the esophagus.

Bio Tip

Health: Aspirin and ethyl alcohol are absorbed directly into the bloodstream through the stomach.

Why does eating too much cause heartburn?

Check Your Understanding

6. Beginning with the mouth, describe the path food takes as it moves through the digestive system.
7. What causes an ulcer?
8. Identify the differences between the digestive process of a human and a hydra.
9. **Critical Thinking:** How do antacids reduce heartburn?
10. Biology and Reading: Name three organs that are not part of the digestive tube. How do these organs aid the digestive process?

TEACH

Independent Practice

Study Guide/*Teacher Resource Package*, p. 60. Use the Study Guide shown at the bottom of this page for independent practice.

Check for Understanding

Have students respond to the first three questions in Check Your Understanding.

Reteach

Reteaching/*Teacher Resource Package*, p. 27. Use this worksheet to give students additional practice in understanding problems of the digestive system.

Extension: Assign Critical Thinking, Biology and Reading, or some of the **OPTIONS** available with this lesson.

3 APPLY

Software

The Digestion Simulator, Cambridge Development Laboratories.

4 CLOSE

Audiovisual

Show the filmstrip *The Digestive System*, Clearvue, Inc.

Answers to Check Your Understanding

6. mouth, esophagus, stomach, small intestine, large intestine, and anus
7. enzymes and stomach acid digest the stomach lining
8. human – two openings, specialized organs; hydra – one opening, no digestive organs
9. They neutralize the stomach acid.
10. salivary glands – produce digestive enzymes and mucus; pancreas – produces digestive enzymes; liver – produces digestive enzymes and bile; gallbladder – stores bile made by the liver

STUDY GUIDE 59

STUDY GUIDE 60

RETEACHING 27

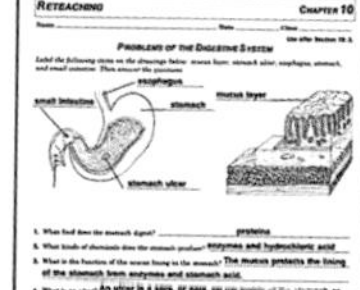

In addition to presenting strategies for teaching the lesson, the margin contains many options for reteaching and extension.

And you will really enjoy our two-page **Planning Guide** that precedes each chapter. It gives you a quick reference to objectives, materials, ancillaries, and other available resources.

Digestion

PLANNING GUIDE

CONTENT	TEXT FEATURES	TEACHER RESOURCE PACKAGE	OTHER COMPONENTS
(1 1/2 days) 10:1 The Process of Digestion Breakdown of Food Physical and Chemical Changes	Skill Check: *Experiments*, p. 205 Lab 10-1: *Digestion*, p. 207 Idea Map, p. 205 Check Your Understanding, p. 206	Reteaching: *Digestion*, p. 25 Critical Thinking/Problem Solving: *What Can Teeth Reveal About Diet?* p. 10 Focus: *Breaking Down Food*, p. 19 Study Guide: *The Process of Digestion*, p. 55 Lab 10-1: *Digestion*, pp. 37-38	
(4 days) 10:2 The Human Digestive System Nutrients Are Digested A Trip Through the Digestive System Moving Digested Food Into Body Cells Digestion in Other Animals Problems of the Digestive System	Skill Check: *Understand Science Words*, p. 212 Mini Lab: *How Long Is the Digestive System?* p. 210 Mini Lab: *How Do Villi Aid Absorption?* p. 214 Career Close-Up: *Dietician*, p. 211 Lab 10-2: *Digestive System*, p. 213 Idea Map, p. 212 Check Your Understanding, p. 217	Application: *Gallstones, a Problem of the Digestive System*, p. 10 Enrichment: *Digesting Different Nutrients*, p. 10 Reteaching: *Digestive Systems of Animals*, p. 26 Reteaching: *Problems of the Digestive System*, p. 27 Skill: *Outline*, pp. 10-11 Transparency Master: *Human Digestive System*, p. 45 Study Guide: *The Human Digestive System*, pp. 56-58 Study Guide: *Problems of the Digestive System*, p. 59 Study Guide: *Vocabulary*, p. 60 Lab 10-2: *Digestive System*, pp. 39-40	**Laboratory Manual:** *How Do Digestive System Lengths Compare?* p. 79 **Laboratory Manual:** *How Does the Fish Digestive System Work?* p. 83 Color Transparency 10: *The Human Digestive System*
Chapter Review	Summary Key Science Words Testing Yourself Finding Main Ideas Using Main Ideas Skill Review	Chapter Review, pp. 50-51 Chapter Test, pp. 52-54	**Test Bank**

MATERIALS NEEDED

LAB 10-1, p. 207	LAB 10-2, p. 213	MARGIN FEATURES
4 paper cups gelatin water 4 applicator sticks 4 plastic spoons enzyme A enzyme B refrigerator (optional)	five diagrams of the digestive system colored pencils: red, blue, green, yellow, and purple	Skill Check, p. 205 2 sugar cubes glass warm water Skill Check, p. 212 dictionary Mini Lab, p. 210 pencil paper Mini Lab, p. 214 water paper towels beaker

OBJECTIVES

SECTION	OBJECTIVE	OBJECTIVES CORRELATION: CHECK YOUR UNDERSTANDING	CHAPTER REVIEW	TRP CHAPTER REVIEW	TRP CHAPTER TEST
10:1	1. **Relate** the importance of the digestive system.	1	3	28	7, 47
	2. **Compare** a physical change and a chemical change in the digestive system.	2, 4	1, 5, 6, 13, 21	8, 33	10, 31, 32, 33, 34, 46, 48
	3. **Explain** the role of enzymes in a chemical change.	3	4, 10, 12	11, 12, 13, 14, 15, 16, 17, 30	44
10:2	4. **Trace** the path of food from the mouth to the body cells.	6, 8	2, 8, 9, 11, 14, 17, 20	1, 3, 6, 9, 10, 11, 12, 13, 14, 15, 16, 17, 18, 19, 20, 21, 22, 23, 24, 25, 26, 27, 28, 29, 31, 32, 34, 35	1, 2, 3, 6, 8, 11, 12, 13, 14, 15, 16, 17, 18, 19, 20, 21, 22, 23, 24, 25, 26, 35, 36, 37, 38, 43, 45
	5. **Compare** the human digestive system with those of other animals.	8, 10	15, 18, 19	4, 5, 7	4, 9, 27, 28, 29, 30
	6. **Identify** the problems of the digestive system.	7, 9	16, 22	2	5, 41, 42

TEACHER EDITION

Teacher Resource Booklets Provide Options for Every Step of Your Lesson Plan

Biology: An Everyday Experience offers the most comprehensive resource package available. Each of the program components are designed to support your teaching style and create a positive atmosphere for learning.

- **Teacher Resource Guide** includes complete program planning charts, lab safety worksheets, and other valuable resources.
- **Focus** directs student attention to the new ideas and concepts presented in each chapter.
- **Study Guide** reinforces comprehension as students read their text.
- **Skill** gives you practice exercises for different study skills and essential science skills.
- **Lab Worksheets** enable students to record data, observations and conclusions from in-text labs.
- **Application** exercises will help your students apply the chapter content to real world experiences.
- **Critical Thinking/Problem Solving** reinforces the use of critical thinking skills in solving problems.
- **Reteaching** explores lesson concepts using alternative strategies.
- **Enrichment** extends student knowledge of chapter concepts.
- **Transparency Masters** include blackline reproductions and student worksheets for each of the program's full-color transparencies.
- **Evaluation** includes review exercises and tests for every chapter and unit.
- **Lesson Plans** include complete teaching plans for every lesson in an easy-to-use format.

Additional Program Components Anticipate Your Every Need

An optional **Laboratory Manual** contains two additional activities per chapter providing more hands-on opportunities to reinforce concepts and process skills.

The **Transparency Package** includes 48 full-color transparencies in a three-ring binder with a resource book of blackline masters and student worksheets for each transparency. Excellent for direct instruction, reteaching, and review.

The **Cooperative Learning Booklet** includes student worksheets and detailed instructions using techniques that are proven effective for students of all ability levels.

A **Computer Test Bank,** available in Apple and IBM versions, allows you to create your own tests and re-sequence or add questions.

The student edition **Study Guide** promotes greater comprehension of the chapter concepts as the students read their text.

Spanish Resources provides Spanish translations of chapter objectives and summaries as well as key terms and their definitions.

The **Optical Data** teaching component includes two video discs that allow you to access colorful diagrams, movie clips, and over 1,000 photographs. The visual information correlates to the page topic to enhance your instruction.

The Classroom-Proven Approach To Biology That Has Found Success Throughout The Country

Biology: An Everyday Experience has succeeded for thousands of students and teachers throughout the country because it uses "everyday" analogies and applications to present and reinforce key concepts.

By using this classroom-proven program, biology will come to life, and your students will better understand the importance of biology to the world around them.

Student Edition	0675-02620-2
Teacher Wraparound Edition	0675-02621-0
Teacher Resource Materials	0675-02677-X
Teacher Resource Guide	
Focus	
Study Guide	
Skill	
Lab Worksheets	
Application	
Critical Thinking/Problem Solving	
Reteaching	
Enrichment	
Transparency Masters	
Evaluation	
Lesson Plans	
Laboratory Manual SE	0675-02622-9
Laboratory Manual TE	0675-02623-7
Transparency Package	0675-02628-8
Cooperative Learning Booklet	0675-02637-7
Computer Test Bank (Apple)	0675-02634-2
Computer Test Bank (IBM)	0675-02630-X
Spanish Resources	0675-02640-7
Study Guide SE	0675-02624-5
Laser Disc Correlation Booklet	0675-02638-5

Call or write your nearest regional office for more information.

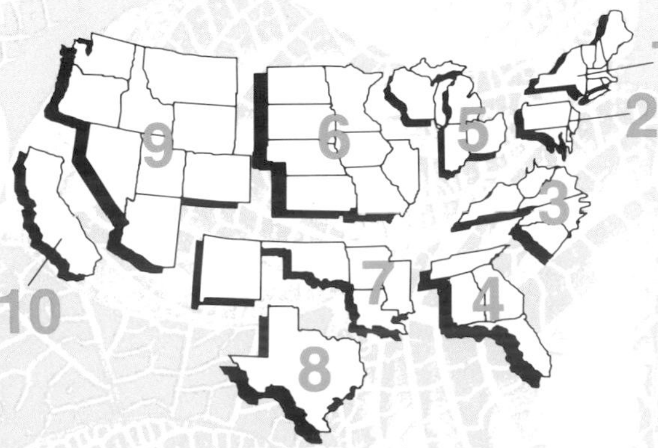

1. NORTHEAST REGION
17 Riverside Drive
Nashua, NH 03062
603-880-4701

2. MID-ATLANTIC REGION
Princeton-Hightstown Road
P.O. Box 409
Hightstown, NJ 08520
609-426-7356

3. ATLANTIC-SOUTHEAST REGION
Brookside Park
One Harbison Way, Suite 101
Columbia, SC 29212
803-732-2365

4. SOUTHEAST REGION
6510 Jimmy Carter Boulevard
Norcross, GA 30071
404-446-7493

5. MID-AMERICA REGION
4635 Hilton Corporate Drive
Columbus, OH 43232
614-759-6600

CATHOLIC SCHOOL REGIONS
BENZIGER PUBLISHING

EAST/SOUTHEAST REGION
Joe McKenney
25 Crescent Street
Stanford, CT 06906
203-964-9109

MIDWEST/WEST REGION
Tim Downs
846 E. Algonquin Road
Schaumburg, IL 60173
708-397-8448

6. MID-CONTINENT REGION
846 East Algonquin Road
Schaumburg, IL 60173
708-397-8448

7. SOUTHWEST REGION
320 Westway Pl., Suite 550
Arlington, TX 76018
817-784-2100

8. TEXAS REGION
320 Westway Pl., Suite 550
Arlington, TX 76018
817-784-2100

9. WESTERN REGION
Glencoe
610 E. 42nd Street, #102
Boise, ID 83714
208-378-4002

10. CALIFORNIA REGION
15319 Chatsworth Street
P.O. Box 9609
Mission Hills, CA 91346
818-898-1391

FOR CANADIAN ORDERS:
Maxwell Macmillan Canada
1200 Eglinton Ave., East
Suite 200
Don Mills, Ontario M3C 3N1
Telephone: 416-449-6030
Telex: 069.59372
Telefax: 416-449-0068

GLENCOE
Macmillan/McGraw-Hill
P.O. Box 508, Columbus, Ohio 43216
90160-X

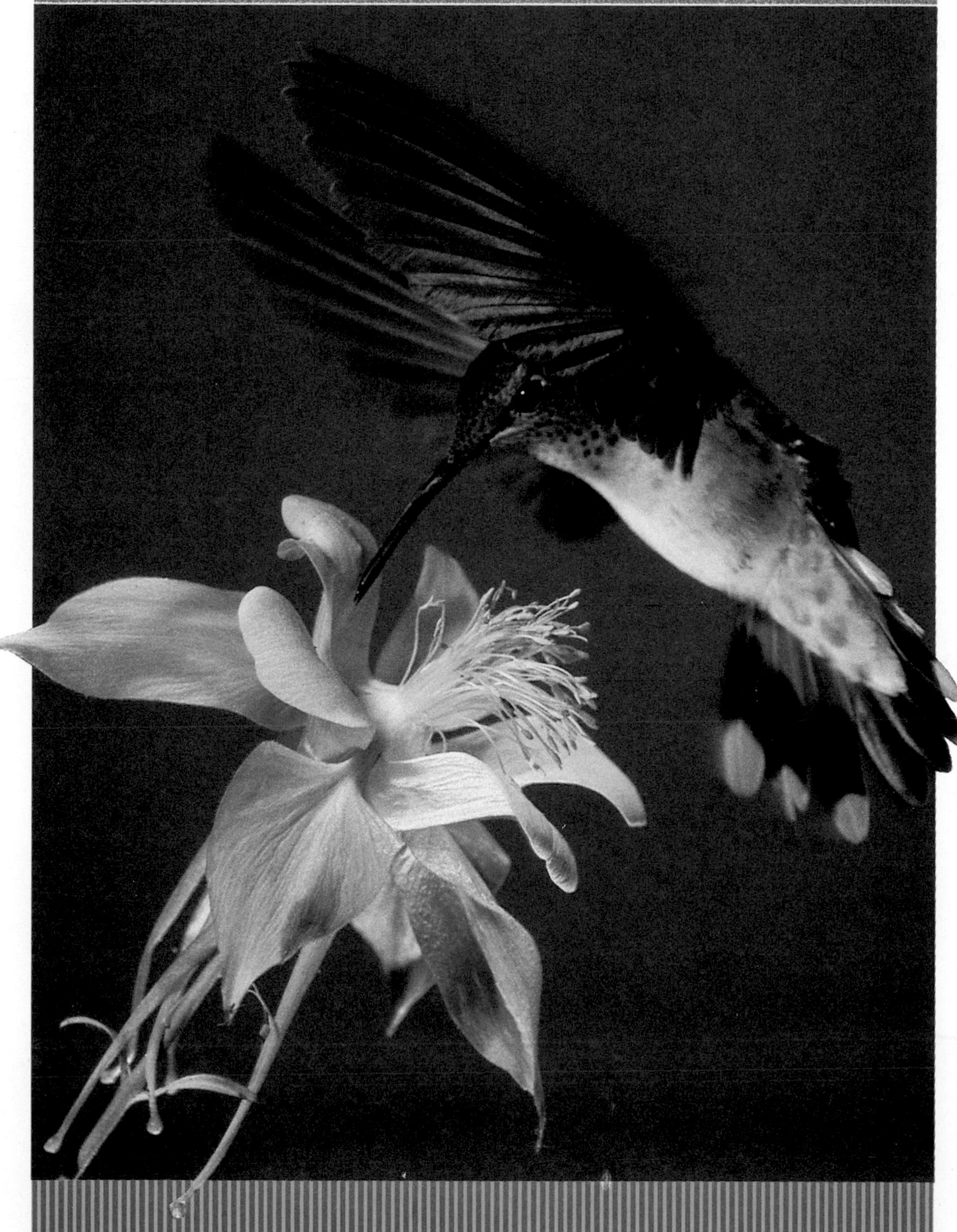

Authors
Albert Kaskel
Paul J. Hummer, Jr.
Lucy Daniel

GLENCOE
Macmillan/McGraw-Hill

Lake Forest, Illinois
Columbus, Ohio
Mission Hills, California
Peoria, Illinois

A MERRILL BIOLOGY PROGRAM

Biology: An Everyday Experience, *Student Edition*
Biology: An Everyday Experience, *Teacher Edition*
Biology: An Everyday Experience, *Teacher Resource Package*
Biology: An Everyday Experience, *Study Guide*
Biology: An Everyday Experience, *Transparency Package*
Biology: An Everyday Experience, *Laboratory Manual, Student Edition*
Biology: An Everyday Experience, *Laboratory Manual, Teacher Edition*
Biology: An Everyday Experience, *Computer Test Bank*

Printed in the United States of America.

ISBN 0-675-02621-0

1 2 3 4 5 6 7 8 9 10–VH–99 98 97 96 95 94 93 92 91

TEACHER GUIDE TABLE OF CONTENTS

Philosophy and Themes

The philosophy of *Biology: An Everyday Experience* is implied in its title. Biology is the study of living things, and living things are part of everyone's everyday experiences. An understanding of biology, therefore, results in a better understanding and appreciation of life. *Biology: An Everyday Experience* thus proceeds with the philosophy that to begin understanding life and life processes depends on a selective yet comprehensive introduction to applied biology.

The approach of this text is interesting, understandable, and practical, but most importantly it aids students who need an introduction to major biological concepts in an easy-to-read form. Difficult concepts are taught using analogies and examples with which students are familiar. Major concepts that may be unfamiliar can thus be learned through understanding rather than through memorization of countless facts. All concepts are presented with the most up-to-date information available with many opportunities for expansion as the needs of individuals or classes dictate. Topics that might be controversial are treated in a balanced and fair manner. In addition, practical applications of biological concepts throughout the text help make biology more "real" for students.

The approach emphasizes the fundamental unity in the diversity of life forms. The text focuses on major life processes. In so doing, each process is discussed using a variety of examples from all five kingdoms of organisms but with particular attention given to humans. In this way, students gain insight into the idea that all organisms, including themselves, carry out the same life functions.

With this philosophy and these ideas in mind, the text is built upon the following unifying themes:

1. There are many different kinds of living things, all of which are alike in some basic ways.
2. Living things depend on body systems that maintain and control body functions.
3. Living things reproduce and pass their traits to their offspring. These traits help a living thing survive in its environment.
4. Living things interact with each other and their environments.

Biology: An Everyday Experience is divided into eight units, organizing the test into major areas of biological study. Unit 1 introduces features of living things and classification. Unit 2 presents each of the five kingdoms. Units 3 and 4 present the structures and functions of animal systems. Unit 5 deals with plants, their parts, and their importance. Ways that living things reproduce, develop, change, and inherit traits are stressed in Units 6 and 7. Unit 8 presents the relationships of living and nonliving things in the environment.

The eight units are divided into 32 chapters that subdivide the units into more specific biological topics. Each chapter is further divided into numbered sections. The numbered sections allow the student to locate specific topics easily and aid the teacher in arranging class and homework assignments. The divisions and subdivisions of the text allow for adaptation to individual classroom needs and make the text useful in situations that require individualized instruction and flexible scheduling.

Text Features

Readability

Biological content with close attention to readability is a major feature of *Biology: An Everyday Experience.* The readability has been designed to promote comprehension, student interest, and student involvement in the subject area. In addition, the readability aids in teaching the material and in classroom management.

In controlling the reading level, several things have been given careful attention. The vocabulary in the text is consistent with the level of the students for whom the text is designed. Words with large numbers of syllables have been avoided wherever possible. Important terms have been printed in boldface type, and in many cases, are followed by phonetic spellings. Each term is clearly defined and reinforced throughout the discussion. Sentence construction and paragraph structure have also been carefully controlled to aid in readability. Readability is also aided by the use of many color photographs and illustrations that tie directly to the printed words. All of the aspects that aid in readability are enhanced by the typeface and type size in which the text is printed.

Photographs and Illustrations

As an aid to comprehension and reinforcement, more than 850 color photographs and illustrations have been included in *Biology: An Everyday Experience.* Each chapter opening includes two photographs that are introduced by the opening paragraphs of the text. The introduction serves to stimulate student interest in the material to be presented in the chapter. In addition, the text photographs and illustrations reinforce and clarify concepts in adjacent paragraphs by directly relating to the printed words. The color artwork included in each Lab serves either as an illustration of the procedure students will follow in doing the lab or as artwork the student will use to complete the lab.

Student Notes

Student notes are placed in the margin to aid in review as well as to serve as a reading aid. Notes are correlated with section objectives and provide thought-provoking questions for students.

Technology

Each unit contains a Technology feature. These features are optional sections that highlight new breakthroughs and applications of the biology found in the chapters in which they occur. The Technology feature can be used to motivate students to seek additional information concerning current issues such as eye "fingerprints," seed banks, and angioplasty.

Problem Solving

The Problem Solving features consist of eight two-page presentations of current and relevant information not directly covered in the text. The information is presented in such a way that students must use photos to solve a problem. Full-color photographs are used extensively in the Problem Solving features to present these topics in an interesting, pleasing manner. Each feature is located in the chapter to which its information pertains and serves to motivate the students to investigate the topics further. The margins of the Problem Solving pages of the *Teacher Edition* contain additional information about and answers to the problems in the feature.

Science and Society

Each unit has a full-page Science and Society feature that introduces students to controversial issues in the sciences. Students are given some background information and then presented with three case studies related to the topic. At the end of each case study are thought-provoking questions that have no right or wrong answers, but invite students to develop and express their own opinions.

Careers

Each unit contains a Career Close-Up feature. Each highlights a career possibility for students to investigate and gives information about the training and schooling required. Each Career Close-Up is contained within the chapter to which it most closely relates. Several of the careers are not typically thought of as biological, but do require some knowledge of biology. The margins of the Career Close-Up pages of the *Teacher Edition* contain additional career information.

Unit Introductions and Closures

The unit-opening pages get students going with large, eye-catching photos and a stimulating introductory paragraph entitled "What would happen if ..." The introductory paragraph encourages students to stretch their imaginations, while integrating science, technology, and society themes.

The unit closures are titled "Connections, Biology in Your World." These pages integrate biology with consumer, leisure, art, history, and geography topics. A single theme unites the connections with a unit. For example, Unit 1 shows the connection between scientific method and Alex Haley's search for his family roots, continental drift, how to build a terrarium, and how to select a bicycle.

Labs

Each chapter of *Biology: An Everyday Experience* contains two pages of labs that enhance student learning of biological concepts through seeing and doing. Each lab includes a materials list, a step-by-step procedure, a skills list, and several questions to test understanding of the lab performed. The end of each lab provides an extension for further exploration of concepts reinforced in the lab. The accompanying color illustrations either show the steps of the procedures or are art that is used by the students in the lab. Additional information about lab safety, care of living materials, and equipment and supplies can be found in this Teacher Guide.

Skill Reinforcement

Skills are reinforced throughout *Biology: An Everyday Experience*. To pique student interest in learning new skills, two kinds of features have been included, Skill Checks and Mini Labs. Skill Checks are quick exercises that students can do in class or as homework assignments. Mini Labs are brief activities that require simple materials that can be found in the classroom or at home. To give students further support with skills, a Skill Handbook is provided at the end of the book. All Mini Labs and Skill Checks provide references to the Skill Handbook for students who need extra help.

Idea Maps

Idea maps outline major concepts in diagram form. They provide a visual summary of the ideas students need to focus on learning. Idea maps can be used as study guides to major concepts and for review and reinforcement. Before students begin a section, have them study the idea map to see what the main ideas of the section are. Then, when they have finished reading the section, have them go over the idea map again. You may wish to have them use the major ideas presented in the idea map and write connecting sentences.

Section- and Chapter-end Materials

Following each numbered section of the text are Check Your Understanding questions. These questions are designed to allow students to check their understanding of previous material. The first three questions correspond to the section objectives. The fourth question stimulates critical thinking, and the fifth question integrates biology with reading, writing, or math. Answers to these questions are provided in the margin of the *Teacher Edition*.

The chapter-end material begins with a Summary that concisely reviews the major concepts and principles of the chapter. Each Summary statement is numbered and corresponds to the section objectives.

The Testing Yourself section of the chapter-end material includes various types of questions. Using Words tests vocabulary understanding. Finding Main Ideas reinforces the reading and locating of important text material. Using Main Ideas requires students to recall important principles and concepts presented in the chapter by asking various types of questions. Skill Review questions review the skills to which students have been introduced in the Skill Checks, Mini Labs, and Labs.

Finding Out More presents Critical Thinking and Application questions to lead the student beyond the material covered in the text. This section is designed to provide a number of open-ended activities such as reports, projects, and experiments.

Appendices

There are four appendices that may be used to expand students' learning or application of concepts. Appendix A shows SI units that students may commonly encounter. A system for easy conversion from one unit to another is described. You may use this section to teach students how to correctly and easily convert SI units. Appendix B includes the classification of living things. Organisms covered in Chapters 4-8 are included in the classification scheme. Appendix C covers root words, prefixes, and suffixes of commonly used biological terms. Appendix D lists rules for safety in the science classroom. Also provided is a chart of safety symbols that appear in the labs.

Glossary and Index

The glossary provides students with a quick reference to key terms and their pronunciations within the text. Page references are provided so students can easily locate the page on which a word is defined. The index allows for easy finding of text material because it is complete and cross-referenced.

Supplementary Materials

Teacher Resource Package

The *Teacher Resource Package* for *Biology: An Everyday Experience* provides background information and comprehensive teaching material to aid in the effective teaching of biology. The following worksheet masters are provided: Application, Enrichment, Focus, Critical Thinking/Problem Solving, Skill, Reteaching, Lab, Study Guide, Transparency, Chapter Review, Chapter Test, and Unit Test.

Each chapter includes Application, Enrichment, Focus, Critical Thinking/Problem Solving, and Skill worksheets. The Application worksheets tie together biological concepts and safety, health, consumer, leisure, and environmental topics. Enrichment worksheets are designed to take students beyond material learned in the text. Focus masters provide five-minute activities to grab the attention of students and get them involved in the lesson. Focus activities require no prior knowledge of the subject matter on the part of the student. Critical Thinking/Problem Solving worksheets help to develop critical thinking skills while applying important concepts learned in the classroom to new situations. Skill worksheets are designed to reinforce process skills.

For each numbered section, a Reteaching master is provided. Reteaching masters are in the form of idea maps, transparencies, and worksheets for students to fill out. Idea maps in the *Teacher Resource Package* coordinate with those found in the *Student Edition* and serve as review and reinforcement aids. Transparencies can be made into overhead masters or passed out to students.

Each lab in the *Student Edition* has an accompanying lab worksheet. The worksheet reproduces the lab page and also includes rules and an expanded data table for students to write in their answers.

Over 160 Transparency masters and worksheets are provided to help you introduce and reinforce the lessons in *Biology: An Everyday Experience.* You can have students fill out their worksheets as you go over the master using the overhead, or the worksheets can be used for homework assignments.

Also included in the *Teacher Resource Package* is an evaluation program. There are two pages of review questions for each text chapter and three pages of test questions. Eight unit tests are included. Each test includes questions and problems of varying difficulty focused on different levels of learning. The reviews and tests can be used not only for assessment but also as learning tools to help students improve their knowledge of biology.

Review and Reinforcement

For your convenience, the Study Guide worksheets in the *Teacher Resource Package* have been bound into a separate booklet.

The *Study Guide* emphasizes the text material by including charts and diagrams for the student to complete. The program concentrates on improving reading skills by making it necessary for the student to reread certain text sections in order to complete the exercises in the *Study Guide.* Besides emphasizing the text material and improved reading, the program offers the student additional reinforcement of important concepts and ideas.

The *Study Guide* can offer flexibility to the teacher. It can be used for in-class work as well as for homework. In addition, the *Study Guide* allows the teacher an additional means for student evaluation.

Laboratory Program

Biology: Laboratory Experiences and *Biology: Laboratory Experiences (Teacher Annotated Edition)* is a learning through doing program of experiments and activities designed to reinforce important concepts. The experiments are written for ease of understanding and the illustrations show the student what to do. Because this program requires inexpensive equipment and materials along with minimum teacher preparation time, the program is easily implemented in a variety of classrooms that differ in sophistication of facilities.

Transparency Package

A transparency package consisting of 48 four-color transparencies accompanied by a Teacher Guide are also available. The transparencies feature original art, text art, or unlabeled diagrams with labels on an overlay.

Computer Test Bank

The *Computer Test Bank* is provided to help you construct chapter and unit tests. The package comes with a convenient teacher guide that includes a printout of all test questions.

Cooperative Learning

The *Cooperative Learning Book* includes worksheets for students and valuable teacher information to help you organize your classes into cooperative groups. Each worksheet reinforces a different biological concept while exposing students to various cooperative learning strategies.

Teaching Cycle

What is the edge for which all teachers search when making a new textbook selection? Teachers anticipate a total program that imparts a wealth of experience they can translate into maximum efficiency, thereby avoiding any teacher's worst enemy—wasted time. The *Teacher Edition* of *Biology: An Everyday Experience* delivers the collective teaching experience of its authors, consultants, and reviewers to you so that you will have the treasure trove of experience teachers search for. By furnishing you with an effective teaching model, this book saves you preparation time and energy. You, in turn, are free to spend that time and energy on your most important responsibility—your students.

As a professional, you will be pleased to find that this program provides you with readily available activities that will engage your students for the entire class period. Each numbered section of every chapter may be considered an individual lesson and includes a comprehensive four-part teaching cycle that, when utilized consistently, will result in better cognitive transfer for your students.

Each chapter begins with two main parts that precede the teaching cycle, a CHAPTER OVERVIEW and a section called GETTING STARTED. The CHAPTER OVERVIEW highlights Key Concepts, Key Science Words, and Skill Development. In addition, it offers a tip for Bridging concepts to be learned with previous lessons. GETTING STARTED offers help on Using the Photos that open the chapter, teaching the MOTIVATION/Try This! activity, and a Chapter Preview. In addition, common student Misconceptions are pointed out to help you get your students off to a good start.

PREPARATION

Before you begin any lesson, thorough PREPARATION is essential. In this step, you gather the Materials Needed to teach the lesson and preview the Key Science Words to be introduced and the Process Skills to be reinforced. With PREPARATION completed, you will have the foundation for keeping your lesson instructionally sound.

1 FOCUS

FOCUS, or the anticipatory set as it is sometimes called, is the first step of the *Biology: An Everyday Experience* teaching cycle that involves student contact. FOCUS helps prepare the students for learning the day's lesson. FOCUS hints may be in the form of Demonstrations, Audiovisuals, Brainstorming, or other innovative ideas that help focus the attention of the class so the lesson can begin. The function of a FOCUS activity is not to teach all of the concepts for the class period, but merely to pique student interest. A FOCUS item may also provide time for students to interact with you, thus enabling you to modify the lesson to fit what students already know. The FOCUS activity usually can be completed within the first five minutes of class and should be a direct lead-in to the concepts that will be presented. By focusing your students, you provide the structural framework for what is to come.

2 TEACH

TEACH, the second step of the teaching cycle, is the heart of any lesson. The primary aim of the *Biology: An Everyday Experience* teaching cycle is to give you the tools to accomplish the admittedly difficult task of getting biological concepts across to your students. Effective teaching strategies as well as alternate ways to teach the lesson are provided in this part of the teaching cycle. MOTIVATION and ACTIVITY ideas appear throughout this step. These ideas can help you develop student interest in the concepts being taught. To help you monitor and adjust your teaching to what the students appear to be learning, Check for Understanding hints are provided. For students who are having trouble, a Reteach suggestion immediately follows the Check for Understanding hint. Reteaching is a way to teach the same concepts or facts differently so they will be more amenable to students' individual learning styles. Also in the TEACH step you will find at least one Enrichment, Challenge, Cooperative Learning, Misconception, Software, and Audiovisual tip.

The authors of *Biology: An Everyday Experience* view teaching as a creative art. As you are aware, teachers work at making the transfer of knowledge as efficient and productive as it can be. One finding of educational researchers is that teachers who closely guide their students during a lesson are usually more effective. To this end, Guided Practice ideas are given. Guided practice takes place when you walk around the room and actively help students begin a task. Independent practice, on the other hand, occurs when students work alone.

Throughout the TEACH step and the rest of the teaching cycle are references to the *Teacher Resource Package* worksheets that go with the lesson. Also included are references to the *Lab Manual* and color *Transparency Package.* With the materials presented in the TEACH step, your efficiency and productivity as a teacher will increase. The TEACH step brings together the major elements that form a sound teaching approach.

3 APPLY

APPLY is the third step of the teaching cycle. In the APPLY step, students have an opportunity for the concepts they have just learned to gel, to become firmer and clearer. In this step, hints may include suggestions for Convergent Questions, Divergent Questions, or Connections. Once students have been taken through the APPLY step, they are ready for the final step, closure.

4 CLOSE

CLOSE is the fourth and final step of the teaching cycle. An excellent CLOSE can be as short as the final minute or two of class, or it can last up to several minutes. There are several purposes to closure. The most important of these is to give students an opportunity to reflect upon what they have learned. One of several kinds of hints may be given in this step. They include Audiovisual suggestions and suggestions for how to Summarize the information.

Answers to Check Your Understanding questions are also presented under CLOSE. Each set of Check Your Understanding questions includes three questions pertaining to concept development, one Critical Thinking question, and one question that connects biology to reading, writing, or math.

As you review the *Teacher Edition* to *Biology: An Everyday Experience,* you will discover that you and your students are considered very important. With the enormous number of teaching strategies provided by the *Teacher Edition*, you should be able to accomplish the goals of your curriculum with a minimum of time and effort. This is true if you are teaching biology for the first time, or are a veteran teacher. The materials allow adaptability and flexibility so that student needs and curricular needs can be met.

Reading Science

Introduction

Scientific writing can be difficult for some students to read. Scientific material is crammed with details, concepts, and interrelationships. Understanding the intricacies of one concept may require an understanding of the subtleties of another. Often, the science textbook is the first experience a student has with trying to read such intensely detailed material. Earlier reading experience may have consisted entirely of descriptive and narrative works. So, the concentration of elements within scientific material may seem overwhelming to the reader who encounters it for the first time.

Science reading requires that students be able to sense relationships and think critically about what is already known and what is currently being read. Students need to possess a degree of competency with study skills in order to read scientific information. They must be able to use the text as a learning tool. They need to be able to interpret not only the printed page, but also the charts, pictures, tables, diagrams, formulas, and experiments. Students who experience difficulty in reading need to be walked through text material. They need to be taught how to read a science book.

Chapter Preview

A chapter preview will serve to acquaint the student with new vocabulary and the organization of the chapter, and will give the student a purpose for reading. The section entitled *Biology and You* at the front of the text instructs students to preview parts of their text and to become familiar with the use of these parts. You may choose to go through the *Biology and You* section step-by-step with your class. Understanding how to use their texts will make students better able to study effectively throughout the school year.

After your class has read and completed *Biology and You,* you still may want to complete a chapter preview to reinforce proper use of the chapter's text material. Students should complete a teacher-directed step-by-step procedure before they thoroughly read a chapter.

Chapter 2, Features of Life and the Cell, is used to exemplify the procedure.

1. Direct students to turn to the table of contents and read the title of Chapter 2.
2. Have students list the numbered sections in order. Point out that 2:1 is the first numbered section of the chapter, 2:2 the second, and so on. Numbered sections are followed by subsections that contain information related to the numbered section. Numbered sections and subsections can be used as a skeletal outline of the chapter.
3. Starting from the beginning of Chapter 2, have students study the list of Key Science Words. Also have them read and become familiar with the section objectives. Have them star the known words and define the others as they read the chapter.
4. Since visual aids are distractors for some readers, the purpose for their inclusion should be discussed before the chapter is read. In this text the visual aids are directly tied to the text words. Have students read the labels that are included on pictures.
5. Read the titles of all charts, tables, or diagrams. Remind students to focus on these visual aids as the chapter is read.
6. Reading the Check Your Understanding sections first can provide a framework that helps students know what to look for in the section.
7. A Summary of Chapter 2 is found on page 44. Have students read this summary before reading the chapter. It gives an overview and identifies the important points.
8. Have students read the list of Key Science Words on page 44. Students may choose other words that are unfamiliar and add them to their personal word lists for study.
9. Guide students to read through the rest of the end matter on pages 44 and 45. The section Using Main Ideas has page references after the questions. If students are expected to complete Finding Out More, a teacher-made study guide could be provided to help students organize and report the information. The questions and activities at the end of the chapter will establish a framework that students can use to study the materials as they read.
10. After the preview, direct students to carefully read the chapter or work with students in reading through the chapter, paying special attention to key terms, visual aids, and information flow.

Special Techniques

You may need to employ special teaching techniques for students who have reading problems. Some teachers prefer to have students read aloud in class. Each student should then restate orally what was just read. You may choose to read to your students for variety, or tape record the text readings and have students use the tapes individually.

Poor reading skills can contribute to other problems. Short attention span, inability to complete task, poor preparation for class, carelessness, easy frustration, and low academic self-concept can all result from reading difficulties. Methods used to help the student with these problems should be designed to help the student achieve some success (no matter how small). To a student accustomed to failure, even a small amount of success is a major first step in improving his or her motivation.

Many teachers find it advisable to work more slowly and cover less material than they would normally. Repetition of main ideas is important. Assignments should be short and practical. Sometimes, working through an assignment step-by-step is beneficial. A student may develop a sense of responsibility for an assignment if the teacher gives each student personal attention and specifically asks for the work.

Making students recopy sloppy work can also help the student to feel more respect for the work he or she has done. These are just a few techniques you may find helpful in trying to develop a feeling of success within the student.

Visual Aids

Visual aids can be considered distracting from the printed text. In many cases, students ignore visual aids and don't understand their relationship to the printed words. The authors of this textbook use pictures, charts, tables, and diagrams to illustrate and condense information. Visual aids are an essential part of a chapter and should be read as carefully as the text. In this textbook, photographs and art are very closely tied to the text words.

At the appropriate time, several questions may be asked about a visual aid to focus attention on it. The authors have included several such questions in the text. Or the teacher may ask questions not provided by the authors.

Paragraph Structure

In order to read science effectively, the student must be aware of the different paragraph forms commonly found in scientific writing. The introductory paragraphs at the beginning of a chapter establish the purpose of the chapter. Notice in Chapter 11 how the first paragraphs introduce the chapter. By using introductory paragraphs as a guide to reading the chapter, the reader can understand the author's purpose for writing.

Definition paragraphs are easy to recognize and can be most helpful for vocabulary clarification. Such paragraphs are particularly important to future understanding of terms when it is the assumption that their meaning is known to the reader.

In scientific writing, paragraphs that present a sequence of events or a chronology are often enumerated. Section 11:2 shows an example of this type of writing. Students many need to be helped to see the relationships and interrelationships of each point.

The transition paragraph is inserted in the discourse to call attention to a shift in time or to change the subject, or just to present an example.

There are many other paragraph forms common to scientific writing, but the authors of this text chose to use these forms most frequently.

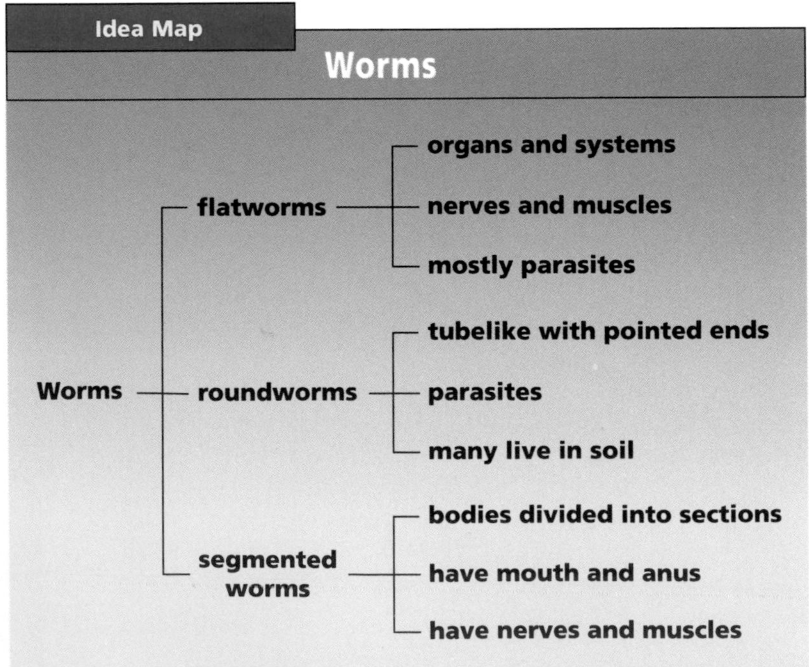

Study Tip: Use this idea map as a study guide to worms. The traits of each worm group are shown.

Note Taking

Note taking can be a difficult and frustrating experience for some students. They often are not aware of how many notes to take. There are several ways note taking can be simplified. Adhering to the numbered sections of the chapter, the teacher can provide a skeletal outline for a chapter. This framework can be provided until students are confident with the outlining process. Completion of the outline should also be teacher-directed. If abbreviations are used, make a key (phy=phylum) to avoid confusion when referring to the outline. The skeletal framework also provides an organizational framework from which students can study.

Other forms of note taking also help students organize their notes, see relationships between ideas, and sort out essential information. A table outline condenses information and is easy to complete once the "features" are identified.

An outline in the form of an idea map provides a visual overview of a chapter or section. With this type of diagram, students can see the relationship of one topic to another. Numerous idea maps are found throughout the chapters. Have students use these as study guides, or have them construct their own.

Vocabulary

The vocabulary of science consists of two types of words: technical and general. The authors of this text have used various methods to define technical vocabulary. Direct definition is characterized by the following format: vocabulary word, linking verb (is), followed by complete definition. This is the method that the authors use most frequently. Students should be directed to the glossary and cautioned that it presents words only as they are used in the text material.

In addition to technical vocabulary, students must be aware of general vocabulary. Certain words in our language have little or no meaning by themselves, but their use in sentences or paragraphs is of the utmost importance. These vocabulary words will be referred to as signal words. The first group is classified as "go" words. These direct the student to continue reading. The most common examples of these signal words are *and, next, in addition, first, second,* and *another.* "Caution" signals alert the reader to pay careful attention to the next point. The most common caution signals are *thus, therefore,* and *as a result.*

The last group of signal words are "turn" signals. These words indicate a different view, or an opposing idea. The most common words in this group are *nevertheless, however,* and *although.*[1]

The teacher's task is to teach the function of these words when they occur in context. It is advisable for the teacher to underline these words in the text so that he or she is alert to their occurrence. It is important to convey their function to the student.

[1] H. Alan Robinson, *Teaching Reading and Study Strategies: The Content Areas* (Boston Massachusetts: Allyn and Bacon, Inc., 1978), pp. 104-106.

Teaching Special Students

	DESCRIPTION	SOURCES OF HELP/INFORMATION
Learning Disabled	All learning disabled students have an academic problem in one or more areas, such as academic learning, language, perception, social-emotional adjustment, memory, or attention.	*Journal of Learning Disabilities* *Learning Disability Quarterly*
Behaviorally Disabled	Students with behavior disorders deviate from standards or expectations of behavior and impair the functioning of others and themselves. These students may also be gifted or learning disabled.	*Exceptional Children* *Journal of Special Education*
Physically Disabled	Students who are physically disabled fall into two categories—those with orthopedic impairments and those with other health impairments. Orthopedically impaired students have the use of one or more limbs severely restricted, so the use of wheelchairs, crutches, or braces may be necessary. Students with other health impairments may require the use of respirators or have other medical equipment.	Batshaw, M.L., and M.Y. Perset. *Children with Handicaps: A Medical Primer.* Baltimore: Paul H. Brooks, 1981. Hale, G. (Ed.). *The Source Book for the Disabled.* NY: Holt, Rinehart & Winston, 1982. *Teaching Exceptional Children*
Visually Disabled	Students who are visually disabled have partial or total loss of sight. Individuals with visual impairments are not significantly different from their sighted peers in ability range or personality. However, blindness can affect cognitive, motor, and social development, especially if early intervention is lacking.	*Journal of Visual Impairment and Blindness* *Education of Visually Handicapped* American Foundation for the Blind
Hearing Impaired	Students who are hearing impaired have partial or total loss of hearing. Individuals with hearing impairments are not significantly different from their hearing peers in ability range or personality. However, deafness can affect cognitive, motor, and social development if early intervention is lacking. Speech development also is often affected.	*American Annals of the Deaf* *Journal of Speech and Hearing Research* *Sign Language Studies*
Multicultural and/or Bilingual	Multicultural and/or bilingual students often speak English as a second language or not at all. The customs and behavior of people in the majority culture may be confusing for some of these students. Cultural values may inhibit some of these students from full participation.	*Teaching English as a Second Language Reporter* Jones, R.L. (Ed.), *Mainstreaming and the Minority Child.* Reston, VA: Council for Exceptional Children, 1976.
Gifted	Although no formal definition exists, these students can be described as having above average ability, task commitment, and creativity. Gifted students rank in the top 5% of their class. They usually finish work more quickly than other students, and are capable of divergent thinking.	*Journal for the Education of the Gifted* *Gifted Child Quarterly* *Gifted/Creative/Talented*

TIPS FOR INSTRUCTION

1. Provide support and structure: clearly specify rules, assignments, and duties.
2. Establish situations that lead to success: use simple vocabulary.
3. Practice skills frequently—use games and drills to help maintain student interest.
4. Allow students to record answers on tape and allow extra time to complete tests and assignments.
5. Provide outlines or tape lecture material.
6. Pair students with peer helpers, and provide classtime for pair interaction.

---

1. Provide a carefully structured environment with regard to scheduling, rules, and room arrangement.
2. Clearly outline objectives and how you will help students obtain objectives. Seek input from them about their strengths, weaknesses, and goals.
3. Reinforce appropriate behavior and model it for students.
4. Do not expect immediate success. Instead, work for long-term improvement.
5. Balance individual needs with group requirements.

---

1. Assume that students understand more than they may be able to communicate.
2. Openly discuss with student any uncertainties you have about when to offer aid.
3. Ask parents or therapists what special devices or procedures are needed, and if any special safety precautions need to be taken.
4. Allow physically disabled students to do everything their peers do, including participating in field trips, special events, and projects.
5. Help nondisabled students and adults understand the characteristics of physically disabled students.

---

1. Help the student become independent—make the student accountable for assignments.
2. Teach classmates how to serve as guides.
3. Eliminate unnecessary noise in the classroom.
4. Encourage students to use their sense of touch. Provide tactile models whenever possible.
5. Describe people and events as they occur in the classroom.
6. Provide taped lectures and reading assignments.
7. Team the student with a sighted peer for laboratory work.

---

1. Seat the students where they can see your lip movements easily, and avoid visual distractions.
2. Avoid standing with your back to a window or light source.
3. Avoid moving around the room or writing on the board while speaking. Instead, use an overhead projector, which allows you to maintain eye contact while writing.
4. Encourage students to face the speaker, even if students must move around during class discussions.
5. Write all assignments on the board, or hand out handwritten instructions.
6. If the student has a manual interpreter, allow both student and interpreter to select the most favorable seating arrangements.

---

1. Do not allow the language a student brings to school to influence your expectations of the student's academic performance; however, beware of reverse discrimination.
2. Try to incorporate the student's language into your instruction. The help of a bilingual aide may be effective.
3. Include information about different cultures in your curriculum to aid students' self-image—avoid cultural stereotypes.
4. Encourage students to share their culture in the classroom.

---

1. Make arrangements for students to take selected subjects early.
2. Let students express themselves in art forms such as drawing, creative writing, or acting.
3. Make public services available through a catalog of resources, such as agencies providing free and inexpensive materials, community services and programs, and people in the community with specific expertise.
4. Ask "what if" questions to develop high-level thinking skills.
5. Emphasize concepts, theories, ideas, relationships, and generalizations.

Performance Objectives

What Is a Performance Objective?

Pick up almost any book on science education and you'll find reasons for teaching science:

"For students to acquire habits of critical thinking...."
"To instill an appreciation for their natural environment...."
"To learn scientific terms, concepts, and principles...."
"So that students will sustain and enhance their natural curiosity...."

This list could go on and on, and no doubt you could add your own reasons as to why you teach science in your classroom. Statements of what science teaching intends to accomplish are no doubt valid and justifiable. The question is: How do you know that you are succeeding in achieving the goals of science education?

What would you see if students really are thinking critically?
What would students be doing if they are appreciating their natural environment?
How could you tell whether or not a student has learned a scientific term, concept, or principle?
How would you know if your teaching enhanced or extinguished a student's natural curiosity?

Therein lies the value of performance objectives—the behaviors which you, the teacher, can observe and which indicate that students are achieving the goals of science education.

For example, let's take the first one: "For students to acquire habits of critical thinking...." Now what might students do if they are thinking critically? Here are some behaviors that you might observe:

Students ask questions related to the topic being discussed.
They gather data or share evidence that supports their answers.
They question or express doubt about the theories posed by others.
They suggest alternate solutions to a problem.
They reject their ideas when the evidence they gather does not support their theories.

Perhaps you could think of other behaviors that would indicate that students are thinking critically. This list is not exhaustive by any means. It only serves as an example of what you might look for if you were accomplishing that goal.

An unlimited number of behaviors could be cited that indicate a student has learned something. Basically, a performance objective is a description of the behavior you might observe in students if they are achieving an educational goal.

What Is a Good Performance Objective?

Statements of performance objectives can usually be divided into three distinct parts. First is a description of the conditions under which the desired behavior will be observed. Here are some examples that describe the condition:

"When presented with pictures of various protists...."
"When asked to list the parts of the plant...."

The second part of a well-stated performance objective is a clear description of exactly what behavior you are looking for. A good performance objective would avoid using such terms as "know about," "appreciate," or "sense the relationship between."

In other words, a good performance objective uses verbs that express some type of observable action. Here are some examples of action verbs that describe observable behaviors: states orally, identifies, watches, matches, lists, states, distinguishes, manipulates, hypothesizes, measures, constructs.

The third part of a well-stated performance objective is a description of some level of performance or criteria that may help you to know if the student or class has performed to the degree that you hoped for.

Why Use Performance Objectives?

A performance objective cannot and should not tell you how to teach. Your teaching strategy is a product of your own creativity as a professional teacher, your knowledge of science and teaching methodology, suggestions from teacher's guides and textbooks, and immediate clues from your students. The purpose of a performance objective is only to give you some idea of what students will be able to do after or during your teaching.

Planning instruction is one use of a performance objective. It can help you decide what materials, classroom conditions, and grouping and teaching strategies you must acquire or develop prior to meeting with your students. This description of conditions is part of the well-stated objective. It helps you think through what you, the teacher, must do to cause the desired behavior to happen.

Another use of a performance objective is to help your gather and provide evidence that students in your class are learning. It allows you to become accountable for time and energy you spend teaching science. It means, however, that you have to evaluate and keep records of student progress. If you do keep such records, then, you or anyone else—parent, teacher, administrator, or supervisor—could observe and evaluate your teaching of science. If anyone were to ask you how you know your students are learning something, you could provide them with some performance evidence that the goals of your science program were being achieved. Of course, students may not exhibit the desired behaviors. If they don't, you have a basis for examining your own teaching, the instructional materials, the classroom, and the school environment and changing them to make them more conducive to learning. But you wouldn't know what changes to make unless you knew what performance outcomes you desired. Part of the well-stated performance objective describes the performance. A precise description tells you what behaviors you should be able to observe if students are achieving the goals of science.

Diagnosing a student's abilities is another use of performance objectives. When you can observe and evaluate certain behaviors, it is easier to determine what students are capable of doing, or what they have accomplished in the past, and what they have yet to master. It more clearly defines the boundaries between what they know and what they don't know. With this information, you can provide a better individualized learning situation for each student. If the students already have demonstrated to you that, for example, they can distinguish between a reflex act and an instinct, why dwell on that? Go on to another objective. Or, perhaps some of your students can do this while others cannot. If it is an important goal, then you'll need to provide some individual or small group activities for some of your students while others might be pursuing other goals. An effective teacher will provide for these individual differences. It is the criterion measure part of the well-stated performance objective that allows you to diagnose which students have accomplished the objective and to what degree they have achieved it.

Where Do Performance Objectives Come From?

Statements of performance objectives come in many forms, and no given number of them constitute a biology curriculum. You could never say that students, having achieved the objectives contained in this *Teacher Edition,* will then "know" biology. The performance objectives for each school, class, group of students, or individual student will vary according to the students, the teacher, the resources available in the learning environment, and the task at hand.

Ultimately, the task of selecting, composing, and evaluating performance objectives is up to you. You should draw on the performance objectives in this *Teacher Edition* and on other sources or other people who could help you. Students are good, if not the best, sources of performance objectives. When they can express to you their questions, their interests, and their goals, then you can cooperatively decide what objectives should be reached.

Any performance objective for teaching science should be based on one or more of the goals of science education. You should be able to say that the reason you're working to accomplish this particular objective is because it's one step or one part of a long-range goal of science education. For example, if one of the goals of science education is to develop the student's ability to utilize some of the methods and processes by which problems are solved scientifically, then one of the purposes of a lesson might be to develop an understanding of what an experiment is. If a student understands what an experiment is:

When asked to define an experiment, he/she will state that it is a test or a way of proving some theory or principle.

When asked what he/she would do to find out what effect exercise has on blood pressure or heartbeat rate, he/she will describe what to do and use the term "experiment" in the description.

When asked for examples of experiments that have been conducted so far this semester, he/she will cite at least three.

Specific performance objectives, such as the above, are only examples of one small part of that larger, broader goal for science education. However, each performance objective should be consistent with one or more of those goals so that you can justify what you are teaching, and so that you can see students progress toward that goal.

Performance objectives are listed for each chapter of *Biology: An Everyday Experience* in the margin and on the interleaf pages preceding each chapter. They are related to the four broad goals of science education.

1. **Attitudes** are behaviors that you might observe as students increase their enjoyment of science activities, and as they demonstrate an interest in the scientific objects and events in their environment. Few of these behaviors are prompted by the teacher. They are voluntary behaviors that indicate an affinity for, an inclination toward, and a preference for science.
2. **Process** goals are behaviors that you might observe as students use the thinking processes of analyzing, experimenting, applying, hypothesizing, theorizing, comparing and contrasting, classifying, and observing.
3. **Knowledge** goals are behaviors that you might observe as students demonstrate that they have gained an understanding of and can use certain terms, concepts, and generalizations of science. Generally, a knowledge objective is one that calls on students to recall or explain information, concepts, or principles that they learned in the past or that were presented in the text and other materials.
4. **Skill** goals are behaviors that you might observe as students gain skill in using scientific equipment correctly and organizing, recording, or reporting information accurately.

You will find that the criterion or level of performance for each objective is not included. The intent was to create guidelines and to state levels of expectancies for you. Only you can decide if 100% or only 50% of your students should be able to accomplish each task. You will need to develop and insert these criterion levels for your own students based on your knowledge of their abilities, the available materials, and your own situation.

How Do You Know You've Achieved Your Objectives?

When you try to find out if students have learned anything, you probably give some form of written test—a true-false, completion, matching, or essay type of examination. All of these forms of evaluation are important in determining whether or not students have achieved some of the objectives.

Cooperative Learning

Cooperative learning groups *learn* things together, not just do things together. Studies show that cooperative learning experiences promote more learning than competitive or individual learning experiences regardless of student age, subject matter, or learning activity. Harder learning tasks, such as problem solving, critical thinking, and conceptual learning, come out far ahead when cooperative strategies are used. Studies show that in classroom settings, adolescents learn more from each other about subject matter than they do from the teacher.

The basic elements of a cooperative learning group are as follows: (1) The students must perceive that they "sink or swim together." (2) Students are responsible for everyone else in the group, as well as for themselves, in learning the assigned material. (3) Students must see that they all have the same goal, that they need to divide up the tasks and share the responsibilities equally, and that they will be given one evaluation or reward that will apply to all the members of the group.

Getting Started

1. *Arrange your room.* Students in groups should face each other as they work together. It is helpful to number the tables so you can refer to groups by number rather than by a student's name. Or, have each group choose a name.

2. *Decide on the size of the group.* Groups work best when teams are composed of two to five students. The materials available might dictate the size of the group.

3. *Assign students to groups.* Groups should reflect real-life situations. The group should be mixed socially, racially, ethnically, sexually, and by learning abilities. If students are allowed to choose their own groups there may be less task-oriented behavior, and the homogeneity that usually results will not allow them the opportunity to hear views that may differ from their own. If a group finds that things are not working out, members may complain that they want to switch groups. If students are told that they can change groups after they have proven their ability to work effectively together for a given time, maybe two weeks, they often decide they don't want to switch. Occasionally a student may insist on working alone. This student may change his or her mind upon seeing that everyone else's grades are better and that the groups are having more fun.

4. *Change groups.* Some teachers keep their groups together for a quarter, a semester, or for a teaching unit. The only criterion would be to have groups stay together long enough to experience success as a group. The advantage of changing groups is that students will have more opportunities to deal with a variety of classmates.

5. *Prepare students for cooperation.* This is a critical step. Tell students about the rationale, procedures, and expected outcomes of this method of instruction. Students need to know that you are not trying to force them to be friends with other people, but asking them to work together as they will later on in life with people who come together for a specific purpose.

Start small. You do not have to incorporate all of this information into your planning for your first cooperative groups. Some ideas you will find easy to adapt to your style while others may be more difficult.

6. *Explain group tasks.* For most activities, each group will need someone to take notes, someone to obtain supplies, someone to summarize as the group progresses, and someone who makes sure everyone is involved. Classes that have less experience using these methods may need to assign these roles to group members at the beginning of each activity. These jobs should be done by different students each time, so that one student does not feel that he or she is being burdened with one job all the time.

7. *Explain the day's lesson.* Develop a transparency that includes the following information or write this information on the chalkboard each day.

▶ **Form Groups:** list the number of students in each group.

▶ **Topic of the Day:** general academic topic.

▶ **Task:** title of lab or other activity. At this time, go over specific instructions, give background, or relate the work to previous learning.

▶ **Goal:** indicate whether students will all do individual work from which you will select one paper or product to grade, or whether they will produce only one product per group. Students' signatures on a product indicate that they will accept the grade.

▶ **Cooperative Skills:** list the specific group skills you will be checking. Start with one or two basic skills. The following skills start from basic and move to more advanced.

a. Stay with your group.
b. Encourage each other to participate.
c. Use each other's names. Use eye contact.
d. Ask your teacher for help only after you have decided as a group that you all need help.
e. Stress that all student contributions are valuable.

After students have some experience working in cooperative groups, you will expect higher-level cooperation skills.

a. Express support and acceptance, both verbal and nonverbal, through eye contact, enthusiasm, and praise.
b. Ask for clarification about what is happening.
c. Suggest new ideas.
d. Use appropriate humor that stays on task.

e. Describe feelings using "I messages."
f. Summarize and elaborate on what others have contributed.
g. Develop memory aids and analogies that are clever ways of remembering important points in the assignment.
h. Criticize ideas, not people.
i. Go beyond the first answer to a question.

What the Teacher Does During Cooperative Group Work

1. *Monitor student behavior.* Just because students have been placed in groups and given instructions does not mean that they will automatically work cooperatively. When you first begin, you will want to observe very closely to see that things are off to a good start. Use a formal observation sheet to count the number of times you observe the behavior expected on that particular assignment for each group. Do not try to count too many different behaviors at the beginning. Reassure students that some of the things you are expecting them to say may sound contrived. Share your observations with each group.

2. *Provide assistance with the task.* Go ahead and clarify instructions, review concepts, or answer questions. But, avoid interfering in the group's process. You have now delegated authority to groups to carry out an assignment. It is of critical importance to let them make decisions *on their own.* Even though they are accountable to you for their work, you must let go and allow the groups to work things through for themselves. Students must be allowed to make mistakes, then evaluate themselves to see where they went wrong. You will find that because of their past experience, students who see you hovering nearby will automatically start asking you questions. Your first response should be, "Have you asked everyone in your group?" Explain to students that they will hear that question often from you.

Students will be doing many of the things you usually do. They will be asking each other questions, keeping each other on task, and encouraging everyone to participate. Your role will be supportive supervisor rather than direct supervisor. For example, as a supportive supervisor, you will help a group that has gotten stuck and is experiencing a high level of frustration. You might do this by asking a few open-ended questions. In a conflict situation, you might ask the group what they think the difficulty is and ask them to come up with some strategies for handling the conflict.

3. *Intervene to teach cooperative skills.* As you observe that some groups have more problems than others with learning cooperative skills, you may wish to intervene by asking the group to think about why they are not being effective and asking them to come up with a solution. If you notice that your groups seem to be having a difficult time coming up with ways of encouraging each other, you might ask them to come up with a list of things to say that would be encouraging and then post it in the room.

4. *Provide closure for the lesson.* Students should be asked to summarize what they have learned and should be able to relate it to what they have previously studied. You may want to review the main points and ask students to give examples and answer any final questions.

5. *Evaluate the group process.* In order for groups to be aware of their progress in learning to work together, they must be given time to evaluate how they are working together. Give a few minutes at the end of the lesson to decide if they achieved the criterion you set up for that particular lesson. Have them rate themselves as a group on a scale of one to ten and write down specified ways they could improve.

6. *Evaluate student learning.* Evaluation tools may include traditional tests and quizzes, group quizzes, and extra points for groups achieving overall high marks.

Keep in mind that cooperative learning doesn't just "happen." The first few days may seem like bedlam, with some students upset, others mistrustful, and others off task. Both you and your students will make mistakes. Just be patient and keep at it. You may wish to read more about cooperative learning groups in the references listed below.

Johnson, David W., and Roger T. Johnson. *Cooperation and Competition, Theory and Research.* Edina, MN: Interaction Book Co., 1989.

Kagan, Spencer. *Cooperative Learning, Resources for Teachers.* Laguna Niguel, CA: Resources for Teachers, 1989.

Slavin, Robert. *Cooperative Learning, Student Teams,* 2nd ed. Washington, DC: National Education Association, 1987.

Planning Guide

Biology: An Everyday Experience is designed with built-in flexibility that both beginning and experienced teachers can appreciate. A planning guide has been provided to assist you with both long- and short-range planning. It is designed to help you provide students with the best possible biology program.

The planning guide presents each chapter and the number of class sessions suggested for that chapter. The entire course assumes 180 class sessions divided into six-week periods. This would be equivalent to 160 hours of combined class and laboratory time for the year (50 minutes per day).

The planning guide classifies the sections of each chapter into two categories: those of primary importance and those of secondary importance. Most biology curricula include those sections designated as being of primary importance. The sections listed in this category provide a minimum program that you can develop more fully as time permits by using the sections designated as being of secondary importance. In some cases, the material designated as being of secondary importance is information that helps relate the information in the chapter to students' experiences. For this reason, it is important to include this information whenever possible to enhance students' appreciation and understanding of biology.

Planning Guide for *Biology: An Everyday Experience*

UNIT	CHAPTER	CLASS SESSIONS	PRIMARY IMPORTANCE	SECONDARY IMPORTANCE
1	1	6	All sections	
1	2	6	All sections	
1	3	6	All sections	
2	4	7	All sections	
2	5	5	All sections	
2	6	5	All sections	
2	7	7	All sections	
2	8	7	All sections	
3	9	7	All sections	
3	10	4	All sections	
3	11	5	11:1, 11:2, 11:3	11:4
3	12	5	12:1, 12:2, 12:4	12:3
3	13	5	13:1, 13:2, 13:4	13:3
3	14	5	14:1, 14:2	14:3
4	15	5	15:1, 15:2, 15:3	15:4
4	16	5	16:1, 16:2	16:3
4	17	4	All sections	
4	18	8	All sections	
5	19	7	19:1, 19:2	19:3
5	20	5	All sections	
5	21	6	21:1, 21:2	21:3
6	22	6	22:1, 22:2	22:3
6	23	5	All sections	
6	24	5	All sections	
6	25	5	All sections	
7	26	6	All sections	
7	27	5	27:1, 27:2	27:3
7	28	6	All sections	
7	29	7	All sections	
8	30	6	30:1, 30:2, 30:3	30:4
8	31	5	31:1, 31:3	31:2
8	32	6	32:1, 32:3	32:2

Alternate Sequence Approach

You may choose to teach the subject matter in a sequence other than that which is presented in Chapters 1-32. When using an altered sequence, students may encounter minor vocabulary and concept difficulties. However, these gaps can easily be remedied by the teacher. The following alternate approach is provided merely as a guide and should not be construed as a rigid plan. Areas of emphasis are included along with the alternate sequence. Selection of topics should depend on the interests and ability levels of the classes you teach.

Ecological Approach

Chapters	Emphasis
1-3	Life characteristics Cell anatomy Classification of life forms into five kingdoms
19, 30-32	Plants and photosynthesis How life forms are dependent upon one another Role of energy in ecosystems Recycling of needed chemicals Population dynamics Human role in disturbing the environment Human problems resulting from a damaged environment Future and current solutions to a damaged environment
22, 26-29	Role of mitosis and meiosis Heredity principles How life forms change as a consequence of natural selection Role of changing environment as selection agent for evolution
4-6 20-21, 23	Survey of life forms (not including animals) Protists, monera, fungi, plants
7-16, 24-25	Survey of animals Major animal systems
17-18	Animal behavior Drugs and behavior

Skill Development and Reinforcement

The development and reinforcement of thinking and manipulative skills is a major goal of *Biology: An Everyday Experience.* Throughout the text, students are involved in many activities that test and strengthen their ability to think and operate in a science setting. Specific skill-related exercises can be found throughout the book in Labs, Check Your Understanding questions, Mini Labs, Skill Checks, Skill Review questions, and the Skill Handbook.

Labs

A lab is designed to reinforce and develop a variety of skills through hands-on activities that follow a scientific procedure. Each lab in *Biology: An Everyday Experience* includes a problem statement, a list of process skills, a list of materials, numbered procedure statements, tables, and two sets of questions: those that ask students about the data and observations collected during the lab, and those that ask students to analyze the data they collected and apply the information learned in the investigation to other situations. Many labs require the formation of a hypothesis. More complex process skills will be developed if students understand that hypotheses are neither right nor wrong and that science processes do not produce correct answers, but rather statements that are either supported or not supported. Finally, there is an extension that asks students to go beyond the lab by designing further experiments or participating in some other type of creative activity.

Check Your Understanding

Within each chapter, five review questions appear at the close of each numbered section. In each instance, the fourth question is labeled Critical Thinking. A critical thinking question requires a student to utilize critical thinking skills to answer a question about information presented in the text. The fifth question makes a connection between biology and reading, writing, or math skills.

Mini Labs and Skill Checks

Mini Labs and Skill Checks are sprinkled throughout each chapter. These activities give students an opportunity to reinforce skills such as sequencing, classifying, observing, inferring, or constructing a table. A reference to the Skill Handbook is provided with each Skill Check and Mini Lab for students who need further help. Mini Labs use simple materials that are readily available at home or in the classroom. Each chapter has a Skill Check on understanding science words. In this skill, science words are broken down into root words, prefixes, and suffixes. Extra help with biology words is found in Appendix C, which lists root words, prefixes, and suffixes that are common in biology.

Skill Review

Within each Chapter Review are four Skill Review questions that review the skills first practiced in the Skill Checks, Mini Labs, and Labs. Students are given one more opportunity to practice valuable skills while learning important concepts in biology.

Skill Handbook

For help with Mini Labs, Skill Checks, and Skill Review questions, students using *Biology: An Everyday Experience* may refer to the Skill Handbook on pages 704-719 of the textbook. The handbook contains instructions on skills and an example of each skill type. The skills in the Skill Handbook are:

- *Practicing Scientific Method
- *Reading Science
- *Using a Microscope
- *Organizing Information
- *Using Numbers

Each skill includes several subcategories. For example, Reading Science includes skills on sequencing, understanding science words, interpreting diagrams, and formulating models.

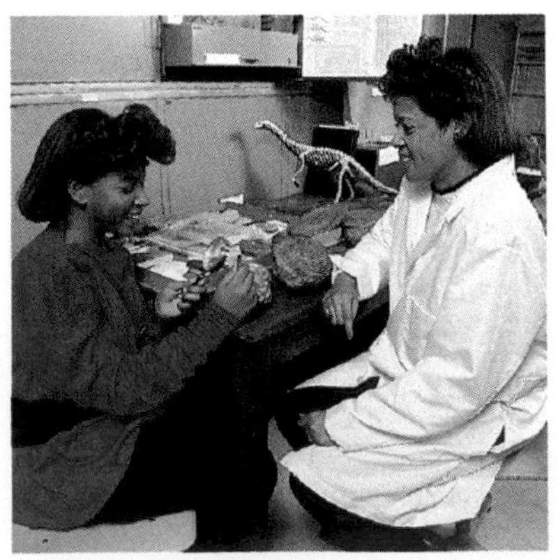

Developing Process Skills

Biology: An Everyday Experience provides experiences that help students both develop and apply critical thinking process skills. These experiences are provided by the use of higher level divergent questions, and lab activities. Students are given the opportunity to use and apply both basic and complex process skills, thus facilitating their advancement toward higher levels of cognitive thinking.

Students able to think in terms of several solutions to a single problem are not limited to concrete activities. Instead, these students can formulate hypotheses as testable ideas in their minds and can demonstrate deductive patterns of thought. Through integration of the important critical thinking process skills listed below, students develop the ability to think logically and abstractly.

Basic Process Skills

Observing: Students use one or more senses to increase their perceptions in order to learn more about objects and events.

Classifying: Students group objects or events based on common properties and/or categorize based on existing relationships among objects or events.

Inferring: Students propose interpretations, explanations, and causes from observed events and collected data.

Communicating: Students convey information verbally, in both oral and written forms, and visually through graphs, charts, pictures, and diagrams.

Recognizing and Using Spatial Relationships: Students estimate the relative positions of moving and nonmoving objects.

Measuring: Students identify and order length, area, volume, mass, and temperature to describe and quantify objects or events.

Predicting: Students propose possible results or outcomes of future events based on observations and inferences drawn from previous events.

Using Numbers: Students transfer or apply ordering, counting, adding, subtracting, multiplying, and dividing to quantify data where appropriate in investigations or experiments.

Complex Process Skills

Interpreting Data: Students explain the meaning of information gathered in scientific situations.

Forming Hypotheses: Students make an assumption in order to draw out and test its logical consequences.

Separating and Controlling Variables: Students recognize the many factors that affect the outcome of events and understand the relationship of the factors to one another so that one factor (variable) can be manipulated while the others are controlled.

Experimenting: Students test hypotheses or predictions under conditions where variables are both controlled and manipulated.

Formulating Models: Students construct mental, verbal, or physical representations of ideas, objects, or events. The models are then used to clarify explanations or to demonstrate relationships.

Defining Operationally: Students form a working definition that is based upon actual experience in which the student has participated.

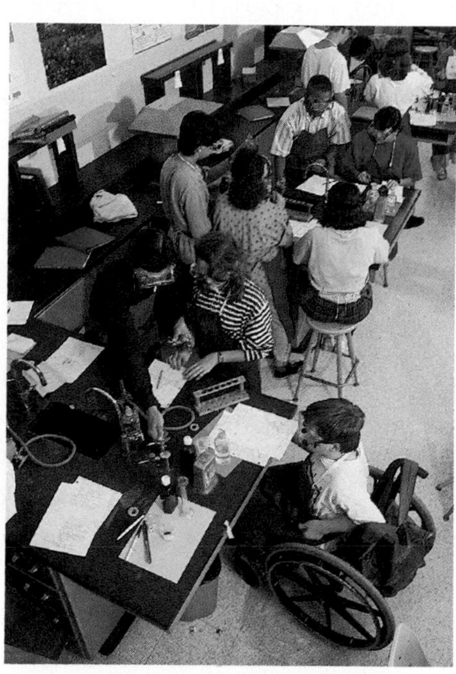

Process Skills Used in Labs

Lab	Process Skills
1-1	observe, recognize and use spatial relationships
1-2	form hypotheses, interpret data, separate and control variables
2-1	make and use tables, interpret data, infer, form hypotheses
2-2	observe, compare, use a microscope
3-1	classify, observe
3-2	classify, communicate, make a table
4-1	observe, recognize and use spatial relationships, formulate a model
4-2	make and use tables, observe, measure in SI, use a microscope
5-1	make and use tables, interpret data, observe, classify, use a microscope
5-2	observe, infer, use a microscope, design an experiment
6-1	make and use tables, interpret data, use a microscope, measure in SI, infer
6-2	make and use tables, observe, use a microscope
7-1	observe, make and use tables, interpret data
7-2	observe, infer, predict, make and use table
8-1	make and use tables, observe, infer
8-2	interpret data, observe, infer
9-1	use numbers, experiment, measure in SI, make and use tables
9-2	form a hypothesis, experiment, make and use tables
10-1	separate and control variables, form a hypothesis, observe, design an experiment
10-2	classify, interpret diagrams
11-1	form a hypothesis, calculate, interpret data, make and use tables
11-2	formulate models, form a hypothesis, measure in SI
12-1	use a microscope, measure in SI, compare
12-2	use a microscope, compare, classify
13-1	form a hypothesis, measure in SI, interpret data
13-2	observe, interpret data, make and use tables, infer
14-1	form a hypothesis, experiment, measure in SI
14-2	formulate a model, experiment, infer
15-1	form a hypothesis, calculate, infer
15-2	experiment, interpret data
16-1	formulate a model, observe, measure in SI
16-2	predict, interpret data, make and use tables

Lab	Process Skills
17-1	predict, separate and control variables, observe, design an experiment
17-2	form hypotheses, observe, make and use tables
18-1	observe, interpret data, experiment
18-2	observe, interpret data, experiment
19-1	measure in SI, interpret diagrams, classify
19-2	observe, infer, experiment
20-1	observe, formulate a model, infer, design an experiment
20-2	observe, classify, form hypotheses, design an experiment
21-1	measure in SI, form hypotheses, interpret data, experiment
21-2	observe, form hypothesis, interpret data
22-1	observe, formulate a model, sequence
22-2	use numbers, make and use tables, form hypotheses, interpret data
23-1	form a hypothesis, experiment, observe
23-2	experiment, observe, measure in SI, infer
24-1	make and use tables, measure in SI, recognize and use spatial relationships, make scale drawings
24-2	make and use graphs, infer, relate cause and effect
25-1	measure in SI, use numbers, infer, make and use graphs
25-2	interpret data, measure in SI, compare
26-1	observe, predict, interpret data
26-2	observe, formulate a model, form hypotheses
27-1	make and use tables, formulate a model, calculate, design an experiment
27-2	observe, make and use tables, interpret data
28-1	formulate a model, interpret diagrams, observe
28-2	observe, infer, interpret data
29-1	form hypotheses, experiment, interpret data, infer, calculate
29-2	formulate a model, observe, infer
30-1	form hypotheses, interpret data, infer, design an experiment
30-2	observe, infer, design an experiment
31-1	observe, form hypotheses, interpret data, infer, design an experiment
31-2	observe, form hypotheses, interpret data, design an experiment
32-1	observe, experiment, interpret data, classify
32-2	observe, form hypotheses, interpret data, design an experiment

Problem Solving

A major challenge faced by teachers is teaching students how to approach problems. When asked to apply a concept or interpret an everyday situation in light of the concepts they have learned, many students become puzzled and confused. To aid you in helping your students develop problem solving skills, each unit of *Biology: An Everyday Experience* includes a Problem Solving feature. The objectives of these features are three-fold. They include helping students (1) become aware of the process they use to solve problems, (2) identify the stages in that process, and (3) identify and choose strategies for problem solving.

Below are some misconceptions most students hold about problem solving.

* A way to solve the problem should be obvious when you read a problem.
* You can't write anything down unless you have the solution worked out in your head.
* No trial-and-error attempts or "playing around" with different approaches to a problem are allowed.
* There is only one "right" way to solve a problem.
* You can't change a problem to make it simpler.
* Problem solving is a step-by-step process that always proceeds in a linear, logical manner.

When faced with a problem, most students focus their attention on getting the "right" answer. Relationships among problems are rarely seen. Instead, each problem is looked on as a completely new, unique situation. Fear of beginning is also an obstacle to problem solving. You may want to present the following overall plan as one way to attack a problem.

1. *Verbalize the problem*—state the problem out loud and believe that you can solve it.
2. *Define the problem*—analyze the information given and determine what you know and what you need to know in order to solve the problem.
3. *Explore*—brainstorm strategies for organizing the given information and finding out what you need to know.
4. *Plan*—decide on a strategy or group of strategies and list steps and substeps of the strategies.
5. *Carry out the plan.*
6. *Assess*—decide what was done, whether or not you are closer to solving the problem, and why or why not.

Once students have an overall plan, they can begin to develop strategies for problem solving. A *strategy* is an organized approach to a problem that breaks down the task of obtaining and organizing information into stages. Having a group of strategies to choose from will help students over the initial panic felt when faced with a problem. Several strategies are listed here.

* construct a table, graph, or figure
* list all possible solutions
* look for a pattern
* talk to an expert
* act out the problem
* make a model
* guess and check
* work backwards
* make a drawing
* solve a simpler or similar problem

Remember that the attitude of students toward problem solving is a big factor in their success or failure. No matter how many models or strategies are given to students, if they think they are no good at solving problems, they will probably fail. Try to overcome this fear of the unknown by including problem solving in your daily teaching. Talk about problem solving as an important skill. Use the words "problem solving" often and consistently to describe the problem solving process. Finally, focus on helping students progress in using the process rather than in getting the "right" answer.

Additional References

Covington, M.V., et. al. *Productive Thinking Program.* Columbus, OH: Merrill Publishing Company, 1984.

deBono, E. *deBono's Thinking Course.* BBC Publication, 35 Marylebone High St., London, WIM 4AA, 1982.

Meiring, Steven P. *Problem Solving . . . A Basic Mathematics Goal: Part 1, Becoming a Better Problem Solver.* Palo Alto, CA: Dale Seymour Publications.

Meiring, Steven P. *Problem Solving . . . A Basic Mathematics Goal: Part 2, A Resource for Problem Solving.* Palo Alto, CA: Dale Seymour Publications.

Safety in the Laboratory

Safety is of prime importance in every classroom. However, the need for safety is even greater when science is taught. Students need to become aware of safety at all times, for themselves and their classmates.

Teachers and students using *Biology: An Everyday Experience* will find that safety awareness is emphasized throughout the book and the laboratory manual. In Labs where potential safety problems might arise, specific safety symbols are used to caution students. Safety symbols that are used in all Glencoe science programs are shown on page 33T. These symbols appear in Labs wherever appropriate. If you take the time to make students aware of them now at the beginning of the course, then they will know immediately what precautions are to be taken as soon as they see a particular symbol. Overall, safety problems can be avoided and accidents prevented with planning on the part of both teacher and student.

In the Laboratory

1. Chemicals in the laboratory.
   Responsible storage, use, and disposal of chemicals in a science lab ensures the safety of you and your students. Follow the guidelines outlined on page 32T for safe and productive behaviors when working with chemicals.
2. Equipment in the laboratory.
   (a) Clean and dry all equipment before storing.
   (b) Label and organize all equipment.
   (c) Protect electronic equipment and microscopes from dust, humidity, and extremes in temperature.
   (d) Be sure all glassware is a heat-treated type that will not shatter.
3. Provide adequate work space and ventilation for activities.
4. Post safety and evacuation guidelines and safety symbols.
5. Check to ensure that safety equipment is accessible and working properly.
6. Provide containers for disposing of chemicals, broken glass, other waste products, and biological specimens. Disposal methods should meet your local guidelines.
7. Use a hot plate for any procedure requiring a heat source. If lab burners are used, a central shutoff valve for the gas supply should be accessible to you. Never use open flames when a flammable solvent is in the same room.

Before the First Lab

1. Distribute and discuss safety rules, first aid guidelines, and safety contract found in the *Teacher Resource Package.*
2. Review the safe use of equipment, chemicals, and living organisms. Review the safety symbols.
3. Review use and location of fire extinguisher.
4. Discuss safe disposal of materials and lab cleanup policy.
5. Have students sign safety contract and return it. Test students' knowledge of safety symbols.

Before Each Lab

1. Perform each activity yourself ahead of time to determine where students may need help.
2. Arrange the lab so that equipment and supplies are clearly labeled and easily accessible.
3. Have available only equipment and supplies needed to complete the assigned Lab.
4. Review the written procedure with students.
5. Be sure all students understand any precautions to be taken.

During the Lab

1. Make sure the lab floors and counters are clean.
2. Insist that all students wear goggles and aprons.
3. Do not allow students to work alone.
4. Insist on caution when students use cutting devices.
5. Shield systems under pressure or vacuum.
6. Caution students not to point the open end of a heated test tube toward anyone.
7. Remove broken or chipped glassware and clean up any spills immediately. Dilute spills with water before removing.
8. Remind students that heated glassware *looks* cool.
9. Prohibit eating and drinking in the lab.

Following the Lab

1. Be certain that students have disposed of broken glassware and chemicals properly.
2. Be sure all equipment is turned off.
3. Insist that each student wash his or her hands when lab work is completed.

Chemical Storage and Disposal

General Guidelines

Be sure to store all chemicals properly. The following are guidelines commonly used. Your school, city, county, or state may have additional requirements for handling chemicals. It is the responsibility of each teacher to become informed as to what rules or guidelines are in effect in his or her area.

1. Separate chemicals by reaction type. Strong acids should be stored together. Likewise, strong bases should be stored together and should be separated from acids. Oxidants should be stored away from easily oxidized materials and so on.
2. Be sure all chemicals are stored in labeled containers indicating contents, concentration, source, date purchased (or prepared), any precautions for handling and storage, and expiration date.
3. Dispose of any outdated or waste chemicals properly according to accepted disposal procedures.
4. Do not store chemicals above eye level.
5. Wood shelving is preferable to metal. All shelving should be firmly attached to walls and have antiroll edges.
6. Store only those chemicals that you plan to use.
7. Hazardous chemicals require special storage containers and conditions. Be sure to know what those chemicals are and the accepted practices for your area. Some substances must even be stored outside the building.
8. When working with chemicals or preparing solutions, observe the same general safety precautions that you would expect from students. These include wearing an apron and goggles. Wear gloves and use the fume hood when necessary. Students will want to do as you do whether they admit it or not.
9. If you are a new teacher in a particular laboratory, it is your responsibility to survey the chemicals stored there and to be sure they are stored properly or disposed of. Consult the rules and laws in your area concerning what chemicals can be kept in your classroom. For disposal, consult up-to-date disposal information from the state and federal governments.

Disposal of Chemicals

Local, state, and federal laws regulate the proper disposal of chemicals. These laws should be consulted before chemical disposal is attempted. Although most substances encountered in high school biology can be flushed down the drain with plenty of water, it is not safe to assume that is always true. It is recommended that teachers who use chemicals consult the following books from the National Research Council.

Prudent Practices for Handling Hazardous Chemicals in Laboratories, Washington, DC: National Academy Press, 1981.

Prudent Practices for Disposal of Chemicals from Laboratories, Washington, DC: National Academy Press, 1983.

These books are useful and still in print, although they are several years old. Current law in your area would, of course, supersede the information in these books.

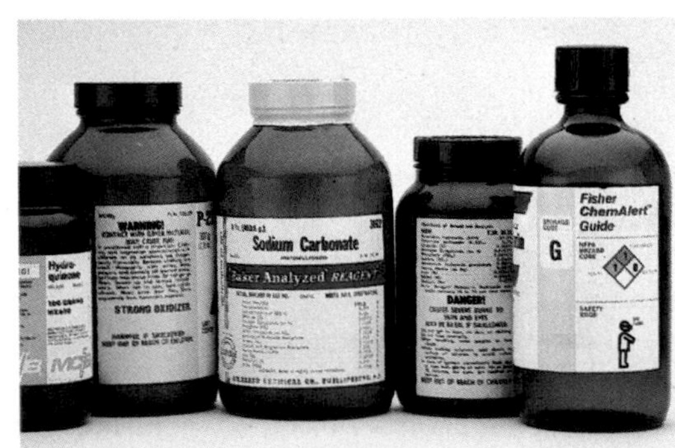

The *Biology: An Everyday Experience* program uses safety symbols to alert you and your students to possible laboratory dangers. These symbols are explained in the chart below. Be sure your students understand each symbol before they begin a lab.

Safety Symbols

	**DISPOSAL ALERT** This symbol appears when care must be taken to dispose of materials properly.		**ANIMAL SAFETY** This symbol appears whenever live animals are studied and the safety of the animals and the students must be ensured.
	**BIOLOGICAL HAZARD** This symbol appears when there is danger involving bacteria, fungi, or protists.		**RADIOACTIVE SAFETY** This symbol appears when radioactive materials are used.
	**OPEN FLAME ALERT** This symbol appears when use of an open flame could cause a fire or an explosion.		**CLOTHING PROTECTION SAFETY** This symbol appears when substances used could stain or burn clothing.
	**THERMAL SAFETY** This symbol appears as a reminder to use caution when handling hot objects.		**FIRE SAFETY** This symbol appears when care should be taken around open flames.
	**SHARP OBJECT SAFETY** This symbol appears when a danger of cuts or punctures caused by the use of sharp objects exists.		**EXPLOSION SAFETY** This symbol appears when the misuse of chemicals could cause an explosion.
	**FUME SAFETY** This symbol appears when chemicals or chemical reactions could cause dangerous fumes.		**EYE SAFETY** This symbol appears when a danger to the eyes exists. Safety goggles should be worn when this symbol appears.
	**ELECTRICAL SAFETY** This symbol appears when care should be taken when using electrical equipment.		**POISON SAFETY** This symbol appears when poisonous substances are used.
	**PLANT SAFETY** This symbol appears when poisonous plants or plants with thorns are handled.		**CHEMICAL SAFETY** This symbol appears when chemicals used can cause burns or are poisonous if absorbed through the skin.

Care of Living Organisms

Think about what made you decide to study biology. Was it curiosity about leaves and bugs? Maybe it was the teacher who hung all those birds' nests from the ceiling. Or was it an afternoon in a lab looking through a microscope at live amoebas? Many people become fascinated with biology as a result of a laboratory experience where they have to grow plants, make wet mount slides of living specimens, or track data on living organisms. From germinating bean seeds to keeping pet turtles, the biology classroom and curriculum comes to life with living things. The student who is bored by the textbook can be revived with a drop of pond water.

Teaching biology offers an opportunity for you to develop in your students a sense of excitement and old-fashioned wonder. Use of live organisms will enhance this wonder and help you reach at least one objective—students will be enthusiastic about coming to class. Many animal groups are described and illustrated in *Biology: An Everyday Experience.* You will not be able to introduce living specimens of all these groups to the classroom, but a few might stimulate student interest. Students will have to understand, of course, that they have an important role in the responsible care of these organisms. A few will probably even be willing to share that responsibility.

In addition, respect of the animals as classroom pets or as organisms to be observed in labs must be fostered. The authors of *Biology: An Everyday Experience* recommend the National Association of Biology Teachers "Guidelines for the Use of Live Animals." These guidelines are published in *The American Biology Teacher,* Vol. 48., No. 2, Feb. 1986. The guidelines are written in clear terms and can be used to stimulate a classroom discussion on the proper care and use of animals in society. The Labs throughout *Biology: An Everyday Experience* avoid the use of dissection and make use of observation of protists, fungi, and arthropods whenever possible. Students who wish to use animals for science fair projects or advanced study projects should use safe and respectful procedures that have been discussed thoroughly with you ahead of time. All work should be supervised for the well-being of both student and project animal.

Many times, students want to bring live animals to class. If facilities are adequate, this can be a great learning tool. However, students will have to understand the importance of providing food, space, fresh water, and adequate light and ventilation for the animals.

Weekends and vacations present problems. All living organisms will require regular feeding and a fresh supply of water. If a custodian cannot help, then students have to realize up front that animal day care is a necessary part of learning, and a regular group of volunteer caretakers will be needed. Students can take part in planning for this. Encourage students to set up teams of volunteers for regular care of organisms.

Equipment and Supplies List

A complete list of equipment and expendables for all the labs in the text is given below. The list will help you in ordering equipment for the entire school year. The amounts listed are for 15 pairs of students. The labs are designed so that simple apparatus can be used. Whenever possible, use materials that can be obtained locally.

Equipment	Quantity	Lab
aquarium (large)	1	13-1
aquarium (small)	15	8-1
balance	2	1-2, 14-1
beaker, 100 mL	30	1-2, 14-1, 23-1, 23-2
beaker, 200 mL	30	9-1
beaker, 250 mL	30	13-1
bolt (with 2 nuts), approximately 3.7 cm x 0.7 cm	30	4-1
bowl	15	30-2
cheese cloth, 20 cm x 20 cm	15	9-1
coins	30	27-1
coverslips	1 box	1-1, 2-2, 5-1, 6-1, 17-1, 30-2
dish (small)	15	7-1, 23-2
dissecting pan	15	7-2
dropper	320	1-1, 2-1, 5-1, 6-1, 6-2, 7-1, 9-1, 9-2, 13-2, 15-1, 17-1, 18-1, 18-2, 20-2, 32-1, 32-2
envelopes (large)	15	3-1
Materials to be placed in each envelope:		
bolt / metal nut		
brass fastener / paper clip		
button / rubber band		
glass slide / safety pin		
hairpin / toothpick		
match / washer		
nail / yarn (small piece)		
feather, down	15	8-2
feather, wing or tail	15	8-2
flashlight	15	7-1, 7-2
forceps	15	1-1, 6-1, 20-2, 30-2, 32-1
funnel	15	9-1
glass tubing	30	11-2
graduated cylinder, 250 mL	15	1-2, 9-1
100 mL	15	29-2
hand lens	15	1-2, 5-2, 6-1, 7-1, 7-2, 8-2, 16-1, 25-2, 31-2
hot plate	15	9-1
jars, baby food	75	2-1
lamp	15	31-1
map, state	15	3-2
metric ruler	15	4-2, 6-1, 8-2, 15-1, 16-1, 19-1, 23-1, 24-1, 24-2, 25-2, 28-2, 29-2, 30-1, 12-1
meter stick	15	11-2
microscopes, light	15	1-1, 2-2, 4-2, 5-1, 5-2,10-1, 10-2, 17-1, 22-2, 24-1, 30-1
microscope slides, glass	2 boxes	1-1, 2-2, 5-1, 6-1, 6-2, 9-2, 13-2, 15-2, 17-1, 18-1, 18-2, 30-2, 32-1
mirror, plane surface	15	17-2
model of foot	15	14-2
net (aquarium fish)	15	8-1, 13-1
pan	15	11-2
paper clips	1 box	2-1
paper punch	15	14-2
pencils, red, blue, green, yellow, purple	15	10-2, 16-2, 24-2
petri dish (with cover)	15	4-2, 11-1, 12-2, 21-2, 24-2, 26-1
plastic dish	15	29-2

plastic stick	15	4-2
plastic squeeze bottle	15	11-2
polystyrene ball	15	4-1
razor blade, single edge	15	21-1, 23-2, 9-2
rubber stopper		
two hole to fit plastic bottle	15	11-2
solid to fit test tubes	90	17-1, 31-1
scalpel	15	5-2, 6-2
scissors	15	8-2, 14-2, 16-1, 23-1, 28-1, 28-2
stereoscopic microscope	15	6-2, 7-1
test tube rack	15	13-2, 15-2, 17-1, 31-1, 32-2
test tubes, 12 cm	90	13-2, 15-2, 17-1, 31-1, 32-2
thermal glove	15	9-1
thermometer	1	13-1
watch (wall clock)	1	11-1, 13-1, 17-2
wire, #22 gauge, 14 cm long	30	4-1

Expendables

Aluminum foil	1 roll	28-2
cardboard piece	15	30-2
cheese cloth	1 package	9-1
chicken bone, a piece	15	14-1
cotton swab	15	7-2
crayons: red, blue, green, yellow	15	28-1
cow bone, a piece	15	14-1
detergent	50 mL	32-2
digestive system diagrams	90	10-2
file card	1 package	14-2
filter paper strips, 13 cm x 4 cm	15	19-2
food samples: apple juice, honey, sweet potato, molasses, maple syrup	15 of each	9-2
gelatin dessert	2 packages	10-1
glucose test paper	2 rolls	13-2, 15-2
glue	1 bottle	30-2
graph paper	30	21-1, 24-2, 30-1
ice	2 cups	13-1
India ink, black	1 bottle	21-1
labels	200	13-1, 17-1, 23-2, 28-2
magazine print letter "e"	15	1-1
marking pen	15	21-2, 31-2
marking pencil	15	12-2, 22-2, 31-1
metal fasteners	1 box	14-2
milk, whole	100 mL	9-1
milk cartons	30	23-1
owl pellet	15	30-2
paper bags	30	26-2
paper cup	120	10-1, 27-1
paper, black	15	16-1, 29-1
paper, heavy	60	28-1
paper, white	105	16-1, 16-2, 17-2, 27-2, 28-1, 29-1
paper dots		
black	450	29-1
white	450	29-1

paper towel	5 rolls	1-2, 6-1, 7-2, 16-2, 21-1, 21-2, 22-2, 26-1, 29-1
pencil	15	6-2, 17-2, 22-1, 23-1, 27-2
permanent marker	15	23-1
pH chart	30	32-1
pH paper, wide range	2 packages	32-1
pig bone, a piece	15	14-1
pipecleaners, 2-cm lengths	360 pieces	4-1
plastic bag, self-sealing	30	1-2, 21-1
plastic cup, clear	70	28-2, 31-2
plastic sheet, clear	1	12-2, 22-2
plastic spoons	60	10-1
rubber bands	15	23-1
salt	10 g	1-2
salt water, varying amounts		13-2, 31-2
soil	40 lb	23-1, 28-2
sticks, for stirring	1 box	10-1, 19-2
straw, drinking	15	2-1
string	1 roll	14-2
sugar, granulated	10 g	solution preparation
tape, masking	2 rolls	1-2, 19-2, 27-1
tape, transparent	1 roll	14-2, 16-1, 21-2, 23-1, 28-1
tissues	1 box	22-2
toothpicks, flat	2 boxes	2-2, 7-1, 21-1, 31-2
tracing paper	60	28-1
turkey bone, a piece	15	14-1
water		
distilled, varying amounts		13-2, 32-2
rain, 300 mL		32-1
tap, varying amounts		1-1, 1-2, 2-2, 7-2, 9-2, 10-1, 14-1, 18-1, 18-2, 26-1, 28-2, 29-2, 23-2, 30-2
wax pencil	15	2-1, 15-2, 18-1, 18-2, 26-1
yeast, dead mixture	150 mL	32-2
yeast, dry	4 packets	2-1, 32-2

Chemicals

acetone	100 mL	solution preparation
alcohol	100 mL	18-2
alcohol testing chemical	10 mL	18-2
ammonia	300 mL	32-1
aspirin	1 small bottle	18-1
aspirin testing chemical	10 mL	18-1
baking soda (sodium bicarbonate)	50 g	32-1
bromthymol blue	1 g	32-2
cola	300 mL	32-1
copper chloride, CuCl	100 g	solution preparation
enzyme	1	9-1
ethyl alcohol	100 mL	6-2
ferric nitrate nonhydrate, $Fe(NO_2)\ 9H_2O$	200 mL	solution preparation
glucose	100 mL	13-2
hydrogen peroxide, 3% solution	1 bottle	32-2
lemon juice	300 mL	32-1
methyl cellulose	25 g	solution preparation
methylene blue stain	25 g	2-2

nitric acid, concentrated	100 mL	solution preparation
oil, vegetable	1/2 L	mini lab
painkiller test solutions	50 mL	18-1
petroleum ether	1 L	solution preparation
phenol red	1 g	2-1
plastic powder (type 2 Jeltrate)	1 L	29-2
potassium iodide	10 g	solution preparation
silver nitrate	10 g	13-2
sodium chloride	100 g	solution preparation
sugar test paper	100 pieces	9-2
test solutions of over-the-counter drugs and household items	50 mL each	18-2
vinegar	3/4 liter	7-2, 32-1

Biological Supplies

Anabaena, prepared slides	15	7-2
bacteria, prepared slide	15	4-2
beans, red	600	26-2
beans, white	600	26-2
bean seedlings, 3 days old	15	21-1
blood, frog, prepared	15	12-1
blood, human, prepared	15	12-1, 12-2
brine shrimp or daphnia	15	7-1
brine shrimp eggs	15	31-2
carrot, root	15	20-2, 23-2
Coleus plant	15 leaves	28-2
corn seeds	900	21-2, 23-1, 26-1
crayfish, live	15	8-1
cultures of:		
amoeba	1	5-1
euglena	1	5-1
hydra	1	7-1
earthworms, live	15	7-2, 11-1
Elodea, several sprigs	45	2-2, 31-1
Enzyme cultures	1	10-1
fern fronds	15	6-2
garlic bulb	15	23-2
grasshopper, stages of metamorphosis	15	25-2
guppy	15	2-1
leaf	15	29-2
leaves, 15 types	45 each	19-1
moss, preserved or live	15	6-1
moth, stages of metamorphosis	15	25-2
mushroom	15	5-2
mushroom basidium, prepared slide	15	5-2
radish root	15	20-2
starfish egg, prepared slide	15	24-1
starfish sperm, prepared slide	15	24-1
urine sample—see Preparation of Solutions		
abnormal		13-2, 15-2
normal		13-2, 15-2
vinegar eels	1	17-1
yam root	15	20-2

Preparation of Solutions

Abnormal urine—Add 2 teaspoons honey to a normal urine mixture.

Alcohol-testing solution—Add 20 g potassium dichromate powder to a glass beaker. Pour 20 mL concentrated sulfuric acid into the beaker. Stir with a glass rod to dissolve most of the powered. *Slowly* add 60 mL distilled water and continue to stir. *Solution becomes very hot.* Allow to cool. Powder may precipitate out after cooling. Pour only the liquid portion of the solution into dropping bottles for student use. Solution has a shelf life of one year.

Aspirin testing solution—Add 2 g ferric nitrate nonhydrate, $Fe(NO_2)$ $9H_2O$ to 50 mL water. Then add 1 mL concentrated nitric acid to this solution.

Aspirin solution—Dissolve 1 aspirin in 50 mL water.

Blue liquid—Add 0.1 g bromthymol blue to 2000 mL water.

Dead yeast mixture—Boil 100 mL live yeast for at least 5 minutes on a hot plate.

Glucose solution—Add 1 teaspoon glucose to 250 mL tap water.

Green liquid—Add 0.1 g bromthymol blue to 2000 mL water. Then exhale into the liquid until a green color appears.

Hydrochloric acid—Pour 85 mL concentrated hydrochloric acid slowly into 1000 mL water. Do not pour water into concentrated acid.

Iodine solution—Dissolve 10 g potassium iodine and 3 g iodine in 1 L water. Store in the dark or in a brown bottle.

Liquid solvent—Combine 92 parts petroleum ether with 8 parts acetone. An alternative solvent is ethyl alcohol.

Live yeast mixture—Add 1 tablespoon each of dry yeast and sugar to 200 mL water.

Methyl cellulose—Add 10 g methyl cellulose powder to 90 mL warm distilled water. Stir gently to avoid bubbles.

Methylene blue stain—Dissolve 1.5 g methylene blue in 100 mL ethyl alcohol. Dilute by adding 10 mL of solution to 90 mL water.

Normal urine—Add 1 teaspoon salt and 4 drops yellow food coloring to 500 mL tap water.

Phenol red—Mix 0.4 g phenol red in 100 mL water to make stock solution. Transfer 1 mL stock solution to 100 mL water to yield a 0.00004% phenol red solution for use.

Salt water—Add 1 teaspoon sodium chloride to 500 mL tap water.

Silver nitrate—Add 4 g silver nitrate to 250 mL distilled water. Store in a brown bottle away from light.

Urine sample—Add 6 drops yellow food coloring to 1000 mL tap water.

Urine sample with glucose—Add 6 drops yellow food coloring to 1000 mL tap water, then add 2 teaspoons glucose or honey.

Yeast solution—Mix 1 teaspoon sugar and 1 teaspoon dry yeast to 200 mL water.

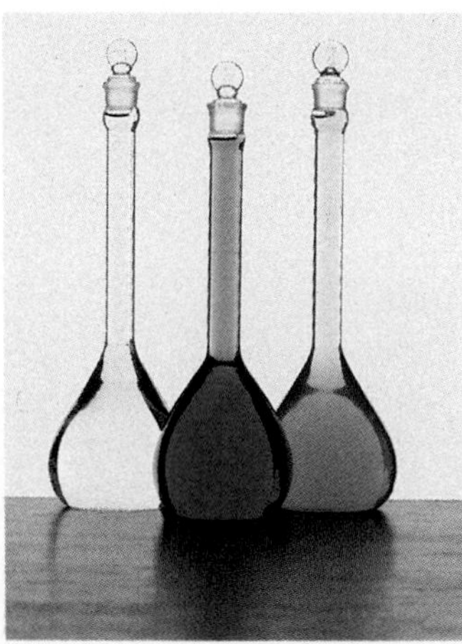

Equipment Suppliers

Carolina Biological Supply Co.
2700 York Rd.
Burlington, NC 27215

Central Scientific Co.
11222 Melrose Ave.
Franklin Park, IL 60131

Fisher Scientific Co.
4901 W. LeMoyne
Chicago, IL 60615

LaPine Scientific Company
6001 S. Knox Ave.
Chicago, IL 60629

McKilligan Supply Corp.
435 Main St.
Johnson City, NY 13790

Nasco
901 Janesville Ave.
Fort Atkinson, WI 53538

Sargent-Welch Scientific Co.
7300 N. Linder
Skokie, IL 60077

Sargent-Welch Scientific of Canada Ltd.
285 Garyray Dr.
Weston, Ontario, Canada M9L 1P3

Science Kit and Boreal Labs
777 E. Park Dr.
Tonawanda, NY 14150

Ward's Natural Science Establishment, Inc.
P.O. Box 1712
Rochester, NY 14603

Materials List by Lab

Lab 1-1
- microscope
- slides
- coverslips
- water
- dropper
- forceps
- small piece magazine print

Lab 1-2
- 2 100 mL beakers
- 40 pinto beans
- balance
- salt
- water
- 2 paper towels
- 50 mL graduated cylinder
- 2 self-sealing plastic bags
- masking tape

Lab 2-1
- 5 baby food jars
- red liquid
- wax pencil
- guppy
- yeast suspension
- dropper
- paper clip
- drinking straw

Lab 2-2
- microscope
- 2 slides
- 2 coverslips
- dropper
- methylene blue stain
- toothpicks, flat type
- *Elodea* leaf
- water

Lab 3-1
- envelopes with 12 items

Lab 3-2
- state maps

Lab 4-1
- bolt
- 2 nuts to fit bolt
- 2 pieces of wire
- polystyrene ball
- pipecleaners

Lab 4-2
- microscope
- prepared slide of *Anabaena*
- prepared slide of bacteria
- petri dish
- metric ruler

Lab 5-1
- microscope
- 3 slides
- 3 coverslips
- 3 droppers
- cultures of:
  - amoeba
  - euglena
  - paramecium

Lab 5-2
- microscope
- hand lens
- scalpel
- prepared mushroom slide
- mushroom gill

Lab 6-1
- stereomicroscope or hand lens
- 3 slides
- cover slip
- dropper
- forceps
- metric ruler
- paper towels
- moss

Lab 6-2
- stereomicroscope
- 2 slides
- scalpel
- dropper
- ethyl alcohol
- whole fern with spore cases
- pencil
- paper

Lab 7-1
- stereomicroscope
- hand lens
- dropper
- small dish
- flashlight
- hydra culture
- daphnia or brine shrimp

Lab 7-2
- hand lens
- shallow pan
- flashlight
- toothpick
- beaker of water
- cotton swab
- paper towels
- vinegar
- live earthworms

Lab 8-1
- small aquarium with crayfish

Lab 8-2
- hand lens
- metric ruler
- scissors
- wing or tail feather
- down feather

Lab 9-1
- 2 200-mL beakers
- dropper
- funnel
- hot plate
- stirring rod
- whole milk
- enzyme
- 250-mL graduated cylinder
- thermal glove
- cheese cloth

Lab 9-2
- slides
- droppers
- razor blade
- food samples for sugar test
- water
- sugar test paper

Lab 10-1
- 4 paper cups
- gelatin
- water
- 4 applicator sticks
- enzyme A
- enzyme B

Lab 10-2
- 5 diagrams of digestive system
- colored pencils

Lab 11-1
- petri dish
- water
- wall clock
- live earthworm

Lab 11-2
- plastic squeeze bottle
- pan or sink
- water
- meterstick
- rubber stopper and tube assembly

Lab 12-1
- microscope
- prepared slides of frog and human blood
- petri dish cover
- metric ruler

Lab 12-2
- sheet of clear plastic
- marking pencil
- microscope
- prepared slide of human blood

Lab 13-1
- 250-mL beaker
- goldfish in aquarium
- thermometer
- net
- watch or wall clock
- ice

Lab 13-2
- 4 test tubes
- test tube rack
- droppers
- labels
- distilled water
- salt water
- glucose
- glucose test tape
- silver nitrate
- normal artificial urine
- abnormal artificial urine
- 4 slides

Lab 14-1
- 100-mL graduated cylinder
- balance
- water
- bones of:
  - chicken
  - cow
  - pig
  - turkey

Lab 14-2
- scissors
- string
- tape
- paper punch
- metal fastener
- index card

Lab 15-1
- metric ruler

Lab 15-2
- test tube
- slides
- 8 droppers
- wax pencil
- normal urine sample
- urine sample from diabetic
- urine samples in test tubes marked C-E
- glucose test paper

Lab 16-1
- metric ruler
- scissors
- hand lens
- clear tape
- white paper
- black paper

Lab 16-2
- white paper
- red and green pencils

Lab 17-1
- microscope
- glass slide
- coverslip
- dropper
- test-tube rack
- 2 test tubes, small
- 2 stoppers to fit tubes
- 2 labels
- vinegar eels

Lab 17-2
- mirror
- watch with second hand
- pencil
- paper

Lab 18-1
- 4 glass slides
- wax marking pencil
- aspirin solution
- 6 test solutions of pain killers
- dropper tube
- aspirin-testing solution in dropper bottle

Lab 18-2
- 4 slides
- wax marking pencil
- 8 droppers
- water
- alcohol
- alcohol testing chemical in dropper bottle
- 6 test solutions of over-the-counter drugs and household chemicals

Lab 19-1
- 15 leaves of different plants
- metric ruler

Lab 19-2
- plant leaf
- coin
- small jar
- metric ruler
- filter paper strip
- liquid solvent
- applicator stick
- masking tape

Lab 20-1
- pencil
- paper towel cut into 10 x 15 cm and 1 x 10 cm strips
- stapler
- large plastic cup

Lab 20-2
- hand lens
- carrot root
- yam root
- radish root
- razor blade
- 3 petri dish halves
- iodine solution
- dropper
- forceps

Lab 21-1
- toothpick
- plastic bag
- paper towel
- graph paper
- razor blade
- India ink
- 2 bean seedlings

Lab 21-2
- petri dish
- marking pen
- 2 paper towels
- transparent tape
- 4 pre-soaked corn seeds

Lab 22-1
- pencil
- paper

Lab 22-2
- clear plastic sheet
- marking pencil
- facial tissue
- microscope

Lab 23-1
- metric ruler
- rubber band
- small beaker
- pencil
- tape
- permanent marker
- 2 milk cartons
- soil
- 20 corn seeds
- water
- stapler
- scissors

Lab 23-2
- garlic bulb
- carrot
- labels
- water
- toothpicks
- small beaker
- metric ruler
- razor blade
- shallow dish

Lab 24-1
- microscope
- prepared slide of starfish eggs
- prepared slide of starfish sperm
- metric ruler
- petri dish for drawing circles

Lab 24-2
- metric ruler
- graph paper
- colored pencils

Lab 25-1
- metric ruler

Lab 25-2
- metric ruler
- hand lens
- grasshopper stages of metamorphosis
- moth stages of metamorphosis

Lab 26-1
- 20 corn seeds
- paper towels
- wax pencil
- petri dish
- water

Lab 26-2
- 40 white beans
- 40 red beans
- 2 paper bags

Lab 27-1
- 2 coins
- paper cup
- masking tape

Lab 27-2
- pencil
- paper

Lab 28-1
- scissors
- tracing paper
- heavy paper
- tape
- blank paper
- crayons

Lab 28-2
- scissors
- clear plastic cup
- aluminum foil
- *Coleus* plant
- soil
- water
- label
- metric ruler

Lab 29-1
- white paper
- black paper
- 30 white dots
- 30 black dots
- damp paper towels

Lab 29-2
- plastic dish
- 100-mL graduated cylinder
- warm water
- metric ruler
- leaf
- plastic powder

Lab 30-1
- metric ruler
- graph paper

Lab 30-2
- light microscope
- slide
- coverslip
- bowl
- forceps
- cardboard
- glue
- owl pellet
- water

Lab 31-1
- 4 test tubes
- wax pencil
- 4 stoppers
- lamp
- blue test liquid
- green test liquid
- 2 *Elodea* sprigs
- 2 test-tube racks

Lab 31-2
- 3 small plastic cups
- marking pen
- hand lens
- flat toothpick
- distilled water
- brine shrimp eggs
- strong salt solution
- weak salt solution

Lab 32-1
- pH paper
- pH chart
- forceps
- marking pencil
- 7 slides
- 7 droppers
- ammonia
- baking soda
- cola
- vinegar
- 2 samples of rainwater
- distilled water

Lab 32-2
- 4 test tubes
- marking pencil
- test-tube rack
- 5 droppers
- blue test liquid
- dead yeast mixture
- live yeast mixture
- detergent
- hydrogen peroxide
- distilled water

Audiovisual and Software Suppliers

AETNA Life and Casualty, Film Library, 151 Farmingham Ave., Hartford, CT 06115
Aims, 626 Justin Ave., Glendale, CA 91201
Almanac Films, Inc., 29 E. Tenth St., New York, NY 10003
American Cancer Society, 777 Third Ave., New York, NY 10017
American Film Registry, 832 S. Wabash, Chicago, IL 60605
American Heart Association, 44 E. 23 St., New York, NY 10010 (or contact local chapter)
Appalachian Hardwood Association, Room 408 NCNB Bldg., High Point, NC 27260
Association Films, Inc., 866 Third Avenue, New York, NY 10022
Audio Productions, Inc., 708 Third Avenue, New York, NY 10017
Audio Visual Center, Indiana University, Bloomington, IN 47405
Bailey Films, Inc., 6509 DeLongpre Ave., Hollywood, CA 90028
Barr Films, P.O. Box 5667, 3490 East Foothill Blvd., Pasadena, CA 91107
Bausch and Lomb, Inc., Film Service, 1400 N. Goodman St., Rochester, NY 14602
Beacon Films, P.O. Box 575, Norwood, MA 02062
Bergwall, Inc., 106 Charles Lindberg Blvd., Uniondale, NY 11553
BFA Educational Media, 2211 Michigan Ave., P.O. Box 1795, Santa Monica, CA 90406
Brancon Films, Inc., 200 W. 57th St., New York, NY 10019
Bray Studios, Inc., (BRAY), 630 Ninth Avenue, New York, NY 10036
Bureau of AV Services, University of Arizona, Tucson, AZ 85721
Carolina Biological Supply Company, Burlington, NC 27215
Chevron Chemical Co., Ortho Distribution (Film Lab), 200 Bush St., San Francisco, CA 94104
CCM Films, Inc., 5547 Ravenswood Ave., Chicago, IL 60640
Centron Educational Films, 108 Wilmont Rd., Deerfield, IL 60015
Churchill Films, 662 Robertson Blvd., Los Angeles, CA 90069
Clearvue, Inc., 6465 Avondale Ave., Chicago, IL 60631
Colonial Films, 71 Walton St., N.W., Atlanta, GA 30303
COMPress, A Div. of Wadsworth Inc., P.O. Box 102, Wentworth, NH 03282
CONDUIT, University of Iowa Oakdale Campus, Iowa City, IA 52242
Conservation Foundation, 1717 Massachusetts Ave. N.W., Washington, DC 20036
Contemporary Films, Inc., 267 W. 25 St., New York, NY 10001
Coronet Films, 108 Wilmont Rd., Deerfield, IL 60015
Cox Enterprises, 2900 S. Sawtelle Blvd., Los Angeles, CA 90064
Cross Educational Software, P.O. Box 1536, Ruston, LA 71270
DM, Inc., One DLM Park, Allen, TX 75002
Davidson & Associates, Inc., 3135 Kashiwa St., Torrence, CA 90505
Denoyer-Geppert Audiovisuals, 355 Lexington Ave., New York, NY 10017
Design Ware, Inc./EduWare Services, Inc., 185 Berry St., San Francisco, CA 94107
Walt Disney Productions, 500 S. Buena Vista Ave., Burbank, CA 91505
Doubleday Multimedia, Box C-19518, 1371 Reynolds, Irvine, CA 92713
EME, Old Mill Plain Road, Box 2805, Danbury, CT 06430
Earling Corp., 2225 Massachusetts Ave., Cambridge, MA 02140
Eastman Kodak Co., Audiovisual Service, 348 State St., Rochester, NY 14608
Education Dimensions Group, P.O. Box 126, Stamford, CT 06904
Educational Activities, 19377 Grand Ave., Baldwin, NY 11510
Educational Development Corp., Learning Resources Division, 4404 S. Florida Ave., Lakeland, FL 33803
Educational Film Library Association, 250 W. 57 St., New York, NY 10019
Educational Images Ltd., P.O. Box 3456 West Side, Elmira, NY 14905
Encyclopedia Brittanica Educational Corp., 425 N. Michigan Ave., Chicago, IL 60611
Eye Gate Media, P.O. Box 303, Jamaica, NY 11435
Farm Film Foundation, 1616 H Street, NW, Washington, DC 20006
Films, Inc, ATTN: Public Media, Inc., 5547 Ravenswood Ave., Chicago, IL 60640
Films for the Humanities and Sciences, P.O. Box 2053, Princeton, NJ 08543
Films of the Nation Distributors, Inc., 305 E. 86 St., New York, NY 10036
Filmstrip House, 6633 W. Howard St., Niles, IL 60648
Focus Media, Inc., 839 Stewart Ave., Box 865, Garden City, NY 11530
Frey Scientific Co., 905 Hickory Lane, Mansfield, OH 44905
Gamco Industries, Box 1911, Big Spring, TX 79720

Gateway Productions, Inc., 1859 Powell St., San Francisco, CA 94133

Golden Key Productions, Inc., Film Distributors, 1921 Hillhurst Ave., Hollywood, CA 90027

Guidance Associates, Inc., Communications Park, Box 3000, Mount Kisco, NY 10549

HRM Software, 175 Tompkins Ave., Pleasantville, NY 10570

Handel Films, 8730 Sunset Blvd., West Hollywood, CA 90069

Hartley Courseware, Inc., 133 Bridge, Dimondale, MI 48821

Hayden Software, 600 Suffolk St., Lowell, MA 01853

Heidenkamp Nature Pictures, 872 Old Hickory Rd., Pittsburgh, PA 15243

Human Relations Media, 175 Tompkins Ave., Pleasantville, NY 10570

IBM, P.O. Box 2150, Atlanta, GA 30055

Ideal Pictures Corp., 58 E. South Water St., Chicago, IL 60648

Indiana University Films, Audio-Visual Center, Bloomington, IN 47405

Insight Media, 121 West 85th Street, New York, NY 10024

Institutional Cinema Service, Inc., 915 Broadway, New York, NY 10075

Instructional Films, Inc., 1150 Wilmette Ave., Wilmette, IL 60091

International Film Bureau, 332 S. Michigan Ave., Chicago, IL 60604

International Film Bureau, Inc., 57 E. Jackson Blvd., Chicago, IL 60604

International Film Foundation, Inc., 200 W. 72nd St., Room 64, New York, NY 10023

JLM Visuals, 920 7th Avenue, Grafton, WI 53024

Jam Handy Organization, 28221 E. Grand Blvd., Detroit, MI 48211

Library Films, Inc., 79 Fifth Ave., New York, NY 10011

McGraw-Hill Text Films, 110 Fifteenth St., Del Mar, CA 92014

McGraw-Hill Publishing Co., Films Division, 330 W. 42 St., New York, NY 10036

Minnesota Educational Computing Corp./MECC, 3490 Lexington Ave., North, St. Paul, MN 55126

Modern Learning Aids, Division of Ward's Natural Science, P.O. Box 1712, Rochester, NY 14603

Modern Talking Picture Service, Inc., 45 Rockefeller Plaza, New York, NY 10020

Moonlight Productions, 2243 Old Middlefield Way, Mountain View, CA 94043

Nasco, 901 Janesville Ave., Fort Atkinson,WI 53538

Nasco West, Inc., P.O. Box 3837, Modesto, CA 95352

National Audubon Society, 1130 Fifth Ave., New York, NY 10028

National Film Board of Canada, 1251 Avenue of the Americas, New York, NY 10020

National Geographic Society, Dept. 86, Washington, DC 20036

National Safety Council, 425 N. Michigan Ave., Chicago, IL 60611

National Wildlife Federation, 1412 16th St. N.W., Washington, DC 20036

NET Film Service, Audio-Visual Center, Indiana University, Bloomington, IN 47401 (also 10 Columbus Circle, New York, NY 10019)

Opportunities for Learning, 20417 Nordhoff St., Chattsworth, CA 91311

Photo Lab, Inc., 3825 Georgia Ave., N.W., Washington, DC 20011

Prentice-Hall Media, 150 White Plains Rd., Tarrytown, NY 10591

Queue, Inc., 338 Commerce Dr., Fairfield, CT 06430

Edwin Shapiro Co., 43-55 Kissena Blvd., Flushing, NY 11355

Scholastic Software, 730 Broadway, New York, NY 10003

Science and Mankind, Inc., Communications Park, Box 200, White plains, NY 10602

Science Software Systems, Inc., 11899 W. Pico Blvd., West Los Angeles, CA 90064

Sensible Software, 210 South Woodward, Ste. 229, Birmingham, MI 48011

Shell Film Library, 1433 Sadlier Circle West Drive, Indianapolis, IN 46239

Society for Visual Education, Inc., 1345 W. Diversey Pkwy, Chicago, IL 60614

Sunburst Communications, Inc., 39 Washington Ave., Pleasantville, NY 10570

Time-Life Films, 100 Eisenhower Dr., Paramus, NJ 07652

United World Films, Inc., 221 Park Ave. South, New York, NY 10003

University of Illinois, Visual Aids Service, Champaign, IL 61820

Vernard Organization, 702 S. Adams St., Peoria, IL 61602

Ward's Natural Science Establishment, P.O. Box 1712, Rochester, NY 14603

Wilner Films and Slides, P.O. Box 231, Cathedral Station, New York, NY 10025

U.S. Government Agencies

Council for Agricultural Science and Technology, 137 Lynn Ave., Ames, IA 50010-7120

Fish and Wildlife Service, U.S. Dept. of the Interior, P.O. Box 128, College Park, MD 20740

National Aeronautics and Space Administration, Washington, DC 20546

National Oceanic and Atmospheric Administration, U.S. Dept. of Commerce, Motion Picture Service, 12231 Welkin Ave., Rockville, MD 20852

Soil Conservation Service, Washington, DC 20251

U.S. Atomic Energy Commission, Washington, DC 20545

U.S. Department of Agriculture, Motion Picture Service, Washington, DC 20251

U.S. Forest Service, U.S. Department of Agriculture, Washington, DC 20251

U.S. Navy Department, Office of Administration, Pentagon Bldg., Washington, DC 20350

U.S. Public Health Service, 200 Independence Avenue SW, Washington, DC 20201

U.S. Public Health Service, Communicable Disease Center, Atlanta, GA 30333

Canada

Audio-Visual Supply Co., Toronto General Trusts Bldg., Winnipeg, Manitoba

Canadian Film Institute, 142 Sparks St., Ottawa, Ontario

General Films Limited, 15334 13th Ave., Regina, Saskatchewan

Radio-Cinema, 5011 Verdun Ave., Montreal, Quebec

Teacher Questionnaire

Perhaps one of the best ways to ensure that effective educational materials are produced is to let authors and publishers know how you feel concerning the materials you are using. Please help us in our planning of revisions and new programs by completing and returning the form found on the next page. After removing the questionnaire from the book, fold and tape it so that the address label shows. We would certainly appreciate hearing from you.

PHOTO CREDITS

5T, Claude Steelman/Tom Stack & Assoc.; **6T,** Mark Newman, Tom Stack & Assoc.; **8T, 9T,** Mark Burnett/ Glencoe; **11T,** Bob Daemmrich; **12T, 13T,** Doug Martin; **19T,** Ted Rice; **20T, 21T,** Bob Daemmrich; **26T,** First Image; **27T,** Bob Daemmrich; **32T,** Chip Clark; **34T,** Doug Martin; **39T,** Ted Rice.

Biology: An Everyday Experience Program© 1992

Circle the number which corresponds most nearly to your opinion of each of the following items of this biology program. Please also star (*) three factors which influence your evaluation or choice of a text.

	Excel-lent	*Very Good*	*Satis-factory*	*Fair*	*Poor*	*Comments*
Student Text						
1. Format	1	2	3	4	5	________
2. Readability	1	2	3	4	5	________
3. Approach	1	2	3	4	5	________
4. Organization	1	2	3	4	5	________
5. Factual accuracy	1	2	3	4	5	________
6. Coverage of science principles	1	2	3	4	5	________
7. Concept development	1	2	3	4	5	________
8. Visual impact	1	2	3	4	5	________
9. Margin notes	1	2	3	4	5	________
10. Treatment of new terms	1	2	3	4	5	________
11. Activities	1	2	3	4	5	________
12. Problems	1	2	3	4	5	________
13. Tables	1	2	3	4	5	________
14. Illustrations	1	2	3	4	5	________
15. Reflect and Review sections	1	2	3	4	5	________
16. Career Close-Ups	1	2	3	4	5	________
17. Photo essays	1	2	3	4	5	________
18. Chapter-end materials	1	2	3	4	5	________
19. Glossary	1	2	3	4	5	________
20. Index	1	2	3	4	5	________
Teacher Edition						
1. Teachability	1	2	3	4	5	________
2. Activity Planning Guide	1	2	3	4	5	________
3. Equipment and Supplies information	1	2	3	4	5	________
4. Special Features information	1	2	3	4	5	________
5. Performance Objectives	1	2	3	4	5	________
6. Career information	1	2	3	4	5	________
7. Audiovisual information	1	2	3	4	5	________
8. Chapter-by-chapter margin material	1	2	3	4	5	________
9. Annotations	1	2	3	4	5	________
Supplements						
1. Teacher Resource Package	1	2	3	4	5	________
2. Review Guide	1	2	3	4	5	________
3. Review Guide, TAE	1	2	3	4	5	________
4. Biology: Laboratory Experiences	1	2	3	4	5	________
5. Biology: Laboratory Experiences, TAE	1	2	3	4	5	________

School Information

1.	Grade level of students	9	10		11	12
2.	Total number of students enrolled in that grade	1–50	51–100		101–200	200+
3.	Total number of students enrolled in biology	1–50	51–100		101–200	200+
4.	Average class size	25 or less	26–30	31–35	36–40	41 or more
5.	Total school enrollment	1–200	201–500		501–1000	1000+
6.	Locale of school	rural	small town		suburban	large city
7.	Ability level of class	below average		average		above average
8.	Appropriateness of text for your class	easy		about right		difficult
9.	Number of years text used	1	2	3	4	5
10.	May we quote you?			yes		no

Please feel free to attach an additional sheet to make further comments.

Name ______________________ Date ______________________

School ______________________ City ____________ State ____________ Zip ______

Fold

Fold

NO POSTAGE NECESSARY IF MAILED IN THE UNITED STATES

BUSINESS REPLY MAIL

FIRST CLASS PERMIT NO. 284 COLUMBUS, OHIO

POSTAGE WILL BE PAID BY ADDRESSEE

GLENCOE PUBLISHING CO.
Editorial Director, Science Dept.
936 EASTWIND DRIVE
WESTERVILLE, OHIO 43081

MERRILL

BIOLOGY

AN EVERYDAY EXPERIENCE

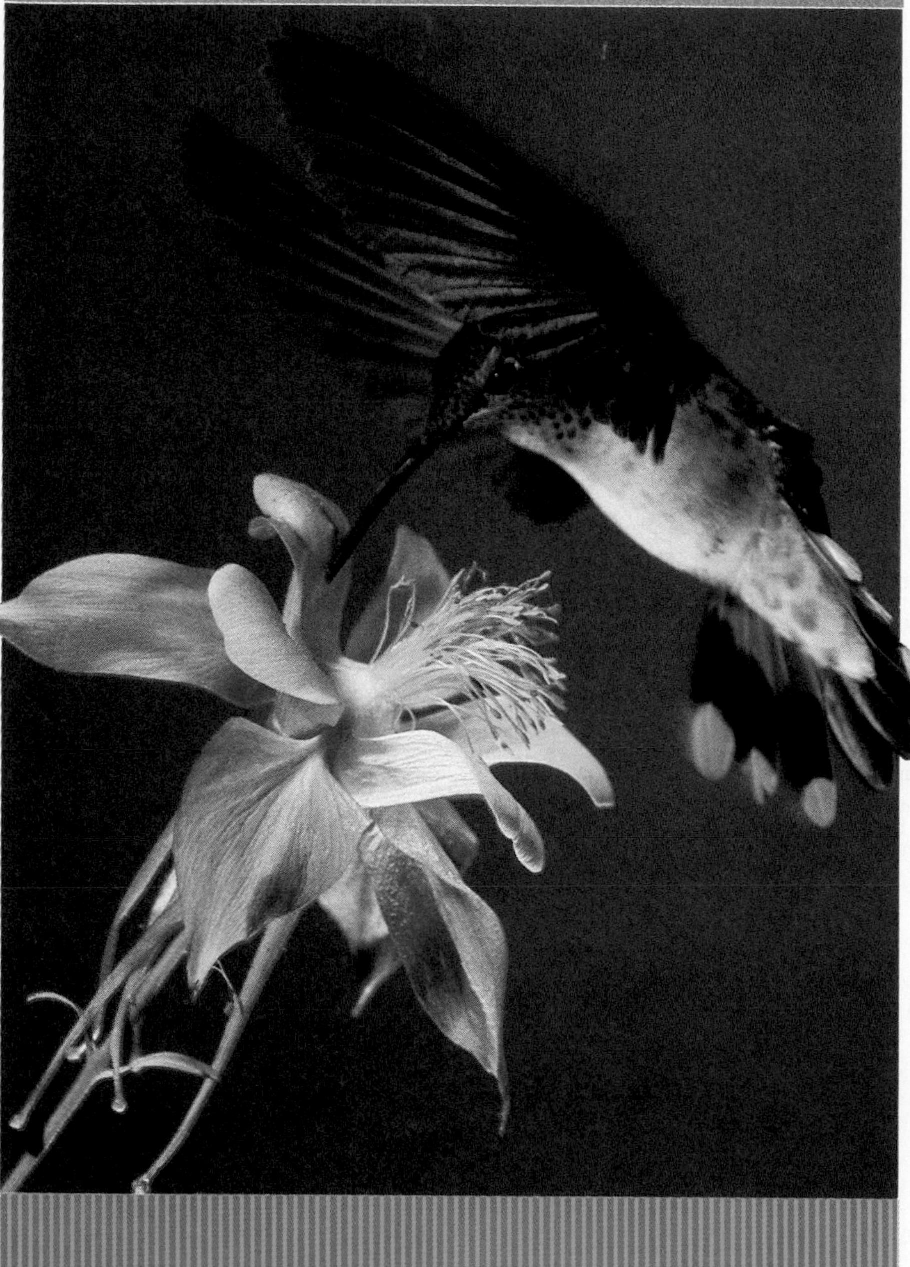

Authors
Albert Kaskel
Paul J. Hummer, Jr.
Lucy Daniel

GLENCOE

Macmillan/McGraw-Hill

Lake Forest, Illinois
Columbus, Ohio
Mission Hills, California
Peoria, Illinois

A MERRILL BIOLOGY PROGRAM

Biology: An Everyday Experience, *Student Edition*
Biology: An Everyday Experience, *Teacher Edition*
Biology: An Everyday Experience, *Teacher Resource Package*
Biology: An Everyday Experience, *Study Guide*
Biology: An Everyday Experience, *Transparency Package*
Biology: An Everyday Experience, *Laboratory Manual, Student Edition*
Biology: An Everyday Experience, *Laboratory Manual, Teacher Edition*
Biology: An Everyday Experience, *Computer Test Bank*

CONTENT CONSULTANTS

David M. Armstrong, Ph.D.
Director, University of Colorado Museum
University of Colorado
Boulder, CO

Mary D. Coyne, Ph.D.
Professor of Biological Sciences
Department of Biological Sciences
Wellesley College
Wellesley, MA

Joe W. Crim, Ph.D.
Associate Professor of Zoology
Department of Zoology
University of Georgia
Athens, GA

Marvin Druger, Ph.D.
Professor of Biology and Science Education
Department of Biology
Syracuse University
Syracuse, NY

David G. Futch, Ph.D.
Associate Professor of Biology
Department of Biology
San Diego State University
San Diego, CA

Carl Gans, Ph.D
Professor of Biology
University of Michigan
Ann Arbor, MI

John Just, Ph.D.
Associate Professor of Biology
School of Biological Sciences
University of Kentucky
Lexington, KY

Richard Storey, Ph.D.
Associate Professor of Biology
Department of Biology
Colorado College
Colorado Springs, CO

James F. Waters, Ph.D.
Professor of Zoology
Department of Biology
Humboldt State University
Arcata, CA

READING CONSULTANT

Barbara S. Pettegrew, Ph.D.
Director of Reading/Study Center
Assistant Professor of Education
Otterbein College
Westerville, OH

REVIEWERS

John A. Beach
Fairless High School
Navarre, OH

Tony Beasley
Science Supervisor
Davidson County School Board
Nashville, TN

Brenda Carrillo
McCollum High School
San Antonio, TX

Renee M. Carroll
Taylor County High School
Perry, FL

Dixie Duncan
Williams Township School
Whiteville, NC

Margorae Freimuth
Argenta-Oreanna High School
Argenta, IL

Raymond P. Gipson
Blue Ridge High School
Morgan Hill, CA

Karen S. Hewitt
Coldspring High School
Coldspring, TX

Marilyn B. Jacobs
Huffman Eastgate High School
Huffman, TX

Rex J. Kartchner
St. David High School
St. David, AZ

Barbara B. Kruse
Alamosa High School
Alamosa, CO

Lynn M. Smith
Waterville High School
Waterville, ME

Ouida E. Thomas
B.F. Terry High School
Rosenberg, TX

1 2 3 4 5 6 7 8 9 10 11 12 13 14 15–VH–98 97 96 95 94 93 92 91

ISBN 0-675-02620-2

Printed in the United States of America.

AUTHORS

Albert Kaskel has thirty-one years experience teaching science. He has extensive teaching experience in the city of Chicago and Evanston Township High School, Evanston, Illinois. His teaching experience includes all ability levels of biological science, physical science, and chemistry. He holds an M.Ed. degree from DePaul University. He received the Outstanding Biology Teacher Award for the State of Illinois in 1984.

Paul J. Hummer, Jr. taught science for twenty-eight years in the Frederick County, Maryland schools. He is currently a biology teacher at Hood College, Frederick, Maryland. He received his B.S.Ed. from Lock Haven State University, Lock Haven, PA, and his M.A.S.T. from Union College in Schenectady, NY. He has experience teaching various ability levels of biology as well as general science and physics. He received the Presidential Award for Excellence in Science and Mathematics Teaching in 1984.

Lucy Daniel teaches biology at Rutherfordton-Spindale High School, Rutherfordton, North Carolina. She has thirty-five years of teaching experience in biology, life science, and general science. She holds a B.S. degree from the University of North Carolina at Greensboro and a M.A.S.E. from Western Carolina University at Cullowhee. She received the Presidential Award for Excellence in Science and Mathematics Teaching in 1984.

iii

Biology *is* an Everyday Experience

This is your life. Biology is not just another science class. It's a subject you already know well, because it's about life.

It's 10:00, do you know where your dinner is? Every day, you eat and drink to stay alive. Where do your food and water come from, and how does your body use them?

Appreciate the environment—it's the only one you have. Trees don't just stand there, they help supply you with oxygen, prevent soil erosion, and make some of your food.

The wonderful world of technology. The field of medicine is closely tied to biology. Advances in medical technology may present you with difficult decisions.

Biology happens! Biology is about every living thing in your world and the relationships among them. The more you learn about biology, the more you will realize that biology *is* an everyday experience.

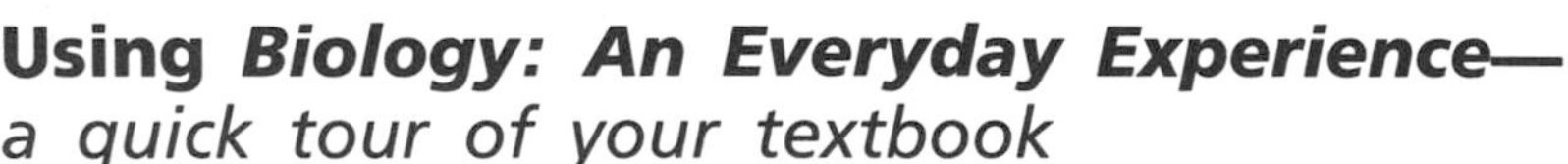

Using *Biology: An Everyday Experience*—*a quick tour of your textbook*

Biology: An Everyday Experience not only presents information, it asks thought-provoking questions. Labs bring the text to life as you use scientific methods to solve problems. You will see how biology affects you as a consumer and learn about careers in biology. Take time now to see what your textbook offers.

iv

from beginning to end, you'll see how biology connects to the world around you

❶ What would happen if. . . there were no mosquitoes? Have you ever thought about it? Each unit opener begins with a thought-provoking question like this. The unit introduction then shows you how even small differences in the relationships between living things can change your world in dramatic ways. So, what would happen if there were no mosquitoes? Read the opener to Unit 8 to find out.

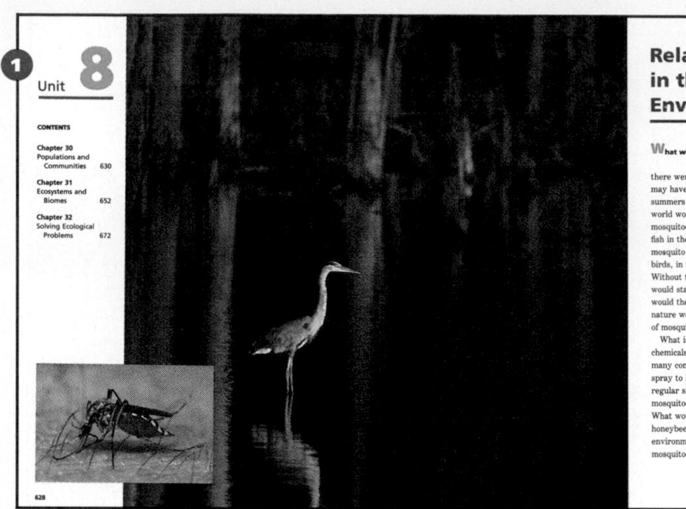

1

Unit 8

CONTENTS

628

Relationships in the Environment

What would happen if...

there were no mosquitoes? You may have memories of hot, itchy summers when you thought the world would be better off without mosquitoes. But, would it? The fish in the photo depend on mosquito larvae for food. Many birds, in turn, depend on the fish. Without the mosquito, many fish would starve to death. Many birds would then starve. The balance of nature would be upset by the lack of mosquitoes.

What is the effect of spraying chemicals to kill mosquitoes? In many communities, trucks that spray to kill mosquitoes are a regular sight. The spray that kills mosquitoes kills honeybees, too. What would be the effect of killing honeybees? What is the cost to the environment of getting rid of mosquitoes? Is the cost too high?

629

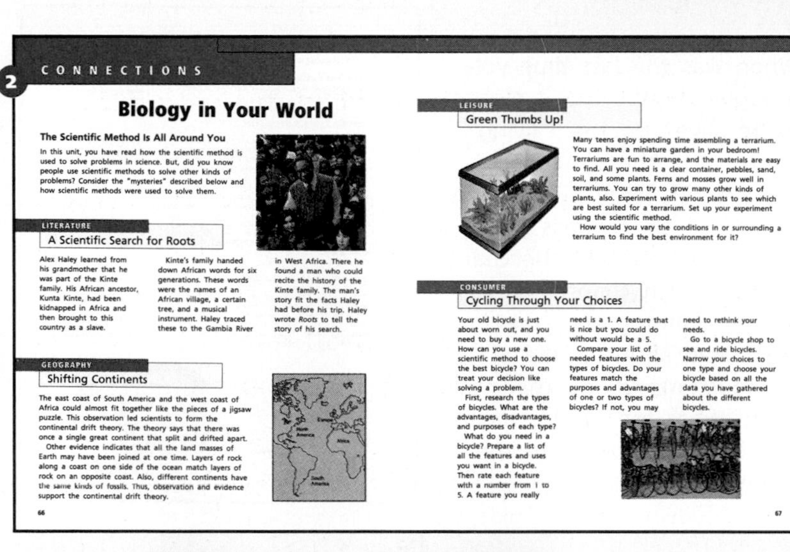

2

CONNECTIONS

Biology in Your World

The Scientific Method Is All Around You

In this unit, you have read how the scientific method is used to solve problems in science. But, did you know people use scientific methods to solve other kinds of problems? Consider the "mysteries" described below and how scientific methods were used to solve them.

LITERATURE

A Scientific Search for Roots

Alex Haley learned from his grandmother that he was part of the Kinte family. His African ancestor, Kunta Kinte, had been kidnapped in Africa and then brought to this country as a slave.

Kinte's family handed down African words for six generations. These words were the names of an African village, a certain tree, and a musical instrument. Haley traced these to the Gambia River in West Africa. There he found a man who could recite the history of the Kinte family. The man's story fit the facts Haley had before his trip. Haley wrote *Roots* to tell the story of his search.

GEOGRAPHY

Shifting Continents

The east coast of South America and the west coast of Africa could almost fit together like the pieces of a jigsaw puzzle. This observation led scientists to form the continental drift theory. The theory says that there was once a single great continent that split and drifted apart.

Other evidence indicates that all the land masses of Earth may have been joined at one time. Layers of rock along a coast on one side of the ocean match layers of rock on an opposite coast. Also, different continents have the same kinds of fossils. Thus, observation and evidence support the continental drift theory.

66

LEISURE

Green Thumbs Up!

Many teens enjoy spending time assembling a terrarium. You can have a miniature garden in your bedroom! Terrariums are fun to arrange, and the materials are easy to find. All you need is a clear container, pebbles, sand, soil, and some plants. Ferns and mosses grow well in terrariums. You can try to grow many other kinds of plants, also. Experiment with various plants to see which are best suited for a terrarium. Set up your experiment using the scientific method.

How would you vary the conditions in or surrounding a terrarium to find the best environment for it?

CONSUMER

Cycling Through Your Choices

Your old bicycle is just about worn out, and you need to buy a new one. How can you use a scientific method to choose the best bicycle? You can treat your decision like solving a problem.

First, research the types of bicycles. What are the advantages, disadvantages, and purposes of each type?

What do you need in a bicycle? Prepare a list of all the features and uses you want in a bicycle. Then rate each feature with a number from 1 to 5. A feature you really need is a 1. A feature that is nice but you could do without would be a 5.

Compare your list of needed features with the types of bicycles. Do your features match the purposes and advantages of one or two types of bicycles? If not, you may need to rethink your needs.

Go to a bicycle shop to see and ride bicycles. Narrow your choices to one type and choose your bicycle based on all the data you have gathered about the different bicycles.

67

❷ What do biology and Alex Haley have in common? A lot, as you'll discover when you read the close to Unit 1. Each unit is closed with mini essays that make connections between biology and consumer issues, leisure activities, art, literature, and history.

v

clearly organized to get you started and keep you going

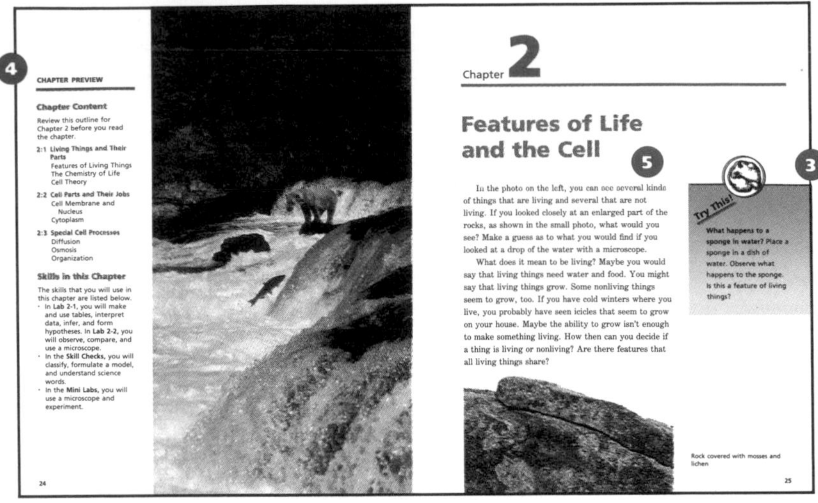
CHAPTER PREVIEW

Chapter Content

Review this outline for Chapter 2 before you read the chapter.

2:1 Living Things and Their Parts
Features of Living Things
The Chemistry of Life
Cell Theory

2:2 Cell Parts and Their Jobs
Cell Membrane and Nucleus
Cytoplasm

2:3 Special Cell Processes
Diffusion
Osmosis
Organization

Skills in this Chapter

The skills that you will use in this chapter are listed below.

- In **Lab 2-1**, you will make and use tables, interpret data, infer, and form hypotheses. In **Lab 2-2**, you will observe, compare, and use a microscope.
- In the **Skill Checks**, you will classify, formulate a model, and understand science words.
- In the **Mini Labs**, you will use a microscope and experiment.

24

Chapter 2

Features of Life and the Cell

In the photo on the left, you can see several kinds of things that are living and several that are not living. If you looked closely at an enlarged part of the rocks, as shown in the small photo, what would you see? Make a guess as to what you would find if you looked at a drop of the water with a microscope.

What does it mean to be living? Maybe you would say that living things need water and food. You might say that living things grow. Some nonliving things seem to grow, too. If you have cold winters where you live, you probably have seen icicles that seem to grow on your house. Maybe the ability to grow isn't enough to make something living. How then can you decide if a thing is living or nonliving? Are there features that all living things share?

Try This!

What happens to a sponge in water? Place a sponge in a dish of water. Observe what happens to the sponge. Is this a feature of living things?

Rock covered with mosses and lichen

25

3 **Try This!**
Each chapter begins with an easy activity to do right at your desk, or at home. It gets you ready for learning.

4 Listed for you in the **Chapter Preview** are the chapter contents. They tell what topics are covered and how they are organized. Study this before you dive into the chapter material. Also listed are skills that you will practice. A skill is something you get better at with practice. *Biology: An Everyday Experience* gives you all the practice you need to master skills that are important for success in biology, your other classes, and your everyday life.

5 When was the last time you thought about what it means to be alive? Do small living things have the same life processes as large ones? These are the kinds of ideas you will ponder as you read the chapter openers. Each chapter opener has two photographs that are talked about in the introduction. As you read, think about what the photos mean and how they relate to the chapter.

15:4 Nervous and Endocrine System Problems

Many health problems are caused by diseases of the nervous and endocrine systems. Luckily, some of these diseases can be treated or cured.

Objectives

8. **Identify** problems that damage the brain.
9. **Explain** the importance of insulin.

Key Science Words

insulin
diabetes mellitus

Nervous System Problems

The brain has many blood vessels covering its surface, Figure 15-15a. The brain receives food and oxygen from these blood vessels. These blood vessels may become weak and break. When this happens, a person is said to have a stroke.

What is a stroke?

What happens when blood vessels of the brain break? It depends on where the blood vessel is and how much blood is lost. Usually, a person loses the use of a part of the brain because the brain cells die when they no longer receive food or oxygen. Losing the use of part of the brain causes the body part that it controls not to work. Figure 15-15b shows what happens when certain parts of the brain lose their oxygen supply.

Endocrine System Problems

The pancreas is a familiar gland. You studied it in Chapter 10 with the digestive system. Refer back to Figure 15-11 to see the location of the pancreas. This gland is also part of the endocrine system. It makes a hormone called insulin (IHN suh lun). **Insulin** is a hormone that lets your body cells take in glucose, a sugar, from your blood.

Figure 15-15 A stroke is the breaking of blood vessels that serve the brain and can result in loss of body functions.

15:4 Nervous and Endocrine System Problems 323

6 Chapters are organized into two to four numbered sections. Each numbered section has several subsections that have red headings. The Objectives at the beginning of the numbered section tell you what major topics you'll be covering and what you should expect to learn about them. The Key Science Words are also listed in the order in which they appear in the section.

vi

lots of ways to help you master important ideas and skills

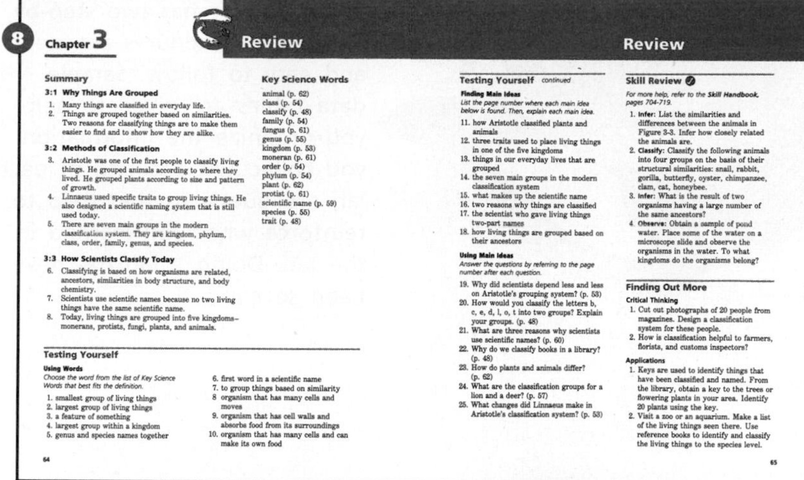

8 Chapter 3 Review

Summary

3:1 Why Things Are Grouped

1. Many things are classified in everyday life.
2. Things are grouped together based on similarities. Two reasons for classifying things are to make them easier to find and to show how they are alike.

3:2 Methods of Classification

3. Aristotle was one of the first people to classify living things. He grouped animals according to where they lived. He grouped plants according to size and pattern of growth.
4. Linnaeus used specific traits to group living things. He also designed a scientific naming system that is still used today.
5. There are seven main groups in the modern classification system. They are kingdom, phylum, class, order, family, genus, and species.

3:3 How Scientists Classify Today

6. Classifying is based on how organisms are related, ancestors, similarities in body structure, and body chemistry.
7. Scientists use scientific names because no two living things have the same scientific name.
8. Today, living things are grouped into five kingdoms–monerans, protists, fungi, plants, and animals.

Key Science Words

animal (p. 62)
class (p. 54)
classify (p. 48)
family (p. 54)
fungus (p. 61)
genus (p. 55)
kingdom (p. 53)
moneran (p. 61)
order (p. 54)
phylum (p. 54)
plant (p. 62)
protist (p. 61)
scientific name (p. 59)
species (p. 55)
trait (p. 48)

Testing Yourself

Using Words

Choose the word from the list of Key Science Words that best fits the definition.

1. smallest group of living things
2. largest group of living things
3. a feature of something
4. largest group within a kingdom
5. genus and species names together
6. first word in a scientific name
7. to group things based on similarity
8. organism that has many cells and moves
9. organism that has cell walls and absorbs food from its surroundings
10. organism that has many cells and can make its own food

64

Review

Testing Yourself *continued*

Finding Main Ideas

List the page number where each main idea below is found. Then, explain each main idea.

11. how Aristotle classified plants and animals
12. three traits used to place living things in one of the five kingdoms
13. things in our everyday lives that are grouped
14. the seven main groups in the modern classification system
15. what makes up the scientific name
16. two reasons why things are classified
17. the scientist who gave living things two-part names
18. how living things are grouped based on their ancestors

Using Main Ideas

Answer the questions by referring to the page number after each question.

19. Why did scientists depend less and less on Aristotle's grouping system? (p. 53)
20. How would you classify the letters b, c, e, d, l, o, t into two groups? Explain your groups. (p. 48)
21. What are three reasons why scientists use scientific names? (p. 60)
22. Why do we classify books in a library? (p. 48)
23. How do plants and animals differ? (p. 62)
24. What are the classification groups for a lion and a deer? (p. 57)
25. What changes did Linnaeus make in Aristotle's classification system? (p. 53)

Skill Review

*For more help, refer to the **Skill Handbook**, pages 704-719.*

1. **Infer**: List the similarities and differences between the animals in Figure 3-3. Infer how closely related the animals are.
2. **Classify**: Classify the following animals into four groups on the basis of their structural similarities: snail, rabbit, gorilla, butterfly, oyster, chimpanzee, clam, cat, honeybee.
3. **Infer**: What is the result of two organisms having a large number of the same ancestors?
4. **Observe**: Obtain a sample of pond water. Place some of the water on a microscope slide and observe the organisms in the water. To what kingdoms do the organisms belong?

Finding Out More

Critical Thinking

1. Cut out photographs of 20 people from magazines. Design a classification system for these people.
2. How is classification helpful to farmers, florists, and customs inspectors?

Applications

1. Keys are used to identify things that have been classified and named. From the library, obtain a key to the trees or flowering plants in your area. Identify 20 plants using the key.
2. Visit a zoo or an aquarium. Make a list of the living things seen there. Use reference books to identify and classify the living things to the species level.

65

7 Here's a chance to sharpen your skills. The **Skill Checks** and **Mini Labs** are good ways to practice skills. Each skill exercise requires only pencil and paper or simple materials you can find at home or get from your teacher. If you have trouble with the skill exercises in the Skill Checks or Mini Labs, there is a reference to the **Skill Handbook** at the back of the book. Here, you can find complete information about a particular skill.

8 **Chapter Reviews** give you an opportunity to reinforce and apply your knowledge.

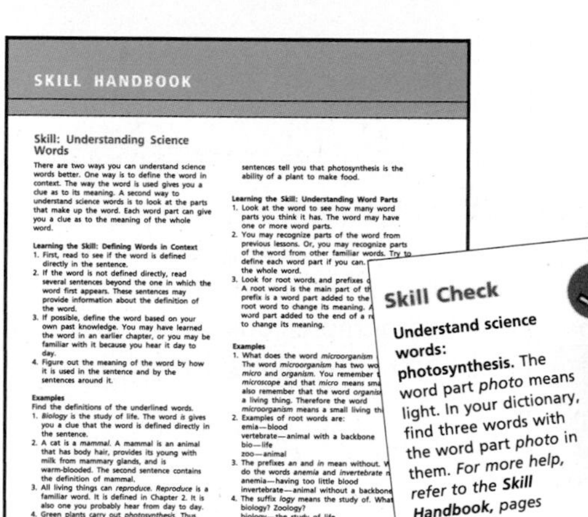

SKILL HANDBOOK

Skill: Understanding Science Words

There are two ways you can understand science words better. One way is to define the word in context. The way the word is used gives you a clue as to its meaning. A second way to understand science words is to look at the parts that make up the word. Each word part can give you a clue as to the meaning of the whole word.

Learning the Skill: Defining Words in Context

1. First, read to see if the word is defined directly in the sentence.
2. If the word is not defined directly, read several sentences beyond the one in which the word first appears. These sentences may provide information about the definition of the word.
3. If possible, define the word based on your own past knowledge. You may have learned the word in an earlier chapter, or you may be familiar with it because you hear it day to day.
4. Figure out the meaning of the word by how it is used in the sentence and by the sentences around it.

Examples

Find the definitions of the underlined words.

1. *Biology* is the study of life. The word *is* gives you a clue that the word is defined directly in the sentence.
2. A cat is a *mammal*. A mammal is an animal that has body hair, provides its young with milk from mammary glands, and is warm-blooded. The second sentence contains the definition of mammal.
3. All living things can *reproduce*. *Reproduce* is a familiar word. It is defined in Chapter 2. It is also one you probably hear from day to day.
4. Green plants carry out *photosynthesis*. Thus, they are able to make their own food. These sentences tell you that photosynthesis is the ability of a plant to make food.

Learning the Skill: Understanding Word Parts

1. Look at the word to see how many word parts you think it has. The word may have one or more word parts.
2. You may recognize parts of the word from previous lessons. Or, you may recognize parts of the word from other familiar words. Try to define each word part if you can. the whole word.
3. Look for root words and prefixes A root word is the main part of th prefix is a word part added to the root word to change its meaning. word part added to the end of a r to change its meaning.

Examples

1. What does the word *microorganism* The word *microorganism* has two wo *micro* and *organism*. You remember *microscope* and that *micro* means sma also remember that the word *organis* a living thing. Therefore the word *microorganism* means a small living th
2. Examples of root words are:
emia—blood
vertebrate—animal with a backbone
bio—life
zoo—animal
3. The prefixes *an* and *in* mean without. do the words *anemia* and *invertebrate* anemia—having too little blood
invertebrate—animal without a backbone
4. The suffix *logy* means the study of. What biology? Zoology?
biology—the study of life
zoology—the study of animals

708 Skill Handbook

Skill Check 7

Understand science words: photosynthesis. The word part *photo* means light. In your dictionary, find three words with the word part *photo* in them. *For more help, refer to the **Skill Handbook**, pages 706-711.*

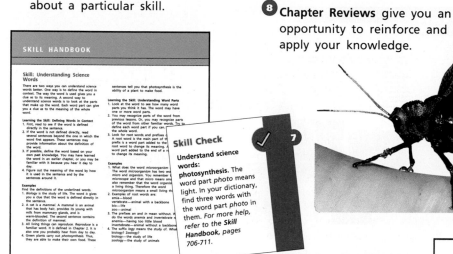

9 If you have trouble remembering and understanding a lesson, help is on the way. Each major concept has an Idea Map that you can use as a study guide. Ideas are summarized in an easy-to-read format. The Idea Maps will help make your study of biology a success.

10 At the end of each major section are five **Check Your Understanding** questions. The first three questions reinforce what you have learned in the section. The fourth question challenges you to think critically about what you have read. The fifth question connects biology with reading, writing, or math.

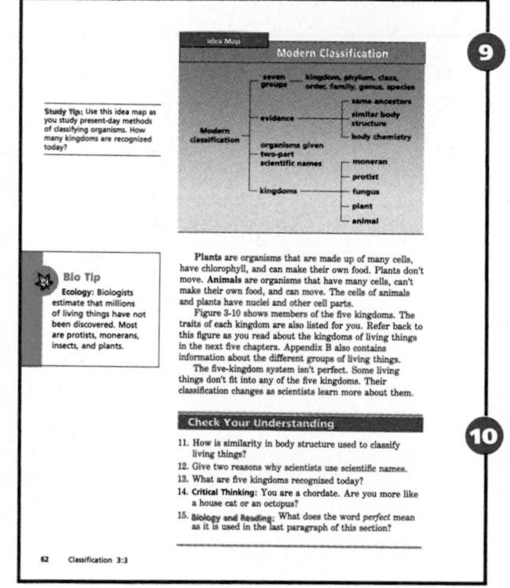

Study Tip: Use this idea map as you study present-day methods of classifying organisms. How many kingdoms are recognized today?

Bio Tip

Ecology: Biologists estimate that millions of living things have not been discovered. Most are protists, monerans, insects, and plants.

Plants are organisms that are made up of many cells, have chlorophyll, and can make their own food. Plants don't move. **Animals** are organisms that have many cells, can't make their own food, and can move. The cells of animals and plants have nuclei and other cell parts.

Figure 3-10 shows members of the five kingdoms. The traits of each kingdom are also listed for you. Refer back to this figure as you read about the kingdoms of living things in the next five chapters. Appendix B also contains information about the different groups of living things.

The five-kingdom system isn't perfect. Some living things don't fit into any of the five kingdoms. Their classification changes as scientists learn more about them.

Check Your Understanding

11. How is similarity in body structure used to classify living things?
12. Give two reasons why scientists use scientific names.
13. What are five kingdoms recognized today?
14. **Critical Thinking:** You are a chordate. Are you more like a house cat or an octopus?
15. **Biology and Reading:** What does the word *perfect* mean as it is used in the last paragraph of this section?

62 Classification 3:3

vii

really experience biology by observing, experimenting, asking questions

11 Every chapter has two step-by-step labs. Procedures are clear and easy to follow. Sample data tables are given to help you organize the information you collect. At the end of each lab are questions that help to reinforce what you learned in the lab. Doing a lab has never been so easy!

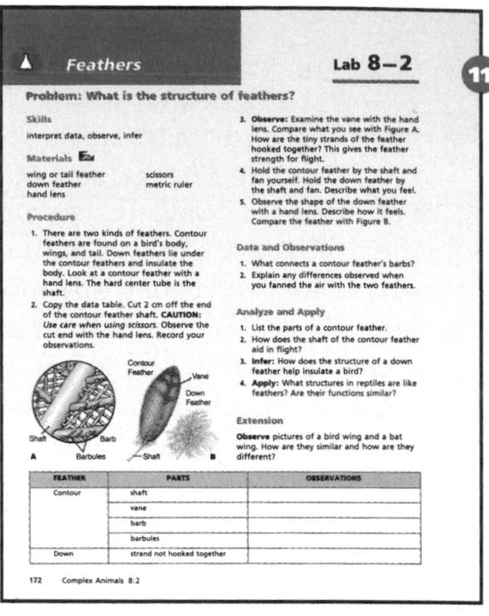

Feathers — Lab 8–2 — 11

Problem: What is the structure of feathers?

Skills

interpret data, observe, infer

Materials

wing or tail feather
down feather
hand lens
scissors
metric ruler

Procedure

1. There are two kinds of feathers. Contour feathers are found on a bird's body, wings, and tail. Down feathers lie under the contour feathers and insulate the body. Look at a contour feather with a hand lens. The hard center tube is the shaft.
2. Copy the data table. Cut 2 cm off the end of the contour feather shaft. **CAUTION:** *Use care when using scissors.* Observe the cut end with the hand lens. Record your observations.
3. **Observe:** Examine the vane with the hand lens. Compare what you see with Figure A. How are the tiny strands of the feather hooked together? This gives the feather strength for flight.
4. Hold the contour feather by the shaft and fan yourself. Hold the down feather by the shaft and fan. Describe what you feel.
5. Observe the shape of the down feather with a hand lens. Describe how it feels. Compare the feather with Figure B.

Data and Observations

1. What connects a contour feather's barbs?
2. Explain any differences observed when you fanned the air with the two feathers.

Analyze and Apply

1. List the parts of a contour feather.
2. How does the shaft of the contour feather aid in flight?
3. **Infer:** How does the structure of a down feather help insulate a bird?
4. **Apply:** What structures in reptiles are like feathers? Are their functions similar?

Extension

Observe pictures of a bird wing and a bat wing. How are they similar and how are they different?

FEATHER	PARTS	OBSERVATIONS
Contour	shaft	
	vane	
	barb	
	barbules	
Down	strand not hooked together	

172 Complex Animals 8:2

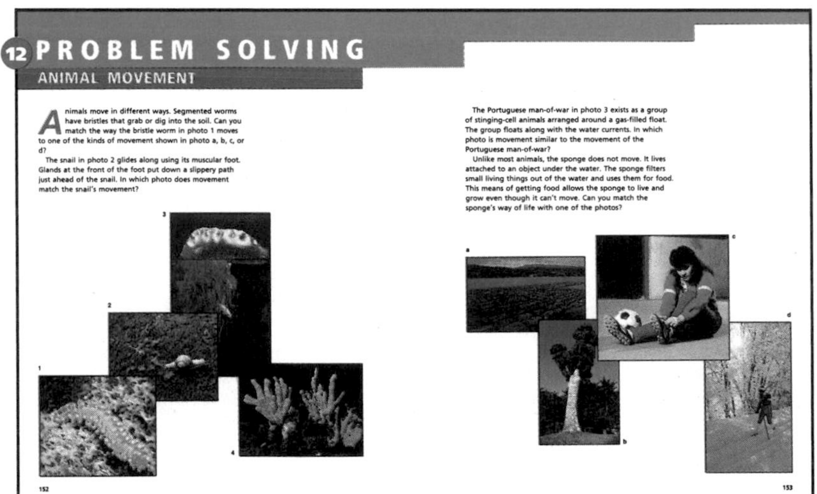

12 PROBLEM SOLVING

ANIMAL MOVEMENT

Animals move in different ways. Segmented worms have bristles that grab or dig into the soil. Can you match the way the bristle worm in photo 1 moves to one of the kinds of movement shown in photo a, b, c, or d?

The snail in photo 2 glides along using its muscular foot. Glands at the front of the foot put down a slippery path just ahead of the snail. In which photo does movement match the snail's movement?

The Portuguese man-of-war in photo 3 exists as a group of stinging-cell animals arranged around a gas-filled float. The group floats along with the water currents. In which photo is movement similar to the movement of the Portuguese man-of-war?

Unlike most animals, the sponge does not move. It lives attached to an object under the water. The sponge filters small living things out of the water and uses them for food. This means of getting food allows the sponge to live and grow even though it can't move. Can you match the sponge's way of life with one of the photos?

152 153

12 Each unit has a two-page Problem Solving feature. Read the short background paragraph, look at the pictures, and solve the puzzle.

viii

explore how biology impacts technology and news-making issues and offers career choices

13

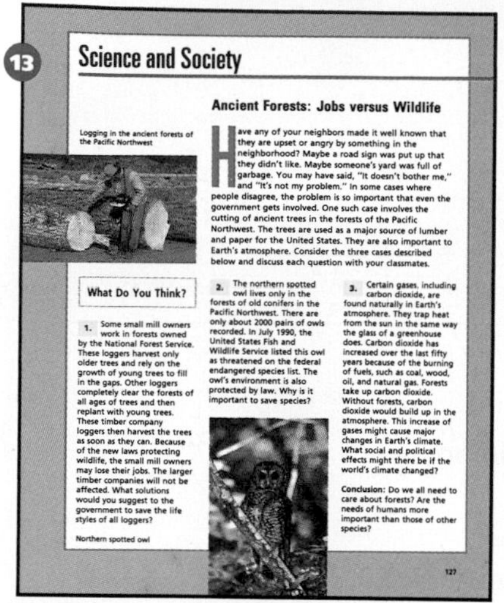

Science and Society

Ancient Forests: Jobs versus Wildlife

Logging in the ancient forests of the Pacific Northwest

Have any of your neighbors made it well known that they are upset or angry by something in the neighborhood? Maybe a road sign was put up that they didn't like. Maybe someone's yard was full of garbage. You may have said, "It doesn't bother me," and "It's not my problem." In some cases where people disagree, the problem is so important that even the government gets involved. One such case involves the cutting of ancient trees in the forests of the Pacific Northwest. The trees are used as a major source of lumber and paper for the United States. They are also important to Earth's atmosphere. Consider the three cases described below and discuss each question with your classmates.

What Do You Think?

1. Some small mill owners work in forests owned by the National Forest Service. These loggers harvest only older trees and rely on the growth of young trees to fill in the gaps. Other loggers completely clear the forests of all ages of trees and then replant with young trees. These timber company loggers then harvest the trees as soon as they can. Because of the new laws protecting wildlife, the small mill owners may lose their jobs. The larger timber companies will not be affected. What solutions would you suggest to the government to save the life styles of all loggers?

2. The northern spotted owl lives only in the forests of old conifers in the Pacific Northwest. There are only about 2000 pairs of owls recorded. In July 1990, the United States Fish and Wildlife Service listed this owl as threatened on the federal endangered species list. The owl's environment is also protected by law. Why is it important to save species?

3. Certain gases, including carbon dioxide, are found naturally in Earth's atmosphere. They trap heat from the sun in the same way the glass of a greenhouse does. Carbon dioxide has increased over the last fifty years because of the burning of fuels, such as coal, wood, oil, and natural gas. Forests take up carbon dioxide. Without forests, carbon dioxide would build up in the atmosphere. This increase of gases might cause major changes in Earth's climate. What social and political effects might there be if the world's climate changed?

Conclusion: Do we all need to care about forests? Are the needs of humans more important than those of other species?

Northern spotted owl

127

13 Are animal experiments necessary? Who decides which person in need of an organ transplant gets one? As you read the Science and Society features, you'll find that the answers to these and other questions are not so easy. The Science and Society features bring you closer to current issues and let you see the impact of technology on society. They prepare you for the day when you may need to participate in making decisions that affect your community and your environment.

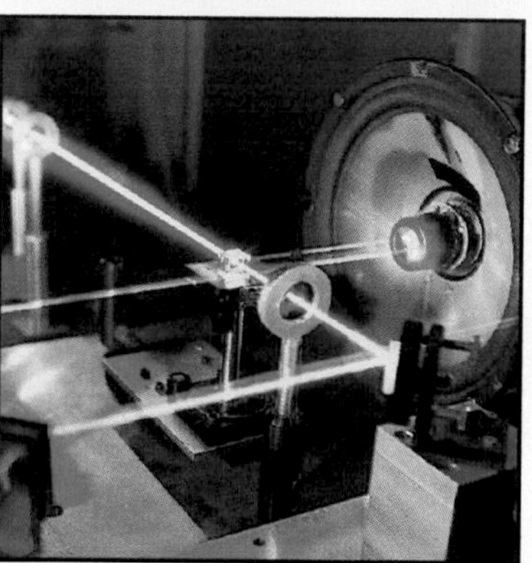

14

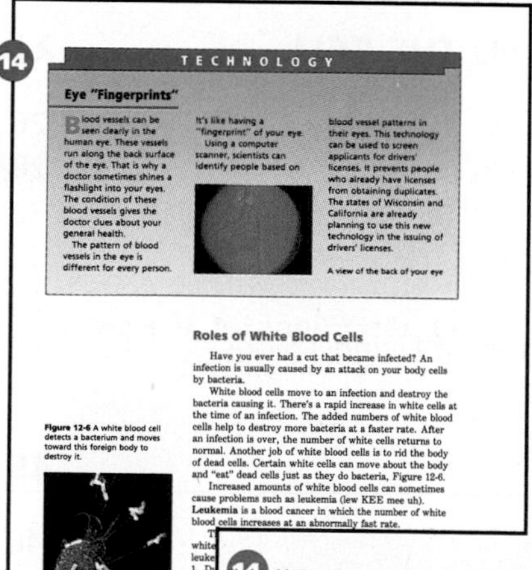

TECHNOLOGY

Eye "Fingerprints"

Blood vessels can be seen clearly in the human eye. These vessels run along the back surface of the eye. That is why a doctor sometimes shines a flashlight into your eyes. The condition of these blood vessels gives the doctor clues about your general health.

The pattern of blood vessels in the eye is different for every person. It's like having a "fingerprint" of your eye.

Using a computer scanner, scientists can identify people based on blood vessel patterns in their eyes. This technology can be used to screen applicants for drivers' licenses. It prevents people who already have licenses from obtaining duplicates. The states of Wisconsin and California are already planning to use this new technology in the issuing of drivers' licenses.

A view of the back of your eye

Roles of White Blood Cells

Have you ever had a cut that became infected? An infection is usually caused by an attack on your body cells by bacteria.

White blood cells move to an infection and destroy the bacteria causing it. There's a rapid increase in white cells at the time of an infection. The added numbers of white blood cells help to destroy more bacteria at a faster rate. After an infection is over, the number of white cells returns to normal. Another job of white blood cells is to rid the body of dead cells. Certain white cells can move about the body and "eat" dead cells just as they do bacteria, Figure 12-6.

Increased amounts of white blood cells can sometimes cause problems such as leukemia (lew KEE mee uh). **Leukemia** is a blood cancer in which the number of white blood cells increases at an abnormally fast rate.

T... white... leuke... 1. D... of bl... the n...

Figure 12-6 A white blood cell detects a bacterium and moves toward this foreign body to destroy it.

250 Blood 12:2

14 "Eyes are the windows to the soul." Did you know that your eyes are also like fingerprints? The patterns made by the vessels in the back of your eye are unique and can be used to identify you. No other person has eyes like you. This and other recent discoveries appear in the Technology features. The Technology features tie together biology and applications of the most recent research in biology. They make biology meaningful to *you.*

15

Career Close-Up

Wildlife Photographer

Photographing wildlife is often a challenging occupation.

John's biology teacher invited a wildlife photographer to visit his class. The photographer brought slides and prints of many living things. Many photographs of flowers and insects were made with a close-up lens or a zoom lens. The photographer showed the students how to use a camera attachment on a light microscope. She told them that her work often took her to outdoor settings.

Students wanted to know about the training needed to be a photographer. She told them that she had taken photography and natural science courses in high school. Then she had taken several courses at a community college. She explained that in this field success depends on a person knowing the subject matter well.

Other students wanted to know where her work was used. She showed them magazines and books that contained her photographs.

Biologists classify living things. Doing so puts organisms in order. It also shows how they are alike. There are over one and one-half million known kinds of living ... e to find information about ... d in some way.

...anding

Give two examples of traits.
...ing at school that is classified.
...gs are classified.
... parts of an animal cell based
...e two other ways to write the ...illion?

15 You may never have thought about a career in biology, but think again. What kinds of interesting careers are there for you in biology? What about wildlife photography? How about being an athletic trainer? Each career feature focuses on one career, telling you the daily ins and outs of the job. Even if you want to work as soon as you graduate from high school, you'll find there are many careers that will let you do just that. Information about career training is given so that if you're interested, you can start planning now.

ix

CONTENTS

x

UNIT 2 KINGDOMS 68

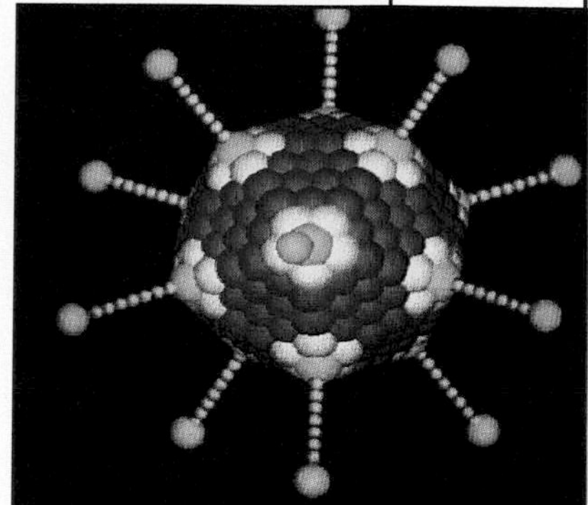

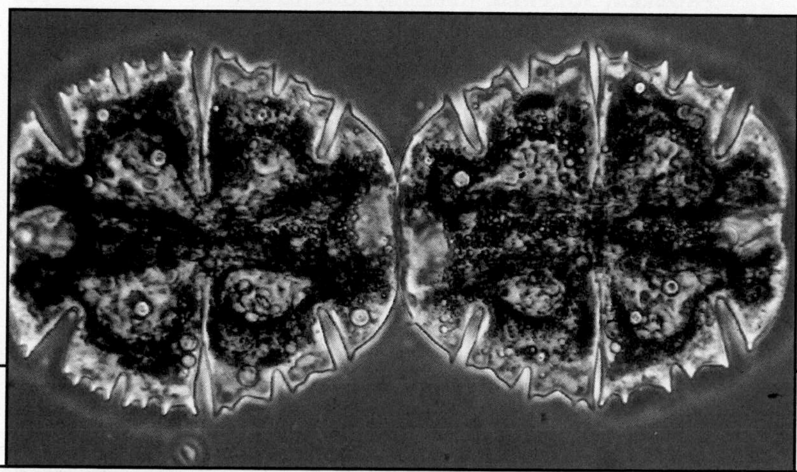

xii

xiii

xiv

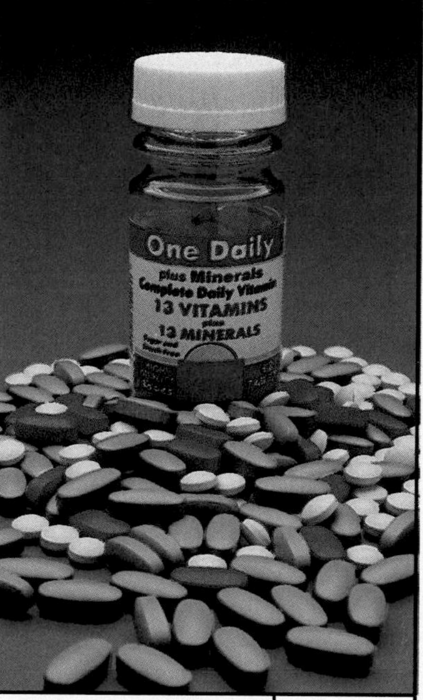

xv

xvi

xvii

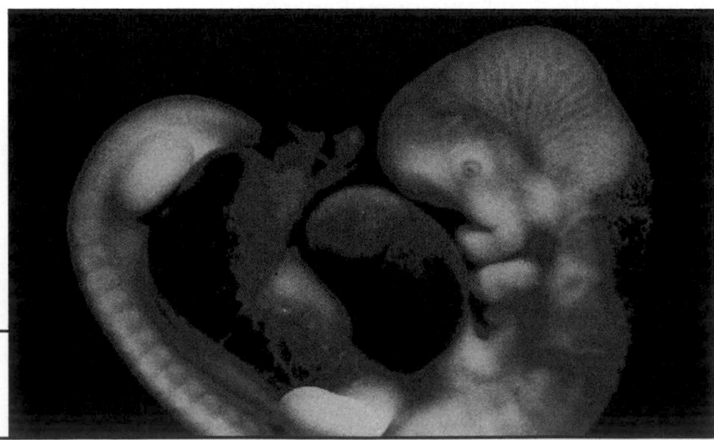

xix

xx

LABS

Have you ever seen an animal capture and eat its prey using tentacles that surround its mouth? You may do this in one of the 64 **Labs** found in your textbook. In another **Lab,** you may watch as protein is digested. In other **Labs,** you test painkillers for the presence of aspirin, build models of viruses, and test the effects of pollution on yeast cells. **Labs** let you use what you have learned to *do* biology.

xxi

SCIENCE AND SOCIETY

Today it is possible for a couple to choose the sex of their child. Should this be done? How will a country's population be affected if all couples chose the sexes of their children? This is an example of a problem in which science and society interact as people line up on both sides of the debate. **Science and Society** features discuss real cases and present questions to help you form your *own* opinion about a current topic of debate in biology. Should animals be used to test the safety of new drugs? Should athletes use steroids to help them reach their goals? These and many other issues involving the environment, health, and conservation are presented in **Science and Society.**

PROBLEM SOLVING

What plants and animals are found in a desert? What information can be found on a food label? These are examples of **Problem Solving** features found in your textbook. You may match the shape of a flower with the shape of the animal that carries the flower's pollen, or you may compare different kinds of animal movement to the movement of other things. In the **Problem Solving** features, you can apply your knowledge of biology to solve biological problems and puzzles.

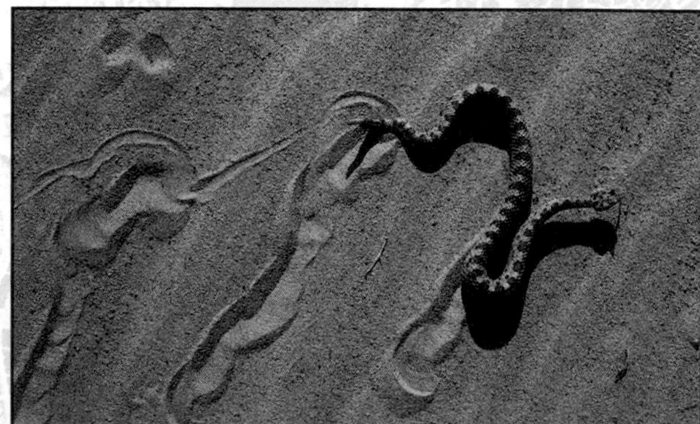

xxii

TECHNOLOGY

What do biologists do with new information about living things? The chemicals in the cells of each human are unique. No two people have the exact same chemical make-up. Learning to put that fact to practical use in solving crimes is one example of technology. Your textbook's **Technology** features show examples of biological knowledge at work. In **Technology**, you learn how bacteria can clean up oil spills and how eye-blinking behavior might help pilots.

CAREER CLOSE-UP

What will you do with everything you learn in your biology course? Maybe you'll begin thinking about a career in a field involving biology. **Career Close-ups** are designed to give you some examples of career paths you might follow. You might become a wildlife photographer and travel around the world photographing living things. Or, you could be an animal breeder working to develop more nutritious beef. Perhaps you would like to become a mushroom farmer. The number of career choices in biology is almost endless.

xxiii

MINI LABS

Would you like to learn how to make a bird feeder or try to design a child-proof drug package? The **Mini Lab** features in your textbook will tell you how.

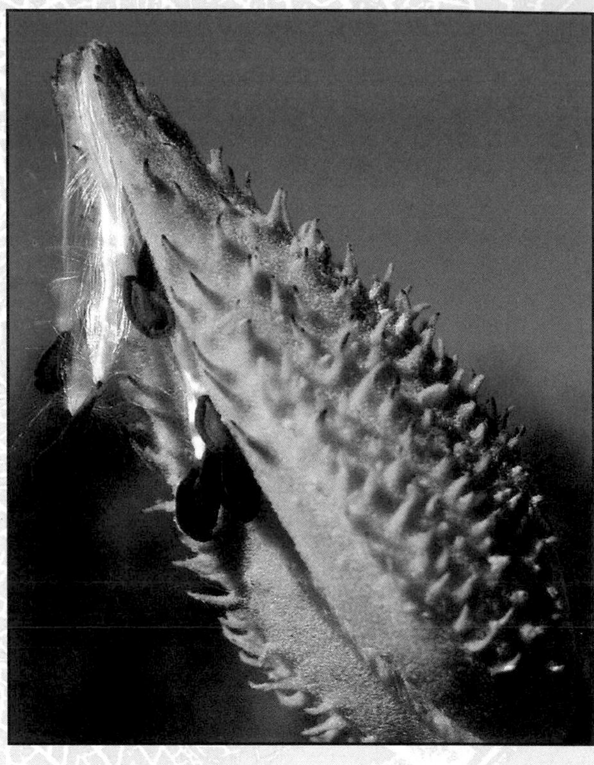

xxiv

SKILL CHECKS

What does the word *photosynthesis* mean? What other words are made of the same word parts? The **Skill Check** features will help you understand science words, as well as give you practice using other skills.

1

Unit 1
Kinds of Life

UNIT OVERVIEW

Unit 1 provides background information for the study of biology. Chapter 1 deals with how biology is used in the present-day world, the tools used by biologists, scientific measurements, and scientific method. The features of living things, the cell as a basic unit of life, and the classification of living things are discussed in Chapters 2 and 3.

Advance Planning

Audiovisual and computer software suggestions are located within each specific chapter under the heading TEACH.

Arrange a field trip to a nearby college for students to see an electron microscope.

Obtain materials for setting up a classroom aquarium to use throughout the year.

To prepare for:

Lab 1-1: Make sure that the light microscopes have been checked and are ready to use. Collect magazines from which to cut the letter *e* and pieces of color photographs.

Lab 1-2: Make sure that you have pinto beans, salt, and self-sealing plastic bags.

Mini Lab: Collect plant cuttings and aspirin.

Lab 2-1: Ask students to bring baby food jars for this lab. Prepare phenol red solution and yeast solution. If you do not have a classroom aquarium, guppies will have to be purchased.

Lab 2-2: Prepare methylene blue satin. Order *Elodea*.

Mini Labs: Cut thin slices of cork. Obtain vanilla extract, a balloon, and a box.

Lab 3-1: Collect the objects to be classified and place them in envelopes.

Lab 3-2: Order state maps.

Unit 1

CONTENTS

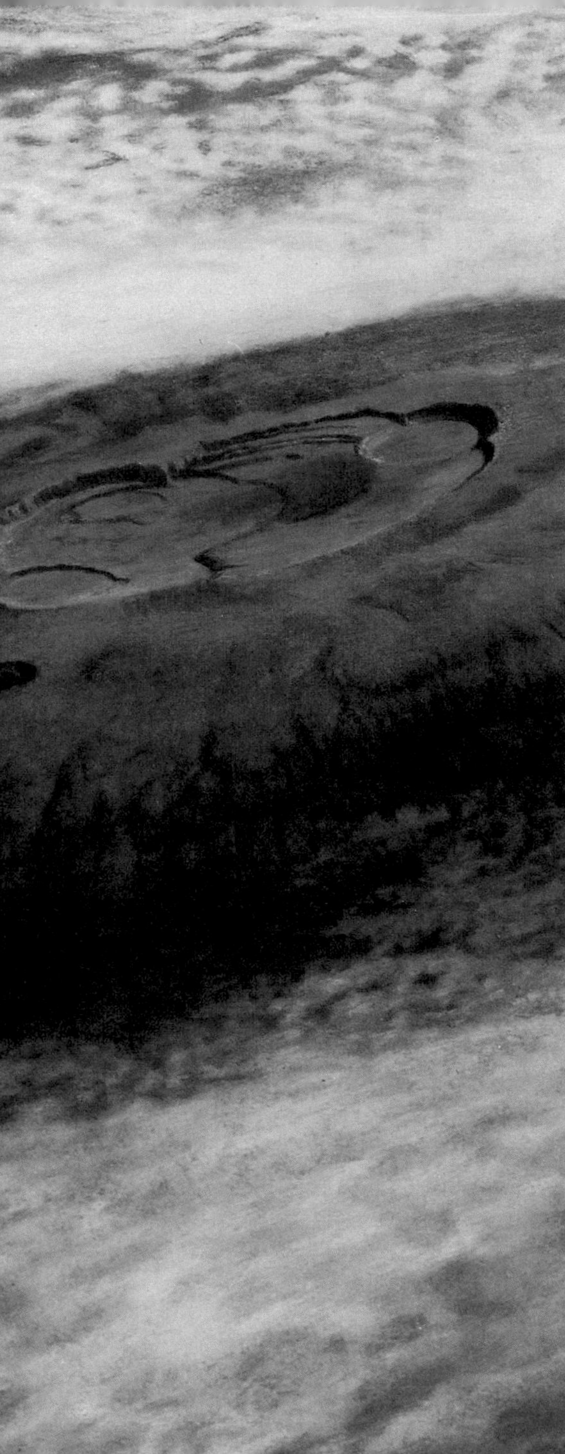

Kinds of Life

What would happen if...

there were life on Mars? Living things as we know them need water, warmth, and protection from radiation from the sun. Does Mars provide these things? Life-forms on Mars would have to survive without any water because all of the water on Mars is frozen. Mars is farther away from the sun than Earth. As a result, the temperature on Mars is always below freezing. The atmosphere of Mars is too thin to block out harmful radiation from the sun. Thus any life on Mars would have to be able to withstand radiation.

Viking probes landed on the surface of Mars in 1976. Martian soil was tested for the presence of life. The tests showed that no life processes as we know them were occurring.

It seems that life does not exist on Mars, at least not as we know it. But are there other types or definitions of life?

UNIT OVERVIEW

Photo Teaching Tip

Have students read the passage that accompanies this pair of unit opening photographs. Open a discussion that will invite students to compare the conditions on Earth and Mars. Have them consider the possibility of the existence of other life-forms in the universe. Explain that scientists need to be open-minded in order to make hypotheses and explore the unknown. New and unusual ideas can often result in scientific breakthroughs. Have students write their own new definitions of life as they imagine it to exist on other planets.

Theme Development

Each organism is made up of cells that help it maintain a balance within its environment. The themes of ecology, homeostasis, and diversity are developed in this unit.

The Study of Life

PLANNING GUIDE

CONTENT	TEXT FEATURES	TEACHER RESOURCE PACKAGE	OTHER COMPONENTS
(1/2 day) 1:1 Biology in Use Who Uses Biology Tools of Biology	Skill Check: *Understand Science Words,* p. 7 Skill Check: *Make and Use Tables,* p. 8 Lab 1-1: *Microscopes,* p. 9 Check Your Understanding, p. 10	Enrichment: *Fields of Science*, p. 1 Reteaching: *Parts of the Microscope*, p. 1 Focus: *How Does Biology Contribute to the Working of a Supermarket?* p. 1 Study Guide: *Biology in Use*, pp. 1-2 Lab 1-1: *Microscopes,* pp. 1-2 Transparency Master: *Tools Used in Biology*, p. 1	**Laboratory Manual:** *How Is the Light Microscope Used?* p. 1 Color Transparency 1: *The Microscope*
(1 1/2 days) 1:2 Measurements Used in Biology Length Volume Weight and Mass Time and Temperature	Skill Check: *Calculate*, p. 12 Check Your Understanding, p. 14	Application: *Safety in the Biology Laboratory*, p. 1 Reteaching: *Measurements Used in Biology*, p. 2 Skills: *Measure in SI*, p. 1 Study Guide: *Measurements Used in Biology*, pp. 3-4	**Laboratory Manual:** *How Are SI Length Measurements Made?* p. 5
(2 days) 1:3 Scientific Method Recognizing and Researching the Problem Forming a Hypothesis Testing a Hypothesis Drawing Conclusions Theory Technology	Mini Lab: *Does Aspirin Help Plants Grow?* p. 16 Lab 1-2: *Scientific Method,* p. 17 Science and Society: *Technology: Helpful or Harmful?* p. 21 Idea Map, p. 15 Check Your Understanding, p. 20	Reteaching: *How Can You Use a Scientific Method to Solve a Problem?* p. 3 Critical Thinking/Problem Solving: *Can You Spot the Scientific Method?* p. 1 Study Guide: *Scientific Method,* p. 5 Study Guide: *Vocabulary,* p. 6 Lab 1-2: *Scientific Method,* pp. 3-4	
Chapter Review	Summary Key Science Words Testing Yourself Finding Main Ideas Using Main Ideas Skill Review	Chapter Review, pp. 1-2 Chapter Test, pp. 3-5	**Test Bank**

MATERIALS NEEDED

LAB 1-1, p. 9	LAB 1-2, p. 17	MARGIN FEATURES
microscope microscope slide coverslips water dropper forceps small piece of magazine print	2 100-mL beakers 40 pinto beans balance salt water 2 paper towels 50-mL graduated cylinder 2 self-sealing plastic bags masking tape	Skill Check, p. 7 dictionary Skill Check, p. 8 pencil paper Skill Check, p. 12 calculator meter stick Mini Lab, p. 16 plants aspirin water

OBJECTIVES

SECTION	OBJECTIVE	OBJECTIVES CORRELATION			
		CHECK YOUR UNDERSTANDING	CHAPTER REVIEW	TRP CHAPTER REVIEW	TRP CHAPTER TEST
1:1	1. **Describe** three jobs that depend on the use of biology.	1, 4	16, 23	3, 26, 36	9, 35, 36, 37, 38, 39
	2. **List** five tools of biologists.	2	19, 29	10, 11, 29	46
	3. **Compare** the features of the light microscope, stereomicroscope, and electron microscope.	3, 5	6, 12, 24	16, 17, 18, 19, 20, 21, 22, 23, 24, 25	1, 3, 15, 16, 17, 18, 19, 20, 21, 22, 23
1:2	4. **Explain** how SI units are grouped.	6, 9	1, 21	2, 4, 32	8, 31, 32, 34
	5. **List** the SI units of measure for length, volume, mass, time, and temperature.	7	2, 4, 13, 25	1, 9, 27, 31, 38	4, 7, 30, 31, 33, 34, 41
	6. **Measure** objects using SI units.	8, 10	17, 18, 27	28, 35	6, 24, 25, 28, 43, 45
1:3	7. **Explain** the steps of the scientific method.	11, 12, 15	3, 7, 10, 11, 14, 15, 20, 22, 28	5, 6, 7, 8, 12, 13, 14, 15, 30, 33, 39	2, 10, 11, 13, 14, 37, 40, 42
	8. **Compare** the difference between a hypothesis and a theory.	13	8	34	12
	9. **Explain** how technology is used to solve everyday problems.	14	9, 26	37	5, 47

The Study of Life

CHAPTER OVERVIEW

Key Concepts

In this chapter, students will study who uses biology, the tools that are used to study it, and how measurements are made using SI. Students also will learn the steps in scientific method and use those steps to solve problems.

Key Science Words

biology	light microscope
Celsius	meter
control	scientific method
data	stereo microscope
experiment	technology
hypothesis	theory
International System of Units	variable
kilogram	volume

Skill Development

In Lab 1-1, students will **observe** and **recognize and use spatial relationships** while learning to use the microscope. In Lab 1-2, they will **form hypotheses, interpret data,** and **separate and control variables** while learning to use scientific method. In the Skill Check on page 7, students will **understand** the **science word** *microscope.* In the Skill Check on page 8, they will **make** and **use tables** to compare microscope magnifications. In the Skill Check on page 12, they will **calculate** area. In the Mini Lab on page 16, they will **design an experiment** to see if plant cuttings will grow faster in aspirin water than plain water.

CHAPTER PREVIEW

Chapter Content

Review this outline for Chapter 1 before you read the chapter.

1:1 Biology in Use
- Who Uses Biology?
- Tools of Biology

1:2 Measurements Used in Biology
- Length
- Volume
- Weight and Mass
- Time and Temperature

1:3 Scientific Method
- Recognizing and Researching the Problem
- Forming a Hypothesis
- Testing a Hypothesis
- Drawing Conclusions
- Theory
- Technology

Skills in this Chapter

The skills that you will use in this chapter are listed below.

- In **Lab 1-1,** you will observe and recognize and use spatial relationships. In **Lab 1-2,** you will form hypotheses, interpret data, and separate and control variables.
- In the **Skill Checks,** you will make and use tables, calculate, and understand science words.
- In the **Mini Labs,** you will design an experiment.

4

Bridging

Students know the differences between things that are living and things that are not living. Discuss these differences and how an understanding of living things is used by many people. For instance, you may want to discuss the work that people in the community do. Students will see how biology is used in everyday life.

Chapter 1

The Study of Life

Look at the photo of the classroom on the left. How many things can you name that are living or were once living? Think about the living or once-living things in your own classroom. The desks, pencils, and books in your classroom are plant products. Chalk comes from tiny living things found in the ocean. Plastics contain materials that come from the remains of plants and animals. Chairs, pens, rulers, and calculators are some of the products that can be made from plastics.

Consider the things that came from living or once-living things in the other parts of the school, such as the gym, cafeteria, or library. You can see many things that you need and use every day are living or were once living. **Biology** is the study of living and once-living things. *Bio-* means life and *-ology* means the study of. A person who studies living and once-living things is called a biologist.

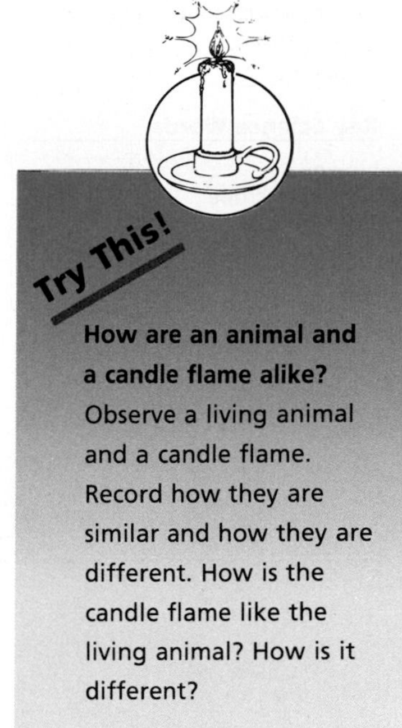

Try This!

How are an animal and a candle flame alike? Observe a living animal and a candle flame. Record how they are similar and how they are different. How is the candle flame like the living animal? How is it different?

GETTING STARTED

Using the Photos

Students may also consider their bedrooms or other rooms in their homes and try to come up with a list of living or once-living things found there. With the widespread use of plastics, there is almost nothing in the home or school environment that is not living or once living.

MOTIVATION/Try This!

How are an animal and a candle flame alike? In the chapter-opening activity, students will **observe** a living and nonliving thing and **record** their observations. Students will see that the candle flame moves, uses energy from the candle, and responds to air currents. They will discover that nonliving things may appear to be living.

Chapter Preview

Have students study the chapter outline before they begin to read the chapter. The chapter introduces the tools, measurements, and problem solving methods of biologists.

Misconception

All people use biology every day. Students may think of people who use biology as those who wear white coats and work in laboratories surrounded by test tubes and beakers.

1:1 Biology in Use

PREPARATION

Materials Needed

Make copies of the Focus, Enrichment, Transparency, Reteaching, Study Guide, and Lab worksheets in the *Teacher Resource Package*.

▶ Gather a Petri dish, Duco cement, and a few pencil shavings for the Focus demonstration. Cut letter e's from a magazine for Lab 1-1.

Key Science Words

biology
light microscope
stereomicroscope

Process Skills

In Lab 1-1, students will observe and recognize and use spatial relationships. In the Skill Checks, students will understand science words and make and use tables.

1 FOCUS

▶ The objectives are listed on the student page. Remind students to preview these objectives as a guide to this numbered section.

MOTIVATION/Demonstration

Fill a Petri dish with water. Place it on the overhead projector. Add 3 or 4 drops of Duco cement. Then add 2 or 3 pencil shavings. Ask students to observe and record their observations. Discuss what life processes can be seen (movement, eating).

Guided Practice

Have students write down their answers to the margin question: to analyze evidence.

Focus/*Teacher Resource Package*, p. 1. Use the Focus worksheet shown at the bottom of this page as an introduction to the uses of biology.

Objectives

1. **Describe** three jobs that depend on the use of biology.
2. **List** five tools of biologists.
3. **Compare** the features of the light microscope, stereomicroscope, and electron microscope.

Key Science Words

biology
light microscope
stereomicroscope

1:1 Biology in Use

The use of biology is not limited to biologists. Many people use biology daily in their hobbies and work. We will look at how you and other people use biology.

Who Uses Biology?

Look at the photos. Are the people shown in the photos using biology in any way?

The beekeeper in Figure 1-1a is removing honey from the hive. A beekeeper must know how bees work together to produce honey. He must know where to place the hives to get the most honey.

How do the police use biology?

Crime lab technicians (tek NISH uhnz) work with different kinds of evidence. Evidence may include cloth fibers, bits of paper, hair, skin, and blood. These things must be studied under a microscope.

If you wear eyeglasses or contact lenses, an optometrist (ahp TAHM uh trust) probably fitted them. The optometrist has studied the eyes and how they work.

Mushrooms are grown in buildings with carefully controlled temperature, moisture, and air flow. Mushroom growers must choose the best soil conditions for their crops. They must know how to identify and treat diseases of mushrooms.

Many people use biology in different ways. You use biology if you have ever asked yourself any of these questions: How can I tell when my plant needs water? What can I do about the fleas on my dog? How can I tell if this plant is poison ivy? The answers to these questions have to do with living things. You use biology all the time and may not even realize it.

Figure 1-1 Beekeepers (a) and optometrists (b) use biology in their work.

a

b

OPTIONS

Science Background

The first microscopes were built around 1600. Galileo observed insects with a compound microscope he had made. Two Dutch spectacles makers, Jan and Zacharias Janssen, are also credited with having developed compound microscopes.

Science Background

Magnets in the electron microscope focus the electron beam onto a fluorescent screen, which produces an image of the specimen.

FOCUS 1

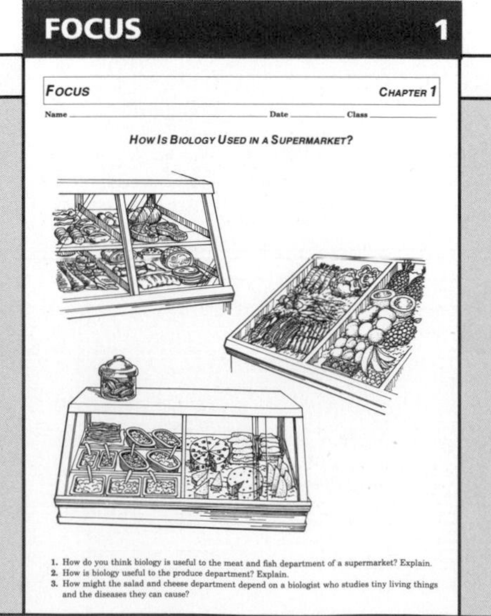

FOCUS CHAPTER 1

Name ______ Date ______ Class ______

HOW IS BIOLOGY USED IN A SUPERMARKET?

1. How do you think biology is useful to the meat and fish department of a supermarket? Explain.
2. How is biology useful to the produce department? Explain.
3. How might the salad and cheese department depend on a biologist who studies tiny living things and the diseases they can cause?

Tools of Biology

Almost every day you use tools to measure and observe. You may use some of the same tools that a biologist uses. Have you ever used a ruler or a magnifying glass? Maybe you have used a pair of binoculars or a microscope.

A hand lens is a type of magnifying glass. It makes an object appear three to five times larger than it is.

A light microscope is one of the most important tools of biology, Figure 1-2. It magnifies small objects similar to the way binoculars magnify far-away objects. Both light microscopes and binoculars have lenses for magnifying objects.

In a **light microscope**, light passes through the object being looked at and then through two or more lenses. What you look at appears larger.

> **Skill Check**
>
> **Understand science words: microscope.** The word part *micro* means small. In your dictionary, find three words with the word part *micro* in them. *For more help, refer to the* ***Skill Handbook****, pages 706-711.*

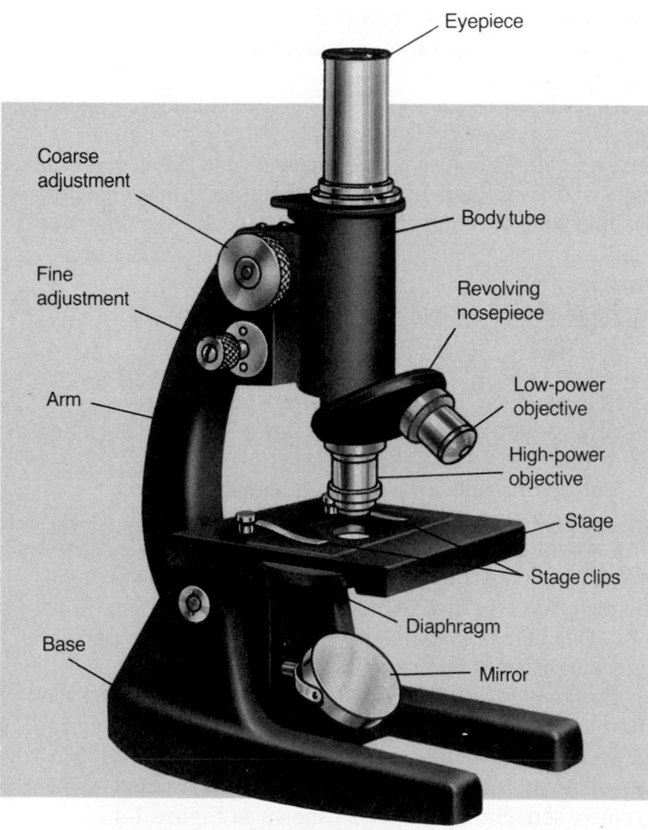

Figure 1-2 A light microscope magnifies small objects.

2 TEACH

MOTIVATION/Brainstorming

Ask students why a paramedic, crime lab technician, or optician needs knowledge of biology.

Concept Development

▶ You may want to introduce the section on tools of biology by showing students a hand lens, a pair of binoculars, and a microscope.

Connection: Language Arts

Have students look through the classified section of the newspaper and circle jobs that use biology.

Independent Practice

Study Guide/*Teacher Resource Package*, p. 1. Use the Study Guide worksheet shown at the bottom of this page for independent practice.

ENRICHMENT 1

ENRICHMENT — *CHAPTER 1*

Name ______ Date ______ Class ______

Use after Section 1:1.

FIELDS OF SCIENCE

Scientists study and investigate nearly every aspect of life on Earth. They work in different fields of science. The names of many of these fields end in the suffix *-logy*. Find this suffix in the dictionary.

What is its meaning? **the science of or study of**

A suffix, such as *-logy*, must be combined with another word part to complete its meaning. When the suffix *-logy* is added to the prefix *bio-*, what does the resulting word mean? **the study of life**

Use a dictionary to find the meanings of the prefixes in the name of each field of science listed below. In the second column of the chart, write a description of what is studied in each field listed in the first column.

Word	Meaning of word
Anthropology	the study of humans, their origins and cultures
Zoology	the study of animals
Ecology	the study of living organisms and their environment
Virology	the study of viruses
Bacteriology	the study of bacteria
Cytology	the study of cell structure
Entomology	the study of insects
Embryology	the study of the formation and development of embryos
Ethology	the study of animal behavior
Herpetology	the study of reptiles
Microbiology	the study of microscopic organisms
Paleontology	the study of plant and animal fossils
Oceanology	the study of marine resources and technology
Physiology	the study of how living things function
Ichthyology	the study of fish

STUDY GUIDE 1

STUDY GUIDE — *CHAPTER 1*

Name ______ Date ______ Class ______

BIOLOGY IN USE

In your textbook, read about people who use biology in Section 1:1. Then, answer the questions below.

1. Many people use biology every day. What do the people shown below need to know about biology?

A florist needs to know how to care for plants.

A coach needs to know about bones and muscles.

A pharmacist needs to know how medicines affect the body.

A farmer needs to know how to raise plants and animals.

A veterinarian needs to know how to keep animals healthy.

A lifeguard needs to know about lungs and breathing.

2. Many people use biology in their hobbies. The column on the right lists ways biology can be used in hobbies. In front of the hobbies on the left, write the letter or letters of the way people use biology in each hobby.

a, c	1. growing houseplants	a. know about different kinds of plants
d	2. jogging	b. know about the habits of birds
b, e	3. bird watching	c. know how to make plants grow
d	4. swimming	d. know about bones and muscles
a, e	5. identifying wild flowers	e. know about classifying things

OPTIONS

How Is the Light Microscope Used?/*Lab Manual*, pp. 1-4. Use this lab to give additional practice with the microscope.

Challenge: Have students expand the list of ways people use biology. Ask if biology might supply the answers to: How could I stay underwater longer? Why do I yawn?

Enrichment/*Teacher Resource Package*, p. 1. Use the Enrichment worksheet shown here to give more information on fields of biology.

TEACH

Concept Development

▶ Explain that the stereoscopic microscope has an ocular lens and an objective lens for each eye. This arrangement of lenses provides a three-dimensional view of the object's surface.

▶ Point out that the electron microscope produces a picture in a manner similar to a television.

▶ Explain to students that a microscope does two things: it magnifies and provides resolving power.

▶ Explain to students that spaces are used to group digits in long numbers because, in some countries, a comma indicates a decimal point.

Guided Practice

Have students write down their answers to the margin questions: objects through which light will not pass.

Cooperative Learning: Divide the class into twos and have students in each group check each other on the parts and functions of the microscope.

Skill Check

Use the Skill Check to make sure that students understand how to find the total magnification of a microscope.

Independent Practice

Study Guide/*Teacher Resource Package*, p. 2. Use the Study Guide worksheet shown at the bottom of this page for independent practice.

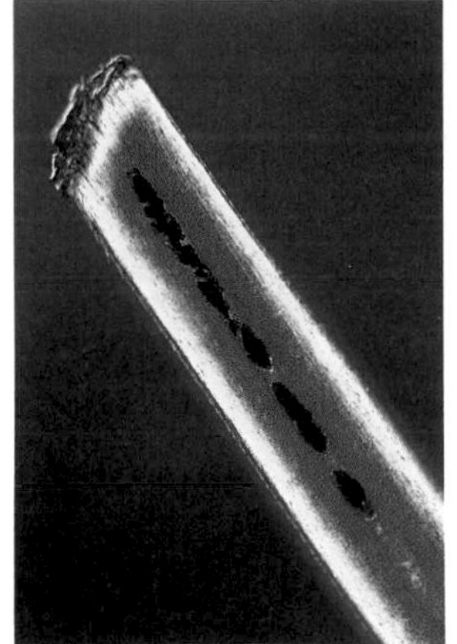

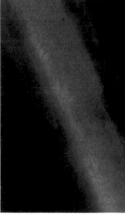

a b c

Figure 1-3 A hair is shown magnified 10 times (a), 100 times (b), and 430 times (c).

Skill Check

Make and use tables: Make a table that compares the magnifying powers of a hand lens, a stereomicroscope, low power and high power of a light microscope, and an electron microscope. *For more help, refer to the* ***Skill Handbook****, pages 715-717.*

What kinds of objects would you view with a stereomicroscope?

The microscope has a lens in the eyepiece. The eyepiece lens magnifies 10 times and is marked 10 ×. If you looked through just the eyepiece, a hair would look like the one in Figure 1-3a.

In addition to the eyepiece lens, a light microscope has one or more objective lenses that magnify the object further. One objective is a low-power lens. It magnifies 10 times and is marked 10 ×. To find the *total magnification* when looking through the eyepiece lens and the objective lens, you multiply the magnification of the two lenses together.

eyepiece lens × objective lens = total magnification

10 times × 10 times = 100 times larger

If you looked at the same hair with the low-power objective and the eyepiece together, you would see something that looks like Figure 1-3b. This hair is enlarged 100 times.

The second objective lens is a high-power lens. High-power objectives can magnify 40, 43, or 100 times. How would an objective that magnifies 43 times be marked? If you looked at the hair with a high-power objective and the eyepiece together, it might look like the hair in Figure 1-3c. This hair is magnified 430 times. The highest-powered light microscopes can magnify objects 2000 times.

Stereomicroscopes (STER ee oh MI kruh skohps) are often used in biology classes. A **stereomicroscope** is used for viewing large objects and things through which light cannot pass, such as insects. The stereomicroscope has an eyepiece lens for each eye, as shown in Figure 1-4.

8

OPTIONS

Enrichment: Investigate preparation techniques for electron microscopy. Investigate the process of taking photographs through a microscope. If you have access to standard photographic equipment, you might try photomicrography.

Transparency Master/*Teacher Resource Package*, p. 1. Use the Transparency Master shown here to teach students about tools used in biology.

STUDY GUIDE 2

STUDY GUIDE — CHAPTER 1

Name ________ Date ________ Class ________

BIOLOGY IN USE

In your textbook, read about the tools of biology in Section 1:1.

3. Biologists use many tools when they study living things. You may use some of the same tools. Label the tools shown below. Fill in the blanks below each picture.

Tool	light microscope	hand lens
Magnification	10× to 2000×	3× to 5×
Use	magnifies objects	magnifies objects

Tool	stereomicroscope	electron microscope	computer
Magnification	10× to 60×	500 000×	
Use	viewing large objects through which light cannot pass	viewing things that cannot be seen with the light microscope	to store, find, and process information

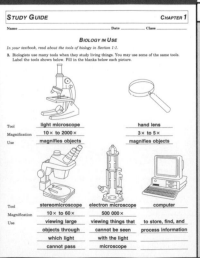

TRANSPARENCY 1

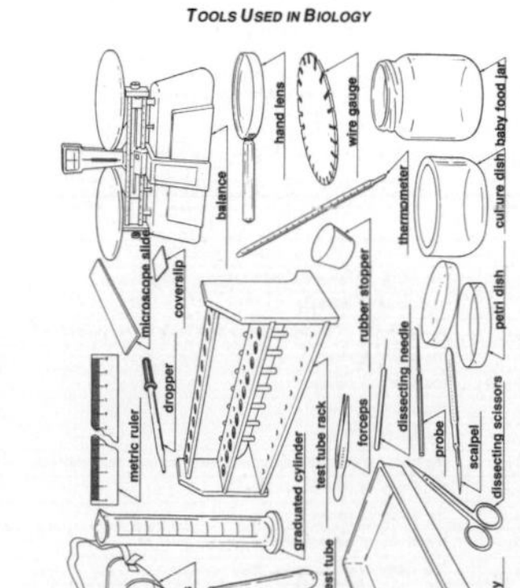

Lab 1–1 Microscopes

Problem: How do you use the microscope?

Skills

observe, recognize spatial relationships

Materials

microscope
microscope slide
coverslip
water
dropper
forceps
small piece of magazine print

Procedure

1. Place a drop of water in the center of a glass slide.
2. With forceps, place a small piece of magazine print in the drop of water. Make sure the piece of magazine has a letter *e* in it.
3. Hold a clean coverslip by the edges at one side of the drop of water. Carefully lower the coverslip onto the drop of water. You have just made a wet mount slide.
4. Place the slide on the stage of the microscope. Put the stage clips into place. Move the slide so that the magazine print is directly over the hole in the stage.
5. Turn the low-power objective into place.
6. Looking from the side, turn the coarse adjustment so that the low-power objective is near the coverslip.
7. Open the diaphragm so that the most light enters the microscope. If your microscope has a mirror, adjust it until you see a circle of light. This circle of light is called the field of view.
8. Look through the eyepiece. Try to keep both eyes open. Raise the body tube until you can see the letters. **CAUTION:** *Never lower the body tube while looking through the eyepiece.*
9. Use the fine adjustment to bring the letters into sharp focus. Find a letter *e*.
10. Adjust the slide so that the letter e is in the center of your field of view.
11. On a separate paper, make a drawing of the letter *e*. Label your drawing with your name and the magnification.
12. **Recognize spatial relationships:** Move the slide to the left, to the right, toward you, and away from you. Note the direction in which the e appears to move.
13. Turn the nosepiece to bring the high-power objective into position. Focus with the fine adjustment. **CAUTION:** *Use only the fine adjustment with the high-power objective.*
14. Draw the letter *e* as it appears under high power. Label your drawing with your name and the magnification.
15. Remove the wet mount. Rinse and dry the slide and coverslip. Set your microscope on low power and put it away.

Data and Observations

1. What happens when you move the slide to the left? To the right? Toward you? Away from you?
2. Describe the appearance of the letter e under high power.

Analyze and Apply

1. What is the purpose of the coverslip?
2. Why should the coverslip be held by the edges?
3. **Apply:** Why must a specimen be very thin to be viewed under the microscope?

Extension

Observe: View other objects, such as a hair or thread under the microscope.

ANSWERS

Data and Observations

1. appeared to move to the right; appeared to move to the left; appeared to move away; appeared to move toward observer
2. Students may observe that the edges of the e are ragged looking; only part of it can be seen.

Analyze and Apply

1. It prevents the objects being viewed from moving and protects the lenses.
2. to prevent fingerprints and smudges
3. Light must pass through it in order for it to be seen.

Lab 1-1 Microscopes

Overview

In this lab, students will use a microscope and observe its magnifying and resolving powers.

Objectives: Upon completing this lab students will be able to (1) **prepare** a wet mount slide, (2) **compare** observations made under high and low powers, (3) **observe** a microscope's magnifying power and resolving power.

Time Allotment: 40 minutes

Preparation

▶ Assemble microscope slides, coverslips, droppers, and forceps. Cut letter e's from magazine print.

Lab 1-1 worksheet/*Teacher Resource Package*, pp. 1-2.

Teaching the Lab

▶ Review with the students the correct procedures for carrying, using, and storing a microscope.

▶ **Troubleshooting:** Make sure the lowercase e is used, not capital E. E is not asymmetrical.

Cooperative Learning: Divide the class into groups of two students. For more information, see pp. 22T-23T in the Teacher Guide.

The Microscope/*Transparency Package*, number 1. Use color transparency number 1 as you teach this lab.

TEACH

Guided Practice

Have students write down their answers to the margin question: biologists use cameras to record an animal's daily habits; they use nets to capture animals and observe them; they use gardens to grow plants and observe them.

Check for Understanding

Have students respond to the first three questions in Check Your Understanding.

Reteach

Reteaching/*Teacher Resource Package*, p. 1. Use this worksheet to give students additional practice with the parts of the microscope.

Extension: Assign Critical Thinking, Biology and Math, or some of the **OPTIONS** available with this lesson.

3 APPLY

Show a videocassette (or filmstrip) on using the microscope.

4 CLOSE

Ask students to list the tools used by biologists studied in this lesson. Then have them give other examples of tools that can detect what the human senses cannot. Radio receivers, infrared and ultraviolet detectors, telescopes, and photographic film are some examples.

Figure 1-4 A stereomicroscope is used for viewing objects through which light will not pass.

How does having two eyepiece lenses help? The advantage of having a lens for each eye is that it makes the object appear three-dimensional. A disadvantage of the stereomicroscope is that its magnifying power is not as great as that of a light microscope. The stereomicroscope magnifies only 10 to 60 times.

An electron microscope is a very high-powered microscope that uses a beam of electrons instead of light to magnify objects. The magnified object is seen on a monitor similar to a TV screen. An advantage of an electron microscope is that it can magnify more than 500 000 times. Objects can be viewed in great detail. A disadvantage is that objects can't be viewed in color. Also, objects must be stained with expensive dyes before they can be viewed under the electron microscope. The staining process requires a great deal of skill and training.

New information about biology is published every day. How could a biologist remember all of it? Many biologists use computers to store, find, and process information. The computer helps biologists search for information and organize it. It saves many hours of library research.

How do biologists use cameras, nets, and gardens?

Biologists use many other tools that you may not associate with biology. For example, biologists use cameras. A wildlife biologist may take photographs of deer to understand the deer's daily habits. Biologists who study fish need boats to take them to where the fish are. They also use nets to catch the fish so they can observe them. Did you ever imagine that a garden could be a biologist's tool? Biologists who study how plants grow use gardens all the time for their work. As you see, biologists use more than laboratory tools to study living things.

Check Your Understanding

1. How does a beekeeper use biology?
2. What are three tools used by biologists?
3. A light microscope has an eyepiece that magnifies 10 × and an objective that is marked 43 ×. What is the total magnification for these two lenses?
4. **Critical Thinking:** How would a farmer use biology to grow corn?
5. **Biology and Math:** If a microscope eyepiece magnifies 4× and the total magnification is 400×, how much does the objective lens magnify?

Answers to Check Your Understanding

1. A beekeeper must know how bees work together to produce honey; he must also know where to place the hives in order to get the most honey.
2. hand lens, ruler, microscope, stereomicroscope, binoculars, computers
3. 430 (10 x 43)
4. The farmer must know the best soil conditions for the corn, know how to identify and treat diseases of corn, and what kinds of fertilizers to use.
5. 100 (400 ÷ 4)

RETEACHING 1

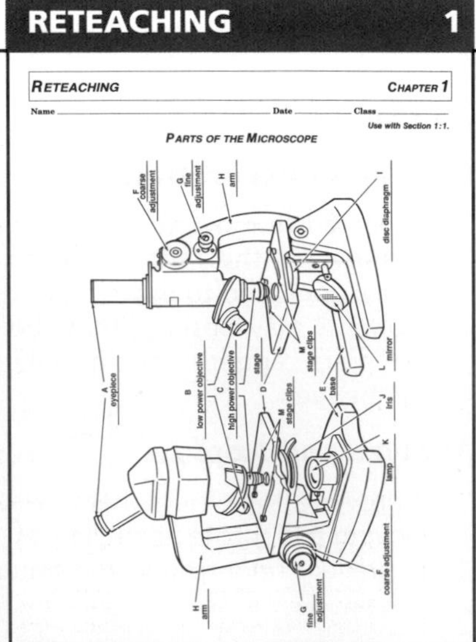

RETEACHING CHAPTER 1

Name ______ Date ______ Class ______

Use with Section 1:1.

PARTS OF THE MICROSCOPE

1:2 Measurements Used in Biology

Objectives

4. **Explain** how SI units are grouped.
5. **List** the SI units of measure for length, volume, mass, time, and temperature.
6. **Measure** objects using SI units.

Key Science Words

International System of Units
meter
volume
kilogram
Celsius

It is 40 kilometers to the nearest city. The soft drink is in a 2-liter bottle. The mass of the bag of potato chips is 184 grams. A football field is 300 feet long. A photographer uses a 35 millimeter camera. The medicine comes in 25-milligram tablets.

In which of these sentences is the unit of measurement different? The football field measurement is different. It is in English units. The other measurements are in metric units. Scientists today use a modern form of the metric system. They use the International System of Units, or SI system. The **International System of Units** is a measuring system based on units of 10. Scientists all over the world use it. Measurements in the SI system are similar to measurements in our money system. Let's see how the two systems compare.

Length

Length is the distance from one point to another. What does our money system have in common with a system for measuring length? The basic unit in our money system is the dollar. As you know, the dollar can be divided into 10 dimes. Each dime can be divided into 10 cents as shown in Figure 1-5.

The SI unit of length is the **meter** (m). Figure 1-5 shows that like a dollar, a meter can be divided into 10 smaller units. The meter is divided into 10 units called decimeters (DES uh meet urz) (dm). Each decimeter can be divided into 10 centimeters (SENT uh meet urz) (cm).

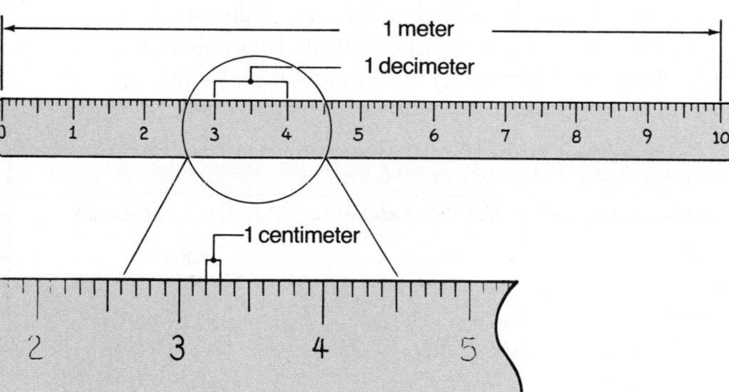

Figure 1-5 The SI system is based on units of 10, just as our money system is.

1:2 Measurements Used in Biology

PREPARATION

Materials Needed

Make copies of the Application, Skill, Reteaching, and Study Guide worksheets in the *Teacher Resource Package*.

▶ Gather measuring instruments for the Focus demonstration.

▶ Gather metric rulers for the Skill Check.

Key Science Words

International System of Units
meter
volume
kilogram
Celsius

Process Skills

In the Skill Check, students will calculate.

1 FOCUS

▶ The objectives are listed on the student page. Remind students to preview these objectives as a guide to this numbered section.

MOTIVATION/Demonstration

Show students measuring instruments such as a clock, rain gauge, barometer, galvanometer, and pedometer. Discuss what each measures in units.

APPLICATION 1

APPLICATION: SAFETY CHAPTER 1

Name ______ Date ______ Class ______

Use after Section 1:1.

SAFETY IN THE BIOLOGY LABORATORY

Working in a biology laboratory can be dangerous if safety rules are not followed.

To prepare yourself for a safe year in the laboratory, complete the exercises below.

1. The phrases below describe student behavior in the laboratory. In the space before each phrase, write *safe* if the behavior is safe or *unsafe* if the behavior is unsafe.
   - **unsafe** holding a frog in your hand while you dissect it
   - **safe** tying back long hair to keep it away from chemicals, burners, or other equipment
   - **unsafe** eating your lunch while waiting for a solution to boil
   - **safe** wearing goggles and a laboratory apron when working with chemicals
   - **unsafe** turning the mirror of your microscope directly toward the sun to get more light
   - **unsafe** identifying a chemical by tasting it
2. Draw a diagram of your laboratory classroom. Show the location of the *fire blanket, fire extinguishers, eyewash station, first aid kit, sand, safety shower,* and *exits*.

   exit, sand, exit, fire extinguisher, first aid kit, fire blanket, eyewash station, safety shower

   Diagrams will depend on the classroom floor plan.
3. Two laboratory accidents are described below. Explain what action should be taken and tell how the accident could have been avoided.
   a. A student's loose sleeve catches on fire as she reaches across a lighted burner.
   Wrap the arm in a fire blanket and get medical help. To avoid such an accident, tie back loose sleeves; do not reach across burners.
   b. A chemical splashes into a student's eye as he heats the chemical in a test tube.
   Wash the eye at the eyewash station and get medical help. To avoid the accident, wear goggles and point the test tube away from anyone.

OPTIONS

Science Background

SI is the form of the metric system used by the scientific community. SI units are metric units. SI is used by scientists all over the world and in everyday life in many countries. SI stands for the French Le Système International d'Unités.

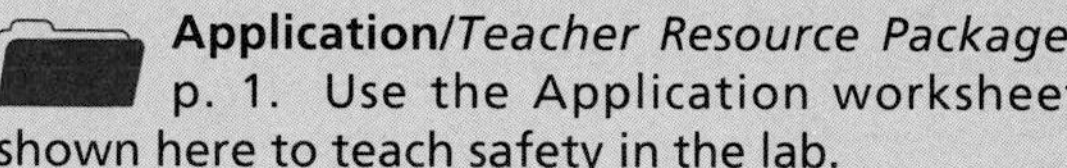

Application/*Teacher Resource Package*, p. 1. Use the Application worksheet shown here to teach safety in the lab.

TEACH

MOTIVATION/Brainstorming

Ask students to list where measurements are made using the SI system. Examples may include sports, soft drink bottles, parts for foreign-made cars.

Concept Development

▶ You will find added information on the SI system included in Appendix A.

▶ Avoid having students convert between the metric and English systems. Encourage students to "think metric."

Connection: Consumer

Ask students to bring in food labels that show metric measurements. Have them convert the measurements on the labels to equivalents in larger or smaller units.

Skill Check

You may have to remind students that area is determined by multiplying length by width.

Guided Practice

Have students answer the margin question by measuring the width of their hands and writing down their answers.

Independent Practice

Study Guide/*Teacher Resource Package*, p. 3. Use the Study Guide worksheet shown at the bottom of this page for independent practice.

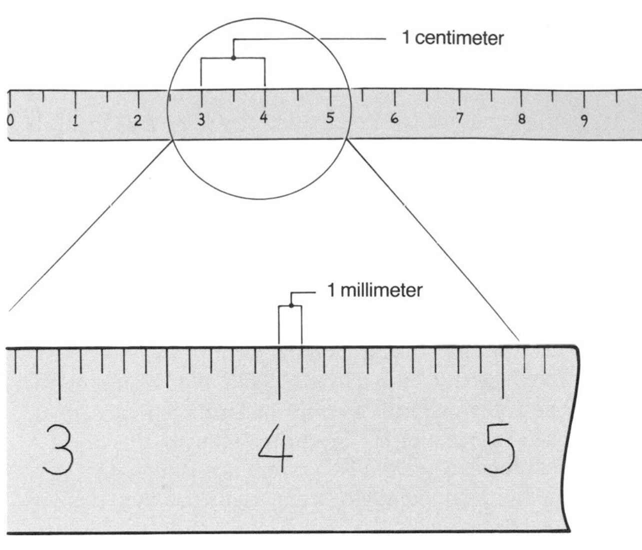

Figure 1-6 There are 10 millimeters in one centimeter.

Skill Check

Calculate: Use a calculator and a meter stick to find the area of your classroom and your desk. *For more help, refer to the **Skill Handbook**, pages 718-719.*

What is the width of your hand in millimeters?

In our money system, the smallest amount of money is one cent. However, the smallest length you can measure is not one centimeter. Figure 1-6 shows that each centimeter can be further divided into 10 units called millimeters (MIHL uh meet urz) (mm). Very small measurements are made in millimeters.

Do we have any units in our money system that are *larger* than the dollar? Yes, we group dollars together into tens, hundreds, and thousands. We also put meters into larger groups. Table 1-1 shows how metric units are grouped. The prefixes shown have special meanings. Notice that the first three prefixes change meters to larger units of measurement. For example, 1000 meters make one *kilo*meter (KIHL uh meet ur) (km). Ten *deci*meters make one meter. One hundred *centi*meters make one meter. The second three prefixes change meters to smaller units of measurement. How many *milli*meters make one meter?

TABLE 1–1. HOW METRIC UNITS ARE GROUPED

Prefix (word part)	Symbol	Meaning
kilo-	k	1000
hecto-	h	100
deka-	da	10
deci-	d	0.1 (1/10)
centi-	c	0.01 (1/100)
milli-	m	0.001 (1/1000)

12

OPTIONS

Enrichment: Explain that the cent is divided into 10 mills and relate that to the division of 1 cm into 10 mm. (The mill is used in tax levies.)

How Are SI Length Measurements Made?/*Lab Manual*, pp. 5-8. Use This lab to give further practice with SI measurements.

Skill/*Teacher Resource Package*, p. 1. Use the Skill worksheet shown here to give students additional practice measuring in SI.

STUDY GUIDE 3

STUDY GUIDE — CHAPTER 1

Name ______ Date ______ Class ______

MEASUREMENTS USED IN BIOLOGY

In your textbook, read about measurements used in biology in Section 1:2.

1. Examine the recipe below and answer the questions. Circle all the measurements on the recipe card.

Whole Wheat Bread

14 g dry yeast — Dissolve yeast in warm water.
826 mL warm water 40°C — Add other parts and mix.
80 mL oil — Knead dough with hands for 10 min.
158 mL honey — Let rise for 1 hour.
7 g salt — Punch dough and work again for 10 min.
120 g white flour — Divide dough into 3 parts.
1135 g wheat flour — Form into loaves each 15 cm long.
Let rise ½ hour.
Makes 3 loaves — Bake in greased pans for 35 min at 200°C.

a. How many milliliters of liquid parts were added together in the recipe? 1064 mL

b. How many grams of dry parts were added together in the recipe? 1276 g

c. Complete the following table using the recipe.

Measurement		What is being measured	
Number	Unit	In general	In this recipe
14	g	mass	yeast
826	mL	volume	warm water
80	mL	volume	oil
1135	g	mass	wheat flour
40	°C	temperature	water temperature
200	°C	temperature	baking temperature
35	min	time	baking time

SKILL 1

SKILL: MEASURE IN SI — CHAPTER 1

Name ______ Date ______ Class ______

For more help, refer to the Skill Handbook, pages 718-719. — *Use after Section 1:2.*

MEASURING IN SCIENCE

Measuring is one of the most important parts of science. The system of measurement used by scientists all over the world is the International System of Units, or SI. You will use SI in your laboratory work.

Check your knowledge of SI by completing the tables below and answering the questions that follow.

Measurement	SI unit	Symbol
length	meter	m
mass	kilogram	kg
volume	cubic meter	m^3
time	second	s

Standard SI units are listed at the left in the table below. Complete the table by writing in the names of the fractions and the multiples of the standard units.

Unit	1/1000	1/100	1	1000
meter	millimeter	centimeter	meter	kilometer
liter	milliliter	centiliter	liter	kiloliter
gram	milligram	centigram	gram	kilogram

1. Scientists measure temperature in degrees Celsius.
2. An SI unit of mass often used instead of kilogram is gram.
3. A microscope slide is 2 centimeters wide. How many millimeters wide is it? 20
4. The number used to change millimeters to centimeters is 10.
5. When changing from large SI units to smaller units, do you multiply or divide? multiply
6. What is the length of this line ______ in centimeters? 2.5 cm

Volume

Volume is the amount of space a substance occupies. Units of volume are based on units of length. If we multiply length by width by height, we get volume. The SI unit of volume is the cubic meter (m^3). This volume is rather large for everyday use, so scientists often use the liter (L) instead. A liter is 1/100 as large as a cubic meter. You use the liter when you do labs in science class, or when you buy soft drinks at the grocery store. One liter equals 1000 milliliters (mL).

Like meters, liters can be put into large groups. One kiloliter means 1000 liters. What does five kiloliters mean?

Into how many smaller units can a liter be divided?

Weight and Mass

The photos in Figure 1-7 show an astronaut on Earth and an astronaut on the moon. The astronaut does not weigh the same in both places. Weight is a measure of the force of gravity on an object. The force of gravity on the moon is less than that on Earth. Therefore, an astronaut weighs less on the moon than on Earth. Even though the astronaut weighs less on the moon than on Earth, his or her mass does not change. Mass is how much matter is in something. Let's look at mass in another way. Consider the masses of two different objects, a box of bricks and a box of cotton. Which has more mass? Mass is measured by comparing an object of unknown mass to an object of known mass. The instrument used to measure mass is a balance.

a

b

Figure 1-7 An astronaut's mass is the same on Earth (a) as it is on the moon (b).

TEACH

Concept Development

▶ Try to give students the idea of the volume of a liter without converting it to the English system (soft drink bottles are an example).

▶ Give students the metric masses of several common items. Examples: loaf of bread-450 g; pair of shoes-1000 g or 1 kg; pencil-10 g.

Check for Understanding

Make flash cards with examples of metric units. When an example is shown, students should respond with the unit of measurement.

Reteach

Show students different pieces of lab equipment. Have them identify the quantity measured and the unit of metric measurement.

Cooperative Learning: Divide the class into cooperative groups of four. Have each group invent a new system for measuring length. Remind each group that a system of measurement must have a standard.

Guided Practice

Have students write down their answers to the margin question: 1000 milliliters.

Independent Practice

Study Guide/*Teacher Resource Package*, p. 4. Use the Study Guide worksheet shown at the bottom of this page for independent practice.

STUDY GUIDE 4

STUDY GUIDE — CHAPTER 1

Name ______ Date ______ Class ______

MEASUREMENTS USED IN BIOLOGY

In your textbook, read about measuring volume in Section 1:2.

2. Look at the graduated cylinder on the right. Note the lines and numbers printed on its sides. The graduated cylinder is filled to the 45 mL mark. Read the level of the liquid in each of the graduated cylinders below. Write the correct volume on the line below each graduated cylinder.

65 mL — 80 mL — 100 mL — 45 mL

850 mL — 750 mL — 1 L (1000 mL)

You may need to explain how to read a meniscus. Students may wonder why the art shows the liquid level curved.

In your textbook, read about measuring temperature in Section 1:2.

3. In each space, write one of the following phrases that best matches the temperature shown. Use these phrases—water for bath, water freezes, water boils, a cool day, and human with fever.

100° water boils
55° water for bath
40° human with fever
20° a cool day
0° water freezes

OPTIONS

Enrichment: Ask students what their approximate weights would be on the moon. Moon weights would be about one-sixth of Earth weights. Ask how their weights would be affected on Jupiter. Jupiter is much larger, and the weights would be much greater. Then ask if their masses would change on the moon and on Jupiter. The answer is no.

The SI unit of mass is the **kilogram** (kg). There are 1000 grams (g) in a kilogram. Grams are used to measure small objects. An egg has a mass of about 60 grams. A gram may be divided into 1000 units called milligrams. Milligrams are often used to measure medicines or ingredients in foods such as breakfast cereals.

Time and Temperature

For what kind of measurement is a kilogram used?

Time is the period between two events. The SI unit for measuring time is the second (s). A stopwatch or a clock with a second hand is used to measure time.

Temperature is a measure of the amount of heat in something. The SI scale for measuring temperature is the Kelvin scale (K). Scientists measure temperature with the **Celsius** (SEL see us) scale because it is easier to use. Temperature scales are divided into units called degrees. On the Celsius scale, the freezing point of water is 0 degrees and the boiling point is 100 degrees. Figure 1-8 shows the temperature in Celsius degrees of other familiar things.

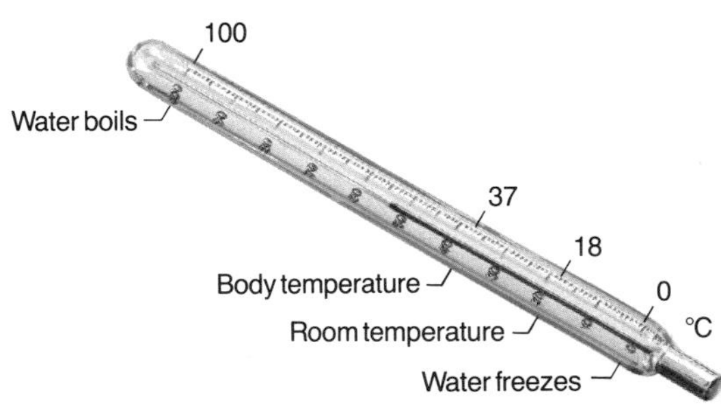

Figure 1-8 The Celsius scale

Check Your Understanding

6. What does the prefix *centi* mean?
7. What are some units used for measuring volume?
8. What is your body temperature in degrees Celsius?
9. **Critical Thinking:** How many centimeters make one kilometer?
10. **Biology and Math:** Suppose a cheetah can run 30 meters per second. How far can it run in 8 seconds?

TEACH

ACTIVITY/Hands-On

Have students use Celsius thermometers to measure room temperature, outdoor temperature, ice water, and boiling water. Caution students about the safety factors regarding boiling water.

Guided Practice

Have students write down their answers to the margin question: mass.

Check for Understanding

Have students respond to the first three questions in Check Your Understanding.

Reteach

Reteaching/*Teacher Resource Package*, p. 2. Use this worksheet to give students additional practice with measuring in SI.

Extension: Assign Critical Thinking, Biology and Math, or some of the **OPTIONS** available with this lesson.

3 APPLY

Software

The Metric System, Queue, Inc.

4 CLOSE

Have students identify the most useful units for measuring the things they can see in the classroom.

Answers to Check Your Understanding

6. 1/100 of something
7. liters and milliliters
8. about 37°
9. 100 centimeters in a meter x 1000 meters in a kilometer = 100 000 cm
10. 240 m (30 x 8)

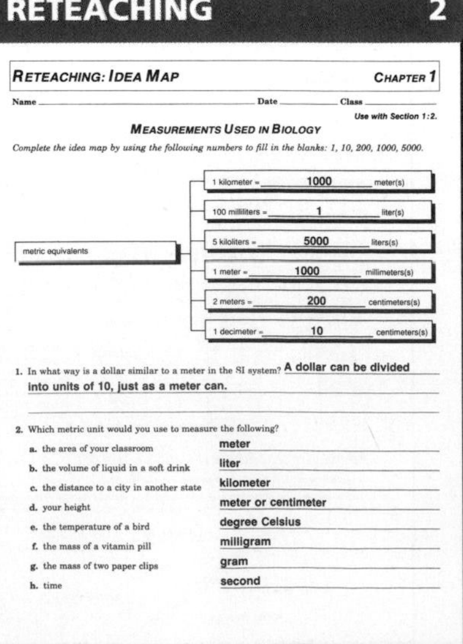
RETEACHING 2

RETEACHING: IDEA MAP CHAPTER 1

Name ______ Date ______ Class ______

Use with Section 1:2.

MEASUREMENTS USED IN BIOLOGY

Complete the idea map by using the following numbers to fill in the blanks: 1, 10, 200, 1000, 5000.

metric equivalents
- 1 kilometer = 1000 meter(s)
- 100 milliliters = 1 liter(s)
- 5 kiloliters = 5000 liters(s)
- 1 meter = 1000 millimeters(s)
- 2 meters = 200 centimeters(s)
- 1 decimeter = 10 centimeters(s)

1. In what way is a dollar similar to a meter in the SI system? **A dollar can be divided into units of 10, just as a meter can.**

2. Which metric unit would you use to measure the following?
   - a. the area of your classroom **meter**
   - b. the volume of liquid in a soft drink **liter**
   - c. the distance to a city in another state **kilometer**
   - d. your height **meter or centimeter**
   - e. the temperature of a bird **degree Celsius**
   - f. the mass of a vitamin pill **milligram**
   - g. the mass of two paper clips **gram**
   - h. time **second**

1:3 Scientific Method

Much of the work of biology is to solve problems. Problems are not solved by flipping a coin or taking a guess as to the outcome. Scientists use a series of steps called a **scientific method** to solve problems. The following steps are often used: recognizing the problem, researching the problem, forming a hypothesis (hi PAHTH uh sus), testing the hypothesis, and drawing conclusions.

Objectives

7. **Explain** the steps of the scientific method.
8. **Compare** the difference between a hypothesis and a theory.
9. **Explain** how technology is used to solve everyday problems.

Key Science Words

scientific method
hypothesis
experiment
variable
control
data
theory
technology

Recognizing and Researching the Problem

Have you ever tried to turn on a light and found that it didn't work? Maybe you have turned the key in a car's ignition and the car didn't start. If you have had problems like those, you probably have used a scientific method to solve them.

A biology class raised guppies for a class project. Paula thought the guppies would have more young if the light in the aquarium was turned off part of the time. Other students thought the light should be left on all the time. But, Paula had observed that her guppies at home had more young than the ones at school. She also knew that she kept her aquarium light turned off part of the time. The class had a problem. What should they do about the aquarium light?

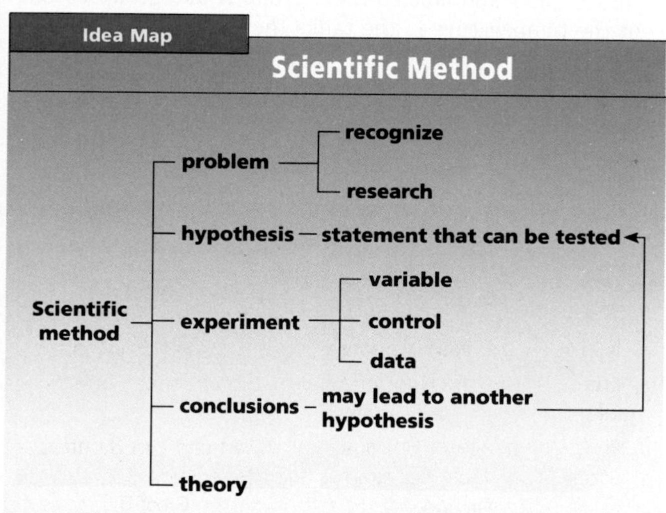

Study Tip: Use this idea map as a study guide to scientific method. Notice that a conclusion may lead to a second hypothesis. The second hypothesis then leads to more experiments and further conclusions.

OPTIONS

Science Background

Scientists obtain information by asking questions, making observations, and trying things out in a systematic way. They use a process called scientific method. A general model of scientific method is presented here.

1:3 Scientific Method

PREPARATION

Materials Needed

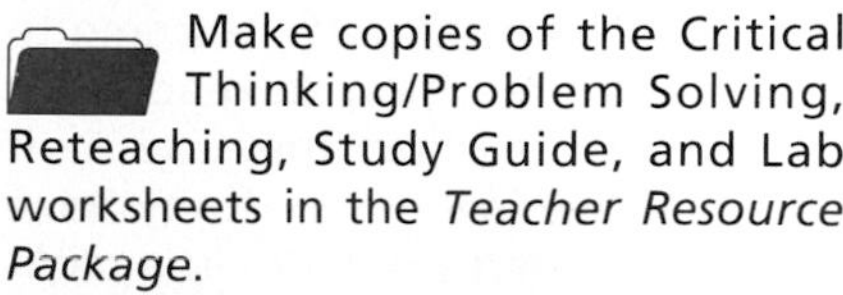

Make copies of the Critical Thinking/Problem Solving, Reteaching, Study Guide, and Lab worksheets in the *Teacher Resource Package*.

▶ For the Focus demonstration, get a slide projector and a screen.

▶ Gather cuttings of ivy, *Coleus,* and *Zebrina,* as well as aspirins for the Mini Lab.

▶ Gather pinto beans, salt, and self-sealing plastic bags for Lab 1-2.

Key Science Words

scientific method	control
hypothesis	data
experiment	theory
variable	technology

Process Skills

In Lab 1-2, students will form hypotheses, interpret data, and separate and control variables. In the Mini Lab, students will design an experiment.

1 FOCUS

▶ The objectives are listed on the student page. Remind students to preview these objectives as a guide to this numbered section.

MOTIVATION/Demonstration

Use a slide projector to set up a problem for students to investigate. Turn on the projector. No light reaches the screen. Have students solve the problem of the malfunctioning projector by using scientific method.

Idea Map

Have students use the idea map as a study guide to the major concepts of this section.

2 TEACH

MOTIVATION/Brainstorm

Ask students to think of ways they use scientific method in their everyday activities. Answers may include analyzing plays in sports, learning to drive a car, learning to read. Ask students to tell how they use their investigative skills. See if any have tried to find out what was in a package before opening it. What procedures did they use?

Concept Development

▶ Explain that using scientific method is similar to using common sense.

▶ Stress that there is no one scientific method.

▶ Point out that scientific method has no set order. The order will depend upon the investigation.

Mini Lab

Have students work in groups of four. Provide cuttings of ivy, *Coleus,* and *Zebrina*. Also provide aspirins and 2-4 small beakers per group.

Guided Practice

Have students write down their answers to the margin question: a statement that can be tested.

Independent Practice

Study Guide/*Teacher Resource Package*, p. 5. Use the Study Guide worksheet shown at the bottom of this page for independent practice.

Mini Lab

Does Aspirin Help Plants Grow?

Design an experiment: Your aunt tells you that plant cuttings will grow faster if aspirin is added to the water. Design and conduct an experiment to find out if this is true. *For more help, refer to the **Skill Handbook**, pages 704-705.*

Paula was able to recognize the problem. Before Paula could work on the solution to the problem, she needed to do some research at the library. She found out what temperature to keep the water and the amount of water needed. However, there was little information about how much light a guppy needs.

Forming a Hypothesis

A **hypothesis** is a statement that can be tested. Paula's hypothesis was: "If the light is turned off part of the time, then the guppies will have more young." Paula knew that her guppies received less light than the ones at school. She also observed two important things. Her tank at home had the same amount of water in it as the one at school. Also, the water temperature was the same in each tank. Paula was pretty sure that the conditions for the guppies were the same at home and at school, except for the amount of light. However, she needed to do a test to be absolutely sure.

Testing a Hypothesis

What is a hypothesis?

Paula's next step was to test her hypothesis. Testing a hypothesis using a series of steps with controlled conditions is called an **experiment**. In her experiment, Paula divided 16 guppies into two equal groups. She put the groups into separate tanks and labeled them group A and group B. She kept the temperature in the tanks the same. She put the same amount of water in each tank. The light for group B was left on 24 hours a day. The light for group A was turned on for 12 hours and off for 12 hours each day.

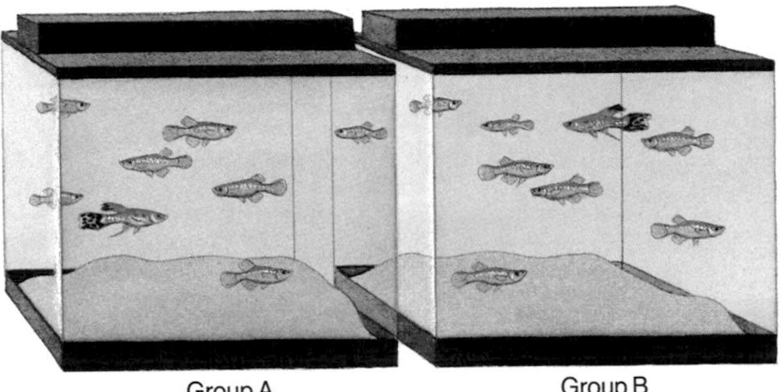

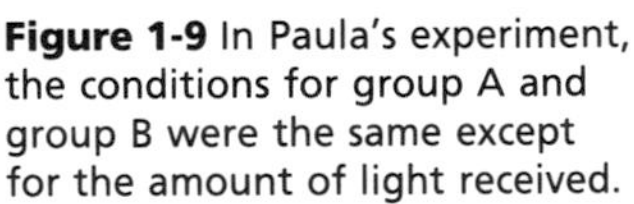

Figure 1-9 In Paula's experiment, the conditions for group A and group B were the same except for the amount of light received.

OPTIONS

Challenge: Have students find out about people such as Salk, Sabin, Fleming, Jenner, Pasteur, and Koch. Encourage them to investigate the ways in which scientists solved problems that have affected our lives.

STUDY GUIDE 5

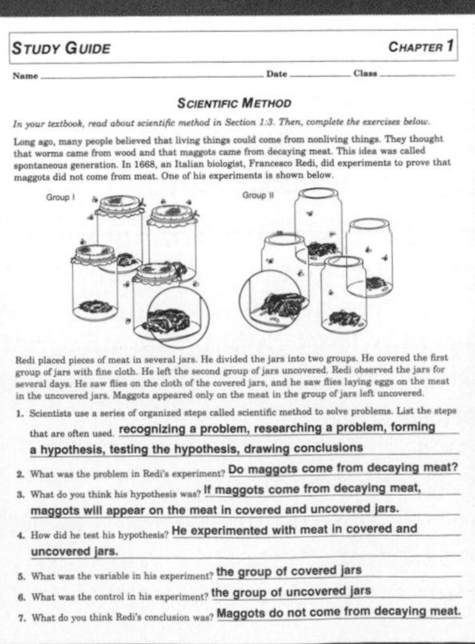

STUDY GUIDE CHAPTER 1

Name ______ Date ______ Class ______

SCIENTIFIC METHOD

In your textbook, read about scientific method in Section 1:3. Then, complete the exercises below.

Long ago, many people believed that living things could come from nonliving things. They thought that worms came from wood and that maggots came from decaying meat. This idea was called spontaneous generation. In 1668, an Italian biologist, Francesco Redi, did experiments to prove that maggots did not come from meat. One of his experiments is shown below.

Group I Group II

Redi placed pieces of meat in several jars. He divided the jars into two groups. He covered the first group of jars with fine cloth. He left the second group of jars uncovered. Redi observed the jars for several days. He saw flies on the cloth of the covered jars, and he saw flies laying eggs on the meat in the uncovered jars. Maggots appeared only on the meat in the group of jars left uncovered.

1. Scientists use a series of organized steps called scientific method to solve problems. List the steps that are often used. **recognizing a problem, researching a problem, forming a hypothesis, testing the hypothesis, drawing conclusions**
2. What was the problem in Redi's experiment? **Do maggots come from decaying meat?**
3. What do you think his hypothesis was? **If maggots come from decaying meat, maggots will appear on the meat in covered and uncovered jars.**
4. How did he test his hypothesis? **He experimented with meat in covered and uncovered jars.**
5. What was the variable in his experiment? **the group of covered jars**
6. What was the control in his experiment? **the group of uncovered jars**
7. What do you think Redi's conclusion was? **Maggots do not come from decaying meat.**

Lab 1–2 Scientific Method

Problem: How is a scientific method used to solve problems?

Skills

form hypotheses, interpret data, separate and control variables

Materials

2 100-mL beakers
40 pinto beans
balance
salt
water
2 paper towels
50-mL graduated cylinder
2 self-sealing plastic bags
masking tape

Procedure

1. Solve this problem using a scientific method: Do seeds grow better when soaked in plain water or salt water?
2. Research the problem. Find out what seeds need in order to grow.
3. Develop a **hypothesis** based on the problem.
4. Conduct the experiment.
   a. Copy the data table.
   b. Label two beakers A and B. Fill each beaker with 50 mL of water.
   c. Add 20 beans to beaker A. Add 20 beans and 2 g salt to beaker B. Label each beaker with your name and set them aside overnight.
   d. On the following day, pour out the water from both beakers.
   e. Wrap the seeds from beaker A with a damp paper towel. Place the paper towel into a plastic bag and close the bag. Label the bag A.
   f. Repeat step e with the seeds in beaker B.

	SEEDS USED	SEEDS THAT GREW
Water	20	17
Salt water	20	0

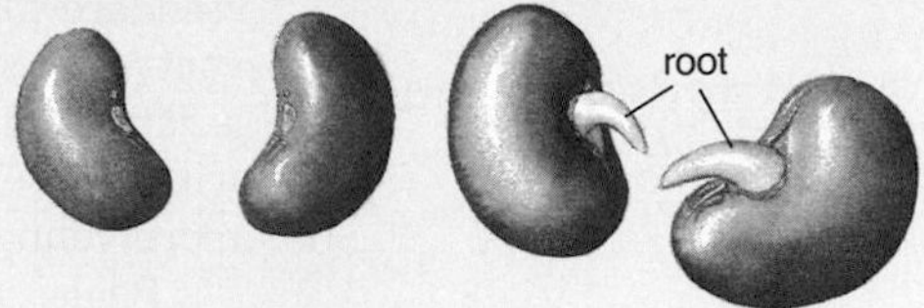

5. Collect the data.
   a. On the next day check the seeds for growth. Look for small white roots.
   b. Count the number of seeds that are growing in each bag. Record these numbers in your data table.
6. Draw conclusions. Based on your data, decide if you need a new hypothesis.
7. If soil and containers are available, you may want to plant the seeds that are growing.

Data and Observations

1. Under what condition, plain water or salt water, did more seeds grow?
2. Under what condition, plain water or salt water, did fewer seeds grow?

Analyze and Apply

1. **Check your hypothesis:** Is your original hypothesis supported by your data? Why or why not?
2. **Infer:** How can you be sure that the conclusion you reached is correct?
3. What variable was being tested in this experiment? What was the control?
4. **Apply:** How do salt water and plain water affect seed growth?

Extension

Design an experiment using distilled water in place of the salt water. Compare your results.

ANSWERS

Data and Observations

1. plain water
2. salt water

Analyze and Apply

1. Students who hypothesized that more seeds would grow in plain water will say their hypotheses were supported.
2. Run another experiment to see if the results are the same.
3. The variable being tested was whether seeds grow better or worse with salt water; the seeds grown with plain water.
4. Salt water slows seed growth. Plain water does not slow seed growth.

Lab 1-2 Scientific Method

Overview

In this lab, students use scientific method to solve a problem.

Objectives: Upon completing this lab, students will be able to (1) **measure** volume and mass in SI units, (2) **form and test hypotheses**, (3) **record** observations.

Time Allotment: 20 minutes day 1, 15 minutes day 2

Preparation

▶ **Alternate Materials:** Other types of seed may be used. Assemble beakers, pinto beans, salt, balances, paper towels, graduated cylinders, and self-sealing plastic bags.

Lab 1-2 worksheet/*Teacher Resource Package*, pp. 3-4.

Teaching the Lab

▶ **Troubleshooting:** The seeds may not germinate overnight. If not, allow 2 days before concluding the lab.

Cooperative Learning: Divide the class into groups of four students. For more information, see pp. 22T-23T in the Teacher Guide.

TEACH

Concept Development

▶ Point out that usually the purpose of an experiment is to test the effect of varying a single condition in an otherwise constant environment. This condition is the independent variable or experimental factor. A control sample is handled exactly the same way as the experimental sample, except that the variable to be tested is either held at a fixed level or omitted. Comparing the results of the control with the results of the experimental sample shows the effect of the variable.

Guided Practice

Have students write down their answers to the margin question: recognizing and researching the problem, forming a hypothesis, testing the hypothesis, drawing conclusions.

Check for Understanding

Have students discuss what would happen if scientific experiments did not include a control. Would the findings of such experiments be valid?

Reteach

Place a control tray of bean seedlings in the light and another identical tray in the dark. Ask students what the variable factor is and what must be kept constant. Have students follow scientific method in observing the effect of sunlight on growth.

What are five steps of the scientific method described in this section?

A **variable** is something that causes the changes observed in an experiment. Some variables in Paula's experiment were water temperature, amount of food given to each group, and number of hours the light was left on. For meaningful results, the effect of only one variable can be tested at a time. Paula tested the effect of having the light on for different lengths of time.

An experiment must also have a control. A **control** is a standard for comparing results. In Paula's experiment, the control was group B, in which the light was left on 24 hours a day. Paula planned to compare her results for group A with her results for group B to see if group A produced more young.

Paula kept a record of the information she gathered. Recording information is called collecting data. **Data** are the recorded facts or measurements from an experiment.

Paula recorded the number of adult guppies she put into each tank. Every day, she recorded the temperature of the water in each of the tanks. Once a week for four weeks, she recorded the number of young produced by each group, Figure 1-11. She removed the new young each week so she could count more easily.

Drawing Conclusions

Paula's last step was to conclude whether or not the problem was solved. At the end of her experiment, the guppies in group A had more young than the guppies in group B, Figure 1-11. Could Paula conclude that 12 hours

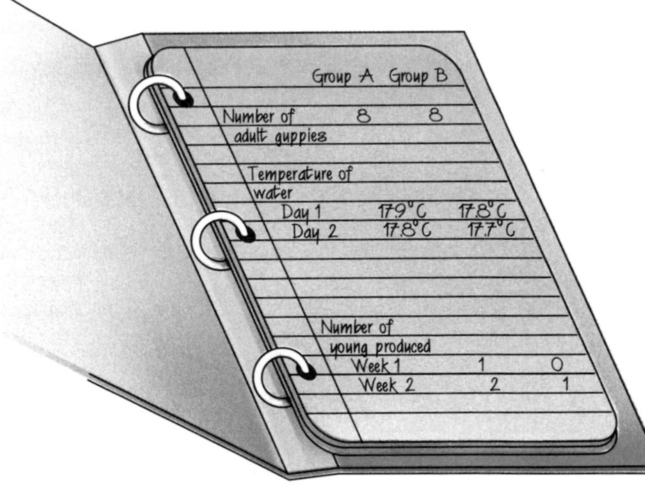

Figure 1-10 Paula recorded the data that she collected.

OPTIONS

Critical Thinking/Problem Solving/ *Teacher Resource Package*, p. 1. Use the Critical Thinking/Problem Solving worksheet shown here as an extension to scientific method.

CRITICAL THINKING 1

CRITICAL THINKING/PROBLEM SOLVING CHAPTER 1

Name ________ Date ________ Class ________

Use after Section 1:3.

CAN YOU SPOT THE SCIENTIFIC METHOD?

Each sentence below describes a step of the scientific method. Match each sentence with a step of the scientific method listed below.

A. recognize a problem
B. form a hypothesis
C. test the hypothesis with an experiment
D. draw conclusions

B 1. Stephen predicted that seeds would start to grow faster if an electric current traveled through the soil in which they were planted.

B 2. Susan said, "If I fertilize my geranium plants, they will blossom."

D 3. Jonathan's data showed that household cockrc ches moved away from raw cucumber slices.

C 4. Rene grew bacteria from the mouth on special plates in the laboratory. She placed drops of different mouthwashes on bacteria on each plate.

C 5. Kathy used a survey to determine how many of her classmates were left-handed and how many were right-handed.

A 6. Dana wanted to know how synthetic fibers were different from natural fibers.

A 7. Jose saw bats catching insects after dark. He asked, "How do bats find the insects in the dark?"

A 8. Justin wondered if dyes could be taken out of plant leaves, flowers, and stems.

C 9. Arjulia soaked six different kinds of seeds in water for 24 hours. Then she planted the seeds in soil at a depth of 1 cm. She used the same amount of water, light, and heat for each kind of seed.

A 10. Bob read about growing plants in water. He wanted to know how plants could grow without soil.

B 11. Kevin said, "If I grow five seedlings in red light, I think the plants will grow faster than the five plants grown in white light."

D 12. Angela's experiment proved that earthworms move away from light.

B 13. Scott said, "If acid rain affects plants in a particular lake, it might affect small animals, such as crayfish, that live in the same water."

D 14. Michael fed different diets to three groups of guinea pigs. His experiment showed that guinea pigs need vitamin C and protein in their diets.

D 15. Kim's experiment showed that chicken egg shells were stronger when she gave the hen feed to which extra calcium had been added.

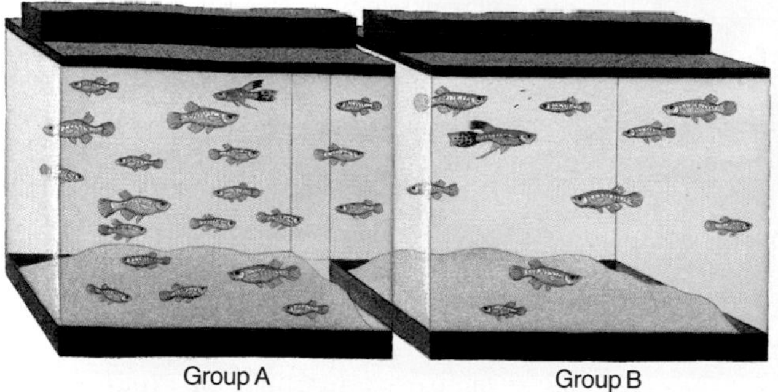

Figure 1-11 At the end of the experiment, group A had more young.

of light and 12 hours of dark caused the difference? She might. One way to be sure of a conclusion is to repeat the experiment. Repeating experiments is how scientists confirm that their hypotheses are correct. To confirm her hypothesis, Paula repeated the experiment three times with different groups of guppies. Each time the same thing happened. The guppies had more young when they were exposed to 12 hours of light and 12 hours of dark each day.

Paula used a scientific method to solve a problem. Let's review the steps that she used.

1. Recognize the problem.
2. Research the problem.
3. Form a hypothesis.
4. Test the hypothesis with an experiment. The experiment should have one variable being tested and a control group.
5. Draw conclusions. If your first hypothesis is wrong, you may need to form another hypothesis and test that.

Theory

If a hypothesis is tested with further experiments and the results are similar, it may become a theory. A **theory** is a hypothesis that has been tested again and again by many scientists, with similar results each time. You may have said at some time, "I think I know why the bus is late. My theory is that it got into a traffic jam on Fifth Street." But, this statement is not a theory. It hasn't been tested. A scientific theory is not a guess. It is the best explanation science has to offer about a problem. Theories can be used to predict future events. In the next chapter you will learn about the cell theory.

Bio Tip

Science: Nonscientists usually use *theory* to mean an idea or thought as opposed to a fact. Scientists use *theory* to describe an idea that has so much supporting evidence that it is almost certainly true.

TEACH

Concept Development

▶ Emphasize the importance of repeating an experiment. A hypothesis cannot be supported or disproved with just one experiment.

▶ Explain to students that the word theory is used outside of science to mean speculation. Many people incorrectly assume that scientists mean the same thing when they speak of scientific theory. A scientific theory is an established, accepted idea that scientists do not usually question until new evidence is presented.

Connection: Social Studies

Stress current events by making a bulletin board entitled Biology News Stories. Place high-interest articles and news stories, such as sports medicine topics, new breakthroughs in cancer research, the effects of steroids, the effects of drugs, and articles on sexually transmitted diseases, on the board. Ask students to bring in articles. Maintain the bulletin board throughout the year.

Independent Practice

Study Guide/*Teacher Resource Package*, p. 6. Use the Study Guide worksheet shown at the bottom of this page for independent practice.

STUDY GUIDE 6

STUDY GUIDE — CHAPTER 1

Name ______ Date ______ Class ______

VOCABULARY

Review the new words in Chapter 1 of your textbook. Then, complete this puzzle.

ACROSS
9. a statement that can be tested
10. SI unit of mass—1000 grams
11. a microscope that has an eyepiece lens and an objective lens for each eye
12. use of scientific discoveries to solve everyday problems
13. something that causes changes in an experiment
14. a hypothesis that has been tested over and over again
15. temperature scale used by scientists
16. recorded facts or measurements from an experiment

DOWN
1. study of living and once-living things
2. International System of Units (abbreviation)
3. method used to solve a problem
4. SI unit of length
5. the standard for comparing results in an experiment
6. the amount of space a substance occupies
7. to test a hypothesis
8. microscope used in class

OPTIONS

Challenge: An example of a well-tested theory is the germ theory of disease, developed from the work of Louis Pasteur. Have students report on the germ theory of disease.

TEACH

Guided Practice

Have students write down their answers to the margin question: they transplant organs and use artificial devices to replace limbs or organs.

Check for Understanding

Have students respond to the first three questions in Check Your Understanding.

Reteach

Reteaching/*Teacher Resource Package*, p. 3. Use this worksheet to give students additional practice using scientific method.

Extension: Assign Critical Thinking, Biology and Reading, or some of the **OPTIONS** available with this lesson.

3 APPLY

Skill

Have students infer which fields of science are responsible for technologies that affect their lives.

4 CLOSE

Refer to a detective television program with which students are familiar. Ask what the detective must do to solve the problem, how he or she finds clues, what is done with the information in order to reach conclusions.

Figure 1-12 Lasers are products of technology.

Bio Tip

Consumer: A laser is a tool that produces a narrow, intense beam of light that can be used as a kind of scalpel. It can be used to remove unhealthy cells and in certain types of eye surgery.

How do doctors use technology to solve medical problems?

Technology

Scientists have played a part in solving many problems in farming, industry, and medicine. The use of scientific discoveries to solve everyday problems is called **technology**. Doctors transplant human organs based on what they know about the human body. Over two million artificial devices are used each year to take the place of limbs or body organs lost to illnesses and accidents. These devices are products of technology.

Improved running shoes, laser surgery, and drugs that clear fats from the walls of blood vessels are also products of technology. These kinds of technological advances promote well-being. Other kinds of advances may be as helpful, but have harmful effects as well. Fertilizers help farmers grow better crops, but they may contribute to water pollution. Chemicals added to food keep foods fresh, but may have harmful effects on people if consumed for long periods of time.

Check Your Understanding

11. What is the variable in an experiment? What is the control?
12. What are five steps in the scientific method described in this section?
13. Why is a theory more accepted than a hypothesis?
14. **Critical Thinking:** Give an example of how you have used technology to solve an everyday problem.
15. **Biology and Reading:** What three steps of the scientific method described in this section should be done before performing an experiment?

Answers to Check Your Understanding

11. The variable is something that causes changes in an experiment. The control is the standard for comparing.
12. recognize the problem, research the problem, form a hypothesis, test the hypothesis with an experiment, draw conclusions
13. A theory has been tested again and again by many scientists with similar results each time.
14. Some students might include getting X rays and vaccinations or using commercial fertilizer to help house plants grow, and so on.
15. recognize the problem, research the problem, form a hypothesis

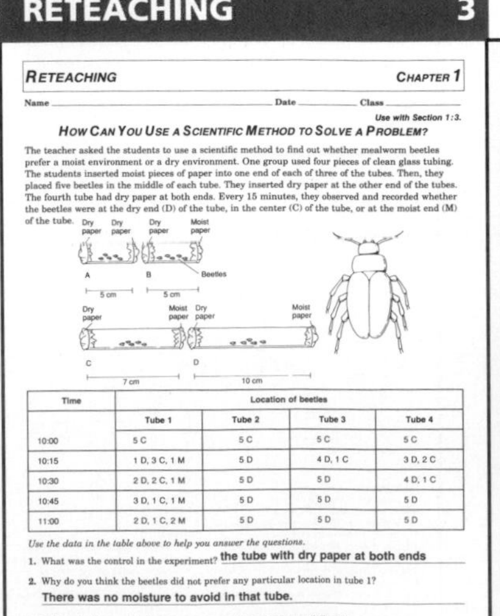

RETEACHING 3

RETEACHING CHAPTER 1

Name ______ Date ______ Class ______

Use with Section 1:3.

HOW CAN YOU USE A SCIENTIFIC METHOD TO SOLVE A PROBLEM?

The teacher asked the students to use a scientific method to find out whether mealworm beetles prefer a moist environment or a dry environment. One group used four pieces of clean glass tubing. The students inserted moist pieces of paper into one end of each of three of the tubes. Then, they placed five beetles in the middle of each tube. They inserted dry paper at the other end of the tubes. The fourth tube had dry paper at both ends. Every 15 minutes, they observed and recorded whether the beetles were at the dry end (D) of the tube, in the center (C) of the tube, or at the moist end (M) of the tube.

Time	Location of beetles			
	Tube 1	Tube 2	Tube 3	Tube 4
10:00	5 C	5 C	5 C	5 C
10:15	1 D, 3 C, 1 M	5 D	4 D, 1 C	3 D, 2 C
10:30	2 D, 2 C, 1 M	5 D	5 D	4 D, 1 C
10:45	3 D, 1 C, 1 M	5 D	5 D	5 D
11:00	2 D, 1 C, 2 M	5 D	5 D	5 D

Use the data in the table above to help you answer the questions.

1. What was the control in the experiment? **the tube with dry paper at both ends**
2. Why do you think the beetles did not prefer any particular location in tube 1? **There was no moisture to avoid in that tube.**
3. Did the beetles react in the same way to moisture and dryness? Explain your answer. **No, they avoided moisture and moved to the dry area.**

Science and Society

Technology: Helpful or Harmful?

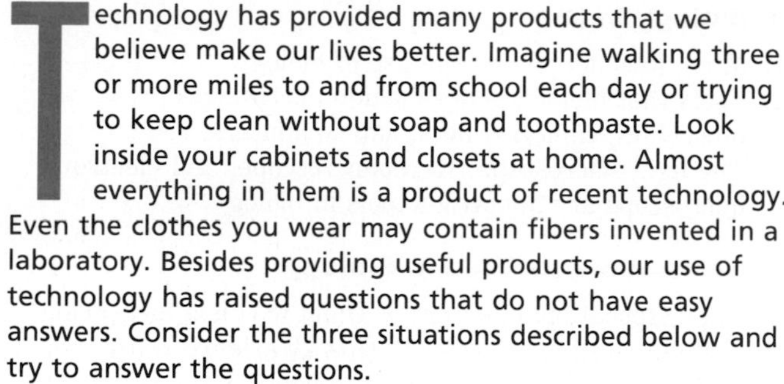

Technology has provided many products that we believe make our lives better. Imagine walking three or more miles to and from school each day or trying to keep clean without soap and toothpaste. Look inside your cabinets and closets at home. Almost everything in them is a product of recent technology. Even the clothes you wear may contain fibers invented in a laboratory. Besides providing useful products, our use of technology has raised questions that do not have easy answers. Consider the three situations described below and try to answer the questions.

What Do You Think?

1. Nuclear energy is an important source of power. Many communities use nuclear energy to generate electricity for lighting homes and businesses. Nuclear power plants do not pollute the air as coal-burning power plants do. Use of nuclear energy, however, does present problems. There is no guaranteed safe way to dispose of used nuclear fuel. Also, many nuclear power plants are being shut down because they are not considered safe. Who is responsible for disposing of nuclear wastes safely? Should we continue to use and build nuclear power plants?

2. Farmers use fertilizers to grow more and better crops. More crops mean a better living for the farmer, a better food supply, and lower prices at the grocery store. Without fertilizers, we might not be able to buy many kinds of fruits and vegetables. Fertilizers, however, can drain from farmland into lakes and streams. Fish can't live in water with fertilizers in it. In some areas, people can't drink the water because of the fertilizers in it. Should laws be passed on when and how much fertilizers can be used?

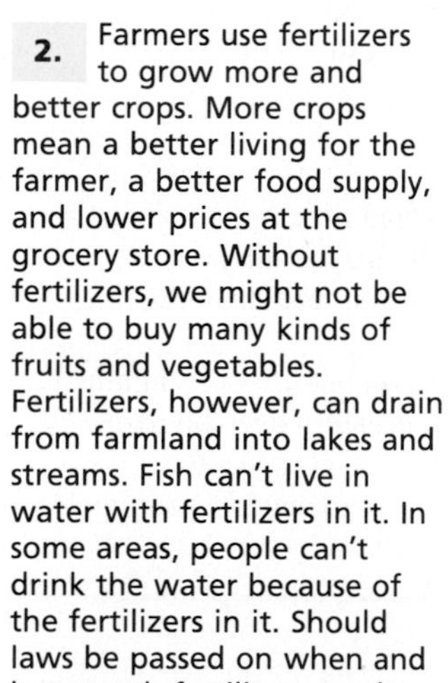

Nuclear power plant

3. A person is rushed to the hospital after an automobile accident. The doctors do not know if there is brain damage, or what the chances of survival are. A quick decision must be made about whether or not to use a life-support system called a respirator. A respirator is a device that helps a person breathe when that person can't breathe on his or her own. The respirator is used. Later, it is discovered that the person shows little brain activity. The person remains in a coma for months. There is little hope for recovery, and the family wants the respirator disconnected. Who should decide when life-support systems are needed?

Conclusion: How does technology help people? Is it possible to misuse technology?

Science and Society

Technology: Helpful or Harmful?

Background

Currently, the Department of Energy (DOE) is planning the construction of a nuclear waste repository that will be used as a storage site for nuclear wastes. Discuss with students alternate energy sources: solar, wind, and geothermal.

A document called the Living Will states that in the event that a person becomes incapacitated, extraordinary life support measures are not used.

Teaching Suggestions

Cooperative Learning: Have students work in cooperative groups of four to compose a letter about each issue and ideas on how to solve the problems.

What Do You Think?

1. Students may argue that there needs to be a uniform set of regulations for disposing of nuclear wastes.
2. Any regulation necessitates monitoring, which creates both cost and bureaucracy.
3. Many students may feel that the patient should not have to pay. Every year, however, many people come out of comas, many of whom were never expected to do so.

Conclusion: Technology is only good as long as it is used to make our lives better and the environment no worse.

Suggested Readings

Sancton, T.A. "What on Earth Are We Doing?" *Time,* Jan. 2, 1989, pp. 24-30.

CHAPTER 1 REVIEW

Summary

Summary statements can be used by students to review the major concepts of this chapter.

Key Science Words

All boldfaced terms from the chapter are listed.

Testing Yourself

Using Words

1. kilogram
2. volume
3. scientific method
4. meter
5. biology
6. light microscope
7. data
8. hypothesis
9. technology
10. experiment
11. variable
12. stereomicroscope

Finding Main Ideas

13. p. 14; Time is measured in seconds.
14. p. 15; A scientific method is a series of steps used to solve a problem.
15. p. 16; An experiment is the testing of a hypothesis.
16. p. 6; People may use biology in hobbies and work, for example beekeeper, crime lab technician, optician, mushroom grower.
17. p. 13; An instrument used to measure mass is a balance.
18. p. 13; Multiply length by width by height to find volume.
19. p. 7; Tools a biologist uses include hand lens, light microscope, electron microscope, and computer.
20. p. 16; A hypothesis is a statement that can be tested.
21. p. 12; Prefixes are combined with a unit of measure to change that unit of measure.
22. p. 18; The part of an experiment that is not changed is the control group.

Chapter 1 Review

Summary

1:1 Biology in Use

1. Many jobs depend on the use of biology.
2. Tools that biologists use include microscopes, binoculars, cameras, nets, and computers.
3. The light microscope, stereomicroscope, and electron microscope are important tools in biology.

1:2 Measurements Used in Biology

4. The International System of Units (SI) is a measuring system based on units of 10 that all scientists use.
5. Meter, cubic meter, kilogram, second, and Celsius degrees are SI measurements.
6. SI units are used to measure length, volume, mass, time, and temperature.

1:3 Scientific Method

7. The steps of the scientific method are: recognizing the problem, researching the problem, forming a hypothesis, testing the hypothesis, and drawing conclusions.
8. A theory is a hypothesis that has been tested again and again by many scientists. Results are the same each time.
9. Technology is used to solve many everyday problems.

Key Science Words

biology (p. 5)
Celsius (p. 14)
control (p. 18)
data (p. 18)
experiment (p. 16)
hypothesis (p. 16)
International System of Units (p. 11)
kilogram (p. 14)
light microscope (p. 7)
meter (p. 11)
scientific method (p. 15)
stereomicroscope (p. 8)
technology (p. 20)
theory (p. 19)
variable (p. 18)
volume (p. 13)

Testing Yourself

Using Words

Choose the word from the list of Key Science Words that best fits the definition.

1. one thousand grams
2. measured in liters
3. series of steps in solving a problem
4. can be divided into 100 units called centimeters
5. study of living things
6. magnifies objects 430 ×
7. recorded measurements in an experiment
8. a statement that can be tested
9. using discoveries in science to solve everyday problems
10. steps used to test a hypothesis
11. something that causes changes in an experiment
12. magnifies objects through which light does not pass

Review

Testing Yourself *continued*

Finding Main Ideas

List the page number where each main idea below is found. Then, explain each main idea.

13. how time is measured
14. what a scientific method is
15. what an experiment is
16. how people use biology
17. instrument used to measure mass
18. how to find volume
19. tools a biologist uses
20. what a hypothesis is
21. how prefixes are used
22. part of an experiment that is not changed

Using Main Ideas

Answer the questions by referring to the page number after each question.

23. What must an optometrist and a mushroom grower know about biology? (p. 6)
24. How is a stereomicroscope different from a light microscope? (p. 8)
25. How are mass and weight different? (p. 13)
26. How are biology and technology related? (p. 20)
27. Which SI units could you use to measure
    (a) the distance to your friend's house? (p. 11)
    (b) the volume of one serving of orange juice? (p. 13)
    (c) the mass of a can of soup? (p. 14)
28. How are a variable and a control different? (p. 18)
29. Why do biologists use computers? (p. 10)

Skill Review ✓

For more help, refer to the ***Skill Handbook,*** *pages 704-719.*

1. **Calculate:** An ostrich has a mass of 155 kg. A hummingbird has a mass of 10 g. How many times greater than the mass of the hummingbird is the mass of the ostrich?
2. **Design an experiment:** Design an experiment to show the effect of sunlight on the growth of bean seedlings.
3. **Observe:** Look around your classroom and name the tools that you observe.
4. **Make and use tables:** Make a table of the different kinds of measurements and the SI units for each.

Finding Out More

Critical Thinking

1. Design a controlled experiment to test the following hypothesis: Radish seeds will germinate faster in light than in darkness.
2. Why is it important to use both a number and a unit when measuring an object?

Applications

1. Report to your class on new technologies in medicine, farming, or industry by reading the newspaper or watching television.
2. Find out which metric units are used by a hospital or pharmacy in preparing medicines. List several examples.

Using Main Ideas

23. An optometrist must know how eyes work, the correct lens to prescribe. A mushroom grower must know soil conditions and mushroom diseases.
24. It does not magnify as much and it allows objects to be viewed that light cannot pass through.
25. The mass of an object remains the same. The weight of an object varies with gravitational pull.
26. Discoveries in biology are used to solve problems in the areas of farming, environment, and disease.
27. The measurements needed are (a) meter or kilometer, (b) milliliters, (c) gram.
28. The control remains the same; the variable is the factor that is being tested.
29. Biologists use computers to keep up with new information about biology.

Skill Review

1. 10 g = .01 kg
   155 kg / .01 kg = 15 500 times as large
2. Have two containers containing the same number of bean seedlings. Keep the containers the same, except one will be kept in the light, one in the dark.
3. Tools can include microscopes (both light and stereo-), balance, graduated cylinders, beakers, and others.
4. Students could list SI units across the top and measurements along the side and then fill in the table.

Finding Out More

Critical Thinking

1. Have two containers with the same number of seeds in each. All the conditions must be kept the same except that one container will be placed in the dark and one will be placed in the light.
2. A number is used to show the amount and a unit is used to tell what is being measured.

Applications

1. Amniocentesis, ultrasound, artificial hearts, organ transplants, insulin pumps, fuel from plants, biological control of insect pests can be used for reports.
2. Volume measurements and mass measurements (liters or milliliters and grams or milligrams or kilograms) are used. Some medications are available in powder form, which must have water added to it. Medications are measured in milligrams per dose.

Chapter Review/*Teacher Resource Package*, pp. 1-2.

Chapter Test/*Teacher Resource Package*, pp. 3-5.

Chapter Test/*Computer Test Bank*

Features of Life and the Cell

PLANNING GUIDE

CONTENT	TEXT FEATURES	TEACHER RESOURCE PACKAGE	OTHER COMPONENTS
(1 1/2 days) 2:1 Living Things and Their Parts Features of Living Things The Chemistry of Life Cell Theory	Skill Check: *Classify,* p. 27 Skill Check: *Formulate a Model,* p. 30 Mini Lab: *What Makes Up Cork?* p. 31 Lab 2-1: *Respiration,* p. 28 Check Your Understanding, p. 31	Enrichment: *The Chemistry of Life,* p. 2 Reteaching: *Living Things and Their Parts,* p. 4 Focus: *Testing for Evidence of Life on Mars,* p. 3 Transparency Master: *Features of Life,* p. 5 Study Guide: *Living Things and Their Parts,* pp. 7-8 Lab 2-1: *Respiration,* pp. 5-6	
(1 1/2 days) 2:2 Cell Parts and Their Jobs Cell Membranes and Nucleus Cytoplasm	Skill Check: *Understand Science Words,* p. 35 Lab 2:2 *Cells,* Idea Map, p. 34 Check Your Understanding, p. 37	Application: *A Cell Is Like a City,* p. 2 Reteaching: *Plant Cell and Animal Cell Structure,* p. 5 Skill: *Interpret Diagrams,* p. 2 Study Guide: *Cell Parts and Their Jobs,* p. 9 Lab 2:2 *Cells,* pp. 7-8	**Laboratory Manual:** *What Cell Parts Can You See with the Microscope?* p. 13 Color Transparency 2a: *Plant and Animal Cells*
(1 day) 2:3 Special Cell Processes Diffusion Osmosis Organization	Mini Lab: *What Is Diffusion?* p. 39 Check Your Understanding, p. 41 Problem Solving: *Features of Living Things,* p. 42	Reteaching: *Cell Processes,* p. 6 Critical Thinking/Problem Solving: *What Happened to Dinner?* p. 2 Study Guide: *Special Cell Processes,* pp. 10-11 Study Guide: *Vocabulary,* p. 12	**Laboratory Manual:** *What Are Diffusion and Osmosis?* p. 9 Color Transparency 2b: *Organization in Living Things*
Chapter Review	Summary Key Science Words Testing Yourself Finding Main Ideas Using Main Ideas Skill Review	Chapter Review, pp. 6-7 Chapter Test, pp. 8-10	**Test Bank**

MATERIALS NEEDED

LAB 2-1, p. 28	LAB 2-2, p. 36	MARGIN FEATURES
5 small baby food jars red liquid wax pencil guppy yeast suspension dropper paper clip drinking straw	light microscope 2 microscope slides 2 cloverslips dropper methylene blue stain toothpicks, flat type *Elodea* leaf water	Skill Check, p. 27 pencil paper Skill Check, p. 30 polystyrene balls toothpicks labels Skill Check, p. 35 dictionary Mini Lab, p. 341 microscope cork slice Mini Lab, p. 39 box vanilla balloon

OBJECTIVES

SECTION	OBJECTIVE	OBJECTIVES CORRELATION: CHECK YOUR UNDERSTANDING	CHAPTER REVIEW	TRP CHAPTER REVIEW	TRP CHAPTER TEST
2:1	1. **Describe** eight features common to all living things.	1, 4, 5	7, 10, 14, 20	4, 19, 11, 12, 13, 14, 28	14, 15, 16, 17, 18, 19, 20, 21, 23, 28
	2. **List** the compounds that make up living things.	2	16	15,16, 17, 18, 19	5, 6, 10, 12, 13
	3. **State** the major ideas of the cell theory.	3	6, 17	1, 2	1, 2, 25, 27, 31
2:2	4. **List** the parts of the cell.	6, 7	1, 4, 23	5, 20, 21, 22, 23, 24, 25, 26, 27, 30, 32	31, 32, 33, 34, 35, 36, 37, 38, 39, 40, 48, 49
	5. **Describe** the functions of the cell parts.	8, 9	2, 12, 18, 23, 26	6, 7, 33, 35, 37, 38, 39	7, 9, 11, 48, 49, 50, 51, 52, 53, 54, 55, 56
2:3	6. **Explain** the process of diffusion in a cell.	11	5, 13, 24, 25	8	26
	7. **Describe** the process of osmosis in a cell.	12, 14	9, 19, 22, 24	36	3, 28, 30
	8. **Communicate** how cells, tissues, organs, and organ systems are organized.	13, 15	3, 8, 11	3, 10	4, 8, 22

Features of Life and the Cell

CHAPTER OVERVIEW

Key Concepts

In this chapter, students will study the eight characteristics that define living things. These characteristics are reproduction, growth, development, need for food, energy consumption, cellular makeup, response to environmental stimuli, and adaptedness. Students also will learn about cell structure and function and the processes by which cells regulate their environments.

Key Science Words

adaptation	nuclear membrane
cell	nucleolus
cell membrane	nucleus
cellular respiration	organ
cell wall	organism
centriole	organ system
chloroplast	osmosis
chromosome	producer
consumer	reproduce
cytoplasm	ribosome
development	tissue
diffusion	vacuole
mitochondria	

Skill Development

In Lab 2-1, students will **make and use tables, interpret data, infer**, and **form hypotheses** to discover different things that give off carbon dioxide. In Lab 2-2, students **use a microscope** as they **observe** and **compare** plant and animal cells. In the Skill Check on page 27, students will **classify** living and once-living things. In the Skill Check on page 30, they will **formulate a model** of a simple molecule. On page 35, they will **understand** the **science word** *chloroplast.* In the Mini Lab on page 31, students will **use a microscope** to examine cork. In the Mini Lab on page 39, they will **experiment** to learn about diffusion.

CHAPTER PREVIEW

Chapter Content

Review this outline for Chapter 2 before you read the chapter.

2:1 Living Things and Their Parts
- Features of Living Things
- The Chemistry of Life
- Cell Theory

2:2 Cell Parts and Their Jobs
- Cell Membrane and Nucleus
- Cytoplasm

2:3 Special Cell Processes
- Diffusion
- Osmosis
- Organization

Skills in this Chapter

The skills that you will use in this chapter are listed below.

- In **Lab 2-1,** you will make and use tables, interpret data, infer, and form hypotheses. In **Lab 2-2,** you will observe, compare, and use a microscope.
- In the **Skill Checks,** you will classify, formulate a model, and understand science words.
- In the **Mini Labs,** you will use a microscope and experiment.

24

Bridging

Students have already learned how scientific measurements are made in Chapter 1. The features of living things can be measured. For example, evidence that a living thing has grown is an increase in mass and length. To show that a living thing is using energy, the volume of CO_2 given off can be measured.

Chapter 2

Features of Life and the Cell

In the photo on the left, you can see several kinds of things that are living and several that are not living. If you looked closely at an enlarged part of the rocks, as shown in the small photo, what would you see? Make a guess as to what you would find if you looked at a drop of the water with a microscope.

What does it mean to be living? Maybe you would say that living things need water and food. You might say that living things grow. Some nonliving things seem to grow, too. If you have cold winters where you live, you probably have seen icicles that seem to grow on your house. Maybe the ability to grow isn't enough to make something living. How then can you decide if a thing is living or nonliving? Are there features that all living things share?

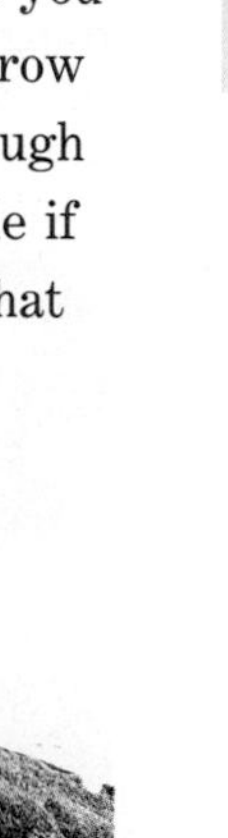

Try This!

What happens to a sponge in water? Place a sponge in a dish of water. Observe what happens to the sponge. Is this a feature of living things?

Rock covered with mosses and lichen

GETTING STARTED

Using the Photos

In looking at the photos, students should try to identify factors that characterize nonliving things. Have students attempt to define the word *life* without using the word *living* in the definition. It is easier to use traits of living things to define life.

MOTIVATION/Try This!

What happens to a sponge in water? Upon completing the chapter-opening activity, students will have gained practice in developing **operational definitions.** As a followup, invite a doctor or nurse to speak about the difficulties of determining when life ends. Students will discover that the definition of a living thing is not always easy to formulate.

Chapter Preview

Have students study the chapter outline before they begin to read the chapter. They should note the overall organization of the chapter, that living things are characterized first, that a feature of living things—the cell—is discussed second, and that cell functions are discussed third.

Misconception

Respiration, the chemical reaction that yields energy within the cell, is one feature of living things. Explain to students that respiration is not the same as breathing.

2:1 Living Things and Their Parts

PREPARATION

Materials Needed

Make copies of the Focus, Transparency Master, Study Guide, Enrichment, Reteaching, and Lab worksheets in the *Teacher Resource Package*.

▶ Prepare phenol red and yeast solutions and obtain small jars, straws, and guppies for Lab 2-1.

▶ Purchase polystyrene balls and toothpicks for the Skill Check.

▶ Prepare slices of cork for the Mini Lab.

Key Science Words

reproduce
development
consumer
producer
cellular respiration
cell
adaptation

Process Skills

In Lab 2-1, students will make and use tables, interpret data, infer, and form hypotheses. In the Skill Checks, students will classify and formulate a model. In the Mini Lab, students will use a microscope.

1 FOCUS

▶ The objectives are listed on the student page. Remind students to preview these objectives as a guide to this numbered section.

MOTIVATION/Bulletin Board

Display a periodic table of the elements and point out common elements and their symbols. Explain that elements can join together to form compounds.

Focus/*Teacher Resource Package*, p. 3. Use the Focus transparency shown at the bottom of this page as an introduction to living things.

2:1 Living Things and Their Parts

Objectives

1. **Describe** eight features common to all living things.
2. **List** the compounds that make up living things.
3. **State** the major ideas of the cell theory.

Key Science Words

reproduce
development
consumer
producer
cellular respiration
cell
adaptation

The word *living* is not easy to define. However, biologists recognize that all living things share certain features. Let's look at some of those features.

Features of Living Things

Feature 1 Living things reproduce.

Reproduce means to form offspring similar to the parents. If living things could not reproduce, there might be nothing alive on Earth today.

Living things reproduce in different ways. For example, a one-celled living thing may split to produce two living things, like the amoeba in Figure 2-1.

Sunflowers grow from seeds made by the parent plants. A sunflower produces many seeds, each of which can become a new sunflower. Bear cubs have a male and a female parent and are born alive.

Feature 2 Living things grow.

A living thing grows by using materials and energy from its environment to increase its size. Young oak saplings grow into large oak trees over a period of many years. A kitten grows into a cat.

Feature 3 Living things develop.

Development is all the changes that occur as a living thing grows. When a tadpole first begins to develop, it does not look like an adult frog, Figure 2-2a. It has no front or hind legs. As the animal grows and develops, legs begin to

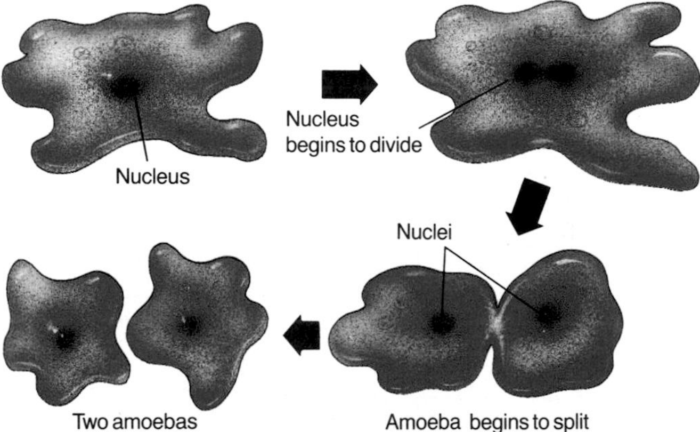

Figure 2-1 An amoeba divides to reproduce.

OPTIONS

Science Background

All the features of living things are needed for the survival of the individual organism, except for reproduction. Reproduction is necessary for the survival of the species.

FOCUS 3

FOCUS CHAPTER 2

Name ________ Date ________ Class ________

TESTING FOR EVIDENCE OF LIFE ON MARS

Viking Lander Spacecraft on Mars

1. The *Viking* Lander took soil samples from Mars' surface. Radioactive nutrients were added to the soil.
2. If living things were present in the soil, they would use the radioactive nutrients to grow.

1. Explain how this experiment could prove to scientists that living things were present in the Martian soil.
2. The Lander did not find materials that make up living things. Do these results prove that life doesn't exist on Mars now? Do they prove that life never existed on Mars? Explain.

a

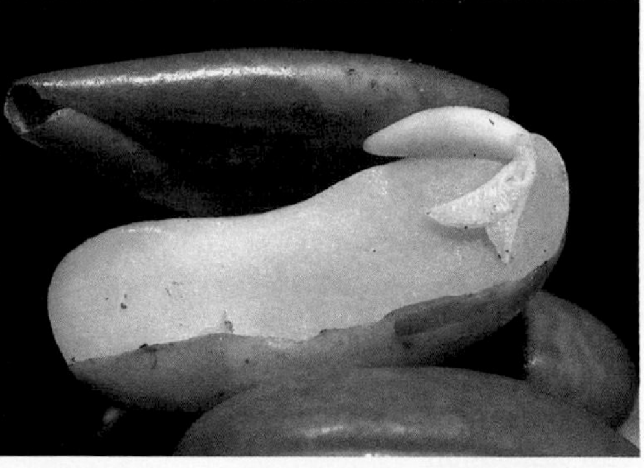

b

Figure 2-2 A tadpole (a) does not look like an adult frog. A developing bean seed (b) does not look like a young bean plant.

form. A young plant in a seed looks different from a fully developed plant, as shown by Figure 2-2b. The young plant does not have roots, stems, or flowers. Many of these parts develop as the plant grows.

Feature 4 Living things need food.

Many animals get food by hunting and eating other animals. Some animals eat only plants. Other animals eat both plants and animals. Animals are consumers. **Consumers** are living things that eat, or consume, other living things. Green plants make their own food. Green plants are producers. **Producers** are living things that make, or produce, their own food.

Skill Check

Classify: Look around you and make a list of things that are living or were once living. How are living things different from things that were once living? *For more help, refer to the **Skill Handbook**, pages 715-717.*

Feature 5 Living things use energy.

Energy is the ability to do work. Moving your arms or legs, blinking your eyes, breathing, and even sleeping require energy. Animals get energy from the food they eat. Plants get energy from the food they make during photosynthesis.

How do living things get energy from food? All living things carry out cellular respiration. **Cellular respiration** is the process by which food is broken down and energy is released. Many living things use oxygen in the process of cellular respiration. Water and a gas called carbon dioxide are given off. The energy given off during cellular respiration is used for other life processes. For example, energy is used to keep human body temperature at 37°C.

What is given off during cellular respiration?

Feature 6 Living things are made of cells.

The **cell** is the basic unit of all living things. Some living things have many cells. Others have only one cell.

2 TEACH

Concept Development

▶ Have students give examples of what consumers eat.

▶ Emphasize that both producers and consumers use food. Some animals eat many times their body weight each day.

▶ You may wish to introduce the concept that energy moves through the living world in one direction. Matter that makes up living things, however, is recycled. These concepts are important in the study of biology.

▶ Emphasize that energy is required for the other features of life.

Skill Check

Living things reproduce, grow, develop, need food, use energy, are made of cells, respond, and adapt. Nonliving things do not have all of these features.

Guided Practice

Have students write down their answers to the margin question: water and carbon dioxide gas.

TRANSPARENCY 5

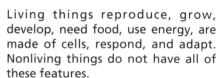

TRANSPARENCY MASTER CHAPTER 2

FEATURES OF LIFE

reproduce | are adapted | develop | grow | need food | use energy | made of cells | respond

OPTIONS

Transparency Master/*Teacher Resource Package*, p. 5. Use the Transparency Master shown here to teach the features of life.

Lab 2-1 Respiration

Overview

In this lab, students use the scientific method to observe that living things give off CO_2. They also learn about humane treatment of animals.

Objectives: Upon completing the lab, students will be able to (1) **state** the purpose of an experimental control, (2) **recognize** that chemical indicators show that chemical reactions are taking place, (3) **observe** that living things give off CO_2.

Time Allotment: 30 minutes

Preparation

▶ **Alternate Materials:** You may wish to substitute a goldfish or a germinating bean seed for the guppy.

▶ For phenol red indicator, mix 0.4 g phenol red in 100 mL water to make stock solution. Use 1 mL stock solution to 100 mL water to yield a 0.00004% solution of phenol red.

▶ For yeast solution, mix 1 teaspoon sugar and 1 teaspoon dry yeast in 200 mL water.

Lab 2-1 worksheet/*Teacher Resource Package*, pp. 5-6.

Teaching the Lab

▶ Phenol red changes from red to yellow or orange in the presence of carbon dioxide.

▶ **Troubleshooting:** Activate the yeast by mixing it with lukewarm water. Do not use hot or cold water.

Cooperative Learning: Divide the class into groups of three students. For more information, see pp. 22T-23T in the Teacher Guide.

Respiration

Lab 2–1

Problem: Do all things give off carbon dioxide?

Materials

5 small baby food jars
red liquid
wax pencil
guppy
yeast suspension
dropper
paper clip
straw

Skills

make and use tables, interpret data, infer, form hypotheses

Procedure

1. Copy the data table.
2. Number the five baby food jars 1 to 5. Fill each of the jars 2/3 full with red liquid.
3. Record in your notebook the color in each jar at the start of the activity.
4. Add the things listed here to the jars. Jar 1—Add nothing. Jar 2—Use the straw to blow gently into the red liquid for 2 minutes. Jar 3—Add 1 guppy. **CAUTION:** *Always use care when handling live animals.* Jar 4—Add 5 drops of yeast solution. Jar 5--Add 1 paper clip. Record what is added to each jar on your table.
5. In your notebook, write a **hypothesis** about which things you think will give off carbon dioxide. You will know when carbon dioxide is given off because the red liquid will turn orange or yellow.
6. Wait 15 minutes. Record in your table the color of the liquid in each jar using red, orange, or yellow as the choices.
7. Return the guppy to your teacher.

Data and Observations

1. In which jars did the color change?
2. In which jars was carbon dioxide present?

Analyze and Apply

1. **Check your hypothesis:** Is your hypothesis supported by your data? Why or why not?
2. What was the purpose of Jar 1?
3. **Interpret data:** Which things gave off carbon dioxide?
4. Which things didn't give off carbon dioxide?
5. What process in living things causes carbon dioxide to be given off?
6. **Apply:** Which of these things give off carbon dioxide: a tree? a bicycle? a fly? a shoe?

Extension

Infer: Look around your classroom. Make a table listing the things that now give off carbon dioxide, things that gave off carbon dioxide when they were living, and things that never gave off carbon dioxide.

JAR	1	2	3	4	5
What was added	nothing	breath	guppy	yeast	paper clip
Color at start	red	red	red	red	red
Color of liquid after 15 minutes	red		yellow	orange	red
Color of liquid in Jar 2 after 2 minutes		yellow			

ANSWERS

Data and Observations

1. 2, 3, 4
2. 2, 3, 4

Analyze and Apply

1. Students who hypothesized that jars 2, 3, and 4 would show the presence of carbon dioxide will say that their hypotheses were supported.
2. control
3. person, guppy, yeast
4. paper clip
5. cellular respiration
6. tree, fly

Figure 2-3 Plants respond to light by growing toward it.

Feature 7 Living things respond.

The plants in Figure 2-3 are responding to the light by growing toward it. When you call your dog, it responds to the sound of your voice. It comes to you. These are examples of living things responding to changes in the environment. The environment is made up of all the living and nonliving things that surround another living thing.

You respond to changes in the environment, too. When you get cold, you shiver. When you run, your heart beats faster. When your body gets warm, you sweat. These are examples of how your body responds to changes.

Feature 8 Living things are adapted to their environments.

A trait that makes a living thing better able to survive is called an **adaptation.** Polar bears are adapted to living in the Arctic. They have thick fur and layers of fat to keep warm. Squirrels are adapted to living in trees. Their bushy tails help them keep their balance.

How can you tell if something is living? It must have all of the features just described. If it does not, it is not living. For example, a burning candle has some features that living things have, Figure 2-4. It gives off carbon dioxide gas and water. It uses oxygen and wax and changes shape. A candle responds. The candle flame flickers when a draft passes over it.

Does having these features mean that a burning candle is alive? The answer is no. A candle does not reproduce. It does not have cells. It does not grow. It is not adapted to its environment. The candle is not living, even though it has a few of the features that a living thing has.

Figure 2-4 A burning candle has some features of living things. What are they? uses energy, responds

TEACH

Concept Development

▶ Responses in plants are usually less obvious than those in animals. A plant that shows rapid response is the mimosa. If you touch a mimosa leaf, all the small leaflets on the branch fold upward.

▶ Point out that organisms are adapted in terms of structure, function, and behavior.

▶ Discuss examples of human adaptations and how each example aids survival.

Independent Practice

Study Guide/*Teacher Resource Package*, pp. 7-8. Use the Study Guide worksheets shown at the bottom of this page for independent practice.

Check for Understanding

Make flash cards by writing one of the eight characteristics of living things on one side and an example of the characteristic on the other. Show an example and have students respond with a characteristic, and vice versa.

Reteach

Have students name the features of living things that can be observed in a classroom aquarium.

STUDY GUIDE 7

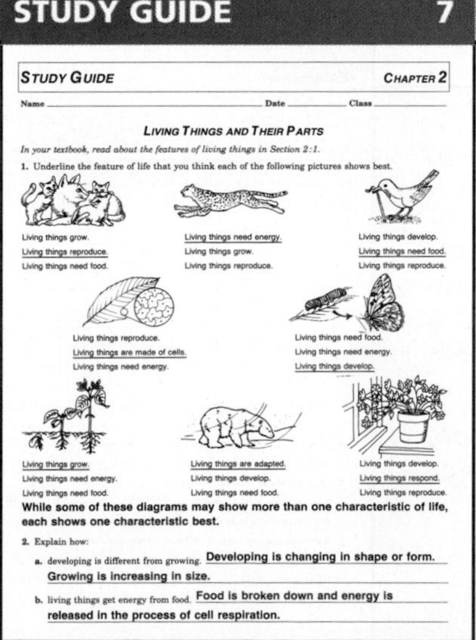

STUDY GUIDE — CHAPTER 2

Name ______ Date ______ Class ______

LIVING THINGS AND THEIR PARTS

In your textbook, read about the features of living things in Section 2:1.

1. Underline the feature of life that you think each of the following pictures shows best.

Living things grow.
Living things reproduce.
Living things need food.

Living things need energy.
Living things grow.
Living things reproduce.

Living things develop.
Living things need food.
Living things reproduce.

Living things reproduce.
Living things are made of cells.
Living things need energy.

Living things need food.
Living things need energy.
Living things develop.

Living things grow.
Living things need energy.
Living things need food.

Living things are adapted.
Living things develop.
Living things need food.

Living things develop.
Living things respond.
Living things reproduce.

While some of these diagrams may show more than one characteristic of life, each shows one characteristic best.

2. Explain how:
   a. developing is different from growing. **Developing is changing in shape or form. Growing is increasing in size.**
   b. living things get energy from food. **Food is broken down and energy is released in the process of cell respiration.**

STUDY GUIDE 8

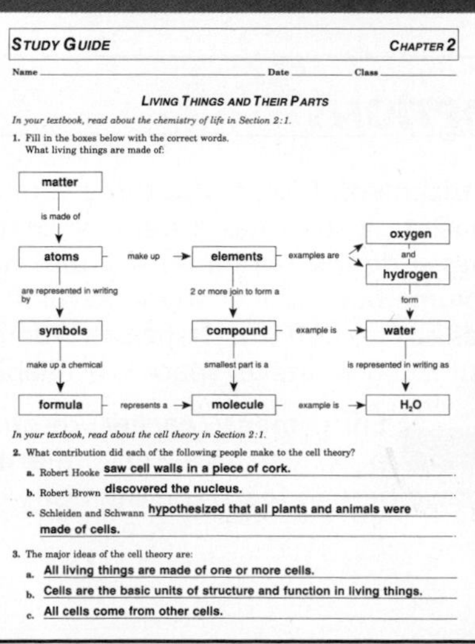

STUDY GUIDE — CHAPTER 2

Name ______ Date ______ Class ______

LIVING THINGS AND THEIR PARTS

In your textbook, read about the chemistry of life in Section 2:1.

1. Fill in the boxes below with the correct words.
   What living things are made of:

matter — is made of → atoms
atoms — make up → elements
elements — examples are → oxygen and hydrogen
atoms — are represented in writing by → symbols
elements — 2 or more join to form a → compound
oxygen and hydrogen — form → water
symbols — make up a chemical → formula
compound — example is → water
compound — smallest part is a → molecule
water — is represented in writing as → H_2O
formula — represents a → molecule
molecule — example is → H_2O

In your textbook, read about the cell theory in Section 2:1.

2. What contribution did each of the following people make to the cell theory?
   a. Robert Hooke **saw cell walls in a piece of cork.**
   b. Robert Brown **discovered the nucleus.**
   c. Schleiden and Schwann **hypothesized that all plants and animals were made of cells.**

3. The major ideas of the cell theory are:
   a. **All living things are made of one or more cells.**
   b. **Cells are the basic units of structure and function in living things.**
   c. **All cells come from other cells.**

TEACH

Concept Development

▶ Point out that even though Earth is filled with billions of things, these things are made of a limited number of elements.

▶ Point out that a compound consists of atoms that are joined together. A chemical formula represents the number and kinds of atoms in a compound.

Skill Check

Have students find a biology or chemistry book that has diagrams of biological molecules. They may use gum drops instead of polystyrene balls.

Guided Practice

Have students write down their answers to the margin question: H_2O.

Cooperative Learning: Divide the class into three groups and have each group make a display of objects made of only one particular element. For example, one group could collect objects made entirely of aluminum; another, objects made entirely of iron; and the third, objects made entirely of copper. Explain that pure gold and silver are too soft for jewelry so other elements are added to give them strength.

Skill Check

Formulate a model: Construct a model of a simple molecule, such as water or carbon dioxide. Use polystyrene balls and toothpicks. Label each atom in the molecule. *For more help, refer to the **Skill Handbook**, pages 706-711.*

The Chemistry of Life

Living things are made of matter. Matter is anything that has mass and takes up space. Matter is made of tiny particles called atoms. Atoms make up elements. An element is a substance that is made up of only one kind of atom. Oxygen and hydrogen are examples of elements.

Matter is often made of two or more different elements joined together to form a compound. Joining different elements can change the way they act. For example, water is a compound made of the elements oxygen and hydrogen. Oxygen and hydrogen are gases. Yet, when they join they make water. As you know, water is a liquid. The smallest part of a compound is a molecule. A molecule of water is the smallest amount of water you can have and still have water.

Scientists use a certain symbol for each different element. When written together, the symbols make a chemical formula. A chemical formula is a way to write the name of a compound using symbols. The symbol for oxygen is O. The symbol for hydrogen is H. The chemical formula for a molecule of water is H_2O. The number 2 shows that there are two hydrogen atoms for every oxygen atom in a molecule of water.

What is the chemical formula for water?

Six elements make up over 97 percent of the matter in living things. Those six elements are carbon, hydrogen, oxygen, nitrogen, phosphorus (FAHS fuh rus), and sulfur, Figure 2-5. They are often called the building blocks of living matter.

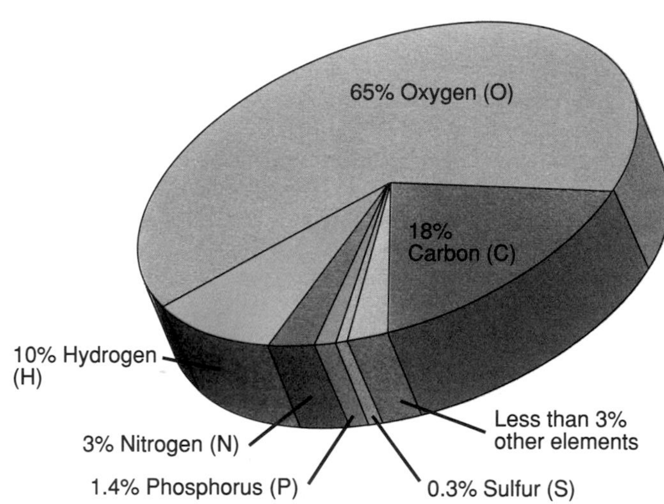

Figure 2-5 Living things are made up of the elements shown here. Which element makes up most of a living thing? oxygen

OPTIONS

Enrichment: Discuss the three common states of matter. A solid has a definite shape and occupies a definite volume. A liquid has a definite volume but changes shape to fill its container. A gas has no definite shape or volume but spreads out to fill whatever space is available.

Enrichment/*Teacher Resource Package*, p. 2. Use the Enrichment worksheet shown here to teach the chemistry of life.

ENRICHMENT 2

ENRICHMENT — CHAPTER 2

Name ______ Date ______ Class ______

Use after Section 2:1.

THE CHEMISTRY OF LIFE

Living matter is composed of many different elements. Elements are made up of small units called atoms. Each atom has a nucleus that is surrounded by particles called electrons. Each electron has a negative charge. A nucleus is usually made up of two types of particles, protons and neutrons. Each proton has a positive charge. Neutrons have no charge. The number of protons in the nucleus of an atom is its atomic number. The number of protons and the number of neutrons added together is the atomic mass. The table below shows facts about the six elements that make up most of your body.

Use the information about atoms and the facts in the table below to answer the questions that follow.

Element	Element symbol	Atomic number	Atomic mass	Percent of human body
hydrogen	H	1	1	9.5
carbon	C	6	12	18.5
nitrogen	N	7	14	3.0
oxygen	O	8	16	65.0
phosphorus	P	15	31	1.0
sulfur	S	16	32	0.3

1. What is the most abundant element in the human body? oxygen
2. What is the symbol of the element in question 1? What is its atomic number? O, 8
3. What element makes up 18.5 percent of the body? What is its symbol? carbon, C
4. Write the atomic number of phosphorus. How many protons does it have? 15, 15
5. Fill in the blanks in this word equation:
   Atomic mass = the number of protons + the number of neutrons.
6. What is the atomic mass of nitrogen? 14
7. How many neutrons are in the nucleus of a nitrogen atom? 7
8. Write the symbol of the element found in 0.3 percent of the human body. S
9. Which element in the chart has no neutrons? hydrogen
10. How many positive charges are in the nucleus of a carbon atom? 6

Cell Theory

In 1665, an English scientist named Robert Hooke looked at thin slices of cork under a microscope. Hooke saw that cork had a lot of empty spaces. Hooke used the word *cells* to describe the empty spaces in cork.

Today, biologists know that Hooke did not see living cells. He saw the walls of cells that were alive at one time.

By the nineteenth century, microscopes had been improved. Scientists could see that the cell had parts. First, Robert Brown discovered the central part of the cell, the nucleus (NEW klee us). Then, two German biologists, Matthias Schleiden and Theodore Schwann, did experiments to see what kinds of living things had cells. They formed hypotheses that all plants and animals were made of cells.

The experiments of Schleiden, Schwann, and other scientists led to the development of the cell theory. The major ideas of the cell theory are listed below.

1. All living things are made of one or more cells.
2. Cells are the basic units of structure and function in living things.
3. All cells come from other cells.

Mini Lab

What Makes Up Cork?

Use a microscope: To see what Robert Hooke saw, slice a thin section from a piece of cork and look at it under the microscope. What do you see in the center of each cell? *For more help refer to the **Skill Handbook**, pages 712-714.*

What events led to the cell theory?

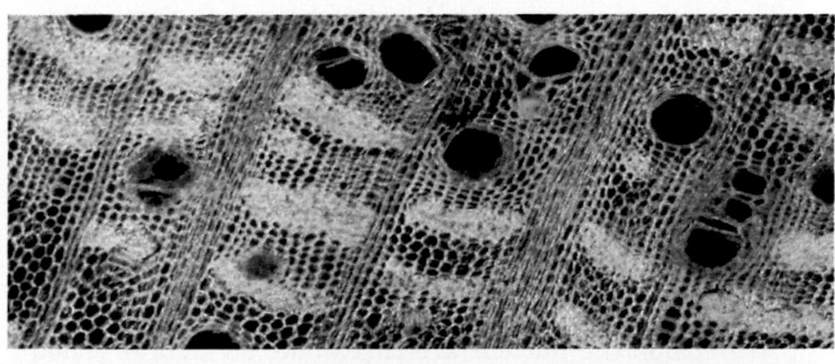

Figure 2-6 These cork cells are similar to what Robert Hooke saw.

Check Your Understanding

1. Name eight features of living things.
2. What six elements make up most of living matter?
3. What is the cell theory?
4. **Critical Thinking:** Why is cellular respiration necessary to living things?
5. **Biology and Writing:** Write a paragraph about a nonliving thing not mentioned in this section. Describe the features of living things that the nonliving thing has.

TEACH

Mini Lab

Students will see cell walls and empty space inside each cell.

Guided Practice

Have students write down their answers to the margin question: experiments of scientists.

Check for Understanding

Have students respond to the first three questions in Check Your Understanding.

Reteach

Reteaching/*Teacher Resource Package*, p. 4. Use this worksheet to give students additional practice with living things and their parts.

Extension: Assign Critical Thinking, Biology and Writing, or some of the **OPTIONS** available with this lesson.

3 APPLY

Connection: History

Have students write reports on Matthias Schleiden, Theodor Schwann, and the cell theory.

4 CLOSE

Show the video *The Living Cell,* Clearvue, Inc.

Answers to Check Your Understanding

1. They reproduce, grow, develop, need food, use energy, are made of cells, respond, and adapt.
2. carbon, hydrogen, oxygen, nitrogen, sulfur, phosphorus
3. All living things are made of one or more cells. Cells are the basic units of structure and function in living things. All cells come from other cells.
4. Food is broken down and energy released.
5. Examples may be a car or a match.

RETEACHING 4

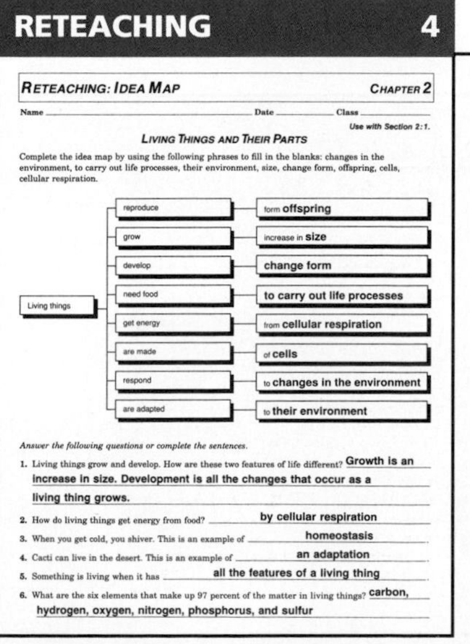

RETEACHING: IDEA MAP — *CHAPTER 2*

Name ______ Date ______ Class ______

Use with Section 2:1.

LIVING THINGS AND THEIR PARTS

Complete the idea map by using the following phrases to fill in the blanks: changes in the environment, to carry out life processes, their environment, size, change form, offspring, cells, cellular respiration.

Living things
- reproduce — form **offspring**
- grow — increase in **size**
- develop — **change form**
- need food — **to carry out life processes**
- get energy — from **cellular respiration**
- are made — of **cells**
- respond — to **changes in the environment**
- are adapted — to **their environment**

Answer the following questions or complete the sentences.

1. Living things grow and develop. How are these two features of life different? **Growth is an increase in size. Development is all the changes that occur as a living thing grows.**
2. How do living things get energy from food? **by cellular respiration**
3. When you get cold, you shiver. This is an example of **homeostasis**.
4. Cacti can live in the desert. This is an example of **an adaptation**.
5. Something is living when it has **all the features of a living thing**.
6. What are the six elements that make up 97 percent of the matter in living things? **carbon, hydrogen, oxygen, nitrogen, phosphorus, and sulfur**

2:2 Cell Parts and Their Jobs

PREPARATION

Materials Needed

Make copies of the Skill, Study Guide, Application, Reteaching, and Lab worksheets in the *Teacher Resource Package*.

▶ Have methylene blue stain and gather *Elodea* and toothpicks for Lab 2-2.

Key Science Words

cell membrane	ribosome
nucleus	mitochondria
nuclear membrane	vacuole
nucleolus	centriole
chromosome	chloroplast
cytoplasm	cell wall

Process Skills

In Lab 2-2, students will observe, compare, and use a microscope.

1 FOCUS

▶ The objectives are listed on the student page. Remind students to preview these objectives as a guide to this numbered section.

MOTIVATION/Bulletin Board

Make a bulletin board showing the parts of an animal cell and a plant cell. As each cell part is studied, identify the part by placing its label on the bulletin board.

Guided Practice

Have students write down their answers to the margin question: cytoplasm.

Objectives

4. **List** the parts of the cell.
5. **Describe** the functions of the cell parts.

Key Science Words

cell membrane
nucleus
nuclear membrane
nucleolus
chromosome
cytoplasm
ribosome
mitochondria
vacuole
centriole
chloroplast
cell wall

2:2 Cell Parts and Their Jobs

Cells are microscopic units that make up all living things. Cells are alive. They do everything needed to stay alive. They carry on cellular respiration. They grow and reproduce. A cell has many different parts to do all of these jobs. As you study the parts of the cell, refer to Figure 2-7. Figure 2-7 shows an animal cell and a plant cell and the cell parts of each.

Cell Membrane and Nucleus

All cells are surrounded by a cell membrane. The **cell membrane** gives the cell shape and holds the cytoplasm. It also helps control what moves into and out of the cell.

The **nucleus** is the cell part that controls most of the cell's activities. It determines how and when proteins will be made. Proteins are complex substances with several different jobs. Some form cell parts. Others regulate activities of the cell. The nucleus also passes traits from parents to offspring.

The **nuclear membrane** is a structure that surrounds the nucleus and separates it from the rest of the cell. The nuclear membrane has openings that allow certain materials to move into and out of the nucleus.

Inside the nucleus is a smaller body called the nucleolus (new KLEE uh lus). The **nucleolus** is the cell part that helps make ribosomes (RI buh sohmz). You will read about ribosomes in the next section. Some cells have more than one nucleolus.

Also inside the nucleus are threadlike structures called chromosomes (KROH muh sohmz). **Chromosomes** are cell parts with information that determines what traits a living thing will have. Examples of traits are hair color, eye color, and sizes and shapes of leaves.

Cytoplasm

What is found between the cell membrane and the nucleus?

The clear, jellylike material between the cell membrane and the nucleus that makes up most of the cell is called **cytoplasm** (SITE uh plaz um). Most of the cell's chemical reactions take place in the cytoplasm. Cytoplasm is mostly water, but it also has other chemicals. In addition, other cell parts that carry on special functions are found in the cytoplasm.

OPTIONS

Science Background

The nucleus determines which proteins will be made and when. Proteins, in turn, regulate most of the other chemical processes in the cell. In this way, the nucleus controls cell activity. Not all cells have nuclei. The red blood cells of mammals have nuclei when they are first formed, but they lose their nuclei before they enter the bloodstream.

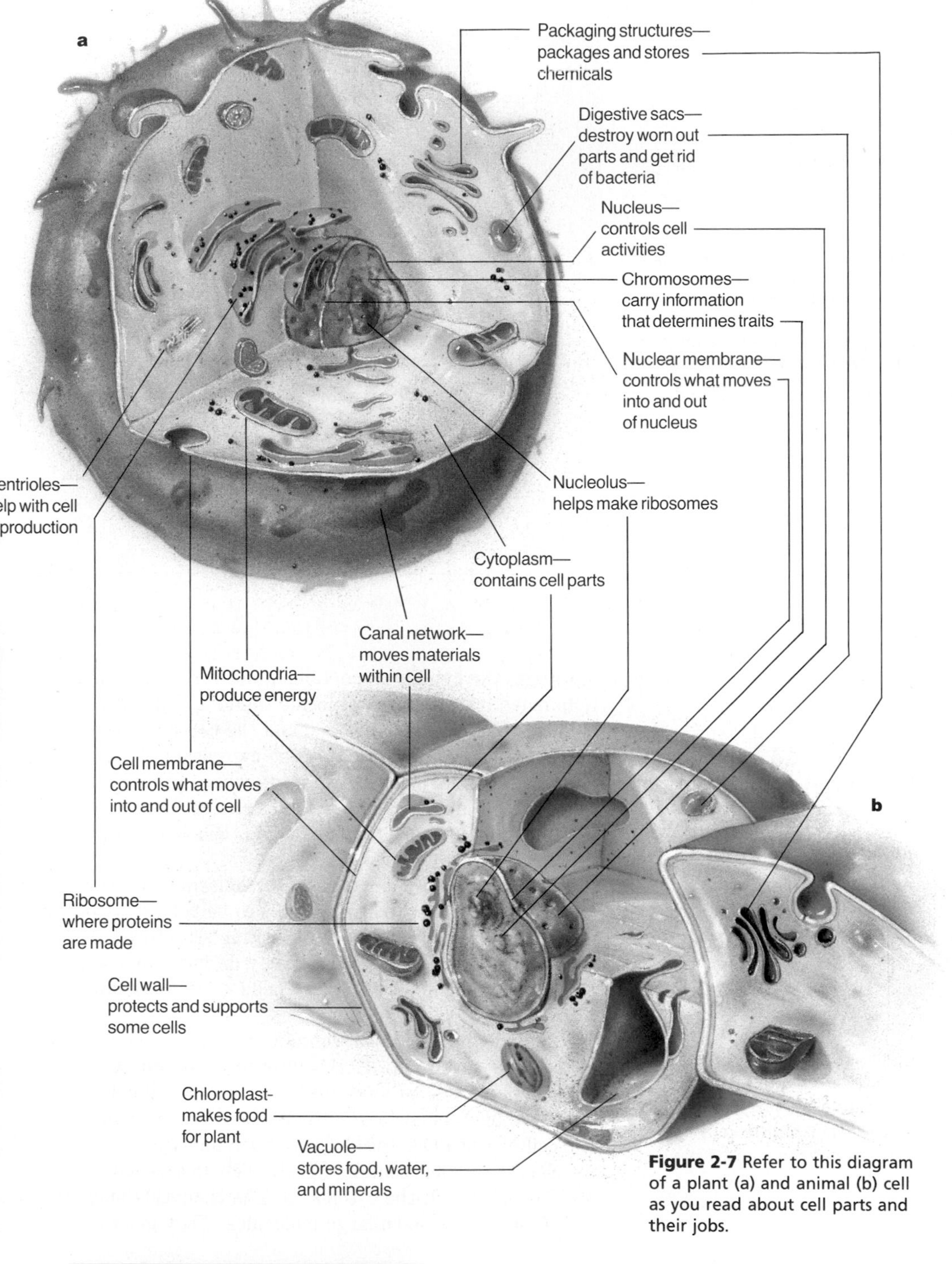

Figure 2-7 Refer to this diagram of a plant (a) and animal (b) cell as you read about cell parts and their jobs.

2 TEACH

MOTIVATION/Software

The Cell: Examination, Structure, and Function, Queue, Inc.

MOTIVATION/Demonstration

Use a projector to show cell parts of both a plant and an animal cell. Prepared slides of frog blood and onion root tip are usually available.

TEACH

Concept Development

▶ Some students may believe a cell wall and a cell membrane to be the same structure. Distinguish between the two, and continue to reinforce the difference as cells are studied.

▶ Explain that a cell wall does not determine what may enter or leave a cell.

▶ Point out that cells of fungi and some one-celled organisms also have cell walls.

▶ Explain that chromosomes carry the hereditary information from one generation of cells to the next.

Cooperative Learning: Divide the class into cooperative groups of six. Have each group be responsible for learning the functions of two cell parts. Once each group has learned its cell parts, have the groups reshuffle and form new groups. Each person in the new group is responsible for explaining the functions of the cell parts he or she has become an "expert" on.

SKILL 2

SKILL: INTERPRET DIAGRAMS — CHAPTER 2

Name ____________ Date ________ Class ________

For more help, refer to the Skill Handbook, pages 706-711. *Use with Section 2:2.*

PLANT AND ANIMAL CELLS

Diagrams in a textbook give information just as words do. They help make the meanings of words clear. Studying Figure 2-7 will help you understand Section 2:2.

Use Section 2:2 and Figure 2-7 to complete the table below.

In the first column, list all the words in Section 2:2 that are printed in bold type. In the second column, tell where in the cell each cell part is located. In the third column, list the function(s) of each cell part.

Cell part	Location	Function(s)
cell membrane	around the cell	gives the cell shape, controls what moves into and out of the cell
nucleus	near the center	controls most of the cell's activities
nuclear membrane	around the nucleus	allows materials to move into and out of the nucleus
nucleolus	in the nucleus	makes ribosomes
chromosomes	in the nucleus	determine what traits a living thing will have
cytoplasm	throughout the cell	makes up most of the cell
ribosomes	in the cytoplasm	where proteins are made
mitochondria	in the cytoplasm	produce energy
vacuole	in the cytoplasm	stores food, water, and minerals
centrioles	in the cytoplasm	help cell reproduction
chloroplasts	in the cytoplasm of plant cells	trap energy for food making
cell wall	surrounds the plant cell	protects and supports the plant cell

OPTIONS

Plant and Animal Cells/*Transparency Package*, number 2a. Use color transparency number 2a as your teach the parts of cells.

Skill/*Teacher Resource Package*, p. 2. Use the Skill worksheet shown here for students to interpret diagrams of plant and animal cells.

TEACH

Concept Development

▶ Explain that cytoplasm consists of many types of proteins and other large molecules.

▶ Point out that mitochondria are most numerous in cells that are active in some way, such as muscle cells and liver cells. In plants, mitochondria are numerous in cells that transport water against the force of gravity.

Idea Map

Have students use the idea map as a study guide to the major concepts of this section.

Guided Practice

Have students write down their answers to the margin question: They are the cell parts where proteins are made.

Idea Map

Cell Parts and Their Jobs

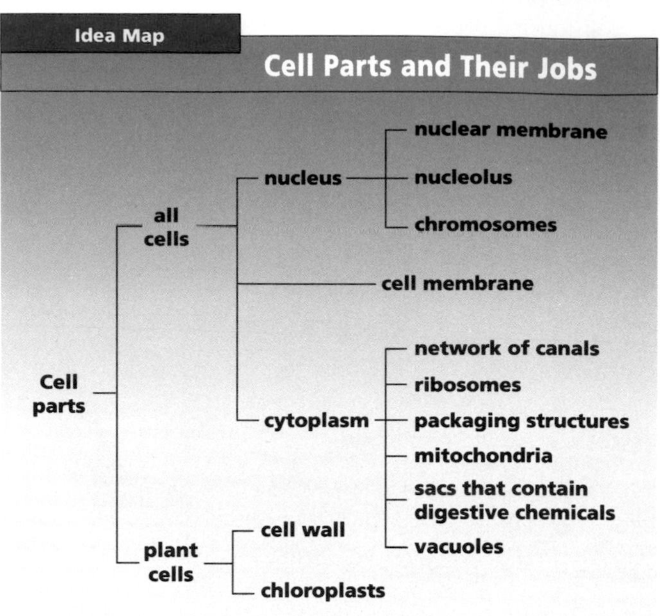

Study Tip: Use this idea map as you study cell parts and their jobs. Remember that only plant cells have cell walls and chloroplasts. All cells have the other cell parts shown in the idea map.

First, the cytoplasm contains a network of canals that help move material around inside the cell. The canals connect the nuclear membrane and the cell membrane.

What is the job of the ribosomes?

A second cell part found in the cytoplasm is the ribosome. **Ribosomes** are cell parts where proteins are made. Large numbers of ribosomes can be found along the canal network, where they are made. Ribosomes can also be found throughout the cytoplasm.

A third cell part found in the cytoplasm is a structure that packages and stores chemicals to be released from the cell. Large numbers of these packaging structures are found in cells that make saliva. Why do you suppose this is so? Large amounts of saliva are needed to break down the foods you eat.

Fourth, the cytoplasm contains rod-shaped bodies called mitochondria (mite uh KAHN dree uh). The **mitochondria** are cell parts that produce energy from food that has been digested. Mitochondria are often called "powerhouses" of the cell because they produce so much energy.

Small sacs that contain digestive chemicals are a fifth structure found in the cytoplasm. The chemicals made in these sacs break down large molecules. They get rid of

Bio Tip

Health: Hair is not made of cells. It is made of protein that is secreted by hair follicle cells. Hair follicle cells surround the root of the hair.

OPTIONS

What Cell Parts Can You See With the Microscope?/*Lab Manual*, pp. 13-16. Use this lab as an extension to studying the parts of cells.

disease-causing bacteria that enter the cell. They also destroy worn-out cell parts and form products that can be used again.

Sixth, most cells have vacuoles (VAK yuh wolz) within the cytoplasm. A **vacuole** is a liquid-filled space that stores food, water, and minerals. Vacuoles also store wastes until the cell is ready to get rid of them. In most plant cells, the vacuole takes up a large amount of space within the cell. The fluid inside the vacuole helps to support the plant.

Centrioles (SEN tree ohlz), a seventh structure within the cytoplasm, are located near the nucleus in animal cells and in some plant cells. **Centrioles** are cell parts that help with cell reproduction. They exist in pairs in the cell.

The cytoplasm of plant cells contains an eighth cell part, chloroplasts (KLOR uh plasts). **Chloroplasts** are cell parts that contain the green pigment, chlorophyll. Chlorophyll traps energy from the sun. Plants use this energy to make food. Chloroplasts give plants their green color.

The cells of plants, algae, fungi, and some bacteria have cell walls. Animal cells do not have cell walls. The **cell wall** is a thick outer covering outside the cell membrane. It protects and supports the cell.

The cell wall often remains after the rest of the cell has died. Wood is made of the walls of dead cells. What did Robert Hooke see when he looked at cork cells?

Skill Check

Understand science words: chloroplast. The word part *chloro* means green. In your dictionary, find three words with the word part *chloro* in them. *For more help, refer to the **Skill Handbook**, pages 706-711.*

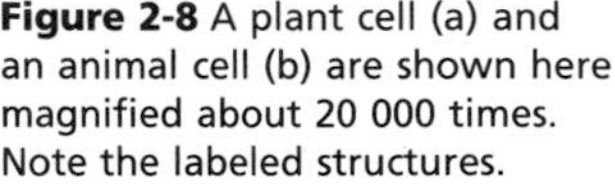

Figure 2-8 A plant cell (a) and an animal cell (b) are shown here magnified about 20 000 times. Note the labeled structures.

a

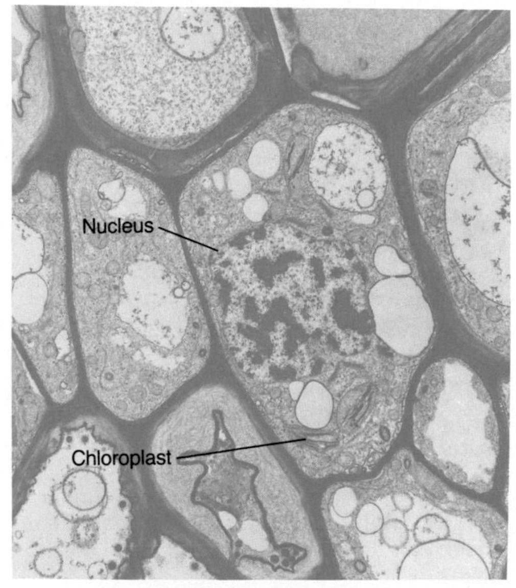

b

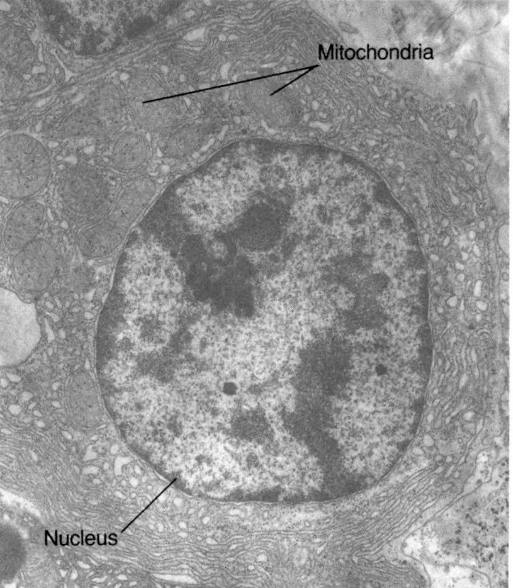

TEACH

Concept Development

▶ Explain that in unicellular organisms, food may be digested within certain vacuoles.

Check for Understanding

Use the overhead projector and a transparency of a typical cell to point out each cell part and where it is located in the cell. Have students identify each part and give its function.

Reteach

Write the function of each cell part on a 3 x 5 card. Have a student draw a card, read the function, name the cell part, and tell where the cell part is located in the cell.

Independent Practice

Study Guide/*Teacher Resource Package*, p. 9. Use the Study Guide worksheet shown at the bottom of this page for independent practice.

APPLICATION 2

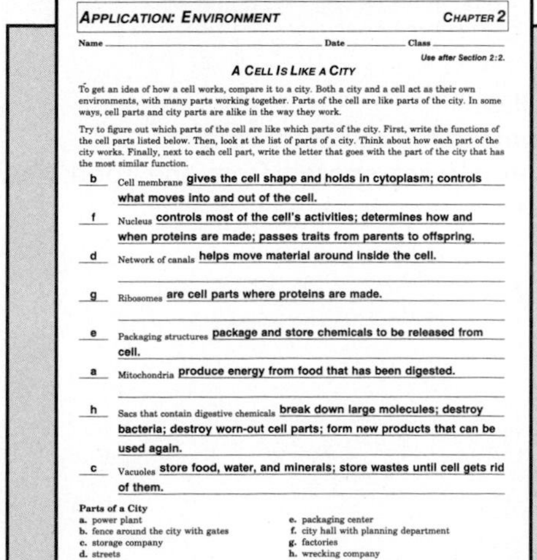

APPLICATION: ENVIRONMENT — CHAPTER 2

Name ______ Date ______ Class ______

Use after Section 2:2.

A CELL IS LIKE A CITY

To get an idea of how a cell works, compare it to a city. Both a city and a cell act as their own environments, with many parts working together. Parts of the cell are like parts of the city. In some ways, cell parts and city parts are alike in the way they work.

Try to figure out which parts of the cell are like which parts of the city. First, write the functions of the cell parts listed below. Then, look at the list of parts of a city. Think about how each part of the city works. Finally, next to each cell part, write the letter that goes with the part of the city that has the most similar function.

b Cell membrane gives the cell shape and holds in cytoplasm; controls what moves into and out of the cell.

f Nucleus controls most of the cell's activities; determines how and when proteins are made; passes traits from parents to offspring.

d Network of canals helps move material around inside the cell.

g Ribosomes are cell parts where proteins are made.

e Packaging structures package and store chemicals to be released from cell.

a Mitochondria produce energy from food that has been digested.

h Sacs that contain digestive chemicals break down large molecules; destroy bacteria; destroy worn-out cell parts; form new products that can be used again.

c Vacuoles store food, water, and minerals; store wastes until cell gets rid of them.

Parts of a City

a. power plant
b. fence around the city with gates
c. storage company
d. streets
e. packaging center
f. city hall with planning department
g. factories
h. wrecking company

STUDY GUIDE 9

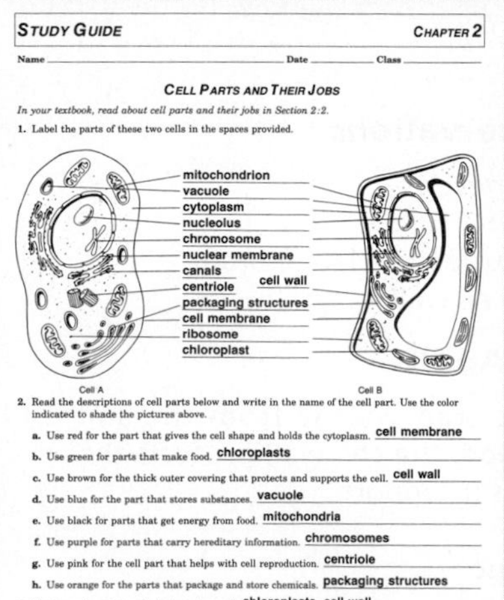

STUDY GUIDE — CHAPTER 2

Name ______ Date ______ Class ______

CELL PARTS AND THEIR JOBS

In your textbook, read about cell parts and their jobs in Section 2:2.

1. Label the parts of these two cells in the spaces provided.

2. Read the descriptions of cell parts below and write in the name of the cell part. Use the color indicated to shade the pictures above.
   a. Use red for the part that gives the cell shape and holds the cytoplasm. cell membrane
   b. Use green for parts that make food. chloroplasts
   c. Use brown for the thick outer covering that protects and supports the cell. cell wall
   d. Use blue for the part that stores substances. vacuole
   e. Use black for parts that get energy from food. mitochondria
   f. Use purple for parts that carry hereditary information. chromosomes
   g. Use pink for the cell part that helps with cell reproduction. centriole
   h. Use orange for the parts that package and store chemicals. packaging structures
3. List two cell parts found only in a plant cell. chloroplasts, cell wall
4. Where in a cell do most chemical reactions take place? in the cytoplasm

OPTIONS

Application/*Teacher Resource Package*, p. 2. Use the Application worksheet shown here to teach how a cell works.

Lab 2-2 Cells

Overview

In this lab, students use the light microscope to compare plant and animal cells. They will stain and observe cell parts.

Objectives: Upon completing this lab, students will be able to (1) **use a microscope** more efficiently, (2) **prepare** stained cells, (3) **compare** the parts of plant and animal cells that are visible with the light microscope.

Time Allotment: 40 minutes

Preparation

▶ **Alternate Materials:** Lettuce can be substituted for *Elodea.*

Lab 2-2 worksheet/*Teacher Resource Package*, pp. 7-8.

Teaching the Lab

▶ Caution students to rub their cheeks gently when obtaining cheek cells with the toothpicks. Also instruct them to properly dispose of the toothpick after use.

Cooperative Learning: Have students work in pairs. For more information, see pp. 22T-23T in the Teacher Guide.

▶ **Troubleshooting:** Too many cheek cells on the slide will result in not being able to see the cells.

Cells

Lab 2–2

Problem: How do animal and plant cells differ?

Materials

light microscope
2 glass slides
2 coverslips
dropper
methylene blue stain
toothpick, flat type
Elodea leaf
water

Skills

observe, compare, use a microscope

Procedure

1. Copy the data table.
2. Put a drop of stain on a slide. Gently scrape the inside of your cheek with a toothpick. **CAUTION:** *Do not scrape hard enough to injure your cheek.*
3. Rub the toothpick in the stain. Break the toothpick in half and discard it as your teacher directs.
4. Cover the slide with a coverslip.
5. **Use a microscope:** Look at the cheek cells under low power, then high power.
6. Locate the nucleus, cytoplasm, and cell membrane. Fill in the table by putting a check mark in the box if the cell part can be seen.
7. Draw and label the nucleus, cytoplasm, and cell membrane of a cheek cell.
8. Prepare a slide of an *Elodea* leaf. Put an *Elodea* leaf in a drop of water on a slide. Add a coverslip.
9. Look at the *Elodea* cells under low power, then high power.
10. Locate the cell wall, chloroplasts, nucleus, and cytoplasm. Fill in the table.
11. Draw and label the cell wall, chloroplasts, nucleus, and cytoplasm of an *Elodea* cell.

CELL PART	CHEEK CELL PARTS PRESENT	*ELODEA* CELL PARTS PRESENT
Cytoplasm	✓	✓
Nucleus	✓	✓
Chloroplast		✓
Cell wall		✓
Cell membrane	✓	✓

Data and Observations

1. Describe the shape of a cheek cell.
2. Describe the shape of an *Elodea* cell.
3. **Compare:** What parts did you see in both cells?
4. What parts are found in plant cells that are absent in animal cells?

Analyze and Apply

1. What do the cell parts found only in plant cells do?
2. Is the nucleus always found in the center of the cell?
3. Which part of an animal cell gives shape to the cell?
4. Which parts of a plant cell give shape to the cell?
5. Why are stains such as methylene blue used when observing cells under the microscope?
6. **Apply:** Why don't animal cells have chloroplasts? (HINT: How do animals get energy?)

Extension

Observe other plant and animal cells under the microscope. How are they different from cheek cells and *Elodea* cells? How are they alike?

ANSWERS

Data and Observations

1. round and uneven
2. rectangular
3. cytoplasm, nucleus, cell membrane
4. chloroplast, cell wall

Analyze and Apply

1. Chloroplasts trap energy from the sun and make food; the cell wall protects the cell and gives it support.
2. no
3. cell membrane
4. cell wall
5. to make the cell parts visible
6. Animals get energy from the food they eat.

Figure 2-9 The maple tree (a), ladybug (b), horse (c), and coral snake (d) are all made of cells.

Your cells and the cells of every living thing around you are complex structures with many parts. Each part has a function that is important to the life of the cell. All of the living things in Figure 2-9 are made of cells. What other living things can you name that are made of cells?

Check Your Understanding

6. Which cell part is being described?
   (a) helps keep cytoplasm inside
   (b) controls most of the cell's activities
   (c) a liquid-filled space for storage
   (d) green parts of plants that trap energy from the sun
   (e) clear, jellylike material in which most of the cell's chemical reactions take place
7. Name two cell parts found in plant cells that are not found in animal cells.
8. Why are mitochondria called "powerhouses" of the cell?
9. **Critical Thinking:** How do mitochondria and chloroplasts differ?
10. **Biology and Writing:** Write three sentences describing the cell parts that make up a wooden table.

RETEACHING 5

RETEACHING CHAPTER 2

Name Date Class

Use with Section 2:2.

PLANT CELL AND ANIMAL CELL STRUCTURES

chloroplast, cell wall, cell membrane, cytoplasm, vacuole, mitochondrion, ribosome, canals, chromosome, nuclear membrane, nucleus, nucleolus, sacs with digestive chemicals, structures that package chemicals, centriole, Plant Cell, Animal Cell

TEACH

Check for Understanding

Have students respond to the first three questions in Check Your Understanding.

Reteach

Reteaching/Teacher Resource Package, p. 5. Use this worksheet to give students additional practice comparing plant cell and animal cell structures.

Extension: Assign Critical Thinking, Biology and Writing, or some of the **OPTIONS** available with this lesson.

3 APPLY

Connection: Language Arts

Have students list the cell parts and use a dictionary to find the origin and meaning of each word.

4 CLOSE

Make a Model

Have students work in pairs with clay and paints to make a model of either a plant or an animal cell.

Answers to Check Your Understanding

6. (a) cell membrane, (b) nucleus, (c) vacuole, (d) chloroplast, (e) cytoplasm
7. cell wall and chloroplast
8. they produce so much energy
9. Chloroplasts trap energy from the sun and change it into food energy. Mitochondria produce energy from food that has been digested.
10. Answers will vary. Students should include cell walls in their answers.

2:3 Special Cell Processes

PREPARATION

Materials Needed

Make copies of the Study Guide, Critical Thinking/ Problem Solving, and Reteaching worksheets in the *Teacher Resource Package*.

▶ Gather beakers and instant coffee for the Focus activity. Have balloons and vanilla extract on hand for the Mini Lab.

Key Science Words

diffusion
osmosis
tissue
organ
organ system
organism

Process Skills

In the Mini Lab, students will experiment.

1 FOCUS

▶ The objectives are listed on the student page. Remind students to preview these objectives as a guide to this numbered section.

ACTIVITY/Hands-On

To see diffusion, divide the class into groups of two and give each group a beaker of water and a small amount of instant coffee. Have students add the coffee to the water, leave it undisturbed, and observe what happens.

Guided Practice

Have students write down their answers to the margin question: movement of a substance from where there is a larger amount to where there is a smaller amount.

2:3 Special Cell Processes

Objectives

6. **Explain** the process of diffusion in a cell.
7. **Describe** the process of osmosis in a cell.
8. **Communicate** how cells, tissues, organs, and organ systems are organized.

Key Science Words

diffusion
osmosis
tissue
organ
organ system
organism

Cells need certain substances to stay alive. These substances include food and oxygen. How does a substance, such as oxygen, get through the cell membrane and into the cell?

Diffusion

Imagine you have a box of marbles. The box is divided in half by a strip of cardboard with an opening. Figure 2-10 shows the box with marbles in it. Notice that all of the marbles are on one side of the cardboard strip.

The marbles are packed very tightly into the box. Some of the marbles roll to the other side of the box through the opening in the cardboard strip. The marbles keep rolling until each side of the box has about equal numbers of marbles. How did this happen?

If you walk near the chemistry lab in your school, you might smell a gas made during a chemistry experiment. How did the gas move from the lab into the hall where you are? The gas moved from where there was a large amount of it, in the lab, to where there was a small amount of it, in the hall. Gas molecules, like marbles, can move about. The movement of a substance from where there is a large amount of it to where there is a small amount of it is called **diffusion** (dif YEW zhun).

What is diffusion?

How does oxygen diffuse into cells? Doesn't the cell membrane get in the way? Think about the box divided by the cardboard strip. Marbles could roll to the other side of the box through the opening in the cardboard strip.

Figure 2-10 Before the marbles roll through the opening in the cardboard strip, they are all on one side of the box (left). The box on the right shows what happens after the marbles roll from one side to the other.

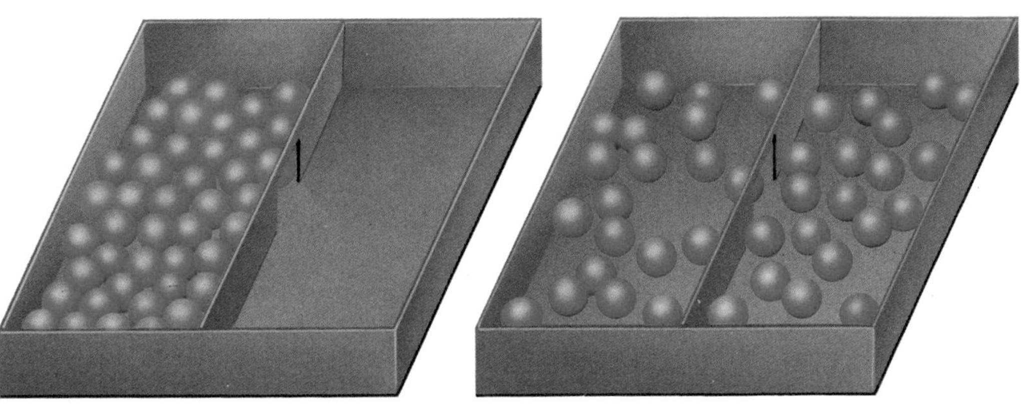

OPTIONS

Science Background

Cell membranes are selectively permeable. Water passes through the membrane but a substance dissolved in the water may or may not pass through. Carrier molecules in the cell membrane permit specific molecules on one side of the membrane to pass through to the other side. The process of diffusion is made easier, or facilitated, by the carrier molecules, so the process is called facilitated diffusion.

What Are Diffusion and Osmosis?/*Lab Manual*, pp. 9-12. Use this lab as an extension to teaching cell processes.

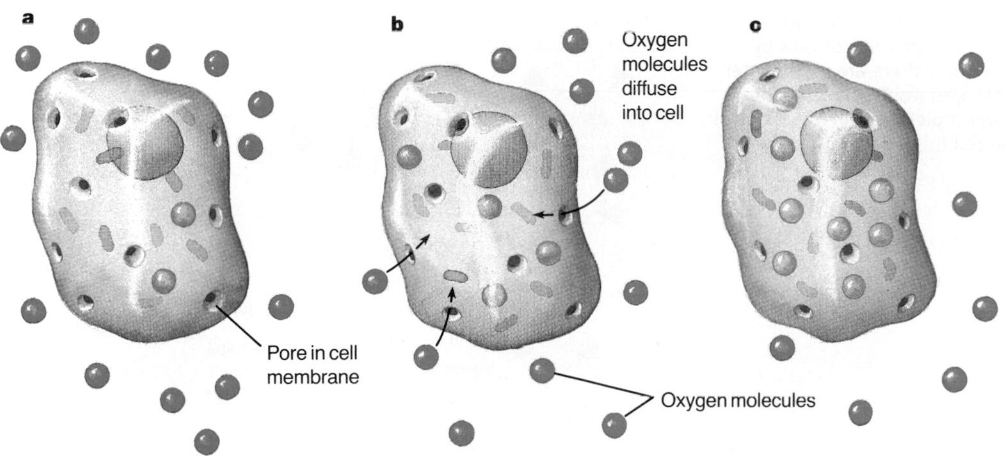

Figure 2-11 Oxygen diffuses into the cell through pores in the membrane.

Membranes also have openings, called pores. Some molecules, such as oxygen, can pass through these pores, Figure 2-11a. The movement of molecules through the pores of a membrane is like the movement of marbles through the opening in the cardboard strip.

In Figure 2-11:

1. There is a large number of oxygen molecules outside the cell.
2. There is a small number of oxygen molecules inside the cell.
3. The oxygen moves from the outside to the inside by diffusion, as shown in Figure 2-11b. The oxygen moves from where there is a large amount of it to where there is a small amount of it. If we look at the cell later, we see about equal numbers of oxygen molecules inside and outside the cell, Figure 2-11c. Remember that at a later time, there were about equal numbers of marbles on both sides of the box.

Osmosis

Water molecules also move across membranes. Like oxygen, they move from where there is a large number of molecules to where there is a small number of molecules. The movement goes on until the number of water molecules is about the same on both sides of the membrane. The movement of water across the cell membrane is called **osmosis** (ahs MOH sus).

Mini Lab

What Is Diffusion?

Experiment: Put 10 drops of vanilla extract inside a balloon. Blow up the balloon, tie it, and place it inside a box. Close the box. After two hours, open the box. What do you smell? *For more help, refer to the* ***Skill Handbook,*** *pages 704-705.*

2 TEACH

MOTIVATION/Demonstration

Place one slice of cucumber, potato, carrot, or celery in salt water and one slice in plain water. Have students observe how the slice in salt water wilts or softens.

Concept Development

▶ Explain that the movement of gas from the chemistry lab is like the diffusion of perfume in the air.

Analogy: Make a comparison between moving molecules and moving marbles in a box.

Independent Practice

Study Guide/*Teacher Resource Package*, p. 10. Use the Study Guide worksheet shown at the bottom of this page for independent practice.

Mini Lab

Students will smell vanilla in the box. The vanilla diffuses through the balloon and into the box.

OPTIONS

Critical Thinking/Problem Solving/ *Teacher Resource Package*, p. 2. Use the Critical Thinking/Problem Solving worksheet shown here for students to understand that foods are affected by osmosis and diffusion.

CRITICAL THINKING 2

CRITICAL THINKING/PROBLEM SOLVING — CHAPTER 2

Name ______ Date ______ Class ______

WHAT HAPPENED TO DINNER? *Use after Section 2:3.*

Jeff's family planned to attend his brother's basketball game on a school night. His mother cooked spaghetti sauce. Jeff offered to make the salad and cook the spaghetti. First, Jeff washed the lettuce. Then, he sliced tomatoes, cucumbers, and radishes. Next, Jeff put some pepper, herbs, oil, and vinegar on the vegetables. Finally, he tossed the salad, covered it, and placed it in the refrigerator. Jeff read the directions for cooking a pound of spaghetti. He was surprised to see that he needed five quarts of water to boil the spaghetti. Jeff read the label on the box of spaghetti. He found that the food was made from ground-up plants. Jeff slid the dry spaghetti into boiling water and waited while it cooked. He drained the spaghetti. It took up much more space now than it had before it was cooked. Almost all the water in the pot was gone. What had happened to the water and the dry spaghetti? Jeff took the salad from the refrigerator. The vegetables were no longer crisp. There was more liquid in the salad bowl than he had added. What had happened to the vegetables?

Analyzing the Problem

1. How did the dry spaghetti increase in size? **The spaghetti absorbed water.**
2. Where did the liquid in the salad bowl come from? **from the vegetables**

Solving the Problem

1. When Jeff made the salad, were more water molecules inside or outside the plant cells? **inside the cells**
2. What happens when the number of water molecules is greater inside a cell than outside? **Water moves out of the cell.**
3. How does your answer to number 2 help to explain what happened to the vegetables in the salad? **Water moved out of the cells by osmosis because there was more water inside the cells of the plants making up the salad than outside.**
4. When Jeff put dry spaghetti into boiling water, was there more water inside or outside the food? **outside the food**
5. What happens when the number of water molecules is greater in one area than another area? **Water moves from the area in which there are more water molecules to the area in which there are fewer water molecules.**
6. How does your answer to number 5 help to explain what happened to the spaghetti? **The water molecules moved from where there were more of them (the water in the pot) to where there were fewer of them (spaghetti).**

STUDY GUIDE 10

STUDY GUIDE — CHAPTER 2

Name ______ Date ______ Class ______

SPECIAL CELL PROCESSES

In your textbook, read about diffusion and osmosis in Section 2:3.

1. The first picture below, labeled *Before*, shows a cell surrounded by oxygen molecules before diffusion takes place. Each of the small black dots represents an oxygen molecule. Which of the three pictures labeled *After* shows where these oxygen molecules would be found after diffusion takes place? Circle your answer. **Students are being asked to show *net* diffusion. Diffusion continues after equilibrium is reached, but net diffusion does not.**

Before — After — After — After

2. What is diffusion? **the movement of a substance from where there is a large amount of it to where there is a small amount of it**
3. How do molecules get through the cell membrane? **The membrane has pores, or small openings, through which the molecules can pass.**
4. What is osmosis? **Osmosis is the movement of water across the cell membrane.**
5. Which way would the water molecules move in the following situations?
   a. cucumber slice is placed in salt water **out of the cucumber**
   b. salt is poured on a snail **out of the snail**
   c. vegetables are sprinkled with water **into the vegetables**
   d. potato slice is placed in pure water **into the potato**
6. Circle the letter in front of the sentence that best explains the process of osmosis.
   (a.) Osmosis is the movement of water into or out of a cell from where it is in large amounts to where it is in small amounts.
   b. Osmosis is the movement of water into or out of a cell from where it is in small amounts to where it is in large amounts.
   c. Osmosis is the movement of salt into or out of a cell from where it is in large amounts to where it is in small amounts.

TEACH

Concept Development

▶ Emphasize that diffusion and osmosis are physical processes over which the cell has no control.

▶ Point out that the concentration of water inside the cucumber would be greater than the concentration of water in the salt water.

▶ Remind students that the cell is the simplest level of organization that is alive.

Guided Practice

Have students write down their answers to the margin question: Cells are surrounded by water molecules. Osmosis allows movement in and out so that the number of molecules inside and the number outside are about the same.

Check for Understanding

Have students list examples of osmosis and diffusion. Suggest smells from a bakery and spraying fruits and vegetables with water.

Reteach

Place a few raisins in a beaker of water and let the beaker stand overnight. Have students explain the process observed.

Independent Practice

Study Guide/*Teacher Resource Package*, p. 11. Use the Study Guide worksheet shown at the bottom of this page for independent practice.

Figure 2-12 Water molecules move into and out of cells by osmosis. If there are more water molecules inside than out, the water molecules will move out of the cell.

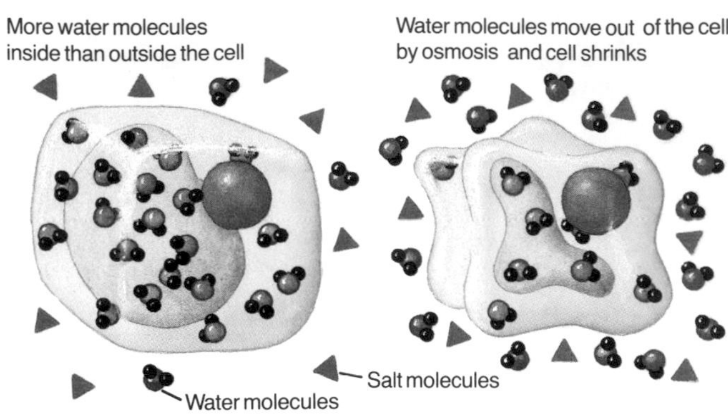
More water molecules inside than outside the cell
Water molecules move out of the cell by osmosis and cell shrinks
Salt molecules
Water molecules

Why is osmosis important to cells?

Osmosis is important to cells because they are surrounded by water molecules. The number of water molecules inside and outside the cell must be about the same. When there are more water molecules outside the cell, they move into the cell. When there are more water molecules inside the cell, they move out.

Suppose you placed some cucumber slices into salt water. What do you think would happen? (HINT: Cucumber cells have nearly pure water inside. Salt water is not pure water because it has salt in it. So, there are more water molecules in a cucumber than in salt water.) The water molecules inside the cucumber would move out, as shown in Figure 2-12. When cells of a plant lose too much water, the plant wilts. What do you think would happen if your cells lost too much water?

Bio Tip

Consumer: Osmosis affects the taste of foods. When steak is salted before it is cooked, water moves out of its cells, making the steak dry and tasteless.

Organization

Living things are organized in special ways. Some living things are made of only one cell. That one cell carries out all the activities necessary for life. It responds to the environment, reproduces, and uses energy.

In living things made of many cells, the cells are organized into groups, Figure 2-13. The cells of each group do special jobs. For example, cells that line the small intestine make chemicals for digestion. Groups of cells, such as those that line the intestine, are called tissues. A **tissue** is a group of similar cells that work together to carry out a special job. Bone, muscle, blood, and nerve are kinds of tissues found in animals. Bark and outer surfaces of leaves are kinds of tissues in plants.

OPTIONS

Science Background

Explain that pressure within a plant cell is called turgor pressure. Turgor pressure is the chief means of support in most nonwoody plants. When plant structures lose too much water, they collapse. The loss of turgor pressure, called plasmolysis, causes plants to wilt.

Organization in Living Things/*Transparency Package,* number 2b. Use color transparency 2b as you teach how living things are organized.

STUDY GUIDE 11

STUDY GUIDE CHAPTER 2

Name ______ Date ______ Class ______

SPECIAL CELL PROCESSES

In your textbook, read about the organization of cells, tissues, and organs in Section 2:3.

7. Place a check mark in the correct column for each phrase or diagram on the left.

	Tissue	Organ	Organ system
Groups of cells all doing the same job	✓		
Stomach, mouth, and intestines all working together			✓
Made up of a group of tissues		✓	
[diagram of cells]	✓		
Small intestine		✓	
[diagram of heart]		✓	
Leaf		✓	
Muscle	✓		
Bark	✓		
Outer surface of a leaf	✓		

8. How is an organ different from a tissue? A tissue is made up of only one kind of cell. An organ is made up of many different kinds of tissues that work together to perform a job. Because the different tissues in an organ are each made up of a different kind of cell, an organ is made up of different kinds of cells.

9. What is an organism? An organism is a living thing.

10. Compare a one-celled organism with a many-celled organism. In a one-celled organism, a single cell carries out all the activities of life. In a many-celled organism, cells are organized into groups and the cells of each group do special jobs.

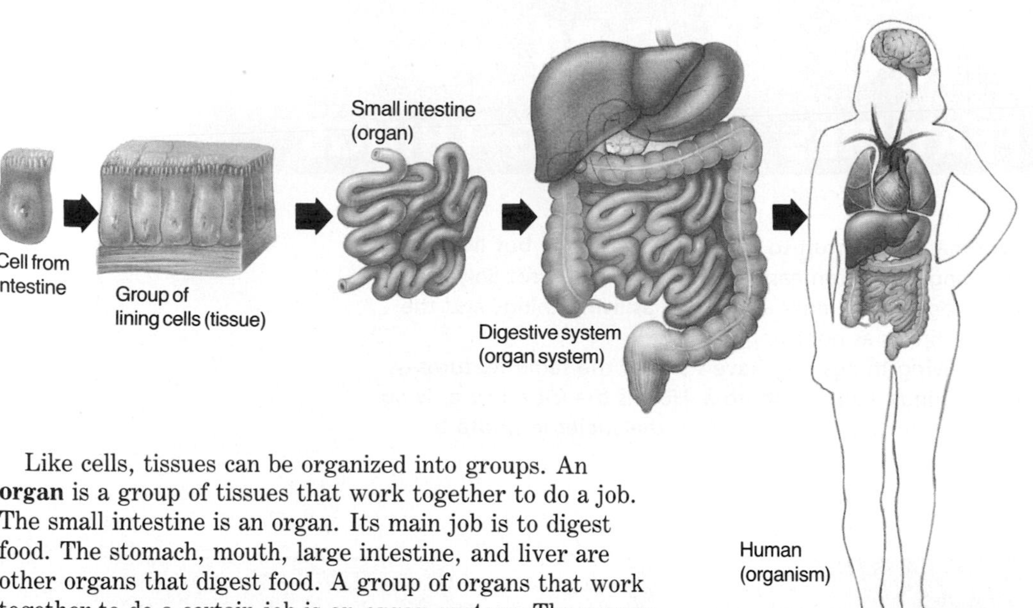

Figure 2-13 Living things (organisms) are organized into cells, tissues, organs, and organ systems.

Like cells, tissues can be organized into groups. An **organ** is a group of tissues that work together to do a job. The small intestine is an organ. Its main job is to digest food. The stomach, mouth, large intestine, and liver are other organs that digest food. A group of organs that work together to do a certain job is an **organ system.** The organs that work together to digest food are called the digestive system.

All the organ systems working together make up an organism (OR guh niz um). An **organism** is a living thing. Many organisms are made of only one cell. Yet, they have all the features of living things. Other organisms have organs and organ systems. Humans are organisms with several organ systems. Among other systems, humans have circulatory, reproductive, and nervous systems. These systems will be explained in Chapters 11, 15, and 24.

What is the relationship among cells, tissues, organs, and organ systems?

Check Your Understanding

11. How does diffusion make it possible for you to smell different odors?
12. In osmosis, which substance diffuses?
13. How are tissues and organs different?
14. **Critical Thinking:** What would happen if you placed a slice of cucumber in distilled water? (HINT: Distilled water is purer than the water inside the cucumber cells.)
15. **Biology and Reading:** What are the living parts that make up an organ system?

RETEACHING 6

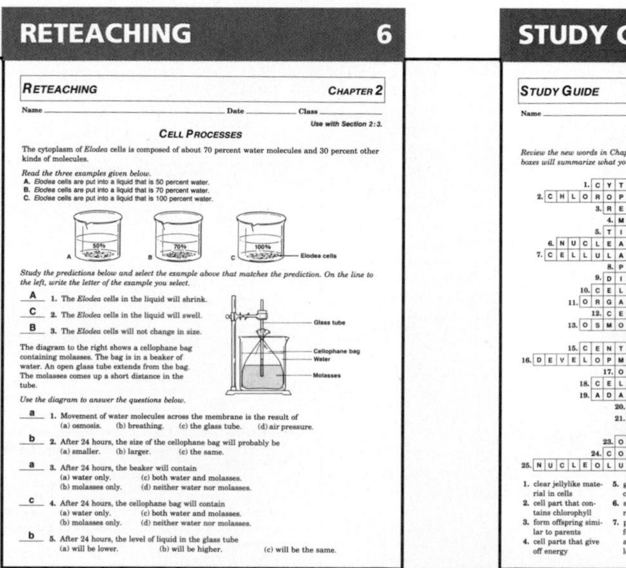

RETEACHING CHAPTER 2

Name ______ Date ______ Class ______

Use with Section 2:3.

CELL PROCESSES

The cytoplasm of *Elodea* cells is composed of about 70 percent water molecules and 30 percent other kinds of molecules.

Read the three examples given below.
A. *Elodea* cells are put into a liquid that is 50 percent water.
B. *Elodea* cells are put into a liquid that is 70 percent water.
C. *Elodea* cells are put into a liquid that is 100 percent water.

Study the predictions below and select the example above that matches the prediction. On the line to the left, write the letter of the example you select.

A 1. The *Elodea* cells in the liquid will shrink.
C 2. The *Elodea* cells in the liquid will swell.
B 3. The *Elodea* cells will not change in size.

The diagram to the right shows a cellophane bag containing molasses. The bag is in a beaker of water. An open glass tube extends from the bag. The molasses comes up a short distance in the tube.

Use the diagram to answer the questions below.

a 1. Movement of water molecules across the membrane is the result of (a) osmosis. (b) breathing. (c) the glass tube. (d) air pressure.
b 2. After 24 hours, the size of the cellophane bag will probably be (a) smaller. (b) larger. (c) the same.
a 3. After 24 hours, the beaker will contain (a) water only. (b) molasses only. (c) both water and molasses. (d) neither water nor molasses.
c 4. After 24 hours, the cellophane bag will contain (a) water only. (b) molasses only. (c) both water and molasses. (d) neither water nor molasses.
b 5. After 24 hours, the level of liquid in the glass tube (a) will be lower. (b) will be higher. (c) will be the same.

STUDY GUIDE 12

STUDY GUIDE CHAPTER 2

Name ______ Date ______ Class ______

VOCABULARY

Review the new words in Chapter 2 of your textbook. Then complete the puzzle. The letters in the dark boxes will summarize what you are studying in Chapter 2.

1. CYTOPLASM
2. CHLOROPLAST
3. REPRODUCE
4. MITOCHONDRIA
5. TISSUE
6. NUCLEAR MEMBRANE
7. CELLULAR RESPIRATION
8. PRODUCER
9. DIFFUSION
10. CELL MEMBRANE
11. ORGAN SYSTEM
12. CELL
13. OSMOSIS
14. VACUOLE
15. CENTRIOLE
16. DEVELOPMENT
17. ORGANISM
18. CELL WALL
19. ADAPTATION
20. CHROMOSOME
21. RIBOSOME
22. NUCLEUS
23. ORGAN
24. CONSUMER
25. NUCLEOLUS

1. clear jellylike material in cells
2. cell part that contains chlorophyll
3. form offspring similar to parents
4. cell parts that give off energy
5. group of similar cells carrying out a job
6. structure that surrounds the nucleus
7. process by which food is broken down and energy is released
8. living thing that makes its own food
9. movement of a substance from where there is a large amount to where there is a small amount of it
10. controls what moves into cells
11. group of organs working together
12. basic unit of all living things
13. movement of water across a membrane
14. stores water, food, and minerals
15. part near the nucleus that helps with reproduction
16. all the changes that occur as a living thing grows
17. living thing
18. thick outer covering of a plant cell
19. trait that helps a living thing survive
20. cell part with information that determines a living thing's traits
21. cell part where protein is made
22. controls the activities of the cell
23. group of tissues that work together
24. living thing that eats other living things
25. smaller body inside the nucleus that helps make ribosomes

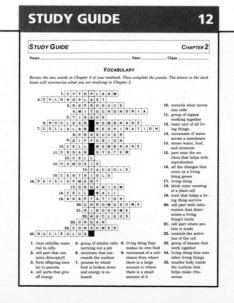

TEACH

Guided Practice

Have students write down their answers to the margin question: cells make up tissues, tissues make up organs, and organs make up organ systems.

Independent Practice

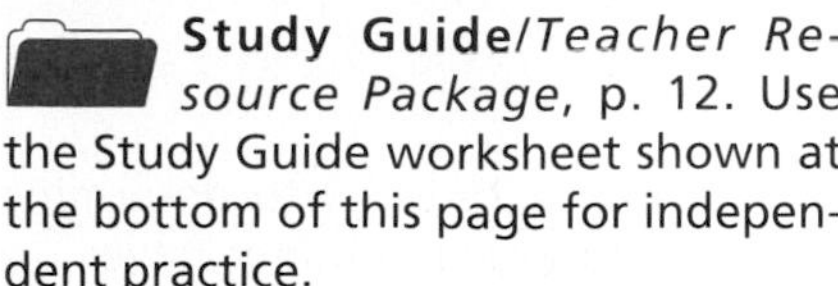

Study Guide/*Teacher Resource Package*, p. 12. Use the Study Guide worksheet shown at the bottom of this page for independent practice.

Check for Understanding

Have students respond to the first three questions in Check Your Understanding.

Reteach

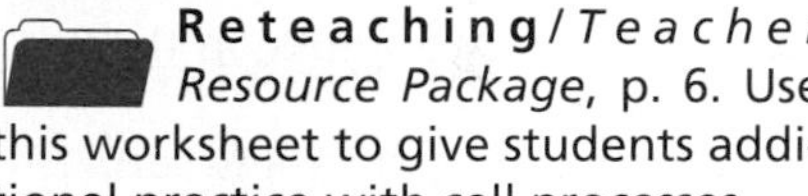

Reteaching/*Teacher Resource Package*, p. 6. Use this worksheet to give students additional practice with cell processes.

Extension: Assign Critical Thinking, Biology and Reading, or some of the **OPTIONS** available with this lesson.

3 APPLY

Brainstorming

Ask students how drying, smoking, and salting preserve foods.

4 CLOSE

Convergent Question

Ask why people cannot use ocean water for drinking.

Answers to Check Your Understanding

11. The molecules diffuse from where they are in large amounts to where they are in small amounts.
12. water
13. An organ is made up of tissues.
14. The slice of cucumber would swell up as water enters.
15. cells, tissues, and organs

Features of Living Things

Problem-solving Strategies

The following strategies can be used to solve the problems in this feature: guess and check, look for a pattern.

Hints

▶ Use pages 26 to 29 to determine what features living things have.

Solving the Problem

a. The icicle increases in size (grows).
b. The copier reproduces.
c. It responds to wind currents.
d. The car needs fuel like the body needs food.
e. It responds to smoke in the environment.
f. It gets energy from the sun.

PROBLEM SOLVING

FEATURES OF LIVING THINGS

It may be difficult to define the word *life*, but living things are often easy to recognize. You probably recognize the deer and plants as living things and the other objects as nonliving things.

Nonliving things may have some of the same features as living things. Look at photo a. How is the icicle like a living thing? What feature of life does the copier in photo b have?

a

b

42

In photo c you see a hot air balloon. How is it similar to a living thing? What feature of life can you identify in photo d? How is the smoke detector in photo e like a living thing? How is the solar panel in photo f like a living thing?

All of the things shown on these pages have features of living things, and yet they are different from the deer and the plants. How are the deer and the plants different from the other things?

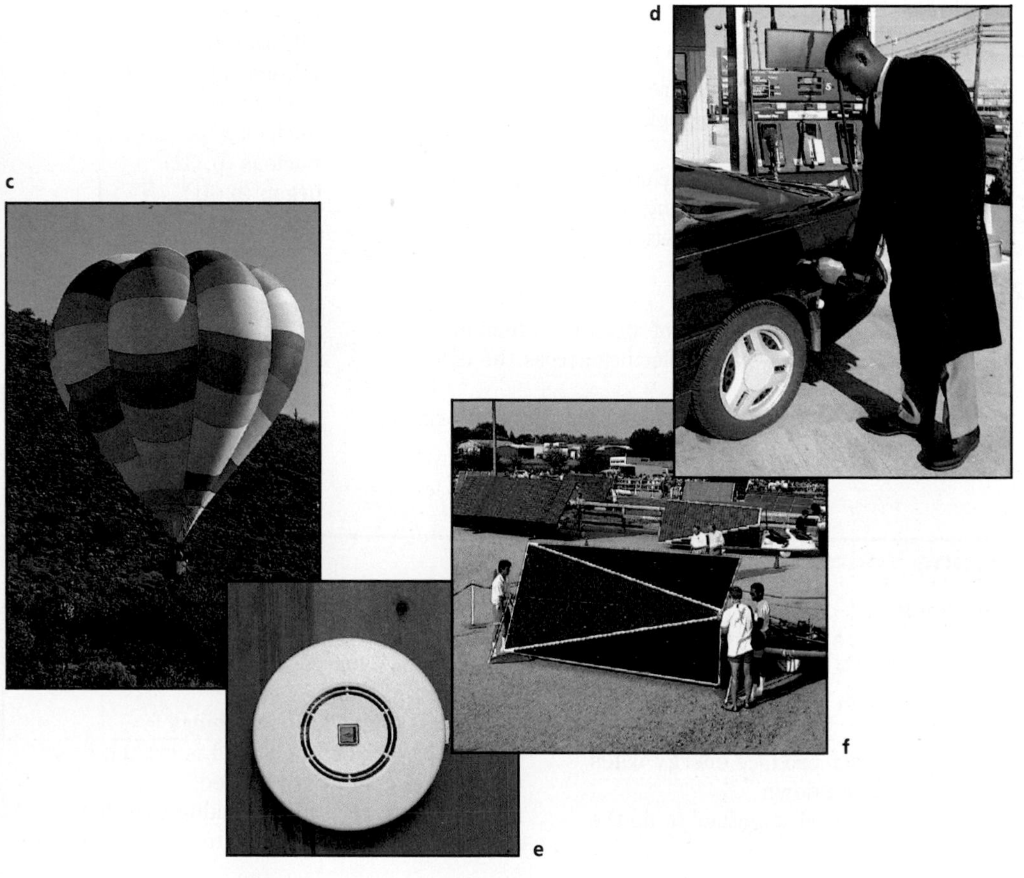
c d e f

Discussing the Problem

▶ Point out that even though non-living things have one or two features of living things, they cannot carry out the processes of life.

▶ Summarize the features of living things.

Extension: Show pictures of other nonliving things and ask students to identify the features each has. You could use a computer, a light, or crystals.

CHAPTER 2 REVIEW

Summary

Summary statements can be used by students to review the major concepts of the chapter.

Key Science Words

All boldfaced terms from the chapter are listed.

Testing Yourself

Using Words

1. chromosome
2. mitochondria
3. organ
4. chloroplast
5. diffusion
6. cell
7. cellular respiration
8. organ system
9. osmosis

Finding Main Ideas

10. p. 29; Living things respond to changes in the environment.
11. p. 4l; An organ system is a group of organs working together.
12. p. 35; Centrioles help with cell reproduction.
13. p. 39; Molecules pass through pores in a membrane.
14. p. 27; Cellular respiration is the process by which food is broken down and energy is released.
15. p. 30; A molecule is the smallest part of a compound.
16. p. 30; The elements carbon, hydrogen, oxygen, nitrogen, sulfur, and phosphorus make up 97 percent of living matter.
17. p. 31; Robert Hooke is the scientist who first observed cells.
18. p. 32; Chromosomes carry information that determines what traits a living thing will have.
19. p. 40; The water molecules are concentrated inside the cell and move out into the salt water where there is less concentration of water molecules.

Chapter 2 Review

Summary

2:1 Living Things and Their Parts

1. Living things have eight features in common. They reproduce, grow, develop, need food, use energy, have cells, respond, and are adapted to their environments.
2. Living things are made of matter. Six elements make up over 97 percent of the matter in living things.
3. The cell theory states: all livining things are made of one or more cells; cells are the basic units of structure and function in living things; all cells come from other cells.

2:2 Cell Parts and Their Jobs

4. The main parts of the cell are the cell membrane, nucleus, chromosomes, cytoplasm, ribosomes, mitochondria, and vacuoles.
5. The jobs of the cell parts include protection, the making of energy, the moving of materials into and out of the cell, and reproduction.

2:3 Special Cell Processes

6. Materials move into or out of a cell by diffusion.
7. The movement of water molecules across the cell membrane is osmosis.
8. Living things are organized into cells, tissues, organs, and organ systems.

Key Science Words

adaptation (p. 29)
cell (p. 27)
cell membrane (p. 32)
cellular respiration (p. 27)
cell wall (p. 35)
centriole (p. 35)
chloroplast (p. 35)
chromosome (p. 32)
consumer (p. 27)
cytoplasm (p. 32)
development (p. 26)
diffusion (p. 38)
mitochondria (p. 34)
nuclear membrane (p. 32)
nucleolus (p. 32)
nucleus (p. 32)
organ (p. 41)
organism (p. 41)
organ system (p. 41)
osmosis (p. 39)
producer (p. 27)
reproduce (p. 26)
ribosome (p. 34)
tissue (p. 40)
vacuole (p. 35)

Testing Yourself

Using Words

Choose the word from the list of Key Science Words that best fits the definition.

1. cell part with information that determines a living thing's trait
2. cell parts that produce energy when food is broken down
3. tissues that work together to do the same job
4. green part inside a plant cell
5. movement of substances, such as oxygen, into a cell
6. basic unit of living things
7. process in which food is broken down and energy is released
8. group of organs working together
9. diffusion of water into or out of a cell

Review

Testing Yourself *continued*

Finding Main Ideas

List the page number where each main idea below is found. Then, explain each main idea.

10. what living things respond to
11. what an organ system is
12. the function of centrioles
13. how molecules pass through a membrane
14. how living things get energy from food
15. what a molecule is
16. the six elements that make up over 97 percent of living matter
17. the scientist who first observed cells
18. the job of chromosomes
19. why cucumbers wilt in salt water

Using Main Ideas

Answer these questions by referring to the page number after the question.

20. How are growing and developing different? (p. 26)
21. Why are humans called organisms? (p. 41)
22. Why will a stalk of celery put in salt water begin to wilt? (p. 40)
23. How do your school and a cell compare? Match the job of each cell part with a part of your school that has a similar job. (pp. 32-35)
    (a) nucleus 1. main office
    (b) vacuole 2. cafeteria
    (c) chloroplasts 3. furnace room
    (d) mitochondria 4. lockers
24. How is osmosis a special kind of diffusion? (p. 39)
25. What is the function of pores in a cell membrane? (p. 39)
26. What characteristics of living things does a cell have? (pp. 26, 27, 29)

Skill Review

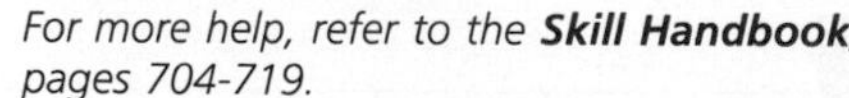

*For more help, refer to the **Skill Handbook**, pages 704-719.*

1. **Make and use tables:** Make a table to show the features of living things shown by a cat, guppy, bird, and maple tree. In your table give examples for each feature of living things shown by these organisms.
2. **Classify:** Classify the following as elements or compounds: hydrogen, oxygen, water, carbon, carbon dioxide, nitrogen, and phosphorus.
3. **Formulate a model:** Construct and label a three-dimensional model of a plant or animal cell.
4. **Infer:** Compare the growth of a single-celled organism with that of a many-celled organism. What is the difference between the two types of growth?

Finding Out More

Critical Thinking

1. Explain why some cells have more mitochondria than others.
2. Make a time line showing the events that led to the cell theory.

Applications

1. What kinds of tissues and organs are you eating when you eat a green salad?
2. Report on ways that desert organisms such as cacti and camels conserve and use water as adaptations for survival.

Using Main Ideas

20. Growing is increasing in size. Developing is changing in shape and form.
21. The human body is a living thing made up of organ systems such as the circulatory, reproductive, and nervous systems.
22. Water will move across a membrane from where it is in large amounts to where it is in small amounts.
23. (a) Nucleus and (1) main office have similar jobs, as do (b) vacuole and (4) lockers, (c) chloroplasts and (2) cafeteria, and (d) mitochondria and (3) furnace room.
24. Diffusion is the movement of molecules, but osmosis is the movement of water molecules.
25. Pores in a membrane allow molecules to pass through.
26. A cell has all the characteristics of living things, including respiration, growth, and reproduction.

Skill Review

1. Have students use the living things as headings across the top, and list the features of living things down the side.
2. Hydrogen, oxygen, carbon, nitrogen, and phosphorus are elements; water and carbon dioxide are compounds.
3. Students should be creative and may use clay, yarn, pipe cleaners, and even edible items. Models should have a key to the cell parts.
4. Many-celled organisms grow by increasing the number of cells; single-celled organisms do not.

Finding Out More

Critical Thinking

1. Cells that move use more energy and have more mitochondria. A muscle cell would have more mitochondria than a skin cell.
2. The time line should begin with 1665. Students should research the cell theory to fill in the time line.

Applications

1. Leaves and stems are tissues, and leaves and roots are organs.
2. Cacti spines are modified leaves that give off almost no water. Camels are able to store quantities of water within their bodies.

Chapter Review/*Teacher Resource Package*, pp. 6-7.

Chapter Test/*Teacher Resource Package*, pp. 8-10.

Chapter Test/*Computer Test Bank*

Classification

PLANNING GUIDE

CONTENT	TEXT FEATURES	TEACHER RESOURCE PACKAGE	OTHER COMPONENTS
(1/2 day) 3:1 Why Things Are Grouped Classifying in Everyday Life How Grouping Helps Us	Lab 3-1: *Classifying,* p. 49 Career Close-Up: *Wildlife Photographer,* p. 50 Check Your Understanding, p. 50	Reteaching: *Grouping Living Things,* p. 7 Study Guide: *Why Things Are Grouped,* pp. 13-14 Lab 3-1: *Classifying,* pp. 9-10	**Laboratory Manual:** *How Can Paper Objects Be Grouped?* p. 17
(1 day) 3:2 Methods of Classification Early Classification The Beginning of Modern Classification	Skill Check: *Understand Science Words,* p. 55 Mini Lab: *How Did Aristotle Classify Animals?* p. 53 Lab 3-2: *Common Names,* p. 52 Idea Map, p. 53 Check Your Understanding, p. 55	Focus: *Classifying Dinosaurs,* p. 5 Reteaching: *Methods of Classification,* p. 8 Study Guide: *Methods of Classification,* p. 15 Lab 3-2: *Common Names,* pp. 11-12 Transparency Master: *Classification of Living Things,* p. 11	
(2 1/2 days) 3:3 How Scientists Classify Today Classifying Based on How Organisms Are Related Other Evidence Used in Classifying Scientific Names Come from Classification Why Scientific Names Are Used Five Kingdom Classification	Skill Check: *Classify,* p. 60 Mini Lab: *What Kingdom?* p. 58 Technology: *Mussels of the Deep,* p. 61 Idea Map, p. 62 Check Your Understanding, p. 62	Application: *Many Ways to Classify,* p. 3 Enrichment: *The Classification of Animals,* p. 3 Reteaching: *The Five Kingdoms,* p. 9 Critical Thinking/Problem Solving: *What Traits Can You Use to Classify Organisms?* p. 3 Skill: *The Five Kingdoms of Living Things,* p. 3 Study Guide: *How Scientists Classify,* pp. 16-17 Study Guide: *Vocabulary,* p. 18	Color Transparency 3: *Five Kingdoms* **Laboratory Manual:** *How Can Living Things Be Grouped?* p. 21
Chapter Review	Summary Key Science Words Testing Yourself Finding Main Ideas Using Main Ideas Skill Review	Chapter Review, pp. 11-12 Chapter Test, pp. 13-15 Unit Test, pp. 16-17	**Test Bank**

MATERIALS NEEDED

LAB 3-1, p. 49	LAB 3-2, p. 52	MARGIN FEATURES
envelope with 12 different items	state map	Skill Check, p. 55 dictionary Skill Check, p. 60 10 leaves key or field guide Mini Lab, p. 53 pencil paper Mini Lab, p. 58 pencil paper

OBJECTIVES

SECTION	OBJECTIVE	OBJECTIVES CORRELATION: CHECK YOUR UNDERSTANDING	CHAPTER REVIEW	TRP CHAPTER REVIEW	TRP CHAPTER TEST
3:1	1. **Give** examples of items in daily life that are grouped.	2, 3	13, 22	1	50
	2. **Explain** how and why we classify things.	1, 4	3, 7, 16, 20	3, 7, 9, 13, 14,15, 16, 19, 21, 26, 28	2, 11, 12, 13, 14, 15, 16, 17, 18, 19, 20
3:2	3. **Explain** Aristotle's classification of living things.	6, 9	11, 19	2	3, 7, 29
	4. **Compare** Linnaeus' system of classification with Aristotle's.	7, 10	1, 2, 4, 17, 25	4	8
	5. **Name** the levels of classification that are used today.	8	14	17, 24	5, 21, 39
	6. **List** traits used in classifying living things.	11, 14	18, 24	10, 12	9, 33
3:3	7. **State** the function of scientific names.	12	5, 6, 15, 21	5, 8, 20, 22	1, 4, 6, 10, 35, 36, 37, 38, 40
	8. **List** the five kingdoms scientists recognize today.	13	8, 9, 10, 12, 23	6, 18, 23	22, 23, 24, 25, 26, 27, 28, 30, 31, 32, 34

Classification

CHAPTER OVERVIEW

Key Concepts

In this chapter, students will study why things are grouped in everyday life. They will learn about the history of classification, how organisms are classified, how scientific names come from classification, and why scientific names are used. They will be introduced to the five kingdom classification system.

Key Science Words

animal	order
class	phylum
classify	plant
family	protist
fungus	scientific name
genus	species
kingdom	trait
moneran	

Skill Development

In Lab 3-1, students will **classify** and **observe** some common objects. In Lab 3-2, they will **classify, communicate,** and **make a table** of name places from a map. In the Skill Check on page 55, students will **understand** the **science word** *phylum.* In the Skill Check on page 60, they will use a key to **classify** leaves. In the Mini Lab on page 53, students will **infer** using Aristotle's classification scheme. In the Mini Lab on page 58, they will **classify** an imaginary organism.

CHAPTER PREVIEW

Chapter Content

Review this outline for Chapter 3 before you read the chapter.

3:1 Why Things Are Grouped
- Classifying in Everyday Life
- How Grouping Helps Us

3:2 Methods of Classification
- Early Classification
- The Beginning of Modern Classification

3:3 How Scientists Classify Today
- Classifying Based on How Organisms Are Related
- Other Evidence Used in Classifying
- Scientific Names Come from Classification
- Why Scientific Names Are Used
- Five Kingdom Classification

Skills in this Chapter

The skills that you will use in this chapter are listed below.

- In **Lab 3-1,** you will classify and observe. In **Lab 3-2,** you will classify, communicate, and make a table.
- In the **Skill Checks,** you will classify and understand science words.
- In the **Mini Labs,** you will infer and classify.

Tubeworms

46

Bridging

Living organisms are classified according to similarities and differences. Bridge this chapter with the section on scientific method in Chapter 1, and relate the classifying of living organisms to data collection. Cell structure is also used in classification. Bridge this section with cells in Chapter 2.

Chapter **3**

Classification

What features do biologists use to group living things? You know that most plants are green and do not move around. You also know that most animals are not green and do move around. The tubeworm on the left lives in the water attached to one spot. It is not green. Is a sponge a plant or an animal? The euglena in the smaller photo is green and moves around in the water. Is it a plant or an animal, or does it belong to some other group?

Biologists have a system for grouping living things. Each living thing has a specific name that biologists all over the world understand. In this chapter, you will learn why we group living things and about the system used to group them.

Try This!

Why do we have two names? Choose a first name that you hear often. Make a list of all the people you know who have the same first name. Can you see why a two-name system is needed?

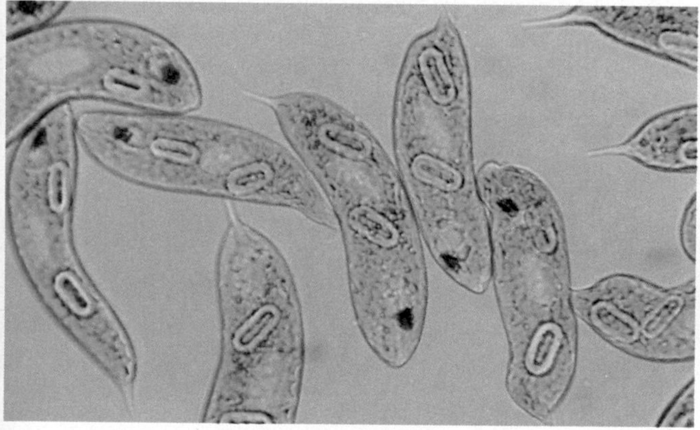

Euglena, 450x

GETTING STARTED

Using the Photos

By looking at the photos, students will see that classifying organisms is more complicated than they thought. Have them try to classify each organism as plant or animal.

MOTIVATION/Try This!

Why do we have two names? When students have completed the chapter opening activity, they will be able to **infer** why two names are needed to identify a person. Then they will apply this to the two-name system used in classification.

Chapter Preview

Have students study the chapter outline to see how the chapter is organized. This chapter discusses how grouping is used. This discussion is followed by the history of classification. The last section explains how scientists classify and name living organisms.

Misconception

Students often think that all organisms fit perfectly into one of the five kingdoms. Point out examples of organisms that have traits of more than one kingdom, such as euglena and slime molds.

3:1 Why Things Are Grouped

PREPARATION

Materials Needed

Make copies of the Application, Study Guide, Reteaching, and Lab worksheets in the *Teacher Resource Package*.

▶ Prepare envelopes for Lab 3-1.

Key Science Words

classify
trait

Process Skills

In Lab 3-1, students will classify and observe.

1 FOCUS

▶ The objectives are listed on the student page. Remind students to preview these objectives as a guide to this numbered section.

MOTIVATION/Demonstration

To introduce how items can be classified, ask each student to place one shoe in a pile in the middle of the floor. Begin sorting the shoes into two piles by using a feature such as right or left shoes or running and nonrunning shoes. Explain that you are using a certain trait to do the sorting. When someone knows what the trait is, have that person suggest another way to sort the shoes. Divide each of the piles further, one pile at a time, and make a simple key on the chalkboard.

Guided Practice

Have students write down their answers to the margin questions: in the produce and bread sections; by a system of numbering.

Objectives

1. **Give examples** of items in daily life that are grouped.
2. **Explain** how and why we classify things.

Key Science Words

classify
trait

3:1 Why Things Are Grouped

How often do you classify things? You probably classify things more often than you think. To **classify** means to group things together based on similarities.

Classifying in Everyday Life

If you were opening a sports store, how would you group the equipment in Figure 3-1? You might put the shoes in one place and the balls in another. You might want items for a certain sport grouped together.

Where would you find lettuce and bread in a grocery store?

Many things in our daily lives have been grouped for us. Think about how food is grouped in a grocery store. Frozen foods, meats, produce, bakery items, and canned foods are found in separate areas.

What subjects are you taking this year? Don't you group your courses? Spanish, French, and German are language courses. Typing and bookkeeping are business courses.

How Grouping Helps Us

There are several reasons to classify things. One reason is to put things in order so that they become easier to find.

How are books arranged in a library?

Your school library must have thousands of books. They are arranged by a system of numbering that makes it easier to find a certain book. Think of trying to find a classroom with the room numbers out of order. Could you find a phone number in a phone book if the names were not in alphabetical order?

A second reason we classify things is to show that they share certain traits. A **trait** is a feature that a thing has. In a library, you see biographies grouped together. What trait do they share?

Figure 3-1 Many everyday objects, such as this sports equipment, are classified.

OPTIONS

Science Background

The science of classifying living things is called taxonomy. More than one and one-half million organisms have been classified. Organisms are classified based on evidence that indicates how closely related they are.

How Can Paper Objects Be Grouped?/*Lab Manual*, pp. 17-20. Use this lab as an extension to classifying everyday objects.

Lab 3–1 Classifying

Problem: How can some common objects be classified?

Skills

classify, observe

Materials

envelope that contains 12 items

Procedure

1. Copy the diagram.
2. Place the objects from your envelope on your desk.
3. Make a list of the objects. Your teacher will help you with their names.
4. These objects will be called Kingdom Objects. List the objects under Kingdom Objects in your diagram.
5. Sort the 12 objects into two groups on your desk. The objects in each group must have a common trait.
6. Call each of these two groups a phylum. Use the common trait as the name of the phylum. Place the phylum name for each group on your diagram.
7. On the diagram, write the name of each object that you placed in Phylum 1 and in Phylum 2.
8. Sort the objects of Phylum 1 into two groups. Each of the two groups must have a common trait.
9. Call each of these two groups a class. Use the common trait as the name of the class. Place the class names for Phylum 1 on your diagram under Classes A and B.
10. Sort the objects in Phylum 2 into two groups. Each of these two groups must have a common trait.
11. Each of these groups represents a class. Place the class names for Phylum 2 on your diagram under Classes C and D.
12. Put the items back into the envelope and return the envelope to your teacher.

Kingdom Objects ____
- Phylum 1 ____
  - Class A ____
  - Class B ____
- Phylum 2 ____
  - Class C ____
  - Class D ____

Data and Observations

1. What traits did you use to classify the kingdom objects into two phyla?
2. What is the name of Phylum 1? Phylum 2?
3. What are the names of Class A and Class B?
4. What are the names of Class C and Class D?
5. What trait do all four classes have in common?
6. What traits do Classes A and B have in common?
7. What traits do Classes C and D have in common?

Analyze and Apply

1. At what level of classification, phylum or class, did all objects share more traits?
2. At what level of classification, phylum or class, did all objects share fewer traits?
3. How could you use the classification method in this lab to group a collection of compact discs?

Extension

Classify the items in your bedroom closet using the same method that you used in this lab.

ANSWERS

Data and Observations

1. metals or nonmetals, flat or not flat, pointed or not pointed
2. same as number 1
3. If the phylum was metals, the class names could be round, not round; steel, not steel.
4. If the phylum was nonmetals, the class names could be white, not white; glass, not glass.
5. All are objects.
6. If the phylum was metals, then classes A and B would both be metals and so on.
7. If the phylum was nonmetals, then classes C and D would both be nonmetals, and so on.

Analyze and Apply

1. phylum
2. class
3. Students should classify their discs first by type of music, then by artist, and so on.

Lab 3-1 Classifying

Overview

In this lab, students will make their own classification system using traits to group common items.

Objectives: Upon completing this lab, students will be able to (1) **devise** a classification system (2) **infer** that any classification system can be correct if proper criteria are followed in formulating it.

Time Allotment: 45 minutes

Preparation

▶ Have 1 envelope for each lab group containing:

hairpin	bolt
paper clip	brass fastener
toothpick	rubber band
nail	yarn (2 cm)
button	glass slide
washer	seed
nut	key

▶ **Alternate Materials:** Similar objects may be substituted.

Lab 3-1 worksheet/*Teacher Resource Package*, pp. 9-10.

Teaching the Lab

▶ Be sure students understand that there is no one correct classification for their objects.

▶ **Troubleshooting:** Make sure all objects in Phylum 1 are separated before students work on Phylum 2.

Cooperative Learning: Divide the class into groups of two students. For more information, see pp. 22T-23T in the Teacher Guide.

Career Close-Up

Wildlife Photographer

Background

The training for a wildlife photographer usually includes training after high school. Success in this field depends on some knowledge of biology.

Related Careers

wildlife illustrator, wildlife biologist

Job Requirements

photography training, an artistic eye, patience

For More Information

Professional Photographers of America
1090 Express Way
Des Plaines, IL 60018

Independent Practice

Study Guide/*Teacher Resource Package*, pp. 13-14. Use the Study Guide worksheets shown at the bottom of this page for independent practice.

3 APPLY

Compare the Library of Congress classification system with the Dewey decimal system.

4 CLOSE

ACTIVITY/Brainstorming

Have students give examples of things they classify.

Answers to Check Your Understanding

1. feature of something; mammals/hair; birds/feathers
2. languages, sports, subjects
3. to make things easier to find; to show how things are alike
4. round: nucleus, nucleolus; long and thin: chromosomes
5. 1 500 000; 1.5×10^6

Career Close-Up

Wildlife Photographer

Photographing wildlife is often a challenging occupation.

John's biology teacher invited a wildlife photographer to visit his class. The photographer brought slides and prints of many living things. Many photographs of flowers and insects were made with a close-up lens or a zoom lens. The photographer showed the students how to use a camera attachment on a light microscope. She told them that her work often took her to outdoor settings.

Students wanted to know about the training needed to be a photographer. She told them that she had taken photography and natural science courses in high school. Then she had taken several courses at a community college. She explained that in this field success depends on a person knowing the subject matter well.

Other students wanted to know where her work was used. She showed them magazines and books that contained her photographs.

Biologists classify living things. Doing so puts organisms in order. It also shows how they are alike. There are over one and one-half million known kinds of living things. It would be impossible to find information about them if they were not grouped in some way.

Check Your Understanding

1. What is meant by a trait? Give two examples of traits.
2. Give an example of something at school that is classified.
3. Give two reasons why things are classified.
4. **Critical Thinking:** Group the parts of an animal cell based on their shapes.
5. **Biology and Math:** What are two other ways to write the number one and one-half million?

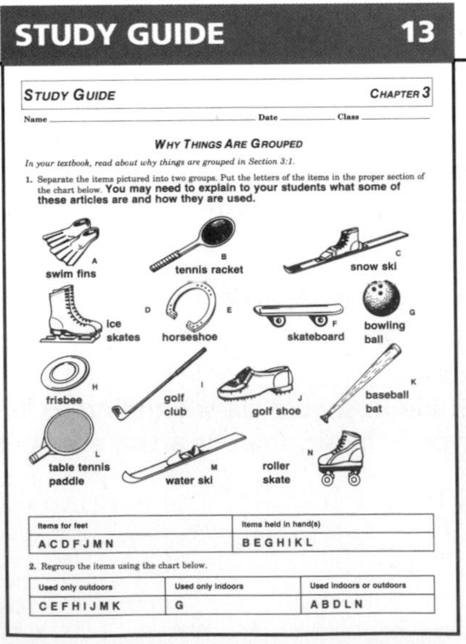

STUDY GUIDE 13

STUDY GUIDE — CHAPTER 3

Name ______ Date ______ Class ______

WHY THINGS ARE GROUPED

In your textbook, read about why things are grouped in Section 3:1.

1. Separate the items pictured into two groups. Put the letters of the items in the proper section of the chart below. **You may need to explain to your students what some of these articles are and how they are used.**

Items for feet	Items held in hand(s)
A C D F J M N	B E G H I K L

2. Regroup the items using the chart below.

Used only outdoors	Used only indoors	Used indoors or outdoors
C E F H I J M K	G	A B D L N

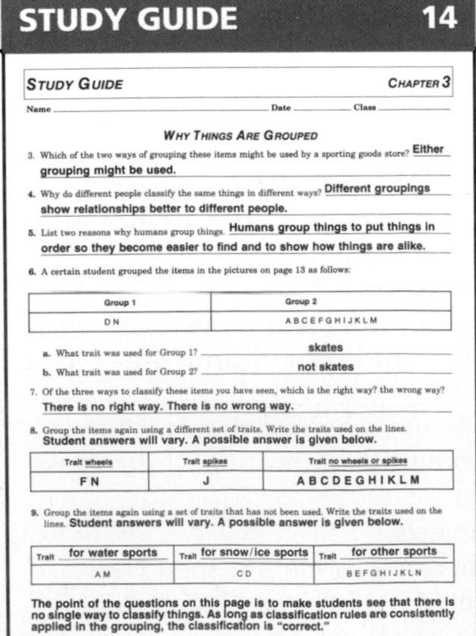

STUDY GUIDE 14

STUDY GUIDE — CHAPTER 3

Name ______ Date ______ Class ______

WHY THINGS ARE GROUPED

3. Which of the two ways of grouping these items might be used by a sporting goods store? **Either grouping might be used.**
4. Why do different people classify the same things in different ways? **Different groupings show relationships better to different people.**
5. List two reasons why humans group things. **Humans group things to put things in order so they become easier to find and to show how things are alike.**
6. A certain student grouped the items in the pictures on page 13 as follows:

Group 1	Group 2
D N	A B C E F G H I J K L M

a. What trait was used for Group 1? **skates**

b. What trait was used for Group 2? **not skates**

7. Of the three ways to classify these items you have seen, which is the right way? the wrong way? **There is no right way. There is no wrong way.**
8. Group the items again using a different set of traits. Write the traits used on the lines. **Student answers will vary. A possible answer is given below.**

Trait wheels	Trait spikes	Trait no wheels or spikes
F N	J	A B C D E G H I K L M

9. Group the items again using a set of traits that has not been used. Write the traits used on the lines. **Student answers will vary. A possible answer is given below.**

Trait for water sports	Trait for snow/ice sports	Trait for other sports
A M	C D	B E F G H I J K L N

The point of the questions on this page is to make students see that there is no single way to classify things. As long as classification rules are consistently applied in the grouping, the classification is "correct."

3:2 Methods of Classification

For hundreds of years, people have been grouping living things. The job has not been easy. What makes the job of classifying hard is that scientists do not always agree on how to group living things.

Objectives

3. **Explain** Aristotle's classification of living things.
4. **Compare** Linnaeus' system of classification with Aristotle's.
5. **Name** the levels of classification that are used today.

Early Classification

Over 2000 years ago, a Greek scientist named Aristotle (AIR uh staht ul) was one of the first people to classify living things. He noticed that living things fit into two main groups—plant and animal. Most plants were green and didn't move. Most animals weren't green and did move.

Aristotle next divided all animals into three groups. He based his groups on where the animals lived as shown in Figure 3-2. Animals that lived in water went into one group. Animals that lived on land went into a second group. Animals that lived in the air and could fly made up a third group.

Aristotle then worked out a system for grouping plants. He based it on size of the plant and pattern of growth. You can see in Figure 3-2 that plants were placed into three smaller groups. Tall plants with one trunk were put into a tree group. Medium plants with many trunks were put into a shrub group. A privet hedge is an example of a shrub. Small plants with soft stems went into an herb group. Herbs included grasses and wildflowers.

Key Science Words

kingdom
phylum
class
order
family
genus
species

How did Aristotle divide his animal group?

Figure 3-2 Aristotle grouped animals into three groups and plants into three groups.

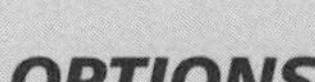

FOCUS 5

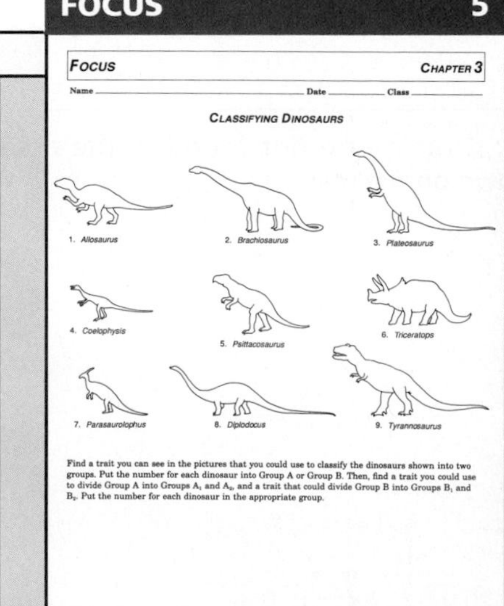

FOCUS CHAPTER 3

Name ____ Date ____ Class ____

CLASSIFYING DINOSAURS

1. Allosaurus 2. Brachiosaurus 3. Plateosaurus 4. Coelophysis 5. Psittacosaurus 6. Triceratops 7. Parasaurolophus 8. Diplodocus 9. Tyrannosaurus

Find a trait you can see in the pictures that you could use to classify the dinosaurs shown into two groups. Put the number for each dinosaur into Group A or Group B. Then, find a trait you could use to divide Group A into Groups A_1 and A_2, and a trait that could divide Group B into Groups B_1 and B_2. Put the number for each dinosaur in the appropriate group.

OPTIONS

Science Background

Aristotle's classification system remained in use almost 2000 years. In the 16th and 17th centuries, there was renewed interest in classification when European explorers brought back many new unidentified plant and animal specimens from other lands. In the 17th century, John Ray developed an improved classification system. He classified plants according to the structure of the seed and gave each organism a Latin name.

3:2 Methods of Classification

PREPARATION

Materials Needed

Make copies of the Focus, Study Guide, Reteaching, and Lab worksheets in the *Teacher Resource Package*.

▶ Gather maps for Lab 3-2.

Key Science Words

kingdom
phylum
class
order
family
genus
species

Process Skills

In Lab 3-2, students will classify, communicate, and make a table. In the Mini Lab, students will infer. In the Skill Check, students will understand science words.

1 FOCUS

▶ The objectives are listed on the student page. Remind students to preview these objectives as a guide to this numbered section.

ACTIVITY/Brainstorming

In groups of five, give students two minutes to brainstorm ways that newspapers, magazines, motor vehicles, sports, and restaurants make use of classification.

Focus/*Teacher Resource Package*, p. 5. Use the Focus transparency shown at the bottom of this page to introduce classification of organisms.

Guided Practice

Have students write down their answers to the margin question: Animals were divided into three groups — animals that lived on the ground, animals that lived in water, and animals that lived in the air and flew.

Lab 3-2 Common Names

Overview

In this lab, students will learn that some places are named for plants and animals. They will see that common names are used.

Objectives: Upon completing this lab, students will be able to: (1) **recognize** that names of living things are used to name places and (2) **relate** that common names are used more by people who are not scientists.

Time Allotment: 35 minutes

Preparation

▶ **Alternate Materials:** Any map may be used.

Lab 3-2 worksheet/*Teacher Resource Package,* pp. 11-12.

Teaching the Lab

▶ Spend some time with students to develop map-reading skills. Point out highways, railroads, rivers, elevations, and parks.

▶ You might want to make an overhead transparency of a map of your area.

Cooperative Learning: Divide the class into groups of two students. For more information, see pp. 22T-23T in the Teacher Guide.

▶ **Troubleshooting:** Check the map to make sure there are places named for plants and animals.

Common Names — Lab 3–2

Problem: How many places are named for animals or plants?

Skills

classify, communicate, make a table

Materials

state map

Procedure

1. **Make a table** in your notebook in which to record your observations. Use the headings Name and Type of Place in your table.
2. Use the map on this page or your state map to find each city or town that has the name of a plant or animal as part of its name. Record the names in your table.
3. Place a (C) after the name so you will know it is a city or town.
4. Use the map to find state or national parks, rivers, lakes, and historical places that have a plant or animal name as part of their names.
5. Record the names of the parks, rivers, lakes, and historical places in your table. Put a (P) after parks, (R) after rivers, (H) after historical places, and (L) after lakes.

Data and Observations

1. Were animal names or plant names used more often on your map?
2. Which animal name appeared most often on your map?
3. Which plant name appeared most?

Analyze and Apply

1. Why do you suppose humans use certain animal and plant names for cities, rivers, and parks?
2. Do cities, parks, or bodies of water seem to have more plant and animal names?
3. Why do humans use the common names of plants and animals rather than the scientific names to name places?
4. **Apply:** Would you expect to find a town called Giraffesville on your map? Explain.

Extension

Communicate: Make a list of other common themes that are used in naming places, for example Indian names. Share your list with the class.

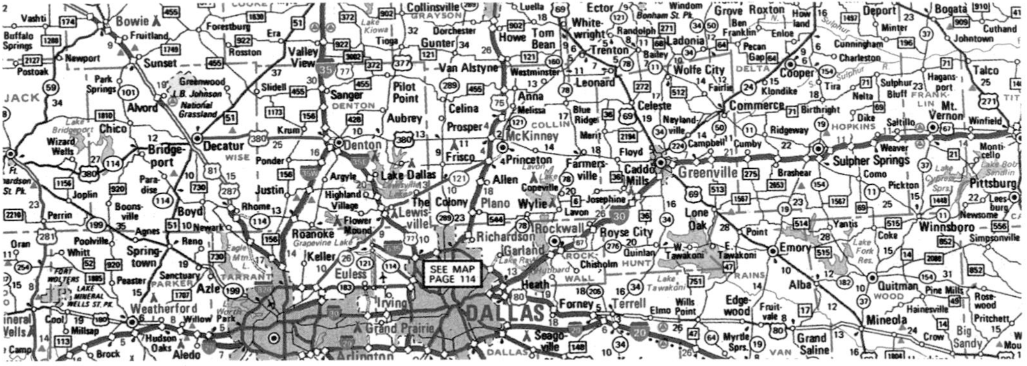

ANSWERS

Data and Observations

1. Answers for this activity will vary according to the map used.
2. Answers will vary according to map used.
3. Answers will vary according to map used.

Analyze and Apply

1. Students may answer that people name places after things with which they are most familiar.
2. Answers may vary.
3. Common names are more familiar.
4. No. Giraffes are not found in the area shown on the map.

The Beginning of Modern Classification

Scientists used Aristotle's system of classification for hundreds of years. However, as scientists found more and more living things, Aristotle's system became less useful. Many of the newly discovered living things did not fit into his system. Many scientists began to question the system because different traits were used to group plants and animals. A useful classification system should use the same traits for classifying all groups.

In 1735, Carolus Linnaeus (lin NAY us) developed a new classification system. He first placed living things into two main groups. He called these groups kingdoms. A **kingdom** is the largest group of living things. Plants made up one kingdom. Animals made up the other kingdom. Linnaeus placed living things with similar traits into the same group and called this group a species. He used very specific traits for his groups. For example, he used flower parts to group plant species. He placed similar species into a larger group called a genus (JEE nus).

Through his work, Linnaeus made a number of important changes in Aristotle's system.

1. He classified plants and animals into more groups.
2. He based his system on specific traits.
3. He gave organisms names that described their traits. These names had two parts. All living things still have two-part names.

How do the classification systems of Aristotle and Linnaeus compare?

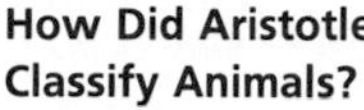

Mini Lab

How Did Aristotle Classify Animals?

Infer: Make a list of animals that you have seen or that you know about from reading magazines and watching television. Classify the animals the way Aristotle would have. *For more help, refer to the* ***Skill Handbook****, pages 706-711.*

Idea Map

Early Classification

- Early classification
  - Aristotle
    - plant
      - trees
      - shrubs
      - herbs
    - animal
      - water
      - land
      - air
  - Linnaeus
    - plant kingdom
      - genus
      - species
    - animal kingdom
      - genus
      - species

Study Tip: Use this idea map as you study the development of classification systems. Aristotle and Linnaeus developed early classification systems.

2 TEACH

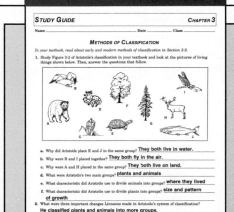

MOTIVATION/Field Trip

Visit a local zoo. Ask students to classify the animals into a phylum. Compare answers in the classroom.

Concept Development

▶ Point out that living things are first placed into large groups. Each large group is then divided into smaller groups.

▶ Emphasize that Linnaeus first based his classification system on flower structures only. He later included other plant structures.

Guided Practice

Have students write down their answers to the margin question: Linnaeus; system is more precise than Aristotle's. Linnaeus used specific traits to group organisms.

Mini Lab

Students should place the animals in groups based on whether they live in water, on land, or fly.

Idea Map

Have students use the idea map as a study guide to the major concepts of this section.

Independent Practice

Study Guide/*Teacher Resource Package*, p. 15. Use the Study Guide worksheet shown at the bottom of this page for independent practice.

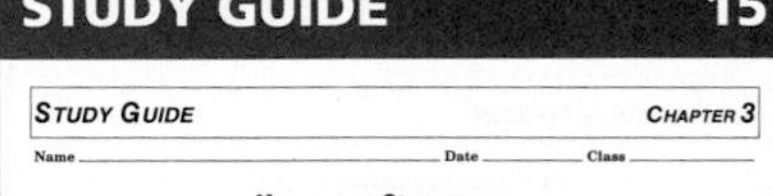

STUDY GUIDE 15

STUDY GUIDE CHAPTER 3

Name ______ Date ______ Class ______

METHODS OF CLASSIFICATION

In your textbook, read about early and modern methods of classification in Section 3:2.

1. Study Figure 3-2 of Aristotle's classification in your textbook and look at the pictures of living things shown below. Then, answer the questions that follow.

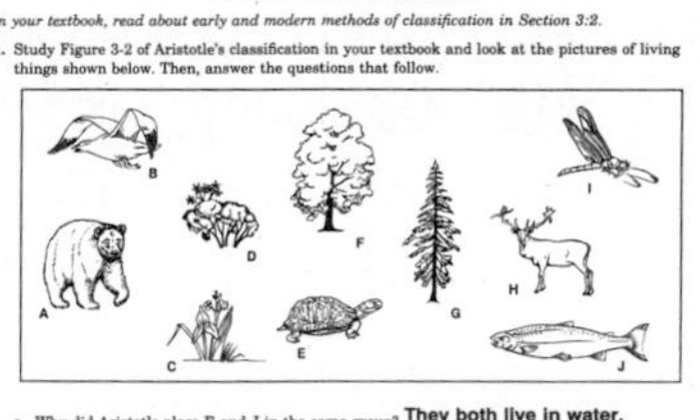

a. Why did Aristotle place E and J in the same group? They both live in water.
b. Why were B and I placed together? They both fly in the air.
c. Why were A and H placed in the same group? They both live on land.
d. What were Aristotle's two main groups? plants and animals
e. What characteristic did Aristotle use to divide animals into groups? where they lived
f. What characteristic did Aristotle use to divide plants into groups? size and pattern of growth

2. What were three important changes Linnaeus made in Aristotle's system of classification?
He classified plants and animals into more groups.
He based his system on specific traits.
He gave organisms names that described their traits.

3. Number these classification divisions in order from the smallest (1) to the largest (7).
1 species 6 phylum 3 family
7 kingdom 4 order 2 genus 5 class

OPTIONS

ACTIVITY/Demonstration

Present students with at least one representative of each kingdom. For the Kingdom Monera, this will need to be done with a picture. Ask students to write descriptions of what they can see from the specimens and pictures in order to describe the kingdom.

TEACH

Check for Understanding

Give students examples of plants and ask which Aristotle would have grouped together. Then ask which Linnaeus would have grouped together.

Reteach

Have students outline how Aristotle divided living things into groups and then compare his system with that of Linnaeus. Outlines should show living things divided into two groups—plants and animals. The animal division should be subdivided into water, land, and air (where they live); the plant division should be subdivided into tall plants, medium plants, and small plants (size). Linnaeus classified plants and animals into more groups based on specific traits. He gave them names that described their traits.

Guided Practice

Have students write down their answers to the margin question: Classification groups and addresses can be arranged from more general to more specific.

TABLE 3–1. COMPARING CLASSIFICATION GROUPS AND ADDRESS INFORMATION

Country	Kingdom
State	Phylum
County	Class
Town	Order
Neighborhood	Family
Street	Genus
House number	Species

Today, there are seven groups for classifying organisms—kingdom, phylum, class, order, family, genus, and species. Why so many? Having more groups makes it easier to place an organism in the proper group. Think of how difficult it would be to find a long-lost cousin's house if all you knew was the country your cousin lived in. Table 3-1 shows the different kinds of address information that could be helpful in finding your cousin's house. How do the classification groups compare to the different kinds of address information?

How can classification groups be compared to addresses?

The kingdom is still the largest group of living things, just as it was in Linnaeus' time. A kingdom can be compared to the country your cousin lives in. Kingdoms are divided into groups called phyla (FI luh) (singular phylum). A **phylum** is the largest group within a kingdom. A phylum can be compared to a state. Phyla are divided into even smaller groups called classes. A **class** is the largest group within a phylum. Classes are divided into groups called orders. An **order** is the largest group within a class. Orders are divided into families. A **family** is the largest group within an order. Notice in Table 3-1 that classes can be compared to counties, orders to towns, and families to neighborhoods.

a

b

Figure 3-3 The praying mantis (a), walking stick (b), and rhinoceros beetle (c) have names that describe their appearance.

OPTIONS

Transparency Master/*Teacher Resource Package*, p.11. Use the Transparency Master shown here to teach the classification groups of living things.

TRANSPARENCY 11

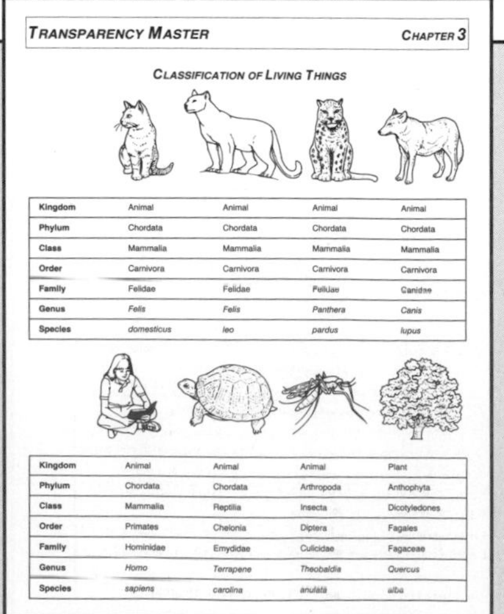

TRANSPARENCY MASTER — CHAPTER 3

CLASSIFICATION OF LIVING THINGS

Kingdom	Animal	Animal	Animal	Animal
Phylum	Chordata	Chordata	Chordata	Chordata
Class	Mammalia	Mammalia	Mammalia	Mammalia
Order	Carnivora	Carnivora	Carnivora	Carnivora
Family	Felidae	Felidae	Felidae	Canidae
Genus	*Felis*	*Felis*	*Panthera*	*Canis*
Species	*domesticus*	*leo*	*pardus*	*lupus*

Kingdom	Animal	Animal	Animal	Plant
Phylum	Chordata	Chordata	Arthropoda	Anthophyta
Class	Mammalia	Reptilia	Insecta	Dicotyledones
Order	Primates	Chelonia	Diptera	Fagales
Family	Hominidae	Emydidae	Culicidae	Fagaceae
Genus	*Homo*	*Terrapene*	*Theobaldia*	*Quercus*
Species	*sapiens*	*carolina*	*anulata*	*alba*

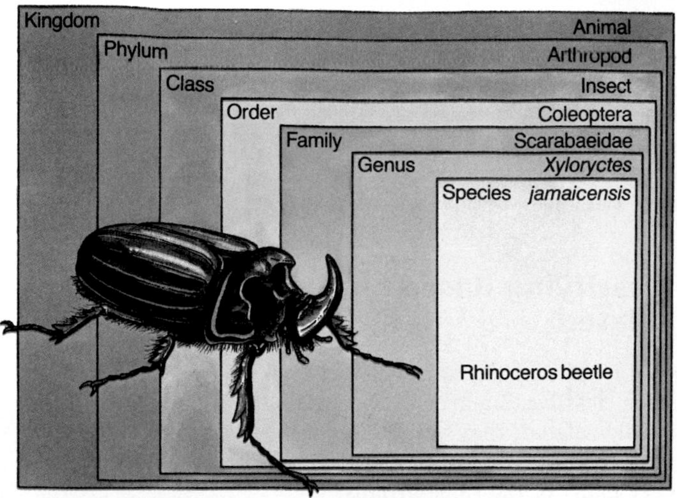

Figure 3-4 Each classification group is a subset of the next-largest group. Of what group is the kingdom a subset? all living things

The names given to the different groups often describe the living things in them. Let's look at an example at the family level. Members of three different insect families are shown in Figure 3-3. Each insect belongs to a different family.

Another way to think of a kingdom is as a set. Think of the other groups, from largest to smallest, as subsets. All seven groups are shown in Figure 3-4. You can see that like classes and orders, families are divided into groups. The largest group within a family is a **genus.** The smallest group of living things is a **species.**

Check Your Understanding

6. What traits were used by Aristotle to divide plants into groups?
7. Linnaeus made important changes in the way living things are classified. Name two.
8. There are seven main classification groups. Name these groups in order from largest to smallest.
9. **Critical Thinking:** A euglena is a one-celled organism that moves on its own and has chloroplasts. Why would Aristotle have trouble classifying this organism?
10. **Biology and Reading:** Who developed a two-kingdom system of classification for plants and animals?

Skill Check

Understand science words: phylum. The word part *phyl* means tribe or race. In your dictionary, find three words with the word part *phyl* in them. *For more help, refer to the* ***Skill Handbook,*** *pages 706-711.*

RETEACHING 8

RETEACHING: IDEA MAP **CHAPTER 3**

Name ______ Date ______ Class ______

Use with Section 3:2.

METHODS OF CLASSIFICATION

Use the following terms to complete the idea map: in water, shrubs, animal, plant, herbs, in the air, plants with specific traits, trees, plants, animals, on land, animals with specific traits.

- Early Classification
  - Aristotle
    - plants
      - trees
      - shrubs
      - herbs
    - animals
      - in water
      - on land
      - in the air
  - Linnaeus
    - plant kingdom
      - plants with specific traits
    - animal kingdom
      - animals with specific traits

1. How does classifying help us? It puts things in order and shows how they are alike.
2. What were the two main groups used by Aristotle and Linnaeus? plants and animals
3. How was Linnaeus' system different from Aristotle's? Linnaeus classified plants and animals into more groups, based on specific traits. He gave organisms two-part names that described their traits.
4. Aristotle's system was inconsistent because he used size to classify plants but not to classify animals. The same system should have been used for both groups.
5. The job of classifying is hard because scientists do not always agree on grouping.

TEACH

Check for Understanding

Have students respond to the first three questions in Check Your Understanding.

Reteach

Reteaching/*Teacher Resource Package,* p. 8. Use this worksheet to give students additional practice with methods of classification.

Extension: Assign Critical Thinking; Biology and Reading, or some of the **OPTIONS** available with this lesson.

3 APPLY

ACTIVITY/Game

Play "What's My Kingdom?". Read a description of an organism without naming it. Have students try to classify it in the proper kingdom.

4 CLOSE

Audiovisual

Show the slide program *The Earth's Five Kingdoms,* JLM Visuals.

Answers to Check Your Understanding

6. size and pattern of growth
7. He classified plants and animals into more groups, based his system on specific traits, and gave organisms names that described their traits.
8. kingdom, phylum, class, order, family, genus, species
9. It has both animal-like characteristics (movement) and plantlike characteristics (chloroplasts).
10. Linnaeus

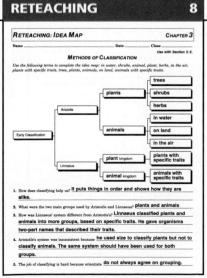

3:3 How Scientists Classify Today

PREPARATION

Materials Needed

Make copies of the Enrichment, Application, Critical Thinking, Skill, Study Guide, and Reteaching worksheets in the *Teacher Resource Package*.

▶ Use bird seed mix to make packets for the Focus activity.

▶ Gather leaves and keys or field guides for the Skill Check.

Key Science Words

scientific name
moneran
protist
fungus
plant
animal

Process Skills

In the Skill Check and Mini Lab, students will classify.

1 FOCUS

▶ The objectives are listed on the student page. Remind students to preview these objectives as a guide to this numbered section.

ACTIVITY/Hands-on

Have students work in pairs for this activity. Give each pair a small packet of bird seed, a hand lens, and a metric ruler. Have them divide the seeds into two groups, then divide the two groups into smaller groups based on traits such as color, size, and shape.

Objectives

6. **List** traits used in classifying living things.
7. **State** the function of scientific names.
8. **List** the five kingdoms scientists recognize today.

Key Science Words

scientific name
moneran
protist
fungi
plant
animal

3:3 How Scientists Classify Today

How do scientists know to which groups an organism belongs? They look at many traits. They compare the traits of one organism with those of another. Scientists also compare organisms living today with those that lived long ago. Let's look at how scientists classify living things.

Classifying Based on How Organisms Are Related

Living things that are closely related are in many of the same classification groups. For example, if two plants are closely related, they will be in almost all of the same groups. If they are not closely related, they will not be in very many of the same groups.

Table 3-2 shows a list of groups to which the house cat shown in Figure 3-5 belongs. It also shows the traits for each group. You may not recognize some of the group names. Many are from the Greek or Latin language.

Compare the lion shown in Figure 3-6 to the house cat. In how many groups are they found together?

TABLE 3–2. CLASSIFYING THE HOUSE CAT

Group	Group name	Group trait
Kingdom	Animal	Has many cells; eats food
Phylum	Chordate	Rodlike structure along the back for support
Class	Mammal	Nurses young; has hair
Order	Carnivore	Eats flesh; has large teeth
Family	Felidae	Sharp claws; large eyes
Genus	*Felis*	Small cats
Species	*catus*	Tame

Figure 3-5 To what classification groups does a house cat belong?

OPTIONS

Science Background

In 1866, Ernst Haeckel proposed a third kingdom called Protista. Robert Whittaker, a biologist at Cornell University, developed the five-kingdom system. It received little support until the 1970s, when extensive work in classifying was done by Lynn Margulis.

Enrichment/*Teacher Resource Package*, p. 3. Use the Enrichment worksheet shown here as an extension to how animals are classified today.

ENRICHMENT 3

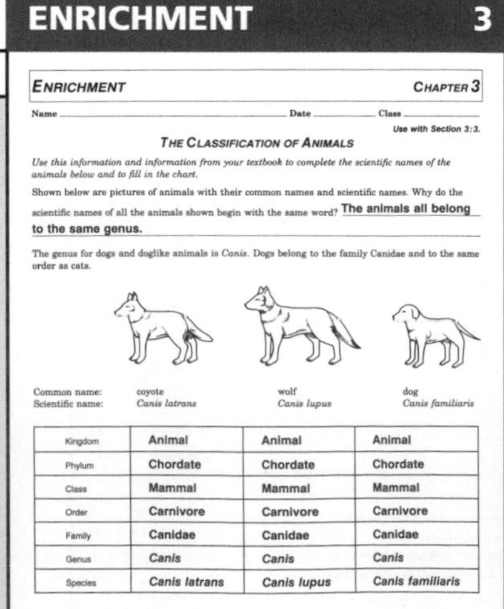

ENRICHMENT CHAPTER 3

Name ______ Date ______ Class ______

Use with Section 3:3.

THE CLASSIFICATION OF ANIMALS

Use this information and information from your textbook to complete the scientific names of the animals below and to fill in the chart.

Shown below are pictures of animals with their common names and scientific names. Why do the scientific names of all the animals shown begin with the same word? **The animals all belong to the same genus.**

The genus for dogs and doglike animals is *Canis*. Dogs belong to the family Canidae and to the same order as cats.

Common name:	coyote	wolf	dog
Scientific name:	*Canis latrans*	*Canis lupus*	*Canis familiaris*

Kingdom	Animal	Animal	Animal
Phylum	Chordate	Chordate	Chordate
Class	Mammal	Mammal	Mammal
Order	Carnivore	Carnivore	Carnivore
Family	Canidae	Canidae	Canidae
Genus	*Canis*	*Canis*	*Canis*
Species	*Canis latrans*	*Canis lupus*	*Canis familiaris*

TABLE 3–3. COMPARING THE HOUSE CAT AND LION			
	House Cat	**Lion**	**Comparison**
Kingdom	Animal	Animal	Same kingdom
Phylum	Chordate	Chordate	Same phylum
Class	Mammal	Mammal	Same class
Order	Carnivore	Carnivore	Same order
Family	Felidae	Felidae	Same family
Genus	*Felis*	*Panthera*	Different genus
Species	*catus*	*leo*	Different species

Table 3-3 shows that five of the seven groups for these two animals are the same. Only the genus and species groups are different. The lion and the house cat are very similar. They have many of the same traits.

Look at the classifications in Table 3-4 for the house cat and deer. These two animals do not share many traits. Notice that only their first three classification groups are the same.

TABLE 3–4. COMPARING THE HOUSE CAT AND DEER			
	House Cat	**Deer**	**Comparison**
Kingdom	Animal	Animal	Same kingdom
Phylum	Chordate	Chordate	Same phylum
Class	Mammal	Mammal	Same class
Order	Carnivore	Artiodactyla	Different order
Family	Felidae	Cervidae	Different family
Genus	*Felis*	*Odocoileus*	Different genus
Species	*catus*	*virginianus*	Different species

Let's compare a house cat with an octopus. They have fewer groups in common than house cats and deer. House cats and deer have backbones and hair. What about an octopus? Table 3-5 shows that for the house cat and the octopus, only the kingdom is the same. The house cat and the octopus are both animals. After the kingdom level, these animals belong to different groups.

TABLE 3–5. COMPARING THE HOUSE CAT AND OCTOPUS			
	House Cat	**Octopus**	**Comparison**
Kingdom	Animal	Animal	Same kingdom
Phylum	Chordate	Mollusk	Different phylum
Class	Mammal	Cephalopod	Different class
Order	Carnivore	Octopoda	Different order
Family	Felidae	Octopodidae	Different family
Genus	*Felis*	*Octopus*	Different genus
Species	*catus*	*vulgaris*	Different species

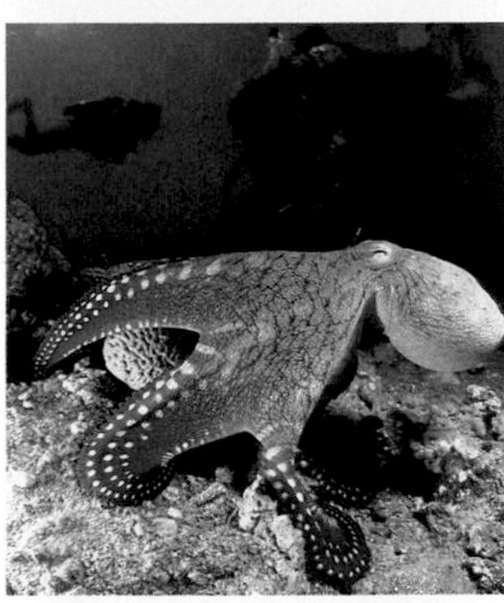

Figure 3-6 How are a lion (top), deer (middle), and octopus (bottom) like a house cat? all are animals; the lion and house cat are classified the same, except for genus and species; the deer and house cat belong to the same phylum and class

2 TEACH

MOTIVATION/Display

Display skeletons of a frog, bird, bat, chicken, cat (whichever are available). Have students identify body parts that have the same structure and origin. Ask what traits a bird and a bat have that are similar and why they are placed in different classes.

Concept Development

▶ Discuss why the classification of living organisms is more difficult than other kinds of classification. There are more different kinds of organisms with many different kinds of traits. Classification is based on the ways organisms are alike and the ways organisms are different.

Cooperative Learning: Point out to students that using a mnemonic device is an easy way to remember the classification system developed by Linnaeus. One example is King Phillip came over for graduation Sunday. Have students work in groups of three to come up with another mnemonic device that could be used.

Independent Practice

Study Guide/*Teacher Resource Package,* p. 16. Use the Study guide worksheet shown at the bottom of this page for independent practice.

STUDY GUIDE 16

STUDY GUIDE — CHAPTER 3

Name ______ Date ______ Class ______

HOW SCIENTISTS CLASSIFY

In your textbook, read about how scientists classify today in Section 3:3. Then, examine the classification of the three animals in the chart below.

	Animal A	Animal B	Animal C
Kingdom	Animal	Animal	Animal
Phylum	Chordate	Chordate	Chordate
Class	Mammal	Aves	Aves
Order	Primates	Passeriformes	Passeriformes
Family	Pongidae	Fringillidae	Fringillidae
Genus	*Pan*	*Spizella*	*Serinus*
Species	*troglodytes*	*passerina*	*canarius*

1. Comparing Animals A and B, how many groups are the same? **2**
2. Comparing Animals A and C, how many groups are the same? **2**
3. Comparing Animals B and C, how many groups are the same? **5**
4. Which two animals (A and B, A and C, or B and C) are most alike in classification? **B and C**
5. Which two animals have more of the same traits? **B and C**
6. Which two animals have more of the same body parts? **B and C**
7. Which two animals are most closely related? **B and C**
8. What is the scientific name of Animal A? ***Pan troglodytes***
9. What does the first word of the scientific name represent? **genus**
10. What does the second word of the scientific name represent? **species**
11. What are three reasons for using scientific names? **No mistake can be made about what living thing is being described. Scientific names of living things seldom change. Scientists throughout the world use the same language to name living things.**

APPLICATION 3

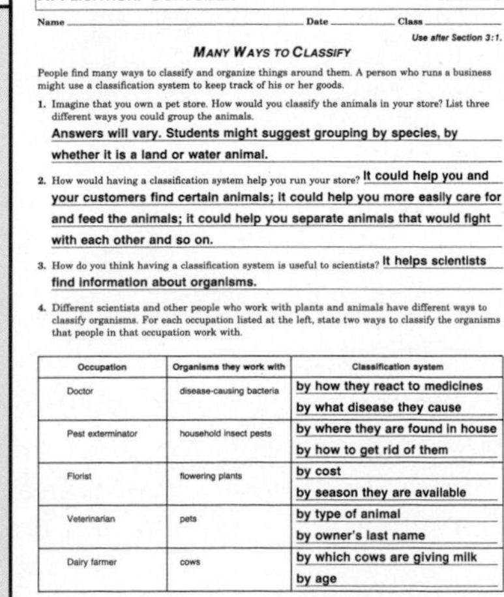

APPLICATION: CONSUMER — CHAPTER 3

Name ______ Date ______ Class ______

Use after Section 3:1.

MANY WAYS TO CLASSIFY

People find many ways to classify and organize things around them. A person who runs a business might use a classification system to keep track of his or her goods.

1. Imagine that you own a pet store. How would you classify the animals in your store? List three different ways you could group the animals. **Answers will vary. Students might suggest grouping by species, by whether it is a land or water animal.**
2. How would having a classification system help you run your store? **It could help you and your customers find certain animals; it could help you more easily care for and feed the animals; it could help you separate animals that would fight with each other and so on.**
3. How do you think having a classification system is useful to scientists? **It helps scientists find information about organisms.**
4. Different scientists and other people who work with plants and animals have different ways to classify organisms. For each occupation listed at the left, state two ways to classify the organisms that people in that occupation work with.

Occupation	Organisms they work with	Classification system
Doctor	disease-causing bacteria	**by how they react to medicines** **by what disease they cause**
Pest exterminator	household insect pests	**by where they are found in house** **by how to get rid of them**
Florist	flowering plants	**by cost** **by season they are available**
Veterinarian	pets	**by type of animal** **by owner's last name**
Dairy farmer	cows	**by which cows are giving milk** **by age**

OPTIONS

Application/*Teacher Resource Package,* p.3. Use the Application worksheet shown here to teach students practical uses for classifying.

TEACH

Concept Development

▶ Make sure that students understand the meaning of the word *ancestor.*

▶ Other kinds of evidence are used in classifying. Chromosome structure and embryology are two examples.

▶ Explain that in the classification system, the number of groups increases from kingdom to species. However, the number of kinds of organisms in each group decreases. At the kingdom level, there are five groups that contain every kind of organism. At the species level, there are millions of groups but only one kind of organism in each group. The more groups that organisms share, the more related the organisms are, and the more ancestors they have in common.

▶ The evolutionary history of a species is called phylogeny.

Misconception: Students may think that the classification system for organisms never changes. The system changes as scientists gain new information.

Mini Lab

Students need to include the major features of the group chosen.

Guided Practice

Have students write down their answers to the margin question: Horseshoe crabs and spiders have similar body chemistry.

Independent Practice

Study Guide/*Teacher Resource Package,* p. 17. Use the Study Guide worksheet shown at the bottom of this page for independent practice.

Mini Lab

What Kingdom?

Classify: Write a description of an imaginary organism so that a person reading the description could classify the organism as a moneran, protist, fungus, plant, or animal. *For more help, refer to the* ***Skill Handbook,*** *pages 715-717.*

Other Evidence Used in Classifying

Classification can be based on a living thing's ancestors. An ancestor is a related organism that lived some time in the past. For example, horses and donkeys have many of the same ancestors. They have more of the same ancestors than horses and goats do. Horses and goats have more of the same ancestors than horses and fish do. Of these pairs, horses and donkeys have the most ancestors in common and are the most related.

Similar body structures often show that living things have common ancestors. This is important in classification. You can see in Figure 3-7 that the front limbs of a human (a), a cat (b), a horse (c), a bird (d), and a bat (e) are similar in their bone structures. These similarities show a common ancestor. Compare the front limbs of animals (a) through (e) with the front limbs of an animal that lived long ago (f). All the limbs are similar even though they do different things. They have similar bones arranged in similar patterns.

Why is the horseshoe crab classified with spiders?

Another way to group living things is by body chemistry. A good example is the horseshoe crab. At first, the horseshoe crab was thought to be like other crabs. The blood of the horseshoe crab, however, is more like that of the spider. As a result, the horseshoe crab is now grouped with spiders.

For many years scientists have debated about how to classify the giant panda. Some classified it with raccoons, while others classified it with bears. Now its body chemistry shows it to be more closely related to bears.

Figure 3-7 Similarity in body structures shows that living things have a common ancestor.

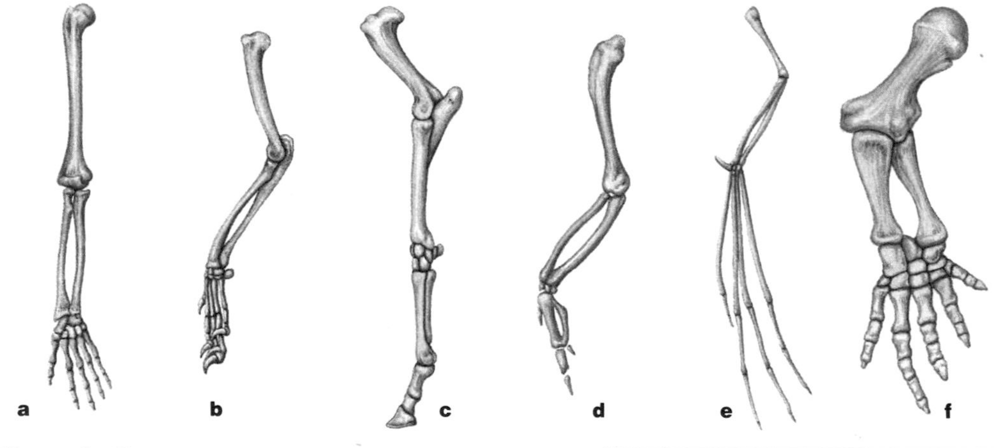

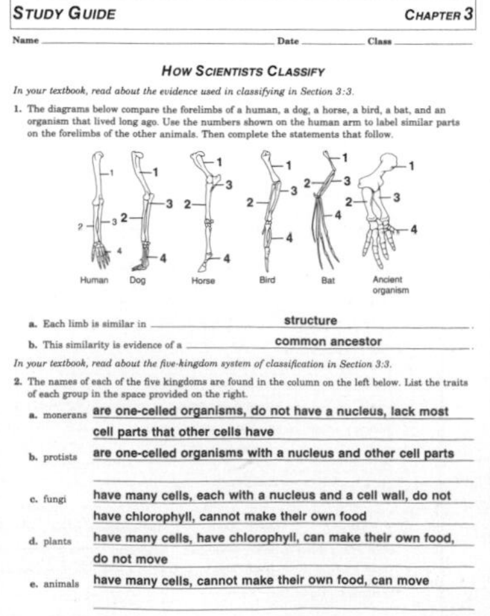

STUDY GUIDE 17

STUDY GUIDE **CHAPTER 3**

Name ______ Date ______ Class ______

HOW SCIENTISTS CLASSIFY

In your textbook, read about the evidence used in classifying in Section 3:3.

1. The diagrams below compare the forelimbs of a human, a dog, a horse, a bird, a bat, and an organism that lived long ago. Use the numbers shown on the human arm to label similar parts on the forelimbs of the other animals. Then complete the statements that follow.

a. Each limb is similar in **structure**.

b. This similarity is evidence of a **common ancestor**.

In your textbook, read about the five-kingdom system of classification in Section 3:3.

2. The names of each of the five kingdoms are found in the column on the left below. List the traits of each group in the space provided on the right.

a. monerans **are one-celled organisms, do not have a nucleus, lack most cell parts that other cells have**

b. protists **are one-celled organisms with a nucleus and other cell parts**

c. fungi **have many cells, each with a nucleus and a cell wall, do not have chlorophyll, cannot make their own food**

d. plants **have many cells, have chlorophyll, can make their own food, do not move**

e. animals **have many cells, cannot make their own food, can move**

Scientific Names Come from Classification

Tables 3-2 to 3-5 showed that living things are classified down to genus and species. The genus and species names together make up the **scientific name.** In Section 3:2, you learned that Linnaeus was the first to give organisms a scientific name with two parts.

The scientific name for a cat is *Felis catus* (FEE lus • CAT us). The name comes from the genus *Felis* and species *catus*. Notice that the genus is always capitalized and the species is not. Both the genus and the species are in italics.

A wolf's scientific name is *Canis lupus* (KAY nus • LEW pus). The name includes the genus *Canis* and species *lupus*. The scientific name for humans is *Homo sapiens*. What are the genus and the species to which humans belong?

Have you ever called a plant or an animal by its scientific name? You have, but you may not have realized it. Figure 3-8 shows some living things that you know about. Table 3-6 shows a list of their scientific names. You probably have used parts of these scientific names many times.

What names make up a scientific name?

Figure 3-8 Many living things have common names that sound like their scientific names.

TABLE 3–6. SCIENTIFIC NAMES OF SOME PLANTS AND ANIMALS

Scientific name	Name you probably use
Pinus sylvestris	Scotch pine
Rosa carolina	rose
Elephas maximus	Asian elephant
Gorilla gorilla	gorilla
Giraffa camelopardalis	giraffe

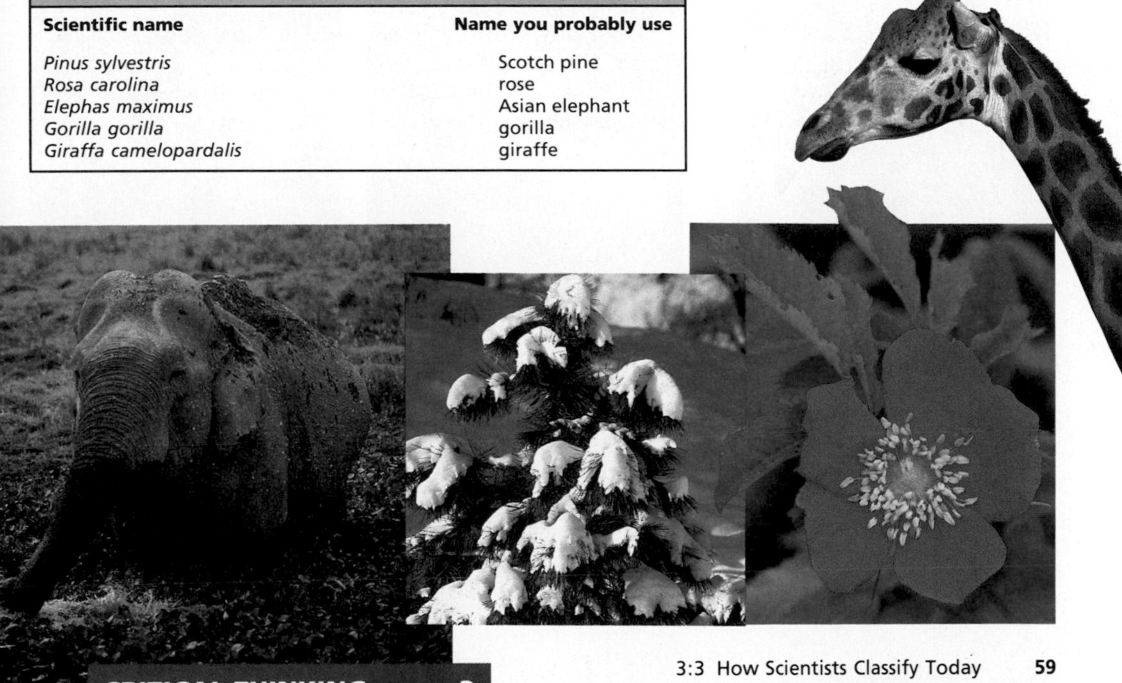

TEACH

Concept Development

▶ Provide students with some scientific names that are easily converted to a common name. Ask the students to name the organisms based on the term which sounds similar.

▶ Point out that Linnaeus' naming system is still used today. His naming system is called binomial nomenclature. It is a system by which each species is given a two-word Latin name.

▶ The second word of a scientific name is an adjective. Often this term is used to describe the species.

▶ Greek and Latin are the languages used for scientific names. Scientists around the world may speak other languages but they all use Latin or Greek for scientific names.

▶ Students need not worry about proper pronunciation or meaning of Greek and Latin names. Some students will enjoy guessing the meanings of some Latin names.

Analogy: An analogy to two-word naming can be found in Chinese names. The first word in a Chinese name is that of the family, and the second and third words are those of the individual. American and European names represent the same idea in reverse order.

Guided Practice

Have students write down their answers to the margin question: The genus and species names make up the scientific name.

CRITICAL THINKING 3

CRITICAL THINKING/PROBLEM SOLVING — CHAPTER 3

Name ______ Date ______ Class ______

Use after Section 3:3.

WHAT TRAITS CAN YOU USE TO CLASSIFY ORGANISMS?

Tell how you would decide into what kingdom each organism described below fits.

Organism A: You are looking at a drop of pond water through a microscope. You discover something you have never seen before. It does not swim around. It is made up of a string of green cells. Each cell is shaped like a shoebox, and has a large nucleus.

Organism B: You are walking along a beach looking at tidepools. In the water you find a soft organism that looks like a thick pink flower. It is about 3 centimeters high. The bottom part is a cylinder. As you watch, a small fish swims toward an opening in the top of the organism. The flowerlike parts catch the fish and slowly push it into the opening.

Organism C: You look at a large bush in the schoolyard. You know that it has been growing in the same place for more than a year. It has green leaves.

Analyzing the Problem

1. What traits help you classify organisms? moves or does not move or swim; green color; takes in food; made up of few or many cells; looks like something I already know
2. If you make a table called Characteristics of Kingdoms, what will you place in these columns:

Protist	microscopic or small; plantlike or animallike
Animal	moves, takes in food
Plant	does not move, makes own food, has many cells
Fungus	do not move, are not green, can't make their own food

Solving the Problem

1. In what kingdom will you classify Organism A? Explain your answer. protist because it is green, small, does not move, and has a nucleus
2. In what kingdom will you classify Organism B? Explain. animal because it takes in food and moves its body
3. In what kingdom will you classify Organism C? Explain. plant because it is green, does not move, has many cells

OPTIONS

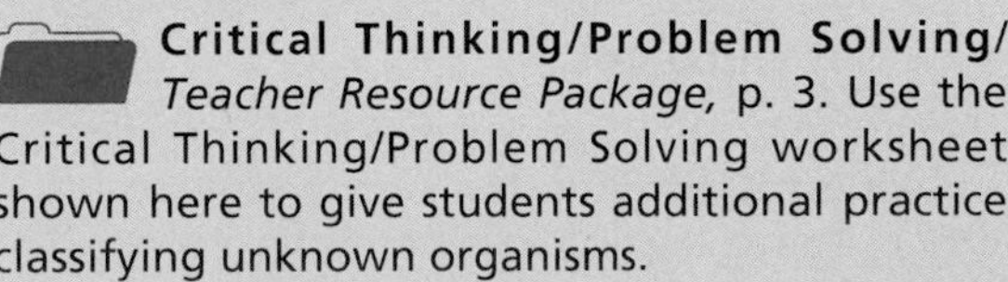

Critical Thinking/Problem Solving/ *Teacher Resource Package*, p. 3. Use the Critical Thinking/Problem Solving worksheet shown here to give students additional practice classifying unknown organisms.

TEACH

Concept Development

▶ Point out that pill bug, sow bug, and wood louse are all names for the same animal. Sweet pepper, bell pepper, mango, and green pepper are all names for *Capsicum frutescens.*

▶ Write the names of organisms on the chalkboard that are given names that are misleading. Examples are ringworm (fungus), acorn worm (vertebrate), sea cucumber (echinoderm), poison oak (herb), ladybug (beetle).

▶ Scientists discovered microscopic organisms that did not seem to fit in the plant or animal kingdom. The microscope encouraged the development of the Protist kingdom.

Skill Check

Provide students with field guides to classify leaves.

Guided Practice

Have students list fish that aren't true fish. Answers could include: crayfish, starfish, jellyfish, and silverfish. Have them write the reasons scientific names are used.

Independent Practice

Study Guide/*Teacher Resource Package,* p. 18. Use the Study Guide worksheet shown at the bottom of this page for independent practice.

Skill Check

Classify: Collect 10 leaves from trees in your neighborhood. Bring the leaves to class and use a key or field guide to find the scientific names of the trees from which the leaves came. *For more help, refer to the* ***Skill Handbook,*** *pages 715-717.*

Why Scientific Names Are Used

You call a robin, seal, apple tree, and house cat by their common names. Common names are names used in everyday language. Scientists prefer to use scientific names. There are several reasons for using scientific names instead of common names.

1. No mistake can be made about which living thing is being described. That's because two different living things don't have the same scientific name. Two different living things, however, may have the same common name. For example, hawk is the common name for several kinds of birds. Only one kind of hawk, however, is named *Buteo jamaicensis* (BOO tee oh • juh may uh KEN sis). This hawk has broad wings and a reddish tail. You may know it as the red-tailed hawk.
2. Scientific names seldom change.
3. Scientific names are written in the same language around the world. Using scientific names allows scientists to communicate no matter what their everyday language is. The language in which scientific names are written is Latin. Latin is used because it does not change.

Figure 3-9 Only one of these hawks is *Buteo jamaicensis* (a).

a

b

c

Five Kingdom Classification

Remember that early scientists grouped living things into two kingdoms—plant and animal. As scientists learned about more living things, they found that some living things did not fit into either kingdom. A new system of classification was needed to group all the living things being discovered.

OPTIONS

ACTIVITY/Project

Have interested students make an insect collection, classifying their organisms to order. The collection can be displayed in class.

How Can Living Things Be Grouped?/*Lab Manual,* pp. 21-24. Use this lab as an extension to the classification of living things.

TECHNOLOGY

Mussels of the Deep

Scientists exploring the ocean floor are making exciting discoveries. Thousands of feet below the ocean's surface live clams, mussels, and tubeworms. These animals live near thermal vents. Hot water from beneath Earth's crust bubbles up through the vents. The hot water carries sulfur compounds. Bacteria living near the vents use these compounds to change carbon dioxide into food. Some animals living near the vents take the bacteria into their bodies and live on the food the bacteria make.

Scientists believed that if organisms could live near thermal vents and use "sulfur-eating" bacteria for food, there must be other organisms that depend on other chemicals for food.

Sure enough, mussels that live on methane gas have been found in the Gulf of Mexico. These mussels are able to thrive on methane gas because of "methane-eating" bacteria that live in their gills. The mussels cluster around oil seeps at depths of about 600 meters. The oil seeps are rich sources of methane. Who knows what other surprises await the curious scientist?

Thermal vent organisms

Today most scientists use this system to classify living things into five kingdoms. The five kingdoms include: monerans (muh NIHR uns), protists (PROH tihsts), fungi, plants, and animals.

Monerans are one-celled organisms that don't have a nucleus. They lack most of the cell parts that other cells have. The kingdom has only two phyla, bacteria and blue-green bacteria.

Protists are mostly single-celled organisms that have a nucleus and other cell parts. Some have chlorophyll and can make their own food. Others must take in food from the surroundings. Some can move and some can't. The organisms in this kingdom are difficult for scientists to classify because they are so different from one another and from most other living things.

Mushrooms, molds, and yeasts are examples of fungi, (singular fungus). **Fungi** are organisms that have cell walls and absorb food from their surroundings. Fungi don't have chlorophyll, so they can't make their own food.

What are two differences between monerans and protists?

SKILL 3

SKILL: CLASSIFY — CHAPTER 3

Name ______ Date ______ Class ______

For more help, refer to the Skill Handbook, pages 715-717. *Use after Section 3:3.*

THE FIVE KINGDOMS OF LIVING THINGS

The pictures at the bottom of the page show organisms that belong in each of the five kingdoms of living things. Classify the organisms in the pictures by filling out the table below. Indicate which organisms belong to which kingdoms by writing the numbers from the appropriate diagrams in the second column. In the third column, list two or more traits of the organisms in each kingdom.

Kingdom	Organisms	Traits of kingdom
Moneran	4, 5	one-celled, do not have a nucleus
Protist	2, 7, 9	mostly one-celled, have a nucleus and other cell parts
Fungus	6, 8	have cell walls, cannot make their own food
Plant	3, 11	many-celled, do not move, make their own food
Animal	1, 10, 12	many-celled, can move, cannot make their own food

1. Starfish 2. Paramecium 3. Moss 4. Blue-green bacteria
5. Bacteria 6. Bread mold 7. Amoeba 8. Mushroom
9. Euglena 10. Butterfly 11. Cactus 12. Earthworm

OPTIONS

Skill/*Teacher Resource Package* p. 3. Use the Skill worksheet shown here to reinforce the skill of classifying.

TECHNOLOGY

Mussels of the Deep

Background

Scientists from Woods Hole Oceanographic Institute in Massachusetts were the first to find organisms in deep-sea vents. The bacteria living there convert chemical energy into food just as plants convert light energy into food. Clams, mussels, tube worms, and other invertebrates eat the bacteria.

Discussion

1. Where do the mussels get their food? (from bacteria)
2. What makes classifying newly discovered organisms difficult? (Scientists cannot agree on how to classify them.)
3. Will other kingdoms be established in future years? Why? (Probably yes, because the traits of newly discovered organisms may not fit the kingdoms already established. In fact, a sixth kingdom has been proposed.)

References

Gilbert, Susan. "Thriving in Darkness: Ecosystems at Deep-Sea Vents Challenge Origin-of-Life Theories." *Science Digest,* Dec. 1985, p. 14.

TEACH

Guided Practice

Have students write down their answers to the margin question: Monerans don't have a nucleus or most of the cell parts other cells have. Protists have a nucleus and other cell parts.

TEACH

Idea Map

Have students use the idea map as a study guide to the major concepts of this section.

Check for Understanding

Have students respond to the first three questions in Check Your Understanding.

Reteach

Reteaching/*Teacher Resource Package*, p. 9. Use this worksheet to give students additional practice with classification.

Extension: Assign Critical Thinking, Biology and Reading, or some of the **OPTIONS** available with this lesson.

3 APPLY

Have each student describe and sketch an imaginary organism that would require a new kingdom. Display the sketches.

4 CLOSE

ACTIVITY/Challenge

Have students make a list of several common living things such as the horsefly, poison ivy, cockroach, etc. Have the students use references to find their scientific names.

Answers to Check Your Understanding

11. Similar body structures often show that living things have common ancestors.
12. Mistakes can be made if common names are used. Scientific names do not usually change. All countries use the same scientific names.
13. Monera, Protist, Fungus, Animal, Plant
14. house cat
15. The word *perfect* means that the present five-kingdom system would never need to be changed.

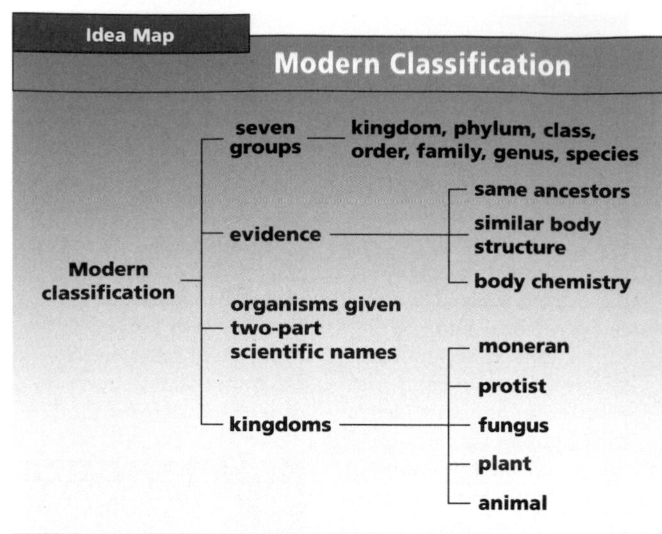

Study Tip: Use this idea map as you study present-day methods of classifying organisms. How many kingdoms are recognized today?

Bio Tip

Ecology: Biologists estimate that millions of living things have not been discovered. Most are protists, monerans, insects, and plants.

Plants are organisms that are made up of many cells, have chlorophyll, and can make their own food. Plants don't move. **Animals** are organisms that have many cells, can't make their own food, and can move. The cells of animals and plants have nuclei and other cell parts.

Figure 3-10 shows members of the five kingdoms. The traits of each kingdom are also listed for you. Refer back to this figure as you read about the kingdoms of living things in the next five chapters. Appendix B also contains information about the different groups of living things.

The five-kingdom system isn't perfect. Some living things don't fit into any of the five kingdoms. Their classification changes as scientists learn more about them.

Check Your Understanding

11. How is similarity in body structure used to classify living things?
12. Give two reasons why scientists use scientific names.
13. What are five kingdoms recognized today?
14. **Critical Thinking:** You are a chordate. Are you more like a house cat or an octopus?
15. **Biology and Reading:** What does the word *perfect* mean as it is used in the last paragraph of this section?

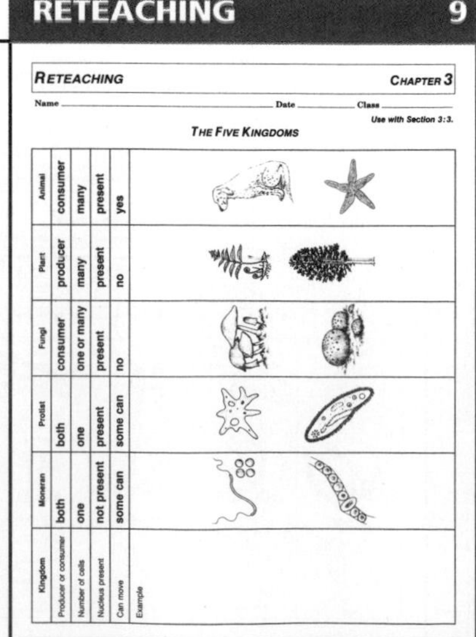
RETEACHING 9

RETEACHING CHAPTER 3

Name ____ Date ____ Class ____

Use with Section 3:3.

THE FIVE KINGDOMS

Kingdom	Producer or consumer	Number of cells	Nucleus present	Can move	Example
Animal	consumer	many	present	yes	
Plant	producer	many	present	no	
Fungi	consumer	one or many	present	no	
Protist	both	one	present	some can	
Moneran	both	one	not present	some can	

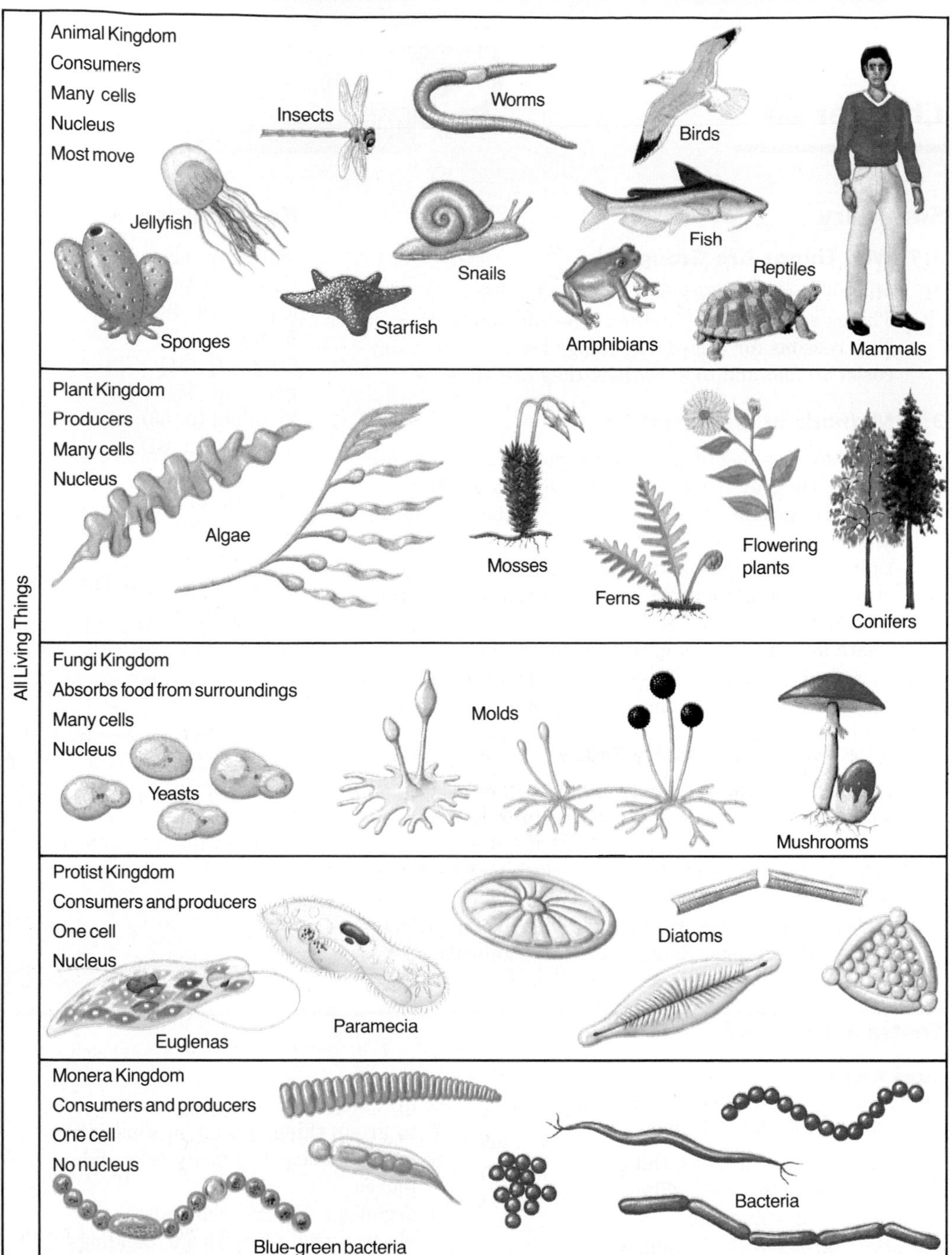

Figure 3-10 Living things are classified into five kingdoms.

OPTIONS

ACTIVITY/Enrichment

Use the microprojector to show prepared slides of bacteria, blue-green bacteria, paramecia, and euglena. This will help students understand the traits used in placing organisms into kingdoms. Observe plants, fungi, and guppies to see the differences in how organisms get food.

Five Kingdoms/*Transparency Package,* number 3. Use color transparency number 3 as you introduce the five kingdoms.

CHAPTER 3 REVIEW

Summary

Summary statements can be used by students to review the major concepts of the chapter.

Key Science Words

All boldfaced terms from the chapter are listed.

Testing Yourself

Using Words

1. species
2. kingdom
3. trait
4. phylum
5. scientific name
6. genus
7. classify
8. animal
9. fungus
10. plant

Finding Main Ideas

11. p. 51; Aristotle classified plants based on how they grew and their size, and animals by where they lived.
12. pp. 61-62; Three traits used to place living things in one of the five kingdoms are number of cells, cell nucleus, and how the living things get food.
13. p. 48; Answers will vary, but some examples of everyday things that are grouped include sports items, groceries, classrooms, classes, and books.
14. p. 54; The seven main groups in the modern classification system are kingdom, phylum, class, order, family, genus, and species.
15. p. 59; The scientific name is made up of the genus and species.
16. pp. 48-50; We classify things to put them in order, to make them easier to find, and to show how things are alike.
17. p. 53; Linnaeus gave living things two-part names.
18. p. 58; The ancestors of two living things give a clue as to how related they are.

Chapter 3 Review

Summary

3:1 Why Things Are Grouped

1. Many things are classified in everyday life.
2. Things are grouped together based on similarities. Two reasons for classifying things are to make them easier to find and to show how they are alike.

3:2 Methods of Classification

3. Aristotle was one of the first people to classify living things. He grouped animals according to where they lived. He grouped plants according to size and pattern of growth.
4. Linnaeus used specific traits to group living things. He also designed a scientific naming system that is still used today.
5. There are seven main groups in the modern classification system. They are kingdom, phylum, class, order, family, genus, and species.

3:3 How Scientists Classify Today

6. Classifying is based on how organisms are related, ancestors, similarities in body structure, and body chemistry.
7. Scientists use scientific names because no two living things have the same scientific name.
8. Today, living things are grouped into five kingdoms–monerans, protists, fungi, plants, and animals.

Key Science Words

animal (p. 62)
class (p. 54)
classify (p. 48)
family (p. 54)
fungus (p. 61)
genus (p. 55)
kingdom (p. 53)
moneran (p. 61)
order (p. 54)
phylum (p. 54)
plant (p. 62)
protist (p. 61)
scientific name (p. 59)
species (p. 55)
trait (p. 48)

Testing Yourself

Using Words

Choose the word from the list of Key Science Words that best fits the definition.

1. smallest group of living things
2. largest group of living things
3. a feature of something
4. largest group within a kingdom
5. genus and species names together
6. first word in a scientific name
7. to group things based on similarity
8 organism that has many cells and moves
9. organism that has cell walls and absorbs food from its surroundings
10. organism that has many cells and can make its own food

64

Using Main Ideas

19. Many of the newly discovered living things did not fit into Aristotle's grouping system.
20. They could all be classified into tall letters and short letters. T, b, 1, and d are tall letters, and c, e, and o are short letters.
21. Scientists use scientific names so that no mistake can be made about what living thing is being described, because they seldom change, and because scientists all over the world use the same Latin names.
22. Books in a library are classified so they will be easier to find.
23. Plants are producers and animals are consumers.
24. Lion – animal kingdom, chordate phylum, mammal class, carnivore order, family Felidae, genus *Panthera,* species *leo;* deer — animal kingdom, chordate phylum, mammal class, order Artiodactyla, family Cervidae, genus *Odocoileus,* species *vivginianus.*
25. Linnaeus used more groups, based his system on specific traits, and gave organisms names that described their traits.

Review

Testing Yourself *continued*

Finding Main Ideas

List the page number where each main idea below is found. Then, explain each main idea.

11. how Aristotle classified plants and animals
12. three traits used to place living things in one of the five kingdoms
13. things in our everyday lives that are grouped
14. the seven main groups in the modern classification system
15. what makes up the scientific name
16. two reasons why things are classified
17. the scientist who gave living things two-part names
18. how living things are grouped based on their ancestors

Using Main Ideas

Answer the questions by referring to the page number after each question.

19. Why did scientists depend less and less on Aristotle's grouping system? (p. 53)
20. How would you classify the letters b, c, e, d, l, o, t into two groups? Explain your groups. (p. 48)
21. What are three reasons why scientists use scientific names? (p. 60)
22. Why do we classify books in a library? (p. 48)
23. How do plants and animals differ? (p. 62)
24. What are the classification groups for a lion and a deer? (p. 57)
25. What changes did Linnaeus make in Aristotle's classification system? (p. 53)

Skill Review ✓

For more help, refer to the ***Skill Handbook,*** *pages 704-719.*

1. **Infer:** List the similarities and differences between the animals in Figure 3-3. Infer how closely related the animals are.
2. **Classify:** Classify the following animals into four groups on the basis of their structural similarities: snail, rabbit, gorilla, butterfly, oyster, chimpanzee, clam, cat, honeybee.
3. **Infer:** What is the result of two organisms having a large number of the same ancestors?
4. **Observe:** Obtain a sample of pond water. Place some of the water on a microscope slide and observe the organisms in the water. To what kingdoms do the organisms belong?

Finding Out More

Critical Thinking

1. Cut out photographs of 20 people from magazines. Design a classification system for these people.
2. How is classification helpful to farmers, florists, and customs inspectors?

Applications

1. Keys are used to identify things that have been classified and named. From the library, obtain a key to the trees or flowering plants in your area. Identify 20 plants using the key.
2. Visit a zoo or an aquarium. Make a list of the living things seen there. Use reference books to identify and classify the living things to the species level.

Skill Review

1. The three insects have different shapes. Two are long and thin, one is round and heavy bodied. All have six legs, all are insects. However, the two long and thin ones are probably more closely related.
2. Students could use the following classes:
   no legs, no wings - snail, oyster, clam
   2 legs, no wings – gorilla, chimpanzee
   4 legs, no wings – rabbit, cat
   6 legs, wings – butterfly, honeybee
3. They share more of the classification categories.
4. Students should see organisms that belong to protist, plant, and animal kingdoms.

Finding Out More

Critical Thinking

1. Race, size, age, hair color, and gender are some traits that can be used in classifying people.
2. Each must be able to classify and identify plants.

Applications

1. Pocket keys with pictures or diagrams are helpful in identifying organisms in the field.
2. Students may ask the zoo or aquarium keeper how the information necessary to classify living things is obtained.

Chapter Review/*Teacher Resource Book,* pp. 11-12.

Chapter Test/*Teacher Resource Book,* pp. 13-15.

Chapter Test/*Computer Test Bank*

Unit Test/*Teacher Resource Package,* pp. 16-17.

Unit 1 Kinds of Life

CONNECTIONS

Biology in Your World

In order to study kinds of life or any other topic, scientists need a plan of action. The scientific method provides a structured way to answer scientific questions and solve problems. This method can be applied to all areas of life, from everyday mysteries to scientific phenomena.

Literature Connection

Alex Haley's (1921-) novel *Roots* documents his family history. Haley managed to trace his family to the village of Juffre in Gambia, West Africa. His great-great-great-great-great-grandfather, Kunta Kinte, was abducted from West Africa in 1767. Kunta was taken on a slave ship to Maryland, where he was sold to a Virginia plantation owner. *Roots* chronicles Haley's family from Kunta to Haley himself. The book was dramatized on television in 1977, and the last episode drew one of the largest audiences in television history.

Geography Connection

According to Alfred Wegener's theory of continental drift, all the continents were once a single land mass called Pangaea. Around 200 million years ago, Pangaea split into two large land masses and these later broke into the present-day continents. The continents drifted about 2.5 cm per year to their present positions.

Wegener showed that plants that once grew in Greenland may be related to plants now growing in the tropics. This finding supports his theory of continental drift.

Today, the theory of plate tectonics is used to explain continental drift. According to this theory, Earth's outer crust is made of rigid plates. Convection currents in Earth's mantle cause the plates to move; thus, the continents drift over the years. Plate movement causes earthquakes, volcanoes, and the formation of mountains and ocean ridges.

CONNECTIONS

Biology in Your World

The Scientific Method Is All Around You

In this unit, you have read how the scientific method is used to solve problems in science. But, did you know people use scientific methods to solve other kinds of problems? Consider the "mysteries" described below and how scientific methods were used to solve them.

LITERATURE

A Scientific Search for Roots

Alex Haley learned from his grandmother that he was part of the Kinte family. His African ancestor, Kunta Kinte, had been kidnapped in Africa and then brought to this country as a slave.

Kinte's family handed down African words for six generations. These words were the names of an African village, a certain tree, and a musical instrument. Haley traced these to the Gambia River in West Africa. There he found a man who could recite the history of the Kinte family. The man's story fit the facts Haley had before his trip. Haley wrote *Roots* to tell the story of his search.

GEOGRAPHY

Shifting Continents

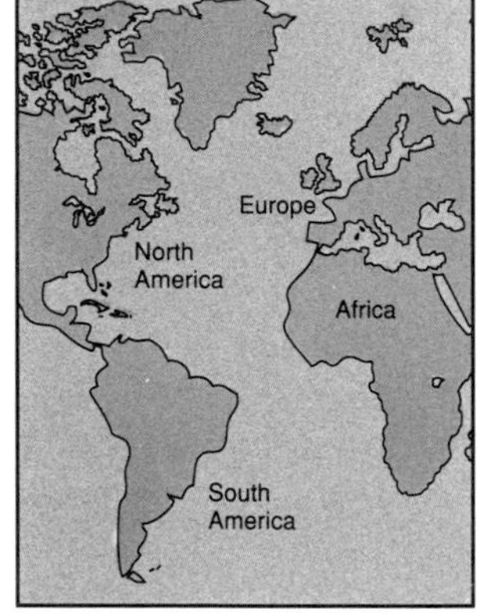

The east coast of South America and the west coast of Africa could almost fit together like the pieces of a jigsaw puzzle. This observation led scientists to form the continental drift theory. The theory says that there was once a single great continent that split and drifted apart.

Other evidence indicates that all the land masses of Earth may have been joined at one time. Layers of rock along a coast on one side of the ocean match layers of rock on an opposite coast. Also, different continents have the same kinds of fossils. Thus, observation and evidence support the continental drift theory.

LEISURE

Green Thumbs Up!

Many teens enjoy spending time assembling a terrarium. You can have a miniature garden in your bedroom! Terrariums are fun to arrange, and the materials are easy to find. All you need is a clear container, pebbles, sand, soil, and some plants. Ferns and mosses grow well in terrariums. You can try to grow many other kinds of plants, also. Experiment with various plants to see which are best suited for a terrarium. Set up your experiment using the scientific method.

How would you vary the conditions in or surrounding a terrarium to find the best environment for it?

CONSUMER

Cycling Through Your Choices

Your old bicycle is just about worn out, and you need to buy a new one. How can you use a scientific method to choose the best bicycle? You can treat your decision like solving a problem.

First, research the types of bicycles. What are the advantages, disadvantages, and purposes of each type?

What do you need in a bicycle? Prepare a list of all the features and uses you want in a bicycle. Then rate each feature with a number from 1 to 5. A feature you really need is a 1. A feature that is nice but you could do without would be a 5.

Compare your list of needed features with the types of bicycles. Do your features match the purposes and advantages of one or two types of bicycles? If not, you may need to rethink your needs.

Go to a bicycle shop to see and ride bicycles. Narrow your choices to one type and choose your bicycle based on all the data you have gathered about the different bicycles.

CONNECTIONS

Leisure Connection

Terrariums can provide plants and animals with ideal growing conditions. If kept moist and given indirect sunlight, a covered terrarium preserves moisture and heat to create a warm, humid environment. Plants that grow well together, such as ferns and ivy, are good choices for terrariums. Small animals such as lizards, toads, salamanders, and small snakes can also thrive in this atmosphere.

Consumer Connection

In listing and rating features of a bicycle, students must consider how they will use a bike. Will it be used for racing, touring, off-road riding, or pleasure riding? Do they want to ride alone or with a partner? Will they carry a lot with them when they ride? Do they want hand or pedal brakes? Do they want a headlight for night-time riding?

Other considerations are the cost, comfort, and look of the bicycle.

References

Haley, Alex. *Roots.* New York: Doubleday & Co., 1976.

Redfern, Ron. *The Making of a Continent.* New York: Times Books, 1983.

Unit 2 Kingdoms

UNIT OVERVIEW

Unit 2 is a survey of the organisms classified in the moneran, protist, fungus, plant, and animal kingdoms. Viruses are also discussed. The major characteristics used in classifying the organisms are identified and the features that distinguish them from other organisms are explained.

Advance Planning

Arrange a field trip to a zoo or a botanical garden. Obtain materials for setting up a classroom terrarium.

Audiovisual and computer software suggestions are located within each chapter under the heading TEACH.

To prepare for:

Lab 4-1:	Purchase 3.7 x 0.7 cm bolts and nuts, #22 gauge wire, 4.5 cm polystyrene balls and pipe cleaners.
Lab 4-2:	Arrange to have prepared slides of *Anabaena* and bacteria, petri dishes, and metric rulers.
Mini Labs:	Assemble beef broth, salt, sugar, vinegar, and water. Obtain yogurt and prepare methylene blue.
Lab 5-1:	Order cultures of: amoeba, euglena, and paramecium.
Lab 5-2:	Arrange to have prepared slides of mushroom basidia.
Mini Lab:	Gather resealable plastic bags.
Lab 6-1:	Collect or order moss plants with spore cases.
Lab 6-2:	Collect or order bracken ferns with spore cases.
Mini Labs:	Purchase blue food coloring. Collect a selection of open and closed pine cones.
Lab 7-1:	Order hydra culture and food (*Daphnia* or brine shrimp).
Lab 7-2:	Order or collect live earthworms.
Mini Labs:	Collect rocks and gather suction cups. Gather wire mesh, funnels, and jars.
Lab 8-1:	Order or collect crayfish.
Lab 8-2:	Arrange to have tail or wing feathers, down feathers.
Mini Labs:	Purchase flour and locate a dew spider web. Assemble wood, a hammer, bottle caps, nails, peanut butter, and bird seed.

Unit 2

CONTENTS

68

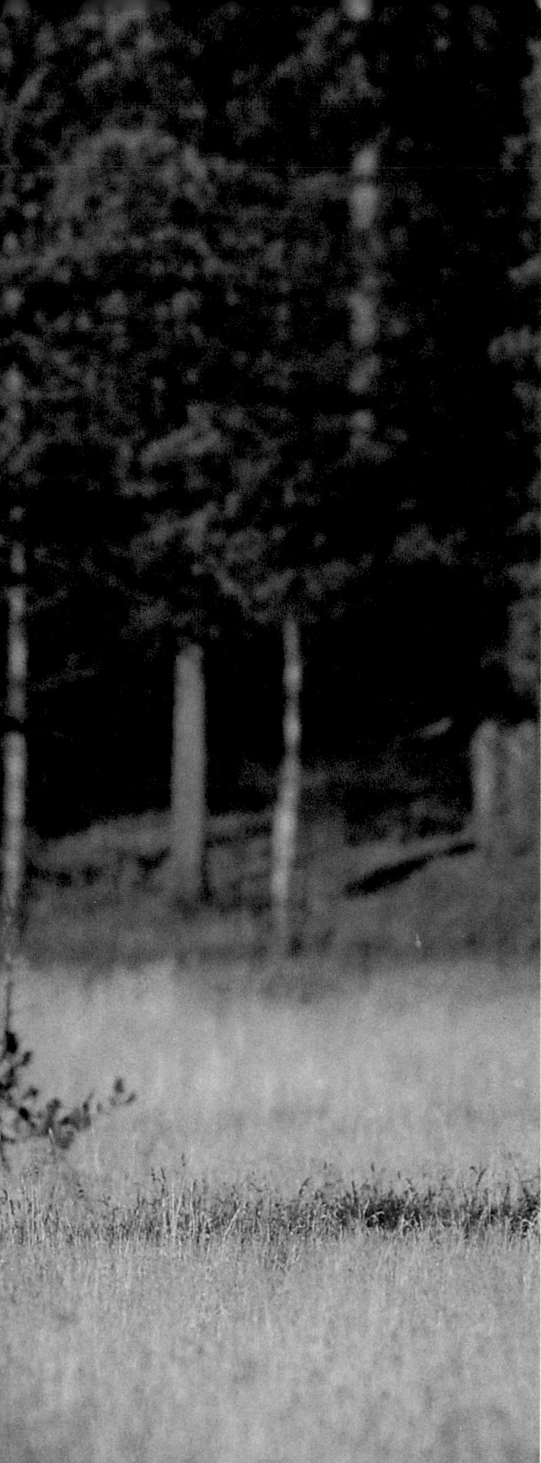

Kingdoms

What would happen if...

there were no fungi? Fungi use and break down substances in rotting logs and other dead organisms. This action releases nutrients into the soil for plants to use. Without fungi, the nutrients in the soil would soon be used up. Then, no plants would grow. Without plants, animals such as the elk in the photo would have no food to eat.

Fungi are also needed to produce many things we've come to depend on. Yeasts, molds, and mushrooms are all fungi. Carbon dioxide gas produced by yeast causes bread to rise. Without yeast, our bread would be flat. Without a certain type of mold, there would be no penicillin. This important antibiotic keeps many deadly diseases under control. Other molds are used to flavor some types of cheeses.

Fungi may be simple and small, but they are a necessary part of our world.

UNIT OVERVIEW

Photo Teaching Tip

Ask students to read the passage and discuss the possible outcomes of life without fungi. Lead students to the understanding that all organisms interact and have important roles in the balance of nature. The discussion may result in the conclusion that all life-forms are valuable and worth protecting.

Theme Development

There are many different kinds of living things, all of which are alike in some basic ways. This unit describes the five kingdoms of living things and how all organisms interact with each other. The themes of diversity and ecology are developed in this unit.

Viruses and Monerans

PLANNING GUIDE

CONTENT	TEXT FEATURES	TEACHER RESOURCE PACKAGE	OTHER COMPONENTS
(1 day) 4:1 Traits of Viruses Viruses and Disease Controlling Viruses	Skill Check: *Interpret Diagrams,* p. 75 Lab 4-1: *Viruses,* p. 76 Idea Map, p. 77 Check Your Understanding, p. 78	Reteaching: *Virus Life Cycles,* p. 10 Study Guide: *Viruses,* pp. 19-20 Lab 4-1: *Viruses,* pp. 13-14	
(3 days) 4:2 Monera Kingdom Traits of Bacteria Bacteria and Disease Helpful Bacteria Controlling Bacteria Blue-green Bacteria	Skill Check: *Understand Science Words,* p. 85 Mini Lab: *What Prevents the Growth of Bacteria?* p. 83 Mini Lab: *What Makes Yogurt?* p. 84 Technology: *Uses of Bacteria,* p. 86 Lab 4-2: *Monerans,* p. 89 Idea Map, p. 87 Check Your Understanding, p. 88	Application: *Ways to Control Bacteria,* p. 4 Enrichment: *Viruses, Monerans, and Disease,* p. 4 Reteaching: *Monerans,* p. 11 Critical Thinking/Problem Solving: *Why Are Medicines Not Used to Treat Virus Diseases?* p. 4 Skill: *Make and Use Tables,* p. 4 Focus: *How Do Bacteria Affect Our Lives?* p. 7 Transparency Master: *Comparing Viruses and Monerans,* p. 15 Study Guide: *Monera Kingdom,* pp. 21-23 Study Guide: *Vocabulary,* p. 24 Lab 4-2: *Monerans,* pp. 15-16	**Laboratory Manual:** *How Can You Test for Bacteria in Foods?* p. 25 **Laboratory Manual:** *Does Soil Contain Bacteria?* p. 27 **Laboratory Manual:** *What Are the Traits of Blue-green Bacteria?* p. 31 Color Transparency 4: *Bacterial and Animal Cells*
Chapter Review	Summary Key Science Words Testing Yourself Finding Main Ideas Using Main Ideas Skill Review	Chapter Review, pp. 18-19 Chapter Test, pp. 20-22	**Test Bank**

MATERIALS NEEDED

LAB 4-1, p. 76	LAB 4-2, p. 89	MARGIN FEATURES
bolt 2 nuts to fit bolt 2 pieces wire polystyrene ball pipecleaners, cut in 2-cm lengths	microscope prepared slide of *Anabaena* prepared slide of bacteria petri dish metric ruler	Skill Check, p. 75 pencil paper Skill Check, p. 85 dictionary Mini Lab, p. 83 4 clean beakers 4 mL beef broth 1 t. salt 1 t. sugar 1 t. vinegar boiling water Mini Lab, p. 84 microscope microscope slide coverslip yogurt water methylene blue stain

OBJECTIVES

SECTION	OBJECTIVE	OBJECTIVES CORRELATION			
		CHECK YOUR UNDERSTANDING	CHAPTER REVIEW	TRP CHAPTER REVIEW	TRP CHAPTER TEST
4:1	1. **Identify** the traits of viruses.	1	10, 11, 21	4, 8, 11, 12	2, 8, 9, 17, 21, 25, 30
	2. **Tell** how viruses reproduce.	2	2, 22	5	7, 27
	3. **List** examples of how viruses affect living things.	3, 4, 5	1, 12, 13, 23, 24	7, 18, 25, 28	5, 6, 25, 29, 32, 43, 49
4:2	4. **Identify** the traits of bacteria.	6	4, 8, 9, 14, 15, 18, 25, 26	2, 6, 9, 10, 13, 21, 29, 30, 31	1, 3, 4, 12, 17
	5. **Explain** how bacteria affect other living things.	7, 9	3, 5, 16, 17, 19, 29, 30	3, 15, 16, 17, 19, 20, 22, 23, 24, 26, 27, 28, 32, 33, 34, 35	10, 11, 13, 21, 26, 31, 33, 34, 35, 36, 37, 38, 39, 40, 41, 42, 44, 45, 46, 47, 48, 50
	6. **Compare** the traits of bacteria and blue-green bacteria.	8	7, 20, 31	1, 14, 15, 30	18, 19, 22, 23, 26

Viruses and Monerans

CHAPTER OVERVIEW

Key Concepts

In this chapter, students will study the traits of viruses and bacteria, how they cause disease, and how they can be controlled. They will also study how bacteria are helpful. Students will study the traits of blue-green bacteria and how they are helpful and harmful.

Key Science Words

antibiotic
asexual reproduction
bacteria
biotechnology
blue-green bacteria
capsule
colony
communicable disease
decomposer
endospore
fission
flagellum
host
interferon
Koch's postulates
parasite
pasteurization
saprophyte
vaccine
virus

Skill Development

In Lab 4-1, students will **observe, recognize and use spatial relationships**, and **formulate a model** to understand the shape of a virus. In Lab 4-2, students will **make and use tables, observe, measure in SI,** and **use a microscope** to compare bacteria with blue-green bacteria. In the Skill Check on page 75, students will **interpret diagrams** to describe how a virus causes disease. On page 85, students will **understand** the **science word** *biotechnology.* In the Mini Lab on page 83, students will **infer** that salt and vinegar retard bacteria. In the Mini Lab on page 84, students will **use a microscope** to observe bacteria in yogurt.

CHAPTER PREVIEW

Chapter Content

Review this outline for Chapter 4 before you read the chapter.

4:1 Viruses
- Traits of Viruses
- Viruses and Disease
- Controlling Viruses

4:2 Monera Kingdom
- Traits of Bacteria
- Bacteria and Disease
- Helpful Bacteria
- Controlling Bacteria
- Blue-green Bacteria

Skills in this Chapter

The skills that you will use in this chapter are listed below.

- In **Lab 4-1**, you will observe, recognize and use spatial relationships, and formulate a model. In **Lab 4-2**, you will make and use tables, observe, measure in SI, and use a microscope.
- In the **Skill Checks**, you will interpret diagrams and understand science words.
- In the **Mini Labs**, you will infer and use a microscope.

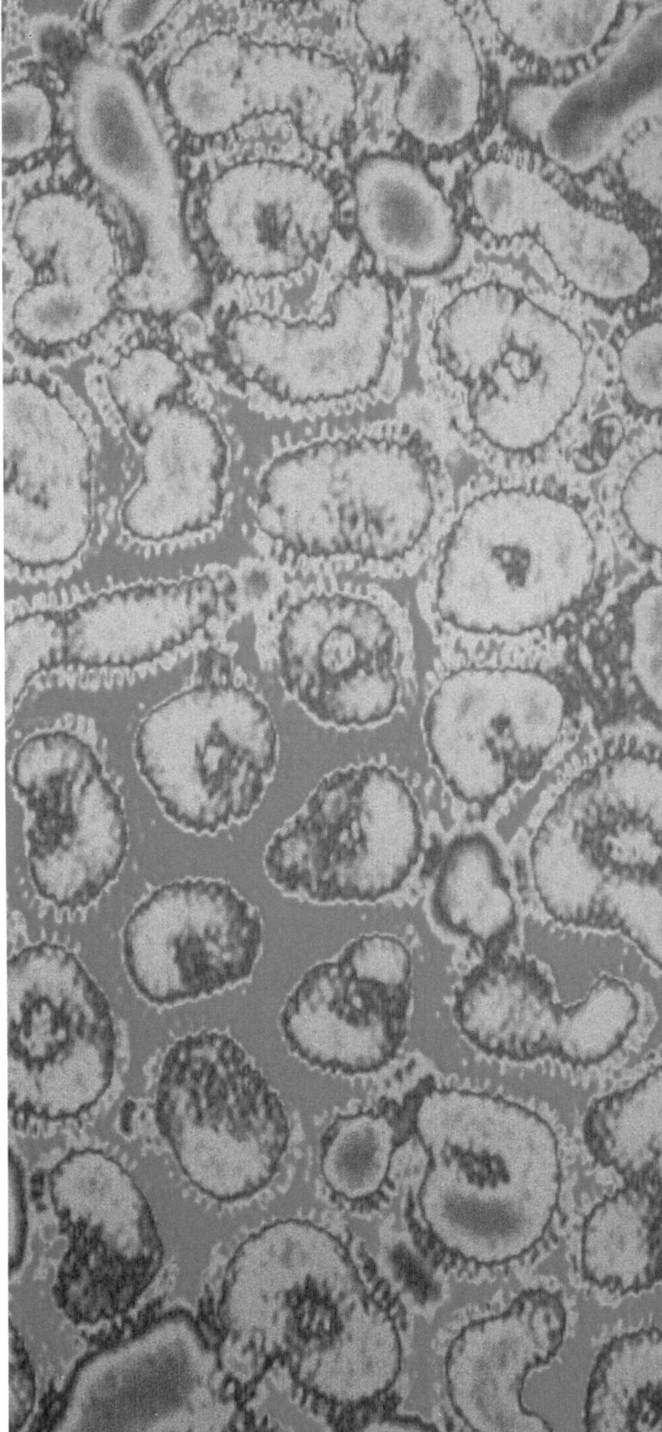

Flu virus

70

Bridging

Review the features of living things and the parts of typical cells in Chapter 2 to help students understand that viruses do not have cell parts and do not have all the features of living things. Bridge this section to bacteria, showing how bacteria are different from other cells.

Chapter **4**

Viruses and Monerans

Have you ever suffered from the flu? If so, you have had a disease caused by a virus. There are several kinds of viruses that cause the flu. You can get the flu more than once a year because you can be infected by different flu viruses. The photo on the left shows one of the viruses that can cause the flu. It is enlarged 120 000 times. What does this tell you about the size of viruses? In the smaller photo you can see bacteria that cause pneumonia. They are enlarged 75 000 times. Are bacteria or viruses larger?

In this chapter you will read about viruses and monerans. Viruses and monerans affect organisms that are billions of times larger than they are.

Try This!

What methods do people use to fight viruses? Interview several people to learn about folk remedies used to treat the common cold. Make a list of the folk remedies. After you have studied viruses, decide which folk remedies would be the most helpful in fighting a cold.

Pneumonia bacteria

GETTING STARTED

Using the Photos

In looking at the photos, students will think at first that bacteria are smaller than viruses. Have students note the different degrees of magnification. By comparing the difference, they will be able to determine that viruses are smaller than bacteria.

MOTIVATION/Try This!

What methods do people use to fight viruses? Upon completing the chapter-opening activity, students will have **communicated** with a number of persons and collected data that they can use in making a decision.

Chapter Preview

Have students study the chapter outline before they begin to read the chapter. The structure of viruses, the role of viruses in causing disease, and how viruses are controlled are studied first. The unique features of the two phyla in the moneran kingdom and their helpful and harmful effects are then discussed.

Misconception

Students may think that medicines cure colds. Medicines provide relief from symptoms, but not a cure. A cure would destroy the cold virus or disable it. We suffer from a cold until we develop antibodies. The medicines simply make us comfortable.

4:1 Viruses

PREPARATION

Materials Needed

Make copies of the Focus, Critical Thinking/Problem-Solving, Study Guide, Reteaching, and Lab worksheets in the *Teacher Resource Package.*

▶ Obtain a basketball, ping-pong ball, and BB shot for the MOTIVATION/Demonstration.

▶ Purchase bolts, nuts, wire, polystyrene balls, and pipecleaners for Lab 4-1.

Key Science Words

virus
host
parasite
interferon
vaccine

Process Skills

In Lab 4-1, students will observe, formulate a model, and recognize and use spatial relationships. In the Skill Check, students will interpret diagrams.

1 FOCUS

▶ The objectives are listed on the student page. Remind students to preview these objectives as a guide to this numbered section.

ACTIVITY/Word Association

The word *virus* comes from the Latin word for poison. Ask students to describe their most recent viral attacks. This will help the class remember the word-root association.

Focus/*Teacher Resource Package*, p. 7. Use the Focus transparency shown at the bottom of this page as an introduction to how bacteria affect our lives.

Objectives

1. **Identify** the traits of viruses.
2. **Tell** how viruses reproduce.
3. **List** examples of how viruses affect living things.

Key Science Words

virus
host
parasite
interferon
vaccine

4:1 Viruses

Viruses are neither living nor nonliving things, and yet they have some traits of both. Viruses are difficult for scientists to classify. What are these unusual things and what are their unusual traits?

Traits of Viruses

Viruses are so small that they can be seen only with an electron microscope. Figure 4-1 shows three kinds of viruses highly magnified. Viruses have many different shapes. Some are round and some are rod-shaped. Other viruses are many-sided.

A **virus** is made of a chromosome-like part surrounded by a protein coat. The chromosome-like part carries the hereditary material. The protein coat is responsible for the different shapes of viruses. The structures of some viruses are shown in Figure 4-00.

Viruses are not made of cells and have no cell parts. They do not grow or respond to changes in the environment as living things do. The trait that viruses share with living things is the ability to reproduce. However, viruses reproduce only inside living cells.

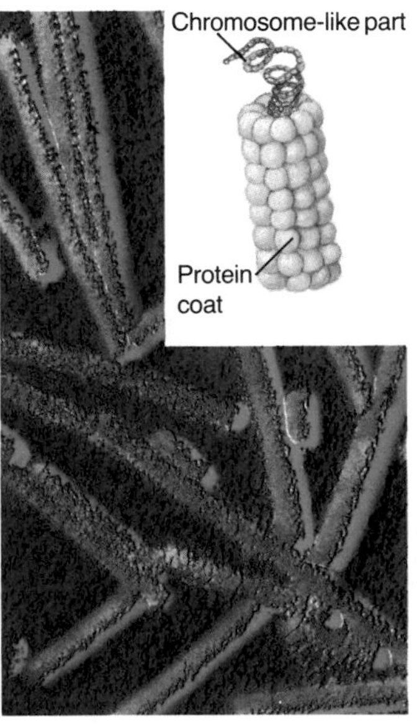

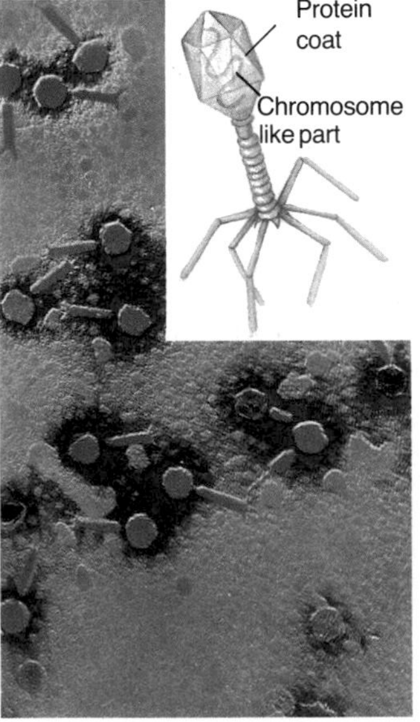

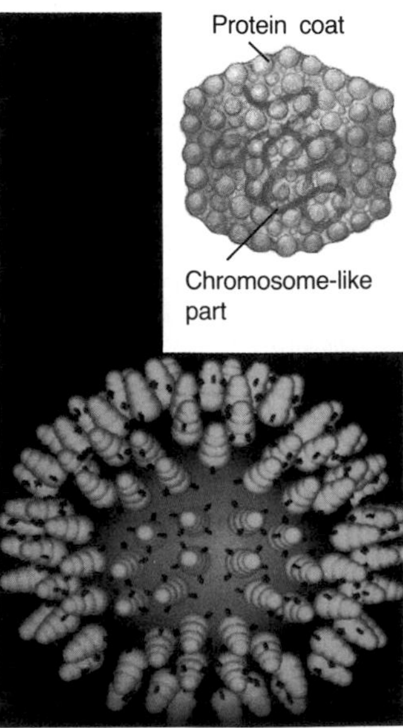

Figure 4-1 All viruses are made of a chromosome-like part and a protein coat.

OPTIONS

Science Background

In 1892, Dimitri Ivanoski, a Russian botanist, discovered that something smaller than bacteria could cause tobacco mosaic disease. In 1953, Dr. Wendell Stanley isolated the first virus, tobacco mosaic virus, and showed that viruses could be crystallized.

FOCUS 7

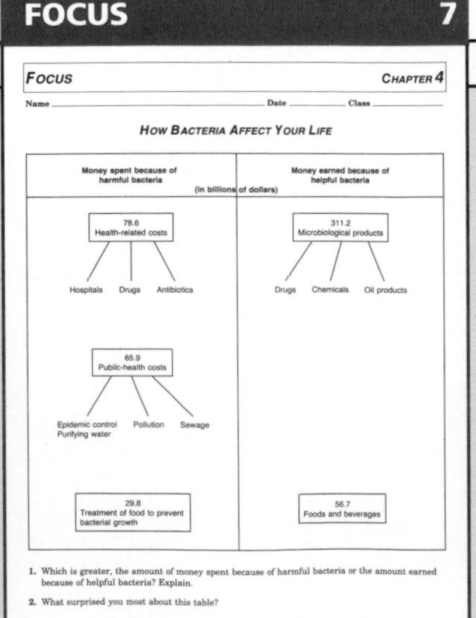
Focus CHAPTER 4

Name ______ Date ______ Class ______

HOW BACTERIA AFFECT YOUR LIFE

Money spent because of harmful bacteria	Money earned because of helpful bacteria
(in billions of dollars)	
78.6 Health-related costs: Hospitals, Drugs, Antibiotics	311.2 Microbiological products: Drugs, Chemicals, Oil products
65.9 Public-health costs: Epidemic control, Purifying water, Pollution, Sewage	
29.8 Treatment of food to prevent bacterial growth	56.7 Foods and beverages

1. Which is greater, the amount of money spent because of harmful bacteria or the amount earned because of helpful bacteria? Explain.
2. What surprised you most about this table?

Parts of viruses that look like crystals were stored in labs for as long as 50 years. Scientists then placed the viruses inside living cells. The viruses grew and reproduced. You can see why some scientists consider viruses to be living and others consider them nonliving. For this reason, viruses are not grouped into any kingdom.

One trait used to group viruses is the kind of cell they infect. Plants, animals, fungi, monerans, and protists all serve as hosts to different kinds of viruses. A **host** is an organism that provides food for a parasite (PAR uh site). A **parasite** is an organism that lives in or on another living thing and gets food from it. In this example, viruses act like parasites.

Each kind of virus infects a certain host. For example, the tobacco mosaic virus in Figure 4-2 will infect tobacco plants, but not corn or wheat plants. Some viruses will infect only certain parts of their hosts. The rabies virus will infect only the nervous system of mammals. Common cold viruses will infect only the cells along the air pathway to the lungs. The shape of the protein coat and size of the virus are two other traits that scientists use to classify viruses.

Some scientists think that viruses came into being before cells existed. Others say that viruses are parts of early cells. Still another idea is that they may have come from disease-causing bacteria.

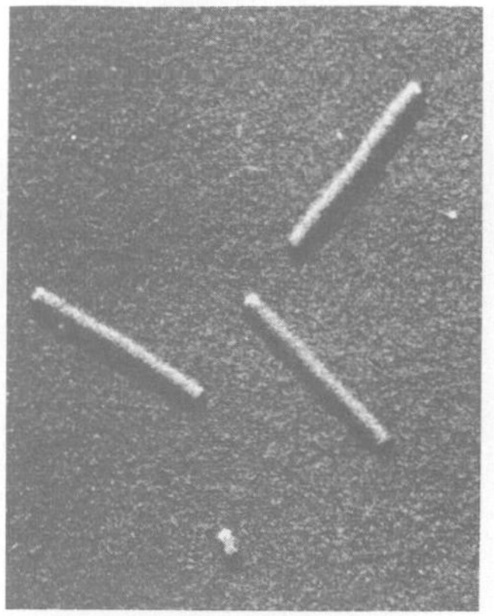

Figure 4-2 Tobacco mosaic virus, magnified 100 000 times

What traits are used to classify viruses?

Viruses and Disease

In spite of their small size, viruses cause many serious diseases in humans and other living things. Some of these diseases are listed in Table 4-1. Viruses may spread from one infected organism to another. In humans, viruses are spread by insects, air, water, food, and other people.

TABLE 4–1. DISEASES CAUSED BY VIRUSES

Animal Diseases	Human Diseases	Plant Diseases
Rabies in dogs	Common cold, flu	Mosaic disease in tobacco
Foot and mouth disease in cattle	German measles, mumps	Bushy stunt in tomato
Newcastle disease in chickens	Measles, chickenpox	Maize dwarf mosaic
Distemper in dogs	Mononucleosis, cold sores	Mosaic disease in alfalfa
Cowpox in cows	Hepatitis, warts	Curly top in sugar beet
Feline leukemia in cats	Polio, smallpox	Dwarfism in rice
	Herpes, AIDS	

Bio Tip

Health: An influenza virus can survive five minutes on human skin and 1.5 days on a kitchen counter top.

2 TEACH

MOTIVATION/Demonstration

Show students a basketball, a ping-pong ball, and a BB shot. Tell them that one represents a human cheek cell, one represents a bacterium, and one represents a virus. Ask which each one represents.

MOTIVATION/Software

Microbiology Techniques, EME.

Concept Development

▶ Before starting this section, you may want to have students discuss whether viruses are living or nonliving. List their ideas on the chalkboard under the headings "Living" and "Nonliving."

▶ Mention that many different viruses are responsible for the large variety of colds and flus that infect humans.

▶ Encourage your students to bring in newspaper and magazine articles concerning viruses.

▶ Point out that scientists could not see viruses until after the electron microscope came into use in the 1940s.

▶ Point out the number of colds a person gets per year tends to decrease with age. It is possible that older people have more antibodies against most of the cold viruses.

Guided Practice

Have students write down their answers to the margin question: the shape of the protein coat and size of the virus.

OPTIONS

Science Background

Until the discovery of viroids, viruses were thought to be the smallest things to cause disease. Viroids are short, naked strands of RNA. They are only a fraction of the size of viruses. They lack the protein coat of viruses. As with viruses, they reproduce only within a living cell. They are known to cause several plant diseases. They may also cause some diseases in animals and humans.

TEACH

Concept Development

▶ You may want to mention that some viruses may be considered to be beneficial. A variety of tulip has been cultivated because of the ornamental coloring produced by a virus that infects the tulip. Some viruses are used in research.

Guided Practice

Have students write down their answers to the margin question: Insects break through the cell walls of the plant cells and let the virus enter.

MOTIVATION/Demonstration

Use the overhead projector or the chalkboard to draw diagrams to explain viral replication. The reproduction of viruses is often called viral replication to distinguish it from the reproduction of cells.

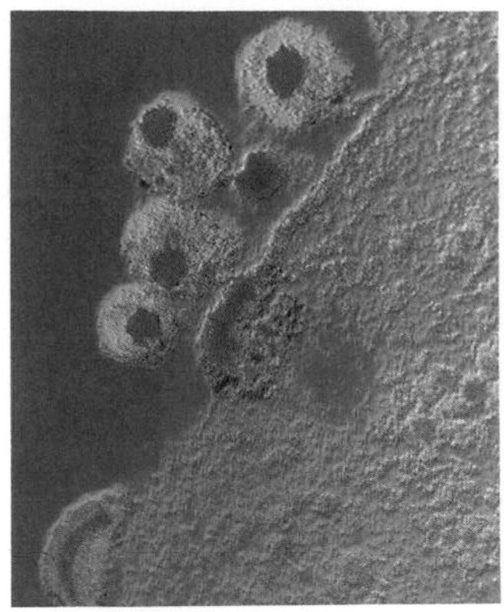

Figure 4-3 AIDS virus being released from an infected cell.

Acquired immune deficiency syndrome (AIDS) is a viral disease that destroys the body's immune system. When the immune system does not work properly, the body can't fight infections. People with AIDS die from diseases that most others can resist. Even a common cold can be life-threatening. The AIDS virus, Figure 4-3, is spread in four ways. It is spread by sexual contact, blood products, the sharing of contaminated needles, and from a pregnant woman to her developing baby. Scientists studying AIDS have not yet discovered a cure.

How do viruses get into plant cells?

Plant viruses may be spread by the wind or by insects. Chewing or sucking insects, such as aphids (AY fudz), whiteflies, and beetles, spread most plant viruses. Many plant viruses are unable to enter a plant without the help of an insect. While feeding, the insect breaks through the cell wall of the plant. This break in the cell wall lets the virus get into the host cell. Viruses may infect one or two leaves or an entire plant. Insects or wind then carry the viruses to other plants.

How do viruses cause disease? Some reproduce rapidly and cause the cell to break open and release viruses, as shown in Figure 4-5. When this type of virus comes in

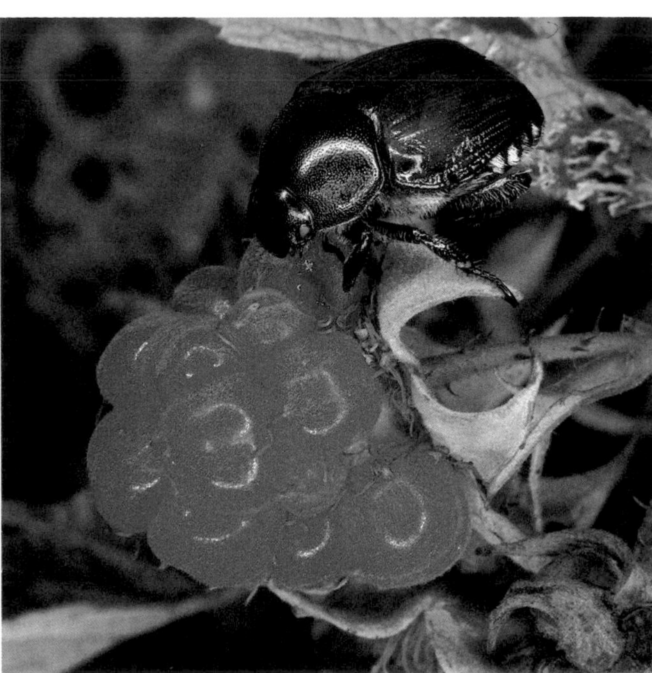

Figure 4-4 Chewing and sucking insects break cell walls and allow viruses to enter plants.

OPTIONS

Science Background

Traditionally, plant and animal viruses have been named for the diseases they cause (e.g., smallpox, rabies, tobacco mosaic virus), while bacteriophages have been assigned number and letter codes (e.g., T2, T4, etc.).

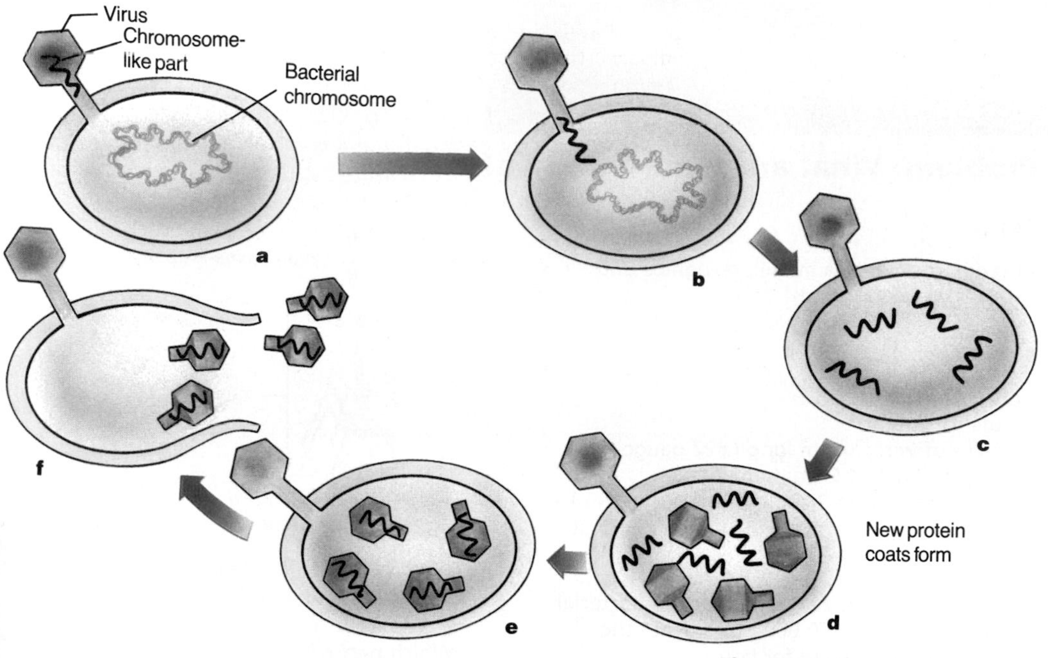

Figure 4-5 Life cycle of a bacterial virus

contact with a host cell, it attaches itself to the cell (a). The chromosome-like part enters the cell (b). Then the chromosome-like part takes over the cell (c). The virus changes the hereditary material in the host cell so that the host cell produces more viruses instead of performing its usual work (d-e). The cell breaks open and releases the new viruses, which then invade other cells (f). Tissue damage and disease result. Viruses that cause polio, mumps, rabies, and flu in humans act this way.

Other viruses remain hidden in the cell a long time without reproducing. Cold sores are blisters around the lips. They are caused by a virus. No symptoms appear until something such as a fever or sunburn causes the virus to become active. The cold sores may disappear for long periods of time, but the virus remains in the body. As long as the virus does not reproduce, no cold sores appear. When the virus begins reproducing again, the cold sores reappear.

Other viruses cause the host cells to reproduce both themselves and the viruses. Groups of infected cells become lumps called tumors. Some tumors are harmless. A wart is an example of a harmless tumor. Examples of harmful tumors are some kinds of cancer.

Skill Check

Interpret diagrams: Look at Figure 4-5 and tell how a virus causes disease. Describe what is taking place in each lettered step. *For more help, refer to the* ***Skill Handbook****, pages 706-711.*

TEACH

Concept Development

▶ Point out that viruses that cause lysis of their host are called virulent phages. A phage may complete a life cycle in 25 to 45 minutes and give off several hundred new phages.

Skill Check

Point out to students that the letters in the text correspond to the letters in the diagram.

Independent Practice

Study Guide/*Teacher Resource Package*, p. 19. Use the Study Guide worksheet shown at the bottom of this page for independent practice.

STUDY GUIDE 19

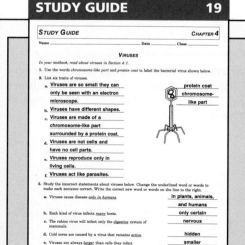

STUDY GUIDE — CHAPTER 4

Name ______ Date ______ Class ______

VIRUSES

In your textbook, read about viruses in Section 4:1.

1. Use the words *chromosome-like part* and *protein coat* to label the bacterial virus shown below.

protein coat
chromosome-like part

2. List six traits of viruses.
   a. Viruses are so small they can only be seen with an electron microscope.
   b. Viruses have different shapes.
   c. Viruses are made of a chromosome-like part surrounded by a protein coat.
   d. Viruses are not cells and have no cell parts.
   e. Viruses reproduce only in living cells.
   f. Viruses act like parasites.

3. Study the incorrect statements about viruses below. Change the underlined word or words to make each sentence correct. Write the correct new word or words on the line to the right.
   a. Viruses cause disease *only in humans*. — in plants, animals, and humans
   b. Each kind of virus infects *many* hosts. — only certain
   c. The rabies virus will infect only the *digestive* system of mammals. — nervous
   d. Cold sores are caused by a virus that remains *active*. — hidden
   e. Viruses are always *larger* than cells they infect. — smaller
   f. Viruses reproduce *outside* of living cells. — inside
   g. Viruses *do not change* the hereditary material in the host cell. — change

OPTIONS

Science Background

The viral disease rubella, also called German measles, is generally mild in children. But it can cause a serious problem if a woman has the disease during the fourth through the twelfth weeks of pregnancy. The developing fetus can suffer damage to the heart, the lens of the eye, the inner ear, and the brain.

Lab 4-1 Viruses

Overview

In this lab, students assemble three-dimensional models of two kinds of viruses to learn the structure of viruses. The lack of cell parts in the models will enable them to learn what viruses are not.

Objectives: Upon completing the lab, students will be able to (1) **describe** the shapes of viruses, (2) **relate** the basic parts of viruses, (3) **demonstrate** how a virus attacks a healthy cell.

Time Allotment: 45 minutes

Preparation

▶ **Alternate Materials:** Toothpicks may be used for pipecleaners. Other sizes of bolts and nuts may be used.

▶ Cut #22 gauge wire in 14-cm lengths. Cut pipecleaners in 2-cm lengths.

Lab 4-1 worksheet/*Teacher Resource Package*, pp. 13-14.

Teaching the Lab

▶ **Troubleshooting:** If the wire is not strong enough to hold the model up, fold the wire, twist it, and then place it on the bolt.

Cooperative Learning: Have students work in pairs to do the lab. For more information, see pp. 22T-23T in the Teacher Guide.

Viruses — Lab 4—1

Problem: What are some shapes of viruses?

Skills

observe, formulate a model, recognize and use spatial relationships

Materials

bolt, 3.7 cm × 0.7 cm
2 nuts to fit bolt
2 pieces of wire, 14 cm long (#22 gauge)
polystyrene ball, 4.5 cm in diameter
pipecleaners, cut in 2-cm lengths

Procedure

1. **Observe:** Look at Figure A of the bacterial virus enlarged 260 000 times. Note the three parts labeled for you.
2. **Formulate a Model:** To build a model of the virus, attach two nuts onto the bolt as shown in Figure C.
3. Twist the wires around the bolt as in Figure D. Make them as tight as possible.
4. Fold down the wire ends and bend them as in Figure E.
5. Figure B shows a flu virus enlarged 300 000 times. Build a model of this virus using the polystyrene ball and pipecleaners.

Data and Observations

1. Which virus part is represented by the top of the bolt and the nuts in your model?
2. Which virus part is represented by the threaded part of the bolt and the wires?

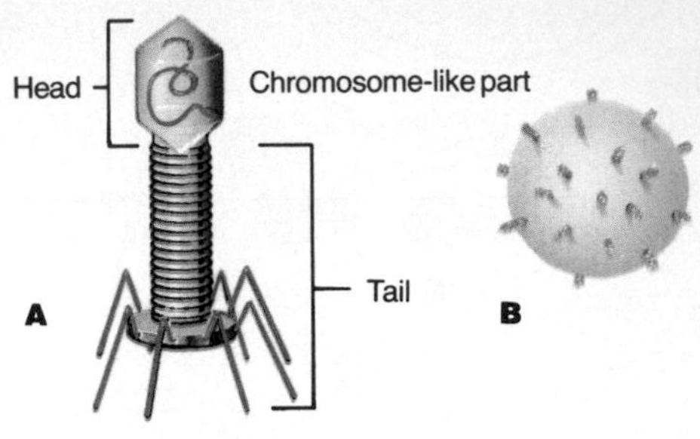

Analyze and Apply

1. What chemical in a real virus would make up the threaded part of the bolt and the wires?
2. Which part of a virus would attach to the host's cell membrane?
3. Which parts would not enter a cell?
4. Which part does enter a cell?
5. If your flu virus model were a real virus, what would you expect to find inside the ball?
6. What chemical would you expect to make up the covering on the ball?
7. What are the basic parts of a virus?
8. **Apply:** How does the structure of a virus differ from that of a bacterial cell?

Extension

Formulate a model: Using references, look up the shapes of some other viruses. Build models with common household items.

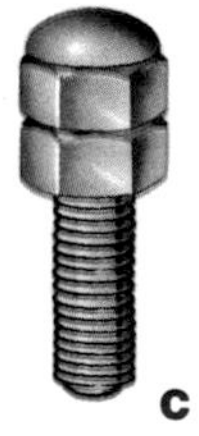

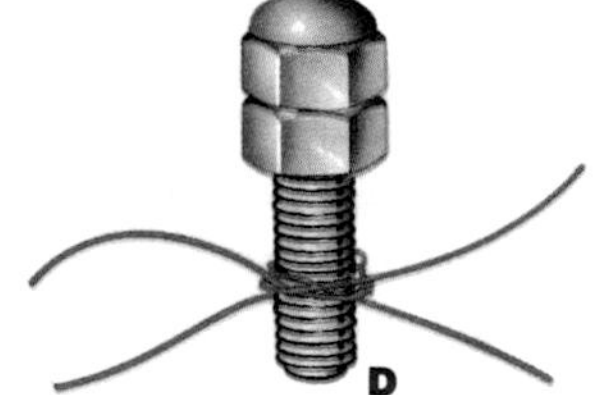

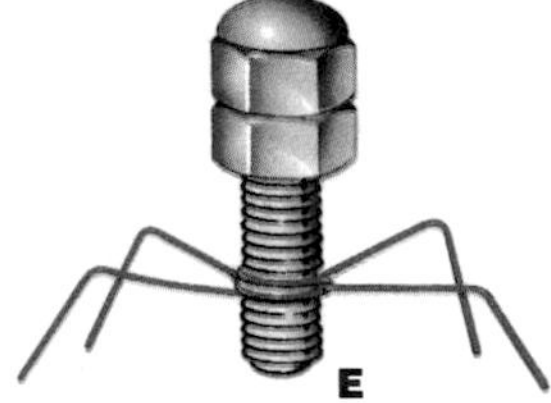

ANSWERS

Data and Observations

1. head
2. tail

Analyze and Apply

1. protein
2. tail
3. the head and tail
4. the chromosome-like part
5. the chromosome-like part
6. protein
7. head, tail, and chromosome-like part
8. Viruses are smaller. They are not green, and they do not live in colonies. The cells are single. *Anabaena* is green, has two kinds of cells, and lives in colonies.

Controlling Viruses

Diseases caused by viruses are hard to treat or cure. There are no known drugs that destroy viruses. However, humans and other animals are protected against some viruses in several ways. Certain white blood cells can surround and destroy a virus. If the virus is not captured and destroyed by these white blood cells, other white blood cells make chemicals called antibodies (ANT ih bohd eez). Antibodies help destroy viruses or harmful bacteria by attaching to them. The virus or bacterium may be destroyed directly by the antibody or it may be held captive by the antibody until white blood cells can surround and destroy it. Each antibody acts only on one specific kind of virus or bacteria.

When human cells are first attacked by a virus, the cells produce interferon (ihnt ur FIHR ahn). **Interferon** is a chemical substance that interferes with the way viruses reproduce. When infected cells burst and release more viruses, they also release interferon. It is believed that the interferon warns nearby cells that a viral infection is taking place. The cells then produce their own chemicals to fight the viruses. Unlike antibodies, interferon will affect any type of virus that invades the body. The interferon produced in one species will work only in that species. For example, interferon produced by a horse will not work in humans.

What does a human cell do when it is attacked by a virus?

Idea Map

Viruses

- **Viruses**
  - **structure**
    - **chromosome-like part**
    - **protein coat**
  - **traits**
    - **reproduce only in living cells**
    - **each infects a certain host**
    - **causes disease**
  - **control**
    - **white blood cells - antibodies**
    - **interferon**
    - **vaccines**

Study Tip: Use this idea map as a study guide to viruses. The features of viruses and how viruses are controlled are shown.

TEACH

Concept Development

▶ Point out that scientists now believe that some people may be prone to cancer because their bodies do not produce enough interferon.

Guided Practice

Have students write down their answers to the margin question: It produces interferon.

Idea Map

Have students use the idea map as a study guide to the major concepts of this section.

Cooperative Learning: Divide the class into groups of four. Have each group research and report on the topics: culturing of viruses in tissues, such as the chick embryo; how interferon works; Burkitt's lymphoma; viroids; and viruses.

Independent Practice

Study Guide/*Teacher Resource Package*, p. 20. Use the Study Guide worksheet shown at the bottom of this page for independent practice.

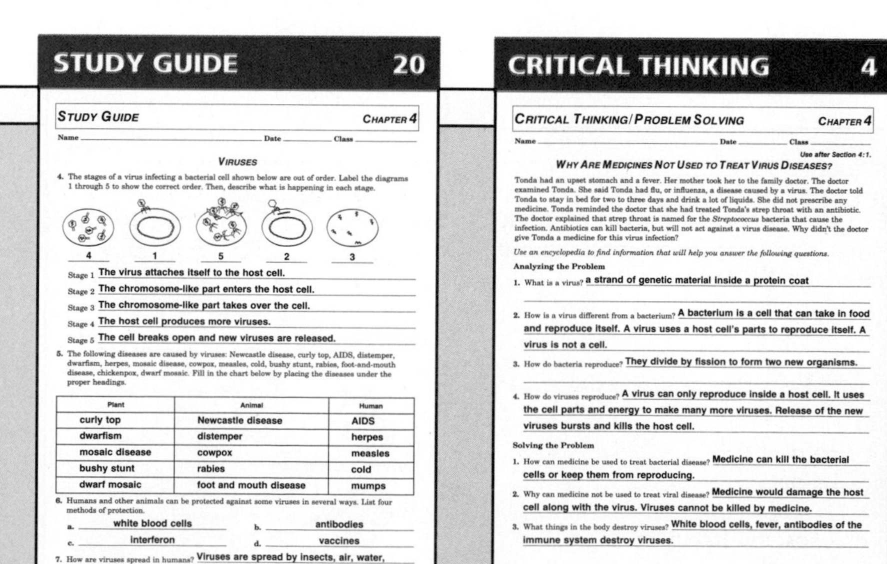

STUDY GUIDE 20

STUDY GUIDE CHAPTER 4

Name ______ Date ______ Class ______

VIRUSES

4. The stages of a virus infecting a bacterial cell shown below are out of order. Label the diagrams 1 through 5 to show the correct order. Then, describe what is happening in each stage.

4 1 5 2 3

Stage 1 The virus attaches itself to the host cell.

Stage 2 The chromosome-like part enters the host cell.

Stage 3 The chromosome-like part takes over the cell.

Stage 4 The host cell produces more viruses.

Stage 5 The cell breaks open and new viruses are released.

5. The following diseases are caused by viruses: Newcastle disease, curly top, AIDS, distemper, dwarfism, herpes, mosaic disease, cowpox, measles, cold, bushy stunt, rabies, foot-and-mouth disease, chickenpox, dwarf mosaic. Fill in the chart below by placing the diseases under the proper headings.

Plant	Animal	Human
curly top	Newcastle disease	AIDS
dwarfism	distemper	herpes
mosaic disease	cowpox	measles
bushy stunt	rabies	cold
dwarf mosaic	foot and mouth disease	mumps

6. Humans and other animals can be protected against some viruses in several ways. List four methods of protection.

a. white blood cells b. antibodies

c. interferon d. vaccines

7. How are viruses spread in humans? Viruses are spread by insects, air, water, food, and other people.

CRITICAL THINKING 4

CRITICAL THINKING/PROBLEM SOLVING CHAPTER 4

Name ______ Date ______ Class ______

Use after Section 4:1.

WHY ARE MEDICINES NOT USED TO TREAT VIRUS DISEASES?

Tonda had an upset stomach and a fever. Her mother took her to the family doctor. The doctor examined Tonda. She said Tonda had flu, or influenza, a disease caused by a virus. The doctor told Tonda to stay in bed for two to three days and drink a lot of liquids. She did not prescribe any medicine. Tonda reminded the doctor that she had treated Tonda's strep throat with an antibiotic. The doctor explained that strep throat is named for the *Streptococcus* bacteria that cause the infection. Antibiotics can kill bacteria, but will not act against a virus disease. Why didn't the doctor give Tonda a medicine for this virus infection?

Use an encyclopedia to find information that will help you answer the following questions.

Analyzing the Problem

1. What is a virus? a strand of genetic material inside a protein coat

2. How is a virus different from a bacterium? A bacterium is a cell that can take in food and reproduce itself. A virus uses a host cell's parts to reproduce itself. A virus is not a cell.

3. How do bacteria reproduce? They divide by fission to form two new organisms.

4. How do viruses reproduce? A virus can only reproduce inside a host cell. It uses the cell parts and energy to make many more viruses. Release of the new viruses bursts and kills the host cell.

Solving the Problem

1. How can medicine be used to treat bacterial disease? Medicine can kill the bacterial cells or keep them from reproducing.

2. Why can medicine not be used to treat viral disease? Medicine would damage the host cell along with the virus. Viruses cannot be killed by medicine.

3. What things in the body destroy viruses? White blood cells, fever, antibodies of the immune system destroy viruses.

OPTIONS

Critical Thinking/Problem Solving/ *Teacher Resource Package*, p. 4. Use the worksheet shown here to reinforce why medicines are not used to treat viral diseases.

TEACH

Concept Development

▶ The World Health Organization has declared the world free of the killing form of smallpox. The smallpox vaccine has been the major factor in eliminating smallpox.

Check for Understanding

Have students respond to the first three questions in Check Your Understanding.

Reteach

Reteaching/*Teacher Resource Package*, p. 10. Use this worksheet to give students additional practice with the life cycle of a virus.

Extension: Assign Critical Thinking, Biology and Writing, or some of the **OPTIONS** available with this lesson.

3 APPLY

Videocassette

Show the videocassette *Viruses*, Coronet.

4 CLOSE

Overhead

Make transparencies of the following viral groups: papovaviruses, adenoviruses, and herpesviruses.

Answers to Check Your Understanding

1. A virus has no cell parts and does not grow like a living thing.
2. inside a living cell
3. It produces antibodies, interferon, and certain white cells that destroy viruses.
4. In response to both infection and a vaccine, the body produces antibodies.
5. The mosquito and the horse are the hosts. The bacteria are parasites.

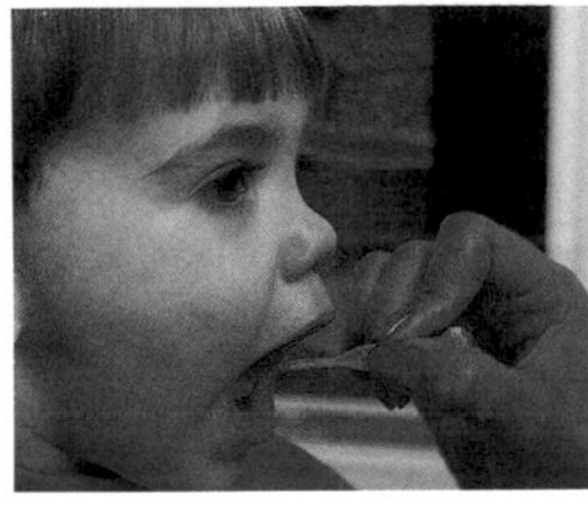

a

b

Figure 4-6 A person takes polio vaccine for protection against the disease (a). Burning infected plants prevents the spread of plant diseases caused by viruses (b).

Vaccines are substances made from weakened or dead viruses. They can be used to treat some viral or bacterial diseases. There are vaccines for polio, rubella, measles, and influenza. Figure 4-6a shows a person getting the polio vaccine. The body reacts to a vaccine by producing antibodies to protect against the disease. In addition to people, pets and farm animals receive vaccines for protection against disease.

It is usually impossible to treat viral infections in plants. Therefore, farmers try to prevent the spread of viral infections by burning infected plants.

Check Your Understanding

1. List two ways viruses differ from living things.
2. Where must viruses be found if they are to reproduce?
3. What are three ways the human body protects itself against viruses?
4. **Critical Thinking:** How is the body's reaction to a vaccine similar to its reaction when it is attacked by a virus?
5. **Biology and Writing:** A mosquito contains some viruses and bites a horse. The horse becomes sick with a disease caused by the viruses from the mosquito. Use a complete sentence to tell which two living things are the hosts. What is the parasite?

OPTIONS

Enrichment: Explain the development of polio vaccines and the way that mass vaccinations were conducted in the 1960s.

RETEACHING 10

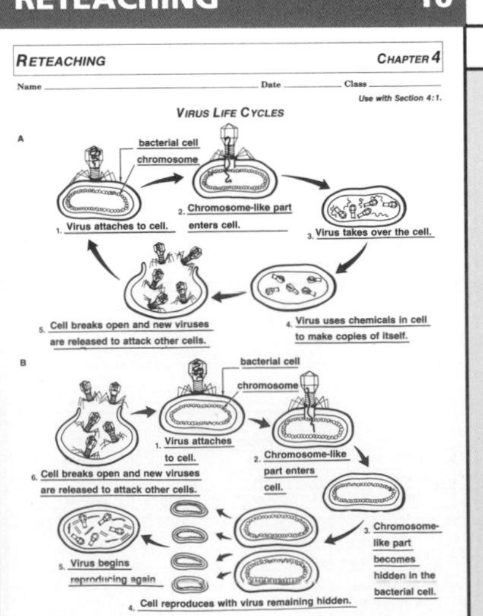

RETEACHING CHAPTER 4

Name ______ Date ______ Class ______

Use with Section 4:1.

VIRUS LIFE CYCLES

4:2 Monera Kingdom

Monerans are one-celled organisms that lack a nucleus, but do have nuclear material within the cell wall. They also lack many of the cell parts found in plant and animal cells. The two groups of monerans, bacteria and blue-green bacteria, are found everywhere around you. They live as single cells or in groups of cells.

Objectives

4. **Identify** the traits of bacteria.
5. **Explain** how bacteria affect other living things.
6. **Compare** the traits of blue-green bacteria and other bacteria.

Key Science Words

bacteria
colony
capsule
flagellum
fission
asexual reproduction
endospore
saprophyte
decomposer
Koch's postulates
communicable disease
antibiotic
biotechnology
pasteurization
blue-green bacteria

Traits of Bacteria

What are bacteria? **Bacteria** are very small, one-celled monerans. They are larger than viruses, but are too small to be seen without a microscope. They are so small that 300 could fit side by side across the period at the end of this sentence.

Bacteria can be found almost everywhere. They live in water, air, soil, food, and on almost every object. They are on your skin and even inside your body. Bacteria have been found in arctic ice as well as in hot springs. Bacteria are so widespread because almost any material may be food for some kind of bacteria.

Bacteria are classified into three groups according to shape. Some bacteria are round. Some are shaped like rods. Others are spiral, Figure 4-7. Bacteria can live as single cells, or they can be found in pairs and colonies. A **colony** is a group of similar cells attached to each other. They may join together in clusters or chains. The cells in a colony do not depend on one another.

a

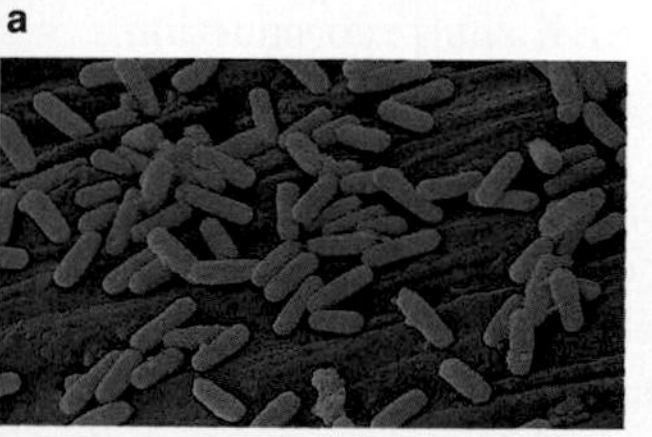

b

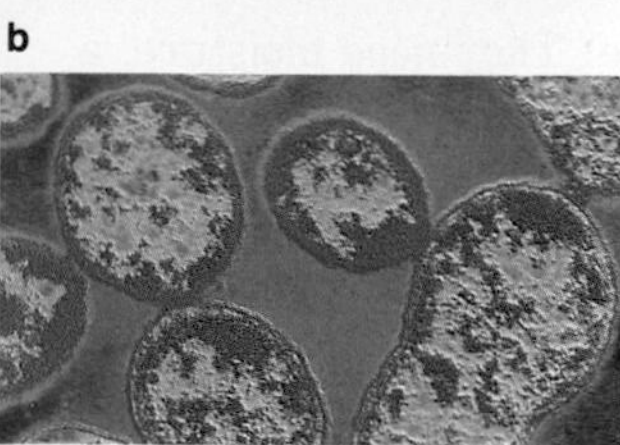

c

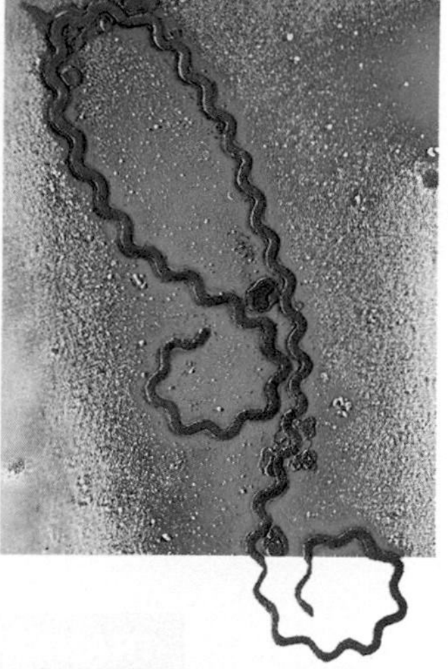

Figure 4-7 Rod-shaped bacteria (a), round bacteria (b), and spiral bacteria (c) highly magnified

OPTIONS

Science Background

Rod-shaped bacteria are called bacilli. Spherical bacteria are called cocci. Spiral-shaped bacteria are called spirilla.

Bacterial and Animal Cells/ *Transparency Package,* number 4. Use color transparency number 4 as you teach the cell parts of bacteria.

4:2 Monera Kingdom

PREPARATION

Materials Needed

Make copies of the Transparency Master, Skill, Study Guide, Application, Enrichment, Reteaching, and Lab worksheets in the *Teacher Resource Package.*

▶ Obtain beef broth, salt, sugar, vinegar, and plain yogurt for the Mini Labs.

▶ Obtain prepared slides of *Anabaena* and bacteria for Lab 4-2.

Key Science Words

bacteria
colony
capsule
flagellum
fission
asexual reproduction
endospore
saprophyte
decomposer
Koch's postulates
communicable disease
antibiotic
biotechnology
pasteurization
blue-green bacteria

Process Skills

In Lab 4-2, students will make and use tables, observe, measure in SI, and use a microscope. In the Skill Check, students will understand science words. In the Mini Labs, students will infer and use a microscope.

1 FOCUS

▶ The objectives are listed on the student page. Remind students to preview these objectives as a guide to this numbered section.

MOTIVATION/Bulletin Board

Put the title Monerans – Helpful and Harmful on a bulletin board. Display pictures of items such as yogurt, cheese, sauerkraut, buttermilk, vinegar, antibiotics, tooth decay, crown gall, fire blight, and cows eating. Have students decide in which column the pictures should be placed.

2 TEACH

MOTIVATION/Demonstration

Draw a bacterial cell and an animal cell on the chalkboard. Use colored chalk to draw in the cell parts. Have the students compare the two cells.

MOTIVATION/Brainstorming

Have students name some skin diseases caused by bacteria (acne, pimples, boils).

Concept Development

▶ Point out that the most unusual trait of bacteria is not size or shape, but chemical makeup. Because of their versatility, bacteria can be found almost everywhere.

▶ Explain that the interval from one fission to the next is highly variable. *E. coli,* a bacterium found in the human intestinal system, divides every 20 minutes under ideal conditions. *Treponema pallidum*, a bacterium that causes syphilis, can divide every 33 hours. Bacteria that cause leprosy reproduce only once every 12 days.

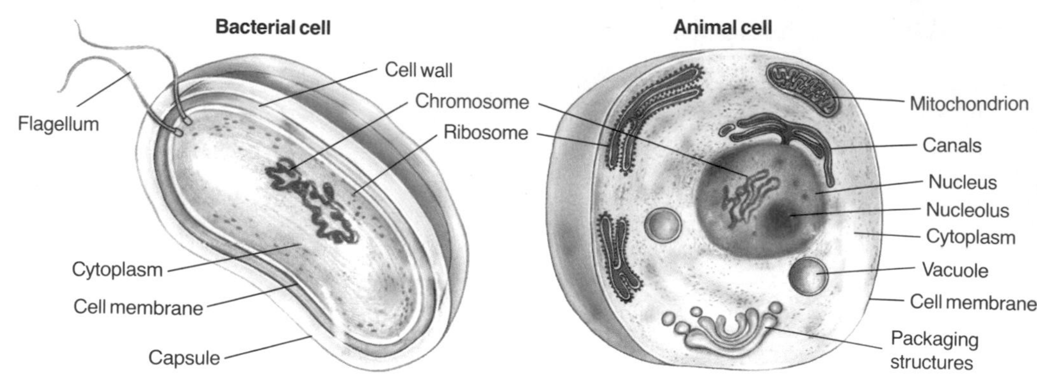

Figure 4-8 Structures of bacterial and animal cells. What structures are found in a bacterial cell but not in an animal cell? flagellum, cell wall, capsule

Under a microscope, bacteria look very different from other cells you have studied. Notice that the bacterial cell in Figure 4-8 does not have a nucleus. It has one main chromosome. The animal cell does have a nucleus. The bacterial cell also does not have most cell parts seen in the animal cell.

Even without certain cell parts, bacteria carry on the same jobs as other cells. Bacteria still reproduce, grow, and carry out cellular respiration.

Bacterial cells have a cell wall as well as a cell membrane. Some bacteria have a sticky outer layer called a **capsule,** Figure 4-8. The capsule keeps the cell from drying out and helps the cell stick to food and other cells. Some bacteria move with a long, whiplike thread called a **flagellum** (fluh JEL um).

Bacteria reproduce by fission (FIHSH un). **Fission** is the process of one organism dividing into two organisms. Fission is a kind of asexual (ay SEK shul) reproduction. **Asexual reproduction** is the reproducing of a living thing from only one parent. Bacteria reproduce by asexual reproduction. The circular chromosome of the bacterial cell makes a copy of itself, and the cell divides, Figure 4-9. The time that it takes a bacterial cell to grow and divide into two cells varies. If growing conditions are right, it can take only about 20 minutes.

What do bacteria need to live? They need moisture, a certain temperature, and food. A few bacteria can live at 0°C and others can live at temperatures of 75°C. Those that cause disease in humans live at 37°C, normal body temperature. Most bacteria grow best in darkness. Most need oxygen to live. Others cannot live in the presence of oxygen.

Bio Tip

Consumer: Bacteria cause much of the metal corrosion in the United States, at an annual cost that may be more than $600 for every man, woman, and child in the country.

Figure 4-9 A bacterial cell divides to form two new cells. What is this form of reproduction called? fission

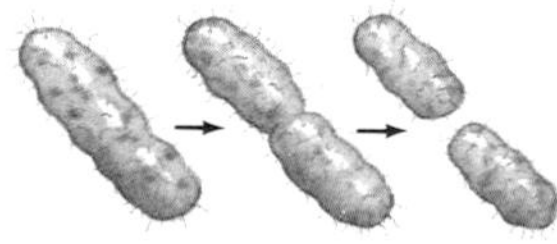

OPTIONS

Science Background

The classification of monerans is controversial. Kingdom Monera includes the archaebacteria or "ancient" bacteria and the Eubacteria, or "true" bacteria. Only two groups of Eubacteria are included here.

Transparency Master/*Teacher Resource Package,* p. 15. Use the Transparency Master shown here to help students compare viruses and monerans.

TRANSPARENCY 15

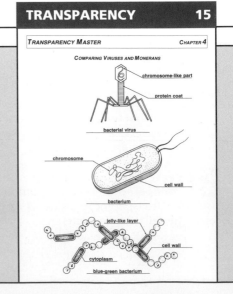

TRANSPARENCY MASTER — CHAPTER 4

COMPARING VIRUSES AND MONERANS

chromosome-like part
protein coat
bacterial virus
chromosome
cell wall
bacterium
jelly-like layer
cell wall
cytoplasm
blue-green bacterium

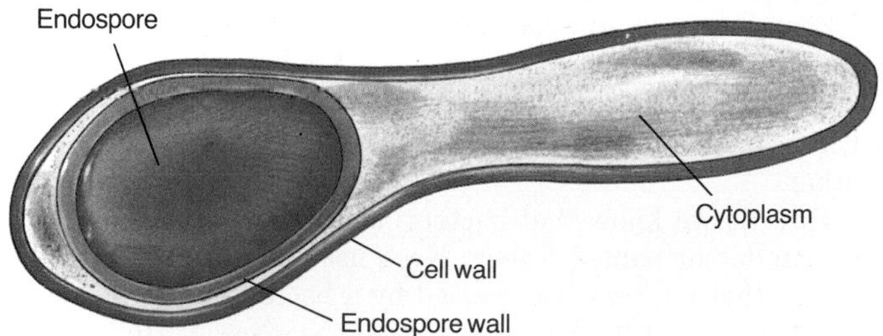

Figure 4-10 An endospore has a thick, protective wall that allows the bacterium to withstand harsh conditions.

If living conditions are not right for bacteria to grow, they can survive by forming endospores (EN duh sporz), Figure 4-10. An **endospore** is a thick-walled structure that forms inside the cell, enclosing all the nuclear material and some cytoplasm. Some endospores can survive for many years. They can withstand boiling, freezing, and extremely dry conditions without damage. When conditions return to normal, endospores develop into bacteria. Endospores are not used for reproduction. They let bacteria survive when living conditions are not ideal.

Most bacteria feed on other living things or on dead things. Bacteria that feed on living things are parasites. Bacteria that live on dead things are called saprophytes (SAP ruh fites). **Saprophytes** are organisms that use dead materials for food. They get energy by breaking down, or decomposing, dead materials. **Decomposers** are living things that get their food from breaking down dead matter into simpler chemicals. Decomposers are important because they return minerals and other materials to the soil, where other organisms can use them.

What do bacteria use for food?

Some bacteria can make their own food. Some use the energy of the sun to make food. Others use the energy in substances containing iron and sulfur to make food.

Bacteria and Disease

Some bacteria are parasites in humans. They can cause a variety of diseases. Human diseases caused by bacteria include strep throat, tuberculosis, certain kinds of pneumonia (noo MOH nyuh), gonorrhea (gahn uh REE uh), and meningitis.

Plants and animals other than humans also may have bacterial diseases. Fire blight and crown gall, Figure 4-11, are plant diseases caused by bacteria. The bacteria that cause fire blight are spread by rain.

Figure 4-11 Crown gall is a plant disease caused by bacteria.

TEACH

Concept Development

▶ Point out that most bacteria that form endospores are harmless. However, some such as bacteria that cause tetanus and botulism are extremely dangerous.

▶ You may wish to mention that some bacteria make their own food by chemosynthesis. Chemosynthesis is similar to photosynthesis except that sunlight is not necessary.

▶ Point out that many bacteria obtain food by secreting digestive enzymes through their cell walls. The digestive enzymes break down food molecules into smaller molecules that can be absorbed by the bacteria.

▶ You might mention that other bacterial diseases include toxic shock syndrome, impetigo, sinusitis, ear infections, scarlet fever, tetanus, food poisoning, whooping cough, and leprosy.

Guided Practice

Have students write down their answers to the margin question: other living things or dead things.

OPTIONS

Does Soil Contain Bacteria?/*Lab Manual*, pp. 27-30. Use this lab as an extension to where bacteria are found.

TEACH

Concept Development

▶ Explain how Koch's postulates are being used today to identify disease-causing organisms. Have students bring in newspaper and magazine articles on disease research.

Guided Practice

Have students write down their answers to the margin question: They show that bacteria taken from one host causes the same disease in a second host.

Some bacterial diseases that occur in animals can be passed on to humans. Anthrax, a disease found in livestock, is one example. It is usually passed on to people who work with animals, such as butchers and handlers of wool and leather.

How do we know that bacteria cause disease? In 1876, a German doctor named Robert Koch used a scientific method to show that anthrax was caused by a bacterium. He made a hypothesis that a bacterium caused the disease. He experimented to test the hypothesis. The experiments supported his hypothesis, so he formed a theory about the cause of disease.

How can scientists prove that bacteria cause disease?

Koch's postulates (KAHKS • PAHS chuh lutz) are steps for proving that a disease is caused by a certain microscopic organism. Here are Koch's postulates.

1. The organism must be present in a living thing when the disease occurs.
2. The organism must be taken from the host and grown in the laboratory, Figure 4-12a, b.
3. When the organisms from the laboratory are injected into healthy hosts, they must cause the same disease in the healthy hosts, Figure 4-12c.
4. The organism must be removed from the new hosts, grown in the laboratory, and shown to be the same as the organism from the first host.

Figure 4-12 Using Koch's postulates to prove the cause of a disease

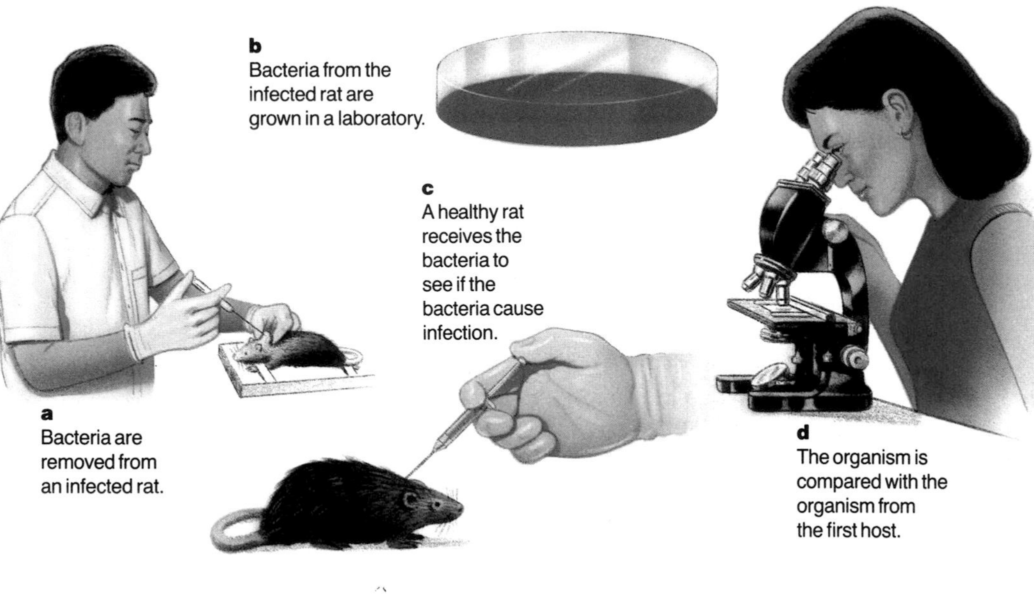

b
Bacteria from the infected rat are grown in a laboratory.
c
A healthy rat receives the bacteria to see if the bacteria cause infection.
a
Bacteria are removed from an infected rat.
d
The organism is compared with the organism from the first host.

OPTIONS

ACTIVITY/Challenge

Find out from the school nurse what diseases students are expected to be vaccinated against by the time they enter school. Have students research to determine which diseases are caused by bacteria and which are caused by viruses. Have them explain why vaccination for these diseases is important.

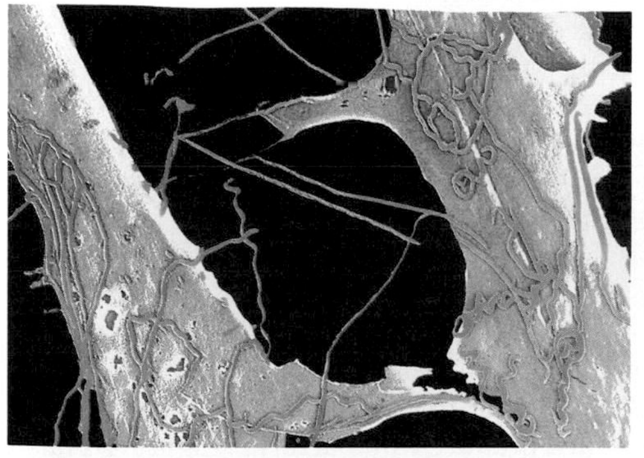

a

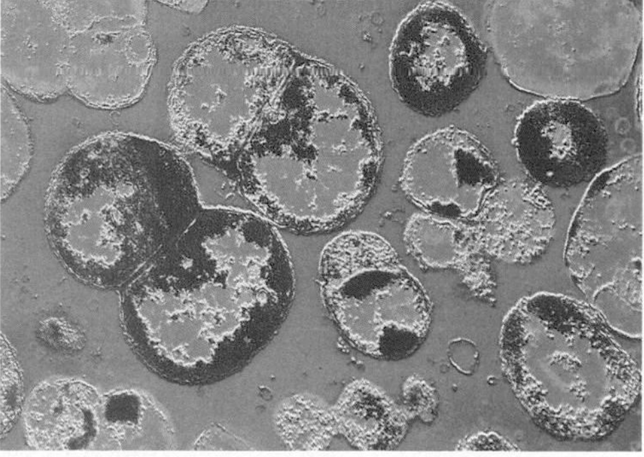

b

Figure 4-13 The spiral bacteria that cause syphilis (a) and the round bacteria that cause gonorrhea (b)

Scientists still use Koch's postulates today. The procedure helps identify bacteria and other disease-causing organisms.

Some diseases caused by bacteria and viruses are called communicable (kuh MYEW nih kuh bul) diseases. **Communicable diseases** are ones that can be passed from one organism to another. They may be spread in several ways. Some diseases are spread by air when a person sneezes or coughs. Pneumonia, strep throat, and tuberculosis are spread through the air. Communicable diseases can also be spread by touching anything an infected organism has touched. Common items that might have bacteria are clothes, food, silverware, or toothbrushes. Another way of spreading diseases is by drinking water that contains bacteria. Some of the more serious diseases are those spread by sexual contact. Syphilis (SIHF uh lus) and gonorrhea are sexually transmitted diseases caused by bacteria, Figures 4-13a, b.

Insects also spread diseases. Flies, fleas, cockroaches, and mosquitoes carry disease organisms.

Helpful Bacteria

You may be surprised to learn that there are more helpful bacteria than harmful ones. Most kinds of bacteria are helpful to humans. Bacteria are needed to decompose dead matter. Bacteria get energy from dead matter as they break it down into materials that other living things can use. In this way, the chemicals that are found in dead matter are recycled so that other organisms can use them to grow.

Mini Lab

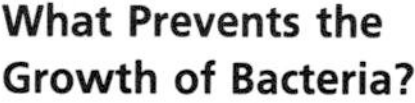

What Prevents the Growth of Bacteria?

Infer: Pour 100 mL beef broth into each of 4 beakers: A, B, C, D. Add 1 tsp. salt to B, 1 tsp. sugar to C, and 1 tsp. vinegar to D. Observe after 2 days. What prevents bacterial growth? *For more help, refer to the **Skill Handbook,** pages 706-711.*

TEACH

ACTIVITY/Guest Speaker

Invite someone from the local health department to discuss sexually transmitted diseases.

MOTIVATION/Brainstorming

Brainstorm how bacterial diseases are spread. Discussions might center around why it is important to (1) wash hands after using the bathroom; (2) cover your mouth when sneezing or coughing; (3) see a doctor if bitten by an animal.

Mini Lab

The beakers with salt and vinegar will be less cloudy than the control. The one with sugar will be more cloudy. Sugar provides food for bacterial growth.

Independent Practice

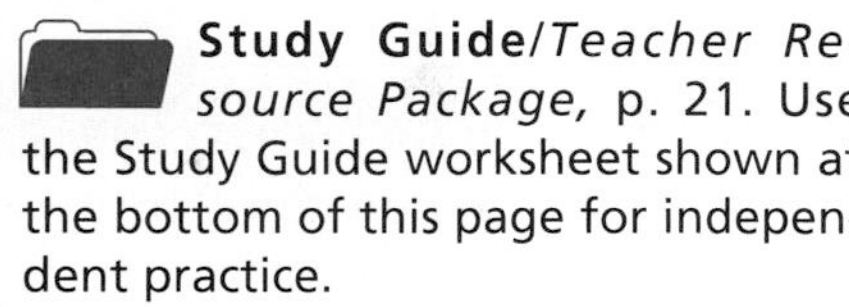

Study Guide/*Teacher Resource Package,* p. 21. Use the Study Guide worksheet shown at the bottom of this page for independent practice.

OPTIONS

Science Background

Robert Koch discovered that the microorganisms causing African sleeping sickness are transmitted to humans by tsetse flies. He also discovered the tuberculosis bacterium and developed the first test to indicate if a person had ever been exposed to the bacterium.

STUDY GUIDE 21

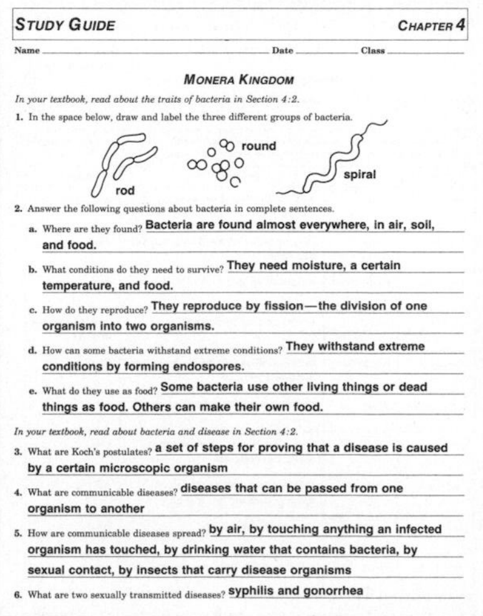

STUDY GUIDE CHAPTER 4

Name ______ Date ______ Class ______

MONERA KINGDOM

In your textbook, read about the traits of bacteria in Section 4:2.

1. In the space below, draw and label the three different groups of bacteria.

2. Answer the following questions about bacteria in complete sentences.
   a. Where are they found? **Bacteria are found almost everywhere, in air, soil, and food.**
   b. What conditions do they need to survive? **They need moisture, a certain temperature, and food.**
   c. How do they reproduce? **They reproduce by fission—the division of one organism into two organisms.**
   d. How can some bacteria withstand extreme conditions? **They withstand extreme conditions by forming endospores.**
   e. What do they use as food? **Some bacteria use other living things or dead things as food. Others can make their own food.**

In your textbook, read about bacteria and disease in Section 4:2.

3. What are Koch's postulates? **a set of steps for proving that a disease is caused by a certain microscopic organism**
4. What are communicable diseases? **diseases that can be passed from one organism to another**
5. How are communicable diseases spread? **by air, by touching anything an infected organism has touched, by drinking water that contains bacteria, by sexual contact, by insects that carry disease organisms**
6. What are two sexually transmitted diseases? **syphilis and gonorrhea**

TEACH

Concept Development

▶ Point out that millions of *E. coli* live in the human intestinal system where they carry out many beneficial functions such as aiding digestion and producing vitamins.

▶ Make sure students understand the difference between antibodies and antibiotics.

▶ Explain that antibiotics inhibit growth of bacteria by interfering with development of cell walls. Antibiotics are not effective against viruses. Remind students that viruses reproduce by using chemicals in living cells. Any substance that interferes with the virus would also kill the living cells.

▶ You may want to have a student contact a pharmacist or doctor to get a list of different antibiotics that are used today. Then discuss the use of the antibiotics.

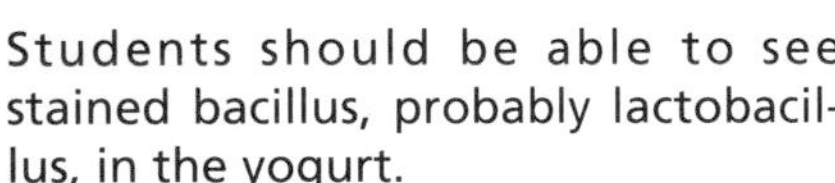

Mini Lab

Students should be able to see stained bacillus, probably lactobacillus, in the yogurt.

MOTIVATION/Display

Display food (containers may be used) made with bacteria – cottage cheese, yogurt, sour cream, buttermilk, sauerkraut, vinegar, pickles, coffee, and cocoa. Discuss the role of bacteria in making the foods.

Mini Lab

What Makes Yogurt?

Use a microscope: Thin plain yogurt with water. Place a drop on a slide. Add a drop of methylene blue and a coverslip. Observe under high power. What do you see in the yogurt? *For more help, refer to the **Skill Handbook**, pages 712-714.*

Some bacteria grow in other living things and help them. Bacteria in the stomach of a cow break down grass and hay. In this way, the grass and hay can be used as food by both the bacteria and the cow. Without the action of bacteria, plants would have little food value for cows, sheep, and deer. Bacteria in your intestine make vitamins that you need.

Bacteria are used to make many products that are useful to us. Some bacteria break down the fibers of plants used to make linen and rope. Some are used in making leather from skins. Some of today's most useful antibiotics (an ti bi AHT iks) are produced by bacteria, Figure 4-14a. **Antibiotics** are chemical substances that kill or slow the growth of bacteria. Some antibiotics have a specific effect, working only on certain types of bacteria. Others destroy many types of bacteria.

Some foods owe their taste or texture to bacteria. Many dairy products are made by adding certain species of bacteria to milk. For example, cottage cheese, Swiss cheese, yogurt, sour cream, and buttermilk are all made by bacteria growing in milk. The flavors of coffee and cocoa are due to bacteria, Figure 4-14b. Sauerkraut is made by the action of bacteria on chopped cabbage. Bacteria also help change alcohol to vinegar.

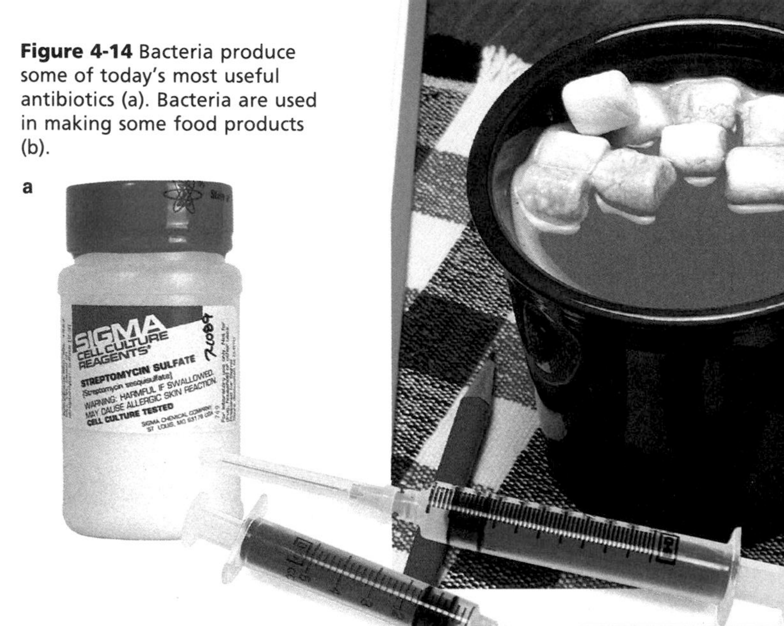

Figure 4-14 Bacteria produce some of today's most useful antibiotics (a). Bacteria are used in making some food products (b).

OPTIONS

How Can You Test for Bacteria in Foods?/*Lab Manual*, p. 25. Use this lab as an extension to studying bacteria in foods.

Enrichment/*Teacher Resource Package*, p. 4. Use the Enrichment worksheet shown here to help students understand whether a virus or moneran causes a certain disease and whether a vaccine is available for that disease.

ENRICHMENT 4

ENRICHMENT — CHAPTER 4

Name ______ Date ______ Class ______

Use after Section 4:2.

VIRUSES, MONERANS, AND DISEASE

Viruses and bacteria cause many human diseases. Some of these diseases are listed in the first column of the table below.

Look up the diseases in your textbook or in a dictionary or an encyclopedia. Then fill in the table below. Tell whether the disease is caused by a virus or by a bacterium, tell what effect the disease has on the body, and tell whether there is a vaccine to prevent the disease.

Disease	Cause	Effect on the body	Vaccine?
rabies	virus	affects the nervous system, causing convulsions and death	yes
measles	virus	red, circular spots break out on the skin	yes
strep throat	bacterium	inflamed throat and high fever	no
influenza	virus	fever, aches, and pains	yes, for some strains
meningitis	bacterium	inflammation of the membranes around the brain	no
mononucleosis	virus	abnormal white blood cells	no
polio	virus	fever, paralysis, and wasting away of muscles	yes
chicken pox	virus	low-grade fever and rash of itching blisters on the skin	no
tuberculosis	bacterium	damages the lungs	no
AIDS	virus	destroys the immune system	no

Bacteria are very important in the field of biotechnology (bi oh tek NAHL uh jee). **Biotechnology** is the use of living things to solve practical problems. Bacteria are being used to produce natural gas and detergents. Some are used to produce human insulin. Insulin is a chemical that the body normally makes to control the level of sugar in the blood. Some people cannot make insulin, so they must use the insulin produced by bacteria.

Controlling Bacteria

If food is put into containers and heated to a high enough temperature, the bacteria inside can be destroyed. The containers can then be sealed while they are hot. Food can remain in them for long periods of time without spoiling, as long as the seals are not broken and the cans remain airtight. The process of sealing food in airtight cans or jars after killing the bacteria is called canning. Endospores can be killed by the canning process. They are a major cause of food poisoning.

The process of heating milk to kill harmful bacteria is called **pasteurization** (pas chuh ruh ZAY shun). The milk you buy in stores is pasteurized. Even pasteurized milk that has not been opened will finally spoil. Can you explain why?

Cooling food to a low temperature slows the growth of bacteria. You keep food in the refrigerator to slow bacterial growth. Freezing food is also used to slow bacterial growth. Frozen food can be stored safely for several months. Items kept in a freezer last longer than those kept in the refrigerator. Why?

Skill Check

Understand science words: biotechnology. The word part *bio* means life. In your dictionary, find three words with the word part *bio* in them. *For more help, refer to the* ***Skill Handbook****, pages 706-711.*

Figure 4-15 Canning is a way to prevent bacteria from spoiling food.

TEACH

Concept Development

▶ Point out that cans of food that bulge should be discarded. The bulge may be due to the presence of gases produced by botulism-causing bacteria growing inside.

▶ Discuss why refrigeration prevents food poisoning. Mention also the importance of cleanliness of food preparers and of the materials and equipment used in food preparation.

Cooperative Learning: Divide the class into groups of four and have each group obtain information on an example of biotechnology, such as using bacteria in genetic engineering, cleaning up toxic waste areas, or making insecticides, and share the information with the class.

Independent Practice

Study Guide/*Teacher Resource Package,* p. 22. Use the Study Guide worksheet shown at the bottom of this page for independent practice.

APPLICATION 4

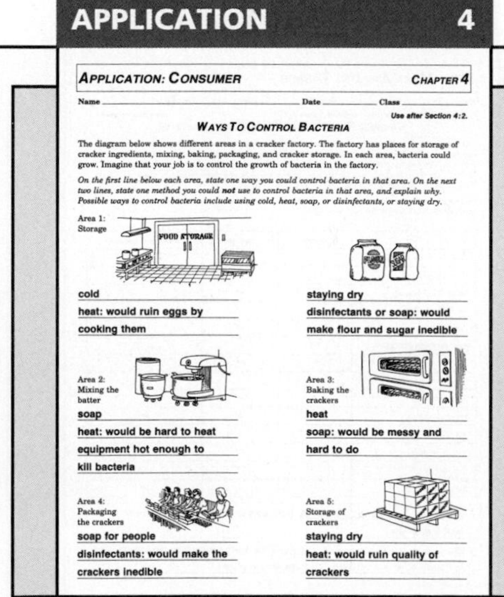

APPLICATION: CONSUMER CHAPTER 4

Name ________ Date ________ Class ________

Use after Section 4:2.

WAYS TO CONTROL BACTERIA

The diagram below shows different areas in a cracker factory. The factory has places for storage of cracker ingredients, mixing, baking, packaging, and cracker storage. In each area, bacteria could grow. Imagine that your job is to control the growth of bacteria in the factory.

On the first line below each area, state one way you could control bacteria in that area. On the next two lines, state one method you could **not** *use to control bacteria in that area, and explain why. Possible ways to control bacteria include using cold, heat, soap, or disinfectants, or staying dry.*

Area 1: Storage

cold
heat: would ruin eggs by cooking them

staying dry
disinfectants or soap: would make flour and sugar inedible

Area 2: Mixing the batter

soap
heat: would be hard to heat equipment hot enough to kill bacteria

Area 3: Baking the crackers

heat
soap: would be messy and hard to do

Area 4: Packaging the crackers

soap for people
disinfectants: would make the crackers inedible

Area 5: Storage of crackers

staying dry
heat: would ruin quality of crackers

STUDY GUIDE 22

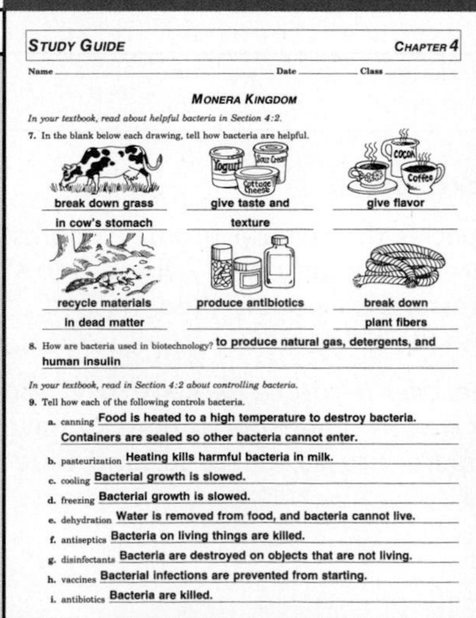

STUDY GUIDE CHAPTER 4

Name ________ Date ________ Class ________

MONERA KINGDOM

In your textbook, read about helpful bacteria in Section 4:2.

7. In the blank below each drawing, tell how bacteria are helpful.

break down grass in cow's stomach

give taste and texture

give flavor

recycle materials in dead matter

produce antibiotics

break down plant fibers

8. How are bacteria used in biotechnology? to produce natural gas, detergents, and human insulin

In your textbook, read in Section 4:2 about controlling bacteria.

9. Tell how each of the following controls bacteria.

a. canning Food is heated to a high temperature to destroy bacteria. Containers are sealed so other bacteria cannot enter.
b. pasteurization Heating kills harmful bacteria in milk.
c. cooling Bacterial growth is slowed.
d. freezing Bacterial growth is slowed.
e. dehydration Water is removed from food, and bacteria cannot live.
f. antiseptics Bacteria on living things are killed.
g. disinfectants Bacteria are destroyed on objects that are not living.
h. vaccines Bacterial infections are prevented from starting.
i. antibiotics Bacteria are killed.

OPTIONS

Science Background

Paul Ehrlich, a German scientist, was the first to find a chemical effective against a bacterial disease. In the early 1900s, he discovered an arsenic compound that destroyed the bacteria that caused syphilis.

Application/*Teacher Resource Package,* p. 4. Use the Application worksheet shown here to reinforce ways to control bacteria.

TECHNOLOGY

Uses of Bacteria

Background

Bacteria are being cultivated by many industrial companies to clean up hazardous pollutants. Because bacteria have rapid reproductive rates, they are able to adapt quickly when any new substance, even a toxic one, is added to their environment. Bacteria that become resistant survive and produce a new, tougher generation. Only the hardiest strains survive.

Discussion

1. How were the number of bacteria increased along Prince William Sound? Fertilizers were added to the water.
2. How does increasing the numbers of bacteria help in cleaning up oil spills and toxic wastes? It increases the chances of bacteria that are resistant to the poison surviving and reproducing.
3. Why are bacteria being cultured to clean up nitroglycerin? Not enough occur naturally, so they are allowed to reproduce in the laboratory and are returned to the soil.

References

Chollar, Susan. "The Poison Eaters." *Discover,* Apr. 1990, pp. 76-78.

TECHNOLOGY

Bacteria are helpful in removing pollutants from soil and groundwater. After an oil spill in Prince William Sound in Alaska, the natural populations of oil-eating bacteria were not large enough to take care of the spill. Researchers added fertilizers to the oil-covered beaches to increase the number of bacteria that lived on the beaches.

At Los Alamos National Laboratory, bacteria that break down explosive wastes are being grown. A researcher has collected soil samples that contain TNT and nitroglycerin. The samples also contain bacteria that have adapted to the explosives and break them down. The bacteria are being cultured in large quantities and transferred back to the contaminated area.

Oil spill

Bacteria are used to mine gold, copper, and other valuable minerals from mines where the concentrations are so low they cannot be mined by traditional methods. Bacteria that release bound-up minerals are added to the ore. The minerals can then be mined.

Figure 4-16 When water is removed from foods, bacteria cannot grow in them.

If water is taken from food, bacteria can't live in the food. Bacteria need the water for growth. For this reason, uncooked noodles and dry cereals can be left open without spoiling. These foods have very little water. Removing the water from food is called dehydration (dee hi DRAY shun). What other foods do you know of that are dehydrated?

Why do you put iodine, hydrogen peroxide, or alcohol on a cut, scrape, or other skin injury? These chemicals are called antiseptics (an ti SEP tiks). The word *antiseptic* means against infection. Antiseptics are chemicals that kill bacteria on living things. Disinfectants (dihs un FEK tunts) are stronger chemicals that are used to destroy bacteria on objects that are not living.

What do we do to get rid of bacteria on or in our bodies? We wash with soap, we brush our teeth, and we use mouthwash. Each time this is done, we wash, brush, kill, or rinse away millions of bacteria. The bacteria can cause body and breath odor and tooth decay.

OPTIONS

Science Background

Only a few species of bacteria produce spores, but their spores are nearly everywhere. Moist heat under pressure is a widely used method of sterilization used to kill spores.

Skill/*Teacher Resource Package*, p. 4. Use the Skill worksheet shown here to have students compare viruses, bacteria, and blue-green bacteria.

SKILL 4

SKILL: MAKE AND USE TABLES CHAPTER 4

Name ____ Date ____ Class ____

For more help, refer to the Skill Handbook, pages 715-717. *Use after Section 4:2.*

VIRUSES, BACTERIA, AND BLUE-GREEN BACTERIA

One way to study and understand information is to organize it into a table. By making a table, you can see at a glance how viruses, bacteria, and blue-green bacteria are the same and how they are different. The first column of the table below lists facts about viruses and monerans. To complete the table, decide whether the fact describes any of the organisms or viruses named in the other columns. Some facts describe more than one type of organism or virus.

Place a check mark in a column if the fact describes that organism or virus. When the table is complete, use it to answer the questions below.

Fact	Viruses	Bacteria	Blue-green bacteria
Some move with a flagellum		✓	
Have a jellylike layer			✓
Some have a capsule		✓	
Reproduce by fission		✓	✓
Live in colonies		✓	✓
Reproduce only in host cells	✓		
May form endospores		✓	
All make their own food			✓
Have no nucleus	✓	✓	✓
Are single-celled		✓	✓
Are not made of cells	✓		
May cause disease	✓	✓	
Can spoil food		✓	
Contain chlorophyll			✓

1. How are viruses similar to bacteria? **They both can cause disease and both lack a nucleus.**
2. How are bacteria similar to blue-green bacteria? **They both reproduce by fission, live in colonies, lack a nucleus, and are single-celled.**

Some medicines help stop bacterial infections after you become sick. You may have been given an antibiotic or other medicine to fight a bacterial infection when you were sick. Vaccines prevent bacterial infections from happening. They protect the body from invading organisms.

Blue-green Bacteria

Blue-green bacteria are small, one-celled monerans that contain chlorophyll and can make their own food. For many years they were called blue-green algae and were classified as plants. Their cell structure is more like that of bacteria than of plants. They do not have nuclei or other typical plant cell parts, Figure 4-17. Each has a cell wall outside a cell membrane. The cell wall of a blue-green bacterium is made of materials different from the cell wall of a plant cell.

Blue-green bacteria contain colored pigments. They are usually a blue-green color, but some blue-green bacteria may appear red, black, brown, or purple. The blue-green bacteria in the Red Sea grow rapidly at certain times of the year, giving the sea its red color and its name.

Where do blue-green bacteria live? They are found in ponds, lakes, moist soils, swimming pools, and sometimes around leaky faucets. Some can even live in salt water and on snow. Others grow in the acid water of hot springs.

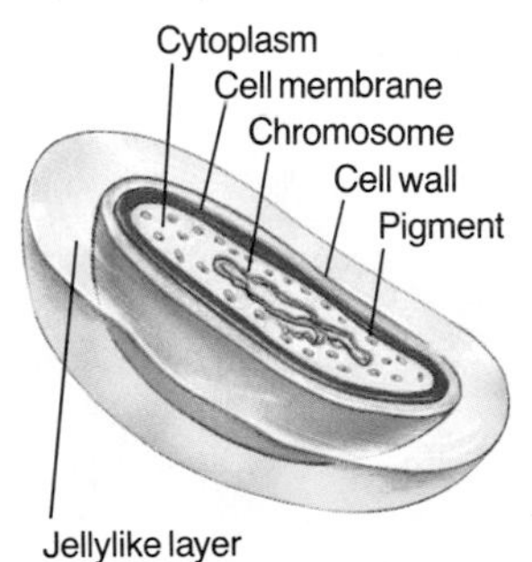

Figure 4-17 Structure of a typical blue-green bacterium. Does it look more like a bacterial cell or an animal cell? bacterial cell

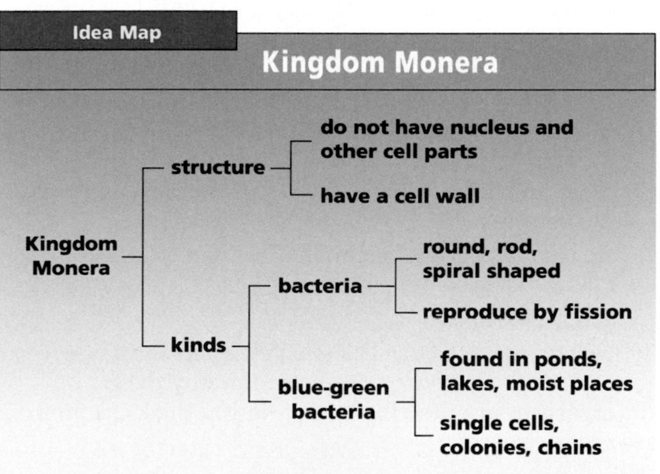

Study Tip: Use this idea map as a study guide to the monerans. Can you give an example of each kind of moneran?

TEACH

Concept Development

▶ Mention that blue-green bacteria are also called cyanobacteria. The color of blue-green bacteria is due to the presence of chlorophyll (green) and phycocyanin (blue).

▶ Point out that many blue-green bacteria take nitrogen from the air and change it to ammonia. Other kinds of bacteria change the ammonia to nitrates. The nitrates can be used by plants.

Idea Map

Have students use the idea map as a study guide to the major concepts of this section.

Check for Understanding

Show prepared slides of bacteria and blue-green bacteria. Have students make a list of characteristics of each. Discuss how they are similar and different.

Reteach

Prepare a list of statements on 3" x 5" cards that describe bacteria and blue-green bacteria. Have each student select a card, read the statement, and tell which one it describes. Some statements may describe both.

Independent Practice

Study Guide/*Teacher Resource Package,* p. 23. Use the Study Guide worksheet at the bottom of this page for independent practice.

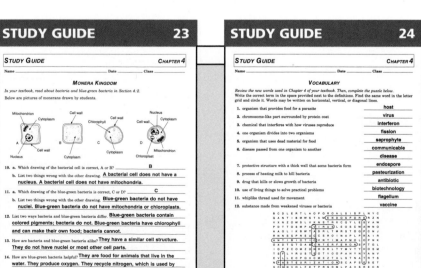

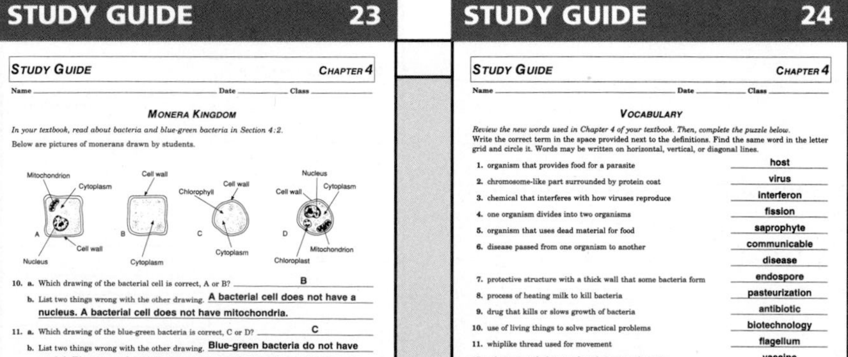

STUDY GUIDE 23

STUDY GUIDE — CHAPTER 4

Name ______ Date ______ Class ______

MONERA KINGDOM

In your textbook, read about bacteria and blue-green bacteria in Section 4:2.

Below are pictures of monerans drawn by students.

10. a. Which drawing of the bacterial cell is correct, A or B? **B**
    b. List two things wrong with the other drawing. **A bacterial cell does not have a nucleus. A bacterial cell does not have mitochondria.**
11. a. Which drawing of the blue-green bacteria is correct, C or D? **C**
    b. List two things wrong with the other drawing. **Blue-green bacteria do not have nuclei. Blue-green bacteria do not have mitochondria or chloroplasts.**
12. List two ways bacteria and blue-green bacteria differ. **Blue-green bacteria contain colored pigments; bacteria do not. Blue-green bacteria have chlorophyll and can make their own food; bacteria cannot.**
13. How are bacteria and blue-green bacteria alike? **They have a similar cell structure. They do not have nuclei or most other cell parts.**
14. How are blue-green bacteria helpful? **They are food for animals that live in the water. They produce oxygen. They recycle nitrogen, which is used by plants.**
15. How are blue-green bacteria harmful? **They grow rapidly in ponds and kill other living things. They make water unfit for drinking and swimming.**

STUDY GUIDE 24

STUDY GUIDE — CHAPTER 4

Name ______ Date ______ Class ______

VOCABULARY

Review the new words used in Chapter 4 of your textbook. Then, complete the puzzle below.
Write the correct term in the space provided next to the definitions. Find the same word in the letter grid and circle it. Words may be written on horizontal, vertical, or diagonal lines.

1. organism that provides food for a parasite **host**
2. chromosome-like part surrounded by protein coat **virus**
3. chemical that interferes with how viruses reproduce **interferon**
4. one organism divides into two organisms **fission**
5. organism that uses dead material for food **saprophyte**
6. disease passed from one organism to another **communicable disease**
7. protective structure with a thick wall that some bacteria form **endospore**
8. process of heating milk to kill bacteria **pasteurization**
9. drug that kills or slows growth of bacteria **antibiotic**
10. use of living things to solve practical problems **biotechnology**
11. whiplike thread used for movement **flagellum**
12. substance made from weakened viruses or bacteria **vaccine**

OPTIONS

ACTIVITY/Challenge

Ask students to find out why blue-green bacteria were once classified as plants and why they are now classified with bacteria (lack of cell parts and cell wall).

TEACH

Guided Practice

Have students write down their answers to the margin question: oxygen.

Check for Understanding

Have students respond to the first three questions in Check Your Understanding.

Reteach

Reteaching/*Teacher Resource Package,* p. 11. Use this worksheet to give students additional practice with monerans.

Extension: Assign Critical Thinking, Biology and Reading, or some of the **OPTIONS** available with this lesson.

3 APPLY

Connection: Math

E. coli bacteria reproduce every 20 minutes. Have students calculate how many can be produced in an eight-hour period.

4 CLOSE

Display

Display food items such as cereal, raisins, pickles, milk, canned food, and frozen food. Ask students to describe methods used to control bacterial growth.

Answers to Check Your Understanding

6. Bacterial cells do not have a nucleus or other cell parts.
7. by air, drinking water, touching, sexual contact, and insects
8. They have chlorophyll and make their own food.
9. Bacteria need water to grow. The water has been removed from these foods.
10. *Cyano* is a prefix that means blue-green.

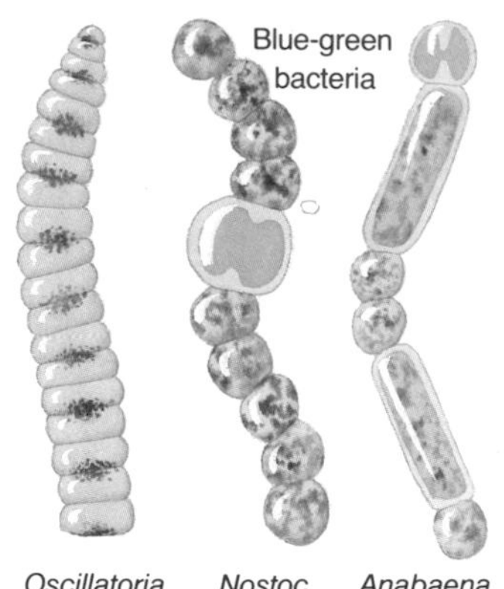

Figure 4-18 Blue-green bacteria (a) can grow very rapidly and cover the surface of a pond (b).

Blue-green bacteria occur as single cells, colonies, and long, threadlike chains. Many have an outer jellylike layer that holds the cell to other cells. Some have gas bubbles that let the cells float at the surface, where they get sun.

Blue-green bacteria serve as food for animals that live in water. They produce oxygen as they make their own food. They are also important in recycling nitrogen that can then be used by plants.

Blue-green bacteria may grow too rapidly and cover an entire pond. When this happens, they can use up the oxygen in the pond and kill other living things. Many blue-green bacteria produce a bad odor. The odor is one clue that the water is unfit for drinking. Substances that pollute water are often used by blue-green bacteria for food. The amount of pollution in water is measured by counting the number of blue-green bacteria.

Check Your Understanding

6. What are two ways that bacterial cells differ from animal cells?
7. What are three ways in which communicable diseases can be spread?
8. How do blue-green bacteria differ from other bacteria?
9. **Critical Thinking:** Why don't foods such as uncooked rice and raisins spoil?
10. **Biology and Reading:** The scientific name for blue-green bacteria is *cyanobacteria.* From the way these organisms are described, what do you think the prefix *cyano-* means?

OPTIONS

What Are the Traits of Blue-green Bacteria?/*Lab Manual*, pp. 31-32. Use this lab as an extension to classifying blue-green bacteria.

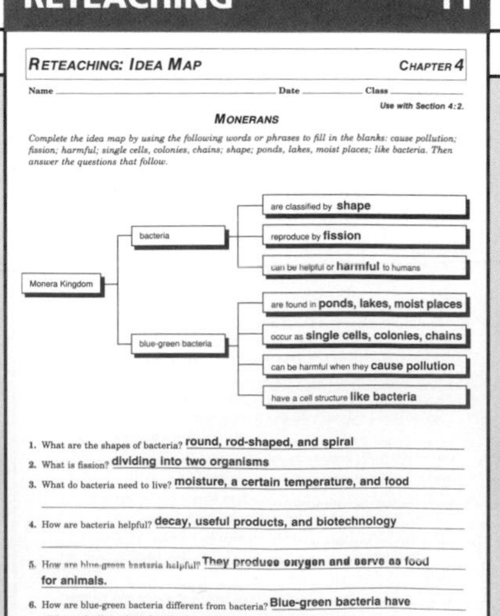

RETEACHING 11

RETEACHING: IDEA MAP CHAPTER 4

Name ______ Date ______ Class ______

Use with Section 4:2.

MONERANS

Complete the idea map by using the following words or phrases to fill in the blanks: cause pollution; fission; harmful; single cells, colonies, chains; shape; ponds, lakes, moist places; like bacteria. Then answer the questions that follow.

Monera Kingdom
- bacteria
  - are classified by **shape**
  - reproduce by **fission**
  - can be helpful or **harmful** to humans
- blue-green bacteria
  - are found in **ponds, lakes, moist places**
  - occur as **single cells, colonies, chains**
  - can be harmful when they **cause pollution**
  - have a cell structure **like bacteria**

1. What are the shapes of bacteria? **round, rod-shaped, and spiral**
2. What is fission? **dividing into two organisms**
3. What do bacteria need to live? **moisture, a certain temperature, and food**
4. How are bacteria helpful? **decay, useful products, and biotechnology**
5. How are blue-green bacteria helpful? **They produce oxygen and serve as food for animals.**
6. How are blue-green bacteria different from bacteria? **Blue-green bacteria have chlorophyll and make their own food; bacteria do not.**

Lab 4–2 Monerans

Problem: How do blue-green bacteria and bacteria compare?

Skills

make and use tables, observe, measure in SI, use a microscope

Materials 

microscope
prepared slide of *Anabaena*
prepared slide of bacteria
petri dish
metric ruler

Procedure

1. Copy the data table.
2. Use the low-power objective to locate a strand of *Anabaena*, Figure A.
3. **Observe:** Switch to the high-power objective of your microscope and observe the *Anabaena*. Look for cell parts inside the cells.
4. Complete the first three rows of the data table for *Anabaena.*
5. Using the petri dish as a guide, draw a circle on a sheet of paper.
6. Look through the eyepiece of the microscope. Draw one cell in the circle. (Pretend that the circle is the view through the eyepiece. Draw the cell the same size it appears through the eyepiece. This is called drawing to scale.)
7. **Measure in SI:** Measure the length of your *Anabaena* diagram in millimeters.
8. Record this number in your data table.
9. To find the actual length of the cell, multiply the length of your diagram by 0.0035. Use a calculator to help you. Record your answer.
10. Repeat steps 2 through 9 with the bacteria slide. See Figure B.

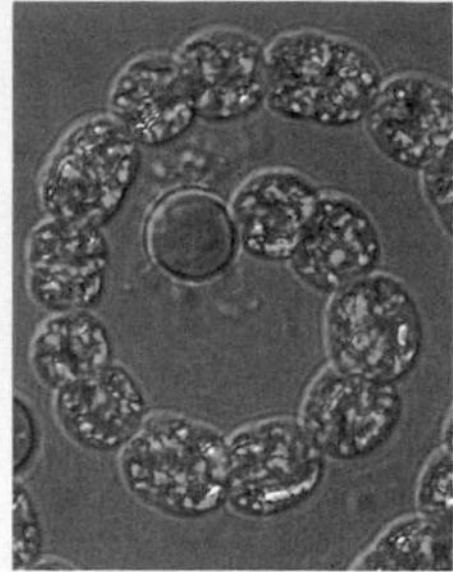

A

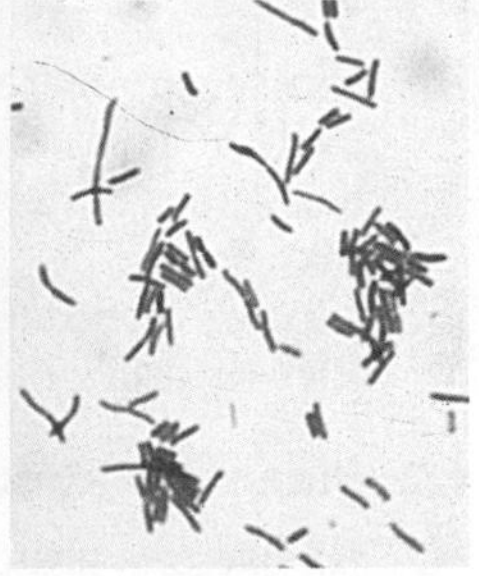

B

Data and Observations

1. Which organism is smaller?
2. Which organism lives in colonies?

	ANABAENA	*BACTERIUM*
Shape of cells	round and oblong	rod
Single cell or colony	colony	single cell
Color	green	pink
Length of diagram	10 mm	4 mm
Actual length of cell	0.035	0.014

Analyze and Apply

1. Which organism can make its own food?
2. To which kingdom do *Anabaena* and bacteria belong? How do you know?
3. **Apply:** How do blue-green bacteria and other bacteria compare?

Extension

Observe other bacteria and blue-green bacteria under the microscope. Compare these with *Anabaena* and the bacteria in this lab.

Lab 4-2 Monerans

Overview

In this lab, students observe bacteria and blue-green bacteria to compare their traits. They will also make scale drawings and measure.

Objectives: Upon completing this lab, students will be able to (1) **determine** which is larger, bacteria or blue-green bacteria, (2) **determine** which makes its own food, (3) **recognize** traits of monerans.

Time Allotment: 25 minutes

Preparation

▶ If your school does not have prepared slides of Anabaena and bacteria, have students use the photos on this page.

 **Lab 4-2 worksheet**/*Teacher Resource Package,* pp. 15-16.

 **Lab 4-2 Computer Program**/ *Teacher Resource Package,* p. vi. Use the computer program shown at the bottom of this page as you teach this lab.

Teaching the Lab

▶ Explain to students that bacteria are normally colorless. The slides have been stained pink as a method of identifying the bacteria.

 **Cooperative Learning:** Have students work in pairs for this lab. For more information, see pp. 22T-23T in the Teacher Guide.

COMPUTER PROGRAM VI

COMPUTER PROGRAM LAB 4-2 MONERANS

```
]POKE 33,33

]LIST

10  GOSUB 390
20  HOME
30  PRINT "              ---------------------------";
33  PRINT "              !   ANABAENA  ! BACTERIUM  !";
35  PRINT "-----------------------------------------";
40  PRINT "!LENGTH IN  !              !            !";
50  PRINT "!MILLIMETERS!              !            !";
60  PRINT "!OF DIAGRAM !              !            !";
70  PRINT "-----------------------------------------";
80  PRINT "!ACTUAL     !              !            !";
90  PRINT "!LENGTH OF  !              !            !";
100  PRINT "!CELL IN    !              !            !";
110  PRINT "!MILLIMETERS!              !            !";
120  PRINT "-----------------------------------------";
130  PRINT "!SKIN   !         !            !        !";
140  PRINT "-----------------------------------------"
150  FOR X = 1 TO 2
160  VTAB V(X): HTAB H(X): FLASH : PRINT " ";: NORMAL
170  VTAB 15: HTAB 1: CALL  - 958
180  PRINT "ENTER YOUR VALUE FOR THIS SPACE";
190  INPUT ": ";A
195 N(X) = A
200  VTAB V(X): HTAB H(X): PRINT A
210  NEXT
220  VTAB 15: HTAB 1: CALL  - 958
230  PRINT "ARE THESE NUMBERS                        ENTERED CORRECTLY? (
    Y/N): ";: GET A$
240  IF A$ = "N" OR A$ = "n" THEN GOTO 20
250  IF A$ < > "Y" AND A$ < > "y" THEN 220
260  VTAB 15: HTAB 1: CALL  - 958: PRINT
270  PRINT  "PRESS THE ";: INVERSE : PRINT "SPACE BAR";: NORMAL : PRINT "
     TO SEE               THE ACTUAL LENGTHS IN MILLIMETERS";: GET A$
280  VTAB 16: HTAB 1: CALL  - 958
290  FOR X = 3 TO 4
300  VTAB V(X): HTAB H(X)
310  PRINT N(X - 2) * .0035
320  NEXT
330  INVERSE : PRINT
340  PRINT : PRINT "DO YOU WANT THIS PRINTED (Y/N)?:";: GET A$
345  NORMAL
348  VTAB 15: HTAB 1: CALL  - 958
350  IF A$ = "N" OR A$ = "n" THEN  END
360  IF A$ < > "Y" AND A$ < > "y" THEN GOTO 340
370  GOSUB 2000
380  END
390  TEXT : HOME : PRINT "LAB 4-1                           MONERANS"
400  PRINT : PRINT
410  PRINT "YOU WILL BE ASKED TO TYPE IN YOUR      RESULTS FOR ONLY THE
     LAST TWO ROWS OF   THE DATA TABLE USED IN THE EXPERIMENT."
430  PRINT
```

ANSWERS

Data and Observations

1. bacteria
2. *Anabaena*

Analyze and Apply

1. *Anabaena*
2. Monera; they do not have nuclei.
3. Bacteria are smaller. They are not green and do not live in colonies. The cells are single. *Anabaena* is green, has two kinds of cells, and lives in colonies.

CHAPTER 4 REVIEW

Summary

Summary statements can be used by students to review the major concepts of the chapter.

Key Science Words

All boldfaced terms from the chapter are listed.

Testing Yourself

Using Words

1. parasite
2. interferon
3. pasteurization
4. colony
5. biotechnology
6. antibiotic
7. blue-green bacteria
8. fission
9. flagellum
10. virus

Finding Main Ideas

11. p. 73; They are classified by the kind of cell they infect.
12. p. 73; They are spread by insects, air, water, food, and other people.
13. pp. 77-78; Certain white blood cells destroy viruses, some white blood cells produce antibodies, vaccines are used to treat some diseases, and cells produce interferon.
14. p. 79; They are found almost everywhere–water, air, soil, food, on your skin, in your body.
15. p. 79; They are classified by their shape–round, rod, and spiral.
16. p. 83; They may be spread by air, touching anything an infected person has touched, drinking water that contains bacteria, and sexual contact.
17. p. 81; Fire blight and crown gall are plant diseases caused by bacteria.
18. pp. 85-87; High and low temperatures, canning, pasteurization, dehydration, antiseptics, washing, and medicines are all methods to control bacteria.
19. p. 83; They change dead matter into materials that other living things can use.
20. p. 88; They grow rapidly and cause water pollution in lakes and ponds.

Chapter 4

Review

Summary

4:1 Viruses

1. Viruses are not cells and have no cell parts. They are made of a chromosome-like part that carries the hereditary material. They are surrounded by a protein coat.
2. Viruses reproduce only inside living cells.
3. Viruses cause diseases in many living things.

4:2 Monera Kingdom

4. All bacteria are one-celled, have no nucleus, and are either round, rod-shaped, or spiral. Other bacteria cannot make their own food or make oxygen.
5. Some bacteria cause serious diseases. They may be spread by air, food, water, sexual contact, or insects.
6. Blue-green bacteria can make their own food and make oxygen. They occur as single cells, colonies, or long chains.

Key Science Words

antibiotic (p. 84)
asexual reproduction (p. 80)
bacteria (p. 79)
biotechnology (p. 85)
blue-green bacteria (p. 87)
capsule (p. 80)
colony (p. 79)
communicable disease (p. 83)
decomposer (p. 81)
endospore (p. 81)
fission (p. 80)
flagellum (p. 80)
host (p. 73)
interferon (p. 77)
Koch's postulates (p. 82)
parasite (p. 73)
pasteurization (p. 85)
saprophyte (p. 81)
vaccine (p. 78)
virus (p. 72)

Testing Yourself

Using Words

Choose the word from the list of Key Science Words that best fits the definition.

1. organism that lives on or in another living thing and causes harm to it
2. substance that interferes with how a virus reproduces
3. process of heating milk to kill harmful bacteria
4. group of similar cells attached to each other
5. the use of living things to solve practical problems
6. chemical that kills or slows the growth of bacteria
7. monerans that contain chlorophyll and can make their own food
8. dividing in half to form two new cells
9. whiplike thread used for movement
10. chromosome-like part surrounded by a protein coat

Finding Main Ideas

List the page number where each main idea below is found. Then, explain each main idea.

11. how viruses are classified
12. how human viruses are spread
13. how humans and other animals protect themselves from viruses

90

Using Main Ideas

21. Viruses are so small they can only be seen with an electron microscope. They have many different shapes. They are made of a chromosome-like part surrounded by a protein coat. They have no cell parts. They reproduce only inside living cells.
22. Chewing or sucking insects break through the plant cell wall and allow the virus to come in contact with the host cell.
23. (1) The chromosome-like part enters a host cell and takes over the cell. The virus makes copies of itself, breaks open, and sends the new viruses out to invade more cells. (2) Viruses remain hidden in cells without reproducing until something causes them to become active.
24. Interferon binds to the cell membrane of other body cells the first time a person has flu. It helps the cells resist other viruses.

Review

Testing Yourself *continued*

14. where bacteria are found
15. how bacteria are classified
16. how communicable diseases are spread
17. two plant diseases caused by bacteria
18. methods by which bacteria can be controlled
19. how decay-causing bacteria are important
20. how blue-green bacteria are harmful

Using Main Ideas

Answer the questions by referring to the page number after each question.

21. What are some traits of viruses? (p. 72)
22. How do insects spread plant viruses? (p. 74)
23. In what two ways do viruses cause disease? (p. 74)
24. How does interferon act against viruses? (p. 77)
25. What are the differences between a bacterial cell and an animal cell? (p. 80)
26. How can bacteria survive when growing conditions are not favorable? (p. 81)
27. How do antiseptics and disinfectants differ from one another? (p. 86)
28. How are Koch's postulates used today? (p. 83)
29. In what ways are bacteria useful to humans? (p. 83)
30. How do blue-green bacteria differ from bacteria? (p. 87)
31. Where can blue-green bacteria be found? (p. 87)

Skill Review ✓

For more help, refer to the ***Skill Handbook,*** *pages 704-719.*

1. **Formulate a model:** Place several green marbles in a bag filled with water. What organism does this represent?
2. **Interpret diagrams:** Look at Figure 4-8 and compare the parts of a bacterium with those of an animal cell. What cell parts does an animal cell have that a bacterium does not have?
3. **Infer:** Blue-green bacteria were once classified as algae. They are now classified as bacteria. The organisms have not changed. Why do you think their classification has changed?
4. **Make and use tables:** Make a table showing the cause of: measles, AIDS, pneumonia, cold, crown gall, flu, syphilis, warts, gonorrhea, tooth decay, fire blight, herpes.

Finding Out More

Critical Thinking

1. Bacteria that live on teeth produce an acid that causes decay. Why do people who do not brush regularly have more cavities than those who do?
2. Few people get the diseases measles and polio. Why are the vaccines still required in many states?

Applications

1. Report on the economic effects of viral diseases on crops.
2. Make a collage of ads for products such as deodorants, soaps, and toothpastes that control bacteria.

Using Main Ideas

25. A bacterial cell does not have a nucleus or other cell parts. An animal cell has a nucleus and other cell parts.
26. They form endospores. A thick wall forms inside the cell, enclosing all the nuclear material and some cytoplasm.
27. Antiseptics are used to kill bacteria on living things. Disinfectants are used to kill bacteria on nonliving objects.
28. They are used to identify bacteria and other disease-causing organisms.
29. Bacteria break down dead matter; break down grass and hay so that it can be digested by animals; produce vitamins; make linen, rope, leather, antibiotics, and many foods.
30. They have chlorophyll and can make their own food.
31. They are found in ponds, lakes, moist soils, swimming pools, and sometimes around leaky faucets.

Skill Review

1. a blue-green bacterium
2. nucleus, mitochondrion, vacuole, Golgi body, nucleolus, endoplasmic reticulum
3. Their cell structure is more like bacteria than algae.
4. Students may like to place headings of Virus and Bacteria across the top and list Human and Plant along the side, then fill in the diseases.

Finding Out More

Critical Thinking

1. Not brushing leaves particles on teeth that bacteria can use for food. This encourages bacterial growth.
2. If several people did not get the vaccine and contracted the diseases, the weakened viruses in the vaccines might not be effective against the active ones.

Applications

1. Common plant viruses include tobacco mosaic disease, turnip yellow mosaic, and tomato bushy stunt.
2. Collect old magazines for students to use.

Chapter Review/*Teacher Resource Package*, pp. 18-19.

Chapter Test/*Teacher Resource Package*, pp. 20-22.

Chapter Test/*Computer Test Bank*

Protists and Fungi

PLANNING GUIDE

CONTENT	TEXT FEATURES	TEACHER RESOURCE PACKAGE	OTHER COMPONENTS
(2 days) 5:1 Protist Kingdom Animal-like Protists Plantlike Protists Funguslike Protists	Skill Check: *Understand Science Words,* p. 97 Skill Check: *Interpret Diagrams,* p. 100 Mini Lab: *Is There Life in a Mud Puddle?* p. 96 Lab 5-1: *Protists,* p. 101 Idea Map, p. 108 Check Your Understanding, p. 108	Reteaching: *Protist Kingdom,* p. 12 Transparency Master: *Kinds of Protists,* p. 19 Study Guide: *Protist Kingdom,* pp. 25-26 Lab 5-1: *Protists,* pp. 17-18	**Laboratory Manual:** *Where Are Protists Found?* p. 33
(2 days) 5:2 Fungus Kingdom Traits of Fungi Kinds of Fungi Lichens	Mini Lab: *What Do Fungi Need to Grow?* p. 104 Career Close-Up: *Mushroom Farmer,* p. 103 Lab 5-2: *Fungi,* p. 109 Check Your Understanding, p. 102	Application: *Learning About Mushrooms,* p. 5 Enrichment: *Ten-pin Protists and Fungi,* p. 5 Reteaching: *Comparing Fungi,* p. 13 Critical Thinking/Problem Solving: *How Do Mushrooms Form Fairy Rings?* p. 5 Skill: *Sequence,* p. 5 Focus: *Mildew Makes Things Musty,* p. 9 Study Guide: *Fungus Kingdom,* pp. 27-29 Study Guide: *Vocabulary,* p. 30 Lab 5-2: *Fungi,* pp. 19-20	**Laboratory Manual:** *What Do Molds Need in Order to Grow?* p. 37 Color Transparency 5a: *Slime Mold Life Cycle* Color Transparency 5b: *How Fungi Get Their Food*
Chapter Review	Summary Key Science Words Testing Yourself Finding Main Ideas Using Main Ideas Skill Review	Chapter Review, pp. 23-24 Chapter Test, pp. 25-27	**Test Bank**

MATERIALS NEEDED

LAB 5-1, p. 101	LAB 5-2, p. 104	MARGIN FEATURES
microscope 3 microscope slides 3 coverslips 3 droppers cultures of: amoeba euglena paramecium	microscope hand lens scalpel prepared mushroom slide mushroom	Skill Check, p. 97 dictionary Mini Lab, p. 96 microscope microscope slide coverslip dropper muddy water Mini Lab, p. 104 bread water plastic bag

OBJECTIVES

		OBJECTIVES CORRELATION			
SECTION	OBJECTIVE	CHECK YOUR UNDERSTANDING	CHAPTER REVIEW	TRP CHAPTER REVIEW	TRP CHAPTER TEST
5:1	1. **Identify** the general characteristics of protists.	1, 4	7, 14, 24, 32	18	5, 26
	2. **Compare** the traits of animal-like protists, plant-like protists, and fungus-like protists.	3	5, 6, 9, 16, 26, 27, 29, 36	6, 7, 8, 30, 34	1, 3, 4, 6, 8, 10, 13, 23, 24, 25, 28, 29, 30, 31, 32, 41, 42, 55, 56, 57
	3. **Give an example** of each kind of protist.	2	8, 11, 17, 21, 22, 23	9, 10, 11, 12, 13, 14, 15, 16, 17, 31, 32, 37	2, 36, 37, 38, 39, 40, 41, 42, 43
5:2	4. **List** the traits of fungi and compare the traits of the major kinds of fungi.	6, 8, 9	2, 3, 10, 12, 13, 15, 18, 19, 25, 28, 30, 33	2, 5, 19, 21, 22, 29, 33, 36, 38	9, 11, 12, 15, 17, 19, 43, 44, 45, 49, 50
	5. **Tell** how fungi can be harmful and helpful.	7	4, 20, 31, 34, 35	1, 3, 4, 22, 25, 26, 27, 28, 29, 30, 31, 32, 33, 34, 35, 36, 37, 38, 39, 40, 41, 47	7, 14, 16, 18, 22, 46, 47, 48, 51, 54

Protists and Fungi

CHAPTER OVERVIEW

Key Concepts

In this chapter, students will study the structure, traits, and economic importance of protists and fungi. The protists are divided into animal-like, plantlike, and fungilike groups. Students will learn about the kinds of fungi and their methods of reproduction

Key Science Words

algae
budding
cilia
club fungi
hyphae
lichen
multicellular
mutualism
protozoan
sac fungi
slime mold
sporangia
sporangium fungi
spore
sporozoan

Skill Development

In Lab 5-1 students will **make and use tables, interpret data, observe, classify,** and **use a microscope** while observing the traits of protists. In Lab 5-2 they will **observe, infer, use a microscope** and **design an experiment** to study mushroom structure. In the Skill Check on page 97, they will **understand** the **science word** *multicellular.* In the Skill Check on page 100, they will **interpret diagrams** of slime molds. In the Mini Lab on page 96, students will **use a microscope** to observe life from a mud puddle. In the Mini Lab on page 104, they will **observe** the growth of fungi.

CHAPTER PREVIEW

Chapter Content

Review this outline for Chapter 5 before you read the chapter.

5:1 Protist Kingdom
Animal-like Protists
Plantlike Protists
Funguslike Protists

5:2 Fungus Kingdom
Traits of Fungi
Kinds of Fungi
Lichens

Skills in this Chapter

The skills that you will use in this chapter are listed below.

- In **Lab 5-1,** you will make and use tables, interpret data, observe, classify, and use a microscope. In **Lab 5-2,** you will observe, infer, use a microscope, and design an experiment.
- In the **Skill Checks,** you will understand science words and interpret diagrams.
- In the **Mini Labs,** you will use a microscope and observe.

92

Bridging

Students learned the basis for classifying organisms into five kingdoms in Chapter 3. In Chapter 4, they learned that monerans are single-celled. Bridge this to the fact that most protists are also single-celled, but they have cell parts. Bacteria and protists are important in decay.

Chapter 5

Protists and Fungi

Many different protists live in streams, ponds, and oceans. Some have chlorophyll and can make their own food, while others must find food. Some have cell walls and others do not. Most protists are one-celled, but some seaweeds are several meters long. In the small photograph on this page, you can see some of the many kinds of protists that are found in a drop of water from a pond.

The mushroom growing near the pond on the left is a fungus. Mushrooms and other fungi were once grouped with plants. Then it was discovered that fungi have traits that are different from plants. Fungi do have cell walls, but they lack chlorophyll. They absorb food from their surroundings. This is why fungi are grouped in a separate kingdom.

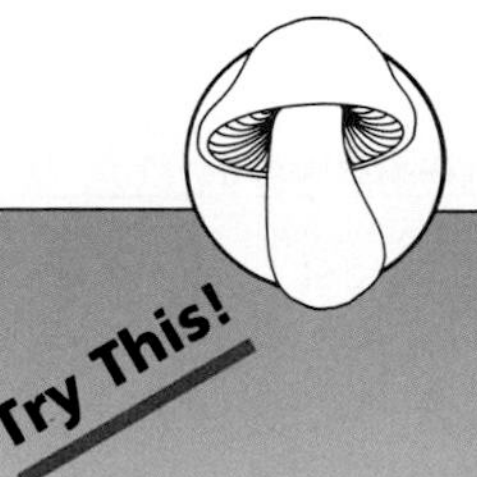

Try This!

Have you ever made mushroom prints? Remove the stalks from several different mushrooms. Place each cap, open side down, on a separate sheet of paper. Cover each one with an inverted bowl or jar and leave overnight. Uncover and remove the caps. What do you see?

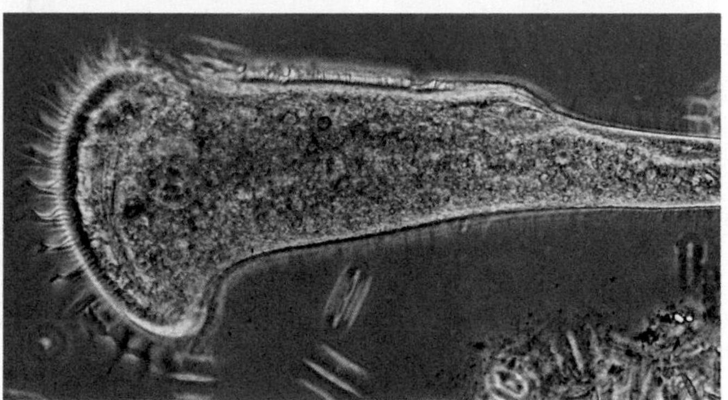

Stentor is a protist that lives in pond water.

GETTING STARTED

Using the Photos

In looking at the photos, students should compare the features of protists and fungi. Have them note features of fungi that are similar to those of plants.

MOTIVATION/Try This!

Have you ever made mushroom prints? Upon completing the chapter-opening activity, students will **observe** that mushrooms have gills under the cap that release spores.

Chapter Preview

Have students study the chapter outline before they begin to read this chapter. They should note that animal-like, plantlike, and funguslike protists are in the Protist Kingdom. The traits of fungi, the kinds of fungi, and lichens are studied in the Fungi Kingdom.

Misconception

Students may think all wild mushrooms are poisonous. Very few species are poisonous, but because they look like the nonpoisonous species, wild mushrooms should never be eaten. Even experts have trouble telling the poisonous species from the nonpoisonous ones.

5:1 Protist Kingdom

PREPARATION

Materials Needed

Make copies of the Transparency Master, Study Guide, Reteaching, and Lab worksheets in the *Teacher Resource Package.*

▶ Obtain different kinds of green algae for Focus activity.

▶ Collect water from a mud puddle for the Mini Lab.

▶ Obtain cultures of amoeba, paramecium, and euglena for Lab 5-1.

Key Science Words

protozoan
cilia
sporozoan
spore
algae
multicellular
slime mold

Process Skills

In Lab 5-1, students will make and use tables, interpret data, observe, classify, and use a microscope. In the Skill Checks, they will interpret diagrams and understand science words. In the Mini Lab, students will use a microscope.

1 FOCUS

▶ The objectives are listed on the student page. Remind students to preview these objectives as a guide to this numbered section.

MOTIVATION/Demonstration

Bring in green algae from flowerpots, ponds, and ditches. Make wet mounts of the samples for students to observe.

Guided Practice

Have students write down their answers to the margin question: one.

5:1 Protist Kingdom

Objectives

1. **Identify** the general characteristics of protists.
2. **Compare** the traits of animal-like protists, plantlike protists, and funguslike protists.
3. **Give an example** of each kind of protist.

Key Science Words

protozoan
cilia
sporozoan
spore
algae
multicellular
slime mold

Protists live almost everywhere. In Chapter 3, protists were described as one-celled organisms that have a nucleus and other cell parts with membranes. Protists are larger than bacteria, but most are so small they can be seen only with a microscope. Protists may be producers or consumers. Most can move about in search of food, light, or a place to live.

Although there are a number of different protist phyla, they can be put into three groups. You can see in Figure 5-1 an example of an animal-like protist, plantlike protist, and a funguslike protist.

Animal-like Protists

How many cells do protozoans have?

Protozoans (proht uh ZOH uhnz) make up the largest group of protists. **Protozoans** are one-celled animal-like organisms with a nucleus. The name *protozoan* comes from the Greek words meaning "first animal." At one time, these organisms were classified in the animal kingdom because scientists thought they looked like tiny animals.

Protozoans, like animals, are consumers. The single cell takes in and digests food. It also reproduces. Most protozoans can move about. They are classified in different phyla depending on how they move. Table 5-1 lists the traits of four protozoan phyla.

Figure 5-1 Protists can be grouped into animal-like protists (a), plantlike protists (b), and funguslike protists (c).

a

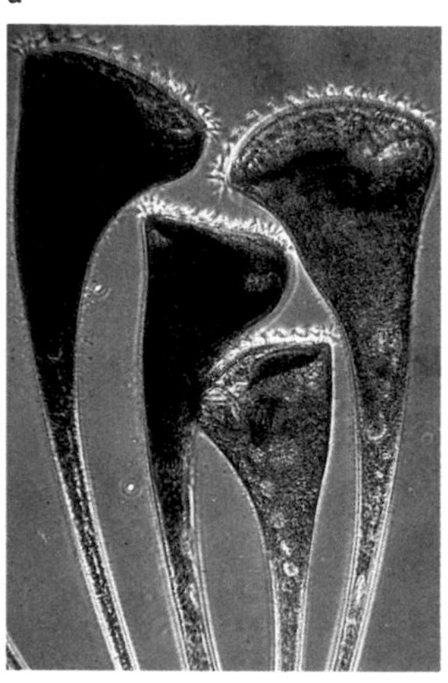

b

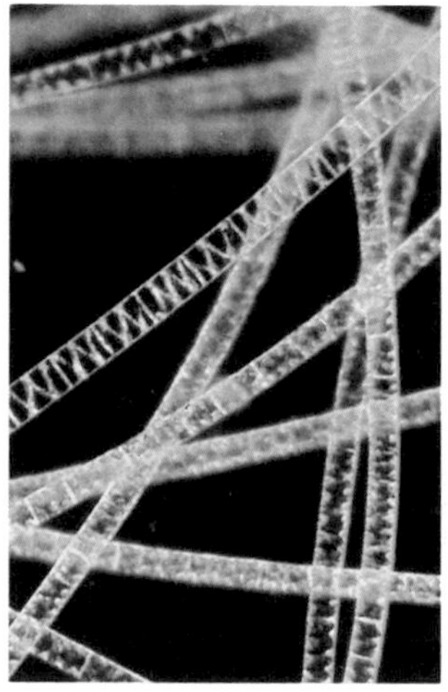

c

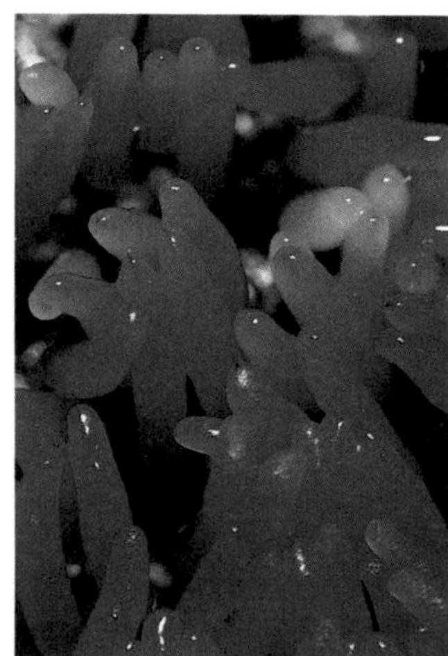

OPTIONS

Science Background

Green algae are classified on the basis of whether the plants are single cells, colonies, or multicellular. Most green algae live in fresh water. Some move by means of flagella. Brown algae are found in salt water. They grow attached to rocks, shells, or other algae.

TABLE 5–1. ANIMAL-LIKE PROTISTS

Traits of Phylum	Example
move with false feet	amoeba
move with cilia	*Paramecium*
do not move; all parasites	*Plasmodium* *(plaz MOH dee uhm)*
move with one or more flagella	trypanosome (trip AN uh some)

Let's look at some of the protozoans. The protozoan in Figure 5-2 is an amoeba (uh MEE buh). The amoeba is a protist that moves by changing shape. It has parts made of cytoplasm that can reach out from the main body. These parts are called false feet. They help the amoeba move about and trap food. Figure 5-3 shows how. First, the amoeba's false feet surround a small protist or a bacterium. Soon the food is trapped inside the amoeba, where it will be digested.

How does an amoeba move?

Like bacteria, amoebas reproduce by fission. A parent cell divides into two new cells. Each of the cells has the same hereditary material as the parent cell.

Most kinds of amoebas are not harmful to humans, but some cause disease. One kind of amoeba causes a severe type of diarrhea called amoebic dysentery (uh MEE bihk • DIHS un ter ee). People get this disease by drinking water or eating food that contains the amoebas. This usually occurs in areas where conditions are not sanitary.

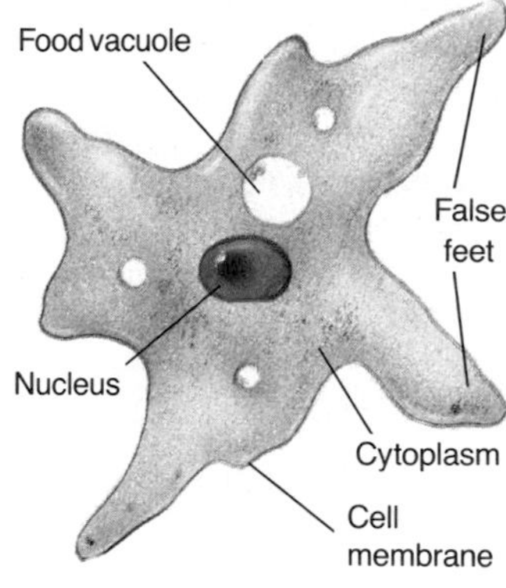

Figure 5-2 Structures of an amoeba. Do amoebas have cell walls? no

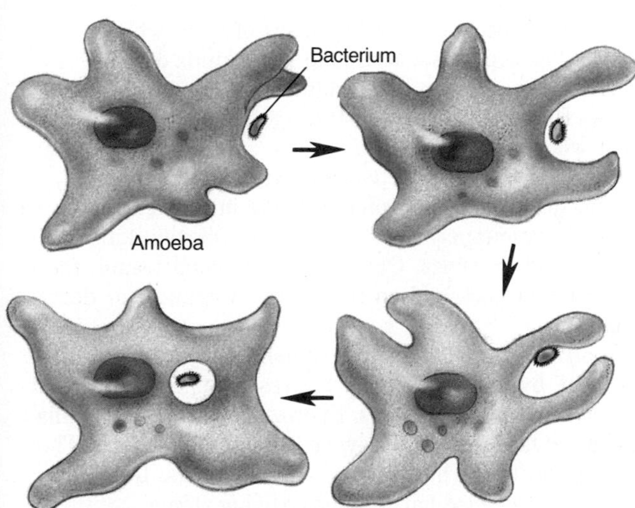

Figure 5-3 Amoebas capture food with their false feet.

2 TEACH

MOTIVATION/Videocassette

Show the videocassette *The Protozoa,* Opportunities for Learning, Inc.

Concept Development

▶ Emphasize that protists occur wherever there is moisture. They may be found in the ocean, fresh water, soil, and bodies of other organisms (plants, animals, other protists).

▶ Point out that animal-like organisms are able to move, feed on other organisms, and have no chlorophyll.

▶ Explain that false feet are called pseudopods.

Guided Practice

Have students write down their answers to the margin question: by changing its shape.

TRANSPARENCY 19

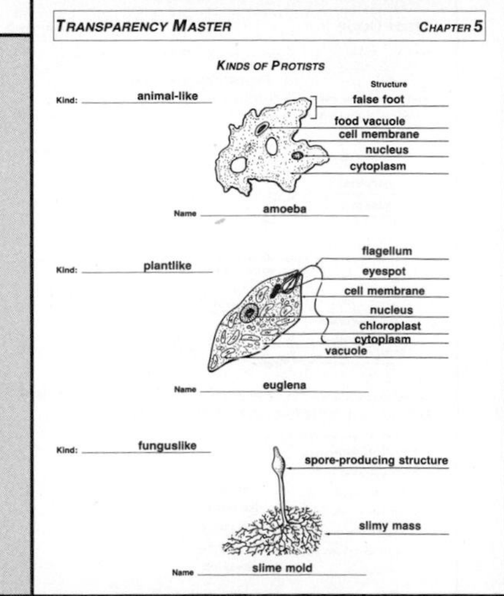

OPTIONS

Transparency Master/*Teacher Resource Package,* p. 19. Use the Transparency Master shown here to teach the kinds of protists.

Where Are Protists Found?/*Lab Manual,* pp. 33-36. Use this lab as an extension to studying the Protist Kingdom.

TEACH

Concept Development

▶ Point out that cilia is plural for cilium, and flagella is the plural of flagellum.

▶ You may wish to review the term *parasite*.

▶ Explain that sporozoans are carried along by currents in the blood and other body fluids of their hosts.

Mini Lab

Students should see different protists. Have them classify their drawings as animal-like or plantlike.

Independent Practice

Study Guide/*Teacher Resource Package,* p. 25. Use the Study Guide worksheet shown at the bottom of this page for independent practice.

Guided Practice

Have students write down their answers to the margin question: sporozoans.

Connection: Social Studies

Have students report to the class on protist-caused diseases such as toxoplasmosis, Chagas disease, and African sleeping sickness.

Figure 5-4 A paramecium (a) and some of its structures (b). What structures does a paramecium use for movement? cilia

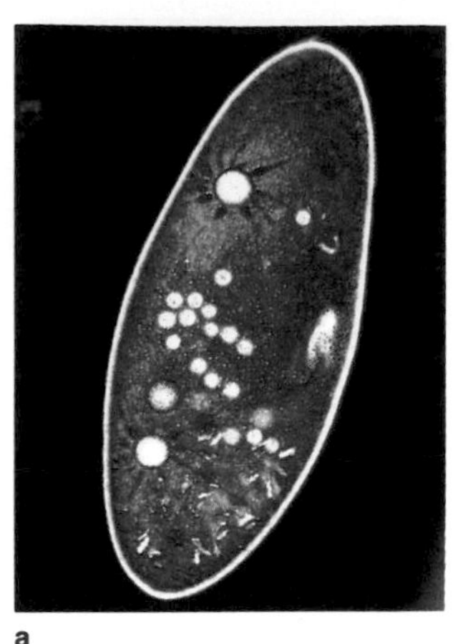

a

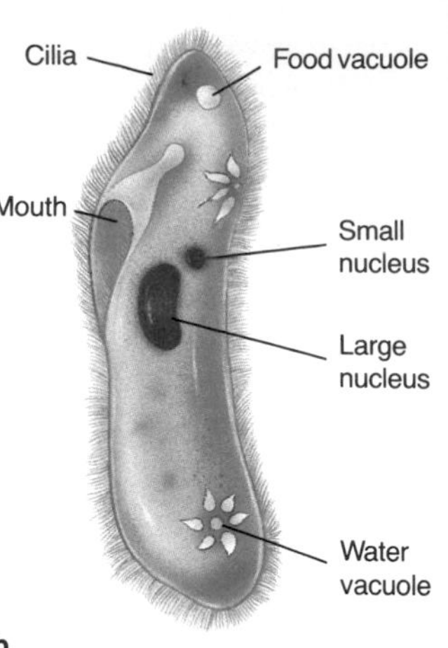

b

Mini Lab

Is There Life in a Mud Puddle?

Use a microscope: Use a dropper to collect a sample of water from a mud puddle. Place a drop on a slide and add a coverslip. Focus on low power and then on high. Draw what you see. *For more help, refer to the* ***Skill Handbook,*** *pages 712-714.*

An example of another type of protozoan is the paramecium. A paramecium is a protozoan that has a definite shape and moves by means of cilia. **Cilia** are short, hairlike parts on the surface of the cell, as seen in Figure 5-4. The cilia move back and forth very fast, causing the organism to move through the water. Protists with cilia are found in most ponds and streams. Most members of this group do not cause diseases in humans.

When a paramecium finds food, such as a bacterium, it sweeps the food into its body with its cilia. The food enters through a mouthlike opening. A vacuole then forms around the food. The food is digested inside the food vacuole and used by the cell.

Some protozoans move by means of long, whiplike flagella. These protists are found in all kinds of water and in the soil. Some even live inside animals, such as the protists that live in the digestive systems of termites and digest wood for the termite.

Some protozoans are parasites and cause disease. Trypanosomes cause sleeping sickness in humans. They are carried from one person to another by a certain kind of fly that is found in Africa. Once inside the bloodstream, these protozoans produce poison that causes weakness or death in humans.

Which protist reproduces by forming spores?

Sporozoans (spor uh ZOH uhnz) are protozoans that reproduce by forming spores. **Spores** are special cells that develop into new organisms. Sporozoans do not have cilia, flagella, or false feet, so they can't move to get food. They live as parasites in humans and other animals. Remember that parasites cause harm to other living things.

STUDY GUIDE 25

STUDY GUIDE CHAPTER 5

Name ______ Date ______ Class ______

PROTIST KINGDOM

In your textbook, read about animal-like protists in Section 5:1.

1. Label the following parts of an amoeba: nucleus, cytoplasm, food vacuole, cell membrane, false foot.

food vacuole
cytoplasm
false foot
cell membrane
nucleus

2. Label the following parts of a paramecium: large nucleus, small nucleus, cytoplasm, vacuole, cell membrane, cilia, mouth. Then, answer the question.

mouth
cell membrane
large nucleus
small nucleus
vacuole
cilia
cytoplasm

Explain how paramecia feed. Food is swept into a mouthlike opening of the body by cilia. A food vacuole forms around the food and digests it.

In your textbook, read about plantlike protists in Section 5:1.

3. Write the phrase *like plants* or *like animals* after each of the following protist traits.

a. can move about — like animals
b. have chlorophyll — like plants
c. have no cell wall — like animals
d. are producers — like plants
e. can make their own food — like plants
f. give off oxygen — like plants

Perhaps you have heard of malaria. The sporozoan named *Plasmodium* causes this disease. It is carried by female *Anopheles* (uh NAHF uh leez) mosquitoes. Humans get the disease when they are bitten by infected mosquitoes. The disease is common in tropical areas where these mosquitoes live.

Plantlike Protists

Algae (AL jee) (singular, alga) are plantlike protists. They are like plants because they have chlorophyll and make their own food. Algae also have other pigments. The other pigments help capture light and pass its energy on to chlorophyll. Algae are producers. They produce large amounts of oxygen, which is used by other living things.

Algae live in fresh and salt water. Some also live in moist soils and on tree bark. Like animals, many algae can move about. They do not have a cell wall. Is this trait like that of a plant or an animal?

Algae may be one-celled or multicellular. **Multicellular** means that an organism has many different cells that do certain jobs for the organism. All algae cells have nuclei. Algae are grouped into different phyla depending on their color and their structures. Note the features of each phylum in Table 5-2.

Skill Check

Understand science words: multicellular. The word part *multi* means many. In your dictionary, find three words with the word part *multi* in them. *For more help, refer to the* ***Skill Handbook****, pages 706-711.*

TABLE 5–2. PLANTLIKE PROTISTS

Traits of Phylum	Example
move with flagellum, one-celled, no cell wall, found mostly in fresh water, green color	euglena
found mostly in salt water, one-celled, gold-brown color	diatom
found mostly in salt water, red or brown color, one-celled	dinoflagellate
green color, found in fresh and salt water and in soil, one-celled, multicellular, or in groups	green algae
brown color, found in salt water, multicellular	kelp

The euglena shown in Figure 5-5 lives in fresh water. A euglena is a one-celled alga that moves with a flagellum. The euglena swims by moving its flagellum back and forth in the water. This causes the cell to move in an unusual wiggling motion. Euglenas have a red eyespot near their front end. The eyespot is sensitive to light and helps the euglena find the light it needs to make food. Are euglenas producers or consumers?

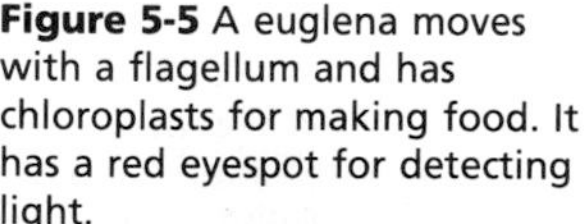

Figure 5-5 A euglena moves with a flagellum and has chloroplasts for making food. It has a red eyespot for detecting light.

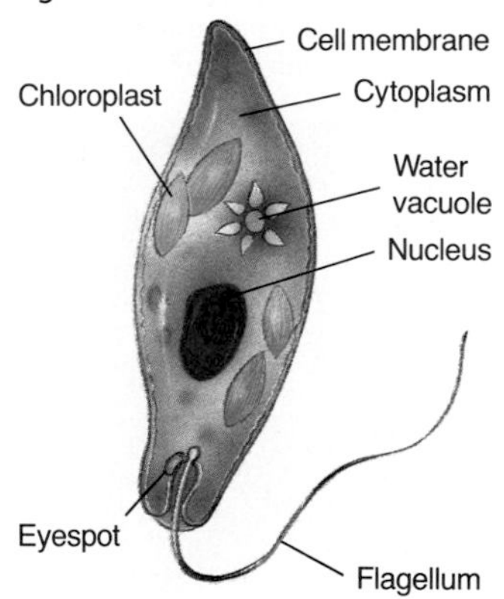

TEACH

Concept Development

▶ Point out that a vector is an animal such as the female *Anopheles* mosquito that carries a protist.

▶ Emphasize the importance of algae as producers. They are the beginning of most food chains in both salt and fresh water.

▶ All cells in one-celled algae are similar to one another and live more or less independently. In multicellular organisms, cells are specialized and dependent on one another.

▶ Stress that all algae contain chlorophyll. They capture light at various wavelengths and pass the energy on to chlorophyll.

▶ The euglena has a depression at the front end of the cell called the reservoir. Near the reservoir is a mass of red pigment called the eyespot. When the euglena senses light, it moves toward the light source. This is a helpful adaptation for a photosynthetic organism.

▶ The euglena reproduces by splitting lengthwise to form two daughter cells.

ACTIVITY/Brainstorming

Have students brainstorm and decide which organism, amoeba, paramecium, or euglena, is the most complex. The paramecium has food and contractile vacuoles, micro- and macronuclei, and is capable of sexual and asexual reproduction.

OPTIONS

Science Background

Red algae contain carrageenan which is used in puddings, preserves, and ice cream. Brown algae is used as animal feed and fertilizer in Northern Europe. Algin, a chemical obtained from brown algae, is often used in the manufacture of latex, ceramic glazes, cosmetics, and ice cream. There is an annual multimillion dollar market for algin in the United States alone.

TEACH

Concept Development

▶ Explain that diatoms store food in the form of oil.

▶ Point out that when boats, fish, or waves disturb some dinoflagellates at night, the water glows with a blue or green light. This is an example of bioluminescence.

▶ Species of dinoflagellates that cause red tides produce powerful nerve poisons that can kill fish. Shellfish such as oysters and clams are not affected by the poisons, but the poisons do collect in their bodies. Humans who eat the shellfish may be paralyzed or even killed.

Independent Practice

Study Guide/*Teacher Resource Package,* p. 26. Use the Study Guide worksheet shown at the bottom of this page for independent practice.

ACTIVITY/Demonstration

Demonstrate the structure of a diatom cell with a petri dish. The top and bottom halves represent the cell wall.

Cooperative Learning: Have students work in groups of four. Assign each group one kind of algae—green, red, or brown—to research. Have them find out what its role is as a food and oxygen producer and its economic importance.

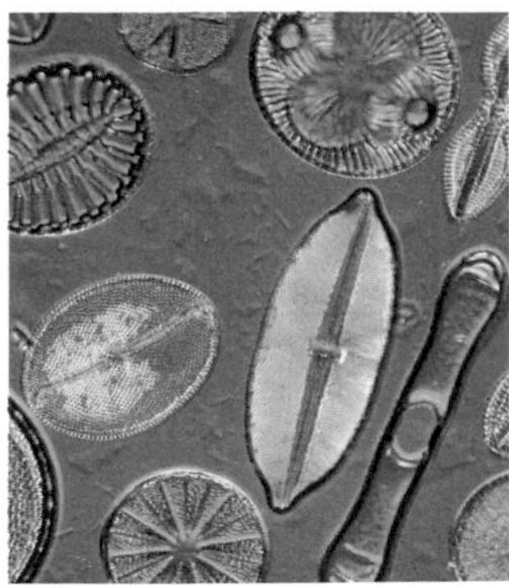

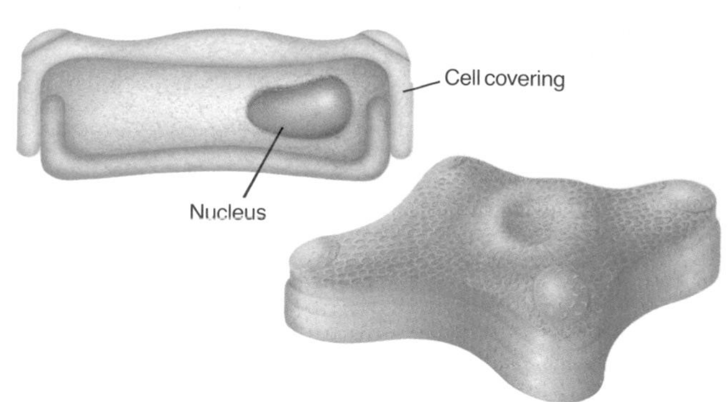

Figure 5-6 Diatoms have many shapes. Each cell has a two-part cell covering.

Diatoms (DI uh tahmz) are beautiful, one-celled protists that have many shapes, Figure 5-6. They are shaped like boats, rods, disks, or triangles. Diatoms are producers. Would you expect them to have chlorophyll? Diatoms can move slowly through the water. They are one of the most important food sources for animals that live in water.

Diatoms have an interesting structure. They have a cell covering made of two parts. The covering overlaps like a box with a lid, as shown in Figure 5-6. It is made of the same material as glass. When diatoms die, they fall to the bottom of the lake or ocean. The coverings do not decay, but form thick layers. The coverings in these layers are used in toothpastes, scouring powders, and filters because they are gritty and are good cleansers.

Dinoflagellates (di noh FLAJ uh luhts) are algae that are usually found in oceans. Only a few types live in fresh water. They are usually red or brown. They have chlorophyll, but their red and brown pigments hide it. They move by beating their two flagella.

Red dinoflagellates are responsible for red tides. They reproduce in such large numbers that the ocean water turns red. Chemicals produced by these protists during red tides can kill thousands of fish. Humans can become ill if they eat shellfish that have absorbed these chemicals. Red tides are common off the coast of Florida and in other warm waters.

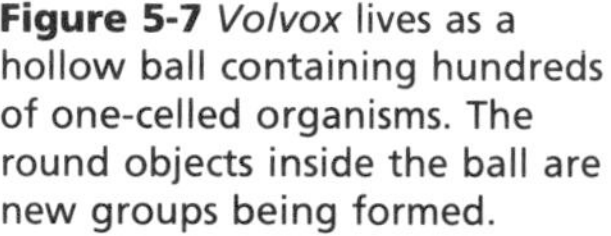

Figure 5-7 *Volvox* lives as a hollow ball containing hundreds of one-celled organisms. The round objects inside the ball are new groups being formed.

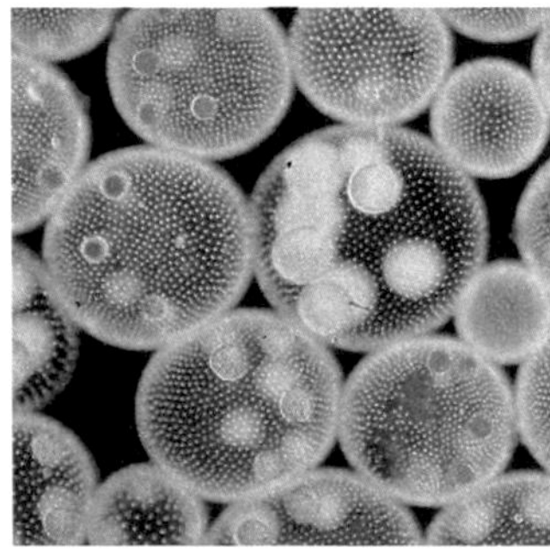

Green algae come in many different forms. They may be one-celled, multicellular, or they may form groups of cells that live together. *Volvox*, the organism shown in Figure 5-7, is a green alga that lives as a hollow ball containing hundreds of one-celled organisms with flagella. The cells are arranged in a single layer with their flagella facing outward. When the flagella beat, the ball of cells spins

OPTIONS

Science Background

The cell walls of diatoms are composed of gelatinous material called pectin. In most diatoms there is also silica, a glassy material rich in silicon. When diatoms die, the outer shell of silica remains intact. The shells accumulate on the ocean floor, forming diatomaceous earth.

STUDY GUIDE 26

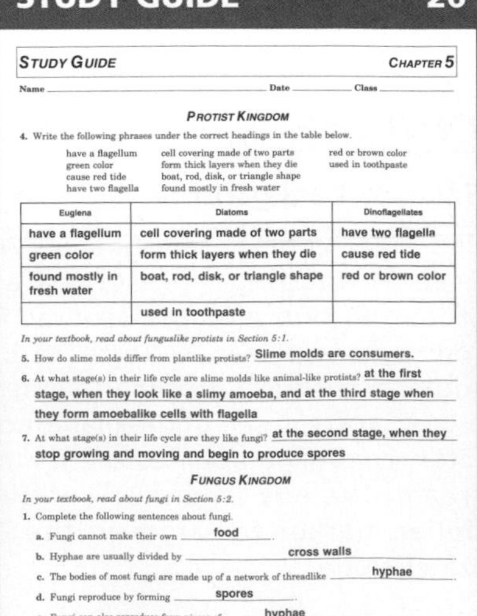

STUDY GUIDE CHAPTER 5

Name ________ Date ________ Class ________

PROTIST KINGDOM

4. Write the following phrases under the correct headings in the table below.

have a flagellum, green color, cause red tide, have two flagella, cell covering made of two parts, form thick layers when they die, boat, rod, disk, or triangle shape, found mostly in fresh water, red or brown color, used in toothpaste

Euglena	Diatoms	Dinoflagellates
have a flagellum	cell covering made of two parts	have two flagella
green color	form thick layers when they die	cause red tide
found mostly in fresh water	boat, rod, disk, or triangle shape	red or brown color
	used in toothpaste	

In your textbook, read about funguslike protists in Section 5:1.

5. How do slime molds differ from plantlike protists? Slime molds are consumers.
6. At what stage(s) in their life cycle are slime molds like animal-like protists? at the first stage, when they look like a slimy amoeba, and at the third stage when they form amoebalike cells with flagella
7. At what stage(s) in their life cycle are they like fungi? at the second stage, when they stop growing and moving and begin to produce spores

FUNGUS KINGDOM

In your textbook, read about fungi in Section 5:2.

1. Complete the following sentences about fungi.
   a. Fungi cannot make their own food.
   b. Hyphae are usually divided by cross walls.
   c. The bodies of most fungi are made up of a network of threadlike hyphae.
   d. Fungi reproduce by forming spores.
   e. Fungi can also reproduce from pieces of hyphae.

through the water. A *Volvox* ball reproduces when some of the cells in the ball come together to form small groups inside the ball. The ball bursts open and releases the small groups of cells.

Multicellular algae have many different shapes. Some form long strands that have many cells. Others have a leaflike shape that looks like lettuce.

Algae are important to us in many ways. They release oxygen into the water and air. The oxygen is used by other living things. Algae are important as food for animals such as fish, snails, and crayfish. Have you ever heard of a seaweed called kelp? Kelp is one kind of brown algae used by many people for food, Figure 5-8. Some scientists think that green algae will be an even more important source of food for humans in the near future.

Are algae products found in any foods that you eat? If you have eaten ice cream or jelly, you probably have eaten certain substances that come from algae. These substances are used to thicken foods.

Figure 5-8 Kelp is a brown alga that many people eat.

Funguslike Protists

Slime molds are funguslike protists that are consumers. They live in cool, damp places, such as the forest floor. They feed on rotting logs and decaying leaves. A few slime molds are parasites.

Bio Tip

Ecology: Slime molds have been known to cover an entire golf course with their slimy masses. The masses creep over the ground, engulfing microorganisms and digesting them.

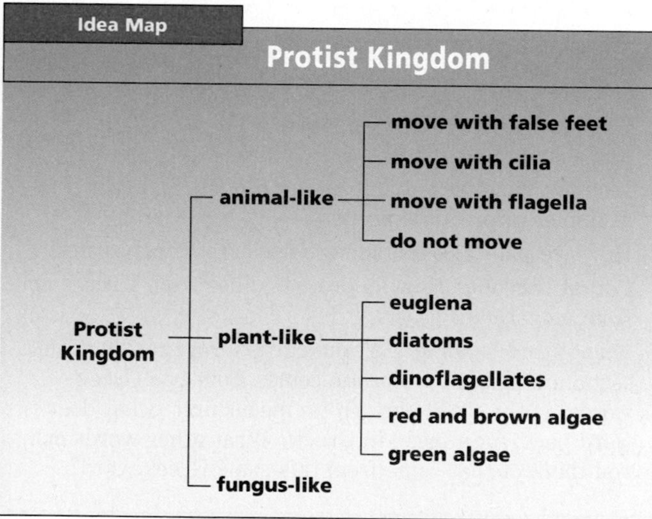

Study Tip: Use this idea map as a study guide to the protist kingdom. The features of the three protist groups are shown.

TEACH

Concept Development

▶ Slime molds are among the least familiar organisms to most students. Use actual specimens to acquaint the class with these organisms.

▶ Point out that slime molds are sometimes classified with fungi because of the way they reproduce (spores) and get their food (absorption).

Check for Understanding

Quiz students on protists, methods of locomotion, how they obtain food, how they are classified and why they are important.

Reteach

Have students make a table to show how protists in this chapter are classified and why they are important.

Idea Map

Have students use the idea map as a study guide to the major concepts of this section.

OPTIONS

Slime Mold Life Cycle/*Transparency Package*, number 5a. Use color transparency number 5a as you teach funguslike protists.

TEACH

Skill Check

The first stage looks like an amoeba and the second stage is like a fungus.

Check for Understanding

Have students respond to the first three questions in Check Your Understanding.

Reteach

Reteaching/*Teacher Resource Package,* p. 12. Use this worksheet to give students additional practice in understanding the Protist Kingdom.

Extension: Assign Critical Thinking, Biology and Reading, or some of the **OPTIONS** available with this lesson.

3 APPLY

ACTIVITY/Software

Protozoa, Opportunities for Learning, Inc.

4 CLOSE

Divergent Question

Ask students to make a list of how protists affect our daily lives.

Answers to Check Your Understanding

1. flagella, cilia, flagellum
2. animal-like: *Paramecium,* amoeba, *Plasmodium,* trypanosome; plantlike: euglena, diatom, dinoflagellate, algae
3. Most plantlike protists have chlorophyll and can make theirown food. Animal-like protists cannot.
4. Protists have cell parts with membranes and a nucleus. Viruses and monerans have only a cell membrane.
5. It means animal. Other examples are zoo, zoology, zoological.

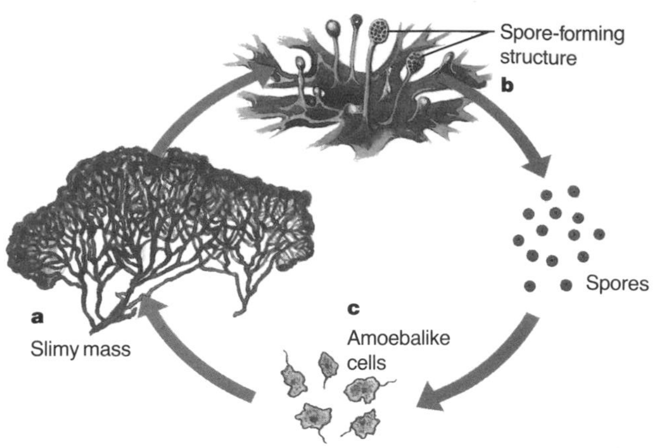

Figure 5-9 The life cycle of a slime mold has three stages: the feeding and growth stage (a), the spore-forming stage (b), and the amoebalike stage (c).

Skill Check

Interpret diagrams: Look at the slime mold in Figure 5-9. Identify the two stages that are like other organisms. What organisms in this chapter do the stages resemble? *For more help, refer to the **Skill Handbook**, pages 706-711.*

There are three stages in the life cycle of a slime mold, Figure 5-9. The first stage looks like a slimy mass. It moves much like an amoeba, by flowing across a surface. The mass may have beautiful colors such as red, yellow, or violet, or it may have no color.

In the second stage, the slime mold stops growing and moving. It produces spores inside a structure on a stalk. The slime mold in this second stage is like a fungus. This stage usually starts when the slime mold has no food.

During the third stage, the spores develop into little amoebalike cells with flagella. Then each of these cells loses its flagella and grows into a slimy mass again.

Check Your Understanding

1. Explain how the following move: a *Volvox* ball, a paramecium, a euglena.
2. List two examples of animal-like protists and two examples of plantlike protists.
3. How are plantlike protists different from protozoans?
4. **Critical Thinking:** How do protists differ from viruses and from monerans?
5. **Biology and Reading:** As you learned from reading this section, the word *protozoan* comes from two Greek words. If the word part *proto-* means first, what does the word part *-zoan* mean in Greek? What other words can you think of that come from this same Greek word?

RETEACHING 12

RETEACHING: IDEA MAP — CHAPTER 5

Name ______________ Date ________ Class ________

Use with Section 5:1.

PROTIST KINGDOM

Use the following terms to complete the idea map: euglena, paramecium, dinoflagellate, amoeba, diatom, sporozoan, slime mold, trypanosome.

Animal-like protists	moves with false feet	amoeba
	moves with cilia	paramecium
	does not move	sporozoan
	moves with flagella	trypanosome
Plantlike protists	moves with flagella	euglena
	has two-part cell covering	diatom
	red or brown color	dinoflagellate
Funguslike protists	has three stages in life cycle	slime mold

1. What traits do animal-like protists have? They are consumers; most move about; and all are one-celled.
2. How are the plantlike protists like plants? All have chlorophyll and make their own food. They produce large amounts of oxygen.
3. How are the funguslike protists like fungi? They live in damp places and feed on decaying material. They reproduce by spores.
4. How do amoebas differ from sporozoans in the way they reproduce? Amoebas reproduce by fission; sporozoans reproduce by forming spores.
5. How are plantlike protists classified? They are classified by their color and their structure.

Lab 5–1 Protists

Problem: What are the traits of protists?

Skills

make and use tables, interpret data, observe, classify, use a microscope

Materials

microscope
3 coverslips
3 droppers
3 glass slides

cultures of:
amoeba
paramecium
euglena

Procedure

1. Copy the data table.
2. Put a drop of amoeba culture on a glass slide. Gently add a coverslip.

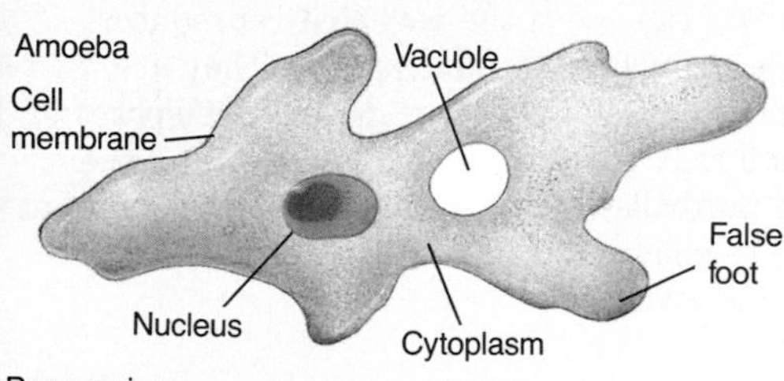

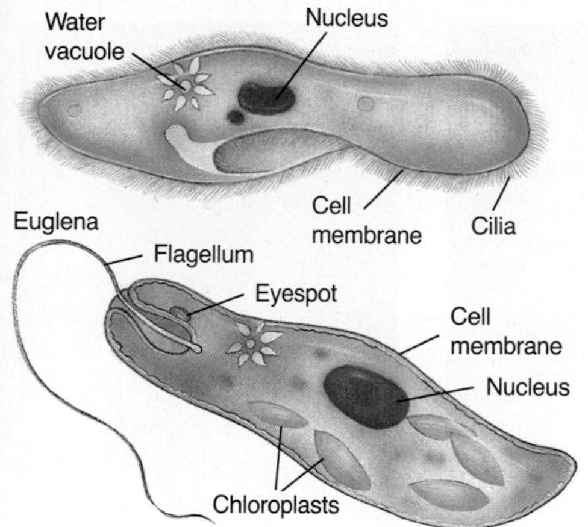

3. **Observe:** Examine the amoeba on low, then high power. Record in your table the parts you see.
4. Repeat steps 2 and 3 with the paramecium and euglena cultures.
5. Wash and dry the glass slides, coverslips, and droppers. Return them to their proper places.

Data and Observations

1. How does the amoeba move?
2. Which protist is green?

	Amoeba	Paramecium	Euglena
Cell membrane	yes	yes	yes
Parts used for movement	false feet	cilia	flagellum
Cell wall	no	no	no
Vacuoles	Answers	will vary.	
Nucleus	yes	yes	yes
Cytoplasm	yes	yes	yes
Green color (chlorophyll)	no	no	yes

Analyze and Apply

1. **Interpret data:** What traits do protists have in common?
2. Which protist moves the slowest? Which moves the fastest?
3. **Apply:** Which protists are like animals? Why? Which protists are like plants? Why?

Extension

Observe a drop of pond water under the microscope. Identify the protists you see.

ANSWERS

Data and Observations

1. Cytoplasm flows in and out of false feet.
2. euglena

Analyze and Apply

1. They have a cell membrane, nucleus, and cytoplasm. They all lack a cell wall.
2. Amoeba moves the slowest. Paramecium moves the fastest.
3. Amoeba and paramecium are like animals because they are consumers and don't make their own food. Euglena are like plants because they have chlorophyll.

Lab 5-1 Protists

Overview

In this lab, students use the microscope to observe the structure of representative protists. They also observe how protists move and any cell parts that are different in the three types.

Objectives: Upon completing this lab, students will be able to (1) **identify** common traits of protists and (2) **recognize** differences between protists.

Time Allotment: 45 minutes

Preparation

▶ Methyl cellulose may be used to slow down paramecia. Add 10 g methyl cellulose powder to 90 mL warmed distilled water. Stir gently to avoid bubbles. Dispense in dropping bottles.

▶ **Alternate Materials:** Strands of cotton fibers may be used to slow protists instead of methyl cellulose.

Lab 5-1 worksheet/*Teacher Resource Package,* pp. 17-18.

Teaching the Lab

Cooperative Learning: Have students work in pairs. For more information, see pp. 22T–23T in the Teacher Guide.

▶ **Troubleshooting:** Remind students never to focus down on a glass slide without watching from the side. The nucleus in euglena may be hard to find if there is an abundance of chloroplasts or if the organisms are very small.

5:2 Fungus Kingdom

PREPARATION

Materials Needed

Make copies of the Focus, Skill, Critical Thinking/ Problem Solving, Application, Study Guide, Enrichment, Reteaching, and Lab worksheets in the *Teacher Resource Package.*

▶ Gather mildew, rust, puffballs, and mushrooms for the Focus activity.

▶ Obtain bread and resealable plastic bags for the Mini Lab.

▶ Obtain prepared slides of mushroom basidium and purchase mushrooms for Lab 5-2.

Key Science Words

hyphae
sporangium fungi
sporangia
club fungi
sac fungi
budding
mutualism
lichen

Process Skills

In the Mini Lab students will observe. In Lab 5-2, they will observe, infer, use a microscope, and design an experiment.

1 FOCUS

▶ The objectives are listed on the student page. Remind students to preview these objectives as a guide to this numbered section.

ACTIVITY/Display

Collect bracket fungi, mildew, rust, puffballs, and mushrooms. Place each in a covered container, label, and display. Use the display to show diversity in fungi. Point out that hyphae are not visible.

Focus/*Teacher Resource Package,* p. 9. Use the Focus transparency shown at the bottom of this page as an introduction to Fungus Kingdom.

5:2 Fungus Kingdom

Objectives

4. **List** the traits of fungi and compare the traits of the major kinds of fungi.
5. **Tell** how fungi can be harmful and helpful.

Key Science Words

hyphae
sporangium fungi
sporangia
club fungi
sac fungi
budding
mutualism
lichen

Mushrooms, molds, mildews, yeasts, rusts, and smuts are all fungi. Fungi are consumers and decomposers. They cannot make their own food. Some are parasites, but most of them are saprophytes. Remember from Chapter 4 that saprophytes live on dead matter. They break down waste and dead materials for food and return them to the soil.

Traits of Fungi

You read in Chapter 3 that a fungus is an organism that has a cell wall and does not make its own food. Cells of fungi often have more than one nucleus. Fungi range in size from one-celled yeasts to large, multicellular mushrooms.

The bodies of most fungi are made of a network of threadlike structures called **hyphae** (HI fee). Hyphae contain cytoplasm and are usually divided by cross walls. The hyphae grow and branch until they cover and digest the food source on which the fungus is growing. Look at the bracket fungi growing on the tree in Figure 5-10b. The hyphae have spread throughout the tree bark. The part of the fungus that you can see is the part that reproduces.

Most fungi reproduce by forming spores. They are classified according to how they form spores. The spores of fungi are so small that you need a microscope to see them. Mushrooms and puffballs release large clouds of spores that are easy to see, as shown in Figure 5-10c. Each cloud contains millions of spores.

Figure 5-10 Hyphae (a) of a fungus usually have cross walls. Bracket fungi (b) grow on trees. Mushrooms (c) reproduce by releasing spores.

a

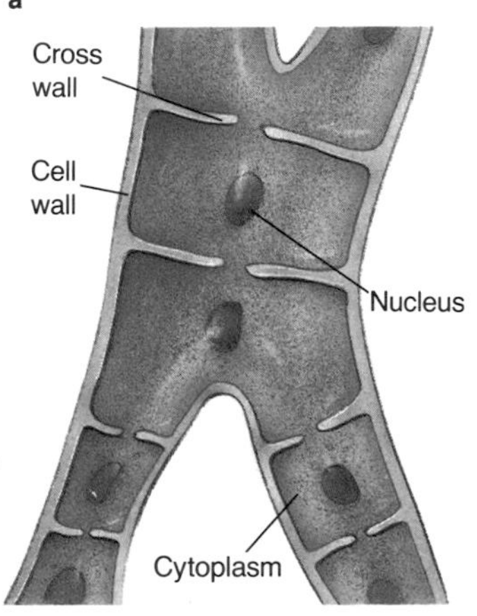

b

c

OPTIONS

Science Background

Amanita muscaria is one of the best known poisonous mushrooms. Its colorful yellow or red cap is covered by white scales. Toxins from *Amanita* become attached to and destroy cells of the liver. Symptoms appear 6 to 12 hours after eating. Death usually occurs in about 4 days. No antidote has been found.

How Fungi Get Their Food/*Transparency Package,* number 5b. Use color transparency number 5b as you teach the fungi.

FOCUS 9

FOCUS
CHAPTER 5
MILDEW MAKES THINGS MUSTY
1. What kinds of objects does mildew grow on?
2. What substance is present in these objects that mildew needs to live?

Chemicals released by hyphae digest dead materials.
Hyphae absorb the digested food.

Figure 5-11 Fungi digest food outside their bodies.

Fungi also reproduce from pieces of hyphae. Sometimes, wind or water carry pieces of broken hyphae to new places. If enough moisture and food are present, the pieces grow into new fungi.

What do fungi use for food?

Most fungi can use once-living things for food. The bracket fungi in Figure 5-10b are feeding on a dead tree. Mildew grows on different items, using them as food. Have you ever seen mildew growing on old clothing? As fungi grow on a once-living thing, they decompose it.

A large amount of waste and dead material is deposited on Earth every day. If it were not for decomposers, the waste would build up and become a problem for all living things. Many of the decomposers that help break down dead materials and return them to the soil are fungi.

Fungi digest food outside their bodies. First, the hyphae release chemicals into the material surrounding them. The chemicals break down the food into small molecules. Then the hyphae absorb the digested food.

Not all fungi feed on dead material. Some feed on living things. They are parasites. Most fungi that are parasites grow on plants. Some attack crops such as corn, wheat, potatoes, and soybeans.

Some fungi are parasites of animals. They cause problems such as athlete's foot by living on human skin cells.

Many fungi grow in and on the roots of living plants, helping the plants get water and minerals. In return, the fungi receive food from the plant. Many trees and other plants can't live without these fungi.

Bio Tip

Health: Ergotism is a serious fungal disease caused by eating fungus-infected rye. It causes severe abdominal pain, hallucinations, gangrene, and even death. The fungus is also a source of lysergic acid diethylamide, also known as LSD.

2 TEACH

MOTIVATION/Audiovisual

Show the slides *Mushrooms and Other Fungi, Parts I and II,* JLM Visuals.

Concept Development

▶ Discuss the nature of a spore as a single cell used for reproduction.

▶ Point out that fungal diseases of plants are still among the greatest threats to human welfare. Hundreds of millions of dollars are spent each year to protect crops with fungicides, to develop new fungicides, and to develop new strains of crops resistant to fungi.

▶ Discuss the amount of waste and dead material that would accumulate if there were no fungi to decompose the organic material.

▶ Explain that a fungus secretes enzymes into its food. These enzymes break large food molecules into molecules that are small enough to be absorbed by hyphae. After the food is absorbed, it travels to all parts of the fungus.

▶ Human fungal diseases cause infections of the skin and of internal organs. Fungus that causes a respiratory infection lives in the soil but becomes a parasite in the lungs if spores or hyphae are inhaled.

Guided Practice

Have students write down their answers to the margin question: Most use once-living things.

SKILL 5

SKILL: SEQUENCE — **CHAPTER 5**

Name ______ Date ______ Class ______

For more help, refer to the Skill Handbook, pages 706-711. *Use after Section 5:2.*

LIFE CYCLES OF FUNGI

The life cycles of two kinds of fungi are shown below. The diagrams show the fungi at different stages of development. They also indicate events or processes that take place at each stage of development.

Study the life cycle of Rhizopus, the bread mold, shown below. Complete the sentences to explain the sequence, or the order, in which the events occur.

In the picture the organisms labeled __A__ are mature bread molds. They produce __spores__ in the structures called __sporangia__. When the __spores__ are released and land on a food source, they develop into __new bread molds__. To show the mold organisms in order from youngest to oldest, you would draw stage __B__ first, then stage __C__, and then stage __A__.

Study the life cycle of the mushroom below and then complete the sentences.

A mushroom reproduces by means of __spores__, which are produced in club-shaped structures in the __gills__ of the mushroom __cap__. These structures are shown in the picture labeled __A__.

Some events in the life cycle of a mushroom are listed below. The events are not in order. Put the events in order by writing the letters of the sentences on the line.

a. Mushroom becomes mature.
b. Spores are released.
c. Mushroom grows and develops.
d. Spore begins to grow.
e. Mushroom produces spores.
f. Spore lands on food source.

f, d, c, a, e, b

OPTIONS

ACTIVITY/Enrichment

Discuss the late blight fungus that caused the Irish potato famine, the chestnut tree fungusthat has killed most of the chestnut trees in North America, and the fungus that causes Dutch elm disease.

Skill/*Teacher Resource Package,* p. 5. Use the Skill worksheet shown here for students to sequence the life cycles of fungi.

TEACH

Concept Development

▶ Explain that sodium propionate is a chemical used by bakeries to inhibit growth of mold in bread. You may want to have students check bread packages for the term.

▶ Point out that an identifying feature of mushrooms is their spore print. A mushroom will drop spores in a pattern that shows the arrangement of gills.

▶ Remind students that the commercial mushrooms are an excellent source of vitamins and the minerals phosphorus and iron. They also contain some proteins.

▶ Hyphae growth rates can exceed 1 kilometer per day. This explains why mushrooms can spring up overnight.

Mini Lab

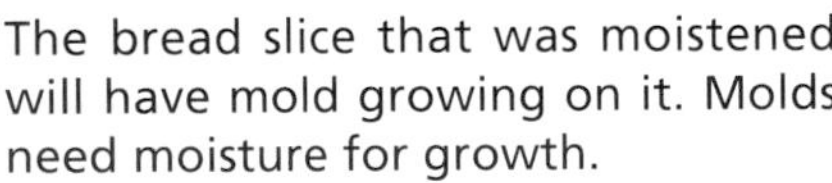

The bread slice that was moistened will have mold growing on it. Molds need moisture for growth.

Mini Lab

What Do Fungi Need?

Observe: Sprinkle a slice of bread with water. Place it in a plastic bag. Place a dry slice in a bag. Seal the bags and set in a warm place for a week. What do fungi need to grow? *For more help, refer to the **Skill Handbook**, pages 704-705.*

Kinds of Fungi

Have you ever seen bread mold—a black, fuzzy substance growing on bread? If so, you have seen a sporangium (spuh RAN jee uhm) fungus. **Sporangium fungi** are fungi that produce spores in sporangia. **Sporangia** are structures, found on the tips of hyphae, that make spores. You can see that the phylum gets its name from these structures.

Let's return to our bread mold. Bread mold produces spores within sporangia that stick up above the bread, as shown in Figure 5-12. Each spore can form a new bread mold. Hyphae grow into the bread. The mold takes in food and water by means of its hyphae. Molds grow best in warm, moist, dark places, but they can grow also in cold places, such as the refrigerator.

Growth of molds on food can be prevented by cleanliness, drying, and the use of chemicals. Chemicals are added to breads to delay the growth of molds. Fruits such as raisins and apricots are preserved by drying.

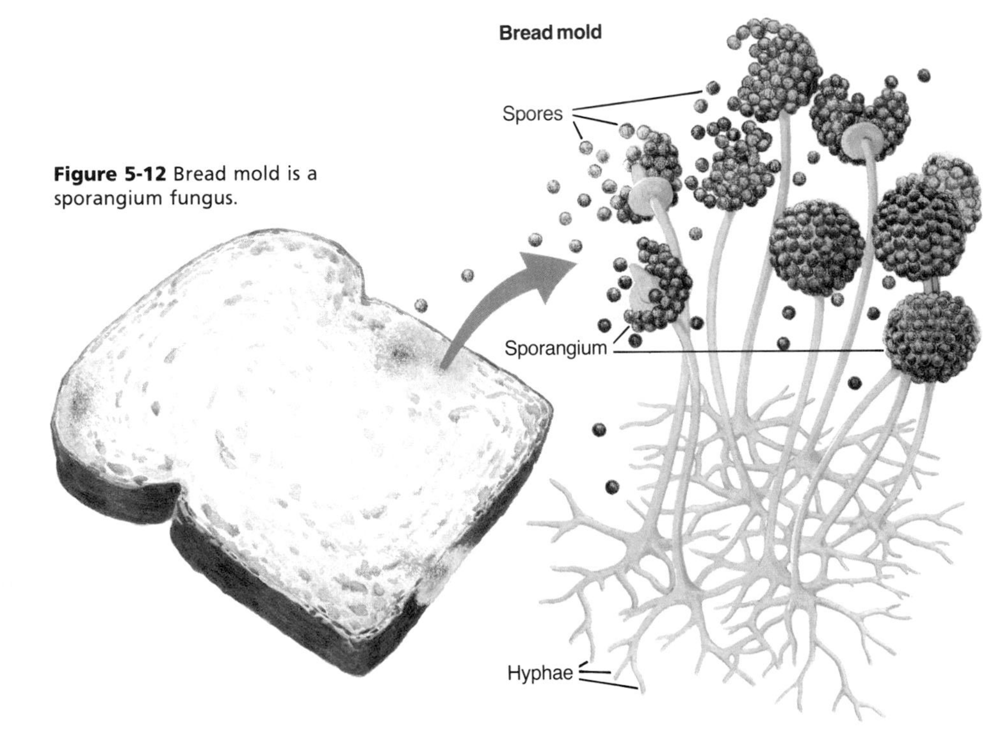

Figure 5-12 Bread mold is a sporangium fungus.

OPTIONS

ACTIVITY/Challenge

Have some students set up an experiment with homemade bread and bakery bread to see which will grow mold faster.

What Do Molds Need in Order to Grow?/*Lab Manual,* pp. 37-40. Use this lab as an extension to the traits of fungi.

Critical Thinking/Problem Solving/ *Teacher Resource Package,* p. 5. Use the Critical Thinking/Problem Solving worksheet shown here to teach how mushrooms grow.

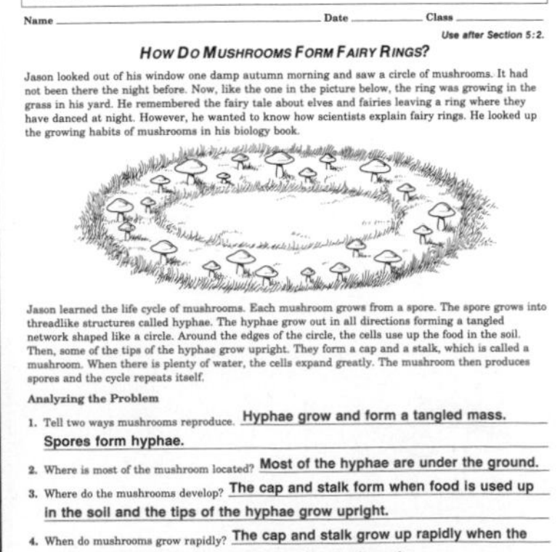

CRITICAL THINKING 5

CRITICAL THINKING/PROBLEM SOLVING — CHAPTER 5

Name ______ Date ______ Class ______

Use after Section 5:2.

HOW DO MUSHROOMS FORM FAIRY RINGS?

Jason looked out of his window one damp autumn morning and saw a circle of mushrooms. It had not been there the night before. Now, like the one in the picture below, the ring was growing in the grass in his yard. He remembered the fairy tale about elves and fairies leaving a ring where they have danced at night. However, he wanted to know how scientists explain fairy rings. He looked up the growing habits of mushrooms in his biology book.

Jason learned the life cycle of mushrooms. Each mushroom grows from a spore. The spore grows into threadlike structures called hyphae. The hyphae grow out in all directions forming a tangled network shaped like a circle. Around the edges of the circle, the cells use up the food in the soil. Then, some of the tips of the hyphae grow upright. They form a cap and a stalk, which is called a mushroom. When there is plenty of water, the cells expand greatly. The mushroom then produces spores and the cycle repeats itself.

Analyzing the Problem

1. Tell two ways mushrooms reproduce. Hyphae grow and form a tangled mass. Spores form hyphae.
2. Where is most of the mushroom located? Most of the hyphae are under the ground.
3. Where do the mushrooms develop? The cap and stalk form when food is used up in the soil and the tips of the hyphae grow upright.
4. When do mushrooms grow rapidly? The cap and stalk grow up rapidly when the ground is very moist, on a damp morning or after rain.

Solving the Problem

1. How do fairy rings form? Mushroom hyphae grow from a spore out into a circle of hyphae. At the edges, mushrooms form. They expand when the ground is very moist, on a damp morning or after rain.

Career Close-Up

Mushroom Farmer

Did you ever wonder where the mushrooms on your pizza came from? Most mushrooms are grown indoors, but some may be grown outdoors or in caves. Equipment is used to control temperature, humidity, and ventilation.

To grow mushrooms, a compost mixture is placed in shallow beds. Spores from mushroom caps are sown on the compost and covered with a thin layer of soil. A mass of hyphae will soon grow through the compost. In seven or eight weeks, mushrooms will appear.

After three months, the mushrooms can be harvested and put into boxes. They will be shipped to markets the same day.

No special schooling is needed for this job, but a knowledge of fungi is very helpful.

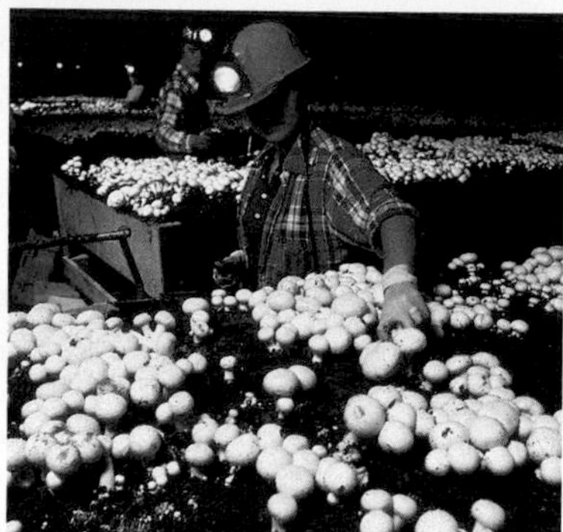

Mushroom farmers grow mushrooms in shallow beds of compost.

Fungi with club-shaped parts that produce spores are called **club fungi,** Figure 5-13. They form networks of branched hyphae underground. Mushrooms are club fungi. Mushrooms get food in much the same way as bread mold.

Mushrooms are an important food crop. Some, however, cause illness and a few types cause death. You should never eat wild mushrooms unless an expert says they are safe.

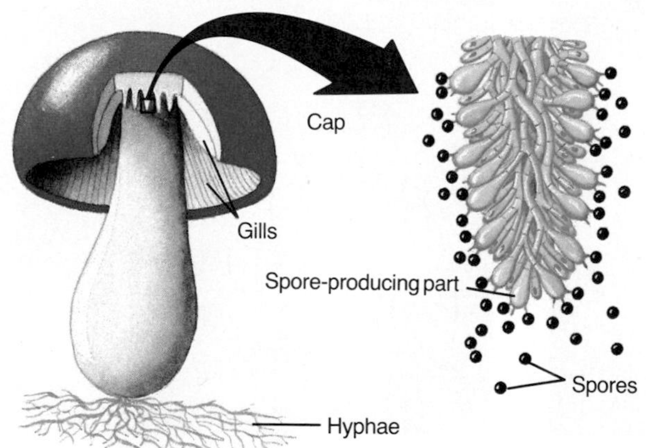

Figure 5-13 Club fungi produce spores in club-shaped structures within gills. Where are the gills located? in the cap

Career Close-Up

Mushroom Farmer

Background

Mushrooms have been used in foods for thousands of years. They grow wild in fields. It was not until the late 1800s that mushrooms were grown commercially in the United States. Mushrooms are eaten fresh, canned, or dried.

Related Careers

plant farmers

Job Requirements

A high school education and community college courses in fungi, business management, and marketing are helpful. Books may be obtained from the local library on the conditions necessary for growing mushrooms and how to start a small business.

For More Information

Mushroom Growers Association
18 South Water Market
Chicago, IL 60608

TEACH

Independent Practice

Study Guide/*Teacher Resource Package,* p. 27. Use the Study Guide worksheet shown at the bottom of this page for independent practice.

APPLICATION 5

APPLICATION: SAFETY CHAPTER 5

Name ____ Date ____ Class ____

Use after Section 5:2.

LEARNING ABOUT MUSHROOMS

Mushrooms provide a food source for people, but some mushrooms are poisonous. Even one bite of a white mushroom called the "destroying angel" can be fatal. Many mushrooms look alike. Some very poisonous species look like common edible species. For this reason, you should never eat a mushroom from the wild unless an adult who knows mushrooms tells you it is safe.

Identifying mushrooms can be difficult. Many plants are identified by their leaves, stems, flowers, or fruits. Mushrooms do not have these parts, so they must be identified in a different way. The special parts of mushrooms can be used to identify them.

1. *Describe each part of the mushroom listed below.*
   Cap the round top of a mushroom
   Hyphae network of threadlike structures
   Spores small reproductive cells

2. Observe a mushroom that you have bought at a grocery.
   Mushroom spores are found in the ridges or "gills" under the cap. Find the gills on your mushroom. If the mushroom is not mature, the gills may be covered by a thin membrane called a veil. Remove the veil if necessary. In the box at the right, make a drawing of the underside of the mushroom, showing the gills.

3. As the spores on the gills mature, the gills become darker. Once the spores are fully developed, they fall from the gills onto the ground. Most spores are hard to see without a magnifying glass. However, you can see a collection of spores by making a spore print. Use a mature mushroom with dark gills. Place the mushroom on a white sheet of paper, gill side down. Cover the mushroom and the paper with a glass jar or bowl to keep the spores from blowing away. Leave it there overnight. The next morning, remove the glass, and carefully lift the mushroom off the paper. You should be able to see a print of the spores as they have fallen from the gills. Share your results with your class.

4. Try to find more than one kind of mushroom in the supermarket. See if the spore patterns are the same or different.

STUDY GUIDE 27

STUDY GUIDE CHAPTER 5

Name ____ Date ____ Class ____

FUNGUS KINGDOM

2. Review the following words from Chapter 4. Then, define them in the spaces below.
   a. saprophyte organism that uses dead material for food
   b. parasite organism that lives in or on another living thing

3. Next to each picture, on the first line write the word *parasite* or *saprophyte,* to describe the kind of fungus shown. On the lower line, explain how you know that the fungus is a saprophyte or a parasite.
   saprophyte — feeds off dead material
   saprophyte — feeds off dead material
   parasite — feeds off living things
   parasite — feeds off living things

4. Put a check mark in the correct place on the table that indicates which traits are found in the different kinds of fungi.

Trait	Sporangium fungi	Club fungi	Sac fungi
reproduce by spores	✓	✓	✓
spores made in a saclike part			✓
cause Dutch elm disease			✓
spores made in a sporangium	✓		
mushrooms belong here		✓	
yeast belongs here			✓
spores made in club-shaped part		✓	

OPTIONS

Application/*Teacher Resource Package,* p. 5. Use the Application worksheet shown here for students to learn safety with mushrooms.

TEACH

Concept Development

▶ Point out that Roquefort, Brie, and Camembert are cheeses that get their special flavors from specific sac fungi used in the production process. The best soy sauces are made by fermenting boiled soybeans and wheat with a sac fungus. The use of fungi to increase the nutrient content of foods is very important in many countries.

▶ Point out that *Penicillium* is one of the six genera of molds from which researchers make antibiotics. *Penicillium* produces penicillins. Molds are used in making well over 1000 different antibiotics.

Guided Practice

Have students write down their answers to the margin question: They are used for baking bread and making alcohol.

Independent Practice

Study Guide/*Teacher Resource Package*, p. 28. Use the Study Guide worksheet shown at the bottom of this page for independent practice.

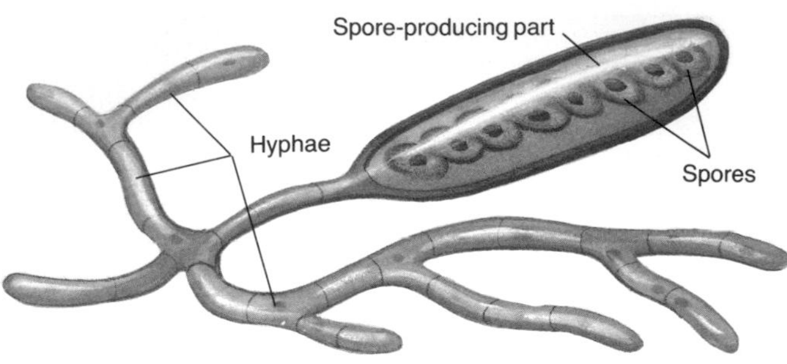

Figure 5-14 Sac fungi produce spores in saclike structures.

Shelf fungi, rusts, smuts, and puffballs are club fungi, too. Many of these fungi are harmful to plants. Rusts and smuts can destroy entire crops of corn, wheat, and oats.

Yeasts, cup fungi, and powdery mildews are called sac fungi. **Sac fungi** produce spores in saclike structures, Figure 5-14. Yeasts are unusual sac fungi because they have only one cell. Yeasts reproduce by budding. **Budding** is reproduction in which a small part of the parent grows into a new organism. The bud grows out of the parent as shown in Figure 5-15b. Budding produces offspring that are identical to the parent. If conditions are not right for growth, the yeast cell can form a spore. When growing conditions improve, the spore forms a new yeast cell.

How are yeasts helpful to humans?

Sac fungi are useful to humans. Yeasts are used for making bread and alcohol. *Penicillium* (pen uh SIL ee uhm) is a fungus used to make the antibiotic penicillin. It is shown in Figure 5-15a. One species of *Penicillium* is used

Figure 5-15 *Penicillium* (a) is a sac fungus used to make penicillin. Yeasts reproduce by budding (b). Is budding sexual or asexual reproduction? asexual

a

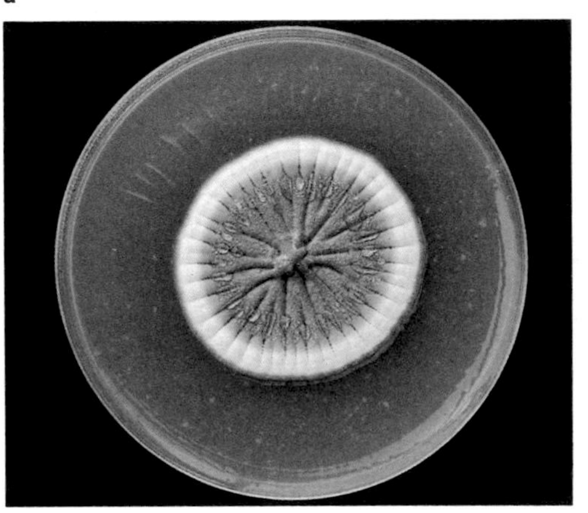

b

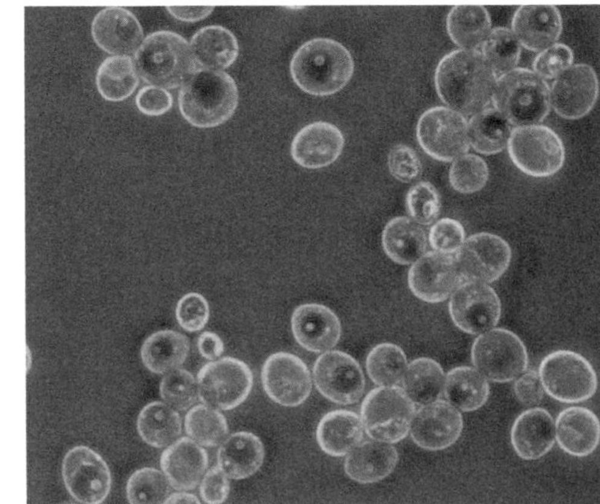

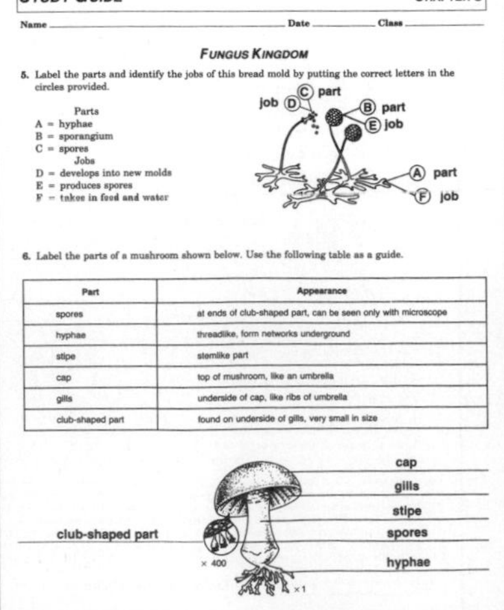

STUDY GUIDE 28

STUDY GUIDE — CHAPTER 5

Name ______ Date ______ Class ______

FUNGUS KINGDOM

5. Label the parts and identify the jobs of this bread mold by putting the correct letters in the circles provided.

Parts
A = hyphae
B = sporangium
C = spores
Jobs
D = develops into new molds
E = produces spores
F = takes in food and water

6. Label the parts of a mushroom shown below. Use the following table as a guide.

Part	Appearance
spores	at ends of club-shaped part, can be seen only with microscope
hyphae	threadlike, form networks underground
stipe	stemlike part
cap	top of mushroom, like an umbrella
gills	underside of cap, like ribs of umbrella
club-shaped part	found on underside of gills, very small in size

TABLE 5–3. HELPFUL AND HARMFUL FUNGI
Helpful Fungi
1. Used as food—mushrooms
2. Used to make blue and Roquefort cheese
3. Used to make wine, beer, and whiskey—yeast
4. Used to make bread rise—yeast
5. Used to make soy sauce
6. Used to make penicillin and other antibiotics
7. Help to break down materials and get rid of wastes
8. Enrich the soil
Harmful Fungi
1. Cause foods, such as fruit and bread, to spoil
2. Cause plant diseases, such as rusts, smuts, Dutch elm disease, and mildew
3. Cause human diseases, such as athlete's foot, ringworm, thrush, and lung infections
4. Destroy leather, fabrics, plastics

to make blue cheeses. While many sac fungi are helpful, one causes Dutch elm disease. This disease has destroyed thousands of elm trees in the United States. Table 5-3 shows some examples of how fungi are helpful and harmful.

Lichens

Some fungi live neither as parasites nor as saprophytes. They get food from other organisms without causing harm. In turn, they may give support or protection. A living arrangement in which both organisms benefit is called **mutualism.**

A **lichen** (LI kun) is a fungus and an organism with chlorophyll that live together. The organism with chlorophyll can be either a green alga or a blue-green bacterium. A lichen looks like a single organism but it is not. The two organisms in the lichen are so closely tangled together that they cannot be easily separated. You may have seen a British-soldier lichen, as shown in Figure 5-16. The green alga provides the food for the fungus. The fungus provides support, and holds water and minerals for the alga. The alga uses the water and minerals to make food for both itself and the fungus. Both organisms benefit.

Lichens are very sensitive to changes in the environment. If the air becomes too polluted, the green organism can't live. If the green organism dies, the fungus also dies.

Bio Tip

Consumer: Most lemon flavoring (citric acid) today is made from a black mold called *Aspergillus niger.*

Figure 5-16 British soldier lichen

TEACH

Concept Development

▶ Point out that lichens can grow in places where few other organisms can live because of their unusual living arrangement.

▶ Explain that most lichens reproduce by fragmentation, in which small pieces break off and blow away.

▶ Point out that the death of an increasing number of lichens in an area may indicate an increase in air pollution.

▶ Many of the chemicals produced by lichens have long been prized as beautiful dyes. Harris tweed is produced with lichen dyes. Litmus, a dye made from lichens, is used to determine whether a solution is an acid or a base.

Check for Understanding

Provide students with diagrams of bread mold, a mushroom, and yeast cells. The diagram should have a place for students to label the fungi, hyphae, and spore-producing structure of each, to add examples of each kind of fungi, and to list how each is helpful or harmful.

Reteach

Discuss why fungi are classified as fungi and the effects of fungi on the environment.

Independent Practice

Study Guide/*Teacher Resource Package,* p. 29. Use the Study Guide worksheet shown at the bottom of this page for independent practice.

ENRICHMENT 5

ENRICHMENT CHAPTER 5

Name ________ Date ________ Class ________

Use after Section 5:2.

TEN-PIN PROTISTS AND FUNGI

Imagine you are bowling. Each of the ten "pins" shown below is a letter in a word related to protists or fungi. The object is to make a word with each group of ten pins. You may form a second word with any letters not used the first time. Score one point for each pin or letter used. If you make a ten-letter word, you have a strike. If you make two words and use all the letters, you have a spare.

Write the word or words in the spaces beneath the pins. Write your score on the score sheet below.

Z N O A / R S O / P O / S — sporozoans

M L M I / E D O / S L / S — slime molds

A R P M / U E C / M I / A — paramecium

O S Q M / E T O / I S / U — mosquitoes

M A I A / E K L / I N / L — animal-like

T N A O / Z O P / R O / S — protozoans

O O T E / S A P / T T / H — toothpaste

L C I I / N P E / I L / N — penicillin

N S I O / F C N / T E / I — infections

G M I U / N R A / O P / S — sporangium

1	2	3	4	5	6	7	8	9	10	Final score
Scores will depend on student answers.										

STUDY GUIDE 29

STUDY GUIDE CHAPTER 5

Name ________ Date ________ Class ________

FUNGUS KINGDOM

7. Refer to Table 5-3 on page 107 of your textbook, and fill in the following blanks.
   a. List three ways in which fungi can be helpful. **Student answers may vary, but may indicate that fungi are used as food, in making food, to make medicine, or to enrich the soil.**
   b. List ways fungi can be harmful to things you own. **Fungi can destroy plants, leather, fabric, and plastic.**
   c. List ways fungi can be harmful to people. **They can cause food to spoil and can cause diseases in humans.**

In your textbook, read about lichens in Section 5:2.

8. What is mutualism? **Mutualism is a living arrangement in which the things living together benefit.**
9. What is a lichen? **A lichen is a fungus and an organism with chlorophyll that live together.**
   a. List two examples of lichens. **British soldier, reindeer moss**
   b. What is the role of the organism with chlorophyll? **It provides food for the fungus.**
   c. What is the role of the fungus? **It provides support and holds water and minerals for the other organism.**
10. Where do lichens live? **on bare rocks, on trees, and on Arctic ice**
   a. How do they help form soil? **Lichens release acids that break down rock. The broken down rock and the dead lichens form soil.**
   b. How do lichens help some animals? **Lichens provide food for some animals.**

OPTIONS

Enrichment/*Teacher Resource Package,* p. 5. Use the Enrichment worksheet shown here to give student practice with words from this chapter.

TEACH

Idea Map

Have students use the idea map as a study guide to the major concepts of this section.

Independent Practice

Study Guide/*Teacher Resource Package,* p. 30. Use the Study Guide worksheet shown at the bottom of this page for independent practice.

Check for Understanding

Have students respond to the first three questions in Check Your Understanding.

Reteach

Reteaching/*Teacher Resource Package,* p. 13. Use this worksheet to give students additional practice in comparing fungi.

Extension: Assign Critical Thinking, Biology and Writing, or some of the **OPTIONS** available with this lesson.

3 APPLY

ACTIVITY/Filmstrip

Show the filmstrip *The Impact of Fungi on Man and His Environment,* Carolina Biological.

4 CLOSE

Ask how fungi are used in pizza making.

Answers to Check Your Understanding

6. spores; from pieces of hyphae
7. sporangium fungi produce spores in sporangia; club fungi produce spores in club-shaped parts
8. to make bread, alcohol, penicillin
9. In fission, bacterium divides into two equal-sized bacteria. In budding, part of the parent grows into a new organism.
10. Fungi may be saprophytes, parasites, or mutualistic.

Study Tip: Use this idea map as a study guide to the fungus kingdom. The features and kinds of fungi are shown.

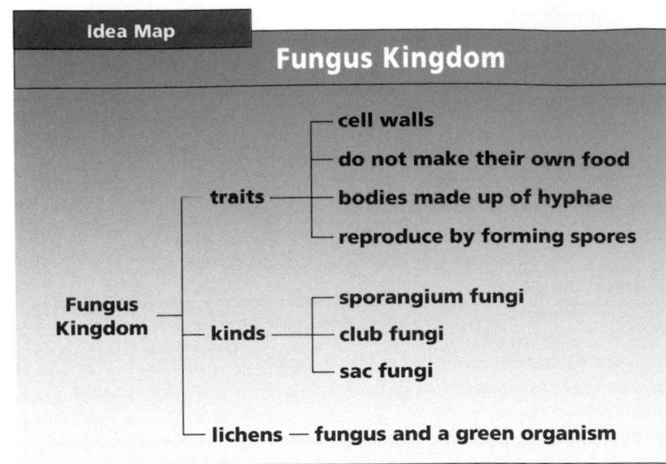

Lichens grow in places where neither fungi nor organisms with chlorophyll can be found alone. They grow on bare rocks, trees, and even on Arctic ice. They are often the first organisms to appear on rocks, such as lava, after a volcano erupts. Lichens release acids that break down the rock. Soil begins to form when the broken down rock mixes with lichens that have died. This process provides a place where other living things can grow.

Some types of lichens provide food for animals. In the Arctic, there is very little plant life. Reindeer moss is eaten by reindeer and caribou (KAIR uh boo), much as cattle graze on grass elsewhere. Caribou are deerlike animals that live in the Arctic.

Check Your Understanding

6. List two ways in which fungi reproduce.
7. How do sporangium fungi differ from club fungi?
8. Name three uses of sac fungi.
9. **Critical Thinking:** How does budding in yeast differ from fission in bacteria?
10. **Biology and Writing:** Combine the following three simple sentences into one compound sentence. Some fungi are saprophytes. Some fungi are parasites. Some fungi are mutualistic.

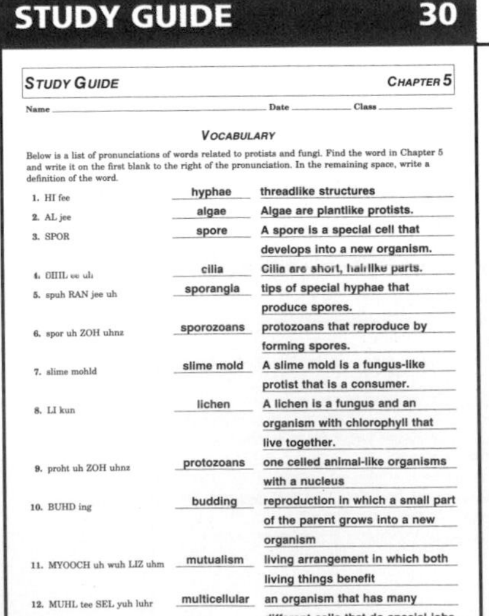
STUDY GUIDE 30

STUDY GUIDE — *CHAPTER 5*

Name ______ Date ______ Class ______

VOCABULARY

Below is a list of pronunciations of words related to protists and fungi. Find the word in Chapter 5 and write it on the first blank to the right of the pronunciation. In the remaining space, write a definition of the word.

Pronunciation	Word	Definition
1. HI fee	hyphae	threadlike structures
2. AL jee	algae	Algae are plantlike protists.
3. SPOR	spore	A spore is a special cell that develops into a new organism.
4. CHIL ee uh	cilia	Cilia are short, hairlike parts.
5. spuh RAN jee uh	sporangia	tips of special hyphae that produce spores.
6. spor uh ZOH uhnz	sporozoans	protozoans that reproduce by forming spores.
7. slime mohld	slime mold	A slime mold is a fungus-like protist that is a consumer.
8. LI kun	lichen	A lichen is a fungus and an organism with chlorophyll that live together.
9. proht uh ZOH uhnz	protozoans	one celled animal-like organisms with a nucleus
10. BUHD ing	budding	reproduction in which a small part of the parent grows into a new organism
11. MYOOCH uh wuh LIZ uhm	mutualism	living arrangement in which both living things benefit
12. MUHL tee SEL yuh luhr	multicellular	an organism that has many different cells that do special jobs.

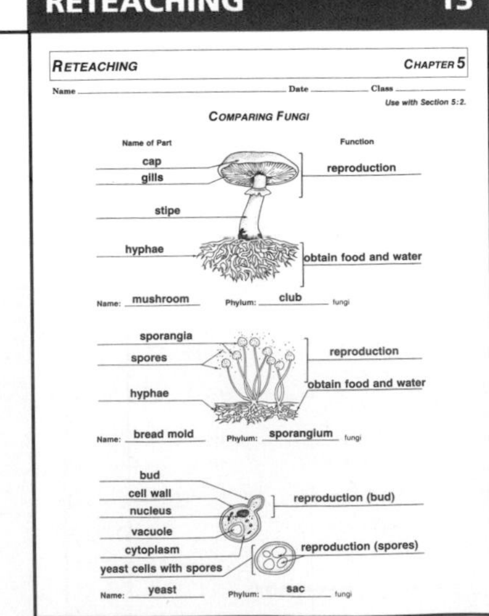
RETEACHING 13

RETEACHING — *CHAPTER 5*

Name ______ Date ______ Class ______

Use with Section 5:2.

COMPARING FUNGI

Name of Part — Function

cap
gills
stipe
hyphae
reproduction
obtain food and water

Name: mushroom Phylum: club fungi

sporangia
spores
hyphae
reproduction
obtain food and water

Name: bread mold Phylum: sporangium fungi

bud
cell wall
nucleus
vacuole
cytoplasm
yeast cells with spores
reproduction (bud)
reproduction (spores)

Name: yeast Phylum: sac fungi

Lab 5–2 Fungi

Problem: Why is a mushroom a fungus and not a plant?

Skills

observe, infer, use a microscope, design an experiment

Materials

scalpel
microscope
hand lens
mushroom
prepared slide of mushroom gill

Procedure

1. Obtain a mushroom and study its structure. Use Figure A to find the parts of the mushroom.
2. Draw and label the parts in your notebook.
3. Cut the mushroom lengthwise through the stipe and cap. **CAUTION:** *Always be careful when using a scalpel.*
4. **Observe:** Examine the cut areas with a hand lens. Locate the hyphae that form the reproductive part. Figure B will help.
5. Use the hand lens to observe the gills on the underside of the cap.
6. **Use a microscope:** Obtain a prepared slide of a mushroom gill. Examine it under low power on the microscope. Locate the structures that produce spores.
7. Locate the spores.
8. Draw and label the spores and the structures that produce them.

Data and Observations

1. What mushroom part supports the cap?
2. Where are the gills located?
3. Where are the reproductive parts of the mushroom located?
4. Describe the color of the mushroom.

Analyze and Apply

1. **Infer:** How would the location of the mushroom's reproductive parts help spread the spores?
2. What is a mushroom's food source?
3. Describe how a mushroom gets its food. Is it a parasite or a saprophyte?
4. **Apply:** How do mushrooms appear in your yard year after year when there is no sign of them between seasons? (HINT: Think about how mushrooms grow.)

Extension

Design an experiment to show what foods a fungus can use for growth.

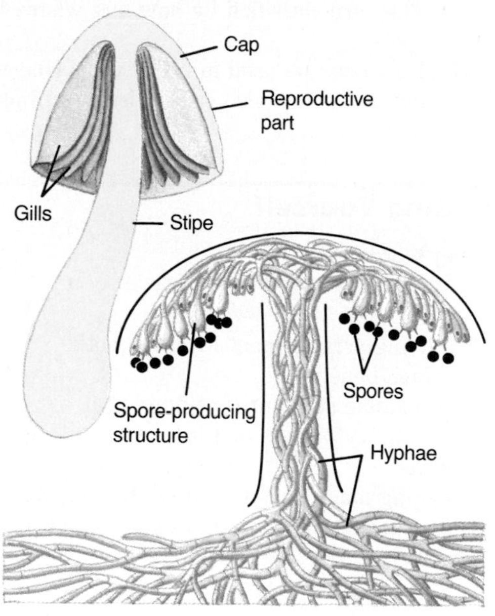

Lab 5-2 Fungi

Overview

In this lab, students will study the structure of a mushroom and determine why it is classified as a fungus and not a plant.

Objectives: Upon completing this lab, students will be able to (1) **identify** the parts of a mushroom and (2) **determine** why a mushroom is a fungus.

Time Allotment: 35 minutes

Preparation

▶ The fresh mushrooms at the grocery store are usually the brown and white varieties of *Agaricus.*

Lab 5-2 worksheet/*Teacher Resource Package,* pp. 19-20.

Teaching the Lab

Cooperative Learning: Have students work in pairs to complete the lab. For more information, see pp. 22T–23T in the Teacher Guide.

▶ **Troubleshooting:** Students may have difficulty in finding all the mushroom parts. Explain that the hyphae of mushrooms are underground. The mushroom is a fruiting body which bears spores. The reproductive structures are located on the gills.

ANSWERS

Data and Observations

1. the stipe
2. underneath the cap
3. on the gills
4. brown or gray

Analyze and Apply

1. The spores can easily be dispersed by the wind or fall to the ground.
2. decaying material
3. It digests its food outside its body. The hyphae release chemicals that break down the food into small molecules, which are then absorbed by the hyphae. Most mushrooms are saprophytes.
4. The spores may be left from the mushrooms present the year before, or hyphae may be left underground. These hyphae can produce new mushrooms.

CHAPTER 5 REVIEW

Summary

Summary statements can be used by students to review the major concepts of the chapter.

Key Science Words

All boldfaced terms from the chapter are listed.

Testing Yourself

Using Words

1. mutualism
2. hyphae
3. multicellular
4. lichen
5. spore
6. budding
7. cilia
8. algae
9. protozoan
10. club fungi
11. slime mold
12. sac fungi
13. sporangia
14. sporozoan

Finding Main Ideas

15. p. 106; Yeasts are one-celled while other fungi are multicellular.
16. p. 96; Sporozoans are protists that do not move.
17. p. 98; A diatom has a two-part cell covering of glasslike material that overlaps.
18. p. 102; Fungi are made of a network of threadlike hyphae.
19. pp. 104-106; The three kinds of fungi are sporangium fungi, club fungi, and sac fungi.
20. p. 106; Sac fungi are used to make bread, alcohol, and antibiotics.
21. p. 98; Red tides are caused by dinoflagellates.
22. p. 100; A slime mold is sometimes a slimy mass of material that flows like an amoeba. In a second stage, it stops flowing and produces spores. In a third stage, the spores become small amoebalike organisms with flagella.
23. p. 99; Most slime molds use rotting logs and decaying leaves for food.
24. pp. 95-97; Some human disease caused by protists are amoebic dysentery, sleeping sickness, and malaria.

Using Main Ideas

25. The green algae provides food and the lichen provides support.
26. An amoeba traps its food with its false feet.
27. A person can get malaria from a sporozoan carried by female *Anopheles* mosquitoes.

Chapter 5 Review

Summary

5:1 Protist Kingdom

1. Protists are usually one-celled, have a nucleus and other cell parts with membranes, and may be either producers or consumers.
2. There are three kinds of protists—animal-like protists, plantlike protists, and funguslike protists. They have different methods of movement, feeding, and reproduction.
3. Amoebas, paramecia, and trypanosomes are animal-like protists. Euglena, diatoms, and *Volvox* are plantlike protists. Slime molds are funguslike protists.

5:2 Fungus Kingdom

4. Fungi have many cells with cell walls and nuclei. They are consumers and feed as saprophytes or parasites. They form mutualistic relationships with green organisms. There are three phyla of fungi. They are classified by how and where they produce spores.
5. Fungi can be used in many ways that are helpful to humans. They also cause diseases in plants and animals.

Key Science Words

algae (p. 97)
budding (p. 106)
cilia (p. 96)
club fungi (p. 105)
hyphae (p. 102)
lichen (p. 107)
multicellular (p. 97)
mutualism (p. 107)
protozoan (p. 94)
sac fungi (p. 106)
slime mold (p. 99)
sporangia (p. 104)
sporangium fungi (p. 104)
spore (p. 96)
sporozoan (p. 96)

Testing Yourself

Using Words

Choose the word from the list of Key Science Words that best fits the definition.

1. a living arrangement in which both things benefit
2. threadlike structures of fungi that contain cytoplasm and have cross walls
3. having many cells that do different jobs
4. fungus and organism with chlorophyll that live together
5. special cell that forms a new organism
6. a way of producing offspring that are identical to the parent
7. tiny, hairlike parts on a cell surface
8. plantlike protist group
9. animal-like protist group
10. fungi with club-shaped parts
11. funguslike protist
12. fungi that have saclike structures
13. structures, on tips of hyphae, that make spores
14. a protozoan that forms spores

Review

Testing Yourself *continued*

Finding Main Ideas

List the page number where each main idea below is found. Then, explain each main idea.

15. how yeasts are different from other fungi
16. the name of protists that do not move
17. the structure of a diatom
18. what fungi are made of
19. the three kinds of fungi
20. why sac fungi are important
21. the cause of red tides
22. the life cycle of a slime mold
23. what most slime molds use for food
24. two human diseases caused by protists

Using Main Ideas

Answer the questions by referring to the page number after each question.

25. What is the role of each organism in a lichen? (p. 107)
26. How does an amoeba get food? (p. 95)
27. How does a person get malaria? (p. 97)
28. How do fungi digest food? (p. 103)
29. How are plantlike protists different from funguslike protists? (pp. 97, 99)
30. How do bracket fungi get food from trees? (p. 102)
31. Why should you not eat wild mushrooms? (p. 105)
32. How do protozoans get food? (p. 94)
33. Where are lichens found? (p. 108)
34 How can growth of molds on food be prevented? (p. 104)
35. How are lichens helpful? (p. 108)
36. How do certain dinoflagellates cause red tides? (p. 98)

Skill Review ✓

For more help, refer to the ***Skill Handbook,*** *pages 704-719.*

1. **Make and use tables:** Make a table to show the three kinds of fungi, where they produce spores, and examples of each.
2. **Classify:** Make a list of the traits of animal-like protists, plantlike protists, and funguslike protists. How are these traits used to classify protists?
3. **Infer:** Mushrooms often appear on a lawn soon after a rain. Using your knowledge of fungi, infer how this happens.
4. **Observe:** Observe a small amount of blue cheese under a stereomicroscope. What makes the cheese blue?

Finding Out More

Critical Thinking

1. What advantages does a lichen have over its fungus and green-organism parts?
2. How would life on Earth be affected if all the algae died?

Applications

1. Make a list of things you can do to keep fungi from growing in your home. Where are fungi most likely to be found in the home?
2. Use the library to learn about fungicides. Report on how they are used to keep fruits and vegetables safe from fungal infection.

111

Using Main Ideas

28. Fungi digest food outside their bodies. They release chemicals that break down the food into small molecules. Then the fungi absorb the digested food.
29. Plantlike protists have chlorophyll and can make their own food, and funguslike protists are consumers.
30. The hyphae spread throughout the tree bark and absorb the food.
31. Some wild mushrooms cause illness and few cause death.
32. The single cell takes in and digests food.
33. Lichens are found on bare rocks, trees, and Arctic ice.
34. Growth of molds can be prevented by cleanliness, drying, and the use of chemicals.
35. Lichens help to form soil and provide food for animals.
36. They reproduce in such large numbers that the water turns red.

Skill Review

1. Have students list the three types of fungi across the top of their table and list the features under each.
2. animal-like protists: animal-like, one-celled, cell nucleus, consumers, move about; plantlike protists: plantlike, one-celled or multicellular, cell nucleus, have chlorophyll, producers, some can move about; funguslike protists: funguslike, multicellular, cell nucleus, consumers or parasites, can move about during part of their life
3. The rain causes spores to be released and creates conditions right for new mushrooms to develop.
4. the sac fungi

Finding Out More

Critical Thinking

1. Lichens can make their own food and have a surface on which to grow.
2. The consumers that depend on algae for food would die. Less carbon dioxide would be removed from the atmosphere, and less oxygen would be placed into the atmosphere.

Applications

1. Fungi can be kept from growing by keeping surfaces dry and clean. Fungi are most likely to be found in damp, dark, places such as wet basements, refrigerators, and bathrooms, and where there are water leaks such as under cabinets.
2. Fungicides are chemical substances used to kill fungi. They are sprayed or dusted on plants to kill rusts, mildew, smuts, and molds.

Chapter Review/*Teacher Resource Package,* pp. 23-24.

Chapter Test/*Teacher Resource Package,* pp. 25-27.

Chapter Test/*Computer Test Bank*

Plants

PLANNING GUIDE

CONTENT	TEXT FEATURES	TEACHER RESOURCE PACKAGE	OTHER COMPONENTS
(2 days) 6:1 Plant Classification Plant Features How Are Plants Grouped?	Skill Check: *Understand Science Words,* p. 115 Mini Lab: *How Does Water Move Up in a Plant?* p. 116 Idea Map, p. 116 Check Your Understanding, p. 116	Reteaching: *Plant Classification,* p. 14 Focus: *How We Use Plants,* p. 11 Study Guide: *Plant Classification,* pp. 31-32 Reteaching: *Life of a Moss,* p. 15 Study Guide: *Nonvascular Plants,* p. 33	**Laboratory Manual:** *What Are the Traits of Vascular and Nonvascular Plants?* p. 41
(2 days) 6:2 Nonvascular Plants Mosses and Liverworts The Life Cycle of a Moss	Lab 6-1: *Nonvascular Plants,* p. 119 Idea Map, p. 118 Check Your Understanding, p. 120	Reteaching: *Life of a Moss,* p. 15 Skill: *Outline,* p. 6 Study Guide: *Nonvascular Plants,* p. 33 Lab 6-1: *Nonvascular Plants,* pp. 21-22	
(2 days) 6:3 Vascular Plants Ferns Conifers Flowering Plants	Skill Check: *Interpret Diagrams,* p. 122 Mini Lab: *What Conditions Cause a Pine Cone to Open?* p. 126 Lab 6-2: *Ferns,* p. 123 Idea Map, p. 121 Check Your Understanding, p. 129	Application: *Poisonous Plants,* p. 6 Enrichment: *Leaf Adaptations,* p. 6 Reteaching: *Comparing Vascular Plants,* p. 16 Critical Thinking/Problem Solving: *What Happened to the Fern?* p. 6 Transparency Master: *Conifer Life Cycle,* p. 25 Study Guide: *Vascular Plants,* pp. 34-35 Study Guide: *Vocabulary,* p. 36 Lab 6-2: *Ferns,* pp. 23-24	**Laboratory Manual:** *How Can Conifers Be Identified?* p. 45 Color Transparency 6a: *Fern Life Cycle* Color Transparency 6b: *Conifer Life Cycle*
Chapter Review	Summary Key Science Words Testing Yourself Finding Main Ideas Using Main Ideas Skill Review	Chapter Review, pp. 28-29 Chapter Test, pp. 30-32	**Test Bank**

MATERIALS NEEDED

LAB 6-1, p. 119	LAB 6-2, p. 123	MARGIN FEATURES
stereomicroscope or hand lens light microscope 3 microscope slides coverslip dropper forceps metric ruler paper towel moss	stereomicroscope 2 microscope slides scalpel dropper ethyl alcohol whole fern for class fern leaves with spore cases pencil paper	Skill Check, p. 115 dictionary Skill Check, p. 122 pencil paper Mini Lab, p. 116 beaker red food coloring white carnation Mini Lab, p. 126 2 plastic bags open and closed pine cones

OBJECTIVES

SECTION	OBJECTIVE	OBJECTIVES CORRELATION			
		CHECK YOUR UNDERSTANDING	CHAPTER REVIEW	TRP CHAPTER REVIEW	TRP CHAPTER TEST
6:1	1. **Describe** two features common to most plants.	1	1, 23	18, 25, 28, 33	1, 14, 21
	2. **Compare** vascular and nonvascular plants.	2, 3, 15	3, 10, 13, 20	10, 12, 13	2, 9, 18, 19, 25, 26, 27, 29, 31
6:2	3. **Compare** mosses and liverworts with other plants.	6, 7	14, 18	7, 17, 22	5, 16, 33, 35, 42, 49
	4. **Sequence** the steps in the life cycle of a moss.	8	2, 17	1, 3, 4, 21	3, 4, 7, 23, 44
	5. **List** three ways mosses are important to other living things.	9	22	35	6, 37, 39
6:3	6. **Compare** the traits of ferns, conifers, and flowering plants.	11	7, 19, 21	2, 6, 11, 14, 20, 23, 24, 26, 27, 29, 30	8, 10, 11, 12, 17, 20, 22
	7. **Explain** how ferns, conifers, and flowering plants reproduce.	12	6, 8, 9, 12, 24	5, 9, 15, 16, 19, 20, 21, 24, 26, 36, 37, 39	7, 13, 15, 28, 41, 43, 44
	8. **Describe** how conifers and flowering plants are important to other living things.	13, 14	15, 16	9	32, 34, 36, 38, 40

PLANTS

CHAPTER OVERVIEW

Key Concepts

In this chapter, students will study the common traits of plants and the characteristics used to group them. Examples of nonvascular plants—mosses and liverworts—and examples of vascular plants—ferns, conifers, and flowering plants—are described. The economic importance of plants is discussed.

Key Science Words

chlorophyll	phloem
conifer	photosynthesis
egg	pollen
embryo	seed
fern	sexual reproduction
fertilization	sperm
flower	vascular plant
flowering plant	xylem
moss	
nonvascular plant	

Skill Development

In Lab 6-1, students will **make and use tables, interpret data, use a microscope, measure in SI,** and **infer** to find traits of nonvascular plants. In Lab 6-2, students will **make and use tables, observe,** and **use a microscope** to study the traits of ferns. In the Skill Check on page 115, students will **understand** the **science word** *photosynthesis.* In the Skill Check on page 122, students will **interpret diagrams** to understand the life cycle of a fern. In the Mini Lab on page 116, students will **experiment** with flowers to learn that vascular stems carry water. In the Mini Lab on page 126, students will **observe** the conditions necessary for pine cones to open.

CHAPTER PREVIEW

Chapter Content

Review this outline for Chapter 6 before you read the chapter.

6:1 Plant Classification
Plant Features
How Are Plants Grouped?

6:2 Nonvascular Plants
Mosses and Liverworts
The Life Cycle of a Moss

6:3 Vascular Plants
Ferns
Conifers
Flowering Plants

Skills in this Chapter

The skills that you will use in this chapter are listed below.

- In **Lab 6-1,** you will make and use tables, interpret data, use a microscope, measure in SI, and infer. In **Lab 6-2,** you will make and use tables, observe, and use a microscope.
- In the **Skill Checks,** you will understand science words and interpret diagrams.
- In the **Mini Labs,** you will experiment and observe.

Bridging

Students have already learned how plants are classified in Chapter 3. Refer students to Figure 3-10 that shows the characteristics used to classify plants.

Chapter 6

Plants

If you were to walk through the forest pictured on the left, you would first see the giant redwood trees. Because of their small size, you might not notice the plants growing around the roots of the trees. Now, look at the tiny water plants in the photo below. These plants live on the surfaces of lakes or ponds.

There are many kinds of plants. They vary in size, shape, color, and life span. Some, like the small water plants, are only a few millimeters long. Others, such as the redwood tree, can grow to 100 meters tall. Some plants change colors and lose their leaves. Others stay green for many years. Some plants live for just a few months. Plants grow almost everywhere on Earth. They are adapted to many kinds of environments. In this chapter, you will read about plants and where they grow.

Try This!

Where does the moisture come from? Cover a small houseplant with a wide-mouth jar. Observe the plant for a day or two. What do you see in the jar? What is its source?

Duckweed

GETTING STARTED

Using the Photos

In looking at the photos, students should compare the size of the redwood trees with the size of the small plants at their bases. They can mark off a few millimeters on a metric ruler to visualize how small water plants can be. Have them look at a meterstick and imagine 100 of them stacked end to end to visualize the height of a redwood tree.

MOTIVATION/Try This!

Where does the moisture come from? When students have completed the chapter-opening activity, they will have **observed** moisture in the jar. The moisture comes from the leaves of the plant.

Chapter Preview

Have students study the chapter outline before they begin to read the chapter. Students will note that plant features and the grouping of plants are studied before nonvascular and vascular plants. Examples of different kinds of plants within each group are discussed.

Misconception

Students may think that plants get everything they need to make food from the soil. Carbon dioxide from the air, energy from sunlight, and chlorophyll are other things that are needed.

6:1 Plant Classification

PREPARATION

Materials Needed

Make copies of the Focus, Study Guide, and Reteaching worksheets in the *Teacher Resource Package.*

▶ Collect plants for the Focus motivation.

▶ Gather beakers, red food coloring, and white carnations for the Mini Lab.

Key Science Words

chlorophyll
photosynthesis
vascular plant
nonvascular plant

Process Skills

In the Mini Lab, students will experiment. In the Skill Check, students will understand science words.

1 FOCUS

▶ The objectives are listed on the student page. Remind students to preview these objectives as a guide to this numbered section.

MOTIVATION/Display

Display a variety of interesting plants such as cacti, medicine plant *(Aloe vera),* sensitive plant *(Mimosa pudica)*, living stones *(Lithops),* and Madagascar sprouting leaf *(Kalanchoe).*

Focus/*Teacher Resource Package* pp. 11-12. Use the Focus transparency shown at the bottom of this page as an introduction to how we use plants.

Guided Practice

Have students write down their answers to the margin question: a stiff cell wall.

6:1 Plant Classification

Objectives

1. **Describe** two features common to most plants.
2. **Compare** vascular and nonvascular plants.

Key Science Words

chlorophyll
photosynthesis
vascular plant
nonvascular plant

There are over 350 000 different kinds of plants. How could you ever know them all? Scientists have grouped plants to make it easier to study and learn them. Just as with all other living things, plants are classified based on their traits.

Plant Features

Although it may seem all plants are different, most have two traits in common. First, almost all plants have green cell parts called chloroplasts (KLOHR uh plasts). A chloroplast is shown in Figure 6-1. Chloroplasts are green because they contain chlorophyll (KLOHR uh fihl). **Chlorophyll** is a chemical that gives plants their green color and traps light energy. Plants trap light energy for photosynthesis (foht oh SIHN thuh sus). **Photosynthesis** is the process in which plants use water, carbon dioxide, and energy from the sun to make food. In the process, they release oxygen. This food-making process of plants occurs only in the chloroplasts.

What feature of cells is common to all plants?

Photosynthesis is the main process that separates plants from animals. Animals can't make their own food. They don't have chlorophyll. Unlike animals, plants can't move about to search for food. They have to take in the materials and energy needed for photosynthesis.

The second trait of plants is a stiff cell wall. The cell wall gives structure to each cell. The cell wall helps to support a plant on land. Fungi, monerans, and many protists also have cell walls, but animal cells don't.

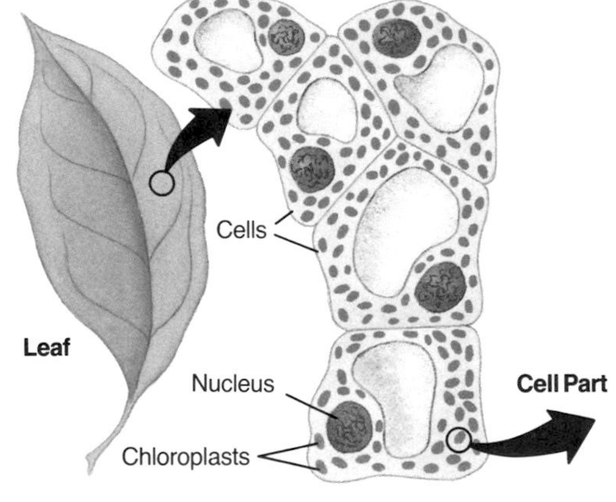

Figure 6-1 A common cell part of almost all plants is the chloroplast, shown here magnified 15 000 times.

OPTIONS

Science Background

The word *division* is often used for phylum in the plant kingdom. Algae make up the first three divisions. Mosses, liverworts, and hornworts are a fourth division. All vascular plants are in a fifth division.

What Are the Traits of Vascular and Nonvascular Plants?/*Lab Manual,* pp. 41-44. Use this lab as an extension to plant classification.

FOCUS 11

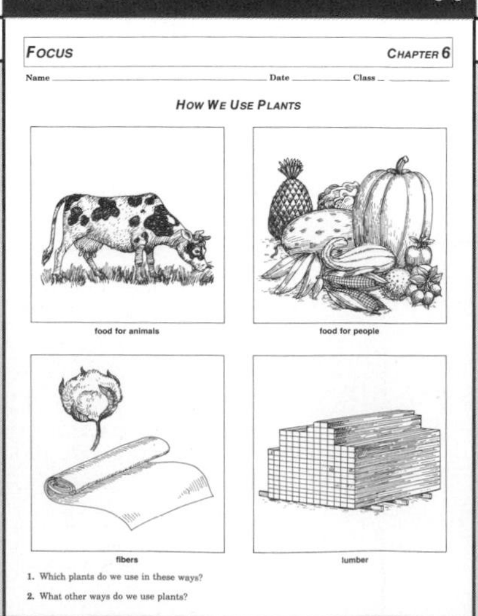

FOCUS CHAPTER 6

Name Date Class

HOW WE USE PLANTS

food for animals
food for people
fibers
lumber

1. Which plants do we use in these ways?
2. What other ways do we use plants?

How Are Plants Grouped?

Plants are grouped in a way similar to how you might group office buildings. If you were to group office buildings by whether they have elevators, you would be able to put them into two groups. Some office buildings have elevators, some don't.

Notice that the taller building in Figure 6-2 has an elevator. The building with only three floors does not have an elevator. Why do we build tall buildings with elevators rather than just stairways? People can get to offices in a tall building more easily if there are elevators in the building. Supplies can also be moved more easily from one floor to another.

Just as there are two groups of buildings, there are also two groups of plants. The two groups of plants are based on whether or not they have cells that form tubes through the length of the plant. Some plants have tubelike cells and some don't. The tubelike cells join end to end and look like water pipes or soda straws joined together. The function of the tubelike cells in plants is much like that of the elevators in a tall building. The elevators carry people up and down within the building. The people can easily reach all the offices. One set of tubelike cells allows water and minerals to move up and down within a plant. A separate set of tubelike cells allows food made by the leaves to move to other parts of the plant. The tubelike cells run through the roots, stems, and leaves of this kind of plant, Figure 6-2. They carry supplies up and down the plant. This is the way that water and food reach all the plant's cells.

Skill Check

Understand science words: photosynthesis. The word part *photo* means light. In your dictionary, find three words with the word part *photo* in them. *For more help, refer to the* ***Skill Handbook****, pages 706-711.*

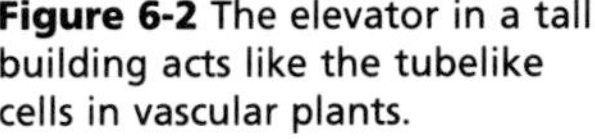

Figure 6-2 The elevator in a tall building acts like the tubelike cells in vascular plants.

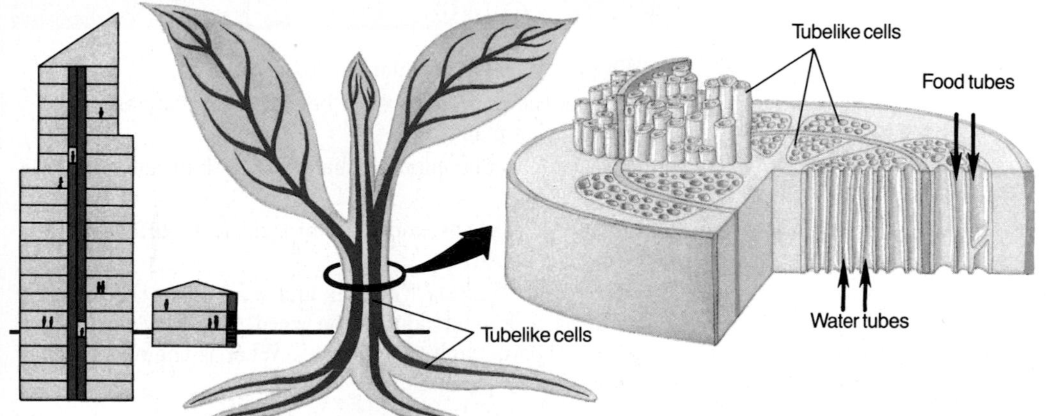

2 TEACH

MOTIVATION/Software

Project Classify: Plants, National Geographic Society.

ACTIVITY/Field Trip

Take a walk around the school or go on a field trip to look at plants. Have students identify the different plants they know.

Concept Development

▶ Review chlorophyll and chloroplasts from Chapter 2.

▶ Point out that mosses and liverworts don't have tubelike cells to carry water and food. Discuss why these plants don't need tubelike cells. Mosses and liverworts are small plants that grow in moist environments.

Using Science Words: You may wish to introduce the terms *xylem* and *phloem* here. Tubelike cells that carry water are called xylem. Tubelike cells that carry food are called phloem.

Independent Practice

Study Guide/*Teacher Resource Package,* pp. 31-32. Use the Study Guide worksheets shown at the bottom of this page for independent practice.

STUDY GUIDE 31

STUDY GUIDE — CHAPTER 6

Name ____ Date ____ Class ____

PLANT CLASSIFICATION

In your textbook, read about plant features in Section 6:1.

1. Shade green those parts of the living things shown below that are usually green.
2. Draw an X through each living thing that does not contain chlorophyll.
3. Circle each living thing that can make its own food.

Green; A height 30 cm; B width 12 cm; C length 2 cm; D height 30 m; Green; E 28 cm; Green

4. Which of the diagrams (A, B, C, D, or E) are plants? **A, D, E**
5. List four features of plants that are different from the features of animals.
   a. **Plants have green parts called chloroplasts that contain chlorophyll.**
   b. **Plants carry on photosynthesis.**
   c. **Plants can't move about.**
   d. **Plants have stiff cell walls.**
6. What is the main difference between plants and animals? **Plants can make their own food, animals can't.**
7. What is photosynthesis? **Photosynthesis is a process in which plants use energy from the sun, carbon dioxide, and water to make food.**
8. Where does photosynthesis occur in plants? **Photosynthesis occurs in the chloroplasts.**

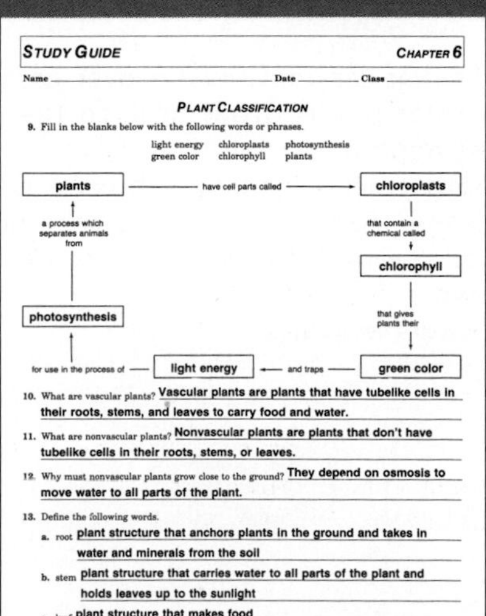

STUDY GUIDE 32

STUDY GUIDE — CHAPTER 6

Name ____ Date ____ Class ____

PLANT CLASSIFICATION

9. Fill in the blanks below with the following words or phrases.

light energy, chloroplasts, photosynthesis, green color, chlorophyll, plants

plants — have cell parts called → **chloroplasts** — that contain a chemical called → **chlorophyll** — that gives plants their → **green color** — and traps → **light energy** — for use in the process of → **photosynthesis** — a process which separates animals from → **plants**

10. What are vascular plants? **Vascular plants are plants that have tubelike cells in their roots, stems, and leaves to carry food and water.**
11. What are nonvascular plants? **Nonvascular plants are plants that don't have tubelike cells in their roots, stems, or leaves.**
12. Why must nonvascular plants grow close to the ground? **They depend on osmosis to move water to all parts of the plant.**
13. Define the following words.
   a. root **plant structure that anchors plants in the ground and takes in water and minerals from the soil**
   b. stem **plant structure that carries water to all parts of the plant and holds leaves up to the sunlight**
   c. leaf **plant structure that makes food**

TEACH

Idea Map

Have students use the idea map as a study guide to the major concepts of this section.

Mini Lab

The flower will turn a shade of red. Tubelike structures take in water and carry it to the flower.

Guided Practice

Have students write down their answers to the margin question: roots.

Check for Understanding

Have students respond to the first three questions in Check Your Understanding.

Reteach

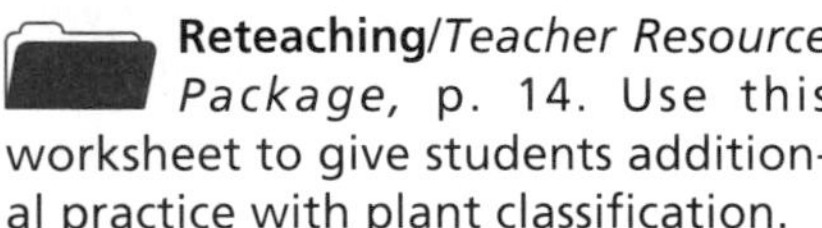

Reteaching/*Teacher Resource Package*, p. 14. Use this worksheet to give students additional practice with plant classification.

Extension: Assign Critical Thinking, Biology and Reading, or some of the **OPTIONS** available with this lesson.

3 APPLY

Demonstration

Set up a bog terrarium. Plant butterwort and cobra lily at one end. Add peat moss to the other end and plant pitcher plant, sundew, and Venus's flytrap.

4 CLOSE

Brainstorming

Have students name as many plant species as they can and group them.

Answers to Check Your Understanding

1. It is used to make food.
2. Vascular plants have tubelike cells; nonvascular plants don't.
3. Vascular plants have tubelike cells that can move water over great distances; nonvascular plants grow close to the ground because they don't have roots.
4. Photosynthesis: carbon dioxide is used, oxygen is released, food is made; cellular respiration: oxygen is used, carbon dioxide is released, food is broken down.
5. Answers will vary.

Study Tip: Use this idea map as a study guide to the traits of plants. Notice how one trait is used to classify plants into two main groups.

Mini Lab

How Does Water Move Up in a Plant?

Experiment: Fill a beaker with water. Add red food coloring. Place a white carnation in the beaker. Explain what happens. *For more help, refer to the* ***Skill Handbook****, pages 704-705.*

What plant part common to vascular plants is absent in nonvascular plants?

Idea Map

Traits of Plants

- **Plants**
  - **features**
    - **chloroplasts**
    - **cell walls give shape and support**
  - **groups**
    - **nonvascular – no tubelike cells**
    - **vascular – have tubelike cells**

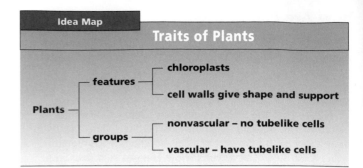

Plants that have tubelike cells in their roots, stems, and leaves to carry food and water are **vascular** (VAS kyuh lur) **plants.** Roots, stems, and leaves are three kinds of organs. In vascular plants, roots anchor plants in the ground and take in water and minerals from the soil. Stems carry water to all parts of the plant and hold the leaves up to the sunlight. Leaves are the main organ for food making. Most of the chloroplasts are in the leaves of a plant.

Plants that don't have tubelike cells are shorter, just as office buildings without elevators are shorter than those with elevators. Plants that don't have tubelike cells in their stems and leaves are **nonvascular** (nahn VAS kyuh lur) **plants.** Nonvascular plants grow close to the ground in moist areas. They don't have roots. They take up water by osmosis through hairlike cells. You have read in Chapter 2 that osmosis is the movement of water across a cell membrane. The water also carries minerals from the soil to the plant.

Check Your Understanding

1. Why is chlorophyll important to plants?
2. What is the main difference between vascular and nonvascular plants?
3. Why are vascular plants usually taller than nonvascular plants?
4. **Critical Thinking:** How does photosynthesis differ from cellular respiration?
5. **Biology and Reading:** Go back and read again the paragraph that introduces the word *photosynthesis*. Then read the paragraph that follows. What is the main idea of these two paragraphs?

RETEACHING 14

RETEACHING: IDEA MAP **CHAPTER 6**

Name ____________ Date ________ Class ________

Use with Section 6:1.

PLANT CLASSIFICATION

Complete the idea map by using the following words or phrases to fill in the blanks: vascular, nonvascular, chloroplasts, cell walls.

- plants
  - features
    - have **chloroplasts**
    - **cell walls** give shape and support
  - groups
    - **nonvascular**— no tubelike cells
    - **vascular**— have tubelike cells

1. What are two traits common to all plants? **Plants make their own food and have stiff cell walls.**
2. What is photosynthesis? **the process in which plants use chlorophyll to trap energy from the sun, and the energy, carbon dioxide, and water are used to make food, and oxygen is given off**
3. What is the function of the tubelike cells in vascular plants? **They allow water and food to pass to all the cells of the plant.**
4. What is the function of roots? **Roots anchor plants in the ground and take in water and minerals from the soil.**
5. What is the function of stems? **Stems carry water to all parts of the plant and hold the leaves up to the sunlight.**
6. What is the function of leaves? **Leaves make food that then moves to other parts of the plants where it is needed.**

6:2 Nonvascular Plants

You may have hiked on the banks of a mossy stream. Mosses are one kind of nonvascular plant. Most nonvascular plants live near water. They grow close to the ground where they can take up water even though they don't have tubelike cells.

Objectives

3. **Compare** mosses and liverworts with other plants.
4. **Sequence** the steps in the life cycle of a moss.
5. **List** three ways mosses are important to other living things.

Key Science Words

moss
sexual reproduction
egg
sperm
fertilization

Mosses and Liverworts

You may have seen mosses as a lush, green, leafy mat on the floor of a forest or on rocks by a stream. A **moss** is a small, nonvascular plant that has both stems and leaves but no roots. If you looked closer to the ground you may have seen smaller patches of green plants that looked wet and slippery. These are liverworts, Figure 6-3.

Mosses and liverworts (LIV uhr wuhrts) are two very similar kinds of nonvascular plants. Unlike vascular plants, mosses and liverworts don't have roots. They are fixed to the surface of the ground or tree trunks by hairlike cells that take up water. Perhaps you have seen mosses and liverworts. If you have, you may have noticed that they are only a few centimeters tall and are common in wet or damp areas.

Mosses have fine, soft stems that often grow upright in mats. These mosses look like short-cropped hair. Some mosses form mats but have stems that creep along the ground. These mosses look like longer hair that is tangled and wavy. The leaves of mosses are only one or two cells thick and will soon dry out if taken from their moist environment. Moss leaves grow from all sides of the stems. Leaf shapes of mosses vary and moss species can be classified by their leaves.

How do leaves and stems of mosses and liverworts differ from those in vascular plants?

a

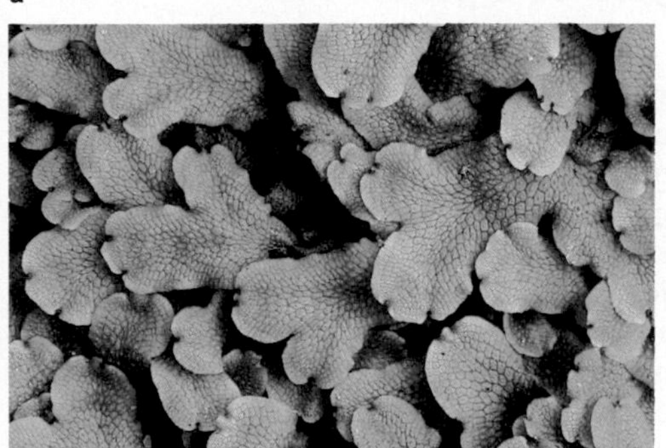

b

Figure 6-3 Liverworts (a) and mosses (b) are nonvascular land plants.

OPTIONS

Science Background

Not all plants called mosses are true mosses. Irish moss is a red marine alga. Reindeer moss is a lichen. Spanish moss is a flowering plant. *Protococcus,* a moss that grows on trees, is a green algae. Club mosses, *Selaginella* and *Lycopodium,* are vascular plants.

6:2 Nonvascular Plants

PREPARATION

Materials Needed

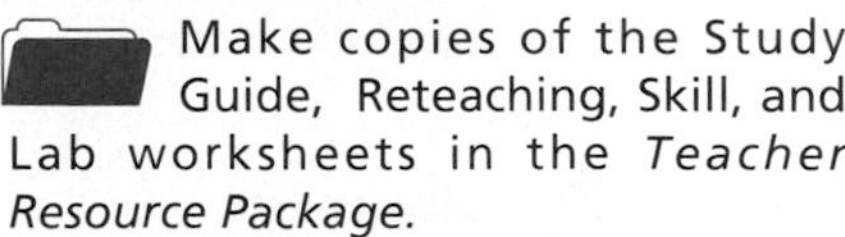

Make copies of the Study Guide, Reteaching, Skill, and Lab worksheets in the *Teacher Resource Package.*

▶ Collect mosses and liverworts for the Focus motivation.

▶ Obtain mosses for Lab 6-1.

Key Science Words

moss
sexual reproduction
egg
sperm
fertilization

Process Skills

In Lab 6-1, students will make and use tables, interpret data, use a microscope, measure in SI, and infer.

1 FOCUS

▶ The objectives are listed on the student page. Remind students to preview these objectives as a guide to this numbered section.

MOTIVATION/Display

Bring in some mosses and liverworts for students to examine.

Guided Practice

Have students write down their answers to the margin question: They are soft, only one or two cells thick, and don't have tubelike cells.

2 TEACH

MOTIVATION/Display

Bring in some sphagnum moss and some peat moss. Place them in separate bowls and allow students to touch and look carefully at each.

Concept Development

▶ Explain that peat is the remains of sphagnum moss that lived long ago.

Idea Map

Have students use the idea map as a study guide to the major concepts of this section.

Guided Practice

Have students write down their answers to the margin question: They are food.

Connection: Math

Obtain some sphagnum moss from a florist or garden store. Have students find the mass of the dry moss. Then place it in water. Have students find the mass of the sphagnum moss after it has been in water for 30 or 40 minutes, and then calculate how much water it absorbed.

Independent Practice

Study Guide/*Teacher Resource Package,* p. 33. Use the Study Guide worksheet shown at the bottom of this page for independent practice.

Study Tip: Use this idea map as a study guide to nonvascular plants. What do mosses and liverworts have in common?

Idea Map

Nonvascular Plants

Plant kingdom
- nonvascular plants
  - mosses
  - liverworts
- vascular plants

Most liverworts don't have roots, stems, or leaves. The body of a liverwort is often a flat, slippery layer of green cells that lies close to the ground. In some species, liverworts look more like mosses. They have creeping stems and small leaves. The main difference between mosses and these leafy liverworts is the arrangement of the leaves. In liverworts, the leaves grow in two or three flattened rows along the stem. Remember that moss leaves grow all around the stems.

How are mosses important to small animals?

Mosses and liverworts are useful to other living things, including you. They are food for some animals such as worms and snails. They also help hold the soil in place to keep it from washing away. Some mosses that live on rocks cause them to break down to form soil.

You may have used sphagnum (SFAHG num) moss in hanging baskets or flowers, Figure 6-4. Have you ever seen a gardener using sphagnum moss? Sometimes called peat moss, sphagnum moss is added to soil to increase the amount of water the soil can hold. Sphagnum moss is an upright moss that forms large, deep mats in bogs. In some areas, peat is cut, dried, and burned as fuel.

Figure 6-4 Moss helps keep moisture around potted flowers.

The Life Cycle of a Moss

Mosses and liverworts need a constant supply of water to survive. They also need water for sexual reproduction. **Sexual reproduction** is the forming of a new organism by the union of two reproductive cells. A female reproductive cell called an **egg** joins with a male reproductive cell called a **sperm.** The joining of the egg and sperm is called **fertilization.** Sexual reproduction occurs in most plants and animals. In many living things, the sperm swims to the egg. The sperm of mosses and liverworts must swim to the eggs to fertilize them. Sperm and eggs of mosses form at the tips of leafy stems.

118

OPTIONS

Skill/*Teacher Resource Package,* p. 6. Use the Skill worksheet shown here to give students practice with outlining.

SKILL 6

SKILL: OUTLINE — CHAPTER 6

Name ______ Date ______ Class ______

For more help, refer to the Skill Handbook, pages 706-711. *Use after Section 6:2.*

CHARACTERISTICS OF PLANT GROUPS

Look at page 112 of your textbook. In the margin is an outline called *Chapter Content.* This outline is like a map—it is a guide to the information you will study in the chapter. The main headings of the outline are the same as the numbered headings in the chapter. The headings tell you that you will learn how plants are classified and will study the two main groups of plants—nonvascular plants and vascular plants. Listed under each main heading are subheadings that match the unnumbered sections in the chapter. These subheadings give you clues to the information you will study in each main section of the chapter. For example, in Section 6:2 Nonvascular Plants, you will study mosses and liverworts and the life cycle of a moss. Outlines are useful aids to studying, learning, and reviewing information.

Below is part of a detailed outline of Section 6:2. Only some of the information has been filled in.

Complete this section of the outline, referring to your textbook if you need to.

Nonvascular Plants

I. Mosses
   A. Characteristics of plant body
      1. green plant
      2. nonvascular (lacks tubelike cells)
      3. does not have **roots**
      4. has short, fine, soft **stems**
      5. has small, very thin **leaves**
   B. Where mosses are found
      1. live near **water**
      2. reason: **They don't have roots to take up water, so they need a good supply.**
   C. Importance of mosses
      1. food for animals
      2. **hold soil in place**
      3. **form soil**
      4. Sphagnum (peat moss) added to soil to help the soil **hold water** or it can be dried and used as **fuel**

II. Liverworts
   A. Characteristics of plant body
      1. **green plants**
      2. **lack tubelike cells**
   B. Where liverworts are found
      1. live **near water**
      2. reason: **They don't have roots so they need a good supply.**
   C. Importance
      1. **food for animals**
      2. **hold soil in place**

III. The life cycle of moss
   A. Carry out sexual reproduction
      1. Egg joins with **a sperm**.
      2. This process is **fertilization**.
   B. Stalk grows from fertilized egg
      1. A **capsule** forms at the tip of the stalk.
      2. The capsule produces **spores** that develop into new plants.

STUDY GUIDE 33

STUDY GUIDE — CHAPTER 6

Name ______ Date ______ Class ______

NONVASCULAR PLANTS

In your textbook, read about mosses and liverworts in Section 6:2. Then answer the following questions.

1. How are mosses and liverworts similar? **They don't have roots, are only a few centimeters tall, and grow in wet or damp places.**
2. How can mosses be classified? **by the shape of their leaves**
3. Describe the leaves and stems of liverworts. **Most have no leaves or stems. Some have two or three flattened rows of leaves on a short, creeping stem.**
4. List three ways that mosses and liverworts are helpful. **They provide food for some animals. They also help hold soil in place, or break down rocks helping to form soil. Sphagnum moss helps increase the amount of water soil can hold. Peat, formed by decayed sphagnum, can be burned as fuel.**
5. Why do mosses and liverworts need water to survive? **The sperm must swim to the eggs to fertilize them.**
6. Where are moss spores produced? **They form in the tip of a stalk that grows from the fertilized egg.**

VASCULAR PLANTS

In your textbook, read about ferns in Section 6:3.

1. Circle the correct word in each sentence.
   a. Ferns are vascular plants that reproduce by seeds / (spores).
   b. Ferns have special tubelike cells called (xylem) / phloem that carry water and dissolved minerals from the roots to the leaves.
   c. The leaves of a fern grow out of a stem that lies (underground) / above ground.
   d. The spore cases of ferns are found on the top / (bottom) side of the leaves.
   e. If a spore lands in a (moist) / dry place, it grows into a small, heart-shaped plant.
   f. The heart-shaped plant produces spores / (sperm and eggs).
   g. Ferns (do) / don't have a vascular system.

Lab 6–1

Nonvascular Plants

Problem: What are some traits of a nonvascular plant?

Skills

make and use tables, interpret data, use a microscope, measure in SI, infer

Materials 

moss
light microscope
3 microscope slides
coverslip
hand lens or stereomicroscope
forceps
paper towel
metric ruler
dropper

Procedure

1. Copy the data table.
2. Place the moss plant on the paper towel and examine it with the hand lens.
3. **Measure in SI:** Find the hairlike cells that act as roots for the moss. Measure their lengths in millimeters. Complete the table.
4. Observe the stem part with the hand lens. Complete the table for this part.
5. Observe the leaf parts with the hand lens. Complete the table for these parts.
6. Use the forceps to remove one of the leaves. Make a wet mount slide and observe the cells under low power.
7. Find the chloroplasts in the cells. Determine how thick the leaf is by moving the focus up and down.

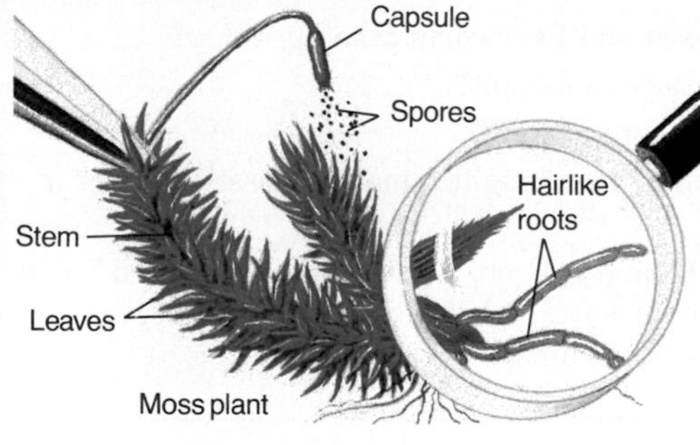

8. Find a spore capsule at the end of a brownish stalk. Observe the spore capsule with the hand lens. Complete the table.
9. Place the spore capsule on a slide. Add two drops of water. Place a second slide on top of the capsule. Press firmly down with your thumb on the top slide so that the capsule is crushed. Carefully remove the top slide. Place a coverslip over the crushed capsule.
10. Examine the released spores under low power. Draw and label the spores.

Data and Observations

1. Which parts of the moss are green?
2. What shapes are moss leaves?

PART	COLOR	SHAPE	LENGTH (mm)
Rootlike hairs	brown	hairlike	1—10
Stem	brown	threadlike	20—80
Leaf	green	round or oval	1—5
Spore case	brown	rounded	2—6

Analyze and Apply

1. **Infer:** How are the green parts used by a moss?
2. Describe the overall size of the plant.
3. How many cell layers are in a moss leaf?
4. **Apply:** Why do moss plants live in moist areas?

Extension

Design an experiment to find out if mosses grow better in wet or dry places.

ANSWERS

Data and Observations

1. the leaves
2. round

Analyze and Apply

1. for photosynthesis
2. about 25 to 100 mm long
3. one or two
4. They don't have vascular tissues.

Lab 6-1 Vascular Plants

Overview

In this lab, students observe the parts of a moss to determine why mosses grow in moist environments and why they do not grow very tall.

Objectives: Upon completing the lab, students will be able to (1) **determine** that mosses do not have vascular tissue, (2) **recognize** that because of the absence of vascular tissue, mosses are incapable of growing tall.

Time Allotment: 35 minutes

Preparation

▶ Mosses collected locally can be kept in cottage cheese containers covered with plastic wrap to prevent water loss. You may wish to place the moss specimens on trays from the supermarket to study.

Lab 6-1 worksheet/*Teacher Resource Package,* pp. 21-22.

Teaching the Lab

▶ **Troubleshooting:** Students may need some help in focusing down through the leaf. Use the overhead projector and a petri dish. Write "bottom" on the bottom and "top" on the top of the dish. When one word is in focus on the overhead, the other will not be. Point out that the same is true with the layers of cells in the leaf.

Cooperative Learning: Have students work in pairs, taking turns using the microscope. For more information, see pp. 22T-23T in the Teacher Guide.

TEACH

Guided Practice

Have students write down their answers to the margin question: spores.

Check for Understanding

Have students respond to the first three questions in Check Your Understanding.

Reteach

Reteaching/*Teacher Resource Package,* p. 15. Use this worksheet to give students additional practice with the life cycle of a moss.

Extension: Assign Critical Thinking, Biology and Reading, or some of the **OPTIONS** available with this lesson.

3 APPLY

Brainstorming

Ask students whether the saying "mosses grow only on the north side of a tree" is a true statement.

4 CLOSE

Audiovisual

Show the slide set *The Plant Kingdom*, Educational Images, Ltd.

Answers to Check Your Understanding

6. by osmosis through hairlike cells that anchor the plant
7. Mosses are food for many animals, help to form soil, help to hold water in soil, and help hold soil in place.
8. sexually by sperm and eggs to form spores
9. Mosses provide a ground cover and help to prevent soil erosion.
10. A drier climate would reduce the number of mosses and liverworts because they require constant water to survive and for reproduction.

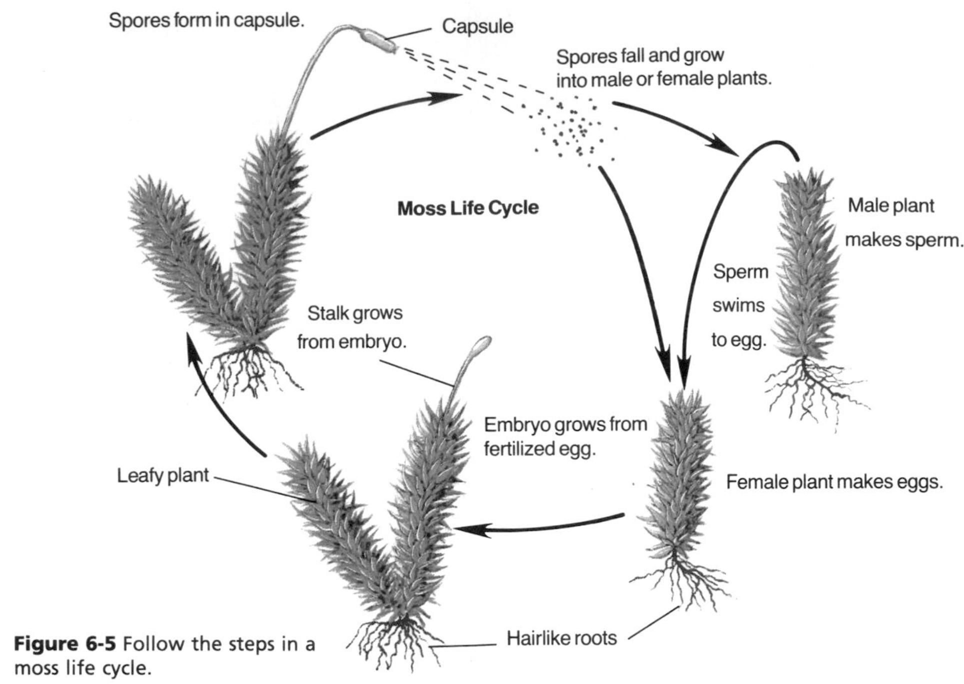

Spores form in capsule.
Capsule
Spores fall and grow into male or female plants.
Moss Life Cycle
Male plant makes sperm.
Sperm swims to egg.
Stalk grows from embryo.
Embryo grows from fertilized egg.
Leafy plant
Female plant makes eggs.
Hairlike roots

Figure 6-5 Follow the steps in a moss life cycle.

What forms inside a moss capsule?

Follow the arrows in Figure 6-5, which shows the steps in the life cycle of a moss. Notice in the figure that after fertilization, a stalk grows from the fertilized egg. Brown capsules form at the tip of each stalk. The capsules contain spores. Many plants make spores. Moss spores are as small and light as powdered sugar. Spores are blown away from the parent plant by wind, and where they land they grow into new leafy plants.

Check Your Understanding

6. How do mosses and liverworts take up water?
7. How are mosses important?
8. How do mosses reproduce?
9. **Critical Thinking:** How might a mat of mosses protect a forest floor?
10. **Biology and Reading:** From what you have learned about mosses and liverworts, what would be the effect on these plants if the climate became drier?

RETEACHING 15

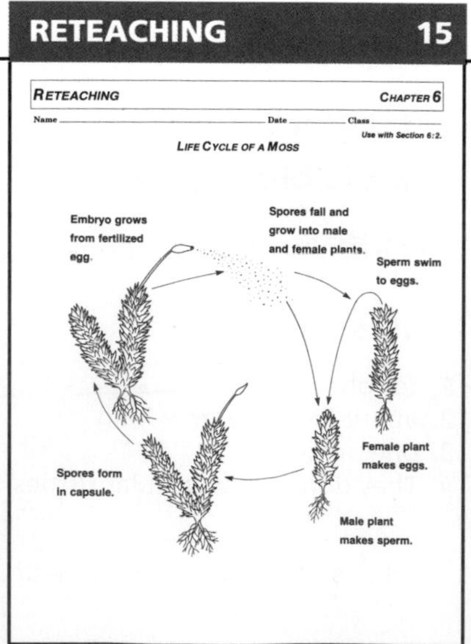
RETEACHING CHAPTER 6

Name ________ Date ________ Class ________

Use with Section 6:2.

LIFE CYCLE OF A MOSS

Embryo grows from fertilized egg.
Spores fall and grow into male and female plants.
Sperm swim to eggs.
Female plant makes eggs.
Spores form in capsule.
Male plant makes sperm.

6:3 Vascular Plants

Most of the plants that you see every day are vascular plants. You have read that vascular plants are plants with tubelike cells in roots, stems, and leaves. The tubelike cells carry food and water throughout the plant. There are two types of tubelike cells in vascular plants. **Xylem** (ZI lum) cells carry water and dissolved minerals from the roots to the leaves. **Phloem** (FLOH em) cells carry food that is made in the leaves to all parts of the plant.

Objectives

6. **Compare** the traits of ferns, conifers, and flowering plants.
7. **Explain** how ferns, conifers, and flowering plants reproduce.
8. **Describe** how conifers and flowering plants are important to other living things.

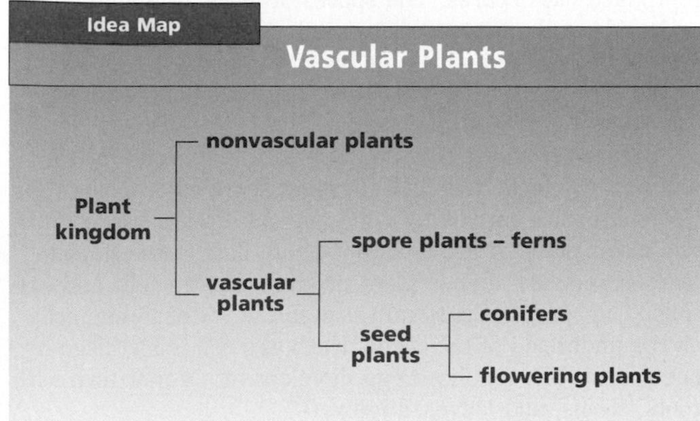

Key Science Words

xylem
phloem
fern
seed
embryo
conifer
pollen
flowering plant
flower

Study Tip: Use this idea map as a study guide to vascular plants. How do ferns differ from other vascular plants?

Ferns

A **fern** is a vascular plant that reproduces with spores. Because of their vascular system, ferns can grow taller than mosses and liverworts. However, one stage of the life cycle of a fern does not have a vascular system at all. For this reason ferns often grow in moist, shaded areas. Some ferns have adapted to much drier climates. Some live in water. Some species called tree ferns live in tropical forests and can grow to a height of 25 meters. There are over 12 000 known species of ferns. About 8000 of these species live in tropical regions.

You might think that a tree fern is unusual. However, over 300 million years ago, most of the plants that grew on Earth were tree ferns or other vascular spore plants. We know that these plants lived at that time because scientists have found ancient, preserved pieces of their stems. These ancient tree ferns lived in swamps. When they died and fell into the swamps, they formed the coal that we use for fuel today.

How are ferns different from conifers and flowering plants?

OPTIONS

Science Background

Seed plants are divided into two groups, based on where the seeds develop. Gymnosperms are plants whose seeds do not develop within ovaries. The largest and most familiar group of gymnosperms is the conifers. The second group of seed plants is angiosperms. They are the flowering plants whose seeds develop within ovaries.

6:3 Vascular Plants

PREPARATION

Materials Needed

Make copies of the Critical Thinking/Problem Solving, Study Guide, Application, Transparency, Enrichment, Reteaching, and Lab worksheets.

▶ Obtain bracken ferns for Lab 6-2.

▶ Collect both open and closed pine cones for the Mini Lab.

Key Science Words

xylem
phloem
fern
seed
embryo
conifer
pollen
flowering plant
flower

Process Skills

In the Skill Check, students will interpret diagrams. In the Mini Lab, students will observe. In Lab 6-2, students will make and use tables, observe, and use a microscope.

1 FOCUS

▶ The objectives are listed on the student page. Remind students to preview these objectives as a guide to this numbered section.

MOTIVATION/Bulletin Board

Arrange pictures of products obtained from plants under the headings: Wood Products, Food, Medicine, and Recreation. Use the bulletin board to discuss the value of plants.

Idea Map

Have students use the idea map as a study guide to the major concepts of this section.

Guided Practice

Have students write down their answers to the margin question: They reproduce with spores.

2 TEACH

MOTIVATION/Display

Display a fern, a conifer with pine cones, and a flowering plant. Point out the fern's lacy leaves and where spores form. Emphasize that cones contain seeds, not spores, and that flowering plants have flowers and seeds that develop within a fruit.

Concept Development

▶ Club mosses and horsetails are not discussed here. You may want to show pictures of both so that students will know they are vascular plants.

▶ Point out that a fern leaf is called a frond. Each frond grows from an underground stem called a rhizome.

▶ Make sure that students understand that spores are not seeds.

▶ Explain that the Christmas fern is believed to have gotten its name from its evergreen nature and the shape of its leaf parts that resemble Christmas stockings.

Guided Practice

Have students write down their answers to the margin question: the leaf.

Misconception: Many people mistake the spore cases on the underside of fern leaves for a disease.

Skill Check

Use Figure 6-7 to make sure students understand the life cycle of a fern.

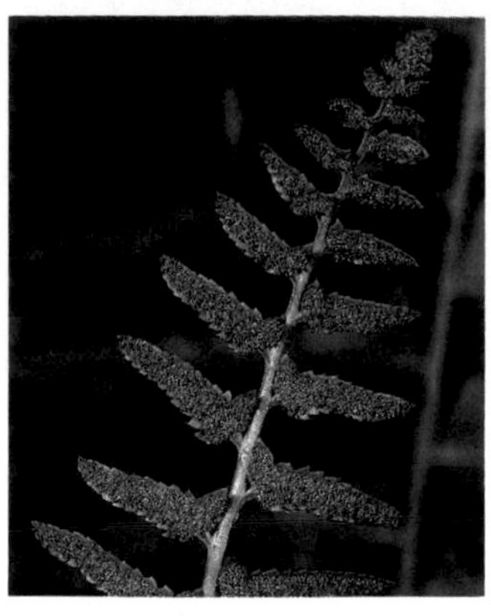

Figure 6-6 A fern produces thousands of spores each year.

What part of a fern plant produces eggs and sperm?

The leaves of a fern grow from a stem that is horizontal and lies underground. The stem stores food and water. Small roots grow down from the underground stem. The roots anchor the plant and take up water and minerals from the soil into the xylem cells.

A fern leaf is often divided into many tiny leaflets that give it a feathery appearance. Many ferns lose their leaves at the end of a growing season. The underground stems remain and produce new leaves each spring. Ferns can be named by looking at the shapes of their leaves.

Ferns are similar to nonvascular plants in that they reproduce with spores. The spores of ferns are found on the underside of the leaves, Figure 6-6. If you have a fern in your school or home, look for brown or orange spots on the leaves. These roundish structures are called spore cases. The spore cases hold the spores.

Figure 6-7 shows the life cycle of a fern. Look for the spore cases on the fern leaf. When a spore case opens, the tiny spores are carried by wind and water. If a spore lands in a moist place, it grows into a small, flat, heart-shaped plant. The heart-shaped plant produces sperm cells and egg cells. The sperm cells swim through the water to egg cells on the underside of the plant. Each egg cell is fertilized by one sperm. The fertilized egg develops into a new fern with roots, stems, and leaves, Figure 6-7.

Skill Check

Interpret diagrams: Look at the fern life cycle in Figure 6-7. What does the spore grow into? Where do the sperm and eggs develop? How do the sperm get to the eggs? *For more help, refer to the **Skill Handbook**, pages 706-711.*

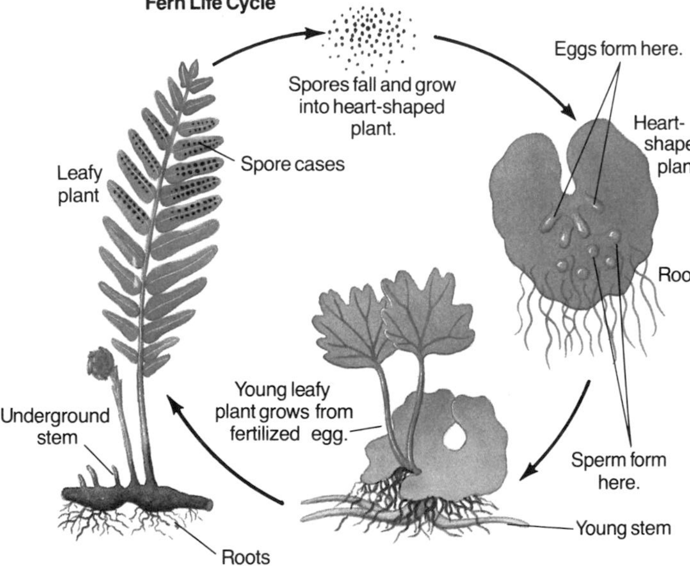

Figure 6-7 Follow the steps in the fern life cycle.

OPTIONS

Fern Life Cycle/*Transparency Package*, number 6a. Use color transparency number 6a as you teach the life cycle of a fern.

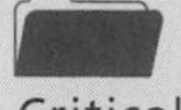

Critical Thinking/Problem Solving/ *Teacher Resource Package*, p. 6. Use the Critical Thinking/Problem Solving worksheet shown here to reinforce traits of ferns.

CRITICAL THINKING 6

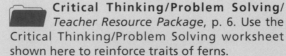

CRITICAL THINKING/PROBLEM SOLVING — CHAPTER 6

Name ______ Date ______ Class ______

Use after Section 6:3.

WHAT HAPPENED TO THE FERN?

A neighbor of Jennie's kept beautiful ferns on her shady porch all summer. Jennie had admired the plants and watched her neighbor care for them. When fall came, Jennie's neighbor carried the plants inside. She had some extra plants, so she gave Jennie two plants to grow in her room. Jennie wondered how much light a fern needs.

Jennie placed one plant in a brightly-lit window. She placed the other plant on the other side of the room. She only watered the plants when the soil was dry. After a few weeks, the leaves of the fern in the window were drooping and turning brown. The fern in the shade looked healthy, but there were powdery, brown spots on the undersides of the leaves. What was happening? Jennie looked at the section on vascular plants in her biology text.

Analyzing the Problem

1. How did Jennie test how much light is needed by ferns? She put one plant in bright light and one in shade.
2. Where do most ferns grow? Ferns usually grow in damp shady woods.
3. Do the powdery, brown spots on the underside of the fern leaf indicate the plant is not healthy? What are they? No, the plant is healthy. The powdery spots are spore cases.

Solving the Problem

1. What can Jennie conclude about how much light ferns need? Ferns need low light. They do not grow well in brighter light.
2. What can Jennie conclude about the brown spots on the underside of the fern leaves? They are part of the fern life cycle. The fern is growing normally.
3. What can Jennie conclude about light conditions for ferns in houses and in the forest? Ferns need low light for healthy growth.

Lab 6–2 Ferns

Problem: What are some traits of ferns?

Skills

make and use tables, observe, use a microscope

Materials

stereomicroscope
2 microscope slides
ethyl alcohol
whole fern plant (for the class)
fern leaf with spore cases
scalpel
dropper
paper and pencil

Procedure

1. **Observe:** Look at a whole fern plant. Locate the horizontal stem at the base.
2. Note how the leaves grow from the stem.
3. Look for veins that indicate xylem and phloem cells in the leaf.
4. Look at the underside of each leaf for brownish-yellow spots. Each spot is made up of a group of spore cases.
5. Draw a table like the one shown. Draw and label your fern plant. Label all the parts as shown in Figure A.
6. Remove a fern leaf. Notice how the cells of the veins connect the stem to the leaf.
7. Obtain a part of a leaf with spore cases.
8. Place a drop of water on a clean slide.
9. Use the scalpel to scrape one of the brownish-yellow spots into the drop of water on the slide. **CAUTION:** *Always cut away from yourself when using a scalpel.*
10. **Use a microscope:** Observe the slide under low power of the stereomicroscope. Look for club-shaped spore cases like the one shown in Figure B.
11. Draw and label a single spore case.
12. Now, make a slide of spores by removing one or two spore cases from your first slide to a clean, dry slide. Add a drop of ethyl alcohol.
13. Observe the slide under low power. Watch what happens to the spore cases.
14. Draw a few of the spores like those shown in Figure C.

Data and Observations

1. What kinds of cells made it difficult to tear fern leaves from the plant?
2. What do fern roots grow from?

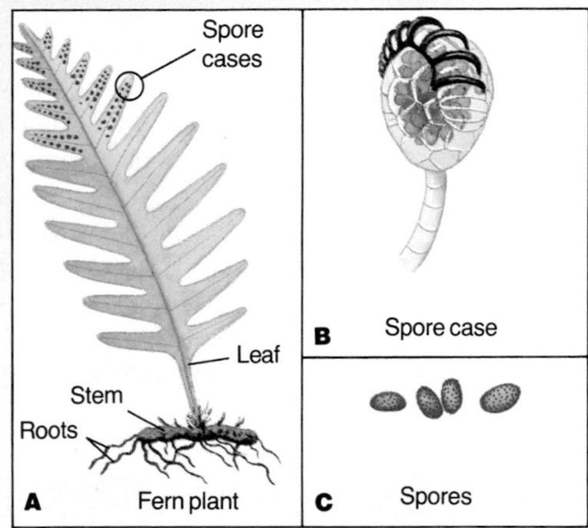

Analyze and Apply

1. What parts of the fern carry on photosynthesis?
2. When are spores produced in a fern life cycle?
3. Why are ferns usually larger than mosses and liverworts?
4. **Apply:** How are the leaves of ferns similar to the leaves of flowering plants?

Extension

Compare the roots of ferns with the rootlike hairs in mosses and liverworts.

ANSWERS

Data and Observations

1. xylem and phloem
2. an underground stem

Analyze and Apply

1. the leaves
2. after the leaves have developed
3. They have a vascular system.
4. They have chlorophyll and veins.

Lab 6-2 Ferns

Overview

In this lab, students examine the structure of a fern and observe spore cases and spores.

Objectives: Upon completing the lab, students will be able to (1) **identify** the structures of a fern plant, (2) **explain** how ferns reproduce.

Time Allotment: 35 minutes

Preparation

▶ **Alternate Materials:** Other kinds of ferns with spore cases may be used.

Lab 6-2 worksheet/*Teacher Resource Package*, pp. 23-24.

Teaching the Lab

Cooperative Learning: Have the students work in pairs. One can prepare slides while the other uses the microscope. For more information, see pp. 22T-23T in the Teacher Guide.

▶ **Troubleshooting:** If too many spore cases are placed on the slide, students will not be able to see the spores. Spores eject from the spore cases when the alcohol is added.

TEACH

Concept Development

▶ Point out that conifers make up about one-third of modern forests. The giant sequoias are conifers and are the largest trees.

Independent Practice

Study Guide/*Teacher Resource Package*, p. 34. Use the Study Guide worksheet shown at the bottom of this page for independent practice.

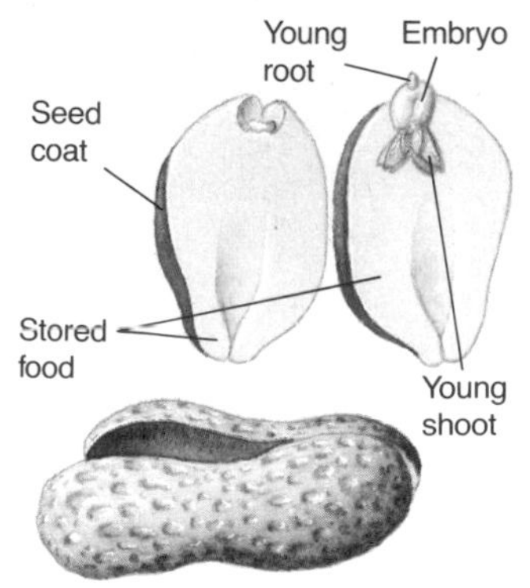

Figure 6-8 A seed has a seed coat to protect the embryo with its food supply. What kind of seed is shown here? a peanut seed

Conifers

The most common land plants are seed plants. Seed plants reproduce by forming seeds. A **seed** is the part of a plant that contains a new, young plant and stored food. The young plant in a seed is the embryo (EM bree oh). An **embryo** is an organism in its earliest stages of growth. A seed has a hard outer covering called the seed coat that protects the embryo, Figure 6-8. The food supply and the seed coat help the embryo survive for long periods of time when conditions are not right for growth.

There are two kinds of seed plants. One kind, called a **conifer** (KAHN uh fur), is a plant that produces seeds in cones. Conifers generally keep their leaves throughout the year. This is why they are sometimes called evergreens. A long time ago there were many different kinds of conifers. Conditions on Earth changed and many of the plants died out. Today, conifers are found mainly in northern areas of the world.

You have probably seen many examples of conifers. Most conifers are evergreen trees with small, needle-shaped leaves. An evergreen tree sheds its leaves in the same way that fur falls from the coat of a dog or cat—not all at once! If you are familiar with pine, spruce, and fir trees and think they are evergreen conifers, you are correct. Check your knowledge of these conifers with Figure 6-9. The larch, dawn redwood, and bald cypress are conifers that lose all their leaves each fall.

Figure 6-9 The pine (a), the spruce (b), and the fir (c) are all conifers with needlelike leaves.

a

b

c

OPTIONS

Science Background

Conifers are examples of evolutionary success by several criteria. They make up about one-third of modern forests. They are the largest living plants. The giant redwoods grow as high as 100 meters. A sequoia contains sufficient wood to build a village of 50 six-room houses. A sequoia is not mature until it is 300 years old.

Conifer Life Cycle/*Transparency Package*, number 6b. Use color transparency number 6b as you teach the life cycle of a conifer.

STUDY GUIDE 34

STUDY GUIDE CHAPTER 6

Name ______ Date ______ Class ______

VASCULAR PLANTS

In your textbook, read about conifers in Section 6:3.

2. In the blanks provided, place a check mark next to the statements that are true for conifers.
   a. ✓ Conifers produce seeds.
   b. ✓ Their leaves are green all year.
   c. ✓ Many have small, needle shaped leaves.
   d. ______ Conifers are nonvascular plants.
   e. ✓ They have woody stems.
   f. ______ They have thin, broad leaves.
   g. ______ Conifers are the smallest group of cone-bearing plants.
   h. ✓ They are often called evergreens.
3. Using Figure 6-10 in your textbook as a guide, write in the blank the part of a conifer described below.
   a. produces pollen — male cone
   b. grains in which sperm form — pollen
   c. produces eggs — female cone
   d. contains a young plant — seed
   e. protects developing embryos — female cone
4. How does pollen reach the female cone? by the wind
5. How do seeds escape from within a cone? When seeds are ripe, cones become dry, they open, and seeds fall to the ground.
6. In what ways are conifers important to humans? They supply three-fourths of the world's lumber; they are used to make paper, cardboard, turpentine, and fuel.

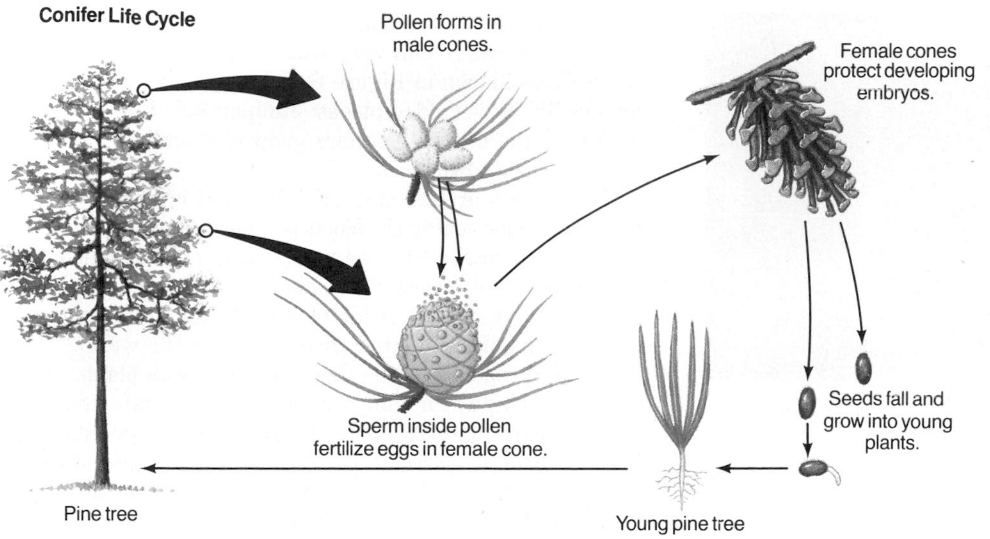
Conifer Life Cycle
Pollen forms in male cones.
Female cones protect developing embryos.
Sperm inside pollen fertilize eggs in female cone.
Seeds fall and grow into young plants.
Pine tree
Young pine tree

Let's look at the life cycle of a pine tree. Have you ever noticed that two different kinds of cones grow on pine trees? Pine trees produce male and female cones. The small cones shown in Figure 6-10 are male cones, which produce pollen. **Pollen** are the tiny yellow grains of seed plants in which sperm develop. You see male cones early in the spring. They open and shed pollen into the air. Wind carries the pollen to the larger female cones. The female cones, as shown in Figure 6-10, contain egg cells. The sperm cells fertilize the egg cells and the seeds form between the woody scales of the cone.

When the seeds are ripe, the cones become dry and the woody scales open. The seeds fall to the ground. When conditions are right, each seed grows into a young plant, Figure 6-10. Some conifers don't have woody cones. The conifer known as a yew produces its seeds inside red, fleshy cuplike parts. Birds eat these juicy cuplike parts and later drop the seeds away from the tree.

The roots, stems, and leaves of conifers are not like the soft stems of ferns. The roots and stems of conifers are hard and woody. The xylem cells have thicker cell walls. Also, the leaves of conifers are tough and needlelike. Examine the different kinds of conifer leaves shown in Figure 6-11. Can you see why some of them are called needles? Other leaves of conifers are scalelike in their shape, but feel quite soft.

Figure 6-10 Follow the steps in the life cycle of a conifer.

Figure 6-11 Conifer leaves are either needlelike as in pines, flattened needles as in hemlock, or scalelike as in arborvitae, a common garden shrub.

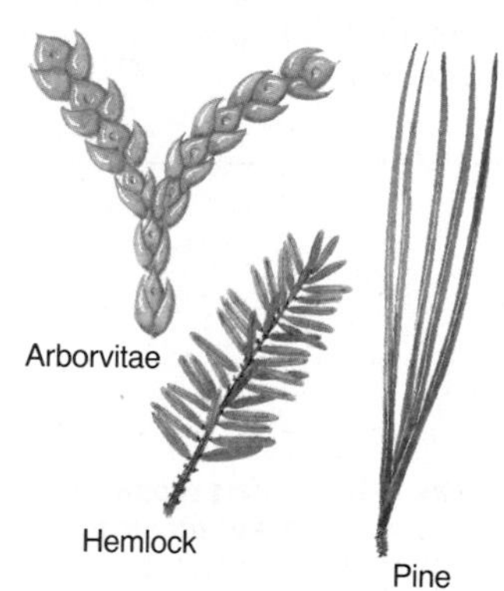
Arborvitae
Hemlock
Pine

TEACH

Concept Development

▶ Mention that a few conifers, such as the yew and the juniper, do not have cones but have individual seeds that develop on branches.

Guided Practice

Give students a photocopied diagram of the life cycle of a pine tree and have them label it.

ACTIVITY/Demonstration

Bring cones of different conifers to class. Indicate that pollen (male) cones are found in clusters at the ends of branches in the spring. The seed (female) cones are larger and more woody than pollen cones and are used to identify various species of conifers. Show the location of seeds on the cone scales. Pull off a cone scale. Two seeds are attached.

TRANSPARENCY 25

TRANSPARENCY MASTER — CHAPTER 6

CONIFER LIFE CYCLE

OPTIONS

Transparency Master/*Teacher Resource Package*, p. 25. Use the Transparency Master shown here to explain the life cycle of a conifer.

How Can Conifers Be Identified?/*Lab Manual*, pp. 45-48. Use this lab as an extension to studying conifers.

TEACH

Concept Development

▶ Point out that many conifers grow well in poor or shallow soil where nutrients are scarce, and where there are often long cold or dry periods.

Mini Lab

Cones that detect moisture will close, and those in a warm, dry place will open. Warm, dry conditions are needed for cones to open. If seeds were released in rainy weather, they would all fall at the bottom of the tree. They are released when the weather is dry so that they will be carried to a suitable spot for germination.

Figure 6-12 A bald cypress is a conifer that lives in swamps.

Conifers can live in many more places than most other plants. Some can live in very wet areas. For example, the bald cypress shown in Figure 6-12 lives in swamps. Other conifers live in very dry places. Junipers are common conifers of the desert. Conifers grow also on high mountain slopes or close to the sea.

Take a look around at everything that is made of wood. Wood is a plant material. Wood is made up mainly of xylem cells. Your pencil, desk, and many parts of your school are probably made of wood. What about your home? What parts of your home are made of wood? Conifers supply three-fourths of the lumber that is used in the world.

You are reading words that are printed on plant material. You pay for things with plant material. You even write on plant material. Why are all these statements true? Paper is made from wood. Cardboard is also made of paper. Think of all the things you buy that are in cardboard boxes. Almost all of the world's paper comes from conifers, Figure 6-13. Conifers also are a source of turpentines, disinfectants, and fuel.

Conifers are very important to other animals for food and shelter. The bark, buds, and seeds of conifers are eaten by insects, birds, squirrels, rabbits, and many other animals.

Mini Lab

What Conditions Cause Pine Cones to Open?

Observe: Place open and closed pine cones into two plastic bags. Add a little water to one. Leave the other in a warm, dry place. Which conditions caused the cones to open? *For more help, refer to the **Skill Handbook**, pages 704-705.*

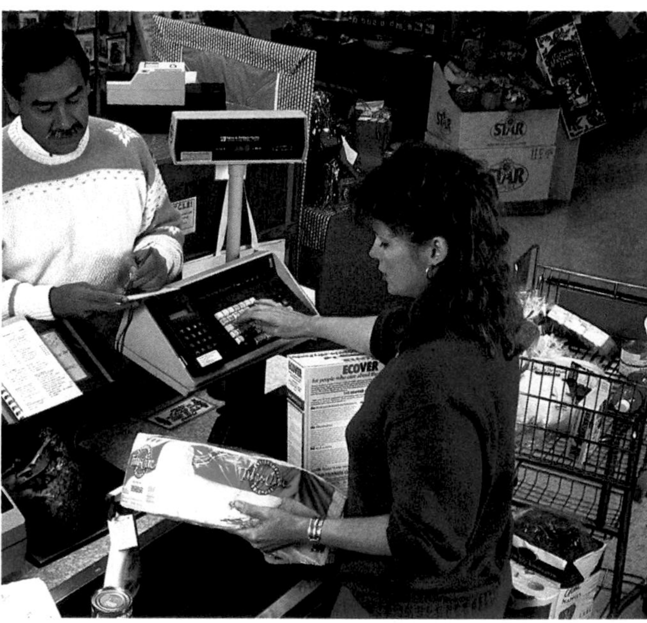

Figure 6-13 Conifers supply most of the world's paper products. Which of these products have you used? Students will probably say all of them.

OPTIONS

ACTIVITY/Challenge

Have students research and illustrate the papermaking process from trees to paper.

Science and Society

Ancient Forests: Jobs versus Wildlife

Logging in the ancient forests of the Pacific Northwest

Have any of your neighbors made it well known that they are upset or angry by something in the neighborhood? Maybe a road sign was put up that they didn't like. Maybe someone's yard was full of garbage. You may have said, "It doesn't bother me," and "It's not my problem." In some cases where people disagree, the problem is so important that even the government gets involved. One such case involves the cutting of ancient trees in the forests of the Pacific Northwest. The trees are used as a major source of lumber and paper for the United States. They are also important to Earth's atmosphere. Consider the three cases described below and discuss each question with your classmates.

What Do You Think?

1. Some small mill owners work in forests owned by the National Forest Service. These loggers harvest only older trees and rely on the growth of young trees to fill in the gaps. Other loggers completely clear the forests of all ages of trees and then replant with young trees. These timber company loggers then harvest the trees as soon as they can. Because of the new laws protecting wildlife, the small mill owners may lose their jobs. The larger timber companies will not be affected. What solutions would you suggest to the government to save the life styles of all loggers?

2. The northern spotted owl lives only in the forests of old conifers in the Pacific Northwest. There are only about 2000 pairs of owls recorded. In July 1990, the United States Fish and Wildlife Service listed this owl as threatened on the federal endangered species list. The owl's environment is also protected by law. Why is it important to save species?

Northern spotted owl

3. Certain gases, including carbon dioxide, are found naturally in Earth's atmosphere. They trap heat from the sun in the same way the glass of a greenhouse does. Carbon dioxide has increased over the last fifty years because of the burning of fuels, such as coal, wood, oil, and natural gas. Forests take up carbon dioxide. Without forests, carbon dioxide would build up in the atmosphere. This increase of gases might cause major changes in Earth's climate. What social and political effects might there be if the world's climate changed?

Conclusion: Do we all need to care about forests? Are the needs of humans more important than those of other species?

127

Science and Society

Ancient Forests: Jobs versus Wildlife

Background

The U.S. Fish and Wildlife Service often becomes involved in controversies that concern the protection of threatened wildlife. If the U.S. Fish and Wildlife Service decides that a species is endangered, it can prohibit activity in a particular area. In the 1970s, construction of the Tellico Dam in Tennessee was halted while environmentalists studied how to protect the small darter fish.

Teaching Suggestions

The questions that appear in the student text should provide the basis for an excellent class debate.

What Do You Think?

There are no incorrect answers to these questions. Students should attempt to answer them based on their own feelings, opinions, or background.

Conclusion: Students should have some understanding of how all living things are dependent on each other. Some may feel that humans are more important, but others will realize that humans can't survive without other living things and need to prevent endangering any species.

Suggested Readings

Satchell, Michael. "The Endangered Logger." *U.S. News and World Report*, June 25, 1990, pp. 27-29.

ENRICHMENT 6

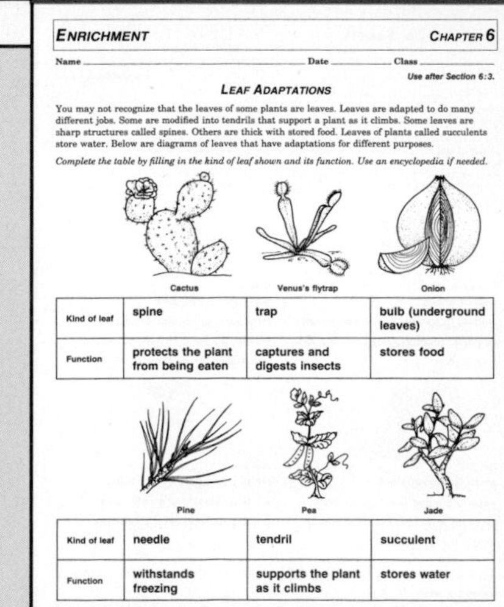

ENRICHMENT CHAPTER 6

Name ______ Date ______ Class ______

Use after Section 6:3.

LEAF ADAPTATIONS

You may not recognize that the leaves of some plants are leaves. Leaves are adapted to do many different jobs. Some are modified into tendrils that support a plant as it climbs. Some leaves are sharp structures called spines. Others are thick with stored food. Leaves of plants called succulents store water. Below are diagrams of leaves that have adaptations for different purposes.

Complete the table by filling in the kind of leaf shown and its function. Use an encyclopedia if needed.

	Cactus	Venus's flytrap	Onion
Kind of leaf	spine	trap	bulb (underground leaves)
Function	protects the plant from being eaten	captures and digests insects	stores food

	Pine	Pea	Jade
Kind of leaf	needle	tendril	succulent
Function	withstands freezing	supports the plant as it climbs	stores water

OPTIONS

Enrichment/*Teacher Resource Package*, p. 6. Use the Enrichment worksheet shown here to help students understand leaf adaptations.

TEACH

Independent Practice

Study Guide/*Teacher Resource Package*, p. 35. Use the Study Guide worksheet shown at the bottom of this page for independent practice.

Cooperative Learning: Have students work in groups of four and prepare an illustrated report on plant adaptations.

Check for Understanding

Take students on a short walk around the school or bring in pictures of a variety of plants. Ask them about each plant. Ask them if the plant is vascular or nonvascular.

Reteach

Show slides or pictures of ferns, conifers, and flowering plants. Have students name the traits each plant has that make it a fern, a conifer, or a flowering plant.

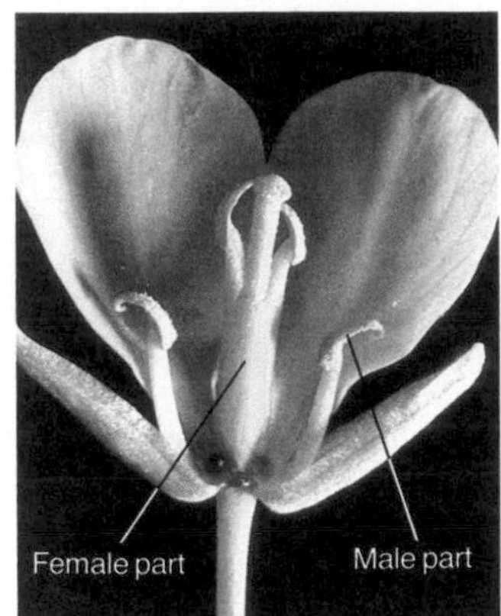

Figure 6-14 A flower is the reproductive part of a flowering plant.

Flowering Plants

The second kind of seed plant produces flowers and forms fruits. This seed plant is a flowering plant. A **flowering plant** is a vascular plant that produces seeds inside a flower. The **flower** is the reproductive part of the plant, Figure 6-14. Flowers have male parts that produce pollen. They also have female parts that produce eggs. A sperm cell produced in a pollen grain must join with an egg for a seed to form. Pollen is carried to the egg cells by wind, insects, or other animals. The female flower parts develop into a fruit that protects the seeds.

There are many more kinds of flowering plants in the world than nonflowering plants. Why might that be? The way the seeds are protected in flowering plants helps to make sure that the new plants survive. Flowering plants are adapted to live in many different environments.

Just because there are many more kinds of flowering plants than nonflowering plants, don't think that you will see mostly flowers when you take a walk outside. Not all flowering plants have big, sweet-smelling flowers. Many flowering plants, such as the maple in Figure 6-15a, have small, non-showy flowers. You may not have known they were flowering plants. Many broadleaved trees, vegetables, grasses, roadside weeds, and thorn bushes have flowers. So you see that not just roses and lilies are examples of flowering plants. Think about grass in lawns, fields, and parks. All grasses have flowers. The flowers on a grass plant are hard to see.

Another reason for not seeing flowers everywhere when you take a walk is that most flowering plants produce their

Bio Tip

Consumer: Did you know that cauliflower and broccoli are heads of tightly packed flower buds? Next time you buy these vegetables, look more closely to find the parts of the flowers.

a

b

Figure 6-15 The flowers of maples (a) are not as showy as those of magnolia trees (b).

OPTIONS

ACTIVITY/Enrichment

Provide a variety of seeds for students to examine and compare their shapes and adaptations for dispersal.

Application/*Teacher Resource Package*, p. 6. Use the Application worksheet shown here to explain poisonous plants.

STUDY GUIDE 35

STUDY GUIDE — CHAPTER 6

Name ______ Date ______ Class ______

VASCULAR PLANTS

7. Decide which of the following sentences are true and which are false. Write the word *true* in the blank next to the sentences that are true. For sentences that are false, replace the underlined word with a word that would make the sentence true. Write that word in the blank.

true a. Seeds of flowering plants are formed inside a flower.
vascular b. Flowering plants are nonvascular.
true c. The flower is involved in reproduction.
male d. Sperm cells are formed within female flower parts.
seed e. In a flowering plant, a fertilized egg forms a flower.
Female f. Male flower parts develop into an embryo.
largest g. Flowering plants make up the smallest group of all types of plants.
true h. Seeds contain a supply of food for the developing embryo.

8. Complete the following table. Put a check mark in the column of each kind of plant that has the trait listed.

Trait	Moss and liverwort	Fern	Conifer	Flowering plant
Nonvascular	✓			
Vascular		✓	✓	✓
Has no tubelike cells	✓			
Has tubelike cells		✓	✓	✓
Has roots, stems, leaves		✓	✓	✓
Doesn't have roots	✓			
Spores	✓	✓		
Seeds			✓	✓
Cones			✓	
Flowers				✓
Most common of plants				✓
Gives off oxygen	✓	✓	✓	✓

APPLICATION 6

APPLICATION: SAFETY — CHAPTER 6

Name ______ Date ______ Class ______

Use after Section 6:3.

POISONOUS PLANTS

Some plants have parts that are poisonous if they are touched or eaten. You can safely explore in woods and gardens if you know which plants to avoid.

Use an encyclopedia or book about plants to find information on the plants listed below. Draw a picture of each plant. On the first line below your picture, tell if the plant is a tree, shrub, vine, or small flowering plant. On the next line, name a part of the plant that you could use to recognize the plant, such as star-shaped flowers or fuzzy leaves. On the last two lines, tell which parts of the plant are poisonous. Include whether the plant is poisonous to the touch or poisonous if swallowed.

Poison ivy
vine or shrub
leaflets in threes; red leaves in fall
all parts; touching plant causes rash
and itching

Rhubarb
small flowering plant
large leaves, reddish leafstalks
leaves; poisonous if swallowed
(leafstalks are edible)

Foxglove
small flowering plant
flowers shaped like tubular bells
all parts, especially leaves; can be
fatal if swallowed

Mistletoe
small plant, parasite on trees
white berries, evergreen leaves
berries; poisonous if swallowed

How does being poisonous help? Being poisonous could protect a plant from being eaten by animals.

flowers only at certain times of the year. For example, many forest trees bloom only in the spring. The garden lily and tomato plants flower in the summer. Some plants even flower at times other than spring and summer, Figure 6-16.

How are flowering plants important to us? You know that showy flowers are often used for decoration, but plants have many more uses. Oranges and potatoes are plant parts you can eat. Bread and cereals are foods that are made from plants. Without plants, there would be no fruits, vegetables, breads, or cereals to eat. What parts of the plants in Figure 6-17 have you eaten?

If there were no plants, could you eat meat instead? No, if there were no plants, there would be no animals. Animals depend on plants or other producers to live.

In what other ways do all animals need plants? Remember that plants make their own food by photosynthesis. Oxygen given off by the plant is needed by both plants and animals for cellular respiration. Much of the oxygen gas that we have on Earth is produced by plants. In turn, the carbon dioxide produced during cellular respiration in plants and animals is needed by plants to make food. You can now see why every living thing depends on every other living thing.

Figure 6-16 Chrysanthemums bloom in late summer. Name some flowers that bloom in the spring. Answers may include daffodils and crocuses.

In what ways do animals need plants?

Figure 6-17 Which part of a plant do you eat—stems, leaves, seeds, or fruits? All of these parts

Check Your Understanding

11. What are three examples of conifers?
12. Where are sperm and egg cells formed in seed plants?
13. How are flowering plants important to us?
14. **Critical Thinking:** Which gas is more important to life on Earth, carbon dioxide or oxygen?
15. **Biology and Reading:** From reading the previous section, what are the three major groups of vascular plants?

RETEACHING 16

Reteaching — *Chapter 6*

Name ____ Date ____ Class ____

Use with Section 6:3.

Comparing Vascular Plants

The chart on this page lists traits found in one or more groups of plants.

If a trait is present in a plant group, place a check mark in the appropriate column.

Traits of land plants	Ferns	Conifers	Flowering plants
Tubelike cells are present.	✓	✓	✓
Is the largest group of plants.			✓
Are made up of cells with a nucleus.	✓	✓	✓
Are usually found in moist places.	✓		
Spores form in a spore case.	✓		
Seeds develop in a cone.		✓	
Have stiff cell walls.	✓	✓	✓
Spores form in a capsule.			
Many species have waxy, needlelike leaves.		✓	
Do not have tubelike cells.			
Cells contain chloroplasts.	✓	✓	✓
Require water for sperm to swim to egg.	✓		
Seeds are enclosed in a fruit.			✓
Seeds contain an embryo surrounded by a protective coat.		✓	✓

STUDY GUIDE 36

Study Guide — *Chapter 6*

Name ____ Date ____ Class ____

Vocabulary

Review the new words used in Chapter 6 of your textbook. Then, complete the exercise. Fill in the blank in each of the sentences below with the correct word from the following list.

chlorophyll	flowers	sexual reproduction	nonvascular plant
xylem	photosynthesis	egg	fertilization
embryo	conifer	vascular plants	moss
sperm	phloem	fern	flowering plant
seed	pollen		

1. The chemical that gives plants their green color is **chlorophyll**.
2. **Nonvascular** plants don't have tubelike cells in their stems and leaves.
3. A small nonvascular plant that has both stems and leaves but no roots is a **moss**.
4. An **egg** is a female reproductive cell.
5. **Vascular plants** have tubelike cells in their roots, stems, and leaves.
6. A **conifer** produces seeds in cones.
7. A male reproductive cell is a **sperm**.
8. A **flowering plant** produces seeds inside a flower.
9. A **fern** is a vascular plant that reproduces with spores.
10. **Phloem** cells carry food from the leaves to all parts of the plant.
11. **Pollen** are the tiny grains of seed plants in which sperm develop.
12. **Flowers** are the reproductive parts of flowering plants.
13. A **seed** contains a new, young plant and stored food.
14. The young plant in a seed is the **embryo**.
15. **Xylem** cells carry water from the roots to the leaves.
16. In **sexual reproduction**, a new organism forms from the union of two reproductive cells.
17. The joining of the egg and the sperm is **fertilization**.
18. **Photosynthesis** is the process in which plants use water, carbon dioxide, and energy from the sun to make food.

TEACH

Guided Practice

Have students write down their answers to the margin question: for food and oxygen.

Independent Practice

Study Guide/*Teacher Resource Package*, p. 36. Use the Study Guide worksheet shown at the bottom of this page for independent practice.

Check for Understanding

Have students respond to the first three questions in Check Your Understanding.

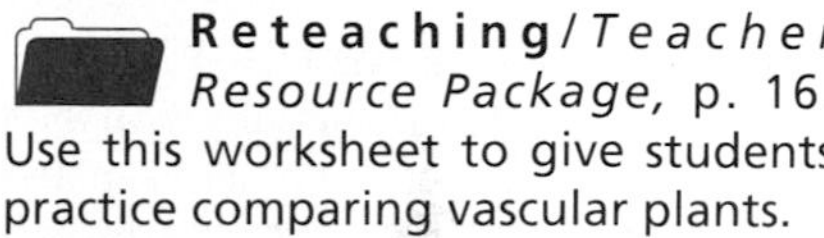

Reteach

Reteaching/*Teacher Resource Package*, p. 16. Use this worksheet to give students practice comparing vascular plants.

Extension: Assign Critical Thinking, Biology and Reading, or some of the **OPTIONS** available with this lesson.

3 APPLY

Connection: Language Arts

Make an illustrated booklet of tree leaves. Use both conifers and flowering plants. Have students look up simple and compound leaves and venation patterns.

4 CLOSE

Cooperative Learning: Have students work in groups of four to make a list of uses of plants.

Answers to Check Your Understanding

11. pines, spruce, and fir trees
12. Sperm is formed in pollen; eggs are formed in the cone or the flower.
13. They are used as decoration and food, and they produce oxygen.
14. Answers will vary, but should show that carbon dioxide and oxygen are equally important.
15. ferns, conifers, and flowering plants

CHAPTER 6 REVIEW

Summary

Summary statements can be used by students to review the major concepts of the chapter.

Key Science Words

All boldfaced terms from the chapter are listed.

Testing Yourself

Using Words

1. chlorophyll
2. fertilization
3. vascular plant
4. sexual reproduction
5. egg
6. seed
7. conifer
8. flowering plant
9. pollen

Finding Main Ideas

10. p. 115; Water and food are carried in tubelike cells.
11. p. 114; Plants use sunlight, carbon dioxide, and water to make food.
12. p. 121; Ferns reproduce by spores.
13. pp. 115-116; Plants are grouped into vascular and nonvascular plants by whether or not they have tubelike cells to carry food and water.
14. p. 117; Mosses have no roots, but have stems and leaves that grow upright in mats; they look like short-cropped hair.
15. p. 129; They are used for decoration and food, and they give off oxygen.

Using Main Ideas

16. Conifers produce three-fourths of the world's lumber, almost all of the world's paper, provide food and shelter for animals, and provide turpentine, resins, and fuel.
17. Mosses form spores by sexual reproduction.
18. They need a constant supply of water to survive, and for sexual reproduction.

Chapter 6 Review

Summary

6:1 Plant Classification

1. Most plants have chlorophyll in chloroplasts that traps light energy for photosynthesis. All plants have stiff cell walls.
2. Nonvascular plants do not have tubelike cells. Vascular plants have tubelike cells that carry food and water.

6:2 Nonvascular Plants

3. Mosses and liverworts are nonvascular plants. They have stems and leaves but no roots.
4. Mosses reproduce by sperm and eggs formed at the tips of leafy stems. The fertilized eggs develop into a stalk with a capsule. Spores are produced in a capsule. New moss plants grow from the spores.
5. Mosses are food for animals. They help form soil and keep it moist. Mosses are used in gardens.

6:3 Vascular Plants

6. Ferns, conifers, and flowering plants all have xylem and phloem cells. Conifers have seeds inside cones. Flowering plants have flowers and seeds.
7. Ferns reproduce by eggs and sperm and by spores on the leaves. Conifers produce sperm in pollen. Pollen and eggs are formed in cones. Flowering plants produce sperm in pollen and eggs in flowers.
8. Conifers are used for lumber and paper. All living things depend on plants for food and oxygen.

Key Science Words

chlorophyll (p. 114)
conifer (p. 124)
egg (p. 118)
embryo (p. 124)
fern (p. 121)
fertilization (p. 118)
flower (p. 128)
flowering plant (p. 128)
moss (p. 117)
nonvascular plant (p. 116)
phloem (p. 121)
photosynthesis (p. 114)
pollen (p. 125)
seed (p. 124)
sexual reproduction (p. 118)
sperm (p. 118)
vascular plant (p. 116)
xylem (p. 121)

Testing Yourself

Using Words

Choose the word from the list of Key Science Words that best fits the definition.

1. chemical that gives plants their green color
2. when a sperm and an egg cell join
3. kind of plant with tubelike cells to carry water and food
4. type of reproduction when a sperm fertilizes an egg
5. female sex cell

Review

Testing Yourself *continued*

6. a structure that contains a small, new plant and a supply of stored food
7. plant that grows from the seeds of woody cones
8. vascular plant that produces seeds inside a flower
9. powderlike structures in seed plants from which sperm develop

Finding Main Ideas

List the page number where each main idea below is found. Then, explain each main idea.

10. what's carried in tubelike cells
11. what plants use to make food
12. how ferns reproduce
13. how plants are grouped
14. what mosses look like
15. how flowering plants are important to other organisms

Using Main Ideas

Answer the questions by referring to the page number after each question.

16. What are several ways that conifers are important? (p. 126)
17. How do mosses reproduce? (p. 118)
18. Why do mosses and liverworts grow in wet or damp places? (p. 117)
19. What are two reasons you may not find flowers on flowering plants? (p. 128)
20. How do nonvascular plants survive without xylem and phloem? (p. 116)
21. What is one way of grouping vascular plants? (pp. 121, 124)
22. What are the uses of mosses? (p. 118)
23. How are plants different from animals? (p. 114)
24. How are spores different from pollen? (pp. 120, 125)

Skill Review ✓

*For more help, refer to the **Skill Handbook**, pages 704-719.*

1. **Infer:** Why are the spores of a fern more likely to be carried by wind than the spores of a moss?
2. **Observe:** Place a flower on a sheet of white paper. Carefully take the flower apart and compare it with the one in Figure 6-14.
3. **Interpret diagrams:** Look at the diagram in Figure 6-10. Why must pollen be formed before fertilization?
4. **Make and use tables:** Make a table to show the importance of mosses and liverworts, ferns, conifers, and flowering plants.

Finding Out More

Critical Thinking

1. How do you think certain medicines from plants were discovered?
2. Compare the methods of reproduction between spore plants and flowering plants.

Applications

1. In an old aquarium or glass jar, set up a terrarium with mosses, liverworts, and small ferns.
2. Report on common poisonous plants. Explain what part of the plant is poisonous, the effects of the poison, and whether there are any known antidotes.

Using Main Ideas

19. Some flowers are small and not showy, some are hard to see, and some plants produce flowers only at certain times of the year.
20. They live close to the ground and take in water by osmosis through hairlike cells.
21. One way of grouping vascular plants is by whether they are flowering or nonflowering.
22. Mosses are food for some animals, they hold soil in place, and they help break up rock to form soil.
23. Plants can make their own food, but animals can't; plants can't move around, but animals can; plants have stiff cell walls, but animals don't.
24. Spores are formed in capsules and form into new plants. Pollen are grains of seed plants. Sperm develops in pollen and then fertilizes egg cells which can then develop into new plants.

Skill Review

1. Mosses grow very close to the ground, but ferns grow tall.
2. Students should be able to see petals and, depending on the type of flower, male and female reproductive parts.
3. Sperm develop in pollen and the sperm fertilize egg cells.
4. Use Mosses and Liverworts, Ferns, Conifers, and Flowering Plants as heads and list the importance of each in columns underneath.

Finding Out More

Critical Thinking

1. Answers will vary, but most students will agree that trial-and-error methods determined that some plants had medicinal value before more scientific methods were developed.
2. Both use sexual reproduction. In spore plants, the fertilized eggs develop into a stalk with a capsule where spores develop. The fertilized eggs in flowering plants produce seeds protected in a fruit.

Applications

1. A five-gallon aquarium is ideal. Plants can be collected from wooded areas, provided they are not protected.
2. Common poisonous plants include the nightshades, yew berries, poinsettia, philodendron, poison ivy, and poison oak.

Chapter Review/*Teacher Resource Package*, pp. 28-29.

Chapter Test/*Teacher Resource Package*, pp. 30-32.

Chapter Test/*Computer Test Bank*

Simple Animals

PLANNING GUIDE

CONTENT	TEXT FEATURES	TEACHER RESOURCE PACKAGE	OTHER COMPONENTS
(1 1/2 days) 7:1 Animal Classification Traits of Animals How Animals Are Classified	Skill Check: *Understand Science Words,* p. 134 Skill Check: *Interpret Diagrams,* p. 135 Check Your Understanding, p. 136	Reteaching: *Animal Classification,* p. 17 Skill: *Interpret Diagrams,* p. 7 Focus: *Finding Relationships Among Simple Animals,* p. 13 Study Guide: *Animal Classification,* p. 37	
(1 1/2 days) 7:2 Sponges and Stinging-cell Animals Sponges Stinging-cell Animals	Mini Lab: *How Does a Sea Anemone Attach Itself?* p. 140 Lab 7-1: *Stinging-cell Animals,* p. 141 Check Your Understanding, p. 140	Reteaching: *Sponges and Stinging-cell Animals,* p. 18 Study Guide: *Sponges and Stinging-cell Animals,* p. 38 Lab 7-1: *Stinging-cell Animals,* pp. 25-26	**Laboratory Manual:** *What Traits Does a Sponge Have for Living in Water?* p. 49 **Laboratory Manual:** *What Are the Parts of a Stinging-cell Animal?* p. 57
(2 days) 7:3 Worms Flatworms Roundworms Segmented Worms	Skill Check: *Infer,* p. 143 Mini Lab: *Where Do You Find Roundworms?* p. 145 Lab 7-2: *Earthworms,* p. 148 Idea Map, p. 147 Check Your Understanding, p. 148	Application: *Tapeworm Life Cycle,* p. 7 Enrichment: *Leeches,* p. 7 Reteaching: *Anatomy of Worms,* p. 19 Study Guide: *Worms,* pp. 39-40 Lab 7-2: *Earthworms,* pp. 27-28	Color Transparency 7a: *Life Cycle of a Pork Tapeworm*
(1 day) 7:4 Soft-bodied Animals Traits of Soft-bodied Animals Classes of Soft-bodied Animals	Check Your Understanding, p. 151 Problem Solving: *Animal Movement,* p. 152	Reteaching: *Classes of Soft-bodied Animals,* p. 20 Critical Thinking/Problem Solving: *What Is Destroying the Tomato Plants?* p. 7 Transparency Master: *Simple Animals,* p. 31 Study Guide: *Soft-bodied Animals,* p. 41 Study Guide: *Vocabulary,* p. 42	**Laboratory Manual:** *What Are the Parts of a Squid?* p. 53 Color Transparency 7b: *How a Squid Moves*
Chapter Review	Summary Key Science Words Testing Yourself Finding Main Ideas Using Main Ideas Skill Review	Chapter Review, pp. 33-34 Chapter Test, pp. 35-37	**Test Bank**

MATERIALS NEEDED

LAB 7-1, p. 141	LAB 7-2, p. 148	MARGIN FEATURES
stereomicroscope hand lens dropper small dish flashlight hydra culture daphnia or brine shrimp	hand lens shallow pan flashlight toothpick cotton swab paper towels beaker of water vinegar live earthworms	Skill Check, p. 134 dictionary Skill Check, p. 135 pencil paper Mini Lab, p. 140 small rock suction cup Mini Lab, p. 145 funnel wire mesh jar alcohol moist soil

OBJECTIVES

SECTION	OBJECTIVE	OBJECTIVES CORRELATION			
		CHECK YOUR UNDERSTANDING	CHAPTER REVIEW	TRP CHAPTER REVIEW	TRP CHAPTER TEST
7:1	1. **List** four traits of animals.	1, 4	26, 30	6, 9, 27, 28, 35	1, 2, 3
	2. **Identify** nine major phyla of animals and give an example of each.	2	9, 13, 15	3, 15, 32	5, 6, 7, 17, 28
7:2	3. **List** the traits of sponges.	6, 10	3, 19, 25	2	10, 14, 21, 23, 24, 26, 31
	4. **Describe** the traits of stinging-cell animals.	7, 8	5, 17, 18, 27	4, 11, 30	8, 11, 12, 15, 19, 22
7:3	5. **List** the three main phyla of worms and give an example of each.	11, 12	1, 7, 12, 20, 33	8, 12, 13, 14, 29, 33	9, 34
	6. **Identify** the main features of flatworms, round worms, and segmented worms.	13, 15	2, 8, 10, 11, 16, 22, 24, 28, 29	1, 5, 7, 16, 17, 18, 19, 20, 21, 22, 23, 24, 25, 26	13, 36, 37, 38, 39, 40, 41, 42, 43, 44, 45, 46, 47, 48, 49, 50, 51, 52, 53
7:4	7. **Identify** the major features of soft-bodied animals.	17, 18	6, 21, 23, 32	31, 34	16, 18, 20, 25, 27, 29, 30, 32, 33, 35
	8. **Explain** how soft-bodied animals are classified.		14	10	4

Simple Animals

CHAPTER OVERVIEW

Key Concepts

This chapter serves as an introduction to the animal kingdom. The traits of the animals in the first six phyla (sponges, stinging-cell animals, flatworms, roundworms, segmented worms, and soft-bodied animals) are examined. Students should see that animals increase in complexity from the first phylum on.

Key Science Words

anus
cyst
flatworm
hookworm
invertebrate
mantle
planarian
pore
roundworm
segmented worm
soft-bodied animal
sponge
stinging-cell animal
symmetry
tapeworm
tentacle
vertebrate

Skill Development

In Lab 7-1, students will **observe, make and use tables,** and **interpret data** dealing with the traits of stinging-cell animals. In Lab 7-2, they will **observe, infer, predict,** and **make and use tables** in relation to the traits of earthworms. In the Skill Check on page 134, they will **understand** the **science word** *invertebrate.* In the Skill Check on page 135, students will **interpret diagrams** of symmetry. In the Skill Check on page 143, they will **infer** why tapeworms affect a person's general health. In the Mini Lab on page 140, students will **infer** how sea anemones attach themselves to rocks. In the Mini Lab on page 145, they will **observe** roundworms.

CHAPTER PREVIEW

Chapter Content

Review this outline for Chapter 7 before you read the chapter.

Skills in this Chapter

The skills that you will use in this chapter are listed below.

- In **Lab 7-1,** you will observe, make and use tables, and interpret data. In **Lab 7-2,** you will observe, infer, predict, and make and use tables.
- In the **Skill Checks,** you will understand science words, interpret diagrams, and infer.
- In the **Mini Labs,** you will infer and observe.

132

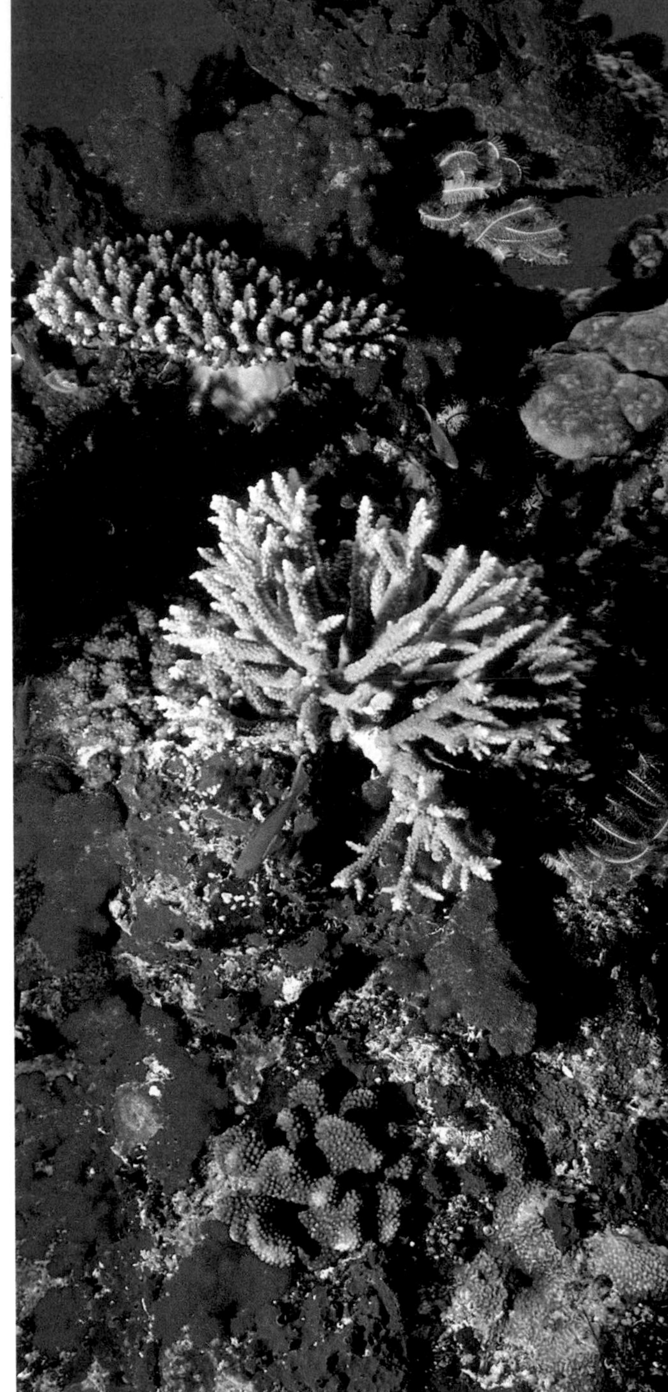

Bridging

In Chapter 3, students learned how the classification scheme for all life forms is organized. Traits of animals were introduced in a very general way. This chapter expands on these traits and gives the student an opportunity to look at various phyla in detail.

Chapter 7

Simple Animals

In the photo on the opposite page, you can see some of the beautiful and unusual animals that are found in the sea. For many years people thought that sponges were plants. The sponges didn't move around by themselves and they didn't seem to capture food, both animal-like traits. Can you tell from the photo how a sponge captures its food? Early scientists couldn't either.

The small photo shows the mouth of a coral. It is surrounded by structures that contain the stinging cells the animal uses to capture food. With careful observation, scientists were able to watch such animal-like traits as food-getting. Today there is no doubt that these organisms are animals.

Try This!

How does a squid move? Inflate a balloon and release it. Observe the movement and direction of the balloon. Compare it with the movement of a squid.

The mouth of a coral is surrounded by tentacles.

GETTING STARTED

Using the Photos

In looking at the photos, students should note the obvious traits of sponges. Have them discuss real sponges that they may have seen or used. They should try to speculate on how a sponge gets its food.

MOTIVATION/Try This!

How does a squid move? Students will **observe** that air leaving the balloon forces it to move in a direction opposite escaping air. A squid moves in a direction opposite escaping water. It squirts water and uses this force to move either forward or backward.

Chapter Preview

Have students study the chapter outline before they begin to read the chapter. They should note the overall organization of the chapter, that the general traits of animals and how they are classified is covered first. Next, the phyla making up sponges and stinging-cell animals are examined. Three different phyla commonly called worms are studied next. Finally, traits and the different classes of soft-bodied animals are studied.

Misconception

Students usually believe that animals having the largest number of different species would be those most familiar to them. This would include vertebrates and, specifically, mammals. However, invertebrates far outnumber the vertebrates. They simply are less obvious to humans because of either their small size or the fact that many live in water habitats.

7:1 Animal Classification

PREPARATION

Materials Needed

Make copies of the Focus, Study Guide, Skill, and Reteaching worksheets in the *Teacher Resource Package.*

▶ Obtain slides for the Focus motivation.

Key Science Words

symmetry
vertebrate
invertebrate

Process Skills

In the Skill Checks, students will interpret diagrams and understand science words.

1 FOCUS

▶ The objectives are listed on the student page. Remind students to preview these objectives as a guide to this numbered section.

MOTIVATION/Demonstration

Obtain prepared slides for all animal phyla. Ask students to group the samples using size, color, where found, and harmful or helpful .

Focus/*Teacher Resource Package,* p. 13. Use the Focus transparency shown at the bottom of this page as an introduction to relations among simple animals.

Objectives

1. **List** four traits of animals.
2. **Identify** nine major phyla of animals and give an example of each.

Key Science Words

vertebrate
invertebrate
symmetry

7:1 Animal Classification

Scientists have discovered and classified about 1 1/2 million different kinds of living things. Of this number, about one million are animals. The different kinds of animals are grouped according to traits they have in common.

Traits of Animals

What are some of the traits that make animals different from other living things? First, animals are consumers and can't make their own food. They must take in food from their surroundings. Some animals eat plants, some eat other animals, and others eat both plants and animals. Most animals digest and store food in their bodies.

Second, most animals can move from place to place. Moving around helps them find food. Animals that don't move have developed other ways to get food.

Third, animals are multicellular organisms. The cells of most animals are organized into tissues and organs that form systems. Many animals have nervous systems, digestive systems, and reproductive systems. Nearly all animals have muscles and systems for getting rid of wastes.

All animals belong to one of two groups—the vertebrates and the invertebrates (in VERT uh brayts). **Vertebrates** are animals with backbones. People and the animals most closely related to us, such as fish, amphibians, reptiles, birds, and other mammals, are vertebrates. **Invertebrates** are animals without backbones. Worms and insects are examples of invertebrates.

Finally, most animals have some kind of symmetry (SIH muh tree). **Symmetry** is the balanced arrangement of body parts around a center point or along a center line. Only a few very simple animals do not show symmetry. These animals grow in a variety of shapes. The sponge in Figure 7-1a does not show symmetry.

Some invertebrates show radial (RAYD ee ul) symmetry. In radial symmetry, the body parts are arranged in a circle around a center point. The sea anemone (uh NEM uh nee) in Figure 7-1b is an example of an animal that has radial symmetry.

All vertebrates and some invertebrates have bilateral (bi LAT uh rul) symmetry. In an animal with bilateral symmetry, the body can be divided lengthwise into two equal sides, a right side and a left side. The bee in Figure

Skill Check

Understand science words: invertebrate. The word part *in* means not. In your dictionary, find three words with the word part *in* in them. *For more help, refer to the **Skill Handbook,** pages 706-711.*

FOCUS 13

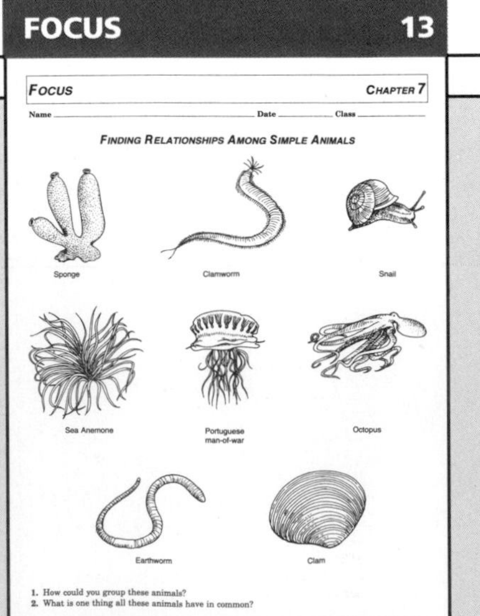
Focus *Chapter 7*

Name ______ Date ______ Class ______

Finding Relationships Among Simple Animals

1. How could you group these animals?
2. What is one thing all these animals have in common?

OPTIONS

Science Background

Phylum names used in this chapter are general terms. Technical terms used in taxonomy to describe the phyla are: Sponges - Porifera; Stinging-cell animals - Coelenterata or Cnidaria; Flatworms - Platyhelminthes; Roundworms - Nematoda; Segmented worms - Annelida; Soft-bodied animals - Mollusca; Jointed-leg animals - Arthropoda; Spiny-skin animals - Echinodermata; Chordates - Chordata.

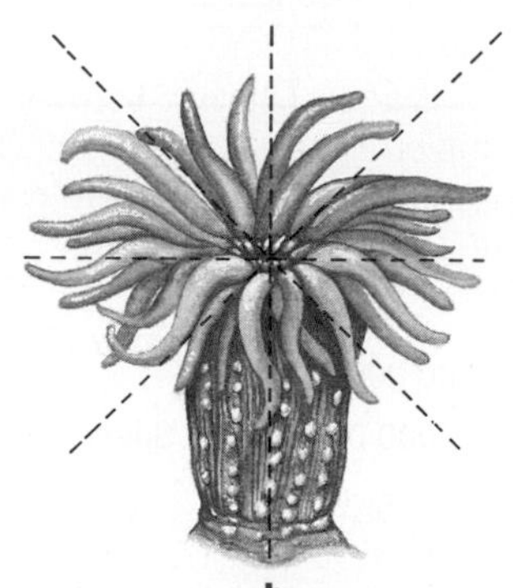

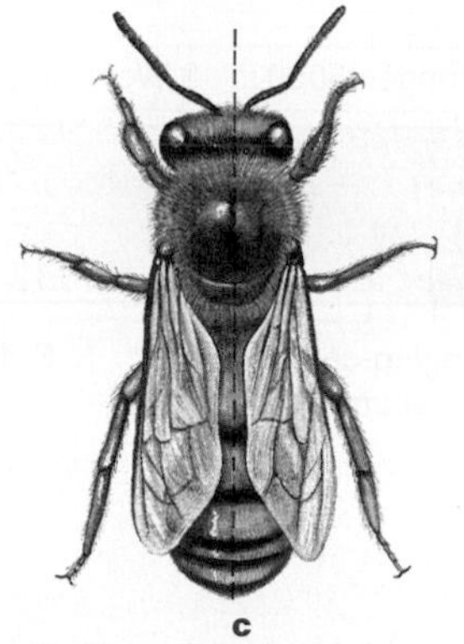

Figure 7-1 A sponge does not have symmetry (a). A sea anemone has radial symmetry (b). A bee has bilateral symmetry (c).

7-1c has bilateral symmetry. Notice that it has a head end and a back end. The head end studies where the animal is going and finds food. The bee also has an upper and a lower side. The lower side moves the animal along a surface.

Let's review the traits of animals.

1. Animals can't make food, but must catch and eat it.
2. Most animals can move from place to place.
3. Animals have many cells. The cells make up tissues and organs that form systems.
4. Most animals have symmetry.

How are an animal's cells organized?

How Animals Are Classified

Scientists group living things into one of five kingdoms. If an organism shows most of the traits just listed, then it is placed in the animal kingdom. If not, then it is placed in one of the other four kingdoms.

How do scientists know to which phylum an animal belongs? Consider the sponges. They have certain traits. If an animal shows these traits, it belongs in the phylum with sponges. If it does not, then it belongs in a different phylum.

Here is an example with which you are familiar. A new student arrives at your school. How does the office staff know whether the student should be placed in the ninth, tenth, eleventh, or twelfth grade? The student can be placed in a certain grade only if he or she has passed a certain number of courses. If the student has passed the number of courses required in the ninth grade, the student is put in the tenth grade. The number of courses passed is the "trait" used to place students into the proper grades.

Skill Check

Interpret diagrams: Make a list of the invertebrates pictured in this chapter. Indicate the type of symmetry shown by each one. *For more help, refer to the* ***Skill Handbook****, pages 706-711.*

2 TEACH

MOTIVATION/Brainstorming

Ask students to describe how animals differ from plants. Ask students how plants and animals are alike.

Concept Development

▶ Ask students to compare the number of plant species (350 000) with the number of animal species.

Cooperative Learning: Divide the class into nine groups. Provide each group with one sample animal. You might use pictures, plastic-embedded, preserved, etc. Each animal should be from a different phylum. Have each group compile a list of the traits that they can see. Have a spokesperson for each group report to the class on their findings.

Guided Practice

Have students write down their answers to the margin question: cells make up tissues and organs that form systems.

Skill Check

Be sure students look at the pictures in the entire chapter, not just the first section. Point out that they are looking for invertebrates.

Independent Practice

Study Guide/*Teacher Resource Package*, p. 37. Use the Study Guide worksheet shown at the bottom of this page for independent practice.

SKILL 7

SKILL: INTERPRET DIAGRAMS: SYMMETRY — CHAPTER 7

Name ____________ Date ________ Class ________

For more help, refer to the Skill Handbook, pages 706-711. — *Use after Section 7:1.*

THE SYMMETRY OF ANIMALS

Review symmetry in Section 7:1 of your textbook. Then, decide whether each animal in the table has radial symmetry or bilateral symmetry. Write your answer in the second column. In the last column, explain how you decided the type of symmetry the animal has. Then, answer the questions.

Animal	Symmetry	Reason
	radial	has body parts around a central point
	bilateral	has two equal sides, a right side and a left side
	radial	has body parts around central point
	bilateral	has two equal sides, a right side and a left side
	bilateral	has two equal sides, a right side and a left side
	bilateral	has two equal sides, a right side and a left side

1. What are the advantages of bilateral symmetry? An animal can move in a specific direction.
2. What are the advantages of radial symmetry? An animal may be able to sense food or the approach of other animals from all sides.

STUDY GUIDE 37

STUDY GUIDE — CHAPTER 7

Name ____________ Date ________ Class ________

ANIMAL CLASSIFICATION

In your textbook, read about how animals are classified in Section 7:1.

1. What is the difference between vertebrates and invertebrates? Vertebrates have a backbone, invertebrates do not.
2. What is symmetry? Symmetry is the balanced arrangement of body parts around a center point or along a center line.
3. What is the difference between radial and bilateral symmetry? In radial symmetry, the body parts are arranged in a circle around a center point. In bilateral symmetry, the body can be divided lengthwise into two equal sides, a right side and a left side.
4. List four traits of animals.
   a. Animals can't make their own food.
   b. Most animals can move from place to place.
   c. Animals have many cells.
   d. Most animals have symmetry.
5. The animal kingdom is one of five kingdoms into which scientists group living things. Scientists group animals into nine major groups.
   a. What are these groups called? phyla
   b. Which group contains the largest number of different kinds of animals? animals with jointed legs
   c. Which group contains the smallest number of different kinds of animals? sponges
   d. Which group contains the simplest animals? sponges
   e. Which group contains the most complex animals? chordates
6. What main group of animals makes up the chordates phylum? vertebrates
7. What main group of animals makes up the rest of the animal kingdom? invertebrates

OPTIONS

ACTIVITY/Project

Have students prepare posters with pictures of animals. Have them divide the animals into vertebrates and invertebrates. There should be at least 20 examples in each category.

Skill/*Teacher Resource Package*, p. 7. Use the Skill worksheet shown here to have students interpret diagrams of animals with symmetry.

TEACH

Guided Practice

Have students write down their answers to the margin question: sponges.

Check for Understanding

Have students respond to the first three questions in Check Your Understanding.

Reteach

Reteaching/Teacher Resource Package, p. 17. Use this worksheet to give students additional practice in animal classification.

Extension: Assign Critical Thinking, Biology and Reading, or some of the **OPTIONS** available with this lesson.

3 APPLY

Summary

Have students discuss animal phyla as being either vertebrates or invertebrates.

4 CLOSE

Convergent Question

Ask students why scientists classify animals.

Answers to Check Your Understanding

1. Animals are consumers, can move about, are multicellular, have symmetry, and are vertebrates or invertebrates.
2. jointed-leg animals; insects, crayfish
3. It can be divided into two equal parts on any plane.
4. It can't be classified as an animal because it makes its own food.
5. An amoeba has no symmetry line; a starfish will have lines from a center point on the body through each part; the person will have a line running lengthwise down the middle.

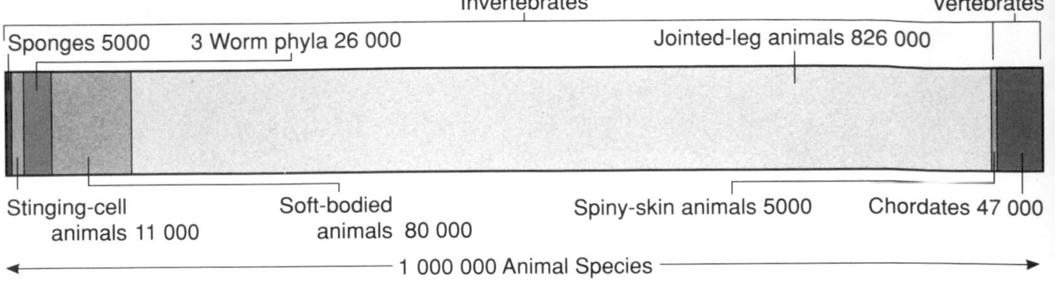

Figure 7-2 Animals are placed in nine major phyla. Which phylum has the most complex animals? chordates

Which phylum contains the simplest animals?

The nine major groups into which animals are placed are shown in Figure 7-2. Each major group is a phylum. Also shown is the number of animal species in each phylum.

The figure shows that some phyla include many different kinds of animals. Other phyla are small. Animals with jointed legs make up the largest phylum. Insects, spiders, and crayfish belong to this phylum. Sponges make up the smallest of the phyla shown.

Figure 7-2 also shows the simplest phyla at the left and the most complex at the right. Sponges are the simplest of all animals. Chordates (KOR dayts) are the most complex. Most chordates are vertebrates. Eight of the nine phyla shown are grouped together as invertebrates. You can see from Figure 7-2 that there are many more invertebrates than vertebrates on Earth.

Check Your Understanding

1. List four traits of animals.
2. Which animal phylum is the largest? Give two examples of members of this phylum.
3. How can an animal body be divided if it has radial symmetry?
4. **Critical Thinking:** An astronaut discovers an organism on a distant planet. It can move around, is multicellular, has bilateral symmetry, and makes its own food. Can this new organism be classified as an animal? Explain.
5. **Biology and Reading:** An amoeba has no symmetry. A starfish has radial symmetry. A human has bilateral symmetry. Draw an amoeba, a starfish, and a person. Draw the line or lines of symmetry for each.

RETEACHING 17

RETEACHING: IDEA MAP CHAPTER 7

Name ____ Date ____ Class ____

Use with Section 7:1.

ANIMAL CLASSIFICATION

Use the following terms to complete the idea map: many cells; tissues, organs, systems; bilateral; invertebrates; food; vertebrates; move; radial.

Animals
- traits
  - cannot make their own **food**
  - most can **move** from place to place
  - multicellular made of **many cells**
  - cells organized into **tissues, organs, systems**
  - symmetry **radial** or **bilateral**
- classification
  - **invertebrates** without backbones
  - **vertebrates** with backbones

1. What traits make animals different from other living things? **They cannot make their own food; can move from place to place; are multicellular; have tissues, organs, and systems; and most have some kind of symmetry.**
2. What are the two groups of animals? **vertebrates and invertebrates**
3. What is radial symmetry? **It is the symmetry in which the body parts are arranged in a circle around a central point.**
4. What is bilateral symmetry? **It is the symmetry in which the body can be divided lengthwise into two equal sides, a right side and a left side.**
5. How do scientists decide in which phylum an animal belongs? **by studying its traits**
6. Which phylum of animals has the largest number of species? **jointed-leg animals**

7:2 Sponges and Stinging-cell Animals

Sponges and stinging-cell animals do not have backbones. They are invertebrates. Sponges are the simplest invertebrates.

Objectives

3. **List** the traits of sponges.
4. **Describe** the traits of stinging-cell animals.

Key Science Words

sponge
pore
stinging-cell animal
tentacle

Sponges

Sponges are simple invertebrates that have pores. A **pore** is a small opening. You may know a sponge as an object that you use when you take a bath or wash cars. Look at the sponges in Figure 7-3. Some look like small trees. Others look like vases. Most sponges have no definite shape. You will also notice that they come in many colors.

What are the traits of sponges? Unlike most other animals, sponges do not move about freely on their own. Most live attached to rocks in shallow oceans. Some sponges live in fresh water. The body of a sponge has many pores. Water enters through these pores and leaves through an opening in the top center of the sponge's body. Many canals carry the water throughout the sponge's body.

How is water carried through the walls of a sponge's body?

Since sponges can't move, how do they get food? All sponges must live in water. Water has small organisms in it that sponges can use for food. The pores in the sponge allow water and any food in the water to flow into the animal. Once inside, the food is trapped by food-getting cells.

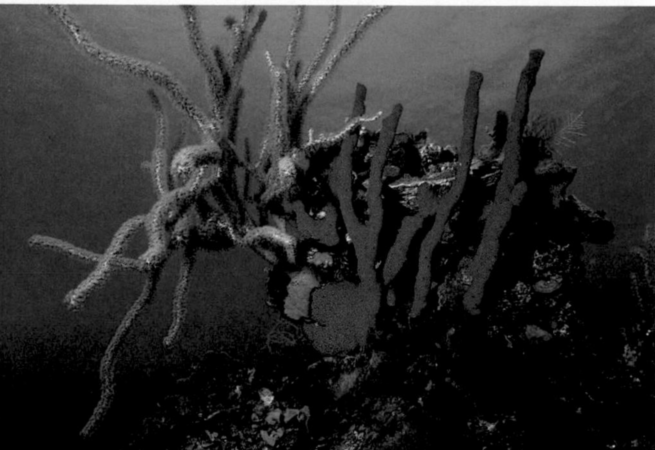

Figure 7-3 Sponges come in a variety of sizes, shapes, and colors.

OPTIONS

Science Background

There are three classes of sponges based on their skeleton composition. These are: Class Calcarea, skeleton of calcium carbonate spicules; Class Hexactinellida, skeleton of glass; Class Demospongiae, skeleton of protein called spongin.

There are three classes of stinging–cell animals. These are: Class Hydrozoa, hydroids such as Hydra and Portuguese man-of-war; Class Scyphozoa, jellyfish; Class Anthozoa, sea anemones and coral.

7:2 Sponges and Stinging-cell Animals

PREPARATION

Materials Needed

Make copies of the Study Guide, Reteaching, and Lab worksheets in the *Teacher Resource Package.*

▶ Have on hand a natural sponge and a plastic sponge for the Focus motivation.

▶ Obtain hydra culture, daphnia or brine shrimp, and flashlights for Lab 7-1.

▶ Obtain a suction cup and small rock for the Mini Lab.

Key Science Words

sponge
pore
stinging-cell animal
tentacle

Process Skills

In the Mini Lab, students will infer. In Lab 7-1, they will observe, make and use tables, and interpret data.

1 FOCUS

▶ The objectives are listed on the student page. Remind students to preview these objectives as a guide to this numbered section.

MOTIVATION/Demonstration

Show students a piece of natural sponge and have them compare it to a commercial plastic type. Have them point out similarities and differences. You may want to prepare wet mounts of these two sponges for further comparison on a microscopic level.

Guided Practice

Have students write down their answers to the margin question: through canals.

2 TEACH

MOTIVATION/Bulletin Board

Arrange pictures of sponges, stinging–cell animals, worms, and mollusks on the bulletin board. Have students place the organisms under the appropriate phylum as the animals are studied. As the traits of the animals are discussed, look for the traits in the pictures.

Concept Development

▶ Explain that sponges are filter feeders, organisms that get their food by filtering it out of the water around them.

▶ The mouth of the sponge is the osculum or excurrent pore.

▶ Explain that the special cells inside sponges for trapping food are collar cells. The collar cells have flagella like those of protists.

▶ The pores of the sponge are incurrent openings. Water is drawn into the sponge and circulated in the central cavity by the beating of the collar cells. Water passes out of the sponge through the osculum.

▶ Point out that most sponges that are now sold are synthetically made. Some places, such as Tarpon Springs, Florida, still catch live sponges for sale.

▶ The sponge is asymmetrical because it lacks symmetry.

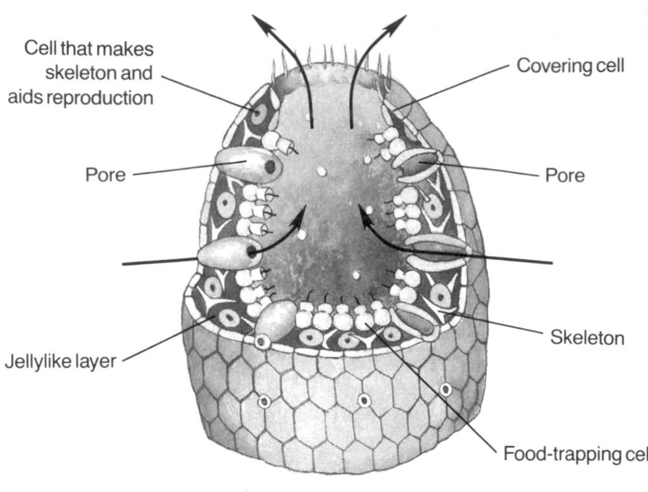

Figure 7-4 Arrows show the direction in which water flows through a sponge. Sponges have three kinds of cells.

Bio Tip

Consumer: Most of the sponges sold today are artificial. They are made from cellulose or synthetic materials. Natural sponges hold much more water than artificial sponges, but they are not commonly used because they are expensive.

Sponges are only two cell layers thick, have no muscle or nerve cells, and have no tissues, organs, or organ systems. Sponges have three main kinds of cells. Each cell type has a certain job. One cell type traps food and moves water through the sponge by beating its flagellum. Other cells cover and protect the sponge. The third cell type produces chemicals that make the skeleton. This third cell type also aids in reproduction and carries food to other cells. The three kinds of cells are shown in Figure 7-4.

Sponges can reproduce both sexually and asexually. In sexual reproduction, the same sponge produces both sperm and eggs, but at different times. It takes two sponges for sexual reproduction to take place. Having both sperm and eggs ensures that sponges near each other can reproduce. Sperm cells produced by one sponge are carried to another sponge by the water. There, the sperm fertilize the eggs. New sponges usually develop on rocks on the ocean floor.

Sponges also reproduce asexually. Small pieces of a sponge's body may break off and form separate, new sponges. Sponges may also form buds. Each bud can develop into a new sponge.

You may have used a natural sponge for cleaning and washing because they hold a lot of water. The skeletons of sponges have many fibers. When the animal dies and decays, the fibers remain. The spaces between these fibers can be filled with water. Because the fibers are elastic, the water can be squeezed out.

OPTIONS

What Traits Does a Sponge Have for Living in Water?/*Lab Manual*, pp. 49-52. Use this lab as an extension to studying sponges.

Stinging-cell Animals

Stinging-cell animals are animals with stinging cells and hollow, sock-shaped bodies that lack organs. Most of these animals live in the ocean. A few live in freshwater lakes and streams. Many stinging-cell animals are beautiful and delicate. They look very different from the animals you may see every day.

It is hard at first to compare hydras, corals, sea fans, jellyfish, and sea anemones with one another. Look at the animals in Figure 7-6. Animals in the stinging-cell animal phylum do not look much alike. Yet, all of them share certain traits.

Many stinging-cell animals have armlike parts called **tentacles** (TENT ih kulz) that surround the mouth. The jellyfish in Figure 7-6a has tentacles. If you were to look closely at corals and sea fans, you would see that these animals also have tentacles. A coral is really a group of many small animals. The same is true of sea fans. A hard structure on the outside of the animals supports and protects them and is made of chemicals produced by the animals. The chemicals harden into different shapes.

Figure 7-5 shows that stinging-cell animals have radial symmetry and sock-shaped bodies made of two cell layers. A jellylike layer lies between the two cell layers. Inside the body of each animal is a body cavity. The cavity has one opening called the mouth. The only way into and out of the body is through the mouth.

Many stinging-cell animals fasten themselves to the ocean bottom or to rocks with a structure called a disc. They do not move from that place. How then do they get food? They catch it with their tentacles.

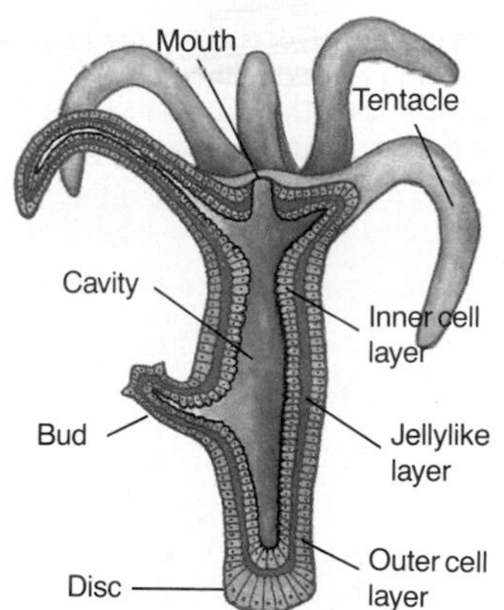

Figure 7-5 Stinging-cell animals have sock-shaped bodies with two cell layers.

How many cell layers does a stinging-cell animal's body contain?

Figure 7-6 Some of the many stinging-cell animals are a jellyfish (a), coral (b), and sea fan (c).

a

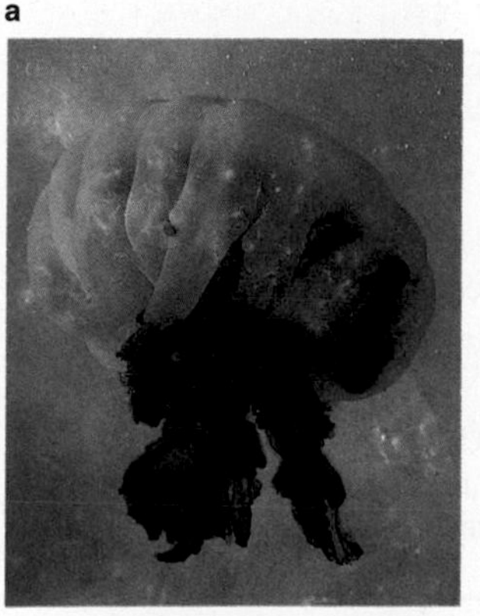

b

c

TEACH

Concept Development

▶ The stinging cells are called nematocysts and release a protein poison that has paralyzing action. Some sea anemones release only a sticky substance.

▶ Explain that common names for animals are often misleading. The jellyfish is not a fish.

▶ The mouth also serves as the anal opening through which wastes are extruded.

Guided Practice

Have students write down their answers to the margin question: two.

Check for Understanding

Have students list the headings Sponges and Stinging-cell animals. Have them list the traits of each under the proper headings.

Reteach

Ask students to prepare a key that will enable them to determine if an animal is a sponge or a stinging-cell animal. Review the process of key construction and provide an example.

Independent Practice

Study Guide/*Teacher Resource Package*, p. 38. Use the Study Guide worksheet shown at the bottom of this page for independent practice.

STUDY GUIDE 38

STUDY GUIDE CHAPTER 7

Name ______ Date ______ Class ______

SPONGES AND STINGING-CELL ANIMALS

In your textbook, read about sponges and stinging-cell animals in Section 7:2.

1. How do sponges get their food? Water flowing through the sponges' pores brings small living things into their bodies. There, the living things are trapped by food-getting cells.
2. How do the different types of cells help a sponge function? Some cells move water and trap food, some cover and protect the sponge's body, and others produce chemicals that make the skeleton.
3. Complete the following sentences about stinging-cell animals.
   a. The body of these animals is a hollow, sock-shaped structure.
   b. Most of these animals live in the ocean.
   c. Their armlike parts are called tentacles.
   d. Each armlike part has many stinging cells.
   e. The body has an opening called a mouth.
   f. The bodies of these animals have two cell layers.
   g. These animals use muscles and nerves to move their armlike parts.
4. Explain how each of the following parts helps the animal function.
   a. disc helps fasten the animals to ocean bottom or to rocks
   b. stinging cells and triggers shoot out darts from the stinging cells and stun passing animals with poison
   c. tentacles push newly-caught meal through mouth and into body cavity
5. Circle the letter of the animal shown below that is not a stinging-cell animal.

   A (B) C D
6. What traits helped you choose your answer for question 5? the lack of tentacles and the presence of pores

OPTIONS

ACTIVITY/Challenge

Have some students set up a saltwater aquarium. Supplies may be purchased from a biological supply house or from aquarium stores.

What Are the Parts of a Stinging-cell Animal?/*Lab Manual*, pp. 57-59. Use this lab as an extension to studying stinging-cell animals.

TEACH

Mini Lab

You may substitute a medicine dropper top (rubber part) and a small pebble for the suction cup and rock.

Check for Understanding

Have students respond to the first three questions in Check Your Understanding.

Reteach

Reteaching/*Teacher Resource Package*, p. 18. Use this worksheet to give students additional practice with sponges and stinging-cell animals.

Extension: Assign Critical Thinking, Biology and Reading, or some of the **OPTIONS** available with this lesson.

3 APPLY

ACTIVITY/Interview

You are a sponge and are being interviewed. Explain what and how you eat, where you live, and what you do.

4 CLOSE

Audiovisual

Show the filmstrip *Survey of the Animal Kingdom, Part I - Sponges, Anemones, Corals and Flatworms,* Educational Images Ltd.

Answers to Check Your Understanding

6. do not move on their own, full of pores, two cell layers thick
7. stun it with darts containing poison and capture it with tentacles
8. have tentacles, stinging-cells, and one opening
9. It allows them to catch food from any direction.
10. probably from the holes, or pores throughout the sponges

Figure 7-7 Hydras catch food by stinging a small animal with a poison dart. The stunned animal is then stuffed into the hydra's mouth.

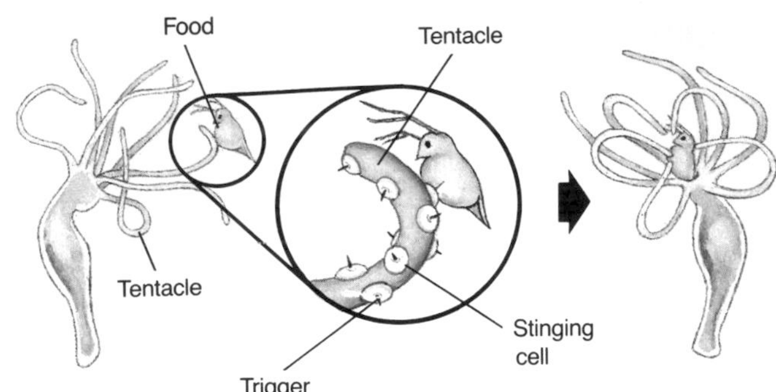

Mini Lab

How Does a Sea Anemone Attach Itself?

Infer: Wet a suction cup and press it against a small rock. Pick the rock up by holding the suction cup. How are you able to lift the rock with the suction cup? *For more help, refer to the **Skill Handbook**, pages 706-711.*

The tentacles have thousands of stinging cells with hairlike triggers. When an animal brushes against the trigger, a stinging dart containing poison shoots into the water. The dart hits the animal and stuns it with the poison. The tentacles then push the newly caught meal through the mouth and into the body cavity, where it is digested. Undigested food leaves the animal through the mouth. Figure 7-7 shows a hydra with food it has caught.

Stinging cells of a jellyfish can cause a very painful sting in people. Anyone who lives near an ocean probably knows not to bother jellyfish that have washed onto shore.

Stinging-cell animals have muscle cells and nerve cells. Animals in this phylum use muscles and nerves to move their tentacles. Jellyfish use muscles to swim.

Stinging-cell animals reproduce sexually by forming eggs and sperm. These are released into the water, where the sperm fertilize the eggs. Some stinging-cell animals, like the hydra, can also reproduce asexually by forming buds. These buds break off and become separate animals.

Check Your Understanding

6. List three traits of sponges.
7. How do stinging-cell animals get food?
8. List three traits of stinging-cell animals.
9. **Critical Thinking:** Why is radial symmetry useful to a stinging-cell animal?
10. **Biology and Reading:** Most of the sponges sold today are made from cellulose, a plant material. How do you think this kind of sponge got its name?

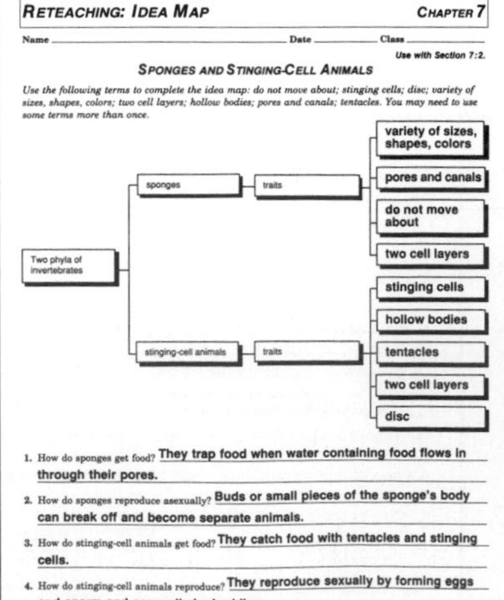

RETEACHING 18

RETEACHING: IDEA MAP — CHAPTER 7

Name ______ Date ______ Class ______

Use with Section 7:2.

SPONGES AND STINGING-CELL ANIMALS

Use the following terms to complete the idea map: do not move about; stinging cells; disc; variety of sizes, shapes, colors; two cell layers; hollow bodies; pores and canals; tentacles. You may need to use some terms more than once.

Two phyla of invertebrates
- sponges — traits: variety of sizes, shapes, colors; pores and canals; do not move about; two cell layers
- stinging-cell animals — traits: stinging cells; hollow bodies; tentacles; two cell layers; disc

1. How do sponges get food? They trap food when water containing food flows in through their pores.
2. How do sponges reproduce asexually? Buds or small pieces of the sponge's body can break off and become separate animals.
3. How do stinging-cell animals get food? They catch food with tentacles and stinging cells.
4. How do stinging-cell animals reproduce? They reproduce sexually by forming eggs and sperm and asexually by budding.

Lab 7–1 Stinging-cell Animals

Problem: What are the traits of a stinging-cell animal?

Skills

observe, make and use tables, interpret data

Materials

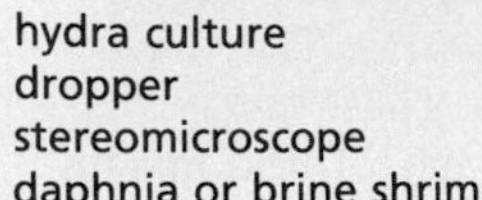

hydra culture
dropper
stereomicroscope
daphnia or brine shrimp
small dish
hand lens
flashlight

Procedure

1. Copy the data tables.
2. Use a dropper to place a hydra and some water from the culture into a small dish.
3. **Observe:** Examine the hydra with a hand lens. Count the number of tentacles. Find the disc by which the animal attaches itself. Find the mouth. Record your observations in Table 1.
4. Tap the dish gently with your finger. Observe how the hydra moves and changes shape. Record your observations.
5. Place the dish on the stage of a stereomicroscope and focus on the hydra.
6. Draw the hydra and label the structures.
7. Drop a daphnia or a small amount of brine shrimp into the dish. Observe and record how the hydra takes in food.
8. Shine a flashlight on the dish. Observe and record the hydra's reaction.
9. Return the hydra to the culture.

Data and Observations

1. How does the hydra react to light?
2. Where is the disc located?

Analyze and Apply

1. How does the hydra capture food?
2. **Interpret data:** Why does the hydra react the way it does when you tap the dish?
3. What is the advantage to the hydra of having a mouth surrounded by tentacles?
4. **Apply:** How does a hydra differ from a sponge in food-getting?

Extension

Observe a hydra when it is near other small animals and protists to determine what a hydra will eat.

TABLE 1.

PART	OBSERVATION
Location of mouth	on top, surrounded by tentacles
Number of tentacles	varies; may be 6 or more
Location of disc	at bottom

TABLE 2.

STIMULUS	REACTION
Touch (tapping on dish)	contracts body and tentacles
Food	surrounds the food with tentacles
Light	contracts body and tentacles

ANSWERS

Data and Observations

1. It contracts its body and tentacles.
2. at the bottom of the hydra

Analyze and Apply

1. It surrounds the food with tentacles. Students may not see the discharge of stinging cells, but they should note that the food animal stops moving as it is stunned.
2. It is protecting itself.
3. The mouth is in a central location for receiving food from any of the tentacles.
4. Sponges get food in the water that enters their bodies through the pores. Special cells trap the food inside the body. Hydras have stinging cells and tentacles that trap food outside the body and then put it in the mouth. Sponges have no mouth.

Lab 7-1 Stinging-cell Animals

Overview

In this lab, students will observe a stinging-cell animal and will be able to study its feeding habits.

Objectives: Upon completion of this lab, students will be able to, (1) **describe** the general shape and characteristics of a hydra, (2) **relate** this animal's response to the presence of a nervous system, and (3) **describe** the method used by hydra in feeding.

Time Allotment: 35 minutes

Preparation

▶ **Alternate Materials:** If prepared slides of hydra are available, then steps 3 and 6 may be done without use of living materials.

▶ Order hydra and daphnia, or brine shrimp in advance from a biological supply house. Purchase from any pet or aquarium shop and follow directions on container for hatching.

Lab 7-1 worksheet/*Teacher Resource Package,* pp. 25-26.

Teaching the Lab

▶ Place several coverslip pieces into the container of hydra overnight. The hydra will stick to the glass. You can remove the glass pieces with attached hydra using tweezers.

7:3 Worms

PREPARATION

Materials Needed

Make copies of the Application, Study Guide, Enrichment, and Reteaching worksheets in the *Teacher Resource Package.*

▶ Gather wire mesh, funnels, and alcohol for the Mini Lab.

Key Science Words

flatworm
tapeworm
cyst
planarian
roundworm
hookworm
anus
segmented worm

Process Skills

In the Skill Check, students will infer. In the Mini Lab, they will observe.

1 FOCUS

▶ The objectives are listed on the student page. Remind students to preview these objectives as a guide to this numbered section.

ACTIVITY/Demonstration

Mark off a distance of 30 meters on the classroom floor. Ask students to imagine an animal of this length inside their body. Advise them that tapeworms have reached this length within human hosts.

Objectives

5. **List** the three main phyla of worms and give an example of each.
6. **Identify** the main features of flatworms, roundworms, and segmented worms.

Key Science Words

flatworm
tapeworm
cyst
planarian
roundworm
hookworm
anus
segmented worm

7:3 Worms

When you hear the word *worm*, you probably think of an earthworm, but there are many different kinds of worms. Worms are invertebrates. They are classified into three main phyla—flatworms, roundworms, and segmented worms, based on their structures.

Flatworms

Worms are more complex than sponges and stinging-cell animals. **Flatworms** are the simplest worms. They have a flattened body and three layers of cells. These layers include an outer layer, an inner layer, and a thick, middle layer. Organs and systems develop from cells of the middle layer.

Most flatworms are parasites. Remember that parasites live in or on other living things and get food from them. The organism that provides the food is the host. Some flatworms can cause serious problems.

A **tapeworm** is a kind of flatworm that has a flattened, ribbonlike body divided into sections. Tapeworms can live in the intestine of almost any kind of vertebrate. A tapeworm has suckers and hooks on one end that are used to hold onto the intestine of its host. Tapeworms have no mouth or organs to digest food. They absorb food that the host has already digested.

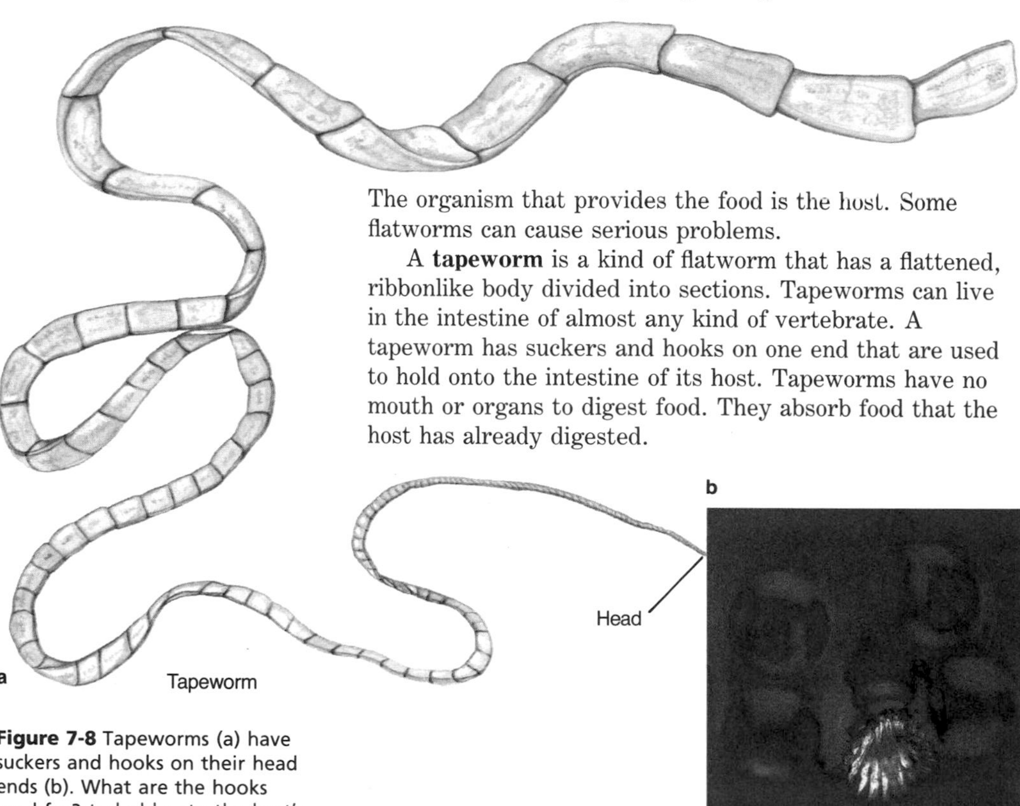

Figure 7-8 Tapeworms (a) have suckers and hooks on their head ends (b). What are the hooks used for? to hold onto the host's intestine

OPTIONS

Science Background

The following classification for each worm phylum is: Phylum Platyhelminthes (flatworms); Class Turbellaria, (planaria); Class Cestoda, (beef tapeworm); Class Trematoda, (flukes); Phylum Nematoda (roundworms); Phylum Annelida (segmented worms); Class Polychaeta (clamworms); Class Oligochaeta (earthworms); Class Hirundinea (leech).

Life Cycle of a Pork Tapeworm/ *Transparency Package,* number 7a. Use color transparency 7a as you teach flatworms.

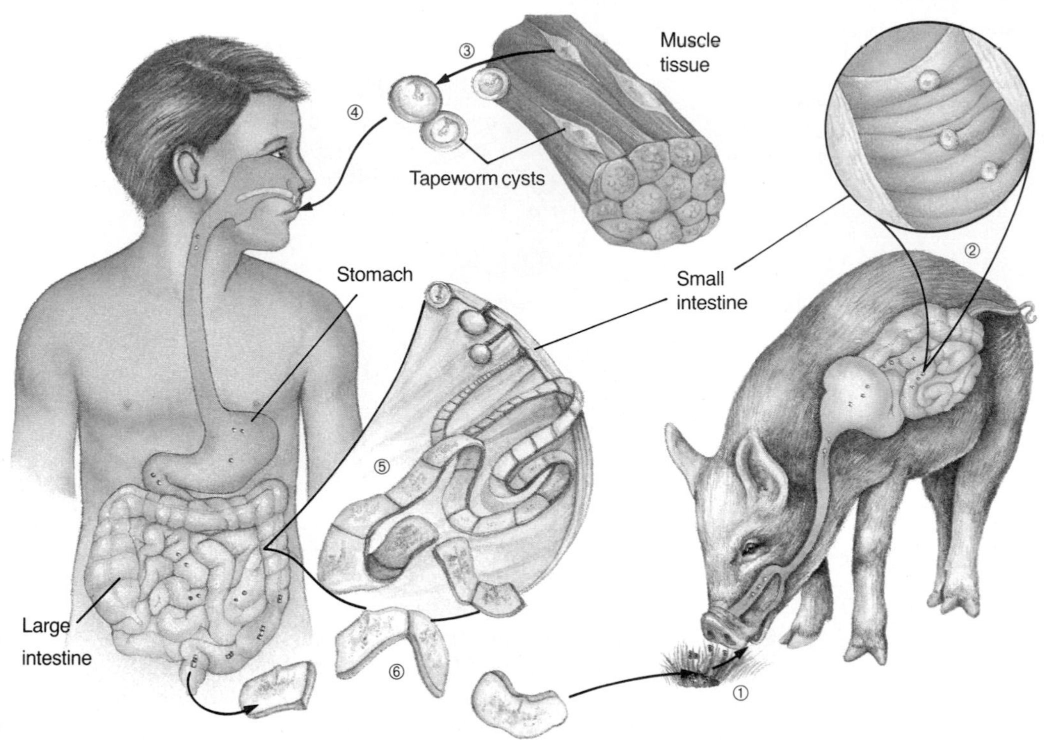

Figure 7-9 Life cycle of a pork tapeworm

The tapeworm in Figure 7-8 is shown life size. Although some are much smaller, this one happens to be very large. Is it any wonder that a worm of this size uses a lot of the host's food?

Tapeworms have life cycles with many stages. Follow the steps of the pork tapeworm life cycle in Figure 7-9.

1. A pig eats tapeworm eggs that are on the ground. The eggs hatch in the pig's intestine.
2. The young worms enter the pig's bloodstream. Then they travel to the muscles and burrow into them.
3. The young worms form cysts (SIHSTZ) in the muscles. A **cyst** is a young worm with a protective covering.
4. If a person eats raw or undercooked meat that contains the cysts, the tapeworms get inside the person's intestine. The worms come out of their cysts, attach to the inside of the intestine, and begin to grow.
5. Tapeworms produce both eggs and sperm in each of their body sections. The sperm fertilize the eggs.
6. The body sections break off and leave the host's body in solid waste through the intestine.

Skill Check

Infer: Someone with tapeworms eats a lot of food but still feels hungry, tired, and loses weight. What is the cause? *For more help, refer to the* ***Skill Handbook****, pages 706-711.*

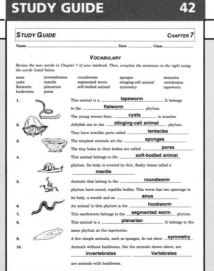

2 TEACH

MOTIVATION/Demonstration

Show the class a preserved specimen of a tapeworm. Lay the worm on a table so students can get a sense of its size.

Concept Development

▶ Point out that tapeworms cause malnutrition or mild vitamin deficiencies in some of their hosts. Some tapeworms cause pernicious anemia because they remove most of the Vitamin B12 from the host's diet.

▶ Medicines have been given to humans who have tapeworms to cause expulsion of the worm.

▶ Several human tapeworms are transmitted by infected pork, beef, or wild game that has not been thoroughly cooked.

▶ One tapeworm section may contain as many as 100 000 eggs.

▶ The tapeworm body is made of sections called proglottids. New sections grow from the head region and push the older ones further back from the head.

Skill Check

Tapeworms absorb nutrients from their host. This person is suffering from lack of necessary nutrients.

Independent Practice

Study Guide/*Teacher Resource Package*, p. 42. Use the Study Guide worksheet shown at the bottom of this page for independent practice.

APPLICATION 7

APPLICATION: HEALTH **CHAPTER 7**

Name ____ Date ____ Class ____

Use after Section 7:3.

PORK TAPEWORM CYCLE

Pork tapeworms are flatworm parasites that can grow in the bodies of pigs and humans. Review the information about tapeworms in Section 7:3 of your text. The diagram below shows the tapeworm life cycle. During their life cycle, tapeworms develop in stages that include fertilized eggs, young worms, cysts, and adult worms.

Fill in the blanks in the diagram to identify the stages of development of the tapeworm.

Which tapeworm stage can be found on the ground or in sewage?
fertilized eggs

Which tapeworm stage develops inside the pig's body?
The pig eats tapeworm eggs. The eggs hatch into young worms in the pig's body. Young worms form cysts.

PORK ROAST

Which tapeworm stage might be found here?
cysts

Describe how the tapeworm can develop inside a person's body.
A person eats undercooked pork containing tapeworm cysts. Adult worms develop from the cysts. They produce eggs and sperm. Body sections with fertilized eggs leave the host's body and get into sewage.

STUDY GUIDE 42

STUDY GUIDE **CHAPTER 7**

Name ____ Date ____ Class ____

VOCABULARY

Review the new words in Chapter 7 of your textbook. Then, complete the sentences on the right using the words listed below.

anus	invertebrates	roundworm	sponges	tentacles
cysts	mantle	segmented worm	stinging-cell animal	vertebrates
flatworm	planarian	soft-bodied animal	symmetry	tapeworm
hookworm	pores			

1. This animal is a **tapeworm**. It belongs to the **flatworm** phylum. The young worms form **cysts** in muscles.
2. Jellyfish are in the **stinging-cell animal** phylum. They have armlike parts called **tentacles**.
3. The simplest animals are the **sponges**. The tiny holes in their bodies are called **pores**.
4. This animal belongs to the **soft-bodied animal** phylum. Its body is covered by thin, fleshy tissue called a **mantle**.
5. Animals that belong to the **roundworm** phylum have round, ropelike bodies. This worm has two openings in its body, a mouth and an **anus**.
6. An animal in this phylum is the **hookworm**.
7. This earthworm belongs to the **segmented worm** phylum.
8. This animal is a **planarian**. It belongs to the same phylum as the tapeworms.
9. A few simple animals, such as sponges, do not show **symmetry**.
10. Animals without backbones, like the animals shown above, are **invertebrates**. **Vertebrates** are animals with backbones.

OPTIONS

Application/*Teacher Resource Package*, p. 7. Use the Application worksheet shown here to teach the life cycle of a tapeworm.

TEACH

Concept Development

▶ Stress the importance of cooking meat thoroughly even though meat inspection prevents most infected meat from reaching the market.

▶ The ventral side of a planarian is covered with cilia. This allows the planarian to glide over a mucous path secreted by glands on its ventral surface.

▶ Emphasize that a planarian's digestive system has only one opening through which both food is taken in and wastes are expelled.

▶ Relate the digestive system of a planarian to that in a stinging-cell animal. Ask students if this feature should be considered simple or complex and why.

Guided Practice

Have students write down their answers to the margin question: planarian.

Independent Practice

Study Guide/*Teacher Resource Package*, p. 39. Use the Study Guide worksheet shown at the bottom of this page for independent practice.

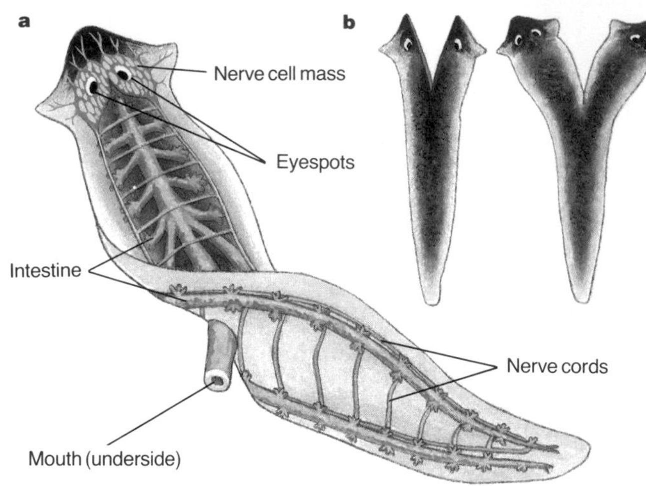

Figure 7-10 A planarian (a) can reproduce asexually by regrowing new parts (b). How many parents are involved in this type of reproduction? one

Tapeworms in humans are not as common in the United States as in some other countries. In the United States, human wastes are treated with chemicals at sewage treatment plants. Meat is inspected for cysts by government inspectors. However, completely cooking meat is the best way to keep from getting tapeworms.

Although most flatworms are parasites, some aren't. Those that are not parasites are said to be free-living. Some of these flatworms live in water, but a few are found on land. A **planarian** (pluh NAIR ee un) is a common freshwater flatworm that is not a parasite. It is less than one centimeter long.

What flatworm has a mouth?

A planarian has the features shown in Figure 7-10a.

1. It has a flat body with muscles.
2. It has a triangular head with two spots that look like eyes. The eyespots have nerve cells that detect light.
3. It has two nerve cords. It also has two masses of nerve cells near the head. These structures allow the planarian to respond to the environment.
4. The mouth is near the middle of the body on the underside.
5. Planarians have an intestine that breaks down food. Undigested food leaves the intestine through the mouth.
6. Each animal has both male and female reproductive organs and produces both sperm and eggs. It reproduces sexually by exchanging sperm with another planarian. Planarians also reproduce asexually by pinching into two parts. Each part then forms a new animal, Figure 7-10b.

STUDY GUIDE 39

STUDY GUIDE — CHAPTER 7

Name ______ Date ______ Class ______

WORMS

In your textbook, read about flatworms in Section 7:3.

1. Study the steps of the pig tapeworm life cycle in Figure 7-9 of your textbook. Then, answer the following questions.
   a. What two host animals are part of the tapeworm's life cycle? pig and human
   b. Which animal will contain cysts of the worm? pig
   c. In which animal will the worm reproduce? human
   d. In which animal will the worm's body sections break off and leave the host's body in its solid waste? human
   e. In which animal will young worms travel to the muscles and burrow into them? pig
   f. In which animal will worms attach to the inside of the intestines? human
2. Why aren't tapeworms common in the United States? These worms aren't common because in the United States human wastes are treated with chemicals at sewage plants, and meats are inspected for cysts.
3. On the blanks below, label the parts of this planarian and briefly describe the job each part does.

   part eyespots — job detect light
   part intestine — job breaks down food
   part nerve cords
   part nerve cell mass — job respond to environment
   part mouth — job takes in and gets rid of undigested food from the body
4. How do planarians differ from most other flatworms? Most flatworms are parasites. Planarians are free-living.

Roundworms

Roundworms are worms that have long bodies with pointed ends. They have three layers of cells. Many of these worms are small and can't be seen without a microscope. Many are parasites. Their hosts are people, dogs, cats, or even plants.

Some roundworms live in great numbers in the soil. A square meter of soil may contain four million worms! These worms are not animal parasites, but some of them may be plant parasites. Most roundworms, however, are free-living.

Hookworms are found in soil in the southeastern part of the United States. A **hookworm** is a roundworm that is a parasite of humans. Hookworms enter the body through the skin of the feet. Once inside, they move to the intestine. There they attach themselves and feed on the host's blood.

Let's take a closer look at a roundworm. Look at Figure 7-11 as you read about the features of this group.

1. These worms have long, rounded bodies. Each end is pointed. A set of muscles runs the length of the body. When roundworms move, they whip about.
2. One end of a roundworm has a mouth. The other end has an anus (AY nus). An **anus** is an opening through which undigested food leaves the body.
3. A roundworm has a tube within its body that connects the mouth and the anus. The tube is an intestine that digests food. Food and wastes do not mix as they do in the stinging-cell animals and flatworms, which have only one opening.
4. Males and females are separate animals.

Mini Lab

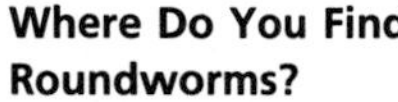

Where Do You Find Roundworms?

Observe: Cover a funnel with wire mesh. Stand it in a jar of alcohol. Place moist soil on the mesh. What do you see in the alcohol when the soil begins to dry out? Why? *For more help, refer to the* ***Skill Handbook****, pages 704-705.*

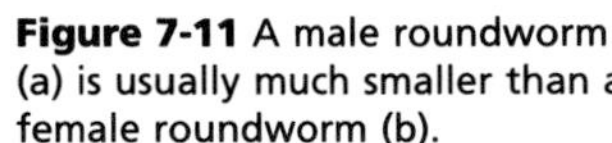

Figure 7-11 A male roundworm (a) is usually much smaller than a female roundworm (b).

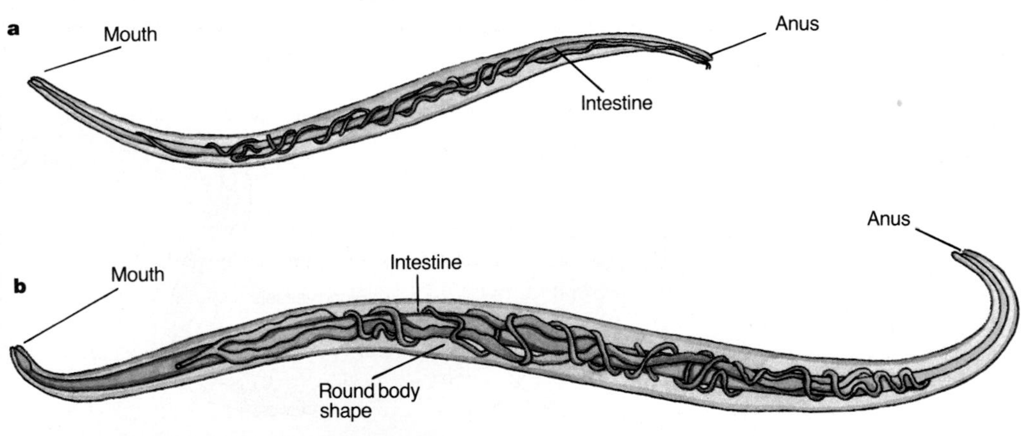

TEACH

Concept Development

▶ Mention that there are over 10 000 species of roundworms.

▶ Mention that hookworms and other roundworms can rupture the intestinal wall causing hemorrhages, infections, and allergic reactions. Sometimes larger worms can burrow into the host causing peritonitis and blocking ducts within the body.

Mini Lab

Any type of alcohol may be used. A light over the soil will speed up the process of soil drying. Students may need a stereoscope or hand lens to examine the alcohol for roundworms.

Independent Practice

Study Guide/*Teacher Resource Package,* p. 40. Use the Study Guide worksheet shown at the bottom of this page for independent practice.

STUDY GUIDE 40

STUDY GUIDE — *CHAPTER 7*

Name ______ Date ______ Class ______

WORMS

In your textbook read about roundworms in Section 7:3.

5. On the blanks provided, label the parts of this roundworm.

mouth; intestine; anus; reproductive organs; round body

In your textbook, read about segmented worms in Section 7:3.

6. Name a segmented worm that is a parasite. leech
7. Name a segmented worm that is not a parasite. earthworm
8. On the blanks below, label the parts of this earthworm and briefly describe the job each part does.

part intestine; job grinds and digests food
part blood vessel; job carries blood to all parts of the body
part mouth; job takes in food
parts hearts; job pump blood
part anus; job gets rid of undigested waste
part bristles; job help animal move

OPTIONS

ACTIVITY/Challenge

Have students prepare wet mounts of the roundworm *Turbatrix aceti* (vinegar eel) to observe roundworm movement. These may be purchased from a biological supply house.

TEACH

Concept Development

▶ Explain that segmentation is internal as well as external.

▶ Explain that a leech can ingest many times its own body weight of blood in one feeding.

▶ Explain that earthworms come near the surface to deposit wastes and to mate, usually at night.

▶ Point out that earthworms have bilateral symmetry.

▶ The bristles are called setae. Birds often have difficulty pulling earthworms out of the ground because the worms' setae dig into the soil.

Check for Understanding

Have students prepare a chart with the headings Tapeworm, Planarian, Hookworm, and Earthworm across the top. Under each heading have them list the phylum name and traits of each.

Reteach

Discuss students' charts from Check for Understanding. Have them fill in any omissions and correct any errors.

a

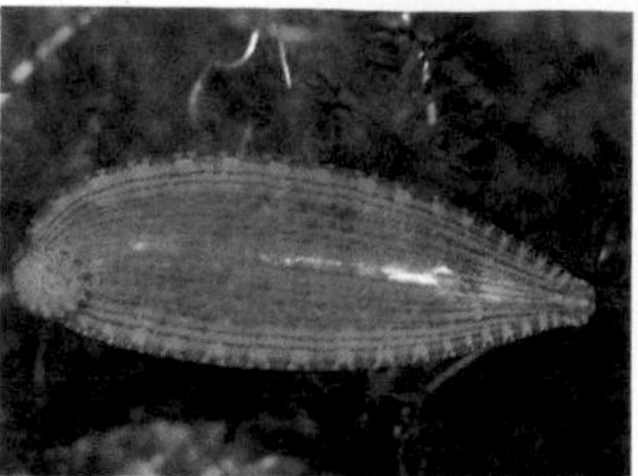

b

Figure 7-12 Earthworms (a) and leeches (b) are segmented worms.

Bio Tip

Health: Leeches are used in medicine to drain excess blood from reattached body parts following surgery. Leeches produce a chemical that prevents blood from clotting. This chemical is used for treating cardiovascular disorders.

Segmented Worms

The **segmented worms** are worms with bodies divided into sections called segments. These worms have three cell layers. They are the most complex of all the worms.

You may be familiar with some of the segmented worms. They live almost everywhere—in fresh water, salt water, and on land. Examples are shown in Figure 7-12. The leech is a segmented worm that is a parasite. Most leeches live in streams and lakes. They attach to the skin of host animals and suck their blood.

The common earthworm is a segmented worm. Figure 7-13 shows some of the earthworm's features. Look at this figure as you read about the earthworm's traits.

1. The body wall has layers of muscles. Each segment has bristles that help the earthworm move by gripping the soil.
2. Earthworms have a mouth and an anus.
3. The intestine is a tube. It has parts for holding food, grinding food, and digesting food.
4. Most segments have organs to get rid of wastes.
5. Two blood vessels run along the body. They meet to form five pairs of simple hearts. The hearts pump blood through the body, carrying oxygen and food to all cells.

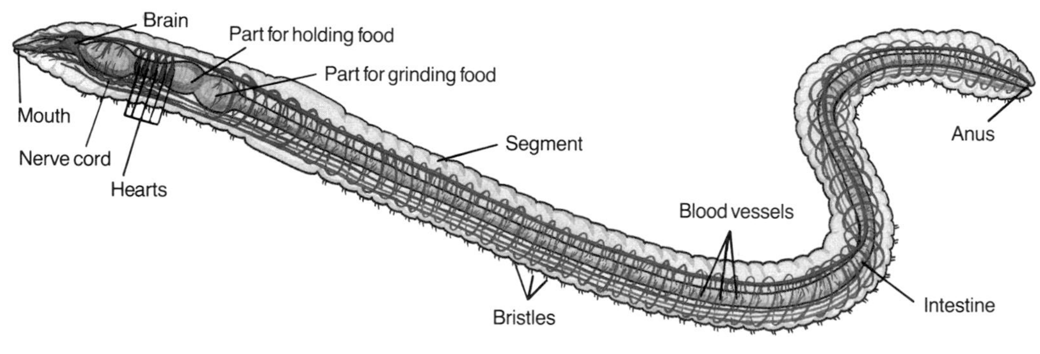

Figure 7-13 Segmented worms, such as earthworms, have a complex structure.

OPTIONS

Science Background

Most of an earthworm's 100 to 150 segments are identical, except for the first and last. A swelling called the clitellum is found between segments 35 and 37. It is important in reproduction.

Enrichment/*Teacher Resource Package*, p. 7. Use the Enrichment worksheet shown here to teach students about leeches.

ENRICHMENT 7

ENRICHMENT CHAPTER 7

Name ______ Date ______ Class ______

Use after Section 7:3.

LEECHES

Read the information below about leeches. Then, answer the questions that follow.

Imagine having four or five leeches attached to your arms, legs, or face. As the leeches suck your blood, they become fatter and fatter. Leeches are segmented worms related to earthworms. Not so long ago, people used leeches on their bodies in just this way. They thought leeches could cure diseases by removing "bad" blood.

People used leeches for removing blood—or bloodletting—for thousands of years. At first, leeches were believed to remove evil spirits from the body. In the 1800s, doctors also used leeches to treat a variety of illnesses, including gout, whooping cough, and mental illness. Millions of these leeches were used each year. They were in such high demand that people began raising leeches on farms. With time, the medical use of leeches became less popular. Some people had died from the overuse of leeches. By the late 1800s, doctors had learned that microorganisms cause diseases. New methods of treating diseases were also developed at that time. For most of the twentieth century, leeches were not used often for medical purposes.

Today, however, people are finding new uses for leeches. For example, doctors are using leeches in plastic surgery. In one case, a boy's ear was reattached after being bitten off by a dog. Leeches were applied around the ear to help drain excess blood. Without draining the blood, the reattached blood vessels would not heal. Researchers have discovered valuable chemicals in the saliva of the giant Amazon leech. One of these chemicals, called hementin, dissolves blood clots. Researchers think hementin might be useful for dissolving blood clots and preventing heart attacks and strokes in humans.

1. Why were leeches in high demand in the 1800s? **Leeches were used to treat many diseases, such as gout, whooping cough, and mental illness.**
2. Why did leeches become less popular in the late 1800s? **Many people had died from the overuse of leeches, doctors were learning more about the causes of diseases, and new methods of treating diseases were being developed.**
3. How are leeches being used in plastic surgery today? **Leeches are used to drain excess blood near the area of the surgery, thereby allowing reattached blood vessels to heal.**
4. What is hementin, and how might it be useful to humans? **Hementin is a chemical found in the saliva of the giant Amazon leech. Since it dissolves blood clots, it might be useful in treating blood clots and possibly preventing heart attacks and strokes in humans.**

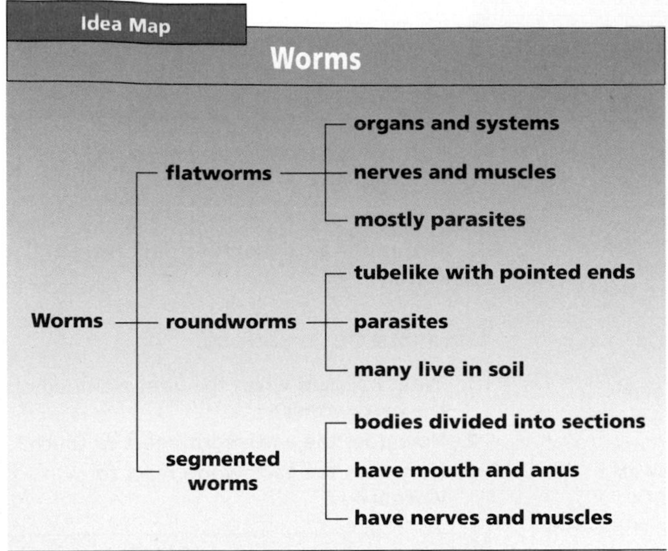

Study Tip: Use this idea map as a study guide to worms. The traits of each worm group are shown.

6. Nerves run the length of the body. There is a simple brain at the front end.
7. Each earthworm has both male and female sex organs. Earthworms reproduce when two worms exchange sperm. Other segmented worms may have separate sexes.

Earthworms take in soil through their mouths. Soil contains decayed matter, such as dead leaves, insects, and seeds. These things are food for the earthworm. The soil itself is not food and passes through the animal's intestine. Soil leaves the intestine through the anus. Earthworms move large amounts of soil from place to place by passing it through their bodies. They enrich the soil and loosen it, helping plants grow.

Why do earthworms seem to eat soil?

Check Your Understanding

11. Give two examples of flatworms.
12. In what way are tapeworms harmful?
13. List three traits of roundworms.
14. **Critical Thinking:** How can you prevent hookworms from entering your body?
15. **Biology and Reading:** List two things that earthworms do that are helpful.

RETEACHING 19

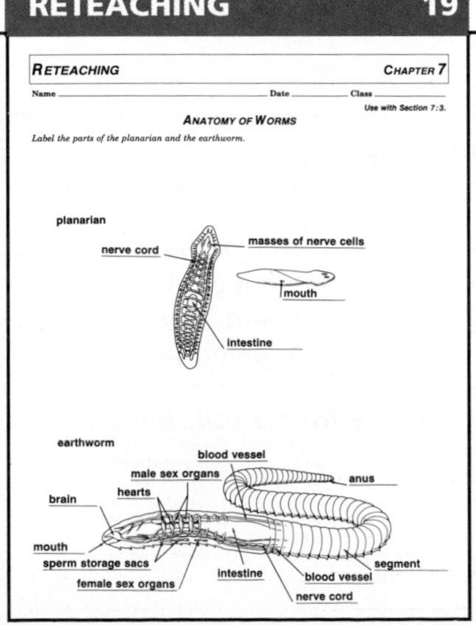
RETEACHING CHAPTER 7

Name ______ Date ______ Class ______

Use with Section 7:3.

ANATOMY OF WORMS

Label the parts of the planarian and the earthworm.

TEACH

Idea Map

Have students use the idea map as a study guide to the major concepts of this section.

Guided Practice

Have students write down their answers to the margin question: They take in soil through the mouth and absorb decayed matter from it.

Check for Understanding

Have students respond to the first three questions in Check Your Understanding.

Reteach

Reteaching/*Teacher Resource Package*, p. 19. Use this worksheet to give students additional practice in understanding the anatomy of worms.

Extension: Assign Critical Thinking, Biology and Reading, or some of the **OPTIONS** available with this lesson.

3 APPLY

ACTIVITY/Challenge

Have students research types of worms that are parasites of humans.

4 CLOSE

Divergent Question

Have students list ways of avoiding parasite infection.

Answers to Check Your Understanding

11. tapeworms and planarians
12. They are parasites and use food of the host animal.
13. long, round bodies; mouth and anus; long digestive tube; separate sexes
14. by wearing shoes outside
15. enrich and loosen soil

Lab 7-2 Earthworms

Overview

In this lab, students examine the external structures of an earthworm and observe how the animal behaves when subjected to stimuli.

Objectives: Upon completion of this lab, students will be able to (1) **describe** structures that appear on the external surface of the animal, (2) **describe** how an earthworm responds to light, touch, and chemicals, and (3) **predict** how its features and behavior aid in its way of life.

Time Allotment: 1 class period

Preparation

▶ Maintain earthworms in a polystyrene container with at least 6-8 cm of soil in the bottom. The soil should be collected at the same site as the earthworms. Keep the soil moist and the container covered. Temperature may range from 5°C to 15°C. Earthworms may be purchased from a biological supply house or purchased from a fish bait shop.

Lab 7-2 worksheet/*Teacher Resource Package*, pp. 27-28.

Teaching the Lab

▶ Stress careful and gentle handling of the animals.

▶ Have students wash their hands when finished with this lab.

Earthworms

Lab 7—2

Problem: What traits does an earthworm have that help it live in soil?

Skills

observe, infer, predict, make and use tables

Materials

live earthworms in a covered container	paper towels
hand lens	beaker of water
shallow pan	vinegar
toothpick	cotton swab
	flashlight

Procedure

1. Copy the data table.
2. Open a container of earthworms and shine the flashlight on the worms. What do the worms do? Record what you see.
3. Wet your hands. Carefully place an earthworm on a moist paper towel in a shallow pan. **CAUTION:** *Do not let the worm dry out.* Keep your hands wet and moisten the worm by sprinkling it with water. Hold the worm gently between your thumb and forefinger. Observe its movements and record them in your table.
4. Rub your fingers gently along the body. Examine the bristles along the earthworm with a hand lens. See the figure for help.
5. **Observe:** With a toothpick, gently touch the earthworm on the front and back ends. Record your observations.
6. **Make and use tables:** Dip a cotton swab in vinegar. Place it in front of the earthworm on the paper towel. Record your observations.
7. Return the earthworm to the covered container.

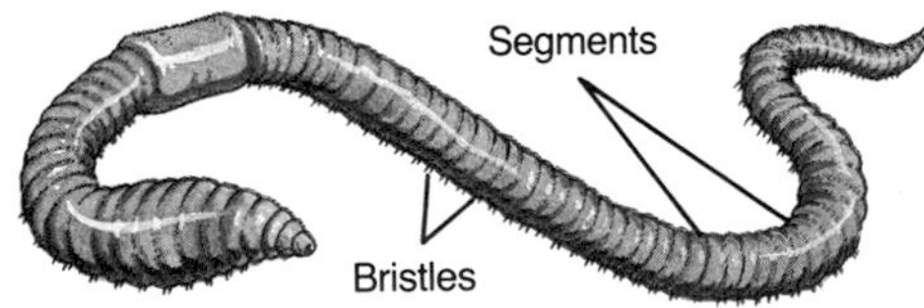

Data and Observations

1. What happens when the light is shined on the earthworms?
2. How does the earthworm react to touch?
3. How does the earthworm react to vinegar?

CONDITION	REACTION
Light	moves away
Holding	tries to free itself
Touch	moves away
Vinegar	moves away

Analyze and Apply

1. **Infer:** How does the earthworm's reaction to light help it to live in the soil?
2. How does the earthworm's reaction to being touched help it to live in the soil?
3. **Predict:** How would you expect an earthworm to react to chemicals like vinegar in the soil?
4. How is the front end of the earthworm helpful for living in soil?
5. How is the long, soft body helpful for living in the soil?
6. How are the bristles useful for living in the soil?
7. **Apply:** How is an earthworm similar to a hookworm?

Extension

Observe a planarian's response to light and touch.

ANSWERS

Data and Observations

1. They move away.
2. It moves away.
3. It moves away.

Analyze and Apply

1. It keeps the worm under the moist soil and away from the light, which has a drying effect.
2. If the worm comes across something in its path, it can turn away.
3. If the worm senses a harmful chemical, it will turn away.
4. It is round and pointed to help the worm move through the soil.
5. It can move with the shape of the soil and move around things easily.
6. They help in movement. They also prevent the worm from being pulled out of the soil.
7. They both live in the soil. Both worms have long bodies.

7:4 Soft-bodied Animals

The soft-bodied animals are more complex than the other invertebrates that you have studied. Soft-bodied animals come in all sizes and live in many different environments. They are placed together in one phylum because of the traits they share.

Objectives

7. **Identify** the major features of soft-bodied animals.
8. **Explain** how soft-bodied animals are classified.

Key Science Words

soft-bodied animal
mantle

Traits of Soft-bodied Animals

Soft-bodied animals are animals with a soft body that is usually protected by a hard shell. Animals in the soft-bodied animal phylum may be familiar to you, no matter where you live. Some live along the ocean on rocks, buried in the sand, or in the water. You may have gathered their shells while walking along a beach, Figure 7-14a. Some of these animals are found around streams and ponds. Others live on land.

Soft-bodied animals have certain traits. The body is covered by a thin, fleshy tissue called a **mantle.** The mantle makes the shell. The shell is the outermost covering. It protects the soft body. Soft-bodied animals have a muscular foot for moving from place to place, Figure 7-14b. Most have a head with a mouth. Many soft-bodied animals have a structure like a tongue covered with teeth inside the mouth. This structure scrapes food from surfaces, such as rocks. A snail has this structure.

What are the traits of soft-bodied animals?

The soft-bodied animals are grouped into classes based on three traits. The three traits are the kind of foot, whether or not a shell is present, and the number of shells.

Figure 7-14 The shells of soft-bodied animals can be found on many beaches (a). Clams use a muscular foot for movement (b).

a

b

7:4 Soft-bodied Animals

PREPARATION

Materials Needed

Make copies of the Transparency Master, Critical Thinking/Problem Solving, Study Guide, Reteaching, and Lab worksheets in the *Teacher Resource Package.*

▶ Obtain earthworms, cotton swabs, vinegar, toothpicks, and flashlight for Lab 7-2.

Key Science Words

soft-bodied animal
mantle

Process Skills

In Lab 7-2, students will observe, predict, and make and use tables.

1 FOCUS

▶ The objectives are listed on the student page. Remind students to preview these objectives as a guide to this numbered section.

ACTIVITY/Brainstorming

Have students name any seafood that they would enjoy eating. List their suggestions on a transparency for the overhead projector. When finished, place a check mark after those foods that are members of the soft-bodied phylum.

Guided Practice

Have students write down their answers to the margin question: soft body, mantle, shell, muscular foot, head with mouth.

TRANSPARENCY 31

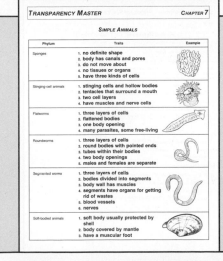

TRANSPARENCY MASTER — CHAPTER 7

SIMPLE ANIMALS

Phylum	Traits	Example
Sponges	1. no definite shape 2. body has canals and pores 3. do not move about 4. no tissues or organs 5. have three kinds of cells	
Stinging-cell animals	1. stinging cells and hollow bodies 2. tentacles that surround a mouth 3. two cell layers 4. have muscles and nerve cells	
Flatworms	1. three layers of cells 2. flattened bodies 3. one body opening 4. many parasites, some free-living	
Roundworms	1. three layers of cells 2. round bodies with pointed ends 3. tubes within their bodies 4. two body openings 5. males and females are separate	
Segmented worms	1. three layers of cells 2. bodies divided into segments 3. body wall has muscles 4. segments have organs for getting rid of wastes 5. blood vessels 6. nerves	
Soft-bodied animals	1. soft body usually protected by shell 2. body covered by mantle 3. have a muscular foot	

OPTIONS

Science Background

The classification for the phylum Mollusca (soft-bodied animals) is as follows: Class Polyplacophora, chitons; Class Scaphopoda, tooth shells; Class Gastropoda, snails and slugs; Class Bivalvia, clams, mussels, oysters; Class Cephalopoda, squid, octopuses.

Transparency Master/*Teacher Resource Package,* p. 31. Use the Transparency Master shown here to reinforce the traits of simple animals.

2 TEACH

MOTIVATION/Audiovisual

Show the video *Biovideo: Introduction to Invertebrates,* Carolina Biological Supply Co.

Concept Development

▶ Soft-bodied animals are commonly called mollusks.

▶ Explain that clams, oysters, and scallops are filter feeders.

▶ Squids reach speeds of about 20 km per hour.

Connection: Language Arts

Have students read the poem "The Chambered Nautilus" by Oliver Wendell Holmes.

Guided Practice

Have students write down their answers to the margin question: snails and slugs; clams, oysters, scallops; octopus, squid, cuttlefish.

Check for Understanding

Have students prepare an outline of Section 7:4. Have them use section titles as the major divisions.

Reteach

Put the headings snails and slugs; clams, oysters, scallops; octopus, squid on the chalkboard. Have students give traits for each.

a

b

Figure 7-15 A snail (a) has a muscular foot. The foot of an octopus (b) is divided into eight arms that surround the head.

What are the three classes of soft-bodied animals?

Classes of Soft-bodied Animals

The first class of soft-bodied animals includes snails and slugs, shown in Figure 7-15a. They live on land and in the water. They glide slowly along by means of a wide, muscular foot. The foot puts down a trail of slime that helps the animal glide. Snails have a single shell and slugs have no shell. Sea and land slugs look like snails without shells. Notice the two pairs of tentacles on the snail's head in Figure 7-15a. They are sense organs. Each of the larger tentacles has an eye that detects light.

The second class of soft-bodied animals includes clams, oysters, and scallops. See Figure 7-14b. Unlike the snails, animals in the second class have two shells that fit together. Many clams spend their lives under water buried in sand or mud. Their foot is shaped like a shovel and is used to burrow in the sand.

How do buried clams get food? Figure 7-16 shows you. These animals usually have two tubes that stick out of the sand into the water. The animal takes in water through one tube. Any food in the water is filtered out by the animal. The water is then forced out through its other tube.

The octopus in Figure 7-15b and squid and cuttlefish belong to the third class of soft-bodied animals. Both squid and cuttlefish have shells inside their bodies. The octopus has no shell. In these animals, the muscular foot is divided into arms, or tentacles, surrounding the head. These animals have very well-developed eyes. They are rapid swimmers and move by shooting a jet of water.

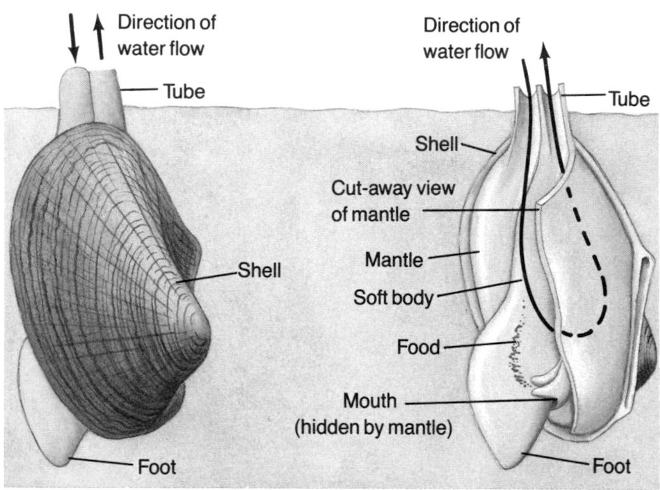

Figure 7-16 Clams filter food out of water. The water is taken into the clam through one tube and forced out through another tube.

OPTIONS

What Are the Parts of the Squid?/*Lab Manual,* pp. 53-56. Use this lab as an extension to studying soft–bodied animals.

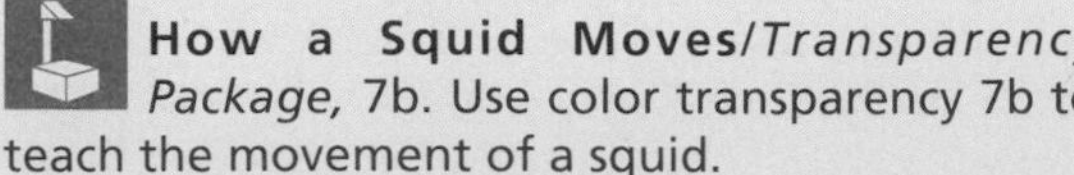

How a Squid Moves/*Transparency Package,* 7b. Use color transparency 7b to teach the movement of a squid.

Critical Thinking/Problem Solving/*Teacher Resource Package,* p. 7. Use the Critical Thinking/Problem Solving worksheet shown here to explain how simple animals can destroy plants.

CRITICAL THINKING 7

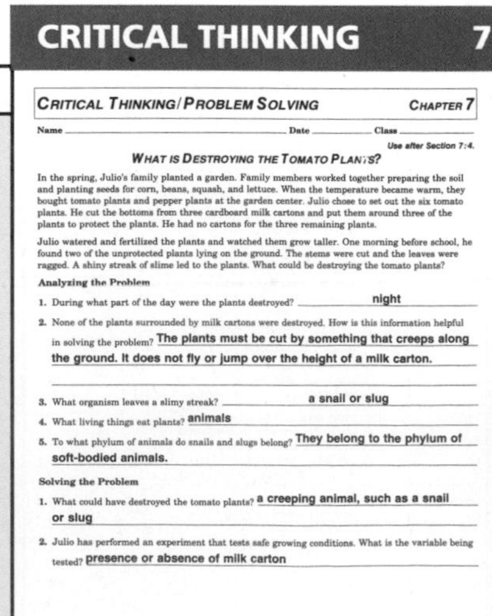

CRITICAL THINKING/PROBLEM SOLVING — CHAPTER 7

Name ______ Date ______ Class ______

Use after Section 7:4.

WHAT IS DESTROYING THE TOMATO PLANTS?

In the spring, Julio's family planted a garden. Family members worked together preparing the soil and planting seeds for corn, beans, squash, and lettuce. When the temperature became warm, they bought tomato plants and pepper plants at the garden center. Julio chose to set out the six tomato plants. He cut the bottoms from three cardboard milk cartons and put them around three of the plants to protect the plants. He had no cartons for the three remaining plants.

Julio watered and fertilized the plants and watched them grow taller. One morning before school, he found two of the unprotected plants lying on the ground. The stems were cut and the leaves were ragged. A shiny streak of slime led to the plants. What could be destroying the tomato plants?

Analyzing the Problem

1. During what part of the day were the plants destroyed? night
2. None of the plants surrounded by milk cartons were destroyed. How is this information helpful in solving the problem? The plants must be cut by something that creeps along the ground. It does not fly or jump over the height of a milk carton.
3. What organism leaves a slimy streak? a snail or slug
4. What living things eat plants? animals
5. To what phylum of animals do snails and slugs belong? They belong to the phylum of soft-bodied animals.

Solving the Problem

1. What could have destroyed the tomato plants? a creeping animal, such as a snail or slug
2. Julio has performed an experiment that tests safe growing conditions. What is the variable being tested? presence or absence of milk carton

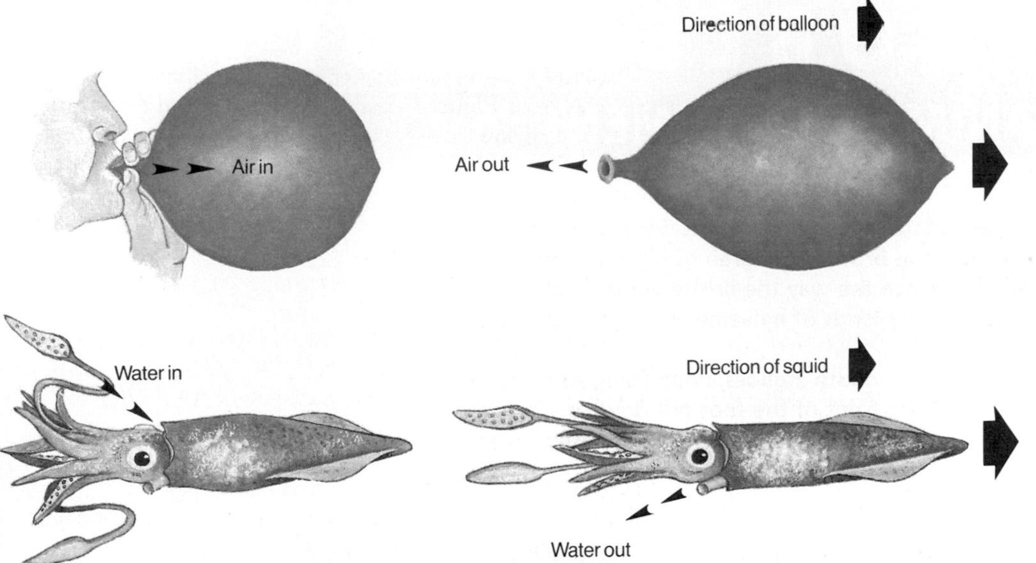

Figure 7-17 Squid move rapidly by shooting a jet of water out of their bodies. Can you think of something else that moves this way? rockets and jet planes

The way a squid moves is shown in Figure 7-17. The movement is similar to that of a balloon. If you let go of a balloon filled with air, it flies in a direction opposite to that of the air coming out of it. The squid also swims in a direction opposite to that of the water coming out of it.

Let's review the features of soft-bodied animals.

1. All are invertebrates. No backbone is present.
2. They have a soft body covered by a mantle.
3. Most have one or two external shells or an internal shell. A few have no shell.
4. Most have a foot by which they move about.

Check Your Understanding

16. What are four traits of soft-bodied animals?
17. How do clams get food?
18. What traits are used to classify soft-bodied animals?
19. **Critical Thinking:** How does the shell of a snail differ from that of a clam? How does the shell of an octopus differ from that of a clam?
20. **Biology and Math:** Giant squid may grow as long as 49 feet. Estimate how many meters long these squid grow.

RETEACHING 20

RETEACHING — CHAPTER 7

Name ______ Date ______ Class ______

Use with Section 7:4.

CLASSES OF SOFT-BODIED ANIMALS

The pictures below show some animals that belong to the phylum of animals with soft bodies.

On the line below each picture, identify the animal shown. Then, use the pictures and your textbook to answer the questions.

octopus — slug — squid

clam — snail — oyster

1. The soft-bodied animals are grouped into three classes. Which of the above animals are grouped together in each class? **snail and slug; squid and octopus; clam and oyster**
2. What traits are used to group the animals into classes? **kind of foot; whether or not a shell is present; kind of shell**
3. What are the sense organs of the snail? **tentacles and the eyes on the tentacles**
4. Which animal has a shell inside its body? **squid**
5. Which animals have no shell? **slug and octopus**
6. Which animals have well-developed eyes? **squid and octopus**
7. Which animal lives buried in the mud? **clam**
8. What makes the shell of the soft-bodied animals? **mantle**
9. How do most soft-bodied animals move? **with a muscular foot**

STUDY GUIDE 41

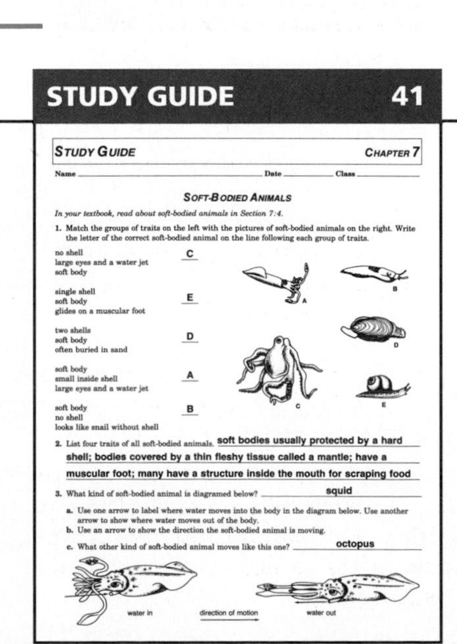

STUDY GUIDE — CHAPTER 7

Name ______ Date ______ Class ______

SOFT-BODIED ANIMALS

In your textbook, read about soft-bodied animals in Section 7:4.

1. Match the groups of traits on the left with the pictures of soft-bodied animals on the right. Write the letter of the correct soft-bodied animal on the line following each group of traits.

no shell, large eyes and a water jet, soft body — **C**

single shell, soft body, glides on a muscular foot — **E**

two shells, soft body, often buried in sand — **D**

soft body, small inside shell, large eyes and a water jet — **A**

soft body, no shell, looks like snail without shell — **B**

2. List four traits of all soft-bodied animals. **soft bodies usually protected by a hard shell; bodies covered by a thin fleshy tissue called a mantle; have a muscular foot; many have a structure inside the mouth for scraping food**
3. What kind of soft-bodied animal is diagramed below? **squid**
   a. Use one arrow to label where water moves into the body in the diagram below. Use another arrow to show where water moves out of the body.
   b. Use an arrow to show the direction the soft-bodied animal is moving.
   c. What other kind of soft-bodied animal moves like this one? **octopus**

water in — direction of motion — water out

TEACH

Independent Practice

Study Guide/*Teacher Resource Package*, p. 41. Use the Study Guide worksheet shown at the bottom of this page for independent practice.

Check for Understanding

Have students respond to the first three questions in Check Your Understanding.

Reteach

Reteaching/*Teacher Resource Package*, p. 20. Use this worksheet to give students additional practice with classes of soft-bodied animals.

Extension: Assign Critical Thinking, Biology and Math, or some of the **OPTIONS** available with this lesson.

3 APPLY

Software

The Animal Kingdom, Part I and II, Queue, Inc.

4 CLOSE

ACTIVITY/Brainstorming

Ask students to explain the importance of soft-bodied animals.

Answers to Check Your Understanding

16. All are invertebrates; have a soft body covered by a mantle; most have one or two shells; most have a foot.
17. It filters food from water.
18. The kind of foot, whether a shell is present, number of shells.
19. (a) A snail's shell is all one part; a clam's shell has two parts. (b) The octopus has no outside shell; the clam has an outside shell with two parts.
20. Accept 14-16 meters.

Animal Movement

Problem-solving Strategies

The following strategies can be used to solve the problem in this feature: construct a table, look for a pattern.

Hints

▶ Certain clues are provided for matching animal with object. For example, setae dig in or grab as do cleats. Sponges do not move nor does a plant. A slimy path would be slippery and so is snow. A Portuguese man-of-war is frequently at the mercy of wind/water currents as is an object floating in the water.

▶ Have students prepare a chart. Ask them to list the following names of animals along the left side: snail, sponge, bristle worm, Portuguese man-of-war. Have them list the following along the top of the chart: Phylum name, Can or cannot move, Muscles present or not, Name of special part used for moving. Have students complete the chart.

▶ Have students describe and list the ways or features that enable those items or objects shown to move. Have them match the items with the animals.

PROBLEM SOLVING

ANIMAL MOVEMENT

Animals move in different ways. Segmented worms have bristles that grab or dig into the soil. Can you match the way the bristle worm in photo 1 moves to one of the kinds of movement shown in photo a, b, c, or d?

The snail in photo 2 glides along using its muscular foot. Glands at the front of the foot put down a slippery path just ahead of the snail. In which photo does movement match the snail's movement?

The Portuguese man-of-war in photo 3 exists as a group of stinging-cell animals arranged around a gas-filled float. The group floats along with the water currents. In which photo is movement similar to the movement of the Portuguese man-of-war?

Unlike most animals, the sponge does not move. It lives attached to an object under the water. The sponge filters small living things out of the water and uses them for food. This means of getting food allows the sponge to live and grow even though it can't move. Can you match the sponge's way of life with one of the photos?

153

Solving the Problem

Photo 1—photo c
Photo 2—photo d
Photo 3—photo a
Photo 4—photo b

Discussing the Problem

▶ This activity involves the technique of using an analogy. Discuss what an analogy is with your students before they begin the activity.

▶ Provide an example such as the commercially available water jet for skimming along the water and the water jet used by a squid.

▶ Provide pictures of other animals such as hydra, sea anemone, clam, and slug and have students compare the methods of movements with the pictures in this Problem Solving.

▶ Have students name body parts used for movement in different animals that they can name.

CHAPTER 7 REVIEW

Summary

Summary statements can be used by students to review the major concepts of the chapter.

Key Science Words

All boldfaced terms from the chapter are listed.

Testing Yourself

Using Words

1. cyst
2. flatworm
3. sponge
4. symmetry
5. tentacle
6. mantle
7. segmented worm
8. tapeworm
9. invertebrate
10. planarian

Finding Main Ideas

11. p. 136; The phylum with the largest number of animal types is the jointed-leg phylum.
12. p. 144; Tapeworms can be avoided by completely cooking meat.
13. p. 144 ; A planarian has eyespots made of nerve cells to detect light.
14. pp. 139-140; Hydra and sea anemones capture their food with tentacles that have stinging cells.
15. p. 138; Sponges have spaces between the many fibers that can fill with water.
16. p. 145; An anus is an opening through which undigested food can pass.
17. p. 151; Water pushed out of the squid moves the squid in a direction opposite to the direction of the water.
18. p. 145; A hookworm enters the body through the skin of the feet.
19. p. 150; Clams have two tubes. They take in water through one tube, filter the food from the water, and then force the water out through the other tube.
20. p. 147; Earthworms eat decayed matter in soil.

Chapter 7 Review

Summary

7:1 Animal Classification

1. Animals can't make their own food. They can move about, are multicellular, and usually have cells organized into tissues, organs, and organ systems.
2. Animals are divided into nine major phyla based on traits they have in common.

7:2 Sponges and Stinging-cell Animals

3. Sponges are invertebrates that live attached to a surface in water.
4. Stinging-cell animals have stinging cells and hollow bodies with one opening.

7:3 Worms

5. Worms are classified into three major phyla—flatworms, roundworms, and segmented worms.
6. Flatworms have flattened bodies. Roundworms have rounded bodies. Segmented worms have segmented bodies.

7:4 Soft-bodied Animals

7. Soft-bodied animals are invertebrates that have a soft body covered by a mantle. They have one, two, or no shells and usually have a foot for movement.
8. Soft-bodied animals are grouped into classes by the kind of foot, whether or not a shell is present, and the number of shells.

Key Science Words

anus (p. 145)
cyst (p. 143)
flatworm (p. 142)
hookworm (p. 145)
invertebrate (p. 134)
mantle (p. 149)
planarian (p. 144)
pore (p. 137)
roundworm (p. 145)
segmented worm (p. 146)
soft-bodied animal (p. 149)
sponge (p. 137)
stinging-cell animal (p. 139)
symmetry (p. 134)
tapeworm (p. 142)
tentacle (p. 139)
vertebrate (p. 134)

Testing Yourself

Using Words

Choose the word from the list of Key Science Words that best fits the definition.

1. young tapeworm with protective covering
2. the simplest worm
3. simplest animal
4. the arrangement of body parts
5. armlike part that surrounds a stinging-cell animal's mouth
6. thin, fleshy tissue that makes a shell
7. earthworm phylum
8. flatworm that lives on the digested food of another animal

154

Using Main Ideas

21. Sponges do not move about, live attached, and have a body with a series of pores or canals.
22. Animals are consumers, can move about, and are multicellular.
23. They cause painful stings.
24. In radial symmetry, body parts are arranged in a circle around a central point. In bilateral symmetry, the body can be divided lengthwise into two equal halves.
25. They enrich the soil and loosen it.
26. Leeches belong to the segmented worm phylum.
27. They attach to the skin of animals and suck blood.
28. Soft-bodied animals are grouped by the kind of foot, whether or not a shell is present, and the number of shells.

Review

Testing Yourself *continued*

9. animal without a backbone
10. flatworm that is not a parasite

Finding Main Ideas

List the page number where each main idea below is found. Then, explain each main idea.

11. the phylum that has the largest number of animal types
12. how to avoid getting a tapeworm
13. what a planarian uses to detect light
14. how animals such as the hydra and sea anemone capture their food
15. why sponges hold water easily
16. what an anus is
17. how a squid moves
18. how a hookworm enters the body
19. how clams buried in the sand get their food
20. what an earthworm eats

Using Main Ideas

Answer the questions by referring to the page number after each question.

21. How do you determine if a living thing belongs to the sponge phylum? (p. 135)
22. What features make animals different from other living things? (p. 134)
23. How are some stinging-cell animals harmful to humans? (p. 140)
24. How does radial symmetry differ from bilateral symmetry? (p. 134)
25. Why are earthworms important to farmers? (p. 147)
26. In which phylum are leeches found? (p. 146)
27. Why are leeches considered to be parasites? (p. 146)
28. What are the three traits used to group soft-bodied animals? (p. 149)

Skill Review 

For more help, refer to the Skill Handbook, pages 704-719.

1. **Observe:** Use a hand lens to observe a natural sponge and a sponge made by humans. Predict which one will hold more water.
2. **Infer:** What can you infer about the fact that a tapeworm has no mouth?
3. **Interpret diagrams:** Look at Figure 7-9. Describe how a human might get tapeworms from a pig.
4. **Make and use tables:** Make a table that compares the traits of flatworms, roundworms, and segmented worms.

Finding Out More

Critical Thinking

1. What advantage does a hydra have over a sponge in getting food?
2. Why is a tapeworm able to live without a digestive system?

Applications

1. Make a poster to illustrate and describe the life cycle of the dog heartworm. List the symptoms of a heartworm infection.
2. Write a report on how pearls are made by oysters. Explain the difference between natural pearls and cultured pearls.

Skill Review

1. A natural sponge will hold more water because it has more holes.
2. It must absorb its food through the body wall.
3. If they eat the meat of the pig uncooked or undercooked.
4. Have students use the headings Flatworms, Roundworms, and Segmented Worms. Have them list the traits under each heading.

Finding Out More

Critical Thinking

1. The hydra can catch food with its stinging cells and tentacles and bring the food to it. A sponge must rely on the water current to bring it food. Hydra can digest larger food items than sponges.
2. It lives in the digestive system of its host and absorbs food that has already been digested.

Applications

1. The larvae of dog heartworms are transmitted to dogs by mosquitoes. The worms develop in the dog's muscles and travel through the veins to the heart. The female reproduces in the heart and causes heart damage. Symptoms include listlessness and heart rhythm abnormalities.
2. Pearls are made when an irritant, such as a grain of sand, gets into the mantle area of an oyster. The mantle secretes the pearl substance around the irritant. For a cultured pearl, the irritant is placed in the oyster; for a natural pearl, the irritant gets into the oyster naturally.

 **Chapter Review**/*Teacher Resource Package*, pp. 33-34.

 **Chapter Test**/*Teacher Resource Package*, pp. 35-37.

Chapter Test/*Computer Test Bank*

Complex Animals

PLANNING GUIDE

CONTENT	TEXT FEATURES	TEACHER RESOURCE PACKAGE	OTHER COMPONENTS
(1 1/2 days) 8:1 Complex Invertebrates Jointed-leg Animals Spiny-skin Animals	Mini Lab: *How Can You Catch a Spider Web?* p. 160 Lab 8-1: *Crayfish,* p. 162 Idea Map, p. 164 Check Your Understanding, p. 164	Reteaching: *Complex Invertebrates,* p. 21 Skill: *Observe,* p. 8 Focus: *Body Coverings,* p. 15 Study Guide: *Invertebrates,* p. 43 Lab 8-1: *Crayfish,* pp. 29-30	**Laboratory Manual:** *What Are the Traits of Certain Jointed-leg Animals?* p. 59 **Laboratory Manual:** *What Are the Parts of a Starfish?* p. 67 Color Transparency 8: *Traits of Jointed-leg Animals*
(2 1/2 days) 8:2 Vertevbrates Chordates Characteristics of fish Jawless Fish Cartilage Fish Bony Fish Amphibians Reptiles Birds Mammals	Skill Check: *Understand Science Words,* p. 169 Skill Check: *Infer,* p. 170 Mini Lab: *How Do You Make a Bird Feeder?* p. 171 Lab 8-2: *Feathers,* p. 172 Science and Society: *Are Animal Experiments Needed?* p. 175 Check Your Understanding, p. 174	Application: *Beak Adaptations,* p. 8 Enrichment: *Orders of Mammals,* p. 8 Reteaching: *Vertebrates,* p. 22 Critical Thinking/Problem Solving: *What Can a Scientific Illustration Tell You?* p. 8 Transparency Master: *Chordate Classes,* p. 37 Study Guide: *Vertebrates,* pp. 44-47 Study Guide: *Vocabulary,* p. 48	**Laboratory Manual:** *How Do Fish Classes Compare?* p. 63
Chapter Review	Summary Key Science Words Testing Yourself Finding Main Ideas Using Main Ideas Skill Review	Chapter Review, pp. 38-39 Chapter Test, pp. 40-42 Unit Test, pp. 43-44	**Test Bank**

MATERIALS NEEDED

LAB 8-1, p. 162	LAB 8-2, p. 172	MARGIN FEATURES
small aquarium with crayfish	hand lens metric ruler scissors wing or tail feather down feather	Skill Check, p. 169 dictionary Mini Lab, p. 160 black paper spider web with dew flour Mini Lab, p. 171 wood nails bottle caps hammer peanut butter bird seed wire or string

OBJECTIVES

SECTION	OBJECTIVE	OBJECTIVES CORRELATION: CHECK YOUR UNDERSTANDING	CHAPTER REVIEW	TRP CHAPTER REVIEW	TRP CHAPTER TEST
8:1	1. **Identify** the major traits of jointed-leg animals.	1	11, 18, 30	1, 2, 11, 14, 15, 17, 33, 38	3, 5, 6, 15, 25
	2. **Compare** insects with other jointed-leg animals.	2, 4	17, 25, 33	6, 9	1, 2, 4, 7, 31, 34, 35, 36, 37, 38, 39, 40, 41, 42, 43, 44
	3. **Describe** the traits of spiny-skin animals.	3	12, 13, 27	7, 16, 18	19, 28
8:2	4. **Compare** the traits of jaw-less fish, cartilage fish, and bony fish.	6	3, 6, 15, 19, 22, 31	10, 23, 24, 26, 31, 36, 37	8, 16, 17, 24, 29, 33, 45, 46, 47, 48, 49, 50, 51, 52, 53, 54
	5. **Describe** the major traits of amphibians, reptiles, and birds.	7	1, 4, 8, 10, 14, 16, 20, 21, 24, 26, 32	5, 12, 20, 21, 22, 27, 28, 29, 32, 34	9, 10, 11, 12, 14, 18, 20, 26, 30, 32
	6. **Identify** the characteristics of mammals.	8	2, 5, 9, 23, 26, 29	3, 4, 8, 12, 13, 19, 25, 30, 35	13, 21, 23, 25, 27

Complex Animals

CHAPTER OVERVIEW

Key Concepts

This chapter surveys the last three animal phyla. Students will learn that chordates are the most complex of animals. They also will learn which features are characteristic of chordates. Two of the phyla to be studied are invertebrates (jointed-leg animals and spiny-skin animals). Chordates are the only phylum studied that are classified as vertebrates.

Key Science Words

amphibian
antennae
appendage
bony fish
cartilage
cartilage fish
chordate
cold-blooded
compound eye
endoskeleton
exoskeleton
gill
hibernation
jawless fish
jointed-leg animal
mammal
mammary gland
molting
reptile
spiny-skin animal
tube feet
warm-blooded

Skill Development

In Lab 8-1, students will **make and use tables, observe,** and **infer** about the traits of jointed-leg animals. In Lab 8-2, they will **interpret data, observe,** and **infer** in relation to the structure of feathers. In the Skill Check on page 169, students will **understand** the **science word** *amphibian.* In the Skill Check on page 170, they will **infer** why reptiles lay fewer eggs than amphibians or fish. In the Mini Lab on page 160, students will **observe** a spider web. On page 171, they will **observe** birds at a bird feeder.

CHAPTER PREVIEW

Chapter Content

Review this outline for Chapter 8 before you read the chapter.

Skills in this Chapter

The skills that you will use in this chapter are listed below.

- In **Lab 8-1,** you will make and use tables, observe, and infer. In **Lab 8-2,** you will interpret data, observe, and infer.
- In the **Skill Checks,** you will understand science words and infer.
- In the **Mini Labs,** you will observe.

156

Bridging

Chapter 7 introduced students to the invertebrate phyla. Chapter 8 continues with this theme. Two remaining invertebrate phyla are covered, and then vertebrates are introduced.

Chapter **8**

Complex Animals

The photograph on the left shows one of the largest animals alive today. How can the elephant grow so big? Now look at the smaller photograph on this page. It is a daphnia, or water flea, magnified many times. Daphnia are found in lakes and ponds. Even though a daphnia is only 1 mm long, it is still a very complex animal. Looking into its transparent body, you can see that it is made up of many parts.

How are the daphnia and the elephant alike? In this chapter you will see what these two animals have in common, and how they differ. You will learn the traits of the more complex animals and how they are grouped.

Try This!

What does a fish scale look like? Place a dried fish scale on dark paper. Use a hand lens to count the wide, lighter bands. What do the bands represent?

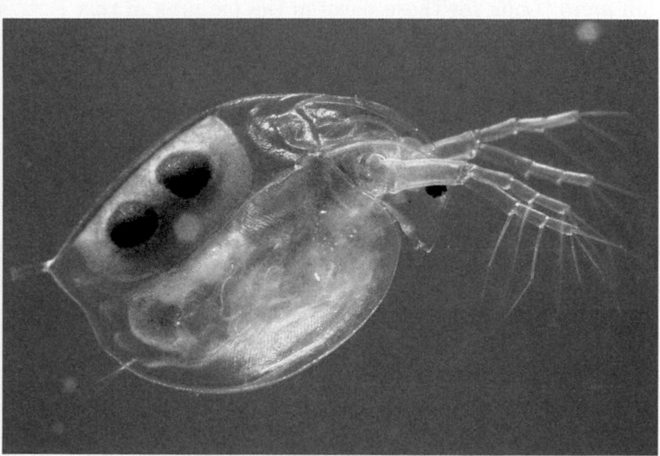

Daphnia

GETTING STARTED

Using the Photos

Elephants have internal skeletons, a trait that allows them to attain massive size. Daphnia have external skeletons, which limits their size. Daphnia have sense organs, digestive systems, and reproductive systems. So do elephants. However, the most significant trait that separates the two is the presence of a backbone in elephants and the absence of one in Daphnia.

MOTIVATION/Try This!

What does a fish scale look like? Obtain fish scales from preserved fish, or by purchasing frozen fish from your local supermarket. Ask students to **observe** and try to determine what they represent. Bands represent rings of growth.

Chapter Preview

Have students study the chapter outline before they begin to read the chapter. They should note the overall organization of the chapter, that the first section still deals with two invertebrate phyla. Next, vertebrates are discussed with only one phylum serving as an example of this group. They should note, however, that the Chordate phylum is divided into seven different classes.

Misconception

There are many misconceptions about animals. Many people think that snakes are slimy when they are really covered with scales and feel cool and dry to the touch. Many beliveve that bats are blind. All bats can see and a few have better vision than people. Most bats, however, don't have an exceptionally keen sense of sight. They rely on their ability to echolocate to navigate. Most people believe that camels store water in their humps. A camel's hump contains fat as an energy reserve that helps it survive in the desert when food and water supplies are low.

8:1 Invertebrates

PREPARATION

Materials Needed

Make copies of the Focus, Skill, Study Guide, Reteaching, and Lab worksheets in the *Teacher Resource Package*.

▶ Make sure that living crayfish have been ordered for Lab 8-1 and that containers are available.

▶ Locate webs and obtain black paper and flour for the Mini Lab.

▶ Obtain 35-mm slides of representative arthropods.

Key Science Words

jointed-leg animal
appendage
exoskeleton
molting
antennae
compound eye
spiny-skin animal
tube feet

Process Skills

In the Mini Lab, students will observe. In Lab 8-1, students will make and use tables, observe, and infer.

1 FOCUS

▶ The objectives are listed on the student page. Remind students to preview these objectives as a guide to this numbered section.

ACTIVITY/Brainstorming

Ask students to list the advantages and disadvantages of a suit of armor. Have them draw parallels to animals having a skeleton on the outside of their body (armor).

Focus/*Teacher Resource Package*, p. 15. Use the Focus transparency shown at the bottom of this page as an introduction to complex animals.

Guided Practice

Have students write down their answers to the margin question: They allow quick movement.

Objectives

1. **Identify** the major traits of jointed-leg animals.
2. **Compare** insects with other jointed-leg animals.
3. **Describe** the traits of spiny-skin animals.

Key Science Words

jointed-leg animal
appendage
exoskeleton
molting
antennae
compound eye
spiny-skin animal
tube feet

8:1 Complex Invertebrates

The animals in the two invertebrate phyla in this chapter are more complex than the animals you studied in Chapter 7. One phylum, containing insects and spiders, is familiar to everyone. Insects are found almost everywhere. It is hard to think of life without insects.

Jointed-leg Animals

Have you ever watched an army of ants moving food back to its nest? Hundreds of these animals work together to carry food that is much larger than they are. Ants crawl along in single file, following a trail that they marked on the way to the food. Back in the nest, hungry ants wait for the hunters to return. Ants are amazing animals!

What is an advantage to jointed appendages?

Ants are jointed-leg animals. A **jointed-leg animal** is an invertebrate with an outside skeleton, bilateral symmetry, and jointed appendages (uh PEN dihj uz). An **appendage** is a structure that grows out of an animal's body. Jointed appendages bend to allow quick movement. Legs, antennae (an TEN ee), and wings are all appendages.

The phylum of jointed-leg animals includes insects, spiders, and crayfish. It has more animal types than any other animal phylum. The graph on page 136 shows that over 80 percent of the known animal types on Earth are jointed-leg animals.

Jointed-leg animals have a segmented body. In many of these animals, the segments are fused into three parts—the head, the thorax (THOR aks), and the abdomen (AB duh mun). Look for these parts in the pictures in this section.

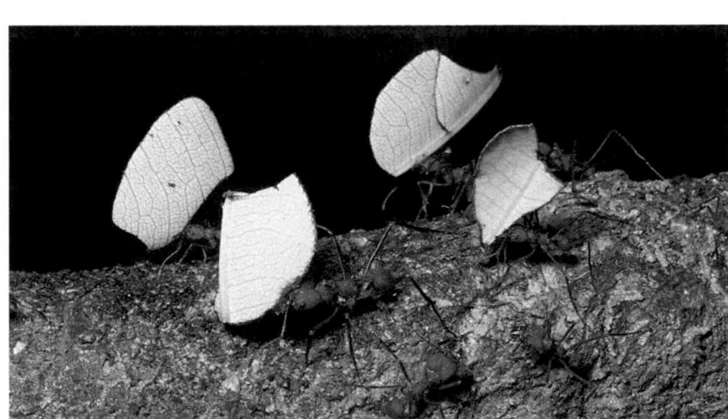

Figure 8-1 Ants work together to carry food back to the nest.

OPTIONS

Science Background

The scientific name for the jointed-leg phylum is Arthropoda. There are six classes within this phylum. They include: horseshoe crabs; spiders, mites, and scorpions; crayfish, barnacles, and shrimp; insects such as ants, bees, and moths; centipedes; millipedes. The spiny-skin animals belong to the phylum Echinodermata. Classes in this phylum include: sea stars (starfish); sea urchins; sea cucumbers; feather stars.

FOCUS 15

FOCUS CHAPTER 8

Name ______ Date ______ Class ______

BODY COVERINGS

Notice that all these animals have different kinds of body coverings. How do you think each kind of body covering helps the animal?

Jointed-leg animals have an exoskeleton. An **exoskeleton** (EK soh skel uht uhn) is a skeleton on the outside of the body. It is made of a hard, waterproof, nonliving substance. It protects the body from drying and injury, and provides a place for muscles to attach.

How does an animal with an exoskeleton grow? The animal must shed its exoskeleton from time to time. Shedding the exoskeleton is called **molting.** After the old skeleton is shed, the body is quite soft. The animal swells by taking in extra water or air while the new skeleton hardens. This swelling gives the animal growing room inside the new skeleton. The animal is not very well protected from its enemies, so it stays hidden until its skeleton hardens.

There are five classes of jointed-leg animals. Crayfish, shrimp, lobsters, crabs, water fleas, and pill bugs are in one class, Figure 8-2. Crayfish and water fleas are found in fresh water. Pill bugs live in damp places on land. The rest of these animals live in the ocean.

Figure 8-3 shows the traits of animals in the first class. Animals in this class have mouthparts that hold, cut, and crush food. They have two pairs of antennae. **Antennae** are appendages of the head that are used for sensing smell and touch. These animals also have compound eyes for seeing. **Compound eyes** are eyes with many lenses. In contrast, you have simple eyes. They each have only one lens.

Most animals in this class have only two body sections. The head and the thorax are fused to make up one section. The abdomen is the second section. These animals usually have five pairs of legs for walking. A clawlike pair of legs at the head grabs and holds food.

The animals in this class are food for many fish and whales. Humans also eat lobsters, shrimp, and crabs.

a

b

Figure 8-2 Crabs (a) and pill bugs (b) belong to the first class of jointed-leg animals.

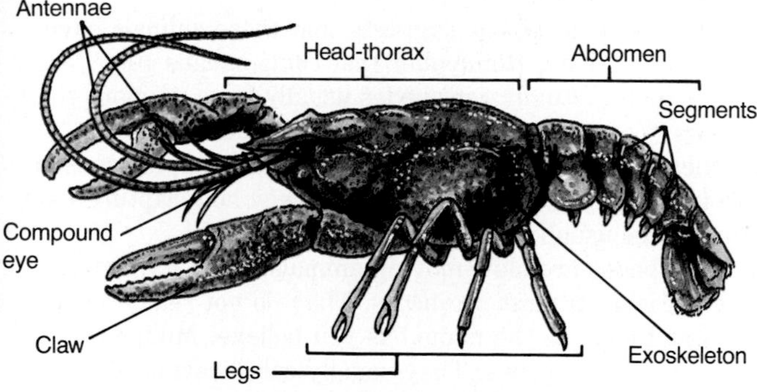

Figure 8-3 Traits of a crayfish

2 TEACH

MOTIVATION/Audiovisual

Show students 35 mm slides of some representative arthropods (any insect, crayfish or shrimp, spider, millipede, centipede). Ask them to list: (a) traits that are shared or are similar in these animals. (b) traits that are different in these animals.

Concept Development

▶ The arthropods are the only invertebrate phylum with members adapted to life in air, land, soil, fresh water, or salt water.

▶ Explain that the jointed-leg animals are the first animals studied so far that have appendages. The mollusk foot is not a true appendage.

▶ The heavy exoskeleton is a greater problem for land animals than it is for those living in water. The buoyancy of the water helps support the exoskeleton of animals that live in water.

▶ Point out that jointed-leg animals also have an open circulatory system, dorsal heart, and ventral nerve cord, and most have a head, thorax, and abdomen.

▶ Point out that most jointed-leg animals undergo four to seven molts before reaching full adult size.

Bridging

Ask students how the body segments of a jointed-leg animal differ from segments in a segmented worm and flatworm.

SKILL 8

SKILL: OBSERVE — CHAPTER 8

Name ______ Date ______ Class ______

For more help, refer to the Skill Handbook, pages 704-705. *Use after Section 8:1.*

THREE JOINTED-LEG ANIMALS

Scientists make observations and keep careful records of what they observe. Develop your observation skills. Examine the jointed-leg animals in the pictures below.

Record your observations in the table. Use the observations to decide to which class of jointed-leg animals each of the organisms belongs. Then answer the questions.

A B C

Trait	Animal A	Animal B	Animal C
Number of body sections	2	2	3
Number of antennae	2 pairs	0	1 pair
Number of legs	5 pairs	4 pairs	3 pairs
Number of eyes visible	2	0	2
Number of wings	0	0	2 pairs

1. What traits do all three animals have? All have appendages and body sections.
2. How do the animals differ from one another? They differ in the number of body sections, number of legs, number of eyes, and presence of wings.
3. Name another animal found in the same class as each animal shown.
   Animal A lobster Animal B spider
   Animal C fly Examples may vary.
4. Which of your observations made it possible for you to decide the class of each organism? number of body sections, number of legs

OPTIONS

Traits of Jointed-leg Animals/*Transparency Package,* number 8. Use color transparency number 8 as you teach about jointed-leg animals.

Skill/*Teacher Resource Package,* p. 8. Use the Skill worksheet shown here to give students practice with traits of jointed-leg animals.

TEACH

Concept Development

▶ Point out that the venom of a scorpion is a neurotoxin that causes paralysis of respiratory and cardiac muscles.

▶ Point out that most spiders are beneficial because they feed on insect pests.

▶ Point out that even though all centipedes are predators and have poison glands, their bite is not lethal. The poison of tropical species with a length of 30 centimeters is not terribly dangerous. The bite can be painful but is no more lethal than a hornet sting.

Mini Lab

If students lightly dust the black paper with flour beforehand, they will be better able to catch and observe a spider web.

MOTIVATION/Display

Display pictures of the black widow spider and the brown recluse spider. Explain that the bites of these two organisms can make a person extremely ill. While some deaths have been reported from spider bites, they usually result from complications rather than from the bite itself. Review first aid for spider bites and other animals' bites and stings. The First Aid Handbook of the American Red Cross is a good reference.

Independent Practice

Study Guide/*Teacher Resource Package*, p. 43. Use the Study Guide worksheet shown below for independent practice.

Figure 8-4 Traits of a spider

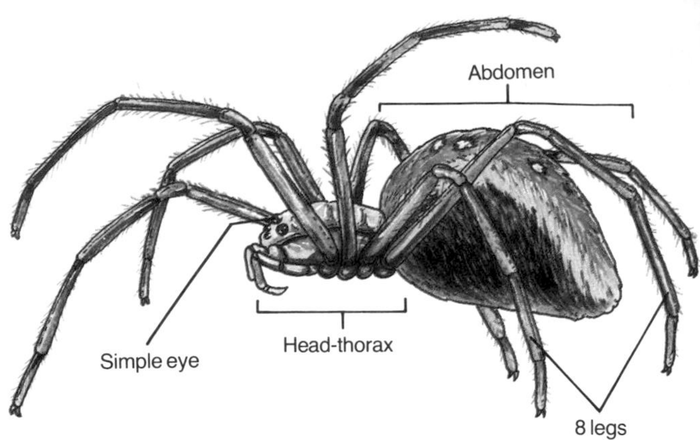

Mini Lab

How Can You Catch a Spider Web?

Observe: Find a spider web covered with dew. Catch the web by placing a piece of black paper against it. Sprinkle some flour over the web on the paper and tap off the excess. What do you see? *For more help, refer to the **Skill Handbook**, pages 704-705.*

Figure 8-5 Centipedes have one pair of legs on each segment.

The second class of jointed-leg animals includes spiders, scorpions (SKOR pee uhnz), ticks, and harvestmen, also called daddy longlegs. Each has four pairs of walking legs, simple eyes, no antennae, and a body with two sections.

Spiders feed on insects. Most spiders trap insects in webs. The head of a spider has a pair of hollow fangs that connect to poison glands. When a spider traps an insect and bites into it, the poison stuns the insect. You may think that all spiders are dangerous to people. However, only a few spiders, like the black widow, have poison that causes serious sickness in people. Scorpions have a pointed stinger on the end of their abdomen. The stinger contains poison. Scorpions use their stinger for protection against enemies, but they can harm people, too.

The third and fourth classes of jointed-leg animals include the centipedes (SENT uh peedz) and millipedes (MIHL uh peedz). Centipedes and millipedes live on land under rocks or wood. They both have heads, long segmented bodies, and many legs.

The name *centipede* suggests that these animals have one hundred legs. Remember that *centi-* means 100. *Pede* means foot. Actually centipedes usually have no more than 30 legs. You can see in Figure 8-5 that each of their segments has one pair of walking legs. The appendages on the first segment are poison claws. They help capture food. Centipedes usually eat insects.

Millipedes are slow-moving animals. They have two pairs of legs on most segments. They do not really have a thousand legs, as the name has you believe. Millipedes do not have poison claws. They usually eat decaying plants.

OPTIONS

ACTIVITY/Challenge

Have students prepare an illustrated report on the various hunting methods of spiders. Include the wolf spider, the trap-door spider, and the bird-eating spider.

What Are the Traits of Certain Jointed-leg Animals?/*Lab Manual*, pp. 59-62. Use this lab as an extension to the lesson on jointed-leg animals.

STUDY GUIDE 43

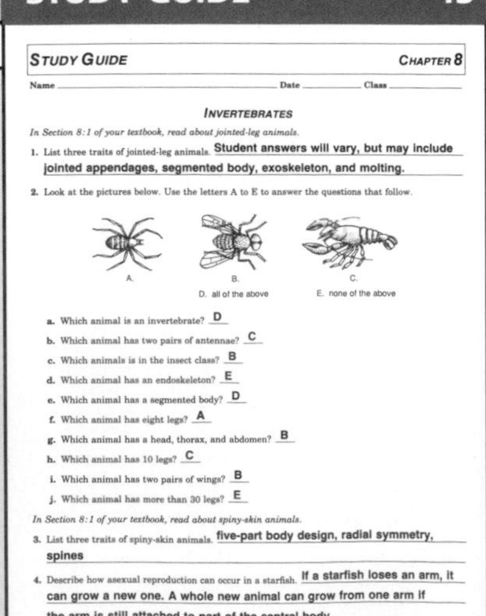

STUDY GUIDE CHAPTER 8

Name ______ Date ______ Class ______

INVERTEBRATES

In Section 8:1 of your textbook, read about jointed-leg animals.

1. List three traits of jointed-leg animals. **Student answers will vary, but may include jointed appendages, segmented body, exoskeleton, and molting.**
2. Look at the pictures below. Use the letters A to E to answer the questions that follow.

A. B. C.
D. all of the above E. none of the above

a. Which animal is an invertebrate? **D**
b. Which animal has two pairs of antennae? **C**
c. Which animals is in the insect class? **B**
d. Which animal has an endoskeleton? **E**
e. Which animal has a segmented body? **D**
f. Which animal has eight legs? **A**
g. Which animal has a head, thorax, and abdomen? **B**
h. Which animal has 10 legs? **C**
i. Which animal has two pairs of wings? **B**
j. Which animal has more than 30 legs? **E**

In Section 8:1 of your textbook, read about spiny-skin animals.

3. List three traits of spiny-skin animals. **five-part body design, radial symmetry, spines**
4. Describe how asexual reproduction can occur in a starfish. **If a starfish loses an arm, it can grow a new one. A whole new animal can grow from one arm if the arm is still attached to part of the central body.**

Insects are the fifth class of jointed-leg animals. There are more kinds of insects than all other animals combined. They live almost everywhere. They live deep in the ocean and high on mountain tops. They live in the air and on the ground, in the tropics and even at the North and South poles. They come in many shapes and colors. They can eat almost anything because they have special mouthparts for chewing, sucking, or lapping.

How can insects eat so many different kinds of food?

How can you tell if an organism is an insect? An insect's body has three main parts as shown in Figure 8-6. The head has two compound eyes and usually three simple eyes, one pair of antennae, and several mouthparts. The thorax has three pairs of walking legs and usually two pairs of wings, so the animal can fly. Insects are the only invertebrates that can fly.

Insects reproduce sexually, with separate sexes producing eggs and sperm. The fertilized eggs are laid in large numbers on leaves or branches of plants.

Insects can be helpful or harmful. Some insects destroy food crops. For example, Mediterranean fruit flies can destroy all of the fruit in an orchard. Moths can eat holes in your clothing when they feed on oils in the fabric or food particles you have left there. Termites destroy wood in buildings and fences. Why do people try to prevent houseflies from touching food? Houseflies carry bacteria that cause diseases.

Some insects help farmers by eating harmful insects. Ladybird beetles, or ladybugs, eat aphids that feed on many types of plants. Bees and other insects carry pollen from flower to flower. Crops must be pollinated in order to reproduce. There are insects that produce food and other useful materials. Honeybees, for example, produce honey.

Bio Tip

Health: Deer ticks carry bacteria that cause Lyme disease. A tick picks up bacteria when it bites a mouse and sucks blood containing the bacteria. Then, when the tick bites a human, the bacteria are transferred. Lyme disease causes rashes and heart damage. It is treated with antibiotics.

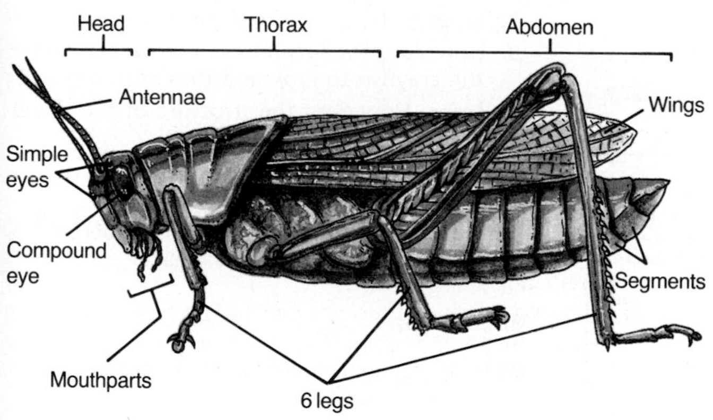

Figure 8-6 Traits of an insect are shown by the grasshopper. How many body sections does an insect have? 3

TEACH

Concept Development

▶ Stress that insects are both helpful and harmful. Students may think that all insects are a nuisance, which is not true.

▶ Point out that mosquitoes do not pass the AIDS virus to people even though they do carry malaria from one person to another.

Guided Practice

Compare the following three jointed-leg animal classes: insect, crayfish, spider. The comparison should consist of a chart with these headings: number of leg pairs, number of body sections, presence of exoskeleton, shows molting, antennae present, eyes present, wings present, lives on land, lives in water. When students are finished, ask them to place a checkmark after the traits shared by all animals. These will be phylum traits.

Guided Practice

Have students write down their answers to the margin question: They have mouthparts for chewing, sucking, or lapping.

ACTIVITY/Demonstration

Students may wish to actually follow the stages of insect development. This can be done by purchasing kits from biological supply houses of cricket, fly, butterfly, and moth life cycles.

OPTIONS

ACTIVITY/Challenge

Pheromones are being used to control many insect pests. Have students find out how they are being used to control fire ants.

ACTIVITY/Project

Prepare a report on the many human diseases carried by insects. Include in the report if the disease is caused by a bacterium, virus, or protist.

Lab 8-1 Crayfish

Overview

Students will become familiar with the traits of animals in the jointed-leg phylum. They will study a crayfish as the representative animal for this phylum.

Objectives: Upon completion of the lab, students will be able to (1) **describe** the main traits for the jointed-leg phylum, (2) **relate** the structure of specific body parts to their function, (3) **state** the adaptive advantages of certain body structures.

Time Allotment: 30 minutes

Preparation

▶ Living crayfish must be ordered in advance from a biological supply house. Make sure that you have sufficient small aquaria (battery jars) to house the animals while students observe them.

▶ **Alternate Materials:** It will be possible to complete this lab using preserved specimens rather than live animals. This may be a cheaper alternative because the same animals are used year after year.

Lab 8-1 worksheet/*Teacher Resource Package,* pp. 29-30.

Teaching the Lab

▶ **Troubleshooting:** It is possible to remove the crayfish from the water for an extended period of time for closer observation. However, caution students about the claws. The animals will pinch fingers. Know your class behavior and do not even suggest removing the animals from water if you anticipate student problems.

▶ It is possible to wrap rubber bands around the front claws to prevent pinching. Do this before class.

Cooperative Learning: Divide the class into groups of two to three students. For more information, see pp. 22T-23T in the Teacher Guide.

Crayfish

Lab 8–1

Problem: What are the traits of a jointed-leg animal?

Skills

make and use tables, observe, infer

Materials

small aquarium with live crayfish

Procedure

1. Make a table similar to the one shown and record your observations as you make them. Use the figure to help you.
2. You will receive a crayfish in a small aquarium from your teacher. **CAUTION:** *Use care when working with live animals.* Leave the crayfish in the aquarium while you make your observations.
3. **Observe:** Touch the crayfish. Observe how it feels. Count the number of body sections.
4. Locate the two pairs of antennae. Are all the antennae the same length?
5. Look closely at the compound eyes. Notice that each eye is located at the top of a short stalk.
6. Locate the first pair of walking legs or claws. On what body section are they found?
7. Observe the other four pairs of walking legs. How are they different from the first pair?
8. Observe the five pairs of swimmerets. On which body section are they found?
9. Find the flipper at the end of the crayfish. How do you think it is used?
10. Return the crayfish to the place your teacher has assigned. Wash your hands.

BODY SECTIONS	PARTS ATTACHED	FUNCTION
Fused head-thorax	1 pr. small antennae	sensory
	1 pr. large antennae	sensory
	2 eyes	sensory
	1 pr. claws	get food
	4 pr. walking legs	movement
Abdomen	5 pr. swimmerets	swim
	flipper	movement

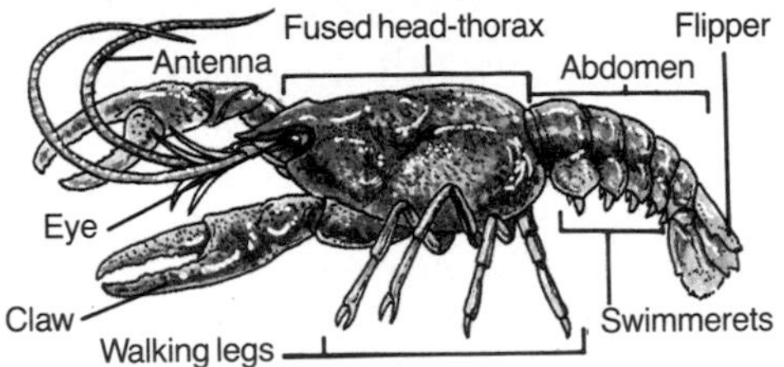

Data and Observations

1. What appendages are attached to the first body section?
2. What appendages are attached to the abdomen?

Analyze and Apply

1. Describe the exoskeleton of the crayfish.
2. What is the function of the exoskeleton?
3. How does the location of the eyes permit the crayfish to look in different directions?
4. **Infer:** How does the structure of the claws aid in getting food?
5. Which parts does the crayfish use to get food?
6. **Apply:** In what way are swimmerets in crayfish and fins in fish similar?

Extension

Observe a spider. Identify the traits that spiders and crayfish have in common.

ANSWERS

Data and Observations

1. the antennae, eyes, claws, and walking legs
2. the swimmerets and flipper

Analyze and Apply

1. The exoskeletion is a hard, waterproof, armorlike structure on the outside of a crayfish.
2. protection from drying and injury; and provides a place for muscles to attach
3. The eyes are on stalks and can move.
4. They are large claws for grabbing and holding food.
5. the claws
6. They are both used for steering the animal through the water.

a

b

c

Figure 8-7 A sea urchin (a), starfish (b), and sand dollar (c) are spiny-skin animals. They all show a five-part body design.

Spiny-skin Animals

The animal in Figure 8-7a looks like a living pincushion. It is a sea urchin. The sea urchin, starfish, and sand dollar belong to the phylum of spiny-skin animals. A **spiny-skin animal** is an invertebrate with a five-part body design, radial symmetry, and spines. Count the arms of the starfish in Figure 8-7b. Sand dollars and sea urchins also show the five-part body design. You may have walked along a beach and seen these animals. They are found only in the oceans. They are very common on rocky shores.

What is the body design of a sand dollar?

What are some other traits of spiny-skin animals? If you look closely at the bottom of a starfish you will see dozens of tube feet, like those in Figure 8-8. **Tube feet** are parts like suction cups that help the starfish move, attach to rocks, and get food. If you ever try to pull a starfish from a rock, you will see how tightly it holds onto the rock with its tube feet. A tube foot works like a medicine dropper. If you squeeze the bulb of a dropper filled with water, you force out the water. If you squeeze the bulb and then place your finger against the open end, you will feel suction when you let go of the bulb. A starfish grips slippery rocks in much the same way. The starfish takes in ocean water and passes it through a series of canals to the tube feet. As this water moves in and out of the tube feet, suction is made and released.

Figure 8-8 Tube feet help a starfish move, attach to rocks, and get food.

TEACH

Concept Development

▶ *Echinoderm* means spiny skin. The term *spiny skin* refers to the spines of calcium found on the outside of these invertebrates. The spines are projections from an endoskeleton that is covered by a layer of skin.

▶ The starfish has radial symmetry, characteristic of spiny-skin animals. Other phylum traits include: no head region or body segmentation, presence of an endoskeleton, and are marine.

Analogy: You might compare the vascular system of the starfish to a hydraulic system.

Guided Practice

Have students write down their answers to the margin question: five-part body design.

Misconception: Students usually believe that all starfish have five arms. Point out that some species have more or fewer than five. You may show pictures of sun stars that have eight or more arms, or the sunflower star of the California coast, which may have up to 20 arms. Emphasize that regardless of the number, the arms are not appendages but outgrowths or lobes of the body.

OPTIONS

Science Background

Because of the spiny external covering, the spiny-skin animals are not usually a source of food for humans. In the West Indies, sea urchin eggs are used for food, and in parts of Asia, dried sea cucumbers are used to make soup.

What Are the Parts of a Starfish?/*Lab Manual*, pp. 67-70. Use this lab as an extension to spiny-skin animals.

TEACH

Idea Map

Have students use the idea map as a study guide to the major concepts of this section.

Check for Understanding

Have students respond to the first three questions in Check Your Understanding.

Reteach

Reteaching/Teacher Resource Package, p. 21. Use this worksheet to give students additional practice in understanding complex invertebrates.

Extension: Assign Critical Thinking, Biology and Reading, or some of the **OPTIONS** available with this lesson.

3 APPLY

ACTIVITY/Bridging

Prepare a list of traits that are similar in segmented worms and jointed-leg animals. Ask students if the list tends to support the idea that both phyla may be related. Are jointed-leg animals more closely related by similar traits to segmented worms or to spiny-skin animals?

4 CLOSE

Audiovisual

Show the videocassette *Spiders; Aggression and Mating*, National Geographic Society Educational Service.

Answers to Check Your Understanding

1. body divided into three parts, jointed appendages, exoskeleton
2. by molting
3. The tube feet act like suction cups.
4. They can live almost everywhere, eat anything, and can fly and walk.
5. Arthritis refers to a disease of the joints.

Figure 8-9 Starfish can grow back missing arms. What type of reproduction is this? asexual

If a starfish loses an arm it can grow a new one, as seen in Figure 8-9. A whole new animal can grow from one arm if the arm is still attached to part of the central body. This is a form of asexual reproduction. Starfish also reproduce sexually with separate sexes producing eggs and sperm.

Study Tip: Use this idea map as a study guide to the invertebrates in this chapter. The features of jointed-leg animals and spiny-skin animals are shown.

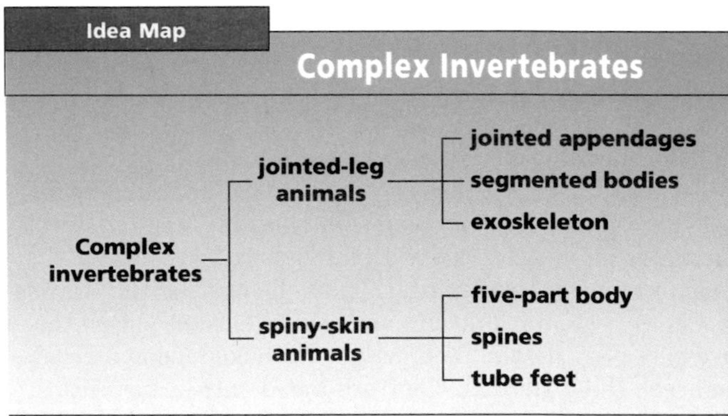

Check Your Understanding

1. List three traits of the jointed-leg animals.
2. How does an animal with an exoskeleton grow?
3. How do starfish use their tube feet for gripping surfaces?
4. **Critical Thinking:** Why are insects able to live in so many more different environments than other animals?
5. **Biology and Reading:** The scientific name for the jointed-leg animals is Arthropoda. The word *arthropoda* is made from two Greek words. The prefix *arthro-* means jointed. The suffix *-poda* means foot. What part of the body do you think the disease arthritis refers to?

OPTIONS

ACTIVITY/Challenge

You discover a "new" animal. Assume that it can talk, understands your questions, and is curled up so you cannot see any of its traits easily. Upon interviewing it, you want to determine to what phylum it belongs. What are some key questions that you might ask it in order to solve the phylum question?

RETEACHING 21

RETEACHING: IDEA MAP CHAPTER 8

Name ______ Date ______ Class ______

Use with Section 8:1.

COMPLEX INVERTEBRATES

Use the following words or phrases to complete the idea map: spines, exoskeleton, five-part body, jointed appendages, tube feet, segmented bodies.

complex invertebrates
- traits of jointed leg animals: jointed appendages; segmented bodies; exoskeleton
- traits of spiny-skin animals: five-part body; spines; tube feet

1. What is an appendage? a structure attached to the body
2. What is a segmented body? a body divided into sections
3. What is an exoskeleton? a skeleton on the outside of the body
4. How do tube feet help the spiny-skin animals move and get food? They are like suction cups allowing the animals to grip slippery rocks and food.
5. What main body parts do most jointed-leg animals have? head, thorax, abdomen
6. What happens to the exoskeleton when an invertebrate grows? The animal sheds the exoskeleton and grows another one.
7. How many legs does each of the following animals have? spider four pairs (8) insect three pairs (6) centipedes one pair per segment millipedes two pairs per segment

8:2 Vertebrates

You have been learning about some of the phyla that make up the invertebrate animals, those with no backbone. Animals that have a backbone are called vertebrates. All vertebrates belong to the chordate phylum. Vertebrates are the most complex organisms in the animal kingdom.

Objectives

4. **Compare** the traits of jawless fish, cartilage fish, and bony fish.
5. **Describe** the major traits of amphibians, reptiles, and birds.
6. **Identify** the characteristics of mammals.

Key Science Words

chordate
endoskeleton
cold-blooded
gill
jawless fish
cartilage
cartilage fish
bony fish
amphibian
hibernation
reptile
warm-blooded
mammal
mammary gland

Chordates

The chordate phylum is probably the most familiar to you. The structures and ways of life of these animals are most like yours. They are your food, your pets, farm animals, the animals you see all around you. Chordates live in water as well as on land. Some chordates, such as bats and birds, are able to fly. You, too, belong to this phylum.

How do you identify a chordate? A **chordate** is an animal that, at some time in its life, has a tough, flexible rod along its back. The chordate phylum is named for this trait.

The chordate phylum contains the largest animals on Earth, one of which is shown in Figure 8-10. How are chordates able to grow so large? They have an endoskeleton (EN doh skel uht uhn). An **endoskeleton** is a skeleton on the inside of the body. An exoskeleton limits growth because it is on the outside of the body. Animals with endoskeletons don't have this problem.

Figure 8-10 A hippopotamus can grow so large because it has an endoskeleton.

8:2 Vertebrates

PREPARATION

Materials Needed

Make copies of the Transparency Master, Critical Thinking/Problem Solving, Application, Enrichment, Study Guide, Reteaching, and Lab worksheets in the *Teacher Resource Package*.

▶ Gather feathers for Lab 8-2.

▶ Obtain materials for bird feeders for the Mini Lab. Collect bird guides.

Key Science Words

chordate	bony fish
endoskeleton	amphibian
cold-blooded	hibernation
gill	reptile
jawless fish	warm-blooded
cartilage	mammal
cartilage fish	mammary gland

Process Skills

In Lab 8-2, they will interpret data, observe, and relate cause and effect. In the Skill Checks, they will understand science words and infer. In the Mini Lab, students will observe.

1 FOCUS

▶ The objectives are listed on the student page. Remind students to preview these objectives as a guide to this numbered section.

ACTIVITY/Brainstorming

Ask students to compare their traits to those of a frog.

TRANSPARENCY 37

TRANSPARENCY MASTER — CHAPTER 8

CHORDATE CLASSES

Class	Traits	Example
Jawless fish	1. tubelike bodies covered with slime 2. do not have paired fins or jaws 3. round mouth lined with teeth 4. skeleton of cartilage 5. cold-blooded	
Cartilage fish	1. skeleton of cartilage 2. jaws 3. toothlike scales on skin 4. paired fins 5. rows of sharp teeth 6. cold-blooded	
Bony fish	1. skeleton of bone 2. skin with scales 3. gill covers 4. jaws 5. cold-blooded	
Amphibians	1. lay eggs in water 2. young have gills, adults have lungs 3. broad mouths with a sticky tongue 4. cold-blooded	
Reptiles	1. dry, scaly skin 2. well-developed lungs 3. two pairs of legs and clawed toes (except snakes) 4. egg has tough shell 5. cold-blooded	
Birds	1. feathers and wings 2. hollow bones and powerful muscles 3. warm-blooded 4. have beaks, no teeth	
Mammals	1. hair 2. feed milk to young 3. warm-blooded	

OPTIONS

Science Background

The Chordate phylum consists of the following: Phylum Chordata; Subphylum Urochordata, or tunicates; Subphylum Cephalochordata, or Amphioxus; Subphylum Vertebrata.

Transparency Master/*Teacher Resource Package*, p. 37. Use the Transparency Master shown here to introduce the seven chordate classes.

2 TEACH

MOTIVATION/Demonstration

Show the class vertebral columns or skeletons of several vertebrates. Point out that vertebrates are distinguished from all other animals by an internal skeleton (endoskeleton) of cartilage and/or bone.

Concept Development

▶ The tough flexible rod present in all chordates is called a notochord. In humans, it was present during embryonic development but was replaced by bony vertebrae. The word *chordate* refers to the chord in notochord.

▶ Many animals that are cold-blooded have some control over their body temperatures because they can move to warmer or cooler places. For example, lizards often sit in the sun. Their bodies warm while they are doing this.

ACTIVITY/Display

Set up numbered specimens of the seven vertebrate classes around the room. Have students write the name of the organisms, its class, and the traits of the class for each specimen.

ACTIVITY/Field Trip

To introduce fish, arrange a field trip to an aquarium. If you have a local aquarium, ask for a guided tour of the back rooms to see how the tanks are maintained and the fish are monitored.

Using Science Word: Explain that the plural form, when referring to more than one species, is fishes and when referring to more than one individual animal is fish.

Independent Practice

Study Guide/*Teacher Resource Package*, p. 44. Use the Study Guide worksheet shown at the bottom of this page for independent practice.

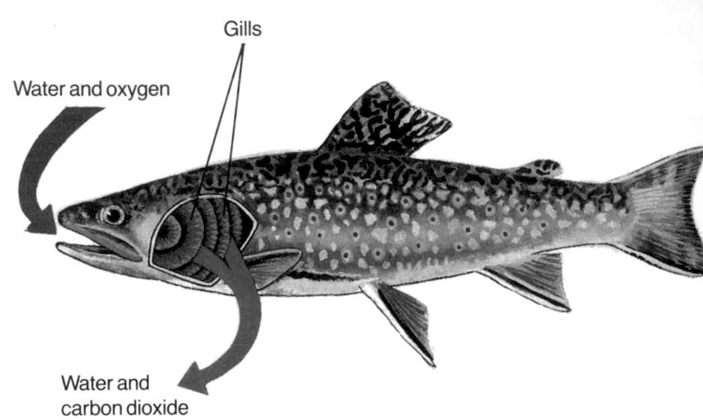

Figure 8-11 Fish have gills that remove oxygen from water. What gas is removed from the fish by the gills? carbon dioxide

Vertebrates are chordates. In most vertebrates, the rod along the back is replaced by a backbone. Vertebrates have well-developed body systems. They have a circulatory system with a heart and blood vessels, a digestive system to change food into a useful form, a skeletal system for support, a respiratory system for gas exchange, and a nervous system for control. Vertebrates have large brains, well-developed senses, and are very intelligent animals. The seven vertebrate classes are jawless fish, cartilage fish, bony fish, amphibians, reptiles, birds, and mammals.

Characteristics of Fish

Three of the seven vertebrate classes are fish. All fish have certain traits in common. Fish are cold-blooded vertebrates that live in water and breathe with gills. **Cold-blooded** means having a body temperature that changes with the temperature of the surroundings. Fish have gills on each side of the throat region. A **gill** is a structure used to breathe in water. The fish pumps water into its mouth and out through the gills, Figure 8-11. The gills pick up oxygen from the water as it passes through.

Most fish have scales that cover and protect their bodies. They also have fins that help them swim. The fins steer the fish as it moves its body from side to side through the water. A lateral line runs along each side of the body. The lateral line is an important sense organ for fish because it detects water movement and the presence of objects.

There are three different classes of fish in the chordate phylum. They are jawless fish, cartilage fish, and bony fish.

OPTIONS

Science Background

Jawless fish, cartilage fish, and bony fish are sometimes grouped into the superclass Pisces. This category denotes movement by body fins.

STUDY GUIDE 44

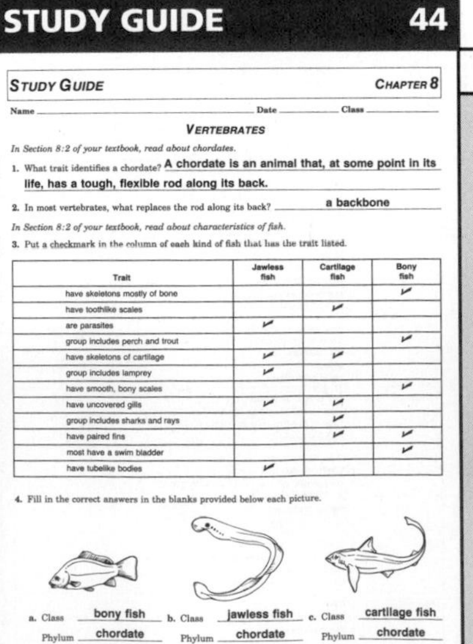

STUDY GUIDE CHAPTER 8

Name ______ Date ______ Class ______

VERTEBRATES

In Section 8:2 of your textbook, read about chordates.

1. What trait identifies a chordate? **A chordate is an animal that, at some point in its life, has a tough, flexible rod along its back.**

2. In most vertebrates, what replaces the rod along its back? **a backbone**

In Section 8:2 of your textbook, read about characteristics of fish.

3. Put a checkmark in the column of each kind of fish that has the trait listed.

Trait	Jawless fish	Cartilage fish	Bony fish
have skeletons mostly of bone			✓
have toothlike scales		✓	
are parasites	✓		
group includes perch and trout			✓
have skeletons of cartilage	✓	✓	
group includes lamprey	✓		
have smooth, bony scales			✓
have uncovered gills	✓	✓	
group includes sharks and rays		✓	
have paired fins		✓	✓
most have a swim bladder			✓
have tubelike bodies	✓		

4. Fill in the correct answers in the blanks provided below each picture.

a. Class **bony fish** Phylum **chordate**
b. Class **jawless fish** Phylum **chordate**
c. Class **cartilage fish** Phylum **chordate**

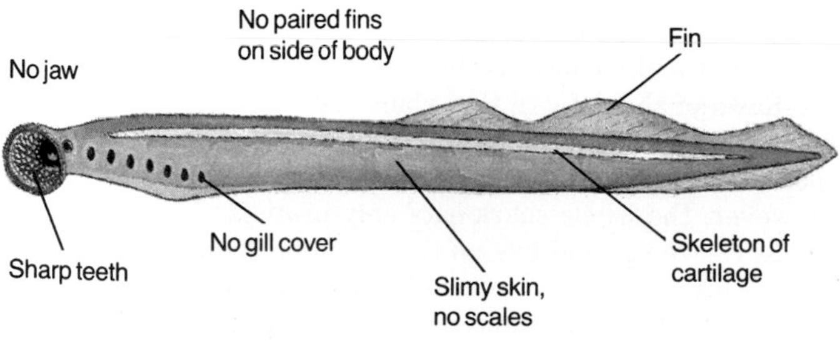

Figure 8-12 Traits of jawless fish are shown by a lamprey.

Jawless Fish

Jawless fish are fish that have no jaws and are not covered with scales. The skeletons of jawless fish are made of cartilage (KART ul ihj). **Cartilage** is a tough, flexible tissue that supports and shapes the body. Your ears and nose tip are made up of cartilage.

The lamprey (LAM pree) shown in Figure 8-12 is a jawless fish. Lampreys have tubelike bodies covered with slime that protects the skin. They don't have paired fins. Lampreys swim by waving their body from side to side.

The lamprey's mouth does not have jaws. It is a round opening lined with toothlike structures. How does the lamprey eat? Many lampreys attach themselves to the sides of other fish with their sharp, toothlike structures. The lamprey cuts a hole through the skin and sucks out the blood and body fluids. Are lampreys parasites?

Cartilage Fish

Cartilage fish are fish in which the entire skeleton is made of cartilage. They have no bone. Unlike the jawless fish, cartilage fish have jaws, toothlike scales, and paired fins. Sharks and rays are cartilage fish. The shark in Figure 8-13 shows these traits.

What kind of skeleton do cartilage fish have?

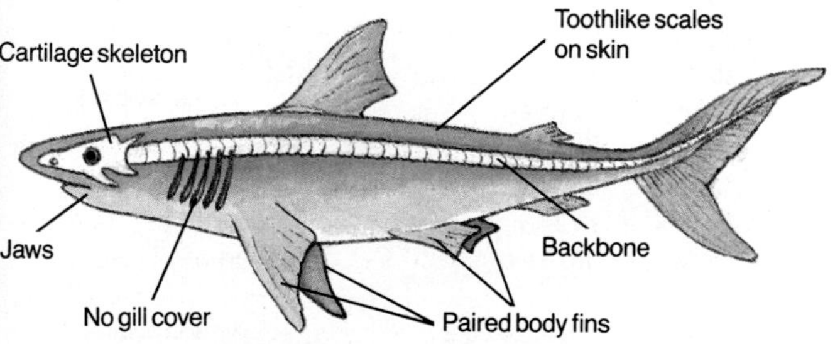

Figure 8-13 Traits of cartilage fish are shown by a shark.

TEACH

Concept Development

▶ Lampreys have one heart, hagfishes have at least four, Hagfish have 5 to 15 pairs of gill openings and mucus-secreting glands over their bodies. The hagfishes have been omitted here.

▶ Point out that sharks and rays can be distinguished by the placement of their gill slits. The gill slits of a shark are always on the side of its head and the ray's gill slits are underneath its wide fins.

▶ Cartilage fish also have 2-chambered hearts.

Connection: Language Arts

Make a list of everyday phrases that describe certain characteristics in terms of animal traits. Ask students to discuss the origin of the phrases and to decide whether the comparisons are valid. Use such phrases as "sly as a fox," "slippery as an eel," "dog tired," "blind as a bat," "eats like a bird," "a memory like an elephant," "free as a bird," and "bee line."

Guided Practice

Have students write down their answers to the margin question: an internal skeleton of cartilage.

CRITICAL THINKING 8

CRITICAL THINKING/PROBLEM SOLVING — CHAPTER 8

Name ______ Date ______ Class ______

Use after Section 8:2.

WHAT CAN A SCIENTIFIC ILLUSTRATION TELL YOU?

Science concepts can be shown with words and with pictures. Some things can be explained best in words, such as experimental results. Illustrations are more helpful for showing structures. For example, many fish have unusual adaptations to their environments.

Use the descriptions below to match the fish to the illustrations. Write the name of each fish next to its picture. Then write how the adaptation might help the fish survive.

Lionfish: Attacks other fish with its sharp fins, which look like feathers. Fins release a poison.

Sargassum Fish: Climbs seaweed with its pawlike fins. Its shaggy body looks like the seaweed.

Porcupine fish: Can fill itself with water and swell up in size. Its skin is covered with spines.

Flounder: Has a flat body that changes color to match its background. Both eyes are on one side of the body.

Flounder — Matches sea floor. Eyes see above.

Porcupine Fish — Puffs up too big to be swallowed.

Sargassum Fish — Is disguised like seaweed.

Lionfish — Attacks food fish with poison fins.

OPTIONS

Enrichment: Mention that in the 1950s one species of sea lamprey threatened the entire Great Lakes fishing industry. The lamprey was partially controlled by chemicals that killed newly hatched larvae.

How Do Fish Classes Compare?/*Lab Manual,* pp. 63-66. Use this lab as an extension to the lesson on fish.

Critical Thinking/Problem Solving/ *Teacher Resource Package,* p. 8. Use the Critical Thinking/Problem Solving worksheet shown here as an extension to fish adaptation.

TEACH

Concept Development

▶ Experiments have shown that sharks use their senses of smell and touch to detect and locate prey. The eyes are used only as they approach the prey.

▶ Students may be interested in knowing that the cartilage fish have no swim bladder. They begin to sink when they stop swimming.

▶ Mention that bony fish also have two-chambered hearts.

ACTIVITY/Demonstration

You may demonstrate camouflage in bony fish by placing a few minnows in each of two beakers. Place one beaker on white cloth and place one on black cloth. Have students observe. Switch the beakers and observe again.

ACTIVITY/Hands-On

You may want to have students dissect a dogfish shark to show the body systems of a cartilage fish. They are available at biological supply houses.

Check for Understanding

Ask students to compare the three fish classes as to: (a) where they live; (b) what makes up the skeleton of each; (c) what they use to move about; (d) number of fins; (e) skin covering; (f) flap covering the gills.

Reteach

Make flash cards of the traits of the three fish classes. On the back of each card, write the class(es) that have the trait. Show students the traits and have them name the corresponding classes.

Independent Practice

Study Guide/*Teacher Resource Package*, p. 45. Use the Study Guide worksheet shown at the bottom of this page for independent practice.

Figure 8-14 A ray has a flat body that is adapted for living on the ocean floor.

Figure 8-15 Catfish have leathery skin instead of scales.

Sharks have slim bodies and paired fins that help with movement and balance. Sharks are fast swimmers.

Rows of sharp teeth that slant backward cover the shark's jaws. The teeth help sharks hold and cut up their food. Most sharks eat other animals that live in the ocean. However, the whale shark eats only protists.

Rays are flat and live on the ocean bottom, Figure 8-14. They eat fish and invertebrates in the ocean. Most rays are harmless to humans, but some stingrays have whiplike tails with stingers that can cause a painful wound.

Bony Fish

Most fish known today belong to the class of bony fish. **Bony fish** have skeletons made mostly of bone, not of cartilage. Many fish that you eat, such as perch, bass, flounder, and trout, are in this group. You may have seen some of these fish in a supermarket.

Figure 8-16 shows the important traits of bony fish. Most bony fish have smooth, bony scales that are covered with a slimy coating, but some, like the catfish in Figure 8-15, have slime-covered leathery skin instead. The slime and scales protect the fish from infections and from enemies. The slime also makes it easier for the fish to glide through the water.

Bony fish have a flap that covers and protects the gills. Jawless fish and cartilage fish do not have this flap. Most bony fish have a swim bladder. A swim bladder is a baglike structure that fills with gases and helps the fish float and go up and down in the water. Fish can change the amount of gas in the swim bladder. As the bladder fills with gas, the fish rises. As the gas is let out, the fish goes deeper.

Most fish need water to reproduce. The female lays large numbers of eggs in the water. The male fish deposits sperm in the water, and some of the eggs are fertilized when the sperm swim to the eggs.

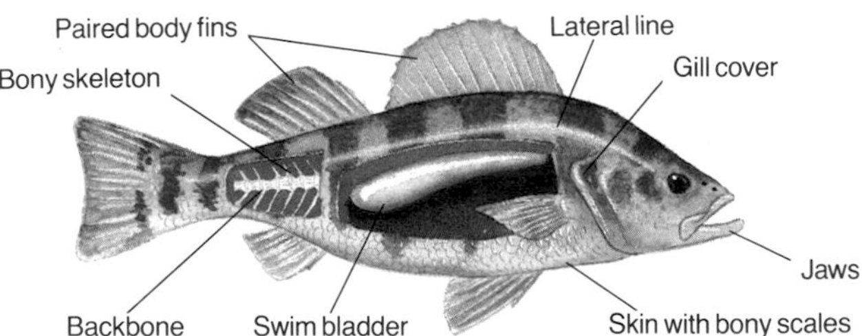
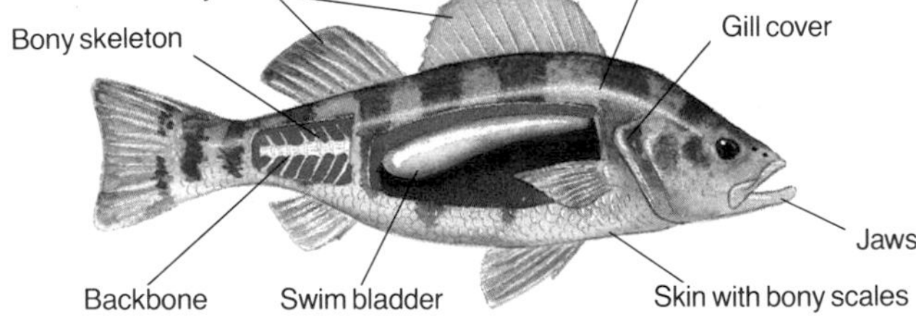

Figure 8-16 Traits of a bony fish. **What is the function of the swim bladder?** It helps the fish go up and down in the water.

OPTIONS

ACTIVITY/Challenge

Have students report on the most dangerous shark waters in the world. Have them include those shark species present.

STUDY GUIDE 45

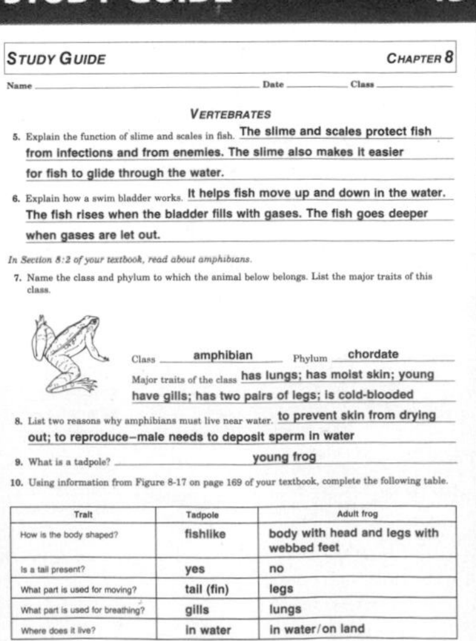

STUDY GUIDE — CHAPTER 8

Name ______ Date ______ Class ______

VERTEBRATES

5. Explain the function of slime and scales in fish. The slime and scales protect fish from infections and from enemies. The slime also makes it easier for fish to glide through the water.
6. Explain how a swim bladder works. It helps fish move up and down in the water. The fish rises when the bladder fills with gases. The fish goes deeper when gases are let out.

In Section 8:2 of your textbook, read about amphibians.

7. Name the class and phylum to which the animal below belongs. List the major traits of this class.

Class amphibian Phylum chordate

Major traits of the class has lungs; has moist skin; young have gills; has two pairs of legs; is cold-blooded

8. List two reasons why amphibians must live near water. to prevent skin from drying out; to reproduce–male needs to deposit sperm in water
9. What is a tadpole? young frog
10. Using information from Figure 8-17 on page 169 of your textbook, complete the following table.

Trait	Tadpole	Adult frog
How is the body shaped?	fishlike	body with head and legs with webbed feet
Is a tail present?	yes	no
What part is used for moving?	tail (fin)	legs
What part is used for breathing?	gills	lungs
Where does it live?	in water	in water/on land

Amphibians

Amphibians (am FIHB ee uns) include frogs, toads, and salamanders. An **amphibian** is an animal that lives part of its life in water and another part of its life on land. Usually, young amphibians live in water and adult amphibians live mostly on land. Amphibians that live mostly on land still need water. Without water, an amphibian's skin dries out. Amphibian eggs are laid in water so they won't dry out. The female lays large numbers of eggs. The male deposits sperm in the water. Only a few eggs are fertilized.

Amphibian young look very different from the adults. Notice that the tadpole in Figure 8-17b is different from an adult frog in many ways. Tadpoles must live in water and breathe with gills. The adults have lungs and can take in oxygen from the air. They also take in oxygen through their moist skins and the linings of their mouths.

Frogs and toads are probably familiar to you. Figure 8-17a shows some of their traits. Most frogs and toads do not have tails. They have broad mouths with long, sticky tongues for catching insects. They have two pairs of legs. The hind legs are much larger and more powerful than the front legs, so the animal can jump great distances. Frogs and toads have webbed feet for swimming. Their eyes stick out from their heads. This trait allows them to hide under the water with only their eyes showing above the surface. When an insect flies by, the frog flicks out its sticky tongue and catches the insect.

Skill Check

Understand science words: amphibian. The word part *amphi* means both. In your dictionary, find three words with the word part *amphi* in them. *For more help, refer to the **Skill Handbook**, pages 706-711.*

a

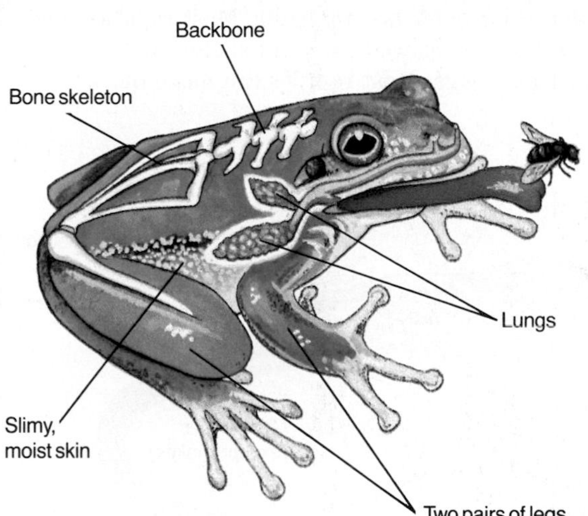

b

Figure 8-17 The traits of an amphibian are shown by a frog (a). A tadpole (b) looks very different from an adult frog and has a different way of life.

TEACH

Concept Development

▶ Point out that many amphibians have poison glands beneath their outer skin. Their poison serves as a protection against natural enemies. Generally these poisons are harmless to humans. However, the South American tree frog Dendrobates secretes a powerful poison used by natives to make poison-tipped arrows.

▶ Remind students that all the amphibian traits are not necessarily present in every animal of each class. For example, Xeno laevis, the South African aquatic frog, has no tongue and rarely leaves the water. There are exceptions for each class (and phylum) that is presented.

ACTIVITY/Demonstration

Use a goldfish or guppy to demonstrate the flow of water across a fish's gills. Have students watch the opening and closing of the mouth and gill covers. Place a drop of food coloring in front of the fish's mouth and see how quickly the water comes out of the gills.

OPTIONS

Science Background

Amphibians, reptiles, birds, and mammals are sometimes grouped into the superclass Tetrapoda. This category denotes movement by legs.

TEACH

Concept Development

▶ Point out that lizards (reptile) and salamanders (amphibian) have similar body shapes but are very different animals.

▶ Emphasize to students that prehistoric reptiles were the dominant animals of their day, just as mammals are dominant today.

ACTIVITY/Demonstration

You might want to introduce the section by displaying a small turtle and having students note the traits.

ACTIVITY/Display

Display pictures of reptiles such as the glass lizard, horned toad, gecko, different kinds of snakes, crocodiles, and alligators. Have students discuss how they are similar.

Skill Check

Reptile eggs have leathery protective coverings. More reptile eggs will hatch and survive; therefore, fewer eggs need to be laid.

Independent Practice

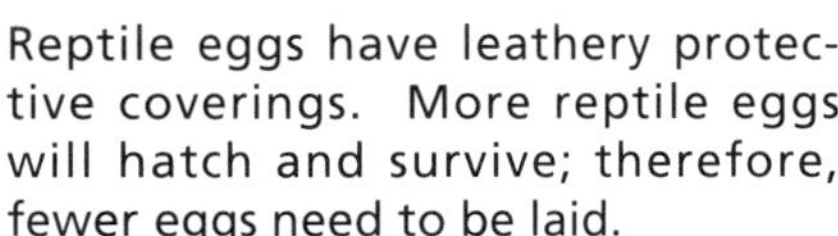

Study Guide/*Teacher Resource Package*, p. 46. Use the Study Guide worksheet at the bottom of this page for independent practice.

a

b

Figure 8-18 A cave salamander (a) and a snake (b) are adapted for living on land.

Salamanders are amphibians with a tail. Their two pairs of legs are about the same size, Figure 8-18a. They live only in moist places. Some salamanders keep their gills throughout their lives and live in water, even as adults.

Amphibians are cold-blooded vertebrates. Their body temperature drops as the temperature of their surroundings drops. Because they are cold-blooded, amphibians become inactive during cold weather. The state of being inactive during cold weather is called **hibernation.** Animals that hibernate eat no food and use only a little oxygen. Their energy needs are met with stored fat.

Amphibians help control insects. Amphibians also are used in life science studies and in medical research. They are eaten by snakes, turtles, birds, and mammals.

Skill Check

Infer: Compare reproduction in reptiles with reproduction in fish and amphibians. Explain why reptiles lay far fewer eggs than amphibians or fish. *For more help, refer to the* ***Skill Handbook,*** *pages 706-711.*

Reptiles

You may have seen a snake at one time and thought it looked slimy. If you touched the snake, you probably were surprised to find that it was not slimy at all. Snakes are reptiles. A **reptile** is an animal that has dry, scaly skin and can live on land. Reptiles were the first vertebrates to live and reproduce entirely on land. Snakes, lizards, turtles, crocodiles, and alligators are all reptiles.

What are the traits of reptiles? Look at Figure 8-19. Reptiles are cold-blooded vertebrates with a backbone and an endoskeleton. Their scaly skin protects them, prevents water loss, and keeps them from drying out. Some reptiles are covered by hard plates instead of scales. They have well-developed lungs for breathing air. Most reptiles have two pairs of legs and clawed toes, but snakes and some lizards don't have legs. Most reptiles can move quickly.

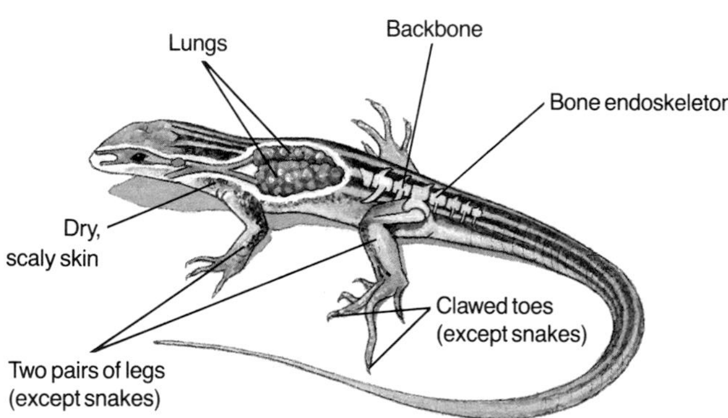

Figure 8-19 A lizard shows the traits of a reptile.

OPTIONS

Science Background

Reptiles have hearts with atria and a single (three-chambered heart) ventricle. Crocodiles have two ventricles (a four-chambered heart).

STUDY GUIDE 46

STUDY GUIDE CHAPTER 8

Name ______ Date ______ Class ______

VERTEBRATES

11. How are cold-blooded animals affected by the temperature in their surroundings? **The temperature of cold-blooded animals drops as the temperature of their surroundings drop.**

12. How does hibernation help amphibians survive? **Animals that are inactive during cold weather eat no food and use only a little oxygen.**

In Section 8:2 of your textbook, read about reptiles.

13. Name the class and phylum to which the animal below belongs. List the major traits of this class.

Class **reptile** Phylum **chordate**

Major traits of the class **cold-blooded; has dry, scaly skin or hard plates; has lungs; has tough, leathery-shelled egg**

14. List five kinds of reptiles. **snakes, lizards, alligators, crocodiles, turtles**

15. List three reasons why a reptile can live entirely on land. **It has dry, scaly skin that prevents it from drying out, well-developed lungs for breathing air, and a tough, leathery-shelled egg that doesn't need to be laid in water.**

In Section 8:2 of your textbook, read about birds.

16. Compare the following traits of birds with those of reptiles. Using the words *same* or *different*, fill in the blanks provided with the answer that applies.

a. warm-blooded	**different**	e. feathers	**different**
b. scaly legs	**same**	f. lungs	**same**
c. shelled eggs	**same**	g. beaks	**different**
d. toes with claws	**same**	h. hollow bones	**different**

They use their claws for running and climbing, and for digging nests in the soil. A reptile egg has a tough, leathery shell that protects it and keeps it from drying out. Because reptile eggs have shells, they can be laid on land instead of in the water. Even though reptiles do not need to live in water, many still do. Alligators, crocodiles, and turtles, for example, spend a good part of their lives in or near the water.

Reptiles eat insects and pests such as rats and mice. In some areas of the world, people eat reptiles and their eggs.

How are reptile eggs protected?

Birds

Birds are vertebrates that have wings, a beak, two legs, and a covering of feathers over most of their bodies. Some of the traits of birds are shown in Figure 8-20. Like reptiles, birds have scales, but the scales are only on their legs. Birds also have claws on their toes. They have well-developed lungs. Female birds, like reptiles, lay eggs with shells from which the young develop.

Most birds are well adapted for flying. They have hollow bones, which makes them light in weight. Birds have powerful muscles to move their wings. Some birds, such as the ostrich, do not fly. Ostriches, however, can run as fast as 48 km an hour, about the speed of a racing bike.

Birds are warm-blooded. **Warm-blooded** means controlling the body temperature so that it stays about the same no matter what the temperature of the surroundings. Feathers help the body keep a constant body temperature.

Mini Lab

How Do You Make a Bird Feeder?

Observe: Nail bottle caps onto a piece of wood. Fill the caps with peanut butter or birdseed. Hang the feeder from a tree with string. Observe the birds that come to the feeder. *For more help, refer to the* ***Skill Handbook,*** *pages 704-705.*

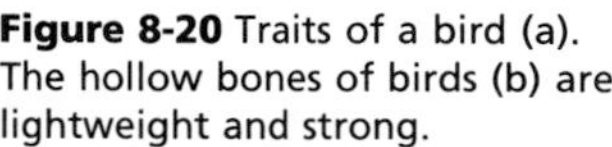

Figure 8-20 Traits of a bird (a). The hollow bones of birds (b) are lightweight and strong.

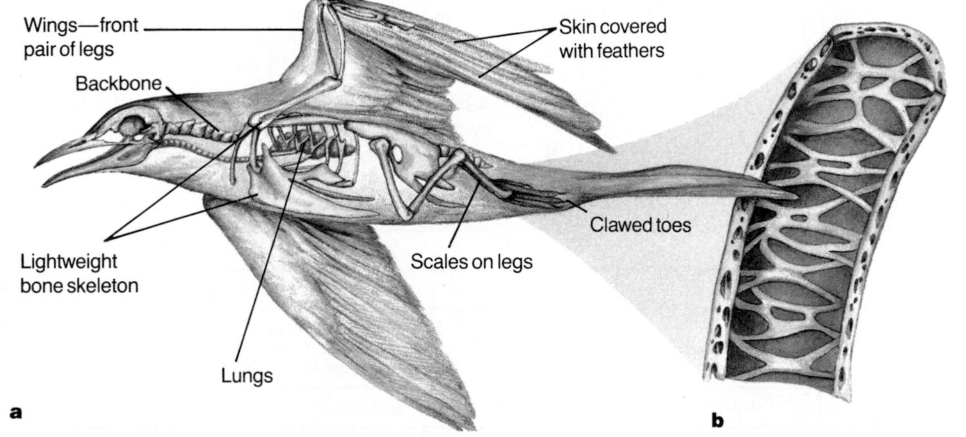

TEACH

Concept Development

▶ Bird skin secretes an oily substance that a bird uses to coat its feathers. This behavior is called preening. Bird feathers are replaced at least once a year by molting. Feathers are usually lost and replaced in pairs, preserving balance for flight.

▶ Point out that warm-blooded animals require more energy to heat their bodies than do cold-blooded animals. Birds must constantly seek food to provide energy to keep their bodies warm.

▶ Stress the importance of the lightweight skeleton of a bird. Bring in chicken bones and beef bones for comparison. Explain that in some birds the weight of the feathers is greater than that of the skeleton.

Mini Lab

Depending on the area in which you live, students should be able to observe sparrows, finches, and woodpeckers. Woodpeckers (and squirrels) are especially attracted to peanut butter.

Guided Practice

Have students write down their answers to the margin question: by a tough, leathery shell.

Independent Practice

Study Guide/*Teacher Resource Package,* p. 47. Use the Study Guide worksheet shown at the bottom of this page for independent practice.

STUDY GUIDE 47

STUDY GUIDE — *CHAPTER 8*

Name ______ Date ______ Class ______

VERTEBRATES

17. Explain the meaning of *warm-blooded.* Warm-blooded means controlling the body temperature so that it stays about the same no matter what the temperature of the surroundings.

18. What do birds have that helps them keep a constant body temperature? feathers

19. How are birds well adapted for flying? They have hollow bones, which makes them light in weight. They have powerful muscles that move their wings.

20. How are the beaks of birds adapted for getting food? The kind (shape and size) of beak they have is related to the kind of food they eat.

In Section 8:2 of your textbook, read about mammals.

21. Name the class and phylum to which the animal below belongs. List the major traits of this class.

Class mammal Phylum chordate

Major traits of the class has hair; is warm-blooded; has mammary glands, nurses young; young are born alive.

22. a. What is a mammal? A mammal is an animal that has hair and feeds milk to its young.

b. Are you a mammal? yes

23. a. What are mammary glands? body parts that produce milk

b. How are male mammary glands different from female mammary glands? Male mammary glands don't produce milk.

24. List two groups of mammals whose young do not develop inside the mother's body. pouched mammals, egg-laying mammals

APPLICATION 8

APPLICATION: LEISURE — *CHAPTER 8*

Name ______ Date ______ Class ______

Use after Section 8:2.

BEAK ADAPTATIONS

Birdwatching is a hobby that many people enjoy. Knowing what kind of food a bird eats can help a birdwatcher know where to find the bird.

To obtain food, a bird uses its beak like a tool. The shape of a bird's beak is related to the type of food the bird eats. Compare the function of each bird's beak to the function of the tools shown below. On the first line next to each bird picture, write the name of the tool whose function most closely resembles that of the bird's beak. Then, consider what kind of food each bird could obtain using its beak. On the second line, write the type of food you think each bird would eat. Refer to the foods and tools listed below. You may use a tool or food choice more than once.

Bird	Tool	Food
woodpecker	awl	insects
parrot	nutcracker	seeds
flamingo	strainer	tiny organisms
vulture	meat knife	fleshy animals
hummingbird	soda straw	nectar
crossbill	nutcracker	seeds
hawk	meat knife	fleshy animals
cardinal	nutcracker	seeds
pelican	scoop	fish

Tools: nutcracker, meat knife, soda straw, strainer, awl (for puncturing), scoop

Foods: seeds, nectar (in flowers), fleshy animals, tiny organisms (in water), insects (under tree bark), fish

OPTIONS

Application/*Teacher Resource Package,* p. 8. Use the worksheet shown here to teach students about beak adaptations.

Lab 8-2 Feathers

Overview

In this lab, students become familiar with the two different types of feathers. They will be able to relate these differences in appearance to the function of each type of feather.

Objectives: Upon completion of the lab, students will be able to (1) **name** the different parts of a typical feather, (2) **list** differences between contour and down feathers, (3) **relate** the differences in structure of the two feather types to the particular function.

Time Allotment: 20 minutes

Preparation

▶ Feathers are available from your local grocery store, local farmers, or some biological supply houses.

▶ Down feathers are available from old discarded pillows or comforters.

▶ Both feather types are available from biological supply houses as prepared slides.

Lab 8-2 worksheet/*Teacher Resource Package*, pp. 31-32.

Teaching the Lab

Cooperative Learning: Divide the class into groups of two to three students. For more information, see pp. 22T-23T in the Teacher Guide.

Feathers

Lab **8–2**

Problem: What is the structure of feathers?

Skills

interpret data, observe, infer

Materials

wing or tail feather
down feather
hand lens
scissors
metric ruler

Procedure

1. There are two kinds of feathers. Contour feathers are found on a bird's body, wings, and tail. Down feathers lie under the contour feathers and insulate the body. Look at a contour feather with a hand lens. The hard center tube is the shaft.
2. Copy the data table. Cut 2 cm off the end of the contour feather shaft. **CAUTION:** *Use care when using scissors.* Observe the cut end with the hand lens. Record your observations.

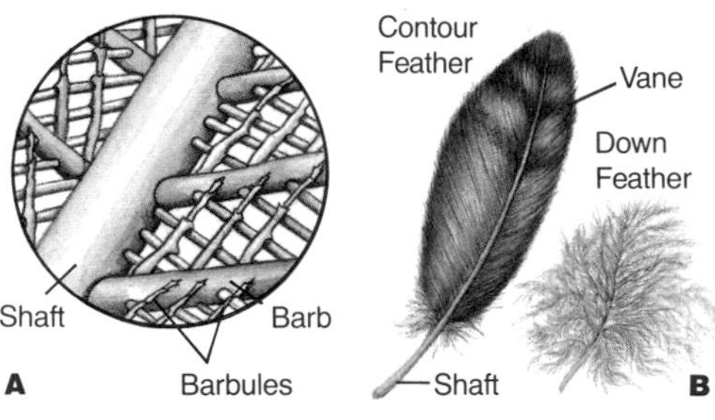

3. **Observe:** Examine the vane with the hand lens. Compare what you see with Figure A. How are the tiny strands of the feather hooked together? This gives the feather strength for flight.
4. Hold the contour feather by the shaft and fan yourself. Hold the down feather by the shaft and fan. Describe what you feel.
5. Observe the shape of the down feather with a hand lens. Describe how it feels. Compare the feather with Figure B.

Data and Observations

1. What connects a contour feather's barbs?
2. Explain any differences observed when you fanned the air with the two feathers.

Analyze and Apply

1. List the parts of a contour feather.
2. How does the shaft of the contour feather aid in flight?
3. **Infer:** How does the structure of a down feather help insulate a bird?
4. **Apply:** What structures in reptiles are like feathers? Are their functions similar?

Extension

Observe pictures of a bird wing and a bat wing. How are they similar and how are they different?

FEATHER	PARTS	OBSERVATIONS
Contour	shaft	hard, smooth, hollow
	vane	tiny strands on either side of the shaft
	barb	make up the vanes
	barbules	hook the barbs together
Down	strand not hooked together	soft, small

ANSWERS

Data and Observations

1. barbules
2. The down feather was not strong or stiff enough to fan air effectively.

Analyze and Apply

1. shaft, barbs, barbules
2. It is strong and stiff and can push air during flight.
3. Because it is soft and fluffy, it can trap air close to the body.
4. Scales; Feathers have the same functions as scales. They have additional functions related to flight.

Figure 8-21 The shape of a bird's beak is related to the kind of food it eats. Woodpecker (a), cardinal (b), and hawk (c). What food does each bird eat? (a) insects, (b) seeds, (c) meat

Birds have no teeth. Instead, they have beaks that they use to get food. The kind of beak a bird has is related to the kind of food it eats. Figure 8-21 shows some examples. Woodpeckers have beaks that cut through tree bark to expose insects. Sparrows and cardinals have thick beaks that crack seeds. Hawks have sharp beaks that tear meat.

Birds are important to us in many ways. They help farmers by eating insects and the seeds of weeds. Some birds eat rats and mice. Chickens and ducks provide eggs and meat. Some people have birds as pets. Many people enjoy watching and feeding wild birds. The bald eagle is the national bird in the United States. Do you know the state bird for your state?

Bio Tip

Leisure: Millions of people in the United States enjoy bird watching. Each year, bird lovers spend over $500 million on birdseed, $100 million on bird feeders, boxes, and baths; and $18 million on field guides.

Mammals

What traits are found in the animals in Figure 8-22? First, they have hair and are warm-blooded. The hair helps keep a constant body temperature. Second, the females have milk glands with which they nurse their young. These animals are mammals (MAM ulz). A **mammal** is an animal that has hair and feeds milk to its young. You are a mammal.

Most animals that you have studied hatch from eggs. Mammals usually develop inside the mother's body and are born alive. After birth, young mammals feed on milk produced by the mother's mammary glands. **Mammary** (MAM uh ree) **glands** are body parts that produce milk. Male mammals also have mammary glands, but they don't produce milk. Besides providing milk, all mammals care for their young.

Figure 8-22 Mammals feed their young with milk from their mammary glands.

TEACH

Concept Development

▶Introduce this section with pictures and specimens of as many different species of mammals as possible.

Cooperative Learning: Divide the class into 7 groups. Each group is to be assigned one chordate class. The task for each group is to prepare five true-false or multiple choice questions that could be used in designing a test. One representative from each group will read off their questions to the class and ask students from other groups to supply the correct answers.

Check for Understanding

Have students compare bird and mammal classes as to: (a) whether cold-or warm blooded; (b) type of body covering; (c) presence of a backbone; (d) appearance of front legs; (e) presence of teeth; (f) if young are provided milk; (g) if mammary glands are present.

Reteach

Make flash cards of the traits of birds and mammals. On the back of each card, write the class(es) that have the trait. Show students the traits and have them name the corresponding classes.

Independent Practice

Study Guide/*Teacher Resource Package,* p. 48. Use the Study Guide worksheet shown at the bottom of this page for independent practice.

STUDY GUIDE 48

STUDY GUIDE — *CHAPTER 8*

Name ______ Date ______ Class ______

VOCABULARY

Review the new words used in Chapter 8 of your textbook. Then, fill in the blanks.

Crayfish, insects, and spiders belong to the phylum of **jointed-leg animals**. These animals have **compound eyes** with many lenses. They also have legs, wings, and **antennae** which are used for sensing smell and touch. These body parts are called **appendages**. Animals in this phylum have a skeleton, called an **exoskeleton**, that is outside their bodies. As the animals grow, they shed their outer skeletons. This process is called **molting**.

The phylum of **spiny-skin animals** includes sea urchins, starfish, and sand dollars. These animals use their **tube feet** to move, attach to rocks, and get food.

The phylum of **chordates** includes animals that have a rod along their back at some time in their lives. Their skeleton, called an **endoskeleton**, is inside their body.

Fish live in water and breathe with **gills**. They are **cold-blooded** animals because their body temperature changes with their surroundings. **Jawless fish** have no jaws, scales, or bones. Their skeleton is made of **cartilage**. **Cartilage fish** have jaws, scales, and a cartilage skeleton. **Bony fish** have jaws, scales, and a bony skeleton.

Amphibians live part of their life in water and part on land.

Hibernation helps animals survive cold weather.

Reptiles have dry, scaly skin, can live on land, and breathe with lungs.

Birds have a beak, wings, and feathers. Their body temperature does not change with the temperature of their surroundings. Thus, they are **warm-blooded** animals.

Mammals also have a constant body temperature. They have hair on their bodies. The females produce milk from their **mammary glands**.

ENRICHMENT 8

ENRICHMENT — *CHAPTER 8*

Name ______ Date ______ Class ______

Use after Section 8:2.

ORDERS OF MAMMALS

Thousands of species of mammals are grouped into orders, each with specific traits. The traits of some of the mammal orders are given in the table below.

Use a dictionary or an encyclopedia to find examples of animals in each of the orders listed. Then, complete the table.

Order name	Traits of the order	Examples
Monotremata	only mammal that lays egg	**duckbilled platypus, echidna (spiny anteater)**
Marsupiala	young are born as embryos; they develop in a pouch while nursing	**opossum, kangaroo, koala bear**
Insectivora	eat insects and burrow in the ground; have pointed teeth and long snouts	**shrew, mole**
Rodentia	have large incisors for gnawing; incisors grow continuously	**mouse, rat, gopher, guinea pig**
Edentata	have long tubular snout with sticky tongue; have reduced teeth or lack teeth altogether; some have bony plates in their skin	**anteater, sloth, armadillo**
Carnivora	have large canine teeth and sharp claws; prey on other animals	**dog, cat, lion, fox**
Chiroptera	forelimbs developed for flying; some fly at night using a sonarlike mechanism to find their way	**bats**
Lagomorpha	have a double row of incisors; incisors grow continuously	**rabbit, hare, pika**
Cetacea	live in fresh water or salt water; forelimbs are flippers; have no hind limbs	**whale, dolphin, porpoise**
Proboscidae	have long muscular nose (trunk) and large paired tusks	**elephant**

OPTIONS

Enrichment/*Teacher Resource Package,* p. 8. Use the Enrichment worksheet shown here to teach students the mammal orders.

TEACH

Guided Practice

Have students write down their answers to the margin question: They crawl into the pouch and attach to mammary glands there.

Check for Understanding

Have students respond to the first three questions in Check Your Understanding

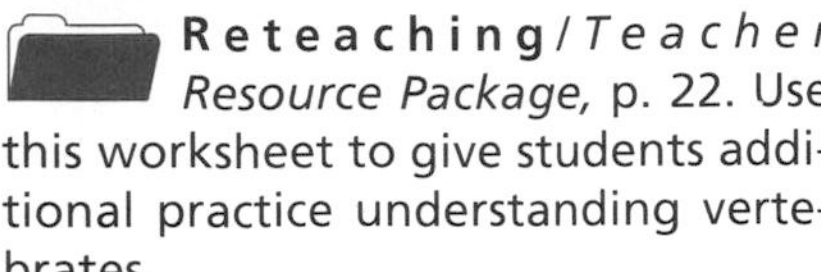

Reteach

Reteaching/*Teacher Resource Package*, p. 22. Use this worksheet to give students additional practice understanding vertebrates.

Extension: Assign Critical Thinking, Biology and Reading, or some of the **OPTIONS** available with this lesson.

3 APPLY

Audiovisual

Show the videocassette *Reptiles*, National Geographic Society Educational Services.

4 CLOSE

ACTIVITY/Software

Project Classify: Mammals, National Geographic Society Educational Services.

a

b

Figure 8-23 Kangaroo young (a) finish developing in the mother's pouch. The duck-billed platypus (b) lays eggs.

How do opossum young finish developing?

TABLE 8–1. CLASSIFICATION OF HUMANS
Kingdom: animal
Phylum: chordate
Subphylum: vertebrate
Class: mammal
Order: primate
Family: hominid
Genus: *Homo*
Species: *sapiens*

Two groups of mammals whose young do not develop inside the mother's body are the pouched mammals and the egg-laying mammals. Kangaroos and opossums are pouched mammals. The young of kangaroos and opossums are not fully developed at birth. After birth, they crawl into a pouch outside the mother's body. There they attach themselves to the mother's mammary glands and feed on milk until they are more fully developed. Egg-laying mammals, such as the duck-billed platypus shown in Figure 8-23b, lay eggs like those of reptiles.

Now that you have studied the entire animal kingdom, let's see where you fit in. Remember that you are also a chordate and a mammal. You can see the smaller subgroups in Table 8-1. The name of your genus is *Homo*. Your species name is *sapiens*. These names make up the scientific name of humans, *Homo sapiens*. The Latin word *Homo* means man and *sapiens* means wise. Together *Homo sapiens* means wise man.

Check Your Understanding

6. Compare the scales of jawless fish, cartilage fish, and bony fish.
7. How do birds get food?
8. What does being warm-blooded mean?
9. **Critical Thinking:** Why do mammals have a relatively small number of young?
10. **Biology and Reading:** Why can chordates grow larger than any other animals? What limits the size of animals that are not chordates?

Answers to Check Your Understanding

6. jawless fish–no scales; cartilage fish–toothlike scales; bony fish– smooth, bony scales
7. with beaks and feet
8. having an internal temperature that remains about the same no matter what the temperature of the surroundings
9. The young must be nursed by the mother and only a small number of young can be nursed at one time.
10. Chordates have an endoskeleton that allows them to grow larger. Some invertebrates do not have the necessary support that would allow them to grow to very large sizes. Other invertebrates have an exoskeleton that limits their size.

RETEACHING 22

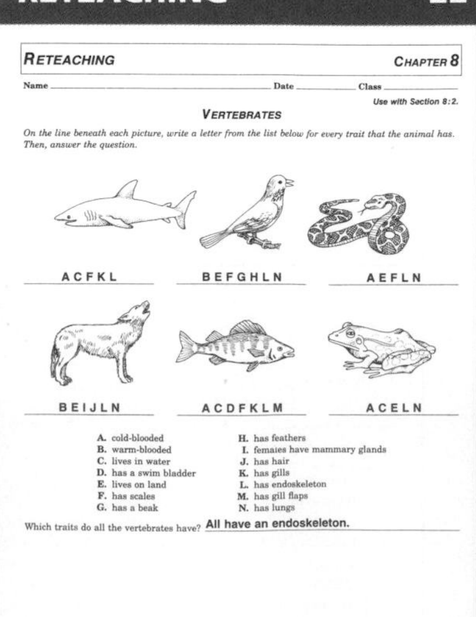

RETEACHING CHAPTER 8

Name ______ Date ______ Class ______

Use with Section 8:2.

VERTEBRATES

On the line beneath each picture, write a letter from the list below for every trait that the animal has. Then, answer the question.

ACFKL — BEFGHLN — AEFLN

BEIJLN — ACDFKLM — ACELN

A. cold-blooded
B. warm-blooded
C. lives in water
D. has a swim bladder
E. lives on land
F. has scales
G. has a beak
H. has feathers
I. females have mammary glands
J. has hair
K. has gills
L. has endoskeleton
M. has gill flaps
N. has lungs

Which traits do all the vertebrates have? **All have an endoskeleton.**

Science and Society

Are Animal Experiments Needed?

Millions of animals are used each year for research conducted in the United States and for dissections in high school classrooms. In most cases, the animals are treated with great care. In other cases, however, the animals are mistreated and many die. Sometimes the research itself is fatal and the animals die. Rats and mice are the animals used most often, but dogs, cats, pigs, rabbits, and frogs are also used. Monkeys and apes are used to study diseases such as cancer and AIDS because these animals are similar to humans. Many high school students dissect frogs, worms, fish, and even mammals. These animals are purchased from companies that usually raise them for the purpose of scientific study, although some animals are captured from the wild.

What Do You Think?

1. Many people in the United States protest the use of animals in experiments and in dissections. These people argue that it is cruel and the animals are made to suffer unnecessarily. They also argue that animals are not enough like humans to give useful results. Should animals be used in laboratory experiments? Should experiments be done if they cause the animals to suffer? Should there be strict laws governing the use of animals in labs?

Animal rights activists

2. Many people defend the use of animals in lab experiments. Doctors studying living animals say the results of experiments allow many human lives to be saved. Vaccines that protect people from diseases were tested on animals before being given to humans. Animals are used to test the safety of drugs and are being used to develop artificial body parts. Do you think human welfare should be placed over animal welfare? If animals are not used, how should new drugs be tested?

3. Many teachers feel that biology students should dissect animals to learn the structure of body systems and how they work. These teachers say that students cannot learn these things by looking at pictures in textbooks. People who disagree say that this is not a good reason for killing animals. Do you think animal dissections are needed for teaching biology students? Does it make a difference whether the animals used are wild animals captured for scientific use or animals raised for sale to schools?

Conclusion: If animals are not used in laboratories, what are the alternatives?

Science and Society

Are Animal Experiments Needed?

Background

Aristotle stated, "Plants exist for the sake of animals and the other animals for the good of man". How have attitudes toward animals changed since Aristotle's time?

Teaching Suggestions

Discuss how nonhuman animals are similar to and different from humans. The discussion will hinge on whether or not students feel that nonhuman animals have rights, equal to those of humans.

What Do You Think?

1. Most students will think that it is moral to use animals in experiments that don't cause suffering. In experiments that cause suffering, students will disagree. Most will agree that strict laws are needed.
2. Explain that many drugs and products can now be tested on cells rather than on whole animals. Discuss whether testing on animals other than humans can give reliable results that translate directly to humans.
3. Students will disagree as to whether or not animals should be dissected for biology class. Many schools are replacing animal dissections with computer simulations and models.

Conclusion: Students may suggest that new products be tested on a representative group of people who would be paid for the experiment. Others may suggest that new drugs be used on a few individuals, with their permission, who need a cure for a disease. Stress the importance of testing new products and drugs before their general widespread use.

Suggested Readings

Miller, Harlan B. and William H. Williams, Eds. *Ethics and Animals.* Clifton, N.J.: Humana Press Inc., 1983.

CHAPTER 8 REVIEW

Summary

Summary statements can be used by students to review the major concepts of the chapter.

Key Science Words

All boldfaced terms from this chapter are listed.

Testing Yourself

Using Words

1. amphibian
2. warm-blooded
3. cartilage
4. molting
5. mammary gland
6. gill
7. endoskeleton
8. cold-blooded
9. chordate
10. reptile
11. compound eye
12. spiny-skin animal

Finding Main Ideas

13. p. 163; Tube feet are used like suction cups to help starfish move.
14. p. 169; Frogs have long, sticky tongues to catch insects.
15. p. 167; A lamprey is a jawless fish that lives as a parasite.
16. p. 159; An animal molts to grow.
17. p. 165; The chordate phylum has the biggest animals.
18. p. 159; An exoskeleton is a skeleton on the outside of the body.
19. p. 168; Sharks eat other animals that live in the sea or protists.
20. p. 169; Amphibian eggs must be laid in water to keep them from drying out.
21. p. 171; Feathers help a bird keep a constant body temperature.
22. p. 168; Bony fish have a swim bladder that helps them to float.
23. p. 173; A mammary gland is a milk gland with which the young are nursed.
24. p. 171; A reptile has an egg with a tough shell that protects it and keeps it from drying out.

Chapter 8 Review

Summary

8:1 Complex Invertebrates

1. Jointed-leg animals have jointed appendages, segmented bodies, and exoskeletons.
2. Insects are jointed-leg animals with one pair of antennae, special mouthparts, and three pairs of walking legs. There are more kinds of insects than all other animals combined.
3. Spiny-skin animals have tube feet and a body design showing five parts.

8:2 Vertebrates

4. There are three classes of fish. Fish have gills. Most fish have scales. The jawless fish and cartilage fish have skeletons made of cartilage. Bony fish have skeletons made of bone. Most bony fish have a swim bladder that helps them go up and down in the water.
5. Amphibians live both in water and on land. Reptiles are animals with dry, scaly skin that can live on land. Birds are warm-blooded. They have feathers, wings, and light, hollow bones.
6. Mammals are warm-blooded and have hair. The females have milk glands with which they nurse the young.

Key Science Words

amphibian (p. 169)
antennae (p. 159)
appendage (p. 158)
bony fish (p. 168)
cartilage (p. 167)
cartilage fish (p. 167)
chordate (p. 165)
cold-blooded (p. 166)
compound eye (p. 159)
endoskeleton (p. 165)
exoskeleton (p. 159)
gill (p. 166)
hibernation (p. 170)
jawless fish (p. 167)
jointed-leg animal (p. 158)
mammal (p. 173)
mammary gland (p. 173)
molting (p. 159)
reptile (p. 170)
spiny-skin animal (p. 163)
tube feet (p. 163)
warm-blooded (p. 171)

Testing Yourself

Using Words

Choose the word from the list of Key Science Words that best fits the definition.

1. animal that lives part of its life in water and another part on land
2. body temperature that stays the same no matter what the temperature of the surroundings
3. tough, flexible tissue that supports and shapes the body
4. shedding of the exoskeleton
5. structure that produces milk
6. used by fish to breathe
7. skeleton inside the body
8. body temperature that changes with the temperature of the environment
9. animal that, sometime in its life, has a stiff rod along the back
10. has dry, scaly skin and lives on land
11. has many lenses
12. has a body design with five parts

176

Using Main Ideas

25. Insects have two compound eyes, three pairs of legs, antennae, and a body in three sections. Spiders have eight legs, no compound eyes, no antennae, and a body in two sections.
26. They all have an endoskeleton and a backbone.
27. A starfish grips slippery rocks with its tube feet.
28. An endoskeleton is on the inside of the body. An exoskeleton is on the outside of the body.
29. They have the largest brains and well developed senses.
30. Centipedes have one pair of legs on each body segment, poison claws, and feed on insects. Millipedes have two pairs of legs on most segments, no poison claws, and eat decaying plants.
31. Sharks have rows of teeth that slant backward and help them hold their food.
32. Tadpoles must live in water because they breathe with gills.
33. Some insects eat harmful insects. Insects carry pollen from flower to flower, and some insects produce food and other useful materials.

Review

Testing Yourself *continued*

Finding Main Ideas

List the page number where each main idea below is found. Then, explain each main idea.

13. how tube feet are used
14. why frogs have long, sticky tongues
15. what a lamprey is
16. why an animal molts
17. which phylum has the biggest animals
18. what an exoskeleton is
19. what sharks eat
20. why amphibian eggs must be laid in water
21. how feathers help a bird
22. what helps a bony fish float
23. what a mammary gland is
24. what kind of egg a reptile has

Using Main Ideas

Answer the questions by referring to the page number after the question.

25. How do insects differ from spiders? (pp. 160, 161)
26. What are two ways that amphibians, reptiles, birds, and mammals are alike? (pp. 169-174)
27. How does a starfish grip slippery rocks? (p. 163)
28. How does an endoskeleton differ from an exoskeleton? (p. 165)
29. Why are vertebrates believed to be the most intelligent animals on Earth? (p. 166)
30. How do centipedes differ from millipedes? (p. 160)
31. What helps sharks hold their food? (p. 168)
32. Why must tadpoles live in water? (p. 169)
33. How are insects helpful? (p. 161)

Skill Review 

*For more help, refer to the **Skill Handbook,** pages 704-719.*

1. **Infer:** Frogs have light coloring on their bottom sides and dark coloring on their top sides. Infer how this coloring can be an advantage to the frog.
2. **Observe:** Examine Figures 8-3 and 8-6. How do crayfish and grasshoppers differ from each other?
3. **Infer:** Animals whose eggs are fertilized outside the body must reproduce in water. Why is this so?
4. **Make and use tables:** Make a table to show the traits of the seven vertebrate classes and give examples of each class.

Finding Out More

Critical Thinking

1. What problems might occur if all the insects in the world were to die?
2. Considering the advantages and disadvantages of endoskeletons and exoskeletons, why do you think there are more kinds of insects than mammals?

Applications

1. Set up a bird feeder at home. Learn what you can do to attract different kinds of birds to your feeder.
2. Write a report about how honeybees communicate with one another. Discuss how communication helps bees make honey.

Skill Review

1. When a predator looks up from underwater, it is looking toward daylight and the light underside of the frog provides camouflage. When a predator looks down into water, it is looking away from the daylight, and the dark top of the frog provides camouflage.
2. Crayfish have two body sections, five pairs of walking legs, and no wings. Insects have three body sections, three pairs of walking legs, and wings.
3. The sperm needs a liquid in which to swim to the egg. Outside the body, water provides that liquid.
4. Students could place the headings Class, Trait, and Example across the top, and the names of the classes along the side. Then they could fill in the rest of the table.

Finding Out More

Critical Thinking

1. There would be widespread famine as crops failed because insects are needed for pollination of many food crops. Many fish, amphibians, reptiles, birds, and mammals would become extinct because they eat only insects.
2. There are more kinds of insects because the exoskeleton can come in many shapes and sizes. The endoskeleton is basically in one pattern and all vertebrates evolved from the same stock.

Applications

1. Various kinds of wild bird seed will attract seed-eaters. Suet balls and pine cones covered with peanut butter will attract insect eaters, and woodpeckers.
2. Bees communicate through a dance that tells the other bees where and how far away a food source is. Encourage students to read *The Dance Language and Orientation of Bees,* by Karl von Frisch.

 **Chapter Review**/*Teacher Resource Package,* pp. 38-39.

 **Chapter Test**/*Teacher Resource Package,* pp. 40-42.

Chapter Test/*Computer Test Bank*

 **Unit Test**/*Teacher Resource Package,* pp. 43-44.

CONNECTIONS

Biology in Your World

In this unit, students learn how organisms are alike and how they are different. Studies of plant and animal groups help students make sense of their world.

Literature Connection

While in Africa, Dian Fossey developed several techniques for observing mountain gorillas. Fossey found that if she stood or walked upright in the gorillas' line of sight, the animals would act frightened. She also found that looking directly at a male gorilla seemed threatening to the animal. The gorillas were most at ease when she imitated their behavior. She tried walking on her hands and knees and staying seated while observing them. When sitting, Fossey would pretend to feed and imitate the sounds gorillas make when content. She then discovered that if she partially hid herself, the animals would come out in the open to get a better view.

Geography Connection

The Great Barrier Reef of Australia sustains 350 species of coral alone. About 1500 species of fish live in the water surrounding the reef. Sea turtles, birds, worms, algae, crabs, and starfish also make the reef their home. Scientists benefit by being able to study this wide variety of life in one place.

CONNECTIONS

Biology in Your World

The Animal World

Classification is used to make sense out of all the many kinds of living things in the world. In this unit, you have seen how organisms are similar. You have also looked at some of the relationships among organisms—from simple, one-celled monerans to complex animals.

LITERATURE

Primate to Primate

Dian Fossey left her home in Kentucky in 1966 to go to Zaire (ZI uhr) and Rwanda (roo AHN duh) in Africa. There, she studied the endangered mountain gorilla in the Virunga (vuh RUN guh) Mountains.

Fossey learned to accept the animals on their own terms. She was able to learn how gorillas form family groups. She saw behaviors that scientists didn't know existed in gorillas.

During her studies, poachers were a constant threat. A poacher is a person who hunts or takes plants or animals illegally. Fossey fought a never-ending battle to protect the gorillas and their natural habitat.

Fossey studied gorillas for 13 years. Her experiences are discussed in her book, *Gorillas in the Mist.*

GEOGRAPHY

Coral Reefs

Coral reefs are found in tropical oceans. Coral reefs are built by animals called coral polyps. These creatures are related to jellyfish. They live in colonies and make hard limestone skeletons around their soft bodies. As old colonies die, new ones grow on top of the old skeletons.

The largest coral reef is the Great Barrier Reef off the coast of Australia. It is over 1900 kilometers long.

Divers often see crabs, worms, fish, octopuses, and sponges living within a coral reef. Coastline development, oil spills, and pollution threaten these fragile and beautiful communities.

LEISURE

Collecting Fossils

You can have fun searching for fossils of organisms that lived long ago. Fossils are often found in rocks such as shale, clay, sandstone, and limestone that were formed underwater. Since fossils are found in layers, try to find exposed areas such as cliffs, quarries, riverbanks, and road or railway cuts. You will need a shovel, hammer, chisel, notebook, and bags for specimens. You may find fossils of sea lilies, which are related to starfish. Fossil clams, snails, and insects are also common.

Take careful notes, and label and wrap all your specimens. You just might turn up something unusual!

CONSUMER

Tasty Morsels from the Sea

Do you enjoy eating lobster, crab, or shrimp? They are all jointed-leg animals. Scallops, clams, oysters, mussels, and snails are soft-bodied animals. To some people, sea urchins and sea cucumbers, both relatives of the starfish, are delicacies. Fish, such as cod, haddock, and tuna, which are vertebrates, are also enjoyed by many people.

You don't have to live near the ocean or go to a fancy restaurant to enjoy good seafood. Many grocery stores have a seafood department that receives fresh or frozen shipments regularly.

Seafood is best fresh and should be properly cooked. Ask at the store when shipments are received. To be considered fresh, seafood should have been received within the last 24 hours. Keep seafood cold and plan to serve it right away. You can freeze it if it hasn't been previously frozen.

Do you like to help in the kitchen? Try a simple recipe, and surprise your family with a seafood dinner.

CONNECTIONS

Leisure Connection

Fossils are common in almost every state. They can be found anywhere sedimentary rock is present. Often, fossils are unearthed by construction crews digging highway or building foundations. In North America, most fossils of mammals are found west of the Mississippi River.

Once a fossil is discovered, scientists classify it by comparing its features to those of other known species. Only the hard parts of an organism remain, so fossils are grouped by the shapes of the shells, teeth, and skeletons.

Consumer Connection

When choosing seafood, price is often a consideration. Fresh or frozen fish is generally the least expensive seafood. Shrimp, crab, and lobster cost more than fish. Exotic or unusual foods, such as sea cucumbers or squid, also cost more. Seafood can be purchased ready to eat, and that preparation adds to the price, too.

References

Arnold, Caroline. *A Walk on the Great Barrier Reef.* Minneapolis: Carolrhonda Books, Inc., 1988.

Fenton, Carroll Lane, and Mildred Adams Fenton. *The Fossil Book.* New York: Doubleday, 1989.

Fossey, Dian. *Gorillas in the Mist.* Boston: Houghton Mifflin, 1983.

Johnson, Sylvia A. *Coral Reefs.* Minneapolis: Lerner Publications Co., 1984.

Unit 3 Body Systems—Maintaining Life

UNIT OVERVIEW

Unit 3 examines animals in detail, with emphasis on humans as the representative animal. A general discussion of nutrients (Chapter 9) is covered first. Then the digestive system (Chapter 10) is explored. Chapters 11 and 12 cover circulation and blood respectively. Chapters 13 and 14 explain the respiratory, urinary, skeletal, and muscular systems.

Advance Planning

Audiovisual and computer software suggestions are located within each chapter under the heading TEACH.

To prepare for:

Lab 9-1: Gather honey, molasses, maple syrup, apple juice, and sweet potato. Obtain sugar test paper.

Lab 9-2: Order enzyme.

Mini Labs: Obtain tomatoes, tomato juice, potatoes, and potato chips.

Lab 10-1: Prepare enzymes A and B. Collect gelatin, plastic spoons, paper cups, and sticks.

Lab 10-2: Make copies of the transparency master of the digestive system. Provide colored pencils.

Lab 11-1: Order or collect live earthworms.

Lab 11-2: Collect plastic squeeze bottles.

Mini Lab: Arrange to borrow a stethoscope.

Lab 12-1: Order prepared slides of human and frog blood. Gather petri dish covers and metric rulers.

Lab 12-2: Order prepared slides of human blood. Provide sheets of clear plastic and marking pencils.

Mini Lab: Provide cooking oil, water, and red food coloring.

Lab 13-1: Order goldfish.

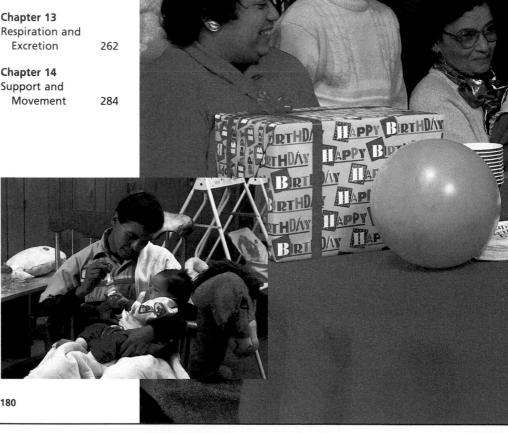

Lab 13-2: Prepare normal and abnormal artificial urine samples and salt water. Prepare silver nitrate and obtain glucose test tape.

Mini Labs: Prepare bromthymol blue and gather drinking straws. Order rubber tubing and filter paper.

Lab 14-1: Collect bones of pigs, cows, chickens, and turkeys.

Lab 14-2: Collect string, metal fasteners, index cards, and a paper punch.

Mini Labs: Purchase cooked chicken legs (thigh and drumstick attached). Prepare 6% hydrochloric acid and obtain chicken bones.

Unit 3

CONTENTS

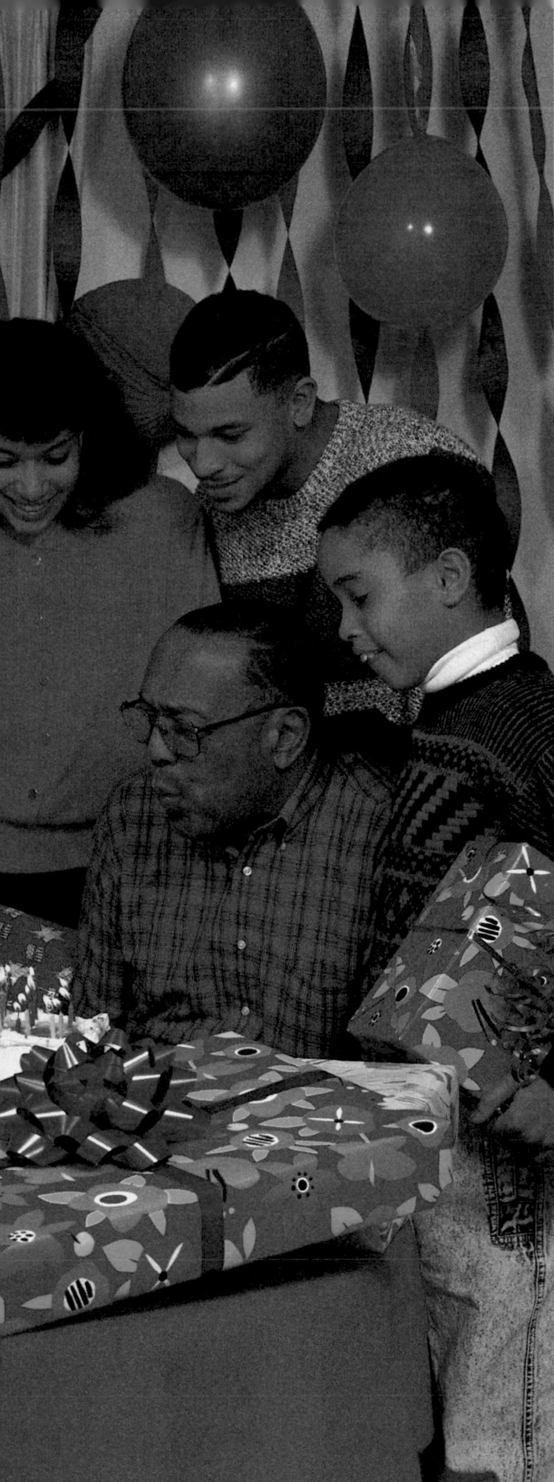

Body Systems— Maintaining Life

What would happen if...

we could live forever? What would it mean? Would we still grow old, or would we stay young? How would everyone's living forever affect the environment? The population would increase at an even greater rate than it does now. We might soon run out of food, space, and resources.

Better medical care and advances in preventing disease have increased the human lifespan. Further advances may increase it more. However, we can't live forever. In the laboratory, human cells die after a set number of divisions.

Should we think more about improving the quality of life than increasing the length of life?

UNIT OVERVIEW

Photo Teaching Tip

Ask students to read the unit opening passage and make a list of all the possible problems that might develop as a result of life without death. Initiate a discussion that first focuses the students' thoughts on your own community and later expand the discussion to include the impact of a growing population on the health of the planet. You may wish to suggest that students write an essay for extra credit on how they would like to use science to improve the quality of life.

Theme Development

Animal life depends on the animal systems that maintain and control regulated functions. This unit uses the human as its major animal example. However, the various systems present in other animal phyla are also referenced. Thus, students will receive a cohesive picture of how animal systems perform needed functions throughout the entire animal kingdom. The theme of homeostasis is developed in this unit. Students will also gain an understanding as to how the various body systems evolved within the animal kingdom.

Nutrition

PLANNING GUIDE

CONTENT	TEXT FEATURES	TEACHER RESOURCE PACKAGE	OTHER COMPONENTS
(3 1/2 days) 9:1 What Are the Nutrients in Food? Proteins, Fats, and Carbohydrates Vitamins Minerals Water Supplying Nutrients to Your Body	Skill Check: *Understand Science Words,* p. 185 Mini Lab: *How Does Salt Content Change in Processed Foods?* p. 189 Mini Lab: *What Are Processed Food Costs?* p. 191 Lab 9-1: *Milk Nutrients,* p. 187 Idea Map, p. 188 Check Your Understanding, p. 192	Enrichment: *Calculating RDA,* p. 9 Reteaching: *Nutrient Needs,* p. 23 Critical Thinking/Problem Solving: *Which Common Foods Provide the Most Nutrients?* p. 9 Skill: *Make a Bar Graph,* p. 9 Focus: *What's Cholesterol All About?* p. 17 Transparency Master: *Reading Food Labels,* p. 41 Study Guide: *What Nutrients Are in Food?* pp. 49-51 Lab 9-1: *Nutrients,* pp. 33-34	**Laboratory Manual:** *What Are the Tests for Fats and Proteins?* p. 71 **Laboratory Manual:** *How Do You Test for Vitamin C in Foods?* p. 75 Color Transparency 9: *Daily Nutrient Requirements*
(1 1/2 days) 9:2 Calories Energy in Food Calorie Content of Food Using Calories	Skill Check: *Infer,* p. 195 Skill Check: *Interpret Data,* p. 197 Lab 9-2: *Energy Foods,* p. 194 Check Your Understanding, p. 198 Problem Solving: *Reading Food Labels,* p. 198	Application: *Comparing Nutrients in Food,* p. 9 Reteaching: *Calories Intake and Output,* p. 24 Study Guide: *Calories,* pp. 52-53 Study Guide: *Vocabulary,* p. 54 Lab 9-2: *Energy Foods,* pp. 35-36	
Chapter Review	Summary Key Science Words Testing Yourself Finding Main Ideas Using Main Ideas Skill Review	Chapter Review, pp. 45-46 Chapter Test, pp. 47-49	**Test Bank**

MATERIALS NEEDED

LAB 9-1, p. 187	LAB 9-2, p. 194	MARGIN FEATURES
2 200-mL beakers thermal glove cheese cloth dropper funnel hot plate stirring rod whole milk enzyme 250-mL graduated cylinder	glass slides droppers razor blade food samples for sugar test water sugar test paper	Skill Check, p. 197 pencil paper Skill Check, p. 185 dictionary Mini Lab, p. 189 tomato canned tomato juice Mini Lab, p. 191 potato potato chips

OBJECTIVES

SECTION	OBJECTIVE	OBJECTIVES CORRELATION: CHECK YOUR UNDERSTANDING	CHAPTER REVIEW	TRP CHAPTER REVIEW	TRP CHAPTER TEST
9:1	1. **List** six important nutrients that the body needs.	1, 4	5, 10, 19, 28	3, 9, 11, 15, 24, 25, 27	1, 2, 10
	2. **Explain** how each of the six important nutrients are used by the body.	2	1, 3, 8, 13, 14, 16, 23	1, 4, 5, 7, 12, 13, 14, 20, 23, 26, 28	4, 6, 8, 9, 11, 12, 16, 17, 18, 19, 20, 21, 22, 28, 29, 30, 31, 32, 33, 34, 35, 36, 37, 38, 40, 41, 42, 43
	3. **Define** a balanced diet.	3	4, 6, 15, 20, 24, 26	6	12, 13
9:2	4. **Describe** how a Calorie is used by the body.	6	2, 18, 25	2, 16, 17, 18, 21	5, 7, 14
	5. **Compare** the number of Calories found in different nutrients.	7	7, 9, 12, 17, 27	22	3, 23, 24, 25, 26, 27
	6. **Compare** the number of Calories used in different activities.	9, 10	11, 21, 22	8, 19	15

Nutrition

CHAPTER OVERVIEW

Key Concepts

In this chapter, students are first introduced to the role and source of the six categories of nutrients. The concept of RDA is described as it relates to the way one maintains a balanced diet. Caloric intake and output are related to gaining or losing weight.

Key Science Words

balanced diet
Calorie
carbohydrate
fat
mineral
nutrient
nutrition
protein
recommended daily allowance
vitamin

Skill Development

In Lab 9-1, students will **use numbers, experiment, measure in SI,** and **make and use tables** in determining nutrients in milk. In Lab 9-2, they will **form a hypothesis, experiment,** and **make and use tables** in determining which foods contain starch and sugar. In the Skill Check on page 185, students will **understand** the **science word** *carbohydrate.* In the Skill Check on page 195, they will infer the number of Calories in fat. In the Skill Check on page 197, they will **interpret data** on Calories used in activities. In the Mini Lab on page 189, students will **interpret data** to compare salt content in fresh and processed foods. In the Mini Lab on page 191, they will **interpret data** to compare the cost of raw and processed foods.

CHAPTER PREVIEW

Chapter Content

Review this outline for Chapter 9 before you read the chapter.

Skills in this Chapter

The skills that you will use in this chapter are listed below.

- In **Lab 9-1,** you will use numbers, experiment, measure in SI, and make and use tables. In **Lab 9-2,** you will form a hypothesis, experiment, and make and use tables.
- In the **Skill Checks,** you will infer, interpret data, and understand science words.
- In the **Mini Labs,** you will interpret data.

182

Bridging

In Chapter 2, students learned about the cell and features of living things. In this chapter, students will be able to associate the fact that the foods that we eat supply nutrients to the cells.

Chapter 9

Nutrition

What influences the types of foods people buy or eat? The photo on the left will give you some clues. It shows foods that can be prepared in a microwave oven. Usually these types of foods can be cooked quickly. Speed of preparation is one thing that influences the kinds of foods we buy. Is price important? Does advertising influence our buying habits? Even ethnic background plays a role in the types of food you eat. You may prefer Greek food as shown in the photo below. Don't stores today have food sections marked ethnic foods?

No matter what influences your choice of food, it's important to your body for several reasons. You will find out how and why food is important as you read this chapter.

Try This!

Where do foods come from? Do most foods that you eat each day come from plants or animals? Make a list of the foods that you ate yesterday. Categorize each food as either "plant" or "animal." What conclusion can be drawn from your list?

A Greek salad

GETTING STARTED

Using the Photos

Discuss convenience, price, and ethnic preference as important considerations when it comes to choosing foods. Ask students to suggest other reasons people have for choosing food.

MOTIVATION/Try This!

Where do foods come from? Students will **observe** that most foods come directly from plants (potatoes, rice, vegetables, fruits). Meats also come from plants because the animals used plants as their original food source.

Chapter Preview

Have students study the chapter outline before they begin to read the chapter. They should note the overall organization of the chapter, that nutrients are studied first, and how the body uses these nutrients is studied next.

Misconception

Students may believe that vitamins supply you with energy, and the more vitamins you take, the healthier you will look and feel. Both are false. No Calories are present in vitamins; therefore, no energy is obtained from them. Certain vitamins, such as the fat-soluble vitamins, in high doses will cause health problems.

9:1 What Nutrients Are in Food?

PREPARATIONS

Materials Needed

Make copies of the Focus, Study Guide, Skill, Transparency Master, Enrichment, Application, Critical Thinking/Problem Solving, Reteaching, and Lab worksheets in the *Teacher Resource Package.*

▶ Obtain enzyme (rennilase), whole milk, and cheese cloth for Lab 9-1.

▶ Obtain starch and sucrose for the Focus activity.

Key Science Words

nutrient	vitamin
nutrition	recommended daily allowance
protein	mineral
fat	balanced diet
carbohydrate	

Process Skills

In Lab 9-1, they will use numbers, experiment, measure in SI, and make and use tables. In the Skill Check, they will understand science words. In the Mini Labs, students will interpret data.

1 FOCUS

▶ The objectives are listed on the student page. Remind students to preview these objectives as a guide to this numbered section.

Guided Practice

Have students write down their answers to the margin question: carbohydrates, proteins, fats, vitamins, minerals, and water.

Focus/*Teacher Resource Book,* p. 17. Use the Focus transparency shown at the bottom of this page as an introduction to nutrients and Calories in food.

9:1 What Are the Nutrients in Food?

Objectives

1. **List** six important nutrients that the body needs.
2. **Explain** how each of the six important nutrients is used by the body.
3. **Define** a balanced diet.

Key Science Words

nutrient
nutrition
protein
fat
carbohydrate
vitamin
recommended daily allowance
mineral
balanced diet

If a car runs out of gas, its motor stops. If you don't add fuel to your body, your motor also stops. Food is the fuel for living things.

Food

The cells of your body must be supplied with food or they stop working. Cells use food for growth and repair. Food must be supplied to your body regularly in the right amount and balance. Your body needs fuel to keep working, just as a motor needs fuel to keep running. You and the motor need the right balance of fuel and oxygen to keep working. Without the proper balance of these substances, your body and the motor will slow down or stop.

What are the six nutrients in food?

To keep all your body cells running properly, you must supply them with the right kinds and amounts of nutrients (NEW tree unts). **Nutrients** are the chemicals in food that cells need. The study of nutrients and how your body uses them is called **nutrition** (new TRISH un). The six different nutrients in food are proteins (PROH teenz), fats, carbohydrates (kar boh HI drayts), vitamins, minerals, and water. Each of these six nutrients will be described in the following sections.

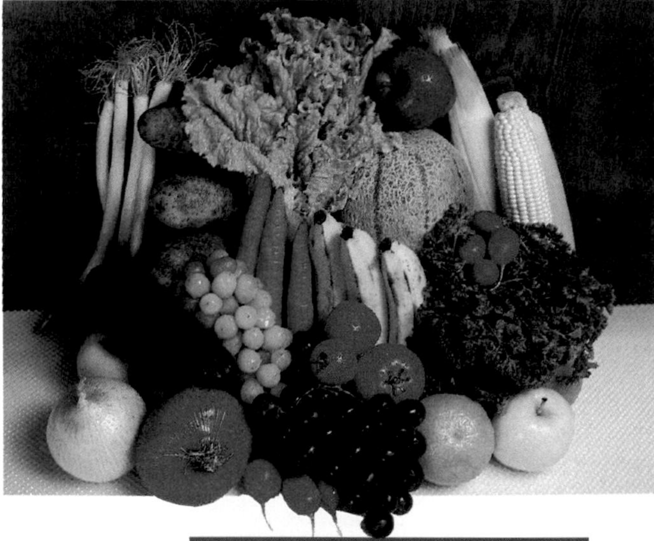

Figure 9-1 Fruits and vegetables provide us with many important nutrients.

OPTIONS

Science Background

Both animal and plant foods supply protein. In general, protein from animals has more nutritional value because it has more of the essential amino acids. Meat, fish, poultry, milk, eggs, legumes, and cereal grains provide most of our protein needs.

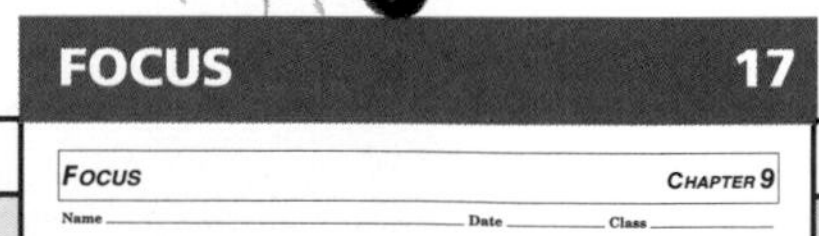

FOCUS 17

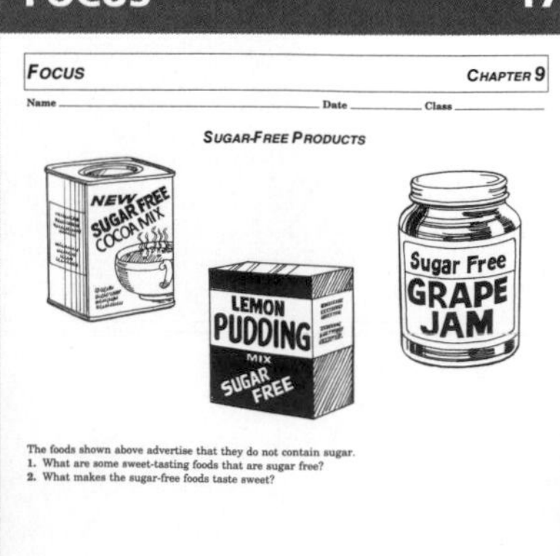

Focus CHAPTER 9

Name ____ Date ____ Class ____

SUGAR-FREE PRODUCTS

The foods shown above advertise that they do not contain sugar.
1. What are some sweet-tasting foods that are sugar free?
2. What makes the sugar-free foods taste sweet?

Figure 9-2 These foods are excellent sources of proteins, fats, and carbohydrates.

Proteins, Fats, and Carbohydrates

Proteins are nutrients that are used to build and repair body parts. Proteins make up large parts of tissues such as bone, muscle, and skin. Foods such as meat, eggs, fish, nuts, and chicken supply you with protein.

Fats are nutrients that are used as a source of energy by your body. Fats are compounds that store large amounts of energy. Salad dressing, butter, and cooking oils are foods high in fat.

Carbohydrates are nutrients that also supply you with energy. What then is the difference between fats and carbohydrates? The difference is that your body may store fats. It uses them as an energy source after it first uses up all of your carbohydrate supply. Foods containing starches and sugars, such as bread and fruit, supply you with carbohydrates.

How much of each nutrient is present in your body? Water is an important nutrient that makes up a large percentage of the human body. Figure 9-3 shows that a male's body is 60 percent water. How does this amount compare with what is present in a female? A male has 18 percent fat. Does a female have more or less of this nutrient? Look at Figure 9-3 and compare amounts of carbohydrate for males and females.

How much of each nutrient do you need each day? You might guess that you need more protein than carbohydrate because protein makes up more of your body. You might also guess that you need very little carbohydrate. After all, this nutrient makes up little of your body.

Skill Check

Understand science words: carbohydrate. The word part *carbo* means coal. In your dictionary, find three words that contain the word part *carbo. For more help, refer to the* ***Skill Handbook****, pages 706-711.*

Figure 9-3 Compare the average percentages of each nutrient in males and females.

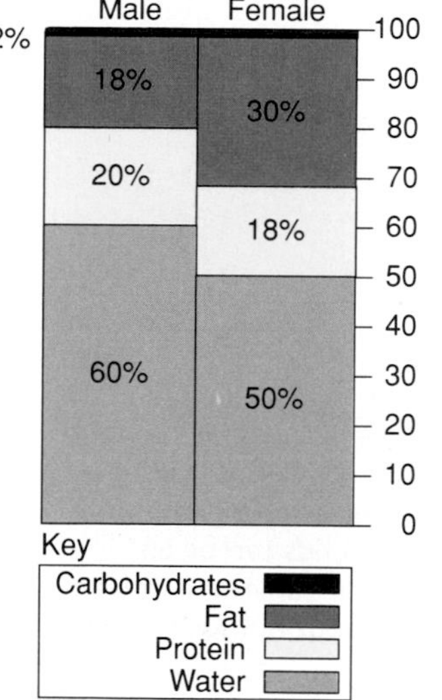

2 TEACH

MOTIVATION/Demonstration

An analogy of the need for a supply of both food and oxygen may be made by burning a candle. The candle wax is the fuel. While burning, the candle uses oxygen from the air. If the candle uses all its fuel, it goes out. If air is excluded, it also goes out. Demonstrate by placing a beaker over the burning candle.

MOTIVATION/Audiovisual

Show the video *Nutrition to Grow On*, Focus Media Inc.

Concept Development

▶ Have students give other examples of protein foods that they are familiar with. Do the same with fats and carbohydrates. You may want to write the students' suggestions on the chalkboard under the proper headings.

▶ Take a survey of what some students had for breakfast or for supper the night before. A typical survey will show that more carbohydrates are eaten than any other food nutrient.

Independent Practice

Study Guide/*Teacher Resource Package*, p. 49. Use the Study Guide worksheet shown at the bottom of this page for independent practice.

STUDY GUIDE 49

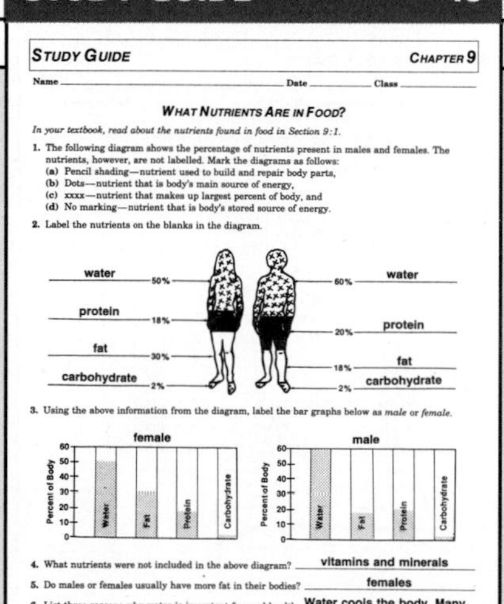

STUDY GUIDE CHAPTER 9

Name ______ Date ______ Class ______

WHAT NUTRIENTS ARE IN FOOD?

In your textbook, read about the nutrients found in food in Section 9:1.

1. The following diagram shows the percentage of nutrients present in males and females. The nutrients, however, are not labelled. Mark the diagrams as follows:
   (a) Pencil shading—nutrient used to build and repair body parts,
   (b) Dots—nutrient that is body's main source of energy,
   (c) xxxx—nutrient that makes up largest percent of body, and
   (d) No marking—nutrient that is body's stored source of energy.
2. Label the nutrients on the blanks in the diagram.

3. Using the above information from the diagram, label the bar graphs below as *male* or *female*.

4. What nutrients were not included in the above diagram? vitamins and minerals
5. Do males or females usually have more fat in their bodies? females
6. List three reasons why water is important for good health. Water cools the body. Many chemical changes take place in water. Water helps carry away body wastes.

OPTIONS

Daily Nutrient Requirements/*Transparency Package*, number 9. Use color transparency number 9 as you teach the nutrients your body needs.

What Are the Tests for Fats and Proteins?/*Lab Manual*, pp. 71-74. Use this lab as an extension to teaching the nutrients in food.

TEACH

Concept Development

▶ Have students use Figure 9-4 to determine how much of each nutrient they need. You may wish to have students construct a chart that summarizes the information.

Connection: Social Studies

Have students determine foods that are mainly fat, protein, and carbohydrate sources in different countries.

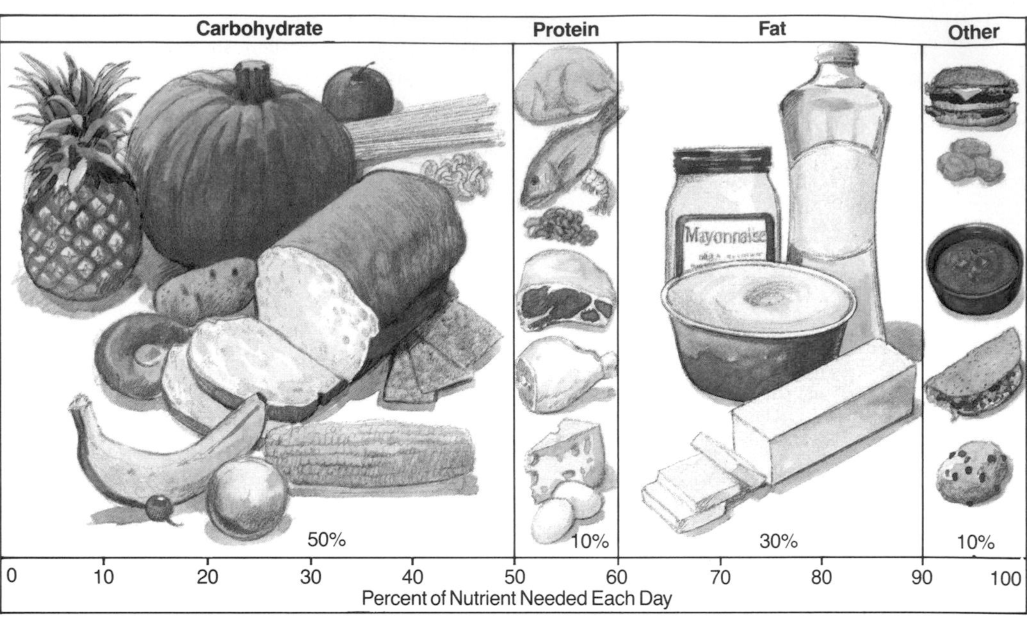

Figure 9-4 Compare the daily amounts of nutrients needed by your body. Which nutrient should you eat most each day? carbohydrate

Something quite different is true. You need more carbohydrate than protein each day. Why? The body uses carbohydrates quickly. Carbohydrates are the body's main source of energy. They are not stored for a long time. Fats and proteins can be stored for a long time.

Figure 9-4 shows how much of each nutrient your body needs each day. Which nutrient is needed in the greatest amount? Which nutrient is needed in the smallest amount? Carbohydrates are needed in the greatest amount and protein is needed in the smallest amount. A person can remain healthy only if he or she takes in the correct amounts of each nutrient. Of course, the amount of each nutrient needed daily may differ slightly for each person. The amount of each nutrient you take in must be balanced with what your body uses. One way to stay healthy is to eat foods that will supply you with the correct amount of each nutrient. Your diet should be about 52 percent carbohydrates, 32 percent fats, and 10 percent protein each day for you to stay healthy.

What parts of your body contain or store nutrients? Protein makes up the cytoplasm in your cells. All the body organs are mostly protein. Fats are stored under skin and around body organs. Carbohydrates are stored in the liver and blood.

Mini Lab

Leisure: Planning a meal for a group of friends can be an enjoyable way to learn about nutrients.

OPTIONS

Skill/*Teacher Resource Package*, p. 9. Use the Skill worksheet shown here for students to make a bar graph of nutrients in cereals.

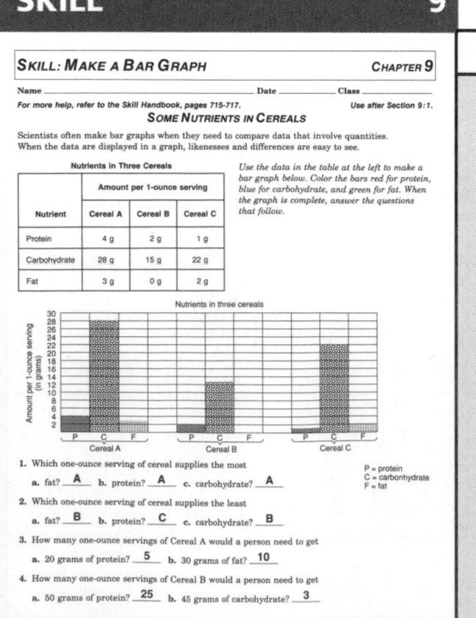

SKILL 9

SKILL: MAKE A BAR GRAPH CHAPTER 9

Name ______ Date ______ Class ______

For more help, refer to the Skill Handbook, pages 715-717. *Use after Section 9:1.*

SOME NUTRIENTS IN CEREALS

Scientists often make bar graphs when they need to compare data that involve quantities. When the data are displayed in a graph, likenesses and differences are easy to see.

Nutrients in Three Cereals

Nutrient	Amount per 1-ounce serving		
	Cereal A	Cereal B	Cereal C
Protein	4 g	2 g	1 g
Carbohydrate	28 g	15 g	22 g
Fat	3 g	0 g	2 g

Use the data in the table at the left to make a bar graph below. Color the bars red for protein, blue for carbohydrate, and green for fat. When the graph is complete, answer the questions that follow.

1. Which one-ounce serving of cereal supplies the most
   a. fat? A b. protein? A c. carbohydrate? A
2. Which one-ounce serving of cereal supplies the least
   a. fat? B b. protein? C c. carbohydrate? B
3. How many one-ounce servings of Cereal A would a person need to get
   a. 20 grams of protein? 5 b. 30 grams of fat? 10
4. How many one-ounce servings of Cereal B would a person need to get
   a. 50 grams of protein? 25 b. 45 grams of carbohydrate? 3

Lab 9–1 Milk Nutrients

Problem: What nutrients are present in milk?

Skills

use numbers, experiment, make and use tables, measure in SI

Materials

whole milk
hot plate
medicine dropper
enzyme
stirring rod
250-mL graduated cylinder
200-mL beakers (2)
thermal glove
cheese cloth
funnel

Procedure

1. Copy the data table.
2. **Measure in SI:** Measure 100 mL of whole milk in the graduated cylinder.
3. Pour the milk into a beaker.
4. Place the beaker of milk onto a hot plate and warm the milk. **CAUTION:** *Use a thermal glove when handling hot objects.*
5. Add 20 drops of the enzyme to the milk.
6. Use a stirring rod to mix the milk and enzyme for several minutes.
7. Continue to stir until the milk separates into a solid white part and a liquid part.
8. Line a funnel with a single layer of wet cheese cloth. Position the funnel so that a beaker is below it, as shown in the figure.
9. Pour the milk into the funnel. Wait 2 to 3 minutes until all the liquid has drained through the cheese cloth.

10. The liquid that drains into the beaker is carbohydrate. Use a graduated cylinder to measure the volume.
11. Record this volume in the data table.
12. The solid material left in the cheese cloth is protein. Record its color and texture in your data table.

Data and Observations

1. What is the percent water in your milk sample?
2. What is the percent protein in your milk sample?

STATE OF MILK	OBSERVATIONS
Original volume of milk used	100 mL
Volume of water in milk sample	80-85 mL
Color and texture of protein	white, soft solid
Color of liquid	clear

Analyze and Apply

1. Why did you add the enzyme to the milk?
2. What three essential nutrients did you study in this lab?
3. Milk can be separated into solid curds and liquid whey. In which step did you do this?
4. **Apply:** If you had tested skim milk instead of whole milk, would nutrients be present in different amounts in the two types of milk?

Extension

Experiment with skim milk and 2-percent milk to measure the same nutrients as those for whole milk.

ANSWERS

Data and Observations

1. 80-85%
2. 15-20%

Analyze and Apply

1. The enzyme helps to separate the protein out of the liquid.
2. carbohydrate, protein, water
3. step 7 after enzyme was added in step 5
4. They would be present in the same amount. Skim milk has less fat, and this nutrient wasn't tested for in this lab.

Lab 9-1 Milk Nutrients

Overview

Students will experimentally measure the amount and/or presence of water, protein, and carbohydrate in milk.

Objectives: Upon completion of this lab, students will be able to (1) **state** that milk contains water, protein, and carbohydrates, (2) **describe** the lab technique used to separate these nutrients, (3) **describe** the test used to detect milk carbohydrate.

Time Allotment: 30 minutes

Preparation

▶ **Alternate Materials:** Vinegar may be substituted in place of rennilase (about 1 teaspoon/100 ml of milk).

▶ Rennilase is available from a biological supply house.

Lab 9-1 worksheet/*Teacher Resource Package,* pp. 33-34.

Teaching the Lab

▶ Review use and proper reading of a graduated cylinder before starting this lab.

▶ Protein may be verified as follows: concentrated nitric acid added to protein will result in a yellow color. *Do as a teacher demo.*

Cooperative Learning: Have students work in groups of two and list their data on the chalkboard. For more information, see pp. 22T-23T in the Teacher Guide.

TEACH

Concept Development

▶ Obtain food labels from a variety of foods. Make photocopies for your students and a transparency, for the overhead projector. Go over the transparency, pointing out the vitamins to familiarize students with the names.

Guided Practice

Have students write down their answers to the margin question: They are needed for growth and tissue repair.

Idea Map

Have students use the idea map as a study guide to the major concepts of this section.

Bio Tip

Consumer: Which has more vitamin C, an orange or a red bell pepper? An orange contains 70 milligrams, while a red bell pepper contains 140 milligrams.

Vitamins

Are you a label reader? Have you ever read a label on a cereal box or bread wrapper? Labels give you useful information about the foods you eat. For example, labels tell you which vitamins are in foods. **Vitamins** are chemical compounds needed in very small amounts for growth and tissue repair of the body. A well-balanced diet will supply you with the vitamins needed each day.

The vitamins have chemical names. For example, ascorbic acid is more commonly known as vitamin C. The chemical name for vitamin A is retinol. When you read a food label, you will see vitamins listed as A, B_1,B_2, B_3, C, and D, or sometimes by their chemical names. Look at Table 9-1 for the names of the vitamins you need each day.

Certain diseases may appear if too much or not enough of a vitamin is in your diet. Taking too much vitamin A, for example, can cause loss of hair or liver problems. Without enough vitamins, many chemical changes cannot take place within your cells. Table 9-1 lists some vitamins that appear on food labels. The table shows how the body uses the vitamins and describes what happens if you do not have enough of them. For example, if you were to go for many months without fresh fruit and vegetables, you may find your mouth sore, your skin rough, and that you bruise easily.

Why are vitamins important?

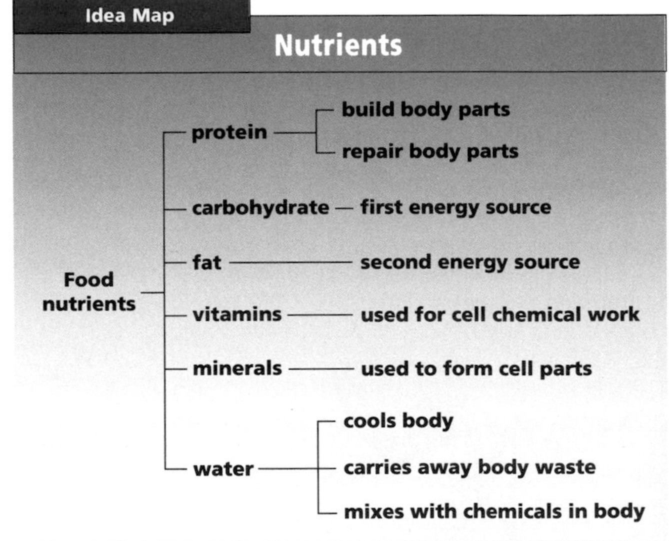

Study Tip: Use this idea map as a study guide to comparing how the body uses each of the six food nutrients.

OPTIONS

Transparency Master/*Teacher Resource Package*, p. 41. Use the Transparency Master shown here to teach how to read food labels.

TRANSPARENCY 41

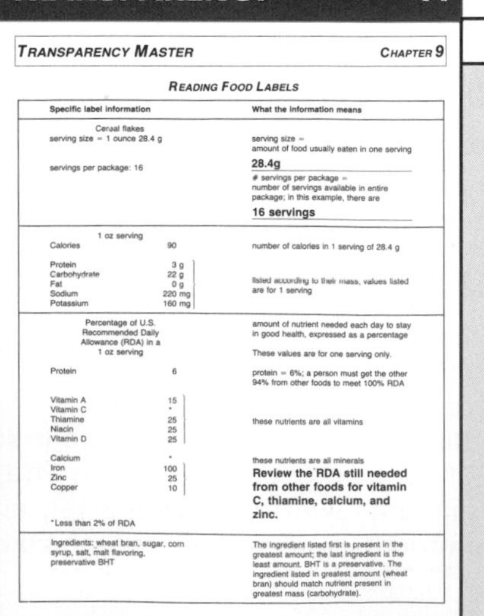

TRANSPARENCY MASTER — CHAPTER 9

READING FOOD LABELS

Specific label information	What the information means
Cereal flakes serving size = 1 ounce 28.4 g servings per package: 16	serving size = amount of food usually eaten in one serving **28.4g** # servings per package = number of servings available in entire package; in this example, there are **16 servings**
1 oz serving Calories 90 Protein 3 g Carbohydrate 22 g Fat 0 g Sodium 220 mg Potassium 160 mg	number of calories in 1 serving of 28.4 g listed according to their mass, values listed are for 1 serving
Percentage of U.S. Recommended Daily Allowance (RDA) in a 1 oz serving Protein 6 Vitamin A 15 Vitamin C * Thiamine 25 Niacin 25 Vitamin D 25 Calcium * Iron 100 Zinc 25 Copper 10 *Less than 2% of RDA	amount of nutrient needed each day to stay in good health, expressed as a percentage These values are for one serving only. protein = 6%; a person must get the other 94% from other foods to meet 100% RDA these nutrients are all vitamins these nutrients are all minerals **Review the RDA still needed from other foods for vitamin C, thiamine, calcium, and zinc.**
Ingredients: wheat bran, sugar, corn syrup, salt, malt flavoring, preservative BHT	The ingredient listed first is present in the greatest amount; the last ingredient is the least amount. BHT is a preservative. The ingredient listed in greatest amount (wheat bran) should match nutrient present in greatest mass (carbohydrate).

TABLE 9-1. VITAMINS				
Vitamin	**How Used in Body**	**Problems if Not Enough**	**Foods**	**RDA**
A (retinol)	vision, healthy skin	night blindness, rough skin	liver, broccoli, carrots	5000 IU
B_1 (thiamine)	allows cells to use carbohydrates	digestive problems, muscle paralysis	ham, eggs, raisins	1.5 mg
B_2 (riboflavin)	allows cells to use carbohydrates and proteins	eye problems, cracking skin	milk, yeast, eggs	1.7 mg
B_3 (niacin)	allows cells to carry out respiration	mental problems, skin rash, diarrhea	peanuts, tuna, chicken	20.0 mg
C (ascorbic acid)	healthy membranes, wound healing	sore mouth and bleeding gums, bruises	green peppers oranges, lemons, tomatoes	60.0 mg
D (calciferol)	bone growth	bowed legs, poor teeth	egg yolk, shrimp, milk, yeast	400 IU

Notice the column marked RDA in Table 9-1. RDA stands for recommended daily allowance. The **recommended daily allowance** is the amount of each vitamin and mineral a person needs each day to stay in good health. The amounts for some of the vitamins are listed as IUs, which stands for International Units. Some of the units in Table 9-1 are listed as mg, or milligrams. Remember from Chapter 1 that one milligram is one thousandth of a gram. A strand of hair has a mass of more than one milligram. You can see that vitamins are needed in very small amounts.

Let's look at a real food label. Figure 9-5 shows a label from tomato juice. Notice that the vitamins have been marked in color. Also note the numbers listed. These numbers are percentages. They show how much of the RDA is in one serving of tomato juice. A serving of this juice gives you 20 percent of the RDA for vitamin A. Notice in the label the nutrients called thiamine, riboflavin, and niacin. These are also known as vitamins B_1, B_2, and B_3, respectively. How much of the RDA for niacin is in one serving of this juice? 6 percent

Mini Lab

How Does Salt Content Change in Processed Foods?

Interpret data: Find out how much salt is present in a tomato. Compare this with the salt in canned tomato juice. How do these amounts compare? *For more help, refer to the **Skill Handbook**, pages 704-705.*

Figure 9-5 Food labels tell which vitamins the packaged food contains. The vitamins are highlighted in the list.

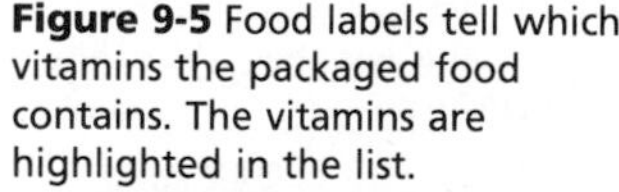
PERCENTAGE OF U.S. RECOMMENDED DAILY ALLOWANCES (U.S. RDA)

PROTEIN . . . . . . 2 NIACIN 6
VITAMIN A . . . . . . 20 CALCIUM . . . . *
VITAMIN C . . . . . . 25 IRON 4
THIAMINE . . . . . . 4 MAGNESIUM 4
RIBOFLAVIN 2

*CONTAINS LESS THAN 2 PERCENT OF THE U.S. RDA OF THIS NUTRIENT.

INGREDIENTS: TOMATOES AND SALT.

TEACH

Concept Development

▶ Remind students that 1000 milligrams equals 1 gram. Show them the mass of 1 gram of a clay ball. Tell them to imagine having to divide this ball into 1000 equal units to help them visualize the size of a milligram.

Mini Lab

Processed foods generally have more salt. 1 tomato (120 g) contains approximately 4 mg of sodium. 1 cup of tomato juice (240 g) contains about 480 mg of sodium.

Cooperative Learning: Divide the class into groups of 4 students. Have each group research the following information for a different vitamin: (a) its RDA, (b) food sources that are high and low in the vitamin, (c) how it is used by the body, (d) signs of vitamin deficiency, (e) side effects due to excess dosage.

ENRICHMENT 9

ENRICHMENT CHAPTER 9

Name ______ Date ______ Class ______

Use after Section 9:1.

CALCULATING RDA

The term *Recommended Daily Allowance* (RDA) is the amount of a nutrient a person needs each day to stay in good health. A check of food labels will show that most nutrients are listed by RDA. Use numbers to answer the questions about RDA that follow.

1. How do you figure out the percent of RDA for a nutrient in a food if you know the amount of that nutrient you have already eaten?
2. How can you figure out the percent of RDA that you still need for that nutrient if the amount you ate didn't supply 100% RDA?

Complete the following table. The first nutrient is done for you as an example.

Nutrient	RDA	Amount taken in	Amount taken in / RDA	× 100 = % RDA taken in that day	% RDA still needed that day
Vitamin B_1	1.5 mg	0.38 mg	$\frac{0.38 \text{ mg}}{1.5 \text{ mg}} = 0.25$	× 100 = 25%	100 − 25 = 75%
		0.75 mg	$\frac{0.75 \text{ mg}}{1.5 \text{ mg}} = 0.50$	× 100 = 50%	50%
Vitamin C	60.0 mg	20.0 mg	$\frac{20.0 \text{ mg}}{60.0 \text{ mg}} = 0.33$	× 100 = 33%	67%
		15.0 mg	$\frac{15.0 \text{ mg}}{60.0 \text{ mg}} = 0.25$	× 100 = 25%	75%
Calcium	1.0 g	0.3 g	$\frac{0.3 \text{ g}}{1.0 \text{ g}} = 0.30$	× 100 = 30%	70%
		0.1 g	$\frac{0.1 \text{ g}}{1.0 \text{ g}} = 0.10$	× 100 = 10%	90%
Protein	50.0 g	12.5 g	$\frac{12.5 \text{ g}}{50.0 \text{ g}} = 0.25$	× 100 = 25%	75%
		37.5 g	$\frac{37.5 \text{ g}}{50.0 \text{ g}} = 0.75$	× 100 = 75%	25%
Fat	5.0 g	1.0 g	$\frac{1.0 \text{ g}}{5.0 \text{ g}} = 0.20$	× 100 = 20%	80%

OPTIONS

Enrichment/*Teacher Resource Package*, p. 9. Use the Enrichment worksheet shown here to have students calculate RDA.

How Do You Test for Vitamin C in Foods?/*Lab Manual*, pp. 75-78. Use this lab as an extension to teaching about vitamins.

TEACH

Concept Development

▶ It may be difficult for students to distinguish between vitamins and minerals when using the chemical names. Use a periodic table of the elements for reference. If a periodic table in chart form is not available, photocopies of the table can be made from any chemistry textbook.

▶ Point out that all the minerals are also elements present on the periodic table.

▶ Ask students to list the minerals present in various foods by reading food labels. They should use the periodic table as a guide.

Independent Practice

Study Guide/*Teacher Resource Package*, p. 50. Use the Study Guide worksheet shown at the bottom of this page for independent practice.

Bio Tip

Health: The American Heart Association recommends that you use only 500 mg of salt each day.

TABLE 9–2. MINERALS

Mineral	How Used in Body	Problems if Not Enough	Foods	RDA
Iron	helps form blood cells, helps blood carry oxygen	anemia, feeling tired	liver, egg yolk, peas, enriched cereals, whole grains	15 mg
Calcium	helps form bones and teeth	bones and teeth become weak or brittle	milk, cheese, sardines, nuts, whole-grain cereals	1 g
Magnesium	helps form bones and teeth	muscles twitch	potatoes, fruits, whole-grain cereals	325 mg
Iodine	helps make thyroid gland chemical	causes thyroid gland to enlarge	seafoods, eggs, milk, iodized table salt	150 μ*
Sodium	muscle contractions, nerve messages	dizziness, tired feeling, cramps	bacon, butter, table salt	1200 mg

*μ = microgram (one microgram is 1/1 000 000 of a gram)

Minerals

Minerals are nutrients needed to help form different cell parts. Minerals, like vitamins, are chemicals. Your body needs minerals in very small amounts. A diet with a variety of foods provides needed minerals.

The list of minerals that your body needs reads like a list of laboratory chemicals. Iron, calcium, iodine, magnesium, and sodium are just a few important minerals. Table 9-2 lists these minerals and how they are used by your body.

The table also tells you what can happen when these minerals are missing from your diet. For example, calcium is a mineral needed to form strong bones and teeth. Lack of calcium may cause bones and teeth to become weak and even brittle.

Figure 9-6 shows you how minerals might be listed on a food label. The minerals are marked in color. Notice the amount of each mineral in a serving of yogurt. These amounts are percentages of the RDA in one serving of yogurt.

Figure 9-6 Labels explain how much of each mineral is contained in the packaged food. The minerals are highlighted in the list. Which mineral in this food label is less than 2% of the U.S. RDA? iron

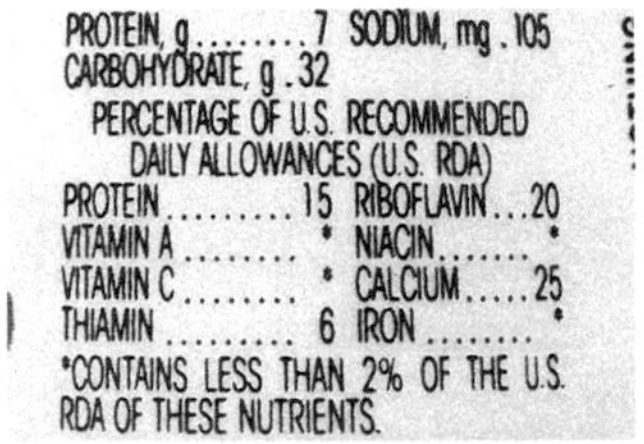
PROTEIN, g........7 SODIUM, mg.105
CARBOHYDRATE, g.32
PERCENTAGE OF U.S. RECOMMENDED DAILY ALLOWANCES (U.S. RDA)
PROTEIN........15 RIBOFLAVIN...20
VITAMIN A........* NIACIN.......*
VITAMIN C........* CALCIUM.....25
THIAMIN........6 IRON........*
*CONTAINS LESS THAN 2% OF THE U.S. RDA OF THESE NUTRIENTS.

OPTIONS

Application/*Teacher Resource Package*, p. 9. Use the Application worksheet shown here to have students compare nutrients in foods.

STUDY GUIDE 50

STUDY GUIDE — *CHAPTER 9*

Name ______ Date ______ Class ______

WHAT NUTRIENTS ARE IN FOOD?

8. Complete the following table by putting check marks in the correct columns.

	Fat	Protein	Carbohydrate
Present in butter, oils	✓		
Body's main energy source			✓
Present in bread and fruit			✓
Makes up bone and muscle		✓	
Need the most of daily			✓
Present in meat, fish		✓	
Used most quickly in body			✓
10% of your diet each day		✓	
Found as cell membranes	✓	✓	
Stored under skin	✓		
Stored in blood and liver			✓

9. Examine these food labels. Then, answer the questions below.

Cereal (1 serving)

Nutrient	RDA
Vitamin A	20
Vitamin C	10
Riboflavin	30
Thiamine	10
Niacin	25
Calcium	40
Iron	60
Potassium	1

Breakfast drink (1 serving)

Nutrient	RDA
Vitamin A	30
Vitamin C	5
Niacin	2
Riboflavin	40
Thiamine	5
Calcium	50
Iron	4
Zinc	1
Phosphorus	1

a. Circle the vitamins on each label. b. Underline the minerals on each label.

c. Which of the two foods supplies more Vitamin C in one serving? cereal

APPLICATION 9

APPLICATION: CONSUMER — *CHAPTER 9*

Name ______ Date ______ Class ______

Use after Section 9:2.

COMPARING NUTRIENTS IN FOODS

Visit a grocery store, and look at the labels of six different breakfast cereals. Look at cereals that are made to appeal more to children and cereals made to appeal more to adults. On each box, find the table that gives the nutrient content and recommended daily allowance (RDA) figures.

Record the information listed below for each cereal. Be sure to use the figures that are given for the cereal alone, without milk added.

Name of cereal (Answers will vary)	% RDA Protein	% RDA Vitamin A	Grams: Carbohydrates
a. Cheerios	6	25	20
b. Special K	10	15	20
c. Puffed Rice	0	0	13
d. Quaker 100% Natural	4	0	18
e. Cap'n Crunch	2	0	24
f. Corn Flakes	4	15	24

Student answers will vary depending on cereals used.

1. Use the information in your table to finish the bar graphs below.

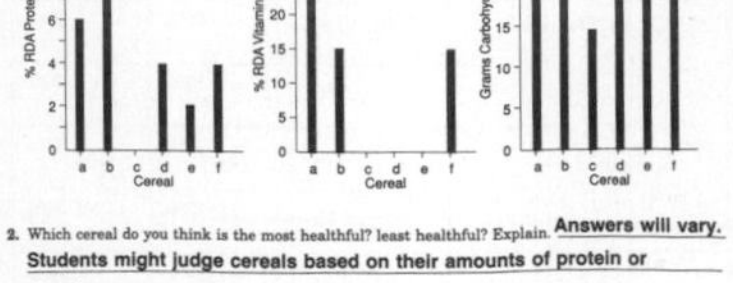

2. Which cereal do you think is the most healthful? least healthful? Explain. Answers will vary. Students might judge cereals based on their amounts of protein or vitamins.

Figure 9-7 You need to replace water that is lost from the body as sweat.

Water

Water is an important nutrient for good health. You learned earlier that the human body is made up of 50 to 60 percent water.

There are three reasons why water is important. First, water cools the body. You see or feel this happening when you sweat, Figure 9-7. Second, many chemicals within the body can combine only with water. Therefore, many chemical changes can take place only in water. Third, water helps carry away body wastes.

The average adult needs about two liters of water each day. Most people don't drink that much water but still get enough of it. Many foods contain water, Figure 9-8. In fact, some foods are over 90 percent water.

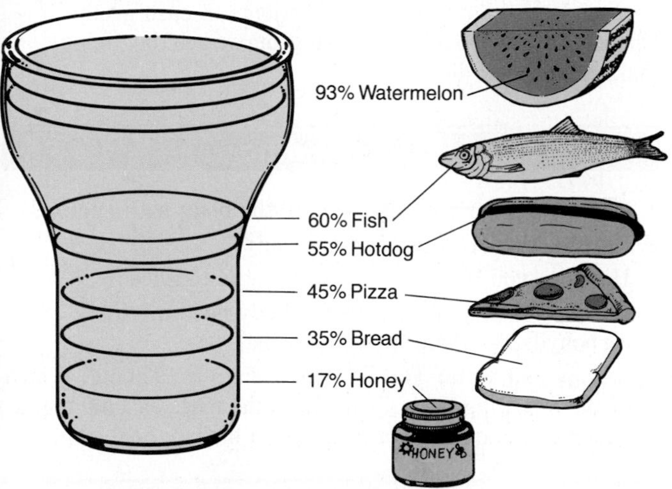

Figure 9-8 Compare the percentage of water in some foods.

Mini Lab

What Are Processed-food Costs?

Interpret data: Find the cost per gram of a raw potato. Compare this with the cost per gram of potato chips. *For more help, refer to the* ***Skill Handbook,*** *pages 704-705.*

TEACH

Concept Development

▶ Ask students how much water they drink in one day. Show them the volume of 2 liters with a graduated cylinder.

Mini Lab

You may actually want to supply students with a potato and have them mass the potato in class. Provide a balance, the cost of the potato, and the cost of a bag of potato chips and the mass of potatoes in the bag.

Check for Understanding

Prepare a transparency of a food label for the overhead. Use the food label to discuss the needs for fat, protein, and carbohydrate; the food group to which the food belongs; the vitamins and minerals present; and the RDA for all vitamins and minerals shown.

Reteach

Prepare a chart with the following headings: Nutrients, Amount in one serving, Role in body, Percent in body of male/female. Supply a copy of a food label. Have students complete the chart using the label and their text as a reference.

CRITICAL THINKING 9

CRITICAL THINKING/PROBLEM SOLVING — CHAPTER 9

Name ______ Date ______ Class ______

Use after Section 9:1.

WHICH COMMON FOODS PROVIDE THE MOST NUTRIENTS?

A balanced diet contains the right percentages of carbohydrate, fat, protein, and water. Find out which foods provide the highest percentage of each. Look at the table below.

Food	Percentage of water	Percentage of carbohydrate	Percentage of fat	Percentage of protein
Milk, whole	87	5	4	4
Bread, white	36	52	4	8
Lettuce	96	3	0	1
Sugar	1	99	0	0
Corn oil	0	0	100	0
Egg	74	1	12	13
Beef, ground	54	0	20	26
Potato	75	21	0	4
Cheese, cheddar	38	4	33	25
Grain cereal	1	84	0	15
Margarine	16	1	82	1
Potato chips	4	50	42	4
Spaghetti	7	77	2	14
Tomato	94	5	0	1
Orange juice	88	10	1	1

Analyzing the Problem

1. Look at the table above. Fill in the foods that provide the highest percentage of each nutrient:
   water **lettuce, tomato, orange juice**
   carbohydrate **sugar, grain cereal**
   fat **corn oil, margarine**
   protein **ground beef, cheddar cheese, grain cereal, spaghetti**
2. People who need to lose weight for health reasons are advised to consume a lower percentage of fats. Which foods might they avoid? **corn oil, margarine, potato chips**
3. Protein is very important in the diet. Which three foods in the table provide high protein without providing high fat content? **grain cereal, spaghetti**

Solving the Problem

1. Can you conclude that a diet of potato chips and fruit juices is all you need to eat to be healthy? Explain. **No, a balanced diet must contain enough of all nutrients.**

OPTIONS

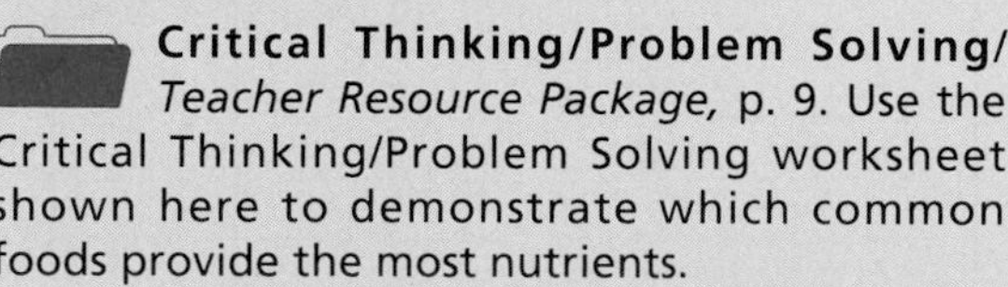

Critical Thinking/Problem Solving/ *Teacher Resource Package,* p. 9. Use the Critical Thinking/Problem Solving worksheet shown here to demonstrate which common foods provide the most nutrients.

TEACH

Guided Practice

Have students write down their answers to the margin question: a diet with the right amount of each nutrient.

Independent Practice

Study Guide/*Teacher Resource Package,* p. 51. Use the Study Guide worksheet shown at the bottom of this page for independent practice.

Check for Understanding

Have students respond to the first three questions in Check Your Understanding.

Reteach

Reteaching/*Teacher Resource Package,* p. 23. Use this worksheet to give students additional practice with nutrient needs.

Extension: Assign Critical Thinking, Biology and Math, or some of the **OPTIONS** available with this lesson.

3 APPLY

Convergent Question

Ask where nutrients come from that are needed by the body if one or two meals are skipped.

4 CLOSE

Software

Buying Nutritious Food, Queue, Inc.

Answers to Check Your Understanding

1. fats and carbohydrates
2. They help form certain cell parts.
3. by choosing food from the milk, meat, fruit, vegetable, and grain groups
4. Carbohydrates are not stored for a long time and are used quickly.
5. a paper clip

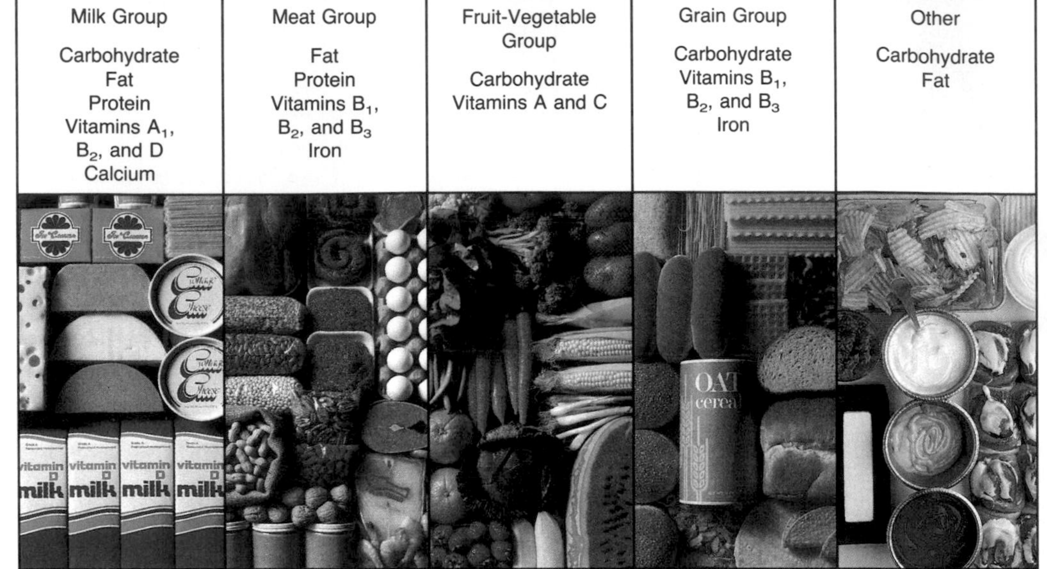

Milk Group
Carbohydrate
Fat
Protein
Vitamins A_1, B_2, and D
Calcium
Meat Group
Fat
Protein
Vitamins B_1, B_2, and B_3
Iron
Fruit-Vegetable Group
Carbohydrate
Vitamins A and C
Grain Group
Carbohydrate
Vitamins B_1, B_2, and B_3
Iron
Other
Carbohydrate
Fat
vitamin D milk
OAT cereal

Figure 9-9 Select foods from each of the five basic food groups to develop a balanced diet. Which food group is a good source of calcium? milk group

What is a balanced diet?

Supplying Nutrients to Your Body

Most foods contain several nutrients. Whole milk is four percent protein, four percent fat, and five percent carbohydrate. It also has vitamins, minerals, and water.

How do you know which foods will give you a balanced diet? A **balanced diet** is a diet with the right amount of each nutrient. Figure 9-9 shows foods placed into five groups. It also lists the major nutrients in each group. Choosing foods from all of these groups each day helps make a balanced diet.

Check Your Understanding

1. Name two nutrients that supply the body with energy.
2. How are minerals used by the body?
3. How can you be sure that your diet is balanced?
4. **Critical Thinking:** Why does the body need more carbohydrates than fats or proteins?
5. **Biology and Math:** The RDA of sodium is 1200 mg. Which of the following have about the same mass as 1200 mg: a paper clip, a quarter, a pencil, or a biology book?

STUDY GUIDE 51

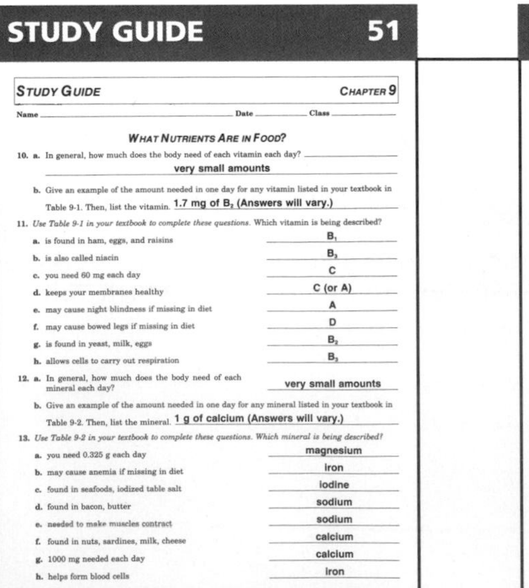

STUDY GUIDE — CHAPTER 9

Name ______ Date ______ Class ______

WHAT NUTRIENTS ARE IN FOOD?

10. a. In general, how much does the body need of each vitamin each day? very small amounts
    b. Give an example of the amount needed in one day for any vitamin listed in your textbook in Table 9-1. Then, list the vitamin. 1.7 mg of B_2 (Answers will vary.)
11. *Use Table 9-1 in your textbook to complete these questions.* Which vitamin is being described?
    a. is found in ham, eggs, and raisins — B_1
    b. is also called niacin — B_3
    c. you need 60 mg each day — C
    d. keeps your membranes healthy — C (or A)
    e. may cause night blindness if missing in diet — A
    f. may cause bowed legs if missing in diet — D
    g. is found in yeast, milk, eggs — B_2
    h. allows cells to carry out respiration — B_3
12. a. In general, how much does the body need of each mineral each day? very small amounts
    b. Give an example of the amount needed in one day for any mineral listed in your textbook in Table 9-2. Then, list the mineral. 1 g of calcium (Answers will vary.)
13. *Use Table 9-2 in your textbook to complete these questions. Which mineral is being described?*
    a. you need 0.325 g each day — magnesium
    b. may cause anemia if missing in diet — iron
    c. found in seafoods, iodized table salt — iodine
    d. found in bacon, butter — sodium
    e. needed to make muscles contract — sodium
    f. found in nuts, sardines, milk, cheese — calcium
    g. 1000 mg needed each day — calcium
    h. helps form blood cells — iron

RETEACHING 23

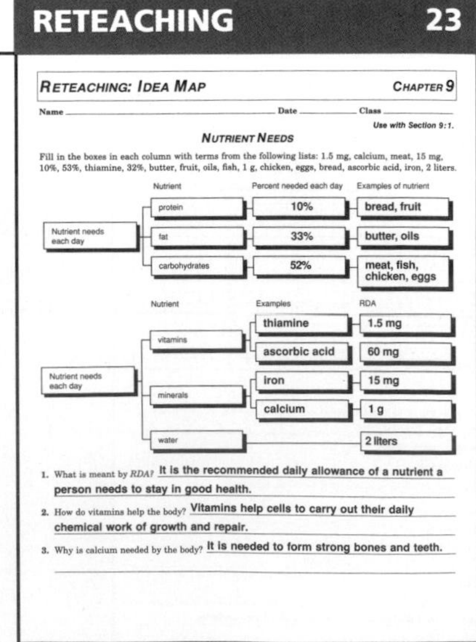

RETEACHING: IDEA MAP — CHAPTER 9

Name ______ Date ______ Class ______

Use with Section 9:1.

NUTRIENT NEEDS

Fill in the boxes in each column with terms from the following lists: 1.5 mg, calcium, meat, 15 mg, 10%, 53%, thiamine, 32%, butter, fruit, oils, fish, 1 g, chicken, eggs, bread, ascorbic acid, iron, 2 liters.

Nutrient needs each day

Nutrient	Percent needed each day	Examples of nutrient
protein	10%	bread, fruit
fat	33%	butter, oils
carbohydrates	52%	meat, fish, chicken, eggs

Nutrient needs each day

Nutrient	Examples	RDA
vitamins	thiamine	1.5 mg
	ascorbic acid	60 mg
minerals	iron	15 mg
	calcium	1 g
water		2 liters

1. What is meant by *RDA*? It is the recommended daily allowance of a nutrient a person needs to stay in good health.
2. How do vitamins help the body? Vitamins help cells to carry out their daily chemical work of growth and repair.
3. Why is calcium needed by the body? It is needed to form strong bones and teeth.

9:2 Calories

Did you ever have a soft drink or candy bar when you wanted to eat something that would give you a lift? Besides supplying your body with nutrients, food gives your body energy. You are able to talk, play sports, and read this book because of the energy food gives you. Let's look at how the energy in food is measured and how the body uses food energy.

Objectives

4. **Describe** how a Calorie is used by the body.
5. **Compare** the number of Calories found in different nutrients.
6. **Compare** the number of Calories used in different activities.

Key Science Words

Calorie

Energy in Food

Have you ever noticed how often TV food commercials mention Calories? A **Calorie** is a measure of the energy in food. Foods high in Calories provide a lot of energy. Low-Calorie foods provide less energy. Diet soft drinks usually contain only one Calorie. A candy bar might contain over 200 Calories. Most of those Calories are in the form of fat and sugar.

Food, like wood or coal, can be burned. The heat given off by burning food can change the temperature of water. Scientists describe a Calorie as the amount of heat it takes to raise the temperature of 1000 g of water 1°C, Figure 9-10. If a slice of bread has 70 Calories, what does it mean? It means that if the slice of bread were burned, it would give off enough heat to raise the temperature of 1000 g of water 70°C.

What is a Calorie?

Of course, in your body, food energy is not used to heat water. Food energy is used to keep your body temperature close to 37°C. It is also used to move your muscles, pump your blood, and send messages along your nerves. Food energy is released when your cells carry on respiration.

a Start with 1000 g of water at 19°C.

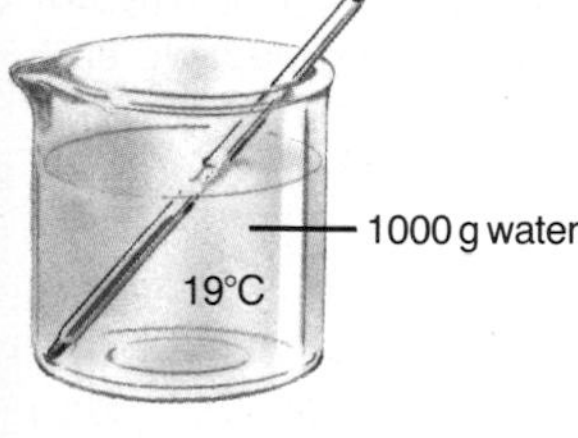

b Burn food to heat the water.

c When one Calorie of food has burned, the temperature of the water is one degree higher.

Figure 9-10 This procedure shows how one Calorie can be measured.

OPTIONS

Science Background

Calories are units of energy. They are arrived at by taking food samples and burning them. The amount of temperature change that occurs during burning is measured and converted into Calories. Food Calories are sometimes called kilocalories and are always capitalized.

9:2 Calories

PREPARATION

Materials Needed

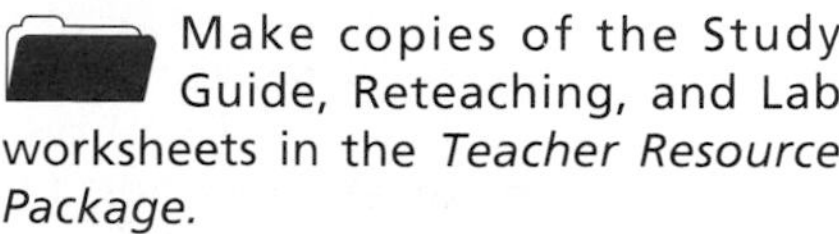

Make copies of the Study Guide, Reteaching, and Lab worksheets in the *Teacher Resource Package.*

▶ Gather food samples needed for Lab 9-2. Purchase sugar (glucose) test paper.

▶ Bring in taco chips for the Focus demonstration.

Key Science Words

Calorie

Process Skills

In Lab 9-2, students will form a hypothesis, experiment, and make and use tables. In the Skill Checks, they will infer and interpret data.

1 FOCUS

▶ The objectives are listed on the student page. Remind students to preview these objectives as a guide to this numbered section.

Guided Practice

Have students write down their answers to the margin question: a measure of the amount of energy in food.

Lab 9-2 Energy Foods

Overview

Students will test foods known to contain sugar. They will then test a number of unknown foods.

Objectives: Upon completing this lab, students will be able to (1) **test** for sugar in a variety of foods, (2) **determine** the purpose of testing for sugar in food.

Time Allotment: 30 minutes

Preparation

▶ Sugar test paper is available in the diabetic needs section of your local drugstore or from a biological supply house.

▶ All sugars such as honey, molasses, and maple syrup must be diluted in water, about 5 parts water to 1 part food, in order for glucose test paper to register a green color. Do not test cooked potato or rice with sugar test paper. They will test positive for sugar.

Lab 9-2 worksheet/*Teacher Resource Package*, pp. 35-36.

Teaching the Lab

▶ **Troubleshooting:** All sugars are carbohydrates but there are many different types of sugars. The test paper being used in this experiment will detect only glucose, a specific sugar type. Table sugar is not glucose. It is sucrose and is not detected with this test paper.

Energy Foods

Lab 9–2

Problem: Which foods contain starch and which contain sugar?

Skills

form a hypothesis, experiment, make and use tables

Materials

glass slides
razor blade
sugar test paper
food samples for sugar test
droppers
water

Procedure

1. Copy the data table.
2. **Form a hypothesis:** Look at the foods you are to test for sugar. In your notebook, write a hypothesis about which foods contain sugar and which don't.
3. Using a dropper, put a drop of honey on a glass slide. Honey is a food that contains sugar.
4. Touch a piece of sugar test paper to the honey. Wait one minute. When the test paper turns green, this shows that sugar is present.
5. Using a different dropper, put a drop of water on a glass slide. Touch a piece of sugar test paper to the water. Wait one minute. No green color shows that sugar is not present.
6. Using a razor blade, cut a small slice from a sweet potato and touch a piece of sugar test paper to the inside of the slice. **CAUTION:** *Always cut away from yourself when using a razor blade.*
7. Record in your table if a green color appears and if sugar is present.
8. Repeat steps 3 and 4 with maple syrup, molasses, and apple juice. Use a different dropper and piece of sugar test paper for each food tested.
9. Dispose of the food samples according to your teacher's directions.

Data and Observations

1. Which foods contained sugar?
2. Which foods did not contain sugar?

FOOD	GREEN COLOR?	SUGAR PRESENT?
Honey	yes	yes
Water	no	no
Sweet potato	yes	yes
Maple syrup	yes	yes
Molasses	yes	yes
Apple juice	yes	yes

Analyze and Apply

1. Explain how you can tell if a food
   (a) contains sugar.
   (b) does not contain sugar.
2. What type of nutrient is sugar?
3. Why was it important to test water for sugar?
4. **Check your hypothesis:** Is your hypothesis supported by your data? Why or why not?
5. To which of the five food groups do each of your food samples belong?
6. **Apply:** What is the role of sugar in the diet?

Extension

Experiment using the same foods and iodine solution to test for the presence of starch.

194 Nutrition 9:2

ANSWERS

Data and Observations

1. In the samples suggested, honey, sweet potato, maple syrup, molasses, and apple juice contain sugar.
2. Water was the only suggested sample with no sugar.

Analyze and Apply

1. (a) Touch a food sample with sugar test paper. After one minute, the presence of sugar will turn the paper a green color.
   (b) If the paper doesn't turn green, there's no sugar present.
2. carbohydrate
3. Water acted as a control in the experiment.
4. Students who hypothesized correctly which foods contain sugar will answer that their hypotheses were correct.
5. Answers will vary depending on sample chosen. The samples suggested here belong mainly to the "other" group and to the fruit and vegetable group.
6. Sugar is a carbohydrate that supplies your body with energy.

Calorie Content of Food

Foods differ in the amount of energy, or Calories, they contain. How many Calories do you think are in a ham sandwich, a small salad, and a glass of milk?

To find the answer, add the Calories next to the list of foods in Table 9-3.

TABLE 9–3. CALORIES IN CERTAIN FOODS

Foods Eaten	Calories
2 slices of white bread	140 (70 in each slice)
1 spoonful of mayonnaise	70
2 slices of ham	148 (74 in each slice)
1/8 head of lettuce	10
1 slice tomato	6
2 spoonfuls of salad dressing	120 (60 in each spoonful)
1 glass milk	150

This lunch would supply 644 Calories.

You can see from the table that not all foods provide the same number of Calories. However, we have not been comparing equal masses of foods to one another. When we do compare equal masses, we find that fats supply the most Calories. For example, let's compare butter with bread. Look at Figure 9-11 as you read. Butter is mostly fat, and bread is mostly carbohydrate. What would happen if you ate an equal mass of butter and bread? The butter would give your body two and one-half times the number of Calories as you would get from the bread.

Equal masses of protein and carbohydrate are both lower in Calories than fats. Let's compare bread with ham, Figure 9-11. Remember that bread is mostly carbohydrate. Ham is mostly protein. There are 70 Calories in a slice of bread and 74 Calories in a slice of ham of the same mass. They have almost equal numbers of Calories.

Skill Check

Infer: Cooking oil and lard are both fats. How will the numbers of Calories found in equal masses of these substances compare? *For more help, refer to the* ***Skill Handbook,*** *pages 706-711.*

Which foods supply the most Calories?

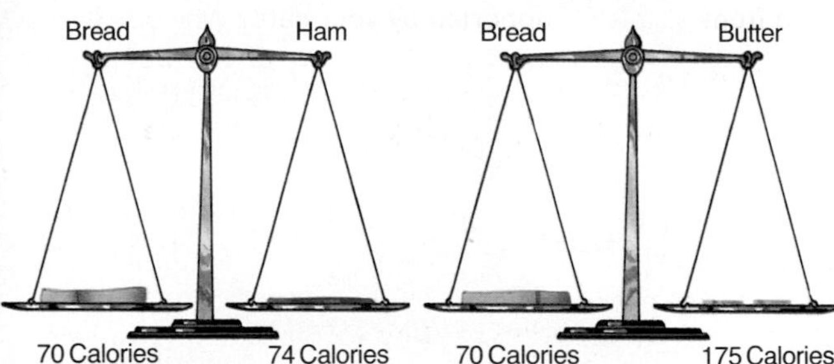

Figure 9-11 Food of equal masses can have very different numbers of Calories.

2 TEACH

MOTIVATION/Demonstration

Illustrate the concept of equal masses of food by bringing to class the number of slices of bread needed to equal the mass of one stick of butter. Find the mass of bread by checking the nutrition label on the package. The mass of one slice will be listed. Calculate the number of slices that equal the mass of one stick of butter. Then the Calories in both foods can be compared.

Concept Development

▶ Food is not burned in the true sense. It is, however, changed chemically and energy is released during cellular respiration.

Guided Practice

Have students write down their answers to the margin question: foods that are high in fat.

Independent Practice

Study Guide/*Teacher Resource Package,* p. 52. Use the Study Guide worksheet shown at the bottom of this page for independent practice.

STUDY GUIDE 52

STUDY GUIDE — CHAPTER 9

Name ____ Date ____ Class ____

CALORIES

In your textbook, read about the energy in food in Section 9:2.

1. Define *Calorie.* A Calorie is a measure of the energy in food.
2. What does it mean if someone says that a food contains 50 Calories? It means that if this food were burned, it would give off enough heat to raise the temperature of 1000 g of water 50° C.
3. What is the energy in food used for in your body? cell work, moving muscles, pumping blood, sending messages along nerves
4. Complete the table below by determining the number of Calories in each food sample and writing the number in the column at the right.

Food sample	Amount of water in beaker	Starting temperature of water before burning food	Final temperature of water after burning food	Number of Calories in food
A	1000 g	18°C	19°C	1
B	1000 g	10°C	15°C	5
C	1000 g	0°C	100°C	100
D	1000 g	55°C	72°C	17

5. A student ate the foods in the table below in one day. Complete the table by determining the total Calories taken in. Then, answer the questions on the following page.

Food	Calories ×	Amount eaten =	Total
Egg	80	2	160
Milk	80	2 glasses	160
Bread	70	4 slices	280
Bologna	60	4 slices	240
Cola	145	4 glasses	580
Hamburger	250	2	500
French fries	100	1 serving	100

OPTIONS

ACTIVITY/Enrichment

Illustrate how to measure the heat energy in food. Place a beaker filled with 1000 mL of water on a metal tripod. Position a regular-sized marshmallow below the beaker using a long needle whose opposite end is stuck into a cork. Record the temperature of the water in the beaker using a Celsius scale. Light the marshmallow with a match and allow it to burn completely. Remeasure the water temperature. The change in temperature indicates the number of Calories in the marshmallow.

TEACH

Concept Development

▶ Explain that runners deplete their stored carbohydrates after about 18-20 miles. They then begin to utilize stored fat for energy. Nonrunners will deplete their carbohydrate stores in about 48 hours if no food is eaten.

Check for Understanding

Have students calculate their Caloric intake for a 24-hour period. Calorie charts are available from your home economics teacher or from any nutrition textbook. This activity works best if students are told in advance to keep a list of the foods they consume and the quantity of each food eaten. Calculators may be helpful.

Reteach

Have students discuss why their Calorie needs are different from those of other students. Have them discuss ways for reducing weight.

Guided Practice

Have students write down their answers to the margin question: A person gains weight.

Independent Practice

Study Guide/*Teacher Resource Package*, p. 53. Use the Study Guide worksheet shown at the bottom of this page for independent practice.

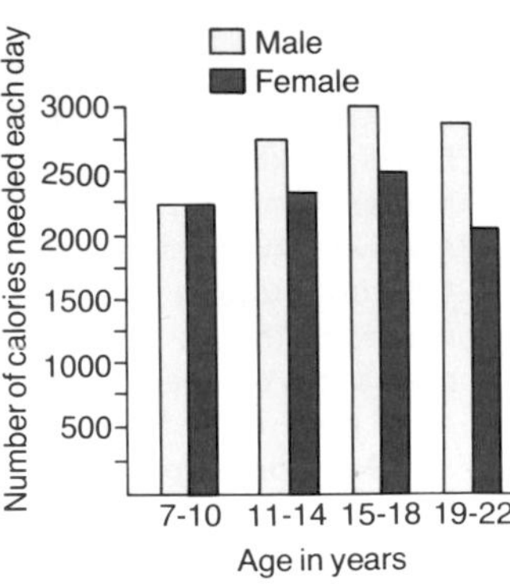

Figure 9-12 Compare the Caloric needs for different ages and sexes. What age group needs the most Calories daily? 15-18

Using Calories

Your body needs a certain number of Calories to keep a proper weight. How many Calories does your body need each day? The answer to that question is not simple. Figure 9-12 shows that age and sex of a person are important in figuring Calorie needs. The easiest way to receive the needed number of Calories is to eat different foods from each of the five groups shown on page 192.

How are Calories used by different people? How a person uses Calories depends on his or her size and on how active he or she is. For example, a larger person uses more Calories than a smaller person doing the same activity. Table 9-4 shows that a person who is 73 kg uses 240 Calories walking for one hour. Someone who is 54 kg uses 180 Calories walking for the same amount of time.

The more energy it takes to do an activity, the more Calories a person uses for that activity. For example, a 63-kg person uses 112 Calories standing for one hour. The same person uses 420 Calories playing tennis for one hour. Playing tennis uses more energy than standing.

What happens if more Calories are taken into the body than are used?

Taking in too many Calories or too little exercise may result in overweight. If the number of Calories taken in are equal to the number of Calories used, body weight stays about the same. If more Calories are taken in than used, weight is gained. What becomes of the extra Calories? They may be stored in the body as fat.

What happens if the body takes in less Calories than it uses? The body makes up the difference by using stored Calories, and the person loses weight. Another way of using stored Calories is by exercising.

Figure 9-13 Taking in more or fewer Calories than are needed can result in overweight or underweight. Neither condition is healthy for the body.

STUDY GUIDE 53

STUDY GUIDE — **CHAPTER 9**

Name ______ Date ______ Class ______

CALORIES

6. Which food gave the student the most Calories? **cola**
7. Were the servings and mass of each food equal? **no**
8. When comparing equal masses of food, which nutrient type will provide the most Calories? **fat**

In your textbook, read about using Calories in Section 9:2.

9. Look at Table 9-4 in your textbook. Use the information in the table and in your textbook to help you answer the following questions.
   a. How many Calories do you need each day? **Answers will vary.**
   b. What two things listed on the graph are important in determining how many Calories a person needs? **age and sex**
   c. How do Calorie needs differ as a person ages from 7 to 18? **Calorie needs increase with age.**
   d. How do Calorie needs differ between males and females above the age of 10? **Males need more Calories than females.**
   e. If a typical female age 18 takes in 1500 Calories each day for one month, will she gain or lose weight? Why? **She will lose weight because she needs 2500 Calories each day. Taking in less Calories than one needs over time will result in weight loss.**
   f. If a typical male age 15 takes in 3500 Calories each day for one month, will he gain or lose weight? Why? **He will gain weight because he needs 3000 Calories each day. Taking in more Calories than one needs over time will result in weight gain.**
   g. How do Calorie needs vary with different kinds of activities a person does? **The more energy it takes to do an activity, the more Calories a person uses to do that activity.**

TABLE 9–4. CALORIES USED IN 1 HOUR

Type of Activity	Mass of Person		
	54 kg	**63 kg**	**73 kg**
Sleeping	48	56	64
Sitting	72	84	96
Eating	84	98	112
Standing	96	112	123
Walking	180	210	240
Playing tennis	380	420	460
Bicycling fast	500	600	700
Running	700	850	1000

Figure 9-14 The number of Calories you will burn during a one-hour walk depends on your body mass.

Skill Check

Interpret data: Study Table 9-4. What happens to the number of Calories used as the type of activity becomes more difficult? *For more help, refer to the* ***Skill Handbook****, pages 704-705.*

Check Your Understanding

6. How are Calories important to the body?
7. Which nutrient supplies the body with the most Calories?
8. Who needs more Calories, a 16-year-old boy or a 16-year-old girl?
9. **Critical Thinking:** A 73-kg person and a 54-kg person run at the same speed for one hour. Which person will use more Calories?
10. **Biology and Math:** Tom has a mass of 63 kg. In a typical day, Tom sleeps for 8 hours, sits for 6 hours, plays tennis for 2 hours, eats for 2 hours, walks for 3 hours, and stands for 3 hours. If Tom consumed 2500 Calories on a given day, would he have gained, maintained, or lost weight?

RETEACHING 24

RETEACHING — CHAPTER 9

Name ______ Date ______ Class ______

CALORIE INTAKE AND OUTPUT — Use after Section 9:2.

A person will gain or lose weight depending on how many Calories he or she takes in and uses up. More Calories taken in over a period of time will result in weight gain.

In the tables below, calculate the number of Calories taken in and used up in one day. Then, answer the questions.

Calories taken in for one day			
Food	Calories	× Amount eaten	= Total
orange juice	110 per glass	× 2 glasses	= 220
muffin	140 each	× 2	= 280
chicken	180 per piece	× 3 pieces	= 540
ham	250 per slice	× 4 slices	= 1000
potato	100 each	× 1	= 100
butter	60 per pat	× 3 pats	= 180
bread	70 per slice	× 4 slices	= 280
total calories taken in for one day			= 2600

Calories used up in one day			
Activity	Hours spent in activity	× Calories used each hour	= Total Calories used
standing	3	× 110	= 330
sitting	8	× 80	= 640
walking	1	× 200	= 200
playing tennis	2	× 400	= 800
eating	1	× 90	= 90
sleeping	9	× 50	= 450
total calories used up in one day			= 2510

1. Which was greater, total Calories taken in or Calories used up? Calories taken in
2. Did the person gain or lose weight that day? gained

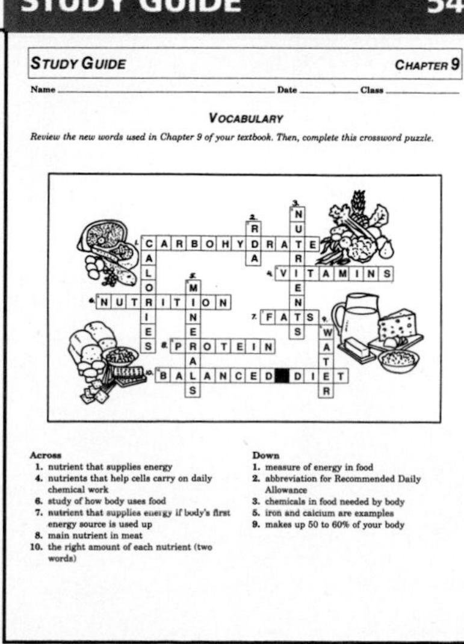

STUDY GUIDE 54

STUDY GUIDE — CHAPTER 9

Name ______ Date ______ Class ______

VOCABULARY

Review the new words used in Chapter 9 of your textbook. Then, complete this crossword puzzle.

Across
1. nutrient that supplies energy
4. nutrients that help cells carry on daily chemical work
6. study of how body uses food
7. nutrient that supplies energy if body's first energy source is used up
8. main nutrient in meat
10. the right amount of each nutrient (two words)

Down
1. measure of energy in food
2. abbreviation for Recommended Daily Allowance
3. chemicals in food needed by body
5. iron and calcium are examples
9. makes up 50 to 60% of your body

TEACH

Independent Practice

Study Guide/*Teacher Resource Package,* p. 54. Use the Study Guide worksheet shown at the bottom of this page for independent practice.

Skill Check

As activity increases or becomes more difficult, the number of Calories used increases.

Check for Understanding

Have students respond to the first three questions in Check Your Understanding.

Reteach

Reteaching/*Teacher Resource Package,* p. 24. Use this worksheet to give students additional practice with Calorie input and output.

Extension: Assign Critical Thinking, Biology and Math, or some of the **OPTIONS** available with this lesson.

3 APPLY

Convergent Question

Have students give reasons why they need food Calories.

4 CLOSE

ACTIVITY/Software

Food, Fitness, and Appearance, Queue, Inc.

Answers to Check Your Understanding

6. They are a measure of the amount of energy in food. The body needs energy to do all its daily activities.
7. fat
8. a 16-year-old boy
9. the 73-Kg person
10. He would lose weight.

PROBLEM SOLVING

Reading Food Labels

Problem-solving Strategies

The following strategies can be used to solve the problems in this feature: construct a table, compare and contrast, and draw conclusions.

Hints

▶ Students should cover the information within the text relating to nutrients and Calories before they attempt to solve this problem.

▶ Remind students that sodium is a reference to salt. Salt is technically called sodium chloride.

Solving the Problem

1. a–Soup B
   b–Soup B
   c–Soup A
   d–They are the same.
   e–Soup B
2. Students need to decide on their own nutritional needs to answer this question. Those who need more carbohydrates, riboflavin, calcium, and fat will choose Soup A; those who need more Vitamin A, thiamine, and iron will choose Soup B. Students also need to weigh the relative importance of sodium, Calories, cholesterol, and protein in the diet.

PROBLEM SOLVING

READING FOOD LABELS

How can you determine which brand of a particular food contains the greatest amount of nutrients? By carefully reading the nutrient information on product labels you can find out the type and amount of nutrients contained in a serving of the product.

1. Compare food labels a and b. Both are soup labels. A single serving of which product will provide
   a) less sodium?
   b) fewer Calories?
   c) more cholesterol?
   d) more protein?
   e) a higher percentage of the RDA for vitamin A?
2. Assume that the cost of a single serving of soup a and soup b is the same. Which soup has the best nutritional value for your dollar? Why?

198

3. Compare food labels c and d. Both are cereal labels. A single serving of which product will provide
   a) more potassium?
   b) less sodium?
   c) less cholesterol?
   d) a higher percentage of the RDA for iron?
   e) more Calories?
4. Assume that the cost of a single serving of cereal c and cereal d is the same. Which cereal has the best nutritional value for your dollar? Why?

c

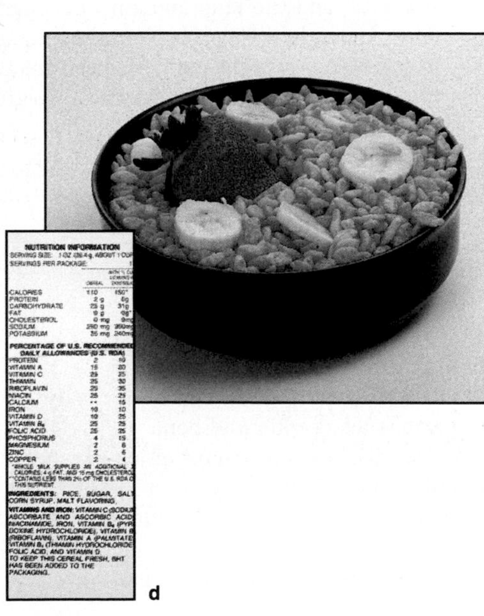

NUTRITION INFORMATION

	CEREAL	WITH ½ CUP VITAMINS A & D SKIM MILK
CALORIES	110	150*
PROTEIN	2 g	6g
CARBOHYDRATE	25 g	31g
FAT	0 g	0g*
CHOLESTEROL	0 mg	0mg
SODIUM	290 mg	350mg
POTASSIUM	35 mg	240mg

PERCENTAGE OF U.S. RECOMMENDED DAILY ALLOWANCES (U.S. RDA)

PROTEIN	2	10
VITAMIN A	15	20
VITAMIN C	25	25
THIAMIN	25	30
RIBOFLAVIN	25	35
NIACIN	25	25
CALCIUM	**	15
IRON	10	10
VITAMIN D	10	25
VITAMIN B_6	25	25
FOLIC ACID	25	25
PHOSPHORUS	4	15
MAGNESIUM	2	6
ZINC	2	6
COPPER	2	4

INGREDIENTS: RICE, SUGAR, SALT, CORN SYRUP, MALT FLAVORING.

TO KEEP THIS CEREAL FRESH, BHT HAS BEEN ADDED TO THE PACKAGING.

d

3. a–Cereal C
   b–Cereal C
   c–Neither cereal contains cholesterol.
   d–Cereal C
   e–Cereal D
4. Students again will need to determine their own nutritional needs. Most students will choose Cereal C because it has more protein, potassium, and iron, less sodium, and more minerals. Neither cereal contains fat or cholesterol and they are close in the amounts of carbohydrates.

Discussing the Problem

▶ Students should be aware of the fact that one person's diet may require less Calories, fat, or sodium than another's. In general, however, the best nutritional food would be the food that supplies the greatest number of different vitamins and minerals, protein, carbohydrates, and the least sodium and fat.

Extensions

▶ Have students not only compare the total number of different minerals and vitamins but also allow them to list the RDA for each one. This would then allow them to compare the different vitamins and minerals in foods A and B.

▶ Have students calculate the number of Calories derived from fat in foods A and B (grams of fat $\times$ 9). A nutritional food should derive not more than 30 percent of its total Calories from fat. Repeat for foods C and D.

Summary

Summary statements can be used by students to review the major concepts of the chapter.

Key Science Words

All boldfaced terms from the chapter are listed.

Testing Yourself

Using Words

1. nutrition
2. Calorie
3. protein
4. balanced diet
5. nutrient
6. recommended daily allowance
7. fat
8. vitamin
9. carbohydrate
10. mineral

Finding Main Ideas

11. p. 196; Calories used depends on a person's size as well as how active the person is.
12. p. 195; Multiply the mass of each food by the number of Calories in a known mass, and then add those numbers together.
13. p. 189; Vitamin C is used for healthy membranes and wound healing. Vitamin D is used for bone growth.
14. p. 191; Water is important for cooling the body, for dissolving chemicals, and for carrying away body wastes.
15. p. 192; Dairy foods contain carbohydrates, fat, protein, water, minerals, and vitamins.
16. p. 196; They are stored as fat.
17. pp. 188-190; Vitamins are needed for growth and tissue repair, while minerals are needed to form cell parts.

Using Main Ideas

18. Vitamin C is supplied by the fruit-vegetable group; carbohydrates are supplied by all groups except meat; water is supplied by all the food groups; magnesium is supplied by the fruit-vegetable and grain groups.

Chapter 9 Review

Summary

9:1 What Are the Nutrients in Food?

1. The body needs six different nutrients to stay healthy—proteins, fats, carbohydrates, vitamins, minerals, and water.
2. Fats and carbohydrates are needed for energy. Proteins are needed to build and repair body parts. Vitamins are needed for chemical work in the cell. Minerals are needed to form certain cell parts. Water cools the body. Chemical changes take place in water. Water carries away body wastes.
3. Choosing a variety of foods from the six nutrients will provide you with a balanced diet.

9:2 Calories

4. A Calorie is a measure of the energy in food.
5. When comparing equal masses of food, fats provide more Calories than any other nutrient.
6. How a person uses Calories depends on his or her age, sex, size, and the kind and amount of activity a person does. Using less Calories than the amount taken in may result in weight gain. Using more Calories than the amount taken in may result in weight loss.

Key Science Words

balanced diet (p. 192)
Calorie (p. 193)
carbohydrate (p. 185)
fat (p. 185)
mineral (p. 190)
nutrient (p. 184)
nutrition (p. 184)
protein (p. 185)
recommended daily allowance (p. 189)
vitamin (p. 188)

Testing Yourself

Using Words

Choose the word from the list of Key Science Words that best fits the definition.

1. study of how your body uses food
2. measure of food energy
3. nutrient used to build and repair body parts, such as skin and bone
4. eating the proper amount of all nutrients each day
5. type of chemical in food needed by all living cells
6. amount of a vitamin needed each day
7. energy food, such as oil or butter
8. nutrient, such as niacin, that aids a cell with its chemical work
9. body's main source of energy
10. nutrients, such as calcium or iron

Finding Main Ideas

List the page number where each main idea below is found. Then, explain each main idea.

11. why the number of Calories used during an activity is different for each person

Review

Testing Yourself *continued*

12. how to find the total number of Calories in a meal
13. the roles of vitamins C and D
14. why water is important
15. the nutrients present in dairy foods
16. what happens to unused Calories in the body
17. ways in which vitamins differ from minerals

Using Main Ideas

Answer the questions by referring to the page number after each question.

18. Which food group supplies the body with vitamin C, carbohydrates, water, and magnesium? (p. 192)
19. How do the numbers of Calories used change as activity increases? (p. 197)
20. Which nutrients are used for growth and repair of skin and bones? (p. 189)
21. What does it mean if a certain food gives you 20 percent of your RDA for niacin? (p. 189)
22. What happens to body weight when
    (a) more Calories are used than taken in? (p. 196)
    (b) more Calories are taken in than used? (p. 196)
23. Which foods would you suggest a person with anemia and muscle twitches eat in an attempt to correct the condition? (p. 190)
24. How many Calories are in equal masses of
    (a) fat and carbohydrate? (p. 195)
    (b) fat and protein? (p. 195)
    (c) carbohydrate and protein? (p. 195)
25. What are the six important nutrients found in food? (p. 184)

Skill Review

*For more help, refer to the **Skill Handbook,** pages 704-719.*

1. **Infer:** Males and females have different amounts of fat in their bodies. What does this tell you about how different sexes store this nutrient?
2. **Use numbers:** Calculate the cost of one gram of canned, cooked kidney beans compared with the cost of an equal amount of plain, uncooked kidney beans. (A can costs $0.85 for 200 gm, while a bag of beans costs $1.25 for 1000 gm.)
3. **Measure in SI:** Use a pan balance to determine the masses of two foods listed in Table 9-3 that have similar Caloric values.
4. **Interpret data:** List the number of Calories that a 63-kg person will use up in one hour of walking and running.

Finding Out More

Critical Thinking

1. If you were a vegetarian, how would you obtain the proteins necessary for a healthy body? Plan two well-balanced vegetarian dinners.
2. If a person takes vitamin and mineral supplements daily, do they still need a variety of foods? Explain your answer.

Applications

1. Build a tin can calorimeter. Measure the Calories in different foods.
2. Use food charts to plan two different dinners—one low in sodium, and one low in carbohydrates.

Using Main Ideas

19. As activity increases, the number of Calories used increases.
20. Proteins are nutrients that build and repair body parts.
21. The food supplies 20 percent of the amount of niacin needed each day to stay in good health.
22. (a) If more Calories are used than taken in, a person will lose weight. (b) If more Calories are taken in than used, a person will gain weight.
23. A person with anemia should eat more liver, eggs, peas, enriched cereals, and whole grains. A person with muscle twitching should eat more potatoes, fruits, and whole grain cereals.
24. (a) Fat has more Calories than an equal mass of carbohydrate. (b) Fat has more Calories than an equal mass of protein. (c) Equal masses of protein and carbohydrate have almost equal numbers of Calories.
25. The six important nutrients found in food are proteins, carbohydrates, fats, water, minerals, and vitamins.

Skill Review

1. Females store more fat than males do.
2. A bag of beans costs less per gram.
3. Answers will vary depending on the foods chosen.
4. walking = 210 Calories; running = 850 Calories

Finding Out More

Critical Thinking

1. Students should use Figure 9–9, Table 9-1, and Table 9-2 for help.
2. Yes. Nutrients other than vitamins and minerals are needed for good health.

Applications

1. Remove the top of a tin can. Make wedge-shaped cuts along the bottom edge and a round opening in the center of the bottom for a water-filled test tube. Place food on a wire stand, turn the can over the stand, and place a tube through the hole. Record the water temperature, ignite the food, and record the final water temperature.
2. Fresh foods will be lower in sodium than processed foods. Dairy and meat products will be lower in carbohydrates than grains and produce.

Chapter Review/*Teacher Resource Package,* pp. 45-46.

Chapter Test/*Teacher Resource Package,* pp. 47-49.

Chapter Test/*Computer Test Bank*

Digestion

PLANNING GUIDE

CONTENT	TEXT FEATURES	TEACHER RESOURCE PACKAGE	OTHER COMPONENTS
(1 1/2 days) 10:1 The Process of Digestion Breakdown of Food Physical and Chemical Changes	Skill Check: *Experiments,* p. 205 Lab 10-1: *Digestion,* p. 207 Idea Map, p. 205 Check Your Understanding, p. 206	Reteaching: *Digestion,* p. 25 Critical Thinking/Problem Solving: *What Can Teeth Reveal About Diet?* p. 10 Focus: *Breaking Down Food,* p. 19 Study Guide: *The Process of Digestion,* p. 55 Lab 10-1: *Digestion,* pp. 37-38	
(4 days) 10:2 The Human Digestive System Nutrients Are Digested A Trip Through the Digestive System Moving Digested Food Into Body Cells Digestion in Other Animals Problems of the Digestive System	Skill Check: *Understand Science Words,* p. 212 Mini Lab: *How Long Is the Digestive System?* p. 210 Mini Lab: *How Do Villi Aid Absorption?* p. 214 Career Close-Up: *Dietician,* p. 211 Lab 10-2: *Digestive System,* p. 213 Idea Map, p. 212 Check Your Understanding, p. 217	Application: *Gallstones, a Problem of the Digestive System,* p. 10 Enrichment: *Digesting Different Nutrients,* p. 10 Reteaching: *Digestive Systems of Animals,* p. 26 Reteaching: *Problems of the Digestive System,* p. 27 Skill: *Outline,* pp. 10-11 Transparency Master: *Human Digestive System,* p. 45 Study Guide: *The Human Digestive System,* pp. 56-58 Study Guide: *Problems of the Digestive System,* p. 59 Study Guide: *Vocabulary,* p. 60 Lab 10-2: *Digestive System,* pp. 39-40	**Laboratory Manual:** *How Do Digestive System Lengths Compare?* p. 79 **Laboratory Manual:** *How Does the Fish Digestive System Work?* p. 83 Color Transparency 10: *The Human Digestive System*
Chapter Review	Summary Key Science Words Testing Yourself Finding Main Ideas Using Main Ideas Skill Review	Chapter Review, pp. 50-51 Chapter Test, pp. 52-54	**Test Bank**

MATERIALS NEEDED

LAB 10-1, p. 207	LAB 10-2, p. 213	MARGIN FEATURES
4 paper cups gelatin water 4 applicator sticks 4 plastic spoons enzyme A enzyme B refrigerator (optional)	five diagrams of the digestive system colored pencils: red, blue, green, yellow, and purple	Skill Check, p. 205 2 sugar cubes glass warm water Skill Check, p. 212 dictionary Mini Lab, p. 210 pencil paper Mini Lab, p. 214 water paper towels beaker

OBJECTIVES

		OBJECTIVES CORRELATION			
SECTION	OBJECTIVE	CHECK YOUR UNDERSTANDING	CHAPTER REVIEW	TRP CHAPTER REVIEW	TRP CHAPTER TEST
10:1	1. **Relate** the importance of the digestive system.	1	3	28	7, 47
	2. **Compare** a physical change and a chemical change in the digestive system.	2, 4	1, 5, 6, 13, 21	8, 33	10, 31, 32, 33, 34, 46, 48
	3. **Explain** the role of enzymes in a chemical change.	3	4, 10, 12	11, 12, 13, 14, 15, 16, 17, 30	44
10:2	4. **Trace** the path of food from the mouth to the body cells.	6, 8	2, 8, 9, 11, 14, 17, 20	1, 3, 6, 9, 10, 11, 12, 13, 14, 15, 16, 17, 18, 19, 20, 21, 22, 23, 24, 25, 26, 27, 28, 29, 31, 32, 34, 35	1, 2 , 3, 6, 8, 11, 12, 13, 14, 15, 16, 17, 18, 19, 20, 21, 22, 23, 24, 25, 26, 35, 36, 37, 38, 43, 45
	5. **Compare** the human digestive system with those of other animals.	8, 10	15, 18, 19	4, 5, 7	4, 9, 27, 28, 29, 30
	6. **Identify** the problems of the digestive system.	7, 9	16, 22	2	5, 41, 42

Digestion

CHAPTER OVERVIEW

Key Concepts

This chapter examines the role of the digestive system and some of its common problems. A meal is followed through the human digestive tract.

Key Science Words

appendix	liver
bile	mucus
chemical change	pancreas
digestion	physical change
digestive system	saliva
enzyme	salivary gland
esophagus	small intestine
gallbladder	stomach
hydrochloric acid	villi
large intestine	

Skill Development

In Lab 10-1, students will **separate and control variables, form a hypothesis, observe,** and **design an experiment.** In Lab 10-2, students will **classify** and **interpret diagrams.** In the Skill Check on page 205, students will **experiment** with dissolving sugar. On page 212, they will **understand the science word** *appendix.* In the Mini Lab on page 210, students will **use numbers** to diagram and label digestive organs. In the Mini Lab on page 214, they will experiment with towels absorbing water.

CHAPTER PREVIEW

Chapter Content

Review this outline for Chapter 10 before you read the chapter.

10:1 The Process of Digestion
- Breakdown of Food
- Physical and Chemical Changes

10:2 The Human Digestive System
- Nutrients Are Digested
- A Trip Through the Digestive System
- Moving Digested Food into Body Cells
- Digestion in Other Animals
- Problems of the Digestive System

Skills in this Chapter

The Skills that you will use in this chapter are listed below.

- In **Lab 10-1,** you will separate and control variables, form a hypothesis, observe, and design an experiment. In **Lab 10-2,** you will classify and interpret diagrams.
- In the **Skill Checks,** you will experiment and understand science words.
- In the **Mini Labs,** you will use numbers and experiment.

202

Bridging

Review digestion by fungi in Chapter 5, by simple invertebrates in Chapter 7, and by complex invertebrates in Chapter 8. Bridge this chapter with these earlier chapters to show how the digestive process becomes more complex as the complexity of the animals increases.

Chapter 10

Digestion

Have you ever watered a very dry houseplant? If so, you probably sprinkled water around the base of the plant rather than flooding one spot with water. Look at the photo on the left. By wetting a large area of soil, the amount of water immediately absorbed by the plant is increased.

Your body needs to absorb nutrients from food just as a houseplant needs to absorb water. This is the job of various organs of your digestive system. One such digestive organ is the small intestine. The picture below shows an enlarged view of the lining of the small intestine. How does the irregular surface of this organ aid in the digestion of food? As you read this chapter, you will discover the answer to this question.

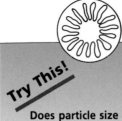

Try This!

Does particle size affect the rate at which a substance dissolves? Predict which would dissolve faster, a copper sulfate crystal or an equal mass of powdered copper sulfate. Check your prediction by placing these substances in two beakers, each with 100 mL of warm water.

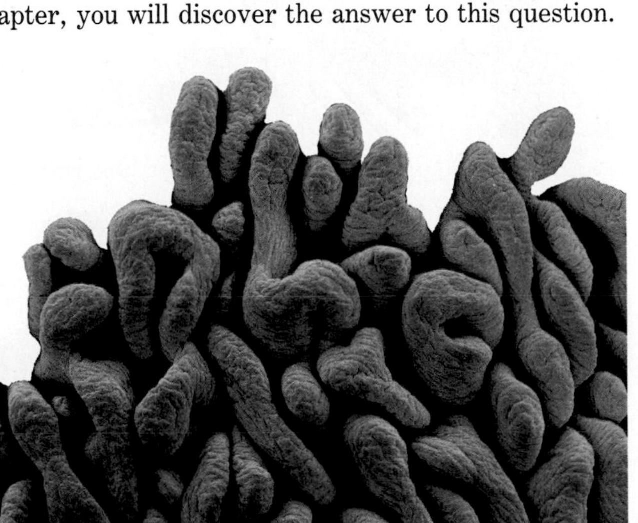

High power view inside the wall of the small intestine

203

GETTING STARTED

Using the Photos

The digestive system changes food both chemically and physically into a form suitable for cell use. The lining of the small intestine has a very large surface area. This structure is designed for rapid absorption of digested food.

MOTIVATION/Try This!

Does particle size affect the rate at which a substance dissolves? Upon completing the chapter opening activity, students will **infer** that smaller particles are broken down faster than larger pieces. Chewing breaks food down physically into smaller pieces. This provides a greater surface area on which enzymes can work. Saliva is able to do a more efficient job with small chunks than with large chunks.

Chapter Preview

Have students study the chapter outline before they begin to read the chapter. They should note the overall organization of the chapter, that the process of digestion is studied first, that nutrients are then covered along with the pathway through the system, and that problems associated with this system are covered last.

Misconception

Ask any student what the most important organ of the digestive system is and they will answer "the stomach." Actually, a person can live without a stomach. It is not a critical organ for digestion.

10:1 The Process of Digestion

PREPARATION

Materials Needed

Make copies of the Focus, Critical Thinking/Problem Solving, Study Guide, Reteaching, and Lab worksheets in the *Teacher Resource Package*.

▶ Gather sugar cubes and warm water for the Skill Check.

▶ Purchase paper cups, gelatin, applicator sticks, plastic spoons, and enzymes for Lab 10-1.

Key Science Words

digestive system
digestion
physical change
chemical change
enzyme

Process Skills

In the Skill Check, students will experiment. In Lab 10-1, students will separate and control variables, form a hypothesis, observe, and design an experiment.

1 FOCUS

▶ The objectives are listed on the student page. Remind students to preview these objectives as a guide to this numbered section.

ACTIVITY/Analogy

On an assembly line, certain tasks are completed in a certain area. Certain steps of digestion are completed in certain areas of the digestive tract.

Guided Practice

Have students write down their answers to the margin question: so that it is in a form that the body cells can use.

Focus/*Teacher Resource Package*, p. 19. Use the Focus transparency shown at the bottom of this page as an introduction to physical digestion.

Objectives

1. **Relate** the importance of the digestive system.
2. **Compare** a physical change and a chemical change in the digestive system.
3. **Explain** the role of enzymes in a chemical change.

Key Science Words

digestive system
digestion
physical change
chemical change
enzyme

Why does food need to be digested?

10:1 The Process of Digestion

When food is first eaten, it is not in a form that can be used by cells in the body. Food must be broken down into a form that cells can use. All cells need food for energy, growth, and repair. How does the body break down food into a form that is usable to cells? The body changes food into a usable form by means of the digestive system. The **digestive system** is a group of organs that take in food and change it into a form the body can use.

Breakdown of Food

Much of your digestive system is hollow. Food moves through it just as materials pass through a tube. To understand how the digestive system works, we can compare it to a factory.

Raw materials are brought into a factory. The materials are transported to different locations in the factory. At each location, the materials are changed. The final products that leave the factory are quite different from the original raw materials. For example, iron ore enters a factory as a raw material. As it moves through the factory, the iron ore is changed to steel. The steel is later changed into new products. Figure 10-1 shows these events.

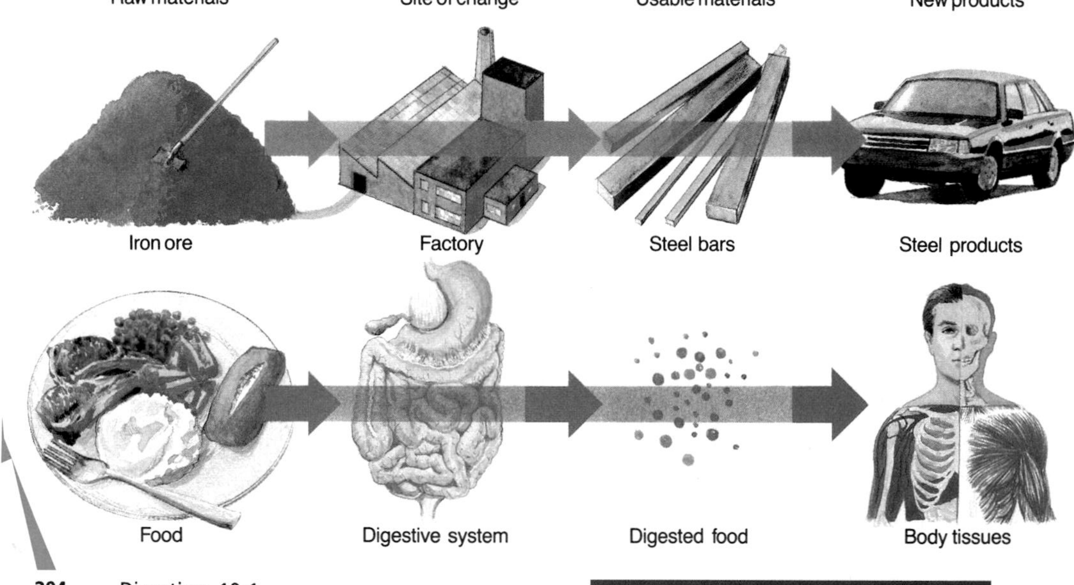

Figure 10-1 The human digestive system is like a factory. Raw materials are used to make products.

OPTIONS

Science Background

Enzymes do not actually change a chemical into new molecules, they simply speed up the reaction. They act as catalysts. It would take years to convert starch to glucose without a catalyst. Within our digestive system, it takes only minutes.

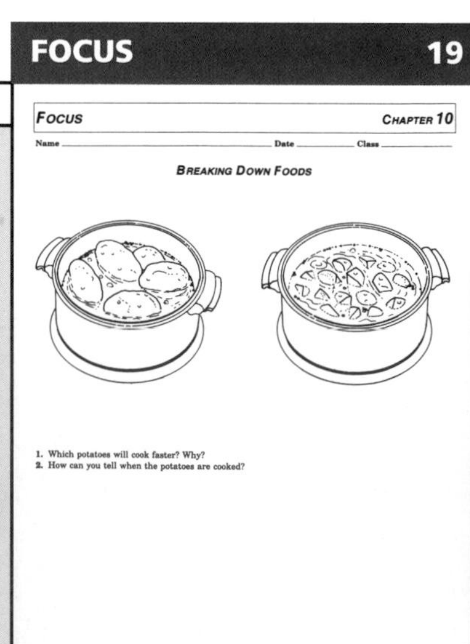
FOCUS 19

FOCUS CHAPTER 10

Name Date Class

BREAKING DOWN FOODS

1. Which potatoes will cook faster? Why?
2. How can you tell when the potatoes are cooked?

Idea Map

Digestion

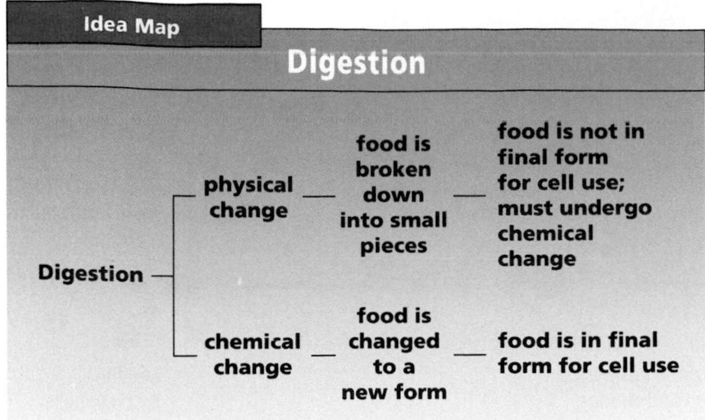
Digestion
physical change
food is broken down into small pieces
food is not in final form for cell use; must undergo chemical change
chemical change
food is changed to a new form
food is in final form for cell use

Study Tip: Use this idea map as a study guide to identifying the differences between physical and chemical changes. Which type of change turns food into a form the body can use?

Your digestive system works in a way similar to the factory. Food is the raw material of your digestive "factory." It enters your digestive system through your mouth. As soon as food enters your body, it begins to change form. The changing of food into a usable form is called **digestion.** As food leaves your mouth, it enters the long tube that makes up your digestive system. The food continuously changes form as it passes through the tube. Finally, the food is in a form that can be used to supply the body with energy or to help make bone, skin, or muscle cells. These are the products of your digestive factory.

Skill Check

Experiment: Compare how long it takes for a sugar cube and a crushed sugar cube to dissolve in a glass of warm water, with or without stirring the water. *For more help, refer to the* ***Skill Handbook****, pages 704-705.*

Physical and Chemical Changes

The digestive system is like a long tube. It is narrow in some places and wide in others. Food is broken down as it moves through this sometimes wide, sometimes narrow tube.

How is food broken down as it passes through the digestive tube? There are two ways. They are physical changes and chemical changes. Physical and chemical changes to food occur at different times and places along the digestive tube.

A **physical change** occurs when large food pieces are broken down into smaller pieces. The food is still in the same form. Only the size and shape of food particles are different. Chewing by the teeth causes a physical change in food. Grinding and mixing also cause a physical change. These physical changes occur farther on down the long tube of the digestive system.

What causes a physical change in food?

2 TEACH

MOTIVATION/Videocassette

Show the videocassette *Eating to Live,* Films for the Humanities.

Idea Map

Have students use the idea map as a study guide to the major concepts of this section.

ACTIVITY/Demonstration

A demonstration of the differences between physical and chemical change may be helpful. Physical change—Break a wood splint into two or four small pieces. Have students examine the wood splint before and after breaking. The starting and final products are exactly the same. Chemical change—Burn the splint. Have students examine the starting and final products. The starting and final products are no longer similar.

Skill Check

The crushed sugar cube should dissolve much more rapidly than the whole sugar cube.

Guided Practice

Have students write down their answers to the margin question: chewing and grinding food with the teeth.

CRITICAL THINKING 10

CRITICAL THINKING/PROBLEM SOLVING — CHAPTER 10

Name ______ Date ______ Class ______

Use after Section 10:1.

WHAT CAN TEETH REVEAL ABOUT DIET?

Humans and many other mammals have four kinds of teeth. The number, size, and shape of each kind of tooth varies in different kinds of mammals. Test this hypothesis: the number and shapes of teeth can be used to predict what an animal eats.

Study the table below. It describes the positions, shapes, and uses of the four kinds of teeth.

Kind	Symbol	Location	Shape	Use
Incisors	I	front of the mouth	chisel	nip, bite, gnaw
Canine	C	behind incisors	chisel	hold, tear
Premolars	P	side of jaw	round, or pointed flat top	chew, grind
Molars	M	back of jaw	large, round, or pointed flat top	chew, grind

I C P M   I C P M   I C P M

Analyzing the Problem

1. Plant eaters have flat molars and premolars. They are called herbivores. Write the numbers of the animals you predict are plant eaters. **Animals 1 and 2**
2. Animals that tear their food are more often eaters of animal flesh. They are called carnivores. Write the numbers of the animals you predict are flesh eaters. Explain your reasons. **Animals 1 and 3, they have large, sharp canines.**
3. Animals that eat both plants and animal flesh are omnivores. Write the number of such an animal and explain your reasons. **Animal 1 has large canines and flat molars**

Solving the Problem

1. Write down the food you ate today. **probably both plant and animal products**
   Do you conclude humans are herbivores, carnivores, or omnivores? **omnivores**
2. The jaws in the pictures are of a human, a giraffe, and a dog. In the blanks, write the number of the jaw of the human **1**, the giraffe **2**, and the dog **3**.

OPTIONS

Critical Thinking/Problem Solving/ *Teacher Resource Package,* p. 10. Use the worksheet shown here to reinforce how teeth are involved in physical digestion.

TEACH

Independent Practice

Study Guide/*Teacher Resource Package,* p. 55. Use the Study Guide worksheet shown at the bottom of this page for independent practice.

Guided Practice

Have students write down their answers to the margin question: They speed up the rate of change.

Check for Understanding

Have students respond to the first three questions in Check Your Understanding.

Reteach

Reteaching/*Teacher Resource Package,* p. 25. Use this worksheet to give students practice in understanding digestion.

Extension: Assign Critical Thinking, Biology and Writing, or some of the **OPTIONS** available with this lesson.

3 APPLY

Audiovisual

Show the videocassette *Breakdown,* Films for the Humanities.

4 CLOSE

ACTIVITY/Brainstorming

Ask: How and where does the digestive system change a slice of bread?

Answers to Check Your Understanding

1. to take in food and change it into a form the body can use
2. physical and chemical changes
3. chemicals that change the rate of a chemical reaction
4. Cells cannot use the starch in bread. It must be broken down into glucose molecules.
5. Answers may include that a factory is not-living and digestion occurs in living things.

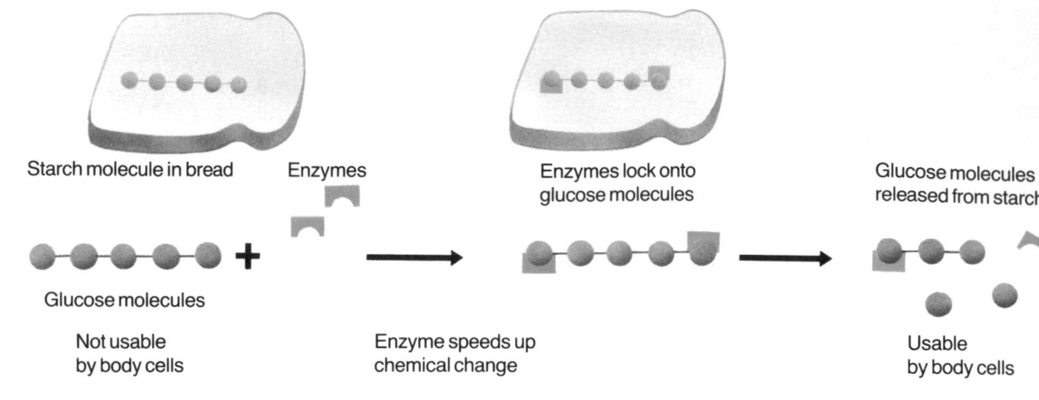

Figure 10-2 Enzymes help speed up chemical reactions.

How do enzymes help chemical changes?

A chemical change occurs when food changes form. How does a chemical change differ from a physical change? A **chemical change** turns food into a form that cells can use. Your digestive system makes chemicals that help with the chemical changes. These chemicals are added to food as it moves through the organs of your digestive system. The chemicals are called enzymes (EN zimes). **Enzymes** are chemicals that speed up the rate of chemical change. Figure 10-2 shows how enzymes work.

Bread is made of a carbohydrate called starch. Bread itself is not usable to cells. It must be digested first. The starch in bread is made of many molecules of a chemical called glucose (GLEW kohs). Glucose is a type of sugar molecule. An enzyme speeds up the change of starch by removing glucose molecules from the starch. Once the glucose molecules are separated, they are in a form your body cells can use.

Check Your Understanding

1. What is the main job of the digestive system?
2. Identify two ways that food is broken down.
3. What are enzymes?
4. **Critical Thinking:** Explain why bread must be digested.
5. **Biology and Writing:** You have learned that the process of digestion is similar to the work of a factory. Write a paragraph that describes the differences between a real factory and digestion.

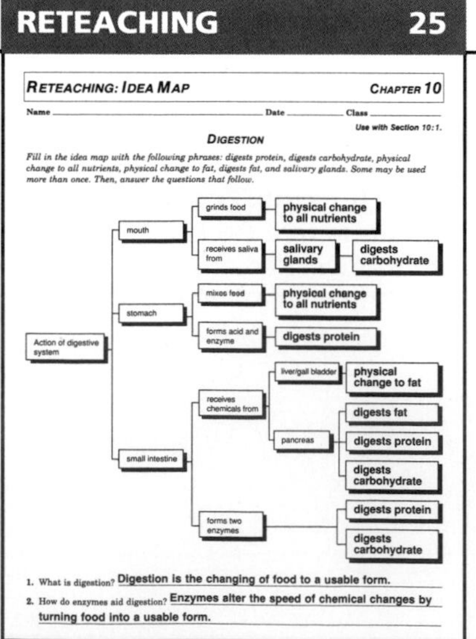

RETEACHING 25

RETEACHING: IDEA MAP — **CHAPTER 10**

Name ________ Date ________ Class ________

Use with Section 10:1.

DIGESTION

Fill in the idea map with the following phrases: digests protein, digests carbohydrate, physical change to all nutrients, physical change to fat, digests fat, and salivary glands. Some may be used more than once. Then, answer the questions that follow.

1. What is digestion? Digestion is the changing of food to a usable form.
2. How do enzymes aid digestion? Enzymes alter the speed of chemical changes by turning food into a usable form.

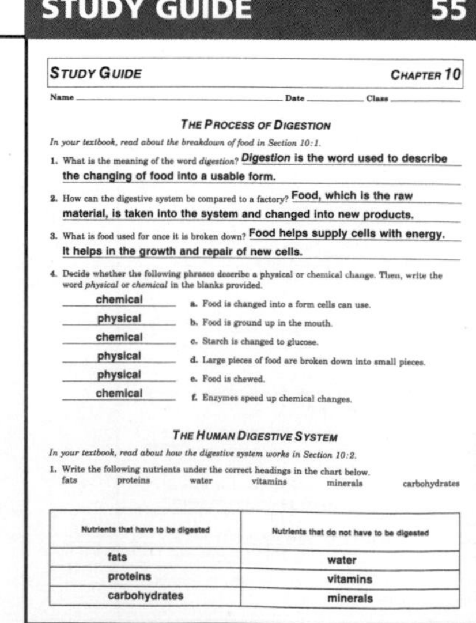

STUDY GUIDE 55

STUDY GUIDE — **CHAPTER 10**

Name ________ Date ________ Class ________

THE PROCESS OF DIGESTION

In your textbook, read about the breakdown of food in Section 10:1.

1. What is the meaning of the word *digestion*? Digestion is the word used to describe the changing of food into a usable form.
2. How can the digestive system be compared to a factory? Food, which is the raw material, is taken into the system and changed into new products.
3. What is food used for once it is broken down? Food helps supply cells with energy. It helps in the growth and repair of new cells.
4. Decide whether the following phrases describe a physical or chemical change. Then, write the word *physical* or *chemical* in the blanks provided.

chemical a. Food is changed into a form cells can use.
physical b. Food is ground up in the mouth.
chemical c. Starch is changed to glucose.
physical d. Large pieces of food are broken down into small pieces.
physical e. Food is chewed.
chemical f. Enzymes speed up chemical changes.

THE HUMAN DIGESTIVE SYSTEM

In your textbook, read about how the digestive system works in Section 10:2.

1. Write the following nutrients under the correct headings in the chart below.
fats proteins water vitamins minerals carbohydrates

Nutrients that have to be digested	Nutrients that do not have to be digested
fats	water
proteins	vitamins
carbohydrates	minerals

Lab 10–1 Digestion

Problem: How are proteins digested?

Skills

separate and control variables, form a hypothesis, observe, design an experiment

Materials

4 paper cups
gelatin
water
4 applicator sticks
refrigerator (optional)
4 plastic spoons
enzyme A
enzyme B

Procedure

1. Copy the data table.
2. Number four paper cups 1 through 4.
3. **Separate and control variables:** Fill each cup as follows:
   Cup 1—2 spoonfuls of gelatin
   This is the control in your experiment.
   Cup 2—2 spoonfuls of gelatin and 1 spoonful of water
   This set up is a variable to show the effect of water on the gelatin.
   Cup 3—2 spoonfuls of gelatin and 1 spoonful of enzyme A
   This set up is a variable to show the effect of enzyme A.
   Cup 4—2 spoonfuls of gelatin and 1 spoonful of enzyme B
   This set up will show the effect of enzyme B.
4. Mix the contents of each cup with a different applicator stick.
5. **Form a hypothesis:** Which cup's contents will show digestion of the gelatin? Write your **hypothesis** in your notebook.
6. Wait 20 minutes. (Or place cups in a refrigerator for 20 minutes.)

CUP	CONTENTS OF CUP	SOLID OR LOOSE?	DIGESTION OCCURRED?
1	Gelatin	solid	no
2	Gelatin + water	solid	no
3	Gelatin + enzyme A	loose	yes
4	Gelatin + enzyme B	solid	no

7. **Observe:** After waiting, record in your table whether or not the gelatin is solid or loose and whether digestion occurred. (NOTE: If gelatin is *solid,* enzyme *did not* digest gelatin. If gelatin is loose, enzyme *did* digest gelatin.)
8. Dispose of the gelatin as indicated by your teacher.

Data and Observations

1. Which cup showed gelatin digestion?
2. What is your evidence?
3. What was added to this cup?

Analyze and Apply

1. What is an enzyme?
2. Where are digestive enzymes usually made?
3. What is your evidence that water is not an enzyme?
4. **Check your hypothesis:** Is your hypothesis supported by your data? Why or why not?
5. **Apply:** Gelatin is a protein. What body organs form enzymes that help digest this nutrient?

Extension

Design an experiment to determine whether saliva contains an enzyme that can digest gelatin. Try your experiment and report the results.

ANSWERS

Data and Observations

1. 3
2. the gelatin became loose
3. enzyme A

Analyze and Apply

1. a chemical that helps to speed up the rate of digestion
2. in the digestive system
3. Cup 2 with water and gelatin alone showed no change in the gelatin.
4. Students who hypothesized that cup 3 would show digestion will answer yes.
5. stomach, pancreas, small intestine

Lab 10-1 Digestion

Overview

In this lab, students will compare visually the action of enzymes on a certain food type.

Objectives: When students have completed this lab, they will have learned that (1) gelatin may be chemically changed when enzymes are added to it, (2) not all enzymes work on the same food.

Time Allotment: 45 minutes

Preparation

▶ Enzyme A is pineapple juice (must be fresh or frozen, *cannot be canned*).

▶ Enzyme B is diastase –mix 10 g diastase with 90 mL water.

▶ Gelatin preparation–add only half the amount of water indicated on the gelatin package.

Lab 10-1 worksheet/*Teacher Resource Package*, pp. 37-38.

Teaching the Lab

▶ **Troubleshooting:** It may take overnight for gelatin to solidify.

10:2 The Human Digestive System

PREPARATION

Materials Needed

Make copies of the Transparency Master, Application, Enrichment, Reteaching, Skill, and Lab worksheets in the *Teacher Resource Package.*

▶ Photocopy diagrams of the digestive system and gather colored pencils for Lab 10-2.

Key Science Words

saliva	liver
salivary gland	bile
esophagus	gallbladder
stomach	large intestine
hydrochloric acid	appendix
small intestine	villi
pancreas	mucus

Process Skills

In the Mini Labs, students will use numbers and experiment. In Lab 10-2, they will classify and interpret diagrams. In the Skill Check, students will understand science words.

1 FOCUS

▶ The objectives are listed on the student page. Remind students to preview these objectives as a guide to this numbered section.

ACTIVITY/Brainstorming

An operation performed on very obese people involves removing a section of the small intestine. Have your students speculate as to why this kind of operation helps with weight loss. Less intestine means less absorption of food.

Objectives

4. **Trace** the path of food from the mouth to body cells.
5. **Compare** the human digestive system with those of other animals.
6. **Identify** the problems of the digestive system.

Key Science Words

saliva
salivary gland
esophagus
stomach
hydrochloric acid
small intestine
pancreas
liver
bile
gallbladder
large intestine
appendix
villi
mucus

10:2 The Human Digestive System

Humans provide a good example of how digestive systems work. If you understand digestion in humans, you should be able to understand it in other animals.

Nutrients Are Digested

Many nutrients must be digested before they can be used, while others are already in a usable form. Table 10-1 shows which nutrients are already usable and which are not.

Water, vitamins, and minerals can move directly from your digestive system into body cells without being changed. Fats, proteins, and carbohydrates must be acted upon by enzymes in your digestive system. There are different kinds of enzymes for each nutrient that must be digested. For example, enzymes that speed up changes in fats cannot change proteins and carbohydrates. Enzymes that speed up changes in proteins cannot help with the breakdown of fats or carbohydrates. The digestive system, therefore, must make different kinds of enzymes for each different nutrient.

TABLE 10–1. NUTRIENTS

Nutrient	Already in Usable Form
Water	yes
Vitamins	yes
Minerals	yes
Fat	no
Protein	no
Carbohydrate	no

A Trip Through the Digestive System

Let's take a trip through the human digestive system to see how it works. To make it a little more interesting, we will look at what happens to a hamburger. Remember that ground meat is mostly protein, mayonnaise is mostly fat, and the bun is mostly carbohydrate. The entire trip of the hamburger through the digestive system takes about 21 hours. Figure 10-3 shows how the entire digestive system looks from one end to the other.

The hamburger enters the system through the mouth. In the mouth, teeth break and grind the food. The breaking and grinding cause the hamburger to change physically. **Saliva** is a liquid that is formed in the mouth and that contains an enzyme. Saliva speeds up chemical changes in the carbohydrates of the bun. It has no chemical effect on proteins or fats. Figure 10-3 shows that saliva is made in the salivary (SAL uh ver ee) glands. **Salivary glands** are three pairs of small glands located under the tongue and behind the jaw. Saliva passes from the glands through small tubes leading to the mouth.

OPTIONS

Science Background

Think of the digestive system as a long tube through which food passes. Each organ of the system makes up the tube or is attached to the tube and helps with the digestion of different food types.

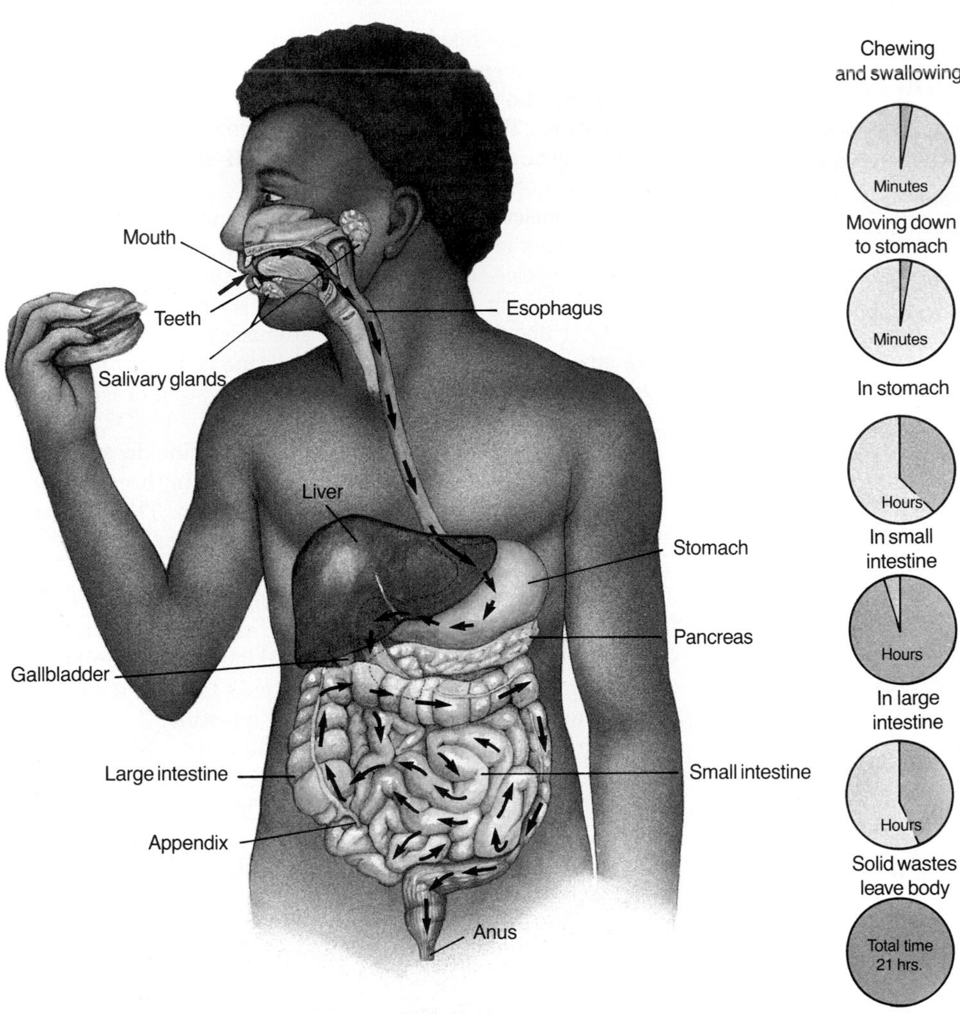

The broken down hamburger remains in the mouth for about one minute. Swallowing moves it from the mouth into the esophagus (ih SAHF uh gus). The **esophagus** is a tube that connects the mouth to the stomach. Muscles in the esophagus push the food toward the stomach. These events are shown in Figure 10-3. This part of the trip takes less than one minute.

As it leaves the esophagus, the food enters the stomach. The **stomach** is a baglike, muscular organ that mixes and chemically changes protein. It can hold about one liter of liquid and food.

Figure 10-3 Follow the path of a meal through the digestive system.

How does food reach your stomach?

STUDY GUIDE 56

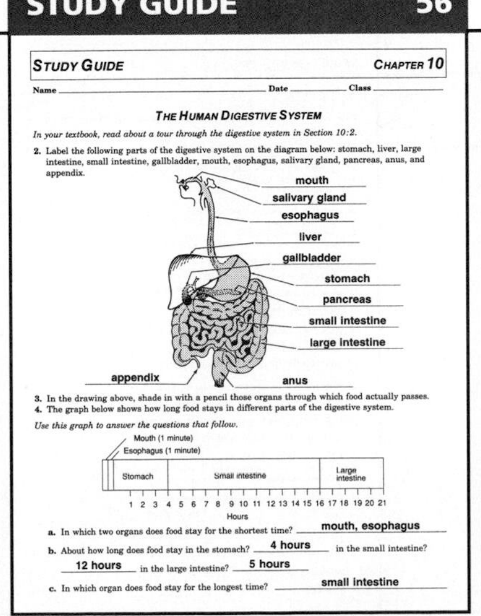

STUDY GUIDE — **CHAPTER 10**

Name ______ Date ______ Class ______

THE HUMAN DIGESTIVE SYSTEM

In your textbook, read about a tour through the digestive system in Section 10:2.

2. Label the following parts of the digestive system on the diagram below: stomach, liver, large intestine, small intestine, gallbladder, mouth, esophagus, salivary gland, pancreas, anus, and appendix.

3. In the drawing above, shade in with a pencil those organs through which food actually passes.
4. The graph below shows how long food stays in different parts of the digestive system.

Use this graph to answer the questions that follow.

a. In which two organs does food stay for the shortest time? **mouth, esophagus**

b. About how long does food stay in the stomach? **4 hours** in the small intestine? **12 hours** in the large intestine? **5 hours**

c. In which organ does food stay for the longest time? **small intestine**

STUDY GUIDE 57

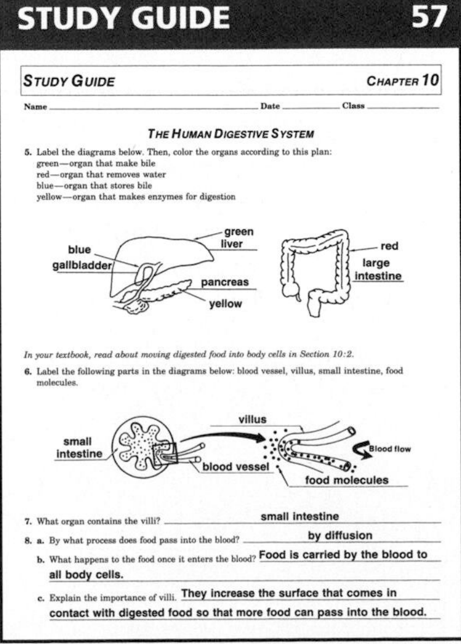

STUDY GUIDE — **CHAPTER 10**

Name ______ Date ______ Class ______

THE HUMAN DIGESTIVE SYSTEM

5. Label the diagrams below. Then, color the organs according to this plan:
green—organ that make bile
red—organ that removes water
blue—organ that stores bile
yellow—organ that makes enzymes for digestion

In your textbook, read about moving digested food into body cells in Section 10:2.

6. Label the following parts in the diagrams below: blood vessel, villus, small intestine, food molecules.

7. What organ contains the villi? **small intestine**

8. a. By what process does food pass into the blood? **by diffusion**

b. What happens to the food once it enters the blood? **Food is carried by the blood to all body cells.**

c. Explain the importance of villi. **They increase the surface that comes in contact with digested food so that more food can pass into the blood.**

2 TEACH

MOTIVATION/Demonstration

Have students observe prepared slides of the intestine (cross section) under the microscope. This will allow students to see the villi. A 35-mm slide projected on the classroom screen would also be an effective way for them to see the extensive surface area of this organ.

Concept Development

▶ The human body may form 250 to 1500 mL of saliva per day.

▶ Point out that the digestive system produces eleven different enzymes. Each enzyme changes a specific nutrient into a usable form.

Guided Practice

Have students write down their answers to the margin question: Muscles in the esophagus move food toward the stomach.

MOTIVATION/Enrichment

Point out that food is prevented from entering the windpipe by the closure of the epiglottis during swallowing. This closure is an example of a reflex action. The muscle contraction called peristalsis is a second example of a reflex. The muscles that line the esophagus contract to push food down into the stomach.

Independent Practice

Study Guide/*Teacher Resource Package*, pp. 56-57. Use the Study Guide worksheets shown at the bottom of this page for independent practice.

TEACH

Concept Development

▶ Explain that food passes directly from the stomach to the small intestine, but the liver, gallbladder, and pancreas pour their chemicals into the small intestine. It is important to emphasize that food does not enter these organs. Figure 10-4, which shows this relationship, should be pointed out to students.

▶ Bile consists of bile salts, cholesterol, and bilirubin (a hemoglobin derivative). The liver produces 500 mL of bile each day.

▶ Mention that the liver has many roles in addition to that of forming bile. You may want to mention that the pancreas also has a dual role and will be discussed in a later chapter.

Mini Lab

Make sure that students recognize that the digestive system is indeed a long tube that is coiled within the human body.

Mini Lab

How Long Is the Digestive System?

Use numbers: Diagram and label the lengths and names of the following digestive organs: esophagus (25 cm), stomach (20 cm), small intestine (700 cm), and large intestine (150 cm). *For more help, refer to the **Skill Handbook,** pages 718-719.*

Cells on the inside of the stomach make two chemicals that help in digestion. One is an enzyme. The enzyme speeds up the chemical change of protein or meat in the hamburger. The other chemical made by the stomach is hydrochloric (hi druh KLOR ik) acid. **Hydrochloric acid** is a chemical often called stomach acid.

The muscular walls of the stomach mix and churn the food. Mixing is a physical part of digestion. Look at Figure 10-3 and notice the small clock next to the stomach. It shows how long foods remains in the stomach.

After about four hours, the stomach pushes food into the small intestine. The **small intestine** is a long, hollow, tubelike organ. Most of the chemical digestion of food takes place in the small intestine.

Before describing what the small intestine does, we must take a short detour. Figure 10-4 shows three different organs that are part of the digestive system. These organs are the pancreas (PAN kree us), liver, and gallbladder. Food doesn't pass through these organs.

The **pancreas** makes three different enzymes. One kind of enzyme helps to break down fats, one kind helps to break down proteins, and the third kind helps to break down carbohydrates. The enzymes pass through a small tube from the pancreas to the small intestine.

The **liver,** the largest organ in the body, makes a chemical called bile. **Bile** is a green liquid that breaks large fat droplets into small fat droplets. This change is physical and takes place in the small intestine. Bile is delivered from the liver to the gallbladder. The **gallbladder** is a small, baglike part located under the liver. It stores bile until it is needed by the small intestine.

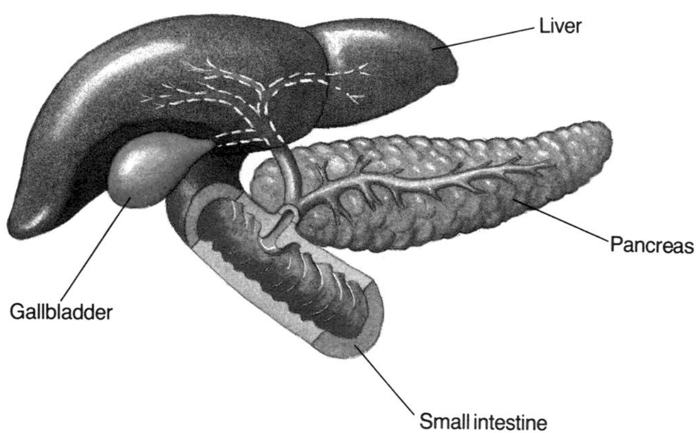

Figure 10-4 Bile from the gallbladder breaks up fat. The pancreas makes three enzymes that help digest fat, protein, and carbohydrates.

OPTIONS

Application/*Teacher Resource Package,* p. 10. Use the Application worksheet shown here to introduce the concept of digestive system disorders.

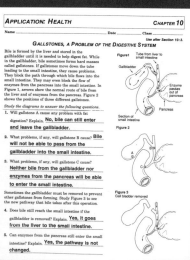

APPLICATION 10

APPLICATION: HEALTH CHAPTER 10

Name ____________ Date ________ Class ________

Use after Section 10:3.

GALLSTONES, A PROBLEM OF THE DIGESTIVE SYSTEM

Bile is formed by the liver and stored in the gallbladder until it is needed to help digest fat. While in the gallbladder, bile sometimes forms hard masses called gallstones. If gallstones move down the tube leading to the small intestine, they cause problems. They block the path through which bile flows into the small intestine. They may even block the flow of enzymes from the pancreas into the small intestine. In Figure 1, arrows show the normal route of bile from the liver and of enzymes from the pancreas. Figure 2 shows the positions of three different gallstones.

Study the diagrams to answer the following questions.

1. Will gallstone A cause any problem with fat digestion? Explain. **No, bile can still enter and leave the gallbladder.**
2. What problems, if any, will gallstone B cause? **Bile will not be able to pass from the gallbladder into the small intestine.**
3. What problems, if any, will gallstone C cause? **Neither bile from the gallbladder nor enzymes from the pancreas will be able to enter the small intestine.**

Sometimes the gallbladder must be removed to prevent other gallstones from forming. Study Figure 3 to see the new pathway that bile takes after this operation.

4. Does bile still reach the small intestine if the gallbladder is removed? Explain. **Yes, it goes from the liver to the small intestine.**
5. Can enzymes from the pancreas still enter the small intestine? Explain. **Yes, the pathway is not changed.**

Figure 1: Tube from liver to small intestine; Gallbladder; Enzyme passes out of pancreas; Pancreas; Section of small intestine

Figure 2: A; B; C

Figure 3: Gall bladder removed

Career Close-Up

Dietitian

Steve was interested in a career as a dietitian. As part of his career day project at school, he decided to interview a dietitian to find out more about the job.

Steve: What is a dietitian?

Dietitian: A dietitian is one who understands nutrition. A dietitian plans diets for groups or individuals. These diets may be regular, balanced meals or diets for patients with special needs.

Steve: What type of training is needed?

Dietitian: Usually a four-year college degree is needed. This background will lead to a Registered Dietitian Degree. A six- to eighteen-month internship in a hospital is required.

Steve: Where are you most likely to find a job?

Dietitian: Hospitals are one place. You could also work for a company, school, university, or nursing home that has its own employee or patient dining hall. You might even work for an eating disorder clinic. Large food companies and drug companies hire dietitians.

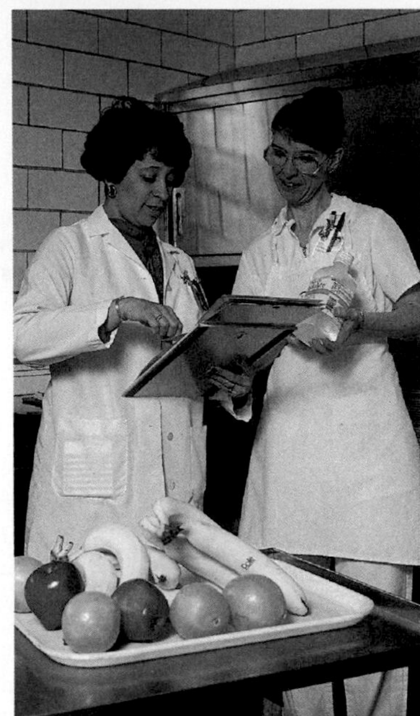

A dietitian approves the meals to be served to hospital patients.

Let's continue our tour and follow the food into the small intestine. Remember, the pancreas and gallbladder have already emptied their chemicals into the small intestine. In addition, the small intestine itself makes several enzymes. Cells that line the small intestine make enzymes that help with digestion of proteins in the hamburger meat and carbohydrates in the bun. All foods that enter the small intestine are finally changed chemically into a form that is usable by the body. The main goal of the digestive system has now been carried out. Figure 10-3 shows these changes. It also shows you that food spends about 12 hours in the small intestine. Why should food spend so much time in this part of the digestive system?

Career Close-Up

Dietician

Background

This field is expanding as the population ages. More and more senior citizen housing centers are employing licensed dieticians to help with the meal planning for these individuals.

Related Careers

Food services in nursing homes, hospitals, and rehabilitation centers are in need of people to prepare, cook, and serve food. A degree as a dietician is not required.

Job Requirements

Becoming a licensed dietician usually requires a two- or four-year college degree and licensing by the state or local government.

For More Information

Check with your school counselor, home economics teacher, or school librarian for more information.

TEACH

Concept Development

▶ The small intestine releases about 1500 mL of liquid per day in the form of digestive enzymes and mucus. It absorbs about 8500 mL of liquid per day.

Independent Practice

Study Guide/*Teacher Resource Package,* p. 58. Use the Study Guide worksheet shown at the bottom of this page for independent practice.

STUDY GUIDE 58

STUDY GUIDE CHAPTER 10

Name ______ Date ______ Class ______

THE HUMAN DIGESTIVE SYSTEM

9. Complete the table below.

Organ	Enzyme formed here? (yes or no)	Food passes through this organ? (yes or no)	Name of nutrient acted upon or digested (fat, protein, carbohydrate, none)	Food absorbed here? (yes or no)	Water absorbed here? (yes or no)	Name of chemical made here
Mouth and salivary glands	yes	yes (mouth)	carbohydrate	no	no	saliva
Esophagus	no	yes	none	no	no	none
Stomach	yes	yes	protein	no	no	hydrochloric acid, enzyme
Liver and gallbladder	no	no	fat	no	no	bile
Pancreas	yes	no	fat, protein, carbohydrate	no	no	enzymes
Small intestine	yes	yes	fat, protein, carbohydrate	yes	no	enzymes
Large intestine	no	yes	none	no	yes	none

10. Decide whether the following statements are true or false. If true, write *true* in the left-hand column. If false, change the underlined word to one that will make the statement true and write the correct word in the blank.

long a. Plant-eating animals usually have short digestive systems.

two b. An earthworm has one opening in its digestive system.

true c. A tapeworm has no digestive system.

short d. Meat-eating animals usually have long digestive systems.

true e. Humans are among the animals that have a complex digestive system.

OPTIONS

The Human Digestive System/*Transparency Package,* number 10. Use color transparency number 10 as you teach the digestive system.

TEACH

Concept Development

▶ Explain that the large intestine aids in the reabsorption of sodium into the bloodstream. The large intestine is composed of three main sections: the ascending colon, the transverse colon, and the descending colon.

ACTIVITY/Display

Obtain a model of the human body (torso). Most models have detachable organs. Ask students to identify all detached organs that compose the digestive system. Have them attempt to reassemble the model correctly.

Idea Map

Have students use the idea map as a study guide to the major concepts of this section.

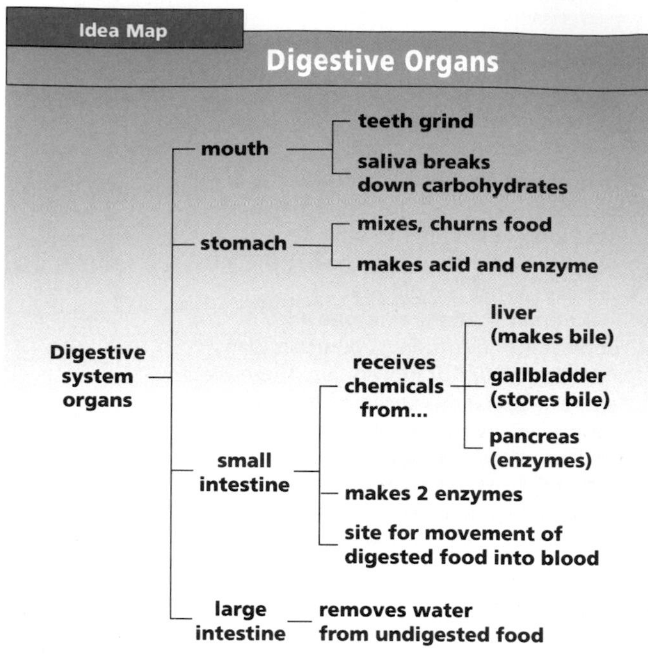

Study Tip: Use this idea map as a study guide to understanding the job of each digestive organ.

After passing through the small intestine, food enters the large intestine. The **large intestine** is a tubelike organ at the end of the digestive tract. It is called the large intestine because of its width. The large intestine is about 5 cm wide, and the small intestine is only 2.5 cm wide. Not much digestion occurs in the large intestine. Its main job is to remove water from undigested food. Water is then returned to the bloodstream. The clock in Figure 10-3 tells you that food spends about five hours in the large intestine. Not all of the food is digested when it reaches the end of the large intestine. It then leaves the body as solid waste through the anus.

One last part of the digestive system should be mentioned. This part is the appendix (uh PEN dihks). The **appendix** is a small fingerlike part found where the small and large intestines meet. The appendix in our body does not take part in the digestion of food.

Altogether your digestive system forms a tube about 900 cm long. The average height of an adult is about 170 cm. Your digestive system is about five times longer than your body! How can such a long tube fit inside of you? Why must it be so long?

Skill Check

Understand science words: appendix. The word part *pend* means to hang. In your dictionary, find three words with the word part *pend* in them. *For more help, refer to the* ***Skill Handbook****, pages 706-711.*

212

OPTIONS

Enrichment/*Teacher Resource Package*, p. 10. Use the Enrichment worksheet shown here to help students.

Transparency Master/*Teacher Resource Package*, p. 45. Use the Transparency Master shown here to help students learn the parts of the digestive system.

ENRICHMENT 10

ENRICHMENT — CHAPTER 10

Name ______ Date ______ Class ______

Use after Section 10:2.

DIGESTING DIFFERENT NUTRIENTS

Use the information below to complete the tables for carbohydrate digestion and protein digestion. Key words for the tables are underlined.

Salivary glands produce the enzyme salivary amylase. The pancreas produces pancreatic amylase. Both enzymes bring about chemical changes, changing carbohydrates to double sugars. Salivary glands release enzymes into the mouth. The pancreas releases enzymes into the small intestine. Glands in the small intestine make carbohydrases, enzymes that bring about the chemical breakdown of double sugars to single sugars. This action occurs in the small intestine.

Proteins are changed into polypeptides in the stomach. An enzyme called pepsin and a chemical called hydrochloric acid, both made by glands in the stomach, aid this chemical change. Trypsin, an enzyme made in the pancreas, is released into the small intestine. Trypsin helps in the chemical breakdown of polypeptides into peptides. Glands in the small intestine release the enzyme erepsin (ee REP sihn). This enzyme chemically changes peptides into amino acids.

Carbohydrate Digestion

Steps in nutrient digestion	Enzyme name	Organ making enzyme	Organ where change occurs	Chemical or physical
Carbohydrate Double sugar	salivary amylase and pancreatic amylase	salivary glands and pancreas	mouth and small intestine	chemical
Single sugar	carbohydrases	small intestine	small intestine	chemical

Protein Digestion

Steps in nutrient digestion	Enzyme or chemical name	Organ making enzyme or chemical	Organ where change occurs	Chemical or physical
Protein Polypeptide	pepsin and hydrochloric acid	stomach	stomach	chemical
Peptide	trypsin	pancreas	small intestine	chemical
Amino acids	erepsin	small intestine	small intestine	chemical

TRANSPARENCY 45

TRANSPARENCY MASTER — CHAPTER 10

HUMAN DIGESTIVE SYSTEM

Human digestive system	Organ name	Main functions, chemical made, and foods acted upon
	Mouth	1. Chewing food begins digestive process. 2. Food enters digestive system.
	Salivary gland	1. An enzyme in saliva starts digestion of carbohydrates. 2. Food is moistened for ease in swallowing. Saliva moves into mouth by way of small tube.
	Esophagus	1. Food is moved by muscle contraction to the stomach.
	Stomach	1. Enzymes and hydrochloric acid are formed here. 2. Protein digestion begins. 3. Muscle movement of stomach mixes food.
	Pancreas	1. Three enzymes are formed here for digestion of fats, proteins, and carbohydrates. 2. All enzymes from pancreas are added to the small intestine.
	Gallbladder and liver	1. Liver forms bile that is stored in the gallbladder. 2. Bile causes fats to break up. 3. Bile is added to the small intestine.
	Small intestine	1. Two enzymes are formed here. One digests protein, and other carbohydrates. 2. Final digestion of fats, protein, and carbohydrates occurs here. 3. All digested foods are absorbed into bloodstream.
	Appendix	1. Performs no known digestive job.
	Large intestine	1. Absorbs large amounts of water. 2. Undigested food given off as solid waste.

- - - → = direction of food
——→ = direction of saliva into mouth from salivary glands
···→ = direction of enzymes into small intestine from pancreas
⇒ = direction of digested food into blood from small intestine
-▲-▲-→ = direction of bile into small intestine from gall bladder

Lab 10–2 Digestive System

Problem: What are the jobs of the digestive system organs?

Skills

classify, interpret diagrams

Materials

five diagrams of the digestive system
colored pencils: red, blue, green, yellow, purple

Procedure

1. Label your five diagrams A, B, C, D, and E.
2. **Classify:** On diagram A, label the liver, esophagus, large intestine, mouth, small intestine, gallbladder, pancreas, salivary gland, stomach, anus, and appendix.
3. With a regular pencil, shade only the parts through which food actually passes.
4. Label the diagram "Human Digestive System and Food Pathway."
5. On diagram B, label the organs that aid the chemical change of carbohydrates. Color these organs red.
6. Label the diagram "Organs that Help to Digest Carbohydrates."
7. On diagram C, label the organs that aid the chemical change of protein. Color these organs blue.
8. Label the diagram "Organs that Help to Digest Protein."

9. On diagram D, label the organs that help with chemical and physical changes of fat. Color these organs green.
10. Label the diagram "Organs that Help to Digest Fat."
11. On diagram E, label the organs of the digestive system where diffusion of digested food into blood occurs. Color these organs yellow.
12. Using the same diagram, E, label the organs where diffusion of water occurs. Color these organs purple.
13. Label the diagram "Organs that Help Remove Digested Food and Water."

Data and Observations

1. Which organs did you color red?
2. Which organs did you color blue?
3. Which organs did you color green?
4. Which organs did you color yellow?
5. Which organs did you color purple?

Analyze and Apply

1. **Interpret diagrams:** Which two organs are the most important in digestion? Explain your answer.
2. Which organs help digest carbohydrates, protein, and fat?
3. **Apply:** Diagram the digestive path of a slice of cheese and pepperoni pizza. Indicate where the crust, cheese, and pepperoni are digested.

Extension

Draw a diagram of the digestive system. Create a color code to indicate where chemical, physical, both physical and chemical, and no changes occur. Then, color your diagram accordingly.

Lab 10-2 Digestive System

Overview

Using diagrams, students will identify the organs responsible for digestion and absorption in the human digestive system.

Objectives: After completing this lab, students will be able (1) to **name** and **describe** the organs of the human digestive system, (2) to **indicate** the organs where absorption of food and water occur, (3) to **name** the specific organs in which carbohydrate, fat, and protein digestion occur.

Time Allotment: 1-2 class periods (See the Cooperative Learning note.)

Preparation

▶ Photocopies of the digestive system must be prepared in advance. Each student will need five copies. (See the Cooperative Learning note.)

Lab 10-2 worksheet/*Teacher Resource Package,* pp. 39-40.

Teaching the Lab

Cooperative Learning: To reduce the amount of time and materials needed, allow students to work in groups of five. Each student would then be responsible for only one diagram and the entire group would turn in one completed set. For more information, see pp. 22T-23T in the Teacher Guide.

ANSWERS

Data and Observations

1. mouth, pancreas, small intestine
2. stomach, pancreas, small intestine
3. pancreas, liver, gallbladder
4. small intestine
5. large intestine

Analyze and Apply

1. the pancreas and small intestine, because most of the digestive enzymes are produced there
2. carbohydrates – mouth, pancreas, and small intestine; protein – stomach, pancreas, and small intestine; fat – pancreas, liver, and gallbladder
3. On a diagram, students will show the crust digested in the mouth and small intestine, the cheese digested in the stomach and small intestine.

TEACH

Using Science Words: Relate the terms *absorption* and *absorb.* Ask students to describe the action of a sponge or paper towel as it soaks up water. What term is often used to describe this action? The towel or sponge absorbs. Relate the term *absorption* to osmosis and diffusion.

ACTIVITY/Brainstorming

Ask students why dieters often increase the amount of vegetables they eat. They may see the connection between eating a lot of foods high in bulk, and not being able to digest as much of one's food. Few nutrients are acquired from these types of foods.

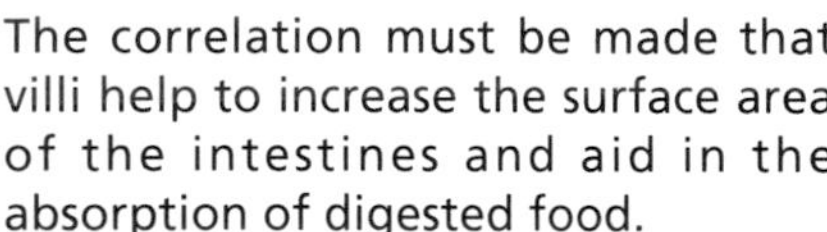

Mini Lab

The correlation must be made that villi help to increase the surface area of the intestines and aid in the absorption of digested food.

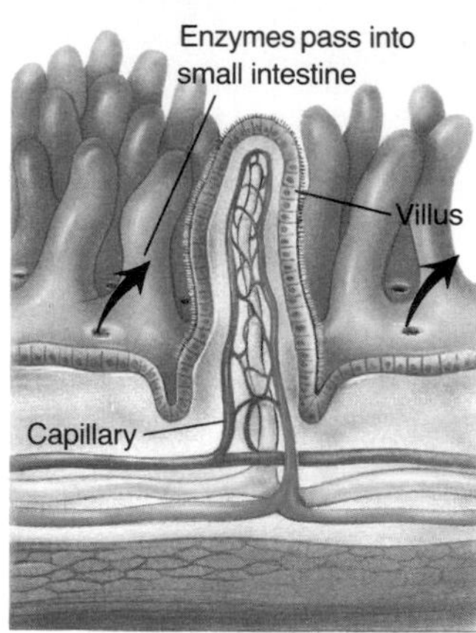

Figure 10-5 The surface area of the small intestine is increased by many hundreds of villi.

Moving Digested Food into Body Cells

Food digested in the small intestine is ready to be used by the body cells. Food cannot stay in the small intestine and do the body any good. It must be carried to all body cells by the blood. How does most food get out of the small intestine and into the blood? Food gets out of the small intestine and into the blood mainly by diffusion. Diffusion is a process that you studied in Chapter 2.

The inside surface of the small intestine helps absorb food molecules. The small intestine is a long, hollow tube much like a garden hose. The main difference between your small intestine and a hose is the inside lining. The lining of your small intestine is not smooth. Figure 10-5 shows that the small intestine has many tiny, fingerlike parts covering its entire inside surface. The fingerlike parts on the lining of the small intestine are called **villi** (VIHL i). Each villus contains blood vessels that carry digested food.

Once inside your blood vessels, digested food is carried by the blood to all body cells. How does digested food get from your blood vessels into your body cells? This happens through a special kind of diffusion. Figure 10-6 shows how food gets into the blood vessels.

The villi allow your small intestine to absorb more digested food than if it were smooth. Why? Villi increase the intestinal surface that comes in contact with digested food. With more intestinal surface, more digested food can pass into the blood.

Mini Lab

How Do Villi Aid Absorption?

Experiment: Compare how one, two, three, and four folded paper towels absorb water. Dip each paper towel into a beaker of water. Record the volume of water left in the beaker. *For more help, refer to the **Skill Handbook,** pages 704-705.*

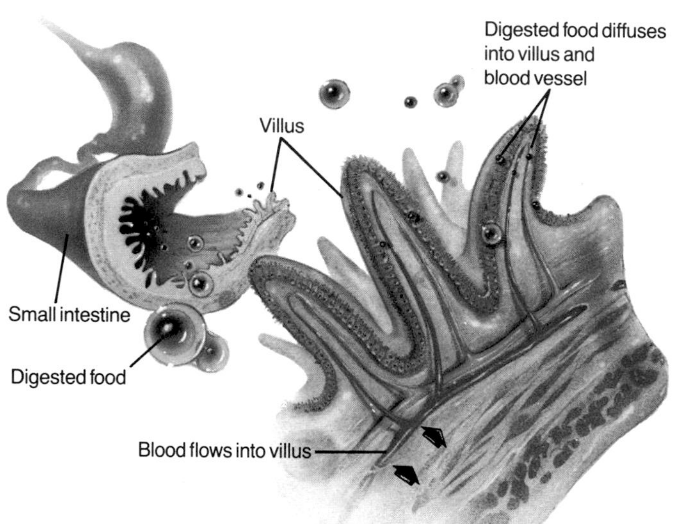

Figure 10-6 Digested food particles pass into the blood through the walls of the villi.

OPTIONS

Skill/*Teacher Resource Package,* p. 10. Use the Skill worksheet shown here to reinforce digestion of nutrients.

How Do Digestive System Lengths Compare?/ *Lab Manual,* pp. 79-82. Use this lab as an extension to the digestive system

SKILL 10

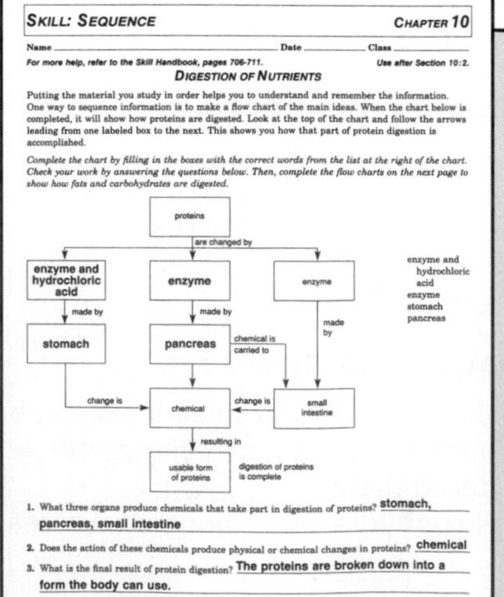

SKILL: SEQUENCE CHAPTER 10

Name ______ Date ______ Class ______

For more help, refer to the Skill Handbook, pages 706-711. *Use after Section 10:2.*

DIGESTION OF NUTRIENTS

Putting the material you study in order helps you to understand and remember the information. One way to sequence information is to make a flow chart of the main ideas. When the chart below is completed, it will show how proteins are digested. Look at the top of the chart and follow the arrows leading from one labeled box to the next. This shows you how that part of protein digestion is accomplished.

Complete the chart by filling in the boxes with the correct words from the list at the right of the chart. Check your work by answering the questions below. Then, complete the flow charts on the next page to show how fats and carbohydrates are digested.

1. What three organs produce chemicals that take part in digestion of proteins? stomach, pancreas, small intestine
2. Does the action of these chemicals produce physical or chemical changes in proteins? chemical
3. What is the final result of protein digestion? The proteins are broken down into a form the body can use.

Consider this example. Trapeze artists may use a small net during their act. If they should fall, the chances of landing in this net are small. If they use a larger net, however, they have a better chance of landing in the net. A similar thing happens with the small intestine. The larger the surface of the intestine, the better the chances are that food molecules will come into contact with it. The more food that contacts the surface of the intestine, the more food that passes through the intestine and is picked up by the blood.

Digestion in Other Animals

How does the human digestive system compare with those of other animals? Different kinds of animals eat different kinds of food. The kind of food eaten is related to the animal's digestive system. Animals that eat plants, such as cows and rabbits, usually have long digestive systems. Animals that eat meat, such as cats and wolves, usually have shorter digestive systems. Plant eaters have longer digestive systems because plants are harder to digest than meat. The longer digestive system gives the food more time to change into a usable form.

Why do plant eaters have long digestive systems?

Like humans, many other animals have digestive systems with two openings. For example, the earthworm also has a mouth and an anus, Figure 10-7. Also like humans, the earthworm's digestive system has different organs that have different jobs. Some of the organs are the sites of chemical changes. Other organs produce physical changes in foods. Dogs, birds, snakes, fish, insects, and squid also have digestive systems with two openings.

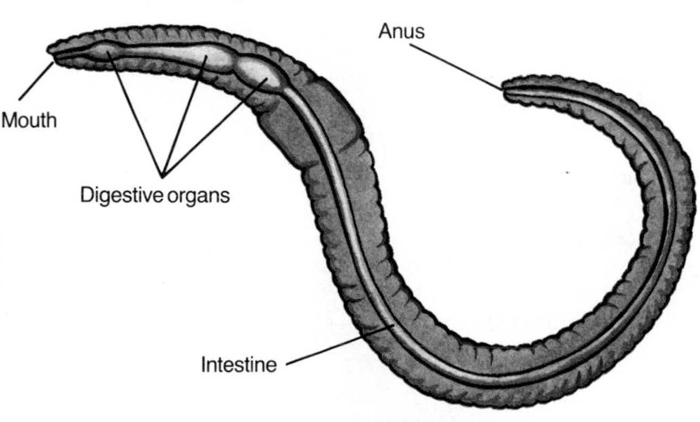

Figure 10-7 There are different organs in the earthworm's digestive system that cause physical or chemical changes in food.

TEACH

Guided Practice

Have students write down their answers to the margin question: Plants are difficult to digest.

Check for Understanding

Ask: Did all the animal phyla studied in Chapters 7 and 8 have a digestive system? Which phyla had one or two openings to the system?

Reteach

Reteaching/*Teacher Resource Package,* p. 26. Use this worksheet to give students additional practice in understanding the digestive systems of animals.

Connection: Math

Have students make a pie graph showing the amount of time food spends in each digestive organ. Times in minutes are: mouth–2; esophagus–1; stomach–240; small intestine–720; large intestine–240.

Have students divide each time by the total time (1200 minutes) and multiply the result by 360 (total number of degrees in the pie). Students can use a protractor to mark the degrees around the circumference, then they can draw a line from each mark to the center.

RETEACHING 26

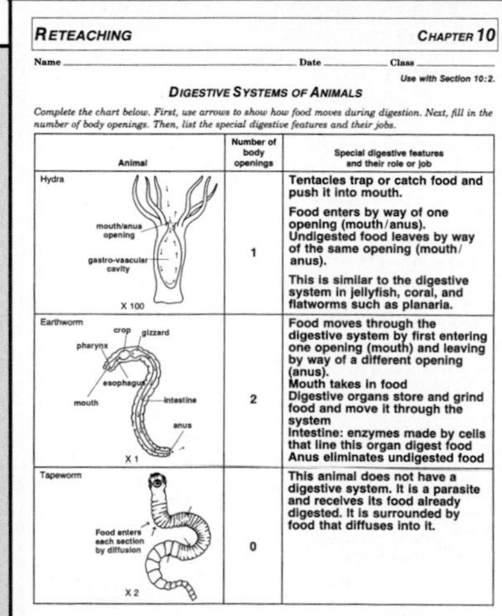

RETEACHING CHAPTER 10

Name ______ Date ______ Class ______

Use with Section 10:2.

DIGESTIVE SYSTEMS OF ANIMALS

Complete the chart below. First, use arrows to show how food moves during digestion. Next, fill in the number of body openings. Then, list the special digestive features and their jobs.

Animal	Number of body openings	Special digestive features and their role or job
Hydra (mouth/anus opening; gastro-vascular cavity; X 100)	1	Tentacles trap or catch food and push it into mouth. Food enters by way of one opening (mouth/anus). Undigested food leaves by way of the same opening (mouth/anus). This is similar to the digestive system in jellyfish, coral, and flatworms such as planaria.
Earthworm (crop; gizzard; pharynx; esophagus; mouth; intestine; anus; X 1)	2	Food moves through the digestive system by first entering one opening (mouth) and leaving by way of a different opening (anus). Mouth takes in food Digestive organs store and grind food and move it through the system Intestine: enzymes made by cells that line this organ digest food Anus eliminates undigested food
Tapeworm (Food enters each section by diffusion; X 2)	0	This animal does not have a digestive system. It is a parasite and receives its food already digested. It is surrounded by food that diffuses into it.

OPTIONS

Science Background

Bacteria within the digestive systems of animals such as cows, sheep, camels, and deer enable these animals to digest plant matter or the cellulose of plant cell walls. Thus, these animals are able to receive considerable nutrition from these foods. Humans cannot benefit from plant matter because we lack these bacteria.

How Does the Fish Digestive System Work?/*Lab Manual,* pp. 83-86. Use this lab as a comparison to the human digestive system.

TEACH

Independent Practice

Study Guide/*Teacher Resource Package,* p. 59. Use the Study Guide worksheet shown at the bottom of this page for independent practice.

Cooperative Learning: Divide the class into two groups: patients and doctors. Have each patient describe his/her digestive complaint to a doctor. The doctor should then diagnose the problem and suggest treatment.

MOTIVATION/Brainstorming

How many commercials on TV advertise products to cure digestive problems? Have students name the products and then discuss them.

ACTIVITY/Demonstration

Add a few drops of dilute hydrochloric acid to several thicknesses of paper. Have students note how rapidly the paper is destroyed by the acid. This simulates the nature of an ulcer.

Repeat the demonstration only this time cover the paper with petroleum jelly (vaseline) before adding the acid. Note the slower action time for the acid. Petroleum jelly simulates the mucus lining of the stomach.

Guided Practice

Have students write down their answers to the margin question on page 217: Excess food from the stomach can back up into the esophagus.

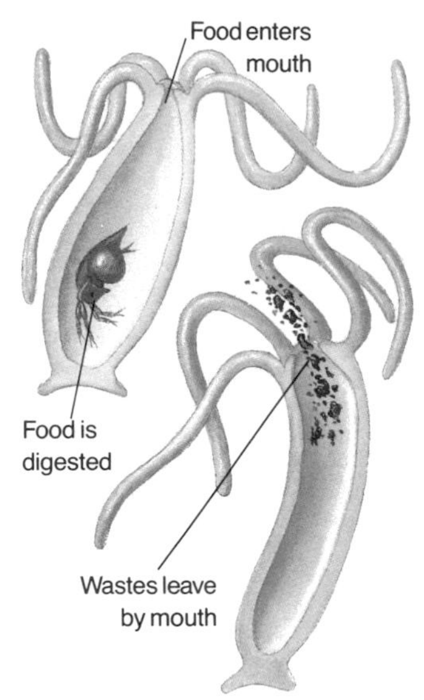

Figure 10-8 The single opening in a hydra acts as both mouth and anus. How are nutrients absorbed by a hydra? into the body cells by diffusion

Some animals have digestive systems with only one opening. The hydra is a small, simple animal with only one opening. Its digestive process is simple. The opening serves as both a mouth and an anus as shown in Figure 10-8. Its stomach is just a hollow sac within the animal's body. What other animals you studied in Chapter 7 have one opening to the digestive system?

A few animals have no digestive system. Animals such as tapeworms are examples. Tapeworms live inside the digestive systems of other animals. Digested food passes into their bodies by diffusion. It may not be a very good arrangement for the animal in whose body the tapeworm lives, but it certainly works for the tapeworm.

Problems of the Digestive System

The digestive system, like any body system, may have problems. You may have heard of ulcers or heartburn. An ulcer (UL sur) is a sore or hole on the inside of either the stomach or the small intestine. Figure 10-9 shows a cut-away view of the inside of a normal stomach and the same view of a stomach with an ulcer. The ulcer is caused by the stomach lining being digested, or "eaten" away. Remember that enzymes and stomach acids are found in the stomach. These enzymes and acids cause the ulcer.

Normally, however, the stomach or intestine does not digest itself. There is usually a chemical covering on the inside. This covering is called mucus (MYEW kus). **Mucus**

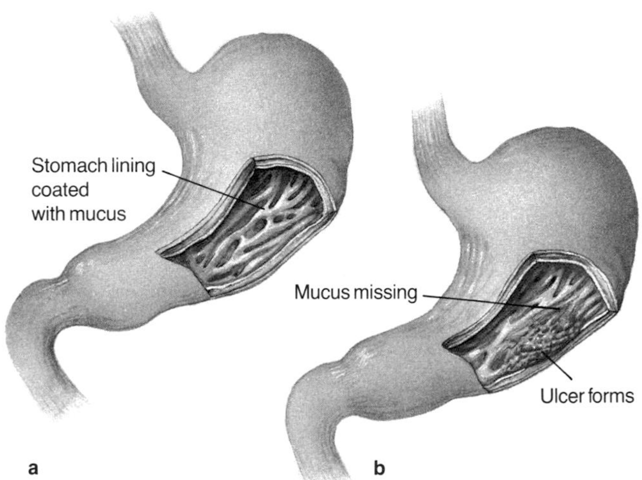

Figure 10-9 A healthy stomach (a) is coated with mucus. A stomach with an ulcer (b) can be very painful.

OPTIONS

ACTIVITY/Challenge

Have students research other problems of the digestive system (appendicitis, liver cancer, gallstones, diarrhea).

Science Background

Ulcers and heartburn are only two of the more common problems associated with digestion. Neither is very serious unless the ulcer results in internal bleeding or perforates the stomach wall resulting in infection of the peritoneal cavity.

STUDY GUIDE 59

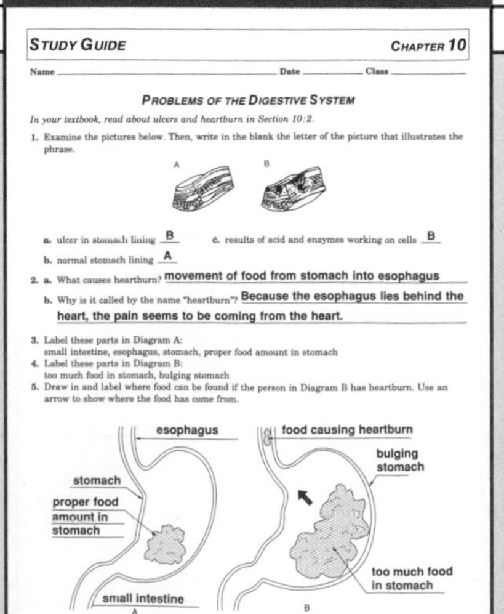

STUDY GUIDE — CHAPTER 10

Name ______ Date ______ Class ______

PROBLEMS OF THE DIGESTIVE SYSTEM

In your textbook, read about ulcers and heartburn in Section 10:2.

1. Examine the pictures below. Then, write in the blank the letter of the picture that illustrates the phrase.

A B

a. ulcer in stomach lining B
b. normal stomach lining A
c. results of acid and enzymes working on cells B

2. a. What causes heartburn? movement of food from stomach into esophagus
   b. Why is it called by the name "heartburn"? Because the esophagus lies behind the heart, the pain seems to be coming from the heart.
3. Label these parts in Diagram A: small intestine, esophagus, stomach, proper food amount in stomach
4. Label these parts in Diagram B: too much food in stomach, bulging stomach
5. Draw in and label where food can be found if the person in Diagram B has heartburn. Use an arrow to show where the food has come from.

Figure 10-10 Eating too many rich or acidic foods can cause heartburn. Which food is more acidic, a pickle, or a potato? a pickle

is a thick, sticky material that protects the stomach and intestinal linings from enzymes and stomach acid. It's the same sticky, thick material that lines your nose.

Heartburn is a problem caused by stomach acids moving into the esophagus. Most of the time, stomach acids stay in the stomach. They then pass into the small intestine. When stomach acids move into the esophagus, they cause a burning feeling. However, nothing is being "burned." The problem also has nothing to do with the heart. The esophagus lies behind the heart. The pain feels like it is coming from the heart, even though it isn't.

Eating too much at one time may result in heartburn, Figure 10-10. The stomach can hold only so much food. If too much is eaten, some may back up into the esophagus.

Bio Tip

Health: Aspirin and ethyl alcohol are absorbed directly into the bloodstream through the stomach.

Why does eating too much cause heartburn?

Check Your Understanding

6. Beginning with the mouth, describe the path food takes as it moves through the digestive system.
7. What causes an ulcer?
8. Identify the differences between the digestive process of a human and a hydra.
9. **Critical Thinking:** How do antacids reduce heartburn?
10. **Biology and Reading:** Name three organs that are not part of the digestive tube. How do these organs aid the digestive process?

STUDY GUIDE 60

STUDY GUIDE — CHAPTER 10

Name ______ Date ______ Class ______

VOCABULARY

Review the new words used in Chapter 10. Use the terms below to fill in the blanks in the sentences that follow.

mucus	digestive system	digestion	stomach	saliva
villi	physical change	esophagus	small intestine	enzymes
bile	chemical change	pancreas	gall bladder	hydrochloric
liver	salivary glands	appendix	large intestine	acid

1. Changing of food into a usable form is called **digestion**.
2. **Enzymes** speed up the rate of chemical change.
3. **Saliva** helps digest carbohydrates in the mouth.
4. **Bile** helps break down fats.
5. The tube that connects the mouth to the stomach is the **esophagus**.
6. **Salivary glands** are located under the tongue and behind the jaw.
7. The **pancreas** is an organ that makes three different enzymes.
8. The **gallbladder** stores bile.
9. Most digestion and absorption of food takes place in the **small intestine**.
10. The **large intestine** removes water from undigested food.
11. The **appendix** is a small fingerlike part located where the small and large intestines meet.
12. The breaking of food into small pieces is **physical change**.
13. Protein digestion begins in the **stomach**.
14. Bile is made in the **liver**.
15. Fingerlike parts on the lining of the small intestine are called **villi**.
16. **Chemical change** turns food into a form that cells can use.
17. The **digestive system** is a group of organs that take in food and change it into a form the body can use.
18. The chemical **hydrochloric acid** is made by the stomach.
19. **Mucus** protects the stomach and intestinal linings.

RETEACHING 27

RETEACHING — CHAPTER 10

Name ______ Date ______ Class ______

Use after Section 10:3.

PROBLEMS OF THE DIGESTIVE SYSTEM

Label the following items on the drawings below: mucus layer, stomach ulcer, esophagus, stomach, and small intestine. Then answer the questions.

1. What food does the stomach digest? **proteins**
2. What kinds of chemicals does the stomach produce? **enzymes and hydrochloric acid**
3. What is the function of the mucus lining in the stomach? **The mucus protects the lining of the stomach from enzymes and stomach acid.**
4. What is an ulcer? **An ulcer is a sore, or hole, on the inside of the stomach or intestine.**
5. What causes a person with an ulcer to feel pain? **The acids and enzymes begin to digest the stomach lining where the ulcer is because the lining is not protected by the mucus there.**
6. What is heartburn? **Heartburn occurs when stomach acids move up into the esophagus.**

TEACH

Independent Practice

Study Guide/*Teacher Resource Package,* p. 60. Use the Study Guide shown at the bottom of this page for independent practice.

Check for Understanding

Have students respond to the first three questions in Check Your Understanding.

Reteach

Reteaching/*Teacher Resource Package,* p. 27. Use this worksheet to give students additional practice in understanding problems of the digestive system.

Extension: Assign Critical Thinking, Biology and Reading, or some of the **OPTIONS** available with this lesson.

3 APPLY

Software

The Digestion Simulator, Cambridge Development Laboratories.

4 CLOSE

Audiovisual

Show the filmstrip *The Digestive System,* Clearvue, Inc.

Answers to Check Your Understanding

6. mouth, esophagus, stomach, small intestine, large intestine, and anus
7. enzymes and stomach acid digest the stomach lining
8. human – two openings, specialized organs; hydra – one opening, no digestive organs
9. They neutralize the stomach acid.
10. salivary glands – produce digestive enzymes and mucus; pancreas – produces digestive enzymes; liver – produces digestive enzymes and bile; gallbladder – stores bile made by the liver

CHAPTER 10 REVIEW

Summary

Summary statements can be used by students to review the major concepts of the chapter.

Key Science Words

All boldfaced terms from the chapter are listed.

Testing Yourself

Using Words

1. physical change
2. esophagus
3. digestion
4. pancreas
5. saliva
6. bile
7. gallbladder
8. villi
9. salivary gland
10. enzyme

Finding Main Ideas

11. pp. 210-212; Food spends four hours in the stomach, twelve hours in the small intestine, and five hours in the large intestine.
12. p. 208; Only one type of enzyme can digest each food type.
13. pp. 204-205; In a factory, raw materials are brought in and changed as they pass from one place to the next. New products are formed. The digestive system does the same thing. The digestive system is like a long tube. Food moves through it in one direction.
14. p. 208; Teeth grind the food, causing a physical change. Salivary glands add saliva to the food, causing chemical changes.
15. p. 215; Different organs can carry out different jobs. Certain organs can carry out physical changes, while others can carry out chemical changes.
16. p. 216; An ulcer is formed when the stomach lining is digested by enzymes and acid.

Using Main Ideas

17. Food passes through the mouth, esophagus, stomach, small intestine, large intestine, and anus.
18. The stomach makes enzymes and hydrochloric acid.

Chapter 10 Review

Summary

10:1 The Process of Digestion

1. The digestive system—a long, hollow tube—takes in food and changes it into a form usable to body cells.
2. Physical changes grind and break down food. Chemicals called enzymes speed up the changing of food into a usable form.
3. Enzymes help to change fats, proteins, and carbohydrates into usable forms by speeding up chemical changes.

10:2 The Human Digestive System

4. Food passes from mouth to esophagus to stomach to small intestine to large intestine. Villi in the small intestine increase surface area and help with the movement of digested food into body cells.
5. Digestive systems in animals differ in length, number of openings, and specialization.

10:3 Problems of the Digestive System

6. An ulcer is formed by a part of the stomach lining being digested. Mucus protects the stomach and intestine linings from enzymes and acid. Heartburn is caused by stomach acids that enter the esophagus. Eating too much at one time may result in heartburn.

Key Science Words

appendix (p. 212)
bile (p. 210)
chemical change (p. 206)
digestion (p. 205)
digestive system (p. 204)
enzyme (p. 206)
esophagus (p. 209)
gallbladder (p. 210)
hydrochloric acid (p. 210)
large intestine (p. 212)
liver (p. 210)
mucus (p. 217)
pancreas (p. 210)
physical change (p. 205)
saliva (p. 208)
salivary gland (p. 208)
small intestine (p. 210)
stomach (p. 209)
villi (p. 214)

Testing Yourself

Using Words

Choose the word from the list of Key Science Words that best fits the definition.

1. breaking of large food pieces into small pieces
2. connects mouth to stomach
3. process of changing food into a usable form
4. organ that makes three different enzymes
5. changes carbohydrates in the mouth
6. liquid that causes a physical change in fats
7. organ that stores bile
8. fingerlike parts on the lining of the small intestine
9. makes saliva
10. chemical that speeds up the changing of food into a usable form

19. A tapeworm has no openings for digestion. A hydra has one opening for digestion, and a human has two openings for digestion.
20. Mucus protects the stomach and intestinal linings from enzymes and stomach acid.
21. A physical change is the breaking of large food pieces into smaller food pieces by the grinding and chewing of the teeth in the mouth. A chemical change is the changing of starch in bread into glucose by enzymes in saliva.
22. Heartburn is caused by eating more food than the stomach can hold. The extra food and stomach acid back up into the esophagus.

Review

Testing Yourself *continued*

Finding Main Ideas

List the page number where each main idea below is found. Then, explain each main idea.

11. how much time food spends in each of the following: the stomach, small intestine, and large intestine
12. why so many different enzymes are needed for digestion
13. how the digestive system is like a factory
14. the body parts that help with physical and chemical changes in the mouth
15. how a digestive system with two openings is more specialized than a digestive system with one opening
16. what causes a stomach ulcer

Using Main Ideas

Answer the questions by referring to the page number after each question.

17. What are the organs through which food passes on its trip through the digestive system? (pp. 209, 210)
18. What two chemicals are made in the stomach? (p. 210)
19. What is an example of an animal with no openings to its digestive system? One opening? Two openings? (pp. 215, 216)
20. What is the function of mucus in the digestive system? (p. 217)
21. What is an example of a physical change and a chemical change that takes place in the digestive system? (pp. 205, 206)
22. What causes heartburn? (p. 217)

Skill Review

*For more help, refer to the **Skill Handbook,** pages 704-719.*

1. **Form a hypothesis:** Which food would enzymes work on more rapidly: a slice of bread or an equal mass of bread crumbs? Explain by using the term *surface area.*
2. **Use numbers:** Determine from Figure 10-3 how long it takes for a meal to pass into the stomach and out into the large intestine.
3. **Interpret diagrams:** Use the information shown in Figure 10-3 to make a bar graph illustrating the amount of time food generally remains in the major digestive organs.
4. **Classify:** Make a list of five foods you have eaten during the past 18 hours. Classify each food according to the main nutrient it contains.

Finding Out More

Critical Thinking

1. Explain how it is possible for a person to live without a stomach.
2. Explain why it is impossible for a person to live without a pancreas.

Applications

1. How do the number and shape of teeth compare among adult animals, such as dogs, cats, cows, and horses? Relate tooth shape with diet.
2. Plants contain the substance cellulose. Report on the relationship between this substance and the length of a plant eater's digestive system.

Chapter Review/*Teacher Resource Package,* pp. 50-51.

Chapter Test/*Teacher Resource Package,* pp. 52-54.

Chapter Test/*Computer Test Bank*

Skill Review

1. bread crumbs; The bread crumbs are already in smaller pieces than a slice of bread and have more surface area on which the enzymes can react.
2. into the stomach – less than 1 minute; stomach – 4 hours; small intestine – 12 hours; digestion in the small intestine takes the longest time.
3. Student graphs should show: stomach – 4 hours; small intestine – 12 hours; large intestine – 5 hours.
4. Students should classify foods as protein, fat, carbohydrate, vitamin, mineral, or water.

Finding Out More

Critical Thinking

1. Most of the absorption of food takes place in the small intestine. If the person eats foods that are already partially broken down, he or she can live without a stomach.
2. Enzymes from the pancreas are necessary to digest carbohydrates, proteins, and fats in the small intestine.

Applications

1. Animals that eat plants have a few large, flat teeth with broad grinding surfaces. Meat eaters have a larger number of smaller teeth with pointed surfaces for ripping and tearing flesh. Animals that eat both plants and animals have both pointed teeth and grinding molars.
2. Cellulose is very difficult to break down. The more cellulose a plant eater eats, the longer its digestive system.

Circulation

PLANNING GUIDE

CONTENT	TEXT FEATURES	TEACHER RESOURCE PACKAGE	OTHER COMPONENTS
(1 day) 11:1 The Process of Circulation Pickup and Delivery Circulation in Animals	Lab 11-1: *Pulse Rate,* p. 224 Idea Map, p. 222 Check Your Understanding, p. 223	Reteaching: *Circulation in Animals,* p. 28 Study Guide: *The Process of Circulation,* p. 61 Lab 11-1: *Pulse Rate,* pp. 41-42	**Laboratory Manual:** *How Do Hearts of Different Animals Compare?* p. 91
(3 days) 11:2 The Human Heart Heart Structure The Pumping of the Heart Heart Valves The Jobs of the Heart	Skill Check: *Understand Science Words,* p. 227 Mini Lab: *How Do the Pulses of Males and Females Compare?* p. 228 Check Your Understanding, p. 231	Enrichment: *Tracing a Heartbeat,* p. 11 Reteaching: *Heartbeat Sequence and Events,* p. 29 Critical Thinking/Problem Solving: *How Are the Heart Valves Arranged?* p. 11 Focus: *Electrocardiograph,* p. 21 Study Guide: *The Human Heart,* pp. 62-63	**Laboratory Manual:** *How Does the Heart Work?* p. 87 Color Transparency 11: *Blood Flow Between Heart and Lungs*
(2 days) 11:3 Blood Vessels Arteries Veins Capillaries	Lab 11-2: *Blood Pressure,* p. 235 Check Your Understanding, p. 234	Reteaching: *Blood Vessels and Blood Flow,* p. 30 Skill: *The Circulatory System,* p. 12 Study Guide: *Blood Vessels,* p. 64 Lab 11-2: *Blood Pressure,* pp. 43-44	
(2 days) 11:4 Problems of the Circulatory System High Blood Pressure Heart Attack Preventing Heart Problems	Technology: *Angioplasty,* p. 238 Check Your Understanding, p. 239	Application: *Blood Pressure,* p. 11 Reteaching: *Circulatory System Problems,* p. 31 Study Guide: *Problems of the Circulatory System,* p. 65 Study Guide: *Vocabulary,* p. 66 Transparency Master: *Circulation Pathway in Humans,* p. 49	
Chapter Review	Summary Key Science Words Testing Yourself Finding Main Ideas Using Main Ideas Skill Review	Chapter Review, pp. 55-56 Chapter Test, pp. 57-59	**Test Bank**

MATERIALS NEEDED

LAB 11-1, p. 224	LAB 11-2, p. 235	MARGIN FEATURES
petri dish water wall clock live earthworm	plastic squeeze bottle pan or sink water meterstick rubber stopper and tube assembly	Skill Check, p. 227 dictionary Mini Lab, p. 228 pencil paper

OBJECTIVES

SECTION	OBJECTIVE	OBJECTIVES CORRELATION: CHECK YOUR UNDERSTANDING	CHAPTER REVIEW	TRP CHAPTER REVIEW	TRP CHAPTER TEST
11:1	1. **Identify** the circulatory system.	1, 2, 4	7, 13, 21	1, 28	5, 12
	2. **Compare** the circulatory systems of earthworms, insects, and humans.	3, 5	13	4	10, 13, 14
11:2	3. **Describe** how blood is pumped through the heart.	6, 9	4, 8, 17, 25	29, 37	45, 48, 49, 50
	4. **Explain** what causes the sounds the heart makes.	7	14, 18, 19	2, 21, 24, 25, 30	7, 24, 46, 47
	5. **Trace** the pathway of blood through the left and right sides of the heart.	8, 10	5, 16, 23, 26	3, 15, 16, 17, 18, 19, 20, 22, 23, 26, 27, 32, 38	1, 16, 17, 18, 19, 21, 22, 23, 25, 26, 27, 28, 29, 30, 31, 32, 39, 40
11:3	6. **Discuss** the importance of arteries.	11	3, 11	9, 10, 13, 31	6, 33, 34, 35, 38, 39, 41, 43
	7. **List** four traits of veins.	12	1, 19	8, 12	2, 36, 44
	8. **Give the function** of capillaries.	13	2	11, 14	4, 37, 38, 42
11:4	9. **Explain** how blood pressure is measured.	16, 19	24	7, 35, 36	8, 9, 11
	10. **Trace** the events before and after a heart attack.	17, 20	6, 9, 15	6, 33, 34	3
	11. **Relate** ways to help prevent and correct heart problems.	18	20, 22	5	15

Circulation

CHAPTER OVERVIEW

Key Concepts

The role of the circulatory system is described using examples from different animal phyla. The anatomy of the human circulatory system is presented. Comparisons are made in the role of the heart, arteries, veins, and capillaries, as well as the blood pressure within them. Problems in the human circulatory system and the role of modern technology in correcting them are also considered.

Key Science Words

aorta
artery
atrium
bicuspid valve
blood pressure
capillary
cholesterol
circulatory system
coronary vessel
heart attack
hypertension
pulmonary artery
pulmonary vein
semilunar valve
tricuspid valve
valve
vein
vena cava
ventricle

Skill Development

In Lab 11-1, students will **form a hypothesis, calculate, interpret data,** and **make and use tables** in comparing worm and human pulse rates. In Lab 11-2, they will **formulate models, form a hypothesis,** and **measure in SI** as they study blood pressure in veins and arteries. In the Skill Check on page 227, students will **understand** the **science word** *semilunar.* In the Mini Lab on page 228, students will **design an experiment** to compare pulse rates of males and females.

CHAPTER PREVIEW

Chapter Content

Review this outline for Chapter 11 before you read the chapter.

Skills in this Chapter

The skills that you will use in this chapter are listed below.

- In **Lab 11-1,** you will form a hypothesis, calculate, interpret data, and make and use tables. In **Lab 11-2,** you will formulate models, form a hypothesis, and measure in SI.
- In the **Skill Checks,** you will understand science words.
- In the **Mini Labs,** you will design an experiment.

220

Bridging

The fate of digested food as studied in the previous chapter can now be followed. Once food passes out of the small intestine, it moves through the body via the bloodstream.

Chapter **11**

Circulation

Look at the photo of the crowded highway shown on the left. All the cars and trucks may have special pickup or delivery jobs. People in cars may be on their way to work, to school, or even going on vacation. Trucks may be picking up or delivering goods to homes, warehouses, or stores.

The photograph below shows a close-up view of human blood moving through a blood vessel. Blood cells are round. Notice that the walls of a blood vessel are very thin.

How are the jobs of cars and trucks on a highway similar to the jobs of blood cells? How is the job of the highway similar to the job of a blood vessel? Can you think of ways in which they are different?

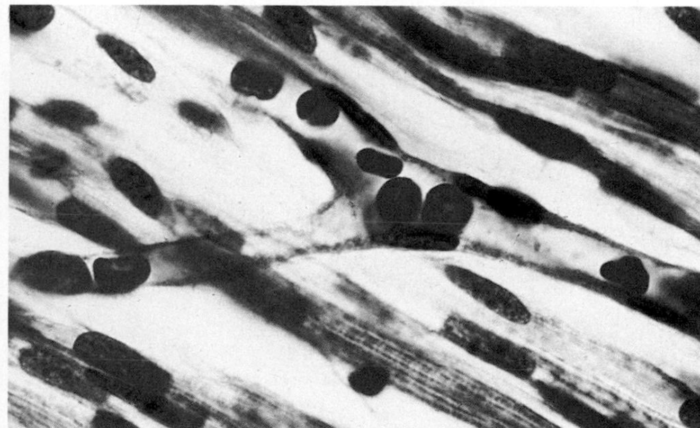

Blood vessel

Try This!

What kinds of sounds does the heart make? Use a stethoscope to listen to the sounds your heart makes. How many different sounds do you hear? Is there a pattern to the sounds? How many sounds do you hear during a one-minute period?

GETTING STARTED

Using the Photos

Use the photo analogy to explain the functions of delivery and pickup performed by the circulatory system. Direct students' attention to the fact that the highway system and the extensive network of blood vessels within the body are very similar in terms of function.

MOTIVATION/Try This!

What kinds of sounds does the heart make? Allow students to listen to their heart sounds for several minutes with stethoscopes. If stethoscopes are not available, students can feel their heartbeat using their hand placed over their chest. Student observations will differ. However, the pattern they **observe** will consist of two distinct sounds occurring close together in a continuous rhythm.

Chapter Preview

Have students study the chapter outline before they begin to read the chapter. They should note the overall organization of the chapter, that the process of circulation is studied first in a very general way, then the human heart is covered in detail. Blood vessel structure and function is next, and finally, problems of the circulatory system and how they may be solved or reduced are studied.

Misconception

Most students do not realize that the human heart is: (a) a muscle (b) hollow inside (c) receives no nourishment or oxygen from the blood being pumped through it (d) divided into two separate sides.

11:1 The Process of Circulation

PREPARATION

Materials Needed

Copy the Study Guide and Reteaching worksheets in the *Teacher Resource Package.*

▶ Order earthworms for Lab 11-1.

Key Science Words

circulatory system

Process Skills

In Lab 11-1, students will form a hypothesis, calculate, interpret data, and make and use tables.

1 FOCUS

▶ The objectives are listed on the student page. Remind students to preview these objectives as a guide to this numbered section.

Idea Map

Have students use the idea map as a study guide to major concepts.

Guided Practice

Have students write down their answers to the margin question: blood, blood vessels, and heart.

Independent Practice

Study Guide/*Teacher Resource Package,* p. 61. Use the Study Guide worksheet shown at the bottom of this page for independent practice.

Objectives

1. **Identify** the circulatory system.
2. **Compare** the circulatory systems of earthworms, insects, and humans.

Key Science Words

circulatory system

11:1 The Process of Circulation

Your body is made of billions of cells. Each cell is like a tiny factory that must be supplied with certain chemicals. You have a pickup and delivery system in your body to supply these chemicals.

Pickup and Delivery

What makes up the circulatory system?

Your body's pickup and delivery system is the circulatory system. Your **circulatory system** is made of your blood, blood vessels, and heart. Blood delivers needed materials, such as oxygen, water, and food, to your cells. Blood picks up the cells' waste products, such as carbon dioxide gas.

Blood travels through a series of tubes called blood vessels. Your heart serves as a pump to help move, or circulate, blood through these vessels.

Circulation in Animals

Not all animals have circulatory systems. Simple animals, such as a sponge, sea anemone, or hydra, do not have circulatory systems. The bodies of these animals are just a few cells thick. Water moves freely in and out of their bodies. Nearly every cell in the animal's body comes in contact with the water. Oxygen and nutrients in the water diffuse into the cells. Wastes, such as carbon dioxide, diffuse out of the cells into the water. The water in which these simple animals live acts as a pickup and delivery service for them.

Study Tip: Use this idea map as a study guide to comparing circulation patterns in different animals.

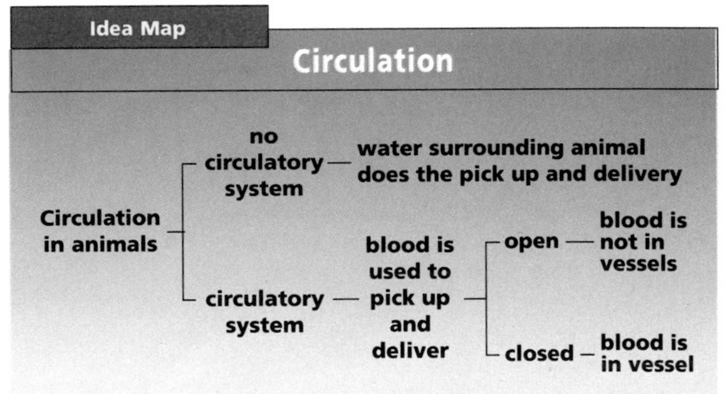

OPTIONS

Science Background

Point out that circulatory systems evolved as body size increased. With a circulatory system, all internal cells can come in contact with blood. The animal is less dependent on an aqueous environment for diffusion of materials into and out of the animal.

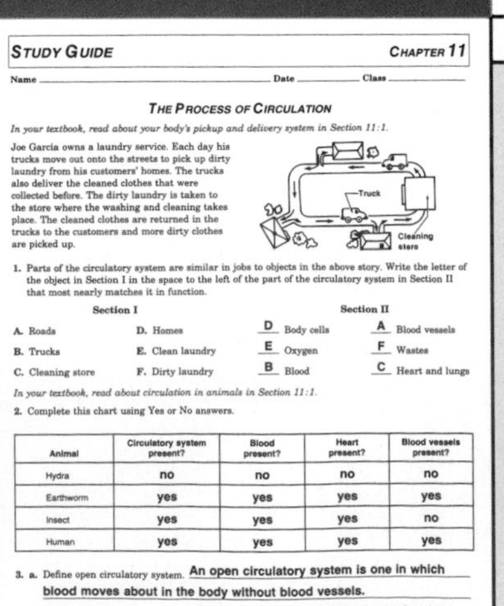

STUDY GUIDE 61

STUDY GUIDE — CHAPTER 11

Name ______ Date ______ Class ______

THE PROCESS OF CIRCULATION

In your textbook, read about your body's pickup and delivery system in Section 11:1.

Joe Garcia owns a laundry service. Each day his trucks move out onto the streets to pick up dirty laundry from his customers' homes. The trucks also deliver the cleaned clothes that were collected before. The dirty laundry is taken to the store where the washing and cleaning takes place. The cleaned clothes are returned in the trucks to the customers and more dirty clothes are picked up.

1. Parts of the circulatory system are similar in jobs to objects in the above story. Write the letter of the object in Section I in the space to the left of the part of the circulatory system in Section II that most nearly matches it in function.

Section I

A. Roads
B. Trucks
C. Cleaning store
D. Homes
E. Clean laundry
F. Dirty laundry

Section II

D Body cells
E Oxygen
B Blood
A Blood vessels
F Wastes
C Heart and lungs

In your textbook, read about circulation in animals in Section 11:1.

2. Complete this chart using Yes or No answers.

Animal	Circulatory system present?	Blood present?	Heart present?	Blood vessels present?
Hydra	no	no	no	no
Earthworm	yes	yes	yes	yes
Insect	yes	yes	yes	no
Human	yes	yes	yes	yes

3. a. Define open circulatory system. An open circulatory system is one in which blood moves about in the body without blood vessels.

   b. Define closed circulatory system. A closed circulatory system is one in which blood moves about in the body within blood vessels.

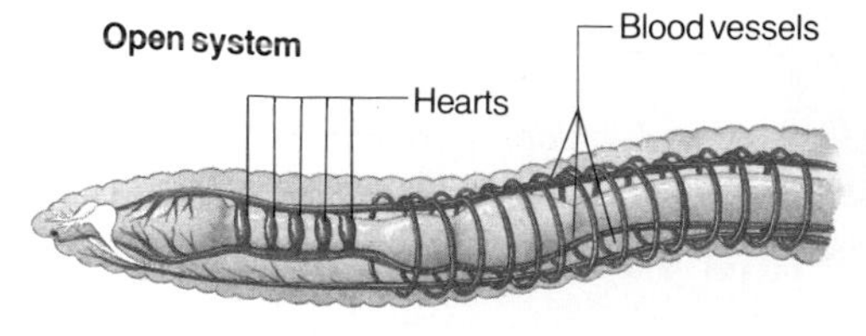

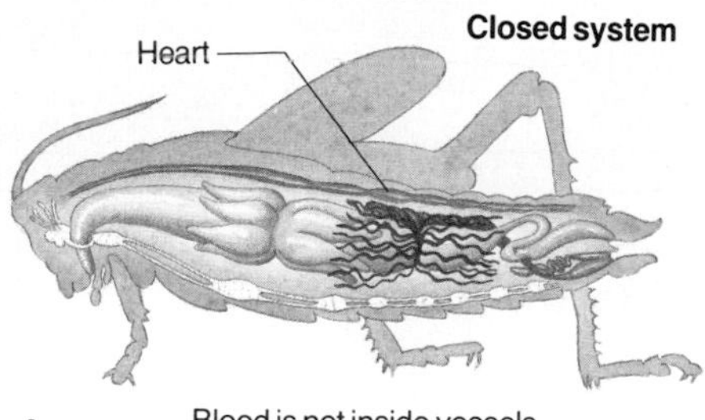

Complex animals, such as earthworms and insects, do have circulatory systems. These animals have many layers of cells and tissues. Oxygen and nutrients would not reach each cell of the animal's body if there were no circulatory system. Look carefully at Figure 11-1 and you will notice an important difference between the circulatory systems of earthworms and insects. Notice that the earthworm has blood vessels and hearts, Figure 11-1b. The circulatory system in the earthworm is said to be closed. Blood is inside vessels. The insect has a heart but no blood vessels contained within. Blood in the insect's body moves about without traveling in vessels. The insect's circulatory system is said to be open. Think about your own body. Your body is made up of many complex systems of organs. You have a closed circulatory system to supply all your cells with the nutrients they need.

Figure 11-1 Earthworms have a closed circulatory system (a). Insects have an open circulatory system (b).

What kind of circulatory system does an insect have?

Check Your Understanding

1. What are the two main jobs of the circulatory system?
2. How do animals that lack a circulatory system get their needed materials?
3. (a) How are the circulatory systems of insects and earthworms alike?
   (b) How are the systems different?
4. **Critical Thinking:** What advantage does a closed circulatory system have over an open circulatory system? (HINT: What would happen if an animal with an open circulatory system got a cut?)
5. **Biology and Reading:** Describe the relationship between the complexity of an animal's body and the type of circulatory system it has.

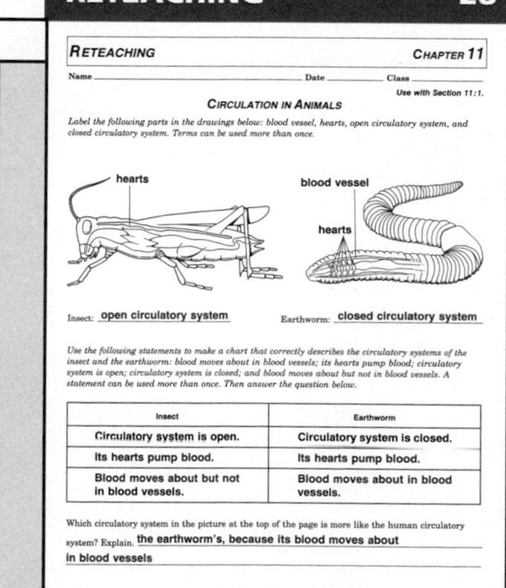

RETEACHING 28

RETEACHING CHAPTER 11

Name ________ Date ________ Class ________

Use with Section 11:1.

CIRCULATION IN ANIMALS

Label the following parts in the drawings below: blood vessel, hearts, open circulatory system, and closed circulatory system. Terms can be used more than once.

Insect: open circulatory system Earthworm: closed circulatory system

Use the following statements to make a chart that correctly describes the circulatory systems of the insect and the earthworm: blood moves about in blood vessels; its hearts pump blood; circulatory system is open; circulatory system is closed; and blood moves about but not in blood vessels. A statement can be used more than once. Then answer the question below.

Insect	Earthworm
Circulatory system is open.	Circulatory system is closed.
Its hearts pump blood.	Its hearts pump blood.
Blood moves about but not in blood vessels.	Blood moves about in blood vessels.

Which circulatory system in the picture at the top of the page is more like the human circulatory system? Explain. the earthworm's, because its blood moves about in blood vessels

OPTIONS

How Do Hearts of Different Animals Compare?/*Lab Manual,* pp. 91-94. Use this lab to give students additional practice with circulation in other animals.

2 TEACH

Guided Practice

Have students write down their answers to the margin question: open; a heart but no blood vessels.

Check for Understanding

Have students respond to the first three questions in Check Your Understanding.

Reteach

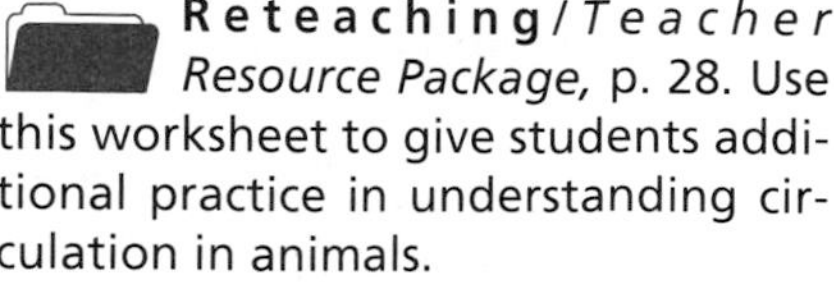

Reteaching/*Teacher Resource Package,* p. 28. Use this worksheet to give students additional practice in understanding circulation in animals.

Extension: Assign Critical Thinking, Biology and Reading, or some of the **OPTIONS** available with this lesson.

3 APPLY

Divergent Question

You discover a very small 10-celled animal living in the ocean. Explain why you are certain that this animal has no circulatory system.

4 CLOSE

Summary

Prepare a list of what exactly is delivered to and picked up from your cells by the circulatory system.

Answers to Check Your Understanding

1. It carries oxygen and nutrients to and removes wastes from cells.
2. Nutrients are obtained from the water by diffusion.
3. (a) They both have the same job and have hearts. (b) Insects have an open system with no blood vessels, while earthworms have a closed system with blood vessels.
4. A closed circulatory system protects the flow of blood through an organism's body.
5. Organisms with closed circulatory systems are more complex.

Lab 11-1 Pulse Rate

Overview

Students will be able to observe the pulsing of blood in an earthworm. This will allow them to count and compare the pulse of an earthworm to their own.

Objectives: Upon completion of the lab, students will be able to (1) **state** that the circulatory system for worms and humans is closed, (2) **calculate** an average pulse for earthworms and humans, (3) **compare** the pulse of an earthworm to their own.

Time Allotment: 1 class period

Preparation

▶ Earthworms may be ordered from a supply house, dug from the soil, or purchased locally from a bait shop.

▶ **Alternate Materials:** Any shallow dish may be used for petri dishes.

Lab 11-1 worksheet/*Teacher Resource Package*, pp. 41-42.

Teaching the Lab

▶ The blood vessel in the earthworm can be observed near the tail.

▶ **Troubleshooting:** You may want to review averaging with students before starting the lab.

Cooperative Learning: Divide the class into groups of two or three. For more information, see pp. 22T-23T in the Teacher Guide.

Lab 11-1 Computer Program/*Teacher Resource Package*, p. viii. Use the computer program shown at the bottom of this page as you teach this lab.

Pulse Rate

Lab 11-1

Problem: How do a worm's pulse and your pulse compare?

Skills

form a hypothesis, calculate, interpret data, make and use tables

Materials

live earthworm
petri dish with cover
water, room temperature
wall clock

Procedure

1. Copy the data table.
2. Place the live earthworm in a petri dish. **CAUTION:** *Keep the earthworm moist by stroking now and again with wet fingers.*
3. Look for the blood vessel along the top surface of the earthworm, Figure A.
4. Count and record the pulse of the earthworm for exactly 15 seconds.
5. Multiply your answer by 4 to get the worm's pulse for one minute. Record your result in the data table.
6. Repeat steps 4 and 5 three more times.
7. **Calculate** an average pulse for the earthworm for one minute. (Add all 4 pulse rates and then divide the total by 4.)
8. Return the earthworm to your teacher.
9. **Form a hypothesis** about how your average pulse rate will compare with that of the earthworm.
10. Use Figure B as a guide or ask your teacher to help you locate your pulse. Take your own pulse for one minute.
11. Record your results in your data table.
12. Repeat step 10 three more times and calculate an average pulse for yourself.

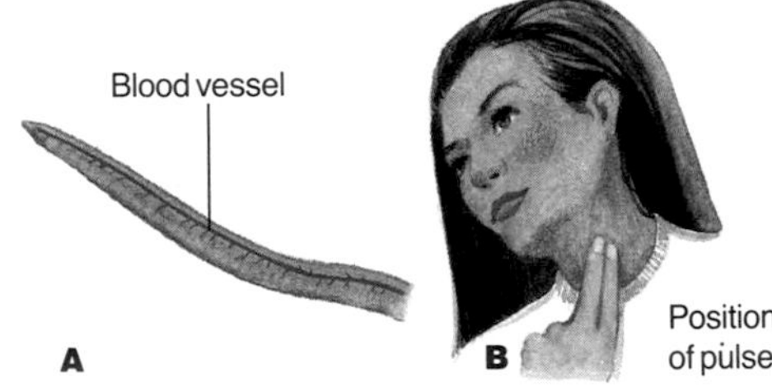

TRIAL	WORM PULSE FOR 15 SECONDS	WORM PULSE FOR 1 MINUTE	YOUR PULSE FOR 1 MINUTE
1	8	32	82
2	6	24	80
3	6	24	78
4	7	28	78
Total	—	108	318
Average	—	27	79.5

Data and Observations

1. What was the earthworm's average pulse over one minute?
2. What was your average pulse?

Analyze and Apply

1. **Check your hypothesis:** Is your hypothesis supported by your data? Why or why not?
2. What is a pulse?
3. Why is it important to repeat measurements in an experiment?
4. **Apply:** Your heartbeat rate slows down when you relax. Explain how this change will affect your pulse rate.

Extension

Design an experiment to determine the effect different kinds of exercise have on your pulse rate.

ANSWERS

Data and Observations

1. about 27 pulses a minute
2. about 79.5 pulses a minute

Analyze and Apply

1. Students who hypothesized that their pulse rates would be higher will answer yes.
2. the rhythmic movement of blood through an artery
3. Measurements vary with each sample taken. The more measurements taken, the less chance of error.
4. As your heartbeat rate slows down, so will your pulse rate. Blood is pumped from your heart into your arteries where you check your pulse rate.

COMPUTER PROGRAM VIII

COMPUTER PROGRAM LAB 11-1 PULSE RATE

```
]POKE 33,33
]LIST

10  GOSUB 390
20  HOME
25 T1 = 0:T2 = 0
30  PRINT "-------------------------------------";
40  PRINT "!     !WORM PULSE!WORM PULSE!YOUR PULSE!";
50  PRINT "!TRIAL!    FOR   !    FOR   !    FOR   !";
60  PRINT "!  #  !15 SECONDS! 1 MINUTE ! 1 MINUTE !";
70  PRINT "-------------------------------------";
75  FOR X = 1 TO 5
80  PRINT "!     !          !          !          !";
90  PRINT "-------------------------------------";
95  NEXT
140  PRINT "-------------------------------------"
143  FOR X = 8 TO 16 STEP 2
145  VTAB X: HTAB 4: PRINT X / 2 - 3
148  NEXT
150 X = 1
160  VTAB V(X): HTAB H(X): FLASH : PRINT " ";: NORMAL
170  VTAB 20: HTAB 1: CALL  - 958
180  PRINT "ENTER YOUR VALUE FOR THIS SPACE";
190  INPUT ": ";A
198 T1 = T1 + A * 4
200  VTAB V(X): HTAB H(X): PRINT A
205  VTAB V(X): HTAB H(X + 1)
207  PRINT A * 4
208  VTAB V(X): HTAB H(X + 2): FLASH : PRINT " ";: NORMAL
209  VTAB 20: HTAB 1: CALL  - 958
210  PRINT "ENTER YOUR VALUE FOR THIS SPACE";: INPUT ": ";A
212 T2 = T2 + A
214  VTAB V(X): HTAB H(X + 2): PRINT A
215 X = X + 3: IF X < 15 THEN  GOTO 160
225  VTAB 20: HTAB 1
230  PRINT "ARE THESE NUMBERS                    ENTERED CORRECTLY? (
    Y/N): ";: GET A$
240  IF A$ = "N" OR A$ = "n" THEN  GOTO 20
250  IF A$ < > "Y" AND A$ < > "y" THEN 220
255  VTAB 18: HTAB 1
260  PRINT "!TOTAL!          !          !          !";
265  PRINT "-------------------------------------";
270  PRINT "!AVG  !          !          !          !";
280  PRINT "-------------------------------------";
290  VTAB V(17): HTAB H(17): PRINT T1;
300  HTAB H(18): PRINT T2
310  VTAB V(20): HTAB H(20): PRINT T1 / 5;
320  HTAB H(21): PRINT T2 / 5
330  INVERSE : PRINT
340  PRINT : PRINT "DO YOU WANT THIS PRINTED (Y/N)? :";: GET A$
345  NORMAL
348  VTAB 22: HTAB 1: CALL  - 958
350  IF A$ = "N" OR A$ = "n" THEN  END
360  IF A$ < > "Y" AND A$ < > "y" THEN  GOTO 340
```

11:2 The Human Heart

Can you believe there is a pump within your chest that started working before you were born? It sounds impossible, but that is what your heart is.

Objectives

3. Describe how blood is pumped through the heart.

4. Explain what causes the sounds the heart makes.

5. Trace the pathway of blood through the left and right sides of the heart.

Key Science Words

atrium
artery
vein
ventricle
valve
tricuspid valve
bicuspid valve
semilunar valve
vena cava
pulmonary artery
pulmonary vein
aorta

Heart Structure

The heart is a muscle that pumps blood through the body. Figure 11-2b shows a photograph of the human heart.

Use Figure 11-2a to learn the parts of the human heart. There are three things to note about this diagram of the heart.

1. It is a cut-away view of the inside of the heart.
2. The colors bright red and blue represent blood within the heart.
3. The uncolored parts are heart muscle.

Because it has two sides, you can think of the heart as two separate pumps, one on the left and one on the right. Figure 11-2a is divided into left and right sides.

You might think that the sides of the heart are backward. The sides are labeled as if the heart were inside someone facing you. So, the heart diagram's right and left sides are opposite to your right and left sides.

Each side of the heart has a small chamber on the top and a large chamber on the bottom. The small, top chambers of the heart are **atria** (AY tree uh). The atria are divided into the right atrium and the left atrium. The large bottom chambers of the heart are called the **ventricles** (VEN trih kulz). The ventricles also are divided into right and left sections.

a

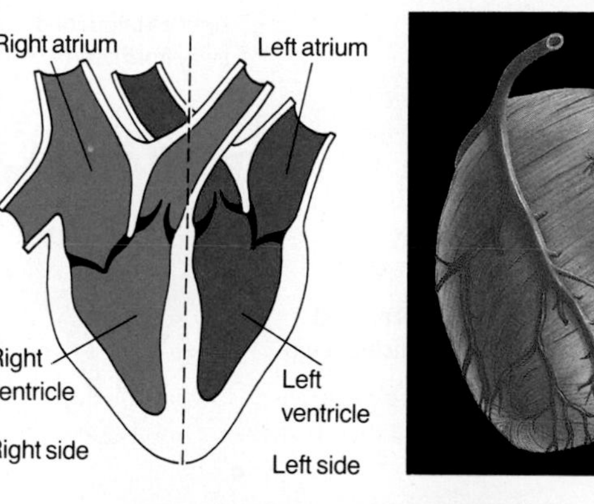

b

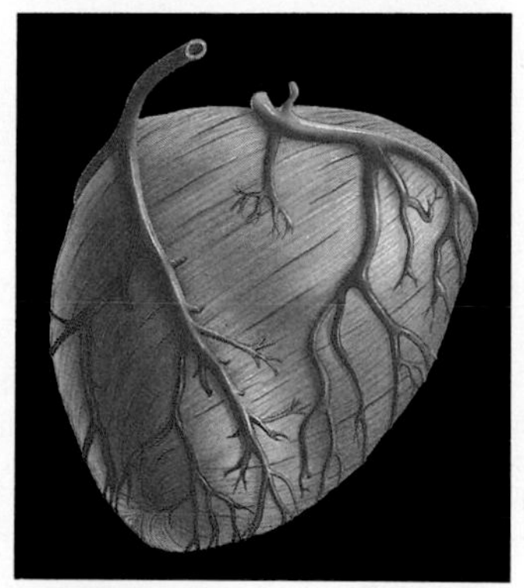

Figure 11-2 The human heart has four compartments. Which compartments of the heart does blood enter from veins? the atria

11:2 The Human Heart

PREPARATION

Material Needed

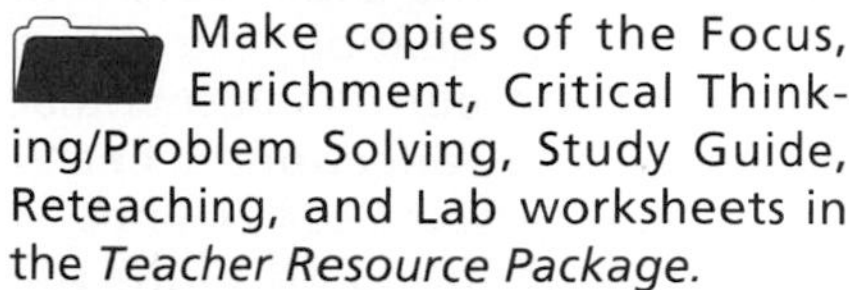

Make copies of the Focus, Enrichment, Critical Thinking/Problem Solving, Study Guide, Reteaching, and Lab worksheets in the *Teacher Resource Package.*

▶ Order a preserved heart from a biological supply house for the Focus activity.

Key Science Words

atrium
ventricle
valve
tricuspid valve
bicuspid valve
semilunar valve
vena cava
pulmonary artery
pulmonary vein
aorta

Process Skills

In the Skill Check, they will understand science words.

1 FOCUS

▶ The objectives are listed on the student page. Remind students to preview these objectives as a guide to this numbered section.

ACTIVITY/Display

Purchase a preserved heart (sheep or pig) from a supply house or use amodel to introduce students to the size and general anatomy of this organ.

Focus/*Teacher Resource Package,* p. 21. Use the Focus transparency shown at the bottom of this page as an introduction to the action of the human heart.

FOCUS 21

FOCUS CHAPTER 11

Name ______ Date ______ Class ______

ELECTROCARDIOGRAPH

A heartbeat begins with a rhythmical electrical discharge in one part of the heart. The electric current then spreads throughout the heart during the rest of the heartbeat. An instrument called an electrocardiograph can record this current. The patient in the picture has wires attached to his chest and arms and to an electrocardiograph.

What might a doctor find out about a patient from his or her electrocardiograph?

OPTIONS

Science Background

The heart is composed of cardiac muscle. The middle and main part of the heart is the myocardium. The inner part is the endocardium. The sac that surrounds the heart is the pericardium.

2 TEACH

MOTIVATION/Demonstration

Have students take their pulse for one minute while resting. Put their pulse rates on the chalkboard and note the wide variation seen within the class. Point out to students that pulse rate is a reflection of heartbeat. One heartbeat corresponds to one surge of blood through the arteries. We call this surge or wave of blood a pulse.

Concept Development

▶ Remind students that when one looks at the front view of a person, the left and right sides are reversed.

▶ Remind students that all diagrams in this chapter are front views.

▶ The first letter of *artery* and the first letter of *away* both begin with an a. This may help students to remember that arteries carry blood away from the heart while veins carry blood in the opposite direction.

Analogy: Ask students if they have ever trapped water between their fists and shot it out at someone. This illustrates the idea graphically because squeezing together the fists requires the action of muscles.

Guided Practice

Have students write down their answers to the margin question: from the atria.

The Pumping of the Heart

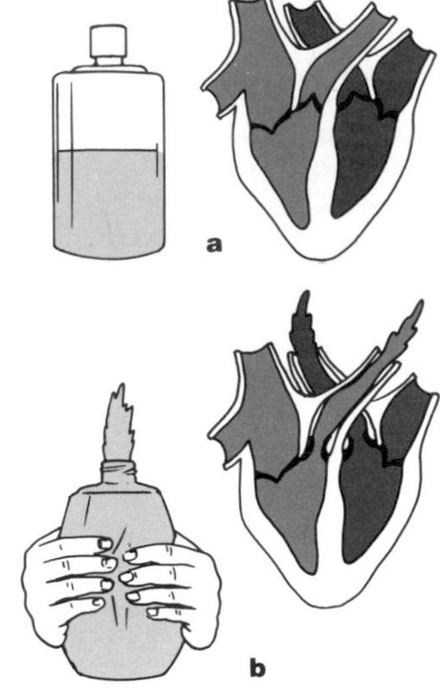

Figure 11-3 When a bottle or heart is not squeezed, no liquid is pushed out. When a bottle or heart is squeezed, liquid is squirted out.

How do the ventricles receive blood?

How does the heart work as a pump? Figure 11-3 shows the heart's squeezing action by comparing it to the squeezing of a plastic bottle. The top picture shows the plastic bottle when it is not squeezed. No liquid is pushed out. The same is true for the heart. If the heart muscle does not squeeze, no blood is pumped. The bottom picture shows the plastic bottle being squeezed and liquid squirting out. The bottom diagram of the heart shows that when muscles of the ventricles squeeze, blood is pushed out.

While a person is resting, the heart pumps 60 to 80 times each minute. After running, the heart may pump 150 times in one minute. Each pump of the heart is called a beat. The structure of the heart allows blood to move through the circulatory system in only one direction. Your heart muscle will pump for more than two billion times during your lifetime!

Figure 11-4 shows several large blood vessels called arteries (ART uh reez) and veins. An **artery** is a blood vessel that carries blood away from the heart. A **vein** is a blood vessel that carries blood back to the heart. The arrows in the diagram show the direction of blood flow.

1. Blood from the veins enters the heart's right and left atria, Figure 11-4a. Neither chamber is pumping.
2. Figure 11-4b shows the atria beginning to pump or squeeze. Right and left ventricles are relaxed and are not pumping. These chambers receive blood from the atria.
3. Figure 11-4c shows the right and left ventricles squeezing blood into two large arteries leading to the body and the lungs. When the ventricles are pumping, the atria are relaxed. Blood returning from the body enters the atria and the entire pumping cycle begins again.

Figure 11-4 Follow the steps that show the pumping action of the heart.

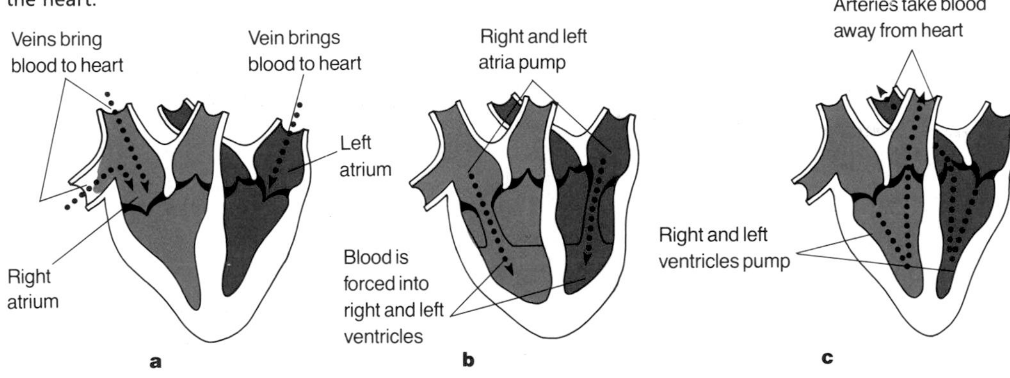

OPTIONS

Enrichment/*Teacher Resource Package*, p. 11. Use the Enrichment worksheet shown here as an extension to the pumping action of the heart.

ENRICHMENT 11

ENRICHMENT CHAPTER 11

Name ______ Date ______ Class ______

Use after Section 11:2.

TRACING A HEARTBEAT

The diagram below shows the tracing made by a beating heart. This tracing is called an electrocardiogram (ECG). The ECG shows the electrical current that is in the heart as it beats. The wavy line on the graph records the electrical activity of the heart over a period of time. The letters **A** through **D** show what takes place during a heartbeat. **A** shows what happens during the contraction of the atria; **B** shows the relaxation of the atria; **C** shows the contraction of the ventricles; **D** shows the relaxation of the ventricles. A heartbeat lasts from the beginning of **A** to the end of **B**. Each vertical line on the diagram represents 0.1 seconds.

A B C D

0 0.2 0.4 0.6 0.8 1 0.2 0.4 0.6 0.8 1 0.2 0.4 0.6 0.8 1

Use this information and the diagram of the ECG to answer the questions.

1. Which parts of the heart start the heartbeat cycle? **atria**
   Which parts of the heart follow next in the heartbeat cycle? **ventricles**
2. How long do the atria contract during one cycle? **0.2 seconds**
   relax? **0.7 seconds**
3. How long do the ventricles contract during one cycle? **0.35 seconds**
   relax? **0.55 seconds**
4. How long does the heart remain totally relaxed during the heartbeat? **0.4 seconds**
5. How long does a single heartbeat last on this ECG? **0.95 seconds**
6. How many complete heartbeats are shown on this ECG? **3**

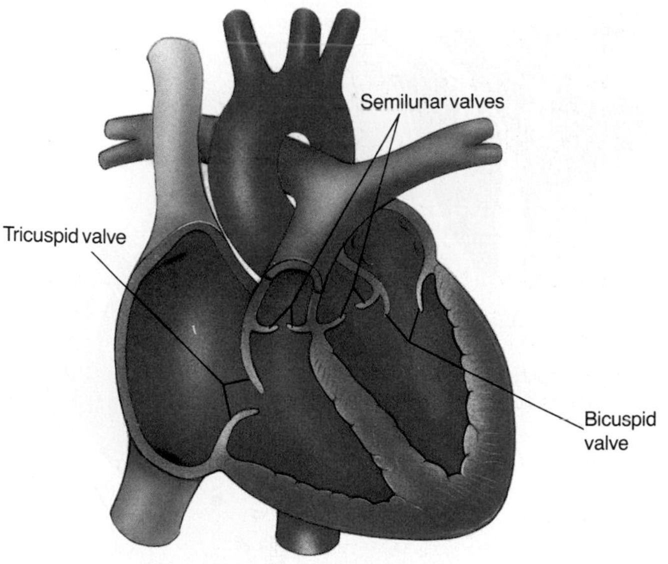

Figure 11-5 Locate the valves of the heart.

Heart Valves

If a pump is to work well, it must keep liquid moving in only one direction. A pump has valves that help with this task. So does the heart. **Valves** are flaps in the heart that keep blood flowing in one direction.

Figure 11-5 shows the location of the valves. Notice that there are two sets of valves. One set is between the atria and ventricles. The valve between the right atrium and right ventricle is called the **tricuspid** (tri KUS pud) **valve.** The valve between the left atrium and the left ventricle is called the **bicuspid** (bi KUS pud) **valve.** Note that these two valves are like one-way doors. They only open downward into the ventricles to keep blood flowing in one direction.

The other valves are the semilunar (sem ih LEW nur) valves. **Semilunar valves** are located between the ventricles and their arteries. Note that these two valves are also like one-way doors. They open only in an upward direction away from the ventricles.

Have you ever heard your heart beat? Do you know what causes the sounds you hear? Some people think they are hearing the heart muscle as it pumps. Actually, the sounds you hear are your heart valves closing. These valves, like doors, make sounds when they close. Doesn't a door make a loud sound when it slams shut?

Skill Check

Understand science words: semilunar. The word part *semi* means half. In your dictionary, find three words with the word part *semi* in them. *For more help, refer to the* ***Skill Handbook****, pages 706-711.*

TEACH

Concept Development

▶ Point out to students that blood on the right and left sides of the heart never mixes directly. Also, it can be noted that the pathway of blood, once within the heart, follows a regular pattern. Blood enters the top chambers, is pumped into the lower chambers, and is then pumped out of the lower chambers to body organs.

▶ Point out to students that a cusp is a flap. The prefix *tri-* refers to three, while the prefix *bi-* refers to two. There are three cusps or sections to the tricuspid valve. The bicuspid valve has two sections or cusps. The term *semilunar* is related to the fact that these valves have a shape similar to a half-moon.

CRITICAL THINKING 11

CRITICAL THINKING/PROBLEM SOLVING CHAPTER 11

Name ______ Date ______ Class ______

Use after Section 11:2.

HOW DOES CIRCULATION VARY WITH DIFFERENT ACTIVITIES?

The circulatory system delivers blood to all cells in your body. However, different parts of your body may receive different amounts of blood, depending on what you are doing. Your brain controls the amount of blood that flows to different parts of your body. A body part that is used more during a particular activity will receive more blood.

The graphs show the relative amounts of blood delivered to certain body parts while a person is doing different activities. The body parts are the small intestine, lungs, skin, and skeletal muscles. The activities are eating, exercising, sitting in a hot, moist sauna, and resting. Each graph shows the amount of blood delivered to one of the body parts. The activities are represented by the letters A, B, C, and D. Study the graphs to determine which activity each letter represents.

Amount of blood in skin — High / Normal — A B C D Activities

Amount of blood in intestine — High / Normal — A B C D Activities

Amount of blood in lungs — High / Normal — A B C D Activities

Amount of blood in skeletal muscles — High / Normal — A B C D Activities

Analyzing the Problem

1. Which of the body parts would receive more blood when a person is eating? Explain. The small intestine receives more blood because there is more digested food to be delivered to body cells.
2. Which body parts would receive more blood when a person is hot? Explain. The skin receives more blood so that more heat can be lost from the body.

Solving the Problem

1. Identify the activities represented by the letters A, B, C, and D. A—exercising; B—resting; C—eating; D—sitting in a sauna

OPTIONS

Critical Thinking/Problem Solving/ *Teacher Resource Package,* p. 11. Use the Critical Thinking/Problem Solving worksheet shown here as an extension to structure and function of heart valves.

TEACH

Concept Development

▶ A murmur is an indication that the heart is not working efficiently. If the deficiency is great, heart enlargement may result.

▶ Explain to students that valve closure is not due directly to muscle action. Valves close due to blood pressure changes occurring within the chambers. As the ventricles contract, they force blood up against the underside of the bicuspid and tricuspid valves, thus forcing them to close. As the ventricles relax, blood in the aorta and pulmonary artery falls back toward the ventricles. The semilunar valves fill with blood, which results in their closure.

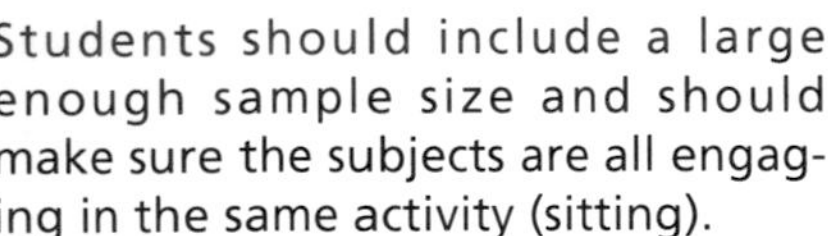

Mini Lab

Students should include a large enough sample size and should make sure the subjects are all engaging in the same activity (sitting).

Guided Practice

Have students write down their answers to the margin question: the heart valves closing.

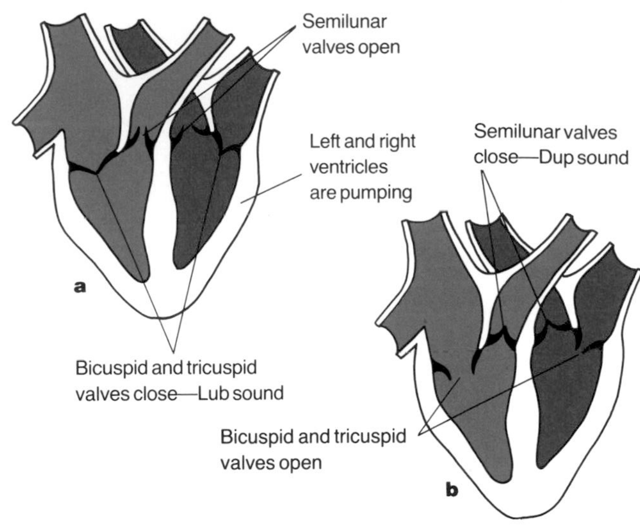

Semilunar valves open
Left and right ventricles are pumping
Semilunar valves close—Dup sound
a
Bicuspid and tricuspid valves close—Lub sound
Bicuspid and tricuspid valves open
b

Figure 11-6 The lub and dup sounds of the heart are caused by the closing of the heart's valves.

Mini Lab

How Do the Pulses of Males and Females Compare?

Design an experiment: Design an experiment to compare the pulse rates of males and females. Carry out the experiment. Write a report. *For more help, refer to the* ***Skill Handbook,*** *pages 704-705.*

Because you have two sets of valves in your heart that close at different times, your heart makes two sounds. The first sound is caused by the closing of your bicuspid and tricuspid valves. Figure 11-6a shows these valves closed. The blood can no longer pass from the atria to the ventricles. When your ventricles squeeze, these valves close and cause a "lub" sound. The second sound occurs when your semilunar valves close. These valves close when your ventricles stop squeezing. A "dup" sound is now heard. Figure 11-6b shows the semilunar valves closed. The blood can no longer pass from the ventricles out of the main arteries.

The two heart sounds heard together make a "lub-dup" sound. The tricuspid and bicuspid valves close harder than the semilunar valves. That is why the sounds differ. A doctor listening to your heart can tell if your heart is working normally. A "lub-dup" sound means your valves are working normally. If the doctor hears a "lub-swish-dup" sound, the bicuspid or tricuspid valves are not closing properly. Blood leaking past the valves causes the "swish" sound. The blood moves in the opposite direction from which it should be going. Blood flowing backward through the heart when valves are not closing tightly is called a heart murmur. Which valves are not closing properly if a doctor hears a "lub-dup-swish" sound? Since the "swish" sound follows the "dup" sound, it must be caused by the semilunar valves not closing properly.

What makes the "lub-dup" sound in your heart?

OPTIONS

ACTIVITY/Challenge

Purchase a preserved heart and allow students to dissect it under your guidance. Make sure that they observe external as well as internal anatomy.

How Does the Heart Work?/*Lab Manual,* pp. 87-90. Use this lab to give students additional practice with heart function.

The Jobs of the Heart

So far we've only seen how your heart pumps. Now let's look at your blood vessels and see how the rest of your circulatory system works. Remember, your heart has a right and left side. Each side has its own job of pumping blood around the body.

Right Side of the Heart

The right side of your heart pumps blood only to your lungs. The path the blood follows can be seen by matching numbers 1 through 5 in Figure 11-7 with statements 1 through 5.

1. Blood enters the heart's right side at the right atrium from a large vein called the vena cava. The **vena cava** (VEE nuh • KAY vuh) is the largest vein in the body and carries blood from the body back to the heart. The blue color is used to show that at this point blood contains a lot of carbon dioxide gas and little oxygen gas.
2. Blood is pumped into the right ventricle.
3. From here, blood is pumped into a large artery. This artery is called the pulmonary (PUL muh ner ee) artery. The **pulmonary artery** carries blood away from the heart to the lungs. Because you have two lungs, the pulmonary artery divides in two. Blood will be pumped to both lungs.
4. Blood enters both lungs. In the lungs, the blood picks up oxygen and loses carbon dioxide. Notice that the color of the blood is now bright red. Blood containing a lot of oxygen is shown in bright red.
5. Blood returns to the heart through the pulmonary veins. **Pulmonary veins** carry blood from the lungs to the left side of the heart. The total time needed for blood to travel from your heart to your lungs and back again is only about 10 seconds.

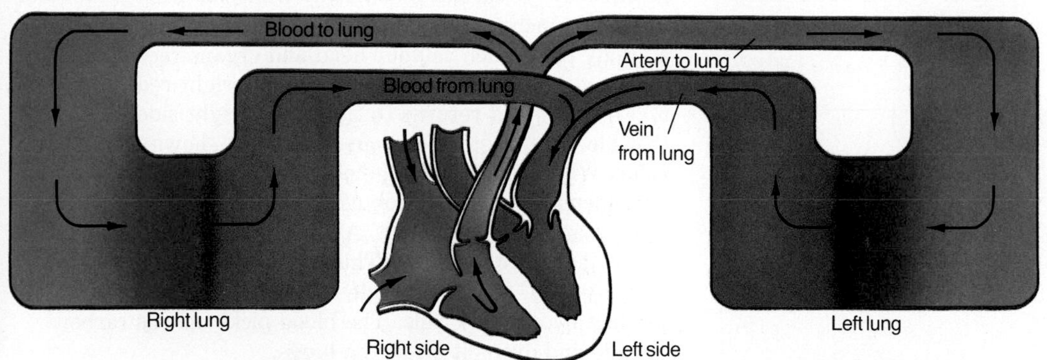

Figure 11-7 Trace the pathway of blood to and from the lungs.

STUDY GUIDE 62

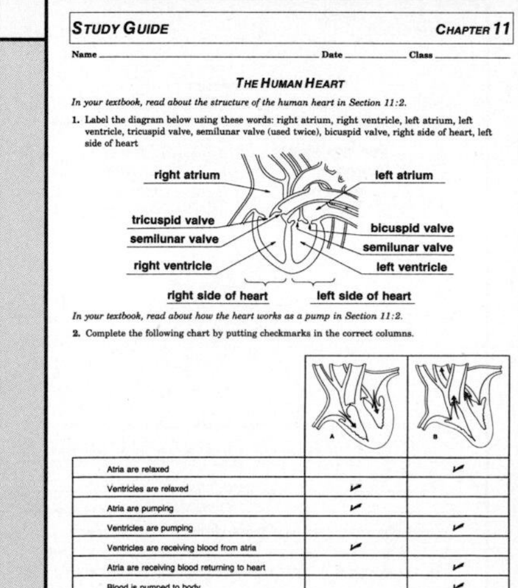

STUDY GUIDE CHAPTER 11

Name ______ Date ______ Class ______

THE HUMAN HEART

In your textbook, read about the structure of the human heart in Section 11:2.

1. Label the diagram below using these words: right atrium, right ventricle, left atrium, left ventricle, tricuspid valve, semilunar valve (used twice), bicuspid valve, right side of heart, left side of heart

In your textbook, read about how the heart works as a pump in Section 11:2.

2. Complete the following chart by putting checkmarks in the correct columns.

	A	B
Atria are relaxed		✓
Ventricles are relaxed	✓	
Atria are pumping	✓	
Ventricles are pumping		✓
Ventricles are receiving blood from atria	✓	
Atria are receiving blood returning to heart		✓
Blood is pumped to body		✓

OPTIONS

Blood Flow Between Heart and Lungs/*Transparency Package,* number 11. Use color transparency number 11 as you teach pulmonary circulation.

TEACH

Concept Development

▶ Stress the following:

1. Blood enters the heart through a vein.
2. The blood in the right side of the heart contains much carbon dioxide. Pictures of the heart always show blood in this condition as being colored blue.
3. The right side of the heart pumps blood only to the lungs.
4. Blood leaves the heart through an artery.
5. Blood loses its supply of carbon dioxide and gains a supply of oxygen in the lungs.

Connection: Math

Have students calculate the volume of blood pumped by the average heart in one minute, one hour, and one day. Use the following information: The left ventricle pumps about 70 mL of blood every time it contracts; the heart beats 70 times in one minute.

Misconception: Emphasize that deoxygenated blood is not blue; it is dark red. Blue is used to illustrate deoxygenated blood because it contrasts well with red.

Cooperative Learning: Divide the class into groups of two students. Give them the following lists of questions: (a) For the right side of the heart, name the chambers, valves, blood vessels that enter the chamber, blood vessels that leave the chamber, condition of blood entering the chamber, condition of blood leaving the chamber, where blood is coming from as it enters the chamber, where blood is going as it leaves the chamber. (b) Give them a second list of questions for the left side of the heart. One team member will ask questions about the left side, the second about the right side. Have the teams continue to ask the questions until all are answered correctly.

Independent Practice

Study Guide/*Teacher Resource Package,* p. 62. Use the Study Guide worksheet shown at the bottom of this page for independent practice.

TEACH

Concept Development

▶ Stress the following:

1. Blood enters the heart through a vein.
2. The blood in the left side of the heart contains much oxygen.
3. The left side of the heart pumps blood to all body organs except the lungs.
4. Blood leaves the heart through an artery.
5. Blood loses its supply of oxygen and gains a supply of carbon dioxide from the body cells.

Check for Understanding

Provide students with a diagram similar to Figure 11-8. Have them label the following: heart chambers, blood vessels, heart valves. Ask them to draw in arrows that show the direction of blood flow.

Reteach

Have students draw a circle and divide it into four quarters. Each quarter will represent the chambers of the human heart. Ask students to label all four chambers and draw in the location of bicuspid and tricuspid valves.

Guided Practice

Have students write down their answers to the margin question: It comes from the lungs where it picked up oxygen.

Independent Practice

Study Guide/*Teacher Resource Package*, p. 63. Use the Study Guide worksheet shown at the bottom of this page for independent practice.

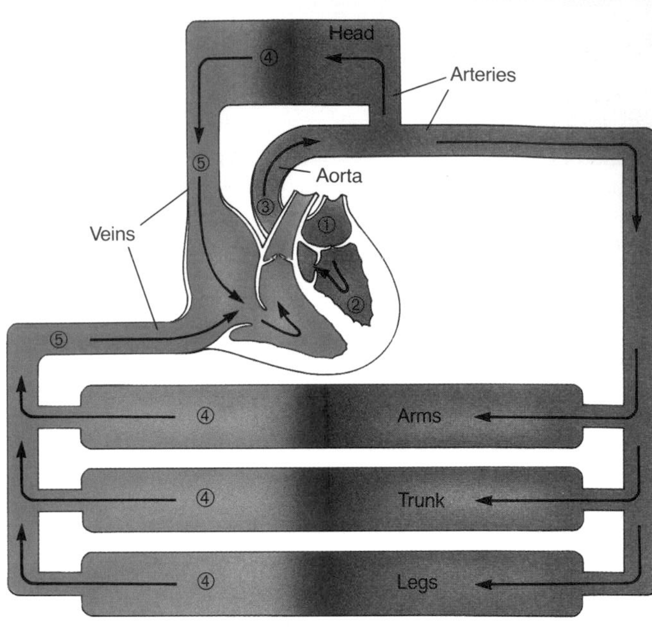

Figure 11-8 Trace the pathway of blood through the body.

Left Side of the Heart

The left side of the heart pumps blood to all parts of the body. The path the blood follows can be seen by matching numbers 1 through 5 in Figure 11-8 with statements 1 through 5.

How is oxygen-rich blood supplied to the left side of the heart?

1. Blood rich in oxygen has just arrived at the left atrium from the lungs.
2. The blood is pumped from the left atrium into the left ventricle.
3. From the left ventricle, blood is pumped out of the heart into the aorta (ay ORT uh). The **aorta** is the largest artery in the body. It carries blood away from the heart's left side. Then it branches and goes to the body or head.
4. Body parts such as your head and organs receive blood that is rich in oxygen as shown by the bright red color.
5. Finally, blood returns to the heart's right side. Notice that blood has lost its oxygen and is now shown as a blue color. Why does this change occur?

Remember, one main job of blood is to carry two gases, oxygen and carbon dioxide. As blood passes through the lungs, it picks up oxygen. This oxygen is then delivered to all body cells. Carbon dioxide is produced as a waste product by all body cells. The blood picks up this carbon dioxide and drops it off at the lungs.

Bio Tip

Health: A resting heart will pump 5 liters of blood through the body each minute.

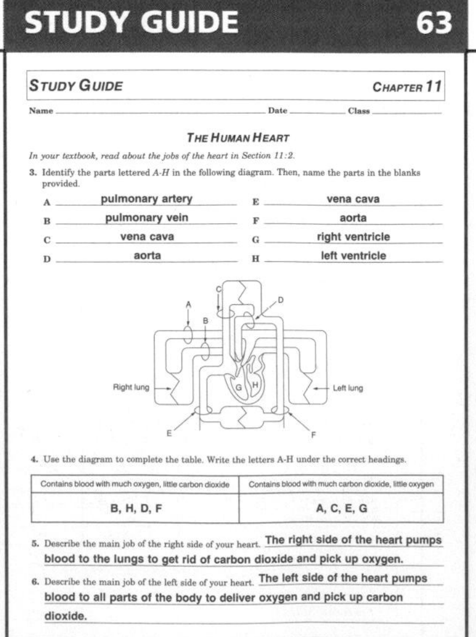

STUDY GUIDE 63

STUDY GUIDE *CHAPTER 11*

Name ________ Date ________ Class ________

THE HUMAN HEART

In your textbook, read about the jobs of the heart in Section 11:2.

3. Identify the parts lettered *A-H* in the following diagram. Then, name the parts in the blanks provided.

A pulmonary artery
B pulmonary vein
C vena cava
D aorta
E vena cava
F aorta
G right ventricle
H left ventricle

4. Use the diagram to complete the table. Write the letters A-H under the correct headings.

Contains blood with much oxygen, little carbon dioxide	Contains blood with much carbon dioxide, little oxygen
B, H, D, F	A, C, E, G

5. Describe the main job of the right side of your heart. The right side of the heart pumps blood to the lungs to get rid of carbon dioxide and pick up oxygen.

6. Describe the main job of the left side of your heart. The left side of the heart pumps blood to all parts of the body to deliver oxygen and pick up carbon dioxide.

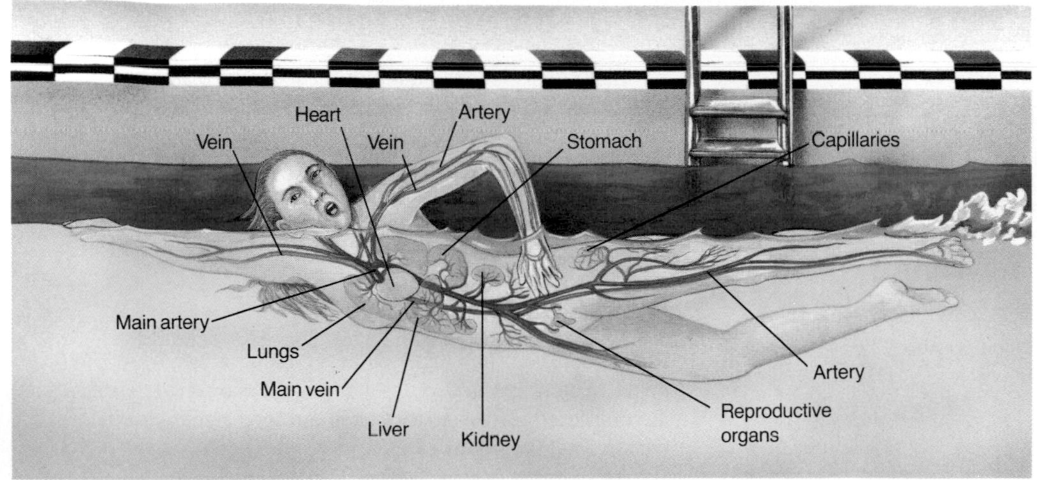

Figure 11-9 Oxygen is delivered to all the organs of your body by arteries. Veins pick up blood that has carbon dioxide in it and return it to the lungs.

There is a very important difference between the left and right sides of your heart. Blood in the right side of your heart contains a lot of carbon dioxide. Blood in the left side of your heart contains a lot of oxygen. Which side of the heart pumps blood only to your lungs? The side with more carbon dioxide. Which side of the heart pumps blood only to your body? The left side. Figure 11-9 helps to show how all the blood vessels supply all the organs of your body.

Check Your Understanding

6. (a) Are ventricles relaxed or pumping when they fill? Describe the condition of the atria as the ventricles fill. (b) Are ventricles relaxed or pumping when they empty? Describe the condition of the atria as the ventricles empty.
7. What causes the sounds of the heart?
8. Trace the pathway of blood once it leaves the (a) left atrium, (b) right atrium, (c) left ventricle, and (d) right ventricle.
9. **Critical Thinking:** An amphibian heart has one ventricle and two atria. How would the blood circulation through an amphibian heart differ from that in a human heart?
10. **Biology and Math:** A person's normal heartbeat rate is 70 beats each minute. About how many times does a person's heart beat in a day?

RETEACHING 29

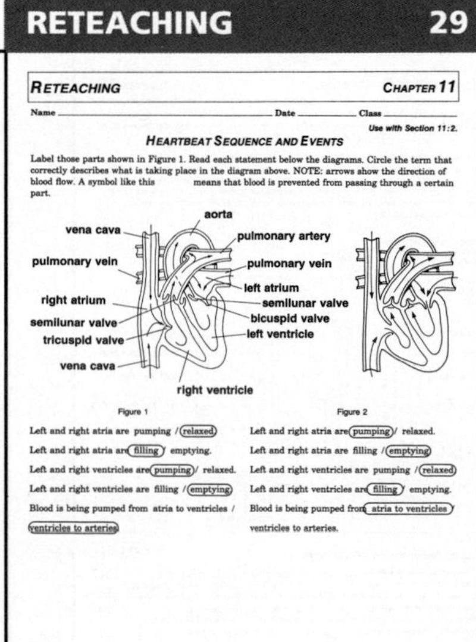

RETEACHING *CHAPTER 11*

Name ______ Date ______ Class ______

Use with Section 11:2.

HEARTBEAT SEQUENCE AND EVENTS

Label those parts shown in Figure 1. Read each statement below the diagrams. Circle the term that correctly describes what is taking place in the diagram above. NOTE: arrows show the direction of blood flow. A symbol like this means that blood is prevented from passing through a certain part.

Figure 1

Left and right atria are pumping / relaxed
Left and right atria are filling / emptying.
Left and right ventricles are pumping / relaxed.
Left and right ventricles are filling / emptying
Blood is being pumped from atria to ventricles / ventricles to arteries

Figure 2

Left and right atria are pumping / relaxed.
Left and right atria are filling / emptying
Left and right ventricles are pumping / relaxed
Left and right ventricles are filling / emptying.
Blood is being pumped from atria to ventricles / ventricles to arteries.

TEACH

Have students respond to the first three questions in Check Your Understanding.

Check for Understanding

Have students respond to the first three questions in Check Your Understanding.

Reteach

Reteaching/*Teacher Resource Package*, p. 29. Use this worksheet to give students additional practice in understanding heartbeat sequence and events.

Extension: Assign Critical Thinking, Biology and Math, or some of the **OPTIONS** available with this lesson.

3 APPLY

ACTIVITY/Software

The Heart Simulator, Cambridge Development Laboratory, Inc.

4 CLOSE

ACTIVITY/Software

The Heart, Queue, Inc.

Answers to Check Your Understanding

6. (a) When the ventricles fill, they are relaxed and the atria are pumping. (b) When the ventricles empty, they are pumping and the atria are relaxed.
7. the closing of the heart valves
8. (a) It enters the left ventricle. (b) It enters the right ventricle. (c) It is pumped into the aorta. (d) It is pumped into the pulmonary artery.
9. Blood from each atrium flows into the same ventricle. There is a mixing in the ventricle of oxygenated and deoxygenated blood.
10. 70 beats per minute $\times$ 60 minutes per hour $\times$ 24 hours = 100 800 beats

11:3 Blood Vessels

PREPARATION

Materials needed

Make copies of the Skill, Study Guide, Reteaching and Lab worksheets in the *Teacher Resource Package.*

▶Build the rubber stopper and tube assembly needed for Lab 11-2.

Key Science Words

artery
blood pressure
vein
capillary

Process Skills

In Lab 11-2, students will formulate models, form a hypothesis, and measure in SI.

1 FOCUS

▶ The objectives are listed on the student page. Remind students to preview these objectives as a guide to this numbered section.

ACTIVITY/Demonstration

Fill a graduated cylinder with 35 mL of red-colored water. Tell students that this is the volume of blood that fills each ventricle when it is relaxed. Therefore, the heart ejects a total of 70 mL of blood per heartbeat. Have students trace the ejected blood. What type of blood vessel does the blood enter when ejected from the heart?

Guided Practice

Have students write down their answers to the margin question: by the pumping action of the heart.

11:3 Blood Vessels

Objectives

6. **Discuss** the importance of arteries.
7. **List** four traits of veins.
8. **Give the function** of capillaries.

Key Science Words

blood pressure
capillary

Blood vessels are tubelike structures through which blood moves. You have about 96 000 kilometers of blood vessels. If they were all placed end-to-end, they would go around Earth about two and one-half times. The three types of blood vessels in your body are arteries, veins, and capillaries (KAP uh ler eez).

Arteries

Remember that arteries carry blood away from the heart. The aorta and pulmonary artery are two arteries you have studied. In what direction is blood being carried within these vessels?

As you can see in Figure 11-11, arteries are round and have thick walls made of many muscle cells. Arteries, such as the aorta, are quite wide in diameter. The aorta can be as wide as a garden hose. Arteries branch into smaller and narrower vessels as they carry blood away from the heart. Look again at Figure 11-9 on page 231 to see what the entire network of arteries might look like.

How is pressure created within arteries?

One important feature of arteries is blood pressure. What do you think would happen if you squeezed the water-filled plastic bottle shown in Figure 11-10? Water would squirt out of the hollow tube. Why does this happen? When you squeeze the bottle, you are reducing its volume. You give the liquid less room inside the bottle. The liquid has to go somewhere, so it squirts out of the tube. The water in the bottle is put under high pressure because of the squeezing. The water moves into the tube where the pressure is lower.

The heart's pumping action on blood is similar to the plastic bottle example. Blood is squeezed by the heart muscle just as water was squeezed out of the bottle by your hand. Just as water moved into the tube, blood is forced into the arteries. The force created when blood pushes against the walls of vessels is called **blood pressure.** This pressure drives the blood through the blood vessels. When you feel your pulse, you are feeling your blood moving through your arteries. Your pulse rate agrees with your heartbeat rate.

The three important traits of arteries are (1) they carry blood away from the heart (2) they carry blood under high pressure (3) they are round in shape and have thick, muscular walls.

Figure 11-10 If a bottle is squeezed, high pressure forces water to squirt out.

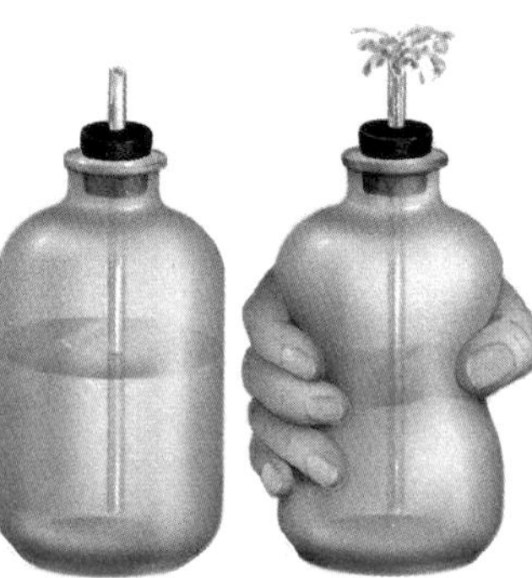

OPTIONS

Science Background

Arteries carry blood away from heart, regardless of condition of blood within them. Veins carry blood to heart, regardless of condition of blood within them.

Skill/*Teacher Resource Package,* p. 12. Use the Skill worksheet shown here to give additional practice with the circulatory system.

SKILL 12

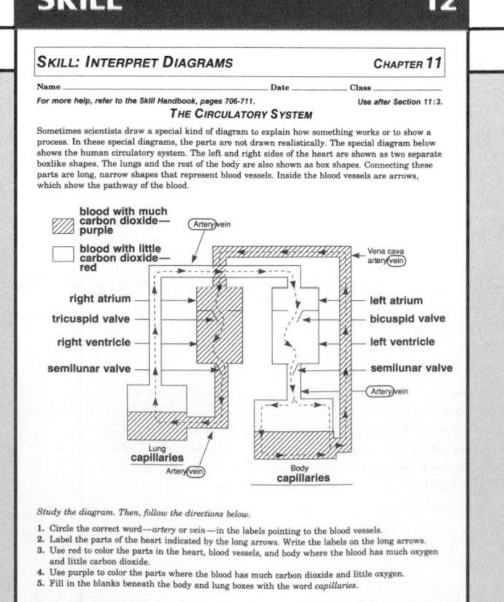

SKILL: INTERPRET DIAGRAMS — CHAPTER 11

Name ______ Date ______ Class ______

For more help, refer to the Skill Handbook, pages 706-711. *Use after Section 11:3.*

THE CIRCULATORY SYSTEM

Sometimes scientists draw a special kind of diagram to explain how something works or to show a process. In these special diagrams, the parts are not drawn realistically. The special diagram below shows the human circulatory system. The left and right sides of the heart are shown as two separate boxlike shapes. The lungs and the rest of the body are also shown as box shapes. Connecting these parts are long, narrow shapes that represent blood vessels. Inside the blood vessels are arrows, which show the pathway of the blood.

Study the diagram. Then, follow the directions below.

1. Circle the correct word—*artery* or *vein*—in the labels pointing to the blood vessels.
2. Label the parts of the heart indicated by the long arrows. Write the labels on the long arrows.
3. Use red to color the parts in the heart, blood vessels, and body where the blood has much oxygen and little carbon dioxide.
4. Use purple to color the parts where the blood has much carbon dioxide and little oxygen.
5. Fill in the blanks beneath the body and lung boxes with the word *capillaries.*

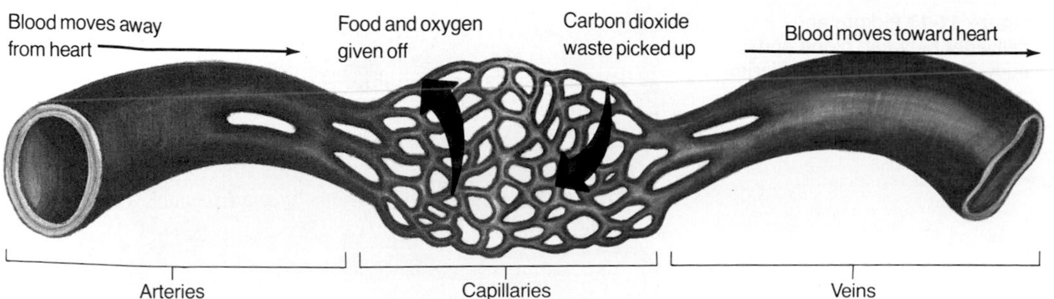

Figure 11-11 The three types of blood vessels are arteries, veins, and capillaries. Where do pickups and deliveries occur? in the capillaries

Veins

Blood must be brought back to the heart in veins. The vena cava and pulmonary vein are two veins you have studied. In what direction is blood being carried within these vessels?

Look again at Figure 11-11. You can see how veins differ from arteries. Veins have less muscle than arteries. Their shape is rather flat, but they may be much wider than arteries. Veins have thinner walls than arteries. Veins in your arms and legs have many one-way valves inside them. These valves keep blood flowing in one direction, toward the heart. Figure 11-12 shows what happens to the valves if blood begins to flow backward away from the heart. The valves are helpful because blood in veins is under low pressure. Without the valves, how would blood in your leg or arm veins return to your heart without flowing back into your feet or hands?

In what direction does blood in the veins travel?

The four important traits of veins are (1) they carry blood to the heart (2) they carry blood under low pressure (3) they are flat in shape and have little muscle (4) they have many one-way valves to keep blood flowing in one direction.

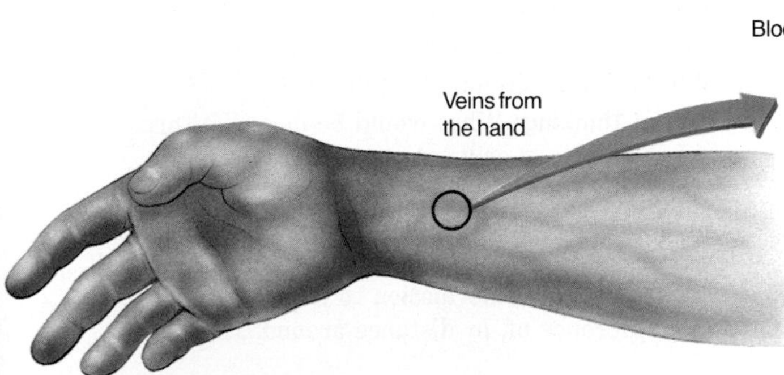

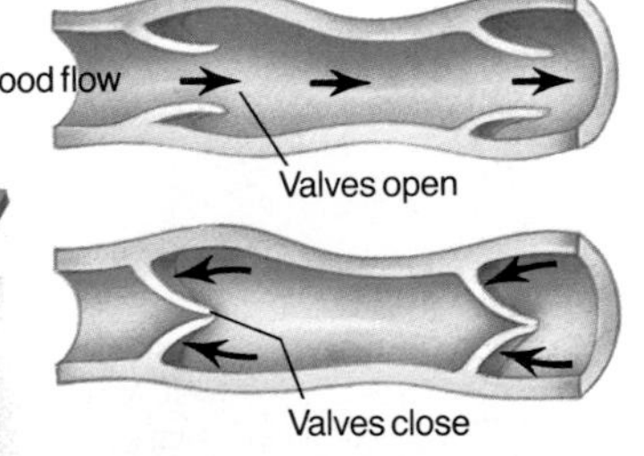

Figure 11-12 One-way valves in veins keep blood flowing in one direction toward the heart.

2 TEACH

MOTIVATION/Videocassette

Show the videocassette, *Life Under Pressure,* Films for the Humanities and Sciences, Inc.

Concept Development

▶ Remind students that all the "work" of delivering and picking up is taking place in the capillaries. Blood cells can move single file through the capillaries.

Misconception: Students may believe that all arteries carry blood with much oxygen, while all veins carry blood with much carbon dioxide. Point out that the pulmonary artery and pulmonary vein are exceptions to this rule.

ACTIVITY/Brainstorming

Make sure students understand which side of the heart must push the blood out under greater pressure. Ask them which side must push blood farther in order to get it where it must go. You may want to point out that the left side of the heart is a much thicker muscle than the right side. Ask students to explain why.

Guided Practice

Have students write down their answers to the margin question: in one direction back to the heart.

Independent Practice

Study Guide/*Teacher Resource Package,* p. 64. Use the Study Guide worksheet shown at the bottom of this page for independent practice.

STUDY GUIDE 64

STUDY GUIDE CHAPTER 11

Name ______ Date ______ Class ______

BLOOD VESSELS

In your textbook, read about arteries, veins, and capillaries in Section 11:3.

1. Circle the word or words that make the statement true.
   a. Arteries carry blood toward / (away from) the heart.
   b. Arteries carry blood under (high) / low pressure.
   c. Arteries have thin / (thick) muscular walls.
   d. An example of an artery is the vena cava / (aorta.)
   e. When your feel your pulse, you are feeling blood moving through your veins / (arteries.)
2. What is the main job of veins? **to carry blood back to the heart**
3. Compare the amount of muscle in veins and arteries. **Veins have thin walls with little muscle. Arteries have thick, muscular walls.**
4. Compare the pressure within veins and arteries. **Veins carry blood under low pressure. Arteries carry blood under high pressure.**
5. Explain how the one-way valves in veins help maintain circulation. **Since blood in these vessels is under low pressure, valves help keep blood flowing in one direction toward the heart.**
6. Place a checkmark next to those statements below that are true.
   ___ a. Blood pressure is higher in capillaries than in arteries.
   ✓ b. Capillary walls are only one cell thick.
   ___ c. The human body has more veins than capillaries.
   ✓ d. Capillaries bring blood close to all body cells.
   ✓ e. All the pickups of carbon dioxide and other cell wastes, and all the deliveries of oxygen, food, and other materials, occur in the capillaries.

OPTIONS

Enrichment: Varicose veins are related to nonfunctioning, poorly functioning, or nonexisting valves along the veins in the legs. As a consequence, blood pools in these vessels, causing them to bulge.

TEACH

Guided Practice

Have students write down their answers to the margin question: oxygen and nutrients diffuse into body cells and waste diffuses out of body cells.

Check for Understanding

Have students respond to the first three questions in Check Your Understanding.

Reteach

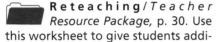

Reteaching/*Teacher Resource Package,* p. 30. Use this worksheet to give students additional practice in understanding blood vessels and blood flow.

Extension: Assign Critical Thinking, Biology and Math, or some of the **OPTIONS** available with this lesson.

3 APPLY

ACTIVITY/Demonstration

Use a variety of tubelike materials to represent arteries and veins.

4 CLOSE

ACTIVITY/Brainstorming

Ask students: Why do you always use an artery to feel your pulse?

Answers to Check Your Understanding

11. They carry blood away from the heart, blood is carried under high pressure, and they have thick, muscular walls.
12. They carry blood to the heart, blood is carried under low pressure, and they have one-way valves to keep blood flowing in one direction.
13. They bring blood cells carrying oxygen and nutrients close to body cells.
14. an artery, because the blood is under high pressure
15. 96 000 km/2.5 = 38 400 km

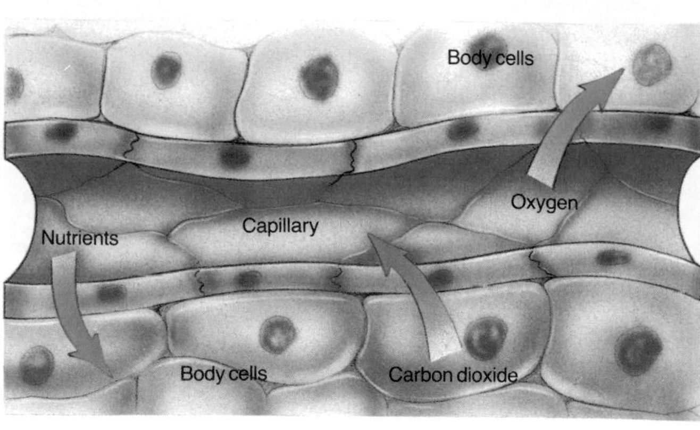

Figure 11-13 Pickups and deliveries between blood and body cells occur in the capillaries.

What occurs in the capillaries?

There are blood vessels in your body that become very narrow until they can no longer be called arteries or veins. A **capillary** is the smallest kind of blood vessel. The wall of a capillary is only one cell thick and may be thinner than a single page in this book. Some blood cells can easily pass between the cells of the capillary wall. You have more capillaries in your body than any other blood vessel type.

Capillaries have a very important job. They bring blood close to every body cell. All the pickups and deliveries occur in the capillaries. Blood in the capillaries can deliver oxygen, food, or other needed materials to all body cells. At the same time, waste chemicals made in body cells, such as carbon dioxide, are picked up by the blood in capillaries. Figure 11-13 shows these events.

Check Your Understanding

11. List three traits of arteries.
12. List four traits of veins.
13. What is the main job of capillaries?
14. **Critical Thinking:** What would be more life-threatening, a cut in an artery or a cut in a vein? Why?
15. **Biology and Math:** You have read that the total length of all your blood vessels is about 96 000 kilometers, enough to go around Earth about two and one-half times. Use this information to calculate the circumference of, or distance around, Earth.

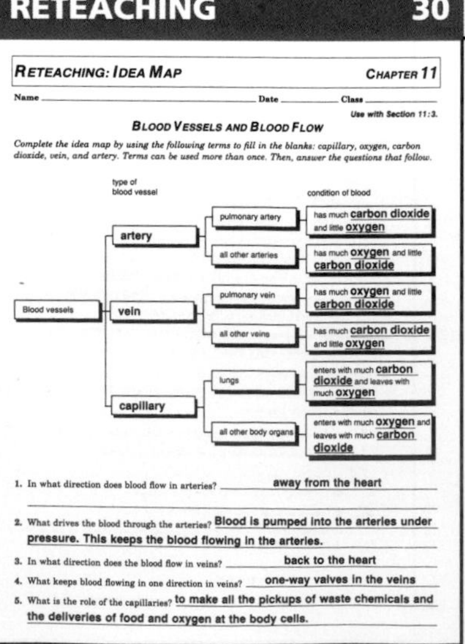

RETEACHING 30

Reteaching: Idea Map — Chapter 11

Name ______ Date ______ Class ______

Use with Section 11:3.

BLOOD VESSELS AND BLOOD FLOW

Complete the idea map by using the following terms to fill in the blanks: capillary, oxygen, carbon dioxide, vein, and artery. Terms can be used more than once. Then, answer the questions that follow.

	type of blood vessel		condition of blood
Blood vessels	artery	pulmonary artery	has much carbon dioxide and little oxygen
		all other arteries	has much oxygen and little carbon dioxide
	vein	pulmonary vein	has much oxygen and little carbon dioxide
		all other veins	has much carbon dioxide and little oxygen
	capillary	lungs	enters with much carbon dioxide and leaves with much oxygen
		all other body organs	enters with much oxygen and leaves with much carbon dioxide

1. In what direction does blood flow in arteries? away from the heart
2. What drives the blood through the arteries? Blood is pumped into the arteries under pressure. This keeps the blood flowing in the arteries.
3. In what direction does the blood flow in veins? back to the heart
4. What keeps blood flowing in one direction in veins? one-way valves in the veins
5. What is the role of the capillaries? to make all the pickups of waste chemicals and the deliveries of food and oxygen at the body cells.

Lab 11-2 Blood Pressure 

Problem: How does blood pressure in arteries and veins compare?

Skills

formulate models, form a hypothesis, measure in SI

Materials

plastic squeeze bottle
pan or sink
rubber stopper and tube assembly
water
meterstick

Procedure

1. Copy the data table.
2. Fill the plastic bottle with water.
3. Insert the rubber stopper and tube assembly into the plastic bottle, Figure A.
4. Position the bottle and meterstick over a pan or sink as shown in Figure B.
5. **Form a hypothesis** about which tube the water will squirt from farther. One tube is glass and the other is plastic.
6. Give the bottle one firm squeeze.
7. Note the distance that water squirts from each tube.
8. **Measure in SI:** Measure in centimeters the distance that water squirts from each tube. Record the distance in your table.
9. Repeat steps 2 through 4 and 6 through 7 two more times.
10. Calculate the average distance water squirted for each tube. (Add the 3 distances and divide the total by 3.)

A
Plastic tube
Plastic bottle
B

TRIAL	DISTANCE WATER SQUIRTS (cm)	
	GLASS TUBE	PLASTIC TUBE
1	42	36
2	38	34
3	37	36
Total	117	106
Average	39	35.3

Data and Observations

1. Which tube squirted water farther?
2. Which tube squirted water the shorter distance?

Analyze and Apply

1. (a) What body organ does the plastic bottle represent?
   (b) What body liquid does the water represent?
2. Arteries are firmer than veins.
   (a) Which tube represents an artery?
   (b) Which tube represents a vein?
3. Which tube was under higher pressure?
4. Which tube was under lower pressure?
5. How does blood pressure in arteries and veins compare?
6. **Check your hypothesis:** Is your hypothesis supported by your data? Why or why not?
7. **Apply:** Why are arteries firmer than veins?

Extension

Design an experiment to show the effect of less salt intake on blood pressure.

Lab 11-2 Blood Pressure

Overview

In this lab, students measure the distance that water squirts when forced through two different tubes. This model will be compared with arteries and veins.

Objectives: Upon completion of the lab, students will be able to (1) **relate** the distance water squirts from two tubes to the pressure within them. (2) **compare** the pressure within arteries and veins.

Time Allotment: 1 class period

Preparation

▶ For the rubber stopper and tube assembly use the following: glass tube 22 cm long, rubber or plastic tube 18 cm long (inner diameter 4 mm), 2-hole rubber stopper (size 6 to 7), lubricant, and cloth towel.

 **Lab 11-2 worksheet**/*Teacher Resource Package,* pp. 43-44.

Teaching the Lab

▶ For safety reasons, the teacher should build the rubber stopper assembly.

Cooperative Learning: Divide the class into groups of two to three students. For more information, see pp. 22T-23T in the Teacher Guide.

Lab 11-2 Computer Program/*Teacher Resource Package,* p. x. Use the computer program shown at the bottom of this page as you teach this lab.

COMPUTER PROGRAM X

COMPUTER PROGRAM LAB 11-2 BLOOD PRESSURE

```
]POKE 33,33
]LIST

 40  DIM GLASS(5),PLASTIC(5)
 70  GOSUB 470
 90  HOME
 100  GOSUB 670
 110  GOSUB 430
 120  PRINT "!  TRIAL  !DISTANCE WATER SQUIRTS (CM) !";
 130  PRINT "!         !-----------------------------";
 140  PRINT "!    #    !GLASS TUBE   !PLASTIC TUBE  !";
 150  GOSUB 430
 160 S1 = 0:S2 = 0
 170  FOR X = 1 TO 5
 180  VTAB (X * 2 + 5): PRINT "!    ";X;"    !";
 190  HTAB 18: INPUT "";GLASS(X)
 200  VTAB (X * 2 + 5): HTAB 25: PRINT "!    ";
 210  INPUT "";PLASTIC(X)
 220  VTAB (X * 2 + 5): HTAB 40: PRINT "!";
 230  GOSUB 430
 240 S1 = S1 + GLASS(X):S2 = S2 + PLASTIC(X)
 250  NEXT X
 270  PRINT "ARE THESE NUMBERS CORRECT? (Y/N)";
 280  GET SPACE$
 290  IF SPACE$ = "N" THEN 80
 300  IF SPACE$ < > "Y" THEN 280
 310  VTAB  PEEK (37) + 1: HTAB 1: CALL  - 868
 320  PRINT "! TOTAL   !";
 330  VTAB 17: HTAB 18: PRINT S1;: HTAB 25: PRINT "!    ";S2;
 340  HTAB 40: PRINT "!";
 350  GOSUB 430
 360  PRINT "! AVERAGE !
 370  VTAB 19: HTAB 18: PRINT S1 / 5;: HTAB 25: PRINT "!    ";S2 / 5;
 380  HTAB 40: PRINT "!";
 390  GOSUB 430
 400  PRINT "DO YOU WANT TO PRINT THIS (Y/N)?";: GET AN$: IF AN$ = "Y" THEN VTA
B  PEEK (37) + 1: HTAB 1: CALL  - 868: GOSUB 1000: END
 410  IF AN$ < > "N" THEN VTAB  PEEK (37) + 1: HTAB 1: CALL  -868: GOTO 400
 420  END
 430  HTAB 1
 440  PRINT "----------------------------------------";
 450  RETURN
 470  TEXT : HOME
 480  GOSUB 670
 490  PRINT : PRINT
 500  PRINT "INSTRUCTIONS:"
 510  PRINT
 580  PRINT : PRINT "YOU WILL BE ASKED TO TYPE IN YOUR       RESULTS FOR THE 5 T
RIALS ONTO A DATA    TABLE ";
 590  PRINT "THAT IS EXACTLY LIKE THE ONE USED IN THE EXPERIMENT."
 600  PRINT
 610  PRINT "AFTER TYPING EACH NUMBER, PRESS THE     RETURN KEY.  AFTER TYPING Y
```

ANSWERS

Data and Observations

1. glass tube
2. plastic tube

Analyze and Apply

1. (a) the heart (b) blood
2. (a) glass tube (b) plastic tube
3. glass tube
4. plastic tube
5. Blood pressure is higher in arteries than in veins.
6. Students who hypothesized that water will squirt farther out of the glass tube will answer yes.
7. They need to be firmer in order to withstand the higher blood pressure.

11:4 Problems of the Circulatory System

PREPARATION

Materials Needed

Make copies of the Application, Transparency Master, Study Guide, and Reteaching worksheets in the *Teacher Resource Package.*

Key Science Words

hypertension
cholesterol
coronary vessel
heart attack

1 FOCUS

▶ The objectives are listed on the student page. Remind students to preview these objectives as a guide to this numbered section.

ACTIVITY/Brainstorming

Ask why the heart needs its own blood vessels when so much blood is passing through it? All pick-ups and deliveries are accomplished in the capillaries. Thus, the heart is no different than any other organ in the body.

Guided Practice

Have students write down their answers to the margin question: upper–ventricles are contracting; lower–ventricles are not contracting.

Objectives

9. **Explain** how blood pressure is measured.
10. **Trace** the events before and after a heart attack.
11. **Relate** ways to help prevent and correct heart problems.

Key Science Words

hypertension
cholesterol
coronary vessel
heart attack

11:4 Problems of the Circulatory System

Like any body part, the circulatory system can develop problems. Many of these problems can be corrected.

High Blood Pressure

When your blood pressure is taken, two measurements are made. One is taken when the ventricles are contracting. This upper pressure is the greater measurement. When the ventricles are not pumping, a lower pressure is taken. The normal range of blood pressure for young adults is 110 to 140 units for the upper pressure and 65 to 90 units for the lower pressure. Blood pressure is recorded as a fraction such as $\frac{120}{80}$. In general, blood pressure increases gradually as a person gets older.

Arteries are partly muscle, which gives them the ability to contract. When the artery contracts, the inside of the artery gets smaller. Blood must now pass through a narrower opening than before. The result is blood pushing through at higher pressure.

Let's use an example with a garden hose representing an artery. Water inside the hose can represent blood.

What happens if you squeeze the hose while the water is on? Water squirts out farther and with more force, Figure 11-14. You have raised the pressure of the water by making it pass through a narrower opening. The same thing happens with arteries.

Hypertension (HI pur ten chun) occurs when blood pressure is extremely high. Hypertension may also refer to a disease caused by high blood pressure. It occurs when arteries are too narrow for easy movement of blood.

Hypertension affects millions of people. Unlike many diseases, hypertension does not always make a person feel ill. Many people with high blood pressure do not know that they have it.

Hypertension can cause damage to body organs. The high pressure makes the heart work harder, which can cause heart failure. It can also cause a blood vessel to burst, which can cause a stroke. For this reason, many people have their blood pressure checked regularly, Figure 11-15. If the blood pressure is high, a doctor may suggest a change in diet or activities. In some cases, medicines are also given to help reduce high blood pressure.

Figure 11-14 The water pressure in a hose is higher when it is squeezed.

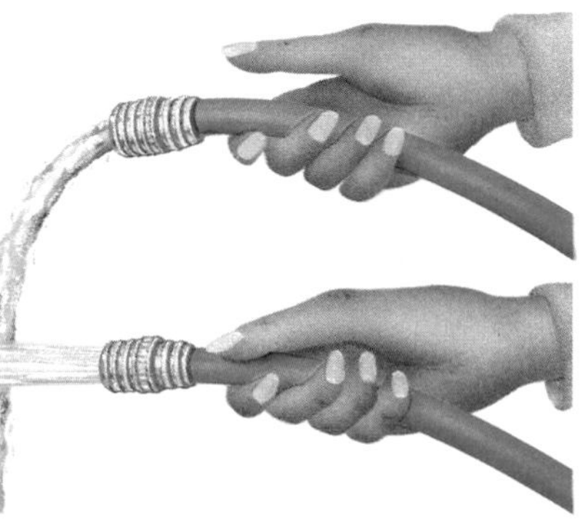

OPTIONS

Science Background

Heart disease does not have a single cause, but has many contributing factors. Heart disease is difficult to control because of these many contributing factors, which are covered in this section.

Application/*Teacher Resource Package,* p. 11. Use the Application worksheet shown here to teach students about blood pressure.

APPLICATION 11

APPLICATION: HEALTH — CHAPTER 11

Name ______ Date ______ Class ______

Use after Section 11:4.

BLOOD PRESSURE

A blood pressure reading is made up of two numbers. The first number indicates the blood pressure when the heart is pumping. The second number indicates the blood pressure when the heart is relaxed. A blood pressure reading is the first number over the second number. For example, the blood pressure reading of a healthy 20-year-old person should be about 110/72.

1. The graph at the right shows the blood pressure of people of different ages.

Blood Pressure Units; Age in years; Blood pressure when heart beats; Blood pressure when heart relaxes

Use the graph to complete the table below.

Age of person (years)	Normal blood pressure when heart is pumping	Normal blood pressure when heart is relaxed	Blood pressure reading
35	128	80	128/80
45	140	82	140/82
60	160	90	160/90
15	102	72	102/72

2. How does blood pressure change with age? It increases with age.

3. A person has high blood pressure if the blood pressure reading is higher than normal for that person's age. A person has low blood pressure if the blood pressure reading is lower than normal for that person's age.

Complete the table below, using the words normal, high, or low to fill in the right-hand column.

Age of person (years)	Blood pressure when heart is pumping	Blood pressure when heart is relaxed	Normal, high, or low blood pressure
35	145	90	high
55	147	68	normal
20	80	40	low
10	100	70	normal

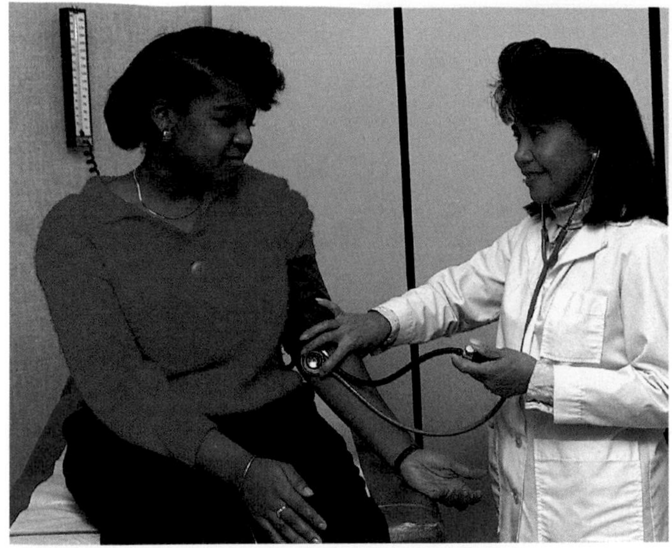

Figure 11-15 Your blood pressure is checked regularly by your doctor.

High blood pressure may be worsened by a person's diet. For example, too much salt in the diet may make hypertension worse. **Cholesterol** (kuh LES tuh ral) is a fatlike chemical found in certain foods. Cholesterol can coat the inside of arteries and cause them to become narrower. This narrowing raises the blood pressure, just as squeezing the hose did.

Bio Tip

Consumer: Foods that come from plants, such as fruit and vegetables, do not contain cholesterol. Natural foods contain much less salt (sodium) than processed foods. The amount of salt in a box of uncooked rice is much less than the amount in a frozen rice dish.

Heart Attack

The heart is made of muscle cells. These cells, just like other cells in the body, must receive oxygen and nutrients. How does the heart receive oxygen and nutrients? The heart has its own supply of blood vessels. The blood vessels that carry blood to and from the heart itself are called **coronary** (KOR uh ner ee) **vessels.** Oxygen and nutrients are carried to the heart by the blood in the coronary vessels.

Coronary vessels, like other blood vessels, can become clogged by cholesterol or a blood clot. When the vessels are clogged, blood cannot reach a part of the heart. This part of the heart then begins to die because of a lack of nutrients and oxygen. The death of a section of heart muscle is called a **heart attack.** If too much heart muscle dies, the heart is unable to pump properly. When blood doesn't deliver enough oxygen to body tissues, the person could die.

What is a heart attack?

STUDY GUIDE 65

STUDY GUIDE — CHAPTER 11

Name ________ Date ________ Class ________

PROBLEMS OF THE CIRCULATORY SYSTEM

In your textbook, read about high blood pressure and heart attacks in Section 11:4.

1. The following diagrams show cross sections of three arteries. Choices A, B, and C may be used more than once and in combinations when answering these questions.

A (normal) B (contracted) C (filled with cholesterol)

a. Which diagram or diagrams *might* have an upper blood pressure value of 160? B, C
Explain why. A narrow opening raises blood pressure.

b. Which diagram or diagrams *might* have an upper blood pressure value of 110? A
Explain why. Diagram A shows a normal opening through which blood should be able to push at a normal pressure value of 110.

2. What are coronary blood vessels? blood vessels that carry blood to and from the heart

3. What can happen if these vessels become clogged? Since blood can't reach a part of the heart, that part begins to die due to lack of nutrients and oxygen. This can result in a heart attack.

In your textbook, read about preventing heart problems in Section 11:4.

4. How can diet help prevent heart problems? Eating a balanced diet can prevent becoming overweight and can reduce cholesterol intake.

5. Why is a smoker more likely to have heart problems than a nonsmoker? Nicotine in tobacco smoke causes blood vessels to narrow in size. This causes the heart to work harder to pump blood.

STUDY GUIDE 66

STUDY GUIDE — CHAPTER 11

Name ________ Date ________ Class ________

VOCABULARY

Review the new words used in Chapter 11 of your textbook. Then, read the statements below.

For each statement, write TRUE or FALSE on the first blank. Make a false statement true by changing the underlined term. Write the correct term on the second blank.

1. TRUE ______ Valves are flaps in the heart and vein.
2. TRUE ______ Arteries carry blood away from the heart.
3. TRUE ______ The circulatory system is made up of blood, blood vessels, and the heart.
4. FALSE vena cava The pulmonary vein is the largest vein.
5. FALSE blood vessels Blood pressure is the force of blood pushing against the walls of the heart.
6. TRUE ______ Atria are the top chambers of the heart.
7. FALSE semilunar The tricuspid valves are located between the ventricles and their arteries.
8. FALSE high Hypertension is caused by low blood pressure.
9. FALSE capillary A vena cava is the smallest kind of blood vessel.
10. TRUE ______ Coronary vessels carry blood to the heart.
11. FALSE Pulmonary veins Capillaries carry blood from the lungs to the left side of the heart.
12. FALSE tricuspid The semilunar valve is located between the right atrium and right ventricle.
13. TRUE ______ A heart attack is the death of a heart muscle.
14. FALSE pulmonary artery The aorta carries blood from the heart to the lungs.
15. TRUE ______ Veins carry blood back to the heart.
16. TRUE ______ The bicuspid valve is located between the left atrium and the left ventricle.
17. TRUE ______ Cholesterol can narrow arteries.
18. FALSE aorta The pulmonary artery is the largest artery.
19. TRUE ______ Ventricles are the bottom chambers of the heart.

2 TEACH

MOTIVATION/Demonstration

This is an excellent place for the use of a heart model or a preserved heart. The coronary blood vessels are usually very prominent on both. Trace the intricate pathway of these blood vessels around the heart.

Concept Development

▶ Students may ask why there is blood pressure even when the heart ventricles are not pumping. The blood is confined to a narrow vessel (the aorta and other major arteries) and still retains pressure from this confinement. Also, the arteries themselves are capable of muscle contraction and contribute to the maintaining of blood pressure.

▶ Coronary blood vessels are normally small in diameter and are highly susceptible to cholesterol deposition. Minor narrowing of these blood vessels can impede blood flow to the heart muscle.

ACTIVITY/Guest Speaker

Ask the school nurse to visit your classroom and demonstrate the use of a sphygmomanometer. If possible, allow several students to take each other's pressure.

Analogy: Compare the buildup of cholesterol in arteries with the accumulation of rust or minerals inside a pipe. The buildup of cholesterol deposits restricts blood flow. The buildup of rust in a pipe reduces water flow.

Guided Practice

Have students write down their answers to the margin question: the death of a section of heart muscle.

Independent Practice

Study Guide/*Teacher Resource Package,* pp. 65-66. Use the Study Guide worksheets shown at the bottom of this page for independent practice.

TECHNOLOGY

Angioplasty

Background

This technique does not require the recuperation time associated with open heart surgery, so it is less costly and traumatic for the patient.

Discussion

Cholesterol is not removed from the blood vessels. It is simply pressed up against the inside of the arteries. Therefore, the procedure must be repeated as cholesterol buildup and subsequent narrowing returns.

References

Popma, J.J. "Management of Patients with Coronary Angioplasty." *American Family Physician,* Jan. 1990, pp. 121-129.

TEACH

Check for Understanding

Ask students to name the part of the circulatory system being affected by: too much cholesterol, too little exercise, too much body fat, smoking.

Reteach

Ask students to prepare an idea map for problems of the circulatory system and their solutions.

Guided Practice

Have students write down their answers to the margin question: nicotine causes blood vessels to narrow in size.

TECHNOLOGY

Angioplasty

Angioplasty is a way of opening blocked arteries using a balloon.

1. A deflated balloon is inserted into an artery.
2. The balloon is inflated and pushes cholesterol against the artery wall.
3. The balloon is deflated and removed. The artery now has an open pathway and blood can flow freely in the vessel.

This type of operation is easier than removing a blocked blood vessel. Patients who have angioplasty may return to normal activities in a few days.

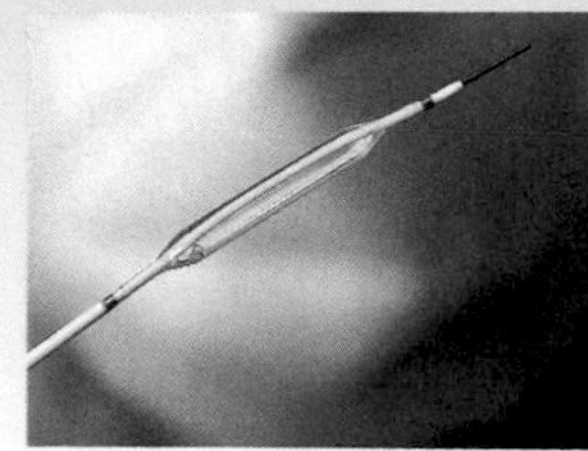

Not all patients can be treated this way. For many patients, replacing clogged vessels is the best form of treatment. A problem with angioplasty is that the cholesterol that caused the problem is still present.

A deflated balloon is prepared for angioplasty.

Preventing Heart Problems

What can a person do to try to prevent heart problems? Scientific research has shown three things that may help. They are exercise, proper diet, and not smoking.

Why is exercise important? Just as leg or arm muscles need exercise, the heart muscle also needs exercise. Physical exercise makes your heart muscle stronger because your heart beats more often when you exercise. Increasing the heartbeat rate regularly is good exercise for your heart.

Diet is also important. Eating a balanced diet can help a person avoid being overweight. Being overweight puts a strain on the heart because fat forms around the heart. The heart has to work harder to pump blood throughout the body. Eating a balanced diet also may help to reduce your cholesterol intake. Table 11-1 shows the cholesterol content of popular foods. How many foods that are high in cholesterol do you eat?

Why is smoking harmful to the heart?

Studies show that a person who smokes is more likely to have heart problems than someone who doesn't smoke. Nicotine, a chemical in tobacco smoke, causes blood vessels to narrow in size. The heart must work harder to pump blood through these narrow vessels.

TABLE 11–1. CHOLESTEROL VALUES FOR CERTAIN FOODS

Food	Cholesterol in One Normal Serving (in milligrams)
Chicken liver	630
Egg yolk	252
Pork spareribs	120
Ham	100
Chicken	90
Flounder	70
Pizza	60
Milk (whole)	34
Butter (1 tbsp.)	20
Milk (skim)	5
Egg white	0

OPTIONS

Science Background

Cholesterol is a naturally-occurring compound in the body, so it is impossible to reduce the presence of cholesterol to zero.

Transparency Master/*Teacher Resource Package*, p.49. Use the Transparency Master shown here as you teach about the effects of cholesterol on the circulatory system.

TRANSPARENCY 49

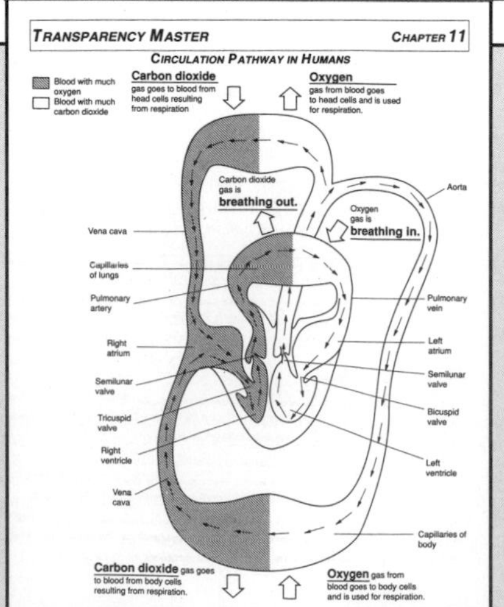

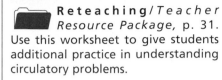

Figure 11-16 Barney Clark was the first person to receive an artificial heart like the one shown (inset). He died in 1983 after living 112 days with the plastic and metal heart.

What can be done for the person who can't be helped with exercise or diet? If blocked coronary vessels are the problem, unclogged vessels from another part of the patient's body can replace those in the heart. There are drugs that dissolve blood clots inside blood vessels. Heart transplant operations are also possible. Hearts are donated by families of persons who die.

An artificial heart made of plastic and metal has been used for heart patients in an emergency until a human heart is donated. There are about 2000 people on the waiting list for a donor heart each year. Figure 11-16 shows what this heart looks like. This type of heart has kept a person alive for over 600 days.

Check Your Understanding

16. What two measurements are made when a person's blood pressure is taken?
17. What causes a section of heart muscle to die?
18. What are three ways of preventing heart problems?
19. **Critical Thinking:** An overweight person's blood pressure is usually higher than the blood pressure of a person of average weight. Why does blood pressure increase with body weight?
20. **Biology and Reading:** A heart attack occurs when blood vessels inside the heart muscle are damaged. The scientific name for a heart attack comes from the name for these blood vessels. What is this name?

RETEACHING 31

RETEACHING: IDEA MAP CHAPTER 11

Name ______ Date ______ Class ______

Use with Section 11:4.

CIRCULATORY SYSTEM PROBLEMS

Use the following terms to complete the idea map below: proper diet, artificial heart, not smoking, drugs to dissolve blood clots, replace blocked vessels, exercise, heart transplants. Then, answer the questions that follow.

Heart problems
- solution for many
  - exercise
  - proper diet
  - not smoking
- solution for some
  - drugs to dissolve blood clots
  - replace blocked vessels
  - heart transplants
  - artificial heart

1. What is the normal upper blood pressure range for young adults? **110-140**
   the normal lower blood pressure range? **65-90**
2. What are some causes of hypertension? **too much salt and too much cholesterol in the diet**
3. Which of the following would be a healthier food in terms of the amount of cholesterol it contains—scrambled eggs or pizza? **pizza**
4. Why is a person who smokes more likely to have heart problems than someone who doesn't? **Nicotine in tobacco smoke causes blood vessels to narrow. The heart has to work harder to pump blood through the narrow vessels.**

OPTIONS

ACTIVITY/Challenge

Have students design a "public information" poster that advises people on how to reduce the risk of heart attack.

TEACH

Check for Understanding

Have students respond to the first three questions in Check Your Understanding.

Reteach

Reteaching/*Teacher Resource Package,* p. 31. Use this worksheet to give students additional practice in understanding circulatory problems.

Extension: Assign Critical Thinking, Biology and Reading, or some of the **OPTIONS** available with this lesson.

3 APPLY

ACTIVITY/Brainstorming

Why it is possible to remove large veins from the body without harm to the person?

4 CLOSE

Convergent Question

Discuss the problem of eating foods that are high in cholesterol. Is it a problem that teenagers should be concerned with now? (Yes, many diseases that appear later in life take many years to develop.)

Answers to Check Your Understanding

16. upper, when the ventricles are contracting, and lower, when the ventricles are at rest
17. if it does not receive enough nutrients and oxygen
18. exercise, proper diet, and not smoking
19. The heart must work harder to pump the blood through the entire body.
20. coronary or coronary attack

CHAPTER 11 REVIEW

Summary

Summary statements can be used by students to review the major concepts of the chapter.

Key Science Words

All boldfaced terms from this chapter are listed.

Testing Yourself

Using Words

1. valve
2. capillary
3. aorta
4. bicuspid valve
5. pulmonary artery
6. heart attack
7. circulatory system
8. ventricle
9. hypertension

Finding Main Ideas

10. p. 228; The heart sounds are caused by the closing of the heart valves.
11. p. 232; Their round shape and thick, muscular walls aid the movement of blood under high pressure.
12. p. 229; Blood leaving the lungs is high in oxygen and low carbon dioxide.
13. p. 222; Simple animals with no circulatory system live in a liquid environment where each body cell is in contact with the liquid.
14. p. 228; A heart murmur is caused by blood leaking past the heart valves when they don't close properly.
15. p. 236; High blood pressure occurs when the arteries are too narrow for free movement of blood.16.pp. 229-230; The right side of the heart pumps blood only to the lungs. The left side of the heart pumps blood to all parts of the body except the lungs.
17. pp. 225, 227; The human heart consists of two atria, two ventricles, a tricuspid valve, a bicuspid valve, and semilunar valves.

Chapter 11

Review

Summary

11:1 The Process of Circulation

1. The circulatory system works as a pickup and delivery system for the body.
2. Insects have an open circulatory system. Earthworms and humans have closed systems.

11:2 The Human Heart

3. Your heart is a muscle with four chambers. Blood is pumped from top to bottom chambers.
4. The closing of heart valves produces heart sounds.
5. The heart's right side pumps blood only to the lungs. The heart's left side supplies blood to the rest of the body.

11:3 Blood Vessels

6. Arteries have thick walls and carry blood away from the heart. Blood in arteries is under high pressure.
7. Veins have valves and carry blood to the heart.
8. Capillaries are very small blood vessels.

11:4 Problems of the Circulatory System

9. Blood pressure is caused by blood pushing against the walls of the blood vessels.
10. A heart attack is caused by blockage of the coronary blood vessels.
11. Many heart problems can be avoided by exercise, proper diet, and not smoking.

Key Science Words

aorta (p. 230)
artery (p. 226)
atrium (p. 225)
bicuspid valve (p. 227)
blood pressure (p. 232)
capillary (p. 234)
cholesterol (p. 237)
circulatory system (p. 222)
coronary vessel (p. 237)
heart attack (p. 237)
hypertension (p. 236)
pulmonary artery (p. 229)
pulmonary vein (p. 229)
semilunar valve (p. 227)
tricuspid valve (p. 227)
valve (p. 227)
vein (p. 226)
vena cava (p. 229)
ventricle (p. 225)

Testing Yourself

Using Words

Choose the word from the list of Key Science Words that best fits the definition.

1. flap in a vein that keeps blood flow going in one direction
2. smallest blood vessel
3. largest artery in body
4. valve between left atrium and ventricle
5. carries blood away from heart to lungs
6. death of a section of heart muscle
7. your heart, blood vessels, and blood
8. bottom heart chamber
9. disease caused by high blood pressure

240

Using Main Ideas

18. The heartbeat is the closing of the tricuspid and bicuspid valves of the heart.
19. Veins carry blood toward the heart, blood in veins is under low pressure, and veins are flat with many one-way valves that keep blood from flowing backwards.
20. Most heart attacks are caused by the blocking of the coronary arteries that supply oxygen and nutrients to the heart.
21. The circulatory system picks up oxygen from the lungs and nutrients from the digestive system and delivers them to the body cells. It also picks up carbon dioxide and wastes from the body cells and delivers them to the lungs and excretory system.
22. Heart attacks can be prevented by exercising, a proper diet, and by not smoking.
23. The tricuspid valve is between the right atrium and the right ventricle. The bicuspid valve is between the left atrium and the left ventricle. The semilunar valves are between the ventricles and their arteries.
24. The upper blood pressure is measured when the ventricles contract. The lower blood pressure is measured when the ventricles are relaxed.

Review

Testing Yourself *continued*

Finding Main Ideas

List the page number where each main idea below is found. Then, explain each main idea.

10. what the "lub-dup" sounds are
11. how the traits of arteries aid blood movement
12. the condition of blood leaving the lungs
13. how simple animals can live without a circulatory system
14. what causes a heart murmur
15. what causes high blood pressure
16. what special jobs the heart's right and left sides have
17. what the main parts of the human heart are

Using Main Ideas

Answer the questions by referring to the page number after each question.

18. What is a heartbeat? (p. 227)
19. What are four traits of veins? (p. 233)
20. What is the cause of most heart attacks? (p. 237)
21. What does your circulatory system pick up and deliver? (p. 222)
22. How can people prevent heart problems? (p. 238)
23. What are the locations and names of all heart valves? (p. 227)
24. What occurs in the heart when one measures the upper and lower blood pressure? (p. 236)
25. How is the pumping action of the heart similar to the squeezing of a plastic bottle? (p. 232)
26. What is the pathway that blood takes as it leaves your heart's right and left ventricles? (p. 226)

Skill Review 

For more help, refer to the ***Skill Handbook,*** *pages 704-719.*

1. **Design an experiment:** Design an experiment to find out whether the average pulse rate of a young child is different from that of a teenager.
2. **Understand science words:** What do the word parts *bi* and *tri* mean?
3. **Formulate a model:** Construct and label a three-dimensional model of the heart and the blood vessels that lead to and from it.
4. **Calculate:** The total sodium (salt) content of a bag of popcorn is 680 mg. The total sodium content of a bag of potato chips is 1140 mg. The popcorn bag contains 4 servings while the bag of potato chips contains 6 servings. Determine the sodium content of a single serving of each snack. Which snack has the lower sodium content?

Finding Out More

Critical Thinking

1. Some babies are born with a hole between the right and left ventricles. Why is this a problem?
2. Suppose you are asked to design an artificial heart. What technical problems might you need to solve?

Applications

1. Design meals for three days that would be suitable for a person who wishes to reduce his cholesterol.
2. Explain why your heartbeat rate speeds up during exercise.

Using Main Ideas

25. When a plastic bottle is squeezed, pressure inside the bottle causes the liquid to be pushed out. When the heart chambers contract, pressure inside the chambers causes blood to be pushed out.
26. When blood leaves the right ventricle, it goes to the lungs through the pulmonary artery. When blood leaves the left ventricle, it goes to the body cells through the aorta.

Skill Review

1. The blood pressure of the teenager should be slightly higher than that of a young child.
2. *Bi* means two, and *tri* means three.
3. The model should contain two atria, two ventricles, a vena cava, an aorta, coronary arteries, a pulmonary artery, and pulmonary veins. There should be valves between the atria and ventricles and between the ventricles and arteries.
4. popcorn–680 mg/4 = 170 mg per serving; potato chips–1140 mg/6 = 190 mg per serving; Popcorn has a lower sodium content per serving than potato chips.

Finding Out More

Critical Thinking

1. The hole between the atria allows high-oxygen blood to mix with low-oxygen blood, making the transport of oxygen to the body cells less efficient.
2. The major problem with an artificial heart is finding a material that won't be rejected by the body. Other concerns include leaking, keeping the pressure, force, and timing of the contractions correct; and preventing the formation of blood clots within the heart.

Applications

1. Answers will vary. The meals should be low in animal fat and high in grains and fruits and vegetables.
2. The heart must pump blood faster to the muscle cells as oxygen is used up during exercise.

 **Chapter Review**/*Teacher Resource Package,* pp. 55-56.

 **Chapter Test**/*Teacher Resource Package,* pp. 57-59.

Chapter Test/*Computer Test Bank*

Blood

PLANNING GUIDE

CONTENT	TEXT FEATURES	TEACHER RESOURCE PACKAGE	OTHER COMPONENTS
(1 day) 12:1 The Role of Blood Blood Functions	Lab 12-1: *Red Blood Cells,* p. 246 Check Your Understanding, p. 245	Reteaching: *Functions of Blood,* p. 32 Study Guide: *The Role of Blood,* p. 67 Lab 12-1: *Red Blood Cells,* pp. 45-46	
(2 days) 12:2 Parts of Human Blood Plasma Red Blood Cells Roles of Red Blood Cells White Blood Cells Roles of White Blood Cells Platelets	Skill Check: *Understand Science Words,* p. 252 Mini Lab: *How Is Human Blood Made Up?* p. 248 Lab 12-2: *Human Blood Cells,* p. 253 Technology: *Eye "Fingerprints,"* p. 250 Check Your Understanding, p. 252	Enrichment: *Red and White Blood Cell Numbers,* p. 12 Reteaching: *Parts of the Blood,* p. 33 Critical Thinking/Problem Solving: *How Are Active and Passive Immunity Different?* p. 12 Study Guide: *Parts of Human Blood,* p. 68 Lab 12-2: *Human Blood Cells,* pp. 47-48	**Laboratory Manual:** *How Can Blood Diseases Be Identified?* p. 95
(1 day) 12:3 Blood Types Blood Types Differ Mixing Blood Types	Check Your Understanding, p. 255	Reteaching: *Blood Types,* p. 34 Study Guide: *Blood Types,* p. 69	**Laboratory Manual:** *What Blood Types Can Be Mixed?* p. 99 Color Transparency 12a: *Blood Types*
(1 day) 12:4 Immunity Your Immune System How the Immune System Works How Shots Keep You Healthy AIDS and the Immune System	Skill Check: *Infer,* p. 258 Check Your Understanding, p. 259	Application: *How Does AIDS Cause Death?* p. 12 Reteaching: *Immunity,* p. 35 Skill: *Outline,* p. 13 Focus: *How Is AIDS Spread?* p. 23 Study Guide: *The Immune System,* pp. 70-71 Study Guide: *Vocabulary,* p. 72 Transparency Master: *AIDS and the Immune System,* p. 53	Color Transparency 12b: *The Immune System*
Chapter Review	Summary Key Science Words Testing Yourself Finding Main Ideas Using Main Ideas Skill Review	Chapter Review, pp. 60-61 Chapter Test, pp. 62-64	**Test Bank**

MATERIALS NEEDED

LAB 12-1, p. 246	LAB 12-2, p. 253	MARGIN FEATURES
microscope prepared slides of human and frog blood petri dish cover metric ruler	sheet of clear plastic marking pencil microscope prepared slide of human blood	Skill Check, p. 252 dictionary Mini Lab, p. 248 oil water red food coloring

OBJECTIVES

		OBJECTIVES CORRELATION			
SECTION	OBJECTIVE	CHECK YOUR UNDERSTANDING	CHAPTER REVIEW	TRP CHAPTER REVIEW	TRP CHAPTER TEST
12:1	1. **Identify** the pickup and delivery jobs of the blood.	1, 2	11, 12	3	1, 7, 11, 12
	2. **Explain** the pickup and delivery system in animals without blood.	3	14, 22	5	13
12:2	3. **Describe** the living and nonliving parts of blood.	6	3, 9, 18	1, 11, 12, 13, 14, 25	18, 19, 20, 21, 22, 23, 24, 30, 35
	4. **Give the functions** of the blood cells and cell-like parts.	7, 10	1, 2, 19	4, 6, 9, 15, 16, 17, 18, 19, 20, 21, 22, 23, 26, 27	2, 5, 6, 10, 22, 23, 24, 25, 28, 29, 30, 31, 33, 46
	5. **Explain** the problems that may occur with blood cells and platelets.	8, 9	4, 5, 8	29	9, 26, 34
12:3	6. **Compare** the red cells and plasma proteins in the four main blood types.	11, 12	10, 21	7, 8, 24	8, 41, 42, 43
	7. **Explain** why blood types can't be mixed.	13, 14	15	9	4, 44, 45
12:4	8. **Describe** how the immune system works.	16, 20	7, 13, 17	10	3, 35, 36, 37, 38, 39, 40
	9. **Explain** how shots prevent disease.	17	20, 23	2	47
	10. **Discuss** the AIDS virus.	18, 19	6, 16	28	14, 48

Blood

CHAPTER OVERVIEW

Key Concepts

This chapter discusses the specific functions of blood and its component parts. Blood types of the AB series are covered. The immune system and how it protects us against disease is discussed.

Key Science Words

AIDS	immune system
anemia	immunity
antibody	leukemia
antigen	plasma
bone marrow	platelet
hemoglobin	red blood cell
hemophilia	white blood cell

Skill Development

In Lab 12-1, students will **use a microscope, measure in SI,** and **compare** red blood cells. In Lab 12-2, they will **use a microscope, compare,** and **classify** human blood cells. In the Skill Check on p. 252, students will **understand** the **science word** *hemophilia.* On page 258, they will **infer** about immunity. In the Mini Lab on p. 248, students will **formulate a model** of blood.

CHAPTER PREVIEW

Chapter Content

Review this outline for Chapter 12 before you read the chapter.

Skills in this Chapter

The skills that you will use in this chapter are listed below.

- In **Lab 12-1,** you will use a microscope, measure in SI, and compare. In **Lab 12-2,** you will use a microscope, compare, and classify.
- In the **Skill Checks,** you will infer and understand science words.
- In the **Mini Lab,** you will formulate a model.

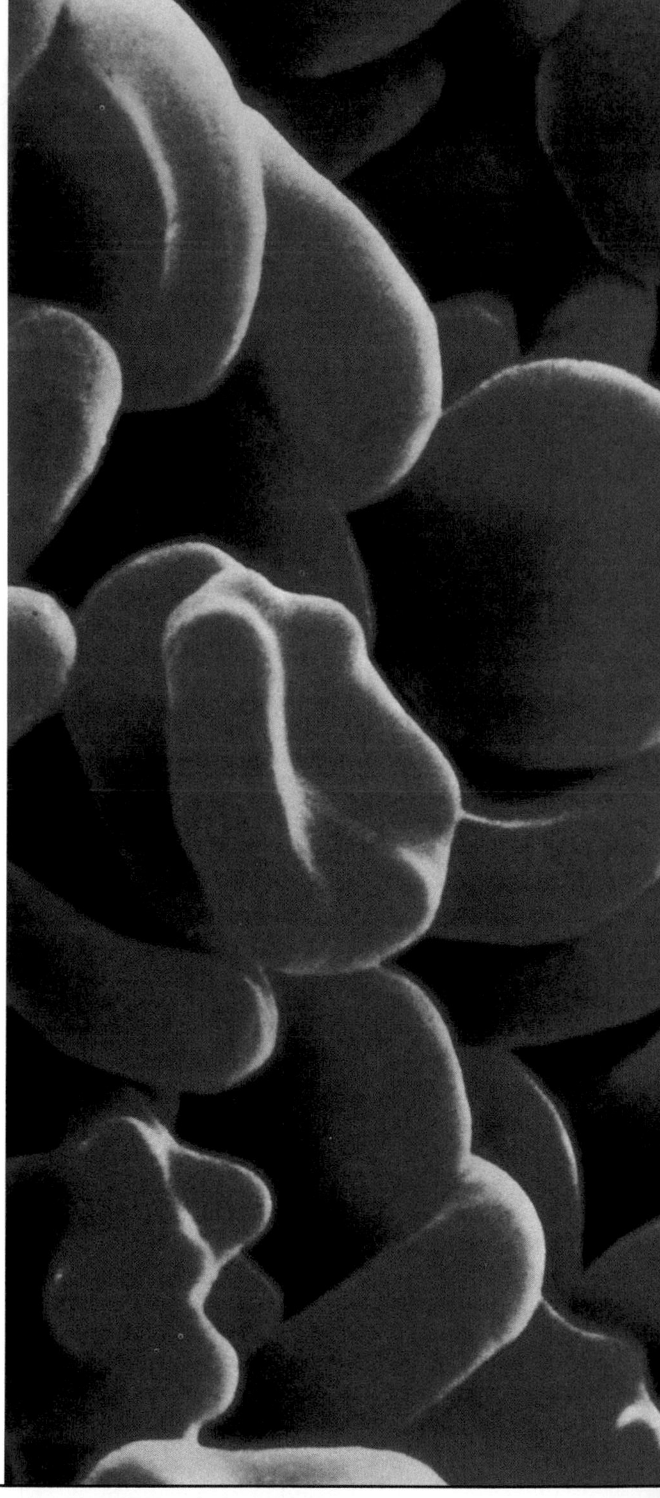

Bridging

The circulatory system was described as a pickup and delivery system. Blood does the actual work of carrying all the chemicals to be picked up and delivered, while the circulatory system pumps the blood.

Chapter 12

Blood

Suppose you were asked to classify blood as either a solid or a liquid. If you have ever had a bloody nose or deep cut, you would probably classify blood as a liquid. But if you viewed blood through a microscope, you might classify it as a solid. The large photograph on the left shows what your blood looks like magnified by an electron microscope. Notice the solid particles. These round, red parts are cells. The small photograph below shows bottles of fruit juices with about the same volume of liquid as you have blood in your body, or about five liters. You may be asking yourself: if blood is made of cells, how can it be liquid in form? After reading this chapter, you will know the answer to this puzzling question.

Try This!

How much blood does the body contain? The body of an adult human contains about 5 liters of blood. List three ways of showing this quantity. For example, your body contains as much blood as 5 quarts of milk. (1 liter is a little more than 1 quart.)

Your body holds five liters of blood.

GETTING STARTED

Using the Photos

Students can discover that blood is composed of cells (pink in color, round). This is apparent only when blood is magnified. It is considered a tissue because it is composed of different cell types.

MOTIVATION/Try This!

How much blood does the body contain? Ways to **measure** could include 5 1-liter soda bottles, a gallon plus a quart, a pail with 5 liters of water in it.

Chapter Preview

Have students study the chapter outline before they begin to read the chapter. They should note the overall organization of the chapter. First the general role of blood is covered, then the various parts of blood are studied, followed by a description of blood types, and finally a study of the immune system.

Misconception

Blood in arteries is thought to be red in color, while blood in veins is thought to be blue. Blood in most arteries is bright red due to the presence of oxygen, while blood in most veins is deep red due to the lack of oxygen.

12:1 The Role of Blood

PREPARATION

Materials Needed

Make copies of the Reteaching, Study Guide, and Lab worksheets in the *Teacher Resource Package.*

▶ Obtain petri dish covers, rulers, and prepared slides for Lab 12–1.

Key Science Words

No new science words will be introduced in this section.

Process Skills

In Lab 12–1, students will use a microscope and measure in SI.

1 FOCUS

▶ The objectives are listed on the student page. Remind students to preview these objectives as a guide to this numbered section.

MOTIVATION/Brainstorming

What do you think is the most important role of blood?

Guided Practice

Have students write down their answers to the margin questions: Carbon dioxide waste goes to the lungs and chemical waste goes to the kidneys.

12:1 The Role of Blood

Objectives

1. **Identify** the pickup and delivery jobs of the blood.
2. **Explain** the pickup and delivery system in animals without blood.

In Chapter 11 you learned that blood is part of your circulatory system. Blood has many important jobs. You will learn about the roles of blood as you read this chapter.

Blood Functions

Blood is a body tissue that is part liquid and part cells. What are the functions of blood? Because it's part of the circulatory system, the blood's functions are to pick up and deliver nutrients and wastes.

First, let's list some of the delivery jobs of blood.

1. Blood delivers digested nutrients from fats, proteins, and carbohydrates to all body cells.
2. Blood delivers oxygen to all body cells.
3. Blood delivers chemical messengers to some body cells.
4. Blood delivers water, minerals, and vitamins to cells.

Next, let's list the pickup jobs of blood.

1. Blood picks up carbon dioxide waste from cells and carries it to the lungs.
2. Blood picks up chemical waste from cells and carries it to the kidneys.
3. Blood moves excess body heat into the skin.

Where does blood carry the wastes that it picks up from body cells?

You may have noticed the red flush that appears on the skin of a person after heavy exercise. Exercise results in the buildup of excess body heat. The red color is due to the widening of blood capillaries in the skin, Figure 12-1.

a

b

Figure 12-1 As you begin to exercise, the body heats up (a). The blood vessels in the skin get wider and excess heat is given off through the skin (b).

OPTIONS

Science Background

Spiders and their relatives have colorless blood. Crustaceans have amoebocytes in their blood to aid in transport of gases. Insects have colorless blood containing amoebocytes.

Blood in most animals consists mainly of plasma with respiratory pigments dissolved in it. These pigments may consist of hemoglobin or chlorocruorin. Hemoglobin makes the blood red; chlorocruorin causes blood to appear green.

Figure 12-2 Many sea animals, such as these sea anemones, have no blood or blood vessels. Water brings oxygen and nutrients to their cells.

Other functions of blood include helping to fight diseases and helping to stop bleeding.

Not all animals have blood. Animals such as sponges, jellyfish, and flatworms have no blood or blood vessels. How do the cells of these animals get oxygen or food? How are they able to get rid of waste chemicals? Most animals without blood live in water. Water serves as their "blood." It brings needed oxygen and food to all cells. It also carries away any waste chemicals from the body.

How is blood to a human like seawater to a jellyfish?

Check Your Understanding

1. What are six substances blood delivers to body cells?
2. What three substances are picked up by blood?
3. How do animals without blood get oxygen or food?
4. **Critical Thinking:** How does blood help a person maintain normal body temperature?
5. **Biology and Reading:** One of the following sentences is a fact. The other sentence can be made into a fact by changing the boldfaced word. Change the word and then write both facts on your paper.

The average adult body contains about five **liters** of blood.
Blood is a body **system** made up of liquid and cells.

RETEACHING 32

RETEACHING — **CHAPTER 12**

Name ______ Date ______ Class ______

Use with Section 12:1.

FUNCTIONS OF BLOOD

List the functions of blood by completing the sentences below. Then, answer the questions that follow.

Blood delivers nutrients to cells.
Blood delivers oxygen to all body cells.
Blood delivers chemical messengers to certain body cells.
Blood delivers water, minerals, and vitamins to all body cells.
Blood picks up carbon dioxide waste from cells and carries it to the lungs.
Blood picks up chemical wastes from cells and carries them to the kidneys.
Blood picks up excess body heat and delivers it to the skin.
Blood is made up of part liquid and part cells.
Blood helps fight diseases.
Blood helps stop bleeding after a cut or injury.

1. Why does a red flush appear on the skin of a person after heavy exercise? The blood capillaries widen in the skin and excess heat escapes through the skin.
2. Why do sponges and jellyfish have no need for blood? All the pickups and deliveries that are done by blood are carried out by the water in which the sponges and jellyfish live.

STUDY GUIDE 67

STUDY GUIDE — **CHAPTER 12**

Name ______ Date ______ Class ______

THE ROLE OF BLOOD

In your textbook, read about the functions of blood in Section 12:1.

Complete this outline of blood functions.

Blood jobs or functions
- 1. Blood picks up
  - a carbon dioxide waste from cells
  - b other chemical wastes from cells
  - c excess body heat
- 2. Blood delivers
  - a nutrients to all cells
  - b oxygen to all cells
  - c chemical messengers to certain cells
  - d water, minerals, and vitamins

PARTS OF HUMAN BLOOD

In your textbook, read about the living and nonliving parts of blood in Section 12:2.

1. Examine the diagram at the right of blood that has been sitting for an hour. Write the letter of the blood part being described in each of the words or phrases below. Write the correct letter next to each word or phrase.

a. plasma A
b. liquid part A
c. blood cell part B
d. nonliving part A
e. living part B
f. mostly water A
g. includes cells that carry oxygen B
h. includes parts that aid in blood clotting B
i. includes proteins, nutrients, salts, and wastes A
j. red B
k. yellow A
l. includes cells that destroy harmful microbes B

A
B

2 TEACH

Independent Practice

Study Guide/*Teacher Resource Package,* p. 67. Use the Study Guide worksheet shown at the bottom of this page for independent practice.

Check for Understanding

Have students respond to the first three questions in Check Your Understanding.

Reteach

Reteaching/*Teacher Resource Package,* p. 32. Use this worksheet to give students additional practice with the functions of blood.

Extension: Assign Critical Thinking, Biology and Reading, or some of the **OPTIONS** available with this lesson.

3 APPLY

Brainstorming

Invent a "fluid" that can be used as a substitute for blood. What would be some of its characteristics?

4 CLOSE

Audiovisual

Show the filmstrip *Blood: River of Life, Mirror of Health,* Human Relations Media.

Answers to Check Your Understanding

1. digested nutrients, oxygen, chemical messengers, water, minerals, and vitamins
2. carbon dioxide waste, chemical waste, and excess body heat
3. from surrounding water
4. Blood picks up excess body heat and moves that heat to the skin where the heat leaves the body.
5. The average adult body contains about five liters of blood. Blood is a body tissue made up of liquid and cells.

Lab 12-1 Red Blood Cells

Overview

This lab will test the observational skills of students and will allow them to compare and contrast blood cells from different animals.

Objective: Upon completing this lab, students will be able to (1) **differentiate** between red blood cells (2) **make** a drawing to scale, and (3) **calculate** cell size.

Time Allotment: 30 minutes

Preparation

▶ Obtain prepared slides of human and frog blood smears.

Lab 12-1 worksheet/*Teacher Resource Package*, pp. 45-46.

Teaching the Lab

▶ If a video camera is available, it can be attached to a microscope and the slides viewed on a television screen.

▶ Review the procedure for finding objects first under low power and then under high power.

▶ Assume that the photo of bird blood cells is shown under high power magnification. Thus, students can measure the cells directly from the page to obtain cell size.

▶ **Troubleshooting:** Students may have difficulty with the math and with measuring/drawing to scale. An example of the steps involved may first be shown on the overhead projector as a demonstration and review.

Cooperative Learning: Divide the class into groups of three students. For more information, see pp. 22T-23T in the Teacher Guide.

Red Blood Cells

Lab 12–1

Problem: How do red blood cells of different animals compare?

Skills

use a microscope, measure in SI, compare

Materials

microscope
petri dish cover
metric ruler
prepared slides of human and frog blood

Procedure

1. Copy the data table.
2. Use the cover of a petri dish to draw a circle on a piece of paper.
3. **Use a microscope:** Look at a prepared slide of human red blood cells under low power on the microscope. Change to high power. Most of the cells you see are red blood cells. Cells that appear blue are not red blood cells.
4. Draw a red blood cell in your circle. Assume your circle is the same as your field of view. Draw the cell to scale.
5. **Measure in SI:** Use a ruler to measure the size in millimeters of the blood cell in your drawing. Record your answer in your data table.
6. Repeat steps 3 through 5 with a prepared slide of frog blood.
7. On your diagrams, check for the presence of a nucleus and a cell membrane. Check these parts in your table if present.
8. Describe and record the shapes of the blood cells in your table. Use the following choices—round or oval.
9. Complete the rest of the data table using the photo of bird blood.

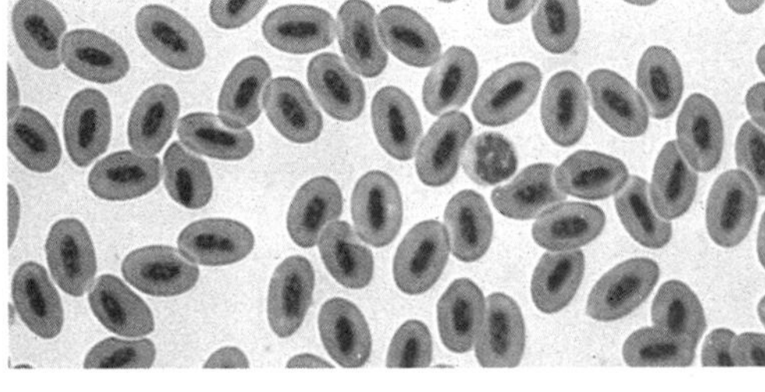

Answers will vary.

BLOOD FROM	SIZE	SHAPE	PARTS PRESENT?	
			NUCLEUS	CELL MEMBRANE
Human	0.01 mm	round	—	√
Frog	0.02 mm	oval	√	√
Bird	—	oval	√	√

Data and Observations

1. Which animals have red blood cells:
   (a) with a nucleus?
   (b) that are round?
   (c) that are oval?
2. Which animal has the larger red blood cells—frog or human?

Analyze and Apply

1. What is the main job of red blood cells?
2. In what blood vessels do red blood cells transport oxygen?
3. **Apply:** Based upon the appearance of red blood cells, which two animals are most closely related?

Extension

Calculate: The photo of bird red blood cells is magnified 1000 times. What is the actual measurement of the diameter of one blood cell?

ANSWERS

Data and Observations

1. (a) frog, bird
   (b) human
   (c) frog, bird
2. frog

Analyze and Apply

1. They carry oxygen to body cells.
2. arteries
3. frog and bird

Extension

0.007 mm

12:2 Parts of Human Blood

Blood is different from most body tissues. Not only is it able to flow, but it's also part living and part nonliving.

Plasma

Let's look at two tubes of blood. The tube on the left in Figure 12-3a shows blood just removed from a person's vein. The blood is a deep red color. No special parts can be seen. Now look at the tube on the right. This tube has been sitting for about an hour. Notice how the blood has separated into two parts. Blood cells have settled to the bottom. A yellow liquid appears on top.

Plasma (PLAZ muh) is the nonliving, yellow liquid part of blood. Blood plasma is 92 percent water. The remaining eight percent includes blood proteins, nutrients, salts, and waste chemicals.

Most of the pickup and delivery jobs of blood are carried out by plasma.

Red Blood Cells

Red blood cells are cells in the blood that carry oxygen to the body tissues. Red blood cells make up most of the blood. There are about five million red blood cells in a small drop of blood. Red blood cells are part of the living portion of blood. They give blood its red color.

Figure 12-3b shows red blood cells as seen under a light microscope. Look at this photograph as you read about red blood cells.

a

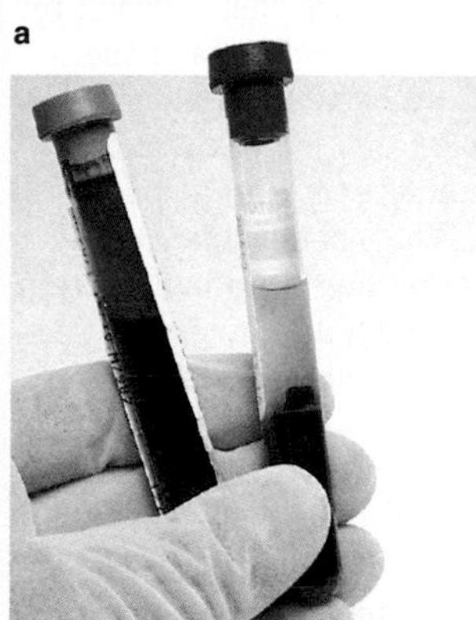

b

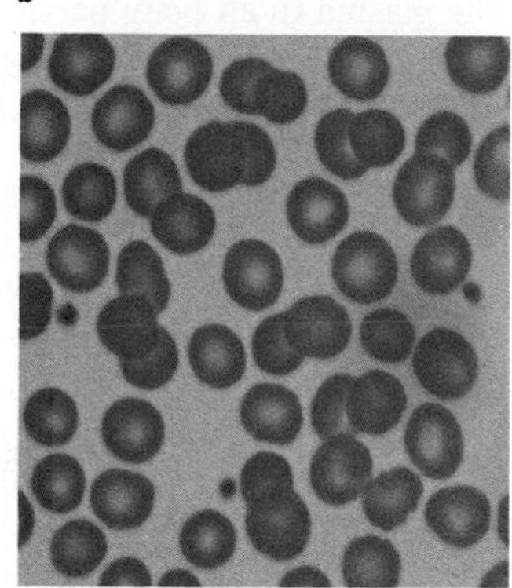

Objectives

3. **Describe** the living and nonliving parts of blood.
4. **Give the functions** of the blood cells and cell-like parts.
5. **Explain** the problems that may occur with blood cells and platelets.

Key Science Words

plasma
red blood cell
bone marrow
hemoglobin
anemia
white blood cell
leukemia
platelet
hemophilia

Which substance makes up the nonliving part of blood?

Figure 12-3 When blood is left to stand (left tube) the red cells and plasma separate out (right tube) (a). Blood cells and plasma can be examined under a light microscope (b).

OPTIONS

Science Background

Blood is an example of a tissue that is rather highly specialized and diverse in function. Each component part, plasma and blood cells, has very specific functions relating to transport of materials as well as to immunity.

12:2 Parts of Human Blood

PREPARATION

Materials Needed

Make copies of the Study Guide, Enrichment, Transparency Master, Critical Thinking/Problem Solving, Reteaching, and Lab worksheets in the *Teacher Resource Package.*

▶ Obtain plastic sheets, marking pencils, and prepared blood slides for Lab 12-2.

▶ Gather cooking oil and red food coloring for the Mini Lab.

Key Science Words

plasma
red blood cell
bone marrow
hemoglobin
anemia
white blood cell
leukemia
platelet
hemophilia

Process Skills

In Lab 12-2, students will use a microscope, compare, and classify. In the Skill Check, they will understand science words. In the Mini Lab, students will formulate a model.

1 FOCUS

▶ The objectives are listed on the student page. Remind students to preview these objectives as a guide to this numbered section.

MOTIVATION/Brainstorming

Describe:
(a) as many different diseases or disorders connected with blood as you can.
(b) as many different single words that describe the appearance or general function of blood as you can.

Guided Practice

Have students write down their answers to the margin question: Plasma is the non-living part of the blood.

2 TEACH

MOTIVATION/Software

The Circulatory System, Queue, Inc.

Concept Development

▶ Ask students to compare the appearance of red blood cells as seen in bone marrow to those seen in blood. Red cells in marrow are immature red blood cells that have not yet lost their nucleus.

Idea Map

Have students use the idea map as a study guide to the major concepts of this section.

Independent Practice

Study Guide/*Teacher Resource Package,* p. 68. Use the Study Guide worksheet shown at the bottom of this page for independent practice.

Guided Practice

Have students write down their answers to the margin question: Anemia is a condition in which there are too few red blood cells. Extra iron in the diet may help.

Mini Lab

Blood that is mixed appears uniformly red. If allowed to stand, however, cells will settle and plasma will appear. This model allows for observing both conditions.

Study Tip: Use this idea map as a study guide for comparing the living and nonliving parts of blood.

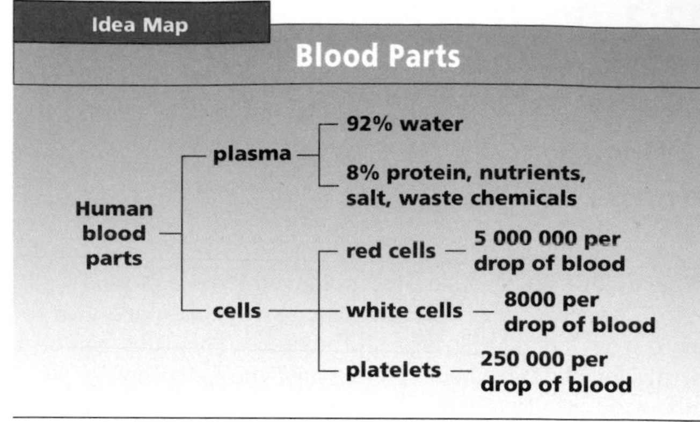

Mini Lab

How Is Blood Made Up?

Formulate a model: Add 20 mL of cooking oil to 20 mL of water and a drop of red food coloring. Shake the tube. Allow the liquids to separate. What do the layers represent? *For more help, refer to the* ***Skill Handbook,*** *pages 706-711.*

Red blood cells are round. They have thin centers and thick edges. They look like doughnuts without holes. Red blood cells have a nucleus only when they are first formed. The nucleus is lost as the cell matures and begins to move through the blood vessels.

Red blood cells have a life span of about 120 days. The body must constantly make new red cells. Red blood cells are made primarily in your bone marrow. **Bone marrow** is the soft center part of the bone.

Roles of Red Blood Cells

Red blood cells are the main part of blood that helps with the blood's job of pickup and delivery. They deliver oxygen to all body cells. Oxygen coming into the lungs is picked up by red blood cells as the cells pass through capillaries in the lungs. Red blood cells are then carried by the plasma to all body parts. Once these cells reach the cells of the body, oxygen is given up by the red blood cells.

How can red blood cells perform this job of oxygen pickup and delivery so well? The answer lies in a special chemical found in red blood cells. This chemical is called hemoglobin (HEE muh gloh bun). **Hemoglobin** is a protein in red blood cells that joins with oxygen and gives the red cells their color. Hemoglobin in blood cells carries oxygen to other body cells.

Hemoglobin contains the mineral iron. If a person's diet is low in iron, the total number of red blood cells and hemoglobin in the blood decreases. This decrease in red blood cells and hemoglobin can lead to anemia. **Anemia** is a

What is anemia? How is it treated?

OPTIONS

ACTIVITY/Challenge

Have students prepare a list of foods that are rich in iron. References can be obtained from a nutrition text. Good sources include: liver, kidney beans, prunes, oatmeal, blackstrap molasses, sweet potato, endive, spinach, figs, and tomato juice

STUDY GUIDE 68

STUDY GUIDE — CHAPTER 12

Name ____ Date ____ Class ____

PARTS OF HUMAN BLOOD

In your textbook, read about blood cells and platelets in Section 12:2.

2. Complete the table below by writing the phrases that follow in the correct column in the table. The first one is done for you.

Red blood cells	White blood cells	Platelets
5 million in a small drop of blood	8000 in small drop of blood	250 000 in a small drop of blood
contain hemoglobin	destroy microbes	not whole cells
transport oxygen	can move between capillaries and among body cells	aid in blood clotting
if number is low, person feels tired	increase during infections	life span of 5 days
life span of 120 days	remove dead cells	results in hemophilia if not working
cell with no nucleus	made in spleen	
look like doughnuts without holes	move like amoebas	
	life span of 10 days	
	increase abnormally during leukemia	
	cell with a nucleus	

8000 in a small drop of blood
250 000 in a small drop of blood
5 million in a small drop of blood
not whole cells
destroy microbes
aid in blood clotting
can move between capillaries and among body cells
increase during infections
contain hemoglobin
remove dead cells
transport oxygen
made in spleen
if number is low, person feels tired
life span of 5 days
life span of 10 days
life span of 120 days
increase abnormally during leukemia
cell with a nucleus
cell with no nucleus
results in hemophilia if not working
look like doughnuts without holes

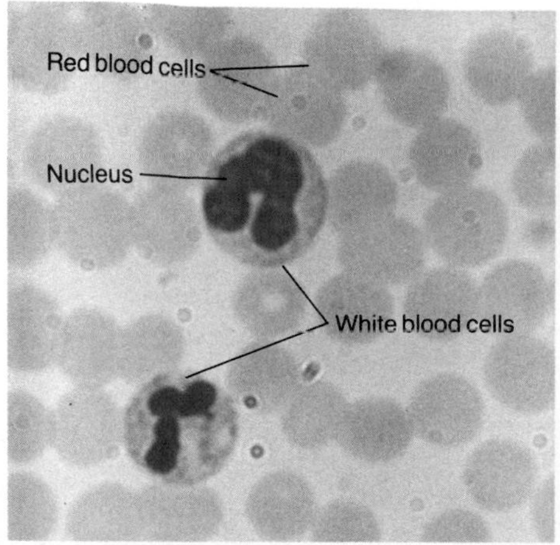

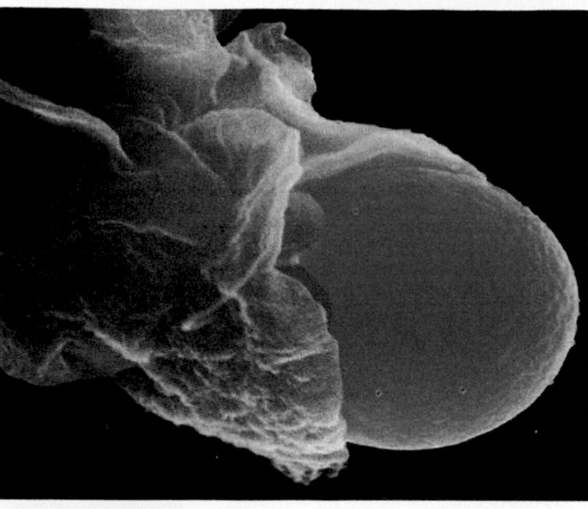

condition in which there are too few red blood cells in the blood. A person with anemia will usually feel weak, tired, and short of breath. These symptoms are caused by too little oxygen reaching body cells. Extra iron in the diet may help solve the problem. How much iron is needed each day? Look back at Table 9-2 on page 190 for the answer.

Figure 12-4 White blood cells as seen under a light microscope (left) are larger than red blood cells. In fact, when a red blood cell dies, white cells surround and destroy it, as shown under an electron microscope (right).

White Blood Cells

The second type of blood cell is the white blood cell. **White blood cells** are the cells in the blood that destroy harmful microbes, remove dead cells, and make proteins that help prevent disease.

White blood cells are part of the living portion of blood. Figure 12-4 shows white blood cells magnified under a light microscope and an electron microscope.

A white blood cell has a nucleus. The nucleus appears dark blue in both cells in Figure 12-4 (left). Also notice that white blood cells are larger than red blood cells. Certain white blood cells may live for months or years, but most have a life span of about 10 days. A healthy person has about 8000 white cells in a very small drop of blood.

Like red cells, white cells are made in bone marrow. Unlike red cells, however, white cells are also made in organs such as the spleen, thymus gland, and tonsils.

Some kinds of white blood cells can move out of capillaries and travel among the body cells. Figure 12-5 shows how white blood cells move like amoebas and at times even look like them.

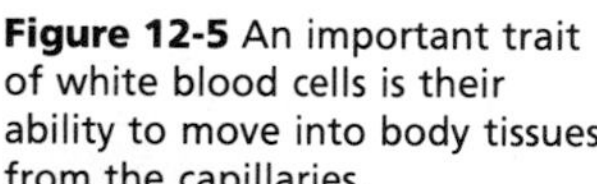

Figure 12-5 An important trait of white blood cells is their ability to move into body tissues from the capillaries.

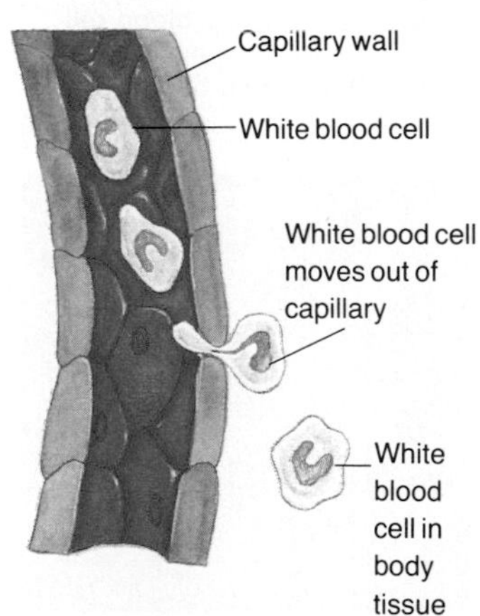

TEACH

Concept Development

▶ The daily iron requirement for females between the ages of 11 and 50 is 18 mg. The requirement for males to age 18 is the same, after which it drops to 10 mg. Ask students to speculate as to why this is so. A menstruating female will lose 1 mg of iron per day during menstruation.

▶ See if students can relate the symptoms of sickle-cell anemia, such as being tired, weak, and short of breath, with the corresponding lack of oxygen in body cells.

▶ Ask students to compare a photo of white cells to one of red cells. They will be able to pick out the major similarities and differences between these two cell types even before reading about them.

▶ The number of white blood cells is used as a diagnostic tool for determining if an infection exists. Ask your students what a doctor might be looking for when a blood test is done on a person who may have appendicitis. Appendicitis is an infection that occurs in the appendix. An elevated white cell count alerts the doctor to a possible infection.

ENRICHMENT 12

ENRICHMENT CHAPTER 12

Name ______ Date ______ Class ______

Use after Section 12:2.

RED AND WHITE BLOOD CELL NUMBERS

You can count the number of cells in a small drop of blood by using a microscope slide with a grid, called a counting chamber. By counting just a sample of blood, you can find out the number of cells in a drop of blood without counting all the cells.

1. Count all the red blood cells in the counting chambers below, marked for persons, A, B, and C. Record the totals in the chart below and calculate the total number of cells in each sample.

A B C

2. Use the same method to find out how many white blood cells are in the samples for persons D, E, and F. Record your results in the chart.

D E F

Person	Red cell count	Add 5 zeros	Total	Person	White cell count	Add 2 zeros	Total
A	73	00000	7 300 000	D	80	00	8 000
B	50	00000	5 000 000	E	173	00	17 300
C	32	00000	3 200 000	F	43	00	4 300

Answer the following questions using information from the chart and from a reference book.

3. Use your text and the results above to find out which persons have the normal number of red cells. B white cells? D

OPTIONS

Enrichment/*Teacher Resource Package*, p. 12. Use the Enrichment worksheet shown here to help students understand blood counts.

TECHNOLOGY

Eye "Fingerprints"

Background

The system works similar to scanners in a supermarket that read bar codes. The eye scanner reads blood vessel patterns present at the back of the eye along the retina.

Discussion

Congress has already passed a law that will require truck drivers and bus drivers to submit to some unique identifying processes before obtaining a license. This will prevent a person from receiving a new license if his or her original has been revoked.

Reference

"Look Me in the Eye." *Discover,* Feb. 1990, pp. 8-11.

TEACH

Concept Development

▶ Discuss the possible treatment of leukemia with radiation. White cell production is decreased in the body as a result of exposure to radiation. Thus, the disease can be slowed through X rays and other radiation treatments.

▶ One way of determining if a person has been accidentally exposed to radiation is to do a white cell count. A very low number of white cells could indicate exposure to radiation.

Misconception: Students believe that white cells eat red cells in leukemia. They do not. The rise in white cell number in leukemia is at the expense of the red and platelet cells. This is because all blood cells, regardless of whether they are to become red, white, or platelet cells,have a common origin, stem cells that differentiate into the different blood cell types.

Blood will clot when it comes in contact with a foreign surface, not when it comes in contact with the air, as is commonly believed.

TECHNOLOGY

Eye "Fingerprints"

Blood vessels can be seen clearly in the human eye. These vessels run along the back surface of the eye. That is why a doctor sometimes shines a flashlight into your eyes. The condition of these blood vessels gives the doctor clues about your general health.

The pattern of blood vessels in the eye is different for every person. It's like having a "fingerprint" of your eye.

Using a computer scanner, scientists can identify people based on blood vessel patterns in their eyes. This technology can be used to screen applicants for drivers' licenses. It prevents people who already have licenses from obtaining duplicates. The states of Wisconsin and California are already planning to use this new technology in the issuing of drivers' licenses.

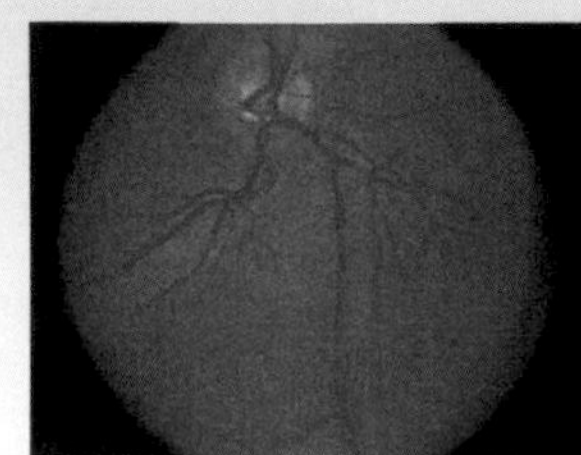

A view of the back of your eye

Roles of White Blood Cells

Have you ever had a cut that became infected? An infection is usually caused by an attack on your body cells by bacteria.

White blood cells move to an infection and destroy the bacteria causing it. There's a rapid increase in white cells at the time of an infection. The added numbers of white blood cells help to destroy more bacteria at a faster rate. After an infection is over, the number of white cells returns to normal. Another job of white blood cells is to rid the body of dead cells. Certain white cells can move about the body and "eat" dead cells just as they do bacteria, Figure 12-6.

Increased amounts of white blood cells can sometimes cause problems such as leukemia (lew KEE mee uh). **Leukemia** is a blood cancer in which the number of white blood cells increases at an abnormally fast rate.

There are three main differences between the rise in white blood cell numbers during an infection and during leukemia.

1. During leukemia, the number of white cells in each drop of blood may reach 100 000 or more. During an infection, the number rarely goes above 30 000.

Figure 12-6 A white blood cell detects a bacterium and moves toward this foreign body to destroy it.

OPTIONS

How Can Blood Diseases Be Identified?/ *Lab Manual,* pp. 96-98. Use this lab as an extension to blood diseases.

2. With leukemia, the number of white cells does not return to normal.
3. The cells formed in such large numbers are not normal cells. They can't do the job performed by normal white blood cells.

Platelets

Cuts and scrapes are common events in our lives. We usually don't worry about these injuries because we know that the flow of blood will stop quickly. A clot forms, and in a few days a scab appears. A blood clot is blood that has formed a plug to stop the bleeding. Figure 12-8 (left) shows a clot starting to form.

The forming of blood clots leads us to the last living part of blood, platelets (PLAYT lutz). **Platelets** are cell parts that aid in forming blood clots. Platelets are not complete cells. However, platelets do come from cells that break apart, so they are still a living part of blood. Notice in Figure 12-8 (right) that the platelets are much smaller than red cells.

When an injury occurs in the body, platelets break apart and release a chemical. This chemical starts the formation of a clot. Several chemicals are involved in clot formation.

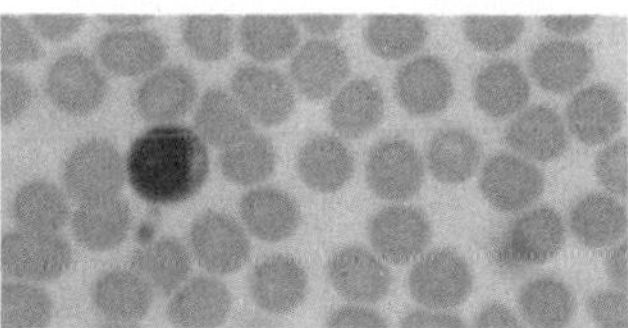

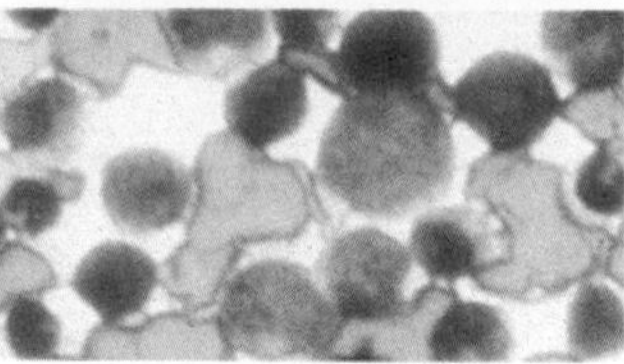

Figure 12-7 Which photo (top or bottom) is from a person with leukemia? bottom

What is the main job of platelets?

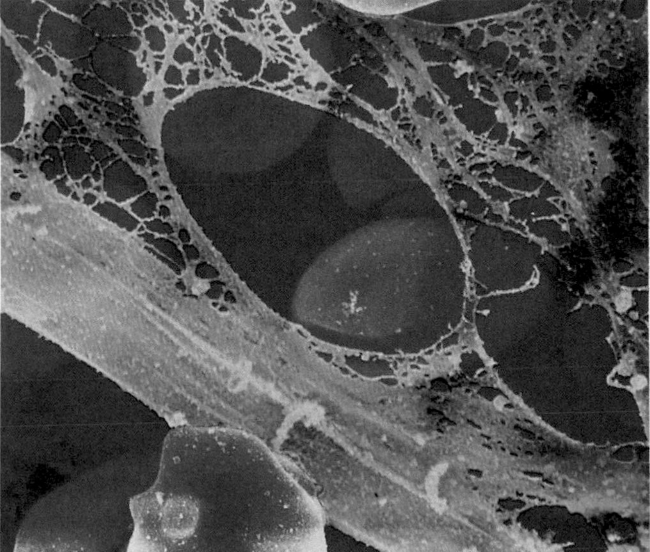

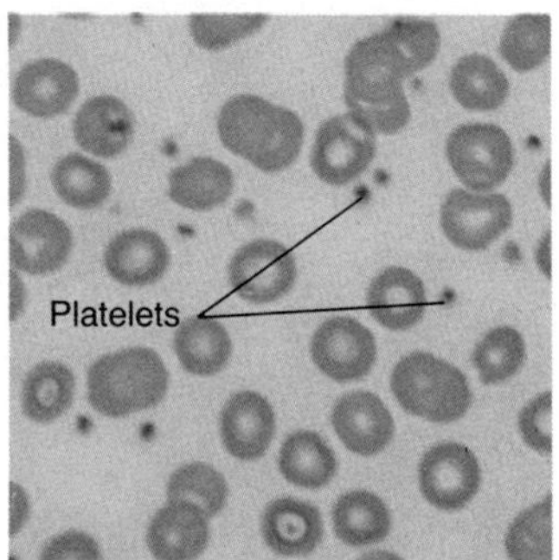

Figure 12-8 Red blood cells caught in fibers form the beginning of a blood clot, as seen under an electron microscope (left). Platelets, as seen under a light microscope (right), produce a chemical that binds the fibers together.

TEACH

Concept Development

▶ Platelets are also called thrombocytes. Students may be familiar with the related terms *thrombus* or *thrombosis.* Both refer to a clot.

Cooperative Learning: Divide the class into 4 groups. Provide them with references that will enable them to gather information on the following diseases or disorders: pernicious anemia, sickle-cell anemia, leukemia, hemophilia. Group 1 determines the cause of each problem. Group 2 determines the symptoms for each problem. Group 3 determines the diagnosis for each problem. Group 4 determines the treatment or cure for each problem. Allow each group to exchange information with the others to gain a complete picture for each disease.

Guided Practice

Have students write down their answers to the margin question: Platelets aid the blood in clotting.

CRITICAL THINKING 12

CRITICAL THINKING/PROBLEM SOLVING — CHAPTER 12

Name ______ Date ______ Class ______

Use after Section 12:2.

HOW ARE ACTIVE AND PASSIVE IMMUNITY DIFFERENT?

The students in a biology class studied immunity. Then they worked in small groups to find examples of active and passive immunity in their own lives. They also asked how the body reacts to foreign proteins.

The students learned about active and passive immunity. Active immunity occurs when a person has a disease and is later immune to it, or when vaccines that contain dead pathogens are introduced into the body. Active immunity is long lasting. Passive immunity results when antibodies are introduced into the body. This kind of immunity lasts only a short time.

Read the report of each group and answer the questions below.

The first group of students studied the inoculations given to young babies. They found diptheria, pertussis, and tetanus injections (DPT) are given to babies at 2, 4, 15, and 18 months old. Each injection contains dead bacteria. The baby develops immunity to the diseases. Most states require another booster before children start school.

The second group studied injections against measles. They found that measles is caused by a virus. The injection contains viruses that are inactive, so they cause a mild form of the disease. After children get a slight rash and fever once, they are not likely to catch that kind of measles again.

The third group studied the injection given after a person is cut by a dirty nail. The injection contains antibodies from the blood of horses and helps to prevent tetanus.

Analyzing the Problem

1. Define immunity. the ability of a person to resist the effects of a disease after the person has once contacted the disease or its cause
2. Define active immunity. long-lasting protection after a person has been infected with a disease-causing bacteria or virus
3. What is a vaccine? a preparation of disease-causing bacteria or viruses that have been treated so they are not able to infect a person with the disease
4. Define passive immunity. short-lasting protection after a person has received antibodies against a specific disease
5. What is an antigen? a protein that stimulates the body to produce antibodies

Solving the Problem

1. Is the DPT injection an example of active or passive immunity? active
2. Is the measles vaccine an example of active or passive immunity? active
3. Is the tetanus injection an example of active or passive immunity? passive

OPTIONS

Science Background

Clotting of blood is a complex series of enzyme reactions that takes place in the body. Not only are platelets needed for the process, but clotting proteins within the plasma are also essential.

Critical Thinking/Problem Solving/ *Teacher Resource Package,* p. 12. Use the Critical Thinking/Problem Solving worksheet shown here to reinforce immunity.

TEACH

Independent Practice

Study Guide/*Teacher Resource Package*, p. 72. Use the Study Guide worksheet shown at the bottom of this page for independent practice.

Check for Understanding

Have students respond to the first three questions in Check Your Understanding.

Reteach

Reteaching/*Teacher Resource Package*, p. 33. Use this worksheet to give students additional practice with parts of the blood.

Extension: Assign Critical Thinking, Biology and Reading, or some of the **OPTIONS** available with this lesson.

3 APPLY

Brainstorming

You have just cut yourself. What kinds of cells are trapped in the clot?

4 CLOSE

Audiovisual

Show the videocassette *Internal Defenses*, Films for the Humanities and Sciences.

Answers to Check Your Understanding

6. red blood cells, white blood cells, and platelets
7. destroy harmful microbes, remove dead cells, and make proteins that help prevent disease
8. During leukemia, the number of white blood cells in a drop of blood may reach 100 000 or more, the number of white blood cells does not return to normal, and the cells formed are abnormal.
9. Iron is one of the nutrients used to make red blood cells.
10. five months or years; about 10 days

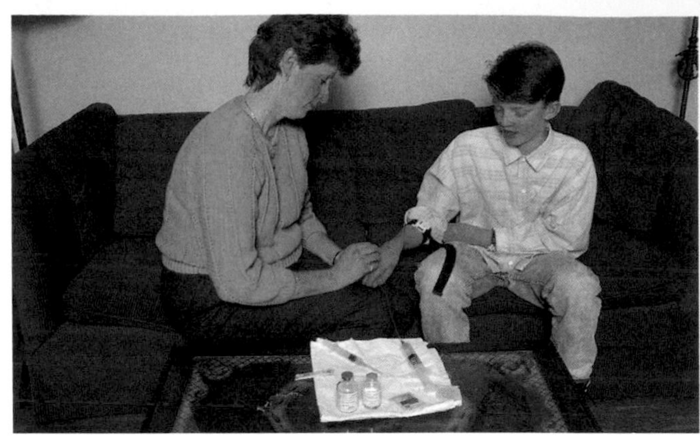

Figure 12-9 A person with hemophilia needs a transfusion of blood clotting factor, even after a minor accident.

Skill Check

Understand science words: hemophilia. The word part *hemo* means blood. In your dictionary, find three words that contain the word part *hemo. For more help, refer to the* ***Skill Handbook****, pages 706-711.*

A small drop of blood contains about 250 000 platelets. The life span of platelets is very short, only about five days. Like red cells and some white cells, platelets are made in the bone marrow.

Two problems can happen with platelets. First if the number of platelets is too low, it's hard for blood clots to form. Second, if platelets lack the clotting chemical, this causes hemophilia (hee muh FIHL ee uh). **Hemophilia** is a disease in which a person's blood won't clot. A minor cut or bruise can be very dangerous to a person with hemophilia because of the large amount of blood that might be lost. Hemophilia is a genetic disease. This means that a person inherits the disease from his or her parents.

Check Your Understanding

6. What substances make up the living part of blood?
7. What are three jobs of white blood cells?
8. What are three ways the rise in white blood cell numbers during leukemia differs from the rise in white blood cell numbers during infection?
9. **Critical Thinking:** You have learned that increasing the amount of iron in one's diet is a way of treating anemia. What does this indicate about the relationship between iron and red blood cells?
10. **Biology and Reading:** What is the maximum life span of a white blood cell? What is the average life span of most white blood cells?

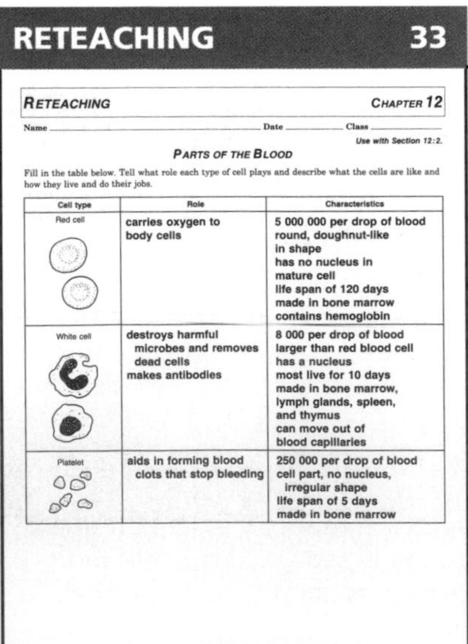

RETEACHING 33

RETEACHING — CHAPTER 12

Name ______ Date ______ Class ______

Use with Section 12:2.

PARTS OF THE BLOOD

Fill in the table below. Tell what role each type of cell plays and describe what the cells are like and how they live and do their jobs.

Cell type	Role	Characteristics
Red cell	carries oxygen to body cells	5 000 000 per drop of blood; round, doughnut-like in shape; has no nucleus in mature cell; life span of 120 days; made in bone marrow; contains hemoglobin
White cell	destroys harmful microbes and removes dead cells; makes antibodies	8 000 per drop of blood; larger than red blood cell; has a nucleus; most live for 10 days; made in bone marrow, lymph glands, spleen, and thymus; can move out of blood capillaries
Platelet	aids in forming blood clots that stop bleeding	250 000 per drop of blood; cell part, no nucleus, irregular shape; life span of 5 days; made in bone marrow

STUDY GUIDE 72

STUDY GUIDE — CHAPTER 12

VOCABULARY

Review the new words used in Chapter 12 of your textbook. Then, use the terms below to fill in the blanks in the sentences that follow.

immunity, antigens, hemophilia, AIDS, bone marrow, immune system, red blood cells, white blood cells, plasma, anemia, leukemia, hemoglobin, platelets, antibodies

1. **Plasma** is the yellow, nonliving part of blood.
2. **Red blood cells** are the cells in the blood that carry oxygen to the tissues.
3. **Hemoglobin** is a protein in red blood cells that joins with oxygen.
4. When a person has **anemia** there are too few red blood cells or too little hemoglobin or both.
5. The cells in the blood that remove microbes and dead cells are **white blood cells**.
6. When a person has **leukemia**, the number of white blood cells increases abnormally.
7. **Platelets** are bloodlike parts important in blood clotting.
8. The blood of a person with **hemophilia** will not clot.
9. The **immune system** helps keep a person free of disease.
10. **Antibodies** are chemicals that destroy bacteria or viruses.
11. **Antigens** are foreign substances that invade the body and cause disease.
12. **Immunity** is the ability of a person who once had a disease to be protected from getting it again.
13. **AIDS** is a disease of the immune system.
14. Red blood cells are made in **bone marrow**, the soft center part of the bone.

Lab 12–2 Human Blood Cells

Problem: How can human blood cells be counted, identified, and compared?

Skills

use a microscope, compare, classify

Materials

sheet of clear plastic
microscope
marking pencil
prepared slide of human blood

Procedure

1. Copy the data table.
2. Figures A and B show what blood cells would look like under the microscope. Each figure represents blood from a healthy person. Place a piece of clear plastic over Figure A.
3. Count and record the number of red blood cells. Use the marking pencil to check the cells counted so that you do not count them twice.
4. Count and record the number of white blood cells.
5. Count and record the number of platelets.
6. Repeat steps 2 through 5 for Figure B.
7. **Use a microscope:** Look at a prepared slide of human blood under low power on the microscope. Change to high power.
8. Draw and label a red blood cell, white blood cell, and platelet.

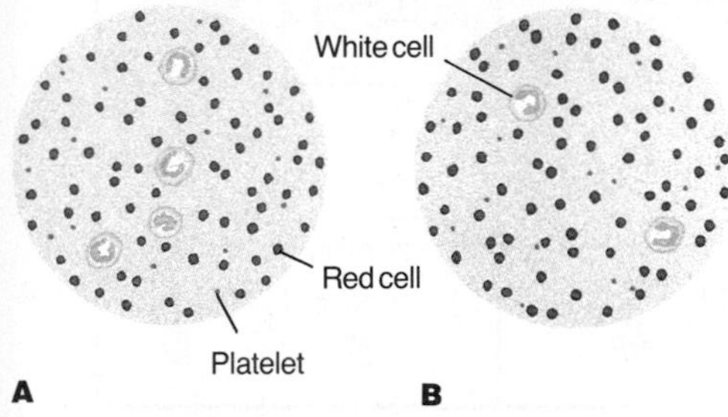

Answers will vary.

NUMBER OF CELLS	FIGURE A	FIGURE B	PREPARED SLIDE
Red cells	75	77	108
White cells	4	2	3
Platelets	14	16	22

9. Record the numbers of red blood cells, white blood cells, and platelets in an area similar to that in the figures.

Data and Observations

1. According to your results with Figures A and B:
   (a) which blood cell type is most common?
   (b) which type is second-most common?
   (c) which type is least common?
2. According to your results with the prepared slide:
   (a) which blood cell type is most common?
   (b) which type is second-most common?
   (c) which type is least common?

Analyze and Apply

1. **Classify:** List three ways that:
   (a) red cells differ from white cells.
   (b) red cells differ from platelets.
2. Which count of cells, from figures or from a prepared slide, is more accurate?
3. **Apply:** How is a cell count important when diagnosing an illness?

Extension

Compare: Examine a prepared slide of frog blood under high power. Count the numbers of red blood cells and white blood cells. Compare frog and human blood.

Lab 12-2 Human Blood Cells

Overview

Students will identify and determine anatomical differences among the three blood cell types. They will also compare the relative numbers of each.

Objectives: Upon completing this lab, students should be able to (1) **distinguish** red, white, and platelet cells, (2) **compare** the numbers of each blood cell type present in normal human blood, and (3) **describe** the changes in blood cell types that take place during anemia and leukemia.

Time Allotment: 30 minutes

Preparation

Lab 12-2 worksheet/*Teacher Resource Package,* p. 47-48.

Lab 12-2 Computer Program/*Teacher Resource Package,* p. xii. Use the computer program shown at the bottom of this page as you teach this lab.

Teaching the Lab

▶ **Troubleshooting:** It may be necessary for students to move the slide slowly along the stage while viewing under high power so that several fields of view are noted. Not all fields will contain white blood cells.

COMPUTER PROGRAM XII

COMPUTER PROGRAM LAB 12-2 HUMAN BLOOD CELLS

```
]POKE 33,33

]LIST

 10  GOSUB 390
 20  HOME
 30  PRINT "-------------------------------------";
 40  PRINT "!  NUMBER    !   FIGURE   !   FIGURE   !";
 50  PRINT "! OF CELLS   !     A      !     B      !";
 70  PRINT "-------------------------------------";
 80  PRINT "!RED CELLS   !            !            !";
 90  PRINT "-------------------------------------";
 100  PRINT "!WHITE CELLS !            !            !";
 120  PRINT "-------------------------------------";
 130  PRINT "!PLATELETS   !            !            !";
 140  PRINT "-------------------------------------";
 150  FOR X = 1 TO 6
 160  VTAB V(X): HTAB H(X): FLASH : PRINT " ";: NORMAL
 170  VTAB 15: HTAB 1: CALL  - 958
 180  PRINT "ENTER YOUR VALUE FOR THIS SPACE";
 190  INPUT ": ";A
 200  VTAB V(X): HTAB H(X): PRINT A
 210  NEXT
 220  VTAB 15: HTAB 1: CALL  - 958
 230  PRINT "ARE THESE NUMBERS                  ENTERED CORRECTLY? (
    Y/N): ";: GET A$
 240  IF A$ = "N" OR A$ = "n" THEN  GOTO 20
 250  IF A$ <  > "Y" AND A$ <  > "y" THEN 220
 260  VTAB 15: HTAB 1: CALL  - 958: PRINT
 270  FLASH : PRINT "PRESS THE SPACE BAR TO SEE CORRECT DATA": GET A$
 278  NORMAL
 280  VTAB 16: HTAB 1: CALL  - 868
 290  FOR X = 1 TO 6
 300  VTAB V(X): HTAB H(X) + 6
 310  READ C: PRINT "(";C;")"
 320  NEXT
 330  INVERSE : PRINT
 340  PRINT : PRINT "DO YOU WANT THIS PRINTED (Y/N)? :";: GET A$
 345  NORMAL
 348  VTAB 14: HTAB 1: CALL  - 958
 350  IF A$ = "N" OR A$ = "n" THEN  END
 360  IF A$ <  > "Y" AND A$ <  > "y" THEN  GOTO 340
 370  GOSUB 2000
 380  END
 390  TEXT : HOME : PRINT "LAB 12-2                HUMAN BLOOD CELLS"
 400  PRINT : PRINT
 410  PRINT "YOU WILL BE ASKED TO TYPE IN YOUR        RESULTS FOR THE 2 HU
    MAN BLOOD SAMPLES  ONTO A DATA TABLE THAT IS EXACTLY LIKE  THE ONE
    USED IN THE EXPERIMENT."
 430  PRINT
 440  PRINT "AFTER TYPING EACH NUMBER, PRESS THE      RETURN KEY. AFTER TY
    PING YOUR DATA, YOU WILL BE ASKED IF THE NUMBERS ARE ENTEREDCORRECTL
    Y.IF CORRECT TYPE THE LETTER Y.IF WRONG, TYPE THE LETTER N."
 450  INVERSE
```

ANSWERS

Data and Observations

1. (a) red cells
   (b) platelets
   (c) white cells
2. (a) red cells
   (b) platelets
   (c) white cells

Analyze and Apply

1. (a) red cells are red, have no nucleus, and are more numerous than white cells; (b) red cells are red and are more numerous than platelets
2. from figures, because the number doesn't vary
3. Too few or too many red or white cells indicates particular illnesses such as anemia and leukemia.

12:3 Blood Types

PREPARATION

Material Needed

Make copies of the Reteaching and Study Guide worksheets in the *Teacher Resource Package.*

Key Science Words

No new science words will be introduced in this section.

1 FOCUS

▶ The objectives are listed on the student page. Remind students to preview these objectives as a guide to this numbered section.

MOTIVATION/Brainstorming

Ask students if they know their blood type. Frequently, parents will know this information.

Guided Practice

Have students write down their answers to the margin questions: Proteins in the plasma of type A blood fit like a puzzle piece with the proteins of red cells in type B blood; mixing the red cell and plasma proteins could cause clumping.

12:3 Blood Types

Objectives

6. **Compare** the red cell and plasma proteins in the four main blood types.
7. **Explain** why blood types can't be mixed.

There are different kinds or types of blood. If you were to donate blood, your blood usually would be given to someone with the same type. If the wrong blood type were given, the person receiving the blood could have serious problems or even die.

Blood Types Differ

How is the plasma protein of type A blood like the red cell protein of type B blood?

There are four main blood types: A, B, AB, and O. What makes each blood type different from the others? The difference is due to proteins found on red blood cells and in blood plasma. Look at Figure 12-10 and notice the different model shapes used to show red cell proteins and plasma proteins. If the protein is on a red blood cell, we shall call it a red cell protein. If it is in the plasma, we shall call it a plasma protein.

Note that the red cell protein shapes on types A and B blood cells are different. Also note that the red cell protein shapes on type AB are the same as both types A and B. Type O red blood cells have no red cell proteins.

Now notice the shapes of the plasma proteins. Type A plasma proteins are different from those in type B. Type AB has no plasma proteins, and type O has plasma proteins like types A and B.

Blood type	Red cell protein present	Plasma protein present	Plasma protein and cell protein
A	Red cell Protein		No fit
B			No fit
AB		None	No fit
O	None		No fit

Figure 12-10 Blood types differ in their proteins. Each blood type has red cell and plasma proteins that don't fit each other.

OPTIONS

Blood Types/*Transparency Package,* number 12a. Use color transparency number 12a as you teach blood types.

What Blood Types Can Be Mixed?/*Lab Manual,* pp. 99-102. Use this lab as an extension to blood types.

Mixing Blood Types

Why is it safe to mix certain blood types and not others? The answer lies in the shapes of the red cell proteins and plasma proteins. Figure 12-10 is a model that shows how the shape of the red cell protein in type A blood can't fit into the shape of its own plasma protein. The red cell and plasma proteins have different shapes. The same is true for B, AB, and O types as well.

What happens when different blood types are mixed? Our models can help explain the result. Let's see what happens when a person with type A blood receives type B blood. Proteins in the plasma of type A blood fit like puzzle pieces into the red cell protein shape of type B blood. Proteins in the plasma of type B blood also fit like puzzle pieces into the red cell protein shape of type A blood. Note this happening in Figure 12-11.

Many type A and B blood cells now join together like all the completed pieces in a puzzle and large clumps of blood cells form. These clumps are too large to pass through capillaries. They plug these blood vessels and prevent the normal flow of blood. If these clumps block vessels in the heart, brain, or lungs, death can occur.

Why wouldn't it be safe for a person with type A blood to receive type AB blood? Why wouldn't it be safe for a person with type O blood to receive blood types A or B? Now you know why most people receive blood that is the same type as their own.

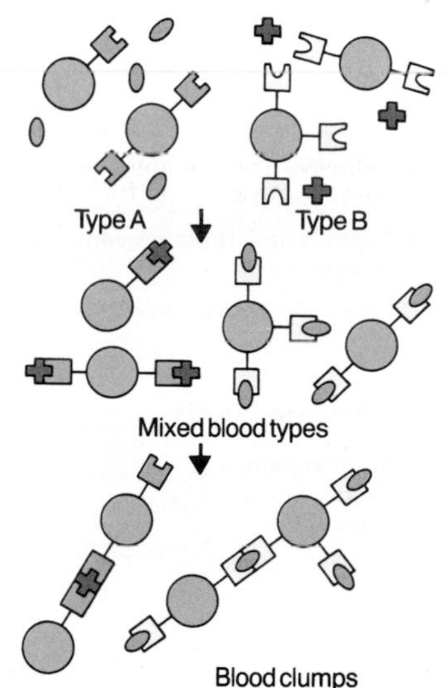

Figure 12-11 Blood clots form when blood types A and B are mixed.

Why can't blood types be mixed?

Check Your Understanding

11. What are the four main blood types?
12. Describe the model shapes of the red cell proteins and plasma proteins found in type O blood.
13. What happens to blood proteins and plasma when blood types A and B are mixed?
14. **Critical Thinking:** Sometimes AB plasma is transfused from one person to another. What trait of this plasma makes it safer to use in a transfusion than whole blood?
15. **Biology and Reading:** Look at Figure 12-10. Notice the shapes of plasma proteins for type O blood. Now, look at the shapes of the red cell proteins for type AB blood. What would happen if you mixed type O blood with type AB blood?

2 TEACH

Independent Practice

Study Guide/*Teacher Resource Package,* p. 69. Use the Study Guide worksheet shown at the bottom of this page for independent practice.

Check for Understanding

Have students respond to the first three questions in Check Your Understanding.

Reteach

Reteaching/*Teacher Resource Package,* p. 34. Use this worksheet to give students additional practice with blood types.

Extension: Assign Critical Thinking, Biology and Reading, or some of the **OPTIONS** available with this lesson.

3 APPLY

Connection: Math

Eighty-five percent of the population in the United States is Rh+ and 15% is Rh-. Ask students to calculate how many people out of 100 are O+ and O- if 50% of the population has blood type O. (Note: O- = .50 × .15 = .0765 or 7 people.)

4 CLOSE

Explain why you must wait at least a month before donating blood again.

Answers to Check Your Understanding

11. A, B, AB, and O
12. Type O red blood cells have no red cell proteins while type O plasma has plasma proteins like those found in types A and B blood.
13. The blood cells join with the plasma proteins and form clumps.
14. Type AB plasma does not contain red blood cell proteins.
15. The blood would clump.

STUDY GUIDE 69

Study Guide — Chapter 12

Name ______ Date ______ Class ______

Blood Types

In your textbook, read about different types of blood in Section 12:3.

Examine the following chart carefully. Then, look at the four tubes of blood shown below. Fill in the spaces with the correct information from the chart and the following labels: red cells, plasma protein shape, red cell protein shape, plasma, red cell. Part of the first one is done for you.

Blood type	Red blood cell protein	Plasma protein	Cell protein plasma protein fit
O	none		no fit
A			no fit
B			no fit
AB		none	no fit

① Plasma protein shape; Plasma; Red cells; Red cell protein shape; Red cell — Type A blood

② Plasma protein shape; Plasma; Red cells; Red cell protein shape; Red cell — Type B blood

③ Plasma protein shape: None; Plasma; Red cells; Red cell protein shape; Red cell — Type AB blood

④ Plasma protein shape; Plasma; Red cells; Red cell protein shape: None; Red cell — Type O blood

RETEACHING 34

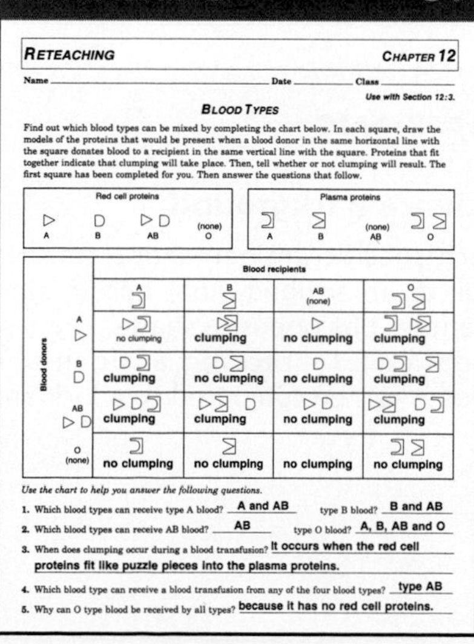

Reteaching — Chapter 12

Name ______ Date ______ Class ______

Use with Section 12:3.

Blood Types

Find out which blood types can be mixed by completing the chart below. In each square, draw the models of the proteins that would be present when a blood donor in the same horizontal line with the square donates blood to a recipient in the same vertical line with the square. Proteins that fit together indicate that clumping will take place. Then, tell whether or not clumping will result. The first square has been completed for you. Then answer the questions that follow.

Red cell proteins: A, B, AB, O (none)

Plasma proteins: A, B, AB (none), O

Blood donors	Blood recipients: A	B	AB (none)	O
A	no clumping	clumping	no clumping	clumping
B	clumping	no clumping	no clumping	clumping
AB	clumping	clumping	no clumping	clumping
O (none)	no clumping	no clumping	no clumping	no clumping

Use the chart to help you answer the following questions.

1. Which blood types can receive type A blood? A and AB type B blood? B and AB
2. Which blood types can receive AB blood? AB type O blood? A, B, AB and O
3. When does clumping occur during a blood transfusion? It occurs when the red cell proteins fit like puzzle pieces into the plasma proteins.
4. Which blood type can receive a blood transfusion from any of the four blood types? type AB
5. Why can O type blood be received by all types? because it has no red cell proteins.

12:4 Immunity

PREPARATION

Materials Needed

Make copies of the Focus, Application, Study Guide, Skill, and Reteaching worksheets in the *Teacher Resource Package.*

Key Science Words

immune system
antibody
antigen
immunity
Acquired Immune Deficiency Syndrome

Process Skills

In the Skill Check, students will infer.

1 FOCUS

▶ The objectives are listed on the student page. Remind students to preview these objectives as a guide to this numbered section.

MOTIVATION/Brainstorming

Ask students why they put a bandage over a cut or scrape? cover their mouth when coughing? receive shots for certain diseases?

Focus/*Teacher Resource Package,* p. 23. Use the Focus transparency shown at the bottom of this page as an introduction to AIDS.

Objectives

8. **Describe** how the immune system works.
9. **Explain** how shots prevent disease.
10. **Discuss** the AIDS virus.

Key Science Words

immune system
antibody
antigen
immunity
AIDS

12:4 Immunity

Another job of your blood helps you stay healthy. Certain blood cells play an important role in helping your body get rid of disease-causing viruses and bacteria.

Your Immune System

Your immune system cures you of the flu, measles, mumps, or even boils. The **immune system** is made of proteins, cells, and tissues that identify and defend the body against foreign chemicals and organisms. It helps to keep you free of disease. Actually, the word *immune* means "to free."

Teardrops, mucus, and skin are part of your immune system. They prevent disease-causing organisms from entering your body. Other parts of the immune system are shown in Figure 12-12. Locate the parts of the immune system and examine their roles.

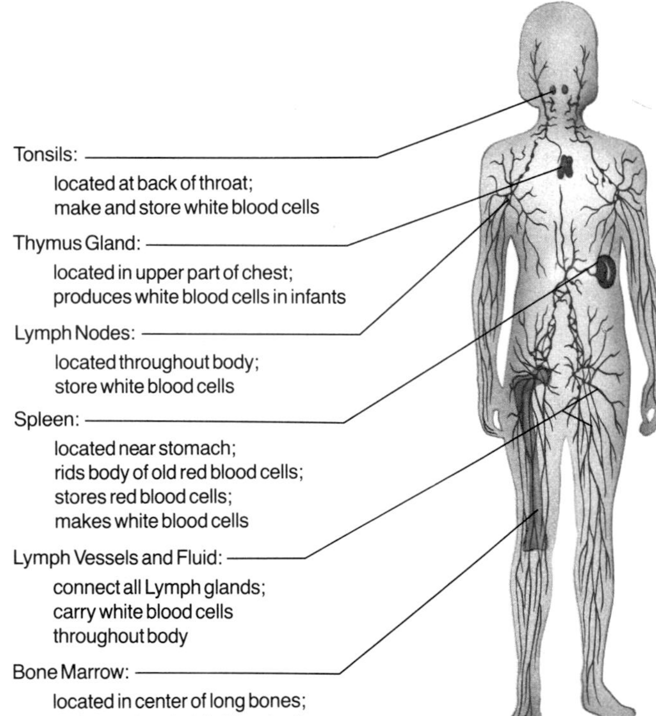
Tonsils:
located at back of throat; make and store white blood cells
Thymus Gland:
located in upper part of chest; produces white blood cells in infants
Lymph Nodes:
located throughout body; store white blood cells
Spleen:
located near stomach; rids body of old red blood cells; stores red blood cells; makes white blood cells
Lymph Vessels and Fluid:
connect all Lymph glands; carry white blood cells throughout body
Bone Marrow:
located in center of long bones; makes red and white blood cells

Figure 12-12 In which organs of the immune system are white cells made? tonsils, thymus gland, spleen, and bones

OPTIONS

Science Background

Each specific antigen shape causes the formation of an antibody that has an almost complementary but opposite shape. The resulting combination of matching antigen and antibody shapes can be compared to a lock and key fit.

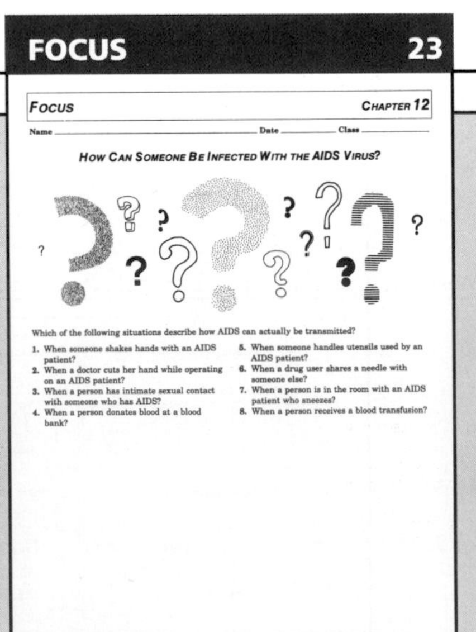
FOCUS 23

FOCUS CHAPTER 12

Name ______ Date ______ Class ______

HOW CAN SOMEONE BE INFECTED WITH THE AIDS VIRUS?

Which of the following situations describe how AIDS can actually be transmitted?

1. When someone shakes hands with an AIDS patient?
2. When a doctor cuts her hand while operating on an AIDS patient?
3. When a person has intimate sexual contact with someone who has AIDS?
4. When a person donates blood at a blood bank?
5. When someone handles utensils used by an AIDS patient?
6. When a drug user shares a needle with someone else?
7. When a person is in the room with an AIDS patient who sneezes?
8. When a person receives a blood transfusion?

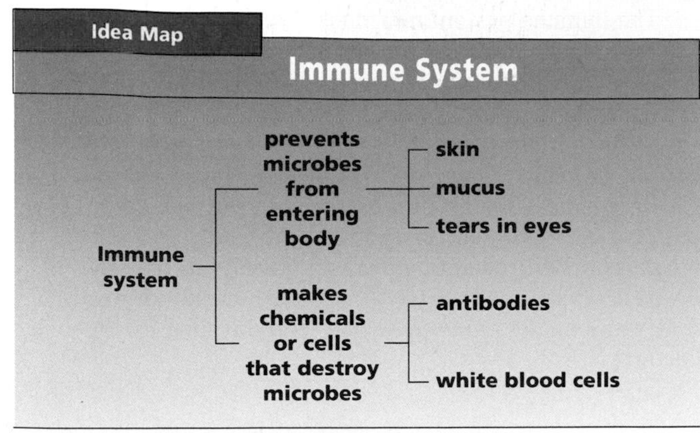

Study Tip: Use this idea map as a study guide for identifying the functions of the immune system.

How the Immune System Works

There are many kinds of white blood cells. Each kind has its own job in the protection of the body. Some white blood cells have the job of making special chemicals called antibodies (ANT ih bohd eez). **Antibodies** are chemicals that help destroy bacteria or viruses. Bacteria, viruses, and other foreign substances are examples of antigens (ANT ih junz) that enter our bodies. **Antigens** are foreign substances, usually proteins, that invade the body and cause diseases.

Models can show how antibodies made by white cells get rid of antigens such as bacteria. Figure 12-13 shows a white blood cell with a model of an antibody on its cell membrane. The antibody looks like the letter *M*. Certain antibodies stay attached to the cell membrane. Other antibodies are released into the blood plasma. These released antibodies match a bacterium that has an exactly opposite "shape" on its surface as shown in Figure 12-13. Note that the antibody and antigen shapes fit together like a lock and key.

When the antigen and antibody on the surface of a white cell fit together correctly, the bacterium may be easily destroyed. First, the cell membrane of the bacterium may break open. When the cell membrane is broken, the bacterium will die. Second, with antibodies stuck to it, the bacterium can now be destroyed by other white blood cells. Each different type of virus or bacterium that enters the body has a different antigen shape on its surface. The white blood cells must have a similar number of different antibody shapes.

Bio Tip

Health: Have you had your shots? Check Table 12-2 on page 258 to see which shots you might need.

What are antigens?

Figure 12-13 An antigen is destroyed when a white cell produces a matching antibody.

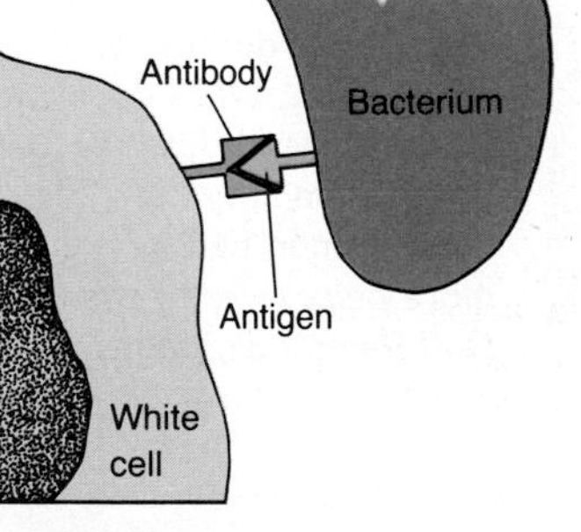

2 TEACH

Concept Development

▶ Discuss the fact that the body may receive its immunity in several ways. Most common to students is naturally acquired immunity. The catching of a disease can lead to the formation of antibodies against a future exposure to the disease. Once infected, a person cannot be reinfected.

▶ The second way of obtaining immunity is through vaccines. This is artificially acquired immunity. A person is given a mild form of a disease to allow the immune system to make antibodies against the disease.

Idea Map

Have students use the idea map as a study guide to the major concepts of this section.

Guided Practice

Have students write down their answers to the margin question: Antigens are foreign substances that invade the body and cause diseases.

Independent Practice

Study Guide/*Teacher Resource Package*, p. 70. Use the Study Guide worksheet shown at the bottom of this page for independent practice.

APPLICATION 12

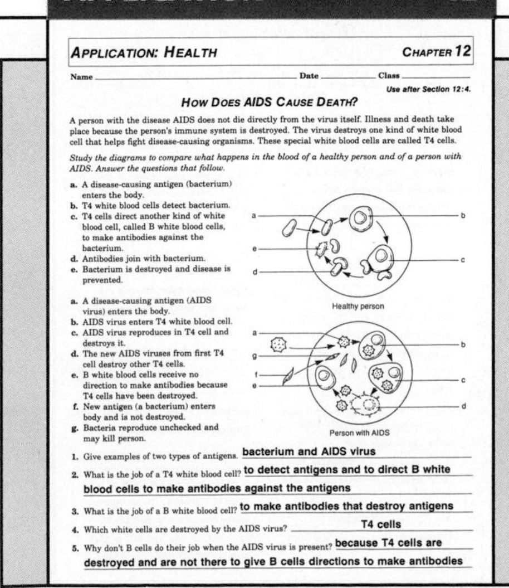

APPLICATION: HEALTH — *CHAPTER 12*

Name ______ Date ______ Class ______

Use after Section 12:4.

HOW DOES AIDS CAUSE DEATH?

A person with the disease AIDS does not die directly from the virus itself. Illness and death take place because the person's immune system is destroyed. The virus destroys one kind of white blood cell that helps fight disease-causing organisms. These special white blood cells are called T4 cells.

Study the diagrams to compare what happens in the blood of a healthy person and of a person with AIDS. Answer the questions that follow.

a. A disease-causing antigen (bacterium) enters the body.
b. T4 white blood cells detect bacterium.
c. T4 cells direct another kind of white blood cell, called B white blood cells, to make antibodies against the bacterium.
d. Antibodies join with bacterium.
e. Bacterium is destroyed and disease is prevented.

a. A disease-causing antigen (AIDS virus) enters the body.
b. AIDS virus enters T4 white blood cell.
c. AIDS virus reproduces in T4 cell and destroys it.
d. The new AIDS viruses from first T4 cell destroy other T4 cells.
e. B white blood cells receive no direction to make antibodies because T4 cells have been destroyed.
f. New antigen (a bacterium) enters body and is not destroyed.
g. Bacteria reproduce unchecked and may kill person.

1. Give examples of two types of antigens. **bacterium and AIDS virus**
2. What is the job of a T4 white blood cell? **to detect antigens and to direct B white blood cells to make antibodies against the antigens**
3. What is the job of a B white blood cell? **to make antibodies that destroy antigens**
4. Which white cells are destroyed by the AIDS virus? **T4 cells**
5. Why don't B cells do their job when the AIDS virus is present? **because T4 cells are destroyed and are not there to give B cells directions to make antibodies**

STUDY GUIDE 70

STUDY GUIDE — *CHAPTER 12*

Name ______ Date ______ Class ______

IMMUNITY

In your textbook, read about immunity in Section 12:4.

1. Define immune system. **proteins, cells, and tissues that identify and defend the body against foreign chemicals and organisms**
2. a. Define antigen. **a foreign substance that causes disease and also antibodies to form**
   b. Are antigens helpful? Explain. **No, they invade the body and cause diseases.**
3. a. Define antibody. **a chemical that helps destroy bacteria or viruses**
   b. Are antibodies helpful? Explain. **Yes, they keep us healthy by getting rid of antigens that enter our bodies.**
4. Figures A, B, C, and D are labeled for you. You are to:
   a. draw the antigen onto the correct cell that normally has antigens on it.
   b. draw the antibody onto the correct cell that normally has antibodies on it.

White cell
A
Bacterium
B
C Antigen
D Antibody

5. How is the meeting of the white blood cell and the bacterium shown in question 4 like the meeting of a lock and a key? **The shape of the white blood cell's antibody will fit together with the shape of the bacterium's antigen.**
6. List two ways that this meeting can result in the death of the bacterium. **By combining with the white blood cell, the membrane of the bacterium may break open. With antibodies stuck to it, the bacterium can then be destroyed by other white blood cells.**

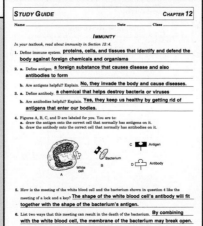

OPTIONS

The Immune System/*Transparency Package*, number 12b. Use color transparency number 12b as you teach the immune system.

Application/*Teacher Resource Package*, p. 12. Use the Application worksheet shown here to reinforce the study of AIDS.

TEACH

Concept Development

▶ The hepatitis virus infects only liver cells and the cold virus infects only nasal cells. The AIDS virus infects only certain white blood cells.

Guided Practice

Have students write down their answers to the margin questions on these two pages: The antigens in the vaccine trigger the immune system to make antibodies to the DPT vaccine. Later, if the person is exposed to the disease, the body is ready with antibodies to destroy the virus; AIDS destroys white cells that fight infections.

Skill Check

The body has a memory for the measles immunity; however, since there are many flu viruses, a person can be invaded by a flu virus of which the body has no memory.

TABLE 12–1. CAUSES OF SOME DISEASES	
Disease	**Cause**
Diphtheria	Bacteria
Tetanus (Lock Jaw)	Bacteria
Pertussis (Whooping cough)	Bacteria
Polio (Infantile paralysis)	Virus
Measles	Virus
Rubella (German measles)	Virus
Mumps	Virus

What occurs in a person's body after receiving a DPT shot?

The immune system now does a remarkable thing. It begins to make many new white blood cells, each with the shape of the antibody just used to get rid of the antigen. It's as if the immune system has a memory. White blood cells will reproduce antibodies in the bloodstream for many months or years. Their job is to prevent future disease caused by the same type of bacteria. If the same type of bacteria gets into your body five years later, the white blood cells with the antibodies will quickly destroy the bacteria. This time, the bacteria are so quickly destroyed that you may not even know you were invaded by the bacteria.

How Shots Keep You Healthy

When you receive shots to prevent a disease, your immune system's memory often is being refreshed. DPT shots against diphtheria (dif THIHR ee uh), pertussis (pur TUH suhs), and tetanus (TET nus) are good examples. The DPT shot is made up of proteins from these three bacterial diseases.

When you receive a DPT shot, it's as if you are getting antigens of these three diseases. Your immune system begins to make antibodies against these antigens. Or, if you have already come into contact with the disease, your body may already have a memory of the antigens. Later on, if the actual bacteria causing these diseases were to enter your body, your immune system would be ready and waiting. You will have gained immunity. Table 12-1 lists other diseases for which you may have received shots. **Immunity** is the ability of a person who once had a disease to be protected from getting the same disease again. Table 12-2 shows the schedule for receiving shots.

Skill Check

Infer: It's common for a person to get the measles only once during his or her lifetime. Yet, a person can get the flu many times during his or her lifetime. What does this indicate about the body's "memory" of these immunities? *For more help, refer to the* ***Skill Handbook****, pages 706-711.*

TABLE 12–2. IMMUNIZATION SCHEDULE FOR PERSONS AGE 7 AND OLDER*		
Spacing	**Vaccines**	**Explanation**
1st visit	Td (adult) TOPV M/M/R	Td—tetanus and diphtheria adult vaccine TOPV—trivalent oral polio vaccine M/M/R—one dose of measles/mumps/rubella combined vaccine
2 months after first	Td (Adult) TOPV	
6—12 months after 2nd	Td (Adult) TOPV	

*who did not begin their immunization series before age 15 months

OPTIONS

Skill/*Teacher Resource Package*, p. 13. Use the Skill worksheet shown here to have students outline the section on the immune system.

Transparency Master/*Teacher Resource Package*, p. 53. Use the Transparency Master worksheet shown here to help students with the role of white blood cells.

TRANSPARENCY 53

TRANSPARENCY MASTER — *CHAPTER 12*

AIDS and the Immune System

Three different kinds of white blood cells are in the blood. One of these, called a lymphocyte, is affected by the AIDS virus.

lymphocyte

There are two main varieties of lymphocytes.

B cells — form antibodies that destroy antigens.

T cells — There are three main kinds of T cells.

Killer T8 cells give off chemicals that destroy antigens and call in more white cells that "eat" antigens.

Helper T4 cells help B cells to form antibodies and increase number of killer T8 cells.

Memory T cells recognize future attacks by similar antigens or other cells and quickly help to form more B and T cells

AIDS virus enters Helper T4 cells

AIDS virus

Helper T4 cell

Effect of AIDS virus on Helper T4 cells

AIDS virus reproduces inside T4 cell.

T4 cell is destroyed as AIDS virus leaves it.

AIDS viruses enter new Helper T4 cells and destroy them. Finally, no Helper T4 cells are left in the body. Then, other diseases can invade the body and cause death.

SKILL 13

SKILL: OUTLINE — *CHAPTER 12*

Name ______ Date ______ Class ______

For more help, refer to the Skill Handbook, pages 706-711. *Use after Section 12:4.*

The Immune System

Complete the outline below by filling in the blanks under the main ideas.

A. What the immune system is
1. Define the immune system. **the proteins, cells, and tissues of the body that identify and defend the body against foreign chemicals and organisms**
2. Name the body parts of the immune system and tell the function of each part. **Tears, skin, and mucus keep organisms out of the body; tonsils, thymus gland, lymph nodes, and spleen store white blood cells; and bone marrow makes white blood cells.**
3. What do white blood cells do in the immune system? **Some white blood cells make antibodies.**
4. What is an antibody? **a chemical that helps destroy bacteria or viruses**

B. How the immune system works
1. What are antigens? **foreign substances that invade the body**
2. What do antigens do? **cause antibodies to form**
3. What happens when an antigen meets an antibody that matches it? **They join like a lock and key.**
4. Name two ways that an antigen such as a bacterium can be destroyed when it has joined an antibody. **The cell membrane of a bacterium may break open. White blood cells destroy the bacterium when antibodies are stuck to it.**

C. How immunity is obtained
1. Explain how the body has lasting immunity after a specific antigen has been destroyed. **White blood cells that produce antibodies against the antigen are formed for years to come.**
2. How does a shot help give lasting immunity? **A shot contains antigens of a specific disease. The antigens cause the immune system to form antibodies that will protect against the disease organisms.**

AIDS and the Immune System

Acquired Immune Deficiency Syndrome, or **AIDS,** is a disease of the immune system. AIDS is caused by a virus that reproduces only inside one kind of white blood cell.

What happens when this type of white blood cell is totally destroyed? Other diseases can then easily invade the body. Diseases that the body's immune system would normally overcome can now cause death.

How can one be infected by the AIDS virus, Figure 12-14? The virus is present in body fluids, such as blood and semen. There are four known ways the virus can be passed from one person to another. One is during intimate sexual contact, when body fluids containing the virus may be passed along through broken body tissues. Second, another way is by sharing needles during drug use. The needle may have a small amount of blood on it. If the blood has the AIDS virus in it, the virus can be injected into the next person's blood. Third, the AIDS virus may be passed from a pregnant woman to her unborn child. Fourth, it's possible to get AIDS from a blood transfusion if the blood is infected. Modern technology has made it possible to test and reject blood that has the AIDS virus.

AIDS is spreading rapidly and there is no known cure for it. Up to October 1990, there have been nearly 155 000 recorded cases of AIDS in the United States. Of this number, nearly 96 000, or over 60 percent, have died of AIDS.

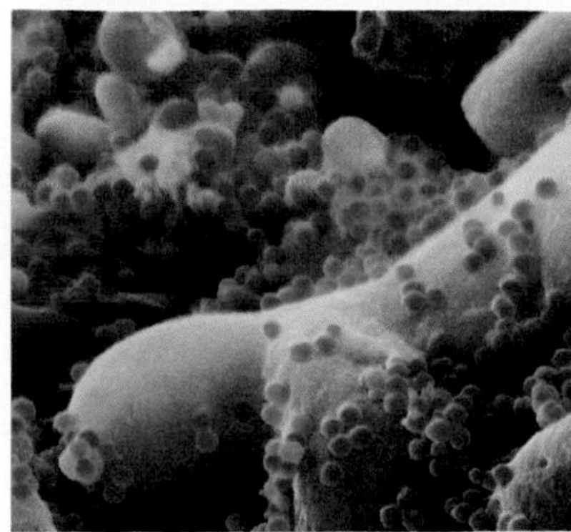

Figure 12-14 AIDS virus particles attack white blood cells and destroy the immune system.

What effect does the AIDS virus have on a person's immune system?

Check Your Understanding

16. Compare antigens and antibodies.
17. What is a DPT shot made up of?
18. What are four ways the AIDS virus can be passed from one person to another?
19. **Critical Thinking:** Why do you think there's not a shot against AIDS?
20. **Biology and Writing:** When a person has an organ transplant, the transplanted organ has antigens different from those of the person receiving the organ. Usually, the person receiving the organ is given drugs that lower the body's immune response. Explain how this treatment might help the transplant procedure.

STUDY GUIDE 71

STUDY GUIDE — CHAPTER 12

Name ______ Date ______ Class ______

IMMUNITY

7. What does the immune system do for months or years after the invasion of a certain antigen? **It will make many new white blood cells, each with the shape of the antibody just used to get rid of the antigen.**
8. If the same type of bacteria enter the body several years later, what will happen? **White blood cells with the necessary antibodies quickly destroy the bacteria.**
9. a. What do the initials *DPT* stand for? **Diphtheria, Tetanus, Pertussis**
   b. What is in a DPT shot? **proteins from these three bacterial diseases**
   c. What happens when you receive this shot? **It's as if you are getting antigens of these three diseases. Your immune system "remembers" the antigens and begins to make antibodies.**
   d. What happens later on if the actual bacteria causing these diseases were to enter your body? **Your immune system would be ready and waiting with the antibodies needed to destroy the antigens.**
10. What is immunity? **the ability of a person who has had a disease once to be protected from getting the same disease again**
11. What do the initials *AIDS* stand for? **Acquired Immune Deficiency Syndrome**
12. Is AIDS caused by a bacterium or a virus? **virus**
13. What type of cells does it attack? **white blood cells**
14. How does AIDS harm the body? **It destroys white blood cells and allows other diseases to invade the body and cause death.**
15. List four ways that AIDS can be spread from one person to another. **during intimate sexual contact, when body fluids containing the virus may be passed along through broken body tissues; by sharing needles during drug use; during pregnancy, the woman may pass the disease to her unborn child; during a blood transfusion of untested blood**

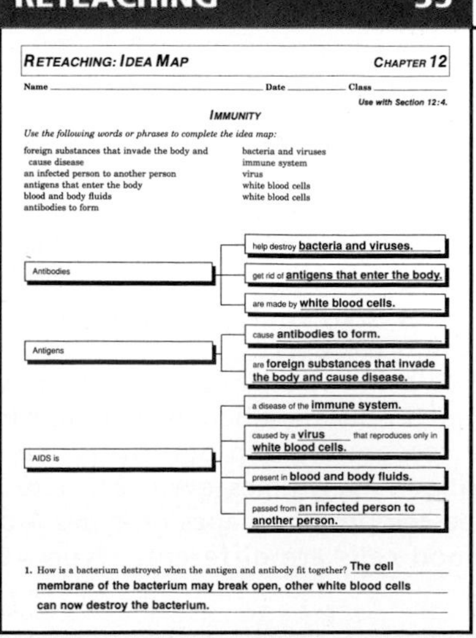

RETEACHING 35

RETEACHING: IDEA MAP — CHAPTER 12

Name ______ Date ______ Class ______

Use with Section 12:4.

IMMUNITY

Use the following words or phrases to complete the idea map:

foreign substances that invade the body and cause disease
an infected person to another person
antigens that enter the body
blood and body fluids
antibodies to form
bacteria and viruses
immune system
virus
white blood cells
white blood cells

Antibodies
- help destroy **bacteria and viruses.**
- get rid of **antigens that enter the body.**
- are made by **white blood cells.**

Antigens
- cause **antibodies to form.**
- are **foreign substances that invade the body and cause disease.**

AIDS is
- a disease of the **immune system.**
- caused by a **virus** that reproduces only in **white blood cells.**
- present in **blood and body fluids.**
- passed from **an infected person to another person.**

1. How is a bacterium destroyed when the antigen and antibody fit together? **The cell membrane of the bacterium may break open, other white blood cells can now destroy the bacterium.**

TEACH

Independent Practice

Study Guide/*Teacher Resource Package,* p. 71. Use the Study Guide worksheet shown at the bottom of this page for independent practice.

Check for Understanding

Have students respond to the first three questions in Check Your Understanding.

Reteach

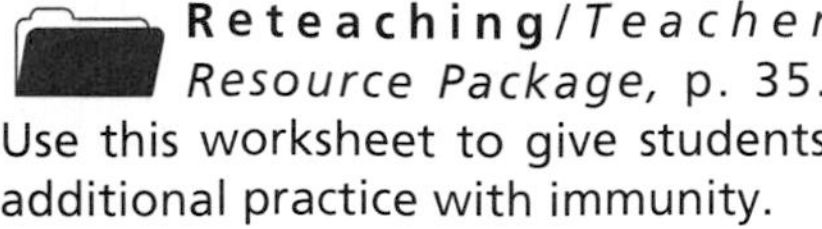

Reteaching/*Teacher Resource Package,* p. 35. Use this worksheet to give students additional practice with immunity.

Extension: Assign Critical Thinking, Biology and Writing, or some of the **OPTIONS** available with this lesson.

3 APPLY

Have students use references to determine and record which disease provides lasting immunity.

4 CLOSE

Audiovisual

Show the videocassette *The Nature and Transmission of AIDS,* Films for the Humanities and Sciences.

Answers to Check Your Understanding

16. Antigens are foreign substances that invade the body and cause disease. Antibodies are chemicals that destroy antigens.
17. proteins from the three different bacterial diseases—diphtheria, pertussis and tetanus.
18. during sexual contact, by sharing needles during drug use, during pregnancy, and by transfusion with infected blood
19. because the AIDS virus has many different forms
20. By receiving drugs that lower the body's immune system, the antibodies that would destroy the organ are not made and the organ is accepted.

CHAPTER 12 REVIEW

Summary

Summary statements can be used by students to review the major concepts of the chapter.

Key Science Words

All boldfaced terms from this chapter are listed.

Testing Yourself

Using Words

1. platelets
2. hemoglobin
3. plasma
4. leukemia
5. anemia
6. AIDS
7. antibody
8. hemophilia
9. red blood cell

Finding Main Ideas

10. p. 254; Blood types differ due to different types of proteins found in the plasma or on the red cells.
11. p. 244; Blood picks up waste chemicals and excess body heat.
12. p. 244; Blood delivers nutrients, oxygen, water, minerals, and chemical messengers.
13. p. 256; Parts of the immune system are tonsils, thymus gland, lymph nodes, spleen, bone marrow. Tears, mucus, and skin can also be included.
14. p. 245; Animals that do not have blood include sponges, jellyfish, and flatworms.
15. p. 255; Blood cell proteins of type A will match with plasma proteins from type B. Blood cell proteins of type B will match with plasma proteins of type A. The result is clumping.
16. p. 259; A person can get AIDS from the exchange of body fluids during sexual contact, by sharing aneedle used by someone with AIDS, and from a pregnant mother to her unborn child.
17. p. 257; Antigens are foreign substances that enter the body and cause disease. Antibodies are chemicals made by the white blood cells to destroy antigens.

Chapter 12

Review

Summary

12:1 The Role of Blood

1. Blood is a body tissue that helps with delivery and pickup of chemicals, nutrients, gases, and wastes.
2. Animals without blood usually live in water. Water delivers oxygen and food to the cells and picks up wastes.

12:2 Parts of Human Blood

3. Blood plasma is a nonliving, yellow liquid that makes up 55 percent of blood. Red blood cells, white blood cells, and platelets are the living parts of blood.
4. Red blood cells carry oxygen in the blood. White blood cells destroy harmful microbes and remove dead cells. Platelets aid in blood clotting.
5. Health problems can occur in people who lack the proper amount of red blood cells, white blood cells, or platelets.

12:3 Blood Types

6. The four main blood types are A, B, AB, O.
7. Different blood types cannot be mixed.

12:4 Immunity

8. The immune system keeps the body free of most diseases. Antibodies destroy antigens that enter the body.
9. Shots help prevent disease.
10. AIDS is a serious disease caused by a virus.

Key Science Words

AIDS (p. 259)
anemia (p. 248)
antibody (p. 257)
antigen (p. 257)
bone marrow (p. 248)
hemoglobin (p. 248)
hemophilia (p. 252)
immune system (p. 256)
immunity (p. 258)
leukemia (p. 250)
plasma (p. 247)
platelet (p. 251)
red blood cell (p. 247)
white blood cell (p. 249)

Testing Yourself

Using Words

Choose the word from the list of Key Science Words that best fits the definition.

1. helps form blood clots
2. gives red blood cells their color
3. part of blood that is nonliving, yellow liquid
4. disease in which white cell numbers increase

Using Main Ideas

18. Plasma is 92% water and 8% other nutrients and salts.
19. Antigens and antibodies have shapes that fit together like lock and key. When they interlock, the bacterium can be easily destroyed by white cells eating it or making it break apart.
20. They act as if they have a memory when they produce antibodies that are capable of recognizing and destroying the same antigen many times, even years later.
21. Red cell protein shapes on types A and B blood cells are different. Type AB red cells have both A and B protein shapes. Type O red cells have no red cell proteins. Type A plasma proteins fit type B cell proteins. Type B plasma proteins fit type A cell proteins. Type AB has no plasma proteins, and type O has both A and B.
22. These animals live in water, which supplies these needs.
23. Shots tell the immune system to make antibodies against certain diseases.

Review

Testing Yourself *continued*

5. a problem resulting from too little hemoglobin in red cells
6. disease caused by a virus that destroys the immune system
7. chemicals that defend the body against foreign chemicals and organisms
8. a disease in which blood does not clot
9. cell with the job of carrying oxygen

Finding Main Ideas

List the page number where each main idea below is found. Then, explain each main idea.

10. why blood types differ
11. what the pickup jobs of blood are
12. several delivery jobs of blood
13. the main parts of your immune system
14. which animal groups do not have blood
15. what happens when blood type A is mixed with type B
16. three ways of getting AIDS
17. how antibodies and antigens differ

Using Main Ideas

Answer the questions by referring to the page number after each question.

18. What are the nutrients that make up blood plasma? (p. 247)
19. How do antibodies help get rid of bacteria? (p. 257)
20. When do white blood cells act as if they have a memory? (p. 258)
21. How do red cell proteins and plasma proteins differ in the four blood types? (p. 254)
22. How do animals with no blood get nutrients and oxygen? (p. 245)
23. How do shots help to prevent diseases? (p. 258)

Skill Review ✔

*For more help, refer to the **Skill Handbook,** pages 704-719.*

1. **Infer:** The common cold is a viral disease that most people survive easily. Explain why a cold can be life-threatening to a person infected with the AIDS virus.
2. **Measure in SI:** The red blood cells in the large photo on page 242 are magnified about 6000 times. Measure the diameter of one cell and determine its actual size in micrometers. (1 mm = 1000 micrometers)
3. **Use a microscope:** Examine a prepared slide of human white blood cells. Compare the sizes of the different kinds of white cells and the different shapes of their nuclei.
4. **Understand science words:** The word part *anti* means against. Define *antibody* and *antigen* using the term *against* in your definitions.

Finding Out More

Critical Thinking

1. Trace the events that occur in your immune system after a mumps shot.
2. A person seriously needs a blood transfusion but none is available. What could be given temporarily to help?

Applications

1. Research the progress of scientists' search for a cure for AIDS.
2. Interview a local dentist to determine how AIDS has altered even the most routine dental procedures.

Skill Review

1. A person with an AIDS infection has an immune system that does not function properly. When this person gets a cold, the body cannot fight infection because the immune system does not work. The infection can therefore continue or get worse, possibly even cause death.
2. If the cell measures 65 mm, then the actual size is:
   $$\frac{65 \times 1000}{8500} = 7.6 \text{ micrometers}$$
3. Students may find five different kinds of white blood cells. Some white blood cells have large, round nuclei that fill the cell; others have lobed nuclei, and some are surrounded by small granules.
4. An antigen is something that fights against good health, such as a bacterium or virus. Antibodies fight against the antigen and help restore good health.

Finding Out More

Critical Thinking

1. When the mumps shot is given, the immune system detects that there is a foreign substance in the body. It identifies the substance, the mumps vaccine, and starts to make antibodies to destroy the antigen. The immune system destroys the antigen and then "remembers" the antibody necessary to do so. If sometime in the future the same antigen enters the body, the immune system kicks in and destroys the antigen again, using the "remembered" antibodies.
2. Type O plasma could be used until a blood match can be obtained, because type O plasma would not contain the red cell proteins.

Applications

1. AIDS is a relatively new disease. Progress is being made, however, and drugs to slow the progression of the disease are being studied. A vaccine is being developed. There is no cure at this time.
2. The AIDS virus is present in blood and body fluids and only a small amount, as little as a drop, of blood is necessary to transmit the disease. Dentists do procedures that can cause bleeding. As a result, dentists take extra care to be sure there is no disease transmission by wearing surgical masks, gloves, and sterilizing all instruments after they are used.

 **Chapter Review**/*Teacher Resource Package,* pp. 60-61.

 **Chapter Test**/*Teacher Resource Package,* pp. 62-64.

Chapter Test/*Computer Test Bank*

Respiration and Excretion

PLANNING GUIDE

CONTENT	TEXT FEATURES	TEACHER RESOURCE PACKAGE	OTHER COMPONENTS
(1 1/2 days) 13:1 The Role of Respiration Gases of Respiration Respiration in Animals	Idea Map, p. 264 Check Your Understanding, p. 265	Reteaching: *Animal Respiratory Systems,* p. 36 Focus: *A Mammal That Can Breathe Like a Fish,* p. 25 Study Guide: *The Role of Respiration,* p. 73	**Laboratory Manual:** *How Does Breathing Occur?* p. 103
(2 days) 13:2 Human Respiratory System Respiratory Organs Gas Exchange Breathing	Skill Check: *Understand Science Words,* p. 267 Mini Lab: *Is Carbon Dioxide Present?* p. 269 Mini Lab: *How Much Air Do You Breathe Out?* p. 271 Lab 13-1: *Breathing Rate,* p. 266 Idea Map, p. 271 Check Your Understanding, p. 271	Reteaching: *Human Respiratory System,* p. 37 Critical Thinking/Problem Solving: *Does Air Breathed In or Out Contain Carbon Dioxide?* p. 13 Skill: *Interpreting Diagrams,* p. 14 Study Guide: *Human Respiratory System,* p. 74 Lab 13-1: *Breathing Rate,* pp. 49-50	Color Transparency 13a: *Breathing In and Out*
(1/2 day) 13:3 Problems of the Respiratory System A Breathing Problem Respiratory Diseases	Skill Check: *Define Words in Context,* p. 273 Check Your Understanding, p. 273	Enrichment: *The Epiglottis,* p. 13 Reteaching: *Respiratory Problems,* p. 38 Study Guide: *Problems of the Respiratory System,* p. 75	
(2 days) 13:4 The Role of Excretion Waste Removal Human Kidneys Excretion and the Skin Problems of the Excretory System	Skill Check: *Interpret Diagrams,* p. 277 Mini Lab: *What Does a Kidney Do?* p. 275 Lab 13-2: *Urine,* p. 278 Science and Society: *Organ Transplants,* p. 281 Check Your Understanding, p. 280	Application: *The Artificial Kidney Machine,* p. 13 Reteaching: *Journey Through the Kidneys,* p. 39 Transparency Master: *Nephron Unit of the Kidney,* p. 59 Study Guide: *The Role of Excretion,* pp. 76-77 Study Guide: *Vocabulary,* p. 78 Lab 13-2: *Urine,* pp. 51-52	**Laboratory Manual:** *What Chemical Wastes Are Removed by the Lungs, Skin, and Kidneys?* p. 107 Color Transparency 13b: *Human Excretory System*
Chapter Review	Summary Key Science Words Testing Yourself Finding Main Ideas Using Main Ideas Skill Review	Chapter Review, pp. 65-66 Chapter Test, pp. 67-69	**Test Bank**

MATERIALS NEEDED

LAB 13-1, p. 266	LAB 13-2, p. 278	MARGIN FEATURES
250-mL beaker goldfish in aquarium thermometer net watch or wall clock ice	4 test tubes test tube rack droppers labels distilled water salt water glucose glucose test tape silver nitrate in dropper bottle normal artificial urine abnormal artificial urine 4 slides	Skill Check, p. 267 dictionary Mini Lab, p. 269 bromthymol blue beaker straw Mini Lab, p. 271 1-L graduated cylinder pan rubber tube water Mini Lab, p. 275 funnel filter paper muddy water

OBJECTIVES

		OBJECTIVES CORRELATION			
SECTION	**OBJECTIVE**	**CHECK YOUR UNDERSTANDING**	**CHAPTER REVIEW**	**TRP CHAPTER REVIEW**	**TRP CHAPTER TEST**
13:1	1. **Define** the role of the respiratory system.	1	12	9	11
	2. **Explain** why cells need oxygen and give off carbon dioxide.	2	10	3	6, 7
	3. **Compare** the respiratory systems of different animals.	3, 4, 5	18	1, 20	2, 12
13:2	4. **Give the function** of different parts of the respiratory system.	6, 10	3, 5, 7	2, 18, 27, 28, 29, 31, 32, 33, 34, 37	14, 15, 16, 17, 18, 19, 20, 21, 22
	5. **Compare** the pathways of gases as they enter and leave the body.	7, 9	16, 19	12, 16, 30	8, 45, 46, 47, 48, 49
	6. **Sequence** the movement of the diaphragm and the rib cage during the breathing process.	8, 14	13, 17	4, 11, 13, 14, 15, 38	39, 40, 41, 42, 43
13:3	7. **Relate** the effects of carbon monoxide poisoning and how to avoid the gas.	11	9, 20	5	5
	8. **Explain** the cause of pneumonia.	12	2	36	9
	9. **Describe** emphysema.	13, 15	15, 21	39	10
13:4	10. **Discuss** the importance of the excretory system.		4, 8	10, 40	3
	11. **Sequence** the steps for filtering of blood in a kidney.	16, 19, 20	1, 11, 20	6, 7, 17, 21, 22, 23, 24, 25, 26, 35, 39	1, 23, 24, 25, 26, 27, 28, 29, 30, 31, 32, 33
	12. **Describe** the skin as part of the excretory system.	18	14	8, 19	4, 13

Respiration and Excretion

CHAPTER OVERVIEW

Key Concepts

In this chapter, students will study the anatomy and physiology of the human respiratory and excretory systems. They will learn the functions of the kidneys, skin, and lungs and the problems associated with these systems. Organ transplants are discussed.

Key Science Words

alveoli	respiratory system
bronchi	trachea
carbon monoxide	urea
diaphragm	ureter
emphysema	urethra
epiglottis	urinary bladder
excretory system	urine
nephron	
pneumonia	

Skill Development

In Lab 13-1, students will **form a hypothesis, measure in SI,** and **interpret data** while determining the effect of temperature on the breathing rate of fish. In Lab 13-2, they will **observe, interpret data, make and use tables,** and **infer** as they detect chemicals in urine. In the Skill Check on page 267, students will **understand** the **science word** *epiglottis.* On page 277, they will **interpret diagrams** while following the pathways of blood, wastes, and water. On page 273, they will **define words in context** while describing a communicable disease. In the Mini Lab on page 269, students will **experiment** to detect carbon dioxide. In the Mini Lab on page 271, they will **design an experiment** to measure air exhaled. In the Mini Lab on page 275, they will **formulate a model** to show how the kidneys work.

CHAPTER PREVIEW

Chapter Content

Review this outline for Chapter 13 before you read the chapter.

Skills in this Chapter

The skills that you will use in this chapter are listed below.

- In **Lab 13-1,** you will form a hypothesis, measure in SI, and interpret data. In **Lab 13-2,** you will observe, interpret data, make and use tables, and infer.
- In the **Skill Checks,** you will understand science words, interpret diagrams, and define words in context.
- In the **Mini Labs,** you will experiment, formulate a model, and design an experiment.

262

Bridging

Chapter 2 introduced the term *cellular respiration.* Students will now have an opportunity to see how oxygen gas is supplied to cells and how carbon dioxide gas is removed from the body.

Chapter 13

Respiration and Excretion

If you were asked, "How much air can your lungs hold?" could you come up with the correct answer? The person in the photo on the left is snorkeling. Different people can stay under water for different lengths of time. This time can vary from a few seconds to several minutes. The small photo below shows one way to measure your own lung volume. What gases enter the lungs when you breathe in? What gases leave the lungs when you breathe out? Why is breathing important? What are some of the effects of breathing in polluted air? This chapter will help you answer these questions.

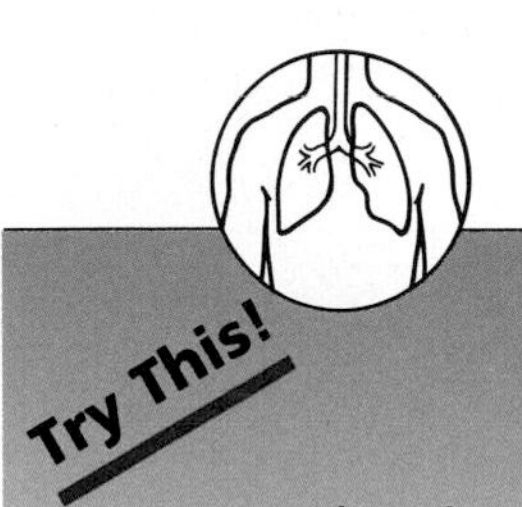

Try This!

How many breaths do you take? Count the number of times you breathe in and out for exactly one minute. What is your breathing rate?

Measuring the volume of air you breathe out

263

GETTING STARTED

Using the Photos

Students will think that oxygen and carbon dioxide are the only gases they breathe in and out. Explain that other gases are present and that they may or may not affect breathing. The connection between breathing and cellular respiration needs to be emphasized. Discuss how lung volume varies with age, sex, and physical condition.

MOTIVATION/Try This!

How many breaths do you take? Students will **observe** that their breathing rate is between 15 to 30 times per minute. A stopwatch will be needed. Students can **calculate** a class average.

Chapter Preview

Have students study the chapter outline before they begin to read the chapter. They should note the overall organization of the chapter, that the role of respiration is presented first, the human respiratory system is discussed next, respiratory problems are then examined, and last, the excretory system is explained.

Misconception

Students often confuse breathing with respiration. Breathing is a mechanical process that forces air into and out of the lungs. Respiration is a chemical process that occurs within all cells.

13:1 The Role of Respiration

PREPARATION

Materials Needed

Make copies of the Focus, Study Guide, and Reteaching worksheets in the *Teacher Resource Package.*

Key Science Words

respiratory system

1 FOCUS

▶ The objectives are listed on the student page. Remind students to preview these objectives as a guide to this numbered section.

MOTIVATION/Brainstorming

Ask students why it is harder to breathe at high altitudes.

Guided Practice

Have students write down their answers to the margin questions: to exchange oxygen and carbon dioxide; carbon dioxide.

Idea Map

Have students use the idea map as a study guide to the major concepts of this section.

Focus/*Teacher Resource Package,* pp. 25-26. Use the Focus transparency shown at the bottom of this page as an introduction to respiration.

13:1 The Role of Respiration

Objectives

1. **Define** the role of the respiratory system.
2. **Explain** why cells need oxygen and give off carbon dioxide.
3. **Compare** the respiratory systems of different animals.

Key Science Words

respiratory system

When you talk of respiration, many people think of breathing. Is there more to respiration than this? Yes, respiration involves more body parts besides the nose and mouth.

Gases of Respiration

Chapter 12 described how your blood delivers oxygen to all your body cells. It also explained how blood removes carbon dioxide from your cells.

What is the role of the respiratory system?

Oxygen is brought into your body by the respiratory (RES pruh tor ee) system. Carbon dioxide is carried out of your body by the respiratory system. Your **respiratory system** is made of body parts that help with the exchange of gases. It brings in oxygen and removes carbon dioxide.

What waste gas is given off by all cells?

What happens to oxygen in cells? Oxygen is a gas used by cells in cellular respiration. During this chemical process, sugar reacts with oxygen, and energy is released for all of the cells' activities. At the same time, carbon dioxide and water are formed. Carbon dioxide is a waste gas given off by all cells. Water is an important nutrient for all cell processes. Remember that cellular respiration occurs in cells of all organisms, including plants. Cellular respiration can be shown as an equation:

$$\underset{\text{Oxygen}}{O_2} + \underset{\text{sugar}}{C_6H_{12}O_6} \xrightarrow{\text{Energy}} \underset{\text{carbon dioxide}}{CO_2} + \underset{\text{water}}{H_2O}$$

Study Tip: Use this idea map as a study guide to the role of the respiratory system. What is the process that releases energy from food?

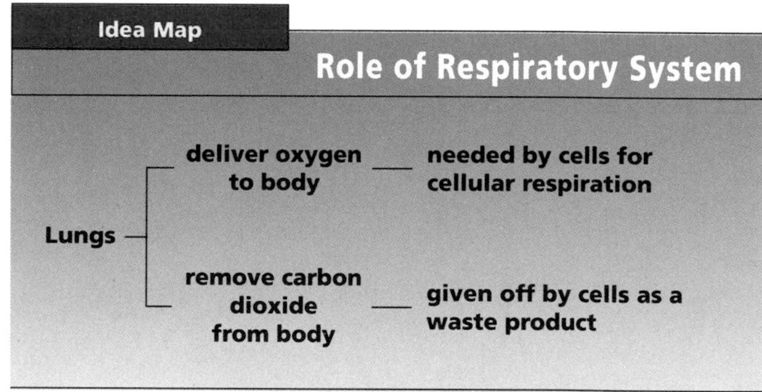
Idea Map
Role of Respiratory System
Lungs
deliver oxygen to body
needed by cells for cellular respiration
remove carbon dioxide from body
given off by cells as a waste product

OPTIONS

Science Background

Certain life forms, such as bacteria and yeast, and body cells, such as muscle cells, can carry on respiration without oxygen. This is called anaerobic respiration. This process yields little available energy for the cell and results in food such as glucose being degraded into either ethyl alcohol or lactic acid. Most life forms, however, carry on aerobic respiration. This process requires oxygen and is more energy efficient than anaerobic respiration.

FOCUS 25

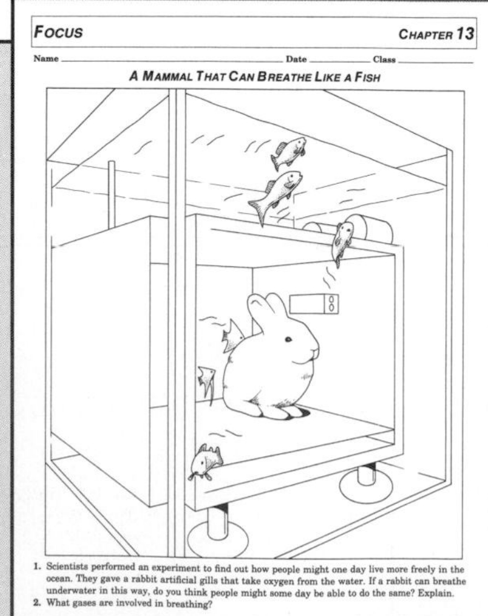
FOCUS CHAPTER 13

Name ____ Date ____ Class ____

A MAMMAL THAT CAN BREATHE LIKE A FISH

1. Scientists performed an experiment to find out how people might one day live more freely in the ocean. They gave a rabbit artificial gills that take oxygen from the water. If a rabbit can breathe underwater in this way, do you think people might some day be able to do the same? Explain.
2. What gases are involved in breathing?

Respiration in Animals

Most animals have respiratory systems to help with the exchange of gases. In Figure 13-1, the blue shading shows the respiratory systems of some animals. Earthworms exchange gases through their skins. Insects have a large network of small tubes that carry air to all body parts. Fish carry on gas exchange through organs called gills. Frogs exchange gases through two types of organs—lungs and skin. Humans, as you know, also have lungs.

How do fish exchange gases?

The systems may look different in different animals, but all these systems are adapted for gas exchange. One important trait of all respiratory systems is that there is a large surface area over which air passes. This large area provides a surface for gases to diffuse into or out of the animals' bodies. In the earthworm, for example, the entire body surface acts as an area for gas exchange.

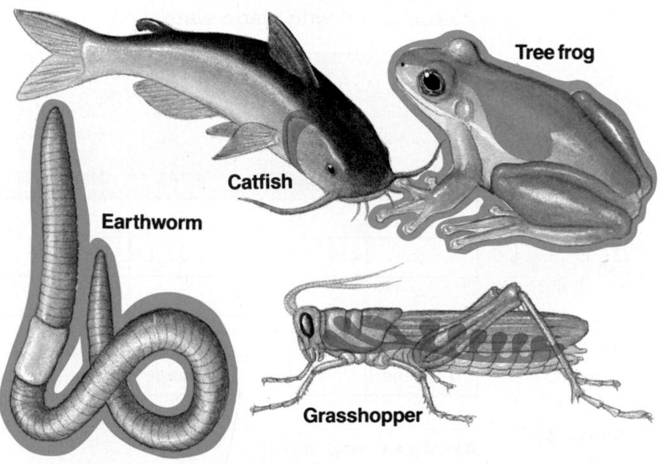

Figure 13-1 Compare the respiratory systems of some animals. The shaded areas in blue show where animals exchange gases with air.

Check Your Understanding

1. Which gases are exchanged by the respiratory system?
2. Why is oxygen needed by our cells?
3. Why do respiratory systems have a large surface area?
4. **Critical Thinking:** Why do birds need a more efficient respiratory system than humans?
5. **Biology and Writing:** Write a four to ten line paragraph that describes one kind of respiratory system.

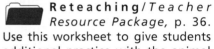

RETEACHING 36

RETEACHING: IDEA MAP — CHAPTER 13

Name ______ Date ______ Class ______

Use with Section 13:1.

ANIMAL RESPIRATORY SYSTEMS

Use the following terms to complete the idea map below: skin, gills, insect, frog, fish, earthworm, skin and lungs, and network of small tubes.

Respiratory System in Animals

Animal	Organ(s) Involved
earthworm	skin
insect	network of small tubes
fish	gills
frog	skin and lungs

1. What respiratory trait is shared by all animals? large surface area for gas exchange
2. What two gases are exchanged during respiration? Oxygen is taken in and carbon dioxide is given off.
3. What products are formed during cellular respiration? carbon dioxide and water
4. Where does cellular respiration take place? Cellular respiration takes place in the cells of all organisms.
5. In what organ does gas exchange take place in humans? Gas exchange takes place in the lungs.
6. Why is a large surface area for gas exchange important? It provides a place where gas can diffuse into or out of the animals' blood or body cells.
7. What chemical process takes place in cellular respiration? Sugar reacts with oxygen, and energy is released.

STUDY GUIDE 73

STUDY GUIDE — CHAPTER 13

Name ______ Date ______ Class ______

THE ROLE OF RESPIRATION

In your textbook, read about respiration in Section 13:1.

1. What is the function of the respiratory system? to help with the exchange of gases; to bring in oxygen and to remove carbon dioxide
2. Explain why a large surface area is needed in a respiratory system. This large area provides a surface for gases to diffuse into or out of the blood or body cells.
3. Match the main methods of getting oxygen with the animals below. Write the letter of the method below each animal.
   A = skin B = skin and lungs C = lungs D = gills E = small tubes

   B A D E C

HUMAN RESPIRATORY SYSTEM

In your textbook, read about respiratory system organs in Section 13:2.

1. Label the parts on the diagram below using these words: bronchus, nose, nasal chamber, lung, trachea, epiglottis, alveoli.

   (C) nose; (E) lung; nasal chamber (A); epiglottis (G); trachea (D); bronchus (F); alveoli (B)

2. Place the letter of the description below in the correct circle next to the labeled part of the diagram.
   A = place where air is warmed or cooled
   B = clusters of air sacs where gas exchange occurs
   C = place where air first enters respiratory system
   D = the windpipe
   E = one of two major organs of respiration
   F = carries air from trachea into lung
   G = flap that prevents food from entering trachea

2 TEACH

Guided Practice

Have students write down their answers to the margin question: through gills.

Independent Practice

Study Guide/*Teacher Resource Package*, p. 73. Use the Study Guide worksheet shown at the bottom of this page for independent practice.

Check for Understanding

Have students respond to the first three questions in Check Your Understanding.

Reteach

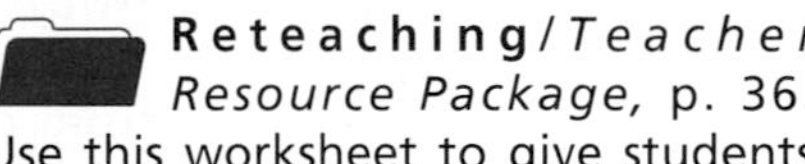

Reteaching/*Teacher Resource Package*, p. 36. Use this worksheet to give students additional practice with the animal respiratory system.

Extension: Assign Critical Thinking, Biology and Writing, or some of the **OPTIONS** available with this lesson.

3 APPLY

Demonstration

Lift up the gill covering on a fresh fish to expose the extensive surface area of the respiratory system.

4 CLOSE

Using Science Words: Have students explain how respiration and breathing differ.

Answers to Check Your Understanding

1. oxygen and carbon dioxide
2. to release energy
3. The larger the surface area, the more gases can be exchanged.
4. They have a higher rate of metabolism than humans.
5. An example is earthworms exchanging gases through skin.

Lab 13-1 Breathing Rate

Overview

In this lab, students will determine if the respiration rate of a fish changes as the amount of oxygen dissolved in the water varies.

Objectives: Upon completing this lab, students will have (1) **measured** the rate at which a fish uses oxygen, (2) **observed** that fish breathe faster in warm water than in cold water.

Time Allotment: 1 class period

Preparation

▶ Pet shops stock feeder goldfish that are very reasonably priced.

Lab 13-1 worksheet/*Teacher Resource Package*, pp. 49-50.

Lab 13-1 Computer Program/*Teacher Resource Package*, p. xiv. Use the computer program shown at the bottom of this page as you teach this lab.

Teaching the Lab

▶ Fish may live in water that is totally covered by ice because the very cold water contains much dissolved oxygen.

Cooperative Learning: Students can work in groups. Each student in the group should make separate counts and average his or her counts. This will increase observer reliability.

Breathing Rate

Lab 13–1

Problem: Does temperature affect the breathing rate of fish?

Skills

form a hypothesis, measure in SI, interpret data

Materials

250-mL beaker
net
ice
goldfish in aquarium tank
thermometer
watch or wall clock

Procedure

1. Copy the data table.
2. Fill the beaker with water from the aquarium.
3. Use a net to transfer one goldfish from the tank to the beaker. **CAUTION:** *Handle animals with care.*
4. Locate the fish's gill cover. Note that the gill cover opens and closes as the fish breathes in and out.
5. **Measure in SI:** Use a thermometer to measure the water temperature in the beaker. Record this temperature in your table.
6. Count the number of times the fish opens its gill cover during one minute. Record this number in your data table.
7. Repeat step 6 two more times, recording your results in the table as trials 2 and 3.
8. Add a small piece of ice to the beaker to slowly drop the water temperature. Continue to add ice until the temperature of the water is 10 degrees lower than at the start. Wait at least 5 minutes before going on to step 9. As you wait, write a **hypothesis** as to whether you think the fish's breathing rate will speed up, slow down, or remain the same with the cooler water.
9. Repeat steps 5 through 7.
10. Complete the data table.
11. Allow the water temperature to rise to room temperature. Then, use the net to return your fish to the aquarium.

Data and Observations

1. What were you measuring when you counted gill cover openings?
2. **Interpret data:** Were there more or fewer gill openings with cold water when compared with warm water?

WATER TEMPERATURE: 24°C		WATER TEMPERATURE: 14°C	
TRIAL	NUMBER OF GILL OPENINGS	TRIAL	NUMBER OF GILL OPENINGS
1	63	1	44
2	58	2	46
3	65	3	45
Total	186	Total	135
Average	62	Average	45

Analyze and Apply

1. Cold water contains more oxygen than warm water. Explain why a fish in cold water breathes more slowly than a fish in warm water.
2. **Check your hypothesis:** Is your hypothesis supported by your data? Explain.
3. **Apply:** Why might a fish die if the water temperature gets too warm?

Extension

Predict the number of gill openings at 5 degrees lower than the water was at the start. Experiment to test your prediction.

ANSWERS

Data and Observations

1. the rate of breathing
2. fewer

Analyze and Apply

1. Oxygen is supplied to the blood faster in colder water.
2. Students who hypothesized that the breathing rate will slow down will answer yes. The oxygen supply is greater in colder water.
3. Warm water has less oxygen and a fish must breathe faster. Eventually a fish may use energy faster than it can take in oxygen, and will die.

COMPUTER PROGRAM XIV

COMPUTER PROGRAM LAB 13-1 BREATHING RATE

```
]LIST

5  DIM YES(5),NO(5)
8  HOME
10  GOSUB 480
40  HOME : VTAB 12: INPUT "ENTER FIRST WATER TEMPERATURE: ";T1
50  INPUT "ENTER SECOND WATER TEMPERATURE: ";T2
60  HOME : GOSUB 450
70 T1$ =  STR$ (T1)
80  IF  LEN (T1$) < 3 THEN T1$ = "0" + T1$: GOTO 80
90 T2$ =  STR$ (T2)
100  IF  LEN (T2$) < 3 THEN T2$ = "0" + T2$: GOTO 100
110  PRINT "! WATER TEMP    "T1$" ! WATER TEMP   "T2$" !";
120  GOSUB 450
130  PRINT "!       ! NUMBER OF !       ! NUMBER OF!";
140  PRINT "! TRIAL !   GILL    ! TRIAL !   GILL   !";
150  PRINT "!       ! OPENINGS  !       ! OPENINGS !";
160  GOSUB 450
170 S1 = 0:S2 = 0
180  FOR X = 1 TO 3
190  VTAB (X * 2 + 8): PRINT "!   ";X;"   !";
200  HTAB 14: INPUT "";NO(X)
210  VTAB (X * 2 + 8): HTAB 21: PRINT "!   ";X;"   !   ";
220  INPUT "";YES(X)
230  VTAB (X * 2 + 8): HTAB 40: PRINT "!";
240  GOSUB 450
250 S1 = S1 + NO(X):S2 = S2 + YES(X)
260  NEXT X
270  GOSUB 450: INPUT "ARE THESE NUMBERS CORRECT? ";S$
280  IF S$ = "N" OR S$ = "n" THEN 80
290  VTAB  PEEK (37) - 1: HTAB 1
300  PRINT "! TOTAL !           ! TOTAL !          !";
310  VTAB 16: HTAB 14: PRINT S1;: HTAB 34: PRINT S2
320  GOSUB 450
330  PRINT "!AVERAGE!           !AVERAGE!          !";
340 A1 =  VAL ( LEFT$ ( STR$ (S1 / 3),6))
350 A2 =  VAL ( LEFT$ ( STR$ (S2 / 3),6))
360  VTAB 18: HTAB 14: PRINT A1;: HTAB 34: PRINT A2;
370  VTAB 18: HTAB 40: PRINT "!";
380  GOSUB 450
390  IF SPACE$ = "N" THEN 80
400  IF SPACE$ = "Y" THEN  END
410  PRINT "DO YOU WANT THIS PRINTED (Y/N)? ";: GET A$
420  IF A$ <  > "Y" AND A$ <  > "N" THEN VTAB 20: HTAB 1: GOTO 410
430  IF A$ = "Y" THEN VTAB 20: HTAB 1: CALL  - 868: GOSUB 670
440  END
450  HTAB 1;
460  PRINT "--------------------------------------";
470  RETURN
480  TEXT : HOME
490  GOSUB 600
500  PRINT : PRINT "YOU WILL BE ASKED TO TYPE IN YOUR WATER TEMPERATURE
    AND RESULTS FOR THE 3 TRIALSONTO A DATA TABLE ";
510  PRINT "THAT IS EXACTLY LIKE  THE ONE USED IN THE EXPERIMENT."
520  PRINT
```

13:2 Human Respiratory System

What are the parts of the human respiratory system and how do they work? When you breathe, all you may feel is the slight movement of your chest. What else is involved in breathing?

Objectives

4. **Give the function** of different parts of the respiratory system.
5. **Compare** the pathways of gases as they enter and leave the body.
6. **Sequence** the movement of the diaphragm and rib cage during the breathing process.

Key Science Words

epiglottis
trachea
bronchi
alveoli
diaphragm

Respiratory Organs

Use Figure 13-2 to tour the respiratory system and study its parts.

1. Our tour starts with the nose. As you breathe in, air enters the nose. Hairs inside the nose trap dust particles and prevent them from entering the lungs.
2. The nasal chamber is a large space above the roof of your mouth. It warms or cools the entering air. Mucus is formed inside the nose. Mucus keeps the air moist as it passes through the nose.
3. Air enters the nose and passes to the windpipe. The windpipe is covered by the epiglottis (ep uh GLAHT uhs). The **epiglottis** is a small flap that closes over the windpipe when you swallow. This closing prevents food or liquid from entering the windpipe when you are eating. If food passed into your windpipe, you would choke.
4. The air passes into your windpipe, which is called the trachea (TRAY kee uh). The **trachea** is a tube about 15 centimeters long that carries air to two shorter tubes that lead into your lungs.
5. **Bronchi** (BRAUN ki) are two short tubes that carry air from the trachea to the left and right lung.

Skill Check

Understand science words: epiglottis. The word part *glott* means language. In your dictionary, find three words with the word part *glott* in them. *For more help, refer to the **Skill Handbook,** pages 706-711.*

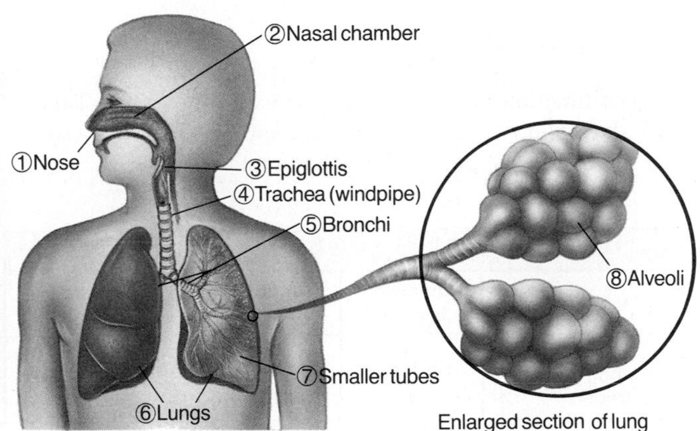

Figure 13-2 Take a tour of the human respiratory system. What structure takes air to the lungs? the trachea

OPTIONS

Science Background

The human respiratory system consists of a series of hollow tubes and air sacs that terminate in and actually form the lungs. Capillaries surround these air sacs and serve as the site for gas exchange between air and blood. Blood carries oxygen to all body cells while carrying carbon dioxide away from the body cells to lung air sacs.

13:2 Human Respiratory System

PREPARATION

Materials Needed

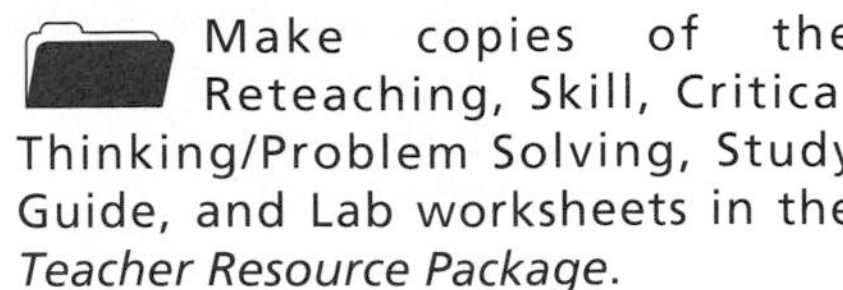

Make copies of the Reteaching, Skill, Critical Thinking/Problem Solving, Study Guide, and Lab worksheets in the *Teacher Resource Package*.

▶ Have goldfish on hand for Lab 13-1.

▶ Gather straws and rubber tubes for the Mini Labs.

Key Science Words

epiglottis
trachea
bronchi
alveoli
diaphragm

Process Skills

In Lab 13-1, students will form a hypothesis, measure in SI, and interpret data. In the Mini Labs, students will experiment and design an experiment. In the Skill Check, they will understand science words.

1 FOCUS

▶ The objectives are listed on the student page. Remind students to preview these objectives as a guide to this numbered section.

ACTIVITY/Brainstorming

Ask students if lungs are made of muscle. Establish that they are not, and ask how lungs pump air into and out of the body.

2 TEACH

MOTIVATION/Demonstration

Use a 1- or 2-liter empty plastic soda bottle to show that pressure influences the movement of air and that air does occupy space. Ask students why air is pushed out of the bottle when the sides are squeezed together and why air rushes back in when the sides return to normal.

Concept Development

▶ Ask students what happens when the epiglottis fails to close quickly. They have all experienced coughing that follows an attempt to clear the windpipe.

▶ Mucus lining the nasal passage and chamber traps dust, foreign matter, and bacteria. The mucus is brought up from the trachea and is either swallowed or spit out.

▶ Nitrogen gas is present in the blood in the same concentration as in the air. It is not utilized in the body but is absorbed into the bloodstream.

Analogy: The branches of the respiratory system can be compared to a tree with many smaller and smaller branches radiating out from the central trunk.

Guided Practice

Have students write down their answers to the margin question: Gases are exchanged in the alveoli.

Cooperative Learning: Divide the class into three groups and have each design an idea map on the respiratory system.

Critical Thinking/Problem Solving/*Teacher Resource Package*, p. 13. Use the Critical Thinking/Problem Solving worksheet shown here to give students practice with components of breathed air.

Skill/*Teacher Resource Package*, p. 14. Use the Skill worksheet shown here to give students practice in interpreting diagrams of the respiratory system.

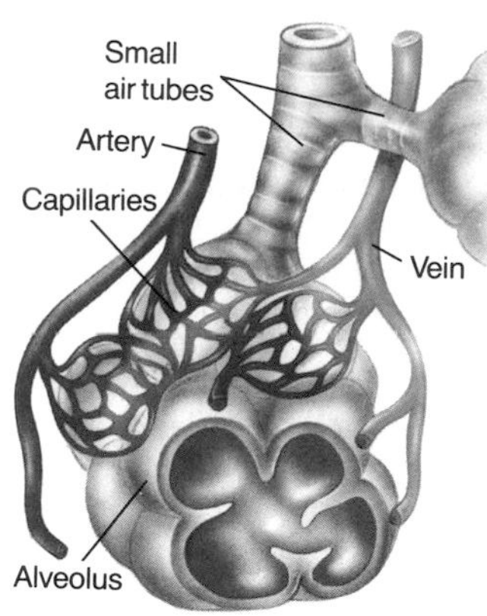

Figure 13-3 In the alveoli, gas exchange takes place in less than one-tenth of a second.

6. The two lungs are major organs in your respiratory system. Lungs are large, soft organs in which oxygen and carbon dioxide are exchanged.
7. As the bronchi enter each lung, they branch into thousands of smaller and smaller tubes. Each tiny tube finally leads into tiny air sacs.
8. There are about 300 million alveoli (al VEE uh li) found in each lung. **Alveoli** are the tiny air sacs of the lungs. The alveoli look like clusters of grapes.

Each air sac, or alveolus, is surrounded by tiny blood vessels called capillaries, Figure 13-3. Oxygen in the air sacs moves through the cell membranes into the blood. Carbon dioxide moves out of the blood into the air sacs. If all the air sacs in a person's lungs were opened and spread out, they would cover an area equal to about 1/5 of the area of a basketball court, Figure 13-4. The air sacs of your lungs provide a large surface area for gases to pass into and out of your blood.

Why are alveoli important?

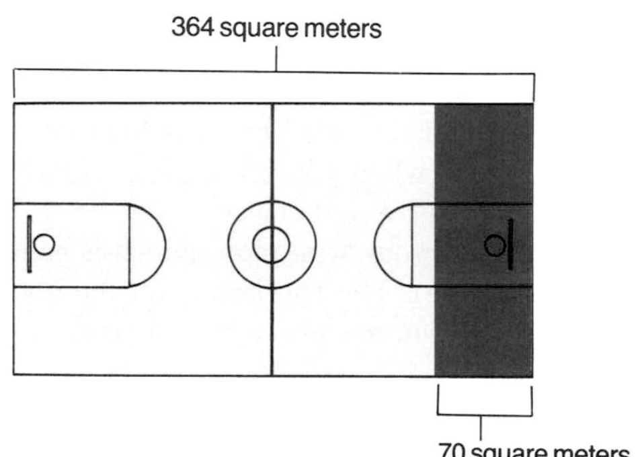

Figure 13-4 The area covered by a person's air sacs equals about one-fifth the area of a basketball court.

Gas Exchange

The function of your lungs is to exchange gases. Table 13-1 shows how much oxygen (O_2), carbon dioxide (CO_2), and nitrogen (N_2) gas we breathe in and out.

TABLE 13–1. MAKEUP OF AIR WE BREATHE

Gas	Chemical Symbol	Air Entering Lungs	Air Leaving Lungs
Oxygen	O_2	19.97%	16.00%
Carbon Dioxide	CO_2	.03%	4.00%
Nitrogen	N_2	80.00%	80.00%

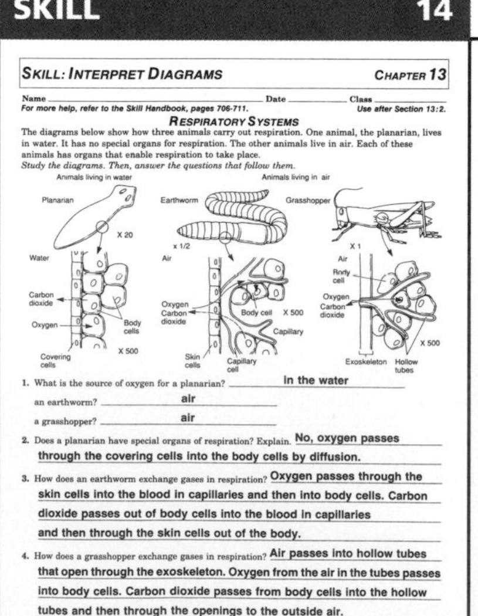

SKILL 14

SKILL: INTERPRET DIAGRAMS — CHAPTER 13

Name ______ Date ______ Class ______

For more help, refer to the Skill Handbook, pages 706-711. *Use after Section 13:2.*

RESPIRATORY SYSTEMS

The diagrams below show how three animals carry out respiration. One animal, the planarian, lives in water. It has no special organs for respiration. The other animals live in air. Each of these animals has organs that enable respiration to take place.

Study the diagrams. Then, answer the questions that follow them.

1. What is the source of oxygen for a planarian? **in the water**
   an earthworm? **air**
   a grasshopper? **air**
2. Does a planarian have special organs of respiration? Explain. **No, oxygen passes through the covering cells into the body cells by diffusion.**
3. How does an earthworm exchange gases in respiration? **Oxygen passes through the skin cells into the blood in capillaries and then into body cells. Carbon dioxide passes out of body cells into the blood in capillaries and then through the skin cells out of the body.**
4. How does a grasshopper exchange gases in respiration? **Air passes into hollow tubes that open through the exoskeleton. Oxygen from the air in the tubes passes into body cells. Carbon dioxide passes from body cells into the hollow tubes and then through the openings to the outside air.**

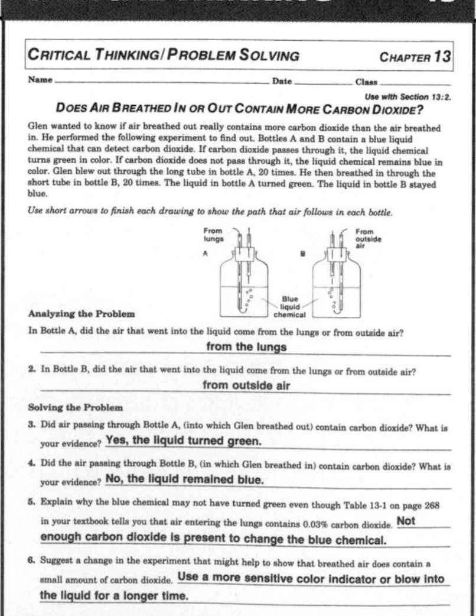

CRITICAL THINKING 13

CRITICAL THINKING/PROBLEM SOLVING — CHAPTER 13

Name ______ Date ______ Class ______

Use with Section 13:2.

DOES AIR BREATHED IN OR OUT CONTAIN MORE CARBON DIOXIDE?

Glen wanted to know if air breathed out really contains more carbon dioxide than the air breathed in. He performed the following experiment to find out. Bottles A and B contain a blue liquid chemical that can detect carbon dioxide. If carbon dioxide passes through it, the liquid chemical turns green in color. If carbon dioxide does not pass through it, the liquid chemical remains blue in color. Glen blew out through the long tube in bottle A, 20 times. He then breathed in through the short tube in bottle B, 20 times. The liquid in bottle A turned green. The liquid in bottle B stayed blue.

Use short arrows to finish each drawing to show the path that air follows in each bottle.

Analyzing the Problem

In Bottle A, did the air that went into the liquid come from the lungs or from outside air? **from the lungs**

2. In Bottle B, did the air that went into the liquid come from the lungs or from outside air? **from outside air**

Solving the Problem

3. Did air passing through Bottle A, (into which Glen breathed out) contain carbon dioxide? What is your evidence? **Yes, the liquid turned green.**
4. Did the air passing through Bottle B, (in which Glen breathed in) contain carbon dioxide? What is your evidence? **No, the liquid remained blue.**
5. Explain why the blue chemical may not have turned green even though Table 13-1 on page 268 in your textbook tells you that air entering the lungs contains 0.03% carbon dioxide. **Not enough carbon dioxide is present to change the blue chemical.**
6. Suggest a change in the experiment that might help to show that breathed air does contain a small amount of carbon dioxide. **Use a more sensitive color indicator or blow into the liquid for a longer time.**

Blood in the capillaries around the alveoli is low in oxygen. As you breathe in, air and the oxygen in it fill each alveolus. Oxygen passes out of the air sacs into the blood of the capillaries by diffusion, Figure 13-5.

Red blood cells carry oxygen to all body cells. The oxygen diffuses into the body cells, Figure 13-6. Why, then, does less oxygen move out of the lungs than goes in as shown in Table 13-1? Less moves out because some oxygen is transported to all your body cells.

Now, why is more carbon dioxide given off than is taken in by the lungs? Carbon dioxide is formed in all body cells as a waste gas during cellular respiration. The gas moves by diffusion from body cells into nearby capillaries, Figure 13-6. In time, blood loaded with carbon dioxide will travel back to the lungs. When blood arrives at the lungs, carbon dioxide diffuses out of the blood in the capillaries and into the alveoli, Figure 13-5. All the carbon dioxide gas given off by your body cells during cellular respiration is carried by your blood to your lungs. Once there, it is given off in the air you breathe out. Do the data in Table 13-1 show this? Why do you think the amount of nitrogen that enters and leaves the lungs stays the same? It's because nitrogen gas is not used by body cells.

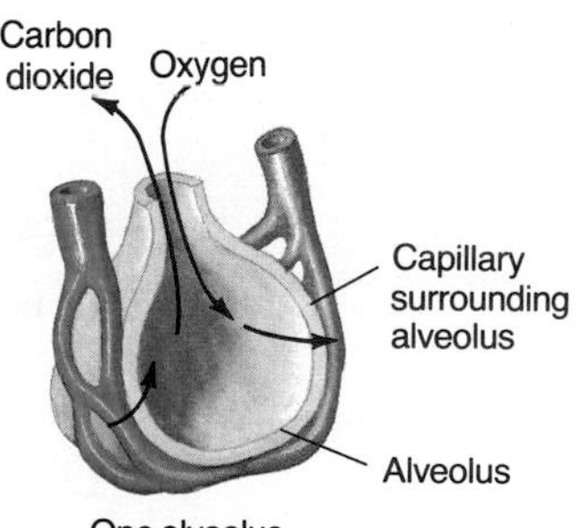

Figure 13-5 The pathways of oxygen and carbon dioxide between the alveolus and its blood capillaries

Why is more carbon dioxide given off than is taken in?

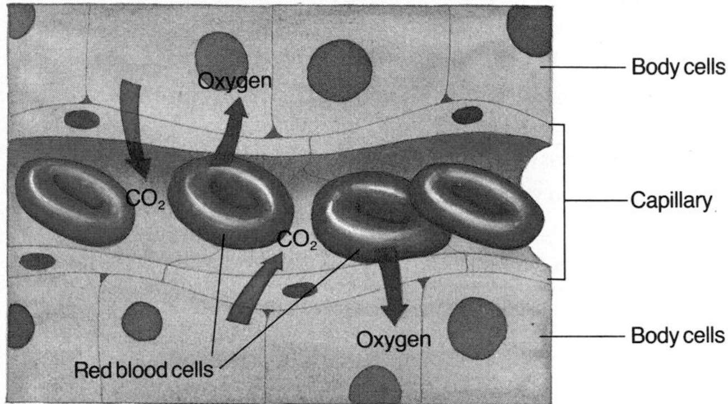

Figure 13-6 Oxygen moves by diffusion from red blood cells into body cells. Carbon dioxide (CO_2) diffuses into capillaries from the cells.

Breathing

Usually, you don't think about your breathing. If you did think about it, however, you would probably notice that you breathe in and out about 12 to 16 times in one minute. How does your breathing work to bring air in and push air out of your lungs? Your rib cage and a muscle at the bottom of your chest help you to breathe.

Mini Lab

Is Carbon Dioxide Present?

Experiment: You can detect carbon dioxide with bromthymol blue. Exhale 40 times through a straw into a beaker filled with the chemical. What color does the chemical turn? *For more help, refer to the* ***Skill Handbook****, pages 704-705.*

TEACH

Guided Practice

Have students write down their answers to the margin question: Carbon dioxide is formed as a waste gas in all body cells.

Check for Understanding

Have students compare and contrast the (a) sites where oxygen and carbon dioxide first enter the blood (alveoli/body capillary); (b) sites where oxygen and carbon dioxide leave blood (body capillary/alveoli); (c) sources of oxygen and carbon dioxide (air/body cells).

Reteach

Have students summarize the events studied by making a table that lists the following across the top: Breathing out, Breathing in. List the following along the side: Direction of diaphragm movement, Condition of diaphragm, Direction of rib movement.

Mini Lab

The Mini Lab will require a solution of 0.1 g bromthymol blue to 2 L of water. The solution will turn green with the presence of CO_2.

Independent Practice

Study Guide/*Teacher Resource Package*, p. 74. Use the Study Guide worksheet shown at the bottom of this page for independent practice.

STUDY GUIDE 74

STUDY GUIDE — CHAPTER 13

Name ______ Date ______ Class ______

HUMAN RESPIRATORY SYSTEM

In your textbook, read about gas exchange in Section 13:2.

3. Examine the first diagram at the right. Then, answer the questions.
   a. What is part A? **alveolus** part B? **capillary**
   b. What gas moves in the direction shown by arrow C? **oxygen** arrow D? **carbon dioxide**
4. Examine the second diagram at the right. Then, answer the questions.
   a. What is part A? **blood cell** part B? **body cell**
   b. What gas moves in the direction shown by arrow C? **carbon dioxide** arrow D? **oxygen**
5. Below are two diagrams of the chest cavity during breathing. Circle the words that correctly complete the statements below each diagram.

Rib cage moves (out) / in.	Rib cage moves out / (in.)
Rib cage moves (up) / down.	Rib cage moves up / (down.)
Diaphragm is relaxed / (working.)	Diaphragm is (relaxed) / working.
Air is (pulled in) / pushed out.	Air is pulled in / (pushed out.)
Diaphragm pushes up / (moves down.)	Diaphragm (pushes up) / moves down.
Lungs get squeezed / (expand.)	Lungs (get squeezed) / expand.
Person is breathing (in) / out.	Person is breathing in / (out.)

OPTIONS

How Does Breathing Occur?/*Lab Manual*, pp. 103-106. Use this lab as an extension to the human respiratory system.

TEACH

Concept Development

▶ Explain that the diaphragm is striated muscle that is normally involuntary, but that may be controlled while singing, holding one's breath, or consciously taking a deep breath.

Divergent Question

Ask students if breathing is usually automatic. Does it speed up during exercise? When may it not be automatic? (breath holding)

Connection: Math

Students can calculate the amount of air they breathe in during one minute and one hour. Assume that humans breathe in about 500 mL of air each time they breathe in. Have students (a) count the number of times they breathe in during one minute, (b) calculate the volume of air breathed in by multiplying their answer from step (a) by 500 mL, (c) calculate the volume of air breathed in during one hour by multiplying their answer from step (b) by 60.

Guided Practice

Have students write down their answers to the margin question: The lungs expand and you breathe in.

ACTIVITY/Enrichment

Have students build a lung model using a plastic soda pop bottle with the bottom cut off, balloons, a Y tube, rubber sheeting, and a rubber stopper.

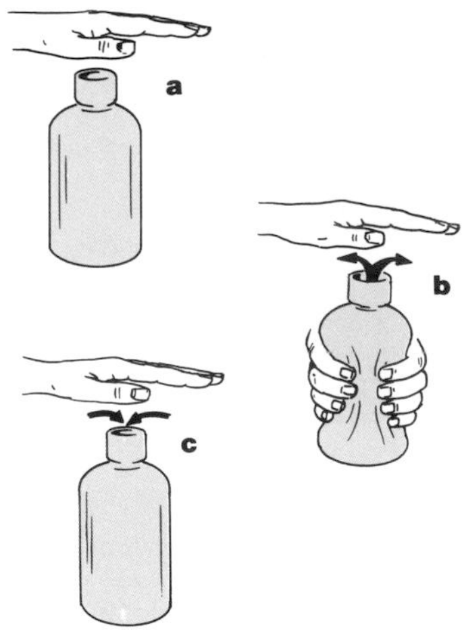

Figure 13-7 No movement of the bottle's sides results in no air moving in or out (a). Pushing the bottle's sides in causes air to move out (b). The bottle sides snap back and air is pulled in (c).

Hold your hand over a plastic bottle such as the one shown in Figure 13-7. You will feel no air moving in or out of the bottle opening. Squeeze the bottle as shown in Figure 13-7. You will feel air rushing out. Why? As the sides of the bottle are pushed in, air is pushed out. Now allow the sides of the bottle to snap back to their original shape, as in Figure 13-7. You can feel air rushing back into the bottle.

Your chest is like the plastic bottle. Its shape and size change, allowing you to breathe in and out. The size of your chest changes due to the action of a muscle located along the bottom of your chest. This muscle is your diaphragm (DI uh fram). The **diaphragm** is a sheetlike muscle that separates the inside of your chest from the intestines and other organs of your abdomen. Read the following statements and match them with parts of the diagram in Figure 13-8.

1. The diaphragm is relaxed. When it relaxes, it is domelike and pushes upward.
2. There is space between the lungs and the inside of the chest wall. The diaphragm pushes up against the lungs, and the space gets smaller.
3. Your lungs are soft. They are squeezed as the space grows smaller.
4. Air is pushed out of the alveoli as the lungs are squeezed. You breathe out.
5. The diaphragm begins to contract. As it tightens up, it flattens and moves downward.
6. The space between the lungs and the inside of the chest wall becomes larger.

What happens when the diaphragm flattens and moves downward?

Figure 13-8 Notice the changes in the diaphragm, lungs, rib cage, and chest cavity during breathing out (a) and breathing in (b).

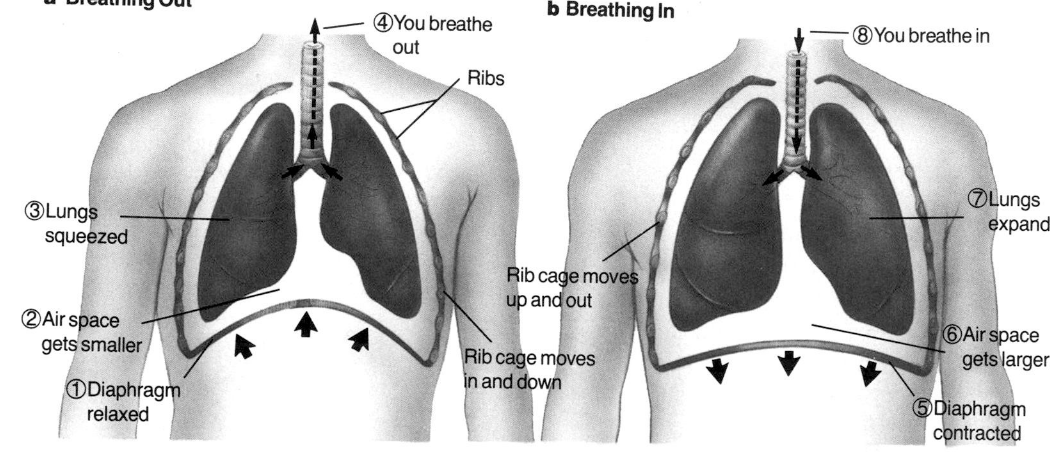

OPTIONS

Breathing In and Out/*Transparency Package*, number 13a. Use color transparency 13a as you teach breathing.

Enrichment/*Teacher Resource Package*, p. 13. Use the Enrichment worksheet shown here to teach the epiglottis.

ENRICHMENT 13

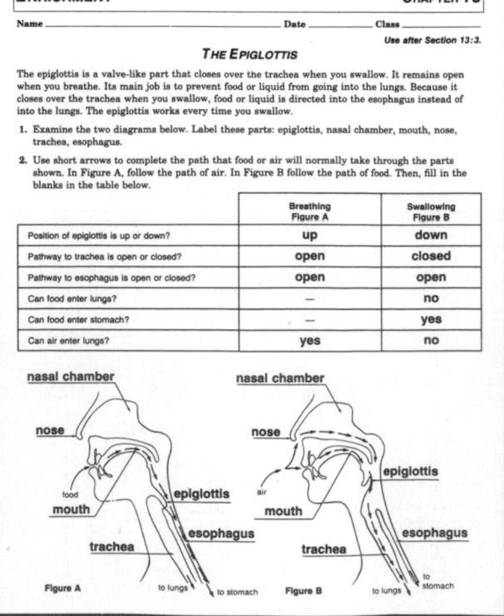

ENRICHMENT CHAPTER 13

Name ______ Date ______ Class ______

Use after Section 13:3.

THE EPIGLOTTIS

The epiglottis is a valve-like part that closes over the trachea when you swallow. It remains open when you breathe. Its main job is to prevent food or liquid from going into the lungs. Because it closes over the trachea when you swallow, food or liquid is directed into the esophagus instead of into the lungs. The epiglottis works every time you swallow.

1. Examine the two diagrams below. Label these parts: epiglottis, nasal chamber, mouth, nose, trachea, esophagus.
2. Use short arrows to complete the path that food or air will normally take through the parts shown. In Figure A, follow the path of air. In Figure B follow the path of food. Then, fill in the blanks in the table below.

	Breathing Figure A	Swallowing Figure B
Position of epiglottis is up or down?	up	down
Pathway to trachea is open or closed?	open	closed
Pathway to esophagus is open or closed?	open	open
Can food enter lungs?	—	no
Can food enter stomach?	—	yes
Can air enter lungs?	yes	no

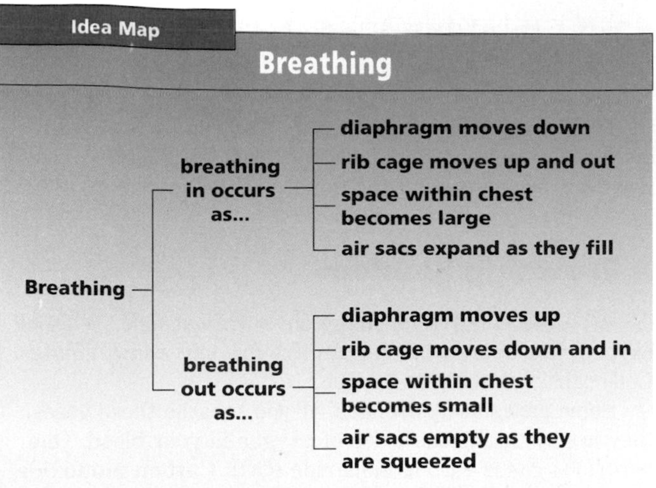

Idea Map
Breathing
Breathing
breathing in occurs as...
diaphragm moves down
rib cage moves up and out
space within chest becomes large
air sacs expand as they fill
breathing out occurs as...
diaphragm moves up
rib cage moves down and in
space within chest becomes small
air sacs empty as they are squeezed

Study Tip: Use this idea map as a study guide to breathing. Does breathing occur in your chest or abdomen?

7. Your lungs expand because the space surrounding the lungs has increased.
8. Air is pulled into the alveoli as the lungs expand. This causes you to breathe in.

Your rib cage also helps with breathing. The rib cage moves in and out as well as up and down, Figure 13-8. The muscles between each rib help with this movement. The ribs can be pulled closer together or moved apart. When your rib cage moves in and slightly down, the ribs close up slightly and the space within your chest gets smaller. Air is squeezed out and you breathe out. As your rib cage moves out and slightly up, the ribs move apart and the space within your chest expands. Air rushes in from the outside and you breathe in.

Mini Lab

How Much Air Do You Breathe Out?

Design an experiment: Use a 1-L graduated cylinder, rubber tube, pan, and water to measure how much air you breathe out. Check with your teacher before doing it. *For more help, refer to the **Skill Handbook,** pages 704-705.*

Check Your Understanding

6. What are the functions of the trachea, bronchi, lungs, and alveoli?
7. How is carbon dioxide formed in your cells, and how does it pass out of your body?
8. In which directions do your rib cage and diaphragm move as you breathe in?
9. **Critical Thinking:** What causes a person to choke?
10. **Biology and Reading:** Where does air go after it leaves the smallest tubes of the bronchi?

RETEACHING 37

RETEACHING — CHAPTER 13

Name — Date — Class — Use with Section 13:2.

HUMAN RESPIRATORY SYSTEM

Oxygen pathway / Carbon dioxide pathway

mouth, esophagus, enlarged view of alveoli X 2000

Respiratory system parts and functions: nose (air enters; hairs block or trap dust and unwanted objects); nasal chamber (warms air and adds moisture as it enters); epiglottis (flap that closes over trachea during swallowing; keeps food and liquid out of lungs); trachea (windpipe) (tube that carries air from nasal chamber to bronchi); bronchus (short tube that carries air from trachea to right and left lungs); lung (main organ of respiratory system; tiny air sacs and blood capillaries where oxygen moves into blood and carbon dioxide moves out); diaphragm (muscle at bottom of chest cavity; moves up when relaxed and helps with breathing out; moves down when contracted and helps with breathing in); capillary (blood vessel that surrounds alveoli; site of gas exchange between blood and air); alveoli (air sacs; site of gas exchange between blood and air)

TEACH

Mini Lab

Water displacement measurements will be between 350-500 mL.

Check for Understanding

Have students respond to the first three questions in Check Your Understanding.

Reteach

Reteaching/Teacher Resource Package, p. 37. Use this worksheet to give students additional practice with the human respiratory system.

Extension: Assign Critical Thinking, Biology and Reading, or some of the **OPTIONS** available with this lesson.

3 APPLY

ACTIVITY/Interview

Interview a molecule of oxygen that just returned from a trip through the human body. Ask it to describe its journey.

4 CLOSE

Audiovisual

Show the videocassette *Breath of Life,* Films for the Humanities and Sciences.

Answers to Check Your Understanding

6. trachea — brings air from nasal chamber to bronchi; bronchi — carry air from trachea to lungs; lungs — help exchange oxygen and carbon dioxide; alveoli — sites of gas exchange between lungs and blood
7. forms during cellular respiration and leaves the body when you breathe out.
8. Rib cage moves up and out as diaphragm moves down.
9. If a person eats when talking, food may fall into the open windpipe.
10. into the alveoli

13:3 Problems of the Respiratory System

PREPARATION

Materials Needed

Make copies of the Reteaching, Enrichment, and Study Guide worksheets in the *Teacher Resource Package*.

Key Science Words

carbon monoxide
pneumonia
emphysema

Process Skills

In the Skill Check, students will define words in context.

1 FOCUS

▶ The objectives are listed on the student page. Remind students to preview these objectives as a guide to this numbered section.

MOTIVATION/Audiovisual

Show the filmstrip *Partners for Life: The Human Heart and Lungs, Part 2 Disease,* Human Relations Media.

Guided Practice

Have students write down their answers to the margin question: They contain carbon monoxide, a poisonous gas.

Independent Practice

Study Guide/*Teacher Resource Package*, p. 75. Use the Study Guide worksheet shown at the bottom of this page for independent practice.

Objectives

7. **Relate** the effects of carbon monoxide poisoning and how to avoid the gas.
8. **Explain** the cause of pneumonia.
9. **Describe** emphysema.

Key Science Words

carbon monoxide
pneumonia
emphysema

13:3 Problems of the Respiratory System

Problems of the respiratory system can be caused by diseases of the respiratory organs. Some problems, however, are caused by the quality of the air we breathe.

A Breathing Problem

A person can live for many days without food. Without oxygen, however, a person can live for only a few minutes. Cells can't live without oxygen.

Some gases are poisonous. If you breathe these gases, they act by taking the place of oxygen in your blood. One poisonous gas is carbon monoxide (CO). **Carbon monoxide** is an odorless, colorless gas sometimes found in the air. If carbon monoxide is inhaled, it is more easily picked up by your red blood cells than oxygen.

Why are exhaust fumes dangerous?

Where does carbon monoxide come from? You know that when fuels are burned, oxygen is used up and carbon dioxide is released—just as in cellular respiration. Carbon monoxide is also given off in small amounts when fuels are burned. For example, carbon monoxide is given off in exhaust fumes when gasoline is burned in a car. The small amount of gas mixes with the surrounding air and is not a health problem. It becomes a serious problem, however, if the exhaust is given off in a closed area, such as a garage. A common cause of carbon monoxide pollution is from the smoke of cigarettes, Figure 13-9.

Bio Tip

Leisure: Swimming is an excellent sport for people with asthma. It provides exercise for the body at the same time as helping a person relax.

Figure 13-9 A person who breathes too much carbon monoxide can't deliver enough oxygen to his or her cells.

OPTIONS

Science Background

There are several different organisms capable of causing pneumonia. These include bacterial, viral, and protist organisms. The most common form, however, is bacterial. This form of pneumonia is caused by the bacterium *Streptococcus pneumoniae*. The form of pneumonia associated with AIDS is caused by a protozoan, *Pneumocystis carinii*.

STUDY GUIDE 75

STUDY GUIDE CHAPTER 13

Name ______ Date ______ Class ______

PROBLEMS OF THE RESPIRATORY SYSTEM

In your textbook, read about respiratory problems in Section 13:3.

A B C D

1. Drawing A shows the normal pathway of 2 oxygen molecules (black dots) going from the alveoli into a lung capillary. Finish the drawing by showing the path that the other 4 oxygen molecules will take in a normal person.
2. Drawing B shows alveoli filled with oxygen and carbon monoxide (squares). Finish the drawing by showing the path that the gas molecules will take when in the lungs of a person with carbon monoxide poisoning.
3. Explain why a person with the problem in diagram B could die. Carbon monoxide gas is picked up more easily than oxygen by red blood cells. If too much is inhaled, too little oxygen will be delivered to the person's cells.
4. Drawing C shows alveoli filled with pus, liquid, and mucus.
   a. What disease may cause this to occur? pneumonia
   b. Can oxygen (black dots) reach the capillaries surrounding these alveoli? no Explain. The alveoli are blocked with pus, liquid, and mucus. This prevents oxygen from getting into the blood.
   c. Is this disease communicable or noncommunicable? communicable Explain. Pneumonia is caused by bacteria or viruses and can be passed from one person to another.
5. Drawing D shows the alveoli of a person with emphysema.
   a. How do these alveoli compare with those of a normal person? The alveoli of a normal person have more surface area. The alveoli of a person with emphysema are broken down.
   b. How is emphysema harmful? A person with emphysema is out of breath because there are not enough alveoli to get oxygen into the blood.

Respiratory Diseases

Pneumonia (noo MOH nyuh) is a lung disease caused by bacteria, a virus, or both. These microbes invade the alveoli and multiply. Their presence causes the lung tissue to form extra mucus. Mucus and pus from microbes fill the alveoli and cause difficulty in breathing. The blocked lungs prevent oxygen from getting into the blood. Because pneumonia is caused by bacteria or viruses, it is communicable. You read in Chapter 4 that a communicable disease is passed from one person to another.

Why is pneumonia communicable?

Some diseases are not passed on from person to person. Emphysema (em fuh SEE muh) is a respiratory disease that is not communicable. **Emphysema** is a lung disease that results in the breakdown of alveoli. A person with emphysema always seems to be out of breath because there are not enough alveoli to get oxygen into the blood. A common cause of emphysema is the breathing in of chemicals while smoking or from air pollution, Figure 13-10.

What happens to a person's lungs with emphysema?

Skill Check

Define words in context: If you say that you are "catching a cold," would this describe a communicable disease? *For more help, refer to the* ***Skill Handbook****, pages 706-711.*

Figure 13-10 More people suffer from respiratory diseases in polluted cities than in cleaner, rural areas.

Check Your Understanding

11. Why is carbon monoxide poisonous?
12. What causes pneumonia?
13. What is emphysema?
14. **Critical Thinking:** A spirometer measures lung capacity and volume. Why are these measurements important?
15. **Biology and Reading:** What happens to the surface area of the lung when alveoli are lost as a result of emphysema?

2 TEACH

Guided Practice

Have students write down their answers to the margin questions: it is caused by bacteria and viruses; they have difficulty with breathing.

Check for Understanding

Have students respond to the first three questions in Check Your Understanding.

Reteach

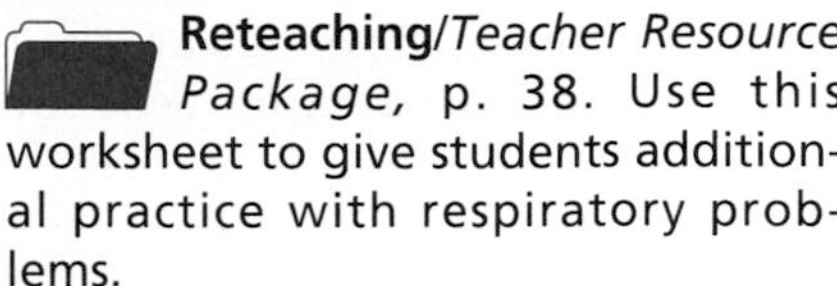

Reteaching/*Teacher Resource Package*, p. 38. Use this worksheet to give students additional practice with respiratory problems.

Extension: Assign Critical Thinking, Biology and Reading, or some of the **OPTIONS** available with this lesson.

3 APPLY

ACTIVITY/Challenge

Have students report on the cause of and problems associated with asthma.

4 CLOSE

Software

Respiratory Diseases and Disorders, Queue, Inc.

RETEACHING 38

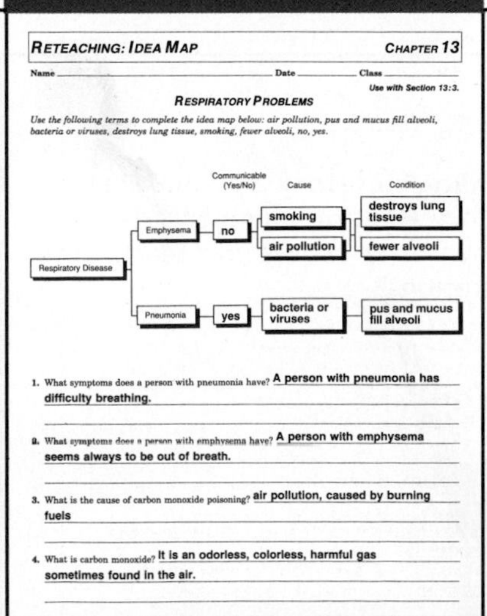

Reteaching: Idea Map **Chapter 13**

Name ______ Date ______ Class ______

Use with Section 13:3.

Respiratory Problems

Use the following terms to complete the idea map below: air pollution, pus and mucus fill alveoli, bacteria or viruses, destroys lung tissue, smoking, fewer alveoli, no, yes.

1. What symptoms does a person with pneumonia have? A person with pneumonia has difficulty breathing.
2. What symptoms does a person with emphysema have? A person with emphysema seems always to be out of breath.
3. What is the cause of carbon monoxide poisoning? air pollution, caused by burning fuels
4. What is carbon monoxide? It is an odorless, colorless, harmful gas sometimes found in the air.

Answers to Check Your Understanding

11. Not enough oxygen is delivered to cells when CO is breathed.
12. bacteria or a virus
13. breakdown of alveoli
14. can show if you have a lung disease
15. Surface area decreases.

13:4 The Role of Excretion

PREPARATION

Materials Needed

Make copies of the Application, Reteaching, Transparency Master, Study Guide, and Lab worksheets in the *Teacher Resource Package*.

▶ Have muddy water for the Mini Lab.

▶ Prepare artificial normal and abnormal urine, silver nitrate, glucose, glucose test tape, and salt water for Lab 13-2.

Key Science Words

excretory system
urea
ureter
urinary bladder
urethra
nephron
urine

Process Skills

In the Mini Lab, students will formulate a model. In Lab 13-2, they will observe, interpret data, make and use tables, and infer. In the Skill Check, they will interpret diagrams.

1 FOCUS

▶ The objectives are listed on the student page. Remind students to preview these objectives as a guide to this numbered section.

ACTIVITY/Demonstration

Use a human torso model to examine and illustrate the number, size, and location of kidneys and the connection of kidneys to blood supply and urinary bladder.

Guided Practice

Have students write down their answers to the margin question: Urea is a poisonous waste product from the breakdown of proteins.

13:4 The Role of Excretion

Objectives

10. **Discuss** the importance of the excretory system.
11. **Sequence** the steps for filtering of blood in a kidney.
12. **Describe** the skin as part of the excretory system.

Key Science Words

excretory system
urea
ureter
urinary bladder
urethra
nephron
urine

Chemical wastes are formed by living cells. Carbon dioxide is removed from your body by your lungs. Other organs, such as your skin and kidneys, help in getting rid of other waste materials.

Waste Removal

Your blood contains many different chemical wastes. These wastes are chemicals that are not needed by the body and may be harmful. If wastes weren't removed from the body, the tissues would fill with poisonous waste products. The wastes would destroy cells and tissues. Fever, poisoning, or even death can result from a buildup of wastes in the tissues.

Wastes are either made by your body cells or are the remains of undigested food in your diet. Getting rid of wastes is called excretion. In Chapter 10, you read that solid wastes are removed by the digestive system. Liquid wastes are removed by the excretory (EK skruh tor ee) system. The **excretory system** is made up of those organs that rid the body of liquid wastes.

Why does urea need to be removed from the body?

Urea (yoo REE uh) is a waste that results from the breakdown of body protein. It's poisonous and must be removed from the body. Urea is picked up from the cells by the blood and carried to the kidneys for removal. The kidneys are the most important organs of the excretory system.

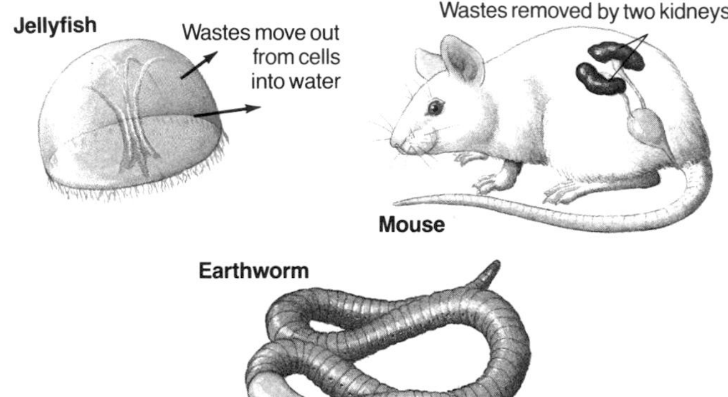

Jellyfish
Wastes move out from cells into water
Wastes removed by two kidneys
Mouse
Earthworm
Wastes removed by tubes connected to outside

Figure 13-11 Compare the excretory organs in a jellyfish, earthworm, and mouse.

OPTIONS

Science Background

Kidneys, lungs, and skin are all involved with excretion of waste chemicals. However, only the kidneys can eliminate urea. Only the lungs can eliminate carbon dioxide. Water and salts are eliminated from several different organs.

Human Excretory System/*Transparency Package*, number 13b. Use color transparency 13b as you teach the role of excretion.

Do all other animals have kidneys as we do? Many animals, such as mice, fish, and frogs, have kidneys. Simpler animals without kidneys, however, must still get rid of wastes. Simple animals such as sponges and jellyfish don't need kidneys. Wastes made by their cells pass out of their cells directly into the water in which they live. Earthworms excrete their wastes through a pair of tubes in each body segment. These tubes connect the inside of the animal to the outside. Compare the organs of excretion in the animals in Figure 13-11.

Human Kidneys

The human body has two kidneys, each about as big as a fist. Kidneys could be described as blood filters. To understand the job of your kidneys, let's look at how a filter works, Figure 13-12. Let's assume you have some muddy water and you want to separate the mud from the water. The muddy water can be poured through filter paper. The mud will be caught by the paper, while the water will pass through. Your kidneys work in a way similar to the filter paper. They filter wastes from your blood. During one day, your kidneys filter up to 200 liters of blood.

If wastes were not removed from your body, they would build up in your blood and act as a poison. In order to carry out their job of removing wastes, your kidneys are hooked up to your blood vessels. Match the following numbered steps to parts of the human excretory system shown in Figure 13-13.

Mini Lab

What Does a Kidney Do?

Formulate a model: Filter some muddy water to model how the kidneys work. *For more help, refer to the **Skill Handbook**, pages 706-711.*

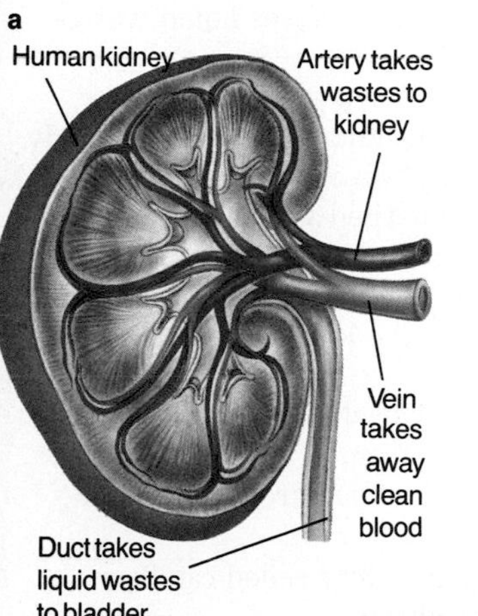

Figure 13-12 The human kidney (a) is a filter for blood. The filter paper catches mud. Clear water passes through the filter (b).

2 TEACH

MOTIVATION/Filmstrip

Show the filmstrip *Your Kidneys – Living Filters,* Clearvue Inc.

Concept Development

▶ Explain that the kidneys selectively filter from the blood excess water, urea, certain ions or salts, and bile pigments resulting from hemoglobin breakdown. The bile pigment gives urine its yellow color.

Mini Lab

Coffee filters may be used if filter paper is not available. Obtaining clear water may require two filterings or double filters. Do the demonstration using water and sand rather than muddy water to hasten the process of filtration. Let students examine the water to be filtered. Make sure that they see the filter paper and its contents, and the pure water that has separated.

Independent Practice

Study Guide/*Teacher Resource Package,* p. 76. Use the Study Guide worksheet shown at the bottom of this page for independent practice.

STUDY GUIDE 76

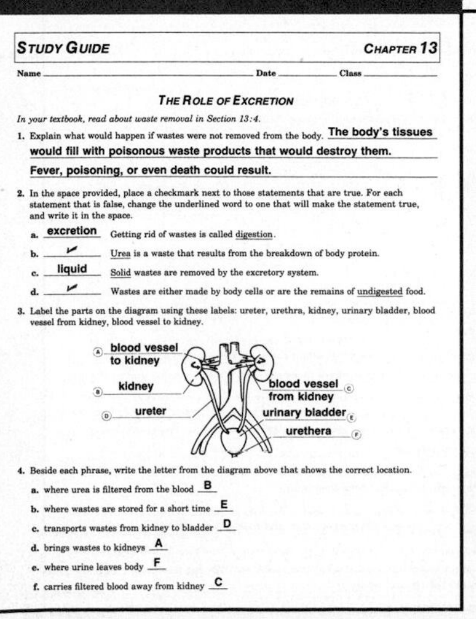

STUDY GUIDE CHAPTER 13

Name ______ Date ______ Class ______

THE ROLE OF EXCRETION

In your textbook, read about waste removal in Section 13:4.

1. Explain what would happen if wastes were not removed from the body. The body's tissues would fill with poisonous waste products that would destroy them. Fever, poisoning, or even death could result.

2. In the space provided, place a checkmark next to those statements that are true. For each statement that is false, change the underlined word to one that will make the statement true, and write it in the space.
   a. excretion Getting rid of wastes is called digestion.
   b. ✔ Urea is a waste that results from the breakdown of body protein.
   c. liquid Solid wastes are removed by the excretory system.
   d. ✔ Wastes are either made by body cells or are the remains of undigested food.

3. Label the parts on the diagram using these labels: ureter, urethra, kidney, urinary bladder, blood vessel from kidney, blood vessel to kidney.

4. Beside each phrase, write the letter from the diagram above that shows the correct location.
   a. where urea is filtered from the blood B
   b. where wastes are stored for a short time E
   c. transports wastes from kidney to bladder D
   d. brings wastes to kidneys A
   e. where urine leaves body F
   f. carries filtered blood away from kidney C

TEACH

Convergent Question

Explain that the kidney is considered to be a body or blood filter. Ask: What does it filter from the blood? What does it not filter from the blood?

MOTIVATION/Audiovisual

Show the filmstrip *Urinary System,* Carolina Biological Supply Co.

Independent Practice

Study Guide/*Teacher Resource Package*, p. 77. Use the Study Guide worksheet shown at the bottom of this page for independent practice.

Guided Practice

Have students write down their answers to the margin question: Wastes diffuse out of the blood into nephrons inside the kidneys. Urea, excess salts, and excess water pass out of the kidneys via the ureters to the urinary bladder and then out of the body via the urethra.

Figure 13-13 Follow the path of blood as it is cleaned by the human excretory system.

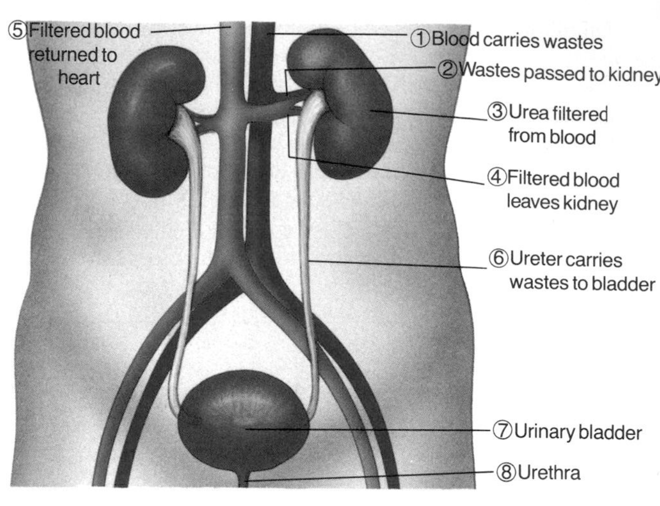

⑤Filtered blood returned to heart
①Blood carries wastes
②Wastes passed to kidney
③Urea filtered from blood
④Filtered blood leaves kidney
⑥Ureter carries wastes to bladder
⑦Urinary bladder
⑧Urethra

1. Blood carrying wastes moves through the body's arteries.
2. Small arteries bring blood to be filtered into each kidney.
3. The kidneys filter urea from the blood.
4. The filtered blood leaves the kidney through a vein. The blood is now free of wastes.
5. The blood in the veins is taken to the heart and other parts of the body.
6. Wastes from the blood leave each kidney through a ureter (YOOR ut ur). A **ureter** is a tube that carries wastes from a kidney to the urinary bladder.
7. The **urinary bladder** is a sac that stores liquid wastes removed from the kidneys.
8. The **urethra** (yoo REE thruh) is a tube that carries liquid wastes from the urinary bladder to outside the body.

What is the path of wastes from the blood through the body?

How do the kidneys do their job of filtering blood? Look at Figure 13-14. It shows an enlarged view of a nephron (NEF rahn), which is a small part of a kidney. A **nephron** is a tiny filter unit of the kidney. Each kidney has about one million nephrons that allow the kidneys to filter your blood every day.

Use the figure and the numbered steps to follow the pathway of blood through a nephron.

1. Blood with blood cells, salts, sugar, urea, and water enters each nephron.
2. The blood first passes into a tightly coiled capillary inside a cuplike part of the nephron.

OPTIONS

Application/*Teacher Resource Package*, p. 13. Use the Application worksheet shown here to give students practice in understanding the operation of an artificial kidney.

STUDY GUIDE 77

STUDY GUIDE CHAPTER 13

Name ______ Date ______ Class ______

THE ROLE OF EXCRETION

5. Complete the chart below by writing the following phrases under the correct organ pictured.

body filter
has sweat glands
helps cool body
removes CO_2
removes water in breath
contains alveoli
removes urea
protective cover
controls water and salt loss

removes CO_2	body filter	has sweat glands
contains alveoli	removes urea	helps cool body
removes water in breath	controls water and salt loss	protective cover

6. In the space provided, place a checkmark next to the statements that are true. For each statement that is false, change the underlined word to one that will make the statement true and write it in the space.

a. nephrons Each kidney has about one million tiny filter units called ureters.
b. ✓ Blood with blood cells, salts, sugar, urea, and water enters each filter unit.
c. ✓ All materials except urea and excess water and salts diffuse back into the blood after filtering.
d. ✓ Filtered waste carried out of the kidney to the bladder is known as urine.
e. salt Each of the body's two to five million sweat glands gives off water and sugar.
f. can't The skin can control water loss.

APPLICATION 13

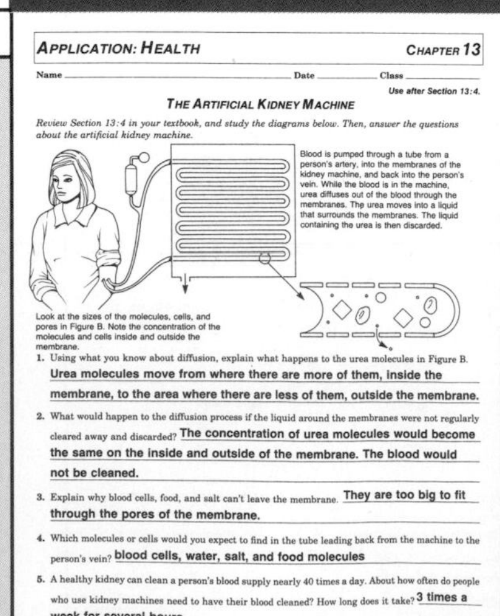

APPLICATION: HEALTH CHAPTER 13

Name ______ Date ______ Class ______

Use after Section 13:4.

THE ARTIFICIAL KIDNEY MACHINE

Review Section 13:4 in your textbook, and study the diagrams below. Then, answer the questions about the artificial kidney machine.

Blood is pumped through a tube from a person's artery, into the membranes of the kidney machine, and back into the person's vein. While the blood is in the machine, urea diffuses out of the blood through the membranes. The urea moves into a liquid that surrounds the membranes. The liquid containing the urea is then discarded.

Look at the sizes of the molecules, cells, and pores in Figure B. Note the concentration of the molecules and cells inside and outside the membrane.

1. Using what you know about diffusion, explain what happens to the urea molecules in Figure B. Urea molecules move from where there are more of them, inside the membrane, to the area where there are less of them, outside the membrane.
2. What would happen to the diffusion process if the liquid around the membranes were not regularly cleared away and discarded? The concentration of urea molecules would become the same on the inside and outside of the membrane. The blood would not be cleaned.
3. Explain why blood cells, food, and salt can't leave the membrane. They are too big to fit through the pores of the membrane.
4. Which molecules or cells would you expect to find in the tube leading back from the machine to the person's vein? blood cells, water, salt, and food molecules
5. A healthy kidney can clean a person's blood supply nearly 40 times a day. About how often do people who use kidney machines need to have their blood cleaned? How long does it take? 3 times a week for several hours

3. Water, salts, sugar, and urea pass into the cuplike part of the nephron. Everything but blood cells is forced out of the blood.
4. Follow the flow shown by the dashed black arrows that indicate the movement of these materials into a long tube.
5. Notice that the capillary with the original blood cells from step 2 now twists itself around the long tube. The movement of blood cells is shown by the dashed red arrows.
6. All materials except urea, water, and salts diffuses back into the blood. This movement is shown by the solid black arrows. Water passes back into the blood by osmosis.
7. The cleaned blood now leaves the kidney and returns to the heart.
8. The filtered wastes stay in the long tube and are carried out of the kidney through the ureter to the bladder. Waste liquid that reaches the ureter is called **urine.** Urine passes out of the body.

Taking in more water or salt means more of these nutrients will be excreted. Less water or salt taken in means less will be excreted. Kidneys regulate the amount of water and salts kept within the body. A healthy person can excrete about one liter of urine each day.

Skill Check

Interpret diagrams: What feature of Figure 13-14 makes it easier for you to follow the pathways of blood, wastes, and water? *For more help, refer to the* ***Skill Handbook****, pages 706-711.*

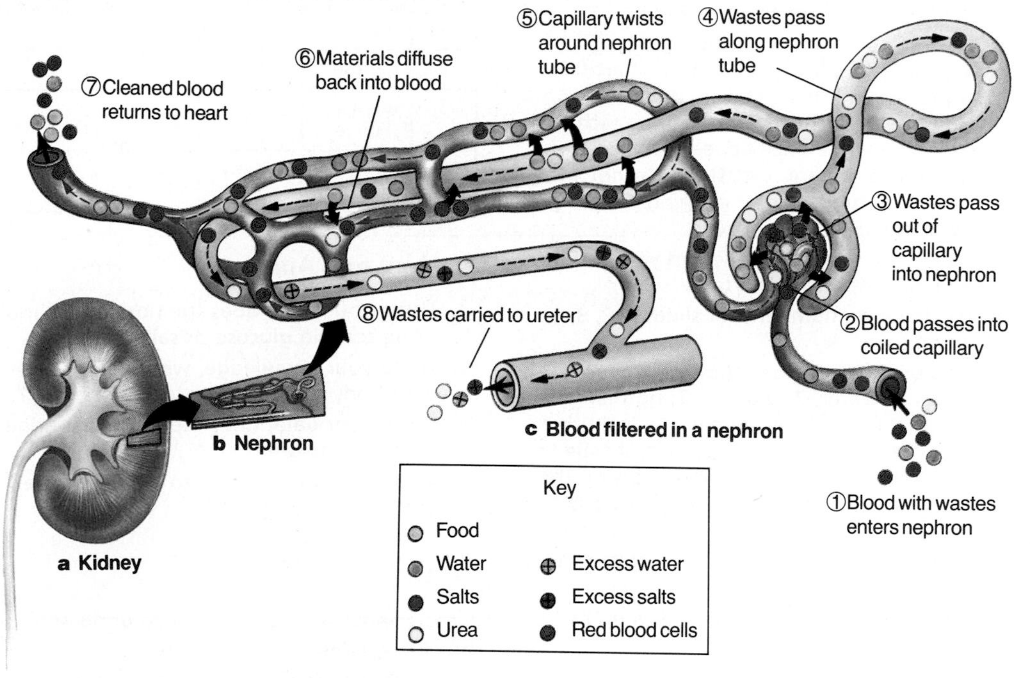

⑤Capillary twists around nephron tube
④Wastes pass along nephron tube
⑥Materials diffuse back into blood
⑦Cleaned blood returns to heart
③Wastes pass out of capillary into nephron
⑧Wastes carried to ureter
②Blood passes into coiled capillary
b Nephron
c Blood filtered in a nephron
①Blood with wastes enters nephron
a Kidney
Key
Food
Water
Salts
Urea
Excess water
Excess salts
Red blood cells

Figure 13-14 A section of a kidney (a) shows the position of a nephron (b). Follow the pathway of materials through a nephron (c).

TEACH

Concept Development

▶ Go over the sequence of events in Figure 13-14. Ask students to follow the pathway of one chemical at a time through the nephron. Be sure to specify whether water and salt are to be considered in excess or as chemicals needed and retained by the body. The pathway that needed water and salts follow will be different from the pathway for excess salt and water.

Guided Practice

Provide students with a list of the following parts: artery entering kidney, vein leaving kidney, kidney, ureter, urethra, nephron, urinary bladder. Ask them to indicate the number of these structures present in the human body.

Check for Understanding

Have students prepare a chart with the following headings: Blood components, Enters kidney by way of artery, Leaves kidney by way of vein, Leaves kidney by way of ureter, Leaves kidney as urine. Under Blood components, list the following items: red cell, needed water, excess water, urea, glucose (food), needed salt, excess salt. Have students complete the chart by placing check marks in the proper columns.

Reteach

Ask students which blood parts or chemicals are needed by the body and which are not needed. Have them use information from Check for Understanding.

TRANSPARENCY 59

TRANSPARENCY MASTER — CHAPTER 13

NEPHRON UNIT OF KIDNEY

artery entering nephron
all chemicals except blood cells are squeezed out from coiled capillary and caught here
cup-like part
food is taken out of tube and put back into blood
tightly coiled capillary
artery leaving coiled capillary
long tube
blood returning to body from nephron
tube leads from nephron
capillary twists itself around long tube
water is taken out of tube and put back into blood
excess
excess
urine
salt is taken out of tube and put back into blood
chemicals in water leave nephron as urine
Key:
Red blood cells = O
Salts = ▲ ▲extra
Food = ●
Urea = ■
Water = ● ●extra

OPTIONS

Transparency Master/*Teacher Resource Package*, p. 59. Use the Transparency Master shown here to teach the nephron unit of the kidney.

Lab 13-2 Urine

Overview

In this lab, students are given an opportunity to check the chemical composition of normal and abnormal urine.

Objectives: Upon completing this lab, students will have learned (1) **to test** for and recognize if salt is present in a liquid, (2) **to test** for and recognize if glucose is present in a liquid, (3) **to test** for the presence or absence of salt and glucose in urine.

Time Allotment: 1 class period

Preparation

▶ For normal urine – add 1 teaspoon sodium chloride (table salt) and 4 drops yellow food coloring to 500 mL tap water.

▶ For abnormal urine – same as above with 1 teaspoon glucose added.

▶ For silver nitrate – add 4 g silver nitrate to 250 mL distilled water.

▶ For glucose – add 1 teaspoon glucose to 250 mL tap water.

▶ For salt water – add 1 teaspoon sodium chloride to 500 mL tap water.

 **Lab 13-2 worksheet**/*Teacher Resource Package,* pp. 51-52.

Teaching the Lab

▶ Remind students to use silver nitrate cautiously.

▶ Use distilled water (available in grocery store) for tube 1 when testing for salt. Some tap water will contain high enough concentrations of salt to yield a false positive test.

▶ Discuss abnormal urine as being like that from a diabetic.

▶ **Troubleshooting:** Emphasize that students will be using artificial urine and that there is no health risk to them.

Urine — Lab 13–2

Problem: What chemicals can be detected in urine?

Skills

observe, interpret data, make and use tables, infer

Materials 

4 test tubes	labels
test-tube rack	glucose
distilled water	glucose test tape
salt water	droppers
normal artificial urine	4 glass slides
abnormal artificial urine	
silver nitrate in bottle with dropper	

Procedure

1. Copy the data table.
2. Use labels to number four test tubes 1, 2, 3, and 4 and place them in a rack.
3. Half fill each tube with the following– 1: water, 2: salt water, 3: normal artificial urine, 4: abnormal artificial urine.
4. Add five drops of silver nitrate to each tube. If a white haze appears, this means that salt is present. **CAUTION:** *Do not spill silver nitrate on skin or clothing. Rinse with water if spillage occurs.*
5. **Make and use tables:** Record your before and after results in the table.
6. Use labels to number four slides 1, 2, 3, and 4.
7. Add one drop of the following to each slide– 1: water, 2: glucose, 3: normal artificial urine, 4: abnormal artificial urine.
8. Touch a small piece of glucose test tape to each drop. If a green color appears on the tape, it means that the sugar glucose is present.
9. Record your before and after results in the table.
10. Dispose of your samples as indicated by your teacher.

Data and Observations

1. How can you tell if a liquid contains salt?
2. How can you tell if a liquid contains glucose?

TUBE	TUBE CONTENTS	HAZE PRESENT BEFORE?	HAZE PRESENT AFTER?	SALT PRESENT?
1	water	no	no	no
2	salt water	no	yes	yes
3	normal urine	no	yes	yes
4	abnormal urine	no	yes	yes
SLIDE	**SLIDE CONTENTS**	**COLOR OF PAPER BEFORE**	**COLOR OF PAPER AFTER**	**GLUCOSE PRESENT?**
1	water	yellow	yellow	no
2	glucose	yellow	green	yes
3	normal urine	yellow	yellow	no
4	abnormal urine	yellow	green	yes

Analyze and Apply

1. Using your data, does the normal artificial urine contain glucose or salt?
2. Using your knowledge, would urine from your body contain glucose or salt? Why?
3. Using your data, does the abnormal urine contain glucose?
4. **Apply:** Why is it useful to know if urine contains salt or glucose?

Extension

Experiment: Add table sugar to urine and test for glucose.

ANSWERS

Data and Observations

1. Silver nitrate makes a liquid hazy in the presence of salt.
2. Glucose test tape turns green in the presence of glucose.

Analyze and Apply

1. salt
2. It would contain salt because excess salt in the blood is excreted. It wouldn't contain glucose because glucose is absorbed back into the blood.
3. yes
4. If urine doesn't contain salt or if it does contain glucose, then the nephrons in the kidneys may not be functioning correctly.

Excretion and the Skin

Skin has three main jobs. First, it protects the body from infection. Second, it is a sense organ. Third, it helps in the excretion of water and salts.

Figure 13-15 shows what a slice through skin looks like. The top layer of this organ is made of a layer of living cells covered with dead cells that are constantly flaking off. A lower layer of skin has capillaries and sweat glands. The sweat glands open onto the surface of the skin. Hair grows from this bottom layer. This layer also has many different types of nerve cells. You will learn in Chapter 16 how nerves in the skin make it an important sense organ.

Your body has two to five million sweat glands like those shown in Figure 13-15. Each gland gives off water and salts much as the kidneys do. Unlike kidneys, however, your skin can't control water or salt loss. It's possible for you to lose half a liter of water each day through the skin without noticing it, unless you sweat heavily.

Does loss of water through the skin help the body? This water loss is one way the body cools itself. You usually sweat more when the weather is warm or when you exercise. Water moving onto the skin from the sweat glands evaporates. The evaporation cools the body.

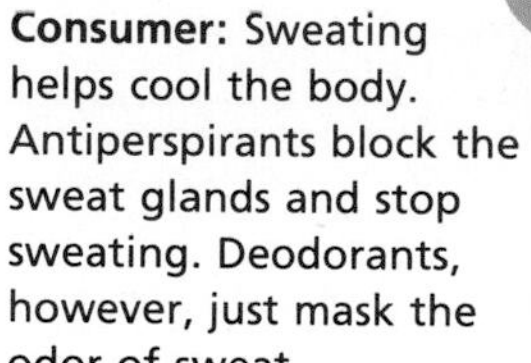

Bio Tip

Consumer: Sweating helps cool the body. Antiperspirants block the sweat glands and stop sweating. Deodorants, however, just mask the odor of sweat.

How does sweat help the body?

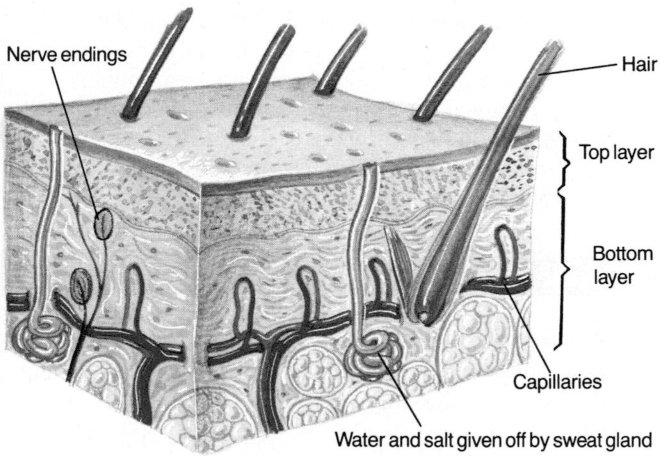

Figure 13-15 The sweat glands are a part of the excretory system. Find these glands in this cross section of skin.

Problems of the Excretory System

Like other organs, the kidneys may become diseased. The kidneys can be damaged over time if a person has high blood pressure. Another cause of kidney damage is infection caused by bacteria.

TEACH

ACTIVITY/Brainstorming

Ask students what the skin protects against. Answers should include preventing disease-causing organisms, such as bacteria, from entering the body and loss of water.

ACTIVITY/Demonstration

Have a student exhale onto a piece of metal or a mirror. Explain that moisture in exhaled air condenses on a cooler surface. Explain that students can see their breath on a cold morning because the water vapor in warm breath condenses in cold air as water droplets.

Guided Practice

Have students write down their answers to the margin question: Sweat cools the surface of the skin, which cools the body.

Independent Practice

Study Guide/*Teacher Resource Package,* p. 78. Use the Study Guide worksheet shown at the bottom of this page for independent practice.

STUDY GUIDE 78

STUDY GUIDE — CHAPTER 13

Name ______ Date ______ Class ______

VOCABULARY

Review the new words used in Chapter 13 of your textbook. Then, complete this puzzle.

1. Put the following words into two groups by adding them to this table under the proper heading: urethra, diaphragm, bronchi, ureter, trachea, nephron, alveoli, epiglottis, urinary bladder, respiratory system, excretory system.

Parts of the respiratory system	Parts of the excretory system
lungs	kidney
rib cage	sweat glands
diaphragm	urethra
bronchi	ureter
trachea	nephron
alveoli	urinary bladder
epiglottis	

2. Put the following words into two groups by writing them in this table under the proper heading: urea, diaphragm, urine, emphysema, excess salt, pneumonia.

Respiration	Excretion
emphysema	urea
pneumonia	urine
diaphragm	excess salt

OPTIONS

What Chemical Wastes Are Removed by the Lungs, Skin, and Kidneys?/*Lab Manual,* pp. 107-110. Use this lab as an extension to the role of excretion.

TEACH

Guided Practice

Have students write down their answers to the margin question: Both remove wastes from a person's blood.

Check for Understanding

Have students respond to the first three questions in Check Your Understanding.

Reteach

Reteaching/*Teacher Resource Package*, p. 39. Use this worksheet to give students additional practice on the route wastes take through the kidneys.

Extension: Assign Critical Thinking, Biology and Reading, or some of the **OPTIONS** available with this lesson.

3 APPLY

Summary

Have students name wastes that are eliminated by the skin and kidneys.

4 CLOSE

Discussion

Discuss why one would test urine for drug use.

Answers to Check Your Understanding

16. ureters — carry liquid waste (urine) from kidneys to urinary bladder; urethra — carries liquid waste from bladder to outside the body
17. excess water, urea, and excess salts
18. sense organ, excretion of salts and water, protects body from infection
19. When the concentration of urea is higher in the tube of the nephron than in the blood, it will pass out of the tube into the blood.
20. the kidney

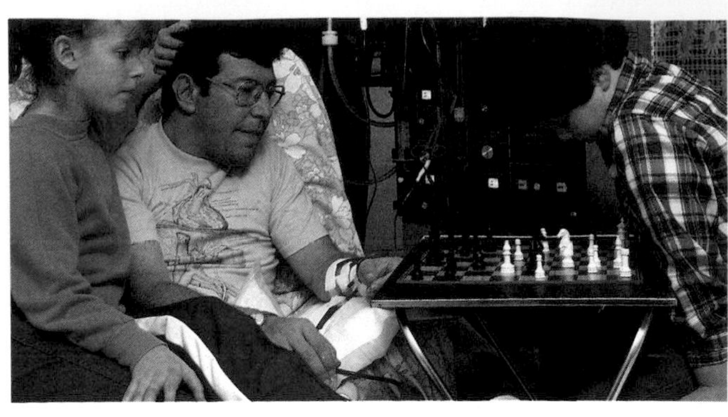

Figure 13-16 Each session on an artificial kidney machine can take up to five hours.

How does a kidney machine compare with a kidney?

Humans are lucky in that they can live with only one kidney. Thus, if one kidney is damaged, we still have the other one to help with excretion. But, what happens when both kidneys are damaged? In such cases, either a kidney machine must be used, or a kidney transplant operation should be performed.

An artificial kidney machine, Figure 13-16, removes urea from the blood when the kidneys can't function. The artificial kidney machine works by passing a person's blood through a very long tube made from a thin membrane. This membrane is surrounded by liquid. Urea in the blood diffuses through the tube membrane and into the liquid. Fresh liquid is constantly added and the used liquid is constantly removed. Blood without urea is then returned to the person. The kidney machine is designed to act just like your nephrons. A person may need up to three sessions a week on the kidney machine.

Check Your Understanding

16. What are the jobs of your ureters and urethra?
17. Name three things that kidneys filter out of the blood.
18. What are the three main jobs of the skin?
19. **Critical Thinking:** How does the process of diffusion allow materials in a nephron to be returned to the blood?
20. **Biology and Reading:** There's a pair of tubes in each body segment of an earthworm that removes wastes made by the cells. What organ in humans has the same function as these tubes in earthworms?

RETEACHING 39

RETEACHING — CHAPTER 13

Name ______ Date ______ Class ______

Use with Section 13:4.

JOURNEY THROUGH THE KIDNEYS

Describe the path of the blood as it travels through the kidneys. Use these terms to fill in the blanks: all body parts, urinary bladder, small arteries, ureters, urea, vein, and urethra.

1. Wastes in blood enter through **small arteries**.
2. Kidneys filter **urea** the blood.
3. Blood leaves a kidney through a **vein**.
4. Veins take clean blood to **all body parts**.
5. Wastes leave kidneys through **ureters**, which carry wastes from the kidneys to the **urinary bladder**.
6. The **urethra** is a tube that carries liquid wastes to outside the body.

Describe the path of the blood as it travels through a single nephron. Fill in the blanks below.

1. The tiny filter units of the kidney are the **nephrons**.
2. Blood enters the capillary of each nephron bringing **blood cells, salts, food, urea, and water**.
3. The **blood cells** remain in the capillary.
4. The **water, salts, food, and urea** pass into the cuplike part of the nephron and flow through a long tube.
5. The **capillary** twists around the long tube.
6. The **food, needed water, and needed salts** pass back into the blood.
7. The **blood cells, needed water, needed salts, and food** leave the nephron and return to the body.
8. The **urea, excess water, and salts** stay in the long tube and are carried out of the body as **urine**.

Answer the following questions.

1. How does loss of water through sweat glands help the body? **It cools the body by lowering the temperature by evaporation.**
2. How does the skin work as an organ of excretion? **It excretes water and salt.**

Science and Society

Organ Transplants

The first successful kidney transplant operation was performed in the 1960s. A kidney was donated from one identical twin to the other. Up to that time, the major problem with organ transplants was that tissues from another person's body were usually rejected. Today, we use drugs that reduce rejection. Kidney transplants are now rather common. Why is the kidney such a good organ for transplants? Remember, each person has two of these organs and could survive with only one. It is not unusual for a healthy person to donate a kidney to another member of his or her family or to an unrelated person. Healthy kidneys are also available from people who have agreed to donate their organs when they die.

After a kidney transplant operation, a person has a new chance to live a long and healthy life.

What Do You Think?

1. There are a greater number of people needing kidney transplants than there are available kidneys. Thousands of patients are now waiting for a healthy kidney donor. The demand is much greater than the supply. Where should the supply of organs come from? Could they be taken from animals such as baboons, terminally ill patients, or from prisoners on death row? At the present time, the most common source is from the bodies of people in fatal auto accidents. Should everyone be expected to carry around a permission card to donate their kidneys?

2. Kidney and other transplant operations are very expensive. Should only those who can afford to pay for the operations be able to have them? If the government or insurance companies pay for the transplant operations, who will decide who gets an organ? Is the life of a four-year-old child worth more than that of a sixty-year-old adult? How should these choices be controlled?

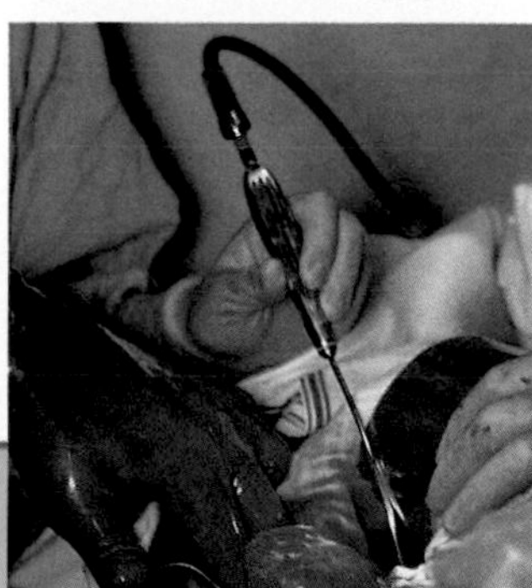

3. An illegal market exists that encourages healthy people to sell one of their kidneys to the highest bidder. Prices as high as $13 000 for a kidney have been reported. Many of these kidneys come to the United States from foreign countries. These organs may not be in a state suitable for transplanting. A person may spend a lot of money and then discover the organ to be useless. Should the United States pass laws that prevent the importing of human organs?

Conclusion: What can be done to assure that anybody who needs a transplant can have one?

A kidney operation

Science and Society

Organ Transplants

Background

The types of transplant operations performed today in decreasing order are: cornea, kidney, bone marrow, skin, liver, lung, heart, and endocrine. The major problem with transplants is the rejection reaction that results from action taken by the recipient's immune system. A drug called cyclosporin A is able to suppress the immune system, so the success rate of transplants has increased in recent years.

Teaching Suggestions

The questions that appear in the student text should provide the basis for an excellent debate. You may wish to assign, for extra credit, the task of defending or rejecting the question being raised.

What Do You Think?

There are no incorrect answers to these questions. Students should attempt to answer them based on their own feelings or opinions.

Conclusion: Students may suggest that the government would have to become more involved in order to keep transplants fair for all people.

Suggested Reading

O'Neil, Paul. "The Heart that Failed." *Discover,* Jan. 1985, pp. 14-15.

CHAPTER 13 REVIEW

Summary

Summary statements can be used by students to review the major concepts of the chapter.

Key Science Words

All boldfaced terms from the chapter are listed.

Testing Yourself

Using Words

1. nephron
2. pneumonia
3. epiglottis
4. ureter
5. alveoli
6. diaphragm
7. bronchi
8. urethra
9. carbon monoxide

Finding Main Ideas

10. p. 264; Carbon dioxide is formed in all body cells as a waste gas during cellular respiration. Carbon dioxide diffuses into the blood and is given off in the air as you breathe out.
11. p. 277; Urea, sugar, water, and salts diffuse out of nephron capillaries .
12. p. 269; Oxygen diffuses into cells, and carbon dioxide diffuses out of cells.
13. p. 270; The domelike diaphragm moves upward and squeezes trapped air in the chest wall. The pressure of the air increases, the lungs are squeezed, and the space gets smaller.
14. p. 279; Water loss through the skin is one way the body cools itself.
15. p. 273; A person with emphysema does not have enough alveoli to get oxygen into the blood.
16. p. 269; Oxygen diffuses into the alveoli from the bronchi and then into blood capillaries surrounding alveoli. Carbon dioxide diffuses out of capillaries into alveoli and then out of alveoli into the bronchi.

Chapter 13 Review

Summary

13:1 The Role of Respiration

1. Oxygen is taken in and carbon dioxide is given off in the respiratory system.
2. Oxygen is used by cells to convert food to energy. Carbon dioxide is given off as waste.
3. Some animals have no respiratory system. Animals with a respiratory system use skin, gills, lungs, or pairs of tubes for gas exchange.

13:2 Human Respiratory System

4. The respiratory system is made up of tubes that supply air to the alveoli in the lungs.
5. Oxygen moves from lungs to blood to body cells. Carbon dioxide moves from body cells to the lungs.
6. Your diaphragm relaxes and the rib cage moves in when you breathe out. Your diaphragm contracts and the rib cage moves out when you breathe in.

13:3 Problems of the Respiratory System

7. Carbon monoxide is a poisonous gas.
8. Pneumonia is caused by bacteria and viruses.
9. Emphysema causes breakdown of lung tissues.

13:4 The Role of Excretion

10. Kidneys filter wastes such as urea, excess water, and salts from the blood.
11. Blood, carrying wastes from body cells, is filtered in nephrons in the kidney.
12. Your skin excretes water and cools the body.

Key Science Words

alveoli (p. 268)
bronchi (p. 267)
carbon monoxide (p. 272)
diaphragm (p. 270)
emphysema (p. 273)
epiglottis (p. 267)
excretory system (p. 274)
nephron (p. 276)
pneumonia (p. 273)
respiratory system (p. 264)
trachea (p. 267)
urea (p. 274)
ureter (p. 276)
urethra (p. 276)
urinary bladder (p. 276)
urine (p. 277)

Testing Yourself

Using Words

Choose the word from the list of Key Science Words that best fits the definition.

1. tiny filter unit of kidney
2. communicable disease of lungs
3. flap that keeps food out of trachea
4. tube that carries urine from kidney to bladder
5. tiny air sacs of lungs
6. sheetlike muscle that separates chest from rest of body

282

Using Main Ideas

17. The diaphragm moves down as it contracts, allowing the chest wall to enlarge. Air pressure in the chest wall decreases, and air rushes in to inflate the lungs.
18. Earthworms exchange gases by diffusion across the skin. Fish carry on gas exchange across organs called gills.
19. Air enters the nose and passes into the trachea. From the trachea, the air moves into two bronchi that lead to the right and left lung.
20. Urea is the waste that results from the breakdown of body protein, while urine is the liquid waste, containing urea, that passes out of the body. The ureters carry liquid waste from the kidneys to the urinary bladder, while the urethra carries liquid waste from the urinary bladder to outside the body. Carbon dioxide is given off as a waste product of cellular respiration. Carbon monoxide is given off in the burning of fossil fuels.
21. Emphysema can be prevented by not smoking and by avoiding air pollution.

Review

Testing Yourself *continued*

7. tubes that carry air from trachea to both lungs
8. tube that carries urine to the outside of your body
9. poisonous gas in exhaust fumes

Finding Main Ideas

List the page number where each main idea below is found. Then, explain each main idea.

10. why more carbon dioxide is given off than taken in
11. which chemicals are forced out of the capillaries of the nephrons
12. which two gases are exchanged during cellular respiration
13. what makes the space around your lungs get smaller as you breathe out
14. why water loss through the skin can be helpful
15. why a person with emphysema is always short of breath
16. the events that take place in the alveoli

Using Main Ideas

Answer the questions by referring to the page number after each question.

17. Why do your lungs expand when your diaphragm contracts? (p. 271)
18. How do the respiratory systems of earthworms and fish compare? (p. 265)
19. What is the sequence of organs through which air passes, starting with the nose? (pp. 267, 268)
20. How do the following pairs of words differ–urea and urine, ureter and urethra, and carbon dioxide and carbon monoxide? (pp. 268, 272, 274, 276, 277)
21. What can be done to lower the chances of getting emphysema? (p. 273)

Skill Review ✓

For more help, refer to the ***Skill Handbook,*** *pages 704-719.*

1. **Experiment:** Blow up a round balloon for 15 seconds. Tie it closed. Run on the spot for one minute, then blow up a second round balloon for 15 seconds. Tie it closed. Compare the volume of each balloon by measuring their circumferences. How did exercise affect your breathing efficiency?
2. **Formulate a model:** Make a model of your lungs using everyday household materials.
3. **Understand science words:** Use the dictionary to find two words closely related to trachea that are used in biology. Give their meanings.
4. **Infer:** Why can you see your breath on a cold morning? What is being excreted?

Finding Out More

Critical Thinking

1. People with high blood pressure are advised to reduce salt intake. What reasons might be given for this?
2. Compare the chemicals in blood entering and leaving the kidney.

Applications

1. Place your hand just below your ribs and feel the movement of your diaphragm and rib cage as you breathe in and out.
2. Which organs of the respiratory system are used when you cough, cry, hiccup, laugh, yawn, and sing?

Skill Review

1. Exercise should increase your breathing efficiency.
2. Plastic squeeze bottles can be used for lungs, and straws for bronchi and trachea.
3. Examples: tracheid – water-conducting tubes in plants; tracheitis – inflammation of the trachea
4. Warm water vapor from the nose meets the cold air and fogs. Water vapor is being excreted.

Finding Out More

Critical Thinking

1. In high blood pressure, the kidneys retain salt and water instead of passing them out. An elevated salt level in the blood causes constriction of blood vessels and less blood gets to kidneys and cells.
2. Blood entering the kidney contains salts, water, blood cells, proteins, urea, and sugar. The blood leaving the kidneys contains blood cells, proteins, and sugar. It also contains salts and water, but in a lower concentration than the blood entering.

Applications

1. The diaphragm will move down as you breathe in and up when you breathe out.
2. The organs include the epiglottis, trachea, lungs, and diaphragm.

Chapter Review/*Teacher Resource Package*, pp. 65-66.

Chapter Test/*Teacher Resource Package*, pp. 67-69.

Chapter Test/*Computer Test Bank*

Support and Movement

PLANNING GUIDE

CONTENT	TEXT FEATURES	TEACHER RESOURCE PACKAGE	OTHER COMPONENTS
(2 days) 14:1 The Role of the Skeleton Functions of the Skeleton Bones in the Skeleton Bone Growth Bone Structure Joints	Mini Lab: *What Happens to Bone When Calcium is Removed?* p. 287 Mini Lab: *How Strong Can a Hollow Bone Be?* p. 289 Lab 14-1: *Bone Density,* p. 290 Idea Map, p. 286 Check Your Understanding, p. 291	Enrichment: *Human Skeletons,* p. 14 Reteaching: *Bone and Skeleton,* p. 40 Study Guide: *The Role of the Skeleton,* pp. 79-80 Lab 14-1: *Bone Density,* pp. 53-54	**Laboratory Manual:** *How Do Male and Female Skeletons Differ?* p. 115 Color Transparency 14: *The Human Skeleton*
(2 days) 14:2 The Role of Muscles Movement Human Muscle Types How Muscles Work Muscles Work in Pairs	Skill Check: *Classify,* p. 294 Skill Check: *Infer,* p. 296 Lab 14-2: *Muscles,* p. 298 Career Close-up: *Athletic Trainer,* p. 293 Check Your Understanding, p. 297	Application: *Exercise and Skeletal Muscles,* p. 14 Reteaching: *Muscles,* p. 41 Critical Thinking/Problem Solving: *What Are the Jobs of Different Muscles?* p. 14 Skill: *Understand Science Words,* p. 15 Focus: *What You Can Do Without Thinking,* p. 29 Transparency Master: *Muscle Types,* p. 65 Study Guide: *The Roles of Muscles,* pp. 81-82 Lab 14-2: *Muscles,* pp. 55-56	
(2 days) 14:3 Bone and Muscle Problems Problems of the Skeletal System Problems of the Muscular System Making Products Fit People	Skill Check: *Understand Science Words,* p. 299 Check Your Understanding, p. 301	Reteaching: *Bone and Muscle Problems,* p. 42 Study Guide: *Bone and Muscle Problems,* p. 83 Study Guide: *Vocabulary,* p. 84	**Laboratory Manual:** *What Causes Sports Injuries?* p. 111
Chapter Review	Summary Key Science Words Testing Yourself Finding Main Ideas Using Main Ideas Skill Review	Chapter Review, pp. 70-71 Chapter Test, pp. 72-74 Unit Test, pp. 75-76	**Test Bank**

MATERIALS NEEDED

LAB 14-1, p. 290	LAB 14-2, p. 298	MARGIN FEATURES
100-mL graduated cylinder balance water bones of chicken, cow, pig, turkey	scissors string tape paper punch metal fastener index card	Skill Check, p. 299 dictionary Mini Lab, p. 287 beaker tweezers chicken bone 6% hydrochloric acid Mini Lab, p. 289 tape paper Mini Lab, p. 295 cooked chicken leg (drumstick attached)

OBJECTIVES

		OBJECTIVES CORRELATION			
SECTION	OBJECTIVE	CHECK YOUR UNDERSTANDING	CHAPTER REVIEW	TRP CHAPTER REVIEW	TRP CHAPTER TEST
14:1	1. **Explain** the functions and growth of the skeleton.	1, 5	11, 16, 19	3, 5, 7, 8, 11, 15, 16, 19, 33	2, 6, 7, 15, 18, 37, 38, 39
	2. **Define** the six tissues of bones.	2	5, 7, 14	13, 23, 34	4, 9, 11, 13
	3. **Identify** three types of joints.	3, 4	10	9, 20, 22, 24, 25, 31	1, 20, 22, 23, 43, 44, 45, 46, 47, 48
14:2	4. **Compare** three kinds of muscles.	6	2, 3, 21	2, 18, 32, 35, 36	12, 26, 27, 28, 29, 30, 31, 32, 40, 41
	5. **Explain** how muscles work to move body parts.	7, 8, 9	6, 23	1, 12, 14, 17, 21	10, 17, 21, 24, 25, 26, 33
	6. **Relate** how muscles work in pairs.	10	8, 15, 22	26, 27, 28, 29, 30	3, 16, 49, 50, 51, 52, 53, 54
14:3	7. **Discuss** problems of the skeletal system.	11	4, 12, 20	4, 6	8, 35, 42
	8. **Give examples** of problems of the muscular system.	12, 14, 15	24	36	5, 19, 36
	9. **Explain** the purpose of new designs for products.	13	17	10	14

Support and Movement

CHAPTER OVERVIEW

Key Concepts

In this chapter, students will study the structure and function of the skeletal and muscular systems. The anatomy of bones and joints is examined. Muscles, muscle pairing, and their relation to movement are discussed. Several problems of the skeletal and muscular systems are examined.

Key Science Words

arthritis	muscular system
ball-and-socket joint	skeletal muscle
cardiac muscle	skeletal system
fixed joint	smooth muscle
hinge joint	solid bone
involuntary muscle	spongy bone
ligament	sprain
muscular dystrophy	tendon
	voluntary muscle

Skill Development

In Lab 14-1, students will **interpret data, form a hypothesis, experiment,** and **measure in SI** while comparing mammal and bird bone density. In Lab 14-2, they will **formulate a model, experiment,** and **infer** while examining muscle function. In the Skill Check on page 294, they will classify muscle types. In the Skill Check on page 296, they will **infer** where muscle tissue goes when it contracts. In the Skill Check on page 299, they will **understand** the **science word** *arthritis.* In the Mini Lab on page 287, they will **experiment** with bone calcium. In the Mini Lab on page 289, they will **formulate a model** of hollow bone. In the Mini Lab on page 295, they will **observe** a chicken thigh.

CHAPTER PREVIEW

Chapter Content

Review this outline for Chapter 14 before you read the chapter.

14:1 The Role of the Skeleton
- Functions of the Skeleton
- Bones in the Skeleton
- Bone Growth
- Bone Structure
- Joints

14:2 The Role of Muscles
- Movement
- Human Muscle Types
- How Muscles Work
- Muscles Work in Pairs

14:3 Bone and Muscle Problems
- Problems of the Skeletal System
- Problems of the Muscular System
- Making Products Fit People

Skills in this Chapter

The skills that you will use in this chapter are listed below.

- In **Lab 14-1,** you will interpret data, form a hypothesis, experiment, and measure in SI. In **Lab 14-2,** you will formulate a model, experiment, and infer.
- In the **Skill Checks,** you will infer, classify, and understand science words.
- In the **Mini Labs,** you will formulate a model, observe, and experiment.

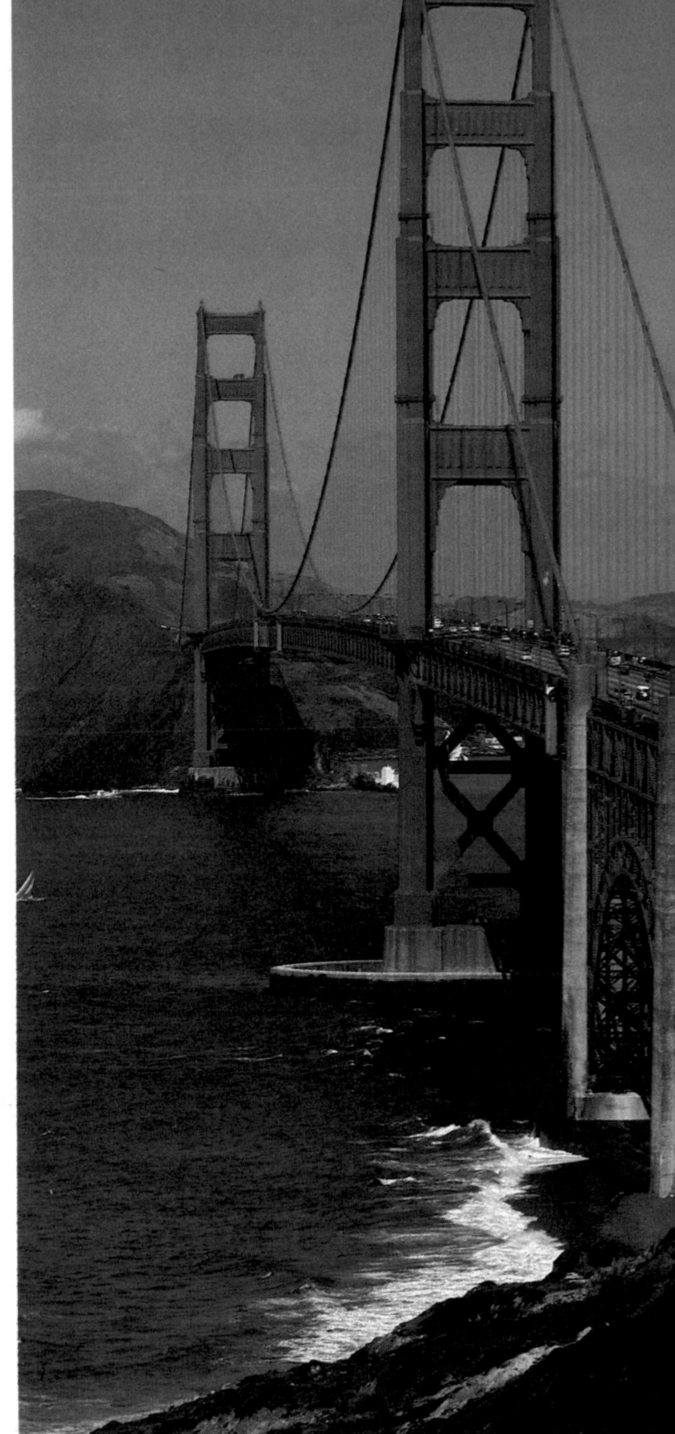

Bridging

The human heart is muscle. The lungs are able to move air in and out as muscles contract. Food moves through the digestive system due to the action of muscles in the stomach and intestine. This chapter will show how these muscles actually work to move the body, blood, air, and food.

Chapter **14**

Support and Movement

All your body systems tackle mighty jobs each day. They help you walk, sit, write, tie your shoelaces, and even watch a TV show. But what about the extra work that you give your body? Do you jog, dance, do judo, lift heavy weights, swim, cycle, or play baseball? These are not activities you need to do to survive. So, how can your body put up with these extra demands?

Your bones and muscles give your body support and strength, just as the steel frame supports the bridge shown in the photo on the left. The strength of your skeleton and muscles can be relied on in most exercises, such as the one shown in the photo below. In this chapter, you will see how the pieces and parts of the skeleton and muscles work together.

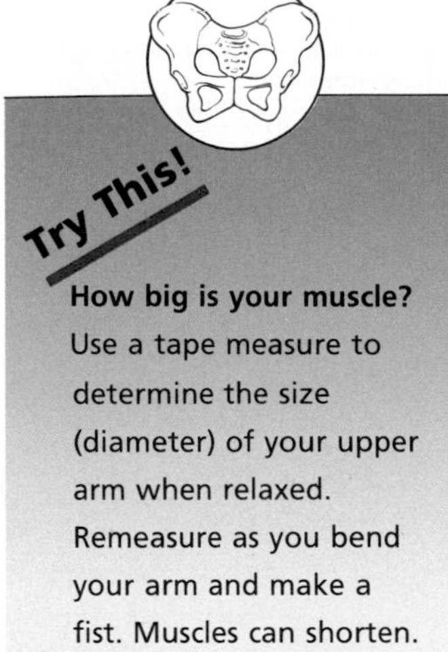

Try This!

How big is your muscle? Use a tape measure to determine the size (diameter) of your upper arm when relaxed. Remeasure as you bend your arm and make a fist. Muscles can shorten. When did your muscle shorten?

GETTING STARTED

Using the Photos

Have students give examples of other types of support systems, living and nonliving. Living support systems include exoskeletons, the hydrostatic skeleton of an earthworm, and cell walls of plants. Nonliving supports include the chassis of a car and the frame of a house. Ask students what all these systems have in common.

MOTIVATION/Try This!

How big is your muscle? A strip of clay that is pushed in from either side will end up thicker in the center. Muscles tend to show the same effect as they shorten. Students will observe that muscle tissue bunches up and as a result, the muscle appears to thicken.

Chapter Preview

Have students study the chapter outline before they begin to read the chapter. They should note the overall organization of the chapter, that the role of the skeleton is covered first, that the study of muscles is next, and that a discussion of bone and muscle problems ends the chapter.

Misconception

Students are not aware of the fact that bone is living tissue. Yet, they realize that a fracture of this body part will heal and repair itself in time. They are also not sure of the fact that the bulk of internal organs is muscle tissue.

14:1 The Role of the Skeleton

PREPARATION

Materials Needed

Make copies of the Enrichment, Reteaching, Study Guide, and Lab worksheets in the *Teacher Resource Package*.

▶ Obtain paper, tape, chicken bones, and hydrochloric acid for the Mini Labs.

▶ Gather bones from the butcher shop for Lab 14-1.

▶ Obtain old X rays from the local hospital for the demonstrations.

Key Science Words

skeletal system
ligament
solid bone
spongy bone
hinge joint
ball-and-socket joint
fixed joint

Process Skills

In Lab 14-1, students will interpret data, form a hypothesis, experiment, and measure in SI. In the Mini Labs, they will experiment and formulate a model.

1 FOCUS

▶ The objectives are listed on the student page. Remind students to preview these objectives as a guide to this numbered section.

ACTIVITY/Demonstration

Obtain outdated X rays from your local hospital. Project them onto the classroom screen using an overhead projector. Ask students if they can identify certain body areas or bones from the X rays.

Idea Map

Have students use the idea map as a study guide to the major concepts of this section.

Objectives

1. **Explain** the functions and growth of the skeleton.
2. **Define** the six tissues of bones.
3. **Identify** three types of joints.

Key Science Words

skeletal system
solid bone
spongy bone
ligament
hinge joint
ball-and-socket joint
fixed joint

14:1 The Role of the Skeleton

All vertebrates, from fish to mammals, have a skeleton. The skeleton provides support to their bodies. It also has other jobs such as protection, storage of materials, production of blood cells, and helping with movement.

Functions of the Skeleton

You know that all body systems are made of organs. Bones are the organs in the skeletal system. The **skeletal system** is the framework of bones in your body. As a framework, the skeleton helps to support the entire body. A skeleton also has other jobs. The skeleton helps to protect certain body organs. Your brain, heart, and lungs are organs with soft tissues. They could easily be damaged. Your skull protects your brain against injury. Ribs form a cage that protects your heart and lungs.

Many bones in your body make blood cells. You learned in Chapter 12 that bone marrow is the soft center part of bone. Blood cells are made within the bone marrow. You may have eaten a ham steak. A ham steak is the muscle of a pig's thigh, and the bone in the steak is a section of the pig's thigh bone. At the center of the bone is the marrow.

What part of bone produces blood cells?

Another job of bone is to store calcium (Ca). Remember that calcium is a mineral used by the body and is part of all bones. Calcium gives bones their strength. Without calcium, your bones would become weak or brittle.

The last job of your skeleton is to provide a place for muscles to attach. If muscles were not attached to your bones, you would not be able to move.

Study Tip: Use this idea map as a study guide to the functions of the skeleton. What bones allow you to write the answer to this question?

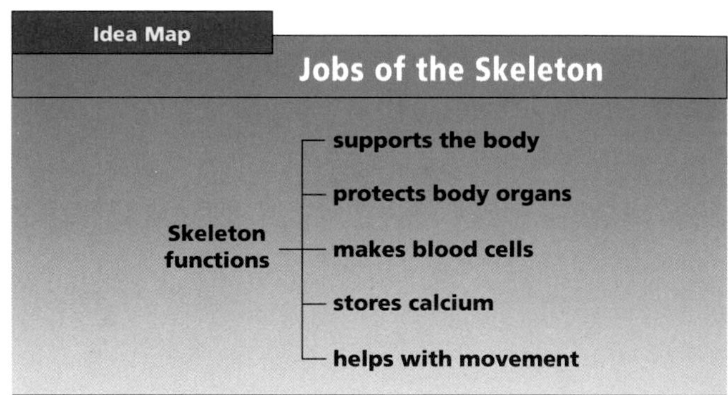
Idea Map
Jobs of the Skeleton
Skeleton functions
supports the body
protects body organs
makes blood cells
stores calcium
helps with movement

OPTIONS

Science Background

The interdependence of the muscular and skeletal systems is developed in this chapter. Muscles contract to move body parts that are usually attached to some part of the skeletal system. This is, of course, particularly true for skeletal muscle.

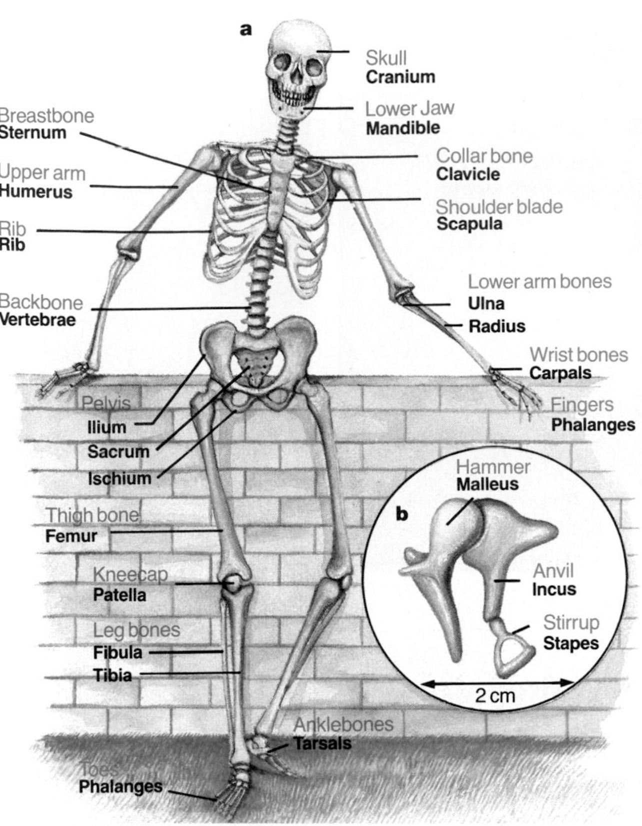

Figure 14-1 The skeleton is made of flat bones in the skull and ribs, irregular bones in the backbone, long bones in the arms and legs, and short bones in the hands and feet (a). The smallest bones are in the ear (b).

Bones in the Skeleton

If you counted all the bones in an adult human skeleton, you would find 206 of them. Examine the human skeleton in Figure 14-1. All the bones can't be counted in this diagram because not all of them are shown. Also, some bones are joined with other bones, making them look like one. For example, there are 22 different bones in the human skull. You can see only a few of these in the diagram.

Notice that the common name of a bone is usually different from the medical name. The common names are printed in blue. The medical names are printed in black. The three small ear bones shown to the bottom right are the body's smallest bones. Together, they measure only two centimeters long. They look so much like a hammer, an anvil, and a stirrup that these are their common names.

Mini Lab

What Happens to Bone When Calcium Is Removed?

Experiment: Place a chicken bone into a beaker with dilute HCl. Leave the bone overnight. Rinse carefully to remove any acid. Now, describe the bone. *For more help, refer to the* ***Skill Handbook****, pages 704-705.*

2 TEACH

MOTIVATION/Demonstration

A skeleton (either real or plastic) would illustrate the major functions being described here.

Concept Development

▶ The top ten rib pairs are attached to the sternum. The lowest two pairs are not attached and are called "floating" ribs.

Guided Practice

Have students write down their answers to the margin question on page 286: marrow.

Connection: Social Studies

Have students investigate some of the benefits and limitations of armor.

Mini Lab

Caution students to use care with hydrochloric acid.

Independent Practice

Study Guide/*Teacher Resource Package*, p. 79. Use the Study Guide worksheet shown at the bottom of this page for independent practice.

The Human Skeleton/*Transparency Package*, number 14. Use color transparency number 14 as you teach the bones of the skeleton.

STUDY GUIDE 79

STUDY GUIDE CHAPTER 14

Name ______ Date ______ Class ______

THE ROLE OF THE SKELETON

In your textbook, read about functions of the skeleton in Section 14:1.

1. Below are five pictures. Under each, write what the item does or is used for. Then, write what job of the skeletal system is similar.

Hinge — How used? help objects move — Skeleton job: helps body move

Catcher's mask — How used? protection — Skeleton job: protects organs

Trunk — How used? storage — Skeleton job: stores calcium

Kite (wooden part) — How used? framework — Skeleton job: support for body

Factory (AUTO MAKER) — Does what? makes things — Skeleton job: makes blood cells

In your textbook, read about bone growth in Section 14:1.

2. A child has 5 wrist bones. An adult has 8 wrist bones.
   a. How can these differences be used as evidence that bone tissue is alive? The increase in the number of bones shows that bone is alive and can make more bone.
   b. How has bone length in your legs changed since you were an infant? My leg bones have increased in length.
   c. How can this change be used as evidence that bone tissue is alive? Something which is living can grow in size.

OPTIONS

ACTIVITY/Challenge

Ask students to use references (anatomy books) in order to determine the regions and number of bones associated with the spinal cord. An "idea map" could be designed from their findings. The five regions of the spine include:

neck or cervical region	7
thoracic	12
lumbar	5
sacrum (5 bones fused)	5
tail or coccyx	4

TEACH

Concept Development

▶ Bone is a combination of organic matter (35%) and mineral salts (65%). The organic part is composed of cells and a protein called collagen. The organic matter makes bone flexible. The mineral salts, such as calcium carbonate or calcium phosphate, make bone hard.

ACTIVITY/Demonstration

Find examples of X rays showing wrists and ankles of a young person and an older person. Place the X rays on an overhead projector and reduce the light in the room. An opaque projector will also work. Compare specific infant bones to the same bones of an older person. Have students compare both the size and number of bones for young and old people.

Guided Practice

Have students write down their answers to the margin question: cartilage, outer membrane, solid bone, spongy bone, marrow, ligaments.

ACTIVITY/Project

Have students test for the presence of calcium in a variety of skeleton-like parts such as snail shells, chicken cartilage, beef bone. A 6 percent solution of hydrochloric acid added to these various tissues will form bubbles if calcium is present.

Enrichment/*Teacher Resource Package*, p. 14. Use the Enrichment worksheet shown here to teach students more about the parts of the skeleton.

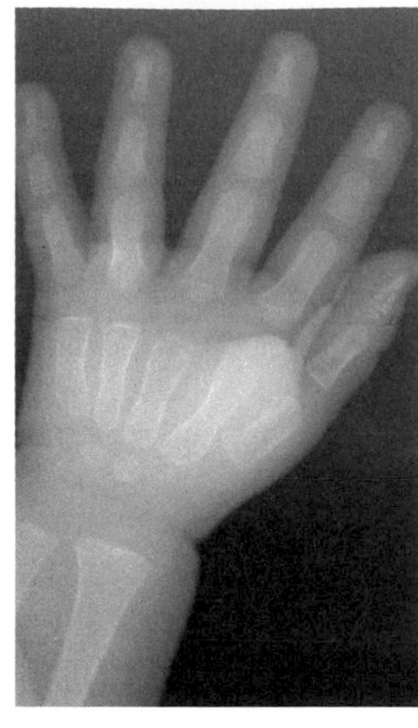

a

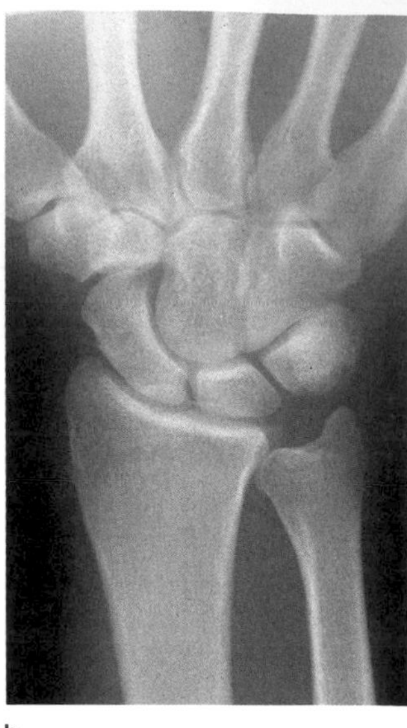

b

Figure 14-2 The hand and wrist bones of an infant (a) and an adult (b) indicate an increase in numbers of bones with age.

Bio Tip

Consumer: Many foods provide you with a natural supply of calcium. They include milk, milk products, green leafy vegetables, oranges, dried peas and beans, and shellfish.

Bone Growth

Bone tissue is alive and is made of cells, just as in other organs. Because bone cells are living, they can reproduce and make more bone. This results in bone growth. You know that bones grow because you are taller now than when you were younger.

Not only does bone size change as you grow, the number of your bones increases. Figure 14-2 shows an X ray of the hand and wrist bones of a three-year-old child. The X-ray photo on the right shows the hand and wrist bones of an adult. It is clear that the size of the bones has increased during growth. Has the number of bones increased? Count the number of bones shown in the wrist of each X ray. An infant's wrist has five bones. An adult's wrist has eight bones.

Bone Structure

What are six tissues of bone?

Most bones are made of six kinds of tissues. Figure 14-3 shows the positions of these six tissues in a bone.

You read in Chapter 8 that cartilage is a tough, flexible tissue that supports and shapes the body. This tissue acts as a cushion where bones come together. Cartilage doesn't

OPTIONS

Science Background

Cartilage is a special tissue consisting of cells called chondrocytes and a protein matrix made up of collagen. Cartilage has no mineral salts such as calcium. No blood vessels run through cartilage. This is why cartilage is so slow to heal if torn or injured.

How Do Male and Female Skeletons Differ?/*Lab Manual*, pp. 115-118. Use this lab as an extension to skeleton structure.

ENRICHMENT 14

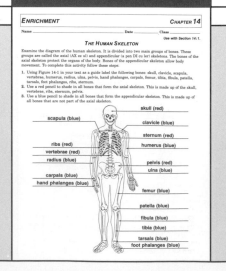

ENRICHMENT CHAPTER 14

Name ______ Date ______ Class ______

Use with Section 14:1.

THE HUMAN SKELETON

Examine the diagram of the human skeleton. It is divided into two main groups of bones. These groups are called the axial (AX ee ul) and appendicular (a pen DI cu ler) skeletons. The bones of the axial skeleton protect the organs of the body. Bones of the appendicular skeleton allow body movement. To complete this activity follow these steps:

1. Using Figure 14-1 in your text as a guide label the following bones: skull, clavicle, scapula, vertebrae, humerus, radius, ulna, pelvis, hand phalanges, carpals, femur, tibia, fibula, patella, tarsals, foot phalanges, ribs, sternum.
2. Use a red pencil to shade in all bones that form the axial skeleton. This is made up of the skull, vertebrae, ribs, sternum, pelvis.
3. Use a blue pencil to shade in all bones that form the appendicular skeleton. This is made up of all bones that are not part of the axial skeleton.

store calcium, so it is much softer than bone. Your ears and the tip of your nose can be bent from side to side. They are shaped by cartilage. When eating chicken, you may have noticed cartilage on the ends of the bones. Cartilage in foods such as chicken and beef is often called gristle.

Bone is covered by a thin sheet of tissue that forms an outer membrane. This membrane has many nerves and blood vessels that supply the bone with blood. This is the part that hurts when a bone gets bumped or bruised. It is also the growth area for new bone.

The inside of a bone shows other tissues. **Solid bone** is the very compact or hard part of a bone. It is usually found along the outer edges of bones. This part of the bone is very strong. Calcium is stored in solid bone and makes it strong.

Spongy bone is the part of a bone that has many empty spaces, much like those in a sponge. Spongy bone is usually found toward the ends of bones. It is strong like solid bone and gives the bone strength. Spongy bone also stores calcium but is lightweight because of the many empty spaces. Bird skeletons are lightweight because much of their bone tissue is spongy bone. How is this feature helpful to birds?

Remember that marrow is the soft center in bone. Blood cells and platelets are made in the marrow.

Ligaments (LIGH uh munts) are tough fibers that hold one bone to another. They are usually found at bone joints where two bones come together.

Mini Lab

How Strong Can a Hollow Bone Be?

Formulate a model: Curl a sheet of paper into a tube about 3 cm in diameter. Tape it so it does not unwind. How many books can be supported on top of the cylinder? *For more help, refer to the* ***Skill Handbook****, pages 706-711.*

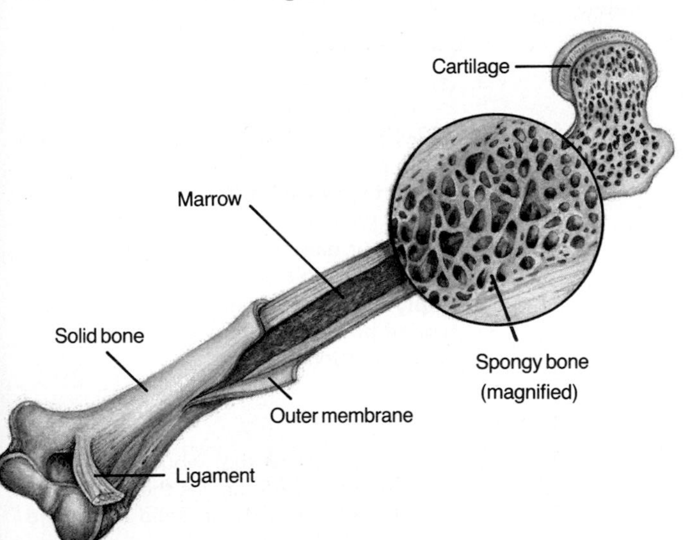

Figure 14-3 The six tissues of bone are shown in this cut-away diagram.

TEACH

ACTIVITY/Demonstration

Bring a beef bone into class for students to examine. If the bone is fresh, students will be able to see the periosteum and to pull off portions of it. Chicken bones show cartilage very well. A beef knee joint with bone above and below the joint will show the many different ligaments holding the bones in place. A long beef bone cut open lengthwise from your butcher will show solid, spongy, and marrow regions.

Mini Lab

The strip of folded paper may require some additional support initially. The weight of the book will usually crumple it before students realize what has occurred. Books will have to be centered onto the cylinders, otherwise they will fall off. Hollow bones, as illustrated by the cylinder of paper, have more strength than solid bones.

Guided Practice

Provide students with a diagram of a cross section of bone. Ask them to label the parts that have been studied.

Check for Understanding

Ask students to name parts of bone that illustrate the following skeletal functions: support, protection, form blood, store calcium, place for muscle attachment.

Reteach

Certain bone parts have specialized functions. Have students classify the following as to whether they add strength, are a covering, or provide cushioning: cartilage, spongy bone, solid bone, periosteum.

Independent Practice

Study Guide/*Teacher Resource Package*, p. 80. Use the Study Guide worksheet shown at the bottom of this page for independent practice.

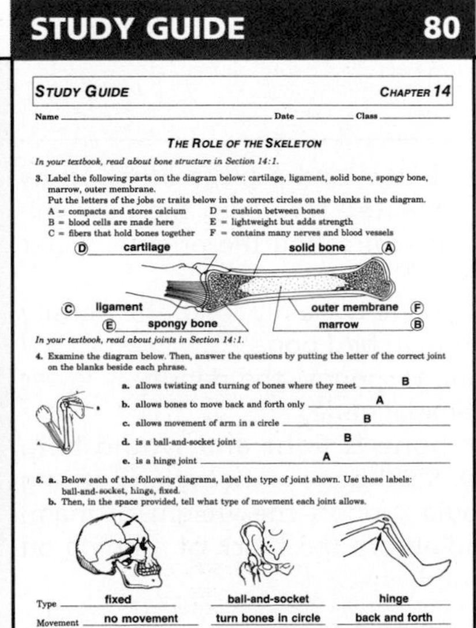

STUDY GUIDE 80

STUDY GUIDE — CHAPTER 14

Name ______ Date ______ Class ______

THE ROLE OF THE SKELETON

In your textbook, read about bone structure in Section 14:1.

3. Label the following parts on the diagram below: cartilage, ligament, solid bone, spongy bone, marrow, outer membrane.
Put the letters of the jobs or traits below in the correct circles on the blanks in the diagram.
A = compacts and stores calcium D = cushion between bones
B = blood cells are made here E = lightweight but adds strength
C = fibers that hold bones together F = contains many nerves and blood vessels

(D) cartilage; solid bone (A); (C) ligament; outer membrane (F); (E) spongy bone; marrow (B)

In your textbook, read about joints in Section 14:1.

4. Examine the diagram below. Then, answer the questions by putting the letter of the correct joint on the blanks beside each phrase.
a. allows twisting and turning of bones where they meet B
b. allows bones to move back and forth only A
c. allows movement of arm in a circle B
d. is a ball-and-socket joint B
e. is a hinge joint A

5. a. Below each of the following diagrams, label the type of joint shown. Use these labels: ball-and-socket, hinge, fixed.
b. Then, in the space provided, tell what type of movement each joint allows.

Type	fixed	ball-and-socket	hinge
Movement	no movement	turn bones in circle	back and forth

Lab 14-1 Bone Density

Overview

Students will learn how to determine the density of bone and use the technique to compare the densities of mammal and bird bones.

Objectives: Upon completion of the lab, students will be able to (1) **calculate** density, (2) **compare** the density of mammal and bird bone, (3) **relate** the lower density of bird bones to a bird's lifestyle.

Time Allotment: 1 class period

Preparation

▶ Use similar (homologous) bones for comparison of densities, for example ribs (beef ribs, pork chops, chicken and turkey breast).

Lab 14-1 worksheet/*Teacher Resource Package*, pp. 53-54.

Teaching the Lab

▶ Review the math involved with density calculations.

Cooperative Learning: Divide the class into groups of three students. For more information, see pp. 22T-23T in the Teacher Guide.

Lab 14-1 Computer Program/ *Teacher Resource Package*, p. xvi. Use the computer program shown at the bottom of page 291.

Bone Density

Lab **14–1**

Problem: How do bird and mammal bone densities compare?

Skills

interpret data, form a hypothesis, experiment, measure in SI

Materials

100-mL graduated cylinder
water
balance
bones of cow, pig, chicken, turkey

Procedure

1. Copy the data table.
2. **Measure in SI:** Use a balance to determine the mass in grams of a cow bone.
3. Record the mass of the bone.
4. Measure 50 mL of water in the graduated cylinder.
5. **Experiment:** Place the bone into the cylinder. Read the new volume of water. Remember to read the volume at eye level.
6. Subtract 50 from the new volume reading. This will give you the volume of the bone in millimeters.
7. Record this volume of the bone in your data table.
8. To calculate the density of the bone, divide the mass of the bone by its volume. (NOTE: Density is a measure of how compact a material is. The more compact it is, the higher its density. The less compact it is, the lower its density.)
9. Write a **hypothesis** in your notebook about which type of bone you think will have higher density, bird or mammal. Justify your hypothesis. (HINT: Read Section 14:1 again.)
10. Repeat steps 2 to 8 using a pig bone, a chicken bone, and a turkey bone.

	MAMMAL BONE		BIRD BONE	
	COW	PIG	CHICKEN	TURKEY
Mass	38 g	13.5 g	34 g	28 g
Volume	23 mL	10 mL	30 mL	25 mL
Density	1.6 g/mL	1.3 g/mL	1.1 g/mL	1.1 g/mL

Data and Observations

1. Which kind of bone, mammal or bird, has the higher density?
2. Which kind of bone, mammal or bird, has the lower density?

Analyze and Apply

1. **Check your hypothesis:** Is your hypothesis supported by your data? Explain.
2. How would you describe a mammal bone in terms of its density? How would you describe a bird bone's density?
3. (a) Which material would be more dense, a piece of steel or a piece of wood?
   (b) What kind of experiment could you do to prove your answer correct?
4. **Interpret your data** to explain if mammal bone is mainly solid or spongy.
5. Using your data, is bird bone mainly solid or spongy? Explain.
6. **Apply:** Using your data, explain how the type of bone might help birds and mammals survive.

Extension

Design an experiment that would help you measure the density of each of the three tissues of bone: spongy bone, solid bone, and marrow.

ANSWERS

Data and Observations

1. mammal
2. bird

Analyze and Apply

1. Students who hypothesized that mammal bones are more dense will say yes. A mammal bone has more solid bone than a bird bone.
2. A mammal bone is more compact. A bird bone is less compact.
3. (a) a piece of steel
   (b) Compare the difference in volume of a piece of steel and a piece of wood by placing in water, recording the new volumes, and subtracting the original water volumes.
4. Mammal bone is mainly solid; the density is higher than bird bone.
5. Bird bone is spongy; the density is lower than mammal bone.
6. Spongy bone is light and would help birds fly. Solid bone is heavy and strong and would support the weight of mammals and absorb the shock of running on the ground.

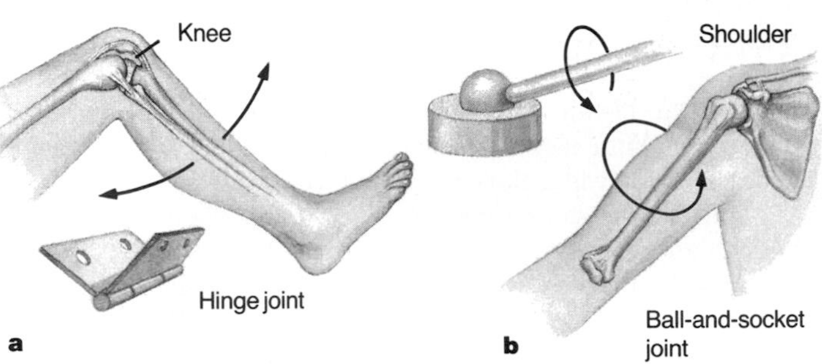

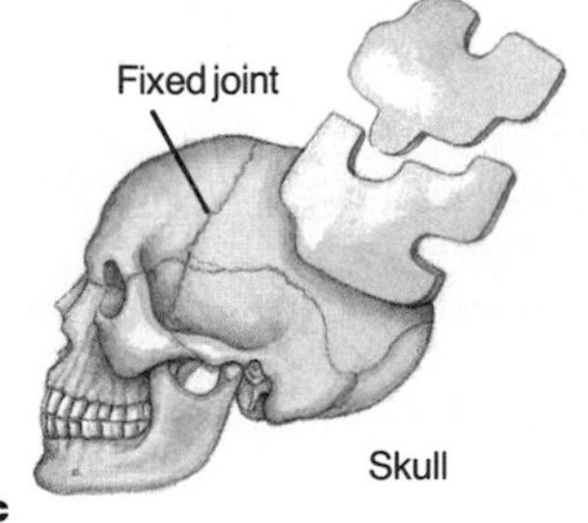

Figure 14-4 Hinge joints allow only back and forth movements, as in the hinge of a door (a). Ball-and-socket joints allow twisting and turning movements, as in a radio antenna (b). Fixed joints in the skull allow no movement, as in a jigsaw puzzle (c).

Joints

The place where bones come together is called a joint. There are several types of joints in the body. Most joints allow for different kinds of bone movement. Another type of joint allows no movement at all.

Hinge joints allow bones to move only back and forth. Your knee and elbow joints are examples of hinge joints, Figure 14-4. Compare a knee and an elbow to a real hinge. Why do you think you can open your mouth? Your lower jaw is attached to the skull by a hinge joint.

What joint allows only back and forth movement?

Your upper arm bone meets the shoulder, and your upper leg bone meets the pelvis in ball-and-socket joints. A **ball-and-socket joint** allows you to twist and turn the bones in a circle where they meet. Figure 14-4 compares the movement of a ball-and-socket joint to an antenna.

The skull has joints where the bones come together. These joints don't move. Joints that don't move are called **fixed joints.** In Figure 14-4, the zigzag lines on the skull are the fixed joints.

Check Your Understanding

1. What mineral supplies strength to bone?
2. Describe the jobs of cartilage, ligaments, and marrow.
3. Describe the movements of a hinge joint and a ball-and-socket joint. Give examples of each.
4. **Critical Thinking:** What are some sports you couldn't do if your shoulder and upper arm were joined by a hinge joint? Explain your answer.
5. **Biology and Math:** Is the smallest bone in the body less than two centimeters long? How do you know?

TEACH

Guided Practice

Have students write down their answers to the margin question: hinge joint.

Check for Understanding

Have students respond to the first three questions in Check Your Understanding.

Reteach

Reteaching/*Teacher Resource Package*, p. 40. Use this worksheet to give students additional practice with bone structure.

Extension: Assign Critical Thinking, Biology and Math, or some of the **OPTIONS** available with this lesson.

3 APPLY

ACTIVITY/Enrichment

Obtain an owl pellet. Carefully remove all hair and feathers to expose the bones within.

4 CLOSE

Software

Human Systems, Series II, Skeletal, Opportunities for Learning, Inc.

Answers to Check Your Understanding

1. calcium
2. Cartilage acts as a cushion between bones; ligaments hold one bone to another; marrow forms blood cells.
3. hinge joint–moves back and forth, elbow or knee; ball-and-socket–moves in a circle, hips or shoulder
4. baseball, volleyball, tennis, football; you couldn't throw overhand with a hinge joint.
5. The smallest bone in the body must be less than two centimeters long because the three bones of the ear measure two centimeters.

COMPUTER PROGRAM XVI

COMPUTER PROGRAM LAB 14-1 BONE DENSITY

```
5  HOME : GOSUB 1000
10  FOR X = 1 TO 4
20  READ ANIMAL$(X)
30  NEXT
40  FOR QUESTIN = 1 TO 4
50  PRINT "ENTER MASS OF "ANIMAL$(QUESTIN)" BONE : ";
60 A$ = "": HTAB 33
61  GET S$: IF S$ =  CHR$ (13) THEN 65
63 A$ = A$ + S$
64  PRINT S$;: GOTO 61
65 MASS(QUESTIN) = VAL (A$)
68  PRINT "g"
69 A$ = ""
70  PRINT "ENTER VOLUME OF "ANIMAL$(QUESTIN);" BONE : ";
75  HTAB 33
80  GET S$: IF S$ = CHR$ (13) THEN 84
81 A$ = A$ + S$
83  PRINT S$;: GOTO 80
84 VOLUME(QUESTIN) = VAL (A$)
85  PRINT "mL": PRINT
90  NEXT
100  PRINT : PRINT " ARE THESE NUMBERS CORRECT? (Y/N) :";: GET A$
110  IF A$ < > "Y" AND A$ < > "N" THEN  VTAB  PEEK (37): HTAB 1: GOTO
    100
120  IF A$ = "N" THEN  HOME : GOTO 40
130  HOME
140  FOR ANIMAL = 1 TO 4
150  PRINT "DENSITY OF "ANIMAL$(ANIMAL)" BONE IS:";
155 D = MASS(ANIMAL) / VOLUME(ANIMAL)
157 d =  INT (D * 100 + .5) / 100
170  HTAB 30: PRINT D"g/mL"
180  PRINT
190  NEXT
200  PRINT : PRINT
210  PRINT "DO YOU WANT THIS PRINTED? (Y/N) :";: GET A$
215  PRINT
220 IF A$ < > "N" AND A$ < > "Y" THEN  VTAB  PEEK (37): HTAB 1: GOTO
    210
230  IF A$ = "N" THEN  END
240  PR# 1
250  FOR ANIMAL = 1 TO 4
260  PRINT "MASS OF "ANIMAL$(ANIMAL)" BONE: "MASS(ANIMAL)"g"
270  PRINT "VOLUME OF "ANIMAL$(ANIMAL)" BONE: "VOLUME(ANIMAL)"mL"
280  PRINT "DENSITY OF "ANIMAL$(ANIMAL)" BONE: "; INT ((MASS(ANIMAL) / V
    OLUME(ANIMAL)) * 100 + .5) / 100"g/mL"
290  PRINT
300  NEXT
310  PR# 0: END
1000  PRINT "LAB 14-1                          BONE DENSITY"
1005  PRINT : INVERSE : PRINT "INSTRUCTIONS:": NORMAL : PRINT : PRINT
1010  PRINT "YOU WILL BE ASKED TO ENTER YOUR DATA     FOR THIS EXPERIMENT
    . A DATA CHART        DIFFERENT FROM THE ONE USED IN THE TEXT WILL AP
    PEAR ON THE SCREEN."
1030  VTAB 24: HTAB 5
```

RETEACHING 40

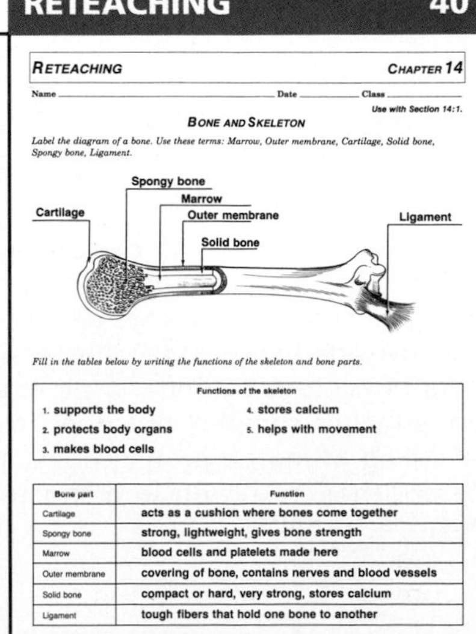

RETEACHING — CHAPTER 14

Name ______________ Date ________ Class ________

Use with Section 14:1.

BONE AND SKELETON

Label the diagram of a bone. Use these terms: Marrow, Outer membrane, Cartilage, Solid bone, Spongy bone, Ligament.

Fill in the tables below by writing the functions of the skeleton and bone parts.

Functions of the skeleton

1. supports the body
2. protects body organs
3. makes blood cells
4. stores calcium
5. helps with movement

Bone part	Function
Cartilage	acts as a cushion where bones come together
Spongy bone	strong, lightweight, gives bone strength
Marrow	blood cells and platelets made here
Outer membrane	covering of bone, contains nerves and blood vessels
Solid bone	compact or hard, very strong, stores calcium
Ligament	tough fibers that hold one bone to another

14:2 The Role of Muscles

PREPARATION

Materials Needed

Make copies of the Transparency Master, Critical Thinking/Problem Solving, Skill, Application, Reteaching, Study Guide, and Lab worksheets in the *Teacher Resource Package*.

▶ Purchase chicken legs for the Mini Lab. Boil them at home prior to bringing them to school.

▶ Obtain file cards, string, tape, and metal fasteners for Lab 14-2.

Key Science Words

muscular system
skeletal muscle
voluntary muscle
cardiac muscle
involuntary muscle
smooth muscle
tendon

Process Skills

In Lab 14-2, students will formulate a model, infer, and experiment. In the Mini Lab, they will observe. In the Skill Checks, they will infer and classify.

1 FOCUS

▶ The objectives are listed on the student page. Remind students to preview these objectives as a guide to this numbered section.

Bridging

Discuss the relationship between muscles and bones.

14:2 The Role of Muscles

Objectives

4. **Compare** three kinds of muscles.
5. **Explain** how muscles work to move body parts.
6. **Relate** how muscles work in pairs.

Key Science Words

muscular system
skeletal muscle
voluntary muscle
cardiac muscle
involuntary muscle
smooth muscle
tendon

The ball flies in your direction and you leap into the air to meet it. Your sister's pass from the other side of the volleyball net was a clever one, but you manage to return the ball. At the same time, you notice your shoelace is undone and you kneel to tie it. In these few seconds, you have used hundreds of different muscles in your body.

Movement

Muscle is a body tissue that can change its shape and length and thus cause movement. The kinds of movements muscles carry out depend on where the muscles are attached. For example, arm and leg muscles allow you to move the bones of your arms and legs, such as when you leap to punch a volley ball, Figure 14-5. Your heart is an organ with very strong muscle tissue. Its main job is to help pump or move blood. Your stomach and intestines also have muscle tissues. The movement of muscles in these organs helps to push food along.

The **muscular system** is all the muscles in your body. Almost all animal groups have a muscular system, which allows them to move about.

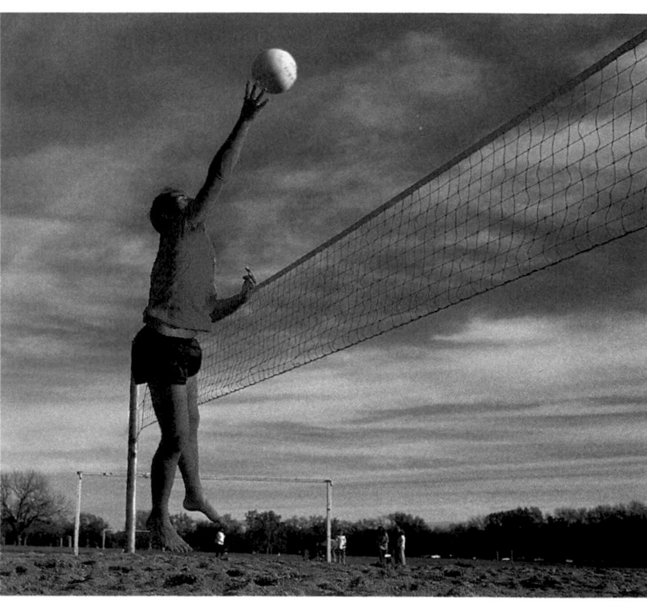

Figure 14-5 Muscles allow your body to perform a variety of different movements.

OPTIONS

Science Background

Muscle tissue is capable of contracting (shortening) when stimulated by a nerve message. These messages are either under voluntary or involuntary control. The actual physiology behind muscle contraction is rather complex but does involve the sliding of muscle protein fibers across one another, resulting in a shortening effect.

Career Close-Up

Athletic Trainer

Are you interested in sports? You might want a job working with athletes. You might want to work with students in high school, but you could also train athletes in college. Maybe one day you will be training a professional team. To become an athletic trainer you will need to understand how muscles and bones make up the human body. Take courses in biology, health, human physiology, chemistry, and physics in order to start your career. Other useful courses include nutrition, drugs, first aid, health, and human anatomy.

In a typical day you may be asked to work directly with athletes. As the trainer, you will supervise exercises and you might be required to treat sprains, muscle cramps, or other minor body injuries. Other activities for an athletic trainer include meal planning, repairing of sports equipment, and ordering of training room supplies.

As an athletic trainer, your future is rewarding. With a college degree, the starting salary can be more than $20 000 per year.

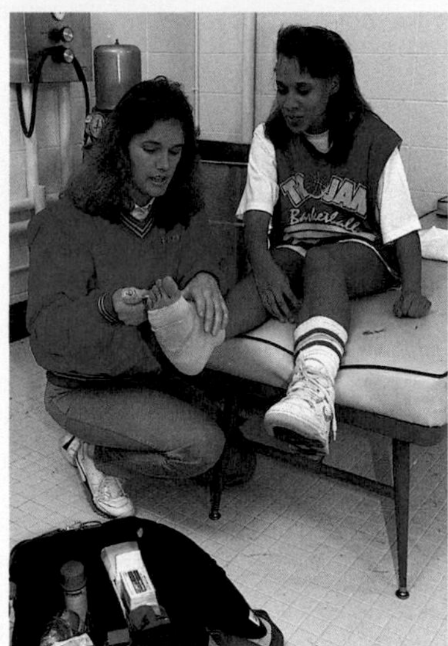

An athletic trainer understands the importance of warm-up exercises to avoid muscle damage.

Human Muscle Types

The human body has three different kinds of muscle. They are skeletal, smooth, and cardiac (KAR dee ac) muscle. Each muscle type has a different structure and pattern that make it different from the other. Each type of muscle has a different job, and each has a different location in the body.

Skeletal muscles are muscles that move the bones of the skeleton. Your arms and legs are moved by this muscle type. Skeletal muscles make up the bulk of your body. Important skeletal muscles for athletic activity include those in the arms, the legs, the abdomen, the chest, and the shoulders.

What are the three different kinds of muscles?

TRANSPARENCY 65

TRANSPARENCY MASTER — *CHAPTER 14*

MUSCLE TYPES

Muscle type—skeletal
Characteristics:
1. bandlike appearance from dark and light stripes
2. long fibers
3. separate cells hard to see
4. cell nucleus present
5. voluntary muscle
6. moves bones

Found in:
1. arms, leg muscles
2. any muscle you have control over

Muscle type—smooth
Characteristics:
1. no bandlike appearance
2. not connected to bones
3. individual cells are easier to see
4. nucleus present
5. involuntary muscle

Found in:
1. digestive organs (stomach, intestines)
2. blood vessels, ureters

Muscle type—cardiac
Characteristics:
1. bandlike appearance from dark and light stripes
2. long fibers that form a "weave" by joining together
3. individual cells hard to see
4. cell nucleus present
5. involuntary
6. not connected to bone

Found in:

heart only

OPTIONS

ACTIVITY/Challenge

Use prepared slides to show the differences among the three muscle types. An alternate suggestion is to obtain 35 mm colored slides. Or, if a video camera is available, project slides through the microscope onto a TV for class viewing.

Transparency Master/*Teacher Resource Package*, p. 65. Use the Transparency Master shown here to teach students about muscle types.

Career Close-Up

Athletic Trainer

Background

Athletic trainers not only work with athletes, they may frequently consult with and discuss problems with the team coach and doctor.

Related Careers

A physical therapist, physical education teacher, or paramedic are careers related to athletic trainers.

Job Requirements

Athletic trainers must be certified by the National Athletic Trainers Association.

For More Information

The Athletic Institute
200 Castlewood Drive
North Palm Beach, FL 33408

2 TEACH

MOTIVATION/Audiovisual

Project 35 mm color slides of all three muscle types onto the screen. Do not tell students what they are looking at. Ask them to describe similarities and differences.

Concept Development

▶ Point out to students that their internal organs are mainly muscle.

Bridging

Do a quick review of the animal kingdom with students. Point out that all phyla except sponges exhibit motion.

Guided Practice

Have students write down their answers to the margin question: skeletal, cardiac, and smooth.

Videocassette

Muscle Power, Films for the Humanities and Sciences.

TEACH

Misconception: Ask students what they are eating when they eat hot dogs, hamburgers, roast, or steak. Students do not realize that meat purchased in a grocery or as a hamburger or hot dog is animal muscle.

Cooperative Learning: Divide the class into five groups. Have each group be responsible for researching and listing as many body organs as possible formed from skeletal, cardiac, and smooth muscle. Each group is to report verbally to the other groups on the findings. Offer some type of reward to the group with the longest list.

Independent Practice

Study Guide/*Teacher Resource Package*, p. 81. Use the Study Guide worksheet shown at the bottom of this page for independent practice.

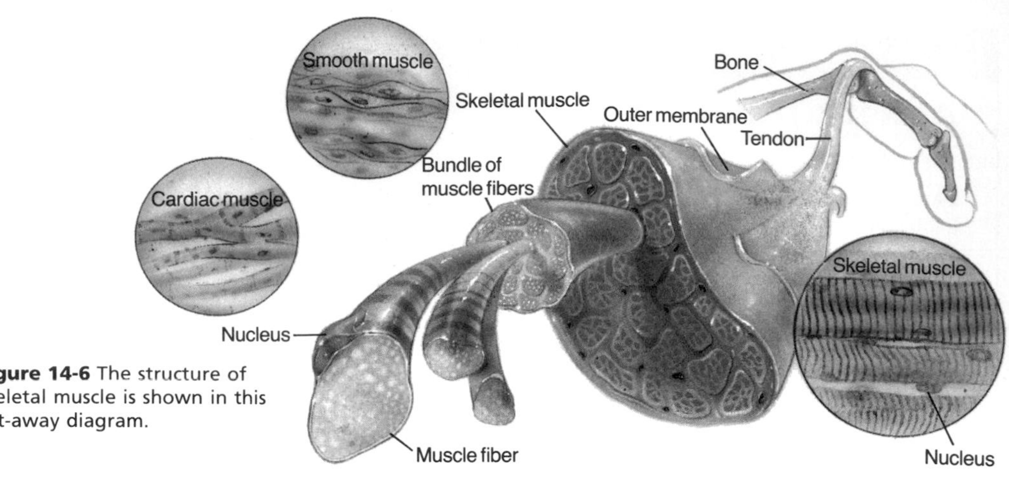

Figure 14-6 The structure of skeletal muscle is shown in this cut-away diagram.

Skill Check

Classify: In what ways are skeletal, cardiac, and smooth muscle alike? How do they differ? *For more help, refer to the **Skill Handbook** pages 715-717.*

Figure 14-7 The heart is the only organ with cardiac muscle.

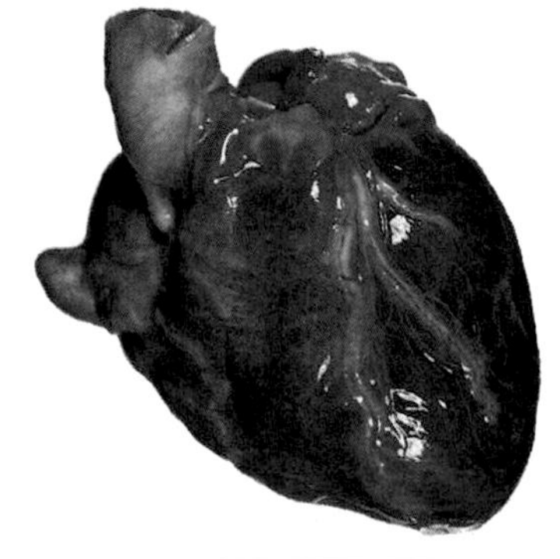

Figure 14-6 shows how skeletal muscle is made of bundles of fibers. Each fiber is a muscle cell. Notice that skeletal muscle looks striped. The stripes are caused by two kinds of proteins that make up the muscle fibers. The whole muscle is surrounded by a layer of fibrous tissue.

Skeletal muscles are voluntary. **Voluntary muscles** are muscles you can control. If you decide to lift something, you control the muscles needed for lifting. If you pull a rope, jump, look out the window, or point, you decide what you want your muscles to do. You control your arm, leg, head, and finger movements.

Most of the animal tissue that people eat is skeletal muscle. If you eat meat, you are usually eating muscle. For example, the parts of a fish that you eat are its muscles. You eat mostly muscle when you eat a chicken drumstick. Hamburger is the ground-up muscle of beef cows.

Cardiac muscle is the muscle that makes up the heart. The heart is the only body organ made of this muscle type. Cardiac muscle is not connected to any bones, Figure 14-7.

Cardiac muscle is made of bundles of fibers, just as in skeletal muscle. Again, this muscle type looks striped. The main difference between cardiac and skeletal muscles is that the bundles of cardiac muscle fibers form a tight weave. The tight weave makes cardiac muscle very strong.

Cardiac muscle is involuntary. **Involuntary muscles** are muscles you can't control. You don't think whether your heart needs to pump slow or fast. Your brain controls this movement as needed.

OPTIONS

ACTIVITY/Challenge

Ask students to prepare a wet mount of a very small amount of fresh hamburger meat. If a small enough sample is used, students will see the individual fibers and striations on the fibers. Proper lighting is critical.

Critical Thinking/Problem Solving/*Teacher Resource Package*, p. 14. Use the Critical Thinking/Problem Solving worksheet shown here as an extension to muscle types.

CRITICAL THINKING 14

CRITICAL THINKING/PROBLEM SOLVING — CHAPTER 14

Name ______ Date ______ Class ______

Use after Section 14:2.

WHAT ARE THE JOBS OF DIFFERENT MUSCLES?

Read the story below. As you read, think about the different types of muscles and what jobs they do. What kinds of activities do you do that depend on certain types of muscles?

It was 11:15 in the morning and time for gym. Alicia enjoyed gym class because she was a good athlete and probably the fastest *runner* (1) in her class. Today they were going outdoors to *run sprints* (2). Alicia *knew* (3) she could win if she did some *leg stretching* (4) exercises first.

It was very *warm outside* (5). After running the sprints and winning, Alicia was aware of how hard she was *breathing* (6). Her *rib cage* (7) was *moving in and out* (8) rapidly. She could even feel her *heart beating* (9). When she *placed her hand* (10) over her neck, she could feel her pulse. A pulse is caused by the pumping of blood through the *arteries* (11).

Usually she did not sweat much, but today she was *sweating a lot* (12). After *showering* (13) and *changing back into her school clothes* (14), Alicia was ready for lunch. She knew lunch was near because she was getting *hunger pangs* (15) in her *stomach* (16). Alicia asked her *gym teacher* (17) before leaving what caused the hunger pangs. The teacher told her that hunger pangs were the result of *movements or contractions* (18) of an empty stomach.

Analyzing the Problem

1. Write the numbers of the phrases that name organs made of muscle. 4, 7, 9, 11, 16
2. Write the numbers of the phrases that name things that your body can do only because you have muscles. 1, 2, 4, 6, 8, 9, 10, 12, 13, 14, 15, 18
3. Write the numbers of the phrases of body parts that best match the kind of muscle listed.
   Smooth: 11, 16 Skeletal: 4, 7 Cardiac: 9
4. Write the numbers of the phrases that name things that your body can do under voluntary control (you can control it). 1, 2, 3, 4, 10, 13, 14
5. Write the numbers of the phrases that name things that your body can do under involuntary control (you can't control it). 6, 8, 9, 12, 15, 18

Solving the Problem

6. Think about the activities you do every day. Write a paragraph like the one above that describes your activities. Underline words that tell what you can do because of muscles. Circle words that list body parts that are made of muscle.
   Student answers will vary.

STUDY GUIDE 81

STUDY GUIDE — CHAPTER 14

Name ______ Date ______ Class ______

THE ROLE OF MUSCLES

In your textbook, read about human muscle types in Section 14:2.

1. Identify these three drawings as smooth, skeletal, or cardiac muscle. Label them correctly. They are about 1500 times natural size.

   skeletal muscle   cardiac muscle   smooth muscle

2. Complete the table by checking the correct column for each trait listed.

Trait or location	Skeletal muscle	Cardiac muscle	Smooth muscle
Makes up your small and large intestines			✓
Makes up your heart		✓	
Makes up your body muscles	✓		
Has stripelike appearance	✓	✓	
Is voluntary	✓		
Can be controlled	✓		
Moves your bones	✓		
Has no stripes			✓
Muscles form a tight weave		✓	
Involuntary		✓	✓
Is not connected to bone		✓	✓
Can't be controlled		✓	✓
Can contract	✓	✓	✓
Can shorten	✓	✓	✓
Most often eaten as meat	✓		

Smooth muscle is involuntary muscle that makes up the intestines, arteries, and many other body organs. You have no control over the working of your intestines or blood vessels. The cells of smooth muscle are long and spindly, but much shorter than the fibers of skeletal muscles. Smooth muscle does not have stripes. Like cardiac muscle, smooth muscle is not connected to any bones.

How Muscles Work

A muscle works by changing its length. For a muscle to do its job, its fibers must shorten. The entire muscle shortens when the muscle fibers contract. The contraction of muscles allows you to move your body parts. Muscles don't lengthen to move body parts, they only shorten.

Let's look at the working of a skeletal muscle. Skeletal muscles are connected to bones by tendons (TEN duhns). A **tendon** is a tough, fibrous tissue that connects muscle to bone. The tendons cause the bone to be pulled when the muscle contracts.

How would your muscles work if you were to pull a boat in to dock with a rope? Look at Figure 14-8a to see the shape of your upper arm muscles before you begin to pull. They are relaxed. The muscle fibers have not contracted or shortened. Figure 14-8b shows how your arm muscles would look while you were pulling on the rope. Your muscle fibers are working. When they work, they contract or shorten. The bulging you see when a muscle is working is due to the thickening of muscle fibers as they shorten.

Mini Lab

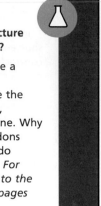

What Is the Structure of a Chicken Leg?

Observe: Examine a cooked chicken drumstick. Locate the muscles, tendons, cartilage, and bone. Why are so many tendons needed? Where do tendons lead to? *For more help, refer to the* ***Skill Handbook****, pages 704-705.*

How do skeletal muscles move body parts?

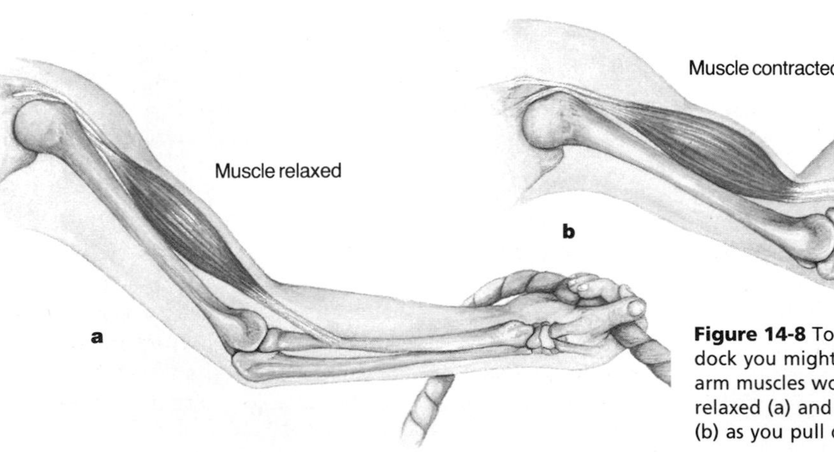

Figure 14-8 To pull a boat into dock you might use a rope. Your arm muscles would first be relaxed (a) and then contracted (b) as you pull on the rope.

TEACH

Concept Development

▶ The end of the muscle that is connected to the bone that does not move is referred to as the origin end. The opposite muscle end is called the insertion end. It is attached to the moving bone.

Mini Lab

Demonstrate muscle movement in a chicken leg by using a chicken thigh with the foot still attached. Most of the leg of a chicken is muscle. Tendons are very tough (almost bone-like) fibers connected to the muscle. Pulling on the various tendons will allow students to see the corresponding movements of the toes, as well as up–and–down movement of the foot.

Guided Practice

Have students write down their answers to the margin question: by contracting.

Analogy: Use a thick rubber band to illustrate muscle contraction.

Using Science Words: Make sure that students know the meaning of the words *contract* and *contraction.* To illustrate, describe someone rolling up into a ball as being contracted.

Independent Practice

Study Guide/*Teacher Resource Package*, p. 82. Use the Study Guide worksheet at the bottom of this page for independent practice.

SKILL 15

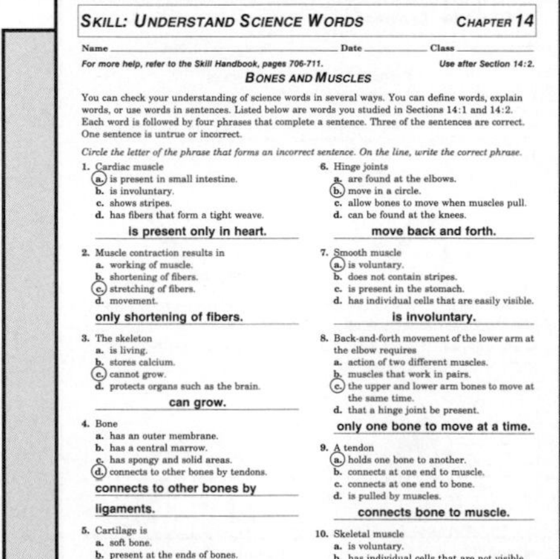

SKILL: UNDERSTAND SCIENCE WORDS — CHAPTER 14

Name ______ Date ______ Class ______

For more help, refer to the Skill Handbook, pages 706-711. — *Use after Section 14:2.*

BONES AND MUSCLES

You can check your understanding of science words in several ways. You can define words, explain words, or use words in sentences. Listed below are words you studied in Sections 14:1 and 14:2. Each word is followed by four phrases that complete a sentence. Three of the sentences are correct. One sentence is untrue or incorrect.

Circle the letter of the phrase that forms an incorrect sentence. On the line, write the correct phrase.

1. Cardiac muscle
   (a.) is present in small intestine.
   b. is involuntary.
   c. shows stripes.
   d. has fibers that form a tight weave.
   is present only in heart.
2. Muscle contraction results in
   a. working of muscle.
   b. shortening of fibers.
   (c.) stretching of fibers.
   d. movement.
   only shortening of fibers.
3. The skeleton
   a. is living.
   b. stores calcium.
   (c.) cannot grow.
   d. protects organs such as the brain.
   can grow.
4. Bone
   a. has an outer membrane.
   b. has a central marrow.
   c. has spongy and solid areas.
   (d.) connects to other bones by tendons.
   connects to other bones by ligaments.
5. Cartilage is
   a. soft bone.
   b. present at the ends of bones.
   (c.) lacking in sodium.
   d. a soft cushion between bones.
   lacking in calcium.
6. Hinge joints
   a. are found at the elbows.
   (b.) move in a circle.
   c. allow bones to move when muscles pull.
   d. can be found at the knees.
   move back and forth.
7. Smooth muscle
   (a.) is voluntary.
   b. does not contain stripes.
   c. is present in the stomach.
   d. has individual cells that are easily visible.
   is involuntary.
8. Back-and-forth movement of the lower arm at the elbow requires
   a. action of two different muscles.
   b. muscles that work in pairs.
   (c.) the upper and lower arm bones to move at the same time.
   d. that a hinge joint be present.
   only one bone to move at a time.
9. A tendon
   (a.) holds one bone to another.
   b. connects at one end to muscle.
   c. connects at one end to bone.
   d. is pulled by muscles.
   connects bone to muscle.
10. Skeletal muscle
    a. is voluntary.
    b. has individual cells that are not visible.
    c. shows stripes.
    (d.) has fibers that form a weave.
    has fibers side by side.

STUDY GUIDE 82

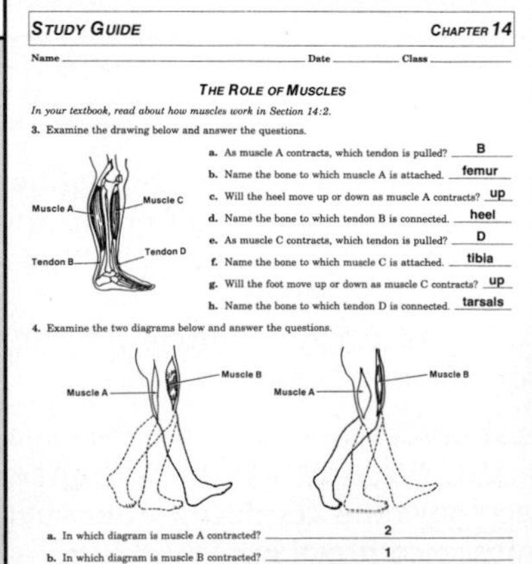

STUDY GUIDE — CHAPTER 14

Name ______ Date ______ Class ______

THE ROLE OF MUSCLES

In your textbook, read about how muscles work in Section 14:2.

3. Examine the drawing below and answer the questions.

   a. As muscle A contracts, which tendon is pulled? **B**
   b. Name the bone to which muscle A is attached. **femur**
   c. Will the heel move up or down as muscle A contracts? **up**
   d. Name the bone to which tendon B is connected. **heel**
   e. As muscle C contracts, which tendon is pulled? **D**
   f. Name the bone to which muscle C is attached. **tibia**
   g. Will the foot move up or down as muscle C contracts? **up**
   h. Name the bone to which tendon D is connected. **tarsals**

4. Examine the two diagrams below and answer the questions.

   a. In which diagram is muscle A contracted? **2**
   b. In which diagram is muscle B contracted? **1**
   c. How can you tell which muscle is contracted? **The contracted muscle is shorter and thicker.**
   d. When one muscle of a pair is contracted, the other is **relaxed**.

5. In each diagram, draw a solid line over the dotted line that shows the correct position of the leg.

OPTIONS

Skill/*Teacher Resource Package*, p. 15. Use the Skill worksheet shown here to help students understand the terminology in this section.

Science Background

The axons of motor nerves terminate in or on muscle tissue. When a stimulus moves down the nerve to the axon, a chemical is released from the axon. The chemical is called a transmitter substance and will stimulate the muscle tissue to contract. This chemical is usually acetylcholine.

TEACH

Misconception: Exercise creates larger muscle cells, not more muscle cells. The number of muscle cells doesn't change.

Skill Check

The muscle tissue forms a bulge where the contracting fibers overlap.

ACTIVITY/Demonstration

Have students feel their calf muscles while standing on tiptoe. Remind them that standing on tiptoe requires that the foot be turned downward. Have them note the contraction of their calf muscles. Then, have them return to a normal standing position as they continue to concentrate on their calf muscles. Holding onto the front of the leg while the foot is turned up will allow them to see that different muscles are needed to raise the foot.

Skill Check

Infer: If muscles shorten when they contract, where does the excess muscle tissue go? *For more help, refer to the **Skill Handbook**, pages 706-711.*

Bones with skeletal muscles also allow you to walk. Walking is an exercise that strengthens muscles because of the continual contracting and stretching of pairs of muscles. Let's look at this movement.

Figure 14-9a shows the muscles that are used to raise or lower your foot. All the muscles in this diagram are relaxed. This means that the foot is not moving up or down. Notice that one end of muscle A is attached to the top of the tibia (TIHB ee uh), your leg bone. This end won't move during contraction. The lower end of the tibia is attached by a tendon to the tops of the tarsals, the bones of your foot. This end moves during contraction. One end of muscle B is attached to the bottom of the femur, your thighbone. This end won't move during contraction. The other end is attached by a tendon to the back of your heel bone. This end moves.

Figure 14-9b shows that muscle A is slightly stretched. You can tell this because the muscle is a little longer than when relaxed, as shown in Figure 14-9a. Muscle B, however, is contracted. You can tell this because it is much shorter than it was in Figure 14-9a. As muscle B contracts, it pulls up the bottom of your heel. A hinge joint in the ankle allows for this movement.

How is your foot pulled up? A different muscle must be used this time. Muscle B is not used. Muscle B in Figure 14-9c is now relaxed. Muscle A is contracted. When it shortens, it pulls up the foot. You can now move forward.

Figure 14-9 When you walk, you lift your feet. At first, your muscles are relaxed (a). Then, the heel is pulled up (b), and the foot is lifted off the ground (c). Why is cycling a good exercise for leg muscles? The muscles are continually stretched.

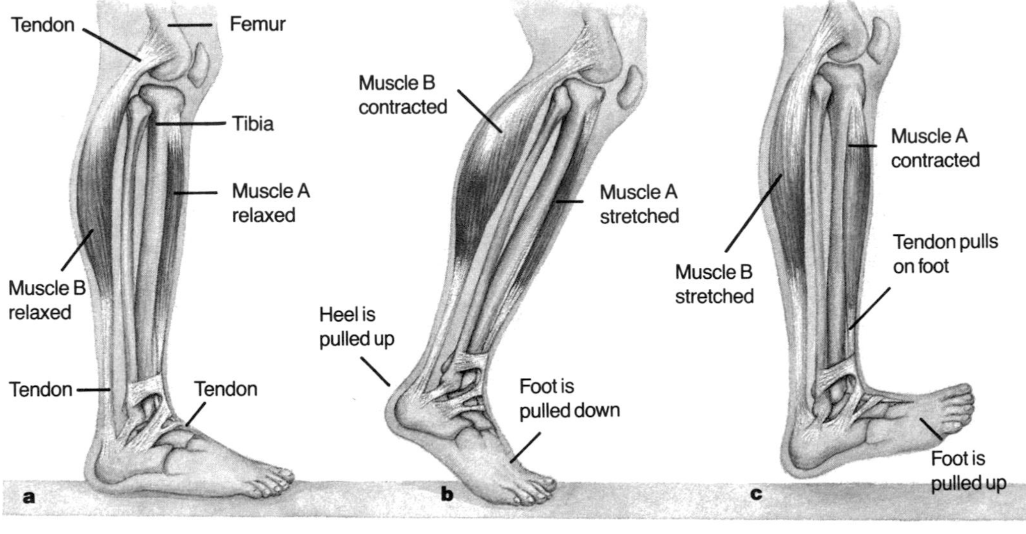

OPTIONS

Enrichment: The pairing of muscles throughout the body is called antagonistic pairing. In the example being used, muscle A is a flexor. It raises the foot. Muscle B is called an extensor. It lowers the foot. Most major muscle pairings include a flexor and an extensor.

Application/*Teacher Resource Package*, p. 14. Use the Application worksheet shown here to show the connection between exercise and muscle contraction.

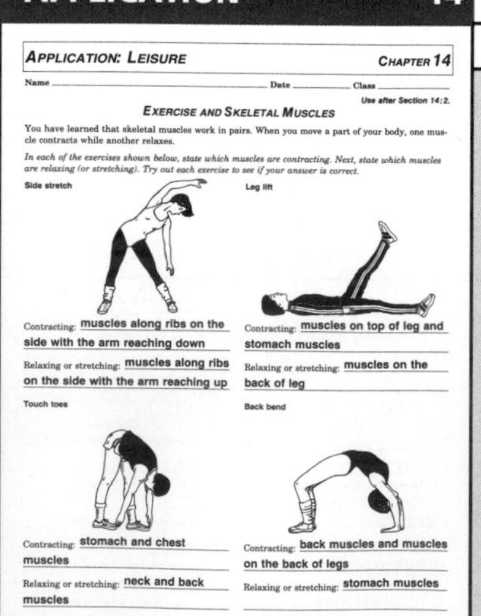

APPLICATION 14

APPLICATION: LEISURE CHAPTER 14

Name ______ Date ______ Class ______

Use after Section 14:2.

EXERCISE AND SKELETAL MUSCLES

You have learned that skeletal muscles work in pairs. When you move a part of your body, one muscle contracts while another relaxes.

In each of the exercises shown below, state which muscles are contracting. Next, state which muscles are relaxing (or stretching). Try out each exercise to see if your answer is correct.

Side stretch

Contracting: muscles along ribs on the side with the arm reaching down

Relaxing or stretching: muscles along ribs on the side with the arm reaching up

Leg lift

Contracting: muscles on top of leg and stomach muscles

Relaxing or stretching: muscles on the back of leg

Touch toes

Contracting: stomach and chest muscles

Relaxing or stretching: neck and back muscles

Back bend

Contracting: back muscles and muscles on the back of legs

Relaxing or stretching: stomach muscles

Moveable joint is here

B

A

D

C

Moveable joint is here

Figure 14-10 Which way will the head and arm move as different muscles contract and relax?

Muscles Work in Pairs

How do skeletal muscles work in pairs?

Because muscles can only shorten, it takes a pair of skeletal muscles to move bones back and forth. When one muscle contracts, the opposite muscle must relax. In the examples just used, one muscle was needed to pull your foot up. A different muscle was needed to lower your foot.

Look at these other examples in Figure 14-10. See if you can figure out which muscle has which job. Remember, muscles move body parts only when they shorten. The body part moves because muscles pull on a bone.

How does the head move when muscle A relaxes and muscle B contracts? The head turns up.

How does the arm move when muscle C contracts and muscle D relaxes? The arm straightens.

Check Your Understanding

6. Give examples of the three types of muscles and where they are found in the body.
7. What is the job of tendons?
8. How does the length of a relaxed muscle compare with that of a contracted muscle?
9. **Critical Thinking:** Muscle cells have more mitochondria than other cells. Why?
10. **Biology and Reading:** You have some muscles in your eye that you can control. Other muscles in your eye work automatically. What two kinds of muscles must control movements in your eye?

TEACH

Guided Practice

Have students write down their answers to the margin question: because muscles can only shorten.

Check for Understanding

Have students respond to the first three questions in Check Your Understanding.

Reteach

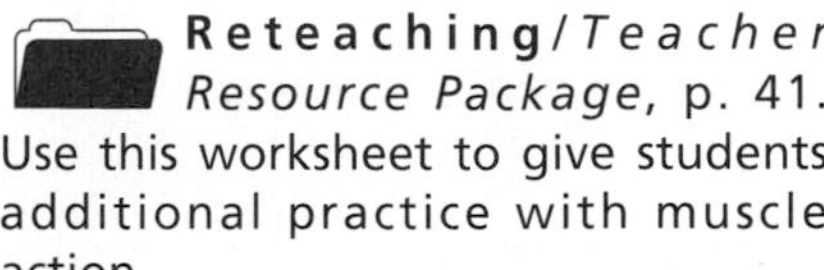

Reteaching/*Teacher Resource Package*, p. 41. Use this worksheet to give students additional practice with muscle action.

Extension: Assign Critical Thinking, Biology and Reading, or some of the **OPTIONS** available with this lesson.

3 APPLY

Software

Human Systems, Series II Muscular, Opportunities for Learning, Inc.

4 CLOSE

ACTIVITY/Enrichment

Have students do a little research to find the answer to the following: Which type of muscle, skeletal, cardiac, or smooth, will fatigue the most rapidly? Least rapidly?

Answers to Check Your Understanding

6. skeletal–arms, legs; cardiac–heart; smooth–stomach, intestines, blood vessels
7. Tendons connect muscle to bone.
8. When contracted, muscle is much shorter and thicker than when relaxed.
9. Muscle cells need more energy for movement than other cells. Mitochondria are where energy is produced from food.
10. You have control over the skeletal muscles that move the eye, but not the smooth muscles.

RETEACHING 41

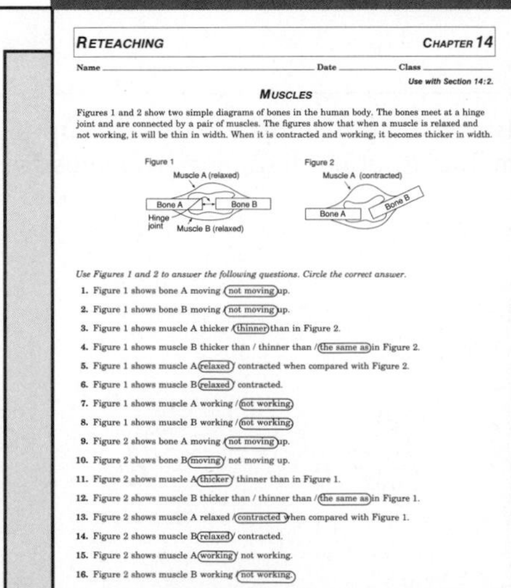

RETEACHING CHAPTER 14

Name ______ Date ______ Class ______

Use with Section 14:2.

MUSCLES

Figures 1 and 2 show two simple diagrams of bones in the human body. The bones meet at a hinge joint and are connected by a pair of muscles. The figures show that when a muscle is relaxed and not working, it will be thin in width. When it is contracted and working, it becomes thicker in width.

Use Figures 1 and 2 to answer the following questions. Circle the correct answer.

1. Figure 1 shows bone A moving / not moving up.
2. Figure 1 shows bone B moving / not moving up.
3. Figure 1 shows muscle A thicker / thinner than in Figure 2.
4. Figure 1 shows muscle B thicker than / thinner than / the same as in Figure 2.
5. Figure 1 shows muscle A relaxed / contracted when compared with Figure 2.
6. Figure 1 shows muscle B relaxed / contracted.
7. Figure 1 shows muscle A working / not working.
8. Figure 1 shows muscle B working / not working.
9. Figure 2 shows bone A moving / not moving up.
10. Figure 2 shows bone B moving / not moving up.
11. Figure 2 shows muscle A thicker / thinner than in Figure 1.
12. Figure 2 shows muscle B thicker than / thinner than / the same as in Figure 1.
13. Figure 2 shows muscle A relaxed / contracted when compared with Figure 1.
14. Figure 2 shows muscle B relaxed / contracted.
15. Figure 2 shows muscle A working / not working.
16. Figure 2 shows muscle B working / not working.

OPTIONS

ACTIVITY/Challenge

Ask students to diagram a muscle, bone, joint, and tendon and show the resulting bone movement when the muscle contracts. Ask students to modify the diagram by including another muscle that can move the bone in the opposite direction. (If Lab 14-2 has been done, ask students to use a set of muscles and bones other than the lower leg and foot).

Lab 14-2 Muscles

Overview

Students will build a paper model of a foot and leg. Antagonistic muscle pairs are demonstrated.

Objectives: Upon completion of the lab, students will be able to (1) build a **model** of the human foot and leg and (2) **demonstrate** the action of muscle pairs in bringing about movement of the foot.

Time Allotment: 30 minutes

Preparation

▶ Prepare patterns of the model foot and leg before class.

Lab 14-2 worksheet/*Teacher Resource Package*, pp. 55-56.

Teaching the Lab

▶ Pulling up on the string means pulling toward the top of the model.

▶ Suggest that the model be taped to the desk along the upper edge of the leg piece. Make sure the tape does not block movement of the strings or foot.

▶ **Troubleshooting:** Remind students that tape must be positioned as shown. It cannot overlap onto other model parts.

Cooperative Learning: Divide the class into groups of two students. For more help, refer to pp. 22T-23T in the Teacher Guide.

Muscles

Lab 14—2

Problem: Do muscles work in pairs?

Skills

formulate models, experiment, infer

Materials

index card
scissors
string
metal fastener
tape
paper punch

Procedure

1. Copy the data table.
2. Cut one index card in half lengthwise. Attach one half of the card to the other half using the metal fastener as shown in Figure A. One half card is the foot, and the other half card is the leg.
3. Punch two holes in the top of the leg bone card, and thread a piece of string, 15 cm long, through each hole. Attach the strings to the base of the foot card as shown in Figure B.
4. **Experiment:** Pull up on string A. Record in your table how the foot part of the model moves. Also note if string B gets shorter or longer between the hole on the leg card and the tape on the foot card.
5. Record your findings in the table.
6. Pull up on string B. Record in your table how the foot part of the model moves. Also note if string A gets shorter or longer between the hole on the leg card and the tape on the foot card.

Data and Observations

1. In your model:
   (a) what does the metal fastener represent?
   (b) what do strings A and B represent?
   (c) what do the pieces of tape represent?
2. When the foot moved down, which string got shorter? Which got longer?

A

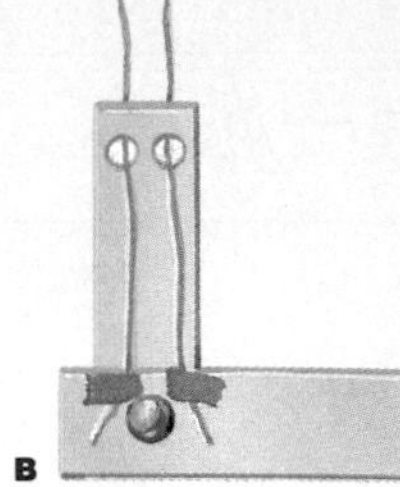

B

3. When the foot moved up, which string got shorter? Which got longer?

	FOOT MOVES UP OR DOWN?	STRING A LENGTHENS OR SHORTENS	STRING B LENGTHENS OR SHORTENS
String A pulled up	down	shortens	lengthens
String B pulled up	up	lengthens	shortens

Analyze and Apply

1. (a) Was a short string supposed to show a contracted or a relaxed muscle?
   (b) Was a long string supposed to show a contracted or a relaxed muscle?
2. Can the same string (muscle) move the foot up and down? Explain.
3. **Apply:** Which other sets of muscles in your body act the same way as those in your model?

Extension

Formulate a model of a weight-lifting machine that would act to strengthen the thigh muscles while moving the leg forward and backward.

ANSWERS

Data and Observations

1. (a) a joint
   (b) a pair of muscles
   (c) tendons
2. A got shorter, B got longer
3. B got shorter, C got longer

Analyze and Apply

1. (a) contracted
   (b) relaxed
2. No. Only a contracted muscle causes movement.
3. Answers may include lower arm, upper arm, hands, upper legs, and neck muscles.

14:3 Bone and Muscle Problems

From studying this chapter, you know that the skeletal and muscular systems work together. So, a problem in one system may cause a problem with the other. Modern science and technology is used to solve some of the problems that affect the skeletal and muscular systems.

Objectives

7. Discuss the problems of the skeletal system.

8. Give examples of problems of the muscular system.

9. Explain the purpose of new designs for products.

Key Science Words

arthritis
sprain
muscular dystrophy

Problems of the Skeletal System

Some problems with the skeletal system are caused by diseases of the joints. **Arthritis** (ar THRIT us) is a disease of bone joints. One type of arthritis results in breakdown of the cartilage at the joints. The result is pain and swelling at the diseased joint, Figure 14-11a. In time, a person may not be able to bend or move the affected part of the body.

What are the effects of arthritis?

Today, there is some help for the problems of arthritis. Artificial joints made of plastic or metal are sometimes used to replace diseased joints. Hip, ankle, and knee joints have been replaced by this technology. Figure 14-11b shows an artificial hip joint. It is made of metal and replaces the ball part on the femur, which is attached to the ball-and-socket joint in the hip.

Bones are strong because they store calcium. If the level of calcium is low, bones will break easily. Bones tend to become brittle as a person ages. Exercise and eating dairy foods helps to keep bones strong.

Skill Check

Understand science words: arthritis. The word part *arthr* means joint. In your dictionary, find three words with the word part *arthr* in them. *For more help, refer to the **Skill Handbook**, pages 706-711.*

Figure 14-11 Arthritis can cause severe disability. The ball part of a ball-and-socket joint can be replaced with metal (inset).

FOCUS 27

FOCUS — CHAPTER 14

Name ______ Date ______ Class ______

WHEN MUSCLES NO LONGER WORK: STEPHEN HAWKING

Normal muscle

Motor Neurons

Impulse from motor neuron causes muscle to contract

Stephen Hawking: Scientist with motor-neuron disease

Shriveled muscle

Damaged motor neuron cannot cause muscle to react

1. What do you think happens when the nerves that make muscles work degenerate or become useless? What kinds of activities are interfered with?
2. Why would a person with damaged nerves find it difficult to talk or eat?

OPTIONS

Science Background

A number of joint replacements are now possible including hip, knee, and ankle. These replacements are often needed as a consequence of arthritis.

Arthritis is considered an autoimmune disease. That is, the body's immune system is responsible for causing the disease. Two general types are recognized: rheumatoid and osteoarthritis. Both result in deterioration of cartilage at the ends of bone.

14:3 Bone and Muscle Problems

PREPARATION

Materials Needed

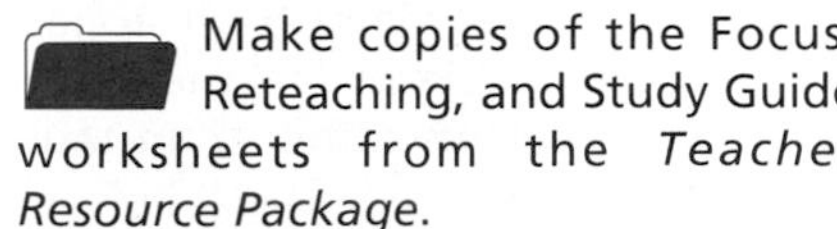

Make copies of the Focus, Reteaching, and Study Guide worksheets from the *Teacher Resource Package*.

▶ Obtain a foot or knee model from a local nursing school, hospital, or orthopedic surgeon for use in the demonstration of ligaments.

Key Science Words

arthritis
sprain
muscular dystrophy

Process Skills

In the Skill Check, students will understand science words.

1 FOCUS

▶ The objectives are listed on the student page. Remind students to preview these objectives as a guide to this numbered section.

Focus/*Teacher Resource Package*, p. 27. Use the Focus transparency shown at the bottom of this page as an introduction to bone and muscle problems.

MOTIVATION/Demonstration

Muscle has a very rich supply of capillaries. This is easily illustrated with a piece of fresh meat. Hold the meat up and blood will drain from the tissue.

Guided Practice

Have students write down their answers to the margin question: a breakdown of cartilage that causes pain and swelling at the joint.

2 TEACH

Bridging

Remind students that a muscle cannot contract without some command. This command comes from the nerve cells associated with the muscle. The vast majority of apparent muscle problems are the result of nerve problems rather than muscle dysfunction.

Check for Understanding

Discuss answers to these questions with students: (a) How does a fracture differ from a sprain? How does a muscle cramp differ from a muscle strain?

Reteach

Prepare an idea map of problems associated with the skeleton and muscle.

Guided Practice

Have students write down their answers to the margin question: a tense muscle due to low oxygen supply.

Independent Practice

Study Guide/*Teacher Resource Package*, pp. 83-84. Use the Study Guide worksheets shown at the bottom of this page for independent practice.

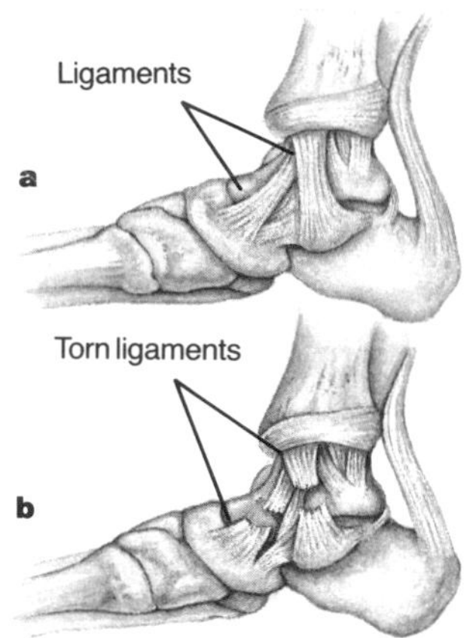

Figure 14-12 Normal (a) and torn (b) ligaments of an ankle with a sprain

What is a cramp?

Most bones in the body are connected by ligaments. Have you ever twisted your ankle? If you have, the pain you felt was caused by injury to your ankle ligaments, Figure 14-2. **Sprains** are injuries that occur to your ligaments at a joint. A sprain results when the ligaments are torn and blood vessels are damaged.

Problems of the Muscular System

Have you ever strained a muscle while lifting or after a sudden move? Have you ever had muscle cramps while swimming or during a long-distance run? Strains and cramps are two quite different problems.

You might strain a muscle if you haven't exercised for a while. A sudden use of a poorly exercised muscle may tear the fibers. Regular exercise will help you avoid straining your muscles. A muscle cramp is when the muscle contracts strongly and then can't relax. Muscle cramps result from a poor supply of oxygen. If you exercise one set of muscles too long, the oxygen supply may run low. When oxygen returns, the muscles will recover.

Skeletal muscles are controlled by nerve cells. A disease called muscular dystrophy (MUS kyuh lur • DIHS truh fee) blocks the nerve messages to muscles. **Muscular dystrophy** is a disease that causes the slow wasting away of skeletal muscle tissue. Muscular dystrophy can be inherited and is most common in males, Figure 14-13.

Figure 14-13 By transplanting healthy muscle cells into a person with muscular dystrophy, scientists have given new hope to many people with this disease.

OPTIONS

What Causes Sports Injuries?/*Lab Manual*, pp. 111-114. Use this lab as an extension to bone and muscle problems.

STUDY GUIDE 83

STUDY GUIDE — CHAPTER 14

Name ____ Date ____ Class ____

BONE AND MUSCLE PROBLEMS

In your textbook, read about bone and muscle problems in Section 14:3.

1. What is arthritis? **Arthritis is a disease of bone joints.**
2. One type of arthritis results in breakdown of the cartilage at the joints. How would this affect a person's life? **This breakdown causes pain and swelling at the diseased joint. In time, a person may not be able to bend or move the affected part of the body.**
3. What can be done to help people whose joints are severely affected by arthritis? **Diseased joints can be replaced with plastic or metal ones.**
4. What can happen to bones if a person doesn't get enough calcium in their diet? **The bones can become brittle and break easily.**
5. What are ligaments? **Ligaments are tough fibers that connect bones to each other.**
6. What happens to ligaments that are sprained? **They are torn and blood vessels are damaged.**
7. a. What is a muscle cramp? **A muscle cramp occurs when a muscle contracts strongly and can't relax.**
   b. When does it occur? **If you exercise some muscles too long, oxygen supply to those muscles may run low.**
8. a. What is muscular dystrophy? **It's a disease that blocks nerve messages to muscle tissue.**
   b. What effect does it have on muscles? **It causes muscles to waste away.**

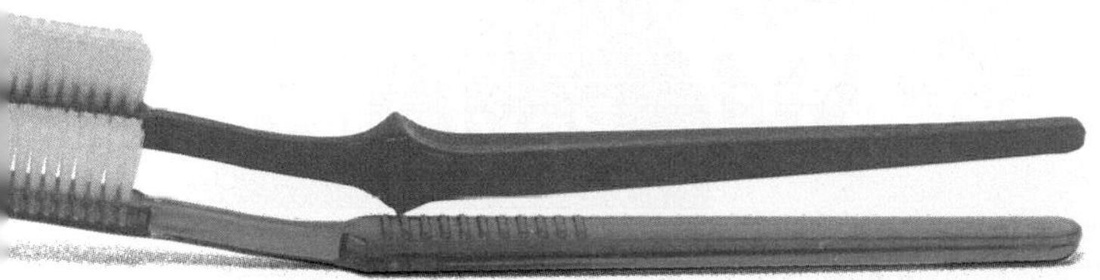

Figure 14-14 How are these toothbrushes designed to fit your body?

Making Products Fit People

How often have you sat in class and complained that the desk or chair was very uncomfortable? Backaches, muscle fatigue, and general discomfort are often the result of poor product design. Why? In the past, the most important thing for a new product was that it should look good. It wasn't important that a product fit the shape of the human body.

All of this is changing, however. New product design that fits the user's body shape is now becoming important. Automakers have put lumbar supports in their car seats. The lumbar region is the "small of the back" that gets tired after long periods of sitting.

Look at the toothbrushes in Figure 14-14. Will their handles reduce the chances of dropping them? Will they feel more comfortable in your hands? Will the bristles reach all the surfaces of your teeth and gums? Their design helps solve these kinds of problems.

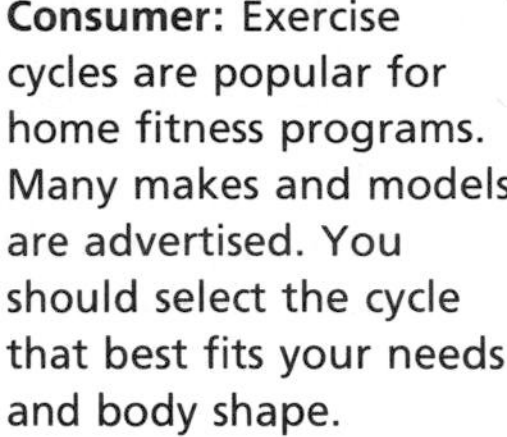

Bio Tip

Consumer: Exercise cycles are popular for home fitness programs. Many makes and models are advertised. You should select the cycle that best fits your needs and body shape.

What kind of product design is becoming popular?

Check Your Understanding

11. What is arthritis?
12. What happens to ligaments when the ankle is sprained?
13. What new design in autos makes drivers more comfortable?
14. **Critical Thinking:** Low back pain and neck pains are often due to muscle spasms related to stress. What might be some ways to avoid these problems?
15. **Biology and Math:** There are several kinds of muscular dystrophy. In the kind of muscular dystrophy that occurs most often in the U.S., 3 out of every 10 000 boys will be expected to show symptoms of the disease. How many boys would be expected to show symptoms of muscular dystrophy in a city of 60 000?

STUDY GUIDE 84

STUDY GUIDE — **CHAPTER 14**

Name ______ Date ______ Class ______

VOCABULARY

Review the new words used in Chapter 14 of your textbook. Then, complete the puzzle. Use the words or phrases to fill in the blanks in the sentences. Do not use any term more than once.

skeletal system	solid bone	fixed joints	ligaments
spongy bone	hinge joints	muscular system	ball-and-socket joint
skeletal muscles	sprain	voluntary muscles	muscular dystrophy
cardiac muscle	tendons	involuntary muscle	smooth muscle
arthritis			

1. **Cardiac muscle** is found only in the heart.
2. Muscle you have no control over is **involuntary muscle**.
3. Bones are held together by **ligaments**. A **sprain** results when they are torn.
4. **Spongy bone** is usually found toward the ends of bones. The outer part of bones is usually **solid bone**.
5. The **skeletal system** is a framework for the body.
6. All the muscles in your body make up the **muscular system**.
7. Muscles are connected to bones by **tendons**.
8. Muscles you can control are **voluntary muscles**.
9. Many body organs, such as arteries, are made up of **smooth muscle**.
10. **Arthritis** is a disease of the joints.
11. **Muscular dystrophy** is a disease that causes the wasting away of muscle tissue.
12. Muscles that move the bones of the skeleton are **skeletal muscles**.
13. Your knees and elbows are **hinge joints**.
14. Bones can turn in a circle at a **ball-and-socket joint**.
15. Joints that don't move are called **fixed joints**.

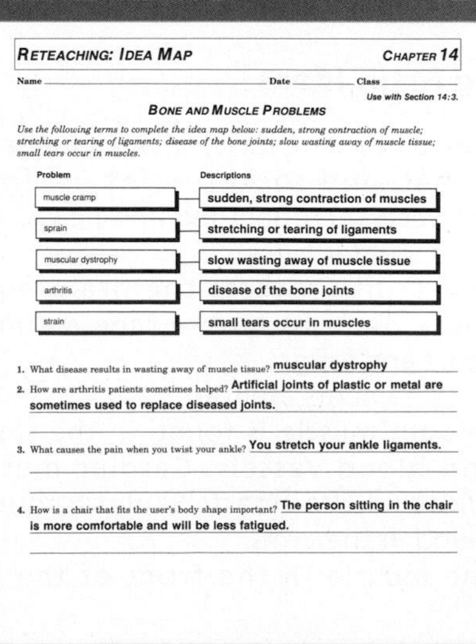

RETEACHING 42

RETEACHING: IDEA MAP — **CHAPTER 14**

Name ______ Date ______ Class ______

Use with Section 14:3.

BONE AND MUSCLE PROBLEMS

Use the following terms to complete the idea map below: sudden, strong contraction of muscle; stretching or tearing of ligaments; disease of the bone joints; slow wasting away of muscle tissue; small tears occur in muscles.

Problem	Descriptions
muscle cramp	sudden, strong contraction of muscles
sprain	stretching or tearing of ligaments
muscular dystrophy	slow wasting away of muscle tissue
arthritis	disease of the bone joints
strain	small tears occur in muscles

1. What disease results in wasting away of muscle tissue? **muscular dystrophy**
2. How are arthritis patients sometimes helped? **Artificial joints of plastic or metal are sometimes used to replace diseased joints.**
3. What causes the pain when you twist your ankle? **You stretch your ankle ligaments.**
4. How is a chair that fits the user's body shape important? **The person sitting in the chair is more comfortable and will be less fatigued.**

TEACH

Guided Practice

Have students write down their answers to the margin question: one that fits the user's body shape.

Check for Understanding

Have students respond to the first three questions in Check Your Understanding.

Reteach

Reteaching/*Teacher Resource Package*, p. 42. Use this worksheet to give students additional practice with bone and muscle problems.

Extension: Assign Critical Thinking, Biology and Math, or some of the **OPTIONS** available with this lesson.

3 APPLY

Divergent Question

The human body may use several systems in order to function normally. Ask students for an example of this type of cooperation using the movement of an arm or leg.

4 CLOSE

A person has a cast on his broken leg for three months. When the cast is removed, he notices that the muscle of the leg has shrunk. Explain why.

Answers to Check Your Understanding

11. a disease of bone joints
12. ligaments are torn
13. a lumbar support that supports the lower back
14. exercising and relaxing
15. In a city of 60 000, 18 boys would be expected to have the disease.

$$3/10\,000 = x/60\,000;$$
$$180\,000/10\,000 = x;$$
$$x = 18$$

CHAPTER 14 REVIEW

Summary

Summary statements can be used by students to review the major concepts of the chapter.

Key Science Words

All boldfaced words from the chapter are listed.

Testing Yourself

Using Words

1. ball-and-socket joint
2. smooth muscle
3. cardiac muscle
4. arthritis
5. solid bone
6. tendon
7. ligament
8. skeletal muscle
9. skeletal system

Finding Main Ideas

10. p. 291; A hinge joint is the elbow or knee. Fixed joints are the skull bones. A ball-and-socket joint is the upper arm and shoulder.
11. p. 299; Artificial joints of plastic or metal are used to replace diseased joints.
12. p. 286; It supports the body, protects organs, stores materials, makes blood cells, and helps with movement.
13. p. 300; A sprain is an injury to a ligament.
14. p. 300; Muscular dystrophy interrups nerve messages to muscles and causes the muscle tissue to waste away.
15. p. 289; The six tissues of bone are cartilage, outer membrane, solid bone, spongy bone, marrow, and ligaments.
16. p. 297; Muscle can only shorten. One muscle moves a bone in only one direction, and a second muscle is needed to move it in the opposite direction.
17. p. 287; The leg bones are the femur, tibia, and fibula. The arm bones are the humerus, radius, and ulna. The collarbone is the clavicle, and the shoulder blade is the scapula.
18. p. 301; Products can be designed that support the lower back and can be adjusted for height and angle.

Chapter 14 Review

Summary

14:1 The Role of the Skeleton

1. The skeleton serves as a framework, protects body organs, makes blood cells, stores calcium, and provides a place for muscle attachment. Bone is alive and grows.
2. The six tissues of bones include a fibrous membrane around solid bone, spongy bone, and marrow, as well as cartilage and ligaments.
3. Three types of joints are hinge, ball-and-socket, and fixed.

14:2 The Role of Muscles

4. Muscles bring about body movement. The three types of muscle are skeletal, cardiac, and smooth.
5. Muscles contract in order to work. They are connected to bone by tendons.
6. Muscles must work in pairs in order to bring about movement of body parts.

14:3 Bone and Muscle Problems

7. Arthritis, lack of calcium, and sprains are three common problems of the skeletal system.
8. Strains and cramps are two common muscle problems. Muscular dystrophy is a more serious and often inherited muscle problem.
9. New products are being designed to fit the shape of the human body.

Key Science Words

arthritis (p. 299)
ball-and-socket joint (p. 291)
cardiac muscle (p. 294)
fixed joint (p. 291)
hinge joint (p. 291)
involuntary muscle (p. 294)
ligament (p. 289)
muscular dystrophy (p. 300)
muscular system (p. 292)
skeletal muscle (p. 293)
skeletal system (p. 286)
smooth muscle (p. 295)
solid bone (p. 289)
spongy bone (p. 289)
sprain (p. 300)
tendon (p. 295)
voluntary muscle (p. 294)

Testing Yourself

Using Words

Choose the word from the list of Key Science Words that best fits the definition.

1. allows arm to move in a full circle
2. involuntary muscle that makes up intestines and blood vessels
3. muscle that makes up the heart
4. a disease of bone joints
5. compact or hard part of bone
6. attaches muscle to bone
7. holds two bones together
8. type of muscle that works in pairs
9. framework of all body bones

Using Main Ideas

19. The joint in the lower jaw is a hinge joint. A ball-and-socket joint is formed between the upper leg and pelvis, and in the shoulder.
20. The skull protects the brain against injury. The ribs form a cage around the heart and lungs.
21. The ligaments are torn.
22. Smooth muscle is found in the stomach and blood vessels. Cardiac muscle is found in the heart. Skeletal muscle is found in the arms.
23. The muscle in the front of the leg is attached at the top of the tibia and at the bottom to the foot bones. When this muscle contracts, the foot is pulled up. Muscle at the back of the leg is attached at the top to the femur and at the bottom to the underside of the heel. When the muscle contracts, the foot is pulled down.
24. You can control voluntary muscles. You can't control involuntary muscles.
25. Muscle cramps result.

Review

Testing Yourself *continued*

Finding Main Ideas

List the page number where each main idea below is found. Then, explain each main idea.

10. examples of the three types of joints in the human body
11. how the problem of arthritis is treated
12. five main jobs of the skeletal system
13. what a sprain is
14. a disease that causes the blocking of nerve messages to muscle
15. the six tissues of bone
16. why two different muscles are needed to move bones back and forth
17. the medical names of the bones of the leg, arm, collar, and shoulder blade
18. how products can be designed to fit the shape of the human body

Using Main Ideas

Answer the questions by referring to the page number after each question.

19. What type of joint is found in each of the following: lower jaw, upper leg and pelvis, and shoulder? (p. 296)
20. What are two examples of bones protecting body organs? (p. 286)
21. Why do you feel pain when you sprain your ankle? (p. 300)
22. What type of muscle is found in or as part of each of the following: stomach, blood vessels, heart, and arms? (pp. 294, 295)
23. How do you move your foot up and down? (p. 296)
24. What is the difference between voluntary and involuntary muscles? (p. 294)
25. What happens to muscle when the oxygen supply runs low? (p. 300)

Skill Review ✓

For more help, refer to the ***Skill Handbook,*** *pages 704-719.*

1. **Infer:** When weight lifters flex their muscles, are the muscles shortening, relaxing, or stretching?
2. **Understand science words:** The word *involuntary* means without choice. The word part *in* means without. In your dictionary, find another meaning of the word part *in*.
3. **Classify:** Which words or statements are not correct for all muscles: voluntary, living, contract, made from cells, and form a tight weave?
4. **Infer:** A muscle that moves your leg up or down depends on what direction of action at your knee joint?

Finding Out More

Critical Thinking

1. Draw an imaginary animal. Build your new animal's skeletal system from balsa wood or paper. Hinge bones together with wire or thread. Explain to the class how your animal is adapted to survive.
2. How does the skeleton of a human compare with the skeleton of an alligator? Explain how each skeleton helps the organism survive.

Applications

1. Find out the causes and problems of rheumatoid arthritis, myasthenia gravis, and gout.
2. Make a list of the different types of bone fractures that can occur.

Chapter Review/*Teacher Resource Package*, pp. 70-71.

Chapter Test/*Teacher Resource Package*, pp. 72-74.

Chapter Test/*Computer Test Bank*

Unit Test/*Teacher Resource Package*, pp. 75-76.

Skill Review

1. The muscles are shortening. A muscle bunches up when it contracts.
2. The word part in also means within or toward.
3. Not all musclus are voluntary or form a tight weave.
4. Movement is the result of a hinge joint.

Finding Out More

Critical Thinking

1. Students should describe how their new animal's skeleton would be beneficial for feeding and protection.
2. The human skeleton is upright and helps with walking. The hands have a thumb that helps with holding objects. The alligator skeleton is on four legs and low to the ground, which allows it to hide and move fast over the ground. It has a long tail that helps it swim.

Applications

1. The cause of rheumatoid arthritis is unknown, but it is thought to be related to deficiencies in the autoimmune system. If severe, it can result in loss of use of the affected joints. Myasthenia gravis is a disease of the muscular system. A person becomes progressively weaker until movement is no longer possible. Gout is a metabolic disorder. The joints become inflamed and very painful.
2. Fractures include closed (simple) and open (compound).

Unit 3 Body Systems—Maintaining Life

CONNECTIONS

Biology in Your World

The human body, an incredible living system, has smaller systems within it that work to maintain life. Students learn in this unit that their mind, body, and behavior all contribute to their health and well-being.

Literature Connection

Norman Cousins teaches future doctors about the biochemistry of the emotions. Cousins has overcome two serious illnesses and believes his positive outlook helped his recoveries. He also feels patients and doctors should work as a team when making decisions about treatment. If patients work together with their doctors, they are less apt to feel helpless. Cousins thinks helplessness and panic contribute to the deaths of some ill people.

Art Connection

Rembrandt's painting *The Anatomy Lecture of Dr. Nicolaes Tulp* was the first of his many important group portraits. Usually, the artist chosen for a guild portrait had political connections. Because a guild member had ties to Rembrandt's art dealer, Rembrandt was selected to paint the autopsy. The surgeons liked the painting, and he was commissioned by many others for group portraits.

CONNECTIONS

Biology in Your World

An Amazing Machine

Even as you sleep, your digestive system is breaking down food. Your circulatory system is delivering oxygen and nutrients to cells. Eating well and getting plenty of exercise will keep your body systems running smoothly as they do their tasks.

LITERATURE

Think Positive

Your heart really pumps life into your body. It is a remarkable, complex machine.

Norman Cousins is an editor and author. For many years he was editor of the magazine *Saturday Review.* He had a massive heart attack in 1980. Instead of giving up, he looked at his illness as a challenge. He began to take part in medical decisions concerning his health. Cousins knew that panic and depression could make his heart condition worse. He used positive thought, humor, and relaxation to avoid panic and depression so his heart could recover. In *The Healing Heart,* Cousins tells about his illness and recovery. He stresses that a person's attitude has a lot to do with recovering from an illness.

ART

The Inside Story

One of the ways medical students learn about the inside parts of the human body is through dissection. In the 1600s, the bodies of executed criminals were used. In 1632, the Dutch painter Rembrandt van Rijn was asked to paint a group portrait of the Amsterdam Guild of Surgeons. His painting, *The Anatomy Lecture of Dr. Nicolaes Tulp,* records a public dissection. In the painting, Dr. Tulp is showing the tendons of the arm. This painting was one of the first group portraits Rembrandt did in Amsterdam. It is considered one of the greatest dramatic group portraits.

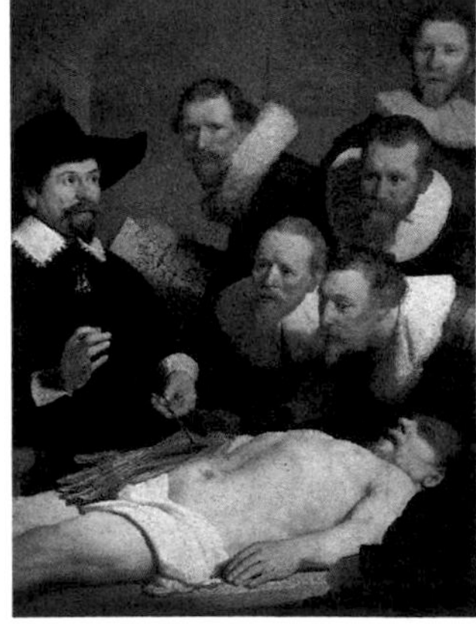

LEISURE

How Fit Are You?

Exercise can be an enjoyable way to spend leisure time. The benefits of exercise are long-lasting. Endurance exercises done on a regular basis will help your heart, lungs, and circulatory system work better. These exercises include walking, jogging, bicycling, and swimming. Lifting weights will build muscle strength, and stretching will increase flexibility.

To improve your overall fitness, plan an exercise program. Before you begin one, get advice from a doctor. Your program need not take large amounts of time or money. You may want to exercise with a friend.

Besides an exercise program, there may be other ways to get exercise. Are there daily activities you could change? Maybe you could walk to the store rather than ride in a car.

CONSUMER

Healthy Dieting

Many people diet to lose weight. What is a safe diet? A safe diet provides the nutrients the body needs every day, but with fewer calories. An effective diet includes an exercise program. Many doctors think a person should lose no more than two pounds per week. Before beginning a diet and exercise program, a person should see a doctor.

How safe are fad diets? Some fad diets promise weight loss without exercise. Others stress eating foods with a lot of a certain nutrient. Some diets promise a loss of several pounds a week. How safe and effective do you think these diets are? How well do they meet safe diet requirements?

CONNECTIONS

Leisure Connection

Leisure exercise activities benefit the body in several ways. Physically fit people can do everyday chores without tiring and are less likely to injure themselves. A fit body resists disease and infection. Exercise reduces the risk of heart disease and can help control adult diabetes and high blood pressure.

Consumer Connection

Many fad diets are nutritionally unbalanced. Some people lose weight quickly on these diets but at the expense of their health. Unbalanced diets can cause fatigue, gall stones, or even death.

The best way to lose or maintain weight is to eat a balanced diet and exercise moderately. Weight taken off slowly is easier to keep off and causes less strain on your body. Groups such as Weight Watchers offer support for dieters.

References

Cousins, Norman. *The Healing Heart: Antidotes to Panic and Helplessness.* New York: W.W. Norton & Co., 1983.

Insel, Paul, and Walton Roth. *Core Concepts in Health. 5th ed.* Mountain View, CA: Mayfield Publishing Co., 1988.

Wardlaw, Gordon, and Paul Insel. *Perspectives in Nutrition.* St. Louis: Times Mirror/Mosby College Publishers, 1990.

White, Christopher. *Rembrandt.* London: Thames and Hudson Ltd., 1984.

Unit 4
Body Systems—Controlling Life

UNIT OVERVIEW

Unit 4 ties together the concepts of coordination and communication among living things. Chapter 15 focuses on the nervous and endocrine systems. Sense organs are discussed in Chapter 17. Chapter 17 concentrates on animal behavior and how it relates to the nervous system. Chapter 18 deals with the effect of drugs upon behavior.

Advance Planning

Audiovisual and computer software suggestions are located within each specific chapter under the heading TEACH. Photocopies of specific items for teaching the chapter or an activity should be prepared in advance.

Prepare a time schedule of chapters in this unit so that any chemicals with a short shelf life may be prepared when needed.

To prepare for:

Lab 15-1: Gather metric rulers.

Lab 15-2: Prepare normal and diabetic "urine" samples. Gather droppers, test tubes, wax pencils, and glucose test paper.

Mini Lab: Arrange to have flashlights available.

Lab 16-1: Gather black and white paper, tape, scissors, and a hand lens.

Lab 16-2: Assemble red and green colored pencils, paper towels, and sugar-free peppermint candy.

Lab 17-1: Order vinegar eels.

Lab 17-2: Collect mirrors.

Mini Labs: Order or collect live earthworms. Ask students to bring in shoe boxes. Obtain black paper. Purchase onions and collect knives.

Lab 18-1: Prepare 6 test solutions of painkillers and aspirin-testing solution in dropper tubes.

Lab 18-2: Prepare 6 test solutions of over-the-counter drugs, household items, and alcohol testing chemical.

Mini Lab: Order bacteria culture and agar. Treat paper disks with onion and garlic.

Unit **4**

CONTENTS

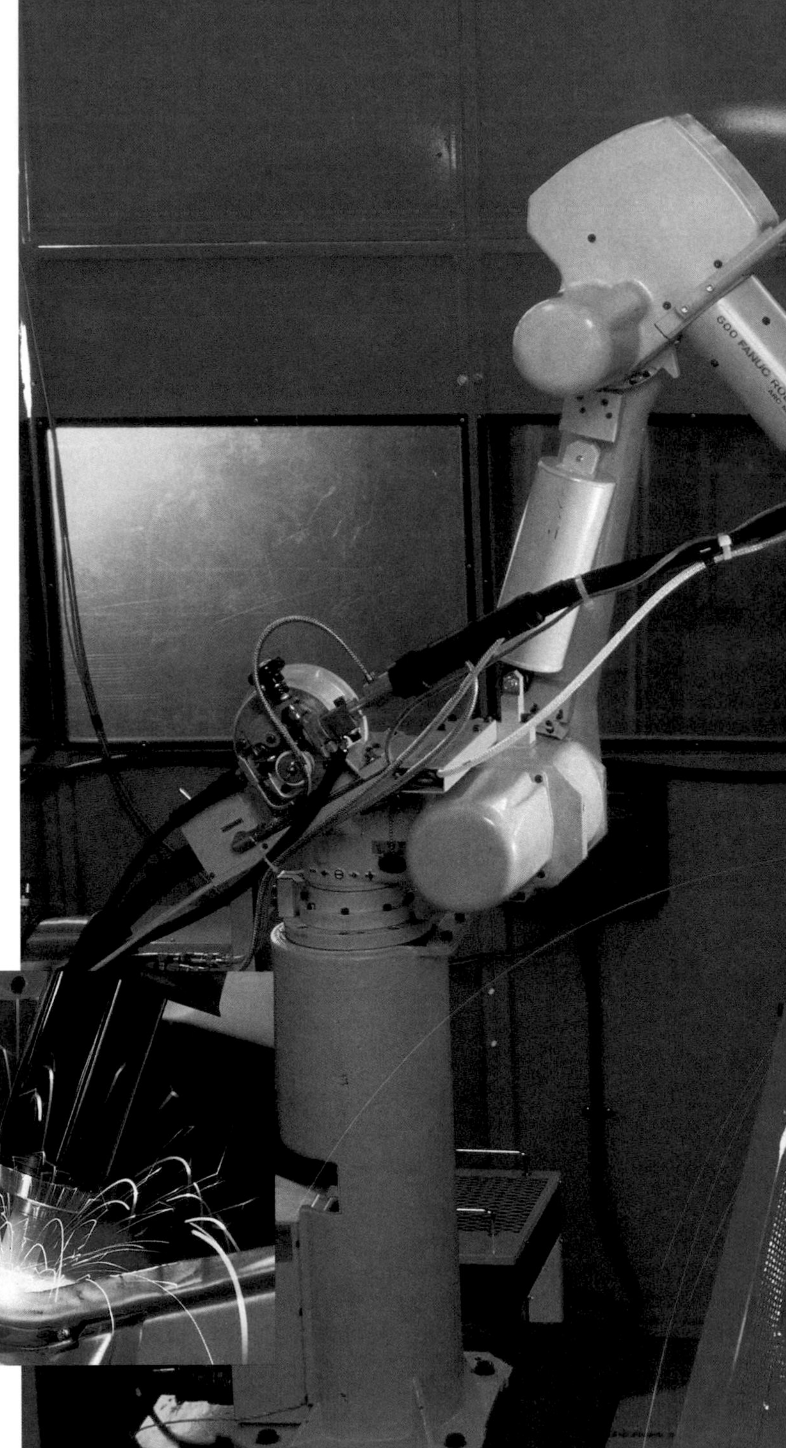

Body Systems—Controlling Life

What would happen if...

robots could think and make decisions? So far, robots can't think, guess, imagine, create, or make decisions. But researchers hope to produce computer programs that mimic human thought.

With such computer programs, the possible uses of robots would increase greatly. More and more jobs could be taken over by robots.

Being able to run a factory or business without people has many advantages. Robots are not paid, and they could work 24 hours a day. Dirty, boring, and dangerous jobs could be done by robots. But, would people who lose their jobs to robots find other jobs or would they become unemployed? What would be the impact on society of increased unemployment?

UNIT OVERVIEW

Photo Teaching Tip

After students have read the passage that accompanies these unit opening photographs of a robot, ask them to make a list of all the things they do each day that they would like to have a personal robot to carry out for them. Have students consider the choice between personal control and being controlled. This could lead the discussion to the misuse and abuse of drugs, which can result in a loss of control over one's own choices. Point out that technology can be used to help us gain more control over our environment and that as scientists we have the choice to use or abuse this control.

Theme Development

Animal life depends on the animal systems that maintain and regulate body functions. This unit, as did the previous one, continues to use the human as its major animal example. The theme of homeostasis is developed in this unit. The nervous and endocrine systems plus the sense organs of various animal phyla other than Chordates are referenced in this unit. Control of life functions is finalized, with special emphasis given to animal behavior and the effect of drugs on behavior.

Nervous and Chemical Control

PLANNING GUIDE

CONTENT	TEXT FEATURES	TEACHER RESOURCE PACKAGE	OTHER COMPONENTS
(1 day) 15:1 The Role of the Nervous System Response Nervous Systems of Animals	Check Your Understanding, p. 311	Reteaching: *Nervous Systems of Invertebrates,* p. 43 Study Guide: *The Role of the Nervous System,* p. 85	
(3 days) 15:2 Human Nervous System Nerve Cells Pathways of Messages Nervous System Parts Jobs of the Brain Reflexes	Skill Check: *Interpret Diagrams,* p. 314 Skill Check: *Understand Science Words,* p. 316 Mini Lab: *What Is an Eye Reflex?* p. 317 Lab 15-1: *Reaction Time,* p. 319 Idea Map, p. 317 Check Your Understanding, p. 318	Application: *Testing Reaction Times,* p. 15 Reteaching: *Parts of the Brain,* p. 44 Focus: *What You Can Do Without Thinking,* p. 29 Transparency Master: *Neuron Parts and Pathways,* p. 69 Study Guide: *The Human Nervous System,* pp. 86-87 Lab 15-1: *Reaction Time,* pp. 57-58	**Laboratory Manual:** *Which Brain Side is Dominant?* p. 119 **Laboratory Manual:** *What Are the Functions of the Brain?* p. 123 Color Transparency 15a: *Movement of a Message Across a Synapse*
(1 1/2 days) 15:3 The Role of the Endocrine System Chemical Control The Pituitary Gland The Thyroid Gland	Idea Map, p. 322 Check Your Understanding, p. 322	Enrichment: *How Pancreas Hormones Work Together,* pp. 15-16 Reteaching: *Endocrine Glands,* p. 45 Critical Thinking/Problem Solving: *How Does the Brain Affect the Amount of Urine Made by the Kidneys?* p. 15 Study Guide: *The Role of the Endocrine System,* p. 88	Color Transparency 15b: *The Endocrine System*
(1 1/2 days) 15:4 Nervous and Endocrine System Problems Nervous System Problems Endocrine System Problems	Lab 15-2: *Diabetes,* p. 325 Check Your Understanding, p. 324 Problem Solving: *Viewing the Human Body,* p. 326	Skill: *Summarize,* p. 16 Study Guide: *Nervous and Endocrine System Problems,* p. 89 Study Guide: *Vocabulary,* p. 90 Lab 15-2: *Diabetes,* pp. 59-60	
Chapter Review	Summary Key Science Words Testing Yourself Finding Main Ideas Using Main Ideas Skill Review	Chapter Review, pp. 77-78 Chapter Test, pp. 79-81	**Test Bank**

MATERIALS NEEDED

LAB 15-1, p. 319	LAB 15-2, p. 325	MARGIN FEATURES
metric ruler	test tube rack microscope slides 8 droppers wax pencils normal urine sample urine sample from diabetic urine samples in test tubes marked C-E glucose test paper	Skill Check, p. 316 dictionary Mini Lab, p. 317 flashlight

OBJECTIVES

SECTION	OBJECTIVE	OBJECTIVES CORRELATION: CHECK YOUR UNDERSTANDING	CHAPTER REVIEW	TRP CHAPTER REVIEW	TRP CHAPTER TEST
15:1	1. **Explain** how animals keep in touch with their body parts and their surroundings.	1, 2, 4	1, 20	9	12, 13, 47
	2. **Compare** the nervous systems of common animals.	3	16	10	14, 48
15:2	3. **Explain** how nerve cells carry messages through the body.	6, 10	3, 6, 18, 25	4, 15, 28, 31	3, 5, 9, 10, 11, 39, 40, 41, 42, 43, 44, 45
	4. **State** the functions of the three major parts of the nervous system.	7, 9	4, 12, 17, 22	1, 3, 6, 8, 11, 17, 20, 23, 24, 32	2, 6, 15, 17, 18, 19, 20, 21, 22, 23, 24, 25, 46, 53
	5. **Describe** a reflex action.	8	10, 15	14, 27	7, 16, 49, 56
15:3	6. **Explain** the function of the endocrine system.	11	9	5, 12, 13, 16, 18, 19, 21, 22, 25, 26	1, 8, 26, 27, 28, 29, 30, 31, 32, 35, 37, 52
	7. **Relate** the importance of the pituitary and thyroid glands.	12, 14, 15	5, 8, 11, 14, 24	29, 33	33, 34, 38, 51, 57
	8. **Identify** problems that damage the brain.	16, 20	21	2	54
	9. **Explain** the importance of insulin.	17, 18	1, 17, 13, 23	7, 30, 34	4, 36, 50, 55

Nervous and Chemical Control

CHAPTER OVERVIEW

Key Concepts

This chapter looks at the body's two major systems of communication, the nervous and endocrine systems. The neuron is described and its role in carrying messages through the nervous system is analyzed. The most common endocrine glands are described, and the way hormones keep themselves in balance is discussed. Certain problems of the nervous and endocrine systems are also examined.

Key Science Words

axon	nerve
brain	nervous system
cerebellum	neuron
cerebrum	pituitary gland
dendrite	reflex
diabetes mellitus	spinal cord
endocrine system	synapse
hormone	thyroid gland
insulin	thyroxine
medulla	

Skill Development

In Lab 15-1, students will **form a hypothesis, calculate**, and **infer** to determine reaction time. In Lab 15-2, they will **experiment** and **interpret data** to determine if glucose is present in urine of a diabetic. In the Skill Check on page 314, students will **interpret diagrams** of synapses. In the Skill Check on page 316, they will **understand** the **science word** *cerebrum.* In the Mini Lab on page 317, they will **observe** eye reflexes.

CHAPTER PREVIEW

Chapter Content

Review this outline for Chapter 15 before you read the chapter.

15:1 The Role of the Nervous System
- Response
- Nervous Systems of Animals

15:2 Human Nervous System
- Nerve Cells
- Pathways of Messages
- Nervous System Parts
- Jobs of the Brain
- Reflexes

15:3 The Role of the Endocrine System
- Chemical Control
- The Pituitary Gland
- The Thyroid Gland

15:4 Nervous and Endocrine System Problems
- Nervous System Problems
- Endocrine System Problems

Skills in this Chapter

The skills that you will use in this chapter are listed below.

- In **Lab 15-1,** you will form a hypothesis, calculate, and infer. In **Lab 15-2,** you will experiment and interpret data.
- In the **Skill Checks,** you will interpret diagrams and understand science words.
- In the **Mini Lab,** you will observe.

308

Bridging

Skeletal muscles contract on a voluntary basis and heart muscle contracts on an involuntary basis. From where within the body do these messages that bring about contraction originate? The nervous system's role in muscle contraction can now be related to an earlier study of muscle action.

Chapter 15

Nervous and Chemical Control

The larger photo on the left is a photograph of a circuit board from a computer. The smaller photo below shows the human brain. It is often said that a computer and the human brain are very much alike. The brain is made of living cells. There are billions of cells in the human brain. Each cell sends and receives messages from nearby cells. These messages are interpreted as sights, sounds, smells, or thoughts. A computer has thousands of computer chips. Each chip sends and receives messages from the other chips in the computer. Both brains and computers process information. How is the processing of information by the brain important? In what other ways are messages carried through the body?

Try This!

Can you control your reflexes? Put on a pair of safety goggles. Have someone toss a paper wad toward your eyes. Do you blink? Can you keep yourself from blinking? What is this involuntary action called?

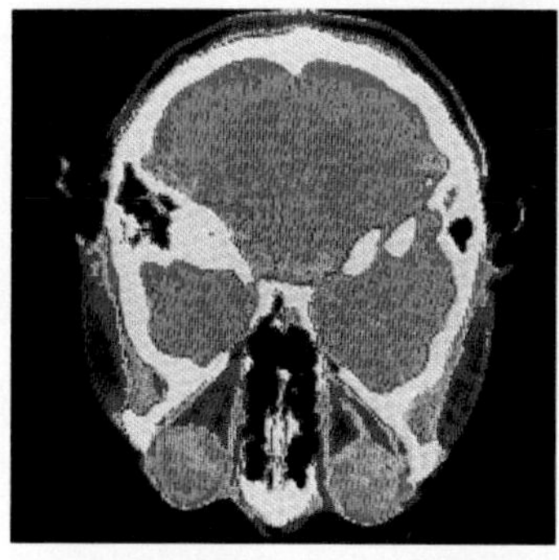

CAT scan of the human brain

GETTING STARTED

Using the Photos

In looking at the photos, students should try to identify similarities and differences between the brain and a circuit board. Both process information. The brain is more complex and can do more than a computer.

MOTIVATION/Try This!

Can you control your reflexes? Students are **experimenting** with a reflex. This type of action is not under voluntary control and will occur each time the same stimulus (wad of paper moving toward the eyes) is detected.

Chapter Preview

Have students study the chapter outline before they begin to read the chapter. They should note the overall organization of the chapter, that the introduction describes the general role of the nervous system and introduces students to the system found in simpler animal phyla. Next, it describes the nature of the human nervous system. The role of the endocrine system is examined next with a detailed study of certain endocrine glands. Last, problems that arise with the endocrine and nervous system are described.

Misconception

Ask students the cause of diabetes and they will tell you that it is related to the kidneys (presence of sugar in urine). In reality, the problem is associated with an endocrine gland and the lack of the hormone insulin.

15:1 The Role of the Nervous System

PREPARATION

Materials Needed

Make copies of the Reteaching and Study Guide worksheets in the *Teacher Resource Package.*

Key Science Words

nervous system

1 FOCUS

▶ The objectives are listed on the student page. Remind students to preview these objectives as a guide to this numbered section.

Convergent Question

Ask students what animals would be unable to do if they had no nervous system. Students will realize that almost all body functions are related directly or indirectly to the nervous system.

Guided Practice

Have students write down their answers to the margin questions: The hydra has a nerve net; animals are able to respond to changes by means of their nervous systems.

15:1 The Role of the Nervous System

Objectives

1. **Explain** how animals keep in touch with their body parts and their surroundings.
2. **Compare** the nervous systems of common animals.

Key Science Words

nervous system

Most animals have special cells and organs that help them keep in touch with parts of their own bodies. They are able to send messages to all body parts and receive messages from those body parts. These special cells also allow an animal to receive messages from its surroundings.

Response

Most animals can quickly detect changes that take place around them. Usually, they respond quickly to these changes. A response is the action of an organism because of a change in its environment.

Let's use an example to show how quickly animals respond to changes around them. Have you ever seen a dog chase a cat? It seems impossible for the dog to catch the cat. Why? First, the cat usually sees the dog. The cat's brain gets the message that something nearby is moving toward it. The brain responds by sending messages to the cat's leg muscles. The cat runs up a tree to protect itself.

The cat sees and responds to the dog because it has a nervous system. A **nervous system** is made of cells and organs that let an animal detect changes and respond to them. This system is made of nerve cells, sense organs, and usually a brain.

Nervous Systems of Animals

The simplest animals to have a nervous system are the stinging-cell animals. Figure 15-1a shows what this system looks like in the hydra. Hydras have a very simple nervous

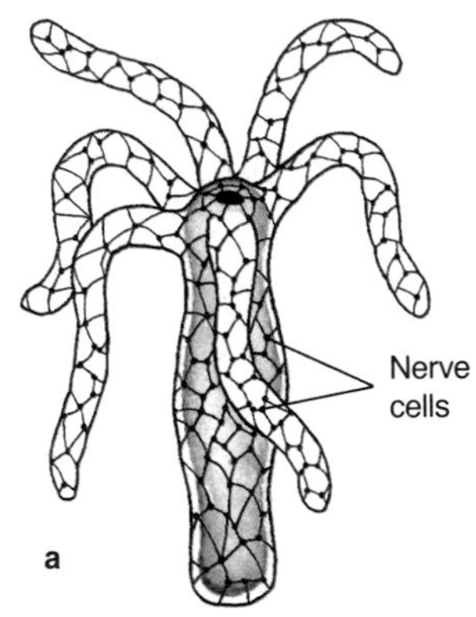

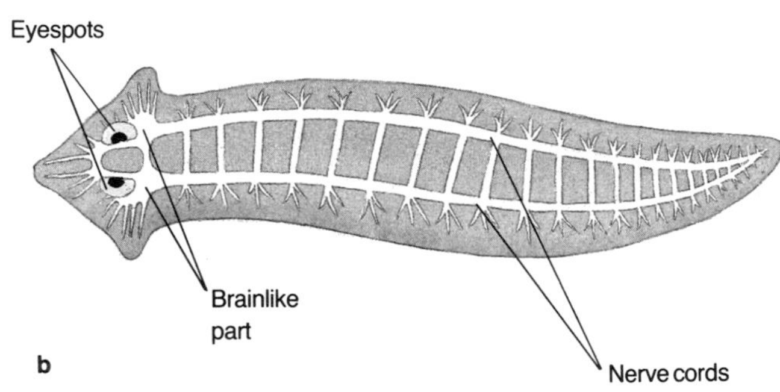

Figure 15-1 Hydras (a) and planarians (b) have simple nervous systems.

OPTIONS

Science Background

A nerve net transmits impulses in all directions. Impulses are weaker, and response time is slower. A nervous system transmits impulses along discrete nerve pathways. Impulses are stronger, and response time is faster.

system made up of nerve cells that form a net throughout the body. This simple grouping of nerve cells lets these animals detect and respond to changes around them.

A flatworm has a nervous system that is more complex than that of the hydra. The nervous system of a flatworm has several parts. You can see in Figure 15-1b that a planarian has three parts that a hydra doesn't have. The planarian has a brainlike part, eyespots, and two nerve cords. Planarians can respond to changes in light with their eyespots. Because they have a brainlike part and nerve cords, they also can respond more quickly than a hydra.

Jointed-leg animals have a more complex nervous system than flatworms. Figure 15-2 shows the inside of a spider. A spider has four pairs of eyes. It has a brain, nerve cord, and many nerves going to its body parts. Spiders can respond even more quickly than planarians.

What kind of nervous system does a hydra have?

How are animals able to respond to changes around them?

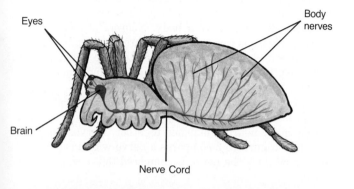

Eyes
Body nerves
Brain
Nerve Cord

Figure 15-2 Nervous system of a spider

Check Your Understanding

1. What is meant by *response?* Give an example not found in this chapter.
2. What is a nervous system? What parts form a nervous system?
3. Compare the nervous systems of a hydra, planarian, and spider.
4. **Critical Thinking:** What cell parts do protists use to respond to changes in the environment?
5. **Biology and Writing:** A planarian has a nervous system. Do you think a planarian can learn? Write a paragraph of at least three sentences to explain your answer.

2 TEACH

Independent Practice

Study Guide/*Teacher Resource Package,* p. 85. Use the Study Guide worksheet shown at the bottom of this page for independent practice.

Check for Understanding

Have students respond to the first three questions in Check Your Understanding.

Reteach

Reteaching/*Teacher Resource Package,* p. 43. Use this worksheet to give students additional practice with the nervous systems of invertebrates.

Extension: Assign Critical Thinking, Biology and Writing, or some of the **OPTIONS** available with this section.

3 APPLY

ACTIVITY/Challenge

Have students research the nervous system in other animal phyla.

4 CLOSE

Show the videocassette *Nervous System,* National Geographic.

Answers to Check Your Understanding

1. It is how an animal reacts to a change in its environment. A robin responds to a worm by grabbing it in its beak.
2. cells and organs that let an animal detect changes and respond to them; nerve cells, sense organs, and possibly a brain
3. The hydra has a nerve net. Flatworms have a brain-like part, eyespots, and two nerve cords. Spiders have a brain, eyes, body nerves, and a nerve cord.
4. nucleus, vacuole, cell membrane
5. Answers will vary but should include that a planarian has a brainlike part.

RETEACHING 43

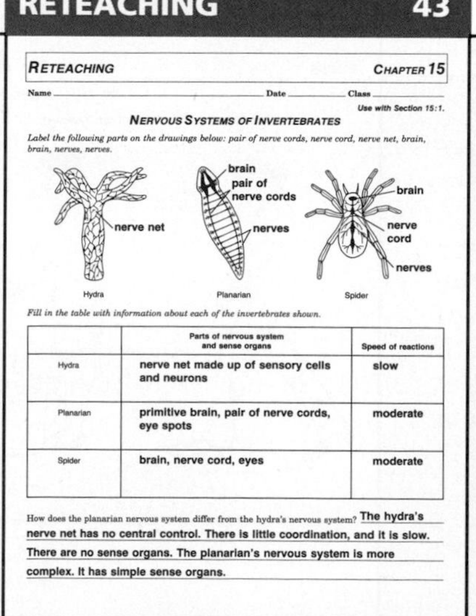

RETEACHING CHAPTER 15

Name ____ Date ____ Class ____

Use with Section 15:1.

NERVOUS SYSTEMS OF INVERTEBRATES

Label the following parts on the drawings below: pair of nerve cords, nerve cord, nerve net, brain, brain, nerves, nerves.

Fill in the table with information about each of the invertebrates shown.

	Parts of nervous system and sense organs	Speed of reactions
Hydra	nerve net made up of sensory cells and neurons	slow
Planarian	primitive brain, pair of nerve cords, eye spots	moderate
Spider	brain, nerve cord, eyes	moderate

How does the planarian nervous system differ from the hydra's nervous system? The hydra's nerve net has no central control. There is little coordination, and it is slow. There are no sense organs. The planarian's nervous system is more complex. It has simple sense organs.

STUDY GUIDE 85

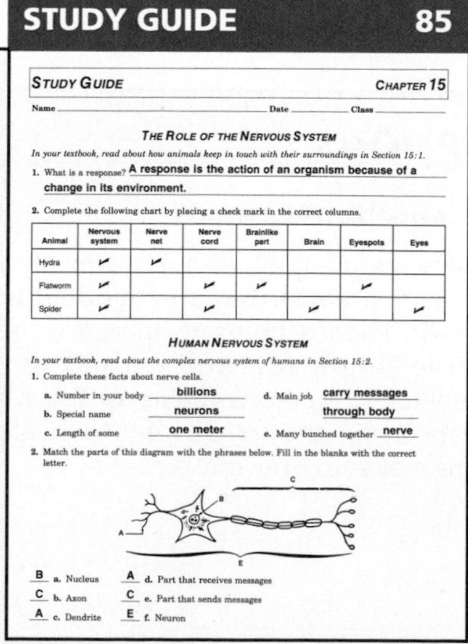

STUDY GUIDE CHAPTER 15

Name ____ Date ____ Class ____

THE ROLE OF THE NERVOUS SYSTEM

In your textbook, read about how animals keep in touch with their surroundings in Section 15:1.

1. What is a response? A response is the action of an organism because of a change in its environment.
2. Complete the following chart by placing a check mark in the correct columns.

Animal	Nervous system	Nerve net	Nerve cord	Brainlike part	Brain	Eyespots	Eyes
Hydra	✓	✓					
Flatworm	✓		✓	✓		✓	
Spider	✓		✓		✓		✓

HUMAN NERVOUS SYSTEM

In your textbook, read about the complex nervous system of humans in Section 15:2.

1. Complete these facts about nerve cells.
   a. Number in your body billions
   b. Special name neurons
   c. Length of some one meter
   d. Main job carry messages through body
   e. Many bunched together nerve
2. Match the parts of this diagram with the phrases below. Fill in the blanks with the correct letter.

B a. Nucleus
C b. Axon
A c. Dendrite
A d. Part that receives messages
C e. Part that sends messages
E f. Neuron

15:2 Human Nervous System

PREPARATION

Materials Needed

Make copies of the Focus, Transparency Master, Application, Study Guide, Reteaching, and Lab worksheets in the *Teacher Resource Package.*

▶ Obtain penlights for the Mini Lab on an eye reflex.

▶ Gather metric rulers for Lab 15-1.

Key Science Words

neuron	spinal cord
nerve	cerebrum
dendrite	cerebellum
axon	medulla
synapse	reflex
brain	

Process Skills

In Lab 15-1, students will form a hypothesis, calculate, and infer. In the Skill Checks, students will understand science words. In the Mini Lab, students will observe and interpret diagrams.

1 FOCUS

▶ The objectives are listed on the student page. Remind students to preview these objectives as a guide to this numbered section.

MOTIVATION/Brainstorming

Ask students to name activities that would be impossible if we had no nervous system and to offer a possible reason for their answer. Ask if it would be possible to remain alive without a nervous system.

Focus/*Teacher Resource Package,* p. 29. Use the Focus Transparency shown at the bottom of this page as an introduction to reflexes.

15:2 Human Nervous System

Objectives

3. **Explain** how nerve cells carry messages through the body.
4. **State** the functions of the three major organs of the nervous system.
5. **Describe** a reflex action.

Key Science Words

neuron
nerve
dendrite
axon
synapse
brain
spinal cord
cerebrum
cerebellum
medulla
reflex

Humans have one of the most complex nervous systems. If you understand how the human nervous system works, then you will have an idea of how nervous systems work in many other animals. Let's look at parts of the human nervous system in more detail.

Nerve Cells

Nerve cells are the main part of any nervous system. They carry messages through the nervous system. Your body contains billions of nerve cells. Nerve cells are called **neurons** (NOO rahnz).

Neurons are often compared to electrical wires. Wires are very thin and long. Wires carry messages and have a covering of insulation around them. Wires usually connect two things, such as an electric outlet and a lamp. Neurons are very thin and can be very long. They are as long as one meter in some parts of your body. Neurons also have a covering. Neurons carry messages through your body. They make it possible for body parts to keep in touch with each other. Figure 15-3 shows how a wire and a neuron compare.

We can also compare a cable with a nerve. A cable is made of many wires bunched together. Cables are thick. A **nerve** is many neurons bunched together. Nerves can be thick, too. Figure 15-3 compares a nerve with a cable. Notice how thick the nerve is compared to the single neuron.

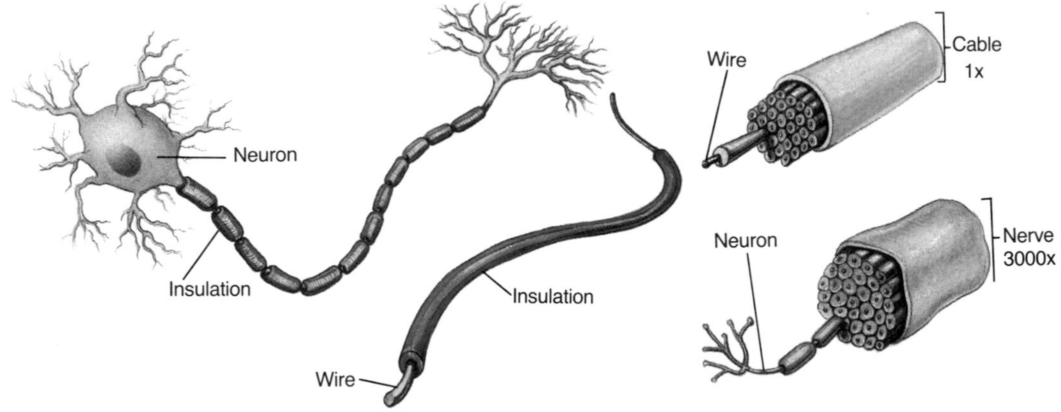

Figure 15-3 Neurons and nerves can be compared to wires and cables.

OPTIONS

Science Background

Many neurons have a fat-containing sheath (myelin sheath) that surrounds the axon. The myelin sheath helps to increase the speed of nerve impulses and insulates the cell. Myelinated neurons make up the white matter in the brain and spinal cord. Unmyelinated neurons make up gray matter.

FOCUS 29

FOCUS CHAPTER 15

Name Date Class

WHAT YOU CAN DO WITHOUT THINKING

1. The people shown are doing things without thinking about them. What are they doing?
2. What other things can you do without thinking about them?

A neuron, shown in Figure 15-4, has many of the same parts that other cells have. There are a few differences, however, between neurons and other cells. Two differences are the length and the shape of the neuron. The long, thin shape helps the neuron do its job well. The third difference between neurons and other cells is in the shape of the ends. Notice the branching shape of both ends of the neuron. One end is called the dendrite. **Dendrites** are parts of the neuron that receive messages from nearby neurons. The other end, usually longer, is called the axon (AK sahn). The **axon** is the part of the neuron that sends messages to surrounding neurons or body organs.

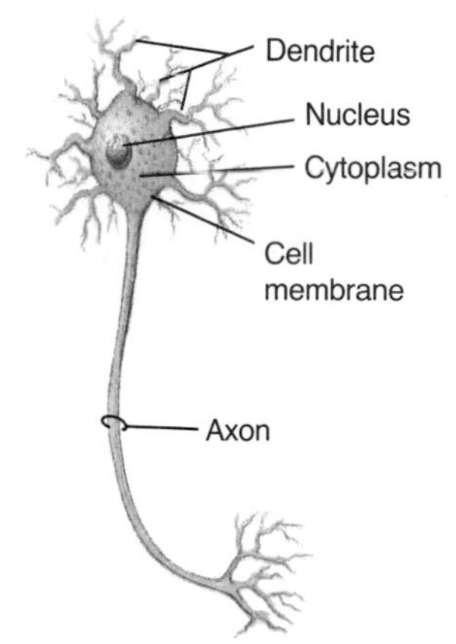

Figure 15-4 The long, thin shape of a neuron helps it do its job of carrying messages.

Pathways of Messages

How do nerves carry messages from one part of your body to another? Figure 15-5 shows what the path of nerves would look like. There are three important things that you should see in the diagram.

1. The pathway that carries messages from brain to hand is not the same pathway that carries messages from hand to brain. The different colored arrows in this diagram show the directions in which messages move along the pathways.
2. The neurons that make up a long pathway do not touch each other. There is a very small space called a synapse (SIN aps) between one neuron and the next. A **synapse** is a small space between the axon of one neuron and the dendrite of a nearby neuron.
3. The dendrites of one neuron are always next to the axon of another neuron.

Figure 15-5 The nerve pathways that carry messages away from the brain are different from the nerve pathways that carry messages to the brain.

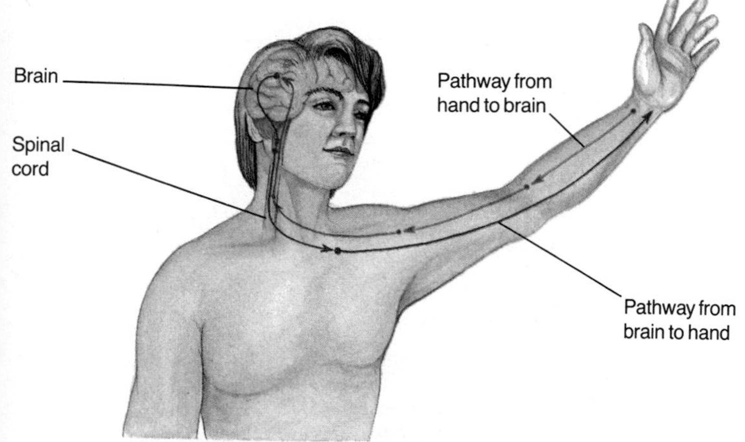

2 TEACH

MOTIVATION/Demonstration

See if your physics department has a wave motion apparatus. It consists of a series of thin metal tubes fastened to a thin metal strip. The motion of the tubes will simulate a wave pattern when the strip is twisted. Such a demonstration will help students visualize how a nerve message is propagated along the length of the nerve.

Concept Development

▶ Understanding the terms *axon, dendrite,* and *synapse* is critical to understanding how the nervous system works. Make sure that students understand these terms before moving on.

▶ The three points listed in the diagram reference are important. Ask students to redraw the diagram of neuron pathways on the chalkboard, making sure that they observe the three rules in their drawings.

▶ Ask students to label the axon and dendrite ends of the neurons that were drawn on the chalkboard. It is important that axon and dendrite labels do appear next to one another, but are labeled on different neurons. Add labels to each synapse.

Analogy: Have students read the comparison between nerve cells and a wire. Ask them to describe differences between the two. Possible answers are that nerves are composed of cells, that they are composed of living matter, and that some nerves can repair themselves, while wires cannot. A cable cut in cross section may be obtained from your shop teacher. It would serve as a good visual aid in making the comparison between nerves and cables more tangible.

TRANSPARENCY 69

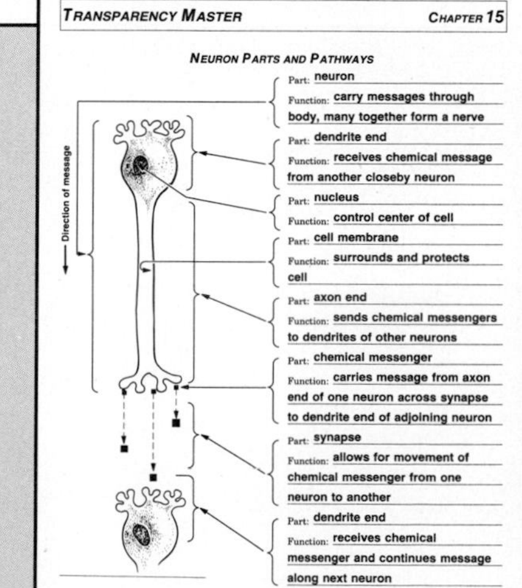

TRANSPARENCY MASTER — CHAPTER 15

NEURON PARTS AND PATHWAYS

Part: neuron
Function: carry messages through body, many together form a nerve

Part: dendrite end
Function: receives chemical message from another closeby neuron

Part: nucleus
Function: control center of cell

Part: cell membrane
Function: surrounds and protects cell

Part: axon end
Function: sends chemical messengers to dendrites of other neurons

Part: chemical messenger
Function: carries message from axon end of one neuron across synapse to dendrite end of adjoining neuron

Part: synapse
Function: allows for movement of chemical messenger from one neuron to another

Part: dendrite end
Function: receives chemical messenger and continues message along next neuron

OPTIONS

Enrichment: The speed of messages along a nerve is about 100 meters per second. If a person could run at that speed, he or she could cover the length of a football field in about one second.

Transparency Master/*Teacher Resource Package,* p. 69. Use the Transparency Master shown here as you teach about neuron pathways.

TEACH

Analogy: An analogy can be made between a radio station transmitting tower, a home radio receiver, and a neuron's axon/dendrite ends. The tower sends out the signal (axon end), while the radio receives the message (dendrite end). Radio signals represent the chemical given off by the axon. Continue the analogy of radio waves by asking if a typical home radio receiver can send messages back to the radio station. It can't. Thus, the rule established for one-way messages along neuron pathways is further illustrated.

Guided Practice

Have students write down their answers to the margin question: Message moves along neuron from dendrite to axon. Message reaches tip of axon. Chemical is given off by axon when message arrives. Chemical passes across synapse and reaches dendrite of next neuron. Chemical restarts the message and message continues along the new neuron.

Skill Check

Messages travel from one neuron to the next by means of chemical messengers that cross the synapse.

Messages move along a neuron from one end to the other. The message is an electrical charge that moves along the axon just as electricity moves along a wire. It flows along the neuron from dendrite end to axon end. How can this message travel across the synapse between one neuron and the next?

How do messages move across a synapse?

Figure 15-6 shows how messages move across a synapse. First, the message moves along a neuron from the dendrite to the axon, Figure 15-6a. Next, the message reaches the tip of the axon, Figure 15-6b. Notice that a chemical is given off by the axon when the message arrives there. This chemical then passes across the synapse and reaches the dendrite of the next neuron as shown in Figure 15-6c. The chemical restarts the message and the message continues along the new neuron.

Now you know why different pathways are needed to carry messages from the brain to the hand and from the hand to the brain. Messages do not travel in both directions along the same neuron. Only the axon of the neuron gives off the chemical that crosses the synapse.

Skill Check

Interpret diagrams: Look at Figure 15-6. How does the message travel from one neuron to the next? *For more help, refer to the* ***Skill Handbook,*** *pages 706-711.*

Nervous System Parts

Nerve cells make up three important parts or areas of your nervous system. These parts are the brain, spinal cord, and body nerves.

The first major organ of the human nervous system is the brain. The **brain** is the organ that sends and receives messages to and from all body parts. It also records and interprets these messages. It is made of billions of neurons.

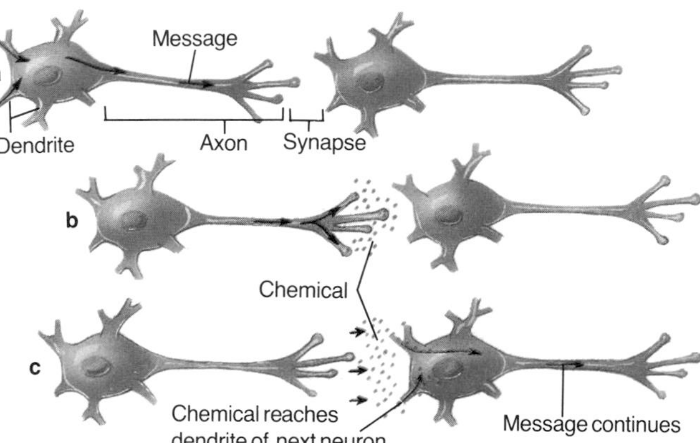

Figure 15-6 Messages move from one neuron to the next with the help of a chemical messenger that crosses the synapse.

OPTIONS

ACTIVITY/Enrichment

You can use a skull to show how well it serves as a protective structure. Most skulls are hinged on top so that students can actually measure the bone thickness of different regions of the skull.

Movement of a Message Across a Synapse/*Transparency Package,* number 15a. Use color transparency 15a as you teach how nerve cells carry messages.

The second major part of the human nervous system is the spinal cord. Your **spinal cord** is the part that carries messages from the brain to body nerves or from body nerves to the brain. Messages travel up the spinal cord on the way to your brain and down the spinal cord to body nerves. The spinal cord is made of millions of neurons. Figure 15-7 shows the location of your spinal cord. It runs down the center of your back. The spinal cord can be compared to the power lines that enter or leave a power plant. The power plant could be compared to the brain.

Figure 15-8 shows how well the brain and spinal cord are protected against injury. Both are covered by bone and membranes. Both are also surrounded by fluid that cushions them. The brain is covered by your skull. The spinal cord is covered by bones called vertebrae. The word *vertebrate,* used in Chapter 7, sounds very similar. What do *vertebrae* and *vertebrate* mean?

The third part of your nervous system is the group of nerves that enter and leave the spinal cord. Body nerves connect organs, muscles, and skin to the spinal cord. Messages move along body nerves from organs or muscles to the spinal cord and then to the brain. Messages also move from the brain to the spinal cord and then along body nerves to organs or muscles. Body nerves are like the wires that lead from the power lines to your house.

What are the three major parts of the nervous system?

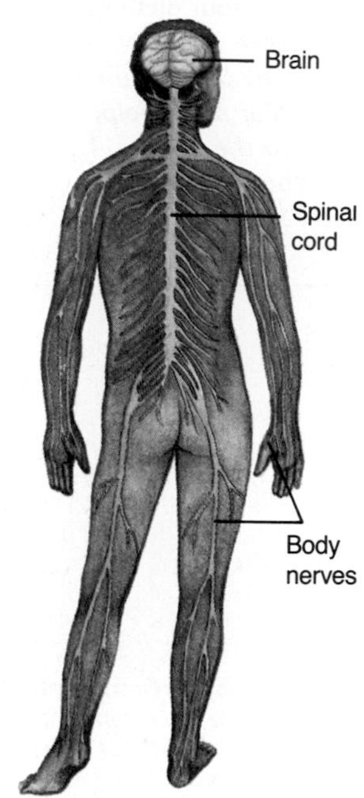

Figure 15-7 The parts of the nervous system include the brain, spinal cord, and body nerves.

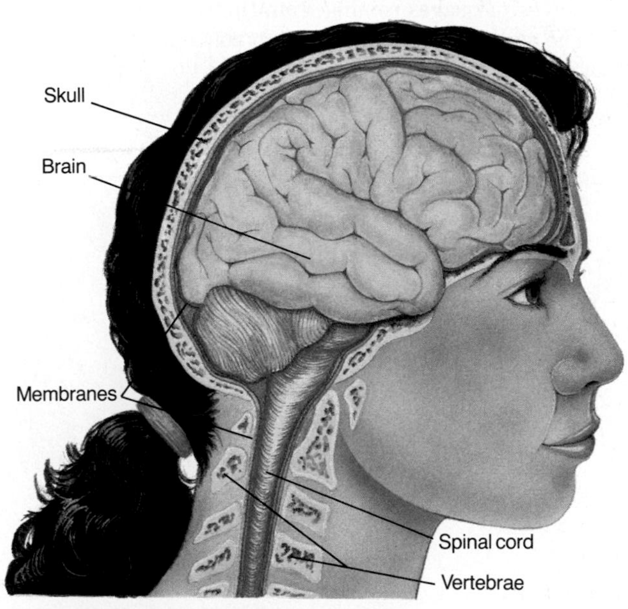

Figure 15-8 The brain and spinal cord are well protected.

STUDY GUIDE 86

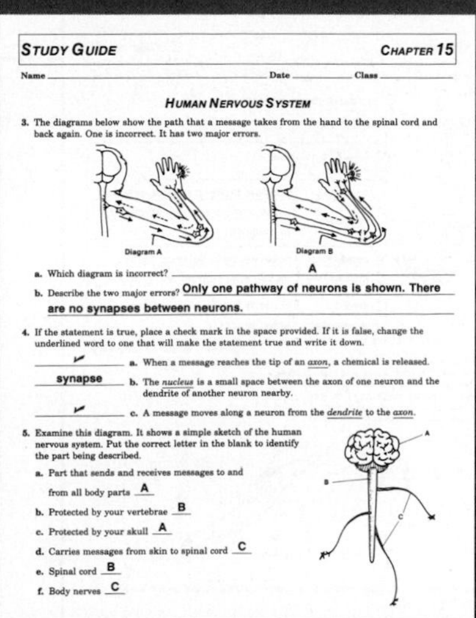

STUDY GUIDE CHAPTER 15

Name ______ Date ______ Class ______

HUMAN NERVOUS SYSTEM

3. The diagrams below show the path that a message takes from the hand to the spinal cord and back again. One is incorrect. It has two major errors.

Diagram A Diagram B

a. Which diagram is incorrect? A

b. Describe the two major errors? Only one pathway of neurons is shown. There are no synapses between neurons.

4. If the statement is true, place a check mark in the space provided. If it is false, change the underlined word to one that will make the statement true and write it down.

✓ a. When a message reaches the tip of an *axon*, a chemical is released.

synapse b. The *nucleus* is a small space between the axon of one neuron and the dendrite of another neuron nearby.

✓ c. A message moves along a neuron from the *dendrite* to the *axon*.

5. Examine this diagram. It shows a simple sketch of the human nervous system. Put the correct letter in the blank to identify the part being described.

a. Part that sends and receives messages to and from all body parts A

b. Protected by your vertebrae B

c. Protected by your skull A

d. Carries messages from skin to spinal cord C

e. Spinal cord B

f. Body nerves C

TEACH

Concept Development

▶ Explain to students that when the spinal cord is injured, nerve function is affected below the point of injury. Incoming messages from sensory neurons cannot reach the brain, and messages from the brain cannot reach the motor neurons. The degree to which nerve function is diminished is related to the severity of the injury. A severed spinal cord results in complete paralysis below the point of injury. Neurons in the central nervous system do not repair themselves.

▶ You may want to introduce the terms *central nervous system* and *peripheral nervous system* at this point. The brain and spinal cord comprise the central nervous system. Body nerves comprise the peripheral nervous system. Some students may have heard of peripheral vision. Peripheral vision refers to vision toward the side. Peripheral nerves are those that extend from the spinal cord toward both sides of the body.

Guided Practice

Have students write down their answers to the margin question: Three major parts of the nervous system are the brain, spinal cord, and body nerves.

Independent Practice

Study Guide/*Teacher Resource Package,* p. 86. Use the Study Guide worksheet shown at the bottom of this page for independent practice.

TEACH

Concept Development

▶ Have students speculate as to the advantage of the brain having a folded surface rather than a flat surface. Surface area is greatly expanded by the folds.

▶ Review the terms *voluntary* and *involuntary.* Ask students why we say "control your tongue" or "control your emotions." These actions are voluntary, and therefore we can control them.

▶ A summary of cerebrum anatomy and function at this point should emphasize that the cerebrum has left and right sides. Each side controls the opposite side of the body. The cerebrum is also divided into front and back halves.

Demonstration

Using a brain model or a preserved brain, locate for students the areas of the brain: cerebrum, cerebellum, medulla. As you point out these areas, remind students of their functions.

Independent Practice

Study Guide/*Teacher Resource Package,* p. 87. Use the Study Guide worksheet shown at the bottom of this page for independent practice.

ACTIVITY/Software

The Nervous System and the Sense Organs, Queue, Inc.

Skill Check

Understand science words: cerebrum. The word part *cerebr* means brain. In your dictionary, find three words with the word part *cerebr* in them. *For more help, refer to the* ***Skill Handbook,*** *pages 706-711.*

Jobs of the Brain

The brain, like other body organs, has several different parts. Each part has a different job. The human brain has three main parts. Let's look at each part. They are the cerebrum (suh REE brum), cerebellum (ser uh BEL uhm), and medulla (muh DUL uh). The **cerebrum** is the brain part that controls thought, reason, and the senses. Look at Figure 15-9. Most of what you see is the cerebrum. It is the largest part of the brain. It looks like a huge walnut because of its folds.

The cerebrum has many jobs. One of its jobs is to store messages. We call stored messages memory. The cerebrum receives messages from all the sense organs. For example, sounds may be interpreted as music, laughter, or a whistle. Sights may be interpreted as brightly colored flowers or dark thunder clouds. The cerebrum is also the center for muscle control. Messages for moving the arms and legs start in the cerebrum. Messages about pain or touch end up in the cerebrum. The cerebrum also controls personality.

Many jobs of the cerebrum are voluntary. Remember from Chapter 14 that voluntary means you have control. For example, you decide if you want to move a toe or foot.

Figure 15-9 also shows a top view of the cerebrum. It is divided into left and right sides. The left side of the cerebrum controls the right side of the body. The left side also receives messages coming from the right side of the body. The right side of the cerebrum controls and receives messages from the left side of the body.

Figure 15-9 The three main parts of the brain are the cerebrum, cerebellum, and medulla. Which part controls involuntary jobs only? the medulla

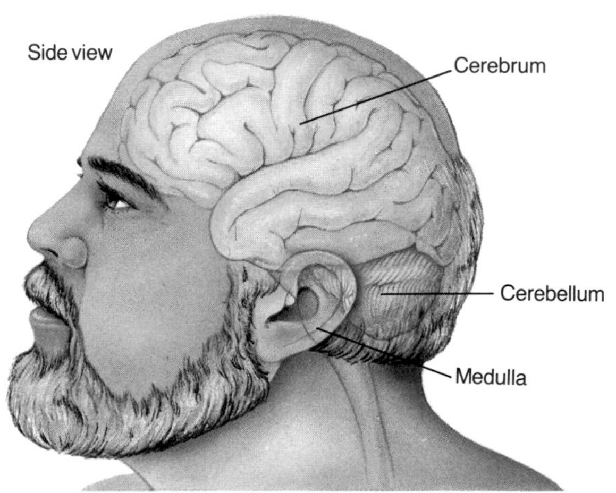

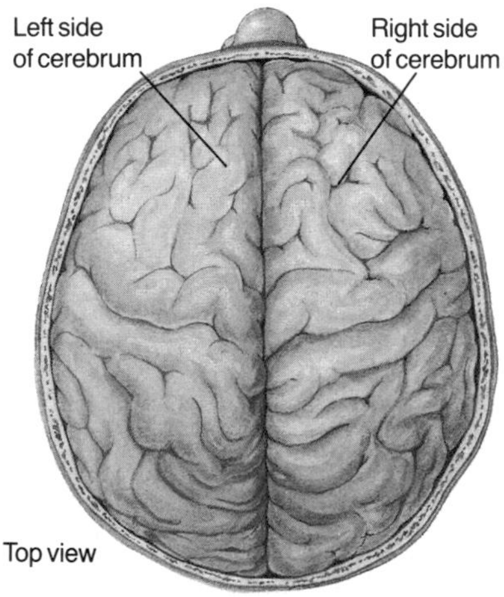

OPTIONS

Enrichment: The human cerebrum has four main regions. They are the frontal lobe, which controls speech and sorting of senses; parietal lobe, which controls body awareness; occipital lobe, which controls vision; temporal lobe, which controls hearing, reading, and smell.

Which Side of the Brain Is Dominant?/*Lab Manual*, pp. 119-122. Use this lab as an extension to brain anatomy and function.

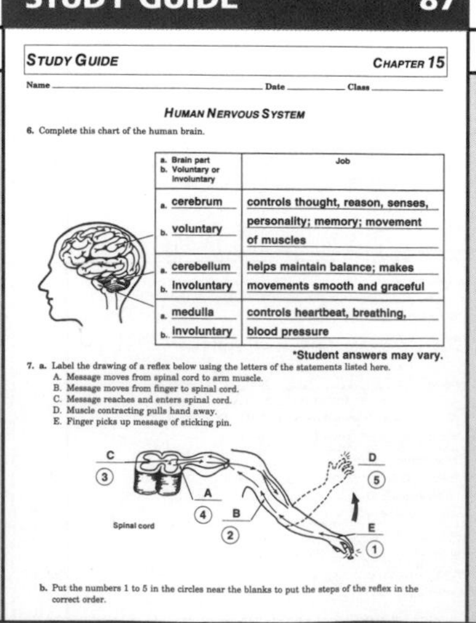

STUDY GUIDE 87

STUDY GUIDE CHAPTER 15

Name ________ Date ________ Class ________

HUMAN NERVOUS SYSTEM

6. Complete this chart of the human brain.

a. Brain part b. Voluntary or involuntary	Job
a. cerebrum b. voluntary	controls thought, reason, senses, personality; memory; movement of muscles
a. cerebellum b. involuntary	helps maintain balance; makes movements smooth and graceful
a. medulla b. involuntary	controls heartbeat, breathing, blood pressure

*Student answers may vary.

7. a. Label the drawing of a reflex below using the letters of the statements listed here.
   A. Message moves from spinal cord to arm muscle.
   B. Message moves from finger to spinal cord.
   C. Message reaches and enters spinal cord.
   D. Muscle contracting pulls hand away.
   E. Finger picks up message of sticking pin.

b. Put the numbers 1 to 5 in the circles near the blanks to put the steps of the reflex in the correct order.

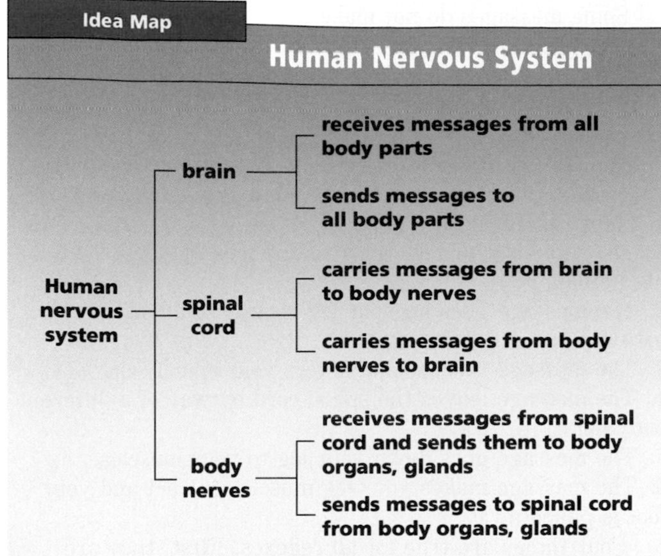

Idea Map
Human Nervous System
Human nervous system
brain
receives messages from all body parts
sends messages to all body parts
spinal cord
carries messages from brain to body nerves
carries messages from body nerves to brain
body nerves
receives messages from spinal cord and sends them to body organs, glands
sends messages to spinal cord from body organs, glands

Study Tip: Use this idea map as you study the three main parts of the human nervous system. What are the main jobs of the brain, spinal cord, and body nerves?

Locate the cerebellum in Figure 15-9. The **cerebellum** is the brain part that helps make your movements smooth and graceful, rather than robotlike. How does the size of the cerebellum compare to that of the cerebrum? Where is the cerebellum located in relation to the front and back of your head? All nerves that enter or leave the brain on their way to and from the muscles deliver messages to the cerebellum. The cerebellum helps you keep your balance. The cerebellum's actions are involuntary. This means that you can't control them.

The third part of the brain is the medulla. The medulla may look as if it were part of the spinal cord, but its job is very different. The **medulla** is the brain part that controls heartbeat, breathing, and blood pressure. All jobs handled by the medulla are involuntary. The medulla works without your thinking about it. When was the last time you thought about keeping your heart beating?

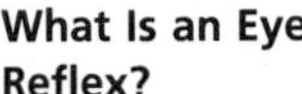

Mini Lab

What Is an Eye Reflex?

Observe: Have a partner cover one eye. Shine a small flashlight into the other eye. Uncover the first eye. Are the pupils the same size? *For more help, refer to the **Skill Handbook**, pages 704-705.*

Reflexes

In most cases, any message received by your body must get to the brain before you can react to it. Think of what happens when you see a ball flying toward you. You raise your arms or duck after your brain gets the message that the ball is coming toward you.

What is a reflex?

TEACH

Idea Map

Have students use the idea map as a study guide to the major concepts of this section.

Mini Lab

Both eyes will respond to the stimulus even though only one eye is receiving the stimulus. As a variation, the classroom lights can be turned off and then turned back on instead of using the flashlight.

Guided Practice

Have students write down their answers to the margin question: Reflexes are involuntary, they happen quickly, they may not involve the brain. Most reflexes are helpful.

Cooperative Learning: Ask students to complete the following, working in groups: one student should be designated the "artist or recorder" and one, the presenter. The task is as follows: (a) draw a diagram of the brain onto a transparency, (b) label the three brain areas, (c) indicate which areas are under voluntary or involuntary control, (d) list functions for each brain area. Have the presenter of each group show the group's transparency to the rest of the class via the overhead projector.

Connection: Social Studies

Have students determine the nature of the following White House occupants' nervous or endocrine system problems: F. D. Roosevelt (polio), John Kennedy (Addisons disease), Barbara Bush (thyroid problems).

Guided Practice

Ask students to list as many functions as possible under the following four nervous system headings: Spinal Cord, Cerebrum, Cerebellum, Medulla. Allow them to use their textbook as a reference.

APPLICATION 15

APPLICATION: SAFETY — CHAPTER 15

Name ______ Date ______ Class ______

REFLEXES PROTECT YOU — *Use after Section 15:2.*

To ride a bike safely, take part in sports, work with tools, or drive a car, you need to react quickly to changes around you. Your nervous system sends messages to your brain to tell you about the changes. Then, your brain sends messages to your body to tell it what to do. Sometimes, you need to react even more quickly. You know that some messages can cause you to react without going to the brain. These reflexes go to the spinal cord and back to the muscles.

1. You blink or duck when a ball or other object flies toward your face. How does this reflex protect you? **Blinking or ducking prevents the object from striking the eyes and injuring them.**
2. Pulling away from a sharp object or from something hot are also reflexes. How does this protect you? **prevents injury or burns**
3. What are some other reflexes? How do they protect you or help keep you safe? **Answers will vary.**
4. You can experience some reflex responses. Sit on a chair with one leg crossed over the other like the girl in the picture. With your fingers, find the soft place below your kneecap. Hit the spot gently but firmly with the edge of your hand as shown.
   a. Describe what happens to your leg. **the leg kicks upward**
   b. How could this reflex help keep you safe? **Answers will vary but students might suggest that the action helps avoid injury from a blow to the knee or allows a quick response.**
5. Tickle your nostrils gently with a fluffy ball of clean cotton.
   a. Describe your response. **Response will probably be a sneeze.**
   b. How could this response protect you? **The sneeze prevents the object that caused it from entering the nose.**

OPTIONS

What Are the Functions of the Brain?/*Lab Manual,* pp. 123-126. Use this lab as an extension to the brain and its functions.

Application/*Teacher Resource Package,* p. 15. Use the Application worksheet shown here to teach students how reflexes are protective.

TEACH

Check for Understanding

Have students respond to the first three questions in Check Your Understanding.

Reteach

Reteaching/*Teacher Resource Package*, p. 44. Use this worksheet to give students additional practice with parts of the brain.

Extension: Assign Critical Thinking, Biology and Reading, or some of the **OPTIONS** available with this section.

3 APPLY

Connection: Health

Have a health professional such as nurse or doctor speak to the class about head injuries.

4 CLOSE

Videocassette

Show the videocassette *Our Talented Brain,* Films for the Humanities and Sciences.

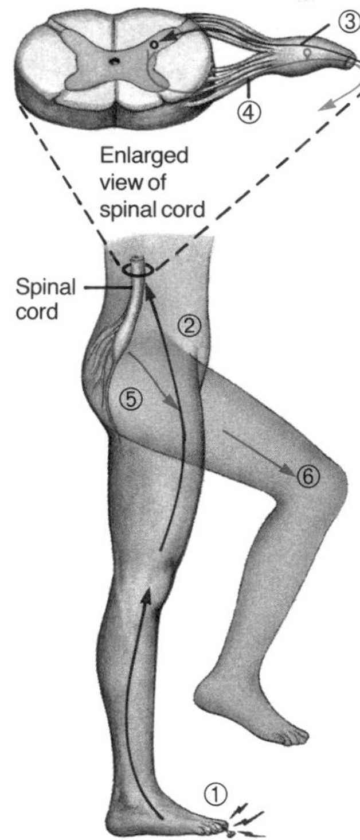

Figure 15-10 In a reflex, the message moves from the body part to the spinal cord and back to the body part.

Some messages do not make it to the brain. They go into the spinal cord and quickly back out to the muscles. The body is able to react in a very short time. Quick, protective reactions that occur within the nervous system are called **reflexes.**

How does a reflex work? Think of what happens when you accidentally step on a tack. Follow the numbered steps in Figure 15-10.

1. The skin on your foot receives the message that it has been stuck.
2. The message goes up your leg by way of a body nerve pathway.
3. The message reaches and enters your spinal cord.
4. The message leaves the spinal cord by way of a different body nerve pathway.
5. The message goes down your leg to your muscles.
6. The message makes your leg muscle contract and your foot is pulled away.

Four things are true for all reflexes. First, they are involuntary. Second, they happen very quickly. The events in Figure 15-10 took a fraction of a second. Third, reflexes may or may not involve the brain. In the tack example, your brain may have received a pain message. But, the message reached the brain *after* you pulled your foot away. If your brain had to receive the pain message before you could react, it would take more time. Injury could result or be more severe. This brings us to the fourth point about reflexes. Most reflexes are helpful. They help protect you from further harm. Coughing, blinking, and swallowing are reflexes. How does coughing or blinking protect you?

Check Your Understanding

6. Compare the jobs of dendrites and axons.
7. Describe the locations and jobs of the brain's three parts.
8. How do reflexes help? Give two examples.
9. **Critical Thinking:** In humans, the cerebrum is very large and folded. How does having a large cerebrum help humans?
10. **Biology and Reading:** You have learned that neurons are like electrical wires. You also learned that neurons have coverings, just as electrical wires do. From this analogy, what are the coverings on neurons for?

Answers to Check Your Understanding

6. Dendrites receive messages from neurons. Axons send messages to neurons.
7. cerebrum—top of brain, controls thought, reason, memory, muscles, and senses; cerebellum—back of brain, makes muscle movements smooth and graceful; medulla—above spinal cord, controls breathing, heartbeat, and blood pressure
8. Reflexes are quick, protective, and involuntary. Coughing and blinking are examples.
9. It allows humans to think and reason.
10. The coverings insulate neurons so they don't touch one another.

RETEACHING 44

RETEACHING: IDEA MAP — CHAPTER 15

Name ______ Date ______ Class ______

Use with Section 15:2.

PARTS OF THE BRAIN

Use these terms to complete the idea map: center of muscle control, controls heartbeat, controls blood pressure, controls personality and memory, helps keep your balance, interprets messages from sense organs, makes your movements smooth, controls breathing, controls thought and reason.

	Brain regions	Functions
Parts of the brain	cerebrum	controls thought and reason
		center of muscle control
		interprets messages from sense organs
		controls personality and memory
	cerebellum	helps keep your balance
		makes your movements smooth
	medulla	controls heartbeat
		controls blood pressure
		controls breathing

1. Which part(s) of the brain control(s) voluntary actions? cerebrum
2. Which part(s) of the brain control(s) involuntary actions? cerebellum and medulla
3. What kinds of actions are not controlled by the brain? reflex actions

Lab 15–1 Reaction Time

Problem: What can change reaction time?

Skills

form a hypothesis, calculate, infer

Materials

metric ruler

Procedure

Reaction time is how long it takes for a message to travel along your nerve pathways.

1. Copy the data table.
2. Have your partner hold a metric ruler at the end with the highest number.
3. Place the thumb and first finger of your left hand close to, but not touching, the end with the lowest number.
4. When your partner drops the ruler, try to catch it between your thumb and finger.
5. Record where the top of your thumb is when you catch the ruler.
6. Repeat steps 2 to 5 three more times.
7. State if you think the ruler will fall farther if you catch it with your right hand. Write your **hypothesis** in your notebook.
8. Repeat steps 2 to 5 four more times using your right hand to catch the ruler.
9. Switch roles and drop the ruler for your partner.
10. **Calculate:** To complete your data table, calculate the time in seconds needed for the ruler to fall. Multiply the distance by 0.01. Use a calculator if you have one.
11. Find the average for each column.

Data and Observations

1. Did you catch the ruler faster with your left hand or your right hand?
2. Which hand is your writing hand?

Analyze and Apply

1. **Check your hypothesis:** Is your hypothesis supported by your data? Why or why not?
2. **Infer:** Compare your results with several classmates. Which hand was faster at catching the ruler? Why? (HINT: Which hand do most people use to write?)
3. Why was it a good idea to run several trials?
4. **Apply:** Explain why a message moving along nerve pathways takes time.

Extension

Design an experiment to show how age affects reaction time.

TRIAL	LEFT HAND		RIGHT HAND	
	DISTANCE RULER FALLS (cm)	TIME IN SECONDS	DISTANCE RULER FALLS	TIME IN SECONDS
1	27	0.23	25	0.22
2	26	0.23	25	0.22
3	28	0.24	23	0.21
4	30	0.24	26	0.23
Total	111	0.94	99	0.88
Average	27.75	0.24	24.75	0.22

Lab 15-1 Reaction Time

Overview

This lab will provide students with a simple means of measuring reaction time.

Objectives: Upon completion of this lab, students will be able to (1) **state** the meaning and causes of reaction time, (2) **measure** reaction time under different conditions, (3) **recognize** that reaction times are not always the same.

Time Allotment: 30 minutes

Preparation

Lab 15-1 worksheet/*Teacher Resource Package,* pp. 57-58.

Lab 15-1 Computer Program/*Teacher Resource Package,* p. xviii. Use the computer program shown at the bottom of this page.

Teaching the Lab

▶ During the prelab have students practice holding the ruler correctly.

▶ If a student is unable to catch the ruler in time, record this as 35 cm.

▶ A more accurate but more complex method of calculating elapsed time may be used with students who have better math skills. It is as follows: (1) Multiply the distance in cm by 2. (2) Divide the result in step 1 by 1000. (3) Calculate the square root of the result in step 2.

Cooperative Learning: Divide the class into groups of two students. For more information, see pp. 22T-23T in the Teacher Guide.

COMPUTER PROGRAM XVIII

COMPUTER PROGRAM LAB 15-1 REACTION TIME

```
]POKE 33,33

]LIST

10  GOSUB 1000
20  DIM LO(5),RO(5),LC(5),RC(5)
25  DIM LA(5),RA(5),LB(5),RB(5)
28  HOME : GOTO 55
30  PRINT "TRIAL!   LEFT HAND   !   RIGHT HAND"
45  PRINT "-----+----------------+------------------"
50  PRINT "     !DISTANCE!TIME ! DISTANCE!TIME": PRINT
51  RETURN
55  GOSUB 30
60  FOR I = 1 TO 5
70  PRINT I;"    ";
80  INPUT "!";LO(I)
85 LA(I) = .01 * LO(I): VTAB (I + 9): HTAB (15): PRINT "!";LA(I);
90  VTAB (I + 9): HTAB 21: PRINT "!";
100  INPUT "";RO(I)
105 RA(I) = .01 * RO(I): VTAB (I + 9): HTAB (31): PRINT "!";RA(I)
110  NEXT
120  VTAB 22: HTAB 3: PRINT "ARE THESE NUMBERS CORRECT? (Y/N):";: GET A$
130  IF A$ = "N" OR A$ = "n" THEN 28
140  IF A$ < > "Y" AND A$ < > "y" THEN 120
150  VTAB 22: HTAB 1: CALL  - 868
170  PRINT "DO YOU WANT TO HAVE THE TOTALS AND      AVERAGE PRINTED? (Y/N):";: G
ET A$
180  IF A$ = "Y" OR A$ = "y" THEN FLAG = 1: GOTO 200
190  IF A$ < > "N" AND A$ < > "n" THEN 150
200  VTAB 23: HTAB 1: CALL  - 868
210  VTAB 22: HTAB 1: CALL  - 868
220  VTAB 22: HTAB 1: INPUT "PRESS RETURN FOR TOTALS. . .";A$
230  HOME : IF FLAG THEN  PR# 1: GOSUB 30
235  PRINT "TOTAL!";: GOSUB 285
236  GOSUB 240
239  PRINT  CHR$ (12): PR# 0: END
240  PRINT "AVG  !";
245 T = 0
250  FOR I = 1 TO 5:T = T + LO(I): NEXT :T = T / 5: PRINT T;
260 T = 0: FOR I = 1 TO 5:T = T + LA(I): NEXT :T = T / 5: HTAB (15): PRINT "!";T
;
270 T = 0: FOR I = 1 TO 5:T = T + RO(I): NEXT :T = T / 5: HTAB (21): PRINT "!";T
;
280 T = 0: FOR I = 1 TO 5:T = T + RA(I): NEXT :T = T / 5: HTAB (31): PRINT "!";T
;
281  PRINT : PRINT : PRINT
283  RETURN
285  REM
300 T = 0: FOR I = 1 TO 5:T = T + LO(I): NEXT : PRINT T;
310 T = 0: FOR I = 1 TO 5:T = T + LA(I): NEXT : HTAB (15): PRINT "!";T;
320 T = 0: FOR I = 1 TO 5:T = T + RO(I): NEXT : HTAB (21): PRINT "!";T;
330 T = 0: FOR I = 1 TO 5:T = T + RA(I): NEXT : HTAB (31): PRINT "!";T
339  RETURN
```

ANSWERS

Data and Observations

1. Answers will vary.
2. Most students will say their right hand.

Analyze and Apply

1. Students who are right-handed and hypothesized the ruler would not fall as far when they tried to catch it with their right hand will probably say their hypotheses were supported.
2. In general, best reaction times will correlate with handedness of student.
3. Times may vary somewhat, and it is best to take an average.
4. Time is needed for the message to move from one neuron to the next.

15:3 The Role of the Endocrine System

PREPARATION

Materials Needed

Make copies of the Enrichment, Critical Thinking, Study Guide, and Reteaching worksheets in the *Teacher Resource Package.*

Key Science Words

endocrine system
hormone
pituitary gland
thyroid gland
thyroxine

1 FOCUS

▶ The objectives are listed on the student page. Remind students to preview these objectives as a guide to this numbered section.

Brainstorming

Pose the following questions to the class: (a) If messages from the endocrine system do not use a nerve pathway, what other pathway for distribution may be available in the body? (b) How might the speed of messages not carried by nerves compare to those carried by nerves?

Guided Practice

Have students write down their answers to the margin question: Hormones are chemicals made in one part of an organism that affect other parts of the organism.

15:3 The Role of the Endocrine System

Objectives

6. **Explain** the function of the endocrine system.
7. **Relate** the importance of the pituitary and thyroid glands.

Key Science Words

endocrine system
hormone
pituitary gland
thyroid gland
thyroxine

Many animals have an additional system for sending messages through their bodies. This system does not use nerve cells. It uses chemicals formed in special glands.

Chemical Control

What are hormones?

The second system that allows different parts of your body to keep in touch is called the endocrine (EN duh krin) system. The **endocrine system** is made of small glands that make chemicals for carrying messages through the body. Endocrine glands are found throughout the body. The chemicals made by endocrine glands are called hormones (HOR mohnz). **Hormones** are chemicals made in one part of an organism that affect other parts of the organism. Hormones are released into the blood. Once in the blood, hormones travel to different organs of the body. Changes take place in the organs when they receive the chemical messages that hormones carry.

Figure 15-11 shows the main endocrine glands in the human body. Note that their jobs, or functions, are also given. Some of these glands will be studied in greater detail in the next few sections.

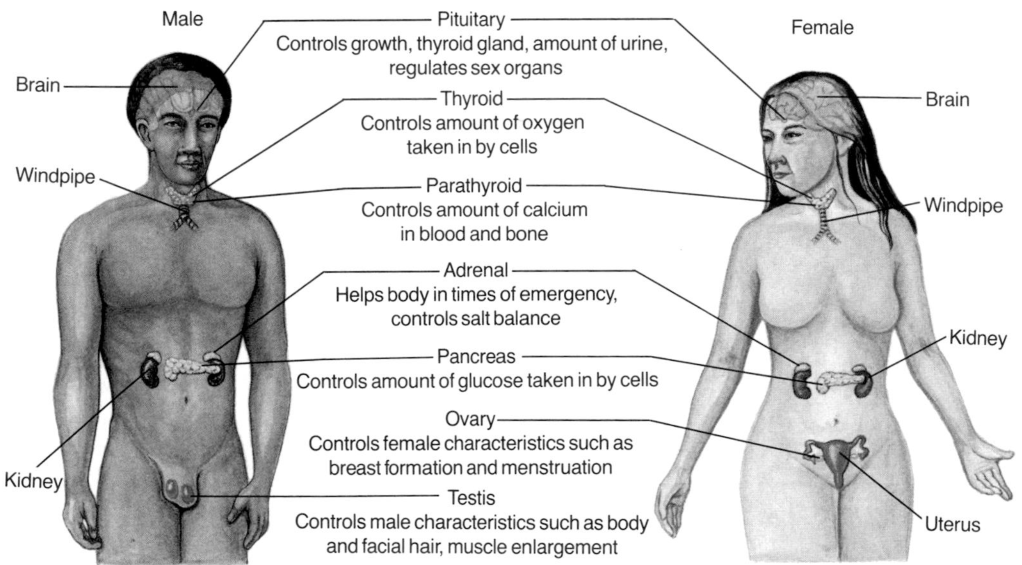

Figure 15-11 The endocrine system is made up of several glands and organs that control different body functions.

OPTIONS

Science Background

The endocrine system consists of a series of ductless glands. Hormones move directly into fluid that bathes body cells. Chemicals made by ducted glands, such as salivary glands, are sent directly to the target organ. Ducted glands are called exocrine glands.

Enrichment/*Teacher Resource Package,* p. 15. Use the Enrichment worksheet shown here as an extension to endocrine system functions.

ENRICHMENT 15

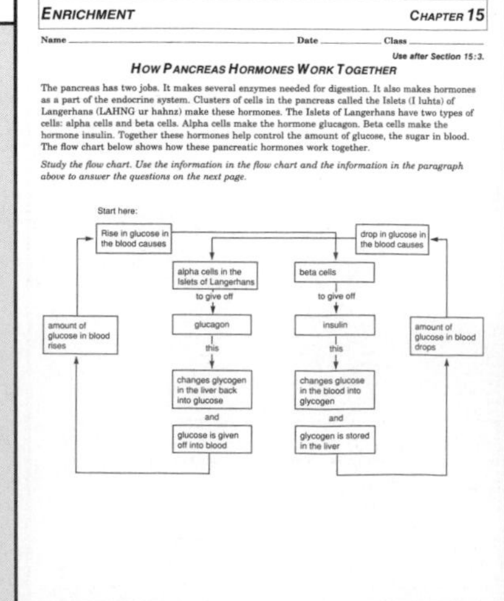
ENRICHMENT CHAPTER 15

Name ______ Date ______ Class ______

Use after Section 15:3.

HOW PANCREAS HORMONES WORK TOGETHER

The pancreas has two jobs. It makes several enzymes needed for digestion. It also makes hormones as a part of the endocrine system. Clusters of cells in the pancreas called the Islets (I luhts) of Langerhans (LAHNG ur hahnz) make these hormones. The Islets of Langerhans have two types of cells: alpha cells and beta cells. Alpha cells make the hormone glucagon. Beta cells make the hormone insulin. Together these hormones help control the amount of glucose, the sugar in blood. The flow chart below shows how these pancreatic hormones work together.

Study the flow chart. Use the information in the flow chart and the information in the paragraph above to answer the questions on the next page.

The Pituitary Gland

The **pituitary** (puh TEW uh ter ee) **gland** is an endocrine gland that forms many different hormones. It is often called the master gland because it makes hormones that regulate other endocrine glands. The pituitary forms more hormones than any other endocrine gland in the body. These hormones control many organs, other endocrine glands, and different body functions. Figure 15-12 shows where the pituitary gland is located in the human body. It is located just below the brain.

As a master gland, the pituitary has many jobs. For example, it makes hormones that control body growth. It causes a person to reach sexual maturity, also called puberty. This gland helps to control the amount of urine that you form.

Let's take a closer look at one hormone made by the pituitary gland. This hormone controls body growth and is called growth hormone. How did biologists find out that the pituitary controls body growth? They used the scientific method. Their experiments are shown in Figure 15-13. Look over their work.

Rats with their pituitary glands removed did not grow. Those with a pituitary gland did grow. The rats that had their pituitary glands removed and received injections of pituitary gland hormone grew like normal rats.

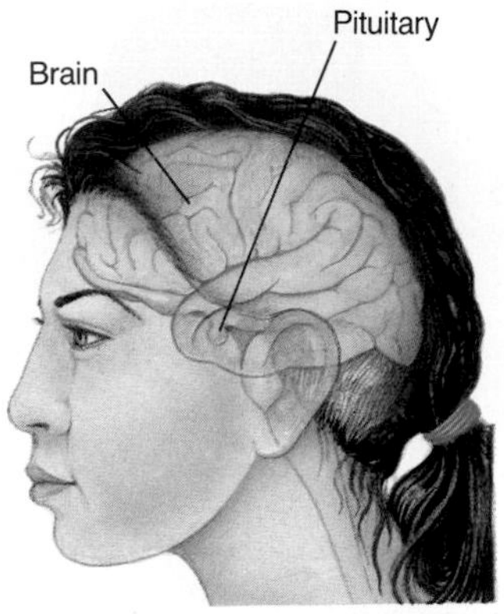

Figure 15-12 The pituitary gland is located below the brain.

How is body growth controlled?

Figure 15-13 The experiment pictured here showed that growth hormone from the pituitary gland controlled growth.

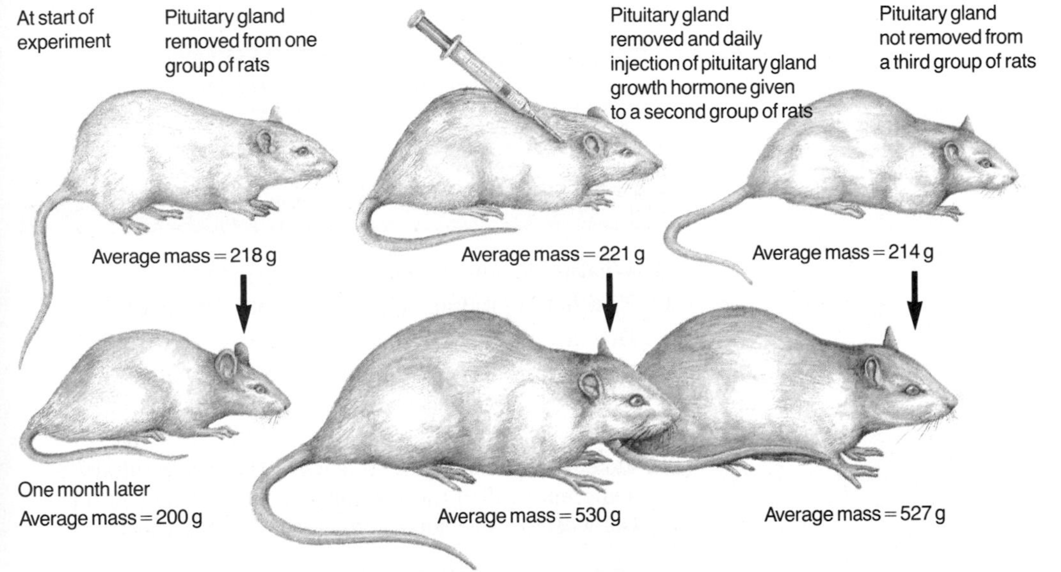

2 TEACH

MOTIVATION/Brainstorming

Ask students to list similarities and differences between the endocrine and nervous systems. Suggest similarities in function, composition, and location. Differences could be related to size, speed of action, and how messages are carried.

Concept Development

▶ Explain that the term *endocrine* comes from Greek, meaning inside (*endo-*) and to separate (*crine*). The endocrine glands are within the body and are separate tissue.

▶ Remind students that even though the pituitary forms eight different hormones, and each one is distributed by the blood, each hormone has a different body part or organ that it influences.

Guided Practice

Have students write down their answers to the margin question: Body growth is controlled by hormones made in the pituitary gland.

MOTIVATION/Demonstration

A mannequin would help show the locations of the endocrine glands.

Independent Practice

Study Guide/*Teacher Resource Package*, p. 88. Use the Study Guide worksheet shown at the bottom of this page for independent practice.

CRITICAL THINKING 15

CRITICAL THINKING/PROBLEM SOLVING — CHAPTER 15

Name ______ Date ______ Class ______

Use after Section 15:3.

HOW DOES THE BRAIN AFFECT THE AMOUNT OF URINE MADE BY THE KIDNEYS?

Your pituitary gland produces a hormone called antidiuretic hormone, or ADH. The word *antidiuretic* (ANT i DI yew RET ihk) means "against water loss." The following diagrams explain how this hormone works. The diagrams show how ADH keeps enough water in the body.

Study the diagrams and answer the questions that follow.

Person drinks very little water for 24 hours.
Brain detects blood is low in water.
Pituitary gland
ADH
Result: Pituitary releases ADH into blood.
ADH causes kidney to return more water to blood.
Low urine output results.

Person drinks very much water for 24 hours.
Brain detects blood contains much water.
Pituitary gland
Result: Pituitary does not release ADH into blood.
Kidney returns little water to blood.
High urine output results.

1. What gland produces ADH? pituitary
2. What organ does ADH affect? kidney
3. When will ADH be released? Circle the correct answer.
   a. when the amount of water drunk is (very low) / very high
   b. when the blood contains more / (less) water than usual
4. How does the body respond to ADH?
   a. Kidneys respond to ADH by returning more water to the blood.
   b. This results in a urine output that is low.
   c. Is body water being conserved? yes
5. How does the body respond to a lack of ADH?
   a. Kidneys respond to a lack of ADH by returning less water to the blood.
   b. This results in a urine output that is high.
   c. Is body water being conserved? no

STUDY GUIDE 88

STUDY GUIDE — CHAPTER 15

Name ______ Date ______ Class ______

THE ROLE OF THE ENDOCRINE SYSTEM

In your textbook, read about the endocrine system in Section 15:3.

1. On the blanks below, write the name and job of the glands being shown.

brain
windpipe
kidney
uterus
Female
Male
scrotum

a. pituitary — controls growth; makes hormones that effect kidney and sex organs; makes eight different hormones
b. thyroid — makes thyroxine; controls how fast cells use food
c. parathyroid — controls balance of calcium
d. adrenal — helps body in time of emergency
e. pancreas — controls the amount of sugar in the blood; makes insulin
f. ovary — controls female characteristics
g. testis — controls male characteristics

OPTIONS

Critical Thinking/Problem Solving/*Teacher Resource Package*, p. 15. Use the Critical Thinking/Problem Solving worksheet shown here to give students practice solving problems regarding the pituitary gland.

The Endocrine System/*Transparency Package*, number 15b. Use color transparency number 15b as you teach the functions of the endocrine system.

TEACH

Idea Map

Have students use the idea map as a study guide to the major concepts of this section.

Independent Practice

Study Guide/*Teacher Resource Package,* p. 90. Use the Study Guide worksheet shown at the bottom of this page for independent practice.

Check for Understanding

Have students respond to the first three questions in Check Your Understanding.

Reteach

Reteaching/*Teacher Resource Package,* p. 45. Use this worksheet to give students additional practice with the endocrine glands.

Extension: Assign Critical Thinking, Biology and Reading, or some of the **OPTIONS** available with this section.

3 APPLY

Have students research what mineral is present in thyroxine and why this mineral is important in the diet.

4 CLOSE

Videocassette

Show the video *Messengers,* Films for the Humanities and Sciences.

Answers to Check Your Understanding

11. It sends hormone messages through the body.
12. It releases human growth hormone, which triggers growth.
13. The thyroid gland is an endocrine gland that forms the hormone thyroxine.
14. the thyroid; If thyroxine production is low, the person may gain weight.
15. In this case, master means a gland that controls other glands.

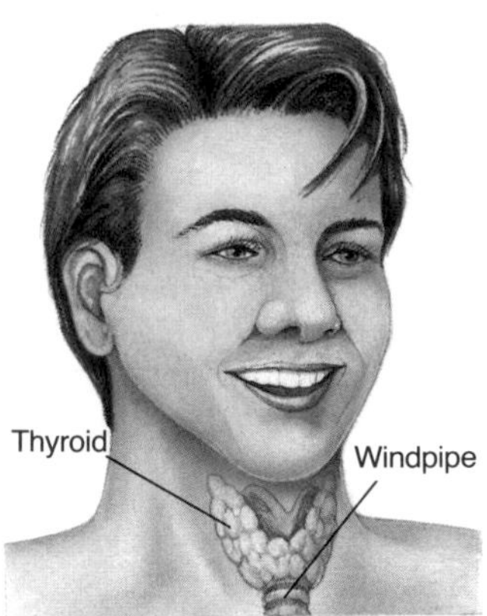

Figure 15-14 The thyroid gland makes a hormone that controls how fast your cells release energy from food.

Study Tip: Use this idea map as you study the human endocrine system. What are the jobs of the endocrine system glands?

The Thyroid Gland

The **thyroid** (THI royd) **gland** is an important endocrine gland found near the lower part of your neck. It lies in front of the windpipe and is about the size of your ear. Figure 15-14 shows its location. The thyroid's job is to make thyroxine (thi RAHK sun). **Thyroxine** is the hormone that controls how fast your cells release energy from food.

Sometimes the body may form too little or too much of a hormone. If the thyroid makes too little thyroxine, a person may gain weight and feel tired. How is this problem related to what thyroxine does? Could it be that food does not release enough energy? If the thyroid makes too much thyroxine, a person may lose weight and feel nervous. How could this problem be related to thyroxine's job?

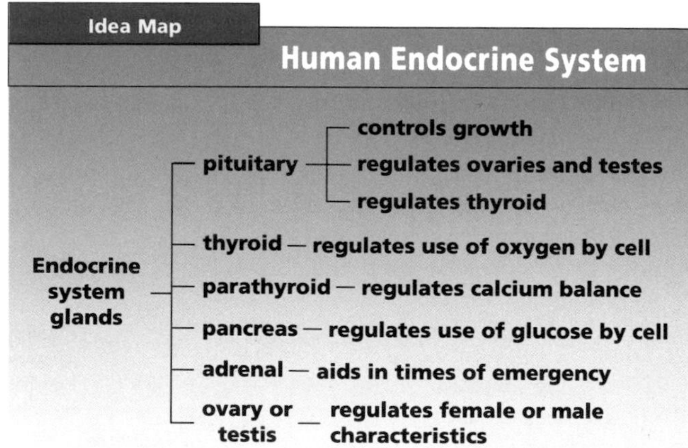

Check Your Understanding

11. What is the job of your endocrine system?
12. How is the pituitary gland important for growth?
13. How are the thyroid gland and thyroxine related?
14. **Critical Thinking:** If a person is overweight and can't lose weight through diet and exercise, what endocrine gland should he or she have checked? Why?
15. **Biology and Reading:** You learned that the pituitary is sometimes called the master gland. What do you think the word *master* means when used in this way?

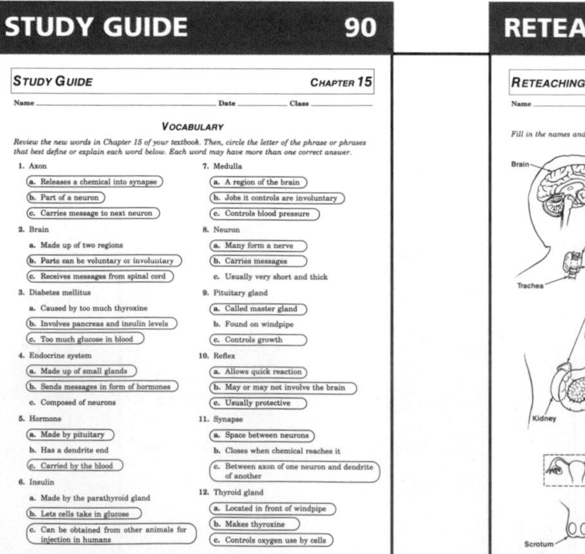

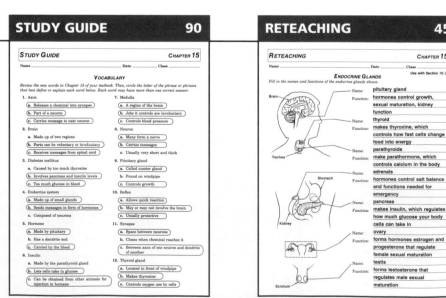

STUDY GUIDE 90

STUDY GUIDE — CHAPTER 15

Name ______ Date ______ Class ______

VOCABULARY

Review the new words in Chapter 15 of your textbook. Then, circle the letter of the phrase or phrases that best define or explain each word below. Each word may have more than one correct answer.

1. Axon
   a. Releases a chemical into synapse
   b. Part of a neuron
   c. Carries message to next neuron
2. Brain
   a. Made up of two regions
   b. Parts can be voluntary or involuntary
   c. Receives messages from spinal cord
3. Diabetes mellitus
   a. Caused by too much thyroxine
   b. Involves pancreas and insulin levels
   c. Too much glucose in blood
4. Endocrine system
   a. Made up of small glands
   b. Sends messages in form of hormones
   c. Composed of neurons
5. Hormone
   a. Made by pituitary
   b. Has a dendrite end
   c. Carried by the blood
6. Insulin
   a. Made by the parathyroid gland
   b. Lets cells take in glucose
   c. Can be obtained from other animals for injection in humans
7. Medulla
   a. A region of the brain
   b. Jobs it controls are involuntary
   c. Controls blood pressure
8. Neuron
   a. Many form a nerve
   b. Carries messages
   c. Usually very short and thick
9. Pituitary gland
   a. Called master gland
   b. Found on windpipe
   c. Controls growth
10. Reflex
    a. Allows quick reaction
    b. May or may not involve the brain
    c. Usually protective
11. Synapse
    a. Space between neurons
    b. Closes when chemical reaches it
    c. Between axon of one neuron and dendrite of another
12. Thyroid gland
    a. Located in front of windpipe
    b. Makes thyroxine
    c. Controls oxygen use by cells

RETEACHING 45

RETEACHING — CHAPTER 15

Name ______ Date ______ Class ______

Use with Section 15:3.

ENDOCRINE GLANDS

Fill in the names and functions of the endocrine glands shown.

Brain
Trachea
Stomach
Kidney
Scrotum

Name: pituitary gland
Function: hormones control growth, sexual maturation, kidney function

Name: thyroid
Function: makes thyroxine, which controls how fast cells change food into energy

Name: parathyroids
Function: make parathormone, which controls calcium in the body

Name: adrenals
Function: hormones control salt balance and functions needed for emergency

Name: pancreas
Function: makes insulin, which regulates how much glucose your body cells can take in

Name: ovary
Function: forms hormones estrogen and progesterone that regulate female sexual maturation

Name: testis
Function: forms testosterone that regulates male sexual maturation

15:4 Nervous and Endocrine System Problems

Many health problems are caused by diseases of the nervous and endocrine systems. Luckily, some of these diseases can be treated or cured.

Objectives

8. **Identify** problems that damage the brain.
9. **Explain** the importance of insulin.

Key Science Words

insulin
diabetes mellitus

Nervous System Problems

The brain has many blood vessels covering its surface, Figure 15-15a. The brain receives food and oxygen from these blood vessels. These blood vessels may become weak and break. When this happens, a person is said to have a stroke.

What is a stroke?

What happens when blood vessels of the brain break? It depends on where the blood vessel is and how much blood is lost. Usually, a person loses the use of a part of the brain because the brain cells die when they no longer receive food or oxygen. Losing the use of part of the brain causes the body part that it controls not to work. Figure 15-15b shows what happens when certain parts of the brain lose their oxygen supply.

Endocrine System Problems

The pancreas is a familiar gland. You studied it in Chapter 10 with the digestive system. Refer back to Figure 15-11 to see the location of the pancreas. This gland is also part of the endocrine system. It makes a hormone called insulin (IHN suh lun). **Insulin** is a hormone that lets your body cells take in glucose, a sugar, from your blood.

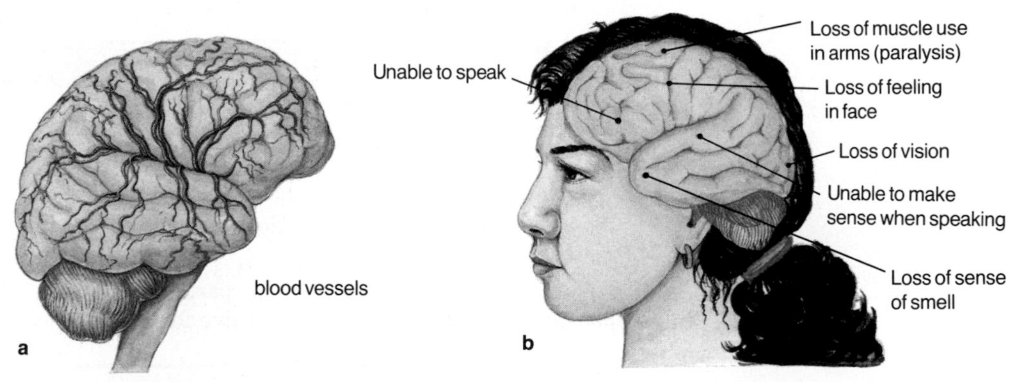

Figure 15-15 A stroke is the breaking of blood vessels that serve the brain and can result in loss of body functions.

15:4 Nervous and Endocrine System Problems

PREPARATION

Materials Needed

Make copies of the Skill Study Guide, and Lab worksheets in the *Teacher Resource Package*.

▶ Purchase glucose test paper and prepare urine samples for Lab 15-2.

Key Science Words

insulin
diabetes mellitus

Process Skills

In Lab 15-2, students will experiment and interpret data.

1 FOCUS

▶ The objectives are listed on the student page. Remind students to preview these objectives as a guide to this numbered section.

MOTIVATION/Demonstration

Use a brain model to review the brain's control of the body.

Guided Practice

Have students write down their answers to the margin question: the breaking of a blood vessel that serves the brain.

SKILL 15

SKILL: SUMMARIZE CHAPTER 15

Name ______ Date ______ Class ______

For more help, refer to the Skill Handbook, pages 706-711. *Use after Section 15:4.*

THE ENDOCRINE SYSTEM

Summarizing is a good way to remember information, check your understanding of a subject, and review what you have studied. After you answer the following questions, you will have a three-part summary—(1) a comparison of the body's two systems of communication, (2) the functions of some organs of the endocrine system, and (3) some effects on the body when certain endocrine glands do not function properly.

Complete the following statements by filling in the blanks with words that make the sentences correct.

1. The body has two communication systems. One is the __nervous__ system. The other is the __endocrine__ system.
2. The nervous system uses __nerves (neurons)__ to detect changes and respond to them. The endocrine system uses __hormones__, which are chemical messengers.
3. The nervous system is made up of organs such as the __brain (spinal cord)__. The endocrine system is made up of __glands__.
4. The nervous system sends messages along __neuron__ pathways. The endocrine system sends messages through the __blood__.

Use the diagram at the right to answer the questions below. Write the letter of the correct choice in the blank.

5. Gland __B__ makes thyroxine.
6. Gland __C__ controls calcium balance.
7. Gland __A__ controls sexual maturity.
8. Gland __B__ controls the speed at which cells use food.
9. Gland __A__ controls body growth.

A
B
C

Complete the following statements by writing ***too much*** *or* ***too little*** *in the blanks.*

10. A person gains weight if __too little__ thyroxine is made.
11. A person may feel nervous if __too much__ thyroxine is made.
12. A person may grow __too little__ if the pituitary gland does not work.
13. Glucose may not pass into cells if __too little__ insulin is made.

OPTIONS

Science Background

Strokes may be caused by or brought on by hypertension, blood clots, and/or atherosclerosis of vessels associated with the cerebrum.

Skill/*Teacher Resource Package,* p. 15. Use the Skill worksheet shown here to give students practice summarizing concepts.

2 TEACH

Guided Practice

Have students write down their answers to the margin question: Insulin lets the body cells take in glucose from the blood.

Independent Practice

Study Guide/*Teacher Resource Package,* p. 89. Use the Study Guide worksheet shown at the bottom of this page for independent practice.

Check for Understanding

Have students respond to the first three questions in Check Your Understanding.

Reteach

Reteaching/*Teacher Resource Package,* p. 46. Use this worksheet to give students additional practice with endocrine system problems.

Extension: Assign Critical Thinking, Biology and Reading, or some of the **OPTIONS** available with this section.

3 APPLY

Interview

Have students research treatment and symptoms of diabetes mellitus.

4 CLOSE

Software

The Human System Series 2, Focus Media, Inc.

Answers to Check Your Understanding

16. Brain cells die.
17. Insulin opens cell membranes and allows sugar to enter cells.
18. failure of the pancreas to make enough insulin
19. test the urine for glucose
20. because vessels that carry food and oxygen to it have broken

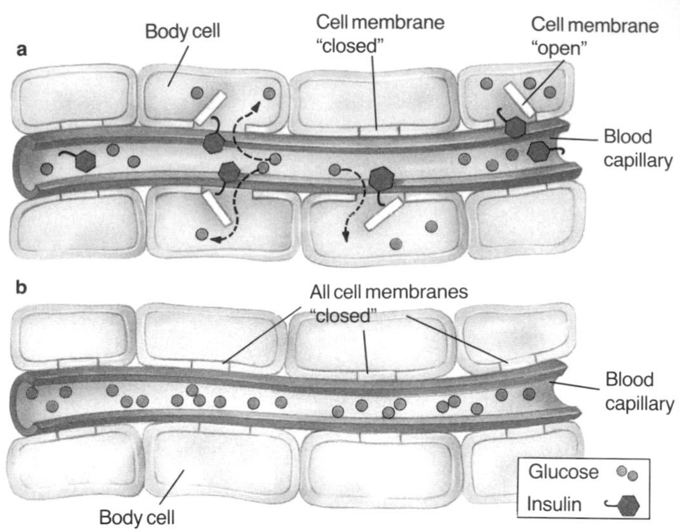

Figure 15-16 Insulin helps cells take in glucose from the blood.

What is insulin?

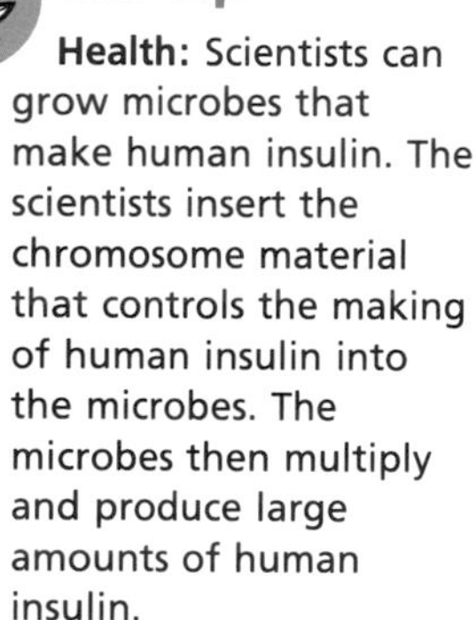

Bio Tip

Health: Scientists can grow microbes that make human insulin. The scientists insert the chromosome material that controls the making of human insulin into the microbes. The microbes then multiply and produce large amounts of human insulin.

Figure 15-16a shows how insulin works. The blue circles stand for glucose. The red figures stand for insulin. Insulin opens the cell membrane, allowing glucose to enter the cells. Once inside your cells, glucose can be used as food.

What if the pancreas stops making insulin? If insulin is missing, glucose can't get into the cells. It remains in the blood. As a result, a person may lose weight. Not treating this problem may lead to blindness, heart disease, or death.

The problem just described has a name. **Diabetes mellitus** (di uh BEET us • MEL uht us) is a disease that results when the pancreas doesn't make enough insulin. People with this disease have too much glucose in their blood and not enough glucose in their cells. The excess glucose that is in the blood leaves the body in the urine.

Check Your Understanding

16. What happens when the brain loses its oxygen supply?
17. How does insulin do its job?
18. What is the cause of diabetes mellitus?
19. **Critical Thinking:** If you were a doctor, how would you test someone for diabetes?
20. **Biology and Reading:** Why does the part of the brain damaged by a stroke no longer receive food or oxygen?

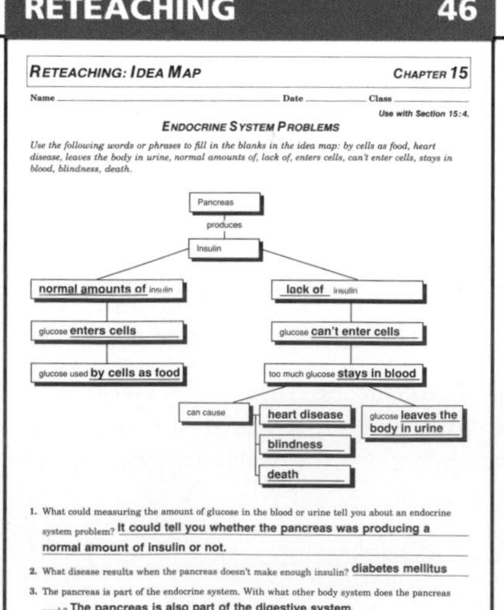

RETEACHING 46

RETEACHING: IDEA MAP — *CHAPTER 15*

Name ______ Date ______ Class ______

Use with Section 15:4.

ENDOCRINE SYSTEM PROBLEMS

Use the following words or phrases to fill in the blanks in the idea map: by cells as food, heart disease, leaves the body in urine, normal amounts of, lack of, enters cells, can't enter cells, stays in blood, blindness, death.

Pancreas
produces
Insulin
normal amounts of insulin
glucose enters cells
glucose used by cells as food
lack of insulin
glucose can't enter cells
too much glucose stays in blood
can cause
heart disease
blindness
death
glucose leaves the body in urine

1. What could measuring the amount of glucose in the blood or urine tell you about an endocrine system problem? **It could tell you whether the pancreas was producing a normal amount of insulin or not.**
2. What disease results when the pancreas doesn't make enough insulin? **diabetes mellitus**
3. The pancreas is part of the endocrine system. With what other body system does the pancreas work? **The pancreas is also part of the digestive system.**

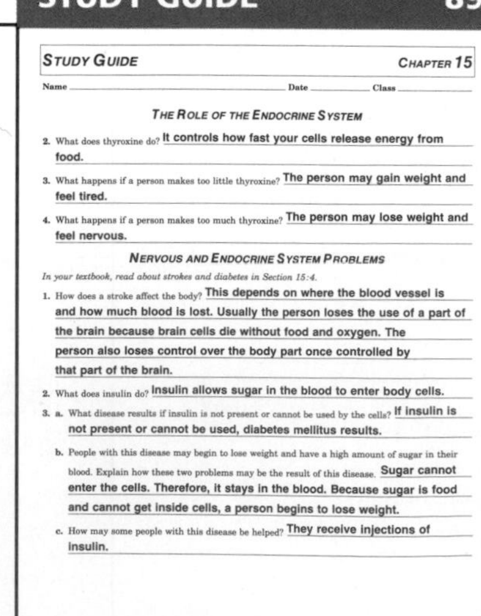

STUDY GUIDE 89

STUDY GUIDE — *CHAPTER 15*

Name ______ Date ______ Class ______

THE ROLE OF THE ENDOCRINE SYSTEM

2. What does thyroxine do? **It controls how fast your cells release energy from food.**
3. What happens if a person makes too little thyroxine? **The person may gain weight and feel tired.**
4. What happens if a person makes too much thyroxine? **The person may lose weight and feel nervous.**

NERVOUS AND ENDOCRINE SYSTEM PROBLEMS

In your textbook, read about strokes and diabetes in Section 15:4.

1. How does a stroke affect the body? **This depends on where the blood vessel is and how much blood is lost. Usually the person loses the use of a part of the brain because brain cells die without food and oxygen. The person also loses control over the body part once controlled by that part of the brain.**
2. What does insulin do? **Insulin allows sugar in the blood to enter body cells.**
3. a. What disease results if insulin is not present or cannot be used by the cells? **If insulin is not present or cannot be used, diabetes mellitus results.**
   b. People with this disease may begin to lose weight and have a high amount of sugar in their blood. Explain how these two problems may be the result of this disease. **Sugar cannot enter the cells. Therefore, it stays in the blood. Because sugar is food and cannot get inside cells, a person begins to lose weight.**
   c. How may some people with this disease be helped? **They receive injections of insulin.**

Lab 15–2 Diabetes

Problem: Is glucose found in the urine of a person with diabetes?

Skills

experiment, interpret data

Materials

glucose test paper
glass slides
normal urine sample (A)
urine sample from diabetic (B)
urine samples in test tubes marked C-E
test-tube rack
wax pencil
8 droppers

Procedure

1. Copy the data table.
2. Use a wax pencil to draw two circles on a glass slide. Mark the circles A and B.
3. Add two drops of normal urine to the circle marked A. Add two drops of urine from a diabetic to the circle marked B.
4. Touch a small piece of glucose test paper to each urine sample. A green color means glucose is present. A yellow color means that no glucose is present. Record the color of the paper in your data table.
5. Draw one circle on each of three slides. Label the slides C to E.
6. Using a dropper, put two drops of urine from test tube C into the circle on slide C. Do the same with test tubes D and E.
7. Test each urine sample with glucose test paper. Record the color of the paper in your table. Complete your data table.
8. Dispose of your samples as directed by your teacher.

Data and Observations

1. In which samples was glucose present?
2. In which samples was glucose not present?

Analyze and Apply

1. **Interpret data:** Which samples tested could be from a normal person? A person with diabetes? Explain.
2. Explain why glucose is present in the urine of a person with diabetes.
3. Name the endocrine gland not working if a person has diabetes.
4. **Apply:** What kinds of foods should a person with diabetes avoid? Why?

Extension

Experiment to test if glucose test paper will detect different amounts of glucose.

SAMPLE	COLOR OF TEST PAPER	GLUCOSE PRESENT?	DIABETES PRESENT?
Normal urine (A)	yellow	no	no
Urine from diabetic (B)	green	yes	yes
C	green	yes	yes
D	green	yes	yes
E	yellow	no	no

*Answers will vary depending on samples used.

ANSWERS

Data and Observations

1. C, D
2. E

Analyze and Apply

1. E; C, D; E has no glucose in it but C, D have glucose in them.
2. Glucose can't get into the body cells because there isn't enough insulin produced.
3. pancreas
4. foods high in sugars; The body cells won't be able to take in the sugars because insulin is lacking.

Lab 15-2 Diabetes

Overview

Students will test for the presence of glucose in urine.

Objectives: Upon completion of the lab, students will be able to (1) **test** for the presence of glucose in urine, (2) **recognize** glucose in urine as a symptom of diabetes mellitus.

Time Allotment: 30 minutes

Preparation

▶ Precut glucose test paper into 1 cm strips.

▶ Urine samples without glucose—for every 1000 mL tap water, use six drops yellow food coloring.

▶ Urine samples with glucose—prepare as above and add 2 teaspoons of glucose or honey.

Lab 15-2 worksheet/*Teacher Resource Package*, pp. 59-60.

Teaching the Lab

▶ Explain that a person with diabetes has excess glucose in his or her blood.

▶ **Troubleshooting:** Caution students not to mix droppers and to rinse and dry slides before reusing them.

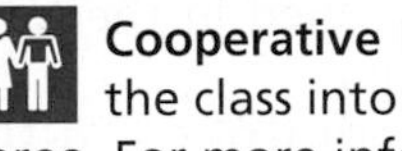

Cooperative Learning: Divide the class into groups of two or three. For more information, see pp. 22T-23T in the Teacher Guide.

PROBLEM SOLVING

Viewing the Human Body

Problem-solving Strategies

The following strategies can be used to solve the problem in this feature: guess and check, make a drawing, review brain anatomy.

Hints

▶ Have students make simple diagrams of body slices such as in figures b, c, and d. Ask them to visualize and include those body organs that would be found along these types of slices.

▶ Brain diagrams within the chapter can be used to point out the location of cerebrum, cerebellum, and medulla.

Solving the Problem

Photo 1 matches a cross section of diagram b.

1. Clues to look for include shape and size of the diagram. Diagram a includes the head, and diagram c includes the arms. Neither of these structures appears in the photo.
2. The red areas are muscle, the blue areas are organs, and the white area is the spinal column
3. The middle part of the cerebrum controls hearing.
4. Vision is controlled in the back of the cerebrum
5. Speaking is controlled in the upper middle part of the cerebrum.
6. Thinking is controlled in the front part of the cerebrum.

PROBLEM SOLVING

VIEWING THE HUMAN BODY

Magnetic resonance imaging (MRI) allows scientists to see inside the body. MRI is different from X rays. X rays allow only hard body parts such as bone to be pictured. Also, the energy given off by X-ray equipment can injure the body. MRI can show all body parts and is not damaging to the body. Photo 1 shows an MRI of part of the human body. Diagrams a, b, and c show three different sections of the human body. Which of these diagrams matches the MRI picture?

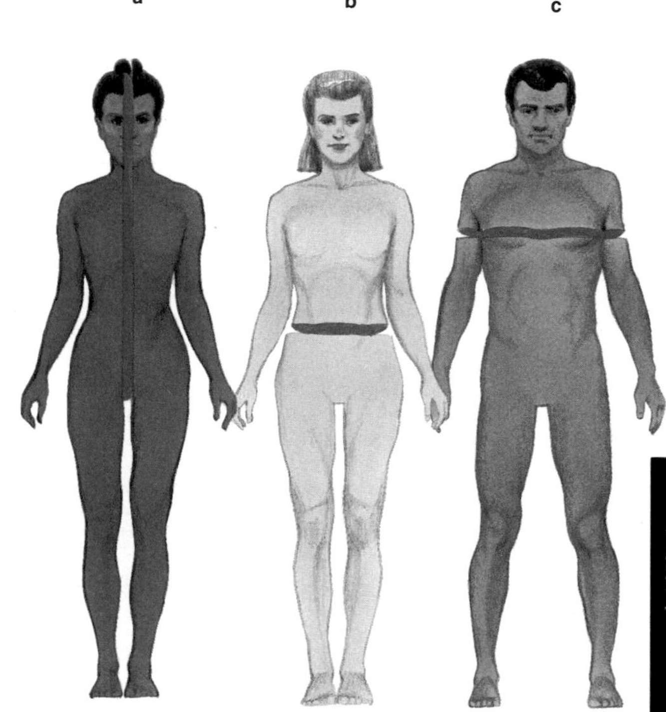

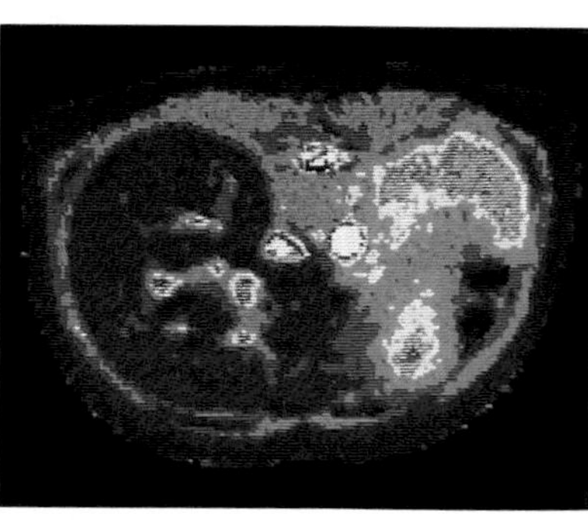

326

1. How were you able to tell which diagram matched photo 1? What clues did you look for?

2. What organs could the red, black, and white areas of photo 1 be?

Positron emission tomography (PET) allows scientists to determine what part of the brain is being used during a certain task. Scientists can also use PET to locate areas of the brain that are not functioning normally. Photo 2 shows side views of the human brain. The front of the head is toward your left. The most active brain area is shown in red. Less active areas are yellow, then green, then blue.

3. Photo 2d is a PET image of a person listening to Beethoven's Fifth Symphony. Which part of the brain is being used?

4. Photo 2e is a PET image of a person looking at a picture. Which part of the brain is being used?

5. Photo 2f is a PET image of a person reciting the alphabet. Which part of the brain is being used?

6. Photo 2g is a PET image of a person solving a math problem. Which part of the brain is being used?

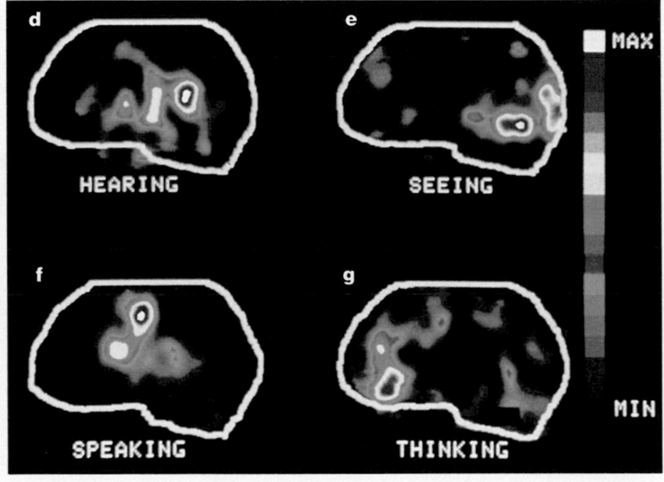

Discussing the Problem

▶ A body slice such as the one in diagram A would include body organs such as brain, head, neck, chest, heart, lungs, etc. These parts are not shown at all in photo 1.

▶ A body slice such as the one in diagram C would include body organs such as heart and lungs, and arms.

Extensions

Ask students to identify the body organs shown in the MRI photo. Have them diagram what an MRI photo might look like if taken through of a slice through diagram C.

Ask students to make PET diagrams that would show what the brain would look like if a person were: (a) smelling a rose, (b) tasting a pizza, (c) moving their legs, (d) deciding right from wrong, (e) talking.

CHAPTER 15 REVIEW

Summary

Summary statements can be used by students to review the major concepts of the chapter.

Key Science Words

All boldfaced terms from the chapter are listed.

Testing Yourself

Using Words

1. reflex
2. diabetes mellitus
3. neuron
4. medulla
5. thyroxine
6. dendrite
7. insulin
8. thyroid
9. endocrine

Finding Main Ideas

10. p. 318; They are involuntary, happen very quickly, may or may not involve the brain, and most are helpful.
11. p. 320; The adrenal gland controls salt balance and helps the body in times of emergency. The pituitary controls growth and is a master gland that controls other glands. The parathyroid controls the amount of calcium in the blood.
12. p. 316; The cerebrum is voluntary; the cerebellum and medulla are involuntary.
13. p. 324; It acts like a gatekeeper. Insulin "opens" the cell membrane allowing glucose to pass into the cell.
14. p. 321; Three rat groups were used. One group (control) had no treatment. The second group had the pituitary removed but received daily injections of the pituitary hormone. The third group had the pituitary removed. The first two groups grew at a normal rate. The third group did not grow at all.
15. p. 318; Skin receives message that tack sticks toe—message travels by way of neurons up leg to spinal cord—message leaves spinal cord and travels down leg to muscle—toe is pulled away.

Chapter 15 Review

Summary

15:1 The Role of the Nervous System

1. The nervous system allows animals to receive messages from their surroundings.
2. Nervous systems become more complex as animal groups become more complex.

15:2 Human Nervous System

3. Neurons are nerve cells. They have ends called dendrites and axons. Neurons make up nerve pathways.
4. The brain, spinal cord, and body nerves form the human nervous system.
5. Reflexes are involuntary, quick reactions of the nervous system that protect the body.

15:3 The Role of the Endocrine System

6. The endocrine system consists of glands that send hormones throughout the body.
7. The pituitary gland makes many hormones that control different body functions. Thyroxine is the hormone made by the thyroid gland.

15:4 Nervous and Endocrine System Problems

8. Blood vessels that supply the brain with food and oxygen may break, resulting in a stroke.
9. Insulin is a hormone made by the pancreas. Insulin controls glucose movement into your cells.

Key Science Words

axon (p. 313)
brain (p. 314)
cerebellum (p. 317)
cerebrum (p. 316)
dendrite (p. 313)
diabetes mellitus (p. 324)
endocrine system (p. 320)
hormone (p. 320)
insulin (p. 323)
medulla (p. 317)
nerve (p. 312)
nervous system (p. 310)
neuron (p. 312)
pituitary gland (p. 321)
reflex (p. 318)
spinal cord (p. 315)
synapse (p. 313)
thyroid gland (p. 322)
thyroxine (p. 322)

Testing Yourself

Using Words

Choose the word from the list of Key Science Words that best fits the definition.

1. quick reaction that is protective
2. disease caused by lack of insulin
3. special name for a nerve cell
4. brain area that controls heartbeat
5. chemical made by the thyroid gland
6. neuron end that receives messages
7. hormone made by the pancreas
8. gland found in the neck
9. system that sends chemical messages through the body

Using Main Ideas

16. Stinging-cell animals have nerve cells spread over their body. Complex animals such as spiders have a brain, nerve cord, and sense organs.
17. Right side of cerebrum receives and controls messages from the left side of body.
18. A message reaches the axon end of a neuron. A chemical is given off. The chemical moves across the space and restarts the message on the dendrite end of the neuron.
19. The pituitary gland is located at the base of the cerebrum; the thyroid is over the windpipe; the parathyroid is located on the thyroid; the pancreas is located below the stomach and even with the kidneys; the adrenal is on top of the kidney; the ovary is in the lower part of the body near the uterus.
20. The nervous system is made of cells that allow an animal to detect changes around it. This same system will allow an animal to respond to these changes.
21. The person loses the use of a part of the brain and the body part controlled by that part of the brain.
22. The brain receives and sends messages to all body parts. These messages enter and

Review

Testing Yourself *continued*

Finding Main Ideas

List the page number where each main idea below is found. Then, explain each main idea.

10. the four main features of a reflex
11. the functions of the adrenal, pituitary, and parathyroid glands
12. the brain regions that are voluntary
13. how insulin works
14. how to prove with experiments that the pituitary gland controls growth
15. the pathway that a reflex follows

Using Main Ideas

Answer these questions by referring to the page number after each question.

16. How do the nervous systems of simple and more complex animal groups differ? (p. 311)
17. Which side of the cerebrum receives and controls messages from the left side of your body? (p. 316)
18. How does a message move from one neuron to the next? (p. 313)
19. Name the locations of the pituitary, thyroid, parathyroid, pancreas, adrenal, and ovary. (p. 320)
20. How do animals keep in touch with their surroundings? (p. 310)
21. What can happen when someone has a stroke? (p. 323)
22. How do the brain and spinal cord work together? (p. 315)
23. What happens if the pancreas does not produce enough insulin? (p. 324)
24. What happens if the thyroid produces too much thyroxine? (p. 322)
25. Why are different pathways needed to carry messages from hand to brain and brain to hand? (p. 313)

Skill Review ✓

*For more help, refer to the **Skill Handbook,** pages 704-719.*

1. **Interpret data:** Which rat in the experiment in Figure 15-13 was the control? Why?
2. **Interpret diagrams:** Study the diagrams of neurons in this chapter. How does the shape of a neuron help it do its job?
3. **Infer:** What would happen to messages traveling along the spinal cord if the spinal cord were cut? How could this type of injury affect body parts?
4. **Observe:** Examine slides of thyroid tissue. Diagram what you see.

Finding Out More

Critical Thinking

1. Find out what the following diseases are and what their causes are: multiple sclerosis, cerebral palsy, epilepsy, polio.
2. What are the symptoms of diabetes mellitus?

Applications

1. Design and build a model of a neuron, a neuron pathway of at least three neurons, and a nerve. (HINT: Spaghetti might work well.)
2. Prepare a large diagram that shows the locations and jobs of the different areas of the cerebrum.

Using Main Ideas

leave the brain by way of the spinal cord.

23. Diabetes mellitus may result.
24. Too much thyroxine will result in weight loss and feeling nervous.
25. Only the axon end of neurons can give off a chemical that keeps the messages moving from one neuron to the next. Thus, messages cannot travel in both directions along the same pathway.

Skill Review

1. The third column was the control because it had nothing done to it.
2. Its long thin shape enables electrical impulses to travel quickly along its length. The ends (axon and dendrite) are close together to allow the impulses to go from one neuron end to the next neuron easily.
3. They would be disrupted because nerves do not repair themselves, unlike other cells. When a body part is not used, it shrinks (atrophies).
4. The diagram will have open spaces surrounded by small cells that will stain dark.

Finding Out More

Critical Thinking

1. Multiple sclerosis results when the covering of nerve cells is somehow destroyed. Cerebral palsy is due to brain damage at birth and may result when oxygen is cut off to the brain during delivery. Epilepsy occurs when the electrical patterns of the central nervous system are disrupted. Polio occurs when the protective covering of the nerve cells is inflamed.
2. Symptoms of diabetes mellitus include: excess sugar in blood and urine, thirst, hunger, and weight loss.

Applications

1. Students could lay spaghetti end to end and glue it to construction paper.
2. Students should include the cerebrum, cerebellum, and medulla.

Chapter Review/*Teacher Resource Package,* pp. 77-78.

Chapter Test/*Teacher Resource Package,* pp. 79-81.

Chapter Test/*Computer Test Bank*

Senses

PLANNING GUIDE

CONTENT	TEXT FEATURES	TEACHER RESOURCE PACKAGE	OTHER COMPONENTS
(1 day) 16:1 Observing the Environment Senses Aid Survival Sense Organs of Animals	Check Your Understanding, p. 333	Reteaching: *Animal Sense Organs,* p. 47 Study Guide: *Observing the Environment,* pp. 91-92	
(3 1/2 days) 16:2 Human Sense Organs The Eye The Tongue and Nose The Ear The Skin	Skill Check: *Interpret Diagrams,* p. 341 Skill Check: *Understand Science Words,* p. 343 Mini Lab: *What Is an Afterimage?* p. 335 Lab 16-1: *The Eye,* p. 337 Lab 16-2: *The Senses,* p. 338 Career Close-Up: *Licensed Practical Nurse,* p. 342 Idea Map, p. 340 Check Your Understanding, p. 343	Enrichment: *Animal Sense Organs,* p. 17 Reteaching: *The Human Eye,* p. 48 Critical Thinking/Problem Solving: *How Are a Camera and a Human Eye Similar?* p. 16 Focus: *An Electrical Sense Organ,* pp. 31-32 Study Guide: *Human Sense Organs,* pp. 93-94 Lab 16-1: *The Eye,* pp. 61-62 Lab 16-2: *The Senses,* pp. 63-64 Transparency Master: *Human Sense Organs I and II,* pp. 75-76	**Laboratory Manual:** *How Are Your Senses Sometimes Fooled?* p. 131 **Laboratory Manual:** *How Can You Test Your Senses?* p. 127 **Laboratory Manual:** *What Are the Parts of an Eye?* p. 135 Color Transparency 16: *Pathway of Light Through the Eye*
(1 1/2 days) 16:3 Problems With Sense Organs Correcting Vision Problems Protecting Against Hearing Loss Correcting Hearing Problems	Check Your Understanding, p. 347	Application: *Skin Disorders,* p. 16 Reteaching: *Vision Problems,* p. 49 Skill: *Relate Cause and Effect,* p. 17 Study Guide: *Problems With Sense Organs,* p. 95 Study Guide: *Vocabulary,* p. 96	
Chapter Review	Summary Key Science Words Testing Yourself Finding Main Ideas Using Main Ideas Skill Review	Chapter Review, pp. 82-83 Chapter Test, pp. 84-86	**Test Bank**

MATERIALS NEEDED

LAB 16-1, p. 337	LAB 16-2, p. 338	MARGIN FEATURES
ruler scissors clear tape white paper black paper top part of hand lens	white paper red and green pencils	Skill Check, p. 343 dictionary Mini Lab, p. 335 pencil paper

OBJECTIVES

SECTION	OBJECTIVE	OBJECTIVES CORRELATION			
		CHECK YOUR UNDERSTANDING	CHAPTER REVIEW	TRP CHAPTER REVIEW	TRP CHAPTER TEST
16:1	1. **Relate** ways a planarian and an earthworm sense light.	2, 4	12, 22	2	3
	2. **Compare** the sense organs of a cricket and a snake.	3	1, 8, 9, 11, 12, 13, 20, 23, 24, 25	5	10, 16, 23
16:2	3. **State** the functions of the parts of the eye.	6, 9, 10	4, 5, 6, 15, 16, 23	3, 9, 25, 26, 27, 28, 29, 30, 31, 32, 36, 38	5, 6, 11, 14, 17, 20, 21, 25, 28, 29, 43, 44, 45, 46, 47, 48, 49, 50, 51, 52
	4. **Explain** the jobs of the nose, tongue, and skin as sense organs.	8	2, 3, 10, 17, 19, 23	7, 8, 34, 35, 39	4, 8, 9, 13, 18, 24, 30
	5. **Describe** the parts of the outer, middle, and inner ear.	7	7, 18, 21	4, 11, 12, 13, 14, 15, 16, 17, 18, 19, 20, 21, 22, 23, 33, 37	1, 7, 26, 31, 32, 33, 34, 35, 36, 37, 38, 39, 40, 41, 42
16:3	6. **Describe** how common vision problems are corrected.	11, 14, 15	14	10, 40	19, 28
	7. **Discuss** reasons for protecting your ears against loud noises.	12	14	1	2
	8. **Explain** ways of correcting hearing problems.	13		6	12, 22, 27

Senses

CHAPTER OVERVIEW

Key Concepts

This chapter begins by pointing out the importance of sense organs. An overview of certain sense organs in the animal kingdom is presented, followed by a detailed look at human sense organs, including the eye, ear, skin, tongue, and nose. Finally, the chapter looks at some of the more familiar problems associated with the senses.

Key Science Words

auditory nerve
cochlea
cone
cornea
dermis
eardrum
epidermis
farsighted
iris
lens
lens muscle
nearsighted
olfactory nerve
optic nerve
pupil
retina
rod
sclera
semicircular canals
sense organ
taste bud
vitreous humor

Skill Development

In Lab 16-1, students will **formulate a model, observe,** and **measure in SI** as they learn how the eye works. In Lab 16-2, they will **predict, interpret data,** and **make and use tables** as they test their sense of vision. In the Skill Check on page 341, students will **interpret a diagram** of the skin. In the Skill Check on page 343, they will **understand** the **science word** *epidermis.* In the Mini Lab on page 335, they will **observe** an afterimage.

CHAPTER PREVIEW

Chapter Content

Review this outline for Chapter 16 before you read the chapter.

Skills in this Chapter

The skills that you will use in this chapter are listed below.

- In **Lab 16-1,** you will formulate a model, observe, and measure in SI. In **Lab 16-2,** you will predict, interpret data, and make and use tables.
- In the **Skill Checks,** you will interpret diagrams and understand science words.
- In the **Mini Lab,** you will observe.

330

Bridging

The nervous system allows animals to monitor their surroundings. This chapter explains to students how the nervous system gets its input or information about the surroundings. Sense organs are an extension of the nervous system, which students have just read about in Chapter 15.

Chapter 16

Senses

Think about all the things you can enjoy because of your senses. You can enjoy the aroma of baking pizza because of your sense of smell. You can savor the rich sweetness of a chocolate chip cookie because of your sense of taste. Your senses let you experience the richness of the world around you.

But, did you realize there are things your senses can't detect? What do you think an insect can see? Insects can see ultraviolet light from the sun that you can't see. The flower on the left is what you see when you look at a flower. The flower on the right is what an insect sees. This flower was photographed in ultraviolet light. The insect's ability to see the middle of the flower as a darkened area helps guide the insect to the flower. Like you, the insect's senses allow it to keep in touch with the world around it.

Try This!

Did you hear that? Listen to the sounds you make as you speak, breathe, and chew. Plug your ears with your fingers and listen to these sounds again. How do the sounds differ? Can you explain why?

Flowers photographed under natural light (left) and ultraviolet light (right)

Misconception

Mention an eye transplant operation and most students will assume that the whole eye is removed and a new one from a donor is inserted. What actually is transplanted is only the cornea, the outer covering of the eye. At this time, one cannot cut a major nerve such as the optic nerve and have it regrow. (See the reference to this research in Chapter 15.) Thus, it is impossible to transplant an entire eye and expect it to function normally.

GETTING STARTED

Using the Photos

The ability to see colors is found in many animals including fish, reptiles, most birds, and some mammals. An insect's eye is made up of thousands of lenses and produces a picture that is somewhat like an image produced by a color TV. Both are composed of small dots. Have students compare the colors of the flowers as they appear to humans and insects. An insect can see UV light but we can't. However, an insect can't distinguish between red and black but we can.

MOTIVATION/Try This!

Did you hear that? Hearing is based on detection of molecules that vibrate or move. These vibrations are usually air molecules in motion; however, they may be vibrations of a solid. Sound heard when the ears are plugged occurs as a result of vibrations through bone. Upon completion of this activity, students will be able to compare sound as a result of air molecule motion with sound as a result of bone vibration.

Chapter Preview

Have students study the chapter outline before they begin to read the chapter. They should note the overall organization of the chapter, that the introduction describes the sense organs of various animals. Next it explains the parts and functions of the human sense organs. Last, it deals with problems associated with sense organs and how certain problems are solved or prevented.

16:1 Observing the Environment

PREPARATION

Materials Needed

Make copies of the Focus, Reteaching, and Study Guide worksheets in the *Teacher Resource Package.*

▶ Obtain plastic mounts or slides for the demonstration.

Key Science Words

sense organ

1 FOCUS

▶ The objectives are listed on the student page. Remind students to preview these objectives as a guide to this numbered section.

MOTIVATION/Demonstration

Show students plastic mounts or 35 mm slides of a planarian, earthworm, cricket, and snake.

Guided Practice

Have students write down their answers to the margin questions: A planarian senses light with its two eyespots; a snake picks up odor molecules with its tongue.

Focus/*Teacher Resource Package,* p. 31. Use the Focus transparency shown at the bottom of this page as an introduction to sense organs.

16:1 Observing the Environment

Objectives

1. **Relate** ways a planarian and an earthworm sense light.
2. **Compare** the sense organs of a cricket and a snake.

Key Science Words

sense organ

Living things must know what is going on around them. They may use eyes. What if they do not have eyes? They will have other ways to keep in contact with their surroundings.

Senses Aid Survival

The human body has many sense organs. **Sense organs** are parts of the nervous system that tell an animal what is going on around it. Eyes, ears, nose, tongue, and even our skin are sense organs.

Could you stay alive for very long without sense organs? It would be very hard. What about other animals? How well would they survive without any sense organs?

Sense Organs of Animals

The sense organs of four different animals will be studied in this section. These animals are a flatworm, a segmented worm, an insect, and a snake.

How does a planarian sense light?

A planarian is a simple, small animal that lives in ponds or streams. Figure 16-1a shows two of its sense organs. Eyespots of a planarian are simple. They can tell only light from dark. A planarian has knobs on its front end that detect the direction of water currents and food.

Earthworms are a little more complex than planarians. If you look at an earthworm's body closely, you cannot see anything that looks like an eye. Yet, the animal can detect light. How? Earthworms have nerve cells just below the skin that detect light.

Figure 16-1b shows three different sense organs of a cricket. The cricket has parts for detecting sound on the

Figure 16-1 A planarian (a) and a cricket (b) have sense organs that help them keep in touch with their surroundings.

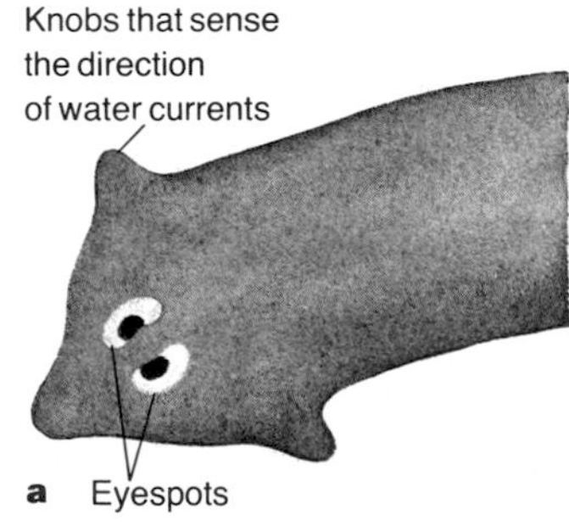

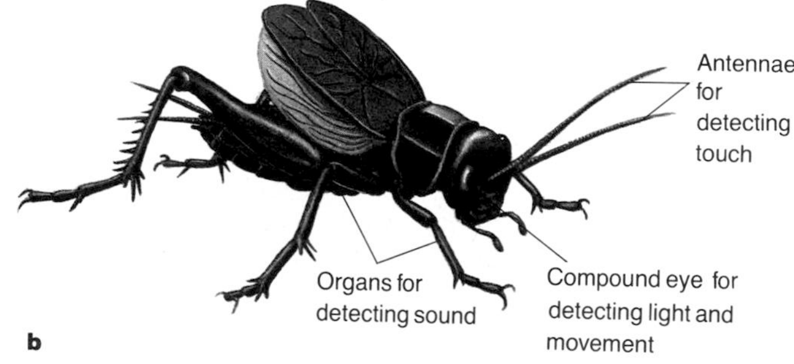

OPTIONS

Science Background

The vast array of different sense organs parallels animal complexity. Simple animals tend to have poorly developed nervous systems and correspondingly poorly developed sense organs. The more complex the nervous system, the greater the complexity and variety of sense organs seen in the animal kingdom.

FOCUS 31

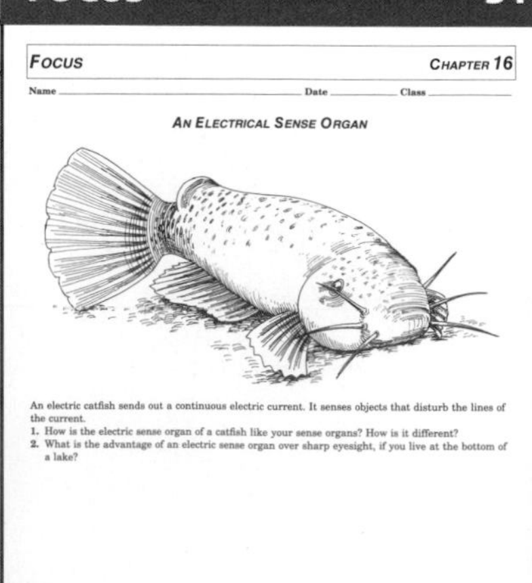
FOCUS CHAPTER 16

Name ______ Date ______ Class ______

AN ELECTRICAL SENSE ORGAN

An electric catfish sends out a continuous electric current. It senses objects that disturb the lines of the current.

1. How is the electric sense organ of a catfish like your sense organs? How is it different?
2. What is the advantage of an electric sense organ over sharp eyesight, if you live at the bottom of a lake?

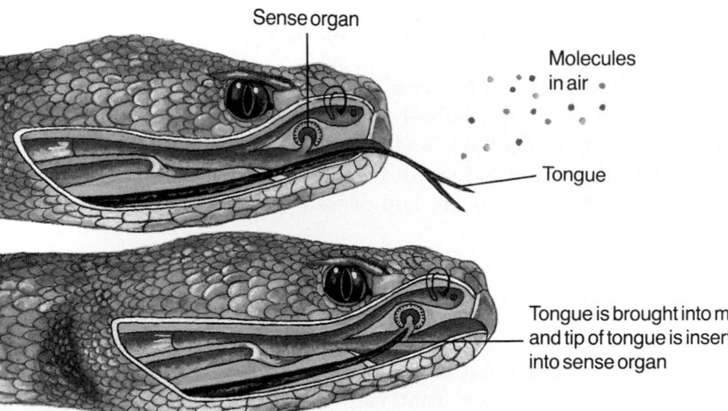

Figure 16-2 A snake has a sense organ in the roof of its mouth for sensing odors.

front legs. The antennae detect touch and chemicals. The eyes detect movement and light and dark. Insects have compound eyes. In this case, the word *compound* means many. A compound eye is made of hundreds or even thousands of very small eyelike parts. These eyelike parts are grouped together to form the compound eye.

The sense organs of snakes and other reptiles are more complex than those of insects. Snakes have eyes similar to human eyes. Their eyes have many of the same parts that human eyes have.

How does a snake smell?

Snakes have a very good sense of smell. Have you ever noticed how a snake darts its tongue in and out? A snake picks up odor molecules in the air with its tongue, then brings it back into its mouth. The snake then sticks the tip of its tongue into special sense organs found on the roof of its mouth. These sense organs look like two curled grooves as shown in Figure 16-2. Nerve cells line these grooves. The nerve cells pick up the molecule messages brought in by the tongue. Messages are then sent to the snake's brain.

Check Your Understanding

1. Name five different sense organs in the human body.
2. Explain how an insect can detect light.
3. How does a snake use its tongue as a sense organ?
4. **Critical Thinking:** Since earthworms live underground, why do they need to detect light?
5. **Biology and Reading:** How do senses aid survival?

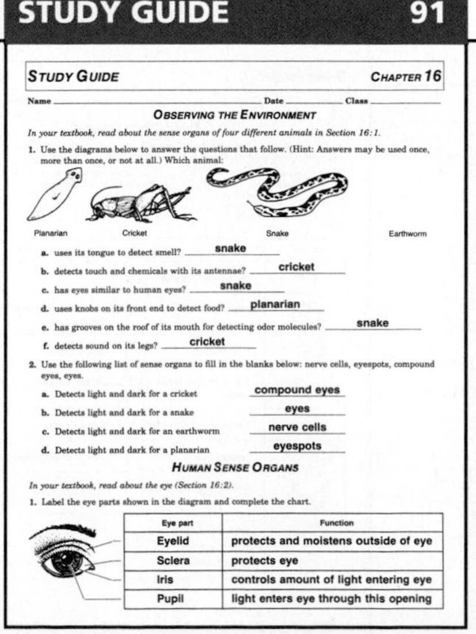

STUDY GUIDE 91

STUDY GUIDE — CHAPTER 16

Name ____ Date ____ Class ____

OBSERVING THE ENVIRONMENT

In your textbook, read about the sense organs of four different animals in Section 16:1.

1. Use the diagrams below to answer the questions that follow. (Hint: Answers may be used once, more than once, or not at all.) Which animal:

Planarian Cricket Snake Earthworm

a. uses its tongue to detect smell? **snake**
b. detects touch and chemicals with its antennae? **cricket**
c. has eyes similar to human eyes? **snake**
d. uses knobs on its front end to detect food? **planarian**
e. has grooves on the roof of its mouth for detecting odor molecules? **snake**
f. detects sound on its legs? **cricket**

2. Use the following list of sense organs to fill in the blanks below: nerve cells, eyespots, compound eyes, eyes.

a. Detects light and dark for a cricket **compound eyes**
b. Detects light and dark for a snake **eyes**
c. Detects light and dark for an earthworm **nerve cells**
d. Detects light and dark for a planarian **eyespots**

HUMAN SENSE ORGANS

In your textbook, read about the eye (Section 16:2).

1. Label the eye parts shown in the diagram and complete the chart.

Eye part	Function
Eyelid	protects and moistens outside of eye
Sclera	protects eye
Iris	controls amount of light entering eye
Pupil	light enters eye through this opening

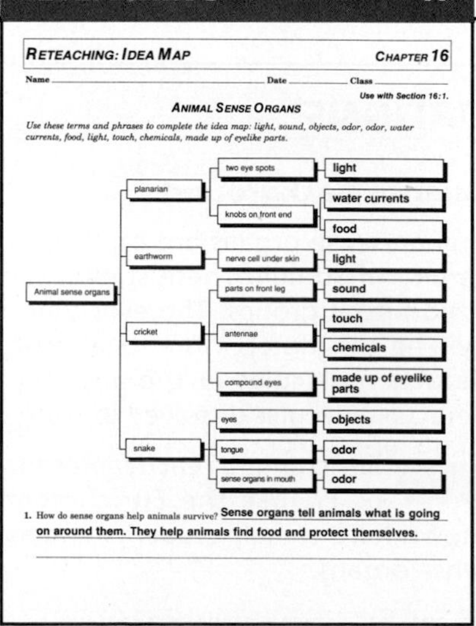

RETEACHING 17

RETEACHING: IDEA MAP — CHAPTER 16

Name ____ Date ____ Class ____

Use with Section 16:1.

ANIMAL SENSE ORGANS

Use these terms and phrases to complete the idea map: light, sound, objects, odor, odor, water currents, food, light, touch, chemicals, made up of eyelike parts.

- Animal sense organs
  - planarian
    - two eye spots — **light**
    - knobs on front end — **water currents**, **food**
  - earthworm
    - nerve cell under skin — **light**
  - cricket
    - parts on front leg — **sound**
    - antennae — **touch**, **chemicals**
    - compound eyes — **made up of eyelike parts**
  - snake
    - eyes — **objects**
    - tongue — **odor**
    - sense organs in mouth — **odor**

1. How do sense organs help animals survive? **Sense organs tell animals what is going on around them. They help animals find food and protect themselves.**

2 TEACH

Independent Practice

Study Guide/*Teacher Resource Package,* p. 91. Use the Study Guide worksheet shown at the bottom of this page for independent practice.

Check for Understanding

Have students respond to the first three questions in Check Your Understanding.

Reteach

Reteaching/*Teacher Resource Package,* p. 17. Use this worksheet to give students additional practice with animal sense organs.

Extension: Assign Critical Thinking, Biology and Reading, or some of the **OPTIONS** available with this lesson.

3 APPLY

ACTIVITY/Demonstration

Show students the lateral line along the side of a preserved fish and explain that it detects vibrations in the water.

4 CLOSE

Discuss how difficult it is to catch a fly. Relate this to the efficiency of the insect eye in detecting motion.

Answers to Check Your Understanding

1. eyes, ears, nose, tongue, skin
2. with its compound eyes.
3. Nerve cells pick up messages brought in by the tongue and transfer them to the brain.
4. They need to detect light because when they do go to the surface, they have to stay out of strong light to avoid drying out.
5. They detect changes in the organism's environment. The organism can then react to those changes, some of which could threaten survival.

16:2 Human Sense Organs

PREPARATION

Materials Needed

Make copies of the Transparency Masters, Reteaching, Critical Thinking/Problem Solving, Enrichment, Study Guide, and Lab worksheets in the *Teacher Resource Package.*

▶ Obtain black and white paper for Lab 16-1. Purchase peppermint candy and gather green and red colored pencils for Lab 16-2.

▶ Gather ear plugs, eye and ear models, and PTC paper for the demonstrations.

Key Science Words

sclera	optic nerve
iris	taste bud
pupil	olfactory nerve
cornea	eardrum
lens	cochlea
lens muscle	auditory nerve
retina	semicircular canal
vitreous humor	epidermis
rod	dermis
cone	

Process Skills

In Lab 16-1, students will observe, measure in SI, and formulate a model. In Lab 16-2, students will predict, interpret data, and make and use tables. In the Skill Checks, students will interpret diagrams and understand science words. In the Mini Lab, students will observe.

1 FOCUS

▶ The objectives are listed on the student page. Remind students to preview these objectives as a guide to this numbered section.

MOTIVATION/Brainstorming

Ask students to name as many sense organs in the human body as they can.

Objectives

3. **State** the functions of the parts of the eye.
4. **Explain** the jobs of the nose, tongue, and skin as sense organs.
5. **Describe** the parts of the outer, middle, and inner ear.

Key Science Words

sclera	cone
iris	optic nerve
pupil	taste bud
cornea	olfactory nerve
lens	eardrum
lens muscle	cochlea
retina	auditory nerve
vitreous humor	semicircular canal
rod	epidermis
	dermis

16:2 Human Sense Organs

The human body has a variety of sense organs. Each sense organ is specialized as to what it can detect. Eyes detect light. The nose and tongue detect chemical molecules. Ears detect moving air molecules. Skin detects heat, cold, pain, touch, and pressure.

The Eye

What are the parts of the eye?

How do our eyes give us information about our surroundings? What are the parts of the human eye? Figure 16-3 shows a front view and a side view of the eye. Let's look at what the parts of the eye do.

The eyelid protects and moistens the outside of the eye. Each time you blink, liquid spreads over the front of your eye.

The **sclera** (SKLER uh) is the tough, white outer covering of the eye. The sclera protects the eye.

The **iris** is a muscle. The iris controls the amount of light entering the eye. It is also the part that gives the eye its color. When you say that someone has blue or brown eyes, you are describing the color of the iris.

The **pupil** is an opening in the center of the iris. Light enters the eye through the pupil. As the amount of light changes, the size of both the iris and the pupil changes. The pupil becomes larger in dim light and smaller in bright light. How does a larger pupil help you see in the dark?

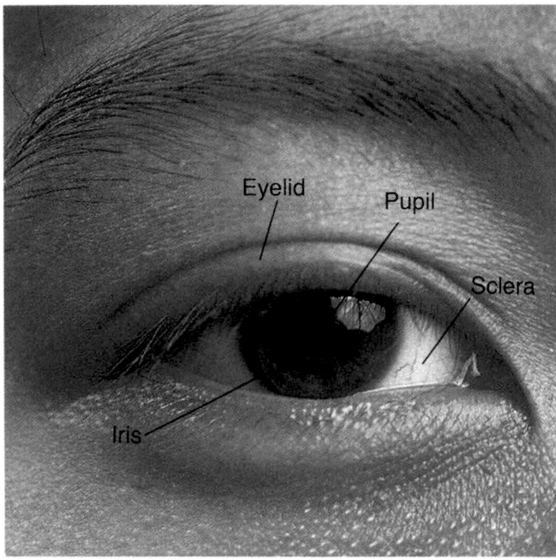

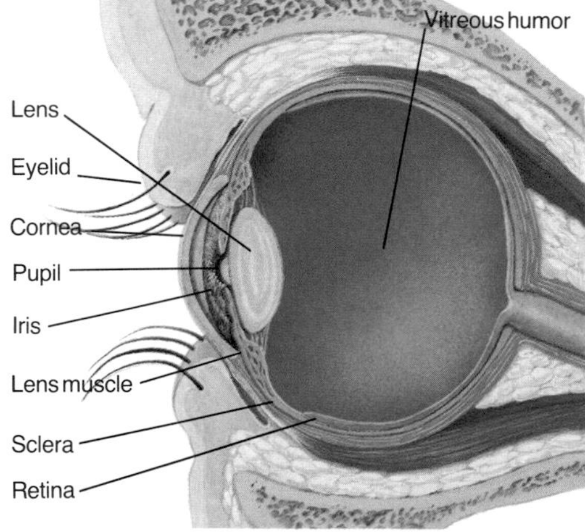

Figure 16-3 The parts of the human eye are shown here.

OPTIONS

Science Background

Human sense organs are capable of detecting a variety of stimuli. These stimuli can be categorized into 3 groups. The eyes detect light energy. The ears detect vibrational energy. The nose detects molecules in the air, and the tongue detects molecules dissolved in water.

Enrichment/*Teacher Resource Package,* p. 17. Use the Enrichment worksheet shown here to help students understand animal sense organs.

ENRICHMENT 17

ENRICHMENT **CHAPTER 16**

Name ______ Date ______ Class ______

Use after Section 16:2.

ANIMAL SENSE ORGANS

Read Section 16:2 and review Chapters 7 and 8 in your textbook. Match the statements about sense organs below with the animals shown. Then write the function of the sense organ in the last column.

nerves	sense organs on the roof of the mouth
lateral line	parts on the front legs
tentacles with eyes	nerve cells
well developed eyes	eyes that stick out
no sense organs	

Animal	Sense organ	Function
	no sense organs	
	nerves	used with muscles to move tentacles
	nerve cells	detect light
	parts on the front legs	detect sound
	tentacles with eyes	detect light
	lateral line	detect water movement
	sense organs on the roof of the mouth	detect odor
	well developed eyes	see predators
	eyes that stick out	see while hidden under water

The clear, outer covering at the front of the eye is the **cornea** (KOR nee uh). It protects the eye and allows light to enter the eye through the pupil. The cornea also helps to focus the light by bending the light rays as they enter the eye.

The **lens** is a clear part of the eye that changes shape as you view things at different distances. The lens muscle attaches to the lens. The **lens muscle** pulls on the lens and changes its shape. This helps to focus objects that are close up or far away.

The **retina** (RET nuh) is a structure at the back of the eye made of light-detecting nerve cells. The retina is often compared to film in a camera.

The **vitreous** (VI tree us) **humor** is a jelly-like material inside the eye. It pushes out on the eye parts. Its main job is to keep the eye round in shape.

Now that we have looked at the parts of the eye, we can follow the path that light takes through the eye. Follow the numbered steps in Figure 16-4.

1. Light rays enter the eye through the cornea. Notice that the cornea slightly bends the light rays. The light rays are bent toward each other.
2. Light passes through the pupil and then through the lens. Light is bent again as it passes through the lens. Again, the light rays are bent toward each other.
3. Because the vitreous humor is clear, light continues to pass through the eye.

Mini Lab

What Is an Afterimage?

Observe: Stare out of the classroom window for at least 30 seconds. Then, close your eyes for 15 seconds. What you see is called an afterimage. What does the afterimage look like? *For more help, refer to the **Skill Handbook**, pages 704-705.*

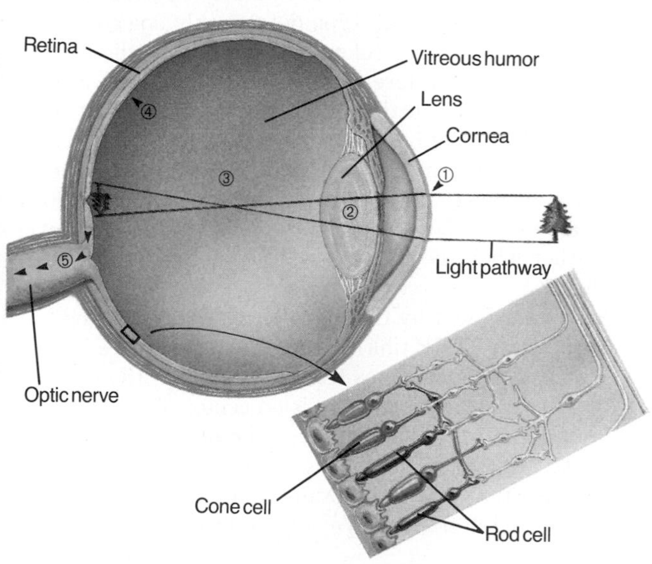

Figure 16-4 Light passes through the cornea, lens, and vitreous humor before it strikes the retina.

2 TEACH

MOTIVATION/Demonstration

A simple demonstration will show that the pupils of the eyes dilate in dim light. Have pairs of students sit so they can see each other's eyes. Darken the classroom as much as possible and leave lights off for at least 30 seconds. Turn them back on and have students note the change in the size of their partner's pupils. It may be necessary to repeat this demonstration several times.

Guided Practice

Have students write down their answers to the margin question: The parts of the eye are sclera, iris, pupil, cornea, lens, retina, and vitreous humor.

Mini Lab

Afterimages are related to the over stimulation of and chemical changes occurring in retinal cells.

Concept Development

▶ Explain that parts of the eye through which light passes are almost devoid of blood vessels, as blood vessels would impair vision. All other parts, however, do contain blood vessels. "Bloodshot" eyes are due to the dilation of capillaries located in the conjunctiva, a thin layer covering the sclera.

▶ Color vision is dependent on three different cone types. Each cone contains either a green, blue, or red receptor. The vast array of colors is due to the many possible combinations of the three basic receptors.

CRITICAL THINKING 16

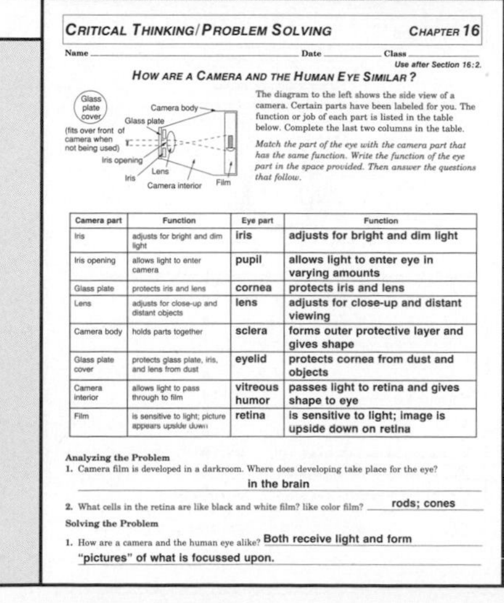

CRITICAL THINKING/PROBLEM SOLVING CHAPTER 16

Name ____ Date ____ Class ____

Use after Section 16:2.

HOW ARE A CAMERA AND THE HUMAN EYE SIMILAR?

The diagram to the left shows the side view of a camera. Certain parts have been labeled for you. The function or job of each part is listed in the table below. Complete the last two columns in the table.

Match the part of the eye with the camera part that has the same function. Write the function of the eye part in the space provided. Then answer the questions that follow.

Camera part	Function	Eye part	Function
Iris	adjusts for bright and dim light	iris	adjusts for bright and dim light
Iris opening	allows light to enter camera	pupil	allows light to enter eye in varying amounts
Glass plate	protects iris and lens	cornea	protects iris and lens
Lens	adjusts for close-up and distant objects	lens	adjusts for close-up and distant viewing
Camera body	holds parts together	sclera	forms outer protective layer and gives shape
Glass plate cover	protects glass plate, iris, and lens from dust	eyelid	protects cornea from dust and objects
Camera interior	allows light to pass through to film	vitreous humor	passes light to retina and gives shape to eye
Film	is sensitive to light; picture appears upside down	retina	is sensitive to light; image is upside down on retina

Analyzing the Problem

1. Camera film is developed in a darkroom. Where does developing take place for the eye? in the brain
2. What cells in the retina are like black and white film? like color film? rods; cones

Solving the Problem

1. How are a camera and the human eye alike? Both receive light and form "pictures" of what is focussed upon.

OPTIONS

Critical Thinking/Problem Solving/ *Teacher Resource Package,* p. 16. Use the worksheet shown here to help students compare a camera and the human eye.

Pathway of Light Through the Eye/ *Transparency Package,* number 16. Use color transparency number 16 as you teach how the eye functions.

What Are the Parts of an Eye?/*Lab Manual,* pp. 135-140. Use this lab to reinforce what students learn about the parts of an eye.

TEACH

Concept Development

▶ Students will often see "floaters" within their eyes when looking into bright light. It is believed that these are blood cells that are floating in the vitreous humor.

▶ An easy way of remembering which cell type does what is to relate the letter c in "cone" to the letter c in "color."

▶ The prefix *opt-* is present in such words as *optician, optometrist, optics.* Ask students if they can name some words sharing the prefix *opt-*. This exercise becomes a useful tool for students when trying to remember the word *optic.*

Independent Practice

Study Guide/*Teacher Resource Package*, p. 92. Use the Study Guide worksheet shown at the bottom of this page for independent practice.

Idea Map

Have students use the idea map as a study guide to the major concepts of this section.

Study Tip: Use this idea map as you study the parts of the human eye and their functions. Write down the function of each eye part.

Idea Map

Eye Parts

- Human eye
  - outer eye parts
    - eyelid
    - sclera
    - cornea
  - space or opening
    - pupil
  - inner eye parts
    - iris
    - lens and lens muscle
    - vitreous humor
    - retina
      - rods
      - cones
    - optic nerve

4. Finally, the light rays strike the retina. Notice that the retina is made of two types of nerve cells. These cells are called rods and cones because of their shapes. **Rods** are nerve cells that detect motion and help us to tell if an object is light or dark. They also help us to detect the shapes of objects. We use our rods when looking at something in dim light.

Cones are nerve cells that can detect color. There are three types of cones. Each type detects only one color: red, green, or blue. All other colors that we see are the result of two or three of the different types of cones acting together. Figure 16-5 shows a section of the retina enlarged 1000 times. Notice the many rods and cones.

Look closely again at the retina in Figure 16-4. When the image of the tree forms on the retina, it is upside down. It appears upside down because the light rays crossed over one another when they were bent. Which two eye parts bend light?

5. The message sent by the light leaves the retina and enters the optic (AHP tihk) nerve. The **optic nerve** is a nerve that carries messages from the retina to the brain. Once a message arrives at the vision center of the cerebrum, two things happen. One, the message is interpreted. In our example, the brain decodes the message and we see a tree. Two, the brain interprets the message as an object right side up. We see the tree in its normal position.

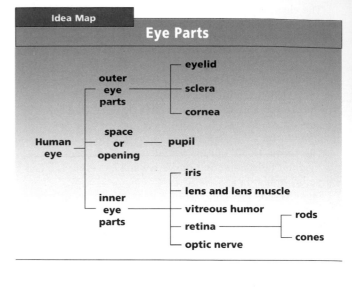

Figure 16-5 The retina is made up of thousands of rods and cones.

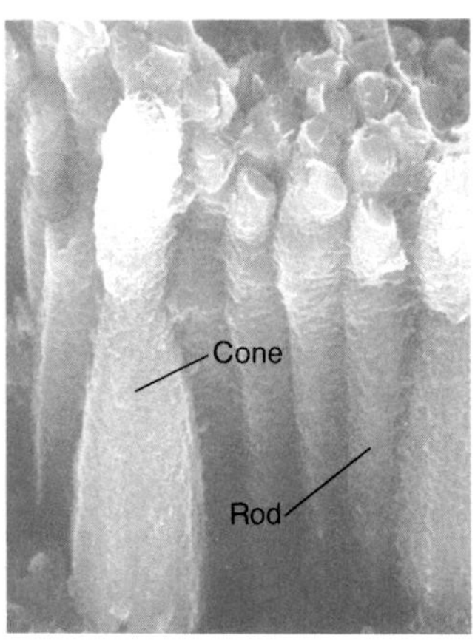

OPTIONS

Science Background

Tears contain an enzyme (lysozyme) that destroys bacteria. Lysozyme helps to fight off bacterial infections and lubricates the eye.

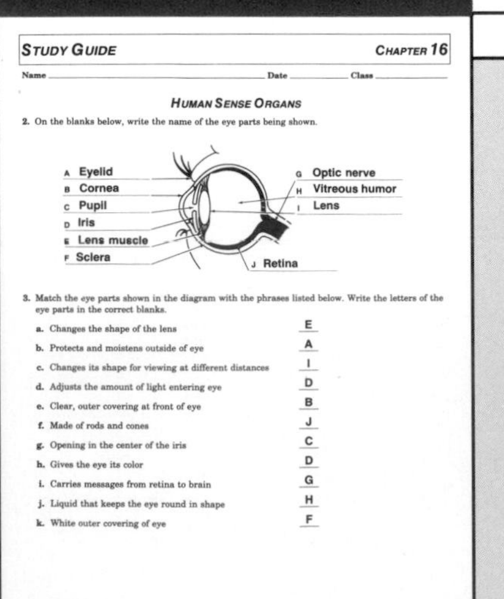

STUDY GUIDE 92

STUDY GUIDE CHAPTER 16

Name ______ Date ______ Class ______

HUMAN SENSE ORGANS

2. On the blanks below, write the name of the eye parts being shown.

A Eyelid
B Cornea
C Pupil
D Iris
E Lens muscle
F Sclera
G Optic nerve
H Vitreous humor
I Lens
J Retina

3. Match the eye parts shown in the diagram with the phrases listed below. Write the letters of the eye parts in the correct blanks.

a. Changes the shape of the lens E
b. Protects and moistens outside of eye A
c. Changes its shape for viewing at different distances I
d. Adjusts the amount of light entering eye D
e. Clear, outer covering at front of eye B
f. Made of rods and cones J
g. Opening in the center of the iris C
h. Gives the eye its color D
i. Carries messages from retina to brain G
j. Liquid that keeps the eye round in shape H
k. White outer covering of eye F

Lab 16-1 The Eye

Problem: How does the eye work?

Skills

observe, measure in SI, formulate a model

Materials

black paper
ruler
clear tape
white paper
scissors
top part of a hand lens

Procedure

1. Make a data table in which to diagram your results.
2. Use a ruler to trace a letter *L* onto black paper. Make the letter 15 cm high and 8 cm long. Make each leg of the *L* 3 cm wide.
3. Cut out the letter and tape it onto the classroom window right side up.
4. Hold a piece of white paper as shown in the figure. The paper should be 40 to 60 cm away from the window.
5. With your back toward the window, look at the white paper.
6. Hold the top of the hand lens about 4 cm from the paper. Move the lens slowly toward and away from the paper until you see the letter *L* clearly on the paper.

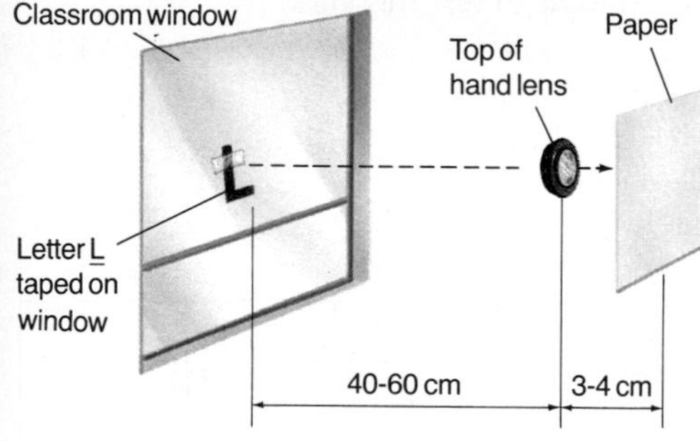

7. Complete the data table by making a diagram of the letter *L* as it appears on the window and on the paper.
8. **Measure in SI:** Measure the distance between the lens and paper in cm. Record this distance in your data table.
9. Determine the shape of the lens by rubbing your fingers over both sides of it. Diagram the shape of the lens in your data table.

Data and Observations

1. What was the appearance of the letter *L* on the window?
2. What was the appearance of the letter *L* on the paper?
3. Which of the following better describes the shape of the lens: (a) thicker toward the edges and thinner toward the center or (b) thinner toward the edges and thicker toward the center?

Analyze and Apply

1. Which part of the human eye is represented by the:
   (a) lens?
   (b) white paper?
2. (a) In a real eye, what structures would make up the paper?
   (b) In a real eye, what shape would the lens have?
3. **Apply:** In this lab, you moved the lens back and forth to obtain a clear view of the letter *L* on the paper. What does the action of moving the lens back and forth represent in the real eye?

Extension

Formulate a model to show what causes nearsightedness. How does the distance between the lens and white paper change?

ANSWERS

Data and Observations

1. right side up and frontwards
2. upside down and backwards
3. b

Analyze and Apply

1. a) lens
   b) retina
2. a) rods and cones
   b) thinner toward the edges and thicker toward the middle
3. focusing

Lab 16-1 The Eye

Overview

Students will construct a simple eye model. This model illustrates the role and shape of the lens. Students will discover that the image that falls upon the retina is inverted.

Objectives: Upon completing the lab, students will be able to (1) **compare** the shape of a hand lens to that of the eye lens, (2) **recognize** the role of the lens and retina, (3) **observe** that the image that falls on the retina is inverted.

Time Allotment: 30 minutes

Preparation

▶ **Alternate Materials:** You may use a hand-held magnifying lens in place of the hand lens.

Lab 16-1 worksheet/*Teacher Resource Package,* pp. 61-62.

Teaching the Lab

▶ **Troubleshooting:** The distance between the lens and the paper is going to be rather short (3-5 cm), as indicated in the diagram.

▶ Alert students to the fact that the image of the letter is indeed inverted.

Cooperative Learning: It will be necessary for students to work in groups of two so as to hold the lens and paper in proper position and measure the distance between them at the same time. For more information, see pp. 22T-23T in the Teacher Guide.

Lab 16-2 The Senses

Overview

Students will determine if their sense organs are 100 percent reliable. They will test their blind spots and color afterimaging. They should conclude that the eye is not totally reliable.

Objectives: Upon completing the lab, students will be able to (1) **test** for the blind spot and (2) **describe** an afterimage.

Time Allotment: 30 minutes

Preparation

▶ **Alternate Materials:** Other strong-tasting candy, such as spearmint, may be used.

Lab 16-2 worksheet/*Teacher Resource Package,* pp. 63-64.

Teaching the Lab

▶ To find the blind spot, have students start with the page at arm's length and move the paper slowly toward them. The blind spot will become apparent when the page is about 20 cm from the eye.

▶ **Troubleshooting:** Students may need to repeat the steps before they see the afterimage. Do not tell them what they are supposed to see.

Cooperative Learning: Divide the class into groups of two or three students. For more information, see pp. 22T-23T in the Teacher Guide.

The Senses

Lab 16-2

Problem: How reliable is your sense of vision?

Skills

predict, interpret data, make and use tables

Materials

white paper
green and red pencils

Procedure

1. Copy the data table.
2. Close your left eye. With your right eye, stare at the cross in the figure for about 10 seconds.
3. Very slowly move the page toward you. At a certain distance, the dot in the figure will disappear. When it disappears, light from the dot is falling on your blind spot. The blind spot is an area on the retina with no rods or cones.
4. Close your right eye. Repeat steps 2 and 3, only this time stare at the circle.
5. Record in your table whether each eye has a blind spot.
6. Stare at the triangles for 30 seconds. Then, look at a blank piece of paper. You will see a similar figure on the blank paper. Record in your table what colors you see in the outer triangle and the inner triangle in the second figure.

TEST		OBSERVATIONS
Blind spot	Right eye	blind spot present
	Left eye	blind spot present
Colors of triangles	Outer triangle	red
	Inner triangle	green

Data and Observations

1. Is your blind spot present in both eyes?
2. What happened to the colors of the triangles when you looked at the white paper?

Analyze and Apply

1. Why aren't you usually aware of your blind spot?
2. Which parts of the eye detect the colors of the triangles?
3. **Apply:** Was the change in color you observed in the triangles taking place in your eyes or in your brain? Explain your answer.

Extension

The size of an object determines how far away the object must be before the light from it falls on your blind spot. **Design an experiment** to test this idea.

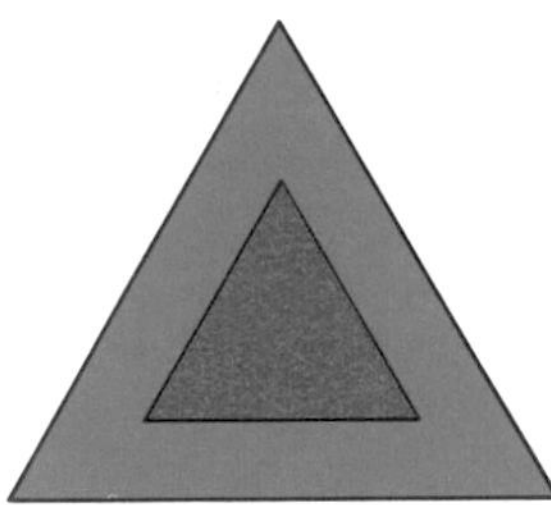

ANSWERS

Data and Observations

1. yes
2. They were reversed.

Analyze and Apply

1. An object must be in a certain position in front of the eyes for the blind spot to be noticed.
2. cones
3. The change was taking place inside the brain. The rods and cones don't interpret messages, the brain does.

The Tongue and the Nose

The tongue is the major sense organ for taste. The tongue detects molecules dissolved in water. The tongue senses different molecules and you taste the sweetness of a candy bar or the sourness of a lemon.

Notice in Figure 16-6a that the surface of the tongue has many small bumps. On each of these bumps are tiny pits that contain taste buds. **Taste buds** are nerve cells in the tongue that detect chemical molecules. You have about 10 000 taste buds. Figure 16-6a shows a greatly magnified view of several taste buds.

There are four different kinds of taste buds on the tongue. Each kind is located in a different area of the tongue. Each area of the tongue detects a certain kind of molecule, or taste. The four different tastes are sour, salty, sweet, and bitter. You know that there are more than just four tastes. What you taste are different combinations of the four basic tastes.

Have you ever had trouble tasting things when you had a cold? That's because the senses of taste and smell work together. They both detect molecules. Your nose detects gas molecules in the air. These gas molecules are then interpreted by the brain as odors.

Figure 16-6b shows how your nose works. Molecules in the form of a gas are detected by neurons that line the top of the nasal chamber. There are seven different types of nerve cells in the nose. Each type detects one kind of odor. The **olfactory** (ohl FAK tree) **nerve** then carries the message to your brain. The cerebrum interprets the message as smoke or perfume or some other odor.

Bio Tip

Science: Your sense of smell is 1000 times more sensitive than your sense of taste.

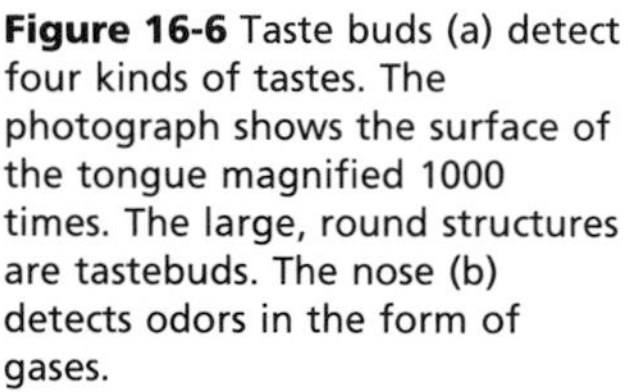

Figure 16-6 Taste buds (a) detect four kinds of tastes. The photograph shows the surface of the tongue magnified 1000 times. The large, round structures are tastebuds. The nose (b) detects odors in the form of gases.

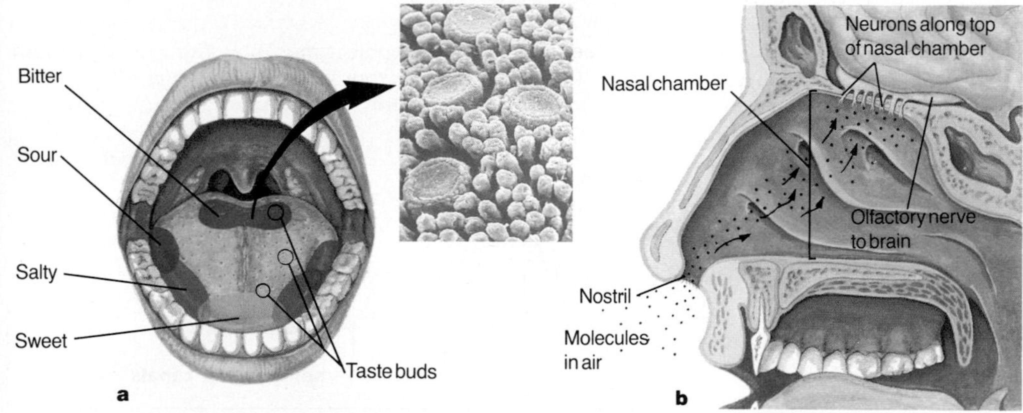

TEACH

Concept Development

▶ Review the term *molecule* with your students. Then ask if it is molecules that one detects on the taste buds. The answer is yes.

MOTIVATION/Demonstration

Ask students if each one perceives the same exact taste for all types of food. Why do people have likes and dislikes when it comes to food? The perception of taste may have some genetic basis. Tell students that the ability to taste certain chemicals is a trait that they may inherit much like eye, skin, or hair color. To illustrate this idea, provide each student with a small piece of PTC paper. (This paper is available from most biological supply houses.) Ask them to taste the paper. About 80 percent of the class will describe its taste as bitter. The remaining 20 percent will describe it as having no taste. Ask the students who tasted nothing to raise their hand.

TRANSPARENCY 75

TRANSPARENCY MASTER — CHAPTER 16

HUMAN SENSE ORGANS I

lens, vitreous humor, eyelid, optic nerve, cornea, pupil, iris, retina, lens muscle, sclera — The Eye

bitter, sour, salty, sweet — The Tongue

olfactory nerve, nerve cells, nasal chamber, nostril — The Nose

OPTIONS

Transparency Master/*Teacher Resource Package*, p. 75. Use the Transparency Master shown here to help students study the human sense organs.

How Can You Test Your Senses?/*Lab Manual*, pp. 127-130. Use this lab as an extension to learning about senses.

TEACH

Concept Development

▶ The small middle-ear bones are called the malleus (hammer), incus (anvil), and stapes (stirrup).

▶ A model of the human ear would help students to visualize the locations and the size relationships of parts being described.

▶ Compare the outer ear (pinna) to a megaphone or an old-fashioned ear trumpet. Ask why people who are hard of hearing often cup their hands in back of their ears when trying to hear. They are trying to direct more sound waves into the outer ear.

Idea Map

Have students use the idea map as a study guide to the major concepts of this section.

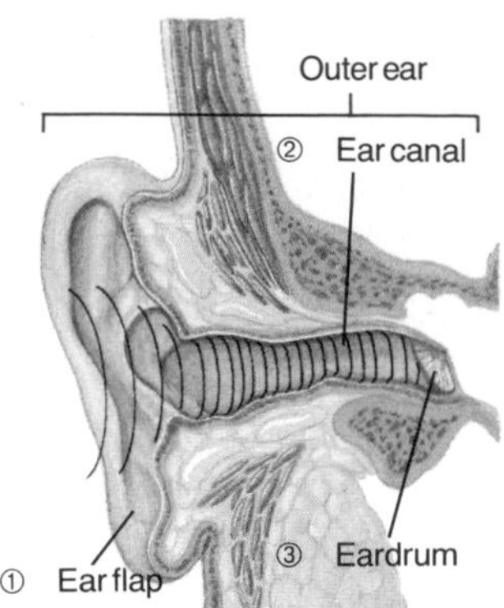

Figure 16-7 Sound waves are directed into the ear by the ear flap and ear canal.

The Ear

Ears are sense organs for detecting sound waves. Sound waves are air molecules in motion. How does the ear detect moving air molecules and allow you to hear?

The human ear is divided into three areas. These areas are called the outer, middle, and inner ear. The following description tells how these parts work together and enable you to hear.

Figure 16-7 shows the three parts of the outer ear. Look at this figure as you read steps 1 through 3.

1. The only part of your ear that you can see is the ear flap. The ear flap helps direct sound waves into a narrow tube leading into the ear. The ear flap is made of cartilage and connective tissue. It is soft and easily bent.
2. The narrow tube leading into the ear is called the ear canal. The ear canal carries sound waves to the middle ear.
3. Sound waves bump against a thin membrane called the eardrum. The **eardrum** is the membrane that vibrates at the end of the ear canal. The vibrations, or back-and-forth movements, are caused by sound waves striking the eardrum. A fatlike chemical, earwax, is made by cells in the ear canal. Earwax helps to keep insects and other foreign matter out of the ear and keeps the eardrum soft.

Figure 16-8 shows the middle ear. It has two main parts. Look at this figure as you read steps 4 and 5.

4. Three small bones make up one of the main parts of the

Study Tip: Use this idea map as you study the parts of the human ear and their functions. Write down the function of each ear part.

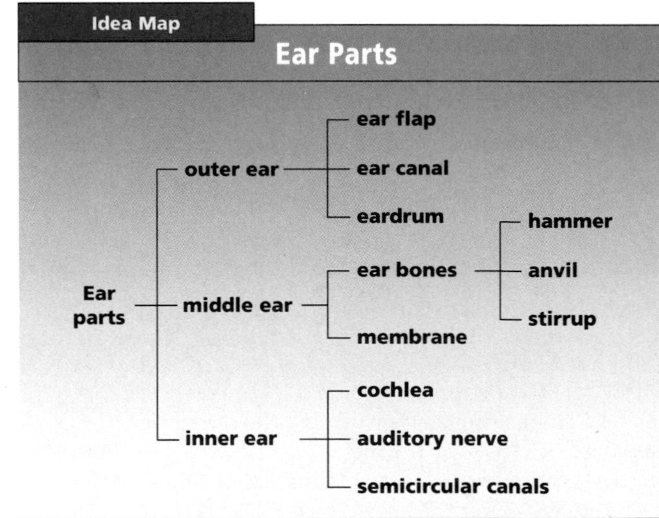

OPTIONS

Transparency Master/*Teacher Resource Package*, p. 77. Use the Transparency Master shown here to help students study the human sense organs.

TRANSPARENCY 77

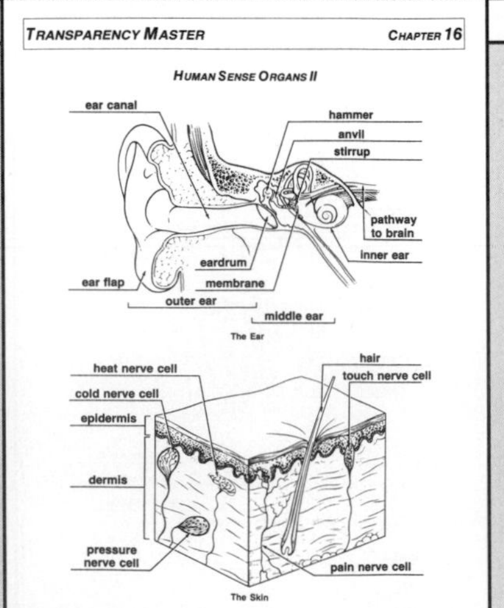

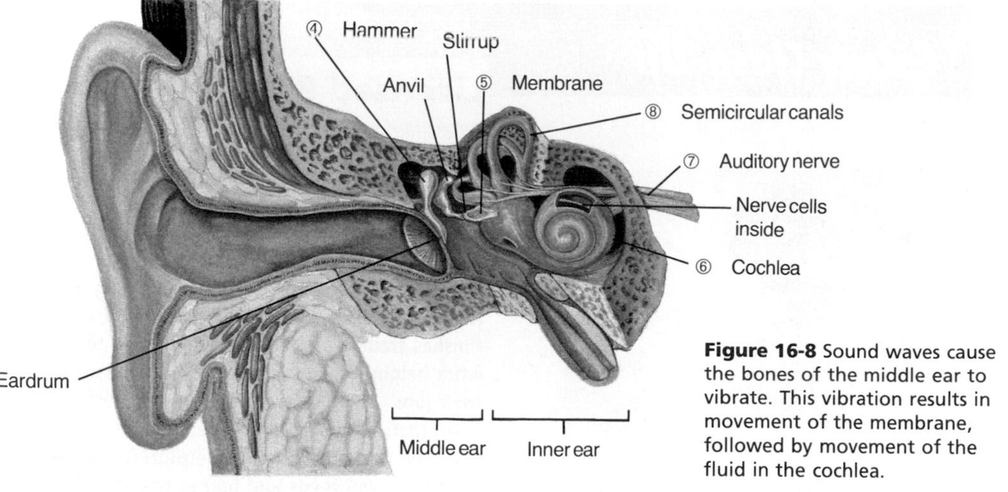

Figure 16-8 Sound waves cause the bones of the middle ear to vibrate. This vibration results in movement of the membrane, followed by movement of the fluid in the cochlea.

middle ear. Because of their shapes, the bones are called the hammer, anvil, and stirrup. These bones are quite small and are connected to one another. The hammer is also connected to the eardrum. When the eardrum vibrates, the hammer moves. The movement of the hammer causes the other two bones to move.

5. The stirrup is connected to a membrane in the middle ear that vibrates with the motion of the ear bones.

The inner ear also has three main parts. Look at Figure 16-8 and read steps 6, 7, and 8 to see what they do.

6. This part is called the cochlea (KAHK lee uh). *Cochlea* is Latin for "snail shell." The **cochlea** is a liquid-filled, coiled chamber in the ear that contains nerve cells. When the middle ear membrane vibrates, it makes the liquid in the cochlea move. The nerve cells in the cochlea detect this movement.

How does the cochlea work?

7. Each nerve cell in the cochlea is connected to a large nerve, the auditory (AHD uh tor ee) nerve. The **auditory nerve** carries messages of sound to the brain.

Once messages reach the cerebrum of your brain, they are interpreted as particular sounds. You hear a whistle, a barking dog, or some other sound.

8. The semicircular canal has a very special job not related to hearing. The **semicircular canals** are inner ear parts that help us keep our balance. Nerve messages pass from these ear parts to your brain's cerebellum. When these messages arrive in the brain, they send messages to body muscles to contract or relax as needed to maintain balance.

Skill Check

Interpret diagrams: Study Figure 16-7. Which of the ear parts shown is the first to respond to sound? *For more help, refer to the* ***Skill Handbook****, pages 706-711.*

TEACH

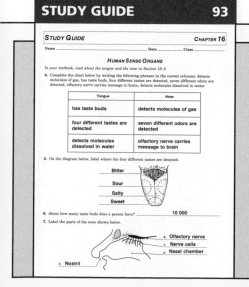

MOTIVATION/Demonstration

You can demonstrate the role of the inner ear bones with a hypodermic syringe (piston removed). As the piston is inserted into the cylinder and pushed inward, the pressure within the cylinder increases. In the analogy, the cylinder represents the inner ear and the piston represents the ear bones. These bones increase the pressure of the sound vibration 22 times. The oval window vibrates more intensely from the increased pressure than did the eardrum when the sound struck it.

Guided Practice

Have students write down their answers to the margin question: The cochlea contains liquid and nerve cells. When the middle ear membrane vibrates, the liquid in the cochlea moves. The nerve cells in the cochlea detect this movement. The nerve cells are connected to the auditory nerve, which carries messages of sound to the brain.

Skill Check

The eardrum is the first ear part that responds to sound.

MOTIVATION/Software

The Ear, Queue, Inc.

Independent Practice

Study Guide/*Teacher Resource Package,* p. 93. Use the Study Guide worksheet shown at the bottom of this page for independent practice.

STUDY GUIDE 93

STUDY GUIDE — CHAPTER 16

Name ______ Date ______ Class ______

HUMAN SENSE ORGANS

In your textbook, read about the tongue and the nose in Section 16:2.

4. Complete the chart below by writing the following phrases in the correct columns: detects molecules of gas, has taste buds, four different tastes are detected, seven different odors are detected, olfactory nerve carries message to brain, detects molecules dissolved in water

Tongue	Nose
has taste buds	detects molecules of gas
four different tastes are detected	seven different odors are detected
detects molecules dissolved in water	olfactory nerve carries message to brain

5. On the diagram below, label where the four different tastes are detected.

Bitter
Sour
Salty
Sweet

6. About how many taste buds does a person have? 10 000

7. Label the parts of the nose shown below.

B Olfactory nerve
C Nerve cells
D Nasal chamber
A Nostril

OPTIONS

How Are Your Senses Sometimes Fooled?/*Lab Manual,* pp. 131-134. Use this lab as an extension to understanding the senses.

Career Close-Up

Licensed Practical Nurse

Background

A practical nurse works with patients in hospitals and nursing homes, and provides in-home care. A practical nurse is involved with many aspects of patient care and works closely with registered nurses and doctors.

Related Careers

Related careers are registered nurse and nurse's aide.

Job Requirements

In order to be a licensed practical nurse, a person must be a high school graduate and take special training at a junior college or hospital.

For More Information

National Federation of Licensed Practical Nurses, Inc., Box 11038, Durham, NC 27703.

TEACH

Guided Practice

Have students write down their answers to the margin question: The skin has nerve cells for detecting pain, pressure, touch, heat, and cold.

Independent Practice

Study Guide/*Teacher Resource Package*, p. 94. Use the Study Guide worksheet shown at the bottom of this page for independent practice.

Career Close-Up

Licensed Practical Nurse

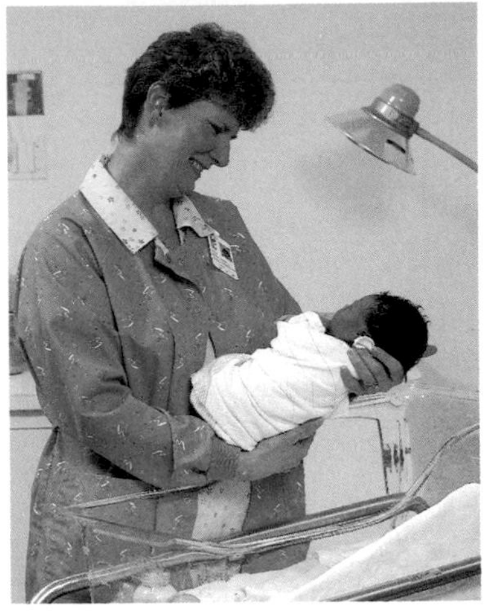

An LPN cares for patients.

Did you know that you can be a nurse without going to college for four years? You can if you become a licensed practical nurse, or LPN. An LPN must graduate from high school and take a year of special training at a junior college or hospital. When the LPN finishes training, he or she can go right to work helping doctors and registered nurses do their jobs.

A practical nurse works directly with patients. The LPN takes temperatures, changes bandages, and feeds and bathes patients. Practical nurses are also licensed to give drugs to patients. They learn about how drugs affect patients and the proper use of drugs.

Practical nurses may work in hospitals, nursing homes, and homes for the elderly. Practical nurses are licensed by the state in which they work.

Have you ever experienced motion sickness? It's a terrible feeling! Motion sickness results when the eyes and semicircular canals receive conflicting messages. For example, when you are in a car, your inner ear will be telling you that you are moving. If for some reason you can't look out of the car to see where you are going, your eyes will be telling you that you aren't moving. The messages are mixed up and you feel ill. One way to prevent motion sickness is to look out the front window of the car. Most drivers don't experience motion sickness because they are always looking out the front window.

The Skin

How does the skin function as a sense organ?

You may not think of your skin as a sense organ. It does, however, have many different kinds of nerve cells that detect changes around the body. Before we describe these nerve cells, let's look at the skin itself. Figure 16-9

OPTIONS

Science Background

One part of the body that has a large number of pain neurons close to the surface is the cornea of the eye. When even a very small object gets into the eye, it causes severe pain.

STUDY GUIDE 94

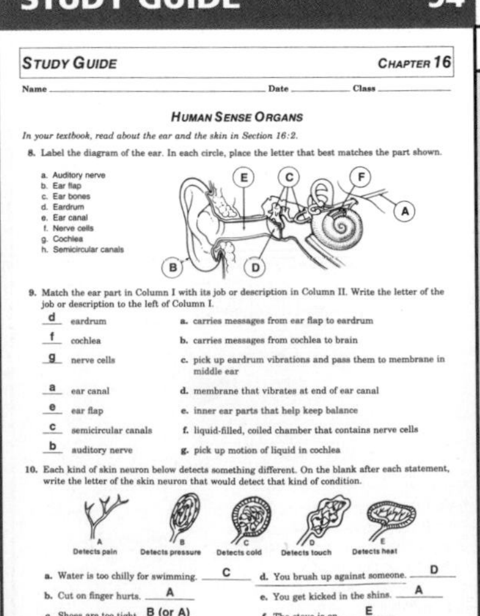

STUDY GUIDE CHAPTER 16

Name ______ Date ______ Class ______

HUMAN SENSE ORGANS

In your textbook, read about the ear and the skin in Section 16:2.

8. Label the diagram of the ear. In each circle, place the letter that best matches the part shown.

a. Auditory nerve
b. Ear flap
c. Ear bones
d. Eardrum
e. Ear canal
f. Nerve cells
g. Cochlea
h. Semicircular canals

9. Match the ear part in Column I with its job or description in Column II. Write the letter of the job or description to the left of Column I.

Column I		Column II
d	eardrum	a. carries messages from ear flap to eardrum
f	cochlea	b. carries messages from cochlea to brain
g	nerve cells	c. pick up eardrum vibrations and pass them to membrane in middle ear
a	ear canal	d. membrane that vibrates at end of ear canal
e	ear flap	e. inner ear parts that help keep balance
c	semicircular canals	f. liquid-filled, coiled chamber that contains nerve cells
b	auditory nerve	g. pick up motion of liquid in cochlea

10. Each kind of skin neuron below detects something different. On the blank after each statement, write the letter of the skin neuron that would detect that kind of condition.

a. Water is too chilly for swimming. C
b. Cut on finger hurts. A
c. Shoes are too tight. B (or A)
d. You brush up against someone. D
e. You get kicked in the shins. A
f. The stove is on. E

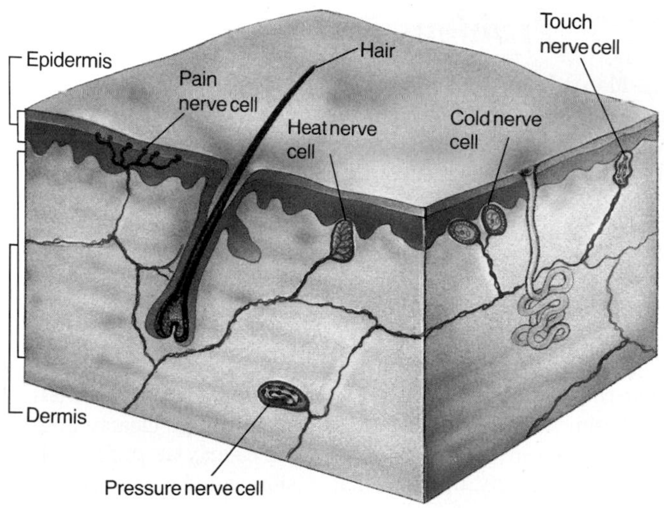

Figure 16-9 The skin contains five kinds of nerve cells.

shows a closeup of a small section of skin. Two different layers form the skin. The **epidermis** (ep uh DUR mus) is the outside layer of cells of an organism. The **dermis** is a thick layer of cells that form in the inner part of the skin.

Notice in Figure 16-9 that five nerve cell types are shown. Each nerve cell detects a different condition. The nerve cells detect pain, pressure, touch, heat, and cold. Note that most nerve cells are found in the dermis. Only nerve cells that detect pain are found in both the epidermis and the dermis.

Like messages from other sense organs, messages from the nerve cells in the skin also travel to the cerebrum. There they are interpreted as hot, cold, pain, pressure, or touch messages.

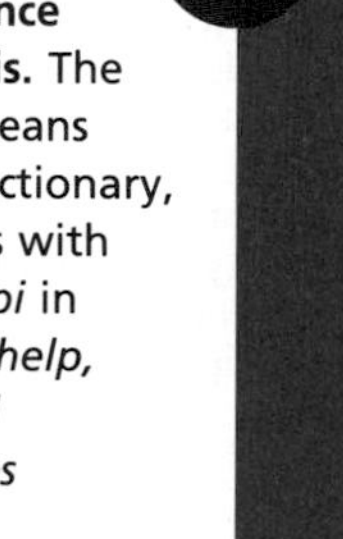

Skill Check

Understand science words: epidermis. The word part *epi* means outer. In your dictionary, find three words with the word part *epi* in them. *For more help, refer to the **Skill Handbook**, pages 706-711.*

Check Your Understanding

6. What is the relationship between the iris and the pupil?
7. How do the bones of the middle ear enable you to hear?
8. How are taste and smell related? How do they differ?
9. **Critical Thinking:** Many animals are active only at night. Would these night creatures have larger or smaller pupils than humans? Why?
10. **Biology and Reading:** Where are the nerve cells of the eye found? What are they called?

TEACH

Check for Understanding

Have students respond to the first three questions in Check Your Understanding.

Reteach

Reteaching/*Teacher Resource Package,* p. 48. Use this worksheet to give students additional practice with the human eye.

Extension: Assign Critical Thinking, Biology and Reading, or some of the **OPTIONS** available with this lesson.

3 APPLY

Demonstration: Provide two or three students with sets of earplugs, such as those used by swimmers. Have them wear the earplugs for the first 20 minutes of class. Then, have them report on what took place during the 20 minutes. Discuss the importance of the senses.

4 CLOSE

Discuss why: (a) foods taste so bland when you have a cold, (b) your ears plug up when riding up or down in an elevator, (c) the entire eye cannot be replaced.

Answers to Check Your Understanding

6. The iris is a muscle in the eye that controls the size of the pupil.
7. When the eardrum vibrates, the hammer moves and causes the other two bones to move. The vibrations are transferred through the inner ear to the auditory nerve, which sends the impulse to the brain, and sound is perceived.
8. Sense organs for taste and smell detect molecules. To detect taste, molecules must be dissolved in water. To detect odor, molecules must be in gas form.
9. larger; to allow in more light
10. Nerve cells of the eye are found in the retina and are called rods and cones.

RETEACHING 48

RETEACHING — **CHAPTER 16**

Name ______ Date ______ Class ______

Use with Section 16:2.

THE HUMAN EYE

Label the parts of the human eye shown below. Use the following terms and phrases to list the name and functions of each part: lens, iris, cornea, retina, vitreous humor, sclera, bends light so objects will be in focus, adjusts the amount of light entering the eye, changes shape to help you see close and far, has light detecting surface like the film of a camera, keeps the eye round in shape, protects eye and gives it shape.

Image
Object

- lens — changes shape to help you see close and far
- cornea — bends light so objects will be in focus
- iris — adjusts the amount of light entering the eye
- vitreous humor — keeps the eye round in shape
- sclera — protects eye and gives it shape
- retina — has light detecting surface llike the film of a camera

1. What is the function of the rods in the retina? The rods detect motion and help us to see in dim light.
2. What is the function of the cones? Each cone can detect one color: red, green, or blue.
3. What is the function of the optic nerve? It carries messages from the retina to the vision center of the cerebrum.

OPTIONS

Challenge: Use reference books to research some eye problems associated with improper muscle action.

Challenge: Interview a teacher of the hearing impaired. Find out the types of problems experienced by hearing impaired students. Ask to learn several words used in signing.

16:3 Problems with Sense Organs

PREPARATION

Materials Needed

Make copies of the Skill, Application, Reteaching, and Study Guide worksheets in the *Teacher Resource Package.*

▶ Obtain an eye chart for testing students' vision. Also obtain a tape recorder for the demonstration.

Key Science Words

nearsighted
farsighted

1 FOCUS

▶ The objectives are listed on the student page. Remind students to preview these objectives as a guide to this numbered section.

MOTIVATION/Demonstration

Use an eye chart to demonstrate that a student volunteer who wears glasses has no trouble reading the chart with glasses but has difficulty reading the same chart at the same distance without glasses. NOTE: If an eye chart is not available, print up a series of block letters that measure exactly 1 cm in height. Have the student stand 20 feet from the chart.

Objectives

6. **Describe** how common vision problems are corrected.
7. **Discuss** reasons for protecting your ears against loud noises.
8. **Explain** ways of correcting hearing problems.

Key Science Words

nearsighted
farsighted

16:3 Problems with Sense Organs

Many people have lost their sense of hearing or vision completely. There are many more people with hearing or vision problems. What causes some of these problems? What can be done to correct them?

Correcting Vision Problems

Have you ever wondered what is meant by 20/20 vision? A person with 20/20 vision is said to have normal vision. Figure 16-10a tells you what the numbers mean. Notice that the units used by eye doctors are not in metric or SI. A person with 20/20 vision sees certain things clearly at 20 feet. A person with 20/60 vision sees clearly at 20 feet what a person with 20/20, or normal, vision would see clearly at 60 feet.

Not everyone has 20/20 vision. Prove it to yourself by looking around the classroom. How many of your classmates are wearing glasses or contact lenses?

Why do some people have normal vision and others have problems seeing clearly? Figures 16-10b-d show you. The lines from the letter *L* to the retina show the path of light into the eye. Notice that the lines in Figure 16-10b meet on the retina. This eye has 20/20 vision. The eye in Figure 16-10c is nearsighted. **Nearsighted** means being able to see clearly close up but not far away. The path of light meets in front of the retina, instead of on it. This is because the farsighted eye is longer from front to back than the normal eye.

Figure 16-10 A person with 20/20 vision can see a 1 cm high letter clearly at 20 feet (a). In a normal eye (b), light rays meet on the retina. In a nearsighted eye (c), light rays meet in front of the retina. In a farsighted eye (d), light rays meet behind the retina.

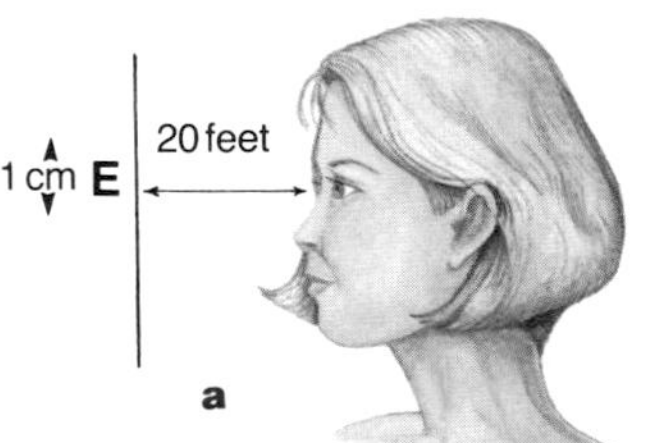

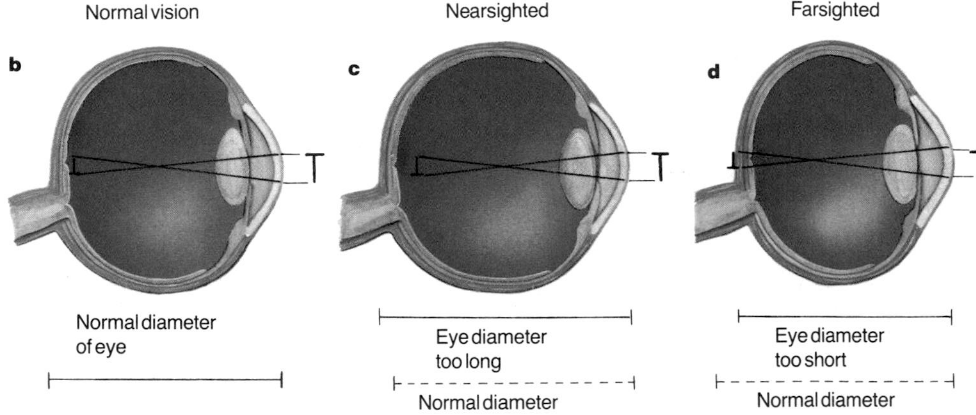

OPTIONS

Science Background

Nearsightedness is also called myopia. It results from improper bending of light by the cornea, by the lens, or by an abnormally long eye. Farsightedness is also called hypermetropia. It results from improper bending of light by the cornea, by the lens, or by an abnormally short eye.

Skill/*Teacher Resource Package,* p. 17. Use the Skill worksheet shown here to help students relate cause and effect.

SKILL 17

SKILL: INFER — **CHAPTER 16**

Name ______ Date ______ Class ______

For more help, refer to the Skill Handbook, pages 706-711. — *Use after Section 16.3.*

SENSE ORGANS

Scientists look for patterns among their observations. One type of pattern they search for is cause and effect. The cause is the reason something happens. The effect is what happens.

In the table below, consider each statement at the left to be a cause. Think about the probable effect of each cause. Write your response in the second column.

Cause	Effect
A virus affects the function of your semicircular canals.	You do not have normal balance.
You have difficulty hearing a speech and cup your hand behind your ear.	Sound waves are directed into the ear and you hear better.
You get a dirt particle in your eye.	You blink and liquid spreads over the front surface of the eye.
You go from bright sunshine into a darkened theater.	The pupils of your eyes become larger.
Particles of perfume reach neurons in your nasal chamber.	The olfactory nerve carries the message to the brain. The cerebrum interprets the message as the odor of perfume.
You have a stuffy head cold when you eat a slice of pizza.	You cannot taste the pizza as well as you normally would.
You touch your tongue to a slice of lemon.	Your taste buds detect a sour taste.
The middle ear bones cannot move back and forth.	Deafness occurs.
Rays of light meet in front of the retina instead of on the retina.	Vision is blurred. The condition is nearsightedness.

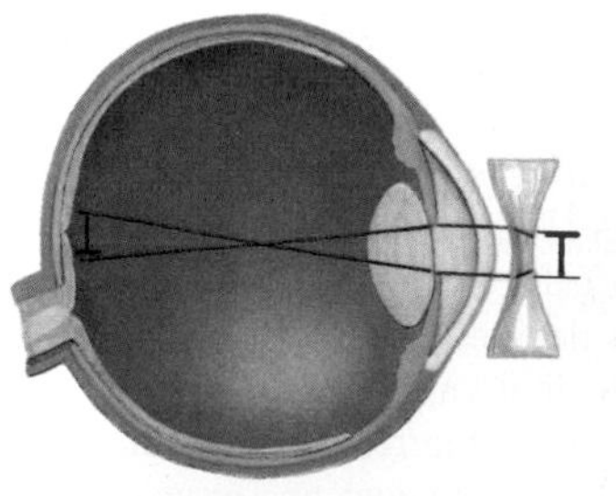

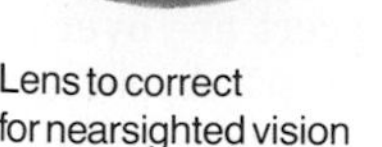

Lens to correct for nearsighted vision

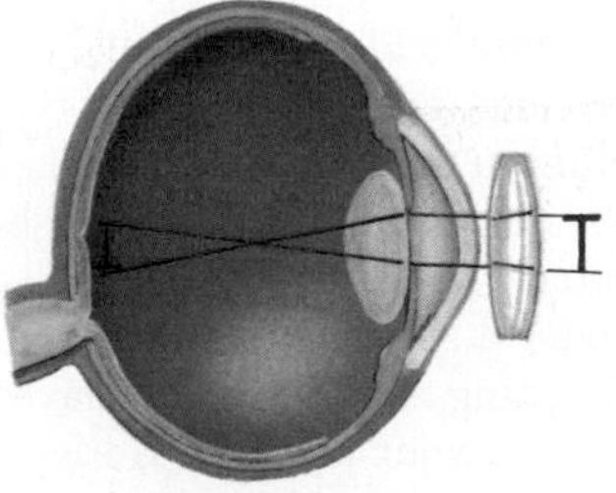

Lens to correct for farsighted vision

Figure 16-11 Lenses bend the light entering the eye and cause it to fall on the retina.

Figure 16-10d shows what happens within the eye when a person is farsighted. **Farsighted** means being able to see objects clearly far away but not close up. When the path of light enters the eye, it meets in back of the retina, instead of on it. Notice in the figure that the farsighted eye is shaped differently than the normal eye. The farsighted eye is shorter from front to back.

How are these kinds of vision problems corrected? They are corrected with lenses people can wear. Figure 16-11 shows how the lenses of glasses or contacts help correct vision problems. The lenses bend the light before it enters the eye. This extra bending allows the light rays to meet on the retina as they do in a normal eye. As a result, objects appear clear and sharp instead of fuzzy or blurry.

Bio Tip

Consumer: Tanning parlors increase the risk of eye cataracts. A cataract is a clouding of the lens. It results in loss of vision and blindness if not treated.

How does wearing glasses correct nearsightedness?

Protecting Against Hearing Loss

Can listening to loud music damage your hearing? The answer to this question is yes. Listening to any kind of loud noise over a long period of time can cause permanent damage to your hearing.

How does listening to loud noises damage hearing? Loud noises damage the inside of the cochlea. The cochlea contains fluid and thousands of hairlike cells. The hairlike cells vibrate as the fluid within the cochlea is set into motion by sound waves. The movement of the hairlike cells starts a message in the auditory nerve leading to the brain. Whenever the ear is exposed to loud noises, some of the hairlike cells become flattened. Once the hairlike cells are flattened, they can no longer send messages to the auditory nerve. If enough hairlike cells are damaged, hearing loss results. Also, the hairlike cells can't repair themselves. Hearing that is damaged this way can't be restored.

STUDY GUIDE 95

STUDY GUIDE — CHAPTER 16

Name ______ Date ______ Class ______

PROBLEMS WITH SENSE ORGANS

In your textbook, read about problems with sense organs in Section 16:3.

1. Examine the diagrams below. Determine what vision problem is shown. In the space provided, name and describe the problem.

Farsighted means being able to see clearly far away but not close up. The path of light meets in back of the retina instead of on it.

Nearsighted means being able to see clearly close up but not far away. The path of light meets in front of the retina, instead of on it.

2. How are these problems corrected? They are corrected with special lenses that cause the path of light to meet on the retina.
3. What are two causes of deafness or hearing loss and how is each one treated?
   a. The nerve cells in the cochlea do not work. An electronic ear can help.
   b. The ear bones cannot move. The stirrup is removed and replaced with a small piece of plastic that vibrates properly.

STUDY GUIDE 96

STUDY GUIDE — CHAPTER 16

Name ______ Date ______ Class ______

VOCABULARY

Review the new words used in Chapter 16 of your textbook. Then, use the terms below to fill in the blanks in the sentences that follow.

auditory nerve	cochlea	eardrum	rods
olfactory nerve	cones	epidermis	sclera
lens muscles	cornea	nearsighted	pupils
vitreous humor	irises	farsighted	retina
optic nerve	lenses	taste buds	dermis
semicircular canals			

1. The **sclera** is a tough, white covering that protects the eye.
2. Your **taste buds** allow you to taste sweet, salty, bitter, and sour.
3. The **olfactory nerve** carries messages from neurons in the nose to the brain.
4. When you focus on distant objects, your **lens muscles** change the shape of the **lenses** in your eyes.
5. When sound waves enter your ear, they cause the **eardrum** to vibrate.
6. The **vitreous humor** keeps your eyes round in shape.
7. The skin is made of two layers: the **dermis** and the **epidermis**.
8. The **retina** is made of two kinds of neurons: **rods** that detect motion and **cones** which detect color.
9. The **cornea** is a clear covering over the pupil.
10. The **semicircular canals** in your inner ear help you keep your balance.
11. Your **irises** determine the color of your eyes.
12. A **farsighted** person might need to wear glasses to read a book. A **nearsighted** person might need to wear glasses to drive a car.
13. The nerve cells in the **cochlea** send messages to the **auditory nerve**, which carries messages of sound to the brain.
14. When you enter a dark room, your **pupils** become larger.
15. The **optic nerve** carries messages from the retina to the brain.

2 TEACH

MOTIVATION/Demonstration

Borrow an earmuff type hearing protection device from a student's parent. Allow the class to try it on with loud music playing. This will help them better understand the degree of protection given by these devices.

Concept Development

▶ Figure 16-10 may require some added explanation. If a person can see a 1 cm high letter clearly at 20 feet, their vision is said to be 20/20. If the smallest letter a person can see clearly at 20 feet is 1.3 cm high, their vision is said to be 20/30.

▶ Obtain a tape recorder and play some music for the students at a normal sound level. Slowly increase the volume. Ask students to raise their hand when the volume becomes irritating to them.

Connection: Consumer

Have students compare the magnifications of binoculars offered for sale in mail order catalogues or stores. What are the ranges of powers recommended for bird watching and opera viewing?

Independent Practice

Study Guide/*Teacher Resource Package,* pp. 95-96. Use the Study Guide worksheets shown at the bottom of this page for independent practice.

Guided Practice

Have students write down their answers to the margin question: Wearing glasses bends the light entering the eye and allows the light rays to meet on the retina.

TEACH

Concept Development

▶ Not all hearing takes place because of sound waves entering the outer ear. Sound conduction by the skull also plays an important role. Sound bypasses the middle ear and stimulates the cochlea. The ability to hear sound conducted by bone is used to determine if a person is suffering from nerve deafness or middle ear deafness.

Guided Practice

Have students write down their answers to the margin questions: A sound of 85 decibels or more can damage hearing. An electronic ear has a wire that is placed inside the cochlea and carries messages from outside the ear to the cochlea.

How loud a sound can damage your hearing?

How loud must a sound be before it damages your hearing? Table 16-1 shows the loudness of different sounds that you hear frequently. The loudness of sound is measured in units called decibels (DEH suh bulz). The softer a sound is, the lower its decibel value will be. The louder a sound is, the higher its decibel value will be. Listening to sounds that have decibel values over 85 can damage your hearing. Notice in the table that the decibel values for a motorcycle, jet, and rock concert are over 85.

What can be done to prevent hearing loss? Avoiding the sources of loud noises is one way. If loud noises can't be avoided, then hearing protection can be used. People who work at airports wear earmuffs to protect their hearing. People who work in factories often use earplugs made of plastic or foam rubber. It is important to prevent hearing loss. Once the hearing has been damaged by loud noises, it can't be restored.

TABLE 16–1. DECIBEL VALUES OF COMMON SOUNDS

20	rustling of leaves	
30	whisper	
50	light traffic	
60	air conditioner	
70	loud talk	
	television	
	vacuum cleaner	
85	food blender	
90	motorcycle at 10 meters	
	shouting	
	power mower	
100	snowmobile	
	jet overhead	hearing damage may result
110	portable radio with headphones	
120	thunderclap	
	rock concert	painful to the ear
140	jet nearby	
160	shotgun	

Correcting Hearing Problems

There are many causes of deafness or hearing loss. Sometimes the problem lies with the auditory nerve or cochlea. Hearing problems can happen if the middle ear bones don't move smoothly. Let's look at some new ways of treating these problems.

A person may become deaf if the nerve cells in the cochlea don't work. An electronic ear can help, Figure 16-12. The electronic ear has a long wire that is placed inside the cochlea. The wire carries messages from outside

OPTIONS

Challenge: Have students research how a hearing aid works. A hearing aid will help with conduction deafness or hearing loss due to the inability of the bones to vibrate and conduct sounds to the cochlea. In contrast, an implant helps with nerve deafness.

Application/*Teacher Resource Package*, p. 16. Use the Application worksheet shown here to help students learn about skin disorders.

APPLICATION 16

APPLICATION: HEALTH — CHAPTER 16

Name ______ Date ______ Class ______

SKIN DISORDERS — *Use after Section 16:3.*

The largest organ of the human body is the skin. Many disorders affect the skin.

Use a dictionary or encyclopedia to find the answers to the following questions.

1. The disorders listed below are caused by infections. For each disorder, tell whether it is caused by a bacteria, virus, fungus, insect, or insect-like creature. Then, describe the symptoms.

   Boils **bacteria; painful red lumps with pus**

   Warts **virus; small, hard lump (Virus gets into skin cells and causes them to multiply rapidly.)**

   Ringworm **fungus; patches of ring-shaped, red, itchy, scaly skin**

   Impetigo **bacteria; thin blisters that burst and form crusts (Occurs mainly in children.)**

   Athlete's foot **fungus; cracks form in the skin between the toes, peeling skin**

2. Burns may be caused by heat from fire, chemicals, electric shock, or overexposure to sunlight or other radiation. Describe the symptoms of the three types of burns below.

   First-degree burns **skin turns red; damages only the epidermis**

   Second-degree burns **skin blisters; damages epidermis and part of the dermis; may leave scars**

   Third-degree burns **skin blisters and/or turns black; damage to all skin layers; scarring; may require skin grafts; may be life-threatening**

3. Tumors are abnormal growths of cells. Some types of tumors form on the skin. They may be malignant or benign. Define these terms.

   Malignant **cancerous; can spread through the body, causing illness or death**

   Benign **not cancerous; will not spread throughout the body**

4. Describe the symptoms of skin cancer caused by overexposure to the sun. **One or more tumors may form on the skin, often on the face. The tumor may look like a pink lump or an ulcer with a crust. In one kind of skin cancer, a new mole may form or an old mole may become sore, itchy, or crusty. It may enlarge or bleed. The cancer can spread and cause death.**

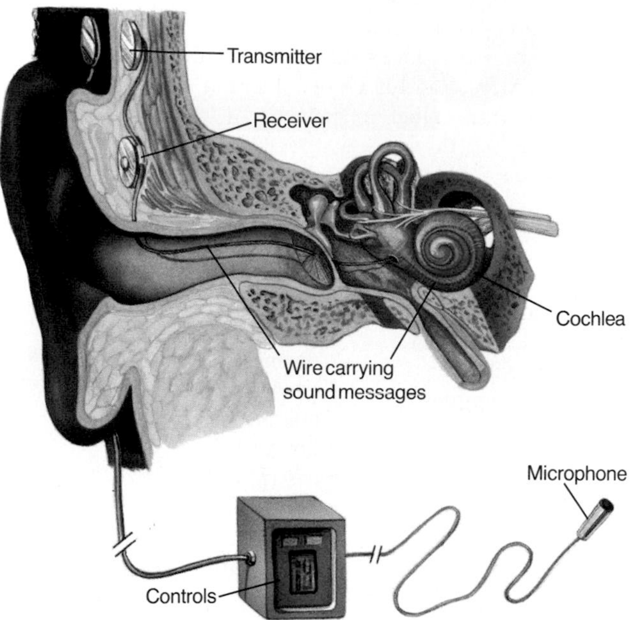

Figure 16-12 An electronic ear helps to restore certain kinds of hearing loss.

the ear to the cochlea. The electronic ear lets people hear sounds that they couldn't hear without it.

Remember that the job of middle ear bones is to move back and forth. Deafness may result if the ear bones can't move. The ear bone that most often gets stuck is the stirrup. When it does, the middle ear membrane can't move, and messages no longer reach the cochlea. To treat this problem, the stirrup is removed during an operation. It is replaced with a small piece of plastic. The plastic stirrup vibrates properly and moves the membrane.

How does an electronic ear work?

Check Your Understanding

11. Explain what causes a person to be nearsighted or farsighted.
12. How does loud noise cause hearing loss?
13. Describe two ways of correcting hearing problems.
14. **Critical Thinking**: How would damage to the optic nerve affect vision?
15. **Biology and Reading**: What system of measurement do eye doctors use?

RETEACHING 49

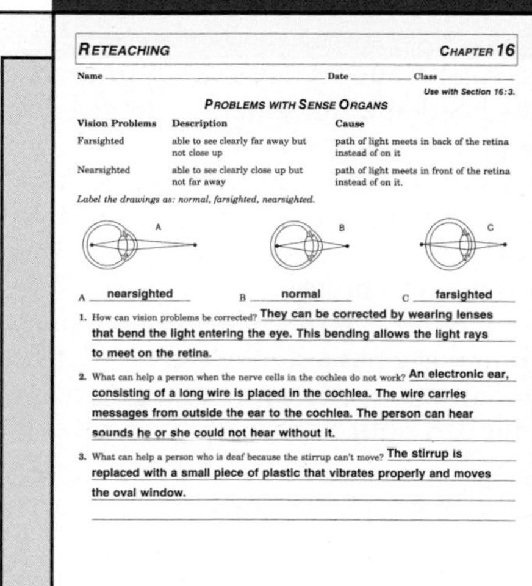

RETEACHING — CHAPTER 16

Name ______ Date ______ Class ______

Use with Section 16:3.

PROBLEMS WITH SENSE ORGANS

Vision Problems	Description	Cause
Farsighted	able to see clearly far away but not close up	path of light meets in back of the retina instead of on it
Nearsighted	able to see clearly close up but not far away	path of light meets in front of the retina instead of on it.

Label the drawings as: normal, farsighted, nearsighted.

A nearsighted B normal C farsighted

1. How can vision problems be corrected? They can be corrected by wearing lenses that bend the light entering the eye. This bending allows the light rays to meet on the retina.
2. What can help a person when the nerve cells in the cochlea do not work? An electronic ear, consisting of a long wire is placed in the cochlea. The wire carries messages from outside the ear to the cochlea. The person can hear sounds he or she could not hear without it.
3. What can help a person who is deaf because the stirrup can't move? The stirrup is replaced with a small piece of plastic that vibrates properly and moves the oval window.

OPTIONS

Enrichment: Ask students to research one of the following questions. Are decibels and hearing range the same thing? How do they differ? What is the hearing range for humans, dogs, dolphins, bats?

Enrichment: Ask students to design a poster that alerts teens to the danger of continuous loud music.

TEACH

Check for Understanding

Have students respond to the first three questions in Check Your Understanding.

Reteach

Reteaching/*Teacher Resource Package,* p. 49. Use this worksheet to give students additional practice with vision problems.

Extension: Assign Critical Thinking, Biology and Reading, or some of the **OPTIONS** available with this lesson.

3 APPLY

Brainstorming

Have students consider the following question: Why might damage to the retina or optic nerve be the most difficult problem to correct?

4 CLOSE

ACTIVITY/Audiovisual

Show the videocassette *Eyes and Ears,* Films for the Humanities and Sciences.

Answers to Check Your Understanding

11. Nearsightedness is caused by an eyeball that is too long. Light focuses in front of the retina. Farsightedness is caused by an eyeball that is too short. Light focuses at the back of the retina.
12. Loud noises damage the inside of the cochlea by flattening the hairlike cells in the cochlea. Once the hairlike cells are flattened, they can't send messages to the auditory nerve.
13. An electronic ear may be used. A stirrup may be replaced with one made of plastic.
14. The person would probably be blind.
15. Doctors who study the eye use standard English measurements.

CHAPTER 16 REVIEW

Summary

Summary statements can be used by students to review the major concepts of this chapter.

Key Science Words

All boldfaced terms from the chapter are listed.

Testing Yourself

Using Words

1. vitreous humor
2. eardrum
3. cochlea
4. olfactory nerve
5. dermis
6. taste bud
7. nearsighted
8. iris
9. cone
10. semicircular canal
11. lens

Finding Main Ideas

12. p. 332; Planaria have two eye spots that detect light and dark. Insects have compound eyes made up of many eyelike parts. Humans have a complex eye that can change for viewing close and distant objects. It can detect colors and motion. Only one lens is present.
13. p. 334; The parts that protect the eye are the eyelid, cornea, and sclera. The iris and pupil adjust the amount of light allowed to enter the eye.
14. p. 347; Causes of deafness can be middle-ear problems, such as immobile bones, or nerve problems involving the inner ear or auditory nerve.
15. p. 343; Nerve cells for pressure and touch are found in the dermis; the nerve cells for pain are found in both the dermis and epidermis.
16. p. 339; Various tastes are a result of combinations of the basic tastes.
17. p. 341; Nerve cells in the cochlea connect to the auditory nerve.
18. pp. 344-345; A nearsighted person sees clearly close up but not far away as a result of an eye that is longer from front to back than a normal eye. A farsighted person sees clearly far away but not close up as a result of an eye that is shorter from front to back than a normal eye.

Using Main Ideas

19. Sound waves cause these parts to vibrate.
20. (a) iris and lens muscle, (b) eyelid, sclera, and cornea, (c) vitreous humor, (d) retina and optic nerve, (e) cornea and lens
21. A person standing 20 feet from an eye chart can see what a person with normal vision can see at 60 feet.
22. Sound is detected by parts on its front legs (ears). Touch is detected by antennae on its head and movement is detected by eyes on its head.
23. The olfactory nerve carries messages from nose to brain, the auditory nerve from cochlea to brain, and the optic nerve from retina to brain.
24. A compound eye has many eyelike parts. A human eye has a single lens.
25. The message is interpreted and messages are flipped right side up.

Chapter 16

Review

Summary

16:1 Observing the Environment

1. Sense organs differ among animals. Planaria have eyespots. Earthworms have light-sensitive skin.
2. Crickets detect sound with their front legs, touch and chemicals with antennae, and light with compound eyes. Snakes smell with their tongues.

16:2 Human Sense Organs

3. The human eye has parts for reducing or increasing the amount of light entering the eye, focusing, and for seeing color or black and white.
4. The tongue detects molecules dissolved in water. It senses sour, salty, sweet, and bitter. The human nose detects molecules or odors in the form of gases. Skin contains nerves that detect pain, pressure, touch, heat, and cold.
5. The human ear detects air molecules in motion. It is divided into an outer, middle, and inner area.

16:3 Problems with Sense Organs

6. Nearsighted and farsighted vision are corrected with glasses or contact lenses to provide 20/20 vision.
7. Loud noise causes hearing loss by damaging the nerve cells in the cochlea.
8. Certain types of deafness can be helped with a plastic stirrup or electronic ear.

Key Science Words

auditory nerve (p. 341)
cochlea (p. 341)
cone (p. 336)
cornea (p. 335)
dermis (p. 343)
eardrum (p. 340)
epidermis (p. 343)
farsighted (p. 345)
iris (p. 334)
lens (p. 335)
lens muscle (p. 335)
nearsighted (p. 344)
olfactory nerve (p. 339)
optic nerve (p. 336)
pupil (p. 334)
retina (p. 335)
rod (p. 336)
sclera (p. 334)
semicircular canals (p. 341)
sense organ (p. 332)
taste bud (p. 339)
vitreous humor (p. 335)

Testing Yourself

Using Words

Choose the word from the list of Key Science Words that best fits the definition.

1. liquid inside the eye
2. membrane at the end of the ear canal
3. liquid-filled chamber of the ear
4. carries messages from the nose to the brain
5. inner layer of the skin
6. detects molecules on the tongue
7. can see clearly close up but not far away
8. adjusts amount of light entering eye
9. nerve cell that detects color
10. helps us keep our balance
11. changes shape for viewing distant and nearby objects

Review

Testing Yourself *continued*

Finding Main Ideas

List the page number where each main idea below is found. Then, explain each main idea.

12. how the eyes of planaria, insects, and humans differ
13. the eye parts that protect the eye and the eye parts that adjust light
14. two causes of deafness
15. layer of skin in which you find many pressure, touch, and pain nerves
16. how you are able to taste more than just four types of taste
17. how the cochlea aids hearing
18. how nearsighted and farsighted vision differ

Using Main Ideas

Answer the questions by referring to the page number after the question.

19. What effect do sound waves have on the eardrum, ear bones, and middle ear membrane? (p. 341)
20. Which eye parts (a) are muscles, (b) protect the eye, (c) give the eye shape, (d) are made of nerves, and (e) bend light? (pp. 334-335)
21. What is meant by 20/60 vision? (p. 344)
22. How does a cricket detect sound, touch, and movement? (p. 333)
23. What is the job and the sense organ associated with the following nerves?
    (a) olfactory (p. 339)
    (b) auditory (p. 341)
    (c) optic (p. 336)
24. How does a compound eye differ from a human eye? (p. 333, pp. 334-336)
25. Describe two jobs of the cerebrum when messages from the eye reach it. (p. 336)

Skill Review

*For more help, refer to the **Skill Handbook,** pages 704-719.*

1. **Interpret diagrams:** Study Figure 16-6. Where on the tongue are the four tastes detected?
2. **Predict:** How would puncturing the eardrum affect the ability to hear?
3. **Observe:** Look at your pupils in dim light, then in bright light. How does the size of the pupil change?
4. **Formulate a model:** Strike a tuning fork with a rubber mallet. Note the sound it makes. Place the tuning fork into a glass of water. What happens to the water? How does this model show what happens within the cochlea?

Finding Out More

Critical Thinking

1. Why is it impossible to transplant the retina or optic nerve? Why is it possible to transplant the cornea?
2. Why is the pupil black?

Applications

1. Design an experiment to test which sense is better developed in most people, taste or smell.
2. Using a large ball and strips of cloth, construct a model of the human eye. Use the cloth to represent the muscles located on the outside of the eye. Determine the job of each muscle pair. Indicate these jobs on your model.

Skill Review

1. Sweet taste is detected on the tip of the tongue, sour on the sides toward the back, bitter on the far back center, and salt on the sides toward the front.
2. Puncturing the eardrum would cause sounds to be distorted, since the eardrum would not be functioning properly. It would not vibrate correctly and that would cause sounds to be perceived differently.
3. The size of the pupil gets larger in dim light, smaller in brighter light. The iris closes partially in order to make the pupil smaller, opens partially to make the pupil larger.
4. The water in the glass will form waves similar to those in a pond when a stone is dropped into it. In the same manner, when a sound wave (vibration) hits the fluid in the cochlea, the liquid sends out waves that are sensed by the nerve cells in the cochlea, which send the message to the auditory nerve.

Finding Out More

Critical Thinking

1. It is impossible to transplant the retina or optic nerve because both are nerve tissue, and nerve tissue, once it is severed, does not regenerate. Corneas, however, can be transplanted because that part of the eye will repair itself.
2. The pupil appears black because light striking the retina is absorbed, not reflected.

Applications

1. Various solutions of different concentrations can be used. Starting with the weakest solution, students could tell at which point they taste or smell the solution.
2. The ball represents the eyeball. Strips of cloth on the top and bottom of the ball would represent the muscles that move the eye upward and downward. Those on the sides would move the eye from side to side.

Chapter Review/*Teacher Resource Package,* pp. 82-83.

Chapter Test/*Teacher Resource Package,* pp. 84-86.

Chapter Test/*Computer Test Bank*

Animal Behavior

PLANNING GUIDE

CONTENT	TEXT FEATURES	TEACHER RESOURCE PACKAGE	OTHER COMPONENTS
(3 days) 17:1 Behavior Steps of Behavior Innate Behavior Learned Behavior	Skill Check: *Understand Science Words,* p. 353 Lab 17-1: *Innate Behavior,* p. 355 Lab 17-2: *Innate and Learned Behavior,* p. 358 Technology: *Blinking Reveals Behavior Secrets,* p. 356 Idea Map, p. 35 Check Your Understanding, p. 357 Mini Lab: *Do Onions Make You Cry?* p. 356	Application: *Driving a Car,* p. 17 Reteaching: *Innate and Learned Behavior,* p. 50 Critical Thinking/Problem Solving: *Where Can You Observe a Circadian Rhythm?* p. 17 Focus: *Animal Behavior,* p. 33 Study Guide: *Behavior,* pp. 97-98 Lab 17-1: *Innate Behavior,* pp. 65-66 Lab 17-2: *Innate and Learned Behavior,* pp. 67-68	**Laboratory Manual:** *What Happens When You Learn Through Trial and Error?* p. 145 Color Transparency 17: *Stimulus and Response*
(3 days) 17:2 Special Behaviors Behaviors for Reproduction Behaviors for Finding Food Protective Behaviors Migration Parental Behavior	Skill Check: *Form Hypotheses,* p. 360 Mini Lab: *How Do Earthworms Behave?* p. 362 Idea Map, p. 364 Check Your Understanding, p. 365	Enrichment: *Sleep Behavior,* p. 18 Reteaching: *Special Types of Behavior,* p. 51 Skill: *Interpret Data,* p. 18 Transparency Master: *Steps of Behavior,* p. 81 Study Guide: *Special Behaviors,* pp. 99-101 Study Guide: *Vocabulary,* p. 102	**Laboratory Manual:** *What Self-protecting Behaviors Do Isopods Show?* p. 141
Chapter Review	Summary Key Science Words Testing Yourself Finding Main Ideas Using Main Ideas Skill Review	Chapter Review, pp. 87-88 Chapter Test, pp. 89-91	**Test Bank**

MATERIALS NEEDED

LAB 17-1, p. 355	LAB 17-2, p. 358	MARGIN FEATURES
microscope glass slide coverslip dropper test tube rack 2 test tubes, small 2 stoppers to fit tubes 2 labels vinegar eels	mirror watch with second hand pencil paper	Skill Check, p. 353 dictionary Mini Lab, p. 362 shoe box black paper live earthworm Mini Lab, p. 356 onion knife

OBJECTIVES

SECTION	OBJECTIVE	OBJECTIVES CORRELATION: CHECK YOUR UNDERSTANDING	CHAPTER REVIEW	TRP CHAPTER REVIEW	TRP CHAPTER TEST
17:1	1. **Explain** the difference between a stimulus and a response.	1	4, 9, 16, 20	1, 3, 9, 17, 29, 33	2, 5, 7, 30, 31, 32, 33, 34, 35
	2. **Explain** innate behavior and give examples.	2, 4	1, 2, 3, 12, 15	18, 20, 23, 24, 32, 37	15, 17, 19, 21, 23, 25, 27, 28, 29
	3. **Describe** how behavior is learned and give examples of learned behavior.	3	1, 3, 18	2, 7, 17, 21, 22, 28	3, 6, 16, 18, 20, 22, 24, 25, 27
17:2	4. **Explain** how courting behaviors help an animal species reproduce.	8	5, 10, 19, 23, 24	5, 11, 15, 30, 34	1, 4, 10, 39, 40, 41
	5. **Describe** how behavior helps an animal find food, shelter, and protection from enemies.	6, 9, 10	7, 8, 14, 22	4, 6, 10, 12, 14, 16, 19, 26, 31	9, 11, 12, 13, 26, 37, 38, 42, 43, 44
	6. **Compare** reproduction in animals that give parental care with reproduction in animals that give no care.	7	6, 11, 21	8, 13, 25	8, 14, 45, 46, 47, 48, 49

Animal Behavior

CHAPTER OVERVIEW

Key Concepts

The chapter develops the concepts of stimulus and response. A distinction is made between innate and learned behavior. Special behaviors that promote survival within the animal kingdom are detailed, with a number of specific examples provided.

Key Science Words

behavior	migration
courting behavior	parental care
innate behavior	pheromone
instinct	social insect
learned behavior	stimulus

Skill Development

In Lab 17-1, students will **predict, separate and control variables, observe,** and **design an experiment** to show vinegar eels' response to gravity. In Lab 17-2, they will **form hypotheses, observe,** and **make and use tables** in a study of innate and learned behavior. In the Skill Check on page 353, students will **understand** the **science word** *innate.* On page 360, they will **form hypotheses** about moth behavior. In the Mini Lab on page 356, students will **infer** if crying from cut onions is learned or innate behavior. On page 362, they will **observe** earthworm protective behavior.

CHAPTER PREVIEW

Chapter Content

Review this outline for Chapter 17 before you read the chapter.

Skills in this Chapter

The skills that you will use in this chapter are listed below.

- In **Lab 17-1,** you will predict, separate and control variables, observe, and design an experiment. In **Lab 17-2,** you will form hypotheses, observe, and make and use tables.
- In the **Skill Checks,** you will understand science words and form hypotheses.
- In the **Mini Labs,** you will infer and observe.

350

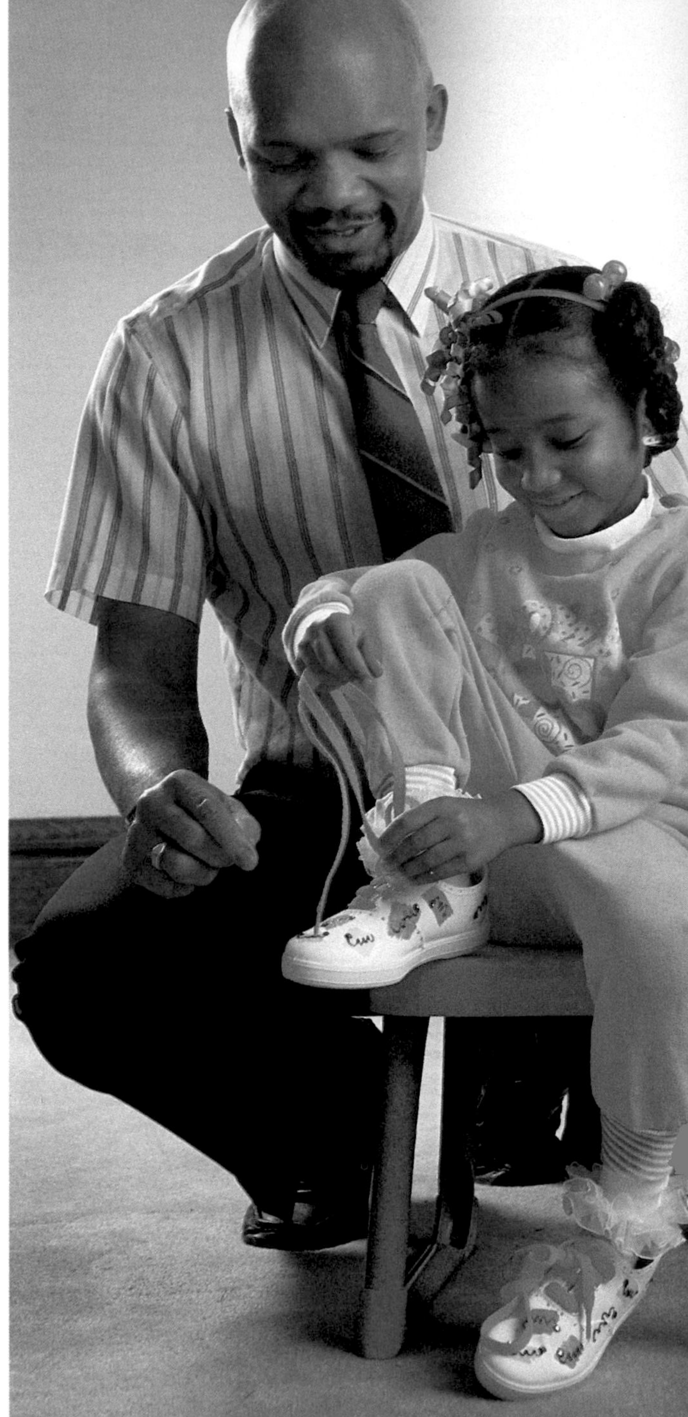

Bridging

Animal behavior is the application of the nervous system in animals. Students will see a correlation between how one acts and the control that the nervous system has over these actions.

Chapter **17**

Animal Behavior

Children must learn how to tie their shoelaces. This skill is learned at home or in school. The child in the photo on the opposite page is being taught to tie her shoelaces. After a lot of practice, she will have learned this skill.

A bird building a nest has never gone to school to learn nest-building. How does the bird shown in the photograph below know how to build a nest without learning about it first? How does learning how to tie shoelaces differ from nest-building? These are some of the questions you will explore in this chapter.

Try This!

How do you learn? Find a book on origami, or paper folding. Follow directions on folding an animal, while you time how long it takes you to do this. Repeat the folding of the same animal several more times. Note how long each new trial takes. Does the length of time change as you practice?

Birds don't have to learn how to build nests.

GETTING STARTED

Using the Photos

The two photos illustrate two kinds of behavior—learned and innate. Have students brainstorm other behaviors that they think belong to one or the other category. Another example of learned behavior you might wish to demonstrate is the tying of a bowtie. Swallowing and salivating are two more examples of innate behavior you might discuss.

MOTIVATION/Try This!

How do you learn? Students will **observe** that the time it takes to repeat the folding process should decrease as the task is repeated and learned. Locate library books that deal with origami for the paper folding.

Chapter Preview

Have students study the chapter outline before they begin to read the chapter. They should note the overall organization of the chapter, that the general nature of behavior is covered first. Next, specific types of behaviors seen in the animal kingdom are covered.

Misconception

Ask students to describe any animal behavior and they will typically describe it in human terms using such words as *pain, emotions,* and *desire.* We have a tendency to relate all animal behavior in terms of human reactions. We do this for all animals, simple or complex. Caution students not to think of animal behavior in terms of how we see it.

17:1 Behavior

PREPARATION

Materials Needed

Make copies of the Focus, Critical Thinking/Problem Solving, Study Guide, Application, Reteaching, and Lab worksheets in the *Teacher Resource Package.*

▶ Order vinegar eels (*Turbatrix aceti*) from a biological supply house for Lab 17-1.

▶ Obtain mirrors from your physics teacher or alert students to bring them to class for Lab 17–2.

▶ Obtain onions for the Mini Lab.

Key Science Words

behavior
stimulus
innate behavior
instinct
learned behavior

Process Skills

In the Mini Lab, students will infer. In Lab 17–1, they will predict, separate and control variables, observe and design an experiment. In Lab 17–2, they will form hypotheses, observe, and make and use tables. In the Skill Check, they will understand science words.

1 FOCUS

▶ The objectives are listed on the student page. Remind students to preview these objectives as a guide to this numbered section.

ACTIVITY/Demonstration

Bang a textbook on the desk without warning the students. Discuss their reaction to the noise. Is this something we learned to do? Ask if a newborn child would be startled by the same noise.

Focus/*Teacher Resource Package,* p. 33. Use the Focus transparency shown at the bottom of this page as an introduction to animal behavior.

Objectives

1. **Explain** the difference between a stimulus and a response.
2. **Explain** innate behavior and give examples.
3. **Describe** how behavior is learned and give examples of learned behavior.

Key Science Words

behavior
stimulus
innate behavior
instinct
learned behavior

17:1 Behavior

How do animals know what is happening around them? How do they react to events occurring in their environment? Animals react to changes around them in many different ways. However, they all use their sense organs, nervous systems, and muscles when they react.

Steps of Behavior

Everything that an animal does is part of its behavior. **Behavior** is the way an animal acts. The way an animal acts depends on what is going on around it.

Let's use an example to see how behavior works. The feeding behavior of an owl can be broken down into steps. Follow the steps in Figure 17-1 as you read.

1. The owl sees a mouse on the ground.
2. Messages pass along nerves from the bird's eyes to its brain.
3. The brain sends out new messages along nerve pathways to muscles.
4. Messages arriving at muscles allow the owl to grab the mouse.

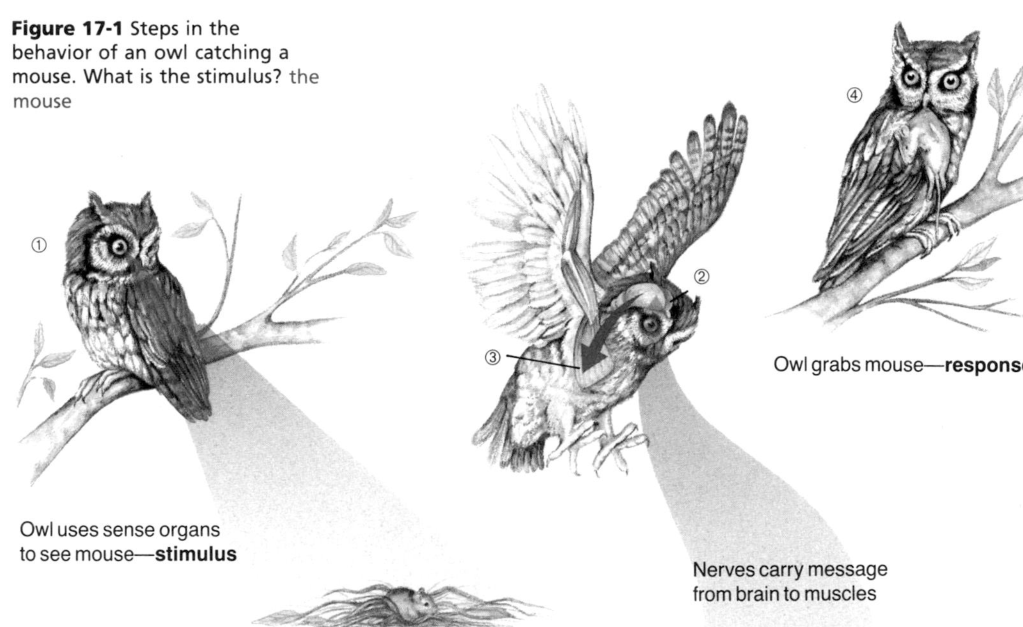
①
②
③
④
Owl uses sense organs to see mouse—**stimulus**
Nerves carry message from brain to muscles
Owl grabs mouse—**response**

Figure 17-1 Steps in the behavior of an owl catching a mouse. What is the stimulus? the mouse

OPTIONS

Science Background

The study of behavior is called ethology. Ethology comes from the Greek word *ethos* meaning character or custom.

Stimulus and Response/*Transparency Package,* number 17. Use color transparency number 17 as you teach the steps of behavior.

FOCUS 33

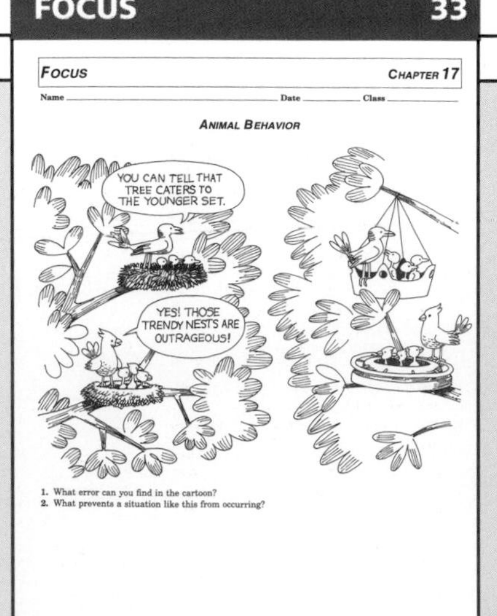

FOCUS CHAPTER 17

Name ______ Date ______ Class ______

ANIMAL BEHAVIOR

YOU CAN TELL THAT TREE CATERS TO THE YOUNGER SET.
YES! THOSE TRENDY NESTS ARE OUTRAGEOUS!

1. What error can you find in the cartoon?
2. What prevents a situation like this from occurring?

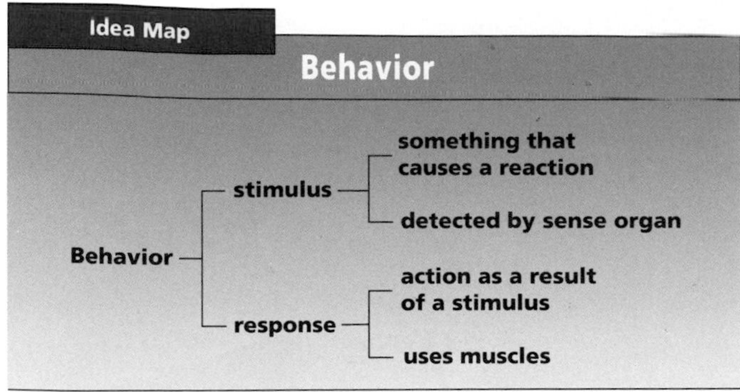

Study Tip: Use this idea map as a study guide to stimulus and response. Can you give an example of a stimulus and its response?

What are the two parts of behavior?

There are two important parts to all behavior. They are stimulus and response. A **stimulus** is something that causes a reaction in an organism. In the owl example, the mouse was the stimulus. Seeing it led to the owl's behavior.

Moving to get the mouse was the owl's response. You read in Chapter 15 that a response is the action of an organism as a result of a change, in this case a stimulus. Notice that the bird's response used muscles. How were they used?

Here is a different example. You are standing in a dark room and you think you are alone. You don't see anyone, but someone else is in the room with you and taps you on the arm. You jump and scream. What was the stimulus in this example? Which sense organs detected the stimulus? What were the responses? Which muscles were used to respond?

Innate Behavior

There are two main types of behavior in animals—innate and learned. When a robin builds a nest, it is using innate behavior. **Innate behavior** is a way of responding that does not require learning. You did not learn to grab for objects, yawn, smile at your mother, or cry as a baby. All of these behaviors are innate. One type of innate behavior is an instinct. An **instinct** is a complex pattern of behavior that an animal is born with. Nest-building and mouse-catching are instincts. They are more complex than simple innate behavior, such as a yawn. In nest-building, for example, the bird must search for the proper material, gather it, and build the nest. The behavior may take several days to complete.

Skill Check

Understand science words: innate. The word part *in* means inside. In your dictionary, find three words with the word part *in* in them. *For more help, refer to the **Skill Handbook,** pages 706-711.*

2 TEACH

MOTIVATION/Brainstorming

Provide students with the following written paragraph: You approach what looks like a friendly dog tied to a leash. The dog snarls and bares its teeth. It begins barking at you and strains at its leash as it tries to reach you. You back away and leave. The dog stops barking.

Ask students:

1. What was the stimulus that started the dog's behavior?
2. What was the dog's response?
3. Did the dog use sense organs to detect the stimulus?

Concept Development

▶ Instinctive behaviors are practiced by an entire species or a large fraction of the population. For example, male fruit flies all vibrate their wings when courting a female.

Using Science Words: Familiarity with the terms *stimulus* and *response* is essential to understanding this chapter. Review the definitions and then give students several examples in which they identify the stimulus and the response.

Idea Map

Have students use the idea map as a study guide to the major concepts of this section.

Guided Practice

Have students write down their answers to the margin question: stimulus and response.

CRITICAL THINKING 17

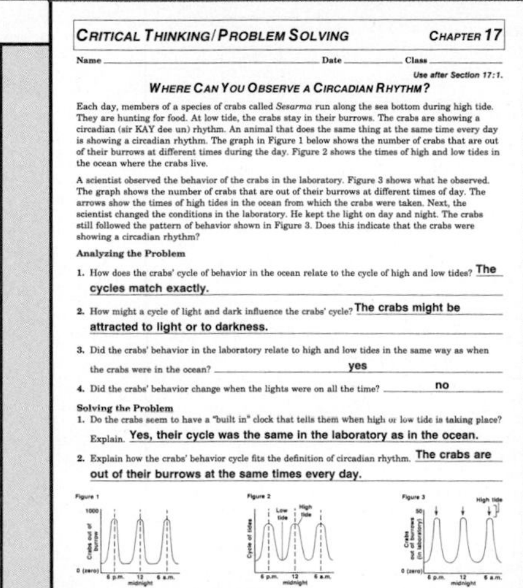

CRITICAL THINKING/PROBLEM SOLVING — CHAPTER 17

Name ______ Date ______ Class ______

Use after Section 17:1.

WHERE CAN YOU OBSERVE A CIRCADIAN RHYTHM?

Each day, members of a species of crabs called *Sesarma* run along the sea bottom during high tide. They are hunting for food. At low tide, the crabs stay in their burrows. The crabs are showing a circadian (sir KAY dee un) rhythm. An animal that does the same thing at the same time every day is showing a circadian rhythm. The graph in Figure 1 below shows the number of crabs that are out of their burrows at different times during the day. Figure 2 shows the times of high and low tides in the ocean where the crabs live.

A scientist observed the behavior of the crabs in the laboratory. Figure 3 shows what he observed. The graph shows the number of crabs that are out of their burrows at different times of day. The arrows show the times of high tides in the ocean from which the crabs were taken. Next, the scientist changed the conditions in the laboratory. He kept the light on day and night. The crabs still followed the pattern of behavior shown in Figure 3. Does this indicate that the crabs were showing a circadian rhythm?

Analyzing the Problem

1. How does the crabs' cycle of behavior in the ocean relate to the cycle of high and low tides? **The cycles match exactly.**
2. How might a cycle of light and dark influence the crabs' cycle? **The crabs might be attracted to light or to darkness.**
3. Did the crabs' behavior in the laboratory relate to high and low tides in the same way as when the crabs were in the ocean? **yes**
4. Did the crabs' behavior change when the lights were on all the time? **no**

Solving the Problem

1. Do the crabs seem to have a "built in" clock that tells them when high or low tide is taking place? Explain. **Yes, their cycle was the same in the laboratory as in the ocean.**
2. Explain how the crabs' behavior cycle fits the definition of circadian rhythm. **The crabs are out of their burrows at the same times every day.**

OPTIONS

Critical Thinking/Problem Solving/ *Teacher Resource Package,* p. 17. Use the worksheet shown here to help students understand circadian rhythms.

TEACH

MOTIVATION/Analogy

Use a tape recorder in class to demonstrate the analogy of innate behavior. Play a short section of a current song. Stop the tape and rewind it. Play the section again. Then ask these questions:

1. (a) Was the song already on the tape when I bought it? (b) Will the same song play each time I start the tape at the same place? (c) Will the tape change if I wait a month? A year?
2. (a) Is a message already in the nervous system when an animal is born? (b) Will the same message be played back with the same response? (c) Does innate behavior ever change?

Independent Practice

Study Guide/*Teacher Resource Package,* pp. 97–98. Use the Study Guide worksheets shown at the bottom of this page for independent practice.

Guided Practice

Have students write down their answers to the margin question: no, innate behavior can't be changed.

MOTIVATION/Brainstorming

Ask students to give examples of other innate behaviors. Some possibilities are: yawning, coughing, sneezing, blinking, crying; growling or snapping in a dog, grooming in a cat.

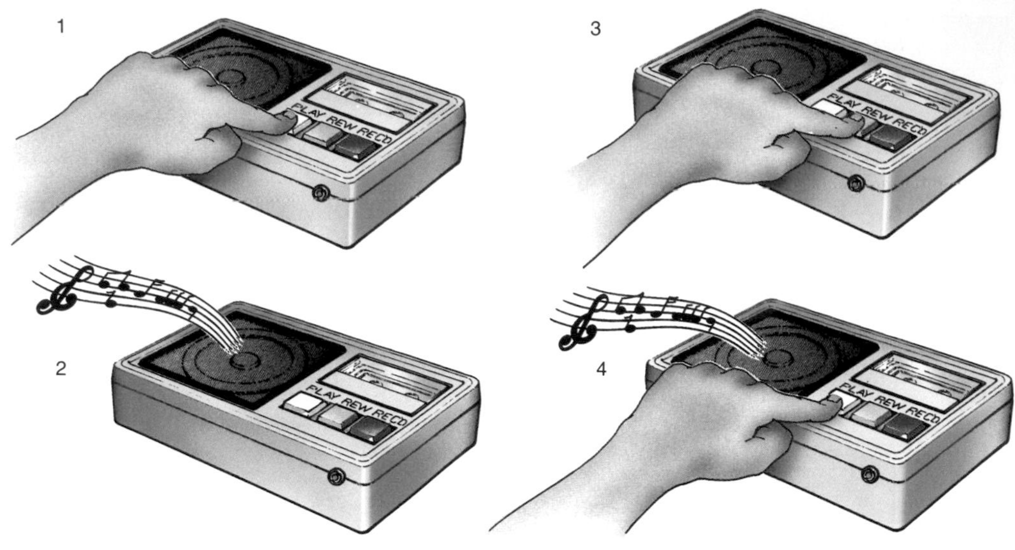

Figure 17-2 Innate behavior can be compared to the playing of a prerecorded tape.

Let's compare innate behavior to running a tape recorder. Follow the steps in Figure 17-2 as you read.
1. You put a tape of your favorite song into a tape recorder. Then you press the play button.
2. The recorder plays the song.
3. You rewind the tape and press play again.
4. The recorder plays the same song as long as you continue to play the same tape.

Innate behavior is similar to playing this pre-recorded tape. Putting the tape into the recorder is like putting the stimulus into the nervous system. The playing song is like the response to the stimulus.

Can innate behavior be changed?

Each time a certain stimulus for an innate behavior occurs, the animal has the same response. Innate behaviors cannot be changed. Wasn't this also the case with our tape recorder? Let's look at a behavior that you have experienced but never had to learn. You swallow, and food goes down your trachea, or windpipe, instead of your esophagus. Your response is to cough. Coughing brings the food up and out of your windpipe. Why is coughing innate behavior? The same thing happens each time. You don't have to think about it and you can't change it.

Instincts, too, are automatic. A robin does not have to think about what kind of nest to build. All robins build the same shape nests, made out of the same materials. They can't change the kind of nest they build.

> **Bio Tip**
>
> **Health:** An innate behavior can be seen in infants when they grasp a rattle. The middle finger always closes on the handle first.

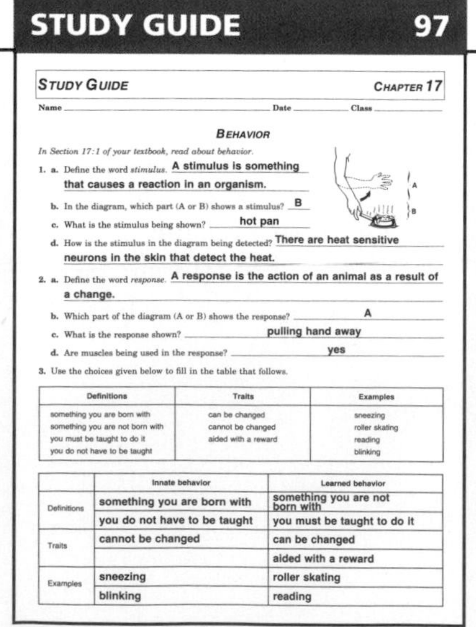

STUDY GUIDE 97

STUDY GUIDE — CHAPTER 17

Name ______ Date ______ Class ______

BEHAVIOR

In Section 17:1 of your textbook, read about behavior.

1. a. Define the word *stimulus.* A stimulus is something that causes a reaction in an organism.
   b. In the diagram, which part (A or B) shows a stimulus? B
   c. What is the stimulus being shown? hot pan
   d. How is the stimulus in the diagram being detected? There are heat sensitive neurons in the skin that detect the heat.
2. a. Define the word *response.* A response is the action of an animal as a result of a change.
   b. Which part of the diagram (A or B) shows the response? A
   c. What is the response shown? pulling hand away
   d. Are muscles being used in the response? yes
3. Use the choices given below to fill in the table that follows.

Definitions	Traits	Examples
something you are born with something you are not born with you must be taught to do it you do not have to be taught	can be changed cannot be changed aided with a reward	sneezing roller skating reading blinking

	Innate behavior	Learned behavior
Definitions	something you are born with	something you are not born with
	you do not have to be taught	you must be taught to do it
Traits	cannot be changed	can be changed
		aided with a reward
Examples	sneezing	roller skating
	blinking	reading

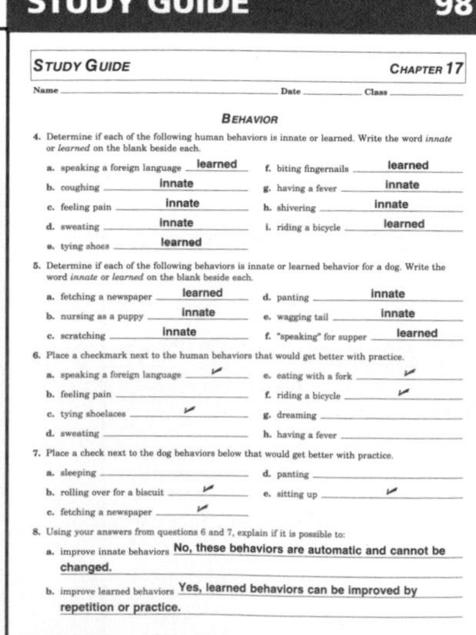

STUDY GUIDE 98

STUDY GUIDE — CHAPTER 17

Name ______ Date ______ Class ______

BEHAVIOR

4. Determine if each of the following human behaviors is innate or learned. Write the word *innate* or *learned* on the blank beside each.
   a. speaking a foreign language learned
   b. coughing innate
   c. feeling pain innate
   d. sweating innate
   e. tying shoes learned
   f. biting fingernails learned
   g. having a fever innate
   h. shivering innate
   i. riding a bicycle learned
5. Determine if each of the following behaviors is innate or learned behavior for a dog. Write the word *innate* or *learned* on the blank beside each.
   a. fetching a newspaper learned
   b. nursing as a puppy innate
   c. scratching innate
   d. panting innate
   e. wagging tail innate
   f. "speaking" for supper learned
6. Place a checkmark next to the human behaviors that would get better with practice.
   a. speaking a foreign language ✓
   b. feeling pain ______
   c. tying shoelaces ✓
   d. sweating ______
   e. eating with a fork ✓
   f. riding a bicycle ✓
   g. dreaming ______
   h. having a fever ______
7. Place a check next to the dog behaviors below that would get better with practice.
   a. sleeping ______
   b. rolling over for a biscuit ✓
   c. fetching a newspaper ✓
   d. panting ______
   e. sitting up ✓
8. Using your answers from questions 6 and 7, explain if it is possible to:
   a. improve innate behaviors No, these behaviors are automatic and cannot be changed.
   b. improve learned behaviors Yes, learned behaviors can be improved by repetition or practice.

Lab 17–1 Innate Behavior

Problem: How do vinegar eels respond to gravity?

Skills

predict, separate and control variables, observe, design an experiment

Materials

microscope	2 test tubes, small
dropper	2 stoppers to fit tubes
glass slide	2 labels
coverslip	test-tube rack
vinegar eels	

Procedure

1. Copy the data table.
2. Use a dropper to place a drop of liquid containing vinegar eels onto a glass slide. Gently add a coverslip.
3. **Observe:** Observe the eels under low power of your microscope. Note their movement.
4. Draw several eels in the circle in the table.
5. **Predict:** Certain animals move toward gravity, while others move against gravity. Predict whether the vinegar eels will move toward gravity, against gravity, or will show no response to gravity.
6. Fill a small test tube with the liquid containing vinegar eels. Stopper the tube. If there is any air in the tube, remove the stopper and add a few more drops of liquid. Replace the stopper.
7. Fill a second tube half full with the liquid containing vinegar eels. Stopper the tube.
8. Place both tubes in the test-tube rack and label them with your name. Let the tubes stand overnight.
9. The following day, note carefully the location of the vinegar eels in each tube. **NOTE:** *Do not move or touch the tubes.*
10. Record on the tube outlines in the table where most of the eels are found.
11. Return the eels to their original container.

OBSERVATIONS OF VINEGAR EELS	
Vinegar eels, 100X	

Data and Observations

1. Describe the appearance and movement of vinegar eels under the microscope.
2. If vinegar eels move toward gravity, they will be found near the bottom of the test tube. If they move away from gravity, they will be found near the top of the test tube. If they do not show any behavior in response to gravity, they will be found evenly throughout the tube. What type of behavior do vinegar eels show toward gravity?

Analyze and Apply

1. What evidence do you have that the animals are responding to gravity and not to the air at the top of the tube?
2. Is the behavior of vinegar eels in response to gravity innate or learned? Explain.
3. **Apply:** How might vinegar eels benefit from the type of behavior that they show in response to gravity?

Extension

Design an experiment to show the type of behavior vinegar eels might show in response to light and dark.

ANSWERS

Data and Observations

1. Vinegar eels are very small, roundworms that show a jerky movement.
2. They move away from gravity. Most eels will be found near the top of the test tube.

Analyze and Apply

1. Vinegar eels in both tubes showed the same response.
2. The response is innate behavior. It does not change.
3. Food or oxygen might be more plentiful at the top.

Lab 17-1 Innate Behavior

Overview

Students will use vinegar eels (members of the phylum Nematoda, or roundworms) to study the behavior of these animals to gravity.

Objectives: Upon completion of the lab, students will be able to (1) **describe** the appearance of these animals (2) **describe** how one can experimentally study behavior of an animal.

Time Allotment: Setup time 20 minutes, following day 10 minutes

Preparation

Lab 17-1 worksheet/*Teacher Resource Package*, pp. 65-66.

Teaching the Lab

▶ Remind students on the following day to look carefully at the tube to determine where the animals are concentrated. A hand lens or magnifying lens might help in observing the vinegar eels.

▶ **Troubleshooting:** The adding of a viscous liquid (methyl cellulose) to the slide will slow movement of the animals.

Cooperative Learning: Students could work in teams of two to conserve on equipment. For more information, see pp. 22T-23T in the Teacher Guide.

TECHNOLOGY

Blinking Reveals Behavior Secrets

Background

According to scientist John Stern of Washington University, blinking is related to behavior states such as excitement, fatigue, and anxiety.

Discussion

Have students perform the following experiment: Determine the average number of blinks per minute for several students in the class who claim they are not tired. Determine the average number of blinks for several students who claim they are very tired. Is there any difference in the averages of the two groups?

References

Chollar, Susan. "In the Blink of an Eye." *Psychology Today*, Mar. 1988, p. 8.

TEACH

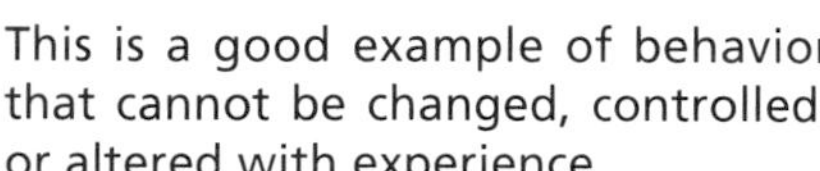

Mini Lab

This is a good example of behavior that cannot be changed, controlled, or altered with experience.

TECHNOLOGY

Blinking Reveals Behavior Secrets

Blinking your eyes is an innate behavior. When you blink your eyes, you are protecting them from dust or smoke, and you are providing moisture for the cornea to prevent it from drying out. You don't have to think about blinking. It happens by itself.

Normally, people blink about 10 to 20 times each minute. Scientists have found that if a person is lying, he or she blinks more often.

Scientists also found that a person who is tired will blink about 30 or 40 times per minute. This information would be helpful in alerting pilots to the fact that they are too tired to be flying airplanes. Scientists could design an instrument that would tell the pilot if his or her blinking has increased beyond the normal rate. Thanks to people who study blinking, flying may be safer in the future.

Airplane pilot

Mini Lab

Do Onions Make You Cry?

Infer: Cut an onion. Hold the cut edge close to your face. Describe what happens. Could you have prevented this behavior? Is this behavior innate or learned? Why? *For more help, refer to the* ***Skill Handbook,*** *pages 706-711.*

Learned Behavior

The second main type of behavior is learned behavior. **Learned behaviors** are behaviors that must be taught. These behaviors must be practiced until a certain stimulus results in a certain response. Behaviors such as tying your shoelaces or writing your name are learned behaviors.

Let's look at how learned behavior compares to recording a tape. Follow the steps in Figure 17-3 as you read.

1. You put a blank tape into a tape recorder. Then you press the play button. You hear nothing.
2. You rewind the tape and record a song.
3. You play back the tape. This time the recorder plays the song you just recorded.

You can continue to record the song until it sounds good to you. You can correct mistakes and record again.

Learned behavior is like recording a tape. There may be no response the first time a stimulus is received. The same kind of thing happens with a blank tape. It plays nothing.

Responding over and over to a stimulus can lead to learned behavior. Recording over and over can lead to a song that sounds good to you. Just as you recorded on the blank tape, the nervous system can "record" a behavior.

OPTIONS

Challenge: Have students relate some behaviors their pets have learned.

Application/*Teacher Resource Package,* p. 17. Use the Application worksheet shown here to show students the importance of learning safety skills for driving a car.

What Happens When You Learn Through Trial and Error?/*Lab Manual,* pp. 145-148. Use this lab as an extension to learning behavior.

APPLICATION 17

APPLICATION: SAFETY — CHAPTER 17

Name ______ Date ______ Class ______

Use after Section 17:1.

LEARNED BEHAVIOR: DRIVING A CAR

You have learned that behaviors that must be taught are called learned behaviors. Many learned behaviors are made up of a series of small steps. To learn to drive a car safely, many behaviors must be learned.

Under each heading below, list the steps that are part of learning to drive. Observe a driver in your family if necessary.

1. To start a car, you would need to learn:
   to have the car in the parking gear
   where to put the key
   how to turn the key in the ignition
2. To make the car move in a straight line at a slow speed, you would also need to learn:
   how to shift gears
   how to work the gas pedal and control your speed
   how to work the brake
   how to hold the steering wheel to make the car go straight
3. To drive on streets and go around corners, you would also need to learn:
   how to stay in your lane
   how to make turns and use your turn signals
   how to read street signs
4. To drive on highways, you would also need to learn:
   how to drive at a high speed
   how to enter a highway on the entrance ramps
   how to shift lanes
5. Many behaviors that involve several steps must be taught in a certain order. Is this true for learning to drive a car? Explain. Yes; a person would have to learn the basic things, like starting a car, before trying something harder, like driving in traffic.

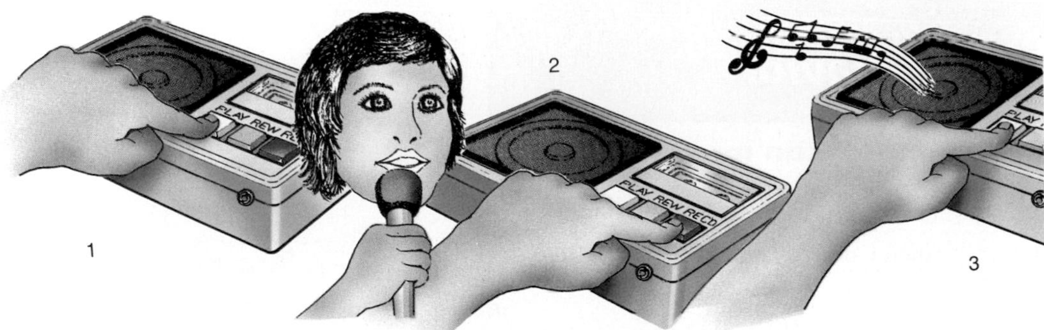

Figure 17-3 Learned behavior can be compared to the recording of a tape.

Suppose you want to teach a dog to raise its paw. When you first tell the dog to raise its paw, nothing happens. Repeat the message over and over and pick up the dog's paw each time. The dog will learn what to do. Then, each time the dog hears the stimulus word, "paw," it will respond the same way. It lifts its paw.

Can learned behavior change? Yes, you can teach a dog to lift its paw and bark at the same time. You can even teach the dog to lift its paw, bark, and then roll over.

Most animals learn new behaviors faster if there is a reward. Animal trainers often use food as a reward when an animal shows the correct behavior. The next time you see dolphins jump through a hoop at an aquarium, look for the reward of fish they receive from their trainer. What do dog trainers give dogs as a reward for correct behaviors?

What helps animals learn faster?

Check Your Understanding

1. What is the difference between stimulus and response? Give an example of each.
2. How does an instinct differ from simple innate behavior?
3. What type of behavior must be practiced?
4. **Critical Thinking:** Why would you expect the behavior of a honeybee to be more complex than that of a sponge?
5. **Biology and Reading:** Read the following sentences. Write the one that summarizes the information in this section.
   a. Behavior is how an animal knows what is happening.
   b. Behavior is everything that an animal does and is made up of unlearned and learned responses.
   c. Behavior is all of the complex learned responses to stimuli by animals that have brains.

RETEACHING 50

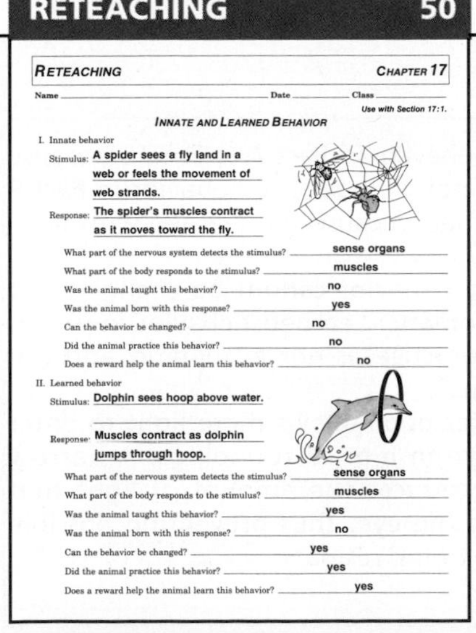

RETEACHING — *CHAPTER 17*

Name ______ Date ______ Class ______

Use with Section 17:1.

INNATE AND LEARNED BEHAVIOR

I. Innate behavior

Stimulus: A spider sees a fly land in a web or feels the movement of web strands.

Response: The spider's muscles contract as it moves toward the fly.

What part of the nervous system detects the stimulus? sense organs
What part of the body responds to the stimulus? muscles
Was the animal taught this behavior? no
Was the animal born with this response? yes
Can the behavior be changed? no
Did the animal practice this behavior? no
Does a reward help the animal learn this behavior? no

II. Learned behavior

Stimulus: Dolphin sees hoop above water.

Response: Muscles contract as dolphin jumps through hoop.

What part of the nervous system detects the stimulus? sense organs
What part of the body responds to the stimulus? muscles
Was the animal taught this behavior? yes
Was the animal born with this response? no
Can the behavior be changed? yes
Did the animal practice this behavior? yes
Does a reward help the animal learn this behavior? yes

TEACH

Guided Practice

Have students write down their answers to the margin question: animals learn faster if there is a reward.

Check for Understanding

Have students respond to the first three questions in Check Your Understanding.

Reteach

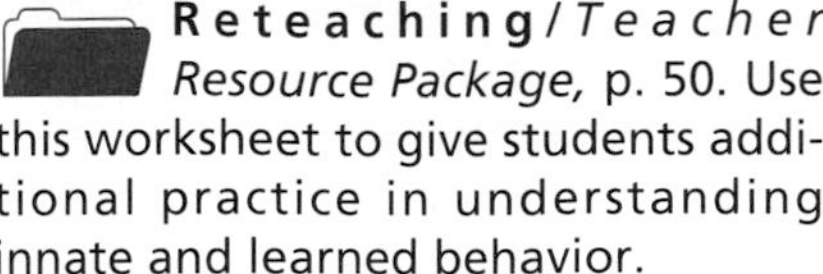

Reteaching/*Teacher Resource Package,* p. 50. Use this worksheet to give students additional practice in understanding innate and learned behavior.

Extension: Assign Critical Thinking, Biology and Reading, or some of the **OPTIONS** available with this lesson.

3 APPLY

Cooperative Learning: Divide the class into small groups. Ask them to name as many behaviors as they can that a baby is innately born with.

4 CLOSE

ACTIVITY/Videocassette

Show the videocassette *Weave and Spin,* Carolina Biological Supply Co.

Answers to Check Your Understanding

1. A stimulus causes a reaction to start or a behavior to begin. A response is the behavior done as a result of the stimulus. Example: stimulus is a bird seeing a worm; response is bird catching the worm.
2. An instinct is a complex pattern of innate behavior.
3. learned behavior
4. A honeybee has a more complex brain and muscular system than a sponge and is capable of both innate and learned behavior.
5. b

Lab 17-2 Behavior

Overview

Students will use change in pupil size as an example of an innate behavior and copying mirror images as an example of learned behavior.

Objectives: Upon completion of the lab, students will be able to (1) **give** pupil size as **an example** for innate human behavior, (2) **recognize** that innate behavior cannot be changed or modified with increasing numbers of trials, (3) **identify** copying a mirror image as a learned behavior that can change.

Time Allotment: 40 minutes

Preparation

Lab 17-2 worksheet/*Teacher Resource Package,* pp. 67-68.

Teaching the Lab

Cooperative Learning: Students can be paired up for the entire experiment. For more information, see pp. 22T-23T in the Teacher Guide.

▶ **Troubleshooting:** Advise students that the change in pupil size will not take very long.

Behavior

Lab 17-2

Problem: How do innate and learned behavior differ?

Skills

form hypotheses, observe, make and use tables

Materials

watch with second hand
pencil and paper
mirror

Procedure

Part A

1. Copy the data table.
2. **Observe:** Look at your eyes in the mirror and note the size of your pupils with the lights on and the lights off.
3. The teacher will turn off the lights. When the lights are turned on, look at the watch. Time how long it takes your pupils to change size. Record your data.
4. Write a **hypothesis** to tell whether the length of time it takes your pupils to change size will increase, decrease, or stay the same with repeated trials.
5. Repeat step 3 four more times.

Part B

1. Write your name on a piece of paper.
2. Position a mirror as shown in Figure B.
3. While looking *only* into the mirror, try to trace your name. Have a partner time you. Record the data in the table.

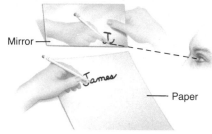

TIME IN SECONDS		
Trial	Pupil Change	Trace Name
1	Time will	Time will
2	not change.	decrease.
3		
4		
5		

A
Iris
Pupil
B
Mirror
Paper

4. Write a **hypothesis** to tell whether the length of time it takes you to trace your name will change with repeated trials.
5. Repeat steps 2 and 3 four more times.

Data and Observations

1. Did the pupils take the same amount of time to change with repeated trials?
2. Did the time needed to trace your name change with repeated trials?

Analyze and Apply

1. **Check your hypotheses:** Are your **hypotheses** supported by your data? Why or why not?
2. Was the behavior in Part A innate or learned? Was the behavior in Part B innate or learned? How do you know?
3. Compare innate and learned behaviors.
4. **Apply:** How does the behavior in Part A help humans with their vision?

Extension

Design an experiment to show if learned behavior is forgotten if it is not practiced.

ANSWERS

Data and Observations

1. The pupils took the same amount of time to change with repeated trials.
2. The time needed to trace a name became shorter with each trial.

Analyze and Apply

1. Answers will vary. Students who hypothesized that the time for Part A would remain the same and the time for Part B would decrease will say that their hypotheses were supported.
2. The behavior in Part A is innate because it did not change. The behavior in Part B is learned because it is learned with practice.
3. Innate behavior cannot be changed and is automatic. Learned behavior improves with practice, is not automatic, and can change.
4. A wider pupil allows more light to enter the eye in dim surroundings. A narrow pupil reduces the amount of light that enters the eye, thus preventing possible injury to the retina.

17:2 Special Behaviors

How do certain behaviors help animals? Some types of behavior help animals find food. Other types may help an animal find a mate. Certain behaviors protect animals from their enemies. Finding a place to live while having young is another type of special behavior.

Objectives

4. **Explain** how courting behaviors help an animal species reproduce.
5. **Describe** how behavior helps an animal find food, shelter, and protection from enemies.
6. **Compare** reproduction in animals that give parental care with reproduction in animals that give no care.

Key Science Words

courting behavior
pheromone
social insects
migration
parental care

Behaviors for Reproduction

Male frogs and crickets make sounds. You may have heard these sounds on a summer night. The males use these sounds to attract females. This behavior brings males and females together for mating. The sounds are the stimulus, and the female responds by finding the male. Does this type of behavior use sense organs or a nervous system? The answer to this question is that both are used. The female must hear the sounds and her brain must send the proper signals to her muscles so she can respond. Is a frog's croaking or a cricket's chirping innate or learned behavior? Why do you think so?

Some animals, such as birds and fish, have complex courting behaviors when they reproduce. **Courting behaviors** are behaviors used by males and females to attract one another for mating. Figure 17-4 shows a peacock with its tail feathers spread. The feather display is a courting behavior. The male uses it to attract the female. The colorful neck flap of certain lizards helps attract females and threaten other males. Figure 17-4 shows the neck flap on an anole lizard.

Bio Tip

Leisure: People enjoy watching fireflies. Males of different species make special flash patterns when they look for mates. A female of the same species flashes back the same signal. He flies down to mate with her. If all species had the same flash, males would mate with the wrong females.

Figure 17-4 Peacocks and anole lizards have colorful courting behavior.

17:2 Special Behaviors

PREPARATION

Materials Needed

Make copies of the Study Guide, Transparency Master, Enrichment, Skill, and Reteaching worksheets in the *Teacher Resource Package*.

▶ Earthworms will be needed for the Mini Lab. Order or obtain locally in bait shops or dig them yourself from soil.

Key Science Words

courting behavior
pheromone
social insect
migration
parental care

Process Skills

In the Mini Lab, students will observe. In the Skill Check, they will form hypotheses.

1 FOCUS

▶ The objectives are listed on the student page. Remind students to preview these objectives as a guide to this numbered section.

ACTIVITY/Brainstorming

What would happen if a newborn child were to fall into deep water? Would it hold its breath and attempt to swim? What would happen if an animal such as a very young cat were placed onto a high ledge? Would it fall off or would it back away from the ledge? Are the behaviors of both the young cat and baby examples of protective behaviors?

Independent Practice

Study Guide/*Teacher Resource Package*, p. 99. Use the Study Guide worksheet shown at the bottom of this page for independent practice.

STUDY GUIDE 99

STUDY GUIDE — CHAPTER 17

Name ______ Date ______ Class ______

SPECIAL BEHAVIORS

In Section 17:2 of your textbook, read about special behaviors that help reproduction.

A (male) B (male) C (female)

1. a. Is frog A making a sound? yes
   b. Is frog B making a sound? no
   c. Is frog C able to make croaking sounds? no
   d. Which frog (A or B) will be able to "mate" with frog C? A
   e. Explain. Its croaking is a reproductive behavior that attracts females.
2. What is a pheromone? a chemical that changes the behavior of animals of the same species
3. A scientist experiments with silk moths. You predict the results and provide a reason why.
   a. Antennae of male moths are removed. The moths are released. Females are 100 meters away.
      Results Males will ignore females.
      Why? They cannot detect the pheromone.
   b. Eyes of female moths are covered. They are then placed in a cage that allows air to enter and leave. Males are released 100 meters away.
      Results Males will fly toward females and attempt to mate.
      Why? Females give off a pheromone that is not dependent on sight.
   c. Antennae of female moths are removed. They are then placed in a cage that allows air to enter and leave. Males are released 100 meters away.
      Results Males will fly toward females and attempt to mate.
      Why? The male can detect the female pheromone with its antennae.
   d. Female moths are placed in an airtight cage. Males are released 100 meters away.
      Results? Males will ignore females.
      Why? They cannot detect the pheromone.

OPTIONS

Science Background

Behaviorists will categorize learned behavior into five main types—habituation, imprinting, classical conditioning, operant conditioning, and insight. This section emphasizes the types of behavior that aid an animal's survival. These examples involve the five types listed above.

2 TEACH

MOTIVATION/Brainstorming

Have students look at the diagrams in Figure 17-5. Assuming this is an example of an innate behavior influenced by a pheromone, have students suggest ways other than removing the antennae that would prove that the male is responding to the specific female pheromone. They may suggest using pheromones from other insects, or using other female species. Ask students what type of control might have been used in this experiment. They should suggest that the male moths should have been tested to see if they would fly to the female when she was not releasing pheromones.

Concept Development

▶ Croaking or chirping is innate. Frogs and crickets are born with this ability. Suggest to students that an animal may inherit certain nerve pathways at birth just as it inherits all other traits.

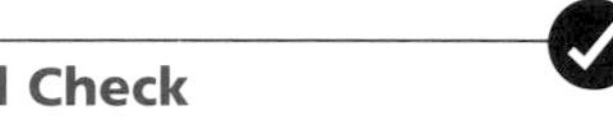

Skill Check

The male moths would fly to the paper with pheromone. They would also fly to where the female moth had been before she was put into the cage.

Guided Practice

Have students write down their answers to the margin question: a chemical that attracts animals of the same species.

What is a pheromone?

Skill Check

Form hypotheses: What would happen to the behavior of the male moths in Figure 17-5 if the pheromone were added to the paper before the female moth was placed in the airtight cage? *For more help, refer to the **Skill Handbook,** pages 704-705.*

Not all male animals make sounds or have displays to attract their mates. Some animals give off chemicals with distinct odors that do the same job. Chemicals that affect the behavior of members of the same species are called **pheromones** (FER uh mohnz).

Many female insects use pheromones to attract mates. One example is the silk moth. The female silk moth attracts the male by giving off a pheromone that is carried by wind currents. Males can detect the odor of the chemical with their antennae from many kilometers away. They respond by flying toward the odor. When the males reach the female, she chooses one male and allows him to mate with her.

How did scientists prove that a chemical attracts the male moth? Find the answer in Figure 17-5. Notice that it doesn't matter whether the males can see the females. They aren't attracted to the females by sight. Males are attracted to the odor of the pheromone, which is given off by the females.

How could you prove that the male senses the chemical with its antennae? You could remove the antennae from the males and note their responses. Scientists did this, and the male moths flew in all different directions. They could not smell the stimulus and find the female.

Figure 17-5 Male moths are attracted to the female's pheromone, as shown in this experiment.

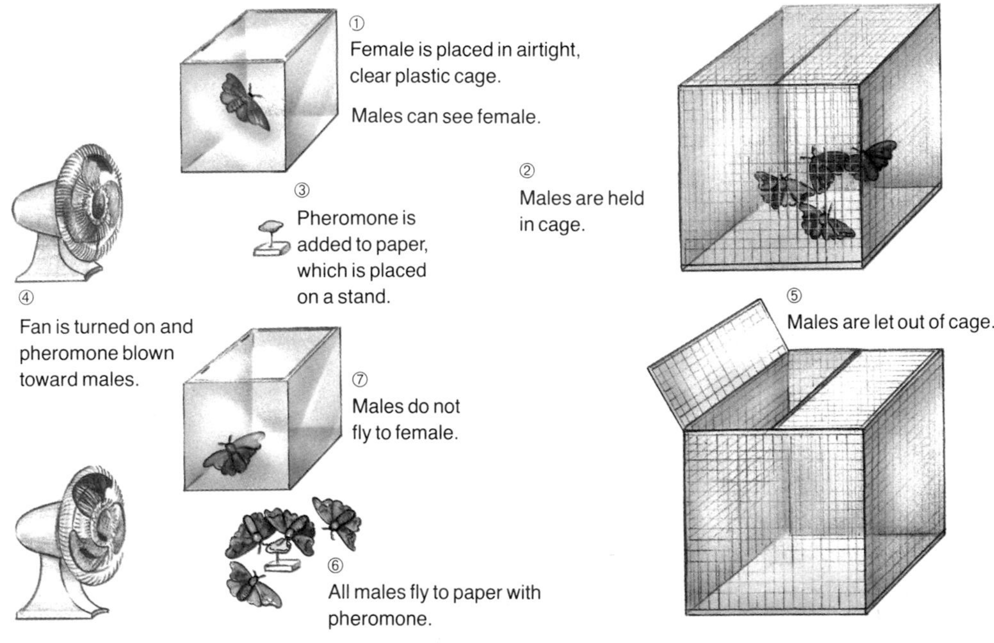

① Female is placed in airtight, clear plastic cage.
Males can see female.
② Males are held in cage.
③ Pheromone is added to paper, which is placed on a stand.
④ Fan is turned on and pheromone blown toward males.
⑤ Males are let out of cage.
⑥ All males fly to paper with pheromone.
⑦ Males do not fly to female.

OPTIONS

Science Background

The female silk moth, *Bombyx* releases a pheromone called bombykol. It is detected by the antennae of the male from distances as far away as one mile. Seventy percent of the male's olfactory receptors detect only this molecule.

Transparency Master/*Teacher Resource Package,* p. 81. Use the Transparency Master shown here to help students understand the steps of behavior.

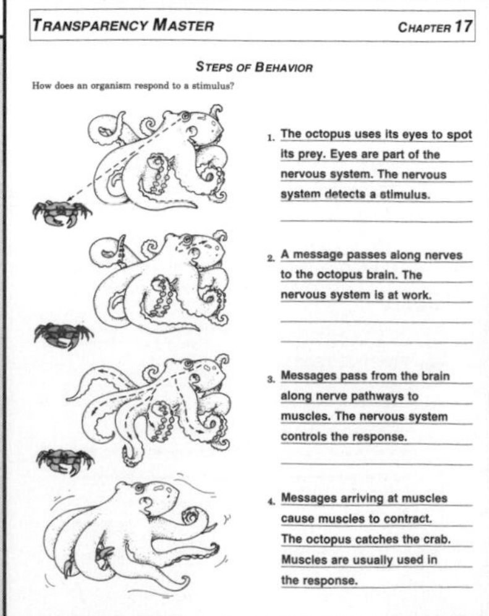

TRANSPARENCY 81

TRANSPARENCY MASTER — CHAPTER 17

STEPS OF BEHAVIOR

How does an organism respond to a stimulus?

1. The octopus uses its eyes to spot its prey. Eyes are part of the nervous system. The nervous system detects a stimulus.
2. A message passes along nerves to the octopus brain. The nervous system is at work.
3. Messages pass from the brain along nerve pathways to muscles. The nervous system controls the response.
4. Messages arriving at muscles cause muscles to contract. The octopus catches the crab. Muscles are usually used in the response.

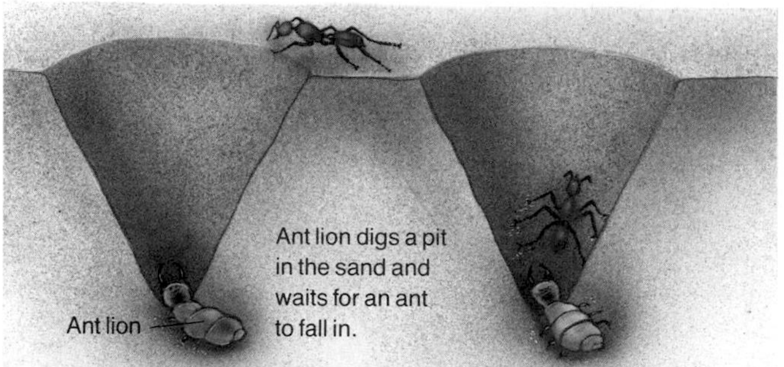

Ant lion digs a pit in the sand and waits for an ant to fall in.
Ant lion

Figure 17-6 An ant lion digs a pit to help in getting food.

Behaviors for Finding Food

How would you like to walk along a beach and fall into a pit? Falling into the pit might not be too bad in itself. What if a hungry animal were waiting for you at the bottom? Things could go downhill very quickly.

Ant lions catch food by building a pit. Figure 17-6 shows how this behavior works. They wait for animals to fall into their pits. When an animal such as an ant falls in, it becomes a meal for the ant lion. Do you think that pit-building is innate or learned? Why do you think so?

Honeybees have complex behavior that helps them find food. They "talk" to one another and tell each other where food is located. The way bees "talk" is explained in Figure 17-7. When bees "talk," they move in a figure eight pattern. The "talking" bee faces the direction of the food when it is in the middle part of the figure eight. How do bees tell one another how far the food is? The "talking" bee wags its abdomen. The number of wags tells the other bees how far the food is from the hive.

Some spiders build webs to trap food. Each species of spider makes a web with a special design, as shown in Figure 17-8. Do you think this behavior is innate or learned?

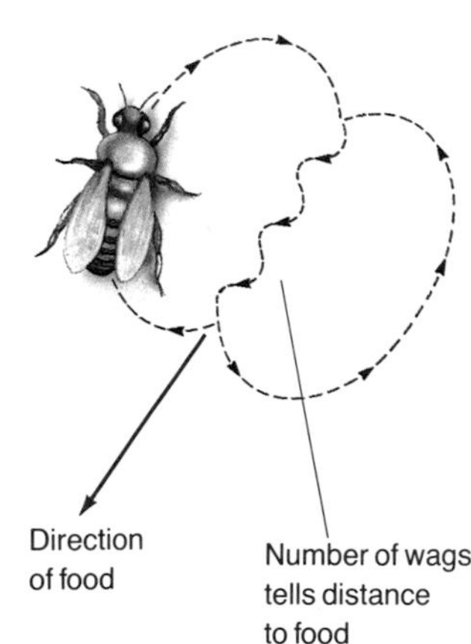

Figure 17-7 Honeybees use special behavior in "talking" to other bees.

Figure 17-8 Spiders use their webs to trap food. Each species of spider builds a web of a unique design.

TEACH

Concept Development

▶ The archer fish, *Toxotes jaculatrix,* spits droplets of water onto insects sitting on twigs that overhang streams and ponds. The droplets of water knock the insects into the water where they become easy prey for the fish.

ACTIVITY/Brainstorming

Ask students to name other animal behaviors that illustrate methods for catching food. They may mention spiders that spin webs, trap door spiders, scorpions, ants that follow trails left by other ants (trails of formic acid).

Independent Practice

Study Guide/*Teacher Resource Package,* p. 100. Use the Study Guide worksheet at the bottom of this page for independent practice.

ACTIVITY/Demonstration

Bring a compass into class. Ask how it works and whether it would be useful in determining the direction to follow to a certain location. Point out that a bee uses a "built-in compass" (its nervous system) to find food location, and is able to communicate the direction to other bees. Also point out that a compass is limited to telling direction. A bee can communicate direction and distance.

ACTIVITY/Project

Ask students to build a maze suitable for a mouse. Have students determine how many trials and the length of time for each trial that it takes for the animal to learn the maze in search of food. Have them report their findingsto the class.

STUDY GUIDE 100

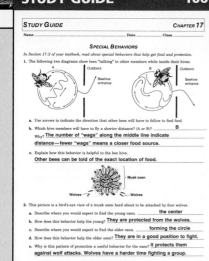

STUDY GUIDE — CHAPTER 17

Name ______ Date ______ Class ______

SPECIAL BEHAVIORS

In Section 17:2 of your textbook, read about special behaviors that help get food and protection.

1. The following two diagrams show bees "talking" to other members while inside their hives.

A — Outdoors — Beehive entrance
B — Outdoors — Beehive entrance

a. Use arrows to indicate the direction that other bees will have to follow to find food.

b. Which hive members will have to fly a shorter distance? (A or B)? **B**
Why? **The number of "wags" along the middle line indicate distance—fewer "wags" means a closer food source.**

c. Explain how this behavior is helpful to the bee hive.
Other bees can be told of the exact location of food.

Musk oxen
Wolves
Wolves

2. This picture is a bird's-eye view of a musk oxen herd about to be attacked by four wolves.

a. Describe where you would expect to find the young oxen. **the center**

b. How does this behavior help the young? **They are protected from the wolves.**

c. Describe where you would expect to find the older oxen. **forming the circle**

d. How does this behavior help the older oxen? **They are in a good position to fight.**

e. Why is this pattern of protection a useful behavior for the oxen? **It protects them against wolf attacks. Wolves have a harder time fighting a group.**

OPTIONS

ACTIVITY/Project

You are to design a short filmstrip that includes both a tape and pictures. Write the script and suggest pictures that could be used to describe any of the special behaviors just studied. (You may want students to work on this project in small groups) Note: You can purchase blank 35 mm filmstrip from Carolina Biological Supply (catalog # 60-4420). Students can draw directly on the film with pencil creating their own filmstrip.

TEACH

Concept Development

▶ Defense behavior in the bombardier beetle consists of spraying its adversary with a chemical from special glands in the abdomen. Reactions that take place at the time of spraying raise the temperature of the chemical to 100°C.

▶ Antipredator, or protection, behaviors are exhibited by many species. Marmosets issue shrill calls to warn other members of the group about possible predators. When pursued by predators, many birds flock together. Fish form schools and antelopes form herds. Herding makes it difficult for the predator to single out one victim.

ACTIVITY/Brainstorming

Most students are familiar with the fact that fish often swim in groups called schools. Ask why this is considered a protective behavior. When a fish swims alone, it is more vulnerable to being caught.

Mini Lab

This Mini Lab will illustrate a protective behavior carried out by earthworms. Ask students to try and analyze why the earthworm avoids bright light. Can they name other animals that tend to do the same thing?

Guided Practice

Have students write down their answers to the margin question: for protection.

Mini Lab

How Do Earthworms Behave?

Observe: Place an earthworm in a box. Cover half the box with black paper. Note if the worm moves toward or away from light. What behavior is this? How does it help a worm? *For more help, refer to the **Skill Handbook**, pages 704-705.*

Why do some animals live in groups?

Protective Behaviors

Musk oxen, such as in Figure 17-9a, are mammals that live in the far north of Alaska and Canada. They are never found living alone. They are always found in groups. Living in a group gives them protection.

Imagine a wolf pack moving toward a herd of musk oxen. These wolves hunt the oxen for food. The oxen see, smell, or hear the wolves. They set up a defense against the wolves by forming a ring, as shown in Figure 17-9b. The adults stand on the outside. The young stay inside the ring. If a battle takes place, the older and larger oxen are in a good position to fight. The wolves can't get to the young inside the ring. The wolves also have a harder time fighting a group than they would a single animal. This type of innate group behavior helps to protect all the animals in the herd.

Many social insects have innate protective behaviors. **Social insects** are insects that live in groups, with each individual doing a certain job. Bees, wasps, ants, and termites are social insects. Bees have workers, drones, and a queen. The queen is the only female in the hive to reproduce. Drones are males. They mate with the queen. Workers are females that can't reproduce. Workers gather food, keep the hive clean, and protect it and the queen.

Ants and termites have an additional job. They have soldiers that help to protect the entire group. If an enemy enters an ant or a termite nest, the soldiers respond. They destroy the enemy by cutting it apart with their sharp jaws. A social insect lives in a group for protection.

Figure 17-9 Musk oxen (a) form a ring (b) to defend their young against wolves.

a

b

OPTIONS

Enrichment/*Teacher Resource Package*, p. 18. Use the Enrichment worksheet shown here to help students understand sleep behavior.

What Self-protecting Behaviors Do Isopods Show?/*Lab Manual*, pp. 141-144. Use this lab as an extension to protective behaviors.

ENRICHMENT 18

ENRICHMENT — CHAPTER 17

Name ______ Date ______ Class ______

SLEEP BEHAVIOR — Use after Section 17:2.

Sleep can be divided into different stages. During stage 1, a person begins to drift off to sleep. Following stage 1, the person drifts into deeper sleep and is harder to wake up as he or she goes from stage 2 to stage 4. The person may toss and turn during these stages of sleep. However, he or she does not dream. Dreaming occurs only during REM sleep, which follows stage 4. During REM sleep, the person does not move. People go through each of the stages of sleep several times each night. The graph shows the pattern of these stages of sleep for a teenager.
Use the graph to answer the questions below.

Awake / REM / Stage 1 / Stage 2 / Stage 3 / Stage 4
105 minutes — 97.5 minutes — 90 minutes — 90 minutes
1 2 3 4 5 6 7 8
Hours of Sleep

1. How long did it take for the person to drift off to sleep? about 7.5 minutes
2. How long did it take for the person to reach stage 4 sleep? about 22 minutes
   How long did the person remain in this stage of sleep? about 75 minutes
3. When did the person first begin dreaming? about 105 minutes after falling asleep
   What happened next? The person woke up from the dream and then fell back to sleep again.
4. What pattern do you see in the order of REM sleep and the other stages of sleep? A person must first pass at least through stages 1-3 and back before REM sleep starts.
5. How many times did the person dream during the night? 4 times How many minutes passed between each dream period? about 90 minutes What was the longest period of dreaming? about 45 minutes How did the length of dreaming change during the night? it increased
6. When did the person spend the most time in stage 4 sleep? at the beginning of the night

a

b

Figure 17-10 The fur seal (a) and the Atlantic golden plover (b) migrate to find a better place to live in winter.

Migration

Many animals move from one place to another. **Migration** is a kind of behavior in which animals move from place to place in response to the season of the year. Many birds, such as the Atlantic golden plover in Figure 17-10b, migrate. The plovers' path is shown in Figure 17-11. Plovers spend spring, summer, and fall in northern Canada. As winter comes, the plovers migrate to South America. They fly a total distance of 10 000 kilometers, more than twice the distance across the United States.

When plovers migrate, they find more food. Food is plentiful during the spring through fall in Canada. As winter arrives, food supplies disappear. The plovers migrate to where there is more food.

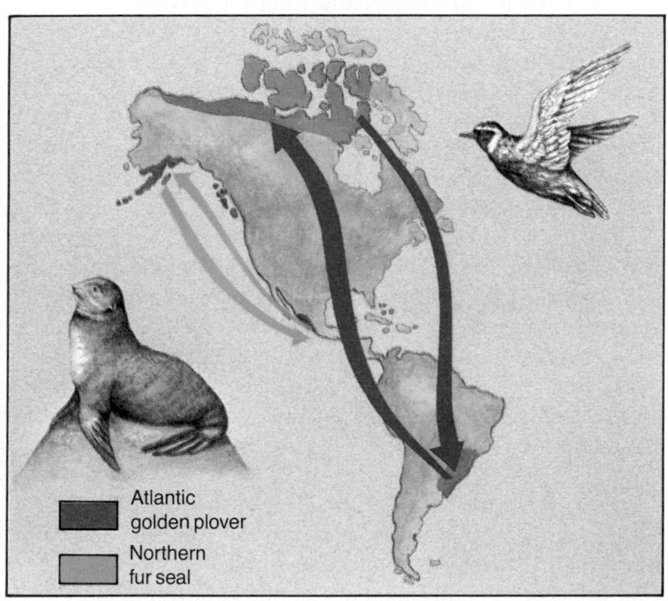

Figure 17-11 Migration routes of the Atlantic golden plover and the Northern fur seal. Why do these animals migrate? to find food and a warmer place

TEACH

Concept Development

▶ Ask where robins go in the winter. Students should realize that these birds migrate to another area (South America). If you live along the Pacific coast, the migration of whales is an annual event. The mechanism these animals use to guide themselves will vary depending on species.

▶ Many birds migrate at night, using the stars to aid in navigation much as the sun is used during the day. Experiments using night migratory birds placed in a planetarium showed this to be true.

▶ Distinguish between migration and homing. Migration occurs seasonally, while homing occurs whenever an animal is moved from its original home.

Connection: Math

The distance between New York and San Francisco is 4800 kilometers, Below is a list of animals and the distance they migrate each year. Calculate how many times these animals could have gone from one coast to the other.

Ruby-throated hummingbird	800 km
Arctic terns	17 600 km
Leatherback turtle	4800 km
Monarch butterfly	2900 km

Independent Practice

Study Guide/*Teacher Resource Package*, p. 102. Use the Study Guide worksheet at the bottom of this page for independent practice.

SKILL 18

SKILL: INTERPRET DATA — **CHAPTER 17**

Name ________ Date ________ Class ________

For more help, refer to the Skill Handbook, pages 704-705. *Use after Section 17:2.*

MIGRATION OF SALMON

When salmon are ready to mate and reproduce, they return from a lake or ocean to the river in which they hatched two years earlier. How do they know when they reach the river from which they hatched? One scientist thought that the fish use their sense of smell to recognize the river. He decided to test this hypothesis.

Six thousand salmon were hatched in large tanks. After three months, the fish were divided equally among three tanks. Chemical A had been added to the water in one tank and chemical B to another tank. The water in the third tank was not treated. The fish in the untreated tank formed the control group. All the fish were marked to show which group they belonged in. When the fish were ready to reproduce, they were released into Lake Michigan. Six small rivers flowed into the lake. Earlier, the scientist had added chemical A to Kewanee River and chemical B to Manitowac River. He had not added chemicals to the other rivers. The scientist and his helpers captured marked salmon from all of the rivers. They counted the number of fish from each river that had the mark of each of the groups in the experiment. The table shows the data they collected.

Number of fish recovered

River	Group A	Group B	Control group
Stony Creek	1	0	47
Annapee River	6	1	78
Kewanee River	1559	20	173
Molash Creek	0	0	24
Manitowac River	4	1311	121
Pigeon River	5	1	204

Interpret the data in the table and answer the questions below.

1. To which river did most of the salmon raised with chemical A return? Kewanee
2. To which river did most of the salmon raised with chemical B return? Manitowac
3. Did the salmon in the control group show a strong preference for a particular river? no
4. Do the data support the hypothesis? Explain why or why not. Yes; almost all the fish raised with chemical A or with chemical B went to the river containing the chemical they were raised with. The controls had no special preference.
5. What type of behavior—learned or innate—did the salmon show? learned

STUDY GUIDE 102

STUDY GUIDE — **CHAPTER 17**

Name ________ Date ________ Class ________

VOCABULARY

Review the new words used in Chapter 17 of your textbook.

Write the words next to their definitions below. Then, find and circle the words in the puzzle. The words are written forwards or backwards in either a horizontal, vertical, or diagonal direction.

1. a chemical that changes the behavior of animals of the same species — pheromone
2. behavior that must be taught — learned behavior
3. movement of animals in response to the season of the year — migration
4. the way an animal acts — behavior
5. adults giving food, protection, and warmth to eggs or young — parental care
6. behavior that does not require learning — innate behavior
7. something that causes an animal to react — stimulus
8. complex pattern of behavior an animal is born with — instinct
9. used by males and females to attract one another — courting behavior
10. lives in a group in which each individual does a certain job — social insect

OPTIONS

Science Background

Ruby-throated hummingbirds migrate 800 km twice a year across the Gulf of Mexico. Arctic terns migrate 35 000 km each year from the Artic Circle to South America. Leatherback turtles migrate 5000 km from French Guiana to Africa. Monarch butterflies migrate 3000 km from southern Canada to Mexico.

Skill/*Teacher Resource Package*, p. 18. Use the Skill worksheet shown here to help students practice interpreting data.

TEACH

Concept Development

▶ Circadian rhythm refers to changes in behavior that are based on a 24-hour clock. Circannual rhythm occurs on a yearly basis. Both types of behavior may be the result of an internal biological clock mechanism.

▶ Whales spend considerable time in the food-rich cold waters of northern oceans. In the fall, they migrate from the cold waters to more temperate regions where calving takes place.

▶ Animals use a variety of navigational devices to find their way. Polarized light is a directional cue that honeybees use. The positions of the stars are also used by many species, including migratory birds.

ACTIVITY/Brainstorming

Find out what students know about homing pigeons and their homing abilities. Discuss possible experiments to find out how pigeons find their way around. What are the various senses that pigeons use? (Pigeons may be sensitive to different orientations of the sun and stars, or they may be influenced by magnetic fields surrounding Earth.)

Idea Map

Have students use the idea map as a study guide to the major concepts of this section.

Independent Practice

Study Guide/*Teacher Resource Package*, p. 101. Use the Study Guide worksheet at the bottom of this page for independent practice.

Study Tip: Use this idea map as a study guide to special behaviors. How many other examples can you give?

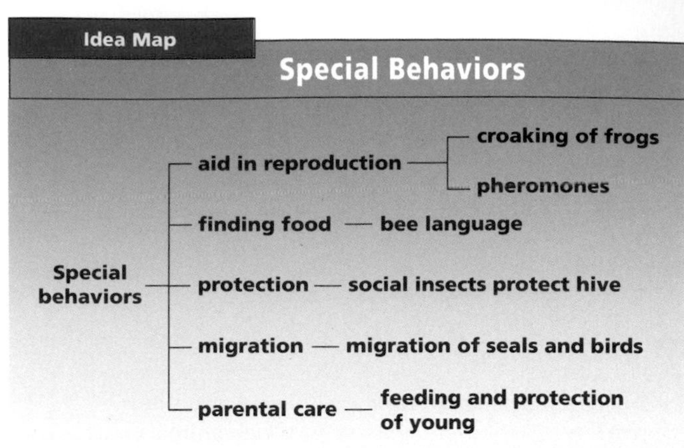

Fur seals, shown in Figure 17-10a, migrate every year. They swim from the coast of Alaska to the coast of Mexico and back again. That's a total distance of about 7000 kilometers each year, the distance between Chicago and England! Their path of migration is also shown in Figure 17-11.

The fur seals' migration helps the animals to reproduce. By moving south, seals find better places to reproduce and care for their young. Seals mate and raise their young on land. It is easier to raise young where it is warm.

How do animals that migrate find their way? This question is of great interest to scientists. Some of the answers can be found in studies made with penguins. Adelie (uh DAY lee) penguins, shown in Figure 17-12, live in the Antarctic. They have nests along the coast, where they live and reproduce. Could these animals find their way back to their nests from miles away?

Scientists moved the penguins far away from their nests and followed them. They found that the penguins used the sun for direction. On sunny days, the penguins moved in a straight line toward their original nests. On cloudy days, the penguins did not move in the correct direction.

Is this type of behavior innate or learned? Here is a clue. Scientists moved baby penguins to a new location. The babies also used the sun to find their way back. They did not have the adults to follow.

How do birds that migrate at night find their way? Scientists found that some birds use the stars for migration. Other birds seem to have built-in "compasses" that tell them the direction of the magnetic north pole.

Figure 17-12 Adelie penguins use the sun's position to find their way.

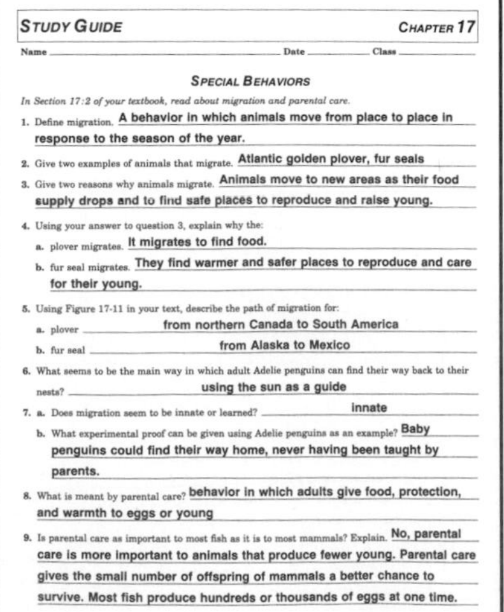

STUDY GUIDE 101

STUDY GUIDE — CHAPTER 17

Name ______ Date ______ Class ______

SPECIAL BEHAVIORS

In Section 17:2 of your textbook, read about migration and parental care.

1. Define migration. A behavior in which animals move from place to place in response to the season of the year.
2. Give two examples of animals that migrate. Atlantic golden plover, fur seals
3. Give two reasons why animals migrate. Animals move to new areas as their food supply drops and to find safe places to reproduce and raise young.
4. Using your answer to question 3, explain why the:
   a. plover migrates. It migrates to find food.
   b. fur seal migrates. They find warmer and safer places to reproduce and care for their young.
5. Using Figure 17-11 in your text, describe the path of migration for:
   a. plover from northern Canada to South America
   b. fur seal from Alaska to Mexico
6. What seems to be the main way in which adult Adelie penguins can find their way back to their nests? using the sun as a guide
7. a. Does migration seem to be innate or learned? innate
   b. What experimental proof can be given using Adelie penguins as an example? Baby penguins could find their way home, never having been taught by parents.
8. What is meant by parental care? behavior in which adults give food, protection, and warmth to eggs or young
9. Is parental care as important to most fish as it is to most mammals? Explain. No, parental care is more important to animals that produce fewer young. Parental care gives the small number of offspring of mammals a better chance to survive. Most fish produce hundreds or thousands of eggs at one time.

Parental Behavior

After you were born, many things had to be done for you. You could not get your own food. You could not find a safe place to live. You could not protect yourself in any way. You would have died if your parents or other adults hadn't taken care of you. Are humans the only animals that care for their young? Most other mammals and birds care for their young. Some fish, amphibians, and reptiles provide protection for their eggs until they hatch.

Parental care is a behavior in which adults give food, protection, and warmth to eggs or young, Figure 17-13. The female parent is often the one to give parental care. The male parent also may protect the eggs or young. Male penguins often care for eggs while the female is feeding.

Parental care becomes more important in animals that produce fewer young. Most fish produce hundreds or thousands of eggs at a time, but do not provide any care at all. Some eggs are eaten, some never hatch, and some survive and grow to adulthood. Large numbers of eggs must be produced to be sure that some will survive.

Animals that provide better parental care can produce fewer young and have them survive. Wolves, squirrels, and birds give lots of parental care to their young. These animals usually have no more than six young at a time. Most of the young live because of the care they receive from their parents.

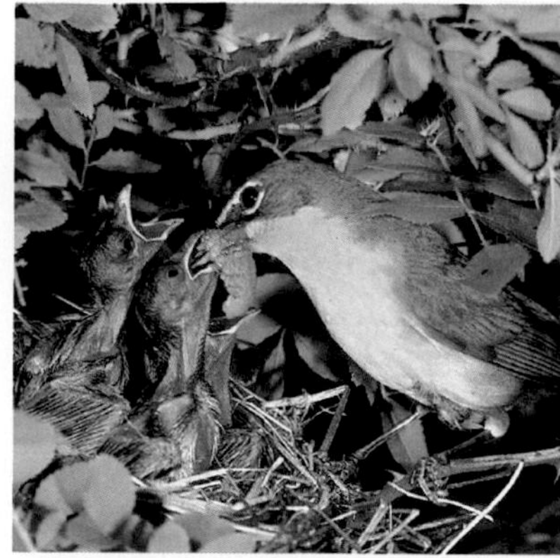

Figure 17-13 Many animals, such as birds, feed and protect their young. What is this kind of behavior called? parental care

Why is parental care important in animals that produce few young?

Check Your Understanding

6. How do crickets and silk moths differ in courting behavior?
7. Describe the path of migration for Atlantic golden plovers, and tell why this behavior helps the animals.
8. Why must an animal that has few young give parental care?
9. **Critical Thinking:** What advantages might a blackbird have by living in a flock of blackbirds rather than by living alone?
10. **Biology and Reading:** In this section you learned that social insects live in groups and have protective behaviors. What word means the opposite of *social* as used in the sentence above? Name an insect that can be described using this word.

TEACH

Guided Practice

Have students write down their answers to the margin question: it is important that all or most of the young survive.

Check for Understanding

Have students respond to the first three questions in Check Your Understanding.

Reteach

Reteaching/*Teacher Resource Package,* p. 51. Use this worksheet to give students additional practice in understanding special types of behavior.

Extension: Assign Critical Thinking, Biology and Reading, or some of the **OPTIONS** available with this lesson.

3 APPLY

Misconception: Many students may not think of human behavior as animal behavior. Show the filmstrip *Experiments in Human Behavior,* Human Relations Media.

4 CLOSE

ACTIVITY/Videocassette

Show the videocassette *Never Cry Wolf,* Walt Disney Studios. Discuss the behaviors seen in the video.

Answers to Check Your Understanding

6. Crickets use sound to attract mates while silk moths use pheromones.
7. Atlantic golden plovers fly from Canada to South America and back again each year. Migration allows them to move to where there is more food in the winter.
8. It must be sure that those offspring survive.
9. It would get protection from the flock and be able to find food more easily.
10. The opposite of social is solitary. *Single, alone, by itself,* or similar terms may also be used. Solitary insects include a fly, butterfly, grasshopper, beetle.

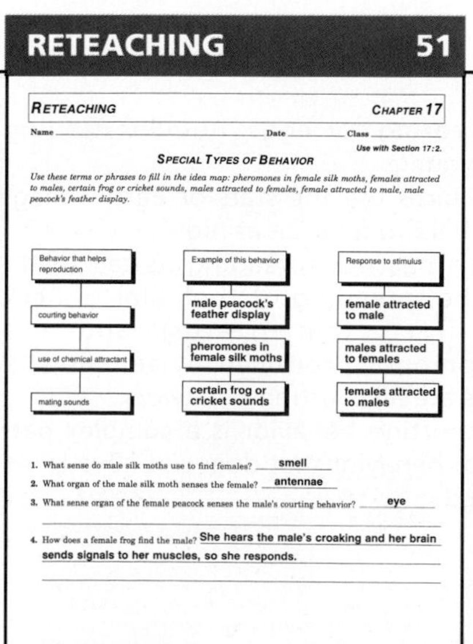

RETEACHING 51

RETEACHING CHAPTER 17

Name ______ Date ______ Class ______

Use with Section 17:2.

SPECIAL TYPES OF BEHAVIOR

Use these terms or phrases to fill in the idea map: pheromones in female silk moths, females attracted to males, certain frog or cricket sounds, males attracted to females, female attracted to male, male peacock's feather display.

Behavior that helps reproduction	Example of this behavior	Response to stimulus
courting behavior	male peacock's feather display	female attracted to male
use of chemical attractant	pheromones in female silk moths	males attracted to females
mating sounds	certain frog or cricket sounds	females attracted to males

1. What sense do male silk moths use to find females? smell
2. What organ of the male silk moth senses the female? antennae
3. What sense organ of the female peacock senses the male's courting behavior? eye
4. How does a female frog find the male? She hears the male's croaking and her brain sends signals to her muscles, so she responds.

CHAPTER 17 REVIEW

Summary

Summary statements can be used by students to review the major concepts of the chapter.

Key Science Words

All boldfaced terms from the chapter are listed.

Testing Yourself

Using Words

1. learned behavior
2. innate behavior
3. behavior
4. instinct
5. courting behavior
6. parental care
7. migration
8. social insect
9. stimulus
10. pheromone

Finding Main Ideas

11. p. 365; Animals that give parental care have fewer young, but more of them survive. Animals that do not give parental care have more young, but fewer of them survive.
12. p. 361; A bee dances for the other bees to tell them where and how far away the food is.
13. p. 356; The first time a stimulus occurs, no response occurs, like a blank tape. Responding over and over to a stimulus can lead to learned behavior that records the behavior on the nervous system, like information is recorded on a tape.
14. pp. 363-364; Migration allows animals to move to areas where there is more food or better breeding sites.
15. p. 354; A prerecorded tape plays the same song every time it is put into a recorder. An innate response produces the same behavior each time the stimulus occurs.
16. p. 353; Sense organs detect the stimulus and muscles perform the behavior response.
17. p. 364; Penguins moved far away from their nests used the sun for direction and found their way back. Baby penguins that did not have the chance to learn from the adults could also find their way back.
18. p. 357; New behaviors are learned faster if there is a reward.

Using Main Ideas

19. If the antennae are removed from the male moths, they cannot find the source of the pheromone.
20. The bird sees the mouse and messages pass along nerves from the bird's eyes to the brain. The brain sends out messages along nerves to the muscles causing the bird to move and catch the mouse.
21. birds caring for eggs; humans feeding their young
22. Some birds use the stars or Earth's magnetic field to migrate at night.
23. A male peacock spreading its tail feathers, the spreading of the colorful neck flap in certain lizards, and the pheromones produced by female silk moths are all courting behaviors.
24. Yes, courting behavior is a complex pattern of behavior that does not have to be learned.

Chapter 17 Review

Summary

17:1 Behavior

1. Behavior is the way an animal acts. All behavior is a response to a stimulus.
2. Innate behavior does not require learning. An animal is born with it. Instincts are complex patterns of innate behavior.
3. Learned behavior must be taught. Animals are not born with it. Learned behavior must be practiced, can be changed, and can be learned more quickly if a reward is given.

17:2 Special Behaviors

4. Courting behavior and response to pheromones are innate behaviors that help reproduction.
5. Many animals use special innate behaviors for catching or finding food. Some animals protect themselves from attack by staying in large groups. Social insects live in groups and have specialized behavior. Animals migrate in response to seasonal changes.
6. Certain animals care for their young. Young animals that receive parental care have a better chance of surviving than those that do not.

Key Science Words

behavior (p. 352)
courting behavior (p. 359)
innate behavior (p. 353)
instinct (p. 353)
learned behavior (p. 356)
migration (p. 363)
parental care (p. 365)
pheromone (p. 360)
social insects (p. 362)
stimulus (p. 353)

Testing Yourself

Using Words

Choose the word from the list of Key Science Words that best fits the definition.

1. behavior that must be taught
2. behavior that does not have to be learned
3. the way an animal acts
4. a complex pattern of responding to a stimulus that is not learned
5. behavior used to attract males or females for mating
6. adults giving food or protection to young
7. moving from place to place in response to the season
8. insects that may have workers, drones, soldiers, and a queen
9. something that causes a reaction
10. chemical that affects the behavior of other members of the same species

Review

Testing Yourself *continued*

Finding Main Ideas

List the page number where each main idea below is found. Then, explain each main idea.

11. how the number of young produced and the number that live compare between animals that give parental care and those that do not
12. how a bee tells others where food is
13. why learned behavior may be compared to recording a tape
14. why animals migrate great distances each year
15. why innate behavior may be compared to playing a prerecorded tape
16. how sense organs and muscles are related to stimulus and response
17. the experimental evidence used to show that penguins use innate behavior to find their nests
18. why a reward might be given when teaching a new behavior

Using Main Ideas

Answer the questions by referring to the page number after the question.

19. What experimental evidence shows that male silk moths use their antennae to detect pheromones? (p. 360)
20. What is the sequence of stimulus and response when a bird sees and catches a mouse? (p. 352)
21. What are two examples of parental care? (p. 365)
22. How do birds find their way while migrating at night? (p. 364)
23. What are three examples of courting behavior in animals? (p. 359)
24. Is courting behavior an instinct? Explain your answer. (p. 353)

Skill Review 

For more help, refer to the ***Skill Handbook,*** *pages 704-719.*

1. **Infer:** Why was pheromone used to attract the male moths in Figure 17-5?
2. **Infer:** How do you know that Adelie penguins use the sun to find the way?
3. **Form hypotheses:** You train goldfish to come to the top of a fish tank to eat when you turn on the light. The next time you feed them, you tap the tank instead of turning on the light. Hypothesize what the fish will do.
4. **Make and use tables:** Make a table with five examples each of human innate and learned behaviors.

Finding Out More

Critical Thinking

1. Decide if the following human baby behaviors are innate or learned: crying, suckling, grasping, crawling, toilet training, yawning, putting on clothes. Explain your answers.
2. Male killer bees are attracted by a pheromone given off by a female. How might the number of bees be reduced?

Applications

1. Design a plan to teach a dog to fetch the newspaper. Include the following terms: stimulus, nervous system, brain, response, sense organs, reward, practice.
2. Make a list of animals that give parental care and those that don't. Find out how many offspring each produces. Relate amount of care to the number and survival rate of offspring.

Skill Review

1. to show that it was the pheromone and not the sight of the female that was the stimulus
2. because they can't find their nests on cloudy days
3. The fish will not come to the top of the tank because the light is their stimulus.
4. Examples may include: innate–coughing, sneezing, yawning, hiccups, jerking your hand back after touching something hot; learned–tying your shoes, reading, writing, solving problems, driving a car

Finding Out More

Critical Thinking

1. crying–innate; suckling–innate; grasping–innate; crawling–learned; toilet training–learned; yawning–innate; putting on clothes–learned. Crying, suckling, grasping and yawning are performed perfectly the first time. Crawling, toilet training, and putting on clothes are all learned because although the initial ability may be innate, the behaviors improve with practice.
2. Traps baited with female pheromones can be placed out to attract male killer bees.

Applications

1. Answers will vary. Accept all suitable answers.
2. Animals that provide more infant care will be more complex than those that provide little care. Those animals that provide little care usually produce more offspring.

 **Chapter Review/***Teacher Resource Package,* pp. 87-88.

 **Chapter Test/***Teacher Resource Package,* pp. 89-91.

Chapter Test/*Computer Test Bank*

Drugs and Behavior

PLANNING GUIDE

CONTENT	TEXT FEATURES	TEACHER RESOURCE PACKAGE	OTHER COMPONENTS
(2 days) 18:1 An Introduction to Drugs What Is a Drug? Obtaining Drugs Legally Reading Drug Labels Speed of Drug Action	Mini Lab: *Are Garlic and Onions Antibodies?* p. 371 Mini Lab: *Can a Drug Package Be Made Childproof?* p. 372 Lab 18-1: *Aspirin,* p. 373 Check Your Understanding, p. 375	Reteaching: *Drugs in the Body,* p. 52 Study Guide: *An Introduction to Drugs,* pp. 103-104 Lab 18-1: *Aspirin,* pp. 69-70	**Laboratory Manual:** *How Do Drugs Affect the Ability of Seeds to Grow Into Plants?* p. 153 Color Transparency 18: *Path of a Swallowed Drug*
(2 1/2 days) 18:2 How Drugs Affect Behavior Stimulants Depressants Psychedelic Drugs	Skill Check: *Sequence,* p. 377 Idea Map, p. 379 Check Your Understanding, p. 379	Enrichment: *Sleep Behavior,* p. 18 Reteaching: *How Drugs Work on Neurons,* p. 53 Study Guide: *How Drugs Affect Behavior,* p. 105	
(1 1/2 days) 18:3 Uses of Over-the-Counter Drugs Antihistimines Cough Suppressants Antacids	Skill Check: *Understand Science Words,* p. 380 Mini Lab: *What Determines the Price of a Drug?* p. 381 Check Your Understanding, p. 382	Reteaching: *Over-the-Counter Drugs,* p. 54 Study Guide: *Uses of Over-the-Counter Drugs,* p. 106	**Laboratory Manual:** *Which Antacid Works Best?* p. 149
(2 days) 18:4 Careless Drug Use Drug Misuse and Abuse Cocaine Caffeine and Nicotine Alcohol	Skill Check: *Make and Use Tables,* p. 388 Lab 18-2: *Alcohol,* p. 387 Science and Society: *Steroids,* p. 389 Check Your Understanding, p. 388	Application: *Smoking and Lung Cancer,* p. 18 Reteaching: *Careless Use of Drugs,* p. 55 Critical Thinking/Problem Solving: *How Unsafe is Blood Alcohol Level?* p. 18 Skill: *Classify,* p. 19 Focus: *Attempts to Give Up Smoking,* pp. 35-36 Transparency Master: *Review of Drugs,* p. 85 Study Guide: *Careless Drug Use,* p. 107 Study Guide: *Vocabulary,* p. 108 Lab 18-2: *Alcohol,* pp. 71-72	
Chapter Review	Summary Key Science Words Testing Yourself Finding Main Ideas Using Main Ideas Skill Review	Chapter Review, pp. 92-93 Chapter Test, pp. 94-96 Unit Test, pp. 97-98	**Test Bank**

MATERIALS NEEDED

LAB 18-1, p. 373	LAB 18-2, p. 387	MARGIN FEATURES
4 glass slides 8 dropers wax marking pencil water aspirin solution 6 test solutions of pain killers aspirin-testing solution in dropper bottle	4 glass slides wax marking pencil 8 droppers water alcohol alcohol-testing chemical in dropper bottle 6 test solutions of over-the-counter drugs and household chemicals	Skill Check, p. 377 pencil paper Skill Check, p. 380 dictionary Mini Lab, p. 371 petri dish agar bacteria culture paper disks treated with onion and garlic Mini Lab, p. 372 paper pencil

OBJECTIVES

SECTION	OBJECTIVE	OBJECTIVES CORRELATION			
		CHECK YOUR UNDERSTANDING	CHAPTER REVIEW	TRP CHAPTER REVIEW	TRP CHAPTER TEST
18:1	1. **Compare** prescription and over-the-counter drugs.	2, 4	2, 6, 10, 14	2, 7, 10, 11, 26	10, 12, 26, 27
	2. **Relate** the importance of information listed on drug labels.	3, 5	3, 4, 5	4, 8, 13, 14, 17, 20	1, 4, 7, 19, 43, 44, 45, 46, 47
	3. **Describe** how drugs stop pain.	1	16	3, 12, 14	11, 15
18:2	4. **Describe** the effects of stimulants and depressants on the body.	6, 9, 10	7, 9, 19, 22	16, 18	3, 17, 25, 28, 29, 31, 33
	5. **Discuss** how psychedelic drugs and inhalants affect the body.	7	15, 17, 26	1, 9, 16	14, 30
18:3	6. **Give the function** of antihistimines and cough suppressants.	11	12, 24, 25	25	2, 14, 20, 21
	7. **Explain** the role of antacids in the body.	13	11, 25	22	5, 9, 24
18:4	8. **List** reasons for not using other people's drugs.	16	20, 21, 23	5, 15, 19, 23	8, 16, 18, 23, 31, 32, 33, 34
	9. **Discuss** the problems caused by using caffeine, nicotine, cocaine, and alcohol.	17, 18, 19, 20	1, 8, 13, 18 22	6, 16, 21, 24	6, 13, 15, 22, 35, 36, 37, 38, 39, 40, 41, 42

Drugs and Behavior

CHAPTER OVERVIEW

Key Concepts

This chapter looks at the physiological action of drugs on the human body. Useful consumer information is provided about drug dose, reading drug labels, and common drugs such as antacids and antihistamines. Stimulants, depressants, and commonly abused drugs are also examined.

Key Science Words

antacid
antihistamine
caffeine
cocaine
controlled drug
dependence
depressant
dosage
drug
drug abuse
ethyl alcohol
inhalant
nicotine
overdose
over-the-counter drug
prescription drug
psychedelic drug
side effect
stimulant
symptom

Skill Development

In Lab 18-1, they will **observe, interpret data,** and **experiment** in determining which medicines contain aspirin. In Lab 18-2, they will **observe, interpret data,** and **experiment,** in determining the presence of alcohol in over-the-counter drugs and household items. In the Skill Check on page 377, students will **sequence** the message path from neuron to neuron. On page 380, they will **understand** the **science word** *antihistamine.* In the Skill Check on page 388, they will **make and use tables** to show alcohol slows down body activities. In the Mini Lab on page 371, students will experiment with an antibiotic. On page 372, they will **observe** drug packaging. One page 381, they will infer the cost of drugs.

CHAPTER PREVIEW

Chapter Content

Review this outline for Chapter 18 before you read the chapter.

18:1 An Introduction to Drugs
- What Is a Drug?
- Obtaining Drugs Legally
- Reading Drug Labels
- Speed of Drug Action

18:2 How Drugs Affect Behavior
- Stimulants
- Depressants
- Psychedelic Drugs

18:3 Uses of Over-the-Counter Drugs
- Antihistamines
- Cough Suppressants
- Antacids

18:4 Careless Drug Use
- Drug Misuse and Abuse
- Cocaine
- Caffeine and Nicotine
- Alcohol

Skills in this Chapter

The skills that you will use in this chapter are listed below.

- In **Labs 18-1** and **18-2,** you will observe, interpret data, and experiment.
- In the **Skill Checks,** you will sequence, understand science words, and make and use tables.
- In the **Mini Labs,** you will experiment, observe, and infer.

368

Bridging

Chapter 15 described the synapse as a space between adjoining neurons. A chemical messenger released from one neuron would move across the synapse and stimulate the adjoining neuron, thus completing a pathway for the nervous system. Students will now be taught the fact that stimulants and depressants operate by influencing the chemicals that move across the synapse, thus allowing a drug to either speed up or slow down messages.

Chapter **18**

Drugs and Behavior

The plant in the photo on the opposite page is foxglove, a member of the genus *Digitalis*. The small photo on this page shows several pills. What do the plant and the pills have in common? Foxglove leaves are used to produce a drug called digoxin. Digoxin is used to treat heart failure, a disease that is caused by damaged heart muscle. The digoxin pills in the small photo help to increase the force of the heart contractions so the weakened heart can pump blood to all parts of the body.

Try This!

What drugs have you bought? Prepare a list of all the different types of drugs that you have purchased in a drugstore this past year. Describe why you bought each drug.

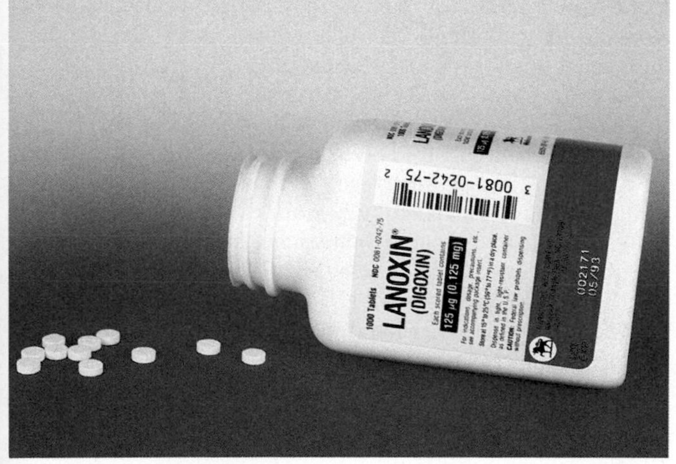

Digoxin tablets

GETTING STARTED

Using the Photos

Use the photos to point out to students that many of our modern medicines originally were derived from parts of plants. Bark from the Peruvian Cinchong tree was probably the most valuable of medical discoveries. The drug quinine extracted from the bark of the tree, is effective against malaria which was widespread disease in the 17th century. You may wish to discuss how the search for new drugs has been one of the major forces in history behind world exploration. Discuss how a country's economy may be controlled by exports of drugs such as tobacco and caffeine.

MOTIVATION/Try This

What drugs have you bought? As a society, we are drug oriented and students will **observe** that there seems to be a legal drug available (over-the-counter) for almost every different ailment as well as for every different behavioral change being sought.

Chapter Preview

Have students study the chapter outline before they begin to read the chapter. They should note the overall organization of the chapter, that the first topic described is a general introduction to drugs. This is followed by a section dealing with how drugs affect behavior. Next, a section deals with the use of over-the-counter drugs. Last, the chapter discusses careless drug use.

Misconception

Students hear and read mainly about illegal drug use. They are not aware of the drug industries' major contribution to our well being and health. Pharmaceutical companies spend alarge portion of their profits on researching and developing drugs to fight as well as to counteract diseases and their symptoms.

18:1 An Introduction to Drugs

PREPARATION

Materials Needed

Make copies of the Study Guide, Lab, and Reteaching worksheets in the *Teacher Resource Package.*

▶ Gather materials needed for Lab 18-1. Prepare aspirin testing solution.

▶ Prepare petri dishes and broth cultures for the Mini Lab.

▶ Obtain garlic and onion bulbs for the Mini Lab

Key Science Words

drug
symptom
controlled drug
prescription drug
over-the-counter drug
side effect
dosage
overdose

Process Skills

In the Mini Lab, students will experiment. In Lab 18-1, they will observe, and interpret data, experiment.

1 FOCUS

▶ The objectives are listed on the student page. Remind students to preview these objectives as a guide to this numbered section.

MOTIVATION/Videocassette

Show the videocassette *Altering Our Living Chemistry,* Human Relations Media.

Objectives

1. **Compare** prescription and over-the-counter drugs.
2. **Relate** the importance of information listed on drug labels.
3. **Describe** how drugs stop pain.

Key Science Words

drug
symptom
controlled drug
prescription drug
over-the-counter drug
side effect
dosage
overdose

18:1 An Introduction to Drugs

Where do most drugs come from? The answer may surprise you. Most drugs come from plants. Aspirin comes from the willow tree. Castor oil comes from the seeds of the castor bean. Marijuana comes from the hemp plant. Some drugs come from fungi. In Chapter 5 you learned that the drug penicillin comes from a fungus called *Penicillium.* Other drugs come from bacteria, and a few come from animals.

What Is a Drug?

What is a drug? A **drug** is a chemical that changes the way a living thing functions when it is taken into the body. Drugs are used for the treatment, cure, and prevention of disease. Drugs may be familiar chemicals such as those found in tea, coffee, or cigarettes. Did you brush your teeth today? If you did, you probably used a drug called fluoride in your toothpaste.

Why do people use drugs? Most drugs are used for medical reasons. These drugs are often called medicines. Doctors use certain drugs to kill organisms that cause diseases. Have you ever had strep throat? This disease is caused by bacteria. Doctors prescribe drugs like penicillin to cure strep throat.

People use other drugs to treat disease symptoms. **Symptoms** are changes that occur in your body as a result of a disease. You may know you have strep throat when your throat is so sore that it hurts to swallow. A sore throat is a symptom. Coughing and rashes are other examples of symptoms. These symptoms can be treated with cough medicines and ointments.

Most drugs are used to help people. If drugs are used incorrectly, however, they can harm people. For this reason, the manufacture and sale of many drugs that might be dangerous if used incorrectly are controlled by law. Drugs that are controlled by law are called **controlled drugs.** Marijuana, cocaine, and tranquilizers are all controlled drugs. Many people use controlled drugs illegally to change their behavior.

If you need a controlled drug for medical reasons, a doctor will direct you to take it, and you will be able to buy it or get it legally from the doctor. If you use a controlled drug without getting it from a doctor or drugstore, you are using the drug illegally.

Figure 18-1 Medicines, and the fluoride in toothpaste, are drugs.

OPTIONS

Science Background

Examples of drugs derived from plants include: pectin from lemon peel and used in antidiarrheal medicines; digitalis from foxglove and used in treating heart disorders; aloe from Aloe vera and used as an ointment for sunburn; castor oil from seeds of castor bean and used as a cathartic.

How Do Drugs Affect the Ability of Seeds to Grow into Young Plants?/*Lab Manual,* pp. 153-156. Use this lab as an extension to the effects of drugs.

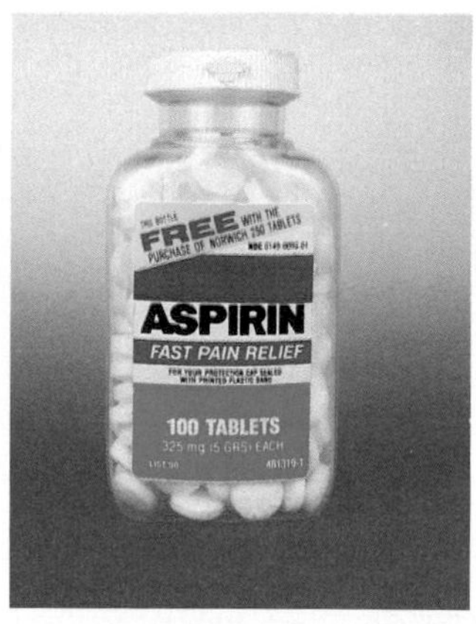

Figure 18-2 Of all the over-the-counter drugs, aspirin is bought most often.

Obtaining Drugs Legally

A legal drug is a drug used legally to treat a disease or its symptoms. There are two ways to obtain drugs legally. One way is with a prescription, and the other way is by buying them over the counter without a prescription.

A **prescription drug** is one that a doctor must tell you to take. The word *prescription* means direction. The doctor directs you to take a certain drug. Drugs obtained this way are legal.

What is a prescription drug?

Why do you need a doctor to tell you which drug to take? Do you know which drug will help your specific illness? Do you know how much of the drug to take? How would you know of any problems that could result from using the drug? You can see why a doctor must prescribe certain drugs for you. Some drugs are harmful if used incorrectly.

Over-the-counter drugs are those that you can buy legally without a prescription. They are also called nonprescription drugs. Figure 18-2 shows the huge selection of over-the-counter drugs in a supermarket. It includes everything from cough medicine to sunburn ointment to aspirin.

Mini Lab

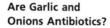

Are Garlic and Onions Antibiotics?

Experiment: Apply bacteria to a petri dish of agar. Add paper disks treated with garlic or onion juice. Use a plain disk as a control. Observe growth after two days. What do you see? *For more help, refer to the* ***Skill Handbook,*** *pages 704-705.*

Reading Drug Labels

What can you learn from a drug label? Most drug labels tell you what the drug can be used for. The label also may have special instructions on what to do before using the drug.

OPTIONS

Science Background

Over-the-counter (OTC) drugs are also called nonprescription drugs. There are about 350 000 OTC products with annual sales of $5 billion. OTC drugs that are subject to abuse include cough syrups, sleeping aids, and appetite suppressants.

ACTIVITY/Challenge

Have students prepare a brief table/chart on one over-the-counter drug of their choice. Their table/chart should include the following information: (a)drug use, (b)any special directions prior to drug use, (c)how often and how much of a drug to take (dosage), (d)any listed warning and (e)any listed cautions.

2 TEACH

MOTIVATION/Story

Relate the discovery of penicillin by Dr. Alexander Fleming in 1928. He noted that a colony of mold appearing by accident upon one of his petri dishes prevented the growth of bacteria near the mold. His observation of this unexpected result led to the discovery of penicillin and all future antibiotics.

Concept Development

▶ The Controlled Substance Act of 1970 established five categories for controlled drugs. The criteria for categorizing drugs are: (1) potential for abuse, (2) pharmacological effects, (3) scientific knowledge regarding the drug, (4) history and patterns of abuse, (5) scope, duration, and significance of abuse, (6) risk to the public health, (7) potential for psychological or physiological dependence, (8) whether the drug is a precursor of a substance already controlled.

▶ Over-the-counter and prescription drugs are not generally covered under the Controlled Substances Act.

Guided Practice

Have students write down their answers to the margin question: a drug that a doctor must tell you to take.

Mini Lab

Purchase sterile agar plates and broth from a supply house or prepare your own. Inoculate broth with *E. Coli* available from supply houses. Onions and garlic juice may be added to paperdiscs. These discs are positioned on inoculated petri dishes. A circle of inhibition will be seen surrounding the disks after 24 hours of incubation.

TEACH

Concept Development

▶ Remind students that the stomach contains an acid and enzymes that could alter the nature of a drug. This is why certain drugs are injected.

ACTIVITY/Demonstration

Make an overhead transparency of some common drug labels to help students locate the information on the label as it is being presented.

Mini Lab

Students should be encouraged to use whatever design they feel is suitable for their product. Ask them to not duplicate those types of tamperproof packaging already available and used.

Guided Practice

Have students write down their answers to the margin question: what the drug can be used for, special instructions for using the drug, special side effects, cautions, dosage.

ACTIVITY/Display

Ask your druggist for a copy of the warnings placed on drugs.

Independent Practice

Study Guide/*Teacher Resource Package*, p. 103. Use the Study Guide worksheet shown at the bottom of this page for independent practice.

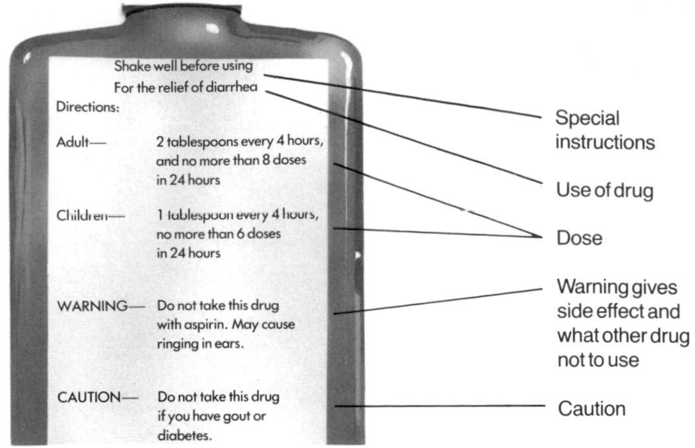
Shake well before using
For the relief of diarrhea
Directions:
Adult— 2 tablespoons every 4 hours, and no more than 8 doses in 24 hours
Children— 1 tablespoon every 4 hours, no more than 6 doses in 24 hours
WARNING— Do not take this drug with aspirin. May cause ringing in ears.
CAUTION— Do not take this drug if you have gout or diabetes.
Special instructions
Use of drug
Dose
Warning gives side effect and what other drug not to use
Caution

Figure 18-3 Warnings, special instructions, and side effects are present on all legal drug labels.

> ### Mini Lab
>
> **Can a Drug Package Be Made Childproof?**
>
> **Observe:** Survey the methods used to make over-the-counter drugs tamperproof and childproof. Design a childproof package for a product that you now use. *For more help, refer to the **Skill Handbook**, pages 704-705.*

Look at the drug label in Figure 18-3. One of the most important parts of a label is the warning. Warnings tell about possible side effects. A **side effect** is a change other than the expected change caused by a drug. This change often is not wanted or desirable. What is the side effect that may take place with use of the drug in Figure 18-3?

Warnings also tell you which foods or other drugs must not be taken with the drug. Mixing drugs with certain other drugs or foods can be dangerous. Mixing drugs can cause an unexpected and unwanted change in the body. For example, some cold medicines help get rid of cold symptoms. If used with certain diet pills, a steep rise in blood pressure, confusion, and nervousness can result.

Drug labels also include cautions. A caution may tell you to keep the drug away from children.

What do drug labels tell you?

Another very important thing a drug label tells you is the dosage. The **dosage** is how much and how often to take a drug. "Take one pill every four hours" is an example of a drug dosage.

Age influences drug dosage. Very young children must receive smaller amounts of a drug than adults. It is important to make sure that a child is not given too much of a drug. Drug dosage also is related to body size. Most drugs taken into the body leave it quickly or are changed into a different form by the body. The kidney, lungs, and liver are three organs that help the body get rid of drugs. For a drug to do its job, a certain amount of it must be in the body for a certain length of time. There must be enough drug taken in to make up for the amount leaving. This amount varies with body size.

OPTIONS

ACTIVITY/Challenge

Ask students to discuss the problem of drug interactions with a druggist and share the information with the class. They should prepare a report, citing specific examples.

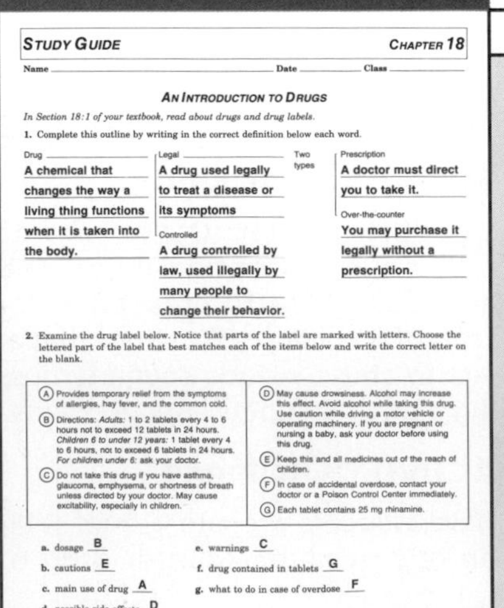

STUDY GUIDE 103

STUDY GUIDE CHAPTER 18

Name ______ Date ______ Class ______

AN INTRODUCTION TO DRUGS

In Section 18:1 of your textbook, read about drugs and drug labels.

1. Complete this outline by writing in the correct definition below each word.

Drug: A chemical that changes the way a living thing functions when it is taken into the body.

Legal: A drug used legally to treat a disease or its symptoms

Two types:
- Prescription: A doctor must direct you to take it.
- Over-the-counter: You may purchase it legally without a prescription.

Controlled: A drug controlled by law, used illegally by many people to change their behavior.

2. Examine the drug label below. Notice that parts of the label are marked with letters. Choose the lettered part of the label that best matches each of the items below and write the correct letter on the blank.

(A) Provides temporary relief from the symptoms of allergies, hay fever, and the common cold.

(B) Directions: *Adults:* 1 to 2 tablets every 4 to 6 hours not to exceed 12 tablets in 24 hours. *Children 6 to under 12 years:* 1 tablet every 4 to 6 hours, not to exceed 6 tablets in 24 hours. *For children under 6:* ask your doctor.

(C) Do not take this drug if you have asthma, glaucoma, emphysema, or shortness of breath unless directed by your doctor. May cause excitability, especially in children.

(D) May cause drowsiness. Alcohol may increase this effect. Avoid alcohol while taking this drug. Use caution while driving a motor vehicle or operating machinery. If you are pregnant or nursing a baby, ask your doctor before using this drug.

(E) Keep this and all medicines out of the reach of children.

(F) In case of accidental overdose, contact your doctor or a Poison Control Center immediately.

(G) Each tablet contains 25 mg rhinamine.

a. dosage B
b. cautions E
c. main use of drug A
d. possible side effects D
e. warnings C
f. drug contained in tablets G
g. what to do in case of overdose F

Lab 18–1 Aspirin

Problem: Which medicines contain aspirin?

Skills

observe, interpret data, experiment

Materials

4 glass slides
wax marking pencil
aspirin-testing chemical, in dropper bottle
6 test solutions of painkillers
8 droppers
water
aspirin solution

Procedure

1. Copy the data table.
2. Use a marking pencil to draw two circles on a glass slide. Label the circles 1 and 2.
3. Add one drop of water to circle 1. Use a clean dropper to add one drop of aspirin solution to circle 2.
4. Add one drop of aspirin-testing chemical to each circle. **CAUTION:** *Aspirin-testing chemical is poisonous and can burn the skin.*
5. **Observe:** Wait one minute. Note the color in each circle. A violet color means that aspirin is present. Record your results.
6. Draw two circles on each of three more glass slides. Label the circles A through F.
7. Record in your data table the name of each medicine being tested.
8. Add a drop of a different test solution to each circle. Use a clean dropper for each solution.
9. Add one drop of aspirin-testing chemical to each circle.
10. Wait one minute. Record the color that appears in each circle. Complete the last column of your data table.
11. Dispose of your solutions and wash your glassware.

Data and Observations

1. Which circles showed a violet color?
2. Which circles did not show a violet color?

CIRCLE	CONTENTS	COLOR WITH TEST CHEMICAL	ASPIRIN PRESENT?
1	water	clear	no
2	aspirin	violet	yes
A	Advil	clear	no
B	Excedrin	clear	no
C	Nuprin	clear	no
D	Bufferin	violet	yes
E	Midol	clear	no
F	Tylenol	clear	no

Analyze and Apply

1. What was the purpose of the slide labeled circle 1 and circle 2?
2. Where should aspirin be listed if it is present in a medicine?
3. Ask your teacher to show you the labels from the medicines tested. Which medicines contain aspirin? Does this agree with your data?
4. **Apply:** Why should aspirin be listed as an ingredient if it is present in a medicine?

Extension

Caffeine is often added to aspirin products because the aspirin works more rapidly if taken with caffeine. Check the labels of aspirin products available at a drugstore to see which products contain caffeine. **Make a table** of the products that contain both drugs and those that contain only aspirin.

ANSWERS

Data and Observations

1. Answers will vary. Bufferin and other aspirin products will show violet color.
2. Answers will vary. Advil, Excedrin, Nuprin, Midol, and Tylenol will not show a violet color.

Analyze and Apply

1. to show that aspirin causes a violet color and that the test chemical does not turn violet without aspirin
2. on the drug label under "ingredients"
3. Answers will vary. Products that gave a positive test will have aspirin in them; products that did not turn violet with the test chemical will not contain aspirin.
4. Some people might want to avoid taking aspirin because they are allergic to it.

Lab 18-1 Aspirin

Overview

Students will test a known aspirin and a known nonaspirin solution with an aspirin-detecting chemical. They will then determine if aspirin is or is not present in a number of painkilling drugs. NOTE: Aspirin-testing chemical is an acid solution. Advise students to use caution and avoid spillage. Rinse with water if spillage occurs on skin or clothing.

Objectives: Upon completion of this lab, students will be able to: (1) **determine** how to test for the presence or absence of aspirin in a drug, (2) **test** a variety of painkilling drugs for the presence of aspirin.

Time Allotment: 30 minutes

Preparation

Lab 18-1 worksheet/*Teacher Resource Package,* pp. 69-70.

▶ The aspirin-testing chemical has a shelf life of more than one year.

▶ To make the aspirin solution, dissolve one aspirin tablet in 50 mL of warm water.

▶ To make the aspirin-detecting solution, add 2 g ferric nitrate nonahydrate, $Fe(NO_3)_3 \bullet 9H_2O$, to 50 mL water. Then add 1 mL concentrated nitric acid. **CAUTION:** *Nitric acid is very corrosive.*

▶ **Alternate Materials:** Use different painkilling drugs if available.

Teaching the Lab

▶ Keep the boxes and bottles of the pain killers. The students may then compare labels and lab results.

▶ **Troubleshooting:** (a) Placing aspirin-detecting solution in marked dropping bottles will reduce chances for spillage. (b) Placing aspirin solutions in marked dropping bottles will reduce spillage accidents and will reduce contamination and errors that result from mixing up clean and used droppers.

▶ Use fresh solutions of drugs. Advil may give a false positive.

▶ Pretest the aspirin-detecting solution before class.

TEACH

ACTIVITY/Demonstration

A demonstration can be done with a funnel to illustrate proper dose and overdose. Pour water into a funnel at such a rate that as much water enters as leaves the funnel. This corresponds to the proper dose. To demonstrate an overdose, pour water more rapidly than it flows out, so that it eventually spills over the edge of the funnel.

Guided Practice

Have students prepare an idea map that compares the two ways of taking drugs, swallowing and injection.

Independent Practice

Study Guide/*Teacher Resource Package*, p. 104. Use the Study Guide worksheet shown at the bottom of this page for independent practice.

ACTIVITY/Brainstorming

Ask your students how a drug is able to move from the blood to the nervous system. Drugs can diffuse from cell to cell, eventually diffusing into nerve cells.

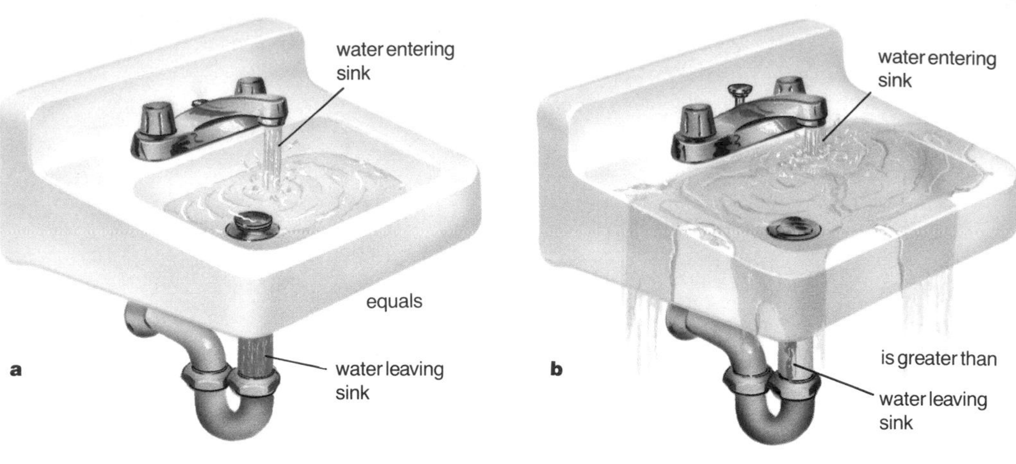

Figure 18-4 Normal drug dose (a) – the amount of drug entering the body equals the amount leaving the body. Overdose (b) – the amount of drug entering the body is greater than the amount leaving the body.

Figure 18-4a uses a leaking sink to help explain how the body balances the amount of drug entering and leaving it. Think of the water going into the sink as a drug entering the body. The leaking stopper stands for the organ removing the drug. If the water entering the sink is equal to the water leaving it, the water will not overflow. Nor will the sink become empty. The same type of thing happens with the proper drug dosage. The amount of drug entering the body equals the amount leaving it.

What happens if a person does not take the correct drug dose? Not taking enough of a drug may result in the drug not doing its job. Taking too much of a drug can result in a drug overdose. An **overdose** is the result of too much of a drug in the body. Let's look at the sink example again. Figure 18-4b shows what might lead to a drug overdose. Too much of a drug is added to the body. The body can't get rid of the drug fast enough, and a drug overdose results. Drug overdoses are dangerous because they prevent the body from working properly.

Bio Tip

Health: Do not store any medicine in the glove compartment of a car. High temperatures may alter the chemicals in the drug.

Speed of Drug Action

There are two ways that people commonly take drugs. These ways are swallowing or getting a shot. Suppose a pain comes from your toe. How can swallowing a pill or getting a shot stop that pain? Look at Figure 18-5 as you read the following steps.

OPTIONS

Science Background

A drug that is injected is generally fast-acting, and dosage is more accurately controlled. A drawback to drug injection is that sterile conditions must be maintained.

STUDY GUIDE 104

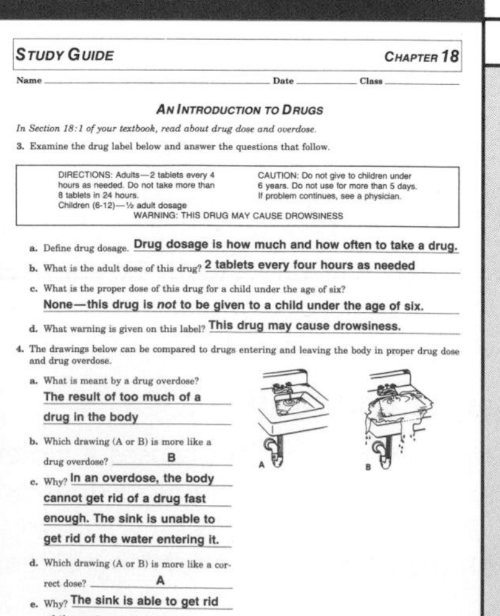

STUDY GUIDE — CHAPTER 18

Name ______ Date ______ Class ______

AN INTRODUCTION TO DRUGS

In Section 18:1 of your textbook, read about drug dose and overdose.

3. Examine the drug label below and answer the questions that follow.

DIRECTIONS: Adults—2 tablets every 4 hours as needed. Do not take more than 8 tablets in 24 hours.
Children (6-12)—½ adult dosage
CAUTION: Do not give to children under 6 years. Do not use for more than 5 days. If problem continues, see a physician.
WARNING: THIS DRUG MAY CAUSE DROWSINESS

a. Define drug dosage. **Drug dosage is how much and how often to take a drug.**
b. What is the adult dose of this drug? **2 tablets every four hours as needed**
c. What is the proper dose of this drug for a child under the age of six? **None—this drug is *not* to be given to a child under the age of six.**
d. What warning is given on this label? **This drug may cause drowsiness.**

4. The drawings below can be compared to drugs entering and leaving the body in proper drug dose and drug overdose.

a. What is meant by a drug overdose? **The result of too much of a drug in the body**
b. Which drawing (A or B) is more like a drug overdose? **B**
c. Why? **In an overdose, the body cannot get rid of a drug fast enough. The sink is unable to get rid of the water entering it.**
d. Which drawing (A or B) is more like a correct dose? **A**
e. Why? **The sink is able to get rid of the water entering it.**

A B

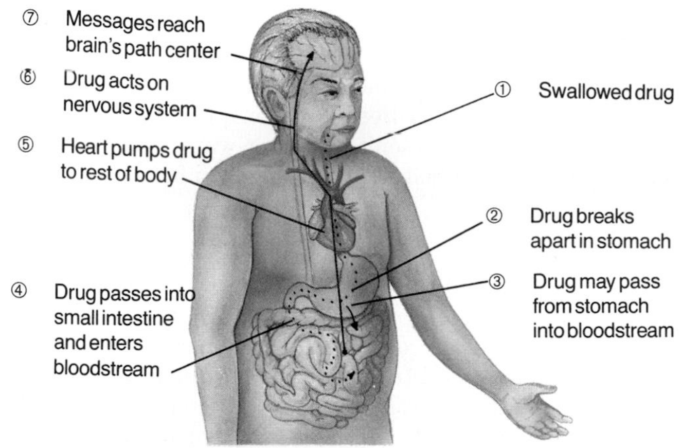
⑦ Messages reach brain's path center
⑥ Drug acts on nervous system
⑤ Heart pumps drug to rest of body
④ Drug passes into small intestine and enters bloodstream
① Swallowed drug
② Drug breaks apart in stomach
③ Drug may pass from stomach into bloodstream

Figure 18-5 Path followed by a swallowed drug. What body system is responsible for pain relief? nervous system

1. A person swallows a drug.
2. The drug reaches the stomach and begins to break up.
3. Some of the drug may pass from the stomach directly into the bloodstream. The rest will continue into the small intestine and then into the bloodstream.
4. Once the drug is in the blood, the heart pumps it to all parts of the body.
5. The drug acts on the nervous system. The nervous system sends messages to the brain and shuts off the brain's pain center.

How does a painkiller stop pain after it is swallowed?

Drugs taken by mouth don't work as quickly as injected drugs. Injected drugs go directly into blood capillaries. They don't have to spend any time passing through the digestive system first.

Check Your Understanding

1. How is buying a prescription drug different from buying an over-the-counter drug?
2. Name four things that a drug label tells you.
3. Describe how a drug stops pain in the body.
4. **Critical Thinking:** If you are very sick, the doctor may give you a shot of antibiotic in the office and then give you pills to take later. Why do you think he or she gave you both a shot and pills? Why not just pills?
5. **Biology and Reading:** Look at the drug label in Figure 18-3. Why should this drug be taken? How often should the person take this drug?

TEACH

Guided Practice

Have students write down their answers to the margin question: It blocks the movement of messengers at the synapse in the brain.

Check for Understanding

Have students respond to the first three questions in Check Your Understanding.

Reteach

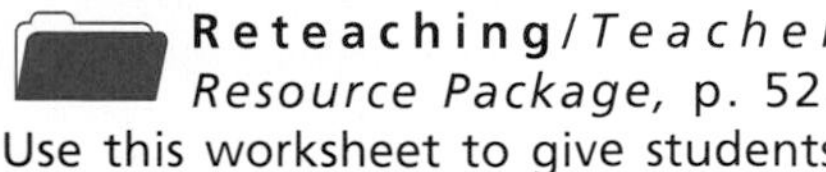
Reteaching/*Teacher Resource Package,* p. 52. Use this worksheet to give students additional practice in understanding special types of behavior.

Extension: Assign Critical Thinking, Biology and Reading, or some of the **OPTIONS** available with this lesson.

3 APPLY

ACTIVITY/Videocassette

Show the videocassette *Chemicals in a Chemical Body,* Human Relations Media.

4 CLOSE

Software

Drugs: Who's in Control? Opportunities for Learning.

Answers to Check Your Understanding

1. A doctor must prescribe a prescription drug.
2. drug use, special instructions on what to do before taking the drug, warnings on side effects or mixing with certain foods or other drugs, drug dosage
3. The drug stops the movement of the chemical messenger at the synapse in the brain.
4. The shot works faster than the pills. Pills give longer-lasting relief.
5. for the relief of diarrhea; every four hours

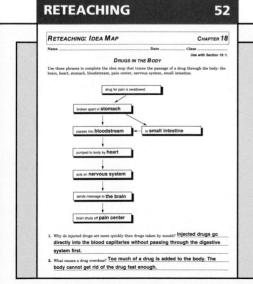

RETEACHING 52

RETEACHING: IDEA MAP — CHAPTER 18

Name ________ Date ________ Class ________

Use with Section 18:1.

DRUGS IN THE BODY

Use these phrases to complete the idea map that traces the passage of a drug through the body: the brain, heart, stomach, bloodstream, pain center, nervous system, small intestine.

drug for pain is swallowed → broken apart in **stomach** → passes into **bloodstream** (← to **small intestine**) → pumped to body by **heart** → acts on **nervous system** → sends message to **the brain** → brain shuts off **pain center**

1. Why do injected drugs act more quickly than drugs taken by mouth? **Injected drugs go directly into the blood capillaries without passing through the digestive system first.**
2. What causes a drug overdose? **Too much of a drug is added to the body. The body cannot get rid of the drug fast enough.**

OPTIONS

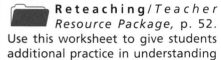

Path of a Swallowed Drug/*Transparency Package,* number 18. Use color transparency number 18 as you teach the speed of drug action.

18:2 How Drugs Affect Behavior

PREPARATION

Materials Needed

Make copies of the Study Guide and Reteaching worksheets in the *Teacher Resource Package.*

Key Science Words

stimulant
depressant
psychedelic drug
inhalant

Process Skills

In the Skill Check, students will sequence.

1 FOCUS

▶ The objectives are listed on the student page. Remind students to preview these objectives as a guide to this numbered section.

ACTIVITY/Word Association

Ask students to take the four words listed under Key Science Words and
a) define the terms in their own words.
b) list dictionary words that are derived from or are similar to them.

Bridging

Review nerve physiology, particularly the role and location of axon, synapse, and dendrite ends.

Objectives

4. **Describe** the effects of stimulants and depressants on the body.
5. **Discuss** how psychedelic drugs and inhalants affect the body.

Key Science Words

stimulant
depressant
psychedelic drug
inhalant

Bio Tip

Consumer: An average of four prescription drugs per year, at a yearly cost of $22, are used by people age 16 or younger. Eighteen prescription drugs per year, at a yearly cost of $138, are used by those 65 or older.

18:2 How Drugs Affect Behavior

Three of the ways in which drugs affect the body are to speed up the body's activities, slow down the body's activities, or affect a person's senses or way of thinking. These changes in the body cause changes in behavior.

Stimulants

A **stimulant** (STIHM yuh lunt) is a drug that speeds up body activities that are controlled by the nervous system. Many stimulants are controlled drugs. Examples of stimulants that are controlled drugs are cocaine and amphetamines (am FEHT uh meenz). Caffeine and nicotine are also stimulants, but they are not controlled drugs.

How does a stimulant speed up the body's activities? To answer this question, we must look at nerve cells in the brain.

In Chapter 15 you learned how neurons carry messages. Chemical messengers given off by the axon end of one neuron move across the synapse and are picked up by the dendrite end of the next neuron. Usually these chemical messengers are destroyed after crossing the synapse. This prevents the original message from going on continuously. Figure 18-6 shows how this works.

How do stimulants change this pattern? They may cause the axon of a neuron to give off more of the chemical

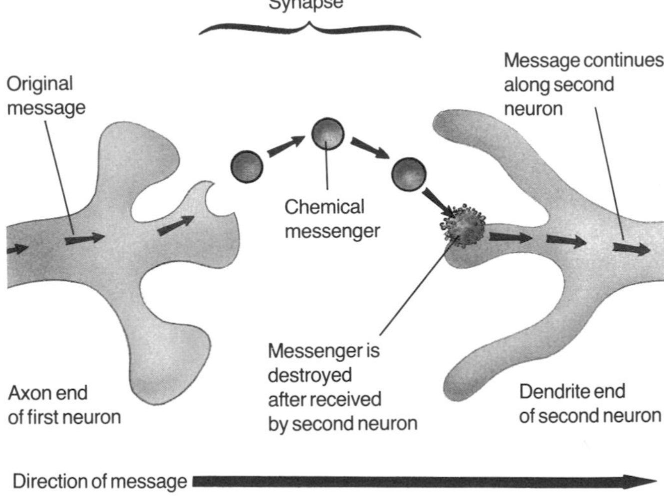

Figure 18-6 Messages move from one neuron to the next across a synapse using a chemical messenger.

OPTIONS

Science Background

LSD stands for lysergic acid diethylamide. Users of LSD report hallucinations, visions, great euphoria, panic, fear, depression. PCP stands for phencyclidine. PCP has been labeled as the most devastating of the hallucinogens because of its severe, long-lasting effects. With chronic use, memory loss, slurred speech, nervousness, anxiety, severe depression, overt aggressive behavior, delirium, convulsions, muscle rigidity, and coma may be experienced.

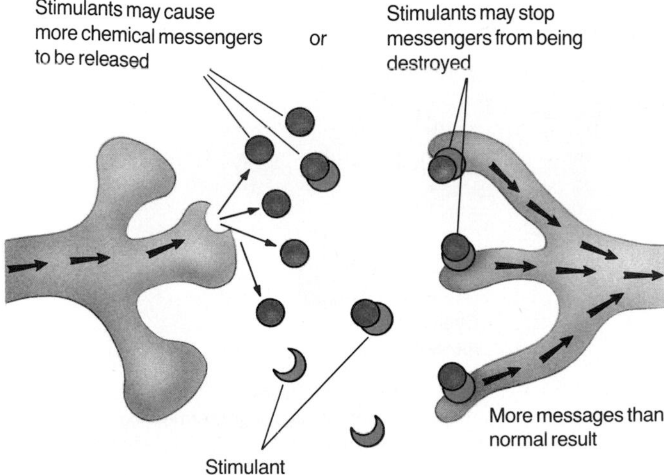

Figure 18-7 There are two ways that stimulants can change the chemical messengers in a synapse.

messenger than normal. Or, stimulants may prevent the chemical messenger from being destroyed once it reaches the dendrite of the next neuron. In both cases, the second neuron keeps receiving chemical messengers. Figure 18-7 shows changes caused by stimulants. With stimulants, messages move from one neuron to the next for a longer time.

How does a stimulant affect the nervous system?

What are some effects of stimulants on the body? Stimulants speed up the heart rate. They increase blood pressure. There is a decrease in appetite. A person taking stimulants has a speeded-up feeling. He or she may feel very alert. Over time, these changes may harm the body because they use up the body's supply of nutrients and energy too quickly.

Depressants

The word *depress* means to push down. A **depressant** (dih PRES unt) is a drug that slows down messages in the nervous system. Depressants slow down the body the way brakes slow down a car. Depressants are controlled drugs.

The main roles of depressants are to calm behavior, reduce pain, and help people sleep. Many mild sleep aids are sold over the counter, even though they are controlled drugs. Codeine (KOH deen), morphine, and barbiturates (bahr BICH uh ruhts) are other depressants. These are legal drugs that may be prescribed by doctors.

Skill Check

Sequence: Draw the path that a message takes to go from one neuron to another. Then draw the same path to show what happens if a depressant is present. *For more help, refer to the **Skill Handbook**, pages 706-711.*

OPTIONS

Science Background

Examples of neurotransmitters are acetylcholine, dopa, dopamine, epinephrine, norepinephrine also known as adrenaline and noradrenaline, glutamic acid, serotonin, and gamma-aminobutyric acid.

2 TEACH

MOTIVATION/Brainstorming

Ask students to name the general region of the nervous system where a stimulant is working if it is used to prevent sleep.

Analogy: Use the analogy of a phone message to reinforce normal nerve physiology. Think of what happens with a telephone. You call someone and talk for a while. When you hang up, the message stops moving across the telephone line. You must make another call if you wish to continue the conversation.

Concept Development

▶ Make sure students understand Figure 18-7. A stimulant will continue to stimulate the dendrite ends of the adjoining neurons for a long period of time, in spite of the fact that no new messages are passing along the nerve. Use the telephone analogy again. Think of what happens if you hang up the phone and the line remains open. Your phone is still connected. You just pick up the phone if you wish to talk to the same person.

ACTIVITY/Brainstorming

Have students identify the axon and dendrite ends of the nerves in Figure 18-6. Ask which nerve end would be blocked from giving off the chemical messenger.

Guided Practice

Have students write down their answers to the margin question: It causes the neuron to give off more chemical messenger than normal or prevents the chemical messenger frombeing destroyed once it reaches the next neuron.

Skill Check

Student drawings should be similar to the sequences shown in Figures 18-6 and 18-8.

TEACH

Concept Development

▶ Inhalants result in euphoria, hallucinations, irritability, anxiety, panic, heart arrhymias, fatigue, depression, and liver failure.

Check for Understanding

Have students prepare a table that lists the following: (a) Side effects on the body when using stimulants, depressants, psychedelics. (b) Change brought about at the synapse when using stimulants, depressants.

Reteach

Have students define the words *stimulate, depress,* and *psychedelic.* Ask them to write three different sentences using the three words in a nondrug-related context. Ask students to give examples of the three drug types. Ask them to speculate on how the synapse is being influenced by psychedelics.

Independent Practice

Study Guide/*Teacher Resource Package,* p. 105. Use the Study Guide worksheet shown at the bottom of this page for independent practice.

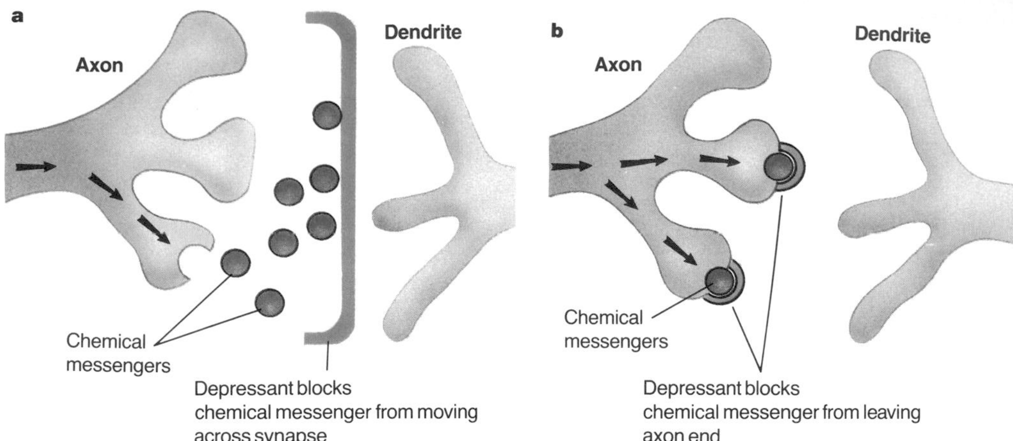

Figure 18-8 Depressants change chemical messengers at a synapse in two ways.

Let's see how a depressant stops pain. Suppose you had a bad toothache. Neurons carry the pain message to your brain. At the brain, the message enters the brain's pain center. Then you feel the discomfort called pain.

Painkillers work in your brain at the synapse, just as stimulants do. Certain depressants may block the movement of chemical messengers across the synapse. This is shown in Figure 18-8a. Some depressants block the axon of a neuron from giving off the chemical messenger. This is shown in Figure 18-8b. Painkillers don't change what causes the pain. They simply keep you from feeling pain by stopping the chemical messenger from doing its job.

Figure 18-9 The leaves, stems, flowers, and pollen of marijuana contain several drugs.

Psychedelic Drugs

A third group of drugs that change behavior is the psychedelic (si kuh DEL ihk) drugs. A **psychedelic drug** is one that alters the way the mind works and changes the signals we receive from our sense organs. Hearing, seeing, and thinking are changed. For example, someone may say that an object appears brighter than it really is. Sounds become louder. Senses blend together. Someone may report "tasting colors" or "seeing music."

There are two general groups of psychedelic drugs. One group is found in nature. Natural psychedelic drugs are those found in certain kinds of mushrooms, cactus plants, marijuana, and the leaves of other desert and jungle plants. The second group of psychedelic drugs is synthetic, or made by humans. Drugs in both groups are controlled.

OPTIONS

Science Background

Inhalants include the following chemical compounds: toluene, benzene, kerosene, gasoline, and Freon (a fluorocarbon found in refrigerators and air conditioners as a coolant).

Inhalants typically act on the nervous system as does alcohol. They "short circuit" the nervous system's normal pathways causing neurons to send messages spontaneously without their receiving of normal messages from sense organs.

STUDY GUIDE 105

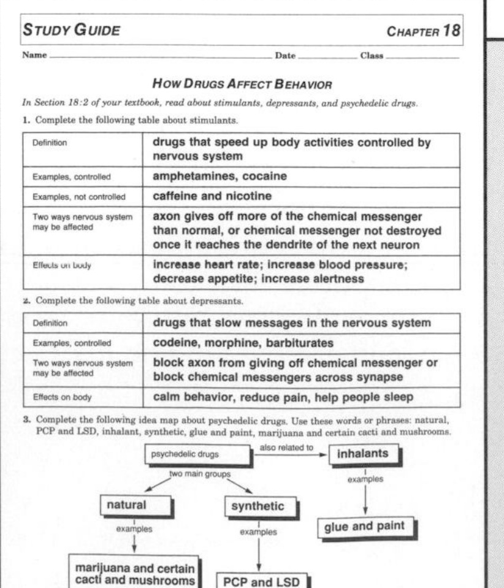

STUDY GUIDE CHAPTER 18

Name ______ Date ______ Class ______

HOW DRUGS AFFECT BEHAVIOR

In Section 18:2 of your textbook, read about stimulants, depressants, and psychedelic drugs.

1. Complete the following table about stimulants.

Definition	**drugs that speed up body activities controlled by nervous system**
Examples, controlled	**amphetamines, cocaine**
Examples, not controlled	**caffeine and nicotine**
Two ways nervous system may be affected	**axon gives off more of the chemical messenger than normal, or chemical messenger not destroyed once it reaches the dendrite of the next neuron**
Effects on body	**increase heart rate; increase blood pressure; decrease appetite; increase alertness**

2. Complete the following table about depressants.

Definition	**drugs that slow messages in the nervous system**
Examples, controlled	**codeine, morphine, barbiturates**
Two ways nervous system may be affected	**block axon from giving off chemical messenger or block chemical messengers across synapse**
Effects on body	**calm behavior, reduce pain, help people sleep**

3. Complete the following idea map about psychedelic drugs. Use these words or phrases: natural, PCP and LSD, inhalant, synthetic, glue and paint, marijuana and certain cacti and mushrooms.

psychedelic drugs — also related to → **inhalants**
inhalants — examples → **glue and paint**
psychedelic drugs — two main groups → **natural**, **synthetic**
natural — examples → **marijuana and certain cacti and mushrooms**
synthetic — examples → **PCP and LSD**

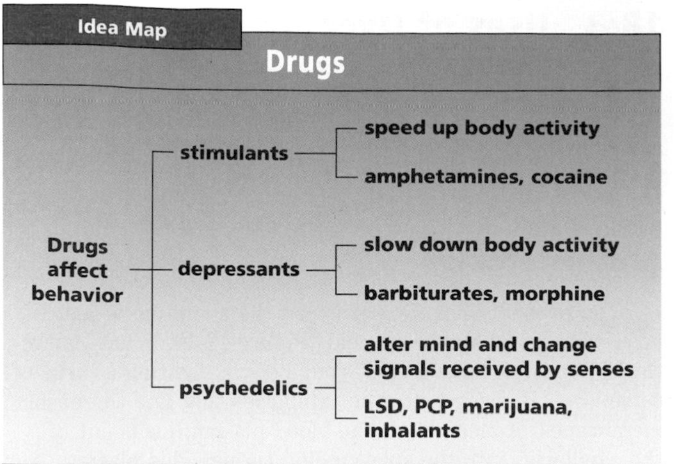

Study Tip: Use this idea map as a study guide to drugs that affect behavior. How many other examples can you give?

Synthetic drugs that alter the mind include PCP and LSD. PCP is also known as "angel dust." Use of PCP causes a variety of physical changes. These include high blood pressure, difficulties with walking or standing, and numbness. PCP also causes changes in behavior. Users of PCP may become very violent. They may also have a loss in memory or try to harm themselves.

What problems can psychedelic drugs cause?

Related to the psychedelics are inhalants. An **inhalant** is a drug breathed in through the lungs in order to cause a behavior change. The chemicals in glues, paints, and typewriter correction fluid are inhalants. Their use can cause irregular heartbeat and liver damage. The heart may stop beating, and death may occur.

Check Your Understanding

6. Describe the action of a stimulant on the nervous system.
7. What behavior changes are caused by psychedelic drugs?
8. What are the main roles of depressants in the body?
9. **Critical Thinking:** How do diet pills work at the nerve level? Are they stimulants or depressants?
10. **Biology and Reading:** According to what you learned in this section, what word means the opposite of depressant?

RETEACHING 53

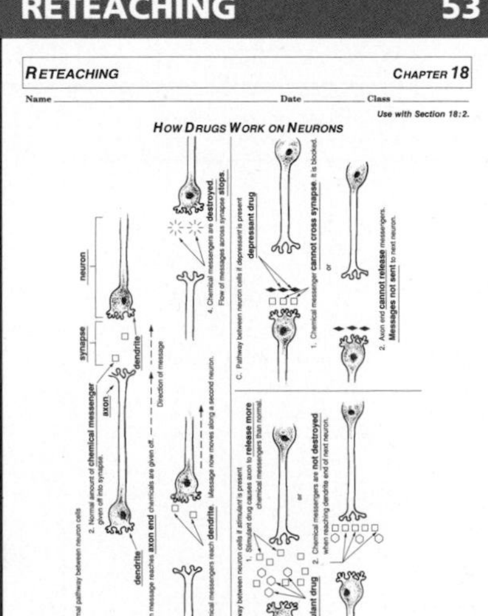
RETEACHING CHAPTER 18

Name ______ Date ______ Class ______

Use with Section 18:2.

HOW DRUGS WORK ON NEURONS

Answers to Check Your Understanding

6. It causes the neuron to give off more chemical messenger than normal or prevents the chemical messenger from being destroyed once it reaches the next neuron.
7. Hearing, seeing, and thinking are changed. Objects may look brighter than normal. Senses blend together.
8. to stop pain, calm behavior, or help people sleep
9. They are stimulants. Messages move from one neuron to the next for a longer time. They decrease the appetite.
10. stimulant

TEACH

Idea Map

Have students use the idea map as a study guide to the major concepts of this section.

Guided Practice

Have students write down their answers to the margin question: they change the way the mind works and change the signals received from the sense organs.

Check for Understanding

Have students respond to the first three questions in Check Your Understanding.

Reteach

Reteaching/*Teacher Resource Package,* p. 53. Use this worksheet to give students additional practice in understanding drugs in the body.

Extension: Assign Critical Thinking, Biology and Reading, or some of the **OPTIONS** available with this lesson.

3 APPLY

ACTIVITY/Filmstrip

Show the filmstrip *A Capsule Look at What Drugs Do to You,* Carolina Biological Supply Co.

4 CLOSE

Audiovisual

Show the filmstrip *Alcohol: America's Drug of Choice,* Carolina Biological Supply Co.

18:3 Uses of Over-the-counter Drugs

PREPARATION

Materials Needed

Make copies of the Study Guide and Reteaching worksheets in the *Teacher Resource Package.*

▶ Obtain sodium bicarbonate (baking soda), vinegar, and litmus paper for the Focus motivation.

▶ Obtain antacid tablets and powders, assemble equipment, and prepare lime water for demonstration of carbon dioxide release.

Key Science Words

antihistamine
antacid

Process Skills

In the Mini Lab, students will infer. In the Skill Check, they will understand science words.

1 FOCUS

▶ The objectives are listed on the student page. Remind students to preview these objectives as a guide to this numbered section.

MOTIVATION/Demonstration

The action of sodium bicarbonate or any other antacid can be demonstrated. Fill a small beaker with vinegar (or any other dilute acid). Use a chemical indicator that will show whether a solution is acidic or basic. Add the sodium bicarbonate to the acid. A foam will appear, which indicates production of carbon dioxide gas. The indicator will change color showing that acid is no longer present in the beaker. If using litmus paper, theneutral solution that results will neither change blue nor red litmus. Repeat the demonstration with other antacids purchased from a drugstore.

18:3 Uses of Over-the-Counter Drugs

Objectives

6. **Give the function** of antihistamines and cough suppressants.
7. **Explain** the role of antacids in the body.

Key Science Words

antihistamine
antacid

There are thousands of over-the-counter drugs available. They relieve minor symptoms of illnesses, but they do not cure diseases. How do they work?

Antihistamines

You probably have experienced the symptom of a stuffy nose when you have had a cold, Figure 18-10. What causes this? When you have a cold, your body is fighting a virus of some kind. Blood goes to the capillaries that line the nasal membranes. A clear fluid, the blood plasma, leaks out of the capillaries into the surrounding tissue. This plasma causes the tissues in your nose to swell. The swelling is what you feel when you have a stuffy nose.

Do you use a nasal spray or nose drops when your nose is stuffy? Nasal sprays and nose drops contain chemicals called antihistamines (ANT i HIHS tuh meenz). An **antihistamine** is a drug that reduces swelling of the tissues by stopping the leaking of blood plasma from capillaries. Most nasal sprays cause the leaking and swelling to stop. Then the stuffy feeling goes away. Antihistamines are also found in pills. They are used to reduce symptoms of hay fever, bee stings, and colds.

Skill Check

Understand science words: antihistamine. The word part *anti* means against. In your dictionary, find three words with the word part *anti* in them. *For more help, refer to the* ***Skill Handbook****, pages 706-711.*

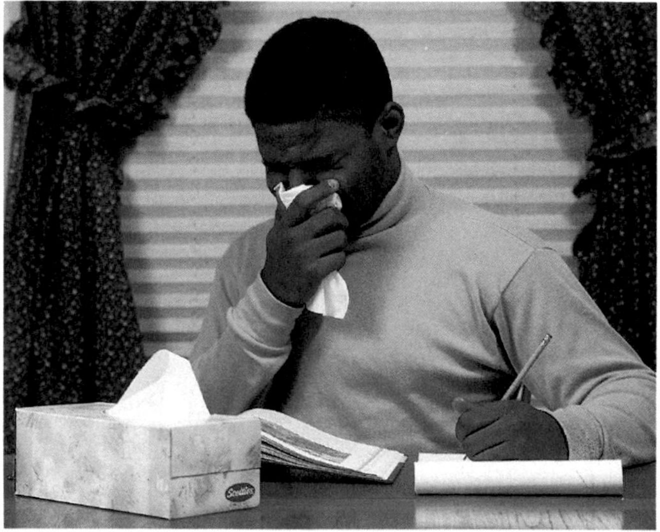

Figure 18-10 Antihistamines relieve the stuffy feeling of a cold. How do antihistamines work? they stop plasma from leaking out of capillaries

OPTIONS

Science Background

An invasion of microbes into the body stimulates certain white blood cells to release a chemical called histamine. This chemical causes blood capillary dilation and permeability. The increased permeability results in fluid loss and swelling. In a cold, histamine causes added mucus production and the typical runny nose associated with a cold. Antihistamines counteract the action of histamines.

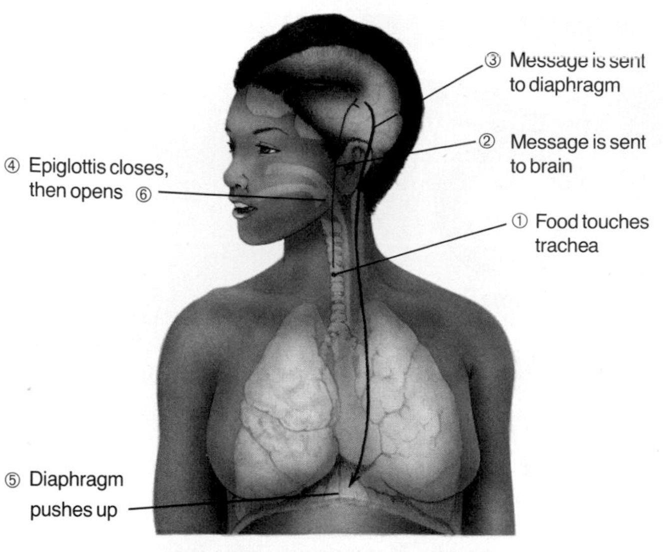
③ Message is sent to diaphragm
② Message is sent to brain
④ Epiglottis closes, then opens ⑥
① Food touches trachea
⑤ Diaphragm pushes up

Figure 18-11 How and why you cough

Cough Suppressants

Coughing is your body's way of getting rid of whatever blocks your windpipe or lungs. Figure 18-11 shows why you cough. Something, such as food, may be touching the sides of your trachea. Nerves in the trachea sense the food and send a message to the part of the brain that controls coughing. The brain then sends the message to your diaphragm and your epiglottis, the flap that covers the opening of your windpipe. The epiglottis closes. Your diaphragm pushes up into your chest. Pressure builds up within your chest and the epiglottis opens. A burst of air under high pressure is pushed from your lungs, and you cough.

What is the role of cough suppressants in coughing? Suppressants are medicines that slow down or suppress the part of the brain that controls coughing. Cough medicines usually contain depressants. These drugs work on the chemical messenger of the synapse in the same way as other depressants.

Mini Lab

What Determines the Price of a Drug?

Infer: Compare the price of a "name brand" drug with a less known brand. Determine the cost per dose for each. Name some factors that might affect the price. *For more help, refer to the* ***Skill Handbook****, pages 706-711.*

What kind of drug do cough suppressants contain?

Figure 18-12 Cough suppressants are available in many different forms.

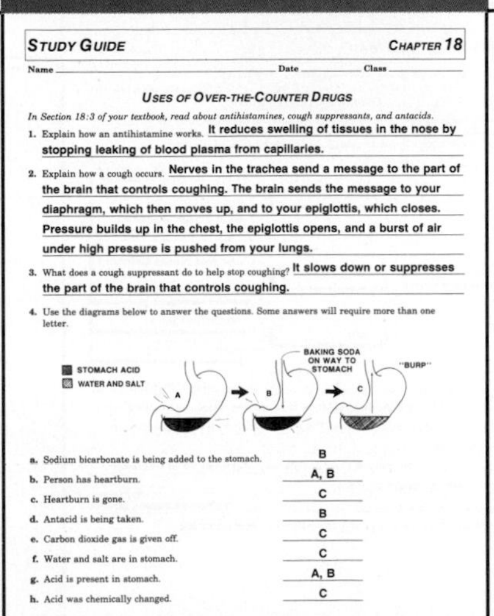

STUDY GUIDE 106

STUDY GUIDE CHAPTER 18

Name ______ Date ______ Class ______

USES OF OVER-THE-COUNTER DRUGS

In Section 18:3 of your textbook, read about antihistamines, cough suppressants, and antacids.

1. Explain how an antihistamine works. It reduces swelling of tissues in the nose by stopping leaking of blood plasma from capillaries.
2. Explain how a cough occurs. Nerves in the trachea send a message to the part of the brain that controls coughing. The brain sends the message to your diaphragm, which then moves up, and to your epiglottis, which closes. Pressure builds up in the chest, the epiglottis opens, and a burst of air under high pressure is pushed from your lungs.
3. What does a cough suppressant do to help stop coughing? It slows down or suppresses the part of the brain that controls coughing.
4. Use the diagrams below to answer the questions. Some answers will require more than one letter.

STOMACH ACID
WATER AND SALT
A → B → C
BAKING SODA ON WAY TO STOMACH
"BURP"

a. Sodium bicarbonate is being added to the stomach. B
b. Person has heartburn. A, B
c. Heartburn is gone. C
d. Antacid is being taken. B
e. Carbon dioxide gas is given off. C
f. Water and salt are in stomach. C
g. Acid is present in stomach. A, B
h. Acid was chemically changed. C

2 TEACH

ACTIVITY/Brainstorming

Ask your students if coughing is voluntary or involuntary. It can be both. The term *reflex* best describes involuntary coughing.

Concept Development

▶ Most students have experienced swelling of the nose membranes. The swelling is due to the formation of histamine.

▶ Histamine is a chemical that is released from cells when they are injured. In the case of a cold, the cells of the nasal chamber membranes are injured by the cold virus.

▶ Histamine not only causes tissue swelling, but it also stimulates the secretion of mucus.

Mini Lab

Students may have to compare price based on cost per size of container if easier than computing per dose. It may be necessary for you to review the math required to solve this Mini Lab problem.

Independent Practice

Study Guide/*Teacher Resource Package,* p. 106. Use the Study Guide worksheet shown at the bottom of this page for independent practice.

Guided Practice

Have students write down their answers to the margin question: a depressant.

TEACH

Guided Practice

Have students write down their answers to the margin question: It changes the acid to water and a salt.

Check for Understanding

Have students respond to the first three questions in Check Your Understanding.

Reteach

Reteaching/Teacher Resource Package, p. 54. Use this worksheet to give students additional practice in understanding how drugs work on neurons.

Extension: Assign Critical Thinking, Biology and Reading, or some of the **OPTIONS** available with this lesson.

3 APPLY

ACTIVITY/Videocassette

Show the videocassette *Over-the-counter Drugs and Valium,* Human Relations Media.

4 CLOSE

ACTIVITY/Brainstorming

Ask students to force a cough. Have them note the changes that take place in the throat, epiglottis, diaphragm, and chest wall. Ask what normally triggers a cough. Is it voluntary or involuntary? How did the forcing of a cough differ from normal coughing in terms of being voluntary or involuntary?

Answers to Check Your Understanding

11. Antihistamines stop blood plasma from leaking out of capillaries. Tissue swelling decreases.
12. depressants
13. It combines with stomach acid to form water and salt.
14. usually involuntary; reflex pathway
15. depressants

+

=

Figure 18-13 Baking soda can change an acid to water and a salt.

Antacids

Sodium bicarbonate (bi KAR buh nate) is the chemical name for baking soda. Many people have it in their homes. It is used to make cakes rise during baking. It is also useful as a drug. Let's see how. The stomach normally makes acid for digestion. When the stomach makes too much acid, you might get heartburn. Baking soda gets rid of the extra acid by causing a chemical change. You see this change in Figure 18-13. In the figure, baking soda has changed vinegar, an acid, to water and a salt. It does the same thing to stomach acid. The chemical change releases carbon dioxide gas. You burp the gas. The pain goes away because water and salt do not irritate the stomach as the acid did.

What does an antacid do to an acid?

Drugs like baking soda are called antacids (ant AS udz). An **antacid** is a drug that changes acid into water and a salt. The word *antacid* means against acid.

Check Your Understanding

11. Describe the changes that take place in your nose when you use an antihistamine during a cold.
12. What type of drug is present in cough medicines?
13. How does an antacid help relieve heartburn?
14. **Critical Thinking:** Is coughing voluntary or involuntary? What nerve pathway is involved in coughing?
15. **Biology and Reading:** What class of drug that you read about in Section 18:2 is similar to the suppressants that you read about in this section?

OPTIONS

ACTIVITY/Challenge

Ask students to use a chemistry text to determine the chemical equation for the antacid reaction. This is a neutralization (acid-base) reaction. The acid and the sodium bicarbonate form dioxide gas and a salt.

Which Antacid Works Best?/*Lab Manual,* pp. 149-152. Use this lab as an extension to understanding antacids.

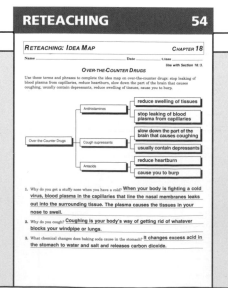

RETEACHING 54

Reteaching: Idea Map — *Chapter 18*

Name ________ Date ________ Class ________

Use with Section 18:3.

Over-the-Counter Drugs

Use these terms and phrases to complete the idea map on over-the-counter drugs: stop leaking of blood plasma from capillaries, reduce heartburn, slow down the part of the brain that causes coughing, usually contain depressants, reduce swelling of tissues, cause you to burp.

- Over-the-Counter Drugs
  - Antihistamines
    - reduce swelling of tissues
    - stop leaking of blood plasma from capillaries
  - Cough supressants
    - slow down the part of the brain that causes coughing
    - usually contain depressants
  - Antacids
    - reduce heartburn
    - cause you to burp

1. Why do you get a stuffy nose when you have a cold? **When your body is fighting a cold virus, blood plasma in the capillaries that line the nasal membranes leaks out into the surrounding tissue. The plasma causes the tissues in your nose to swell.**
2. Why do you cough? **Coughing is your body's way of getting rid of whatever blocks your windpipe or lungs.**
3. What chemical changes does baking soda cause in the stomach? **It changes excess acid in the stomach to water and salt and releases carbon dioxide.**

18:4 Careless Drug Use

Most people use drugs in a wise and careful way. When drug use becomes careless, serious problems can result.

Objectives

8. **List** reasons for not using other people's drugs.
9. **Discuss** the problems caused by using caffeine, nicotine, cocaine, and alcohol.

Key Science Words

drug abuse
dependence
cocaine
caffeine
nicotine
ethyl alcohol

Drug Misuse and Abuse

"Not feeling well? Why don't you try some of my pills?" Have you ever heard someone say that? Should you use drugs that a doctor has told someone else to use? The answer is *no*. Using someone else's drugs is dangerous.

Why is using someone else's drugs dangerous? First, a doctor prescribed the drug for a health problem someone else had. You may not have the same problem.

Second, the dose prescribed for someone else may not be correct for you. Dosage varies with a person's weight and age.

Third, you may be allergic (uh LUR jik) to the drug. If you have a drug allergy (AL ur gee), you are sensitive to a particular drug. You could end up with a rash, itchy eyes, or a runny nose. Sometimes the results are much more serious. An allergic reaction to a drug can make you unable to breathe, or it might cause a drop in blood pressure. These kinds of allergic reactions may cause death.

What are three reasons for not taking another person's drugs?

Using a drug for a health purpose, but using it in the wrong way or amount, is called drug misuse. Using drugs when they are not needed at all is another problem. For example, cocaine and morphine are painkillers. They often end up being abused. **Drug abuse** is the incorrect or improper use of a drug. Taking a controlled drug illegally is drug abuse.

Drug abuse can lead to dependence. **Dependence** means needing a certain drug in order to carry out normal daily activities. Many drugs cause dependence. Morphine, heroin, codeine, alcohol, and even the drugs in coffee, tobacco, and some soft drinks are drugs that people may become dependent upon.

If a person becomes dependent on a drug and stops using it, that person will suffer from withdrawal. Withdrawal sickness causes loss of appetite, vomiting, stomach pains, and other symptoms. These symptoms continue until the person's nervous system has recovered from the effects of the drug. Withdrawal symptoms can be so severe that sudden withdrawal from certain drugs can cause death.

Figure 18-14 The flower of the opium poppy is the source of morphine and codeine.

18:4 Careless Drug Use

PREPARATION

Materials Needed

Make copies of the Focus, Enrichment, Application, Skill, Transparency Master, Critical Thinking/Problem Solving, Study Guide, and Reteaching worksheets in the *Teacher Resource Package.*

▶ Prepare test solutions and alcohol-testing chemical for Lab 18-2.

Key Science Words

drug abuse	caffeine
dependence	nicotine
cocaine	ethyl alcohol

Process Skills

In Lab 18-2, they will observe, interpret data, and experiment. In the Skill Check they will make and use tables.

1 FOCUS

▶ The objectives are listed on the student page. Remind students to preview these objectives as a guide to this numbered section.

ACTIVITY/Filmstrip

Show the filmstrip *Teen Substance Abusers,* Carolina Biological Supply Co.

Guided Practice

Have students write down their answers to the margin question: a drug is prescribed for a certain health problem that you may not have, the dosage may not be correct for you, you may be allergic to the drug.

Focus/*Teacher Resource Package,* p. 35. Use the Focus transparency shown at the bottom of this page as an introduction to careless drug use in relation to smoking.

FOCUS 35

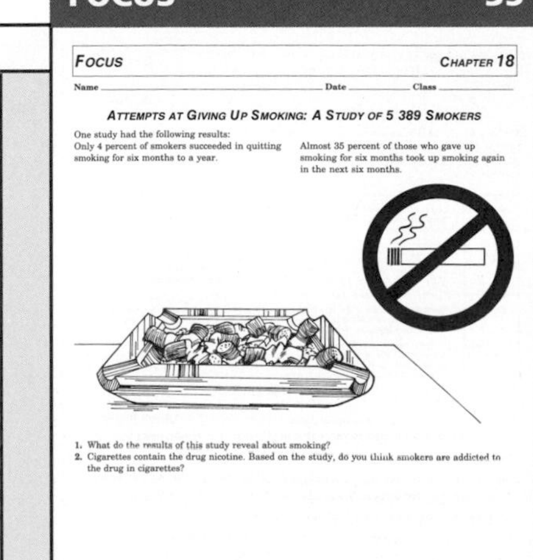

Focus — Chapter 18

Name ______ Date ______ Class ______

Attempts at Giving Up Smoking: A Study of 5 389 Smokers

One study had the following results:
Only 4 percent of smokers succeeded in quitting smoking for six months to a year.

Almost 35 percent of those who gave up smoking for six months took up smoking again in the next six months.

1. What do the results of this study reveal about smoking?
2. Cigarettes contain the drug nicotine. Based on the study, do you think smokers are addicted to the drug in cigarettes?

OPTIONS

Science Background

Dependence may be physical or psychological. A person can be either or both. Dependence can develop as a result of periodic or prolonged use of a drug.

2 TEACH

MOTIVATION/Videocassette

Show the videocassette *Cocaine and Crack: Formula for Failure,* Human Relations Media.

Concept Development

▶ The most harmful effect of cocaine use may be that this drug is a potential local anesthetic. It has been the cause of heart stoppage due to the blocking of messages to heart muscle, preventing the heart from contracting.

Independent Practice

Study Guide/*Teacher Resource Package,* p. 108. Use the Study Guide worksheet shown at the bottom of this page for independent practice.

Guided Practice

Have students write down their answers to the margin question: a strong form of cocaine.

Cocaine

The leaves of a coca bush are used to make a drug called cocaine. **Cocaine** is a controlled drug used for its stimulant effects. Cocaine is a major cause of drug-related deaths in the United States. It may be injected with a needle, inhaled through the nose, or smoked. When inhaled, the drug enters capillaries in the nose and then goes through the circulatory system to the brain.

Upon first taking cocaine, a person may become more active. Blood pressure rises, and breathing and heart rate speed up. If too much of the drug is taken, the reverse may occur. The activity of the medulla slows down greatly. Remember from Section 15:2 that the medulla controls involuntary actions, such as breathing and heart rate. The slowing of the activity of the medulla can cause breathing or heart rate to slow or stop suddenly. It is not known how large a dose is needed for this to happen, and the drug acts differently in different people.

What is crack?

Crack is a very strong form of cocaine. Crack is made from cocaine that has been formed into a paste and then allowed to dry and harden. When smoked, the drug enters the blood by way of the lungs. In this way, it acts on the body in a matter of seconds. Use of crack can cause heart attacks and lung damage. Crack is so dangerous that it can cause death, even after the first use.

Crank, also called "ice," is another drug that is smoked. Crank is even more dangerous than crack because it causes quicker dependence than crack. Crank often causes death.

Figure 18-15 Police often find large quantities of illegal drugs (a) when they make a raid (b).

a

b

OPTIONS

Enrichment/*Teacher Resource Package,* p. 19. Use the Enrichment worksheet shown here to help students understand how the body rids itself of drugs.

STUDY GUIDE 108

STUDY GUIDE **CHAPTER 18**

Name ______ Date ______ Class ______

VOCABULARY

Review the new words in Chapter 18 of your textbook. Then, write the term that each of the phrases below describes on the blank that follows the phrase.

1. a drug that slows messages in the nervous system — depressant
2. too much of a drug — overdose
3. will form carbon dioxide in the stomach — antacid
4. a drug in cigarettes — nicotine
5. a chemical that changes the way a living thing functions when it is taken into the body — drug
6. a drug that speeds up body activities controlled by the nervous system — stimulant
7. the incorrect or improper use of a drug — drug abuse
8. a change that is not expected caused by a drug — side effect
9. drug that relieves a stuffy nose — antihistamine
10. a drug you can buy legally without a prescription — over-the-counter drug
11. a change that takes place in the body due to disease — symptom
12. needing a certain drug in order to carry out normal daily activities — dependence
13. a drug in cola, tea, and coffee — caffeine
14. a drug that a doctor must tell you to take — prescription drug
15. drug made from the leaves of the coca bush — cocaine
16. drugs that are controlled by law — controlled drug
17. how much and how often to take a drug — dosage
18. drug that changes the signals from the sense organs — psychedelic drug
19. drug breathed in through the lungs — inhalant
20. drug found in alcoholic drinks — ethyl alcohol

ENRICHMENT 19

ENRICHMENT **CHAPTER 18**

Name ______ Date ______ Class ______

Use after Section 18:4.

HOW THE BODY RIDS ITSELF OF DRUGS

The body has a number of ways of ridding itself of different kinds of drugs. The table shows the different organs or body fluids involved in the process.

Read the table. Use your textbook to review how the body systems or organs work. Then answer the questions below.

Kidneys	Some drugs are water soluble. This type of drug will end up in the blood when taken into the body. Water-soluble drugs are filtered from blood as the blood moves through the kidneys. The drugs pass out of the body in the urine.
Liver	Some drugs are fat soluble. The liver can change fat-soluble drugs into water-soluble drugs. Once changed into water-soluble drugs, the kidneys filter them from the blood. They pass out of the body in the urine. The liver also breaks down alcohol into simpler substances.
Bile	Some drugs dissolve in bile. Bile is a fluid made in the liver. Drugs that are changed in the liver may leave the liver in bile. Bile passes into the intestine and is eliminated with undigested foods through the anus.
Lungs	Some gases taken in through the lungs, such as those used to put a patient to sleep during surgery, pass into the blood. They are given off from the blood back into the lungs, where they are exhaled. Ethyl alcohol also passes from the blood to the lungs where it is exhaled.

1. How does the body rid itself of water-soluble drugs? Water-soluble drugs are filtered from the blood as it moves through the kidneys. The drugs pass from the body in the urine.
2. How does the body rid itself of fat-soluble drugs? The liver changes fat-soluble drugs into water-soluble drugs. The drugs are filtered out of the blood by the kidneys and pass from the body in the urine.
3. How does bile help rid the body of drugs? Some drugs dissolve in bile. The bile passes out of the liver into the intestine. Eventually the bile is eliminated from the body through the anus with other digestive wastes.
4. How do the lungs help rid the body of drugs? Some drugs move from the blood to the lungs, where they pass out of the body when air is exhaled.

Caffeine and Nicotine

Caffeine is a drug found in coffee and tea. It also is found in cocoa, chocolate, and some soft drinks. Some over-the-counter drugs, such as cold remedies and diet pills, have caffeine.

How does caffeine affect a person? You can almost guess by what people say about coffee. "It helps me wake up." "It gives me a lift." Caffeine is a stimulant.

How much caffeine is found in certain foods? Table 18-1 shows you.

TABLE 18–1. CAFFEINE CONTENT OF SOME FOODS

Food or drug	Milligrams of caffeine
cup of coffee	80
cup of tea	40
regular cola soft drink, 1 can	40
chocolate bar	10
chocolate chip cookie	4

How much caffeine causes a change in behavior? As little as 100 milligrams may cause a change. A person may feel more awake and alert. He or she will notice that the heart rate speeds up. Caffeine may make it hard to sleep. Caffeine also causes dependence.

Nicotine is a stimulant found in tobacco. Nicotine speeds up the heart and increases blood pressure. Cigarettes, cigars, snuff, and chewing tobacco have nicotine.

Figure 18-16 Coffee beans are the seeds of the coffee tree and the source of the stimulant caffeine. People in the United States drink about 400 million cups of coffee each day.

Bio Tip

Health: In the United States, there are 359 000 tobacco-related deaths a year. This is equal to 1000 deaths each day.

TEACH

Concept Development

▶ Caffeine is one of the most widely used stimulants in the world. It affects the central nervous system and the heart.

▶ Nicotine is a central nervous system stimulant. It also stimulates the adrenal glands to release epinephrine. The results are symptoms associated with the fight or flight mechanism. These symptoms include increased blood pressure, increased heart rate, and increased blood flow to muscles.

▶ Nicotine is classified chemically as an alkaloid, as are caffeine, opium, and cocaine. This means that it contains nitrogen, usually in the form of an amine.

▶ Review *milligram* with students, and point out that the amounts listed in Table 18-1 are small. Ask students if small amounts of a drug are capable of causing obvious changes in behavior.

Connection: History

Have students research and report on early history and use of cocaine.

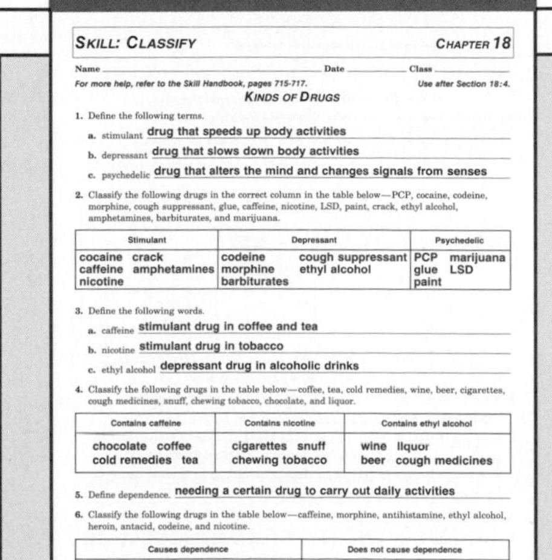

SKILL 19

SKILL: CLASSIFY — CHAPTER 18

Name ______ Date ______ Class ______

For more help, refer to the Skill Handbook, pages 715-717. *Use after Section 18:4.*

KINDS OF DRUGS

1. Define the following terms.
   a. stimulant **drug that speeds up body activities**
   b. depressant **drug that slows down body activities**
   c. psychedelic **drug that alters the mind and changes signals from senses**
2. Classify the following drugs in the correct column in the table below—PCP, cocaine, codeine, morphine, cough suppressant, glue, caffeine, nicotine, LSD, paint, crack, ethyl alcohol, amphetamines, barbiturates, and marijuana.

Stimulant	Depressant	Psychedelic
cocaine crack caffeine amphetamines nicotine	codeine cough suppressant morphine ethyl alcohol barbiturates	PCP marijuana glue LSD paint

3. Define the following words.
   a. caffeine **stimulant drug in coffee and tea**
   b. nicotine **stimulant drug in tobacco**
   c. ethyl alcohol **depressant drug in alcoholic drinks**
4. Classify the following drugs in the table below—coffee, tea, cold remedies, wine, beer, cigarettes, cough medicines, snuff, chewing tobacco, chocolate, and liquor.

Contains caffeine	Contains nicotine	Contains ethyl alcohol
chocolate coffee cold remedies tea	cigarettes snuff chewing tobacco	wine liquor beer cough medicines

5. Define dependence. **needing a certain drug to carry out daily activities**
6. Classify the following drugs in the table below—caffeine, morphine, antihistamine, ethyl alcohol, heroin, antacid, codeine, and nicotine.

Causes dependence	Does not cause dependence
caffeine ethyl alcohol codeine morphine heroin nicotine	antihistamine antacid

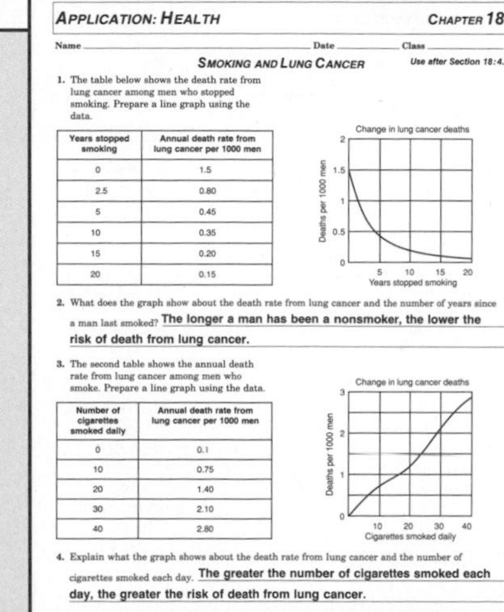

APPLICATION 18

APPLICATION: HEALTH — CHAPTER 18

Name ______ Date ______ Class ______

SMOKING AND LUNG CANCER *Use after Section 18:4.*

1. The table below shows the death rate from lung cancer among men who stopped smoking. Prepare a line graph using the data.

Years stopped smoking	Annual death rate from lung cancer per 1000 men
0	1.5
2.5	0.80
5	0.45
10	0.35
15	0.20
20	0.15

2. What does the graph show about the death rate from lung cancer and the number of years since a man last smoked? **The longer a man has been a nonsmoker, the lower the risk of death from lung cancer.**
3. The second table shows the annual death rate from lung cancer among men who smoke. Prepare a line graph using the data.

Number of cigarettes smoked daily	Annual death rate from lung cancer per 1000 men
0	0.1
10	0.75
20	1.40
30	2.10
40	2.80

4. Explain what the graph shows about the death rate from lung cancer and the number of cigarettes smoked each day. **The greater the number of cigarettes smoked each day, the greater the risk of death from lung cancer.**

OPTIONS

Application/*Teacher Resource Package,* p. 18. Use the Application worksheet shown here to help students understand the effects of smoking on health.

Skill/*Teacher Resource Package,* p. 19. Use the Skill worksheet shown here to help students with classifying drugs.

TEACH

ACTIVITY/Brainstorming

Ask students how snuff, chewing tobacco, and cigarettes differ in the way nicotine enters the body. Students may not realize that many drugs can be absorbed into the bloodstream by way of the small capillaries that line the mouth and cheeks.

ACTIVITY/Demonstration

Use the alcohol-testing chemical from Lab 18-2 to determine if alcohol is formed by yeast. Prepare a small flask of water (50 mL), table sugar (1 teaspoon), and packet of dry yeast. Mix and allow to stand overnight. Add one drop of liquid to a glass slide and test for presence of alcohol. See Lab 18-2 for details in interpretation of any color changes. Use water as a control to show that no color change occurs.

Figure 18-17 Tobacco products all contain nicotine.

What problems are caused by using tobacco? First, the nicotine in tobacco causes dependence. Second, the other chemicals in tobacco cause lung, throat, and mouth cancer. Third, smoking is strongly linked with heart disease. Warning labels appear on all cigarette packages. Fourth, second-hand smoke can harm people who are not smoking but who breathe other people's smoke. Tobacco smoke contains poisonous gases.

Alcohol

Beer, wine, and whiskey contain a drug called ethyl (ETH ul) alcohol. **Ethyl alcohol** is a drug formed from sugars by yeast and is found in all alcoholic drinks. Some over-the-counter drugs, such as cough medicines, contain ethyl alcohol. There are other types of alcohol, such as rubbing alcohol, but they are not used in drugs because they are poisonous.

Figure 18-18 shows the path of swallowed alcohol in the body. Alcohol enters the blood from the stomach. Once in the blood, alcohol acts on the nervous system.

Many people think that alcohol is a stimulant because it speeds up heart and breathing rates. Alcohol is actually a depressant because it slows down the nervous system, leading to dangerous changes.

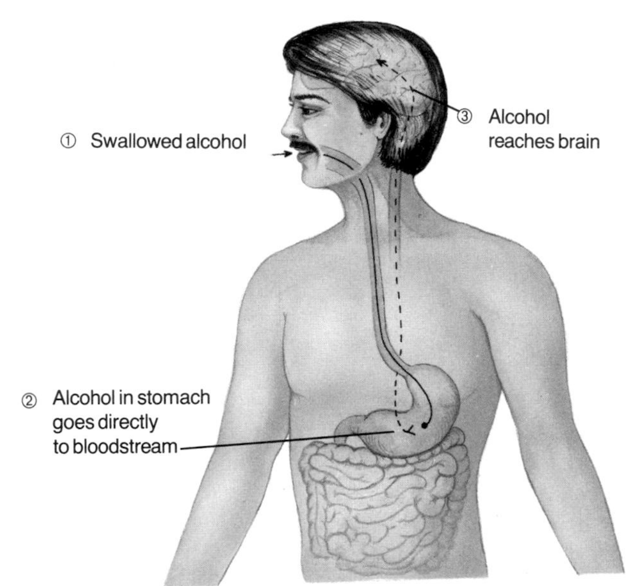

Figure 18-18 Swallowed alcohol goes quickly into the bloodstream and reaches the brain. What kind of drug is alcohol? depressant

386

OPTIONS

Transparency Master/*Teacher Resource Package*, p. 85. Use the Transparency Master shown here to help students review drugs.

Critical Thinking/Problem Solving/ *Teaching Resource Package*, p. 18. Use the worksheet shown here to help students understand unsafe blood alcohol levels.

TRANSPARENCY 85

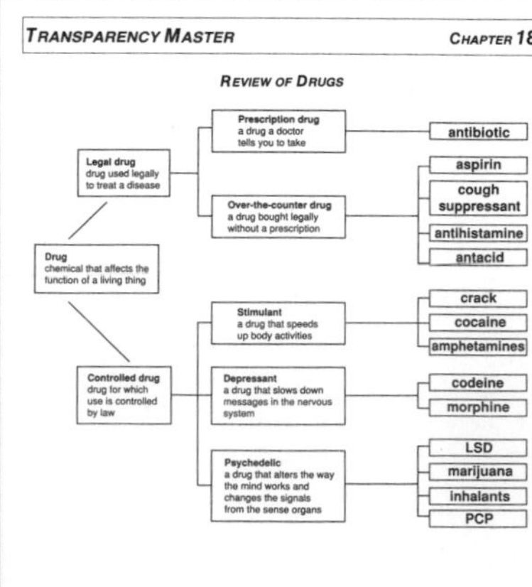

CRITICAL THINKING 18

CRITICAL THINKING/PROBLEM SOLVING — CHAPTER 18

Name ______ Date ______ Class ______

Use after Section 18:4.

HOW IS BLOOD ALCOHOL CONCENTRATION USEFUL?

Alcohol has many effects on a person's body. Some of these effects impair the ability to drive a car safely. The same amount of alcohol consumed can affect different people differently. Blood alcohol concentration (BAC) describes the amount of alcohol in 100 mL of blood. Blood alcohol concentration can show how a person's behavior will be affected by alcohol. Factors that affect the blood alcohol concentration include how much and how quickly alcohol is consumed, the person's body mass, and whether there is food in the stomach. Blood alcohol concentration is used to determine when a person is legally drunk.

Table 1

Blood alcohol concentration (BAC) in %			
Number of drinks in 1 hour	Body weight 45 kg	64 kg	82 kg
1	0.03	0.02	0.02
2	0.06	0.04	0.03
3	0.10	0.07	0.05
4	0.13	0.09	0.07

Table 2

Blood alcohol concentration (BAC) in %			
Number of drinks in 3 hours	Body weight 45 kg	64 kg	82 kg
1	0.01	0.005	0.005
2	0.02	0.01	0.01
3	0.06	0.03	0.01
4	0.10	0.06	0.03

Analyzing the Problem

1. What is the BAC of a 45 kg person having two drinks in one hour and a 45 kg person having two drinks in three hours. one hour: 0.06%; three hours: 0.02%
2. How does time affect BAC? BAC is lower when drinks are consumed over a longer period of time.
3. Compare the BAC if a 45 kg person has two drinks in one hour with the BAC if the same person has four drinks in one hour. Two drinks results in a BAC of 0.06%; four drinks results in a BAC of 0.13%. Blood alcohol concentration is twice as high when twice as much alcohol is consumed.

Solving the Problem

1. In most states, a person is considered legally drunk when the blood alcohol concentration is 0.1%. However, a BAC as low as 0.01% can interfere with a person's ability to drive safely. When does the table suggest it might be safe for a person to drive after consuming one drink? It might be safe for a person weighing 64 kg or more to drive three hours after consuming one drink.

Lab 18–2 Alcohol

Problem: Is alcohol present in over-the-counter drugs and household items?

Skills

observe, interpret data, experiment

Materials

4 glass slides
wax marking pencil
water
alcohol
8 droppers
alcohol-testing chemical, in dropper bottle
6 test solutions of over-the-counter drugs and household items

Procedure

1. Copy the data table.
2. Use a marking pencil to draw two circles on a slide. Label the circles 1 and 2.
3. Add one drop of water to circle 1. Use a clean dropper to add one drop of alcohol to circle 2.
4. Add one drop of alcohol-testing chemical to each circle. **CAUTION:** *Rinse immediately with water if alcohol-testing chemical is spilled on skin or clothing.*
5. **Observe:** Wait five minutes. Look for a color change. A yellow to orange color means alcohol *is not present.* A green, deep green, or blue color means that alcohol *is present.* Record your results.
6. Draw two circles on each of three glass slides. Label the circles A through F.
7. Record in your data table the name of each drug or household item being tested.
8. Add a drop of a different test solution to each circle. Use a clean dropper for each.
9. Add one drop of alcohol-testing chemical to each circle.
10. Wait five minutes. Record any color changes. Complete the last column of your data table.
11. Dispose of your solutions and wash your glassware.

CIRCLE	CONTENTS	COLOR WITH TEST CHEMICAL	ALCOHOL PRESENT?
1	water	orange	no
2	alcohol	blue	yes
A	cough syrup	blue	yes
B	rubbing alcohol	blue	yes
C	mouthwash 1	orange	no
D	mouthwash 2	blue	yes
E	soft drink	orange	no
F	Geritol	blue	yes

Data and Observations

1. Which products showed a color change to blue or green?
2. Which products did not show a color change to blue or green?

Analyze and Apply

1. What was the purpose of circles 1 and 2?
2. Ask your teacher to show you the labels from the products tested. Do your data agree with the labels?
3. Did all the products that contained alcohol also show alcohol listed on their labels?
4. What does your answer to question 3 tell you about the accuracy of these labels?
5. **Apply:** Why is it important that alcohol be listed if it is present in a product?

Extension

There are many different kinds of alcohol (rubbing, grain, wood, etc.). Will the alcohol-testing chemical detect all types of alcohol? **Design an experiment** to test this.

ANSWERS

Data and Observations

1. Answers will vary. Products that contain alcohol will show a color change to blue or green.
2. Products that do not contain alcohol will show a yellow or orange color.

Analyze and Apply

1. to show what a positive alcohol test looks like and to show that the test chemical does not turn blue or green unless alcohol is present
2. Answers will vary with the products tested.
3. Products that contain alcohol should list alcohol on the label.
4. Drug labels must be accurate for safety and health reasons.
5. A person may not be able to tolerate alcohol or may have to avoid alcohol for health reasons.

Lab 18-2 Alcohol

Overview

In this lab, students will test a known alcohol and a known nonalcohol solution with a chemical. They will then determine if alcohol is present in other solutions.

Objectives: Upon completion of this lab, students will be able to (1) **determine** how to test for the presence of alcohol (2) **test** a variety of items for alcohol.

Time Allotment: 30 minutes

Preparation

▶ Alcohol: use ethyl or denatured alcohol from a supply house or use rubbing alcohol from a drugstore.

▶ Alcohol-testing chemical: add 20 g potassium dichromate powder to a glass beaker. Pour 20 mL concentrated sulfuric acid to the beaker. Stir with glass rod to dissolve most of powder. *Slowly* add 60 mL distilled water and continue to stir. *Solution becomes very hot.* Allow to cool. Powder may precipitate out after cooling. Pour only liquid portion of solution into dropping bottles for students use. Solution has a shelf life of one year.

▶ **Alternate Materials:** Use different over-the-counter drugs and household items. NOTE: Do not use any household items or drugs that are green or blue in color.

Lab 18-2 worksheet/*Teacher Resource Package,* pp. 71-72.

Teaching the Lab

▶ Tell students that ethyl alcohol found in alcoholic beverages is not the same as isopropyl, or rubbing alcohol, which is poisonous.

▶ **Troubleshooting:** Placing all liquids in marked dropping bottles will reduce spillage and contamination.

▶ Alcohol-testing chemical is an acid. Advise students to use caution. Rinse with water if spillage occurs on skin or clothing.

TEACH

Skill Check

Table 18-2 clearly shows that with the increase in blood alcohol concentration there is an increase in the lack of body control, even up to the point of death.

Independent Practice

Study Guide/*Teacher Resource Package,* p. 107. Use the Study Guide shown at the bottom of page 389 for independent practice.

Check for Understanding

Have students respond to the first three questions in Check Your Understanding.

Reteach

Reteaching/*Teacher Resource Package,* p. 55. Use this worksheet to give students additional practice in understanding the careless use of drugs.

Extension: Assign Critical Thinking, Biology and Reading, or some of the **OPTIONS** available with this lesson.

3 APPLY

Software

Alcohol, Opportunities for Learning.

4 CLOSE

Audiovisual

Show the video *Maybe I Am: The Story of a Teenage Alcoholic,* Human Relations Media.

Answers to Check Your Understanding

16. You may not have the same health problem, the dosage may not be correct for you, and you may be allergic to the drug.
17. addiction, breathing and heart rate problems, death
18. coffee, tea, cocoa, soft drink
19. Answers will vary. A person can get help from a peer group.
20. Answers will vary—to warn people not to use drugs.

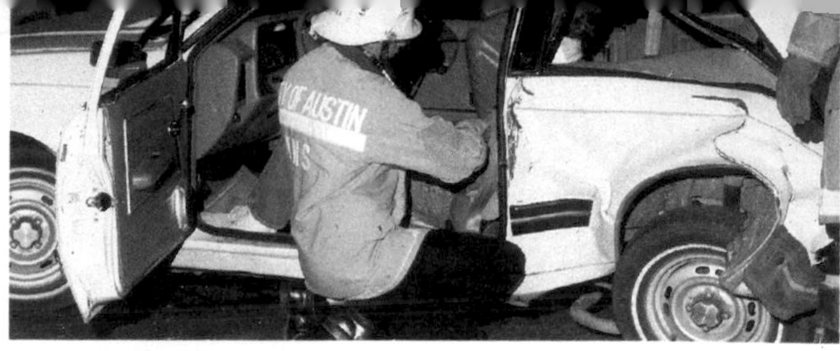

Figure 18-19 About one half of all car accident deaths involve the use of alcohol.

Table 18-2 shows what happens to the body as the amount of alcohol in the blood increases. The letters *BAC* mean *b*lood *a*lcohol *c*oncentration. The BAC is a way of describing the amount of alcohol in 100 mL of blood.

TABLE 18–2. EFFECTS OF ALCOHOL ON THE BODY

% BAC	Effect
0.01 – 0.05	heart and breathing rates increase, judgment decreases
0.06 – 0.10	alertness, coordination, and judgment decrease
0.11 – 0.15	reaction time is slower, speech is slurred, balance is upset
0.16 – 0.29	frequent staggering or falling, loss of awareness
0.30 – 0.39	stupor, as if under an anesthetic
0.40 and up	unconsciousness, breathing stops, death

Skill Check

Make and use tables: Alcohol is a depressant. How does Table 18-2 show that drinking alcohol slows down body activities? *For more help, refer to the* ***Skill Handbook,*** *pages 715-717.*

Another problem is the effect of alcohol on unborn babies. Alcohol passes from mother to baby during pregnancy. The baby can be born with very serious health problems such as fetal alcohol syndrome. These babies are smaller than normal, may be mentally retarded, and have heart defects. Many are born dependent on alcohol.

Check Your Understanding

16. Give three reasons a person should not use someone else's drugs.
17. Describe problems caused by using cocaine and crack.
18. Name four foods that contain caffeine.
19. **Critical Thinking:** Think of a way that might help people stop abusing alcohol or tobacco.
20. **Biology and Reading:** From what you learned in this section, what do you believe was the author's purpose for writing about drugs?

RETEACHING 55

RETEACHING — *CHAPTER 18*

Name ______ Date ______ Class ______

Use with Section 18:4.

CARELESS USE OF DRUGS

1. List the reasons why using drugs prescribed for someone else is dangerous:
   a. **You may not have the same problem.**
   b. **The dose prescribed for someone else may not be correct for you.**
   c. **You may be allergic to the drug, which could give you a rash, itchy eyes, or a runny nose. It might make you unable to breathe or cause your blood pressure to drop.**
2. Place a checkmark in the blank next to the drugs(s) that may cause dependence.

   morphine ✓ alcohol ✓
   heroin ✓ caffeine in coffee ✓
   codeine ✓ nicotine in tobacco ✓
3. What are two opposite effects of cocaine? **At first a person's blood pressure rises and heart rate speeds up; later the action of the medulla slows down greatly, so breathing and heart rate may slow or stop suddenly.**
4. What are two dangerous effects of crack? **It may cause a heart attack and lung damage.**
5. How can caffeine affect the body? **It can make a person feel alert and may make it hard to sleep.**
6. What are the effects of nicotine on the body? **It causes lung, throat, and mouth cancer. It is also strongly linked with heart disease.**
7. What is meant by fetal alcohol syndrome? **When alcohol passes from mother to baby during pregnancy, the baby may be smaller than normal, mentally retarded, and have heart defects.**

Science and Society

Steroids

Testes in the male have two jobs. Not only do they make sperm cells, but they also make a hormone called testosterone (teh STAHS tuh rohn). Testosterone causes the male voice to deepen, hair to grow on the face, and muscles to increase in size. All of this is normal when it occurs at puberty. It is now possible to increase the amount of this hormone in the body by taking testosterone-like drugs. These drugs are called anabolic steroids (an uh BAHL ik • STIHR oydz). They cause a person's muscles to become larger and stronger, and they increase endurance. These changes occur faster than through normal exercise. Some athletes see these drugs as helpful.

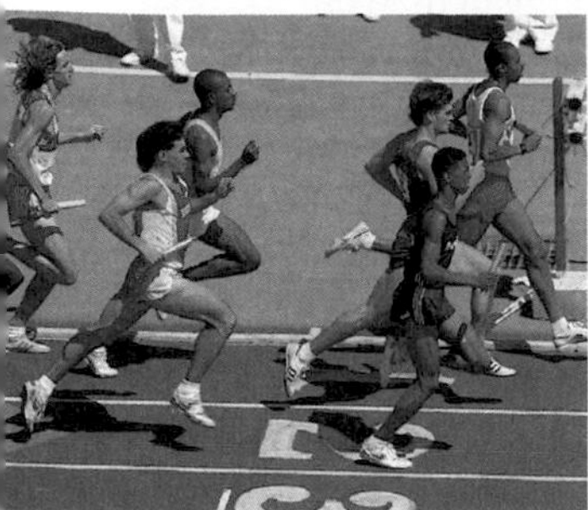

What Do You Think?

1. Athletes who use steroids are finding that the drugs can make them the strongest, fastest, or biggest person around. Many of these athletes train for years, and sports are their lives. Taking steroids is as much a part of their training routine as lifting weights or running. Taking the drugs is helping them to win medals. Many athletes, however, have been kicked off teams or stripped of their medals when it was discovered they were taking steroids. Should an athlete be allowed to use drugs and then compete? Would it be fair to you if you were in a contest with a person who was using anabolic steroids?

2. Many sports organizations, high schools, and colleges test all participating athletes for the presence of drugs in their urine. If drugs are found, the athlete is usually suspended for a length of time and prevented from competing. These drug tests are required of all athletes. The United States Constitution guarantees all citizens the right to privacy. Do you think these drug tests violate the right to privacy? What would happen if an athlete refused to be tested?

3. Steroids cause major health problems. Their use causes liver damage, heart disease, high blood pressure, and sterility. They can cause baldness, growth of breasts, and personality changes in males. Females may develop facial hair, a deep voice, stopping of the menstrual cycle, or a decrease in breast size. Many of these changes are not reversed when the athlete stops taking the drug. Who will pay the athletes' medical bills?

Conclusion: Should laws be passed that prevent or limit the use of steroids by athletes? Is it a government's business what a person does with his or her body?

Bodybuilders may be tested for drugs before they can compete.

STUDY GUIDE 107

STUDY GUIDE — **CHAPTER 18**

Name ______ Date ______ Class ______

CARELESS DRUG USE

In Section 18:4 of your textbook, read about careless drug use.

Place a checkmark in front of those sentences that are true.

______ 1. It is safe to use the drugs that a physician has told someone else to use.

______ 2. The dose of a drug prescribed by a physician for someone else is always the same as the dose that you would need.

__✓__ 3. A drug allergy means that you are sensitive to a particular drug.

______ 4. Allergic drug reactions can never cause death.

__✓__ 5. Drug abuse is the incorrect or improper use of a drug.

______ 6. Drug abuse can never lead to drug dependence.

__✓__ 7. Codeine, alcohol, and heroin are examples of drugs that may cause dependence.

8. Complete the following table by placing checkmarks in the correct columns.

	Cocaine	Caffeine	Nicotine	Alcohol
May cause breathing or heart to stop suddenly	✓			
Causes feeling of alertness and difficulty in falling asleep		✓		
Stimulant	✓*	✓	✓	
Depressant				✓
Leads to dependence	✓	✓	✓	✓
When BAC is 0.4-0.5, unconsciousness or coma can occur				✓
Causes cancer and linked to heart disease			✓	
One form, crack, can cause death with first use	✓			
Can lead to withdrawal symptoms if stopped after dependent use	✓	✓	✓	✓

*Large doses can result in severe depressant effects.

Suggested Readings

Toufexis, Anastasia. "Shortcut to the Rambo Look." *Time,* Jan. 30, 1989, p. 78.

King, Peter. "We Can Clean It Up." *Sports Illustrated,* July 9, 1990, pp. 34-38.

Science and Society

Steroids

Background

Steroids are hormones composed of complex rings of carbon and hydrogen. The steroid hormones include sex hormones and those secreted by the adrenal cortex. Steroids are used legally to treat disorders such as allergies and skin disorders, but can't be used for long periods of time because of side effects. The majority of abuse is with anabolic (tissue-building) steroids.

Teaching Suggestions

Emphasize that taken under prescription, steroids are a legitimate medicine.

What Do You Think?

1. Students will not think it is fair that some use steroids and others don't. Most will feel that steroids should be banned to make the sport fair to everyone.
2. Most students will probably say that they agree with drug testing just to make sports competitions fair.However, they may then discuss how drug testing of innocent people is not fair.
3. Most students will feel that the medical costs are the responsibility of the person who takes the steroid because he or she has a choice.

Conclusion: The subject of government intervention may cause some controversy. Some students may feel that the government shouldn't have any right to say what a person does with his or her body.

CHAPTER 18 REVIEW

Summary

Summary statements can be used to review the major concepts of the chapter.

Key Science Words

All boldfaced terms from the chapter are listed.

Testing Yourself

Using Words

1. drug abuse
2. over-the-counter drug
3. side effect
4. overdose
5. dosage
6. controlled drug
7. stimulant
8. caffeine
9. depressant
10. prescription drug

Finding Main Ideas

11. p. 382; Baking soda changes acid into water and salt.
12. p. 380; An antihistamine stops the leaking of plasma from blood capillaries in the nasal tissue.
13. p. 388; Heart and breathing rate increase, alertness and coordination decrease, reaction time decreases, the person staggers and falls. Increased use can cause stupor, depression of breathing, and death.
14. p. 371; A doctor must tell you to take a prescription drug, while no prescription is needed for over-the-counter drug.
15. p. 379; Blood pressure rises, the person may be unable to walk or stand, experience numbness, and behavior may become violent.
16. p. 375; The drug reaches the stomach, moves from the stomach to the small intestine, and then into the bloodstream. The drug reaches all the neurons and changesthe messengers being sent to the brain. The pain center in the brain is shut off.
17. p. 383; The nervous system is still being affected by the drug until the effects wear off.
18. p. 374; The kidney and the liver get rid of drugs.
19. p. 376; A stimulant causes a neuron to produce more chemical messenger or prevents the messenger from being destroyed after it has done its job.

Using Main Ideas

20. They may have a rash, itchy eyes, a runny nose, not be able to breathe and a drop in blood pressure.
21. The age and body size of a person.
22. Stimulants include caffeine, nicotine, amphetamines, and cocaine. Depressants include ethyl alcohol, morphine, and barbiturates.
23. Drug dependence means that a person must have a certain drug in order to carry out normal daily activities. Morphine, heroine, codeine, nicotine, and alcohol cause dependence.
24. Something may be touching your trachea. Nerves in the trachea sense this and send messages to the brain's cough center. Messages are then sent to the diaphragm and epiglottis and you cough.
25. Antacids change stomach acid to water and a salt. Antihistamines reduce swelling and plasma loss from blood. Cough medicine acts as a depressant on the cough center of the brain.

Chapter 18 Review

Summary

18:1 An Introduction to Drugs

1. Prescription drugs are obtained through a doctor. Over-the-counter drugs are obtained without a prescription.
2. Drug labels give the use, dosage, and warnings against side effects.
3. Drugs that are injected work faster in the body than those that are swallowed.

18:2 How Drugs Affect Behavior

4. Stimulants increase the amount of chemical messenger given off into a synapse. Depressants keep messages from moving across a synapse.
5. Psychedelic drugs and inhalants alter the mind by changing messages received by sense organs.

18:3 Uses of Over-the-Counter Drugs

6. Antihistamines stop plasma loss from capillaries. Cough suppressants slow the brain's cough center.
7. Antacids change acid into water and a salt.

18:4 Careless Drug Use

8. Using someone else's drugs can be dangerous.
9. Cocaine is a controlled stimulant. Caffeine and nicotine are both stimulants. Alcohol is a depressant. All of these drugs cause dependence.

Key Science Words

antacid (p. 382)
antihistamine (p. 380)
caffeine (p. 385)
cocaine (p. 384)
controlled drug (p. 370)
dependence (p. 383)
depressant (p. 377)
dosage (p. 372)
drug (p. 370)
drug abuse (p. 383)
ethyl alcohol (p. 386)
inhalant (p. 379)
nicotine (p. 385)
overdose (p. 374)
over-the-counter drug (p. 371)
prescription drug (p. 371)
psychedelic drug (p. 378)
side effect (p. 372)
stimulant (p. 376)
symptom (p. 370)

Testing Yourself

Using Words

Choose the word from the list of Key Science Words that best fits the definition.

1. using drugs incorrectly or improperly
2. drug bought legally without a prescription
3. unexpected change while using a drug
4. having too much of a drug in the body
5. how much and how often a drug should be used
6. drug whose manufacture and sale are controlled by law
7. drug that speeds up the nervous system
8. drug found in coffee or tea

Review

Testing Yourself *continued*

9. drug that slows the nervous system
10. drug that a doctor must prescribe

Finding Main Ideas

List the page number where each main idea below is found. Then, explain each main idea.

11. how baking soda works in the stomach
12. how an antihistamine works
13. problems that result as blood alcohol concentration increases
14. the difference between prescription and over-the-counter drugs
15. changes that a psychedelic drug, such as PCP, may cause
16. the path that a swallowed drug takes to reach the brain's pain center
17. what causes withdrawal sickness
18. how the body gets rid of drugs
19. how a stimulant speeds up the body

Using Main Ideas

Answer these questions by referring to the page number after each question.

20. What happens when a person has an allergy to a drug? (p. 383)
21. What two factors are used to determine a drug dose? (p. 372)
22. Is each of the following drugs a stimulant or a depressant? caffeine, nicotine, ethyl alcohol, morphine, cocaine, amphetamine (pp. 376-377)
23. What is dependence and what drugs can you become dependent on? (p. 383)
24. Why and how do you cough? (p. 381)
25. How do each of the following drugs work? antacids (p. 382); antihistamines (p. 380); cough suppressants (p. 381)
26. What is a controlled drug and why must it be controlled? (p. 370)

Skill Review ✓

*For more help, refer to the **Skill Handbook**, pages 704-719.*

1. **Make and use tables:** Using Table 18-1, estimate the average amount of caffeine you consume in a day. How can you decrease this amount?
2. **Infer:** Use the sink and running water idea to infer what happens when a child takes an adult dose of a drug rather than the correct child dose.
3. **Interpret data:** If you do the Mini Lab on page 371, how do you know that the paper disk itself does not prevent bacteria from growing?
4. **Sequence:** List the steps that lead to a cough. What step is blocked by a cough suppressant?

Finding Out More

Critical Thinking

1. Drivers suspected of drinking while intoxicated blow up a balloon, and the police test the air in the balloon for alcohol. How does alcohol get into the suspect's breath?
2. Explain why urine can be tested to determine if a person has used drugs.

Applications

1. Examine the labels of two over-the-counter drugs. List and compare the following for each drug: use, dosage, how often it should be used, when to use, warnings.
2. Make a report on fetal alcohol syndrome or the effect of crack on an unborn baby.

Using Main Ideas

26. A controlled drug is one in which the manufacture and distribution is controlled by law. Drugs that may be dangerous if used incorrectly are controlled drugs.

Skill Review

1. Answers will vary depending on the amounts of caffeine thatindividual students consume. Students might suggest that they could consume more decaffeinated beverages and eat foods with less chocolate.
2. If the child takes a children's dosage of the drug, the amount of the drug entering the body equals the amount leaving, like a leaking sink. If the child takes an adult dosage, the amount entering is greater than the amount leaving and the sink overflows.
3. You must have a control. One disk should not be treated with the onion juice.
4. (a) irritation to the trachea, (b) nerves in the trachea send messages to the brain's cough center, (c) messages are received by the cough center, (d) messages are sent from the brain to the diaphragm and epiglottis; (e) you cough. Step (c) is suppressed.

Finding Out More

Critical Thinking

1. The lungs help get rid of drugs.
2. The kidneys help get rid of drugs.

Applications

1. Answer will vary according to the drug labels used.
2. Fetal alcohol syndrome can cause low birth weight babies, premature birth, brain damage, and alcohol dependence in the fetus. Crack can cause the same symptoms in a fetus as alcohol, but the effects are more acute.

Chapter Review/*Teacher Resource Package,* pp. 92-93.

Chapter Test/*Teacher Resource Package,* pp. 94-96.

Chapter Test/*Computer Test Bank*

Unit Test/*Teacher Resource Package,* pp. 97-98.

Unit 4 Body Systems—Controlling Life

CONNECTIONS

Biology in Your World

The body systems and body parts that control our bodies are also involved in how we receive and respond to stimuli. The sense organs receive information from the environment. Students need to understand the importance of their sense organs and how to protect them.

Literature Connection

With the help of Anne Sullivan, Helen Keller (1880-1968) learned the manual alphabet and how to read and write in Braille in just three years. Keller then began speech lessons and eventually spoke well enough to attend high school and college.

After college, she worked to improve conditions for the blind. She traveled, lectured, raised money, and wrote books and articles for her cause. Keller wrote seven books, including *The Story of My Life.*

Art Connection

George Seurat (1859-1891) was influenced by the impressionist painters' subjects and use of bright colors. Impressionists tended to paint what the eye sees at a glance. However, Seurat did not favor this loose style. Seurat used a more scientific approach to painting. He studied theories on color and light to develop pointillism. His paintings look smooth and unbroken from a distance, but up close they are a series of unconnected dots of color. Seurat's style influenced many painters of the early 1900s.

C O N N E C T I O N S

Biology in Your World

Appreciating Our Senses

In this unit, you learned how body systems are controlled. Our bodies can receive information from outside our bodies. Our ears, eyes, nose, mouth, and skin collect this outside information. Factors such as disease and injury can cause damage to any of our sense organs.

LITERATURE

A Silent and Dark World?

In 1881, illness left 18-month-old Helen Keller unable to see, hear, or talk. Most people thought she would not be able to learn. For the next six years, Keller lived in a world she described as a "no-world."

When Keller was 7 years old, a young teacher named Anne Sullivan came to live with her. Sullivan opened up the world for Keller. Using the manual alphabet and braille, Keller was able to communicate. In the manual alphabet, finger positions stand for letters. Braille is a method of reading and writing using raised dots.

At age 22, Keller wrote *The Story of My Life.* Her writings have helped educators design training programs for blind and deaf people. They have also inspired many blind and deaf people to overcome their handicaps.

ART

Optical Painting

Must an artist mix paints to get certain shades? No, mixing of colors can take place in the brain. George Seurat (suh ROH) was a French painter who wanted his paintings to show the colors of nature in a scientific way. He covered his canvases with tiny dots of pure color. Because the dots are so small and regular, the eye does the mixing. This technique, called pointillism, is seen in Seurat's 1885 painting, *Le Bec du Hoc, Grandcamp.* Look closely at the colors to see for yourself.

392

LEISURE

World Without Sound

All during your waking hours, and sometimes in your sleep, sounds surround you. How much do you depend on sound? How would a hearing loss affect your activities? To find out, wear earplugs while at home some evening or on a Saturday. Be sure to insert the earplugs carefully. Do not participate in an activity that would be unsafe without your hearing. As you participate in an indoor hobby, sport, or relaxation activity, make a list of the ways your "hearing loss" affects the activity. You may find that you can't do some of your usual activities. You may find that you don't enjoy the activity as much with reduced hearing. Did you also find that you could do some things better?

You may notice that your "hearing loss" affects other people. Did you have to turn the television volume up so high that it became too loud for others? Did others have to speak more loudly to get your attention?

CONSUMER

Protect Your Sight

With many types of sunglasses available, you can be sure to make a fashion statement. But you also need to make choices when it comes to the level of protection sunglasses offer. It is important to protect your eyes from the effects of harmful ultraviolet (UV) radiation. Scientists think that too much UV radiation can lead to a clouding of the lens of the eye.

Sunglasses do not have to be expensive to be effective. Some inexpensive sunglasses provide good UV protection. Several grades of UV blockage are available. Look for a stamp on the lens that tells you the grade.

The next time you consider buying sunglasses, remember that your eyes are worth protecting—you only have one pair.

393

CONNECTIONS

Leisure Connection

Many hearing-impaired people live safely and independently. Hearing aids can help most people with hearing loss. For people with more severe hearing loss, telephones can be attached to a video screen and keyboard. A decoder connected to a television set makes close-captioning visible. Doorbells and alarm clocks can be connected to lights that flash.

Other hearing-impaired persons own hearing dogs. The dogs are trained in much the same way as seeing eye dogs. They alert their owners to doorbells, alarm clocks, a crying baby, or a smoke alarm.

Consumer Connection

Besides the possibility of causing clouding of the lenses, overexposure to U.V. radiation can cause swelling and inflammation of the eyes. Also, ulcers and tumors may develop in the eyes.

Another consideration in eye protection is glare. Polarized lenses block much of the light reflected from such surfaces as snow and water. With less glare, the eye can see objects more clearly.

References

Keller, Helen. *The Story of My Life.* New York: Doubleday & Co., 1905.

Rewald, John. *Seurat: A Biography.* New York: Abrams, 1990.

Silverstein, Alvin, and Virginia B. Silverstein. *Glasses and Contact Lenses: Your Guide to Eyes, Eyewear, and Eye Care.* New York: J.B. Lippincott, 1989.

Unit 5
Plant Systems And Functions

UNIT OVERVIEW

Unit 5 focuses on plant organs and tissues and how these function. Chapter 19 deals with leaf structure and photosynthesis. Chapter 20 discusses roots and stems and the ways in which they support the plant and transport food and water. Chapter 21 deals with tropisms caused by hormones, growth of plant parts, and some diseases and insects that affect plants.

Advance Planning

Audiovisual and software suggestions are located within each specific chapter under the heading TEACH.

To prepare for:

Lab 19-1:	Collect leaves for student teams. These can be found and dried weeks in advance.
Lab 19-2:	Collect leaves and cut filter paper into strips.
Mini Lab:	Purchase waxed paper and collect leaves.
Lab 20-1:	Cut paper towels into strips prior to the lab.
Lab 20-2:	Purchase yams, radishes, and carrots. Prepare iodine solution.
Mini Lab:	Find a tree stump or log.
Lab 21-1:	Germinate the bean seeds for at least 4 days prior to the lab.
Lab 21-2:	Germinate the corn seeds for at least 4 days prior to the lab.
Mini Lab:	Purchase radish seeds.

Unit 5

CONTENTS

394

Plant Systems and Functions

What would happen if...

there were no forests? Without forests there would be more land available for farming. Then, perhaps enough food could be produced to feed the world's population. Also, more land would be usable for housing, factories, and other types of development.

Without forests, though, there would be no shelter or food for many animals. There would not be enough lumber and other wood products for our needs. Plants use carbon dioxide and give off oxygen during photosynthesis. Without forests, the amount of carbon dioxide might increase and there might not be enough oxygen.

Can we keep our forests and still meet our food and space needs? Scientists are looking for ways to better manage our resources so we can meet our needs without upsetting the environment.

UNIT OVERVIEW

Photo Teaching Tip

The passage that introduces this unit may not have as much impact on your students if you live in a prairie or desert region of the United States as it will on students from a more forested region. First, point out that forests cover a major part of the tropics as well as the northern, coastal, and more mountainous regions of the United States. Then, have students list the disadvantages of a treeless landscape. Make students aware that a forest is not just a collection of trees but that it provides a home, food, and shelter for countless other organisms.

Theme Development

Living things depend on the many body parts that maintain and control functions of the entire organism. The theme of homeostasis is developed in this unit. Students will study the different parts of a plant and how they maintain and control the function of the organism. Students may not be aware that plants, like other living things, also have parts that carry out numerous processes necessary for life. The main organs of a plant are leaf, root, and stem.

The Importance of Leaves

PLANNING GUIDE

CONTENT	TEXT FEATURES	TEACHER RESOURCE PACKAGE	OTHER COMPONENTS
(1 1/2 days) 19:1 The Structure of Leaves Leaf Traits Cells of the Leaf Water Loss in Plants	Skill Check: *Understand Science Words,* p. 403 Mini Lab: *How Does a Leaf Epidermis Do It's Work?* p. 402 Mini Lab: *Why Do Leaves Wilt?* p. 404 Lab 19-1: *Leaves,* p. 400 Check Your Understanding, p. 404	Enrichment: *The Effects of Sunlight and Water on Leaves,* p. 20 Reteaching: *Cells in a Leaf,* p. 56 Critical Thinking/Problem Solving: *How Do Drops of Water Form on Leaves?* p. 19 Transparency Master: *Water Loss in Plant,* p. 89 Study Guide: *The Structure of Leaves,* pp. 109-111 Lab 19-1: *Leaves,* pp. 73-74	**Laboratory Manual:** *What Do the Inside Parts of Leaves Look Like?* p. 157 Color Transparency 19: *Cross Section of a Leaf*
(1 1/2 days) 19:2 Leaves Make Food Building From Raw Materials Changing Raw Materials into Sugar How Is Sugar Used?	Skill Check: *Infer,* p. 408 Idea Map, p. 407 Check Your Understanding, p. 409	Application: *The Greenhouse Effect,* p. 19 Reteaching: *Photosynthesis,* p. 57 Skill: *Make and Use a Line Graph,* p. 20 Focus: *Effects of Sunlight on Growth,* p. 37 Study Guide: *Leaves Make Food,* p. 112	
(1 1/2 days) 19:3 Leaves for Food Animals Depend on Leaves Practical Uses of Leaves Changes in Leaves	Lab 19-2: *Pigments,* p. 415 Science and Society: *Farms of the Future,* p. 413 Idea Map, p. 410 Check Your Understanding, p. 414	Reteaching: *Features of Leaves,* p. 58 Study Guide: *Leaves for Food,* p. 113 Study Guide: *Vocabulary,* p. 114 Lab 19-2: *Pigments,* pp. 75-76	**Laboratory Manual:** *Where in a Leaf Does Photosynthesis Take Place?* p. 161
Chapter Review	Summary Key Science Words Testing Yourself Finding Main Ideas Using Main Ideas Skill Review	Chapter Review, pp. 99-100 Chapter Test, pp. 101-103	**Test Bank**

MATERIALS NEEDED

LAB 19-1, p. 400	LAB 19-2, p. 415	MARGIN FEATURES
15 leaves of different plants metric ruler	plant leaf coin small jar metric ruler filter paper strip liquid solvent applicator stick masking tape	Skill Check, p. 403 dictionary Mini Lab, p. 402 water waxed paper paper towel leaf Mini Lab, p. 404 leaf paper towel

OBJECTIVES

SECTION	OBJECTIVE	OBJECTIVES CORRELATION: CHECK YOUR UNDERSTANDING	CHAPTER REVIEW	TRP CHAPTER REVIEW	TRP CHAPTER TEST
19:1	1. **Examine** and **compare** the parts of a leaf in different plants.	1	3, 6, 19	1, 2, 17, 18, 19, 28, 35	1, 5, 7, 10, 26, 30, 47, 52
	2. **Give the functions** of the cells in a leaf.	4, 5	1, 7, 16	15, 20, 21, 22, 23, 24, 25, 26, 29, 30, 31, 32, 34	4, 8, 11, 12, 14, 15, 16, 17, 18, 27, 29, 32, 34, 35, 36, 37, 38, 39, 40, 41, 42, 43, 44, 45, 46, 48, 49, 50, 51
	3. **Explain** the process of transpiration.	2, 3	2, 4, 5, 10, 18	3, 7, 27, 33	3, 53, 55
19:2	4. **Describe** the process of photosynthesis.	6	8, 9, 24	13, 16	24, 25, 33, 54
	5. **Explain** the chemical equation for photosynthesis.	10	11, 20, 22, 23, 27	11, 12	21, 22, 23, 28
	6. **Compare** the importance of sugar in photosynthesis and respiration.	7	12, 15	4, 5, 14	19
19:3	7. **Determine** why plants are important to other things.	8, 9, 11, 14	14, 21	6, 9	2
	8. **List** different uses of leaves.	12, 15	13, 18	8	9, 13
	9. **Explain** why leaves change color.	13	24	10	6, 20, 31

The Importance of Leaves

CHAPTER OVERVIEW

Key Concepts

In this chapter, students will study photosynthesis as the chief function of leaves. They will compare the structure and internal parts of the leaves. Students will also study the importance of leaves as food for animals and as food and medicines for humans.

Key Science Words

blade	spongy layer
epidermis	stoma
guard cell	transpiration
midrib	wilting
palisade layer	

Skill Development

In Lab 19-1, students will **classify, interpret diagrams,** and **measure in SI** to determine the traits of different leaves. In Lab 19-2, students will **experiment, observe,** and **infer** to discover pigments found in leaves. In the Skill Check on page 403, students will **understand** the **science word** *transpiration.* In the Skill Check on page 408, students will **infer** what happens to plants that are covered. In the Mini Lab on page 402, students will **experiment** with leaf epidermis. In the Mini Lab on page 404, students will **observe** a leaf wilting.

CHAPTER PREVIEW

Chapter Content

Review this outline for Chapter 19 before you read the chapter.

19:1 The Structure of Leaves
- Leaf Traits
- Cells of the Leaf
- Water Loss in Plants

19:2 Leaves Make Food
- Building from Raw Materials
- Changing Raw Materials into Sugar
- How Is Sugar Used?

19:3 Leaves for Food
- Animals Depend on Plants
- Practical Uses of Leaves
- Changes in Leaves

Skills in this Chapter

The skills that you will use in this chapter are listed below.

- In **Lab 19-1,** you will measure in SI, interpret diagrams, and classify. In **Lab 19-2,** you will observe, infer, and experiment.
- In the **Skill Checks,** you will understand science words and infer.
- In the **Mini Labs,** you will observe and experiment.

Bridging

Students learned about the parts of plant cells in Chapter 2 and plant classification in Chapter 6. In this chapter, they will learn the cell in a leaf and how to classify plants by the features of their leaves.

Chapter 19

The Importance of Leaves

Have you ever wondered where your energy to run, cycle, or play sports comes from? How were you able to grow from the size of a book bag as a baby to the size you are today? The answer to both of these questions is food. The baker in the photo to the left and the leaves in the photo below are both making food. Energy is needed to bake the bread and for the leaves to make food. Where does the energy come from to bake the bread? Where do the leaves get the energy to make food?

The baker is making food for himself and other humans. The leaves are making food for the leaf cells and other plant parts. Why do you need food? Why do plants need food? They don't move about as you do, but they do grow.

Try This!

How do leaves vary? Search around your area for the largest and the smallest leaf. Compare the colors, shapes, and sizes of the two leaves.

GETTING STARTED

Using the Photos

In looking at the photos, students should relate how baking bread and photosynthesis in leaves are both food-making processes. Point out that carbon dioxide gas, which they cannot see, and water on a leaf are two raw materials needed for photosynthesis. Both processes use energy; bread making uses heat, and photosynthesis uses light.

MOTIVATION/Try This!

How do leaves vary? Upon completing the chapter-opening activity, students will have gained practice in **observing** similarities and differences among leaves.

Chapter Preview

Have students study the chapter outline before they begin to read the chapter. They should note that the structure of leaves is discussed first and that the food-making process of leaves is discussed second. The uses of and changes in leaves is discussed in the last section.

Misconception

Students are aware that plants take in water through the roots but may fail to realize that plants wilt because they lose water through the leaves.

19:1 The Structure of Leaves

PREPARATION

Materials Needed

Make copies of the Study Guide, Critical Thinking/Problem Solving, Enrichment, Transparency Master, Reteaching, and Lab worksheets in the *Teacher Resource Package.*

▶ Gather leaves for Lab 19-1.

▶ Have a potted plant on hand for the Mini Labs.

Key Science Words

blade
midrib
epidermis
palisade layer
spongy layer
stoma
guard cell
transpiration
wilting

Process Skills

In Lab 19-1, students will classify, interpret diagrams, and measure in SI. In the Skill Check, students will understand science words. In the Mini Labs, students will experiment and observe.

1 FOCUS

▶ The objectives are listed on the student page. Remind students to preview these objectives as a guide to this numbered section.

MOTIVATION/Brainstorming

Have students make a list of leaves they eat. Compile a list on the chalkboard.

Objectives

1. **Examine and compare** the parts of a leaf in different plants.
2. **Give the function** of the cells in a leaf.
3. **Explain** the process of transpiration.

Key Science Words

blade
midrib
epidermis
palisade layer
spongy layer
stoma
guard cell
transpiration
wilting

19:1 The Structure of Leaves

Look around your neighborhood for plants. Apart from flowers, the plant parts that most catch your eye are probably leaves. Leaves are usually green but may show other colors. A plant often can be named just from looking at one of its leaves. Each species has a distinct set of leaf traits.

Leaf Traits

Most leaves are flat and green. The thin, flat part of a leaf is the **blade.** The blades of leaves can be round, heart-shaped, long and narrow, or short and broad. There are leaf blades that don't even look like leaves. The leaf blades of pine trees look like bundles of needles. The leaf blades of cedar trees look like the scales on a fish. Some leaves are adapted to one type of environment. The fleshy leaves of a jade plant are adapted for life in a dry, hot desert. The leaf blade is the main part of a plant that makes food.

A thin stalk usually joins the leaf to the stem. Stalks can be many different lengths and thicknesses. The part of the celery plant that you eat is the leaf stalk. It may be four to eight centimeters wide at the bottom. Many leaf stalks are no larger around than your pencil lead. Some plants, such as corn and grass, have leaves that are not attached to the stem by stalks. The leaf blades are joined directly to the stem. Figure 19-1 shows the stalk and the blade of a leaf.

Remember from Chapter 6 that there are two kinds of cells in the vascular tissue of plants. The stalk of a leaf contains veins with phloem and xylem vessels. These

Bio Tip

Health: Humans get poison ivy rashes when their skin comes in contact with the leaves of the poison ivy plant. You can identify poison ivy by its leaves that have three leaflets.

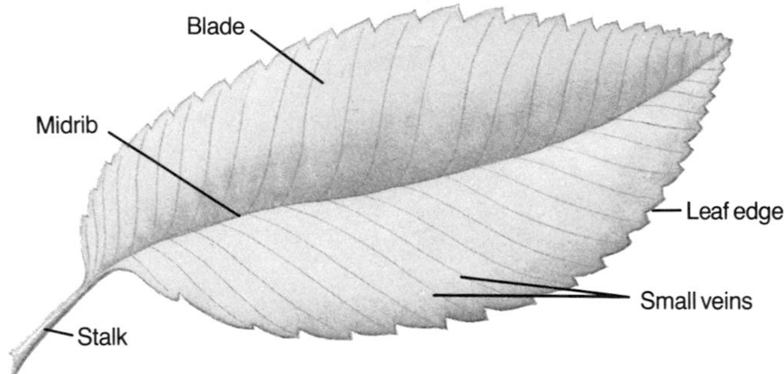

Figure 19-1 A leaf has two main parts—a stalk and a blade.

OPTIONS

Science Background

Scientists showed that plants produce oxygen during photosynthesis by doing the following experiment. A plant was placed in one jar, a mouse in a second jar, and a mouse and plant in a third jar. The mouse in the second jar died from lack of oxygen, but the mouse in the third jar survived.

a

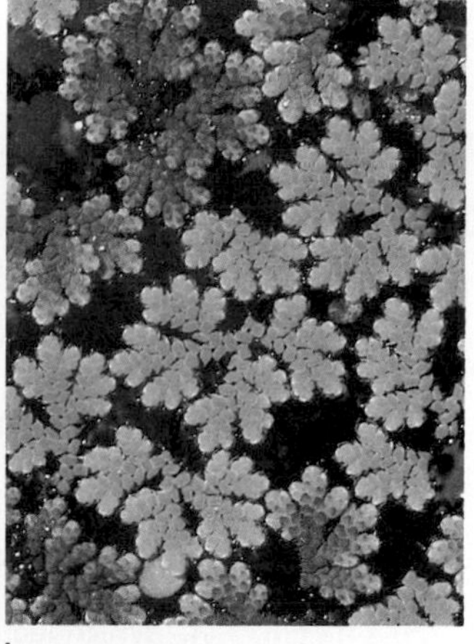

b

Figure 19-2 A royal water lily leaf (a) can be large enough to support a baby, and a water fern (b) has leaves smaller than your fingernail.

vessels, just like the blood vessels in your body, transport nutrients around the tissues of the plant. In the leaf stalk, vessels carry food and water between stem and leaf.

The stalk of a leaf appears to run into the blade and continues to the tip of the leaf. This part of the leaf blade is the midrib. The **midrib** is the main vein of the leaf. Notice in Figure 19-1 the smaller veins branching from the midrib. The midrib and smaller veins are made of phloem and xylem vessels that carry food and water in the leaf. The midribs and veins form different patterns in different leaves.

What leaf traits do scientists use to identify plants?

Scientists use leaf traits to identify and group plants. They use leaf shape, kind of edge, vein pattern, and the arrangement on the stem. It would be difficult to show all the different sizes and shapes of leaves. Look at Figure 19-2. Compare the size of the royal water lily leaf from South America with that of a water fern leaf from North America. Some tropical palm trees have leaves that are as long as a three-story building is high!

How would you describe the shape of grass leaves? Bladelike? Think of some other plants that have leaves shaped like grass leaves. Look at the different leaf shapes in Figure 19-3. Which are shaped like grass leaves?

The leaves in Figure 19-3 also show different kinds of edges. Leaves may have smooth edges or a toothed edge. There may be hundreds of teeth along the edge of a leaf. Notice also in Figure 19-3 that the edges of some leaves curve in and out again to form "fingers" or lobes. The numbers and shapes of lobes are used to identify some plants.

Figure 19-3 Leaves have many shapes and vein patterns. Which of these leaves have parallel veins? grass and corn

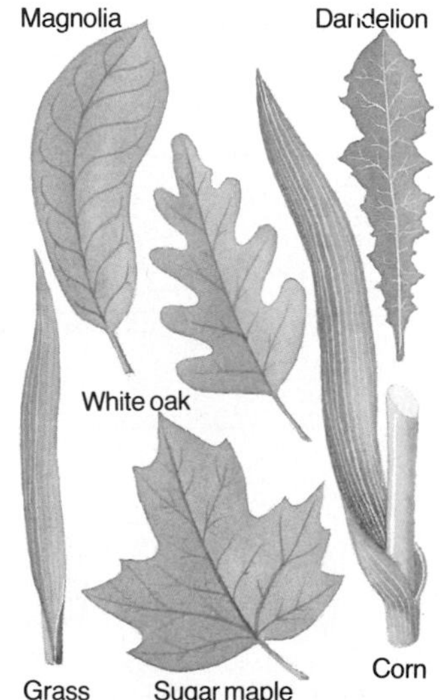

2 TEACH

MOTIVATION/Demonstration

Place dried, pressed leaves on an overhead projector. Point out the differences in shapes and edges of the leaves.

Concept Development

▶ Explain to students that the spines on a cactus plant and the red petal-like flowers of a poinsettia are modified leaves.

▶ Emphasize that veins are found in roots, stems, and leaves because they are the pipeline for water and food for the plant.

▶ Emphasize that the edges, veins, and shape are the main features of a leaf blade used to identify a particular species of plants. Students will use the same features when they do Lab 19-1.

Guided Practice

Have the student make a drawing of a leaf showing the features of the edge, size, and vein pattern. Have them label the appropriate parts.

Independent Practice

Study Guide/*Teacher Resource Package,* p. 109. Use the Study Guide worksheet shown at the bottom of this page for independent practice.

Guided Practice

Have students write down their answers to the margin question: shapes, edges, patterns of veins, and arrangement on stem.

OPTIONS

ACTIVITY/Enrichment

Bring in some fresh spinach, kale, or other greens that have a stalk attached to the leaf. Point out how the veins of the stalk run into the blade. Show students how to trace the vein from the stalk to the blade.

STUDY GUIDE 109

STUDY GUIDE — CHAPTER 19

Name ______ Date ______ Class ______

THE STRUCTURE OF LEAVES

In your textbook, read about leaf traits in Section 19:1.

1. Label the following parts of this diagram: stalk, midrib, blade, smaller vein.

stalk
midrib
smaller vein
blade

In your textbook, read about the cells in a leaf in Section 19:1.

2. Label the following parts of this diagram of a leaf section: air spaces, upper epidermis, lower epidermis, wax layer, guard cell, wax layer, vein, stoma, spongy layer, palisade layer.

wax layer (yellow)
upper epidermis (red)
palisade layer (green)
spongy layer (green)
air spaces
vein (blue)
lower epidermis (red)
guard cell (green)
stoma
wax layer (yellow)

3. Using these colors, shade in the following parts on the diagram above:
Green—leaf cells that make food
Blue—leaf cells that carry water and food
Red—leaf cells that protect
Yellow—waterproof layer

Lab 19-1 Leaves

Overview

In this lab, students will observe 15 different leaves and note their shapes, edges, and vein patterns. They will try to find out which of the patterns are the most common.

Objectives: Upon completing the lab, students will be able to: (1) **measure** various leaf parts, (2) **compare** the leaf parts with pictures.

Time Allotment: 45 minutes

Preparation

▶ Use previously collected leaves.

Lab 19-1 worksheet/*Teacher Resource Package*, pp. 73-74.

Teaching the Lab

Cooperative Learning: Divide the class into teams of two students. For more information, see pp. 22T-23T in the Teacher Guide.

▶ **Troubleshooting:** Make sure the students handle the specimens carefully as leaves can break easily when dry.

Leaves

Lab 19–1

Problem: What are some traits of leaves?

Skills

classify, interpret diagrams, measure in SI

Materials

15 leaves of different plants
metric ruler

Procedure

1. Copy the data table and make a row for each one of your 15 leaves.
2. **Measure in SI:** Choose a leaf. Measure the length of the leaf blade in centimeters from the tip of the leaf blade to its base. For help, see Figure A.
3. Compare the leaf with the shapes given in Figure B. Record the leaf shape.
4. Compare the leaf edge with those in Figure C. Record the leaf edge.
5. Compare and record the vein pattern on your leaf with the vein patterns in Figure D.
6. Repeat steps 2 through 5 with the other 14 leaves.

TRAITS OF LEAVES

Leaf	Blade Length (cm)	Shape	Edge	Veins
1	17.5	oval	no teeth	feather
2	13	star	small teeth	palm

Data and Observations

1. Which leaves were the longest?
2. How many of your leaves had parallel veins? How many had palm veins?

Analyze and Apply

1. Which type of leaf edge is most common in your leaf samples?
2. These are the traits of two leaves: (a) oval, seven pointed lobes, small toothed edge, feather veins; (b) star shape, small teeth, palm veins. Are these two leaves the same species? Explain your answer.
3. **Apply:** How are leaf traits important?

Extension

Classify the 15 leaves by using a field guide.

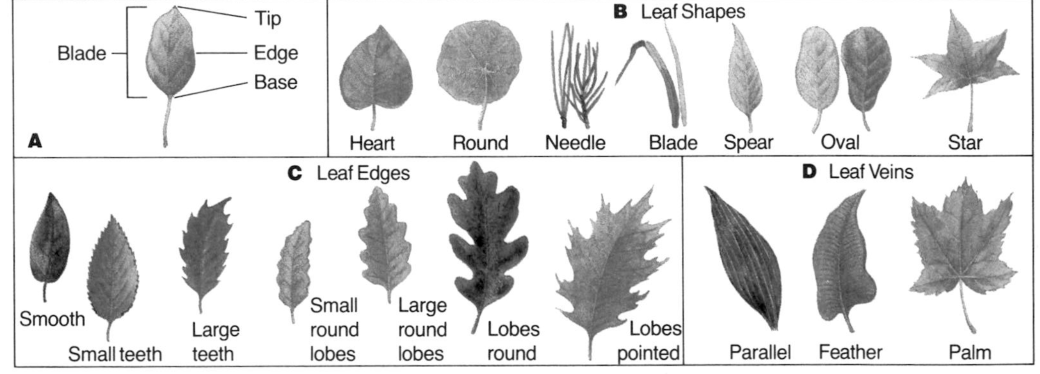

ANSWERS

Data and Observations

1. Answers will vary depending on leaf selection.
2. Answers will vary. Examine each student's data table.

Analyze and Apply

1. Answers will vary. Examine student data.
2. The two leaves are very different in leaf shape, leaf edge, and leaf veins. They are probably two separate species.
3. Leaf traits help in the classifying of plants.

Leaves are arranged in different ways on the stems. Figure 19-4 shows three main leaf arrangements along a stem. Some plants have pairs of leaves opposite each other along the stem. Some plants have one leaf at each point along the stem. They alternate from one side to the other up the stem. In some plants, there are three or more leaves attached around one point on the stem to form a circle or whorled pattern. No matter how they are arranged, the leaves seldom overlap. Each leaf is arranged on the stem to catch the most sunlight it can.

Figure 19-4 Leaves are arranged in an opposite, alternate, or whorled pattern on the stem.

Cells of the Leaf

If you cut a leaf blade in half, you would see its cells. The cells inside a leaf blade are arranged in layers as shown in Figure 19-5. Most leaves are covered with a waxy layer. The waxy layer protects the leaf from water loss and from feeding insects. This layer is not made of cells. Did you ever notice how water forms beads on a newly waxed car? This layer of wax forms a protective coat for the paint on a car. Water cannot pass through the waxy layer on a car, nor can water leak through the waxy layer of a plant. The layer of wax on leaves makes them appear shiny, just as the wax makes a car shiny.

Beneath the waxy layer of a leaf is a layer of cells called the epidermis (ep uh DUR mus). The **epidermis** is the outer layer of cells of a plant. The epidermis is like a skin and is usually only one cell thick.

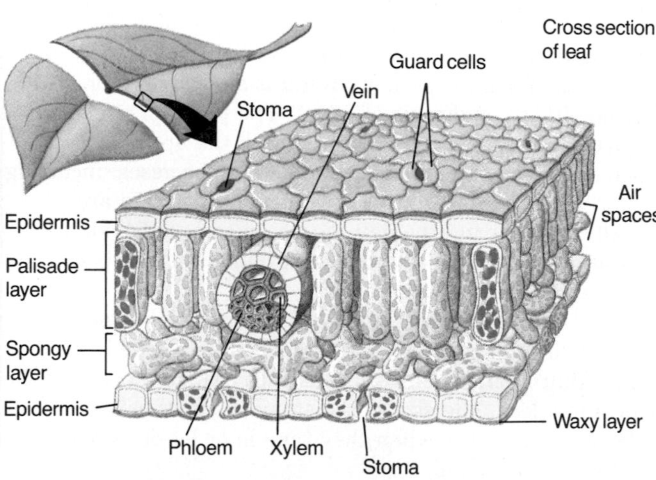

Figure 19-5 The cells of a leaf are arranged in layers. In which layer are there air spaces? the spongy layer

TEACH

Concept Development

▶ Explain that only a few trees have the whorled pattern on the stem.

▶ Point out that the leaf has two layers of epidermis and both of these layers protect the leaf.

▶ Inform students that some leaf epidermis has small hairs projecting through the waxy layer and may not appear smooth if they were to look at it through a hand lens.

Cooperative Learning: Have students in groups of two or three collect and press leaves in a herbarium press or large catalog. After a week of drying and pressing, have students mount their leaves on construction paper and identify the leaves using common names.

Misconception: Explain to students that the waxy layer is the only nonliving layer on a leaf. Students may believe that it is a living layer because it is attached to the leaf.

CRITICAL THINKING 19

CRITICAL THINKING/PROBLEM SOLVING — CHAPTER 19

Name ________ Date ________ Class ________

Use after Section 19:2.

HOW DO DROPS OF WATER FORM ON LEAVES?

As Anita walked into school she noticed the small grass plants growing in the cracks of the pavement and in a nearby vacant lot. Small drops of water shone on the surfaces of each blade of grass. She wondered how the drops formed. She could think of several hypotheses. The water might come from inside the leaf. Or it might be dew condensing from the air. Or, the water might be evaporating from the soil. In her biology class, the teacher suggested she and a team might study transpiration.

Anita and her team decided to try several experiments using plants in pots to answer their questions. First, they would observe the time of day when the droplets formed. Second, they would cover the soil and pot, to prevent evaporation. Also, they would cover plants with glass jars and find out if drops of water still formed. Finally, they would look at the leaves with a microscope. Would they see tiny holes in the leaves?

Analyzing the Problem

1. The students observed droplets at several different times of day. Did this information help them decide if the water came from dew or from the plant cells? **Yes, dew is found in the morning, so the drops are probably not dew.**
2. The students covered the pots and the soil of several plants with plastic, to prevent evaporation from the soil. Then they covered the whole pot and plant with a larger jar. In the morning, the plants inside the jars had drops of water on the leaves. What could they hypothesize about the drops on the plants in jars? **The drops of water came from inside the plants, not from evaporation from the soil.**
3. The students looked at the leaf under the microscope. They could see a large number of pores on the leaves. There were more on the underside than on the tops of the leaves. They compared them to a picture in their textbook. What are the pores called? **stomata**
   In what form does water enter and leave through the stomata? **water vapor**
   If the air outside is cooler, what can happen to the water vapor? **It can condense into water droplets on the leaves.**

Solving the Problem

1. Now the students could decide where the water drops came from, and how water passes out of a plant. Write your conclusion here. **The water forms inside the plant cells and passes out as vapor through the stomata. Then, it condenses on the leaves.**

OPTIONS

Critical Thinking/Problem Solving/ *Teacher Resource Package*, p. 19. Use the Critical Thinking/Problem Solving worksheet shown here for students to learn how drops of water form on leaves.

Cross Section of a Leaf/*Transparency Package*, number 19. Use color transparency 19 as you teach the cells found in a leaf.

TEACH

Concept Development

▶ Point out that some leaves may have as many as 200 stomata per square millimeters.

Guided Practice

Have students write down their answers to the margin question: layer of long, green cells in a leaf just below the upper epidermis.

Mini Lab

The water was absorbed by the towel. The waxed paper and leaf have a layer of wax that keeps water from being absorbed.

Independent Practice

Study Guide/*Teacher Resource Package,* p. 110. Use the Study Guide worksheet shown at the bottom of this page for independent practice.

Check for Understanding

Have the students make a list of the cells in the leaf from top to bottom and write a function for the parts.

Reteach

Have students relate shape and size of cells to their function. (epidermal–brick-shaped, protection; palisade–long, balloonlike, make food; spongy cells–like wet sponge with air holes, make food; guard cell–bean-shaped, lets water in or out).

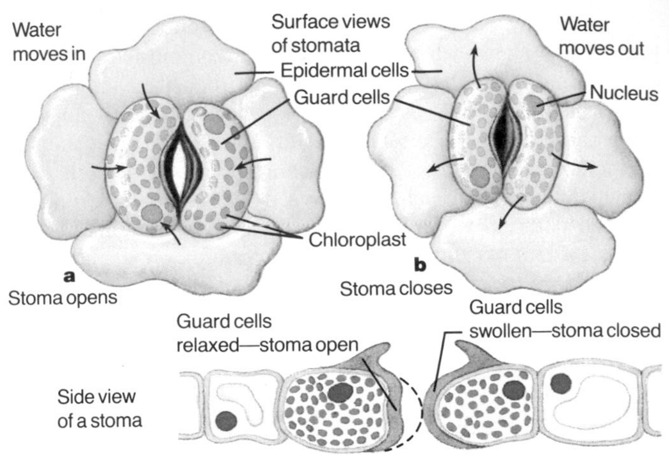

Figure 19-6 Water enters the guard cells and causes them to swell. The stoma opens (a) because the guard cells push apart. The stoma closes (b) when water leaves the guard cells. Below is a cross section through a stoma.

What is the palisade layer?

Examine Figure 19-5 again. Look at the layer of cells below the epidermis. The layer of long, green cells below the upper epidermis of a leaf is the **palisade layer.** Cells of the palisade layer make most of the food for the plant. These cells contain a lot of chloroplasts. Remember that chlorophyll is the green pigment in chloroplasts that helps the plant make food.

Directly below the palisade layer of a leaf is a layer of round, green cells called the **spongy layer.** These cells are loosely arranged and have spaces between filled with water vapor and air. The cells of the spongy layer also make food for the leaf. Leaf veins are often found among the palisade and spongy layers of cells.

Below the spongy layer is another layer of epidermis with its waxy layer. Find a stoma (STOH muh) in the lower epidermis of Figure 19-5. A **stoma** is a small pore or opening in the epidermis of a leaf. The plural of stoma is stomata. Leaves have stomata on both the upper and lower epidermis. The stoma acts as a doorway for gases, including water vapor, to enter and leave the leaf. Stomata are usually open during the day to take in carbon dioxide for photosynthesis. They are closed at night when carbon dioxide isn't needed.

The size of a stoma changes. How does this happen? Around the stoma are two bean-shaped cells called guard cells. **Guard cells** are green cells that change the size of the stoma in a leaf. The size of the stoma changes as the guard cells swell or shrink when they take in or let out water by osmosis, Figure 19-6.

Mini Lab

How Does a Leaf Epidermis Do Its Work?

Experiment: Put two drops of water on waxed paper, on a paper towel, and on a leaf from a potted plant. Compare what happened to the drops of water.

*For more help, refer to the **Skill Handbook,** pages 704-705.*

OPTIONS

Enrichment/*Teacher Resource Package,* p. 20. Use the Enrichment worksheet shown here to teach the effect of sunlight and water on leaves.

What Do the Inside Parts of Leaves Look Like?/*Lab Manual,* pp. 157-160. Use this lab as an extension to the cellular structure of leaves.

STUDY GUIDE 110

STUDY GUIDE CHAPTER 19

Name ______ Date ______ Class ______

THE STRUCTURE OF LEAVES

4. *The chart below describes several different kinds of leaves and gives an example of each. Read each description and example. Examine the diagrams carefully. Then, write the letter of the leaf type on the blank next to the diagram that it best matches.*

Shape	Other traits	Example	
Fan		Ginkgo	(a)
Heart	Edges have teeth.	Cottonwood	(b)
Heart	Edges are smooth. Tip is very pointed.	Catalpa	(c)
Heart	Edges are smooth. Tip is not very pointed.	Redbud	(d)
Oval	Edges are smooth.	Magnolia	(e)
Oval	Edges have a few large teeth.	Holly	(f)
Oval	Edges have many small teeth.	Elm	(g)
Needle	Needles are in twos.	Virginia pine	(h)
Needle	Needles are in threes.	Pitch pine	(i)
Needle	Needles are in fives.	White pine	(j)
5-part	All leaflets attach at same point.	Buckeye	(k)
5-part	Three leaflets attach at top, two near bottom.	Shagbark hickory	(l)
More than 5-parts	Edges have teeth. Leaflets are oppositely attached.	Sumac	(m)
More than 5-parts	Edges are smooth. Leaflets are oppositely attached.	White ash	(n)
Oval	Edges are toothed. Tip is very pointed.	Hackberry	(o)
Wavy lobed	Lobes are pointed.	Pin oak	(p)
Wavy lobed	Lobes are rounded.	White oak	(q)

ENRICHMENT 20

ENRICHMENT CHAPTER 19

Name ______ Date ______ Class ______

Use after Section 19:2.

THE EFFECT OF SUNLIGHT AND WATER ON LEAVES

The amount of sunlight and water a plant gets affects the cells of its leaves. They may develop more layers of cells or fewer layers of cells depending on the amount of sunlight and water they receive.

Study the drawings of leaf sections below. The levels of sunlight and water each leaf gets is given below each cross section. Compare the drawings of the leaf sections, then answer the questions that follow.

Normal sun Normal water — Most sun Normal water — Normal sun Most water — Most sun Little water

1. What type of cells cause Leaf B to be thicker than Leaf A? **The extra palisade cells cause Leaf B to be thicker.**
2. Does Leaf B get more or less sun than the other leaves? **Leaf B gets more sun than Leaf A and Leaf C.**
3. What cell layer is thickest in Leaf C? Is Leaf C getting more water than Leaf A? **The spongy layer is thickest. Leaf C is getting more water than Leaf A.**
4. What nutrient do the extra cells in Leaf C store? **These cells store water.**
5. What is this stored nutrient used for in Leaf C? **Water is used in making food by photosynthesis.**
6. Leaf D gets little water but lives in very bright sunlight. What differences do you notice in Leaf D? **Leaf D has a thicker epidermis and fewer stomata than the other leaves.**
7. How is Leaf D helped by having these differences? **The thicker epidermis and fewer stomata prevent too much water loss.**
8. Where might you find a plant with leaves like Leaf D? **A plant with leaves similar to Leaf D would most likely be found in hot, dry places.**

Figure 19-7 Transpiration is most obvious over the treetops of a tropical forest.

Water Loss in Plants

What is transpiration?

Plants lose water daily through their stomata. The process of water passing out through the stomata of leaves is **transpiration** (trans puh RAY shun). Each day, a plant may lose up to 90 percent of the water it takes up through its roots.

Plant cells are mostly water. Water in a plant keeps the cells firm. Sometimes, a plant loses too much water and wilts. **Wilting** is when a plant loses water faster than it can be replaced. A punctured tire losing air is similar to a plant losing water. The tire goes flat if the escaping air is not replaced at the same rate. The plant shown in Figure 19-8 wilted when it didn't get watered for several days.

During hot, dry days, water loss is greater than usual and the stomata close. On cooler, damp days, water loss slows down and the stomata remain open.

Skill Check

Understand science words: transpiration. The word part *trans* means through. In your dictionary, find three words with the word part *trans* in them. *For more help, refer to the **Skill Handbook**, pages 706-711.*

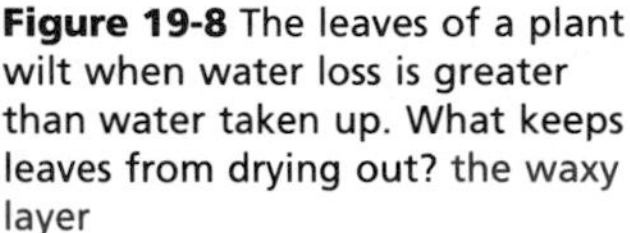

Figure 19-8 The leaves of a plant wilt when water loss is greater than water taken up. What keeps leaves from drying out? the waxy layer

TEACH

Concept Development

▶ Point out that curling of a leaf is an adaptation that helps prevent a leaf from losing water. A curled leaf loses less water than a flat or rigid leaf.

▶ Explain that water can be lost through the stems, but most of the water loss in plants is through the leaves.

▶ Emphasize that temperature, wind, humidity, and light affect transpiration.

▶ Tell students that a single corn plant can transpire about two liters of water a day.

▶ Point out that the number of stomata on a leaf affects the amount of water transpired through a leaf.

Guided Practice

Have students write down their answers to the margin question: process of water passing out through the stomata of leaves.

TRANSPARENCY 89

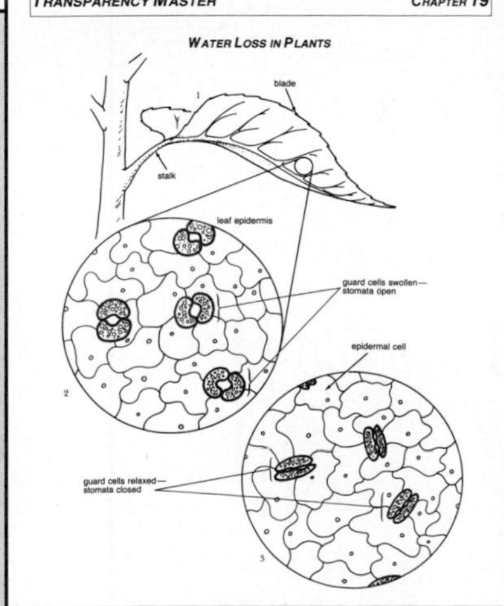

OPTIONS

Transparency Master/*Teacher Resource Package*, p. 89. Use the Transparency Master shown here to teach water loss in plants.

TEACH

Mini Lab

The leaf is firm at the start, and limp as it loses water.

Check for Understanding

Have students respond to the first three questions in Check Your Understanding.

Independent Practice

Study Guide/*Teacher Resource Package,* p. 111. Use the Study Guide worksheet shown at the bottom of the page for independent practice.

Reteach

Reteaching/*Teacher Resource Package,* p. 56. Use this worksheet to give students additional practice with cells in a leaf.

Extension: Assign Critical Thinking, Biology and Math, or some of the **OPTIONS** available with this lesson.

3 APPLY

Demonstration

Show water loss in a plant by placing a clear plastic bag over a well-watered plant. Place in a lighted area and later point out condensation on the side of the bag.

4 CLOSE

Connection: Writing

Have students write a paragraph on the differences between leaves in cool and warm climates.

Answers to Check Your Understanding

1. stalk, blade, veins
2. guard cells
3. A plant wilts when water is lost faster than it can be replaced.
4. To avoid losing too much water, a desert plant has fewer stomata than a forest plant.
5. 1 percent

Figure 19-9 A greenhouse provides a warm, wet environment for plants.

Mini Lab

Why Do Leaves Wilt?

Observe: Remove a leaf from a potted plant and place it on a paper towel at the start of class. What is the texture of the leaf at the start and end of the period? Explain what happened to the leaf. *For more help, refer to the* ***Skill Handbook,*** *pages 704-705.*

Do you have a houseplant at home? If you placed this plant outdoors, would it survive? It's unlikely the houseplant would be adapted to your local climate. For example, many ferns couldn't grow where it is hot and dry. Houseplants are often grown first in greenhouses before they are sold to you, Figure 19-9. If you have ever been inside a greenhouse, you may have noticed how humid and warm it is. The temperature is kept the same at all times. The air is kept moist so plants lose less water through their stomata.

Enough water passes through the plants in a small field of corn in 100 days to fill a bathtub at least 10 000 times. Each corn plant may lose up to 500 liters of water in one season. Now you may understand why farmers need to be concerned about the weather. Without rain, their corn crops would suffer.

Check Your Understanding

1. What three parts of most leaves can you see without a microscope?
2. What cells of the epidermis control sizes of stomata?
3. Explain what causes a plant to wilt.
4. **Critical Thinking:** Would a desert plant have as many stomata in its leaves as a forest plant? Explain.
5. **Biology and Math:** Plants normally lose about 99 percent of the water they absorb. What part of the water they absorb is used for growth?

STUDY GUIDE 111

STUDY GUIDE — CHAPTER 19

Name ______ Date ______ Class ______

THE STRUCTURE OF LEAVES

In your textbook, read about water loss in plants in Section 19:1.

5. The path of water movement through a plant is shown below. Complete the diagram by writing each of these sentences in the place that best shows what is stated.
   Water moves into the leaves where some is used in photosynthesis.
   Water enters roots through the root hairs.
   Water escapes from stomata into the air during transpiration.
   Tubelike cells (xylem) carry water through the stem to the leaves.

6. Circle the conditions under which a plant will lose much water through its stomata.
   (a.) Hot, dry days b. Cool, damp days c. In humid greenhouse
7. Circle the conditions under which a plant will lose little water through its stomata.
   a. Hot, dry days (b.) Cool, damp days (c.) In humid greenhouse
8. a. The diagram below shows the outline of a plant in two conditions. Assume the plant receives no water through its roots and its stomata are open. Complete the diagram by drawing over the dashed lines that best show what the plant would look like.
   b. Which of the following words best describes what has happened to the plant from position A to position B? (Circle one.)
   transpiration, (wilting,) respiration, photosynthesis

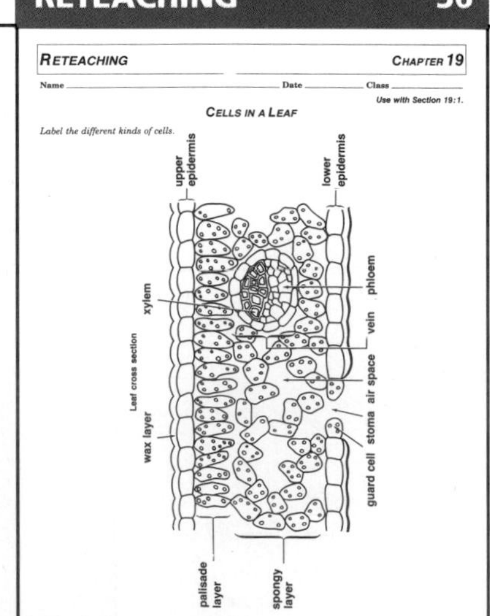

RETEACHING 56

RETEACHING — CHAPTER 19

Name ______ Date ______ Class ______

Use with Section 19:1.

CELLS IN A LEAF

Label the different kinds of cells.

19:2 Leaves Make Food

Plants use materials from their environment to make their own food. The food made by plants is also used by other living things. In meadows, deserts, forests, oceans, and rivers, animals depend on green plants for food.

Objectives

4. **Describe** the process of photosynthesis.
5. **Explain** the chemical equation for photosynthesis.
6. **Compare** the importance of sugar in photosynthesis and respiration.

Building from Raw Materials

At one time, people thought that plants got their food from the soil. Experiments have since shown that as a plant grows taller and heavier, the amount of soil around its roots hardly changes. Today, we know that plants make their own food. The leaf is the main part of a plant that makes food.

Figure 19-10 shows a carpenter building a house. The way a green leaf makes food by photosynthesis can be compared to the way a carpenter builds a house. Both processes build a product from raw materials.

How is building a house like photosynthesis?

A carpenter starts out by using raw materials such as lumber, nails, and shingles. As the carpenter builds, these raw materials begin to take on the shape of a building. Energy is needed to build a house. Human energy is used to carry, arrange, and join materials, and to drive nails into wood. Electrical energy is used to run power saws or drills.

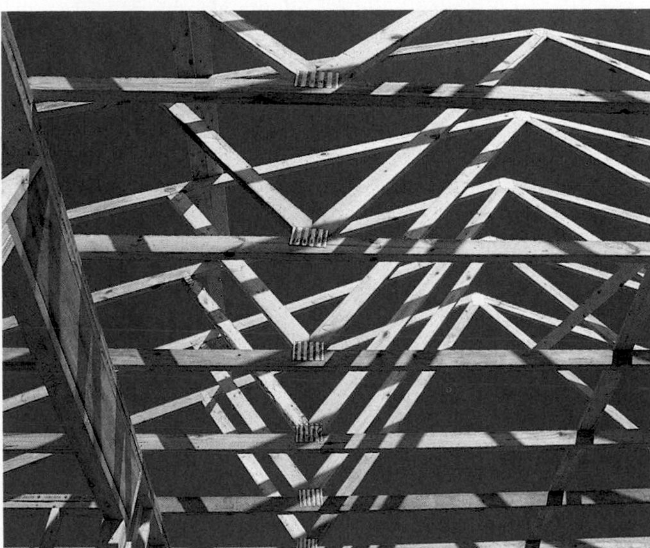

Figure 19-10 The raw materials for building a house include wood and nails.

19:2 Leaves Make Food

PREPARATION

Materials Needed

Make copies of the Focus, Study Guide, Application, Skill, and Reteaching worksheets in the *Teacher Resource Package*.

Key Science Words

No new science words will be introduced in this section.

Process Skills

In the Skill Check, students will infer.

1 FOCUS

▶ The objectives are listed on the student page. Remind students to preview these objectives as a guide to this numbered section.

Convergent Question

Ask students to make a list of materials a plant needs to get its food.

Guided Practice

Have students write down their answers to the margin question: They both use energy to combine raw materials to make a product and produce wastes.

Focus/*Teacher Resource Package*, p. 37. Use the Focus Transparency shown at the bottom of this page as an introduction to the effect of sunlight on growth.

FOCUS 37

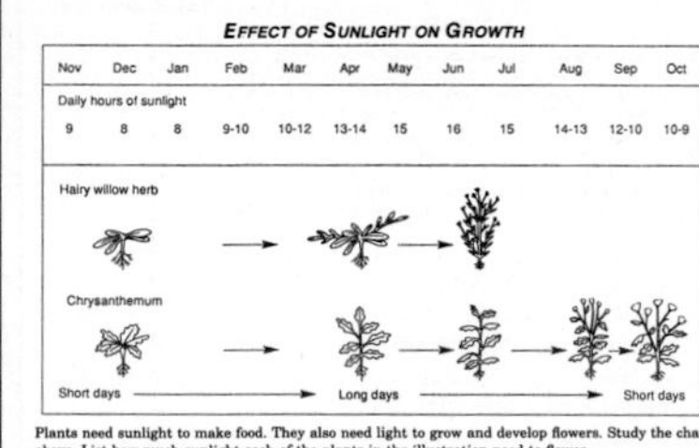

FOCUS CHAPTER 19

Name ______ Date ______ Class ______

EFFECT OF SUNLIGHT ON GROWTH

Nov	Dec	Jan	Feb	Mar	Apr	May	Jun	Jul	Aug	Sep	Oct
Daily hours of sunlight											
9	8	8	9-10	10-12	13-14	15	16	15	14-13	12-10	10-9

Plants need sunlight to make food. They also need light to grow and develop flowers. Study the chart above. List how much sunlight each of the plants in the illustration need to flower.

OPTIONS

Science Background

Many different processes occur in the leaf but photosynthesis is the most important one because food is made for use by the live cells of other plant parts. All chemical energy used by animals and humans started in the plants.

2 TEACH

MOTIVATION/Video

Show the video *Introduction to Photosynthesis,* Insight Media.

Concept Development

- ▶ Explain that soil actually supplies plants with minerals that are needed for many life processes.
- ▶ Emphasize that a specific amount of light, carbon dioxide, and water, as well as a suitable temperature are necessary factors for photosynthesis.
- ▶ Point out that oxygen, the waste product of photosynthesis, is needed by both plants and animals for respiration.
- ▶ Explain that plants are dependent on animals for carbon dioxide for photosynthesis.
- ▶ Explain that plants also get carbon dioxide from the weathering of rocks and volcanoes.

Misconception: Students may think plants get food by taking it in through roots. They are confusing uptake of minerals and water with the food making process of leaves.

Analogy: Make sure that students understand that building a house is a physical process of putting raw materials together; photosynthesis is a chemical process of putting raw materials together. Stress that both require raw materials and end with a usable product.

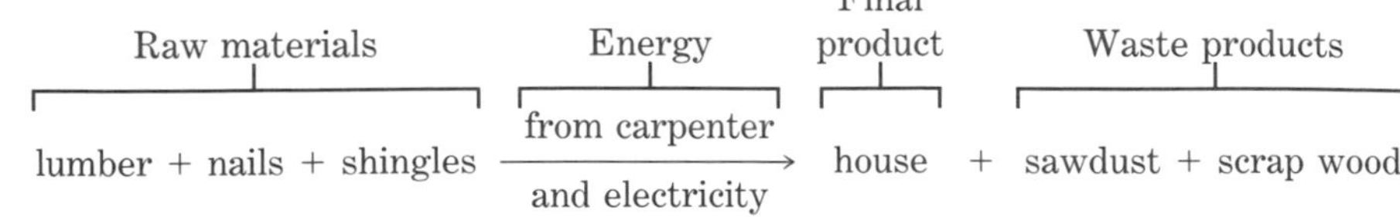

Bio Tip

Consumer: Fertilizer for houseplants is often called plant food. Look at a label on a packet of fertilizer to find out what it really contains.

When a house is built, some waste products are formed. Sawdust and scrap wood are waste products. If collected, the sawdust or wood scraps may be used for some other purpose. The equation above shows a formula for building a house. Notice how the raw materials are combined using energy to give a product and waste materials.

Keeping the example of house building in mind, let's think about the raw materials needed for photosynthesis. This process of food-making uses water and carbon dioxide gas as raw materials. Use Figure 19-11 to trace the path of carbon dioxide and water as they enter a plant. Plant roots take water from the soil. Water passes from the roots, up the stem, and into the leaves. Carbon dioxide in the air enters the leaves through the stomata.

Changing Raw Materials into Sugar

The product of photosynthesis is food in the form of sugar. Just as in house building, plants also have waste products from building food.

How does a plant make sugar? Remember that the chemical formula for carbon dioxide is CO_2. The letter C stands for the element carbon. The letter O stands for the element oxygen. The number 2 means there are two atoms of oxygen in each molecule of carbon dioxide.

Figure 19-11 The raw materials for photosynthesis are the waste products of cellular respiration.

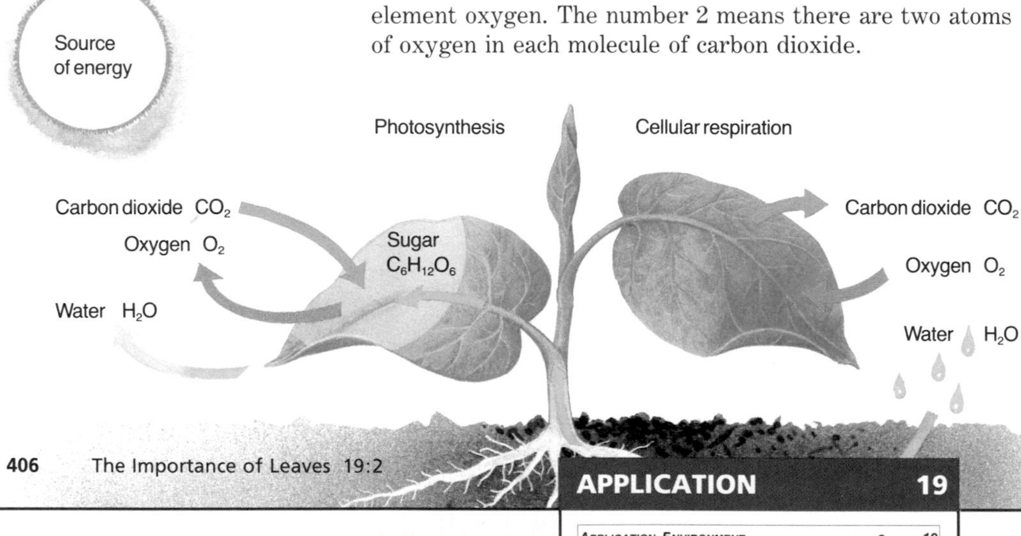

OPTIONS

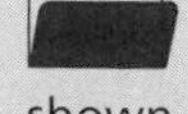

Application/*Teacher Resource Package,* p. 19. Use the Application worksheet shown here to teach the greenhouse effect.

APPLICATION 19

APPLICATION: ENVIRONMENT — **CHAPTER 19**

Name ______ Date ______ Class ______

Use after Section 19:2.

THE GREENHOUSE EFFECT

Earth's atmosphere acts like the glass walls and roof of a greenhouse. It lets in the light of the sun. The light energy then changes into heat energy. The heat energy does not move easily out through the atmosphere, just as heat does not escape easily from a greenhouse. As a result, Earth, like the greenhouse, stays warm. The way the atmosphere helps warm Earth is called the greenhouse effect.

Perhaps you have heard that the greenhouse effect can cause a problem if too much heat is trapped. Extra heat is trapped because Earth's atmosphere is changing. The amount of carbon dioxide in the atmosphere is increasing. Some of the extra carbon dioxide is produced by burning fuels. Some of these fuels include wood, coal, oil, and natural gas. Also, when trees and other plants are destroyed, the problem gets worse. Living plants use up some carbon dioxide through photosynthesis. When the plants are destroyed, the carbon dioxide level continues to rise.

1. What are two ways that people could help lessen the greenhouse effect? **People can burn less fuel and destroy fewer trees and other plants.**
2. Why is the burning of forests a double problem? **The burning creates carbon dioxide, and trees, which could have used up carbon dioxide, are destroyed.**
3. How do you think the recycling of paper could help lessen the greenhouse effect? **Fewer trees would be cut down to make paper.**
4. Does Earth benefit from the greenhouse effect? Explain. **Yes, Earth is kept warm enough for life to exist. Without the atmosphere to hold in heat, Earth would be too cold.**
5. Would planting trees help lessen the greenhouse effect? Explain. **Yes, more trees would use up more carbon dioxide through photosynthesis.**
6. Look for a news report on the greenhouse effect in a newspaper or magazine. Report your findings. **Answers will vary.**

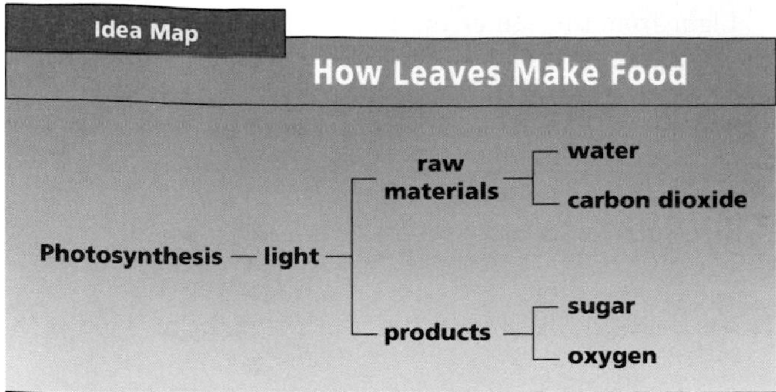

Study Tip: Use this idea map as a study guide to how leaves make food. From where does a plant get its raw materials?

The chemical formula for water is H_2O. The letter H stands for hydrogen. The formula tells us that a water molecule is made of two atoms of hydrogen and one atom of oxygen. The three elements found in carbon dioxide and water—carbon, oxygen, and hydrogen—are the same raw materials that plants need to make sugar, Figure 19-11.

What three elements make up sugar?

The general formula for sugar is $C_6H_{12}O_6$. This is a simple sugar called glucose. The three elements taken in by the plant are arranged in different ways in the leaf to make sugars. All sugars are made of carbon, hydrogen, and oxygen. During photosynthesis, plants first make glucose. This simple sugar is used by the plant to make other more complex carbohydrates such as starch. When food is moved around the plant, another sugar called sucrose is made. Sucrose is the same as your table sugar.

Leaves use six molecules of water and six molecules of carbon dioxide to make one molecule of sugar. How can a leaf cause molecules to change?

Remember how the carpenter used human and electric energy to build the house. Plants also use energy to make sugar. This energy comes from light, Figure 19-12.

The chemical equation for photosynthesis is:

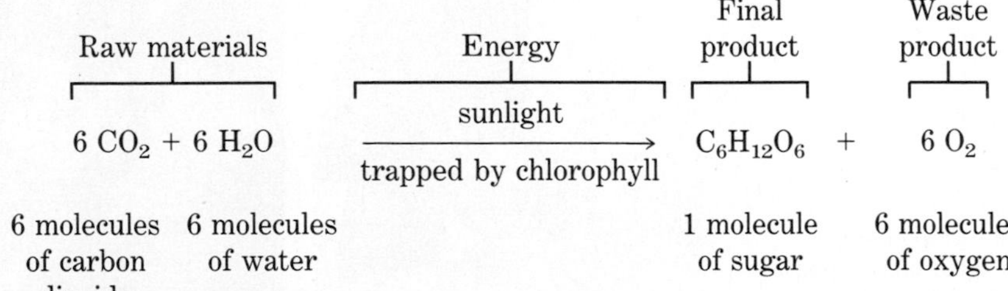

TEACH

Concept Development

▶ Explain that photosynthesis occurs only in cells that have chlorophyll, and those cells are like factories.

Connection: History

Have students investigate and report on Van Helmont's experiments with plant growth. Students can also make a time line to show how many discoveries led up to the current understanding we have about photosynthesis.

Idea Map

Have students use the idea map as a study guide to the major concepts of this section.

Guided Practice

Have students write down their answers to the margin question: carbon, hydrogen, and oxygen.

Independent Practice

Study Guide/*Teacher Resource Package*, p. 112. Use the Study Guide worksheet shown at the bottom of this page for independent practice.

STUDY GUIDE 112

STUDY GUIDE — CHAPTER 19

Name ____ Date ____ Class ____

LEAVES MAKE FOOD

In your textbook, read about photosynthesis in Section 19:2.

The two columns of pictures below relate a carpenter's building a house to a leaf's making food. For each step in both processes, fill in the blanks with the name of what is being produced or used.

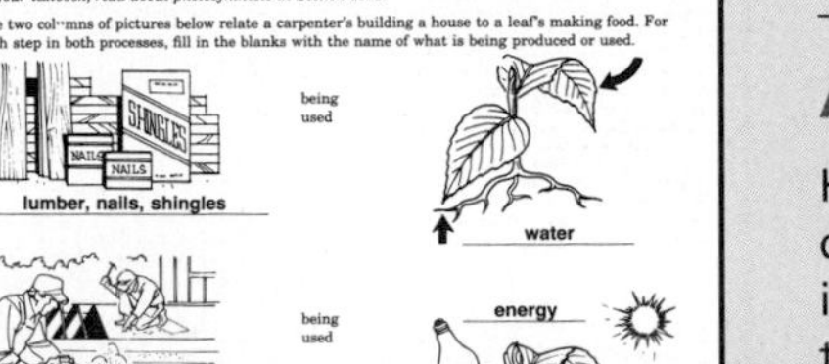

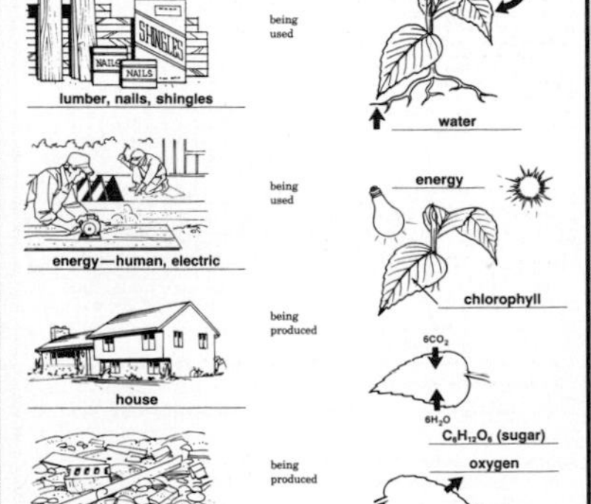

Carpenter		Leaf
lumber, nails, shingles	being used	water
energy—human, electric	being used	energy; chlorophyll
house	being produced	$C_6H_{12}O_6$ (sugar)
sawdust, scrap (waste products)	being produced	oxygen

OPTIONS

ACTIVITY/Challenge

Have students demonstrate that oxygen is made during photosynthesis. Have them place *Elodea* in a test tube filled with water and place the tube near a bright light source. After several minutes, students will see bubbles coming from the plant. Allow them to explain their observations.

TEACH

Concept Development

▶ Point out that plants use only about 1 percent of the light that strikes them during photosynthesis.

▶ Explain that leaves are too small to store all the food made during photosynthesis, but plants also store food in roots, stems, and seeds.

MOTIVATION/Brainstorming

Point out that 90 percent of the photosynthesis in the world occurs in algae. Ask how oxygen gets from water to land.

Check for Understanding

Have students make a parallel chart showing the processes of building a house and photosynthesis. Have them label the raw materials and products.

Reteach

Have students make posters of the two processes, building a house and photosynthesis, and display them. Have some explain their posters.

Guided Practice

Have students draw a plant and trace the paths of water and carbon dioxide through a plant.

Skill Check

Infer: Plants growing beneath other plants sometimes turn yellow. Infer what will happen to these plants if they continue to be covered. *For more help, refer to the **Skill Handbook,** pages 706-711.*

Light from the sun or even light from a light bulb is the source of energy used by plants. How does a plant use light energy to make sugar? You have read in Chapter 6 that plants have chlorophyll. The chlorophyll in the leaves is able to trap light energy. Once trapped, the energy is used by the plant to make sugar.

The word formula for photosynthesis is:

$$\text{Carbon dioxide} + \text{Water} \xrightarrow[\text{by chlorophyll}]{\text{Light trapped}} \text{Sugar} + \text{Oxygen}$$

Oxygen is a waste product of photosynthesis. Just as the carpenter can recycle the waste products sawdust and wood scraps after building a house, a plant can recycle the oxygen from photosynthesis. Plants and other living things use the oxygen for cellular respiration.

How Is Sugar Used?

Suppose you wanted to tear down an old house. Some of the materials in the old house could be reused to build other things such as a shed or garage. The sugar made during photosynthesis is also broken down and used to build other molecules for growth in the plant. When sugar is broken down, energy is released. Remember from Chapter 2 that this process is called cellular respiration. The energy released when sugar is broken down is used for life processes by all living things.

You have read that plants use carbon dioxide and water to make sugar, with oxygen as a waste product. In

a

b

Figure 19-12 A carpenter uses electrical energy to build a house (a). Plants use light energy to make sugars (b).

OPTIONS

Skill/*Teacher Resource Package,* p. 20. Use the Skill worksheet shown here and have students make a line graph on light and photosynthesis.

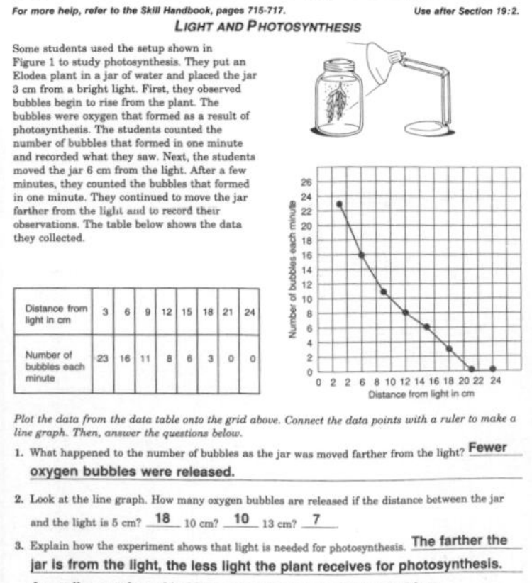

SKILL 20

SKILL: MAKE AND USE A LINE GRAPH CHAPTER 19

Name ______ Date ______ Class ______

For more help, refer to the Skill Handbook, pages 715-717. *Use after Section 19:2.*

LIGHT AND PHOTOSYNTHESIS

Some students used the setup shown in Figure 1 to study photosynthesis. They put an Elodea plant in a jar of water and placed the jar 3 cm from a bright light. First, they observed bubbles begin to rise from the plant. The bubbles were oxygen that formed as a result of photosynthesis. The students counted the number of bubbles that formed in one minute and recorded what they saw. Next, the students moved the jar 6 cm from the light. After a few minutes, they counted the bubbles that formed in one minute. They continued to move the jar farther from the light and to record their observations. The table below shows the data they collected.

Distance from light in cm	3	6	9	12	15	18	21	24
Number of bubbles each minute	23	16	11	8	6	3	0	0

Plot the data from the data table onto the grid above. Connect the data points with a ruler to make a line graph. Then, answer the questions below.

1. What happened to the number of bubbles as the jar was moved farther from the light? **Fewer oxygen bubbles were released.**
2. Look at the line graph. How many oxygen bubbles are released if the distance between the jar and the light is 5 cm? **18** 10 cm? **10** 13 cm? **7**
3. Explain how the experiment shows that light is needed for photosynthesis. **The farther the jar is from the light, the less light the plant receives for photosynthesis. A smaller number of bubbles are released, indicating that less photosynthesis is occurring.**

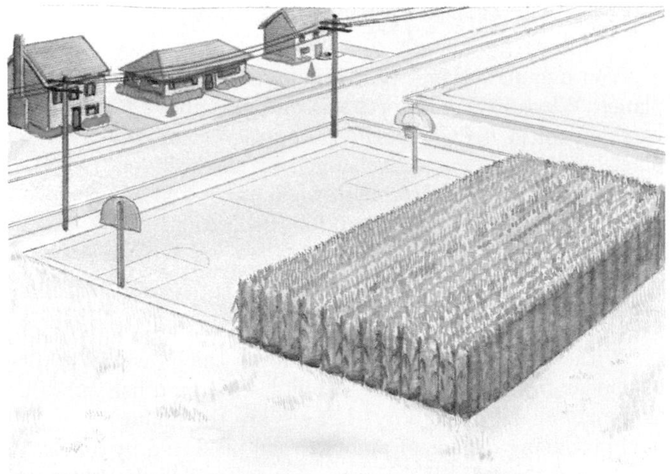

Figure 19-13 If the energy stored in this field of corn could be converted to electrical energy, you and two of your neighbors would have enough electricity for your homes for one year.

respiration, plants and animals use oxygen to break down sugar. Carbon dioxide and water are the waste products. Notice in Figure 19-11 that the raw materials of photosynthesis are the waste products in cellular respiration. The raw materials for respiration are the products in photosynthesis.

Plants store large amounts of energy in the sugar they make during photosynthesis. Suppose plants could change the chemical energy in the food they make into electrical energy. In 100 days, a cornfield the size of a basketball court could make enough electricity in three homes to run their lights, appliances, and heating systems for one year! Plants are a major source of energy for all living things.

How is energy stored in plants?

Check Your Understanding

6. What is the energy source for photosynthesis?
7. What chemical elements are found in sugar made by plants? What chemical elements are used by a plant for photosynthesis?
8. How is the sugar made during photosynthesis important to the plant and to animals?
9. **Critical Thinking:** Why can't animals use the energy from sunlight to make sugar?
10. **Biology and Math:** The formula for sugar is $C_6H_{12}O_6$. How many atoms of each kind are in the formula?

TEACH

Guided Practice

Have students write down their answers to the margin question: in the sugar they make.

Check for Understanding

Have students respond to the first three questions in Check Your Understanding.

Reteach

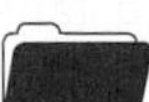 Reteaching/*Teacher Resource Package*, p. 57. Use this worksheet to give students additional practice with photosynthesis.

Extension: Assign Critical Thinking, Biology and Math, or some of the **OPTIONS** available with this lesson.

3 APPLY

Divergent Question

Ask students to predict what would happen if all the plants on Earth were to die tomorrow.

4 CLOSE

Software

Photosynthesis and Transport, Queue, Inc.

RETEACHING 57

RETEACHING: IDEA MAP — *CHAPTER 19*

Name ______ Date ______ Class ______

Use with Section 19:2.

PHOTOSYNTHESIS

Use the following terms to help you complete the idea map: trapped by chlorophyll, carbon dioxide, sunlight, oxygen, water, sugar, waste, useful.

Photosynthesis
- energy: sunlight; trapped by chlorophyll
- raw materials: water; carbon dioxide
- products: useful — sugar; waste — oxygen

1. What is the useful product of photosynthesis? **sugar**
2. What are the raw materials of photosynthesis? **water and carbon dioxide**
3. What elements make up water? **hydrogen and oxygen**
4. What elements make up carbon dioxide? **carbon and oxygen**
5. How does chlorophyll aid in photosynthesis? **It helps trap sunlight.**

Answers to Check Your Understanding

6. light from the sun
7. carbon, oxygen, and hydrogen; carbon, oxygen, and hydrogen
8. Plants use sugar for energy. When animals eat plants, they eat energy.
9. They don't have chloroplasts with chlorophyll.
10. There are 6 atoms of carbon, 12 atoms of hydrogen, and 6 atoms of oxygen.

19:3 Leaves for Food

PREPARATION

Materials Needed

Make copies of the Study Guide, Reteaching, and Lab worksheets in the *Teacher Resource Package.*

▶ Gather plant leaves, coins, small jars, filter paper, liquid solvent, applicator sticks, and masking tape for Lab 19-2.

▶ Purchase produce for the Focus display.

Key Science Words

No new science words will be introduced in this section.

Process Skills

In Lab 19-2, students will experiment, observe, and infer.

1 FOCUS

▶ The objectives are listed on the student page. Remind students to preview these objectives as a guide to this numbered section.

MOTIVATION/Display

Display some produce from the grocery store that has edible leaves. Have students tell you how they know the materials are leaves.

Guided Practice

Have students write down their answers to the margin question: food and energy.

Idea Map

Have students use the idea map as a study guide to the major concepts of this section.

19:3 Leaves for Food

Objectives

7. **Determine** why plants are important to other living things.
8. **List** different uses of leaves.
9. **Explain** why leaves change color.

You live on a planet that is sometimes called the green planet. Why? Flying a few hundred miles above Earth, you would see it as green. Much of the green color comes from plant leaves. The gases exchanged by all these leaves make Earth the perfect environment for humans and all other living things that need oxygen for respiration.

Animals Depend on Plants

What do leaves provide to most living things?

Without photosynthesis, most living things would disappear from Earth. Mice, rabbits, owls, and fish as well as humans would die. Why? Leaves are the major food-producing organs of plants. Food produced by leaves and stored throughout a plant is eaten by animals. Plant eaters digest the plant food and use the released energy for all their life processes.

Many insects are consumers of plant tissues. Figure 19-14a shows insects called leaf miners eating their way through the inside of a leaf. Note the odd-shaped tunnels they make. The tunnels show where they have eaten through the inside of the leaf. Which cells of the leaf have they eaten? All the layers of cells with green chlorophyll have been eaten. These are the cells that produce sugar.

In Figure 19-14b notice the caterpillar eating a leaf. Does a caterpillar eat a leaf in the same way as a leaf miner? What cells are being eaten by the caterpillar?

Animals that eat plants are a source of energy for animals that feed only on other animals. Figure 19-14c shows this kind of consumer eating another animal. The

Study Tip: Use this idea map as a study guide to the importance of leaves. What are two ways that both humans and other animals depend on plants?

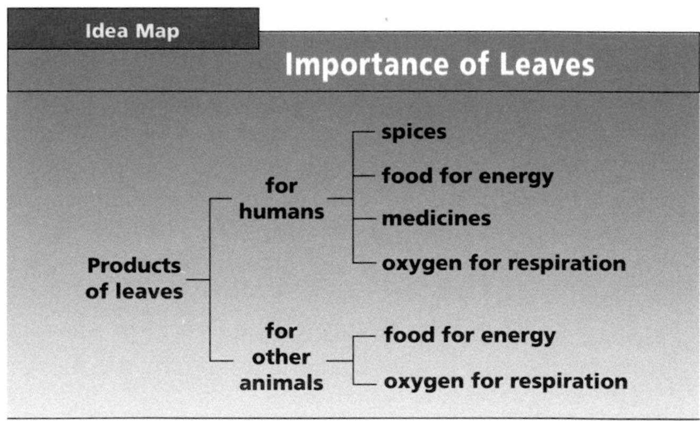

OPTIONS

Science Background

Leaves are important to all other living things on Earth because they are the food source for the plant eaters. The plant eaters are food for the animal eaters. Leaves also supply humans with food, medicines, and numerous products that can be extracted from leaves.

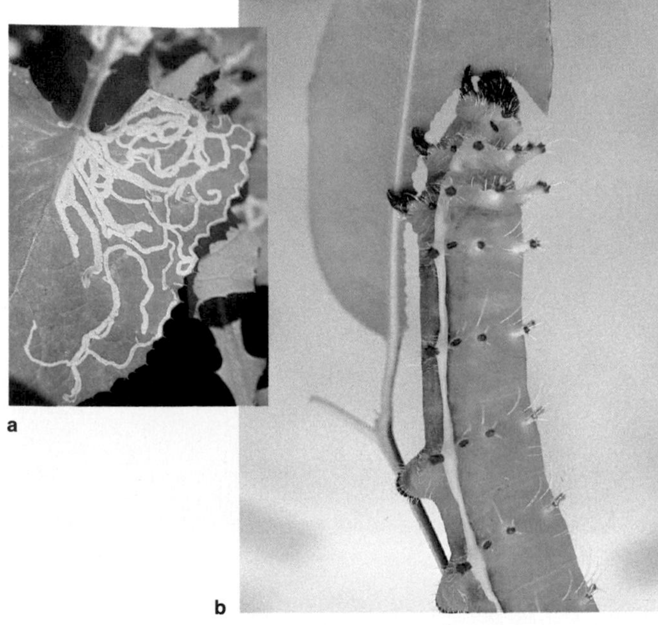

Figure 19-14 Leaf miners tunnel through leaves (a), caterpillars eat whole leaves (b), and birds eat insects that feed on leaves (c).

bird uses the energy from the caterpillar for its own growth and other life processes. The energy from the caterpillar came originally from the leaf of the plant. In turn, the leaf trapped the energy from sunlight. Where do you think your energy for running or cycling comes from? If you follow the chain of feeding back from your hamburger or hot dog you will come to a lot of plants. These plants trap the energy that you use each day.

What if all plants died? Can you predict what would happen to all the plant-eating consumers? They would die because the plants that they depend on for food would be dead. If there were no insects or other plant eaters, such as mice and rabbits, other consumers that eat animals would die. If there were no leaves, there would be less oxygen. Most living things depend on oxygen for respiration.

Practical Uses of Leaves

Many animals, including humans, use leaves for food. You know that cattle, sheep, and other grazing animals eat the leaves of grass. What leaves have you eaten? You may have tried the leaves of cabbage, lettuce, spinach, or onions. In the produce section of a grocery store, you could make a list of many of the leaves people eat.

Bio Tip

Leisure: Develop a vegetable garden. You can grow tomatoes, lettuce, carrots, and radishes in an area less than ten square feet and with very little effort.

2 TEACH

MOTIVATION/Brainstorming

Ask students how humans and animals use leaves.

Concept Development

- Remind students that the palisade and spongy cells are the cells in a leaf that contain chlorophyll.
- Stress that plants are the beginning link in any food chain.
- Reinforce the fact that plants as well as animals need oxygen for respiration.

OPTIONS

Where in a Leaf Does Photosynthesis Take Place?/*Lab Manual,* pp. 161-164. Use this lab as an extension to ways in which animals depend on plants for food.

TEACH

ACTIVITY/Hands-On

Have students place sprouted bean plants in each of two small cups of soil. Add water and place one in a lighted area and the other in a dark area. Have students observe at daily intervals and record changes in the color of the leaves. The plants in the dark should develop yellow leaves.

Check for Understanding

Have students explain the conditions that cause a leaf to turn from green to another color.

Reteach

Divide students into teams and give each team a *Coleus* plant. Have them write a paragraph explaining why the plant has three different colors on the leaf.

Independent Practice

Study Guide/*Teacher Resource Package*, p. 113. Use the Study Guide worksheet shown at the bottom of the page for independent practice.

Guided Practice

Have students write down their answers to the margin question: to produce the chemical digitalis that is used to treat heart disease.

Figure 19-15 Leaves have many uses.

Some leaves are used for flavorings or for spices. If you drink tea, you are drinking boiled water in which tea leaves have been soaked. Peppermint and spearmint are two other flavorings from leaves. Sage, bay, and parsley are leaves used as spices in cooking. Looking at the spice shelves of a grocery store would help you think of other leaves used as spices. Which of the products from plant leaves in Figure 19-15 have you used?

What are foxglove leaves used for?

Many plant leaves contain drugs that are useful in treating diseases. The foxglove is a flowering plant that produces the chemical digitalis (dihj uh TAL us) used as a drug to treat heart disease. As you can see, leaves are very useful to humans.

Changes in Leaves

Have you ever seen grass that has been growing under a board for several days? The grass may have changed color from green to yellow. What happened to the grass under the board? Grass leaves and many other plant leaves contain pigments other than chlorophyll. Two other common pigments are yellow and red in color. Usually leaves are green because the green pigments in chlorophyll cover up any other pigments present. Chlorophyll forms only when there is a supply of light. When the grass leaves were covered by the board, no chlorophyll was made and the green color was lost.

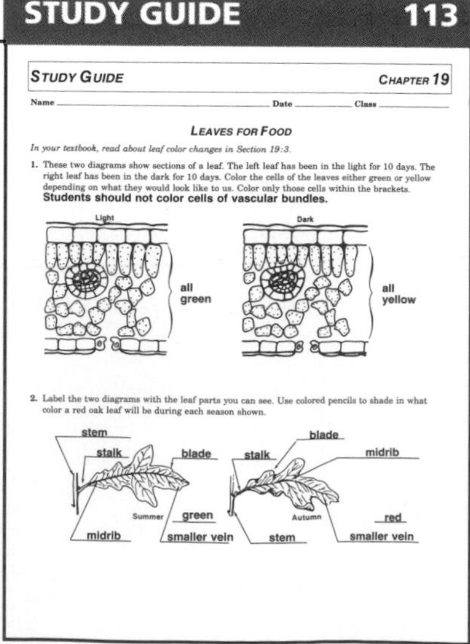
STUDY GUIDE 113

STUDY GUIDE — CHAPTER 19

Name ______ Date ______ Class ______

LEAVES FOR FOOD

In your textbook, read about leaf color changes in Section 19:3.

1. These two diagrams show sections of a leaf. The left leaf has been in the light for 10 days. The right leaf has been in the dark for 10 days. Color the cells of the leaves either green or yellow depending on what they would look like to us. Color only those cells within the brackets. **Students should not color cells of vascular bundles.**

2. Label the two diagrams with the leaf parts you can see. Use colored pencils to shade in what color a red oak leaf will be during each season shown.

Science and Society

Farms of the Future

Growing plants without soil

Farmland that once was used to grow crops for food is now being sold for housing or industry. Less land for farming and growing crops could mean less food for humans. Scientists are now growing plants in the laboratory without soil. They found that as long as light was available, plants could grow while supported only in water that contained minerals. Can this technique of growing plants without soil be used to grow food crops for humans? One plant factory in Illinois grows plants such as lettuce and spinach in four weeks. Containers of sprouted seeds are placed on a slow-moving conveyer belt and given a certain amount of light, water, and minerals. Minerals are added as they are used by the plants. A sprout of lettuce uses 2.5 liters of water and the water is recycled. The same lettuce planted in the field would take six to nine weeks to grow and would use 25 liters of water.

What Do You Think?

1. In an artificial environment, there are no pests, such as weeds or insects, to harm the crops. If the plants were outside, the farmer would have to use pesticides. Inside the factory, the farmer needs to supply the plants with heating, cooling, and lighting. All of these things need electricity. In the fields outside, the farmer would use the energy from the sun. Is it more economical to grow plants in factories or in fields?

2. If we can't afford to build more plant factories, will we be able to grow enough food? If you look around where you live, you might notice that there are more houses, hotels, and offices than there were ten years ago. Did this land once have farm crops? As the human population expands each year, we will build more houses and use up more crop land. What will we all eat? Will we eat more meat?

Which apple would you eat?

3. When you buy a head of lettuce, do you put it back if you see a bruise or leaves with holes? If you bought factory grown plants, they wouldn't have holes from insects. If you bought plants grown in the fields and not sprayed with pesticides, you would probably see some insect damage. How important is it for your vegetables to be perfect? Would you put up with insect-damaged fruits if you knew you were helping to reduce use of chemicals in the environment?

Conclusion: Could plant factories completely change farming all over the world?

Suggested Readings

Collett, R.K. "Hydroponic Gardening." *Flower and Garden,* Mar.-Apr. 1989, pp. 70-72.

Ed. "Fresh Veggies Anywhere." *The Futurist,* Mar.-Apr. 1989, p. 51.

Field, Roger. "Old MacDonald Has a Factory." *Discover,* Dec. 1988, pp. 46-51.

Farms of the Future

Background

Growing plants in greenhouses and without soil has been done for many decades and is called hydroponics. Growing them in a windowless building is a new approach. Light, minerals, and water are carefully controlled. Basil, bibb lettuce, and watercress are the three main crops produced.

Teaching Suggestions

Have the students make a flow chart to show (1) how the raw materials are supplied for photosynthesis, and (2) how any of the raw materials are recycled. Have students find out how raw materials are supplied and recycled in a regular greenhouse. Have them compare a greenhouse with a hydroponics building.

What Do You Think?

1. Answers will vary, but many will say that field-grown produce is more economical.
2. Answers will vary, but some will mention improving methods of food production to make better use of land. Point out that raising beef cattle and other meat sources also requires large tracts of land.
3. Answers will vary. Students who are more ecology-minded will want to reduce the use of chemicals.

Conclusion: Students may see these factories as an answer to areas with drought, little land suitable for farming, and severe insect problems. Have students consider the cost of building large factories and the number of factories necessary to supply world populations. Have them consider the amount and cost of electricity and minerals needed to grow the crops. Remind students that countries suffering from lack of food are already poor and probably could not afford these factories.

TEACH

Guided Practice

Have students write down their answers to the margin question: It breaks down.

Independent Practice

Study Guide/*Teacher Resource Package,* p. 114. Use the Study Guide worksheet shown at the bottom of this page for independent practice.

Check for Understanding

Have students respond to the first three questions in Check Your Understanding.

Reteach

Reteaching/*Teacher Resource Package,* p. 58. Use this worksheet to give students additional practice with the features of leaves.

Extension: Assign Critical Thinking, Biology and Reading, or some of the **OPTIONS** available with this lesson.

3 APPLY

ACTIVITY/Project

Have students list useful leaf products. Have them put product names on tag board strips.

4 CLOSE

Summary

Use the tag board strips for review.

Answers to Check Your Understanding

11. Leaves are the major organs of food producing. Animals eat plants and use the released energy for life processes.
12. for food, spices, flavorings, and medicines
13. Chlorophyll breaks down and other pigments show through.
14. Plants wouldn't photosynthesize, and all living things would die.
15. sage, bay, and parsley

a

b

Figure 19-16 Some plants have pigments that make them show colors other than green (a). Maple trees in the northeastern parts of the United States give a spectacular show of colors in the autumn (b).

What happens to chlorophyll in the autumn?

Some leaves are always a color other than green. Examine the *Coleus* plant in Figure 19-16. How do you explain the colors of the *Coleus* leaves? Have you noticed other plants with colored leaves?

In the area where you live, the leaves of trees may change colors in autumn. When chlorophyll breaks down in autumn, the other pigments in the leaves can be seen. If a leaf contains red and yellow pigments, it will turn red or orange when the chlorophyll is gone.

Why do leaves change their colors in autumn? In the fall, the flow of sap in the stem slows down. The temperature drops and there are fewer hours of sunlight in the autumn. With fewer nutrients and less light, chlorophyll breaks down and the other colored pigments in the leaves show through.

Check Your Understanding

11. Why would most living things disappear from Earth if plants didn't undergo photosynthesis?
12. In what ways are leaves useful to people?
13. Why do some leaves change color in autumn?
14. **Critical Thinking:** If Earth's climate changed so that there was always a thick cover of clouds, what might happen to plants and other living things?
15. **Biology and Reading:** List three leaves that you read about that are used as spices.

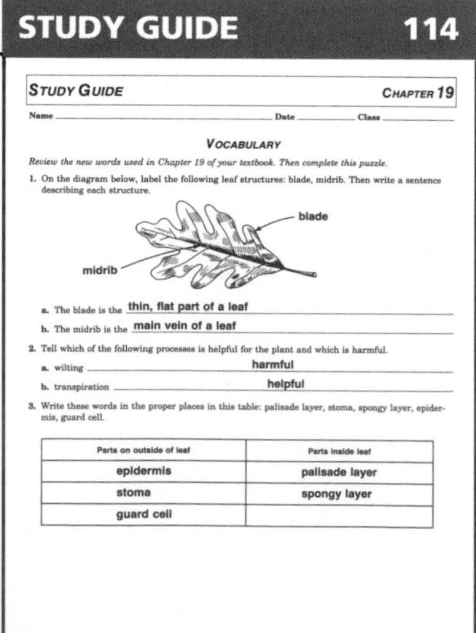

STUDY GUIDE 114

STUDY GUIDE — CHAPTER 19

Name ______ Date ______ Class ______

VOCABULARY

Review the new words used in Chapter 19 of your textbook. Then complete this puzzle.

1. On the diagram below, label the following leaf structures: blade, midrib. Then write a sentence describing each structure.

a. The blade is the thin, flat part of a leaf
b. The midrib is the main vein of a leaf

2. Tell which of the following processes is helpful for the plant and which is harmful.
a. wilting harmful
b. transpiration helpful

3. Write these words in the proper places in this table: palisade layer, stoma, spongy layer, epidermis, guard cell.

Parts on outside of leaf	Parts inside leaf
epidermis	palisade layer
stoma	spongy layer
guard cell	

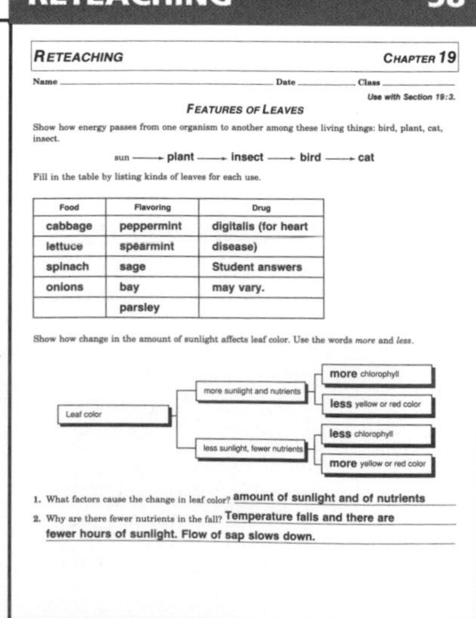

RETEACHING 58

RETEACHING — CHAPTER 19

Name ______ Date ______ Class ______

Use with Section 19:3.

FEATURES OF LEAVES

Show how energy passes from one organism to another among these living things: bird, plant, cat, insect.

sun → plant → insect → bird → cat

Fill in the table by listing kinds of leaves for each use.

Food	Flavoring	Drug
cabbage	peppermint	digitalis (for heart
lettuce	spearmint	disease)
spinach	sage	Student answers
onions	bay	may vary.
	parsley	

Show how change in the amount of sunlight affects leaf color. Use the words *more* and *less*.

1. What factors cause the change in leaf color? amount of sunlight and of nutrients
2. Why are there fewer nutrients in the fall? Temperature falls and there are fewer hours of sunlight. Flow of sap slows down.

Lab 19–2

Pigments

Problem: What pigments are found in a leaf?

Skills

experiment, observe, infer

Materials

plant leaf
coin
small jar
metric ruler
filter paper strip (13 x 2 cm)
liquid solvent
applicator stick
masking tape

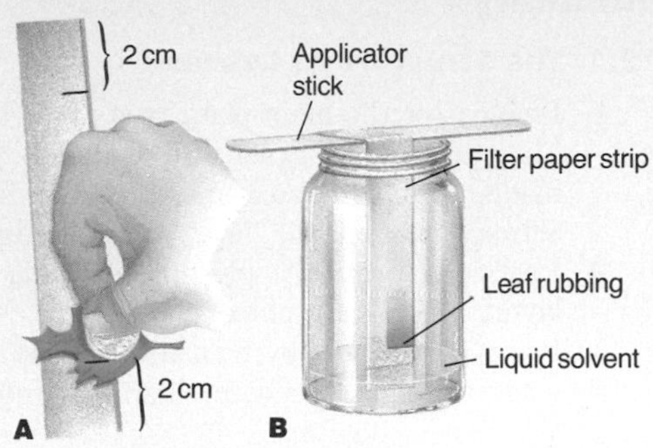

Procedure

1. Lay the leaf across the filter paper, 2 cm from one end. Rub the coin back and forth over the leaf as shown in Figure A. This action will make a dark green line at the 2-cm mark.
2. Pour the liquid solvent into the jar up to a depth of 1 cm. **CAUTION:** *Fumes from liquid solvent are dangerous. Do not breathe in the fumes. Do not use near a flame. Use a fume hood if you have one.*
3. Attach the strip of filter paper to the stick with masking tape, as shown in Figure B. The end with the leaf rubbing should hang down.
4. Hang the end of the paper strip with the leaf-rubbing line on it down into the solvent as shown in Figure B. Make sure the solvent level does not come above the green line. The paper strip may touch the bottom of the jar as long as the solvent level does not cover the leaf-rubbing line.
5. **Experiment:** Allow solvent to move up the paper until it is 2 cm from the top. Watch it carefully so that it doesn't run off the top of the strip.
6. Remove the paper and allow it to dry. Use a fume hood if you have one.
7. Dispose of the solvent as indicated by your teacher.

Data and Observation

1. What color was the paper strip at the leaf-rubbing line before you put the strip in the solvent?
2. What happened to the color of the paper strip at the leaf-rubbing line when the solvent reached it?
3. What colors showed up on the paper strip between the starting and ending lines?

Analyze and Apply

1. Did you see all of the colors the leaf contained before the paper strip was put in the solvent? Explain your answer.
2. **Infer:** Is there more than one shade of any color? If so, what might this mean?
3. Do you think chlorophyll was present? How do you know?
4. **Apply:** How could you find out whether other leaves have the same colors as the one you used in this activity?

Extension

Experiment with a multi-colored leaf and compare the results with those here.

Lab 19-2 Pigments

Overview

In this lab, students will experiment to find out what color pigments are found in a leaf.

Objectives: Completing the lab, students will be able to: (1) **determine** the number of pigments in a leaf, (2) **analyze** the pigments in a leaf.

Time Allotment: 45 minutes

Preparation

▶ Use rolls of filter paper, 2 cm wide.

▶ Most labs will not have fume hoods, so you may want to pour the solvent in the chemistry lab hood prior to the class period.

▶ To avoid pressure buildup on the stopper, don't stopper or cap too tightly.

▶ **Alternate Materials:** You may wish to substitute fingernail polish remover for the solvent.

Lab 19-2 worksheet/*Teacher Resource Package,* pp. 75-76.

Teaching the Lab

▶ As the alcohol goes up the paper strip the students will see different color bands of pigments.

▶ **Troubleshooting:** Make sure that the leaf rubbing is above the solvent level.

Cooperative Learning: Divide the class into teams of two students. For more information, see pp. 22T–23T in the Teacher Guide.

ANSWERS

Data and Observations

1. dark green
2. It began to break up; feather, and move up with the solvent.
3. Answers will depend on leaf used. Many will show green and yellow.

Analyze and Apply

1. No, the different colors separated out after the solvent passed through them.
2. Yes, there are probably more than one kind of chlorophyll and of other pigments.
3. Yes, one of the pigment colors was green. Chlorophyll is a green pigment.
4. Carry out the same experiment using different leaves.

CHAPTER 19 REVIEW

Summary

Summary statements can be used by students to review the major concepts of the chapter.

Key Science Words

All boldfaced terms from the chapter are listed.

Testing Yourself

Using Words

1. palisade layer
2. stoma
3. blade
4. wilting
5. transpiration
6. midrib
7. epidermis

Finding Main Ideas

8. p. 407; Plants need carbon, oxygen, hydrogen, and energy to make sugar.
9. p. 407; Carbon, oxygen, and hydrogen are raw materials that are changed into sugar.
10. p. 403; Wilting is when a plant loses water too fast.
11. p. 408; The products of photosynthesis are sugar and oxygen.
12. pp. 407-408; Sugar is broken down and energy is released during cellular respiration.
13. pp. 411-412; Leaves are used by people for food, spices, and medicines.
14. p. 410; Plants are the major source of energy for all living things.

Using Main Ideas

15. It is broken down and energy is released.
16. The layers of leaf cells that carry on photosynthesis are the palisade and spongy layers.
17. Both are processes in which a plant loses water.
18. The chemical digitalis is made from foxglove.
19. Leaves can be identified by their edges, size, shape, and the way they are arranged on a stem.
20. The elements carbon, oxygen, and hydrogen make up sugar.

Chapter 19 Review

Summary

19:1 The Structure of Leaves

1. Leaves are the main plant parts that make food. They are usually green and are made up of a stalk, a blade, a midrib, and veins. Leaves differ in arrangement, shape, size, and leaf edges.
2. Leaf cells form an epidermis, palisade layer, spongy layer, xylem, and phloem.
3. Plants lose water by transpiration. Wilting occurs when water is lost faster than it is replaced.

19:2 Leaves Make Food

4. In photosynthesis, leaves with chlorophyll use sunlight energy, carbon dioxide, and water to make sugar. This sugar is used as food by living things.
5. The raw materials for photosynthesis are carbon dioxide and water. The products are sugar and oxygen, a waste product. The energy source is sunlight, which is trapped by chlorophyll.
6. Sugar is broken down by cellular respiration into carbon dioxide and water. A large amount of energy is released during respiration.

19:3 Leaves for Food

7. Plants are necessary to supply animals, including humans, with food and oxygen.
8. Leaves are used by people for flavorings, spices, foods, and medicines.
9. Less light and cooler temperatures in autumn cause less chlorophyll to be made in leaves.

Key Science Words

blade (p. 398)
epidermis (p. 401)
guard cell (p. 402)
midrib (p. 399)
palisade layer (p. 402)
spongy layer (p. 402)
stoma (p. 402)
transpiration (p. 403)
wilting (p. 403)

Testing Yourself

Using Words

Choose the word from the list of Key Science Words that best fits the definition.

1. layer of long, thin cells in a leaf
2. small pore in a leaf's epidermis
3. thin, flat part of a leaf
4. process in which plants lose water faster than it can be replaced
5. process in which plants lose water

Review

Testing Yourself *continued*

6. main vein of a leaf
7. cells on the surface of a leaf blade

Finding Main Ideas

List the page number where each main idea below is found. Then, explain each main idea.

8. what plants need to make sugar
9. what raw materials are changed into sugar in a leaf
10. the result of plants losing water too fast
11. the products of photosynthesis
12. what happens to the sugar made during photosynthesis
13. the uses people have for leaves
14. why animals depend on plants

Using Main Ideas

Answer the questions by referring to the page number after each question.

15. What happens to the sugar that a plant makes? (p. 408)
16. What two layers of leaf cells can carry on photosynthesis? (p. 402)
17. What is the relationship between wilting and transpiration? (p. 403)
18. What is the drug from foxglove leaves? (p. 412)
19. What features can you use to identify different kinds of leaves? (p. 398)
20. What elements make up sugar? (p. 407)
21. How are plants, insects, and birds connected by the process of photosynthesis? (p. 410)
22. What are the raw materials needed for photosynthesis? (p. 407)
23. Other than raw materials, what else do leaves need for photosynthesis? (p. 408)
24. Why do leaves change color? (p. 414)

Skill Review 

For more help, refer to the ***Skill Handbook,*** *pages 704-719.*

1. **Classify:** Classify the leaves of plants near your home by shape, edge, and vein pattern.
2. **Measure in SI:** Grow a bean plant from a seed. Measure the volume of water that you use to water the plant each week. After four weeks, find the total volume of water the plant was given. Be careful not to overwater the plant.
3. **Understand science words:** Use a dictionary to find the meaning of the word part *derm.* Find two other words that have this word part.
4. **Interpret diagrams:** Look at Figure 19-6. Which of the drawings shows the stoma in cross section?

Finding Out More

Critical Thinking

1. If plants require water for photosynthesis, how is it possible for desert plants to make food during the dry season?
2. Explain why the number of humans that can live on Earth is related to the rate of photosynthesis in plants.

Applications

1. Make a collection of leaves. Press the leaves in a catalog for two weeks, then use a field guide to identify them.
2. Visit the produce and spice areas of a grocery store. List the leaves or leaf parts that are for sale as food.

Using Main Ideas

21. Insects gain energy from eating plants, and birds gain energy from eating insects.
22. Carbon, oxygen, and hydrogen are raw materials needed for photosynthesis.
23. Leaves use energy from light in photosynthesis.
24. In the fall, there is less light and chlorophyll breaks down, allowing other pigments to show through.

Skill Review

1. Students may want to group leaves within each classification.
2. Students will need to make a chart to keep track of the amount of water used.
3. *Dermis* means skin. Dermatosis is a disease of the skin, *dermal* means derived from skin.
4. The lower drawing shows a cross section through a stoma.

Finding Out More

Critical Thinking

1. Desert plants store water for use during dry seasons.
2. Plants produce oxygen that is necessary for human respiration.

Applications

1. Students can collect grass and other small plant leaves as well as tree leaves.
2. Students will find that the green spices come from leaves, but other colors of spices come from different plant parts.

Chapter Review/ *Teacher Resource Package*, pp. 99-100.

Chapter Test/*Teacher Resource Package*, pp. 101-103.

Chapter Test/*Computer Test Bank*

Plant Support and Transport

PLANNING GUIDE

CONTENT	TEXT FEATURES	TEACHER RESOURCE PACKAGE	OTHER COMPONENTS
(1 1/2 days) 20:1 Stem Structure Herbaceous Stems Woody Stems Stem Growth	Mini Lab: *How Can You Find the Age of a Woody Stem?* p. 423 Career Close-Up: *Nursery Worker,* p. 422 Check Your Understanding, p. 423	Enrichment: *How a Twig Grows,* p. 21 Reteaching: *Important Words for Stems,* p. 59 Skill: *Interpret Diagrams,* p. 21 Focus: *The History of a Tree's Growth,* p. 39 Transparency Master: *Cells in Herbaceous Stems,* p. 93 Study Guide: *Stem Structure,* pp. 115-116	**Laboratory Manual:** *What Does a Woody Stem Look Like Inside?* p. 165 Color Transparency 20: *Cells of a Woody Stem*
(1 1/2 days) 20:2 The Jobs of Stems Transport Storage How Are Stems Used?	Skill Check: *Make and Use Tables,* p. 427 Technology: *Newer Medicines From Plants,* p. 426 Check Your Understanding, p. 427	Reteaching: *The Jobs of Stems,* p. 60 Study Guide: *The Job of Stems,* p. 117	
(1 day) 20:3 Root Structure Taproots and Fibrous Roots Cells of a Root Root Growth	Skill Check: *Understand Science Words,* p. 429 Check Your Understanding, p. 430	Reteaching: *Cells in a Root,* p. 60 Study Guide: *Root Structure,* p. 119	**Laboratory Manual:** *What Do the Inside Parts of a Root Look Like?* p. 169
(2 days) 20:4 The Jobs of Roots Absorption Anchorage and Storage How Are Roots Used?	Skill Check: *Sequence,* p. 431 Lab 20-1: *Absorption,* p. 432 Lab 20-2: *Storage,* p. 434 Idea Map, p. 433 Check Your Understanding, p. 435	Application: *Importance of Stems and Roots,* p. 20 Reteaching: *The Jobs of Roots,* p. 62 Critical Thinking/Problem Solving: *What Caused the Trees to Die?* p. 20 Study Guide: *The Job of Roots,* p. 119 Study Guide: *Vocabulary,* p. 120 Lab 20-1: *Absorption,* pp. 77-78 Lab 20-2: *Storage,* pp. 79-80	
Chapter Review	Summary Key Science Words Testing Yourself Finding Main Ideas Using Main Ideas Skill Review	Chapter Review, pp. 104-105 Chapter Test, pp. 106-108	**Test Bank**

MATERIALS NEEDED

LAB 20-1, p. 432	LAB 20-2, p. 434	MARGIN FEATURES
pencil paper towel strips: 1–10 x 15 cm 4–1 x 10 cm stapler large plastic cup	hand lens carrot root yam root radish root razor blade 3 petri dish halves iodine solution dropper forceps	Skill Check, p. 427 pencil paper Skill Check, p. 429 dictionary Skill Check, p. 431 pencil paper Mini Lab, p. 423 tree stump or leg

OBJECTIVES

SECTION	OBJECTIVE	OBJECTIVES CORRELATION: CHECK YOUR UNDERSTANDING	CHAPTER REVIEW	TRP CHAPTER REVIEW	TRP CHAPTER TEST
20:1	1. **Discuss** the traits of herbaceous stems.	3	8, 22	27	5, 8, 53
	2. **Describe** the five layers of a woody stem.	1	1, 19	5, 7, 8, 11, 15, 16, 31	13, 14, 23, 24, 25, 27, 28, 29, 30, 31, 32, 46, 47, 48, 49, 50, 51
	3. **Explain** how stems grow.	2	5, 6, 7, 18	9, 13, 14, 32, 34	10, 11, 12
20:2	4. **Explain** how a stem serves as a transport system.	7, 9	13, 19	12	26
	5. **Discuss** the storage function of stems.	6	11, 12, 24	10	7
	6. **Identify** how stems are useful to humans.	8	14	6	9
20:3	7. **Compare** taproots and fibrous roots.	11, 15	2	28, 33	2, 15, 16, 17, 18, 19, 20, 21, 22
	8. **Sequence** the layers of root cells.	12, 14	4, 10, 20	17, 18, 19, 20, 21, 22, 26, 30	33, 34, 35, 36, 37, 38, 39, 40, 41, 42, 43, 44, 45, 52
	9. **Describe** how roots grow.	13	16, 17	1	6
20:4	10. **Describe** root hairs and their function.	17	3, 15	4, 23, 29	3
	11. **Relate** how roots anchor the plant and serve as storage.	16	23	24, 25	1
	12. **Discuss** the benefits and problems of roots.	18, 20	21	2, 3	4

Plant Support and Transport

CHAPTER OVERVIEW

Key Concepts

This chapter emphasizes the structures and functions of roots and stems. The chapter points out that some cells found in the roots are continuous throughout the stem and leaves. The economic importance of roots and stems to humans is also presented.

Key Science Words

annual ring	herbaceous stem
cambium	lateral bud
cork	root hair
cortex	taproot
endodermis	terminal bud
fibrous root	woody stem

Skill Development

In Lab 20-1, students will **observe, formulate a model, infer,** and **design an experiment** in relation to root hair function. In Lab 20-2, they will **observe, classify, form hypotheses,** and **design an experiment** while studying starch storage in roots. In the Skill Check on page 427, students will **make and use tables** of plants used by humans. In the Skill Check on page 429, they will **understand** the **science word** *fibrous root.* In the Skill Check on page 431, they will **sequence** plant parts through which water passes. In the Mini Lab on page 423, students will **use numbers** to find the age of a woody stem.

CHAPTER PREVIEW

Chapter Content

Review this outline for Chapter 20 before you read the chapter.

Skills in this Chapter

The skills that you will use in this chapter are listed below.

- In **Lab 20-1,** you will observe, formulate a model, infer, and design an experiment. In **Lab 20-2,** you will observe, classify, form hypotheses, and design an experiment.
- In the **Skill Checks,** you will sequence, make and use tables, and understand science words.
- In the **Mini Labs,** you will use numbers.

418

Bridging

In Chapter 19, students learned about the features used to classify leaves, and the parts and functions of the external and internal parts of leaves. In this chapter, they will learn about the external and internal parts of stems and roots.

Chapter 20

Plant Support and Transport

Plants, like animals, support themselves. Unlike animals, plants have no skeleton. How do you suppose the plants in the photo on the left stay upright without a skeleton? Which plant part supports them?

You may have noticed how pipes supply your home with water and gas. Look at the water pipes in the photo below. Like these pipes, the cells of a plant carry needed materials to all parts of the plant. Which parts of a plant supply the plant with these materials? Look again at the picture on the facing page. How do you suppose the plants get some of their needed materials? Can you tell where the root stops and the stem begins? How is a root different from a stem?

Try This!

Do roots of plants grow only in soil? Find a plant that grows up the sides of buildings. Some of these plants are called vines. Find out which part of the vine attaches to the building.

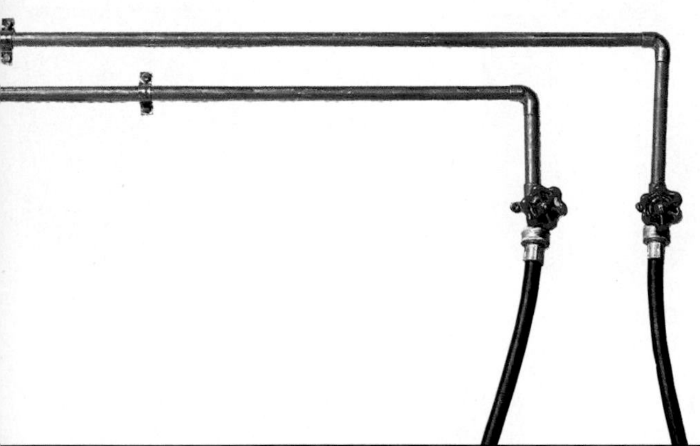

Water pipes supply a home.

GETTING STARTED

Using the Photos

Students should be able to relate how the roots anchor the plants in soil and how the stems support the leaves. Point out that larger plants need a larger root system to carry out the plant's functions. Tell them that the roots spread out in soil as far as the leaves spread out above the ground.

MOTIVATION/Try This!

Do roots of plants grow only in soil? Students will **observe** that some vines that grow up walls send out roots from the sides of the stems. These are called adventitious roots. Examples of plants with adventitious roots are ivy and grape vines.

Chapter Preview

Have students study the chapter outline before they begin to read the chapter. They should note the overall organization of the chapter, that the first topic is stem structure followed by the jobs of stems and how stems are used by humans. These topics are followed by root structures, the jobs of roots, and lastly, by how roots are important to humans.

Misconception

Students may believe falsely that sap rises in a tree in the spring and goes down to the roots in the fall. There is water in a stem all year.

20:1 Stem Structure

PREPARATION

Materials Needed

Make copies of the Focus, Enrichment, Skill, Reteaching, and Study Guide worksheets in the *Teacher Resource Package.*

▶ Obtain cornstalks for the demonstration activity.

▶ Obtain a tree stump or fireplace log for the Mini Lab.

Key Science Words

herbaceous stem	cambium
cortex	terminal bud
woody stem	lateral bud
cork	annual ring

Process Skills

In the Mini Lab, students will use numbers.

1 FOCUS

▶ The objectives are listed on the student page. Remind students to preview these objectives as a guide to this numbered section.

ACTIVITY/Brainstorming

Ask students to give you the names of several plants they have seen on their way to school. Tell them to group their plants into two groups: those with green stems and those with bark. Ask them which plants are taller, those with green stems or those with bark. Ask them why they think one type of plant may grow taller than the other.

Focus/*Teacher Resource Package*, pp. 39-40. Use the Focus transparency shown at the bottom of this page as an introduction to woody stems.

Guided Practice

Have students write down their answers to the margin question: they don't have enough xylem cells.

20:1 Stem Structure

Objectives

1. **Discuss** the traits of herbaceous stems.
2. **Describe** the five layers of woody stems.
3. **Explain** how stems grow.

Key Science Words

herbaceous stem
cortex
woody stem
cork
cambium
terminal bud
lateral bud
annual ring

A stem is a plant part that supports the plant and transports materials. Roots are on one end of a stem and leaves are attached along the stem's length. The external parts of stems have features that help identify plants. Think how the stem of a daisy differs from the stem of an oak tree.

Herbaceous Stems

Why aren't herbaceous stems tall?

There are two stem types found in plants. They are either woody or herbaceous (hur BAY shus). **Herbaceous stems** are soft, green stems. Plants with herbaceous stems usually grow no taller than two meters. If they grew taller, they would probably fall over. Why? Herbaceous stems don't have many xylem cells. Xylem cells help support a plant stem. Recall from Chapter 6 that xylem tissue has tubelike cells that carry water and minerals throughout a plant.

Bean plants have herbaceous stems. If you slice the stem of a bean plant and look at a section under a microscope, it looks like Figure 20-1a. Many herbaceous vegetables have this pattern. Notice how the bundles of xylem and phloem cells are arranged in a circle. Other herbaceous stems, such as corn, lily, and wheat, have scattered bundles of xylem and phloem, as in Figure 20-1b.

Notice the cortex in the two herbaceous stems. The **cortex** is a food storage tissue in plants. Food is usually stored in plants in the form of starch. The epidermis of a herbaceous stem makes up its outer covering.

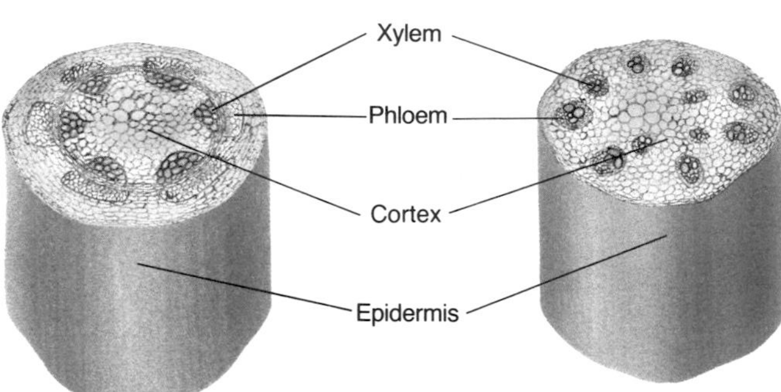

Figure 20-1 There are two patterns of xylem and phloem bundles in herbaceous stems.

OPTIONS

Science Background

There are two kinds of stems, woody and herbaceous. The stems of herbaceous plants are soft and green, while woody stems are hard and not green. Some woody stems can grow to a height of 100 meters, while most herbaceous stems grow to a height of 0.5-2 meters. As they grow, stems increase in length and thickness.

Cells of a Woody Stem/*Transparency Package*, number 20. Use color transparency number 20 as you teach stem structure.

FOCUS 39

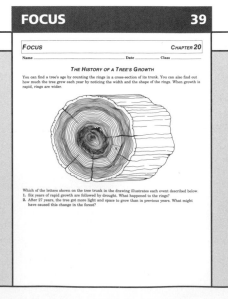

FOCUS CHAPTER 20

Name ________ Date ________ Class ________

THE HISTORY OF A TREE'S GROWTH

You can find a tree's age by counting the rings in a cross-section of its trunk. You can also find out how much the tree grew each year by noticing the width and the shape of the rings. When growth is rapid, rings are wider.

Which of the letters shown on the tree trunk in the drawing illustrates each event described below.

1. Six years of rapid growth are followed by drought. What happened to the rings?
2. After 27 years, the tree got more light and space to grow than in previous years. What might have caused this change in the forest?

Woody Stems

Trees and shrubs have woody stems. A **woody stem** is a nongreen stem that grows to be thick and hard. The rough outer covering of a woody stem is called the bark. Bark protects a woody stem better than epidermis protects a herbaceous stem. If you ever look at a tree stump, look for the dark outer covering. This is the bark. Many trees can be identified by the traits of their bark. The bark of some trees is very smooth, Figure 20-2. Other trees have rough bark. The bark of some trees is scaly.

A woody stem is made up of five different cell layers, or tissues. Each layer has a certain job. By following the numbers in Figure 20-3, you will be able to see where these layers are found.

1. The outer layer of a woody stem is the **cork.** Cork is made of dead cells and protects the stem from insects, disease, and water loss.
2. Inside the cork layer is the layer of cells called the cortex. Remember that cortex cells store food.
3. Inside the cortex is a ring of phloem cells. Recall that phloem carries food from leaves to all parts of the plant.
4. The next layer is the cambium. **Cambium** is a thin layer of cells that divides to form new phloem on the outside and new xylem on the inside. Each year, the cambium produces new xylem and phloem cells that make the stem thicker. Thus, woody stems grow wider with age. The four layers—cork, cortex, phloem, and cambium—together make up the bark of a woody stem.

Figure 20-2 Beech trees can be identified by their smooth bark.

What is the outer layer of a woody stem?

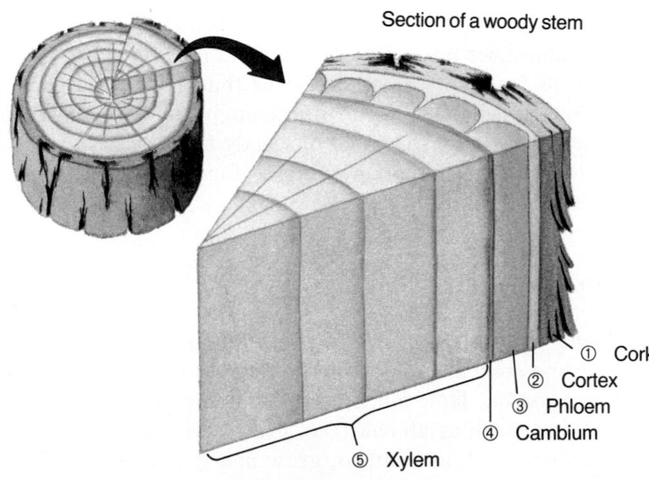

Figure 20-3 A woody stem is made of five cell layers. How many layers make up bark? four

2 TEACH

MOTIVATION/Demonstration

Obtain some dry cornstalks in the fall. You can use these to demonstrate strings or veins in plants.

Guided Practice

Have students write down their answers to the margin question: bark.

ACTIVITY/Display

Make photocopies of the cross sections of pieces of small tree trunks or limbs. These can be put on display with the question "Can you tell the age of these woody stems?"

Independent Practice

Study Guide/*Teacher Resource Package,* p. 115. Use the Study Guide worksheet shown at the bottom of this page for independent practice.

SKILL 21

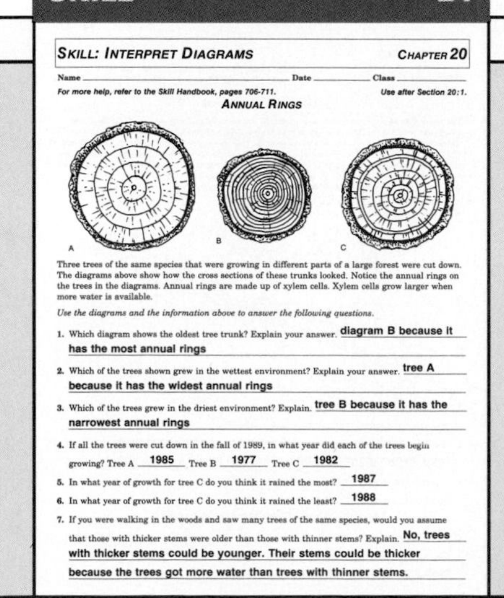

SKILL: INTERPRET DIAGRAMS — CHAPTER 20

Name ______ Date ______ Class ______

For more help, refer to the Skill Handbook, pages 706-711. *Use after Section 20:1.*

ANNUAL RINGS

A B C

Three trees of the same species that were growing in different parts of a large forest were cut down. The diagrams above show how the cross sections of these trunks looked. Notice the annual rings on the trees in the diagrams. Annual rings are made up of xylem cells. Xylem cells grow larger when more water is available.

Use the diagrams and the information above to answer the following questions.

1. Which diagram shows the oldest tree trunk? Explain your answer. **diagram B because it has the most annual rings**
2. Which of the trees shown grew in the wettest environment? Explain your answer. **tree A because it has the widest annual rings**
3. Which of the trees grew in the driest environment? Explain. **tree B because it has the narrowest annual rings**
4. If all the trees were cut down in the fall of 1989, in what year did each of the trees begin growing? Tree A **1985** Tree B **1977** Tree C **1982**
5. In what year of growth for tree C do you think it rained the most? **1987**
6. In what year of growth for tree C do you think it rained the least? **1988**
7. If you were walking in the woods and saw many trees of the same species, would you assume that those with thicker stems were older than those with thinner stems? Explain. **No, trees with thicker stems could be younger. Their stems could be thicker because the trees got more water than trees with thinner stems.**

STUDY GUIDE 115

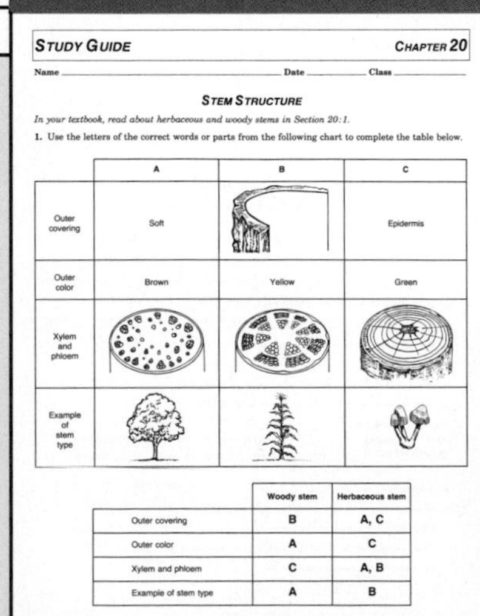

STUDY GUIDE — CHAPTER 20

Name ______ Date ______ Class ______

STEM STRUCTURE

In your textbook, read about herbaceous and woody stems in Section 20:1.

1. Use the letters of the correct words or parts from the following chart to complete the table below.

	A	B	C
Outer covering	Soft		Epidermis
Outer color	Brown	Yellow	Green
Xylem and phloem			
Example of stem type			

	Woody stem	Herbaceous stem
Outer covering	B	A, C
Outer color	A	C
Xylem and phloem	C	A, B
Example of stem type	A	B

OPTIONS

ACTIVITY/Challenge

Have students write a statement to explain what would happen if sap did not rise in a woody stem each spring. Let several students read their statement to the class.

Skill/*Teacher Resource Package,* p. 21. Use the Skill worksheet shown here to give additional practice with aging woody stems.

Career Close-Up

Nursery Worker

A nursery worker must know how to select the best quality plants.

Many people visit a nursery for gardening advice and to buy plants for their garden. In a large nursery, there are often several nursery workers who are there to help you.

The job of nursery worker includes planting a variety of plants, either at the nursery or a customer's home. Being able to understand the measurements in a landscape plan is an important skill for this job. The worker is responsible for preparing the soil and then setting out the plants.

When a nursery worker is not tending plants, he or she may spend some time repairing equipment. During colder months, he or she may help care for houseplants.

A high school education is important for a career as a nursery worker. You should have a general interest in caring for plants. As a nursery worker, you will need to learn about pruning, plant diseases, and insect pests. A class in horticulture (HOR tuh kul chur) will provide you with this knowledge. Most plant nurseries offer excellent on-the-job training.

5. The innermost layer of a woody stem is xylem. The xylem cells have very thick cell walls that help support the plant. Xylem cells take water up through the stem. Dead xylem cells make up the wood of woody stems. This means that wood used for building homes or furniture came from the xylem of a tree.

Stem Growth

Plants with herbaceous stems usually grow for only one year or one season. Plants with woody stems grow for more than one season. How much do plant stems grow in one year? Some, such as an oak tree, grow less than 15 cm while others, such as bamboo, grow nearly six meters.

Career Close-Up

Nursery Worker

Background

More people want to spend their leisure time away from the chores of yard work and depend on nurseries to solve their yard management problems.

Related Careers

lawn manager, horticulture technician, and landscape management

Job Requirements

high school diploma with on-the-job training

For More Information

Check the library for government publications listing careers.

TEACH

Independent Practice

Study Guide/*Teacher Resource Package,* p. 116. Use the Study Guide worksheet shown at the bottom of this page for independent practice.

OPTIONS

Science Background

Point out that tree rings tell something about environmental conditions. Thick annual rings denote good years of growth because the environmental factors were optimum. Thinner annual rings denote less than optimum factors.

Enrichment/*Teacher Resource Package,* p. 21. Use the Enrichment worksheet shown here as an extension to stem growth.

STUDY GUIDE 116

STUDY GUIDE — CHAPTER 20

Name ____ Date ____ Class ____

STEM STRUCTURE

In your textbook, read about stem growth in Section 20:1.

2. Examine the diagram of a core sample taken from a tree. Then, answer the following questions.

a. What is counted to determine the age of a tree? **rings of xylem**
b. In what part of the year do the dark bands form? **summer**
c. Why are they dark? **The xylem cells are smaller (because growth is slower).**
d. In what part of the year do the light bands form? **spring**
e. Why are they light? **The xylem cells are larger (because growth is faster).**
f. How old was this tree when the core sample was taken? **8 years old**
g. Which band (A, B, or C) shows the poorest year of growth? **B**
h. Which band (A, B, or C) shows the year with the most rainfall? **A**

3. Examine the diagram below of a core sample taken in 1991.

Students may need help identifying growth rings.

a. How old was this tree in 1991? **6 years old**
b. What year was rainfall the least where this tree was growing? **1988**
c. What year did the tree grow the least? **1988**
d. What year was rainfall the most where this tree was growing? **1989**
e. What year did the tree grow the most? **1989**

ENRICHMENT 21

ENRICHMENT — CHAPTER 20

Name ____ Date ____ Class ____

Use after Section 20:1.

HOW A TWIG GROWS

The picture shows a twig that is several years old. At the tip of the twig is the terminal bud. The twig grows from the tip. The cells just behind the terminal bud elongate. Bud scales surround and protect the terminal bud. At the end of the year the twig stops growing and the bud scales fall off. The bud scales leave a scar called a bud-scale scar. The bud-scale scar looks like a set of rings going all the way around the twig. Each year's growth is marked by the bud-scale scars. Leaves also make scars on the twig when they fall off in the autumn. These scars are called leaf scars. Lateral buds form on the sides of a twig. These buds show where new twigs will form.

Label each of the structures mentioned above on the drawing of the twig. Then answer the questions that follow.

1. How many centimeters did the twig grow in its first year? **5 cm** In its second year? **4 cm** How many centimeters did it grow last year? **3.5 cm**
2. How old is the twig? How can you tell? **4 years old. The bud-scale scars show 3-years growth and the terminal bud shows a fourth year.**
3. How many leaves grew on the twig last year? **1** How many leaves grew on the twig during its first year? **3** During which year did the twig have the most leaves? Explain how you know. **The second year. There are four leaf scars.**
4. How old is the smaller twig that is growing from the base of the larger twig? **3 years** Will the larger twig sprout any new twigs this year? Explain. **Yes. There are lateral buds just above the last bud-scale scar.**

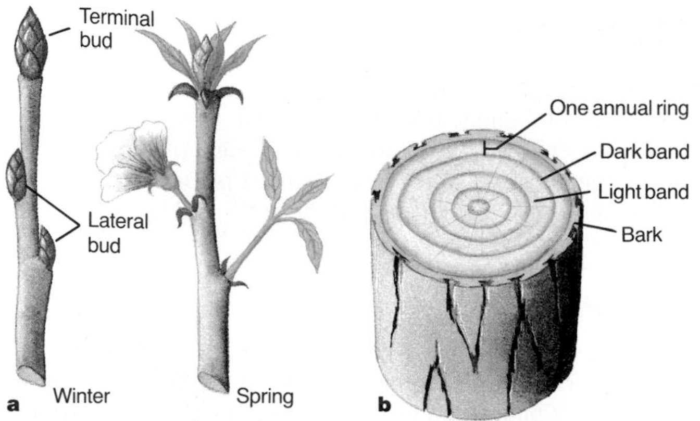

Figure 20-4 Plants grow in length from terminal buds. New branches, leaves, or flowers grow from lateral buds (a). A tree trunk is made of annual rings of wood (b).

What is a terminal bud?

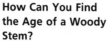

How do stems grow in length? Look at Figure 20-4a. Notice that there are two kinds of buds on the stem. The **terminal bud** is the bud at the tip of a stem. This bud is responsible for the plant's growth in length. Along the sides of a stem are **lateral buds** that give rise to new branches, leaves, or flowers.

A cross section of a tree trunk shows the trunk is made up of a series of rings, Figure 20-4b. Remember that the cambium forms a ring of new xylem cells each year. Each ring of xylem is called an **annual ring**. Each annual ring is often made up of a dark band and a light band of cells. The lighter band forms in the spring when there is plenty of rain and xylem growth is more rapid. The band looks lighter because the xylem cells are larger. Growth is slower in the summer when there is less rain. The band looks darker because the xylem cells are smaller.

Mini Lab

How Can You Find the Age of a Woody Stem?

Use numbers: Find a tree stump or fireplace log and look at the rings. Calculate the age of the woody stem. *For more help, refer to the* ***Skill Handbook,*** *pages 718-719.*

Check Your Understanding

1. List two common plants with herbaceous stems.
2. How can woody stems be used to help identify trees?
3. How does the cambium cause a woody stem to grow?
4. **Critical Thinking:** If you drive a nail into a young tree trunk two feet from the ground, how high up the trunk do you think the nail will be in twenty years?
5. **Biology and Writing:** Plants have two ____ of stems. They are either woody or soft and green. Which word best fits in the blank? kinds, lengths, colors

TEACH

Guided Practice

Have students write down their answers to the margin question: the bud at the tip of stems.

Mini Lab

Make sure that students count the light and dark rings as one year of growth.

Check for Understanding

Have students respond to the first three questions in Check Your Understanding.

Reteach

Reteaching/Teacher Resource Package, p. 59. Use this worksheet to give students additional practice with parts of a stem.

Extension: Assign Critical Thinking, Biology and Writing, or some of the **OPTIONS** available with this lesson.

3 APPLY

ACTIVITY/Field Trip

Take students on a field trip around the school yard or a city park to compare herbaceous and woody stems.

4 CLOSE

ACTIVITY/Challenge

Have students find out how they can tell the age of a tree without cutting it down.

Answers to Check Your Understanding

1. Answers will vary. Examples are corn, lilies, and most vegetables.
2. the texture and kind of bark found on the tree
3. The cambium cells produce new layers of xylem cells. The added cells make the stems thicker.
4. The nail will still be 2 feet from the ground.
5. kinds

RETEACHING 59

RETEACHING — **CHAPTER 20**

Name ____ Date ____ Class ____

Use with Section 20:1.

IMPORTANT WORDS FOR STEMS

Using Vocabulary
Review the science words as you read Section 20:1. Study the definitions of the boldfaced words. Then complete the exercise below. Each science word has two choices that are correct.

Write the letters of both correct choices on the line to the left.

a, c 1. Cambium
(a) forms new xylem and phloem.
(b) is found only in leaves of herbaceous plants.
(c) is found between xylem and phloem.

a, c 2. Bark
(a) is found in plants with woody stems.
(b) is part of xylem in stems.
(c) is made of cork, phloem, cambium, and cortex cells.

b, c 3. Herbaceous stems
(a) are hard with rough bark.
(b) are usually soft and green.
(c) usually have less xylem than woody stems.

a, c 4. Woody stems
(a) are the thick hard stems of certain plants.
(b) are soft and green.
(c) are the nongreen stems of trees.

a, c 5. Cork
(a) forms the outer layer of a woody stem.
(b) is made of living cells.
(c) is made of dead cells that protect the stem.

a, c 6. A lateral bud
(a) forms a new leaf or flower.
(b) is found at the tip of all stems.
(c) is found along the sides of branches.

a, b 7. Cortex
(a) of an herbaceous stem is soft like a sponge.
(b) is the food storage area of the stem.
(c) is where food is made.

OPTIONS

What Does a Woody Stem Look Like Inside?/*Lab Manual,* pp. 165-168. Use this lab as an extension to stem structure.

20:2 The Jobs of Stems

PREPARATION

Materials Needed

Make copies of the Transparency, Study Guide, and Reteaching worksheets in the *Teacher Resource Package*.

▶ Obtain a potted plant for the Focus activity.

▶ Obtain maple syrup and other plant products for the demonstration. Gather a sponge and glass of water for the demonstration.

Key Science Words

No new science words will be introduced in this section.

Process Skills

In the Skill Check, students will make and use tables.

1 FOCUS

▶ The objectives are listed on the student page. Remind students to preview these objectives as a guide to this numbered section.

ACTIVITY/Brainstorming

Show students a potted plant and ask them to work in groups of two or three and try to answer the questions: Where do roots end and stems start? How do you know? How could you find out?

Guided Practice

Have students write down their answers to the margin question: xylem.

20:2 The Jobs of Stems

Objectives

4. **Explain** how a stem serves as a transport system.
5. **Discuss** the storage function of stems.
6. **Identify** how stems are useful to humans.

The stem is an important link between the roots and the leaves of a plant. Roots take up and store materials that leaves need. Leaves produce materials that roots and stems need. The stem is the part of the plant through which materials travel between the roots and leaves.

Transport

Water and minerals are needed by plant parts for growth. Leaves, as you read in Chapter 19, make food for the plant by photosynthesis. Water enters the leaves from the stems. How does the stem get this water? The water is taken up by the roots of the plant.

Water taken in by the roots is transported up through the stem. Minerals from the soil are dissolved in this water and are also carried up the stem. All water and minerals are carried up in the long, tubelike cells called xylem.

What cells in a stem carry water and minerals?

What causes water to move through a plant from its roots to its leaves? Biologists have developed a theory that explains how water moves upward in a plant. One part of the theory is that water moves through a plant much as water moves into a paper towel, Figure 20-5. If you put a dry paper towel into water, the water moves up into the towel by diffusion.

The second part of the theory explains how water passes up and out of a plant. Water moves up the plant through xylem cells and is lost from the leaves through the stomata. You read in Chapter 19 that transpiration is the loss of water through the stomata of leaves. This movement of water through a plant is like a thread being pulled through a straw, Figure 20-6a. The molecules of water stick together in a threadlike stream through a plant.

Figure 20-6b shows how important the stem is as a link between the leaves and roots. As water moves out of the leaves, more water is pulled into the leaves from the stem. The water in the stem is pulled up from the roots. New water enters the roots by osmosis.

Food made in leaves is also transported through stems. Food in the form of sugars moves down the stem through the tubelike cells called phloem. Why does food move downward? Root cells are alive and also need energy in order to stay alive. They would die without food. The sugars made in the leaf are used by the roots and all the other cells of the plant.

Figure 20-5 Water moves into a plant the same way it moves up a paper towel. What is the name of this process? diffusion

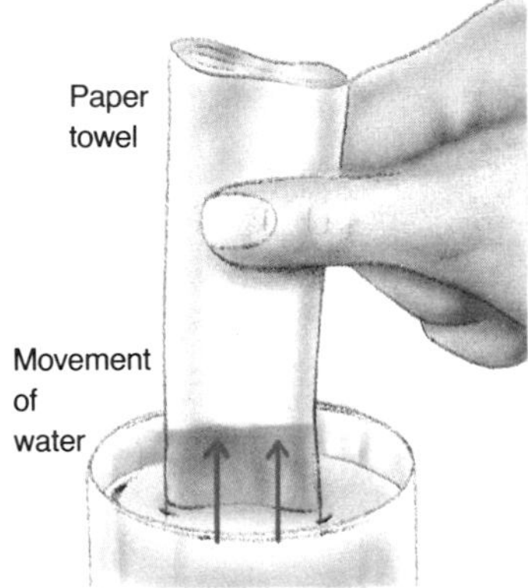

OPTIONS

Science Background

The stem connects the roots to the leaves. Water absorbed by the roots moves through the stem to the leaf for photosynthesis. The food made in the leaf is transported to the stem and roots for storage. This food can be used by all plant cells for respiration.

Transparency Master/*Teacher Resource Package,* p. 93. Use the Transparency Master shown here as you teach structure and function of stems.

TRANSPARENCY 93

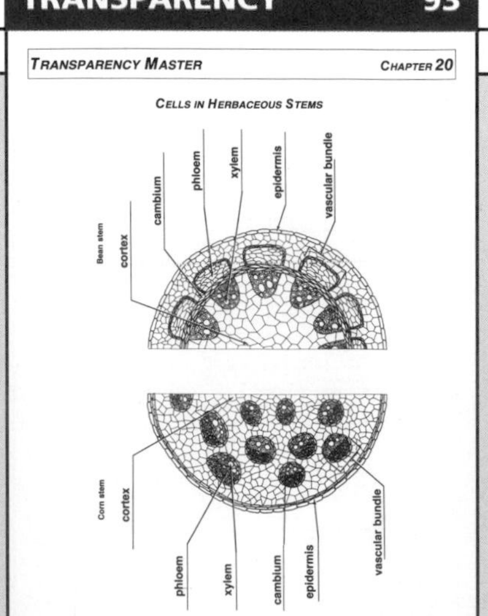

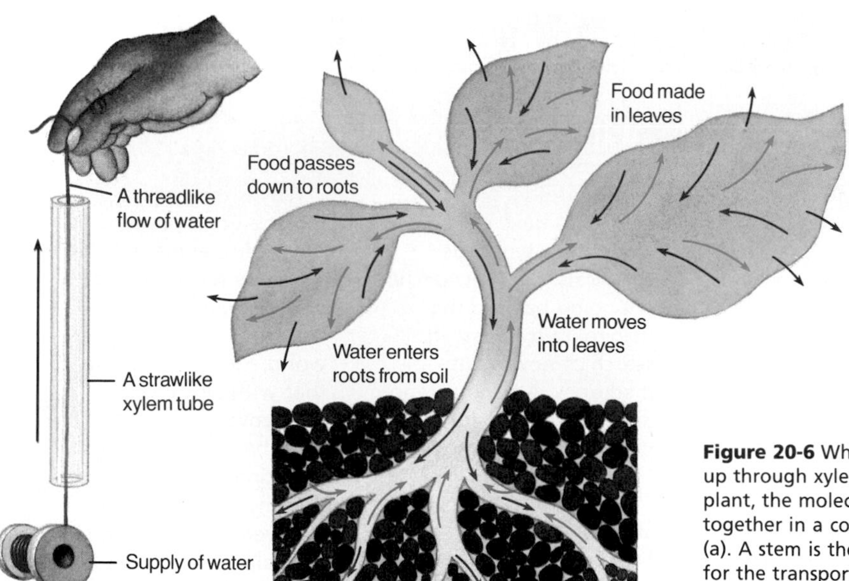

Figure 20-6 When water moves up through xylem tubes in a plant, the molecules stick together in a continuous stream (a). A stem is the plant's organ for the transport of water and food between the roots and the leaves (b).

Storage

Look at the food products stored in containers on the pantry shelf. A container is opened when food is needed. Stems also store materials that are used when needed. What types of materials are stored by the stem? Stems store water, and food in the form of starch. Water comes from the roots and the starch is made from sugars that are carried from the leaves.

One benefit of water storage in herbaceous stems is that it prevents wilting. Water helps keep the cells of the stems stiff. You might say that these stiff cells support a plant like the skeleton supports an animal's body. Plants that live in dry areas have stems that store large amounts of water. A cactus stores a lot of water in the stem. This water is used for photosynthesis during the long, dry season.

Some stems store large amounts of starch. Starch is stored in stems until needed by a plant for its new growth. This food is a reserve supply for other plant parts. When needed, the starch is changed back into sugar. The sugar moves through the phloem cells from the stem to the root or the leaves. Many plants use much of their stored food for new growth each spring.

How does water storage help a plant?

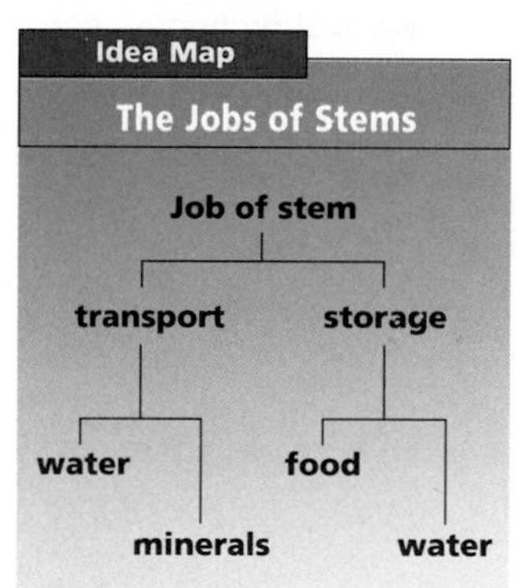

Study Tip: Use this idea map as a study guide to the jobs of stems. What cells transport water in stems?

STUDY GUIDE 117

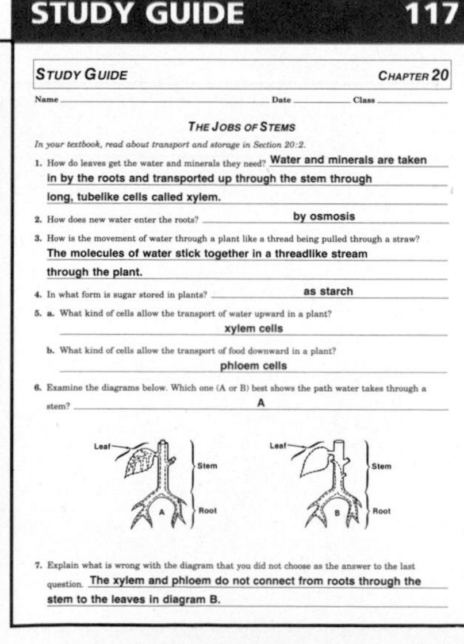

STUDY GUIDE CHAPTER 20

Name ______ Date ______ Class ______

THE JOBS OF STEMS

In your textbook, read about transport and storage in Section 20:2.

1. How do leaves get the water and minerals they need? Water and minerals are taken in by the roots and transported up through the stem through long, tubelike cells called xylem.
2. How does new water enter the roots? by osmosis
3. How is the movement of water through a plant like a thread being pulled through a straw? The molecules of water stick together in a threadlike stream through the plant.
4. In what form is sugar stored in plants? as starch
5. a. What kind of cells allow the transport of water upward in a plant? xylem cells

   b. What kind of cells allow the transport of food downward in a plant? phloem cells
6. Examine the diagrams below. Which one (A or B) best shows the path water takes through a stem? A

   Leaf Stem Root A — Leaf Stem Root B
7. Explain what is wrong with the diagram that you did not choose as the answer to the last question. The xylem and phloem do not connect from roots through the stem to the leaves in diagram B.

2 TEACH

MOTIVATION/Demonstration

Show students various products of plant stems. Suggestions include maple syrup, sugar, turpentine, asparagus. Have students give you the names of other materials they think come from stems.

Concept Development

▶ Make sure students understand that most of a plant's water is lost through the leaves, while very little is lost through the stem.

Idea Map

Have students use the idea map as a study guide to the major concepts of this section.

Check for Understanding

Have students write a short paragraph explaining what materials are moved through the stem.

Reteach

Give students a diagram of a plant with roots, stem, and leaves. Have them draw arrows to show direction of water and food movement.

Guided Practice

Have students write down their answers to the margin question: It prevents wilting.

Independent Practice

Study Guide/*Teacher Resource Package*, p. 117. Use the Study Guide worksheet shown at the bottom of this page for independent practice.

TECHNOLOGY

Newer Medicines from Plants

Background

Explorers to the New World returned with unknown plants that had useful medicinal properties. The explorers had bartered with the natives for information and the plants themselves. A closer study of plants was started as a result of this.

Discussion

Let students know that one of the most promising places that new medicinal plants are being found today is in the tropical rain forests of the world. Since the tropical forests are disappearing at a rapid rate, we may be losing some valuable sources of medicines.

Reference

Dodge, Bertha. *It Started in Eden.* New York: McGraw-Hill Book Company, 1979.

Lehane, Brenden. *The Power of Plants.* New York: McGraw-Hill Book Company, 1977.

TEACH

Guided Practice

Have students write down their answers to the margin question: woody.

TECHNOLOGY

Newer Medicines from Plants

Several centuries ago, explorers brought plants from the tropical forests of the New World back to Europe. The explorers had discovered that these plants were being used for medicines by native peoples.

For example, quinine was found to be used as a cure for malaria. The natives of South America had made an extract of quinine by soaking the bark of the *Cinchona* (sihn CHOH nuh) tree in water. Drinking the water that contained the bark extract helped cure malaria.

Plants use the sugar from photosynthesis and minerals from the soil to make many different compounds that have medicinal properties. Many of the original plant medicines have since been made from synthetic chemicals. Now, researchers are going back to the tropical rain forests in search of new plant medicines. AIDS and cancer are two diseases for which we need new medicines.

Why is the tropical rain forest a good place to hunt for medicinal plants? There are more species of plants in the tropical rain forests than anywhere else in the world. Scientists believe that with all these undiscovered species, there must be some with new medicinal value.

Many plant scientists are involved in the search for new plants in the world's rain forests. The work is very time consuming. Will all of this effort help society? Imagine the benefits of discovering a plant that produces a chemical that can cure AIDS.

A chemical from the bark of the Peruvian Cinchona tree helps cure malaria all over the world.

How Are Stems Used?

Does paper come from woody or herbaceous stems?

The most important product we get from stems is wood. When you write with a wooden pencil, you are using a product from a stem. Look around your home or classroom and you will find many places where wood is used. You read in Chapter 6 how conifers are important for paper products. Paper products you use come from the wood of these tree stems. This book, dollar bills, food packets, and many other paper products are part of your daily life, Figure 20-7a. Your life would be very different without stems.

OPTIONS

ACTIVITY/Challenge

Have students find pictures in magazines of products that come from stems of plants. Have them make a collage of pictures on a large piece of poster board. Have them make a list of the products and how humans use them.

a

b

Figure 20-7 Plants provide us with paper products (a) and sap or liquid products (b).

Stems are useful also as food. When you eat asparagus, cauliflower, and broccoli, you are eating the flower stems of these plants. People in some countries grow bamboo plants and eat the young, soft stems. Food seasonings such as cinnamon and dill are from stems. Some foods are made by taking sap from trees. Maple sugar is made from the sap of sugar maple trees. Sap is the liquid that flows up the stem in the xylem cells. In spring, the sap contains up to four percent sugar, which was stored in the roots over the winter.

Rubber, turpentine, and materials for making chewing gum are made from other liquids in the stems of different trees. After the liquids are collected from the trees, they are processed for our use, Figure 20-7b.

Skill Check

Make and use tables: Use reference materials to make a table of plant products. Examples include corn syrup and corn starch. *For more help, refer to the **Skill Handbook**, pages 715-717.*

Check Your Understanding

6. What happens to minerals in the soil before they can get into roots?
7. How does water storage help herbaceous stems?
8. What are five products we get from stems?
9. **Critical Thinking:** How would the rate of water movement through a plant on a rainy day compare with the rate on a hot, sunny day?
10. **Biology and Writing:** Make a complete sentence from each of the three sentence fragments.
    1. A stem supports a plant and transports
    2. are dissolved in water and carried through roots.
    3. One benefit of water storage in herbaceous stems

TEACH

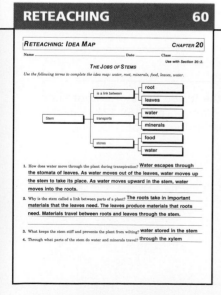

Check for Understanding

Have students respond to the first three questions in Check Your Understanding.

Reteach

Reteaching/*Teacher Resource Package,* p. 60. Use this worksheet to give students additional practice with jobs of stems.

Extension: Assign Critical Thinking, Biology and Writing, or some of the **OPTIONS** available with the lesson.

3 APPLY

Software

How Plants Grow: The Inside Story, Opportunities for Learning.

4 CLOSE

ACTIVITY/Interview

Have students visit a lumberyard and find out the names of some hardwoods and softwoods that are sold there. Have them find out why these woods are called hardwoods and softwoods.

Answers to Check Your Understanding

6. They have to be dissolved in water.
7. It prevents the plant from wilting.
8. Answers will vary. Examples are rubber, turpentine, medicines, maple sugar, food, and paper.
9. The rate of water flow through a plant would be higher on a hot, sunny day because water would evaporate faster into the atmosphere.
10. 1. A stem supports a plant and transports materials.
    2. Materials from the soil are dissolved in water and are carried through the roots.
    3. One benefit of water storage in herbaceous stems is that it prevents wilting.

RETEACHING 60

RETEACHING: IDEA MAP — **CHAPTER 20**

Name ______ Date ______ Class ______

Use with Section 20:2.

THE JOBS OF STEMS

Use the following terms to complete the idea map: water, root, minerals, food, leaves, water.

Stem
- is a link between: root, leaves
- transports: water, minerals
- stores: food, water

1. How does water move through the plant during transpiration? **Water escapes through the stomata of leaves. As water moves out of the leaves, water moves up the stem to take its place. As water moves upward in the stem, water moves into the roots.**
2. Why is the stem called a link between parts of a plant? **The roots take in important materials that the leaves need. The leaves produce materials that roots need. Materials travel between roots and leaves through the stem.**
3. What keeps the stem stiff and prevents the plant from wilting? **water stored in the stem**
4. Through what parts of the stem do water and minerals travel? **through the xylem**

20:3 Root Structure

PREPARATION

Materials Needed

Make copies of the Reteaching and Study Guide worksheets in the *Teacher Resource Package*.

Key Science Words

taproot
fibrous root
root hair
endodermis

Process Skills

In the Skill Check, students will understand science words.

1 FOCUS

▶ The objectives are listed on the student page. Remind students to preview these objectives as a guide to this numbered section.

ACTIVITY/Discussion

Have students discuss what is meant by the word *root* in each phrase below. Have them discuss how the phrase ties in with plant roots.
family roots
root of a problem
rooting around

ACTIVITY/Filmstrip

Show the filmstrip *Roots, Stems, and Leaves,* Clearvue, Inc.

Guided Practice

Have students write down their answers to the margin question: a large, simple root with smaller side roots.

Objectives

7. **Compare** taproots and fibrous roots.
8. **Sequence** the layers of root cells.
9. **Describe** how roots grow.

Key Science Words

taproot
fibrous root
root hair
endodermis

What is a taproot?

20:3 Root Structure

A root is the plant part that takes in water and minerals for the plant. The following sections will describe the structures of roots and how they grow.

Taproots and Fibrous Roots

There are two basic types of root systems—taproots and fibrous roots. The part of a carrot that we eat is the root. In plants like the carrot, there is one main root called a taproot. A **taproot** is a large, single root with smaller side roots. The thick taproots of some plants store water and food during dry or cold periods. In the vegetable section of a grocery store, you can see many different kinds of taproots. Beets, carrots, and turnips are common vegetables that are taproots.

If you weed a garden or lawn, you know that some weeds such as dandelions are very hard to pull out of the soil, Figure 20-8a. Their long, thick taproots will usually break off before you can pull the plant from the soil.

Not all plants have taproots. Some plants have fibrous (FI brus) roots, Figure 20-8b. **Fibrous roots** are many-branched roots that grow in clusters. Unlike the taproot, there is no main, large root. As the name suggests, the roots are fiberlike. Fibrous roots spread out over a large area. Thus, fibrous roots collect water from a larger area than reached by taproots.

Oak trees and hickory trees have long, thick taproots. Some maple trees and beech trees have fibrous roots. Which kind of tree is more likely to blow over in a harsh windstorm?

a

b

Figure 20-8 A taproot has stored food (a), and a fibrous root has many branches (b).

OPTIONS

Science Background

Roots are classified by structure and by the size and number of primary roots present. Taproots have a large primary root that grows straight down into the soil. Numerous secondary roots branch off this root. Fibrous roots have many stringlike primary roots with many more secondary roots branching from the primary roots. Some of the cells found in the stem are also found in the roots. Roots can grow in length and thickness like a stem.

What Do the Inside Parts of a Root Look Like?/*Lab Manual,* pp. 169-172. Use this lab as an extension to root structure.

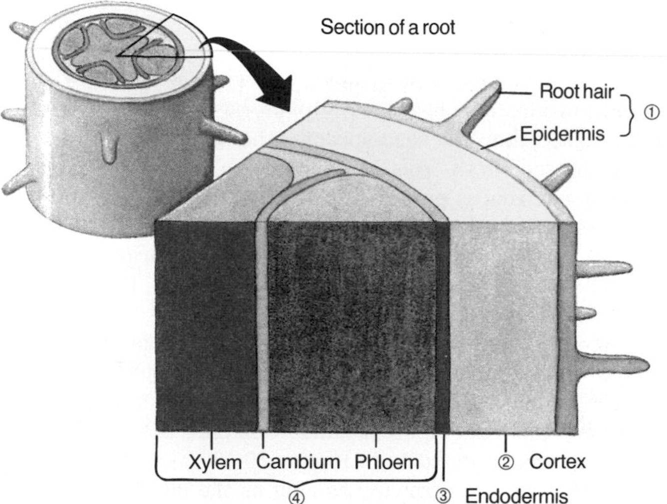

Figure 20-9 A root is made of four main layers of cells. From which layer do root hairs grow? the epidermis

Cells of a Root

The root is made of several layers of cells. The different layers have different jobs. Using Figure 20-9, let's examine the cell layers of a root.

1. The outside layer of a root is the epidermis, which protects the root. Growing from the epidermis are the root hairs. **Root hairs** are threadlike cells of the epidermis that absorb water and minerals for a plant.
2. Inside the epidermis is the layer of cells called the cortex. Just as in a stem, the cells of the cortex store food.
3. The next layer is the endodermis. The **endodermis** is a ring of waxy cells that surrounds the xylem in roots. This layer of cells helps the plant retain the water taken in by the xylem.
4. Inside the endodermis, notice the bundles of xylem. Between these xylem cells are phloem cells. You know that xylem and phloem carry materials in the plant. Xylem cells in the roots carry water and minerals up to the stem. Phloem cells bring food from the leaves.

If you eat a raw or cooked carrot, you might notice a difference in the feel and taste between the outer and inner layers of the carrot root. The outer ring is softer and sweeter. This is the cortex with its stored food. The inner part is tougher and not as sweet. What makes this layer taste different? This layer is made of the xylem and phloem. There are also more fibers in this ring.

What is the outer layer of a root?

Skill Check

Understand science words: fibrous root. The word part *fibr* means threadlike. In your dictionary, find three words with the word part *fibr* in them. *For more help, refer to the **Skill Handbook**, pages 706-711.*

STUDY GUIDE 118

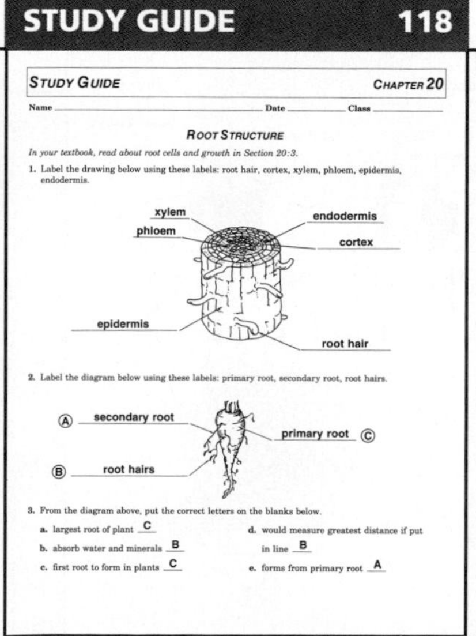

STUDY GUIDE CHAPTER 20

Name ______ Date ______ Class ______

ROOT STRUCTURE

In your textbook, read about root cells and growth in Section 20:3.

1. Label the drawing below using these labels: root hair, cortex, xylem, phloem, epidermis, endodermis.

2. Label the diagram below using these labels: primary root, secondary root, root hairs.

3. From the diagram above, put the correct letters on the blanks below.
   a. largest root of plant C
   b. absorb water and minerals B
   c. first root to form in plants C
   d. would measure greatest distance if put in line B
   e. forms from primary root A

2 TEACH

MOTIVATION/Demonstration

Cut a carrot into enough thin sections so that each student has one. Tell them to hold the carrot toward the light and locate the inner and outer rings. Point out that the xylem and phloem are thick-walled, smaller diameter cells in the inner ring, and the cortex is thinner-walled, large diameter cells in the outer ring.

Concept Development

▶ Point out that cortex cells occupy most of the space in a root because they store food for the plant.

Check Your Understanding

Have students list the cells found in a root from the outside to the center and write a function for each.

Reteach

Set up several microscopes showing a cross section of a root. Place a specific cell at the end of the pointer. Have students identify the cell. Go over all the cell types, and review the size and shape of each according to its function.

Guided Practice

Have students write down their answers to the margin question: epidermis.

Independent Practice

Study Guide/*Teacher Resource Package,* p. 118. Use the Study Guide worksheet shown at the bottom of this page for independent practice.

TEACH

Guided Practice

Have students write down their answers to the margin question: straight down from a seed.

Check for Understanding

Have students respond to the first three questions in Check Your Understanding.

Reteach

Reteaching/*Teacher Resource Package*, p. 61. Use this worksheet to give students additional practice with root structure.

Extension: Assign Critical Thinking, Biology and Reading, or some of the **OPTIONS** available with this section.

APPLY

ACTIVITY/Software

Plant Biology, From the Ground Up, Opportunities for Learning.

CLOSE

Filmstrip

Show the filmstrip *Plants: Parts and Processes—Roots, Stems, and Leaves*, National Geographic Society.

Answers to Check Your Understanding

11. A taproot is a single, large root with many small secondary roots attached. A fibrous root has several large roots growing in a cluster.
12. epidermis–protection; cortex–food storage; xylem–carry water; phloem–carry food
13. They form from the simple primary root as branches of the primary root.
14. epidermis, cortex, xylem, phloem
15. tomato plant because it is less firmly rooted

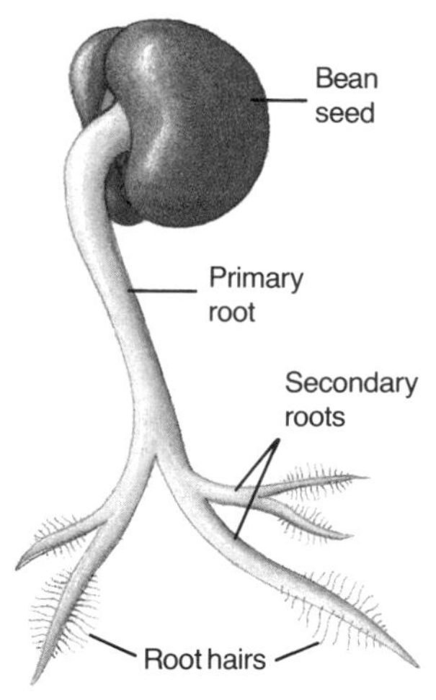

Figure 20-10 The first root of a new plant is its primary root. Other roots are secondary roots.

How does a primary root grow?

Root Growth

If you split open a bean seed, you will see the plant embryo inside. This new, young plant has leaves, a stem, and a root. When the seed sprouts, the first part to grow out of the seed is the root.

Only one root is present in the seed. When it grows out of the seed, it is the primary root. The word *primary* means first. The primary root is the first and largest root to form in a plant. It usually grows straight down, toward the water in the soil.

Later, secondary roots form. Secondary roots are smaller roots that branch from the primary root. The thinner, shorter, threadlike parts near the tips of the secondary roots are the root hairs. Compare the primary roots and secondary roots in Figure 20-10.

Most roots keep growing as long as the plant lives. When roots grow, new cells are added to the tips of the roots. This is how the root grows down into the soil.

How large can a root system grow? In 1926, an American scientist asked the same question. To find the answer, he collected a lot of data. First he carefully removed all the fibrous roots of a rye plant, a grasslike cereal plant. He then measured the lengths of each of the roots and added all the lengths together. The results showed that if the roots were placed end to end, they could form a line 612 km long, as long as the state of Tennessee!

Next, the scientist measured the root hairs. The lengths of all the root hairs were added together. If every root hair were put end to end, the line would go from the east to the west coast of the United States and back again! You can see that the rye plant has a very large root system.

Check Your Understanding

11. How does a taproot differ from a fibrous root?
12. List the layers of cells found in a root and describe the job of each.
13. How do secondary roots form?
14. **Critical Thinking:** Which layers of cells do roots and stems have in common?
15. **Biology and Reading:** Which would be easier to pull up—a dandelion that has a taproot, or a tomato plant that has a fibrous root system?

OPTIONS

ACTIVITY/Challenge

Have teams germinate and grow corn and bean seeds in different kinds of soil to see in which type of soil the roots appear to grow best. Use potting soil, clay soil, and sandy soil. Add the same amount of water to each type of soil.

Science Background

Roots of woody plants can grow from 0.5 to 10 meters into the soil. Most herbaceous plants have roots that grow 0.3 to 0.5 meter into the soil.

RETEACHING 61

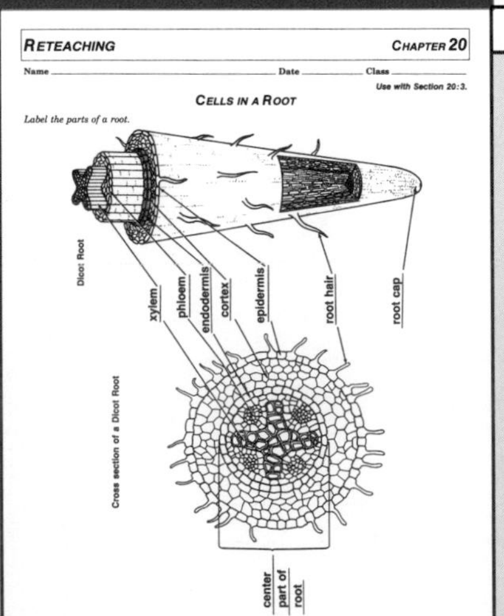

RETEACHING CHAPTER 20

Name Date Class

Use with Section 20:3.

CELLS IN A ROOT

Label the parts of a root.

20:4 The Jobs of Roots

Is the root vital to a plant? The plant would die if its roots were removed. Roots anchor the plant in one place and supply a plant with nutrients.

Objectives

10. Describe root hairs and their function.

11. Relate how roots anchor the plant and serve as storage.

12. Discuss the benefits and problems of roots.

Absorption

Plants get needed materials for growth through their roots. Roots absorb water from their surroundings by osmosis. In Chapter 2, you read that osmosis is the movement of water molecules across a cell membrane. Roots also take in minerals from their surroundings with the water they absorb.

How does water enter a root?

Water enters the root through the root hairs. Root hairs increase the surface area of the root and so increase the amount of water that can be absorbed or taken in by the plant. When a gardener moves a plant from one part of a garden to another, the plant's root hairs may be torn off. The amount of water these plants can absorb is reduced. To protect the plant, the gardener digs up a ball of soil around the plant's roots and moves this soil along with the plant, Figure 20-11a. This protects the root hairs.

The root supplies the plant with raw materials. Water is a raw material for photosynthesis. Minerals are raw materials for the plant to make proteins and other chemicals such as chlorophyll.

Like all living cells, root cells must be supplied with oxygen. Root cells get oxygen from air in the spaces between soil particles. Gardeners and landscapers break up the soil around plants to ensure that air gets into the soil, Figure 20-11b. Sandy soils or soils rich in organic material have more air spaces than clay soils.

Skill Check

Sequence: List the parts of a plant in the order in which water passes in and out of the plant. *For more help, refer to the* ***Skill Handbook****, pages 718-719.*

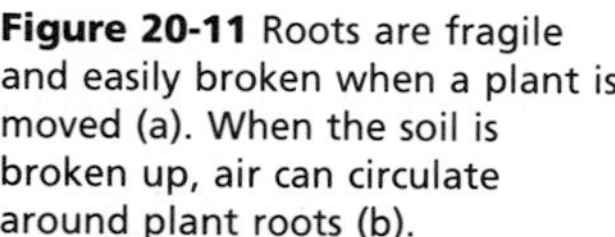

a

b

Figure 20-11 Roots are fragile and easily broken when a plant is moved (a). When the soil is broken up, air can circulate around plant roots (b).

20:4 The Jobs of Roots

PREPARATION

Materials Needed

Make copies of the Critical Thinking/Problem Solving, Application, Reteaching, Study Guide, and Lab worksheets in the *Teacher Resource Package*.

▶ Cut paper towel strips for Lab 20-1. Collect carrot, yam, and radish roots for Lab 20-2.

▶ Germinate the radish seeds before you do the demonstration.

Key Science Words

No new science words will be introduced in this section.

Process Skills

In Lab 20-1, students will observe, formulate a model, infer, and design an experiment. In Lab 20-2, they will observe, classify, form hypotheses, and design an experiment. In the Skill Check, they will sequence.

1 FOCUS

▶ The objectives are listed on the student page. Remind students to preview these objectives as a guide to this numbered section.

Guided Practice

Have students write down their answers to the margin question: by osmosis through the root hairs.

CRITICAL THINKING 20

CRITICAL THINKING/PROBLEM SOLVING — CHAPTER 20

Name ____________ Date ________ Class ________

Use after Section 20:4.

WHAT CAUSED THE TREES TO DIE?

Two students were walking up a street in a new housing development. Sewer lines had just been laid, and the street had just been paved. They noticed that some of the trees by the side of the road looked unhealthy. The leaves were wilted and falling, although it was still summer. The students wondered why this was happening. They also wondered if the trees could recover.

The students listed what could have damaged the trees. Had earthmoving equipment hit the trees? The trunks did not look as if they had been bumped. Perhaps the paving material was bad for the trees. The trees were a few meters from the road. The students had read that the root system grows as far out from the trunk as the branches spread out. They also knew that nutrients travel inside the trunk to the leaves. The students made a hypothesis that the roots and trunks were somehow affected by the new street development.

Analyzing the Problem

1. What are three functions of roots? Roots anchor the plant in the soil, absorb water and minerals, and store food made in the leaves.
2. What two materials do roots take in from the soil? Roots take in water and minerals.
3. By what processes do the materials get into the roots from the soil? absorption and diffusion
4. How are materials carried from the roots to the leaves? Materials travel up the trunk in tubes called xylem.

Solving the Problem

1. If soil and pavement were packed heavily on the roots how could the tree be affected? Water and dissolved minerals would diffuse into the roots more slowly.
2. What will happen to the support tissues in the trunk if they do not have enough water? They become dry and cannot carry water to the leaves.
3. Could the root system be disturbed by paving if the trees are a few meters from the road? Yes, because the roots spread out widely.
4. Can the root system repair itself with time? It might regrow under the road, because cell division happens actively at the tips of roots.

OPTIONS

Critical Thinking/Problem Solving/ *Teacher Resource Package*, p. 20. Use the Critical Thinking/Problem Solving worksheet shown here as an extension to root functions.

Lab 20-1 Absorption

Overview

Students will build a model of a root hair. They can observe how water enters a root hair and is further transported into the epidermal cell.

Objectives: After completing this lab, students will be able to: (1) **formulate a model** of a root hair, (2) **observe** how water moves in the root hair model, (3) **define** root hair.

Time Allotment: 45 minutes

Preparation

▶ Prepare the paper towel strips prior to class. Use a thick paper towel like that found in most school lavatories as these towels will not fall apart during use.

Lab 20-1 worksheet/*Teacher Resource Package,* pp. 77-78.

Teaching the Lab

▶ Make sure students bend the paper towel as suggested. The students should be able to see the water being absorbed rapidly by the paper towel strips.

Cooperative Learning: Divide the class into groups of two students. For more information, see pp. 22T-23T in the Teacher Guide.

Absorption Lab 20–1

Problem: How does a root hair work?

Skills

observe, formulate a model, infer, design an experiment

Materials

paper towel strips:
10 X 15 cm (1 strip)
1 X 10 cm (4 strips)
stapler
large plastic cup
pencil

Procedure

1. Staple the four small paper strips to the larger strip, Figure A. Bend the smaller strips so they are at right angles from the larger strip.
2. Fill the cup to within 2.5 cm of the top with water.
3. Lay a pencil across the rim of the cup. Lay the root model over the pencil. See Figure B. The smaller towel strips will hang down into the water.
4. **Observe** the root model for 20 minutes.
5. Remove the root model from the cup.

Data and Observations

1. What happened to the smaller strips when they were put in water?
2. Did the large strip absorb any water? If so, where did this water come from?

Analyze and Apply

1. Which part of your model represented the root hairs?
2. Which part of your model represented the main root from which root hairs grow?
3. In what way did the small paper strips act like root hairs?
4. Why are there hundreds of root hairs on a single root?
5. **Infer:** What would happen to a plant if its root hairs were damaged?
6. **Apply:** Would you expect desert plants or tropical rain forest plants to have more root hairs? Why?

Extension

Design an experiment that shows the rate of water absorption in a root. Use a carrot, water, and food coloring.

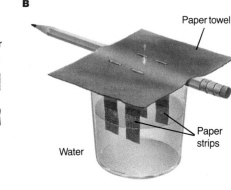

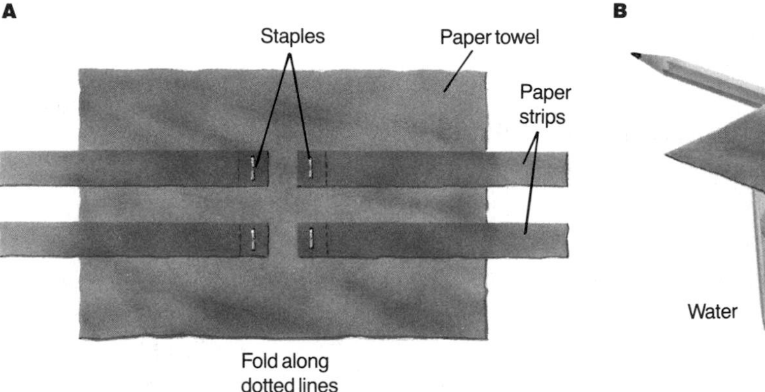

432 Plant Support and Transport 20:4

ANSWERS

Data and Observations

1. Water began to travel up the strips.
2. Yes, the water traveled up the smaller strips into the larger strips.

Analyze and Apply

1. the smaller paper strips
2. the larger paper strips
3. They absorbed water from their surroundings.
4. to provide a larger surface area for water absorption into the plant
5. It would not be able to absorb water and so would wilt and then die.
6. desert plants, because the soil doesn't contain much water, and so the more root hairs, the greater the chance of contacting water

Anchorage and Storage

A major job of a root is to anchor the plant. A root is similar to a boat anchor. An anchor catches on the rocks or soil under the water and holds the boat in one place. The roots of most plants spread through the particles of soil and hold the plant in one place, Figure 20-12a.

Many roots have large cells that store food. The usual food stored is starch. Compare the size of the storage cells with the other cells in Figure 20-12b. You have read that these storage cells make up the cortex. The food in these cells is used later by other cells in the plant. Large amounts of food are stored in taproots. Carrot and turnip roots are good examples of plants that have many food storage cells. The taproot of a dandelion stores food for the plant. You may have noticed that a dandelion will soon grow back if you don't pull up its whole root. It uses its stored food to grow new leaves, stems, and flowers.

Roots store food made in one growing season to use at the start of the next growing season. Many herbaceous plants depend on the stored food in the roots to survive the winter. If food were not stored in the roots for the winter, the plant could not grow new parts the next spring.

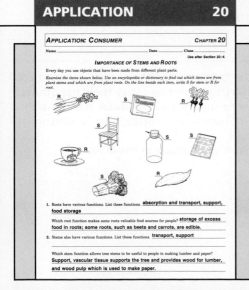

Idea Map

The Job of Roots

- **Job of roots**
  - **absorption**
    - **water enters**
    - **minerals enters**
  - **storage**
    - **stores food**
    - **new growing season**

Study Tip: Use this idea map as a study guide to the jobs of roots. What two things do roots absorb?

Why do roots store food?

How Are Roots Used?

You have already learned that people eat many kinds of roots such as beets, carrots, and sweet potatoes. Products made from the roots are also eaten. Sassafras (SAS uh fras) roots are used to make tea. Horseradish roots are ground and used as a sauce to season other foods. Roots are also used to make products such as perfumes and medicines.

Figure 20-12 Roots anchor a plant in the soil (a). Many roots have stored food in the cells of the cortex (b).

a

b

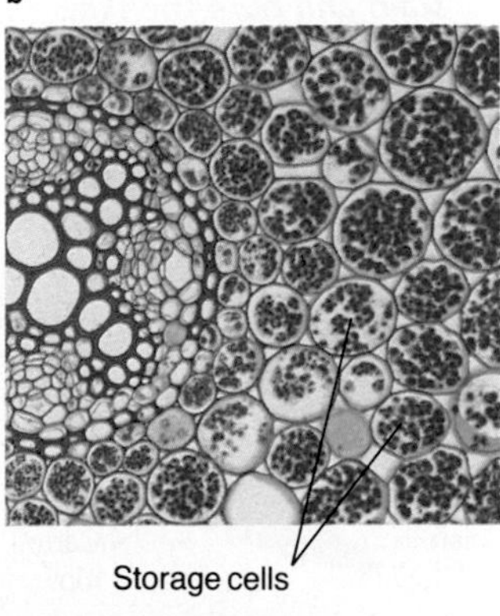

2 TEACH

MOTIVATION/Videocassette

Show the videocassette *The Plant: An Operator's Manual*, Human Relations Media.

ACTIVITY/Demonstration

Root hairs can be shown to students by sprouting radish seeds. Place 50 to 60 radish seeds on a paper towel. Fold the paper towel and wet it. Put the paper towel in a plastic bag. The seeds will sprout within 48 hours. Students can look at root hairs with a hand lens.

Connection: Health

Have students make posters showing the importance of roots and stems to nutrition by cutting pictures from magazines.

Idea Map

Have students use the idea map as a study guide to the major concepts of this section.

Guided Practice

Have students write down their answers to the margin question: to use when needed for growth.

Independent Practice

Study Guide/*Teacher Resource Package*, p. 119. Use the Study Guide worksheet shown at the bottom of this page for independent practice.

APPLICATION 20

APPLICATION: CONSUMER — CHAPTER 20

Name ______ Date ______ Class ______

Use after Section 20:4.

IMPORTANCE OF STEMS AND ROOTS

Every day you use objects that have been made from different plant parts.

Examine the items shown below. Use an encyclopedia or dictionary to find out which items are from plant stems and which are from plant roots. On the line beside each item, write S for stem or R for root.

R S R S S S R S R

1. Roots have various functions. List these functions. **absorption and transport, support, food storage**

   Which root function makes some roots valuable food sources for people? **storage of excess food in roots; some roots, such as beets and carrots, are edible.**

2. Stems also have various functions. List these functions. **transport, support**

   Which stem function allows tree stems to be useful to people in making lumber and paper? **Support, vascular tissue supports the tree and provides wood for lumber, and wood pulp which is used to make paper.**

STUDY GUIDE 119

STUDY GUIDE — CHAPTER 20

Name ______ Date ______ Class ______

ROOT STRUCTURE

In your textbook, read about taproots and fibrous roots in Section 20:4.

4. Examine the drawings below. Then, put A or B on the blank after each phrase or word.
   a. taproot **B**
   b. fibrous roots **A**
   c. often spreads out **A**
   d. often grows very deep **B**

A B

THE JOBS OF ROOTS

In your textbook, read about absorption, anchorage, and storage in Section 20:4.

Examine the pictures below. Beside each picture write a sentence describing what the object pictured does. Then, write a sentence describing a similar job of roots. The first one is done for you.

Sponge, Suitcase, Hair net, Paper clip, Anchor, Paper towels, Stapler, Silo, Tent stake

1. A sponge absorbs water. Roots absorb water and minerals from the soil.
2. **A suitcase helps to store and move items. Roots store food and move water and minerals to the stem.**
3. **A hair net holds hair together. Roots hold soil particles together.**
4. **A paper clip holds things together. Roots hold soil particles together.**
5. **An anchor holds a boat in place. Roots hold a plant in place.**
6. **Paper towels absorb water. Roots absorb water and minerals from the soil.**
7. **A stapler holds papers together. Roots hold soil particles together.**
8. **A silo stores food. A root stores food.**
9. **A tent stake anchors a tent. Roots anchor a plant.**

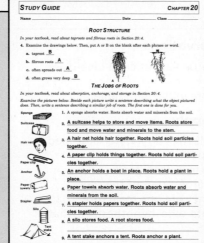

OPTIONS

Science Background

Enrichment: Farmers sometimes plant grasses in their fields as a cover crop in the fall. The fibrous roots bind the soil particles together and prevent soil erosion. In the spring, the grass is plowed under and provides minerals for the new crops.

Application/*Teacher Resource Package*, p. 20. Use the Application worksheet shown here to emphasize the importance of stems and roots.

Lab 20-2 Storage

Overview

Students will discover that roots have a large area in which starch is stored. The iodine test verifies where the cortex, the starch-storage area of a root, is.

Objectives: After completing this lab, students will be able to: (1) **determine** the presence of starch using lab techniques, (2) **identify** where starch is stored in a root, (3) **compare** areas of starch storage in different roots.

Time Allotment: 45 minutes

Preparation

▶ Purchase the roots from the produce section of a grocery store the day before you need them. You may wish to cut the roots prior to the class period.

▶ For *iodine solution;* dissolve 10 g potassium iodide and 3 g iodine in 1000 mL water. Store in a brown bottle.

Lab 20-2 worksheet/*Teacher Resource Package,* pp. 79-80.

Teaching the Lab

▶ Caution the students about getting iodine on their skin. Have them flush the area of the skin with water.

Cooperative Learning: Divide the class into groups of three students. For more information, see pp. 22T-23T in the Teacher Guide.

Storage

Lab 20–2

Problem: What parts of roots store starch?

Skills

observe, classify, form hypotheses, design an experiment

Materials

carrot root	3 petri dish halves
yam root	iodine solution
radish root	dropper
razor blade	hand lens
forceps	

Procedure

1. Copy the data table.
2. Using the razor blade, cut a very thin slice of each root as shown in the figure. **CAUTION:** *Use extreme care with the razor blade.*
3. Place each slice in a separate petri dish.
4. Write a **hypothesis** about which part of the carrot root will show the presence of starch. Will the other roots show the presence of starch? (HINT: Read pages 429 and 433 again.)
5. Add one dropperful of iodine to each root slice as shown in the figure. Make sure each slice has iodine on it at all times. **CAUTION:** *Iodine is poisonous and can stain and burn the skin.*

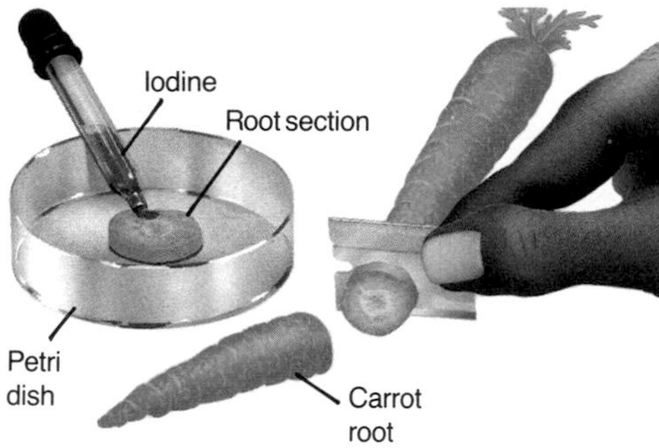

6. **Observe:** During the next 15 minutes, examine the root slices with the hand lens. Look for blue-black areas. A blue-black color means starch is present. Note in your data table in which areas starch is present.
7. Draw each root slice in your notebook. Label the cortex and xylem in each drawing.

Data and Observations

1. Which roots showed starch was present? How could you tell?
2. Which part of each root slice showed more starch present?

TYPE OF ROOT SLICE	BLUE-BLACK AREAS AFTER ADDING IODINE
Carrot	outer ring only
Yam	inside entire root
Radish	inside entire root as small black dots

Analyze and Apply

1. What cells make up the center of the root? What do they do?
2. What cells make up the outer part of the root? What do they do?
3. How are the starch storage areas of the three roots alike?
4. **Classify:** Are the roots used taproots or fibrous roots? Explain your answer.
5. **Check your hypothesis:** Is your hypothesis supported by your data? Why or why not?
6. **Apply:** How is starch made by a plant?

Extension

Design an experiment to test different stems for stored food.

ANSWERS

Data and Observations

1. all roots, because each stained blue-black with iodine
2. See sample data in the data table.

Analyze and Apply

1. xylem and phloem; carry water and food through the root
2. cells of the cortex; store starch
3. make up the largest part of the root
4. all taproots; they are one main root
5. Those students who hypothesized that the outer part of the carrot root contains starch will answer that their hypotheses were supported. The outer part of a carrot root is the cortex, the food-storage cells.
6. from sugar made in the leaves

a

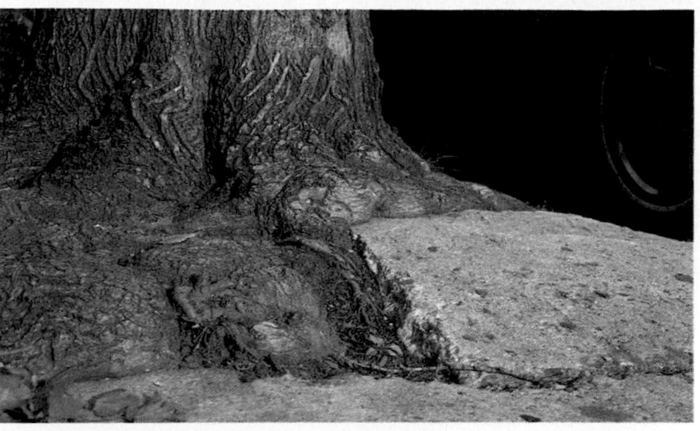

b

Figure 20-13 These root nodules contain bacteria that fix nitrogen for the plant (a). Growth of tree roots can sometimes damage sidewalks or sewage pipes (b).

Roots are beneficial to humans in other ways. If you were to pull up a small clump of grass growing in a yard, you would see soil sticking to the roots. Roots of plants help hold soil together. The soil is not easily carried away by rain, melting snow, or wind.

How do roots help soil?

The roots of many trees and plants, such as beans and clover, help make the soil rich in nitrogen. Some bacteria can change nitrogen in air to a form that plants can use. These bacteria live on plant roots, Figure 20-13a. Soil rich in nitrogen is good for growing corn and other food crops.

Sometimes roots are a nuisance, Figure 20-13b. The roots of some trees, like the willow and maple, grow into underground pipes. Roots can block the pipes that carry water and wastes away from houses. Root growth is so strong it can break pipes. It's a good idea to find out where pipes are laid before planting trees. Sometimes sidewalks or roads are also broken by root growth.

Bio Tip

Biology: Many cities don't plant silver maples and willow trees because their roots cause damage to sewers.

Check Your Understanding

16. Why are root hairs important?
17. What are three jobs of a root?
18. What are three benefits of roots?
19. **Critical Thinking:** You want to plant a shade tree in your yard. What things do you need to find out about the tree and your yard before you plant?
20. **Biology and Reading:** You have read that roots are sometimes a nuisance. What does it mean for a plant's roots to be a nuisance?

TEACH

Guided Practice

Have students write down their answers to the margin question: they hold it together.

Independent Practice

Study Guide/*Teacher Resource Package,* p. 120. Use the Study Guide worksheet shown at the bottom of this page for independent practice.

Check for Understanding

Have students respond to the first three questions in Check Your Understanding.

Reteach

Reteaching/*Teacher Resource Package*, p. 62. Use this worksheet to give students additional practice with roots.

Extension: Assign Critical Thinking, Biology and Reading, or some of the **OPTIONS** available with this lesson.

3 APPLY

ACTIVITY/Field Trip

Have students collect weeds with taproots and fibrous roots.

4 CLOSE

ACTIVITY/Filmstrip

Show the filmstrip *The Primary Plant Body*, Carolina Biological Supply Co.

Answers to Check Your Understanding

16. Root hairs absorb water for the plant from the soil by osmosis.
17. The jobs are absorption, storage, transport, and anchorage.
18. They are used as food and medicines, and hold soil together.
19. You need to find out the location of any underground pipes and cables before you plant.
20. Nuisance means here that roots make problems for people.

RETEACHING 62

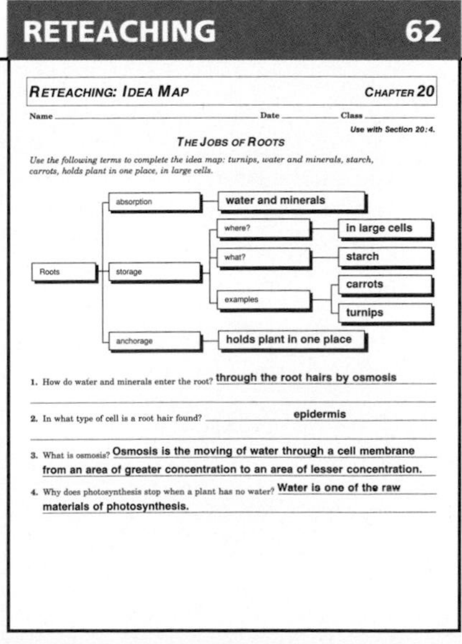

RETEACHING: IDEA MAP — CHAPTER 20

Name ______ Date ______ Class ______

Use with Section 20:4.

THE JOBS OF ROOTS

Use the following terms to complete the idea map: turnips, water and minerals, starch, carrots, holds plant in one place, in large cells.

1. How do water and minerals enter the root? through the root hairs by osmosis
2. In what type of cell is a root hair found? epidermis
3. What is osmosis? Osmosis is the moving of water through a cell membrane from an area of greater concentration to an area of lesser concentration.
4. Why does photosynthesis stop when a plant has no water? Water is one of the raw materials of photosynthesis.

STUDY GUIDE 120

STUDY GUIDE — CHAPTER 20

Name ______ Date ______ Class ______

VOCABULARY

Review the new words used in Chapter 20 of your textbook. Use the glossary in your textbook if you need help.

Complete each sentence using the words below to fill in the blanks. Do not use any words more than once.

lateral buds	root hairs	woody stems
fibrous roots	herbaceous stems	endodermis
annual rings	terminal bud	cortex
cork	taproot	cambium

1. There are two main kinds of roots. A large, single root is called a taproot. Many-branched roots that grow in clusters are fibrous roots.
2. Tiny threadlike root hairs are cells of the epidermis. They absorb water and minerals for the plant.
3. Inside the root and stem, a layer of large, loosely packed cortex cells are present. They are used mainly for food storage.
4. Trees and shrubs have woody stems. Tree stems have an outer covering called cork. It is made up of dead cells and protects the stem.
5. Cambium is a thin layer of cells in a stem that divide to form new phloem and xylem cells.
6. The cross section of a tree trunk shows that the trunk is made up of a series of annual rings, made up of dark and light bands of cells.
7. Soft, green stems are called herbaceous stems.
8. Inside the cortex of a root is a ring of waxy cells called the endodermis.
9. The terminal bud is responsible for a plant's growth in length. The lateral buds give rise to new branches, leaves, or flowers.

CHAPTER 20 REVIEW

Summary

Summary statements can be used by students to review the major concepts of the chapter.

Key Science Words

All boldfaced terms from the chapter are listed.

Testing Yourself

Using Words

1. annual ring
2. taproot
3. root hair
4. cork
5. terminal bud
6. lateral bud
7. cambium
8. herbaceous stem
9. woody stem
10. endodermis
11. cortex

Finding Main Ideas

12. p. 425; Plants store food for the next growing season in the stems.
13. p. 424; Water moves into the roots and up through the stem through xylem cells.
14. p. 426; Stems are used to make paper products, as food, and to make products such as rubber and turpentine.
15. p. 431; Root hairs in the root take in water by osmosis.
16. p. 430; The primary root is the first root to form in a plant. It grows straight down into the soil.

Using Main Ideas

17. The primary root is already present in a seed. The secondary root grows from a primary root.
18. Cambium cells form new xylem cells each year; new xylem cells are formed as rings of new cells.
19. Leaves use water for photosynthesis.
20. The order of cell types in a root is phloem, endodermis, cortex, and epidermis.
21. They can grow into and block underground pipes that carry water and waste from houses. They can break sidewalks and roads as they grow.
22. Xylem and phloem are grouped together in clusters in a corn stem and in a circular pattern in the bean stem.
23. Roots are a good food source for animals because they store large amounts of starch.
24. Water is used for photosynthesis during the dry season.

Chapter 20 Review

Summary

20:1 Stem Structure

1. Herbaceous stems are soft and green.
2. Woody stems are thick and hard. From outside to inside, they are made up of cork, cortex, phloem, cambium, and xylem.
3. Stem growth in length occurs in terminal and lateral buds.

20:2 The Jobs of Stems

4. A stem transports materials from the roots to the leaves.
5. Stems store food and water in the cortex.
6. Stems provide humans with wood, food, seasonings, rubber, and turpentine.

20:3 Root Structure

7. A taproot is a large single root with smaller side roots. Fibrous roots are many-branched roots.
8. Roots are made up of an outer epidermis, cortex, xylem, and phloem.
9. The first root to grow out of a seed is the primary root. Secondary roots grow out from the primary root.

20:4 The Jobs of Roots

10. Root hairs absorb water and minerals by osmosis.
11. Roots anchor the plant and store starch.
12. Roots are used for food and to make medicines. Roots also help hold the soil together.

Key Science Words

annual ring (p. 423)
cambium (p. 421)
cork (p. 421)
cortex (p. 420)
endodermis (p. 429)
fibrous root (p. 428)
herbaceous stem (p. 420)
lateral bud (p. 423)
root hair (p. 429)
taproot (p. 428)
terminal bud (p. 423)
woody stem (p. 421)

Testing Yourself

Using Words

Choose the word from the list of Key Science Words that best fits the definition.

1. a ring of xylem in a woody stem
2. root with a single, large root
3. threadlike cell of the root epidermis
4. dead cells on the outer part of a tree that partly make up bark
5. stem part that causes growth in length
6. gives rise to new branches, leaves, or flowers

Review

Testing Yourself *continued*

7. cells that form new xylem and phloem
8. soft, green stem
9. a nongreen, hard stem
10. ring of waxy cells around the xylem and phloem in the root
11. plant tissue that stores food

Finding Main Ideas

List the page number where each main idea below is found. Then, explain each main idea.

12. stems storing food for the next growing season
13. how water lost in leaves is replaced
14. how stems are useful for paper products
15. how a root takes in water
16. how a primary root develops

Using Main Ideas

Answer the questions by referring to the page number after each question.

17. How are primary and secondary roots different? (p. 430)
18. How does an annual ring form? (p. 423)
19. Why is transporting water to leaves an important function of stems? (p. 424)
20. Starting with the center, what is the order of these cell types as they would occur in a root: cortex, phloem, endodermis, and epidermis? (p. 429)
21. How can roots be a nuisance to humans? (p. 435)
22. How is the arrangement of xylem and phloem different in bean and corn stems? (p. 420)
23. Why are roots a good source of food for animals? (p. 433)
24. Why do plants in dry areas store much water in stems? (p. 425)

Skill Review 

For more help, refer to the ***Skill Handbook,*** *pages 704-719.*

1. **Sequence:** What are the root cells and stem cells in order from the outside to the inside of a root?
2. **Observe:** Observe the plants in the produce section of a grocery store. Make a list of those that are roots.
3. **Classify:** Make a collection of ten weeds from your yard or street. Use a field guide to name them. Group them as either woody or herbaceous.
4. **Use numbers:** Calculate the age of a tree that is 20 cm in diameter if each annual ring is 5 mm thick.

Finding Out More

Critical Thinking

1. What causes knots in wooden boards?
2. What makes a tree ooze sap where limbs are removed? Explain why this happens more often during spring and summer.

Applications

1. Find out which plant parts of onions and white potatoes are the stems.
2. Visit a furniture store and find out what kinds of wood are used in making furniture and why.

Skill Review

1. root cells: epidermis, cortex, endodermis, xylem, and phloem; woody stem cells: cork, cortex, phloem, cambium, and xylem
2. Answers will vary. Some root foods are beets, carrots, sweet potatoes, turnips, sassafras, and horseradish.
3. Remind students that herbaceous stems are soft and green. Woody stems are harder.
4. 10 cm (1/2 the diameter) x 10 mm/cm x 1 yr/5mm = 20 years

Finding Out More

Critical Thinking

1. Knots are caused by the stems of the plant.
2. The fluids within the xylem cells are leaking out. The plant is transporting larger amounts of food and water during the spring and summer than during the winter.

Applications

1. The parts that are eaten are the stems.
2. Oak, maple, cherry, and walnut are often used because they are hard and durable.

 **Chapter Review**/*Teacher Resource Package*, pp. 104-105.

 **Chapter Test**/*Teacher Resource Package*, pp. 106-108.

Chapter Test/*Computer Test Bank*

Plant Response, Growth, and Disease

PLANNING GUIDE

CONTENT	TEXT FEATURES	TEACHER RESOURCE PACKAGE	OTHER COMPONENTS
(2 days) 21:1 Plant Response Growing and Flowering Tropisms Other Plant Responses	Skill Check: *Observe,* p. 444 Skill Check: *Understand Science Words,* p. 446 Lab 21-1: *Root Growth,* p. 442 Lab 21-2: *Plant Responses,* p. 445 Check Your Understanding, p. 446	Application: *Short-day and Long-day Plants,* p. 21 Reteaching: *Plant Responses,* p. 63 Critical Thinking/Problem Solving: *How Do Climbing Plants Respond to Sun?* p. 21 Skill: *Interpret Diagrams,* p. 21 Transparency Master: *Soil Particles and Roots,* p. 97 Study Guide: *Plant Responses,* pp. 121-122 Lab 21-1: *Root Growth,* pp. 81-82 Lab 21-2: *Plant Responses,* pp. 83-84	**Laboratory Manual:** *What Tropisms Can Be Seen in Growing Plants?* p. 173 Color Transparency 21: *Plant Growth Responses*
(1 1/2 days) 21:2 Growth Requirements Seasonal Growth Light Water Minerals Soil Temperature	Mini Lab: *Do Plants Need Light?* p. 448 Idea Map, p. 448 Check Your Understanding, p. 451	Enrichment: *Tolerance in Plants,* pp. 22-23 Reteaching: *Growth Requirements,* p. 64 Focus: *Plant Needs,* p. 41 Study Guide: *Growth Requirements,* pp. 123-124	**Laboratory Manual:** *Is Light an Important Growth Requirement for Plants?* p. 177
(1 day) 21:3 Plant Diseases and Pests Bacteria and Viruses Fungi Insect Pests	Check Your Understanding, p. 453 Problem Solving: *Flowering in Plants,* p. 454	Reteaching: *Plant Diseases and Insects,* p. 65 Study Guide: *Plant Diseases and Insects,* p. 125 Study Guide: *Vocabulary,* p. 126	
Chapter Review	Summary Key Science Words Testing Yourself Finding Main Ideas Using Main Ideas Skill Review	Chapter Review, pp. 109-110 Chapter Test, pp. 111-113 Unit Test, pp. 114-115	**Test Bank**

MATERIALS NEEDED

LAB 21-1, p. 442	LAB 21-2, p. 445	MARGIN FEATURES
toothpick plastic bag paper towel graph paper razor blade India ink 2 bean seedlings	petri dish marking pen 2 paper towels transparent tape 4 pre-soaked corn seeds	Skill Check, p. 444 pencil potted plant Skill Check, p. 446 dictionary Mini Lab, p. 448 2 paper cups 12 radish seeds water soil

OBJECTIVES

SECTION	OBJECTIVE	OBJECTIVES CORRELATION			
		CHECK YOUR UNDERSTANDING	CHAPTER REVIEW	TRP CHAPTER REVIEW	TRP CHAPTER TEST
21:1	1. **Explain** how hormones affect plant growth.	1	2, 14, 20, 23	2, 3, 8, 22	16, 20, 22, 23, 25
	2. **Compare** short-day, long-day, and day-neutral plants.	2, 4	1, 6	10, 11, 27	5, 11, 24, 31, 32, 33, 35, 36, 37, 38, 40
	3. **Distinguish** among tropisms and other plant movements.	3, 5	4, 7, 9, 13, 16, 22	1, 6, 7, 9, 13, 17, 18, 24, 28, 30	1, 8, 10, 12, 14, 15, 34, 39
21:2	4. **Compare** annual, biennial, and perennial plants.	6, 10	8, 10, 18	15, 25	2, 17
	5. **List** the growth requirements of plants.	7, 8, 9	3, 12, 19, 25	4, 19, 20, 21, 26, 29	3, 4, 6, 7, 9, 13, 18, 19, 26, 27, 28, 29, 30, 48, 49, 50, 51, 52, 53
21:3	6. **Explain** how bacteria and viruses affect plants.	11, 15	15, 21	5, 12, 16	21, 41, 44, 47
	7. **Describe** how a fungus can kill a plant.	12	17	12	21, 42, 43, 46,
	8. **Relate** two ways that insects damage plants.	13, 14	1, 2	12, 14, 23	13, 21, 45

Plant Growth and Disease

CHAPTER OVERVIEW

Key Concepts

This chapter points out the role of hormones in various responses of plant growth and flower production. Four growth requirements for plants—light, water, minerals, and temperature—are discussed in terms of their effects on the development of a plant. Plant diseases, insects, and their effects on plant growth are discussed.

Key Science Words

annual	perennial
biennial	phototropism
day-neutral plant	short-day plant
fertilizer	thigmotropism
gravitropism	tropism
long-day plant	

Skill Development

In Lab 21-1 , students will **measure in SI, form hypotheses, interpret data,** and **experiment** with the growth region in a root. In Lab 21-2 , they will **observe, form hypotheses,** and **interpret data** in relation to gravitropism and root growth. In the Skill Check on page 444, students will **observe** thigmotropism. In the Skill Check on page 446, they will **understand** the **science word** *biennial.* In the Mini Lab on page 448, students will **experiment** with plant growth in response to light.

CHAPTER PREVIEW

Chapter Content

Review this outline for Chapter 21 before you read the chapter.

Skills in this Chapter

The skills that you will use in this chapter are listed below.

- In **Lab 21-1,** you will measure in SI, form hypotheses, interpret data, and experiment. In **Lab 21-2,** you will observe, form hypotheses, and interpret data.
- In the **Skill Checks,** you will observe and understand science words.
- In the **Mini Labs,** you will experiment.

438

Bridging

In Chapters 19 and 20 of this unit, students learned about the structures and functions of leaves, roots, and stems. In Chapter 15, they found out about the role of hormones in animals. In this chapter, students will learn how hormones bring about changes in plants. They will find out how hormones, growth requirements, insects, and diseases alter the growth of plants.

Chapter **21**

Plant Growth and Disease

Plants, like animals, respond to changes in their environments. Plants don't have sense organs, nor do they move about. However, plants can still move in response to changes in their environments.

One well known response in plants can be seen in the photo to the left. If you live in the middle or northern states of the United States, you may have seen the new growth of plants in the spring. What causes a plant to grow in the spring, make flowers, or drop its leaves in the fall?

Another change in plants is caused by disease. Plants, like animals, can become sick as shown in the photo below. This chapter will explain how a plant responds to its environment, what it needs to grow, and some of the causes of plant diseases.

Try This!

How can you see a plant move? Place a houseplant in a window. Notice that the stems are straight. Look at the plant after two days. Has the plant moved? In what direction have the stems or leaves moved?

Diseased fruit is not edible.

GETTING STARTED

Using the Photos

Students may not notice that plants have responses because it takes several days to see some of the responses. Point out that the *Mimosa* plant shows a response to touch within a few seconds after the stimulus. The rapid response is caused by loss of water on the underneath side of the leaf. This causes the leaf to curl upward.

MOTIVATION/Try This!

How can you see a plant move? Upon completing the chapter-opening activity, students will have **observed** that plants respond to light. You may want to bring in photos of plants, such as sunflowers, that show response to sunlight. Remind students that they studied stimulus and response in Chapter 17.

Chapter Preview

Have students study the chapter outline before they begin to read the chapter. The first topic deals with how hormones affect plants and how plants respond to a stimulus. This is followed by a discussion of certain growth requirements. The final topic deals with plant diseases and insects that can affect plant growth.

Misconception

Students may believe that the responses they see in a plant are caused by a nervous system or a "desire" on the part of the plant to respond to an environmental factor. Remind students that plants do not have nervous systems.

21:1 Plant Responses

PREPARATION

Materials Needed

Make copies of the Application, Study Guide, Transparency Master, Critical Thinking/Problem Solving, Reteaching, and Lab worksheets in the *Teacher Resource Package.*

▶ Sprout the seeds at least 3-4 days before you start Lab 21-1.

▶ Soak corn seeds the night before you do Lab 21-2.

▶ Obtain a pea seed and a pot of soil for the Skill Check.

Key Science Words

short-day plant
long-day plant
day-neutral plant
tropism
phototropism
gravitropism
thigmotropism

Process Skills

In Lab 21-1, students will measure in SI, form hypotheses, interpret data, and experiment. In Lab 21-2, students will observe, form hypotheses, and interpret data. In the Skill Checks, they will observe and understand science words.

1 FOCUS

▶ The objectives are listed on the student page. Remind students to preview these objectives as a guide to this numbered section.

MOTIVATION/Overhead

Draw a graph on an overhead transparency to show the duration of sunlight in the various seasons. Use the graph to explain that increasing daily sunlight causes flowering in long-day plants and decreasing daily sunlight causes flowering in short-day plants.

Guided Practice

Have students write down their answers to the margin question: A plant will grow bushy.

21:1 Plant Responses

Objectives

1. **Explain** how hormones affect plant growth.
2. **Compare** short-day, long-day, and day-neutral plants.
3. **Distinguish** among tropisms and other plant movements.

Key Science Words

short-day plant
long-day plant
day-neutral plant
tropism
phototropism
gravitropism
thigmotropism

If you took a picture of a bean plant early in the morning and then again later in the day, you would see that some parts of the plant had moved. Early in the morning, bean leaves droop down close to the stem. The photograph taken later in the day would show the leaves held out and away from the stem. Bean leaves respond to a change between night and day. Is the movement of bean leaves a growth response, or do they move by some other means? The following sections describe and explain various plant responses.

Growth and Flowering

The photos in Figure 21-1 are of the same plant. The photos were taken in spring, just a week apart. In just a week, the plant has grown. Growth, flowering, and branching are all plant processes that are controlled by plant growth hormones. In Chapter 15, you read that hormones are chemicals made in one part of an organism that then affect another part of the organism.

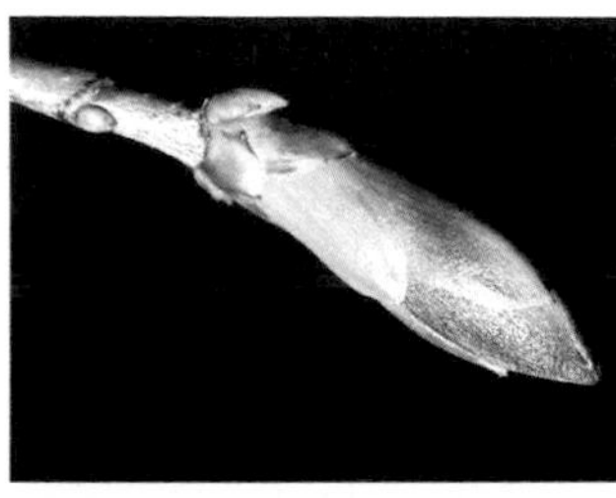

Figure 21-1 A maple tree before (top) and after (bottom) its buds burst open in the spring

Hormones that affect growth are made in the cells of the growing regions of plants. Locate the growth regions of a stem tip and root tip in Figure 21-2a. Growth in the stem tip causes a plant to grow taller and branches to grow larger. Growth in the root tip allows the roots to grow longer. Notice that the cells producing the growth hormones make up only a small area in the growth regions at the very tips of both shoots and roots.

Just what happens when a plant grows? Look at Figure 21-2a. Growth hormones near the root and stem tips cause cells to increase in number. These cell divisions make the root and shoot grow. Farther back from the growing tip, the hormone causes each cell to get longer. The increase in length of the cells pushes the root downward into the soil or the stem higher into the air.

The amount of hormones in lateral buds is higher than in terminal buds. High levels of hormones can slow down the rate of growth. The side branches that usually develop from lateral buds grow more slowly, Figure 21-2b. If you want a tree or shrub to grow more dense and bushy, you could trim off the tips of a few of branches. The lateral buds on these branches will then take over the role of the terminal bud and grow faster. The plant will get bushy because of the new growth of lateral branches.

What happens when you remove terminal buds?

OPTIONS

Science Background

Plant hormones are produced in the same tissues they affect. Plant hormones are sometimes referred to as growth regulators because they can speed up or slow down the growth of different plant parts. The hormone that promotes growth causes cells to elongate in the root and stem tips and stimulates cells to divide. The hormones that inhibit growth cause dormancy in plants.

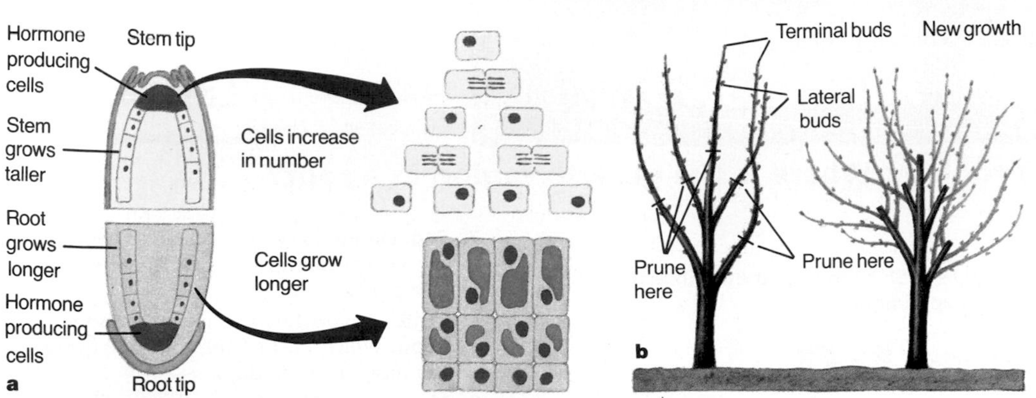

Figure 21-2 Cells in the growth regions of a stem and a root first increase in number at the tips and then get longer farther back (a). If terminal buds are removed, plants grow bushy (b).

You may have noticed that plants don't flower all at the same time. Flowering is controlled by hormones and by the length of time a plant receives light and dark, Figure 21-3. Some plants bloom in the autumn when the days are getting shorter and nights are getting longer. As the days get shorter, there comes a time when a flowering hormone is produced. Plants that flower when the day length falls below 12 to 14 hours are called **short-day plants.** Ragweed, chrysanthemum, and poinsettia are well know short-day plants. Many spring wildflowers are short-day plants. The flower buds form in the fall as the days get shorter. They don't open up until the next spring.

Other plants bloom in the summer as the days get longer. **Long-day plants** are plants that flower when the day length rises above 12 to 14 hours. Long-day plants include lettuce, clover, and gladiolus. Some plants, such as roses and dandelions, can produce flowers at most times of the year. They don't depend on any particular number of hours of light to produce flowering hormones. Once they start flowering, they bloom until frost stops further growth. These plants are day-neutral. **Day-neutral plants** are plants in which flowering doesn't depend on day length.

What plants bloom only in summer?

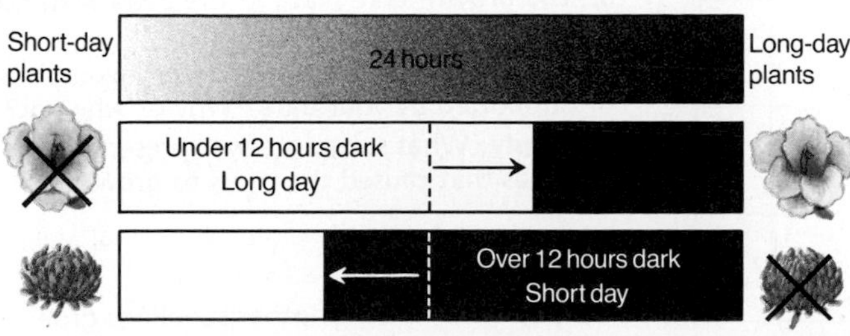

Figure 21-3 Flowering is often controlled by the number of hours of light and dark that a plant receives.

2 TEACH

MOTIVATION/Software

How Plants Grow: The Inside Story, Opportunities for Learning.

Concept Development

▶ Point out that many weed killers are actually hormones.

▶ Mention that growth hormones are added to some plants to speed up the time it takes for growth. The grower can get the produce to market earlier in the season.

Guided Practice

Have students write down their answers to the margin question: long-day plants.

Independent Practice

Study Guide/*Teacher Resource Package,* p. 121. Use the Study Guide worksheet shown at the bottom of this page for independent practice.

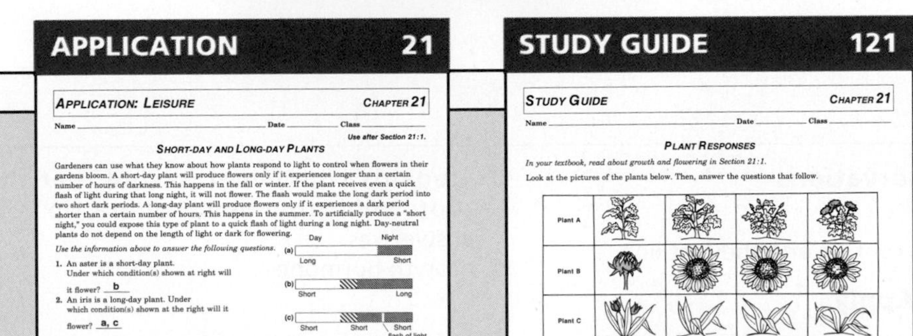

APPLICATION 21

APPLICATION: LEISURE — CHAPTER 21

Name ______ Date ______ Class ______

Use after Section 21:1.

SHORT-DAY AND LONG-DAY PLANTS

Gardeners can use what they know about how plants respond to light to control when flowers in their gardens bloom. A short-day plant will produce flowers only if it experiences longer than a certain number of hours of darkness. This happens in the fall or winter. If the plant receives even a quick flash of light during that long night, it will not flower. The flash would make the long dark period into two short dark periods. A long-day plant will produce flowers only if it experiences a dark period shorter than a certain number of hours. This happens in the summer. To artificially produce a "short night," you could expose this type of plant to a quick flash of light during a long night. Day-neutral plants do not depend on the length of light or dark for flowering.

Use the information above to answer the following questions.

Day / Night
(a) Long / Short
(b) Short / Long
(c) Short / Short / Short — flash of light

1. An aster is a short-day plant. Under which condition(s) shown at right will it flower? b
2. An iris is a long-day plant. Under which condition(s) shown at the right will it flower? a, c
3. Make a check mark in the column to show if a plant is short-day, long-day, or day-neutral.

	Short-day	Long-day	Day-neutral
Daffodils bloom in spring.	✓		
Dandelions bloom in spring, summer, and fall.			✓
Clover blooms in the summer.		✓	
Ragweed blooms in the fall.	✓		

4. Chrysanthemums are short-day plants that normally flower in the fall. How could you keep these plants from flowering until winter? Put lights on the plants at night during the fall to keep the day long and the night short.
5. To create a garden that has flowers in the spring, summer, and fall, would you plant short-day, long-day, or day-neutral plants? You could plant day-neutral plants or a combination of all three types. Short-day plants will flower in spring or fall, and long-day plants will flower in summer. Day-neutral plants will continue to flower throughout the growing season.

STUDY GUIDE 121

STUDY GUIDE — CHAPTER 21

Name ______ Date ______ Class ______

PLANT RESPONSES

In your textbook, read about growth and flowering in Section 21:1.

Look at the pictures of the plants below. Then, answer the questions that follow.

Plant A				
Plant B				
Plant C				
	May 15	June 15	July 15	August 15

1. Which plant is called a short-day plant? plant A
Explain your answer. The plant forms flowers in the fall of the year when the days are getting shorter, thereby providing less sunlight each new day.
2. Which plant is called a long-day plant? plant C
Explain your answer. The plant forms flowers in the spring of the year when the days are getting longer, thereby providing more sunlight each new day.
3. Which plant is called a day-neutral plant? plant B
Explain your answer. The plant forms flowers at most times of the year; it does not depend on day length to produce flowers.

OPTIONS

Application/*Teacher Resource Package,* p. 21. Use the Application worksheet shown here to reinforce short-day and long-day plants.

Lab 21-1 Root Growth

Overview

In this lab, students will learn that the growth region of a root is located in the first 2 mm of the root tip. When they cut off this region in a seedling, the root does not continue to grow. In the seedling where the root tip was not removed, growth is continuous.

Objectives: After completing this lab, students will be able to (1) **measure** the distance between lines on a root, (2) **explain** why the distance between some lines changed, and (3) **infer** where growth takes place in a root.

Time Allotment: 45 minutes setup time and 5-10 minutes per day for 3 days

Preparation

▶ Germinate the seeds 3-4 days prior to the lab.

Lab 21-1 worksheet/*Teacher Resource Package,* pp. 81-82.

Teaching the Lab

▶ **Troubleshooting:** Make sure students give the ink a chance to dry before they put the seedlings in the plastic bag.

Root Growth

Lab 21–1

Problem: Where is the growth region in a root?

Skills

measure in SI, form hypotheses, interpret data, experiment

Materials

2 bean seedlings
black India ink
paper towel
1 mm graph paper
plastic bag
razor blade
toothpick

Procedure

1. Copy the data table.
2. Place a bean seedling on the graph paper. The graph paper will serve as a ruler.
3. **Measure in SI:** Dip a toothpick in the ink. Starting from the tip of the root, draw three lines 2 mm apart, Figure A.
4. Repeat steps 2 and 3 with one more bean.
5. Choose one bean seedling and use a razor blade to remove 2 mm from the root tip. **CAUTION:** *Be careful when using a razor blade.*
6. Label two areas of a paper towel Bean 1 and Bean 2. Bean 2 will be the seedling with no root tip.

DAY	DAY 1		DAY 2		DAY 3	
BEAN NO.	1	2	1	2	1	2
Tip to first mark	3 mm	—	11 mm	—	16 mm	—
First to second mark	3 mm	2 mm	3 mm	2 mm	3 mm	2 mm
Second to third mark	2 mm	2 mm	2 mm	2 mm	2 mm	2 mm

7. **Experiment:** Wet the paper towel. Place the two seedlings in place. Put the towel in a plastic bag.
8. Write a **hypothesis** in your notebook about which part of the root will grow the most in three days.
9. **Measure in SI:** Examine the seedlings for three days. Each day, use the graph paper to measure the distances between the ink marks. Record these data in your table.

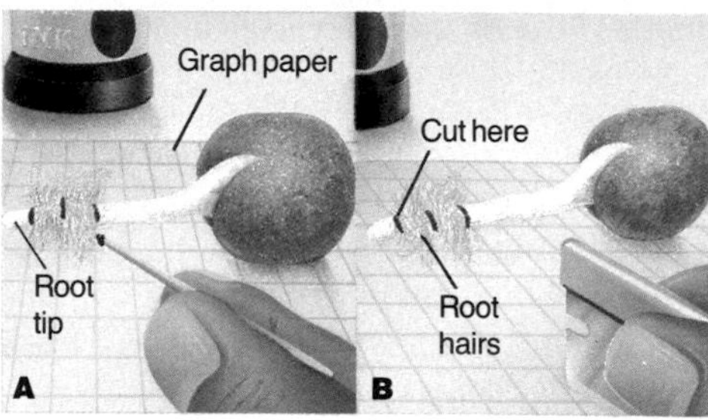

Data and Observations

1. Which bean had the most root growth?
2. In which part of the root tip of Bean 1 was there the most root growth?

Analyze and Apply

1. **Interpret data:** Why did the distance between some lines increase or stay the same?
2. Did growth take place in the bean with no root tip? Explain your answer.
3. **Check your hypothesis:** Is your hypothesis supported by your data? Why or why not?
4. **Apply:** What substance was present in the areas that caused the roots to grow?

Extension

Compare how roots of other seedlings grow.

ANSWERS

Data and Observations

1. bean 1
2. between the root tip and the first line

Analyze and Apply

1. When the distance between lines increased, it meant the cells were dividing more rapidly in these regions.
2. No, the tip is the place where growth hormone is produced.
3. Students who hypothesized that the roots will grow most at the tip will answer yes.
4. growth hormone

Tropisms

Plants respond to stimuli such as light and gravity. Animals respond to stimuli because they have sense organs. How do plants respond to stimuli if they don't have a nervous system? Some plant responses, such as flowering and movement towards light, are caused by changes in growth patterns of cells.

A **tropism** (TROH pihz um) is a movement of a plant caused by a change in growth as a response to a stimulus. You may not have seen a tropism because most of the movements are so slow. When a root grows down or when a stem bends over, the plant is showing a tropism.

One tropism that is easy to recognize is phototropism (foh toh TROH pihz um). **Phototropism** is the growth of a plant in response to light. A plant showing phototropism bends toward the light. When leaf stalks bend toward the light, more light falls on the leaves. How is this useful to the plant? It's clear in Figure 21-4 that light is very important to the growth of sunflowers.

Hormones play a role in tropisms. The growth hormone in a stem tip is affected by light. Light causes the growth hormone to move to the dark side of the stem where it causes the cells to lengthen, Figure 21-5. Because the cells on the dark side of the stem become longer, the stem bends toward the light.

Figure 21-4 Sunflowers were probably named for their obvious response to sunlight.

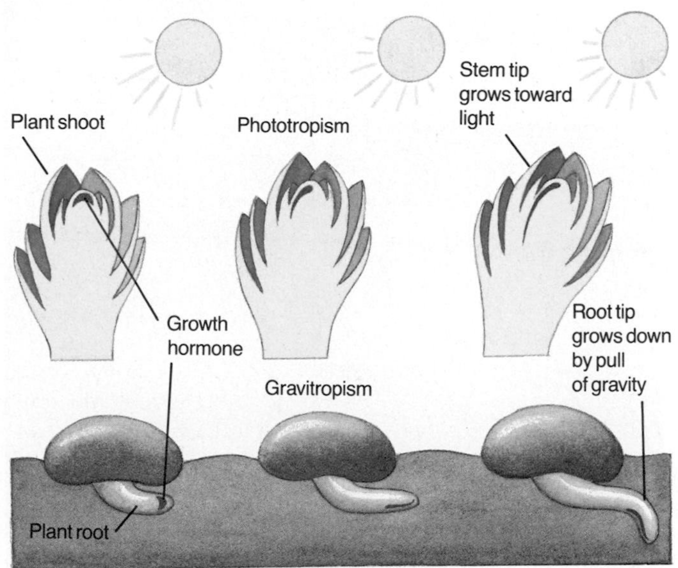

Figure 21-5 Phototropism causes a stem to grow towards light, and gravitropism causes roots to grow down.

TEACH

Concept Development

▶ Explain to students that plant tropisms are actually movements that are caused by unequal growth of some of the plant parts.

▶ Point out that leaves of vines growing on walls or other plants turn outward in response to light.

▶ Explain that hormones also produce effects other than tropisms. A hormone in the leaf stalk helps hold the leaf on the tree during the growing season.

▶ Point out that a tropism is a plant's response to a stimulus. The prefixes *photo-*, *gravi-*, and *thigmo-* define the stimuli.

CRITICAL THINKING 21

CRITICAL THINKING/PROBLEM SOLVING — CHAPTER 21

Name ______ Date ______ Class ______

Use after Section 21:1.

HOW DO CLIMBING PLANTS RESPOND TO THE SUN?

Juan was walking past a chain-link fence in his neighborhood. He noticed that some plants called vines were growing up the fence, curled in and out of its wires. Vines such as ivy were attached to the fence by small rootlike structures. Some, including morning glory plants, had small stems that curled around and around the wire. He knew these were called tendrils.

Juan recalled that his parents put up thin stakes in rows in their garden. They planted ivy, bean, and morning glory plants near the stakes. He examined these plants, too, and found both rootlike structures and tendrils.

Juan also noticed that the morning glory flowers sometimes faced toward, and sometimes away from, the street. He made careful observations, and realized that the stem below the flower twisted around during the day. So did the tendrils. Juan used his textbook to understand how vines respond to their environment.

Analyzing the Problem

1. What is a tropism? the growth response o' a plant to a stimulus in the environment
2. What do most plant tropisms involve? movement
3. What is the substance that travels in the stem of a plant and is involved in plant tropisms? a hormone

Solving the Problem

1. To what stimulus are the stems below the flowers responding when they turn during the day? sunlight
2. What is this tropism called? phototropism
3. To what stimulus are the vines responding when they turn to touch the wire or stake? contact
4. What is this tropism called? thigmotropism
5. How do tendrils become curled? As they grow, they twist around and around the wire or stake they touch.
6. How do stems become curled? As the flowers turn to follow the sun, the stems twist around and around.
7. What is the role of hormones in tropisms? Hormones stimulate some of the cells to grow and divide more quickly. This growth makes the stem or tendril bend.

OPTIONS

What Tropisms Can Be Seen in Growing Plants?/*Lab Manual*, pp. 173-176. Use this lab as an extension to tropisms.

Critical Thinking/Problem Solving/ *Teacher Resource Package*, p. 21. Use the Critical Thinking/Problem Solving worksheet shown here to reinforce how vines respond to the sun.

TEACH

ACTIVITY/Demonstration

Coil a piece of string around a wooden dowel to show how a stem of a climbing plant "holds on" to other objects.

Guided Practice

Have students write down their answers to the margin question: a growth response to contact.

Skill Check

Pea seeds can be purchased in garden or grocery stores. A foam cup can be used for planting the pea seed.

Check for Understanding

Hand out a drawing of a bean plant that shows roots, stems, and leaves. Write the following on the chalkboard: gravitropism, phototropism, and thigmotropism. Tell the students to make a drawing to show how the plant responds to each tropism and write a one-sentence definition for each.

Reteach

Use a sensitive plant to demonstrate its response to touch. Have students compare its response to the three tropisms studied in this chapter.

Independent Practice

Study Guide/*Teacher Resource Package,* p. 122. Use the Study Guide worksheet shown at the bottom of this page for independent practice.

Skill Check

Observe: Observe a climbing plant. Plant a pea seed. Place a pencil in the pot. Observe thigmotropism as the plant grows. *For more help, refer to the* ***Skill Handbook,*** *pages 704-705.*

What is thigmotropism?

Roots grow downward into the soil as a result of gravitropism (grav uh TROH pihz um). *Gravi* means having weight. **Gravitropism** is the response of a plant to gravity. As in the stem, the growth region of the root produces a growth hormone.

If you put a sprouting bean on its side on top of some potting soil, the root will grow downward into the soil within a few days. Large amounts of growth hormone in the root move through the cells to the lower side of the root, as if pulled down by their weight, Figure 21-5. This diffusion is in response to gravity. The hormone slows down the growth in length of the lower cells. The cells above continue to grow longer and the root grows down into the soil.

Grape vines, honeysuckle, and greenbriar are very common climbing plants in the forests of the United States. These climbing plants hold onto trees or fences by thigmotropism. *Thigma* means touch. **Thigmotropism** is a plant growth response to contact. Many climbing plants have twining parts called tendrils that respond to contact with a likely support by coiling around this object. The start of coiling can happen within ten minutes. Peas, beans, and squash are examples of food plants with tendrils that show thigmotropism, Figure 21-6.

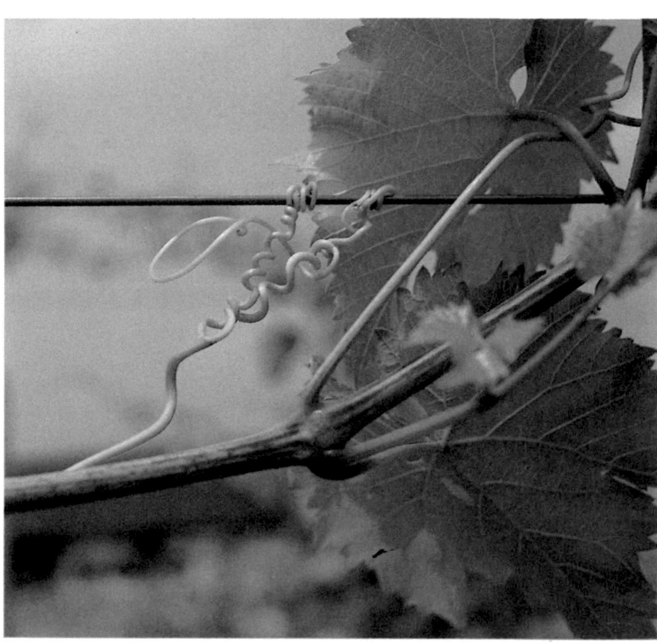

Figure 21-6 Thigmotropism helps a plant climb a fence.

STUDY GUIDE 122

STUDY GUIDE — **CHAPTER 21**

Name ________ Date ________ Class ________

PLANT RESPONSES

In your textbook, read about tropisms in plants in Section 21:1. Then, read the description below and answer the questions that follow.

Some plants in a greenhouse were tipped over and not set upright for several weeks. When the greenhouse manager found them, and stood them up, they looked like those in the diagram.

A B C

4. Which plant(s) were not tipped over? **C** Explain your answer. **The plant roots are growing down into the soil and the stem is growing upward toward the light. This is the way plants normally grow.**
5. Which plant(s) were tipped over? **A and B** Explain your answer. **When a plant is turned on its side, the plant roots begin to grow downward and the stem begins to grow upward.**
6. What is the name of the tropism that describes how the roots are responding? **gravitropism**
7. What is the name of the tropism that describes how the stem is responding? **phototropism**
8. Define each tropism. **Gravitropism is the response of plants to gravity. Phototropism is the response of plants to light.**
9. Which part of the plant responds to gravity? **roots** How can you tell? **Roots grow toward Earth, where the pull of gravity is strongest.**
10. Which part of the plant responds to light? **stem** How can you tell? **Stems grow toward light.**

TRANSPARENCY 97

TRANSPARENCY MASTER — **CHAPTER 21**

SOIL PARTICLES AND ROOTS

Cortex of root

Root hair

Air space

Soil particle

OPTIONS

Transparency Master/*Teacher Resource Package,* p. 97. Use the Transparency Master worksheet shown here to help students with root growth.

Plant Growth Response/*Transparency Package,* number 21. Use color transparency number 21 as you teach plant growth responses.

Lab 21–2 Plant Responses

Problem: How does gravitropism affect the growth of roots?

Skills

observe, form hypotheses, interpret data

Materials

petri dish	transparent tape
2 paper towels	4 presoaked corn seeds
marking pen	

Procedure

1. Copy the data table.
2. Soak two paper towels in water.
3. Wrinkle the towels and place them in the bottom half of the petri dish.
4. Place four presoaked seeds on top of the wet paper towels as shown in Figure A. Place the seeds so the narrow end is pointing toward the center of the dish.
5. Put the top on the petri dish. The lid will press the seeds into the wet towels.
6. Seal the lid with transparent tape.
7. Draw an arrow on the top of the petri dish with a marking pen as shown in Figure B. This will show the direction of the force of gravity.
8. Stand the petri dish on edge so that the arrow is pointing straight down.
9. Write a **hypothesis** in your notebook about which direction you think the roots will grow.
10. **Observe** the seeds for the next four days. Each day, fill in the data table with arrows to show the direction of root growth for each of the four seeds.

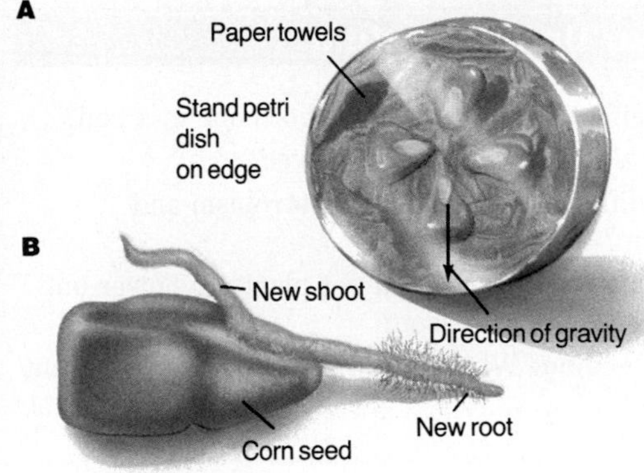

Data and Observations

1. In what direction were the roots growing on Day 1?
2. What is the direction of root growth at the end of four days?

SEED	DIRECTION OF GROWTH OF ROOT			
	Day 1	Day 2	Day 3	Day 4
	→	↘	⤵	⤵
	↓	↓	↓	↓
	↗	↗	→	⤵
	←	↙	↙	↓

Analyze and Apply

1. **Interpret data:** To what factor of the environment are the roots responding?
2. What is this response called?
3. **Check your hypothesis:** Is your hypothesis supported by your data? Why or why not?
4. **Apply:** If this same experiment were carried out in space, would the results be the same? Explain your answer.

Extension

Design an experiment that shows the effect of phototropism.

Lab 21-2 Plant Responses

Overview

In this lab, students will conduct an experiment to find out how roots respond to gravity. Students will see that the roots grow downward shortly after germination.

Objectives: After completing this lab, students will be able to (1) **use** controls and variables in an experiment, (2) **interpret** data from an experiment, and (3) **explain** the effect of gravity on corn roots.

Time Allotment: 45 minutes, then 5-10 minutes per day for 4 days

Preparation

▶ The night before you start this lab, soak the seeds in water. In the morning, place them between wet paper towels in a tray.

Lab 21-2 worksheet/*Teacher Resource Package,* pp. 83-84.

Teaching the Lab

▶ **Troubleshooting:** Make sure students put enough wet paper towels in the petri dish to hold the seeds in place.

Cooperative Learning: Divide the students into teams of two. For more information, see pp. 22T-23T in the Teacher Guide.

ANSWERS

Data and Observations

1. straight towards the center of the dish
2. straight down in the direction of the arrow

Analyze and Apply

1. the force of gravity
2. gravitropism
3. Students who hypothesized that the roots would all grow downward will answer yes.
4. No, the force of gravity is very weak in space. The roots would all grow straight.

TEACH

Check for Understanding

Have students respond to the first three questions in Check Your Understanding.

Reteach

Reteaching/*Teacher Resource Package*, p. 63. Use this worksheet to give students additional practice with plant responses.

Extension: Assign Critical Thinking, Biology and Reading, or some of the **OPTIONS** available with this lesson.

3 APPLY

ACTIVITY/Demonstration

To demonstrate the bending of a stem, inflate a long, thin balloon with air. Draw a grid around the balloon. Let the balloon represent a stem, and the grid the cells of the stem. Bend the balloon (stem) to the right and ask students what happened to the cells on the left. They should respond that the cells became longer. Explain that the increase in length of the cells on one side of a stem causes the stem to bend toward light.

4 CLOSE

Software

The Plant Growth Simulator, Queue, Inc.

Answers to Check Your Understanding

1. The bud grows very slowly.
2. when the day length falls below 12 to 14 hours
3. In plants, phototropism is a growth response to light and thigmotropism is a growth response to contact.
4. Take them indoors and increase or decrease the amount of light they receive.
5. Most plant tropisms occur too slowly to be observed.

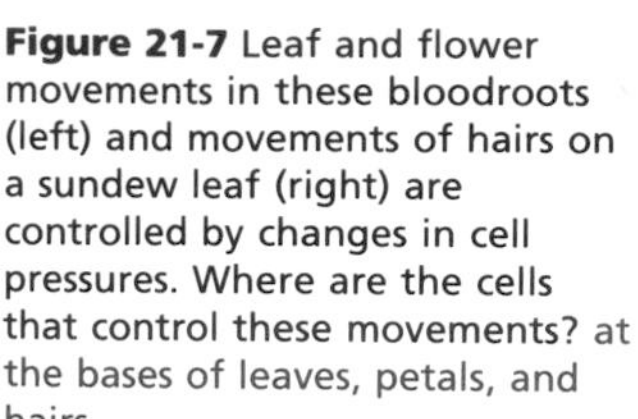

Figure 21-7 Leaf and flower movements in these bloodroots (left) and movements of hairs on a sundew leaf (right) are controlled by changes in cell pressures. Where are the cells that control these movements? at the bases of leaves, petals, and hairs

Skill Check

Understand science words: biennial. The word part *bi* means two. In your dictionary, find three words with the word part *bi* in them. *For more help, refer to the* ***Skill Handbook,*** *pages 706-711.*

Other Plant Responses

Not all responses of plants are caused by hormones. Some plant parts move because of changes in pressure inside the cells. You read in Chapter 19 that stomata in the leaves open and close for gas exchange. Stomata open and close when the water pressure inside the guard cells changes. A stoma opens when the guard cells are full with water. When water is low in the cell, the stoma closes.

There are many other plant movements that are caused by changes in cell pressure. For example, the movement of flowers and leaves shown in Figure 21-7 and described earlier for bean plant leaves are caused by changes in cell pressure. At night, the cells at the bases of petals and leaf stalks in some plants lose water and these parts fold up. The cells regain water in the daytime, and the leaves and flowers open out.

Some plants have leaves that trap insects, Figure 21-7. When the hairs on the leaves are touched, such as when an insect lands on them, the pressure in the cells at the base of hairs changes, causing the hairs to fold over rapidly and trap the insect.

Check Your Understanding

1. What is the effect of a high level of hormone in a bud?
2. What causes a short-day plant to flower?
3. What is the difference between phototropism and thigmotropism?
4. **Critical Thinking:** How could you get plants to flower out of their usual flowering season?
5. **Biology and Reading:** Why is it difficult to observe a plant tropism?

OPTIONS

ACTIVITY/Enrichment

Have a few kinds of insect-eating plants to show students. You can feed the plants wingless fruit flies to see how they respond to the insects.

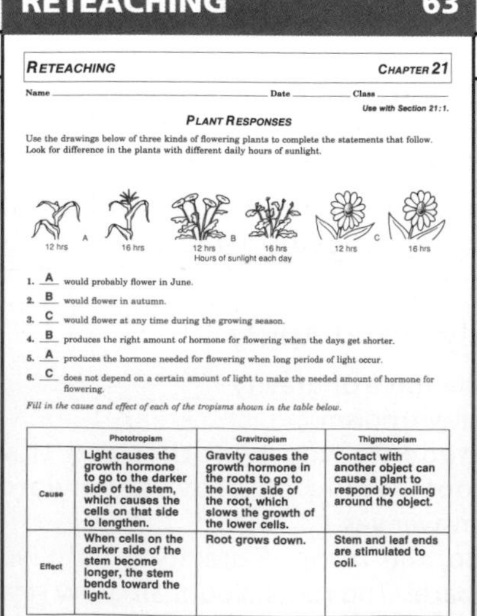

RETEACHING 63

RETEACHING CHAPTER 21

Name ______ Date ______ Class ______

Use with Section 21:1.

PLANT RESPONSES

Use the drawings below of three kinds of flowering plants to complete the statements that follow. Look for difference in the plants with different daily hours of sunlight.

1. A would probably flower in June.
2. B would flower in autumn.
3. C would flower at any time during the growing season.
4. B produces the right amount of hormone for flowering when the days get shorter.
5. A produces the hormone needed for flowering when long periods of light occur.
6. C does not depend on a certain amount of light to make the needed amount of hormone for flowering.

Fill in the cause and effect of each of the tropisms shown in the table below.

	Phototropism	Gravitropism	Thigmotropism
Cause	Light causes the growth hormone to go to the darker side of the stem, which causes the cells on that side to lengthen.	Gravity causes the growth hormone in the roots to go to the lower side of the root, which slows the growth of the lower cells.	Contact with another object can cause a plant to respond by coiling around the object.
Effect	When cells on the darker side of the stem become longer, the stem bends toward the light.	Root grows down.	Stem and leaf ends are stimulated to coil.

21:2 Growth Requirements

Plants can live from a few months to thousands of years. As a plant grows, the numbers of cells increase. Plants use the energy from the sun and water, minerals, and carbon dioxide from the environment to build these new cells. Factors needed by a plant for proper growth are called growth requirements. Growth requirements for plants include light, air, water, minerals, and the right temperature. Water and minerals are usually taken from the soil, so the condition of the soil is often another growth requirement. Growth may be slowed if any of these factors is not present in the right amount.

Objectives

4. **Compare** annual, biennial, and perennial plants.
5. **List** the growth requirements of plants.

Key Science Words

annual
biennial
perennial
fertilizer

Seasonal Growth

What are five growth requirements of plants?

Most of the plants you know, such as oak trees, pine trees, poison ivy, daisies, lettuce, and onions reproduce by seeds. Seed-producing plants can grow from one to many years. Some herbaceous plants complete their growth, produce seeds, and then die within one year. Plants that complete their life cycle within one year are called **annual** (AN yul) plants. Garden plants like corn, peas, and lettuce are annual plants, Figure 21-8a.

Some herbaceous plants need two years to complete growth and produce seeds. These are called biennials, Figure 21-8b. **Biennial** (bi EN ee ul) plants produce seeds at the end of the second year of growth and then die. Cabbages and turnips are biennial plants. This is why you don't see flowers or seeds on a head of cabbage.

When do biennial plants produce seeds?

a

b

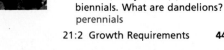

Figure 21-8 Pea plants (a) are annuals, hollyhocks (b) are biennials. What are dandelions? perennials

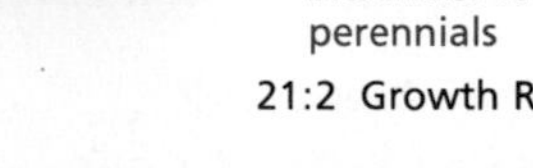

21:2 Growth Requirements

PREPARATION

Materials Needed

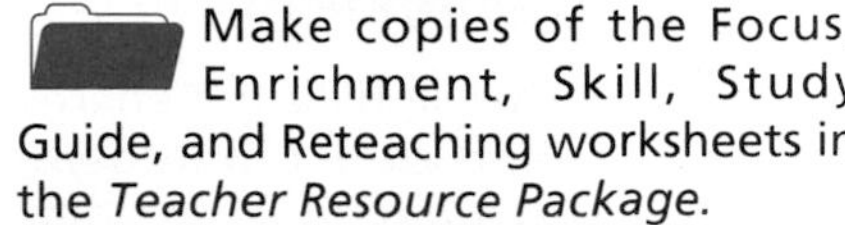

Make copies of the Focus, Enrichment, Skill, Study Guide, and Reteaching worksheets in the *Teacher Resource Package*.

▶ Obtain radish seeds, cups, and soil for the Mini Lab.

Key Science Words

annual
biennial
perennial
fertilizer

Process Skills

In the Mini Lab, students will experiment.

1 FOCUS

▶ The objectives are listed on the student page. Remind students to preview these objectives as a guide to this numbered section.

ACTIVITY/Brainstorming

Ask students to list factors that help a plant grow better.

Guided Practice

Have students write down their answers to the margin questions: light, air, water, minerals, the right temperature; in the second year.

Focus/*Teacher Resource Package*, p. 41. Use the Focus transparency shown at the bottom of this page as an introduction to growth requirements.

FOCUS 41

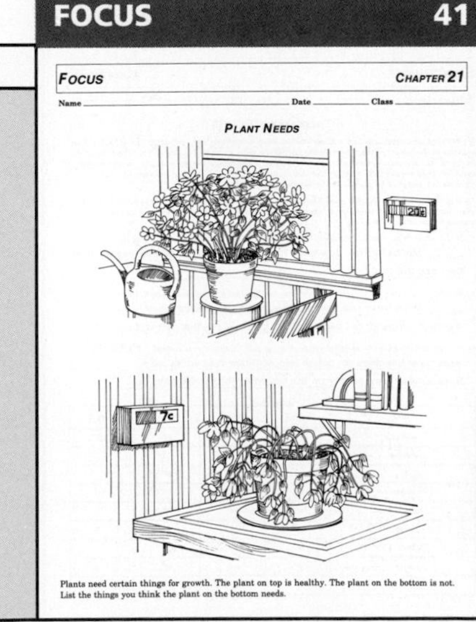

FOCUS
CHAPTER 21
Name
Date
Class
PLANT NEEDS
7°C
Plants need certain things for growth. The plant on top is healthy. The plant on the bottom is not. List the things you think the plant on the bottom needs.

OPTIONS

Science Background

Plants have many requirements for growth. The five listed in this section are the most important. Growth in a plant depends on the interaction of these five factors. Each of these requirements is needed in a specific amount by the plant. For instance, without light the plant would not be able to make chlorophyll even if the other factors were present in optimum amounts.

2 TEACH

MOTIVATION/Filmstrip

Show the filmstrip *Germination and Plant Growth,* Clearvue, Inc.

Concept Development

▶ Point out that light is the energy source for plants during photosynthesis.

▶ Point out that the amount of light a plant gets each day varies with the amount of clouds in the sky.

▶ Explain that some plants have a specific tolerance for shade or direct sunlight.

▶ Explain that biennials store in their roots food that was made during the first year of growth, and they use this food to produce flowers during the second year of growth.

▶ Point out that the annual plants seen in a field or meadow grow from new seeds each year.

Idea Map

Have students use the idea map as a study guide to the major concepts of this section.

Mini Lab

Get potting soil, radish seeds, and cups ready. The plants grown in the dark will be tall, yellow, and thin stemmed, and will not be as straight as those grown in the light.

A plant that lives longer than two years is a perennial (puh REN ee ul). A **perennial** plant is one that doesn't die at the end of one or two years of growth. Perennials usually produce seeds year after year. Many woody plants, such as shrubs and trees, are perennials. Their woody aboveground parts don't die at the end of each growing season. Some herbaceous plants, such as daffodils, onions, and many spring wildflowers, are also perennials. The aboveground parts of herbaceous perennials do die at the end of each growing season. Herbaceous perennials have underground parts with stored food that is used to produce new growth in the spring. Daffodils, onions, and many spring wildflowers are herbaceous perennials.

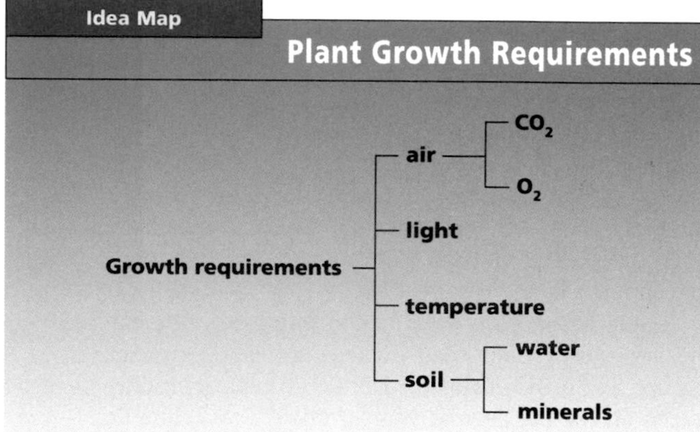

Study Tip: Use this idea map as a study guide to plant growth requirements. Which two requirements are found in soil?

Mini Lab

Do Plants Need Light?

Experiment: Plant 12 radish seeds in moist soil in each of two paper cups. Place one cup in a well-lit area and the other in a cupboard. Compare the growth of the plants for a week. *For more help, refer to the* ***Skill Handbook,*** *pages 704-705.*

Light

Plants need light for proper growth. The amount of light a plant gets controls much of its development. Production of chlorophyll, growth of buds, time of flowering, and ability to make food are all plant processes that need light.

Some plants need direct sunlight in order to grow well, others don't. Impatiens, popular bedding plants with brightly-colored flowers, grow best if they aren't planted in direct sunlight. Tomatoes and corn grow best in direct sunlight. Corn grown in the shaded part of a garden will produce short stalks and small ears. Tomatoes will take longer to ripen if grown in the shade. Plants grown in areas that are too shady will grow tall, be lighter green in color, and have fewer, but larger, leaves.

OPTIONS

Is Light an Important Growth Requirement for Plants?/*Lab Manual,* pp. 177-180. Use this lab as an extension to growth requirements of plants.

Enrichment/*Teacher Resource Package,* p. 22. Use the Enrichment worksheet shown here to help students understand tolerance in plants.

ENRICHMENT 22

ENRICHMENT CHAPTER 21

Name ______ Date ______ Class ______

TOLERANCE IN PLANTS

If you hiked up a mountain that was several thousand kilometers high, you might notice that plants growing at the bottom of the mountain are not all the same as those growing on top. The air and soil on top of the mountain are cooler than at the bottom. Some plants can grow only in warm weather, some can grow only in cold weather, and others can grow in warm and cold weather. The ability of a plant to live and grow in an unfavorable environment is called tolerance.

Look at the drawing on the next page. Then, fill in the table below. Use check marks to show in which zones the plants in the drawing grow. Use the table and a dictionary or encyclopedia to help you answer the questions that follow.

1. Which plant(s) grow in all four areas of the mountain? Explain your answer using the word *tolerance.* **Mosses have a tolerance for wide temperature differences because they can live in all zones.**
2. Which plant(s) grow in only one of the four areas? Explain your answer using the word *tolerance.* **Palm trees and live oak trees have a tolerance for only the warmest temperatures because they grow only in the warmest zones.**
3. Do spruce trees have the same tolerance as white oaks? Explain your answer. **No, spruce trees have tolerance for colder temperatures than white oaks. Spruce trees grow farther up the mountain than white oaks do.**

Plants	Zone A	Zone B	Zone C	Zone D
mosses	✓	✓	✓	✓
white oak	✓	✓		
birch		✓	✓	
hickory	✓	✓		
pine	✓	✓	✓	
live oak	✓			
palm	✓			
spruce	✓	✓	✓	
maple	✓	✓		

a

b

Figure 21-9 The environments of a cactus (a) and a fern (b) are different in rainfall levels.

Water

The two plants shown in Figure 21-9 have different water needs. The cactus can grow in a dry, sandy soil. The fern needs a moist, rich soil to grow well. A desert cactus takes up water from rain that comes only a few times each year. The cactus stores the water for use between rainfalls. The fern isn't adapted to store water. It needs to live in an area where the soil is damp most of the time.

How can some plants live in a desert with little rainfall?

Water has many important uses in plants. Water makes up 30 to 90 percent of a plant's mass. Plants use some of this water for photosynthesis. Minerals taken up by the roots are dissolved in water. Once inside a plant, this water carries the minerals throughout the plant. A farmer or gardener needs to water crops if there isn't enough rain to supply the needs of the plants.

Minerals

Most plants grow in soil. Soil contains many minerals important to plant growth. Plants also use minerals for making chlorophyll and cell walls. Three important minerals used by plants are nitrogen, phosphorus, and potassium.

Plants may absorb more of one type of mineral than another. Why? Since plants need some minerals such as nitrogen, in larger amounts than others, the soil can become drained of that mineral. If the soil of a garden or field is low in one kind of mineral, fertilizer can be added. A **fertilizer** is a substance made of minerals that improves soil for plant growth. When you want to help your flowering plants bloom or your shrubs grow faster, you might apply different types of fertilizer. The labels on fertilizer packets give the percentages of nitrogen, phosphorus, and potassium that the fertilizers contain, Figure 21-10.

Figure 21-10 Fertilizer can supply missing minerals to soil.

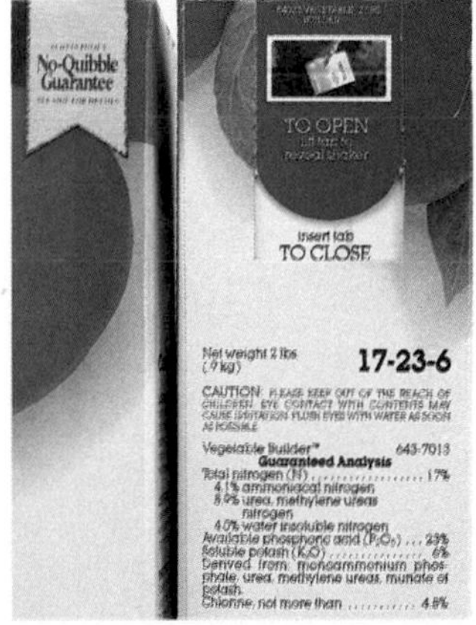

STUDY GUIDE 123

STUDY GUIDE — *CHAPTER 21*

Name ________ Date ________ Class ________

GROWTH REQUIREMENTS

In your textbook, read about growth requirements of plants in Section 21:2. Then, read the following description of a set of experiments on plant growth.

Experiments were done to find what effects the amount of water, light, minerals, and soil had on some plants. In each experiment, the amounts of light, water, minerals, soil, and temperature were kept the same except where shown in the figure on the next page. The plants were grown for nearly two months. Answer the questions after you have studied the diagrams.

1. In experiment 1, which plant grew best? **plant C** How often was this plant watered? **every three days**
2. What would happen to the plant in answer 1 if it were planted in an area where it rained four days each week? **The plant would not grow as well as it did in the experiment.**
3. Does the kind of plant used in experiment 1 grow well with a great amount of water? **no** Explain your answer. **This kind of plant does not grow well if watered too often, such as three times a day or even once a day.**
4. What growth requirement is being tested in experiment 2? **light**
5. In experiment 2, which plant grew best? **plant A** How much sun did the plant receive? **full sun**
6. Suppose you bought several of these plants to put in your flower beds. Where would you *not* plant them? **in shady areas** Why? **This kind of plant does not grow well in the shade.**
7. What growth requirement is being tested in experiment 3? **type of soil needed**
8. In experiment 3, which plant grew best? **plant B** What type of soil was this plant grown in? **potting soil**
9. Could the type of plant in experiment 3 be grown in the desert? **no** Why or why not? **The desert is mostly sandy soil. This plant does not grow well in sandy soil.**

STUDY GUIDE 124

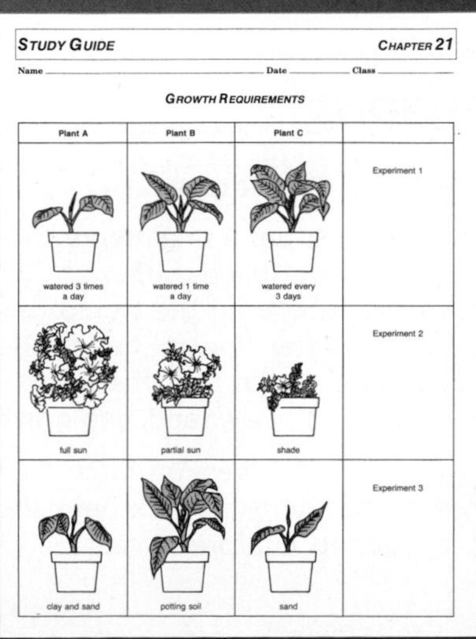

STUDY GUIDE — *CHAPTER 21*

Name ________ Date ________ Class ________

GROWTH REQUIREMENTS

Plant A	Plant B	Plant C	
watered 3 times a day	watered 1 time a day	watered every 3 days	Experiment 1
full sun	partial sun	shade	Experiment 2
clay and sand	potting soil	sand	Experiment 3

TEACH

Concept Development

- ▶ Point out that all growth requirements are needed by plants in order to grow, but that water is the most important. Tell students that 90 percent of the weight of plants is water.
- ▶ Point out that there is a relationship between water and minerals as growth requirements. Minerals have to be dissolved in water before they can be taken in by plants.
- ▶ Explain that the mineral particles in the soil come from rocks being eroded, either by freezing and thawing or by water.
- ▶ Explain that some perennials do not bloom during their first year of growth.

Bridging

Tie in Chapters 19, 20, and 21 by reviewing the importance of water loss in plants. Explain that certain plants, like the cactus, can store lots of water in their waxy coated stems so that they lose very little water. Plants living in drier environments have fewer stomata and smaller leaves to prevent excessive water loss.

ACTIVITY/Display

Cut out sections of several fertilizer bags that list the mineral content. Display these for the students. List below the sections what each type of fertilizer is best used for.

Guided Practice

Have students write down their answers to the margin question: The plants store water.

Independent Practice

Study Guide/*Teacher Resource Package,* pp. 123-124. Use the Study Guide worksheets shown at the bottom of this page for independent practice.

TEACH

Concept Development

▶ Explain that the leaves and stems of plants that die in the fall are broken down into nutrients and recycled by other plants.

▶ Point out that rich soil contains a large amount of dead matter.

▶ Explain that dead matter in soil is food for earthworms and other invertebrates and increases the ability of the soil to hold water.

▶ Emphasize that soil provides oxygen and minerals for plants, and a substrate to which they can attach.

▶ Point out that temperature is the growth requirement that humans are most familiar with.

▶ Explain that temperature varies with the intensity of heat energy.

▶ Reinforce that many plants grow slower when the temperature is lower because chemical reactions are slowed down.

Bio Tip

Leisure: Because flowers bloom at different times of the year, you can design a garden so that you will have flowers all year round.

Soil

You have learned that soil supplies water and minerals to plants. Soil also gives the plant a place to set down its roots. Soil is a mixture that contains minerals, living organisms, dead or decaying matter, air, and water. The minerals come from rocks that have been worn down by wind and rain.

There are three main types of soil, Figure 21-11. Clay soil is hard because the soil particles are small and packed closely together. There are fewer air spaces. Other soil is crumbly because the soil particles are larger. There are more air spaces between the soil particles. Crumbly soil is better for plant growth. The air spaces in this type of soil give roots room to grow. The air spaces also keep roots dry. If roots are soaked too long, they may rot.

If the soil in your garden were like clay, you might first loosen the soil with a hoe. Also, you could add some sand and peat moss. Adding sand and dead organic matter to loosened clay soil increases the number of air spaces and adds nutrients.

Some soils are poor for plant growth. Pure sandy soil is an example of poor soil because it allows water to drain through too fast. The air spaces can't trap and hold water. Plants in desert environments often have enormous root systems to collect as much water as possible.

Temperature

Which plant in Figure 21-12 will be most affected by colder temperatures? Some plants can live in cold climates, while others die when the temperature falls below freezing.

Figure 21-11 Clay soil (a) is very fine; crumbly soil (b) is rich in organic matter; and sandy soil (c) is coarse and can't hold water.

a

b

c

OPTIONS

ACTIVITY/Challenge

Have students put a small spoonful of soil into a large test tube filled with water. Tell them to shake the tube until the clump of soil has broken apart. After the soil has settled overnight, they should notice that the layers from top to bottom are silt, clay, sand, and gravel.

Skill/*Teacher Resource Package,* p. 22. Use the Skill worksheet shown here to have students interpret data.

SKILL 22

SKILL: INTERPRET DATA — **CHAPTER 21**

Name ______ Date ______ Class ______

For more help, refer to the Skill Handbook, pages 704-705. *Use after Section 21:2.*

GROWTH OF FLOWERING PLANTS

Read the following paragraph. Then, study the data in the table and answer the questions.

For their first flower garden, the Smiths bought several kinds of plants. Some of the plants would grow well in the sun and others would grow better in the shade. They also knew they had bought some annuals, some biennials, and some perennials. They planted some of each kind of plant in the shade and the rest in sunny areas. The table shows their record of how the plants grew.

Name of plant	Where planted		When plant bloomed	New growth each spring	Notes
	Sunny	Shady			
Impatiens	X		June-October	No	Stem long, thin; plant droopy
		X	June-October	No	Stems thick, green; many flowers
Mint	X			No	Stems bent over in a month; plants died.
		X	May-June	Yes	Stems green, thick; many flowers
Chrysanthemum	X		September-October	Yes	Stems green; many flowers
		X		No	Stems tall, yellow; died in two months
Foxglove	X		June-July of second year	Only during second spring	Stems tall, green
		X		No	Stems and leaves yellow; died

1. Which of the plants were annuals? Explain. **Impatiens, died after the first season.**
2. Which of the plants were biennials? Explain. **Foxglove, it produced flowers at the end of the second season and then died.**
3. Which of the plants were perennials? Explain. **Mint and chrysanthemum, they did not die at the end of one or two years.**
4. Which of the plants should grow best under trees and shrubs? Explain. **Impatiens and mint, they grow best in shade.**

a

b

Figure 21-12 Some plants live only in cold climates (a), whereas others, such as these palm trees, couldn't survive low temperatures (b).

Temperature affects the rate at which a plant will take up water, and the rates of photosynthesis and growth.

Farmers and gardeners know that they can plant most seeds or plants only after all danger of frost has passed. If they do their planting before this time, their plants will freeze or their seeds won't grow. Some seeds, however, need cold temperatures. For example, one kind of wheat called winter wheat is planted in northern states in the fall. It starts to grow until the temperature gets near freezing. The wheat is then protected by snow cover throughout the winter and begins to grow again in the spring. Some seeds, such as those of apples, will not grow unless they have first been frozen.

Check Your Understanding

6. What are two ways in which annual and perennial plants differ?
7. What are three minerals important to the growth of plants?
8. Compare the light requirements of two different plants.
9. **Critical Thinking:** If you collected plants that were native to Texas and brought them home with you to Maine, what would you need to do to keep your plants alive?
10. **Biology and Reading:** Why don't you see flowers or seeds on a head of cabbage?

TEACH

Independent Practice

Study Guide/*Teacher Resource Packaage,* p. 126. Use the Study Guide worksheet shown at the bottom of this page for independent practice.

Check for Understanding

Have students respond to the first three questions in Check Your Understanding.

Reteach

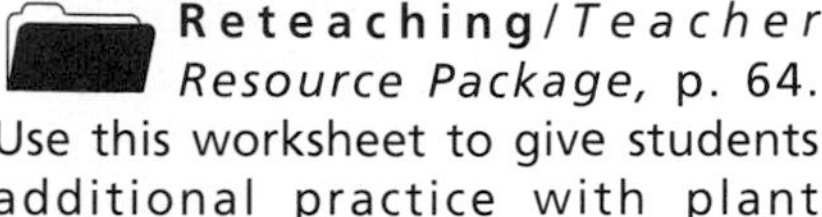

Reteaching/*Teacher Resource Package,* p. 64. Use this worksheet to give students additional practice with plant growth requirements.

Extension: Assign Critical Thinking, Biology and Reading, or some of the **OPTIONS** available with this lesson.

3 APPLY

ACTIVITY/Audiovisual

Show the video *Plant Dynamics,* Carolina Biological Supply.

4 CLOSE

Software

Plants, Opportunities for Learning.

Answers to Check Your Understanding

6. Annual plants complete their life cycle and die within one year. Perennial plants live for more than two years and produce seeds year after year.
7. nitrogen, phosphorus, potassium
8. Some plants, such as tomatoes, need direct sunlight; others, such as impatiens, need shade.
9. You would need artificial light and controlled temperatures similar to those in Texas.
10. Cabbages are biennials and they are eaten in the first year. Flowers and seeds are not formed until the second year.

STUDY GUIDE 126

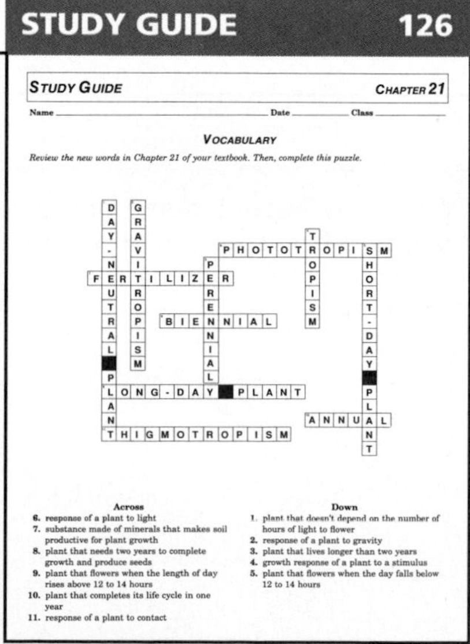

STUDY GUIDE — CHAPTER 21

Name ______ Date ______ Class ______

VOCABULARY

Review the new words in Chapter 21 of your textbook. Then, complete this puzzle.

Across

6. response of a plant to light
7. substance made of minerals that makes soil productive for plant growth
8. plant that needs two years to complete growth and produce seeds
9. plant that flowers when the length of day rises above 12 to 14 hours
10. plant that completes its life cycle in one year
11. response of a plant to contact

Down

1. plant that doesn't depend on the number of hours of light to flower
2. response of a plant to gravity
3. plant that lives longer than two years
4. growth response of a plant to a stimulus
5. plant that flowers when the day falls below 12 to 14 hours

RETEACHING 64

RETEACHING — CHAPTER 21

Name ______ Date ______ Class ______

Use with Section 21:2.

GROWTH REQUIREMENTS

1. The growth requirements of plants are light, water, nutrients, soil, and temperature.
2. If any of the growth requirements are not just right, growth may be slowed.
3. Suppose a group of plants of the same type and age are grown—some of them in a lighted area and some in a dark cabinet.
   a. After seven days the plant growing in the lighted area would have normal leaves and a normal stem.
   b. The plant in the dark area would have a yellowish stem and leaves.
4. Corn grown in the shaded part of the garden will produce short stalks and ears.
5. Cactus plants store water to help them through the dry season.
6. Ferns need to live in an area where the soil is damp most of the time.
7. Water makes up 30 to 90 percent of a plant's mass.
8. Plants can absorb minerals from the soil because they are dissolved in water.
9. Plants use minerals for growth and for making chlorophyll and cell walls.
10. Two kinds of minerals that plants need are nitrates and phosphates.
11. When necessary, fertilizers can supply minerals that are missing from soil.
12. Loosening the soil around plants provides larger air spaces around the roots.
13. Biennial plants produce seeds at the end of the second year of growth.
14. Perennial plants usually do not die at the end of one or two years of growth, and they produce seeds from year to year.

21:3 Plant Diseases and Pests

PREPARATION

Materials Needed

Make copies of the Reteaching and Study Guide worksheets in the *Teacher Resource Package.*

Key Science Words

No new science words will be introduced in this section.

1 FOCUS

▶ The objectives are listed on the student page. Remind students to preview these objectives as a guide to this numbered section.

ACTIVITY/Display

You can preserve many fungi that are plant parasites by putting the plant part with the fungus attached into a preservative such as alcohol. These can be displayed and observed in the lab. Shelf fungi can be air dried. Excellent photos of plant diseases are available from your state Department of Agriculture.

Guided Practice

Have students write down their answers to the margin questions: a virus; it grows into and blocks xylem tissue.

21:3 Plant Diseases and Pests

Objectives

6. **Explain** how bacteria and viruses affect plants.
7. **Describe** how a fungus can kill a plant.
8. **Relate** two ways that insects damage plants.

Diseases and insect pests can slow down or stop plant growth. Diseases affect all plants.

Bacteria and Viruses

Bacteria cause many plant diseases. They can enter a plant through the stomata or small cuts. Once inside, the bacteria destroy plant cells when they invade the cytoplasm. If the bacteria spread throughout the plant, the plant might die. Bacteria are a common cause of blister spots on fruit and leaves, Figure 21-13a.

What causes yellow spotting on leaves?

Viruses also cause plant diseases. Garden plants and houseplants can be affected by a plant virus that causes small yellow spots on leaves. Eventually the yellow spots darken as the tissue dies. This kind of disease is called a mosaic disease, Figure 21-13b.

Viruses often cause the growth of tumors in leaves. The leaves become deformed. Plant viruses don't infect animals so it doesn't hurt you to touch these leaves.

Fungi

How does a fungus destroy an elm tree?

Many plant diseases are caused by fungi, Figure 21-13c. A plant disease caused by a fungus can spread rapidly through entire fields of crops.

Dutch elm disease is caused by a fungus that has killed hundreds of thousands of American elms. A small bark beetle carries the spores of the fungus from infected to healthy trees. The fungus enters the stem, begins to grow, and eventually plugs up the xylem tissue.

Figure 21-13 Plants can be infected by bacteria (a), viruses (b), or fungi (c).

a

b

c

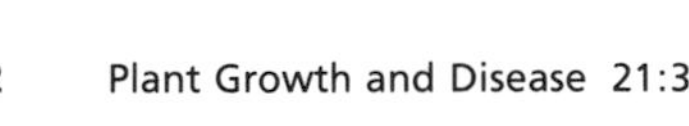

OPTIONS

Science Background

The growth requirements studied in the last section are environmental factors. Living factors, like insects and disease-causing organisms, can also slow down or stop the growth of plants. There are about 200 bacteria, 400 viruses, and 1000 fungi recognized as plant pathogens. Many of these pathogens attack a single species or genus of plants. Insects are responsible for carrying plant diseases from one plant to another. Insects destroy plants by eating plant parts or entire plants. Since they can move about, they sometimes destroy large areas of plants at one time.

a

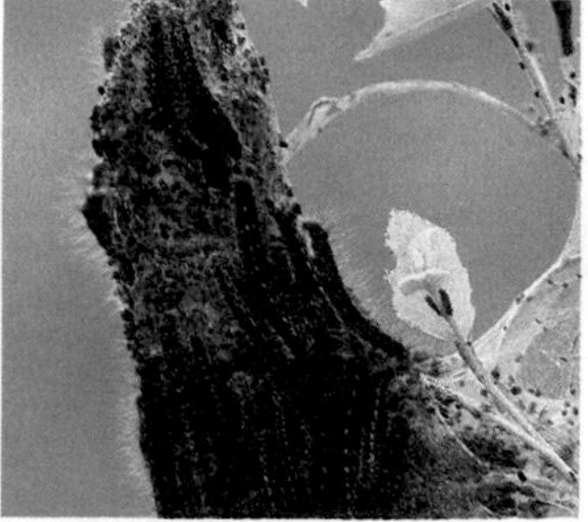
b

Figure 21-14 An insect can transfer viruses from its mouthparts to uninfected plants (a). Tent caterpillars can eat all the leaves on a tree in a few days (b).

Other crop diseases caused by fungi include wheat rusts and corn smuts. There are also a wide variety of fungi that cause fruit and vegetable rot. Recall that spores are the reproductive structures of fungi. Many fungi are spread by the wind and rain that carry the spores.

Insect Pests

In general, insects are a great help to plants. They carry pollen from flower to flower. Sometimes, however, insects cause plant diseases. Suppose an insect visits a plant that has a virus, bacterium, or fungus in its cells. The insect takes in these microbes when it eats tissues of the plant, Figure 21-14a. When the insect visits the next plant, it transfers the disease microbe from its mouthparts to the uninfected plant. The disease soon develops in that plant.

How do insects transfer viruses to plants?

Insects also can damage or even kill plants by eating too many leaves. A plant with damaged leaves can't make as much food. For example, the tent caterpillar, Figure 21-14b, builds a web in a tree and can eat all of the leaves on that tree in a few days.

Bio Tip

Ecology: Insects like praying mantis and lady bugs are helpful to gardeners because they eat harmful insects. Take care not to spray these insects with pesticides.

Check Your Understanding

11. What is mosaic disease?
12. How do spores of Dutch elm disease enter a tree?
13. How can an insect reduce photosynthesis in a plant?
14. **Critical Thinking**: What is a way to control insect pests in your garden without spraying pesticides?
15. **Biology and Reading:** What two kingdoms contain organisms that cause plant diseases?

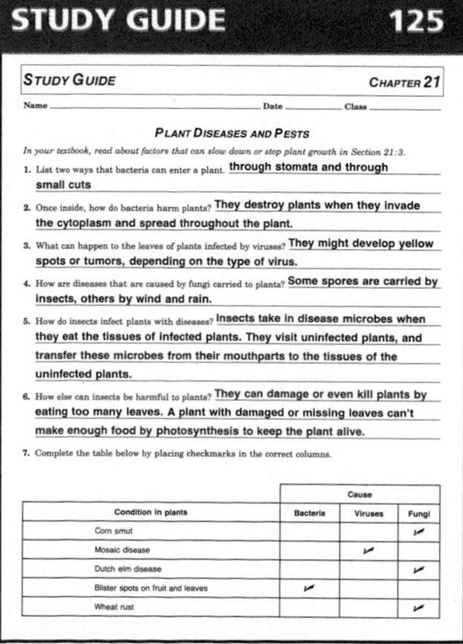

STUDY GUIDE 125

STUDY GUIDE — CHAPTER 21

Name ______ Date ______ Class ______

PLANT DISEASES AND PESTS

In your textbook, read about factors that can slow down or stop plant growth in Section 21:3.

1. List two ways that bacteria can enter a plant. through stomata and through small cuts
2. Once inside, how do bacteria harm plants? They destroy plants when they invade the cytoplasm and spread throughout the plant.
3. What can happen to the leaves of plants infected by viruses? They might develop yellow spots or tumors, depending on the type of virus.
4. How are diseases that are caused by fungi carried to plants? Some spores are carried by insects, others by wind and rain.
5. How do insects infect plants with diseases? Insects take in disease microbes when they eat the tissues of infected plants. They visit uninfected plants, and transfer these microbes from their mouthparts to the tissues of the uninfected plants.
6. How else can insects be harmful to plants? They can damage or even kill plants by eating too many leaves. A plant with damaged or missing leaves can't make enough food by photosynthesis to keep the plant alive.
7. Complete the table below by placing checkmarks in the correct columns.

	Cause		
Condition in plants	Bacteria	Viruses	Fungi
Corn smut			✓
Mosaic disease		✓	
Dutch elm disease			✓
Blister spots on fruit and leaves	✓		
Wheat rust			✓

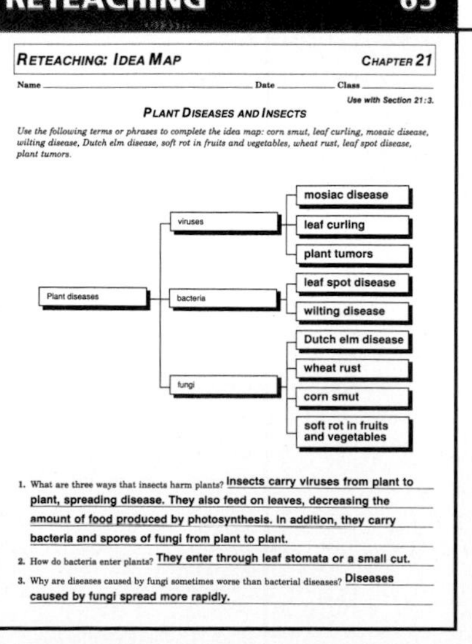

RETEACHING 65

RETEACHING: IDEA MAP — CHAPTER 21

Name ______ Date ______ Class ______

Use with Section 21:3.

PLANT DISEASES AND INSECTS

Use the following terms or phrases to complete the idea map: corn smut, leaf curling, mosaic disease, wilting disease, Dutch elm disease, soft rot in fruits and vegetables, wheat rust, leaf spot disease, plant tumors.

1. What are three ways that insects harm plants? Insects carry viruses from plant to plant, spreading disease. They also feed on leaves, decreasing the amount of food produced by photosynthesis. In addition, they carry bacteria and spores of fungi from plant to plant.
2. How do bacteria enter plants? They enter through leaf stomata or a small cut.
3. Why are diseases caused by fungi sometimes worse than bacterial diseases? Diseases caused by fungi spread more rapidly.

2 TEACH

Guided Practice

Have students write down their answers to the margin question: Insects pass disease microbes on their mouthparts to the next plant.

Independent Practice

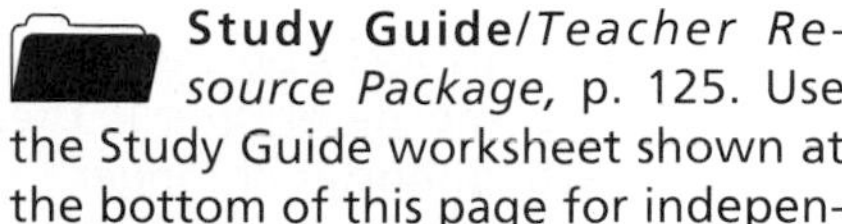

Study Guide/*Teacher Resource Package,* p. 125. Use the Study Guide worksheet shown at the bottom of this page for independent practice.

Check for Understanding

Have students respond to the first three questions in Check Your Understanding.

Reteach

Reteaching/*Teacher Resource Package,* p. 65. Use this worksheet to give students additional practice with plant diseases.

Extension: Assign Critical Thinking, Biology and Reading, or some of the **OPTIONS** available with this lesson.

3 APPLY

Connection: Social Studies

Have students investigate plant diseases that affect humans.

4 CLOSE

ACTIVITY/Guest Speaker

Have a county agricultural agent talk to your class about plant diseases and pests.

Answers to Check Your Understanding

11. a disease caused by a virus that makes yellow spots on leaves
12. The fungus enters the stem.
13. It eats a large number of the plant's leaves.
14. Answers may include collecting pests by hand or using a detergent to wash the leaves.
15. Fungi and Monera

PROBLEM SOLVING

Flowering in Plants

Problem-solving Strategies

The following strategies can be used to solve the problem in this feature: construct a table, look for a pattern, and guess and check.

Hints

▶ Have students focus on the dates of flowering and determine if the days are getting shorter or longer.

Solving the Problem

a. long-day, hollyhock; b. short-day, pansy; c. short-day, chrysanthemum; d. day-neutral, rose; e. day-neutral, blanket flower; f. long-day, gladiolus; g. long-day, iris

PROBLEM SOLVING

FLOWERING IN PLANTS

June 21 is called the longest day of the year. Do you know why? On this day there are more hours of daylight than any other day of the year. After June 21 the days get shorter until December 21. After December 21 the days begin to get longer again until June 21. This cycle is repeated each year.

The change in the amount of daylight and darkness affects the flowering of plants as they grow during the growing season. Long-day plants bloom only when the numbers of hours of daylight get more than a critical number. The critical number of hours varies from species to species. Short-day plants bloom only when the number of daylight hours is less than a critical number. Day-neutral plants are not affected by the lengthening or shortening of the day or night.

a Hollyhock July

c Chrysanthemum September, October

b Pansy August, September

Look at the closeup photos of the flowers. These flowers were in bloom in the months listed with each photo. Make a table of the blooming times and the kind of flower. From your table determine which of the plants are (a) short-day plants, (b) long-day plants, or (c) day-neutral plants.

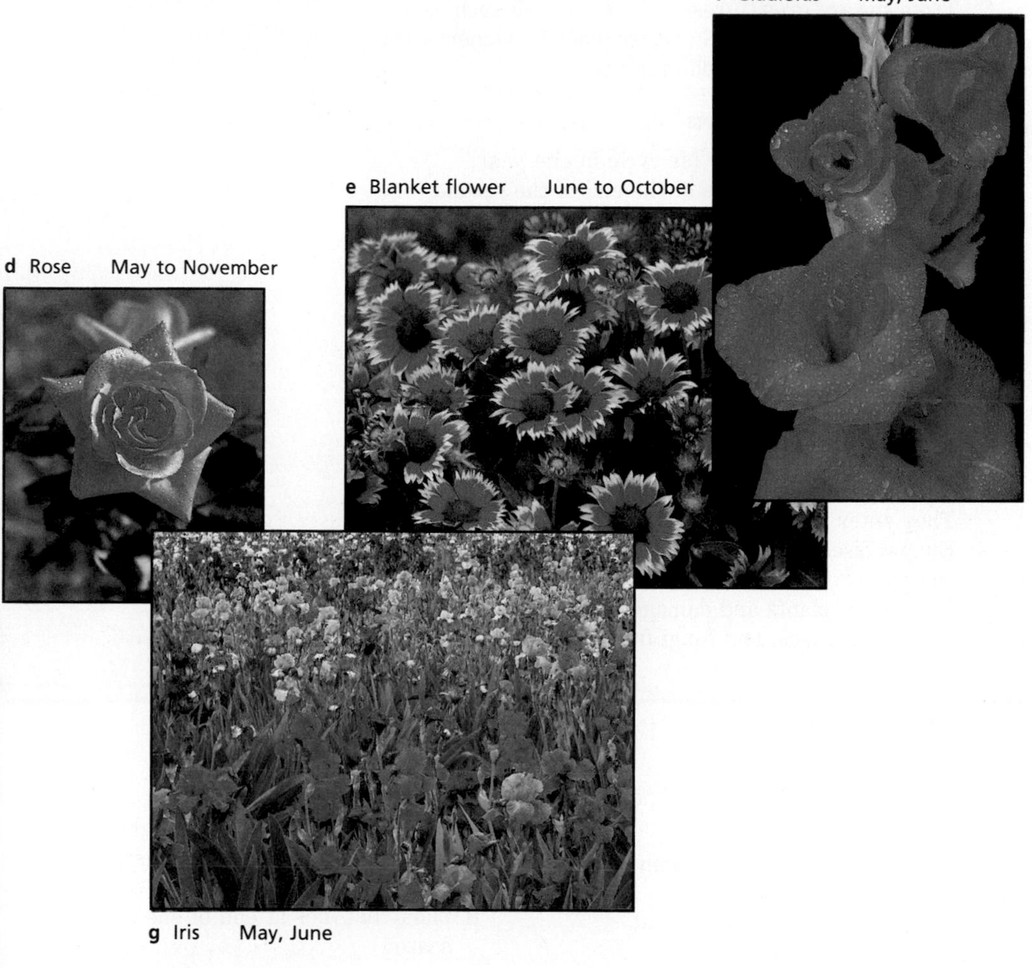

f Gladiolus May, June

e Blanket flower June to October

d Rose May to November

g Iris May, June

Discussing the Problem

▶ It may help students to draw a time line of one year that shows the dates of increasing and decreasing day length. By plotting flowering times on the time line, students can determine in which category each flower belongs.

Extension

Have students research other common plants and use the same strategies to determine each plant's category.

CHAPTER 21 REVIEW

Summary

Summary statements can be used by students to review the major concepts of the chapter.

Key Science Words

All boldfaced terms from the chapter are listed.

Testing Yourself

Using Words

1. short-day plant
2. gravitropism
3. fertilizer
4. tropism
5. phototropism
6. long-day plant
7. thigmotropism
8. annual
9. day-neutral plant
10. perennial

Finding Main Ideas

11. p. 453; Insects spread plant diseases with their mouthparts.
12. p. 449; Minerals such as nitrogen, phosphorus, and potassium are found in soil and used by plants to make chlorophyll and cell walls.
13. p. 443; Growth hormone causes stems to bend toward light.
14. p. 440; If the terminal buds are removed from a plant, bushy growth will result.
15. p. 452; Bacteria destroy the plant cells when they invade the cytoplasm.
16. p. 444; Climbing vines hold onto trees and fences by thigmotropism.
17. p. 452; Dutch elm disease is caused by a fungus.
18. p. 447; Biennial plants produce seeds at the end of the second year of growth.

Using Main Ideas

19. The growth requirements of plants are light, water, soil, nutrients, and temperature.
20. Growth hormones are found in the growing regions of the plant: the terminal bud, lateral bud, and root tip.
21. Bacteria invade a plant through the stomata or a small leaf cut, and cause a disease by destroying the cell's cytoplasm.
22. Three kinds of tropisms in plants are phototropism, gravitropism, and thigmotropism.
23. The terminal bud produces a hormone that keeps the lateral bud from growing as fast as the cells near the terminal bud.
24. Caterpillars eat the leaves and slow down photosynthesis.
25. The three main minerals used by plants are nitrogen, phosphorus, and potassium.

Chapter 21 Review

Summary

21:1 Plant Responses

1. Hormones in plants control growth and flowering.
2. Short-day plants flower when day length shortens. Long-day plants flower when there are longer periods of daylight. The flowering of day-neutral plants does not depend on the length of daylight.
3. Tropisms are growth responses to stimuli such as light, gravity, and touch. Other plant movements are caused by changes in cell pressure.

21:2 Growth Requirements

4. Annuals complete their life cycle in one year. Biennials produce seeds at the end of the second year. Perennial plants can live for many years.
5. Growth requirements for plants include varied amounts of light, water, minerals, air, and temperature. The type of soil is often important.
6. Different plants in different environments need different levels of light, temperature, water, and minerals.

21:3 Plant Diseases and Insects

7. Bacteria and viruses cause many plant diseases. They enter the plant through cuts, stomata, or roots.
8. Fungal diseases spread from plant to plant by spores.
9. Insects eat plants and damage them by carrying bacteria, viruses, and fungi from plant to plant.

Key Science Words

annual (p. 447)
biennial (p. 447)
day-neutral plant (p. 441)
fertilizer (p. 449)
gravitropism (p. 444)
long-day plant (p. 441)
perennial (p. 448)
phototropism (p. 443)
short-day plant (p. 441)
thigmotropism (p. 444)
tropism (p. 443)

Testing Yourself

Using Words

Choose the word from the list of Key Science Words that best fits the definition.

1. plant that blooms in the autumn
2. plant response to gravity
3. substance made of nutrients that improves soil for plant growth
4. plant response to a stimulus
5. the response of a plant to light
6. plant that blooms in the summer
7. plant growth in response to touch
8. plant that dies at end of one growing season

Review

Testing Yourself *continued*

9. plant that blooms from early summer until frost
10. plant that produces seed year after year

Finding Main Ideas

List the page number where each main idea below is found. Then, explain each main idea.

11. how insects spread plant diseases
12. minerals used by a plant to make cell walls and chlorophyll
13. what causes stems to bend toward light
14. how a person could cause bushy growth in plants
15. how plant diseases are caused by bacteria
16. how climbing vines hold onto trees and fences
17. what causes Dutch elm disease
18. when biennial plants produce seeds

Using Main Ideas

Answer the questions by referring to the page number after each question.

19. What are the growth requirements for plants? (p. 447)
20. Where are growth hormones found in plants? (p. 440)
21. How do bacteria invade a plant and cause a disease? (p. 452)
22. What are three kinds of tropisms in plants? (pp. 443, 444)
23. What keeps lateral buds from growing faster than the terminal buds? (p. 440)
24. What effect does a tent caterpillar have on a tree? (p. 453)
25. What are three main minerals used by plants? (p. 449)

Skill Review 

For more help, refer to the ***Skill Handbook,*** *pages 704-719.*

1. **Observe:** Observe plants that are growing in the shade of other plants. Explain how they differ from similar plants growing in the sun.
2. **Experiment:** Germinate two bean seeds with a moist paper towel. Experiment to find the effects of different stimuli on root and shoot growth.
3. **Measure in SI:** For five days, measure the height of a bean plant that you planted.
4. **Interpret data:** You have a garden of roses. One day, you notice some of the leaves have black spots. A week after a heavy rain, you notice that most of the leaves have black spots. The leaves then begin to drop off the plants. What's wrong with your roses?

Finding Out More

Critical Thinking

1. Explain why cutting grass with a mower doesn't stop grass growing.
2. How would a scientist decide whether or not soil is missing some minerals needed for plant growth?

Applications

1. Find out how the amounts of light and water provided for plants are controlled in a greenhouse.
2. Find out the common names of some hormones made by plants. Visit the garden section of a department store or hardware store for help.

Skill Review

1. Plants growing in the shade will be smaller than similar plants growing in the sun.
2. Answers will vary depending on the stimuli chosen. As an example, roots will grow away from light and shoots will grow toward light.
3. The plant will grow higher and develop more leaves as it grows.
4. The roses are probably infected with a fungus whose spores were spread by the rain.

Finding Out More

Critical Thinking

1. Grass grows from the base; the blades of grass are merely leaves. When you mow the grass, you don't cut off the region of growth.
2. The scientist might test the soil to determine its composition, or try growing plants in it to see how well they grow.

Applications

1. Students will find that light and water are controlled by the glass structure of the greenhouse.
2. Rootone, Hormodin, Quick-root, and Rootgro all contain indolebutyric acid, an auxin.

 **Chapter Review**/*Teacher Resource Package,* pp. 109-110.

 **Chapter Test**/*Teacher Resource Package,* pp. 111-113.

Chapter Test/*Computer Test Bank*

 **Unit Test**/*Teacher Resource Package,* pp. 114-115.

CONNECTIONS

Biology in Your World

In this unit, students learn that plants are essential to human existence. Farming is society's structured way of using plants to feed many people. Farmers constantly look for new ways to produce the most crops for the least amount of money. But, they also consider the effect on the environment and the safety of the food supply.

Literature Connection

John Burroughs (1837-1921) was a famous author who wrote about outdoor life. He grew up on a New York farm, where he often read the works of Walt Whitman, Ralph Waldo Emerson, and John James Audubon. He worked for the U.S. Department of the Treasury and as a bank examiner until he moved to his own farm on the Hudson River. Burroughs wrote seven books and many essays about nature's beauty. His friends included Theodore Roosevelt, Henry Ford, and Thomas Edison.

History Connection

From 1845 to 1847, much of Ireland's booming population lived in poverty, and potatoes were a staple of the diet. During the potato famine, 750 000 Irish died of starvation or disease. Hundreds of thousands moved to other countries. Most moved to the United States. Today, late blight can be controlled with fungicides.

CONNECTIONS

Biology in Your World

Healthy Plants, Healthy People, Healthy Environment

In this unit, you learned about plants and their importance. Everyone depends on plants as a food source. Safe farming practices and pest control are needed for healthy food crops. A healthy environment and successful farming are goals of scientists and farmers.

LITERATURE

Deep Woods

John Burroughs was a writer who loved nature and loved to write about it. Many of his essays and books are about his own experiences exploring the Catskill Mountains of New York, where he spent much of his life.

Burroughs brings the out-of-doors to life for his readers. His vivid, interesting writing style makes you feel as if you are with Burroughs in the woods or on a mountaintop.

Deep Woods is a collection of essays from several of Burroughs' books. Included are essays about the Catskills, Maine, Alaska, and Yosemite. Sit back and enjoy Burroughs' descriptions of the beauties and wonders of nature!

HISTORY

The Potato Famine

For more than 100 years, potatoes had been the main part of the diet in Ireland. But in the fall of 1845, the potato crop rotted in about half of Ireland. Starvation and disease followed as crop after crop rotted over the next three years. We know now that a parasitic mold caused crops to rot. The mold had spread rapidly from North America to England, and then to Ireland.

Today, chemicals can be used to control the growth of molds. Use of these chemicals can reduce the loss of crops. The chemicals may also improve the quality of crops. Maybe famines like the one in Ireland will not occur again.

LEISURE

Do You Have a Green Thumb?

You are never too old to enjoy getting dirty! Ask permission to cultivate a small, sunny area of your yard. You will need a spade, a rake, a hoe, and some seed catalogs. Choose several types of fruits and vegetables. All plants have slightly different requirements. You may have better luck with some than with others.

When you prepare your garden, make sure the soil is broken up well for proper drainage. If the soil is mostly clay, add peat moss, sand, or decayed leaves.

At harvest time, notice which fruits and vegetables did well. How can you improve your harvest next year? For each crop you grew, which part do you eat—leaf, stem, fruit, or root?

CONSUMER

Using Chemicals Wisely

Are the fruits and vegetables you buy in grocery stores safe to eat? Aflatoxin is a chemical produced by a fungus. The fungus can grow on grains and other crops. Aflatoxin is a natural cancer-causing agent. It can affect peanuts, corn, and the milk of corn-fed cows.

In 1989, scientists tested corn for the presence of aflatoxin. They found unacceptable levels of the chemical in 6 percent of the tested samples.

A certain chemical works against aflatoxin. The chemical reduces the amount of aflatoxin present in the milk of cows that eat the treated grain.

Should farmers spray their crops with chemicals to kill fungi? Not all fungi are harmful to plants. One soil-living fungus helps plants remove needed nutrients from the soil. Thus, farmers should use caution when applying chemicals so that the chemicals don't enter the soil and kill the fungi there.

CONNECTIONS

Leisure Connection

Some students will not have access to a garden plot. Fortunately, some vegetables grow well in containers. Students should prepare containers as they would for a houseplant.

Dill, parsley, and other herbs do well in small pots on a sunny windowsill. Tomatoes, squash, and pumpkins grow nicely in large tubs. Cherry tomatoes and strawberries thrive in hanging baskets.

Consumer Connection

Many foods contain very low levels of naturally occurring carcinogens. Unfortunately, the levels of aflatoxin found in milk were unsafe. A compound added to dairy cows' grain can control this problem.

However, some people think chemical residues in food are dangerous. Some farmers are reacting to this by producing organically grown food. Organic fruits and vegetables are now available in most supermarkets.

References

"Agriculture." *1991 Science Year.* Chicago: World Book, Inc., 1990.

Burroughs, John. *Deep Woods.* Salt Lake City: Gibbs Smith, 1990.

"Food." *1990 World Book Year Book.* Chicago: World Book, Inc., 1990.

Fry, Peter, and Fiona Somerset Fry. *A History of Ireland.* New York: Routledge London, 1988.

Silcock, Lisa, ed. *The Rainforests.* San Francisco: Chronicle Books, 1990.

Waters, Marjorie. *The Victory Garden Kids' Book.* Boston: Houghton Mifflin, 1988.

Unit 6 Reproduction And Development

UNIT OVERVIEW

Unit 6 is based upon the concept that reproduction is a basic life process and examines both plant and animal reproduction. Meiosis and mitosis are discussed in Chapter 22. Chapter 23 deals with reproduction in plants. Sexual reproduction in animals is discussed in Chapter 24. Chapter 25 studies development in humans.

Advance Planning

Audiovisual and computer software suggestions are located within each specific chapter under the heading TEACH.

Invite someone from the research community to speak about cancer and relate the lack of information on cell reproduction to the difficulty of finding a cure for the disease.

To prepare for:

- Lab 22-2: Purchase a sheet of clear plastic.
- Mini Lab: Purchase radish seedlings.
- Lab 23-1: Purchase carrots and garlic bulbs.
- Lab 23-2: Purchase corn seeds and soak half of them for two days.
- Mini Lab: Soak the bean seeds for two days.
- Lab 24-1: Order prepared slides of starfish eggs and sperm.
- Lab 24-2: Gather colored pencils and graph paper.
- Mini Labs: Order sea urchin eggs and sperm. Order prepared slides of hydra.
- Lab 25-2: Order grasshoppers and moths in various stages of metamorphosis.
- Mini Lab: Prepare glucose solution and gather eggshells.

Unit 6

CONTENTS

Reproduction and Development

What would happen if...

the present rate of population growth continued? The population of North America would increase to about 487 000 000 by the year 2000.

If a population of 487 000 000 people were spread out evenly over all of North America, there would be about 20 people per square kilometer. But the population is not spread out evenly. Few people live in desert and mountain areas. Most people are in cities along rivers, lakes, or oceans. The population density in cities can be hundreds of people per square kilometer.

The world population was about 5 162 000 000 in 1989. At a growth rate of 1.6%, the world population would be about 6 147 000 000 in the year 2000. That's about 41 people per square kilometer. How might this many people affect life on Earth?

461

UNIT OVERVIEW

Photo Teaching Tip

Ask students to read the unit opening passage and look at the photographs. Have students discuss all the places they have visited where they wouldn't like to live. Maybe students have visited a volcano in Hawaii, the swamps of Georgia, or the peaks of the Rocky Mountains. Although these places may be nice to live near, not many people could live in or on them. Now, have students think what it would be like if all the people in the world came to visit their town because it was advertised as the nicest place on Earth. What would be some of the problems of this sudden overcrowding? Explain that this unit will deal with reproduction and that one of the consequences of reproduction in humans is overpopulation. Have students suggest some solutions to the problem of overpopulation.

Theme Development

Living things reproduce and pass traits to offspring. Students will learn that living things reproduce and develop at different rates and go through various stages. They will study mitosis and meiosis, reproduction in various plants and animals, early development, and metamorphosis. Students will also learn about the reproductive system in humans and the development of the human fetus.

Cell Reproduction

PLANNING GUIDE

CONTENT	TEXT FEATURES	TEACHER RESOURCE PACKAGE	OTHER COMPONENTS
(2 days) 22:1 Mitosis Body Growth and Repair An Introduction to Mitosis Steps of Mitosis	Mini Lab: *How Rapid Is Mitosis?* p. 470 Lab 22-1: *Steps of Mitosis,* p. 467 Technology: *Hope for Spinal Cord Injury Patients,* p. 465 Idea Map, p. 466 Check Your Understanding, p. 470	Application: *The Stages of Mitosis,* p. 22 Reteaching: *Mitosis in a Root Tip,* p. 66 Critical Thinking/Problem Solving: *How Can Students Make Slides of Dividing Cells?* p. 22 Focus: *Growing,* p. 43 Transparency Master: *The Steps of Mitosis,* p. 101 Study Guide: *Mitosis,* p. 127 Lab 22-1: *Steps of Mitosis,* pp. 85-86	**Laboratory Manual:** *What Happens When Cells Divide?* p. 181 Color Transparency 22a: *Steps of Mitosis*
(2 1/2 days) 22:2 Meiosis An Introduction to Meiosis Steps of Meiosis Sperm, Eggs, and Fertilization	Skill Check: *Understand Science Words,* p. 474 Idea Map, p. 474 Check Your Understanding, p. 475	Enrichment: *Mitosis, Meiosis, and Number of Chromosomes,* p. 24 Reteaching: *Meiosis and Fertilization,* p. 67 Transparency Master: *The Steps of Meiosis,* p. 103 Study Guide: *Meiosis,* pp. 128-130	Color Transparency 22b: *Meiosis: Halving the Chromosome Number* Color Transparency 22c: *Steps of Meiosis* Color Transparency 22d: *Meiosis in Humans*
(1 1/2 days) 23:3 Changes in the Rate of Mitosis Aging Cancer	Skill Check: *Classify,* p. 479 Lab 22-2: *Rate of Mitosis,* p. 477 Check Your Understanding, p. 479	Reteaching: *Changes in the Rate of Mitosis,* p. 68 Skill: *Form a Hypothesis,* p. 23 Study Guide: *Changes in the Rate of Mitosis,* p. 131 Study Guide: *Vocabulary,* p. 132 Lab 22-2: *Rate of Mitosis,* pp. 87-88	**Laboratory Manual:** *Are There More Dividing Cells or Resting Cells in a Root Tip?* p. 185
Chapter Review	Summary Key Science Words Testing Yourself Finding Main Ideas Using Main Ideas Skill Review	Chapter Review, pp. 116-117 Chapter Test, pp. 118-120	**Test Bank**

MATERIALS NEEDED

LAB 22-1, p. 467	LAB 22-2, p. 477	MARGIN FEATURES
pencil paper	clear plastic sheet marking pencil facial tissue microscope	Skill Check, p. 474 dictionary Mini Lab, p. 470 radish seedling ruler

OBJECTIVES

SECTION	OBJECTIVE	OBJECTIVES CORRELATION			
		CHECK YOUR UNDERSTANDING	CHAPTER REVIEW	TRP CHAPTER REVIEW	TRP CHAPTER TEST
22:1	1. **Relate** some benefits of mitosis.	1, 4	3, 11, 17	3, 11, 18	3, 23, 25, 46, 50
	2. **Identify** cell parts involved in mitosis.	3	—	17, 28	2, 12, 39
	3. **Trace** the steps of mitosis.	2, 5	9, 13, 14	2, 6, 8, 20, 27, 29, 30, 31	1, 5, 10, 15, 18, 20, 28, 32, 36, 38, 40, 41, 42, 44, 48
22:2	4. **Explain** the results of meiosis.	7, 10	10, 16, 17	1, 4, 5, 7	4, 7, 9, 19, 22, 24, 26, 29, 30
	5. **Trace** the steps of meiosis.	6	1	32, 33, 34, 35, 36, 37, 38, 39	14, 37, 43, 45, 47, 49
	6. **Compare** the sex cells of males and females.	8, 9	4, 5, 6, 7	12, 14, 15, 16, 19, 20, 21, 22, 23, 24, 25, 26	11, 13, 17, 21, 27, 34
22:3	7. **Explain** some effects of aging.	11	12, 15	9	33
	8. **Describe** the causes and effects of cancer.	12, 13, 15	2, 8, 18	10	6, 8, 16

Cell Reproduction

CHAPTER OVERVIEW

Key Concepts

The two cell processes of mitosis and meiosis are described in detail. However, the chapter does not use the technical phase names. The role of mitosis in the aging process and its role in cancer are also discussed.

This chapter serves as the basis for the concepts of plant and animal reproduction and genetics.

Key Science Words

body cells
cancer
meiosis
mitosis
ovary
polar body
puberty
sex cell
sister chromatids
testes

Skill Development

In Lab 22-1, students will **observe, formulate models,** and **sequence** to learn the steps in mitosis. In Lab 22-2, they will **use numbers, make and use tables, form hypotheses,** and **interpret data.** In the Skill Check on page 474, students will **understand** the **science word** *ovary*. In the Skill Check on page 479, they will **classify** causes of cancer. In the Mini Lab on page 470, they will **measure in SI** to determine the amount of growth in a radish root.

CHAPTER PREVIEW

Chapter Content

Review this outline for Chapter 22 before you read the chapter.

22:1 Mitosis
- Body Growth and Repair
- An Introduction to Mitosis
- Steps of Mitosis

22:2 Meiosis
- An Introduction to Meiosis
- Steps of Meiosis
- Sperm, Eggs, and Fertilization

22:3 Changes in the Rate of Mitosis
- Aging
- Cancer

Skills in this Chapter

The skills that you will use in this chapter are listed below.

- In **Lab 22-1,** you will observe, formulate a model, and sequence. In **Lab 22-2,** you will use numbers, make and use tables, form hypotheses, and interpret data.
- In the **Skill Checks,** you will classify and understand science words.
- In the **Mini Labs,** you will measure in SI.

462

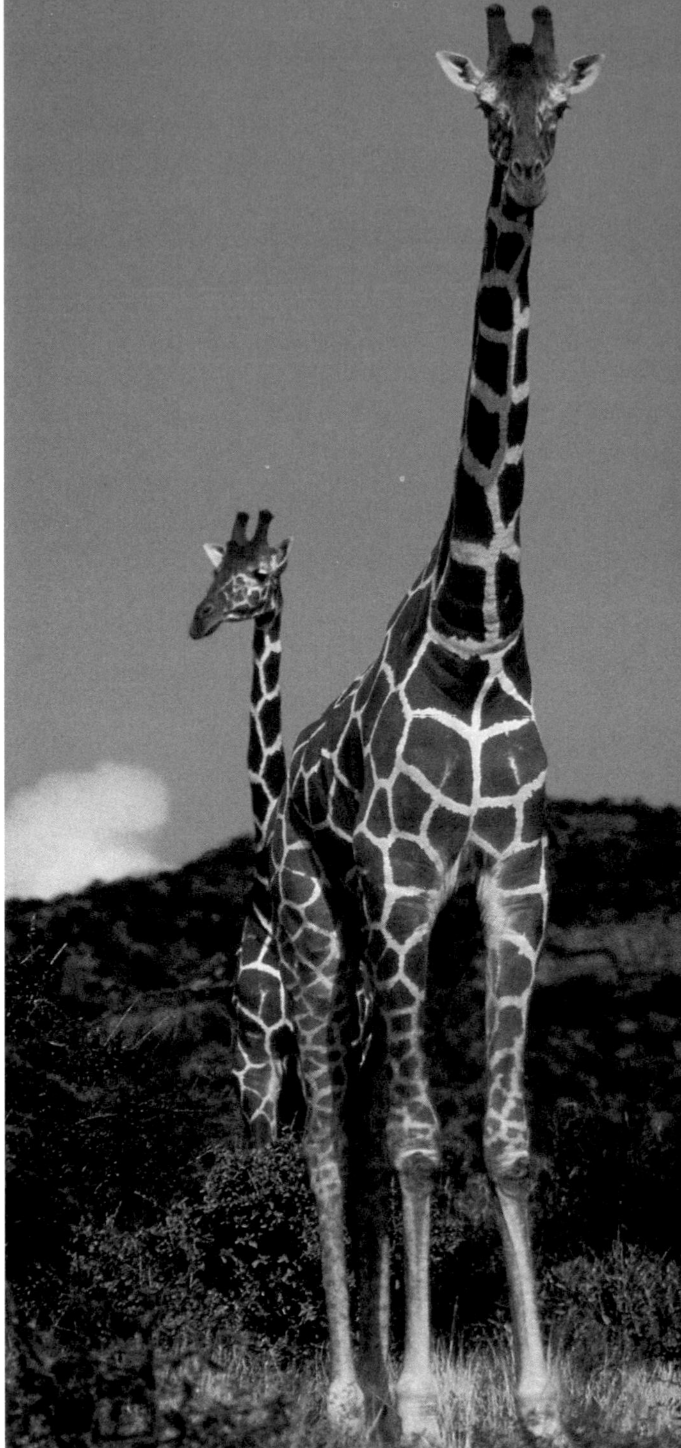

Bridging

Students learned previously that blood cells have a short life span. How does the human body actually replace these blood cells? This chapter looks at this specific process in detail.

Also, the concept of fertilization was introduced in Chapter 6. Why special cells (those with a reduced chromosome number) are needed for this process will become clear.

Chapter 22

Cell Reproduction

Every part of your body is made up of cells. You and all other living things started out as single cells. In some plants and animals, that cell came from a part of one parent. In most plants and animals and in humans, the cell came from the joining of a cell from a male parent and a cell from a female parent. You have learned that these two origins of living things are the difference between asexual and sexual reproduction. Look at the difference in size between the parent and its young in the photo on the left. The larger animal has millions more cells than its offspring. Look at the tree seedling below. You know that the parent tree is much larger. How does one cell become millions of cells? Where do these new cells come from?

Try This!

How many chromosomes do onion cells have? Use a microscope to examine a prepared slide of onion root tip cells under high power. Do all the cells look like they are dividing?

A young tree

GETTING STARTED

Using the Photos

In looking at the photos, students will know that a larger animal or tree has grown more than a smaller one. They should be able to say that growth results from adding cells to the organism. Adding cells is a result of cell division.

MOTIVATION/Try This!

How many chromosomes do onion cells have? Slides of longitudinal onion root tip are to be used. Students must **observe** the region of the onion root tip where cell reproduction is occurring. This region is next to the root cap. Only those cells that are reproducing by mitosis will show chromosomes. All others will show a typical nucleus, but no chromosomes will be visible.

A 35-mm slide of an onion root tip projected onto a screen would allow all students to see the same cellular material and would also allow you to point out those cells that do or do not show chromosomes within the nucleus.

Chapter Preview

Have students study the chapter outline before they begin to read the chapter. They should note the overall organization of the chapter and that the first topic described is the process of mitosis. This is followed by a section dealing with meiosis. Lastly, the chapter deals with the changes associated with aging and cancer.

Misconception

Every cell in a normal human body contains the same number of chromosomes (except for egg and sperm). This number is 46. Each parent has contributed exactly half of this number. That is, your father contributed 23, and your mother contributed 23. You have exactly 1/2 of your father's chromosomes and 1/2 of your mother's chromosomes.

22:1 Mitosis

PREPARATION

Materials Needed

Make copies of the Focus, Application, Critical Thinking/Problem Solving, Transparency Master, Lab, Study Guide, and Reteaching worksheets in the *Teacher Resource Package.*

▶ Obtain radish seeds for the Mini Lab.

Key Science Words

mitosis
body cell
sister chromatids

Process Skills

They will measure in SI in the Mini Lab.

1 FOCUS

▶ The objectives are listed on the student page. Remind students to preview these objectives as a guide to this numbered section.

MOTIVATION/Brainstorming

Ask students how it is possible for their skin to replace itself when scraped or cut off during a fall or injury.

Focus/*Teacher Resource Package,* p. 43. Use the Focus transparency shown at the bottom of this page as an introduction to cell reproduction.

Guided Practice

Have students write down their answers to the margin question: for the body to grow and repair itself.

22:1 Mitosis

Objectives

1. **Relate** some benefits of mitosis.
2. **Identify** cell parts involved in mitosis.
3. **Trace** the steps of mitosis.

Key Science Words

mitosis
body cell
sister chromatids

You started life as a single cell. You now have millions of cells in your body. Somehow, you have grown. The new cells in your body came from cell reproduction.

Body Growth and Repair

Living things grow. You were growing even before you were born. Living things also repair themselves when they are injured. As a child, you probably cut or scraped your skin often. You must have seen new skin grow back on your hands and knees many times. Your body must make new cells to grow and to repair itself. New cells are made by the process of cell reproduction.

Why are new cells important to your body?

One kind of cell reproduction in organisms is called mitosis (mi TOH sus). **Mitosis** is cell reproduction in which two identical cells are made from one cell. Each new cell grows in size until it too is ready to reproduce by mitosis. All body cells in humans are formed by mitosis. **Body cells** are cells that make up most of the body, such as the skin, blood, bones, and stomach. Figure 22-1 shows that all body cells don't live for the same length of time. Cells carry on mitosis at different rates in different organs to replace cells that are worn out. In which body organs do cells carry on mitosis most often? In which organs do cells carry on mitosis least often? In some body cells, such as muscle cells, mitosis never occurs after birth. You are born with all the muscle cells you will ever have.

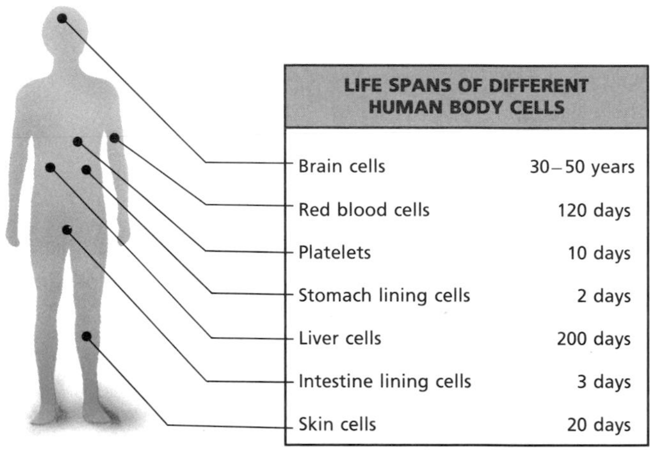

LIFE SPANS OF DIFFERENT HUMAN BODY CELLS	
Brain cells	30–50 years
Red blood cells	120 days
Platelets	10 days
Stomach lining cells	2 days
Liver cells	200 days
Intestine lining cells	3 days
Skin cells	20 days

Figure 22-1 The length of time that human cells live in the body depends on the type of cell.

OPTIONS

Science Background

Prophase corresponds to step one. Step two is metaphase. Step three is anaphase. Step four is telophase.

What Happens When Cells Divide?/*Lab Manual,* p. 181. Use this lab to give additional hands-on practice with mitosis.

FOCUS 43

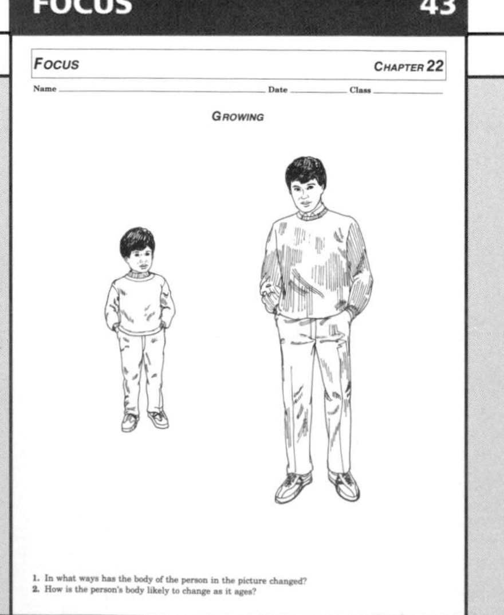

FOCUS CHAPTER 22

Name ______ Date ______ Class ______

GROWING

1. In what ways has the body of the person in the picture changed?
2. How is the person's body likely to change as it ages?

TECHNOLOGY

Hope for Spinal Cord Injury Patients

It has long been thought that nerve cells don't divide by mitosis after you are born. This used to explain why a person with a spinal injury was often permanently disabled. The nerve pathways from brain to body muscles were cut and would never heal.

Recent research shows that nerve cells can regrow and repair themselves. Scientists carried out the following experiment. The optic nerves leading from the eyes to the brains of several hamsters were cut and sections were removed. Normally, this would have meant the loss of sight for the animals. The removed section was then replaced with a piece of nerve taken from another part of the body of each animal. After seven weeks, nerve endings had regrown. The piece of body nerve that was added had somehow acted as a path for the original nerve to follow as it grew. Were the animals able to see again? The scientists have already found that the hamsters could detect changes in light intensity. This means that the optic nerve is working to some extent.

Will this type of scientific breakthrough lead to the healing of spinal cord injuries? As with most scientific research, a long time is needed to solve medical problems.

Hamsters

Mitosis goes on during a person's entire life. You are constantly forming new cells to replace those worn out or lost. Mitosis begins before you are born and continues up to the time you die.

An Introduction to Mitosis

How does mitosis work? We could compare it to how a photocopy machine works. Look at Figure 22-2. Suppose you have a sketch of your pet. Your friend wants a copy. You copy the sketch on a photocopy machine. You now have two identical sketches of your pet.

The process of mitosis is similar. You start with one cell. The end result is two identical cells. The photocopy machine makes a copy in about five seconds. Mitosis may take several hours.

Figure 22-2 How are photocopying and mitosis similar? They each result in an exact copy of the original.

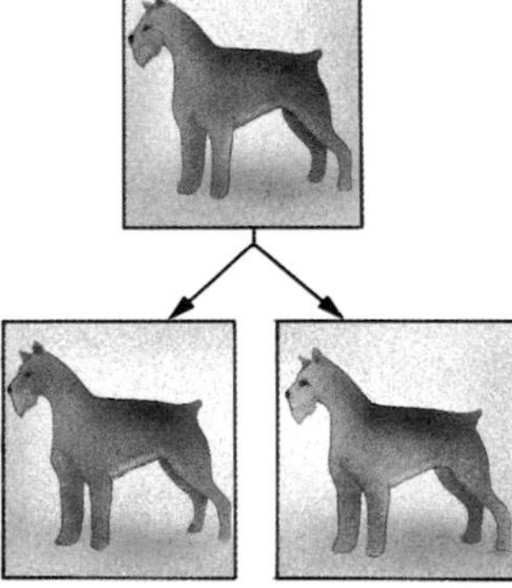

TECHNOLOGY

Hope for Spinal Cord Injury Patients

Background

Mitosis occurs a limited number of times in certain tissues. Nerve tissue is limited as to the number of mitotic divisions it undergoes. Thus, after birth, brain tissue and spinal cord tissue cannot repair itself or regrow.

Discussion

Point out to students that a breakthrough in being able to regrow nerve tissue in the human body must be accomplished in many small steps. Research typically builds on previous findings and many "small steps" are needed before a final satisfactory solution is obtained.

References

Montgomery, Geoffrey. "A Brain Reborn." *Discover,* June 1990, pp. 48-53.

2 TEACH

MOTIVATION/Demonstration

To demonstrate chromosome thickening, use a telephone cord detached from a phone. When stretched out, it is comparable to the chromosomes in a resting phase. When folded up upon itself, shortened and thickened, it is comparable to what happens during prophase.

APPLICATION 22

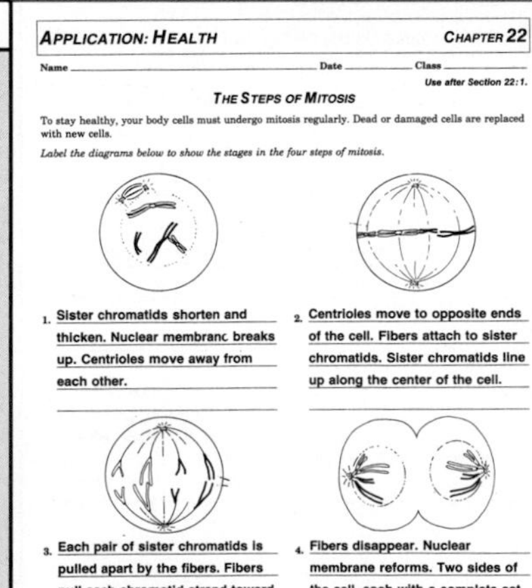

APPLICATION: HEALTH — CHAPTER 22

Name ______ Date ______ Class ______

Use after Section 22:1.

THE STEPS OF MITOSIS

To stay healthy, your body cells must undergo mitosis regularly. Dead or damaged cells are replaced with new cells.

Label the diagrams below to show the stages in the four steps of mitosis.

1. Sister chromatids shorten and thicken. Nuclear membranc breaks up. Centrioles move away from each other.
2. Centrioles move to opposite ends of the cell. Fibers attach to sister chromatids. Sister chromatids line up along the center of the cell.
3. Each pair of sister chromatids is pulled apart by the fibers. Fibers pull each chromatid strand toward centrioles at opposite ends of the cell.
4. Fibers disappear. Nuclear membrane reforms. Two sides of the cell, each with a complete set of chromosomes, separate as the cell membrane pinches the cell in half.

OPTIONS

Enrichment: Most cells are not actively engaged in mitosis all the time. They spend much of their time in interphase. Interphase is sometimes called a "resting" phase. In reality the cell is not resting. Chromosome replication is occurring during this phase. For example, skin cells will spend 15 to 20 days in interphase, while nerve cells spend 50 to 60 years.

Application/*Teacher Resource Package,* p. 22. Use the Application worksheet shown here to review the stages of mitosis.

TEACH

Concept Development

▶ *Chromosome* defines a nuclear structure before it makes a copy of itself (this copying process is covered in Chapter 28). *Sister chromatids* define the structures resulting from replication of the original chromosome.

▶ A key word in this section is *identical*. Identical refers to chromosome number as well as chromosomal makeup or gene traits. Each new cell formed during mitosis is a clone of every other cell in the body, having the same genetic material as every other cell.

▶ The sequence of events described here takes place during interphase. It is important for students to understand that during this phase, the chromosomes are making copies of themselves. The original cell described had only four chromosomes. Now, each chromosome has made a copy of itself, resulting in 8 sister chromatids.

Idea Map

Have students use the idea map as a study guide to the major concepts of this section.

Guided Practice

Have students write down their answers to the margin question: Each chromosome becomes doubled.

Study Tip: Use this idea map as a study guide to mitosis. If you cut your finger, how does mitosis help you?

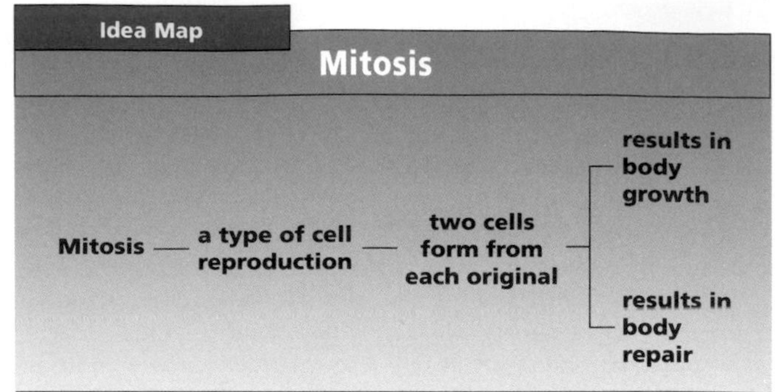

Figure 22-3 Study the parts of an animal cell.

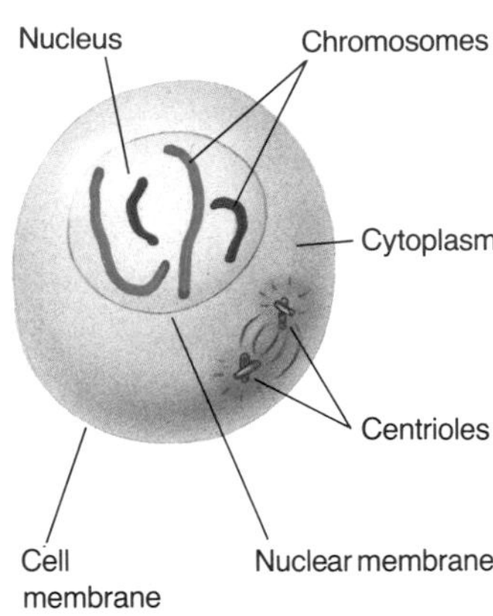

What cell parts are used in mitosis? Figure 22-3 shows what a typical animal cell might look like. Remember from Chapter 2 that the entire cell is surrounded by a cell membrane. Most of the material inside the cell is called cytoplasm. A cell nucleus is present in the cytoplasm. A nuclear membrane surrounds the nucleus. You have also read that inside the nucleus there are chromosomes. They may not be easy to see at this time, but they are there. Notice that there are also centrioles in the cytoplasm.

Most cells contain many chromosomes. To explain how a cell goes through mitosis, let's imagine a cell with just four chromosomes. An important step takes place in the nucleus of every cell before mitosis begins. Each chromosome becomes doubled. Figure 22-4 shows how this works. Notice how each chromosome looks after it has doubled. The two strands of each doubled chromosome are held together at one point. The two strands of a chromosome after it becomes doubled are called **sister chromatids** (KROH muh tidz). Each chromatid is an exact copy of the original chromosome. The centrioles also double just before mitosis begins.

What does each chromosome do before mitosis begins?

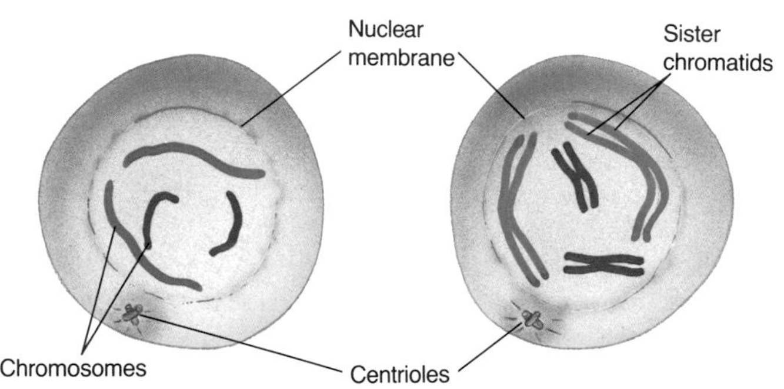

Figure 22-4 Chromosomes become doubled before mitosis begins.

OPTIONS

Critical Thinking/Problem Solving/ *Teacher Resource Package*, p. 22. Use the Critical Thinking worksheet shown here to help students with problem-solving skills.

CRITICAL THINKING 22

CRITICAL THINKING/PROBLEM SOLVING CHAPTER 22

Name ______ Date ______ Class ______

Use after Section 22:1.

HOW CAN STUDENTS MAKE SLIDES OF DIVIDING CELLS?

A class of biology students looked at prepared slides of mitosis and learned the names of the steps. Some of the slides were labeled "onion root tip mitosis." The students wondered how these slides were prepared. The teacher told them how to do a special project.

First, the students obtained six onions that were just beginning to sprout roots. They also collected six jars with mouths that were almost the same diameter as the onions. They filled the jars with water and balanced the onions on the jars. They put the jars on the windowsill. The onions sprouted roots in a few days.

When the roots were about a centimeter long, the students carefully cut off the end 2 to 3 millimeters. They laid each root tip on a glass slide. Then, they put a drop of blue stain on the root. They covered the drop with a coverslip and a cork, and pressed down heavily and carefully on the cork with a thumb. After several minutes, they put the slide under a microscope and looked for cells.

They saw many box-like cells with darkly stained dots in the middle. Some cells looked as if they were full of thread. Some cells looked as if they had a few colored threads in them. By comparing their observations to the figures in their textbook, they were able to identify the steps in mitosis.

Analyzing the Problem

1. What caused the onion roots to sprout? water and growth factors in the onion
2. Where did the onion roots get the energy to grow, divide, and sprout? from stored food
3. Why did the students add the blue stain to the roots? The stain dyes the nucleus and chromosomes a darker color than the rest of the cell.
4. Why did the students squash the root tip under the coverslip and cork? The root is thick, so that it is hard to see individual cells. Squashing spreads out the cells.

Solving the Problem

1. What part of the cell looked like tangled threads? chromosomes
2. What do the chromosomes look like when the cell is not undergoing mitosis? They are not easily seen.

Lab 22–1 Steps of Mitosis

Problem: What do the steps of mitosis look like?

Skills

observe, formulate models, sequence

Materials

paper
pencil

Procedure

1. Look at Figure 22-4 on page 466 showing the stages of mitosis. Notice in Figure 22-4a that the chromosomes have not yet formed sister chromatids. In other words, they're not yet doubled.
2. **Formulate a model:** Trace the cell diagram in Figure 22-4a onto a piece of paper.
3. Draw a new cell that shows the next change before mitosis begins. Trace the diagram in Figure 22-4b.
4. **Sequence:** Use Figure 22-5 on pages 468 and 469 to help you draw the next four steps that would take place in this cell during mitosis.
5. In your diagrams, use the following words to label the parts:
   Original cell—cell membrane, nucleus, centrioles, nuclear membrane, cytoplasm
   Change before mitosis—sister chromatids, centrioles
   Step 1—sister chromatids, centrioles, spindle fibers
   Step 2—centrioles, fibers, sister chromatids at cell center
   Step 3—separation of sister chromatids, fiber, chromosomes
   Step 4—fibers disappearing, pinching in of cell membrane, nuclear membrane reforms, chromosomes
   Body cells—chromosomes, centrioles, nucleus, cell membrane, cytoplasm, body cells

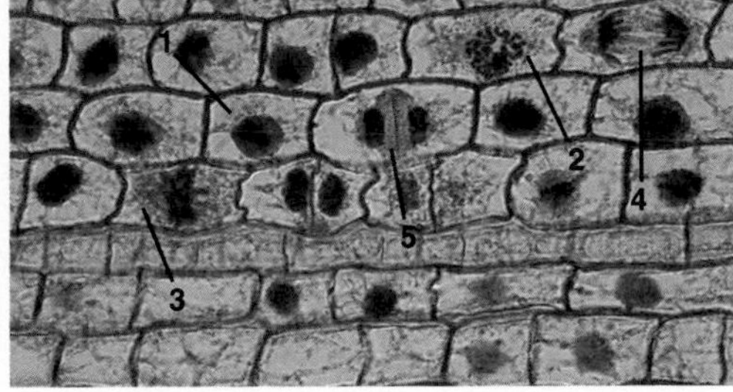

Data and Observations

1. At what step in mitosis do the sister chromatids separate?
2. Would your diagrams differ if two chromosomes had been used? Explain.

Analyze and Apply

1. What is the difference between chromosomes and sister chromatids?
2. How would your diagrams differ if this were meiosis in terms of:
   (a) the final number of cells?
   (b) the final number of chromosomes in each cell if you had started with 46 chromosomes?
   (c) the number of steps needed?
   (d) the labels on the last diagram?
3. **Apply:** Give two examples of human body organs where you would find:
   (a) mitosis taking place.
   (b) meiosis taking place.
4. How are fibers important to cell division?

Extension

Formulate a model: Yarn and paper clips may be used to model the series of changes that occur to two chromosomes before and during mitosis.

Lab 22-1 Steps of Mitosis

Overview

Students will review the sequential changes occurring in cells by diagraming and labeling stages of mitosis.

Objectives: Upon completion of this lab, students will be able to: (1) **identify** changes within cells as mitosis occurs, (2) **label** those cell organelles that appear during the mitotic process, (3) **compare** the changes occurring during mitosis and meiosis.

Time Allotment: 1 class period

Preparation

Lab 22-2 worksheet/*Teacher Resource Package*, pp. 87-88.

Teaching the Lab

▶ You may wish to provide photocopies of outline diagrams from the *Teacher Resource Package* to your students.

▶ Encourage students to use the diagrams in the text as a guide for completion of labels.

▶ **Troubleshooting:** You may want to delay having students answer any questions relating to meiosis until this concept has been covered in class. Students can answer all questions pertinent to mitosis at the conclusion of this lab.

Cooperative Learning: Divide the class into groups of three students. For more information, see pp. 22T-23T in the Teacher Guide.

ANSWERS

Data and Observations

1. step 3
2. No, only in the number of chromosomes. There will be two, not four, chromosomes in the two new cells. The chromosomes all go through the same steps in the same order, no matter how many chromosomes are involved.

Analyze and Apply

1. Sister chromatids are the two strands in a chromosome after it has become doubled.
2. (a) There would be four, not two, cells. (b) There would be 23 chromosomes in each cell. (c) Six steps, not four, are needed for meiosis. (d) One label on the last diagram would be sex cells, not body cells.
3. (a) skin and liver
   (b) testes and ovaries
4. Fibers help move the chromosomes.

TEACH

Concept Development

▶ Point out to students the major changes and accomplishments of mitosis. Remind them of these facts:

1. Two new cells are formed.
2. Each new cell is identical in chromosome number to the other and to the original cell.
3. Each new cell will, in time, undergo mitosis after first entering a resting phase.
4. Body cells are formed by mitosis to replace worn out cells or to form new body cells.
5. Growth takes place as new cells are formed. Repair of an injury might also be occurring.

Cooperative Learning: Divide the class into 5 groups. Each group is to prepare a short written description and a labeled diagram on a transparency of major changes that take place within a cell during a specific stage of mitosis.

Group 1 = describe changes in the cell prior to mitosis.
Group 2 = describe changes during step one.
Group 3 = describe changes during step two.
Group 4 = describe changes during step three.
Group 5 = describe changes during step four.

Guided Practice

Have students write down their answers to the margin question: step two.

Steps of Mitosis

Follow the numbers in Figure 22-5 as you read here about the four steps of mitosis.

Step One

1. Sister chromatids begin to shorten and thicken. If you were to look at a cell in this step of mitosis under a light microscope, you would be able to see the chromosomes. However, you might not be able to see the strands of each sister chromatid.
2. The nuclear membrane begins to break down. The pairs of sister chromatids now look like they are floating in the cytoplasm.
3. The centrioles move away from each other.
4. Fibers form between the centrioles. These fibers are strands of protein that form between the two ends of a cell.

Step Two

1. The centrioles move apart to opposite ends of the cell. The fibers look like they are stretched between the two ends of the cell.
2. Sister chromatids become attached to the fibers at the point where the two strands are joined to each other. The

In which step of mitosis are the chromosomes pulled to the center of the cell?

Figure 22-5 Use these diagrams to help you follow the steps of mitosis as you read the text. How many times does the cell divide? once

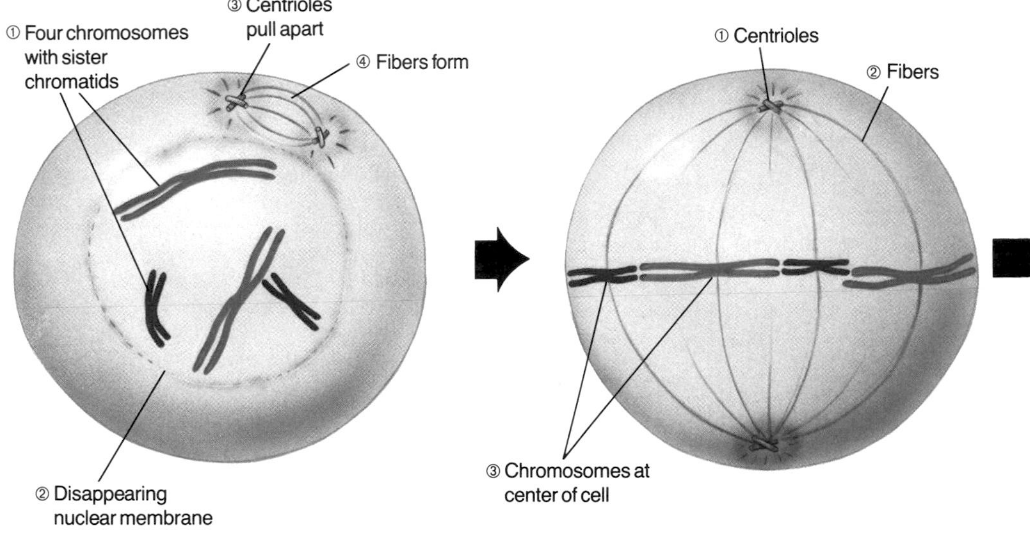

OPTIONS

Transparency Master/*Teacher Resource Package,* p. 101. Use the transparency shown here as you teach mitosis.

Challenge: Have students use a reference to determine the exact name used to describe each phase of mitosis. Having determined these, have students find the meaning of each prefix being used. Each prefix will relate to the events taking place in a very general way.

TRANSPARENCY 101

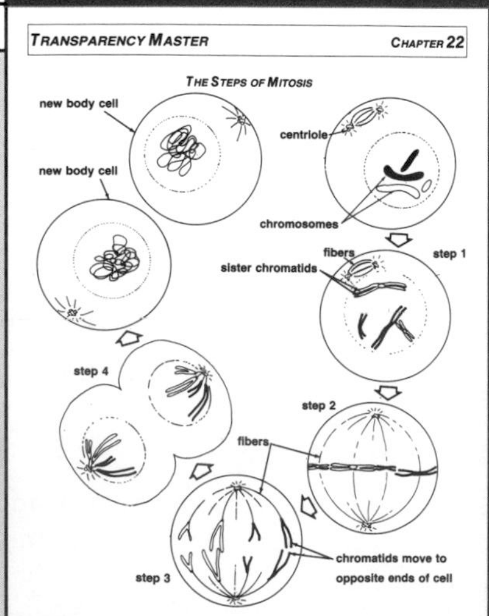

pairs of sister chromatids are pulled toward the center of the cell.

3. The four pairs of sister chromatids are now lined up at the center of the cell.

Step Three

1. The sister chromatids are pulled apart by the fibers. Each chromatid is now separate from its identical partner.
2. The fibers pull each chromatid strand toward the centrioles at opposite ends of the cell. Remember that each chromatid is an exact copy of one original chromosome.

Step Four

1. Each end of the cell now has a complete set of chromosomes. In this example, a complete set is four chromosomes. Notice that this is the same as the number we started with in Step One.
2. The fibers begin to disappear.
3. The nuclear membrane begins to reform.
4. The cell membrane begins to pinch in until the cytoplasm is divided in half. Two new cells have formed. They each have identical chromosomes. They also have the same number of chromosomes as the cell they originally came from.

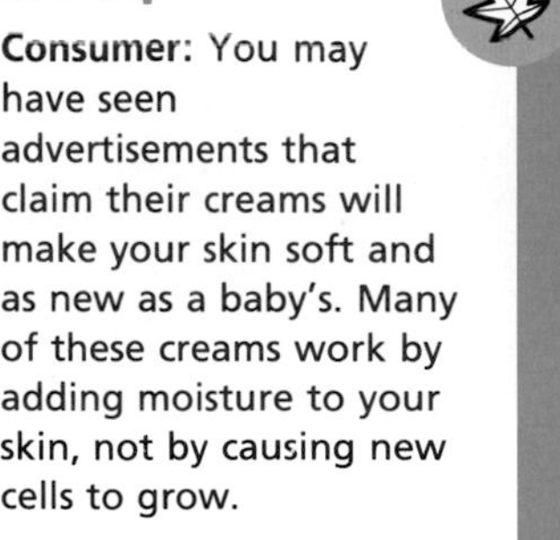
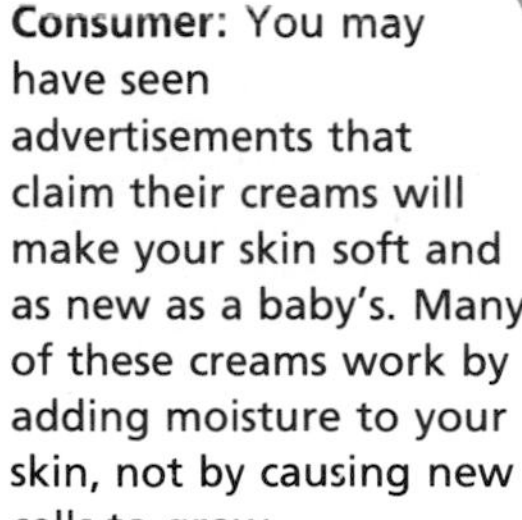

Bio Tip

Consumer: You may have seen advertisements that claim their creams will make your skin soft and as new as a baby's. Many of these creams work by adding moisture to your skin, not by causing new cells to grow.

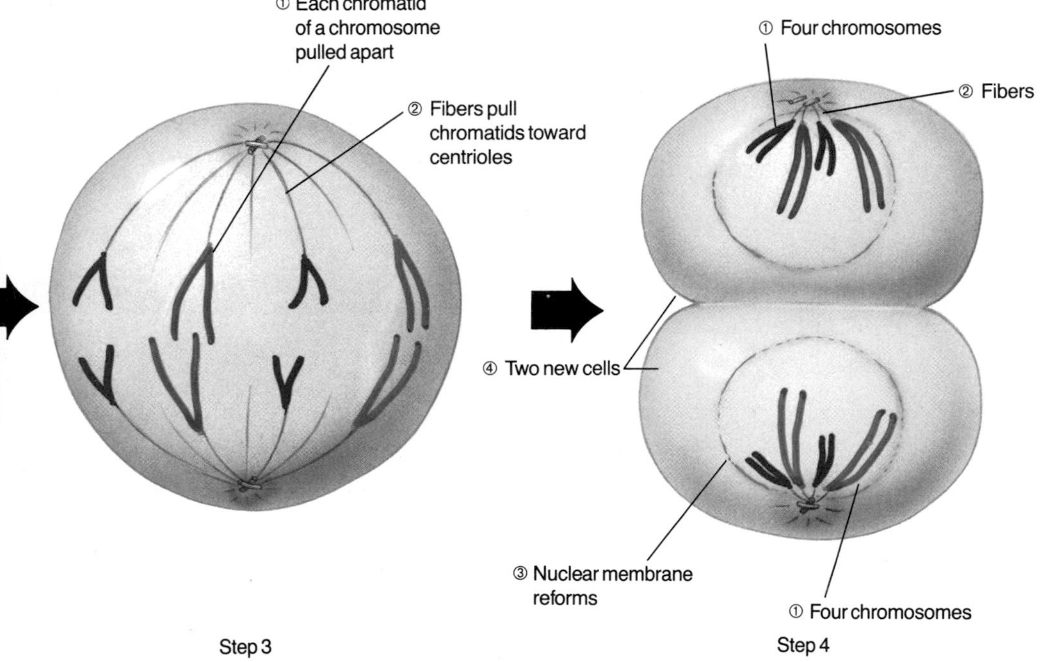

Step 3

Step 4

TEACH

Concept Development

▶ Students can be reminded that step four is almost a step one in reverse. Again, the telephone cord analogy can be used. This time, however, the cord will start out highly twisted and will be stretched out as the chromosomes become less visible.

Guided Practice

Provide students with outline drawings of the cell. Review each step or phase on the overhead projector, writing in the details and drawing in the chromosomes and sister chromatids. Have students record the information and diagrams from the overhead screen.

Connection: Math

Have students start with one cell of a type that undergoes mitosis once every hour and calculate the number of cells there would be at the end of 24 hours. The answer should be approximately 2 followed by 16 zeros (1.7×10^{16}).

Independent Practice

Study Guide/*Teacher Resource Package*, p. 127. Use the Study Guide worksheet shown at the bottom of this page for independent practice.

Guided Practice

Quiz students concerning the number of chromosomes before and after mitosis and the number of sister chromatids during mitosis. Give them one number and have them fill in the other two. Example: If there are 10 chromosomes before mitosis, students should respond that there are 20 sister chromatids and 10 chromosomes in each of the resulting two cells.

STUDY GUIDE 127

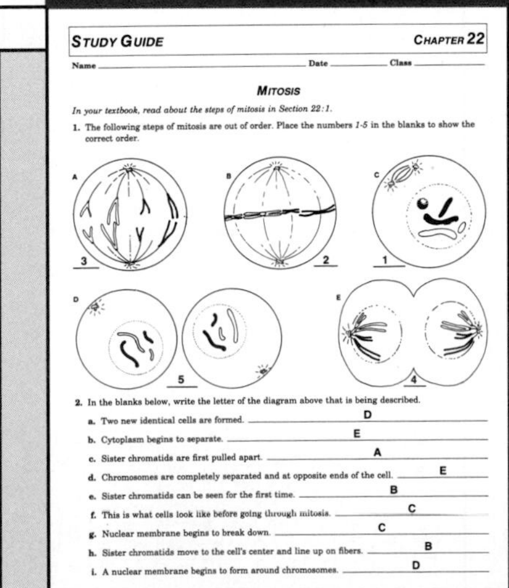

STUDY GUIDE — CHAPTER 22

Name ______ Date ______ Class ______

MITOSIS

In your textbook, read about the steps of mitosis in Section 22:1.

1. The following steps of mitosis are out of order. Place the numbers *1-5* in the blanks to show the correct order.

A: 3 B: 2 C: 1 D: 5 E: 4

2. In the blanks below, write the letter of the diagram above that is being described.

a. Two new identical cells are formed. D
b. Cytoplasm begins to separate. E
c. Sister chromatids are first pulled apart. A
d. Chromosomes are completely separated and at opposite ends of the cell. E
e. Sister chromatids can be seen for the first time. B
f. This is what cells look like before going through mitosis. C
g. Nuclear membrane begins to break down. C
h. Sister chromatids move to the cell's center and line up on fibers. B
i. A nuclear membrane begins to form around chromosomes. D

OPTIONS

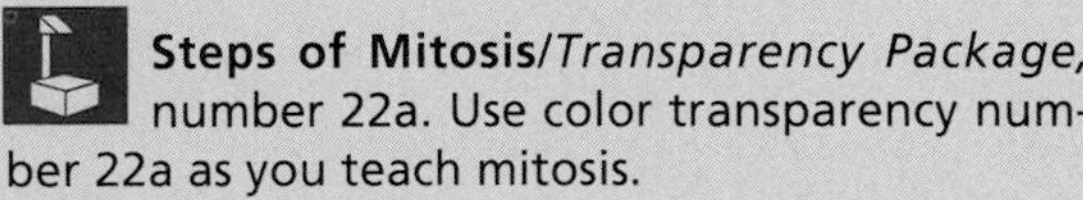

Steps of Mitosis/*Transparency Package*, number 22a. Use color transparency number 22a as you teach mitosis.

TEACH

Mini Lab

Germinate radish seeds by soaking the seeds in water overnight. Remove from water, wrap in damp paper toweling, and place in plastic bag. Radish seeds germinate within 24-36 hours.

Check for Understanding

Have students respond to the first three questions in Check Your Understanding.

Reteach

Reteaching/*Teacher Resource Package,* p. 66 Use this worksheet to give students additional practice in this steps of mitosis.

Extension: Assign Critical Thinking, Biology and Math, or some of the **OPTIONS** available with this lesson.

3 APPLY

Challenge: Design an experiment that measures the rate of growth of fingernails or hair. Carry out the experiment. Relate this growth to mitosis.

4 CLOSE

Explain the following: hair and nails grow, skin flakes off, your body grows, lost blood is replaced, cuts and burns heal.

Answers to Check Your Understanding

1. New cells are needed for growth and repair.
2. Fibers move sister chromatids to the center of the cell and pull them apart.
3. Chromosomes make copies of themselves, the centriole makes a copy of itself.
4. Plant growth in width is from mitosis in cells of the cambium.
5. 4196 cells

a

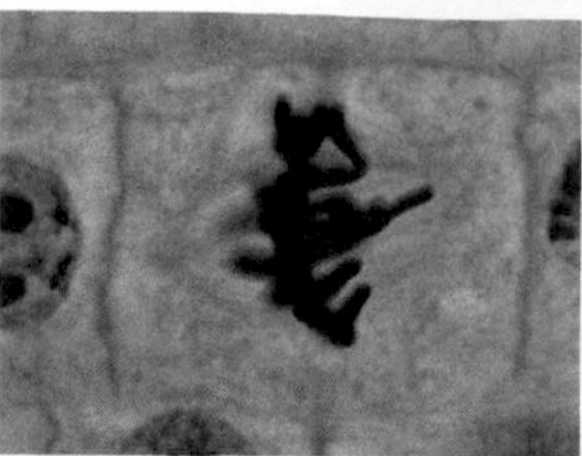
b

c

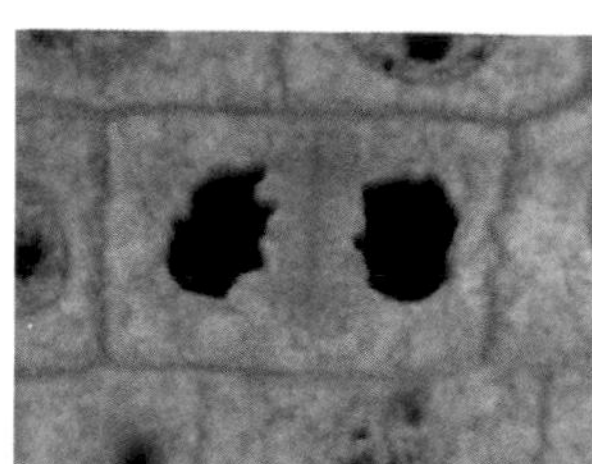
d

Figure 22-6 Mitosis in plant cells: Step One (a), Step Two (b), Step Three (c), Step Four (d)

Mini Lab

How Rapid Is Mitosis?

Measure in SI: Measure the amount of growth in the root and shoot of a radish seedling over a 24 hour period. *For more help, refer to the* ***Skill Handbook,*** *pages 718-719.*

The two new cells are smaller in size than the original. However, each new cell now begins to grow.

What are the benefits of mitosis? First, mitosis helps us grow by producing new cells. Second, mitosis replaces cells lost through cell death and injury, such as when you cut your finger.

Figure 22-6 shows photographs of plant cells in the four steps of mitosis. As you can see, mitosis in plant and animal cells is very similar. Mitosis in plant cells shows two differences from mitosis in animal cells. Plant cells lack centrioles, and at the end of cell division a cell wall is laid down.

Check Your Understanding

1. Why is mitosis important to your body?
2. What are the jobs of protein fibers during mitosis?
3. What happens to chromosomes before the nuclear membrane breaks down in mitosis?
4. **Critical Thinking:** How does mitosis help a plant stem grow in width?
5. **Biology and Math:** Some cells divide every two hours. How many cells would result from mitosis in twenty-four hours if you started with one cell?

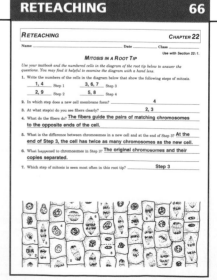

RETEACHING 66

RETEACHING CHAPTER 22

Name ______ Date ______ Class ______

Use with Section 22:1.

MITOSIS IN A ROOT TIP

Use your textbook and the numbered cells in the diagram of the root tip below to answer the questions. You may find it helpful to examine the diagram with a hand lens.

1. Write the numbers of the cells in the diagram below that show the following steps of mitosis.
   1, 4 Step 1 — 3, 6, 7 Step 3
   2, 9 Step 2 — 5, 8 Step 4
2. In which step does a new cell membrane form? 4
3. At what step(s) do you see fibers clearly? 2, 3
4. What do the fibers do? The fibers guide the pairs of matching chromosomes to the opposite ends of the cell.
5. What is the difference between chromosomes in a new cell and at the end of Step 3? At the end of Step 3, the cell has twice as many chromosomes as the new cell.
6. What happened to chromosomes in Step 3? The original chromosomes and their copies separated.
7. Which step of mitosis is seen most often in this root tip? Step 3

22:2 Meiosis

Not all cells reproduce by mitosis. A different type of cell reproduction is important to the passing on of traits to offspring.

An Introduction to Meiosis

Besides body cells, most living things also have sex cells. **Sex cells** are reproductive cells produced in sex organs. Sperm are sex cells made by the male. An egg is a sex cell made by the female. Sex cells are made during meiosis (mi OH sus). **Meiosis** is a kind of cell reproduction that forms eggs and sperm.

To explain how a cell goes through meiosis, let's look again at our cell with four chromosomes, Figure 22-7. The four chromosomes make up two matching pairs.

In meiosis, a cell divides twice. When the cell divides for the first time, each chromosome in a pair moves away from its partner. Each chromosome of a pair goes to a different cell. The sister chromatids stay joined together. The two cells then divide again.

Look at Figure 22-7. How many chromosomes are in each of the four final cells? The number of chromosomes in each cell is one-half the original number. The original cell started with four chromosomes. Each new cell now has only two, or exactly one-half of the original number. Let's examine the process of meiosis in more detail to see how the chromosome number was halved.

Objectives

4. Explain the results of meiosis.

5. Trace the steps of meiosis.

6. Compare the sex cells of males and females.

Key Science Words

sex cell
meiosis
puberty
testes
ovary
polar body

After meiosis, how does the number of chromosomes in a new cell compare with those in the original cell?

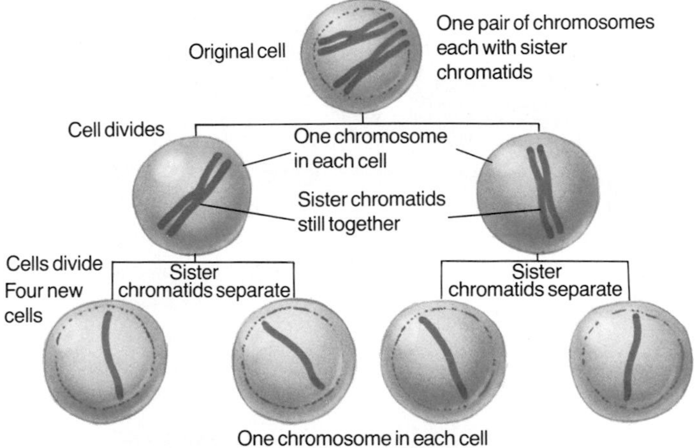

Figure 22-7 Meiosis begins with one cell and results in four cells. Each new cell has one-half the original chromosome number.

22:2 Meiosis

PREPARATION

Materials Needed

Make copies of the Study Guide, Enrichment, and Reteaching worksheets and the Transparency Master in the *Teacher Resource Package.*

Key Science Words

sex cell
meiosis
puberty
testes
ovary
polar body

Process Skills

In the Skill Check, students will understand science words.

1 FOCUS

▶ The objectives are listed on the student page. Remind students to preview these objectives as a guide to this numbered section.

MOTIVATION/Brainstorming

Ask students what would be the result if we got 46 chromosomes from each parent.

Guided Practice

Have students write down their answers to the margin question: there are half the original number of chromosomes in each of the four sex cells.

TRANSPARENCY 103

TRANSPARENCY MASTER CHAPTER 22

THE STEPS OF MEIOSIS

Before meiosis — nuclear membrane disappears
step 1 — four chromosomes
step 2 — pairs of chromosomes move apart
step 3
step 4 — two chromosomes
step 5
step 6 — sister chromatids move apart
4 sex cells

OPTIONS

Science Background

Meiosis means "to reduce" and refers to the fact that meiosis results in a reduction of the number of chromosomes from the diploid to the haploid number. In humans, the diploid number is 46 and the haploid number is 23.

Transparency Master/*Teacher Resource Package*, p. 103. Use the Transparency Master shown here to help you teach the steps of meiosis.

2 TEACH

MOTIVATION/Brainstorming

Ask students: How do the four final copies (new cells) differ from the original in terms of size and number of chromosomes present in original versus the number in each copy?

Concept Development

▶ Provide students with the following problem: A cell is about to undergo meiosis. The cell has 20 chromosomes in its nucleus. Ask students to predict how many new cells will form from the original, as well as the chromosome number of each new cell.

▶ Have students contrast their answers to the effect of mitosis.

▶ Step one shows an important difference between meiosis and mitosis. Point out that no grouping of sister chromatids into fours took place during mitosis. This grouping into fours is called tetrad formation.

▶ Steps two and three differ from mitosis only in that there are groups of four rather than groups of two sister chromatids.

▶ Meiosis is divided into two major phases, meiosis I and meiosis II. In meiosis I, sets of four sister chromatids move together rather than only two, as in mitosis. Steps one through three are part of meiosis I. Steps four through six are part of meiosis II.

Independent Practice

Study Guide/*Teacher Resource Package,* p. 128. Use the Study Guide worksheet shown at the bottom of this page for independent practice.

Steps of Meiosis

Follow the numbers in Figure 22-8 as you read here about the six steps of meiosis. Just as in mitosis, each chromosome forms sister chromatids before meiosis begins.

Step One

1. The sister chromatids shorten and thicken.
2. The nuclear membrane begins to break down.
3. The centrioles begin to move away from one another and fibers form.
4. The matching chromosomes now come together to form pairs. Remember that each chromosome has two strands of sister chromatids. The pair of chromosomes now looks like a set of four strands and can be seen with a light microscope. Remember that in mitosis this pairing step doesn't take place.

Step Two

1. The centrioles have moved to opposite ends of the cell.
2. The sister chromatids become attached to the fibers.
3. Fibers move the two pairs of matching chromosomes to the center of the cell. Note that each chromosome is made up of sister chromatids that are still attached to one another. However, the paired chromosomes are not joined.

Figure 22-8 Follow the steps of meiosis as you read the text. How many times do the cells divide? twice

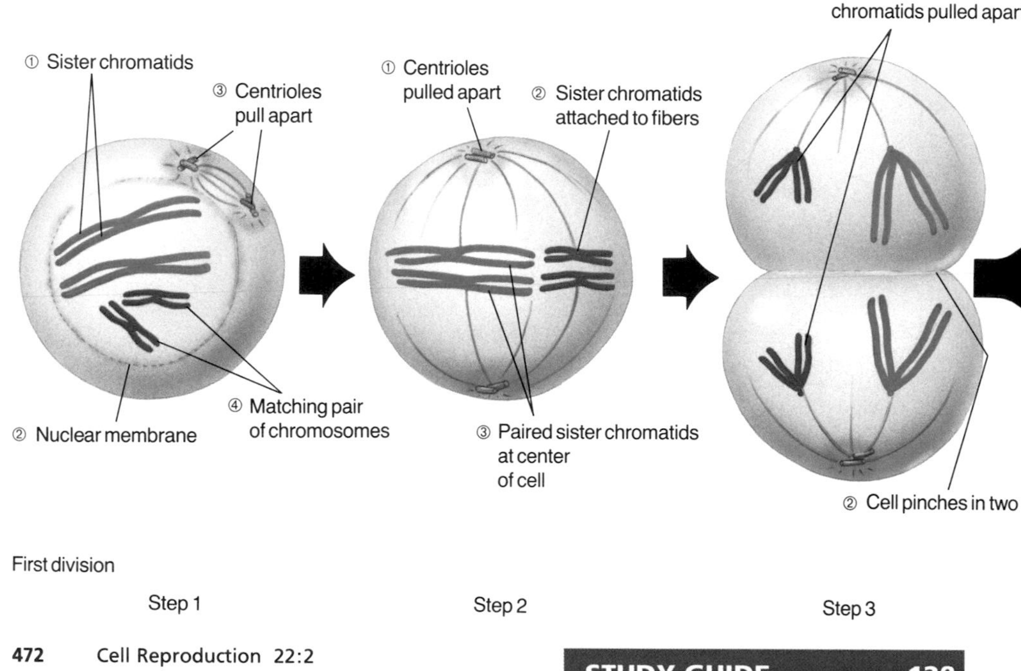

OPTIONS

Meiosis: Halving Chromosome Number/ *Transparency Package,* number 22b. Use color transparency number 22b as you teach meiosis.

STUDY GUIDE 128

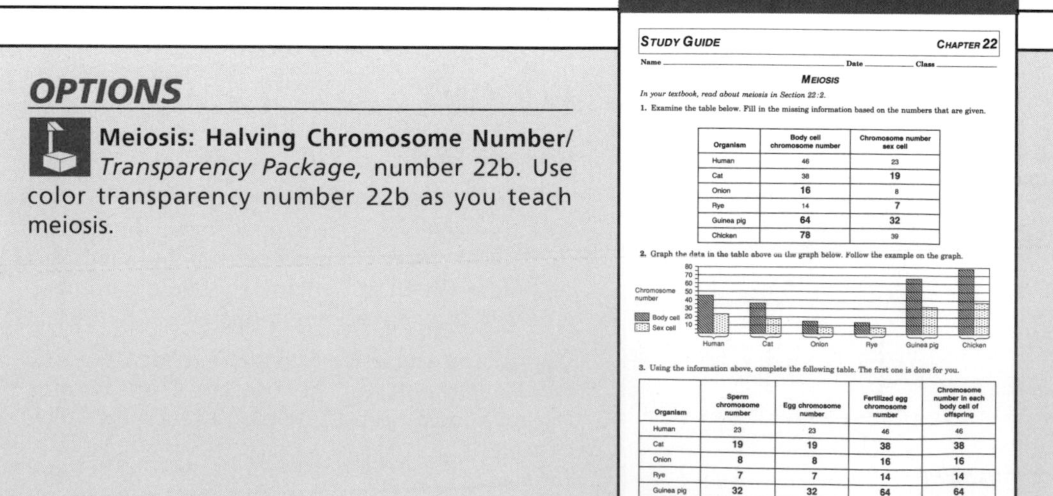

STUDY GUIDE CHAPTER 22

Name ________ Date ________ Class ________

MEIOSIS

In your textbook, read about meiosis in Section 22:2.

1. Examine the table below. Fill in the missing information based on the numbers that are given.

Organism	Body cell chromosome number	Chromosome number sex cell
Human	46	23
Cat	38	19
Onion	16	8
Rye	14	7
Guinea pig	64	32
Chicken	78	39

2. Graph the data in the table above on the graph below. Follow the example on the graph.

3. Using the information above, complete the following table. The first one is done for you.

Organism	Sperm chromosome number	Egg chromosome number	Fertilized egg chromosome number	Chromosome number in each body cell of offspring
Human	23	23	46	46
Cat	19	19	38	38
Onion	8	8	16	16
Rye	7	7	14	14
Guinea pig	32	32	64	64
Chicken	39	39	78	78

Step Three
1. Fibers move the matching chromosomes apart. Remember that in mitosis the sister chromatids came apart. In meiosis, the sister chromatids remain joined, but each matching pair of chromosomes separates.
2. The cell membrane begins to pinch the cell into two and divides the cytoplasm in half.

Step Four
1. Two new cells have now formed. Each cell has two chromosomes, each with sister chromatids.
2. The centrioles double and fibers form again.
3. A new nuclear membrane doesn't form at this time.

Step Five

The second division of meiosis now begins. Steps five and six now occur in both of the new cells. The movement of chromatids is similar to that in steps one to four of mitosis.
1. The centrioles move apart, and the fibers are formed between them.
2. The fibers connect to the sister chromatids at the point where the chromatids are joined together.
3. The sister chromatids are pulled to the center of each cell.

In which step of meiosis do the pairs of sister chromatids separate?

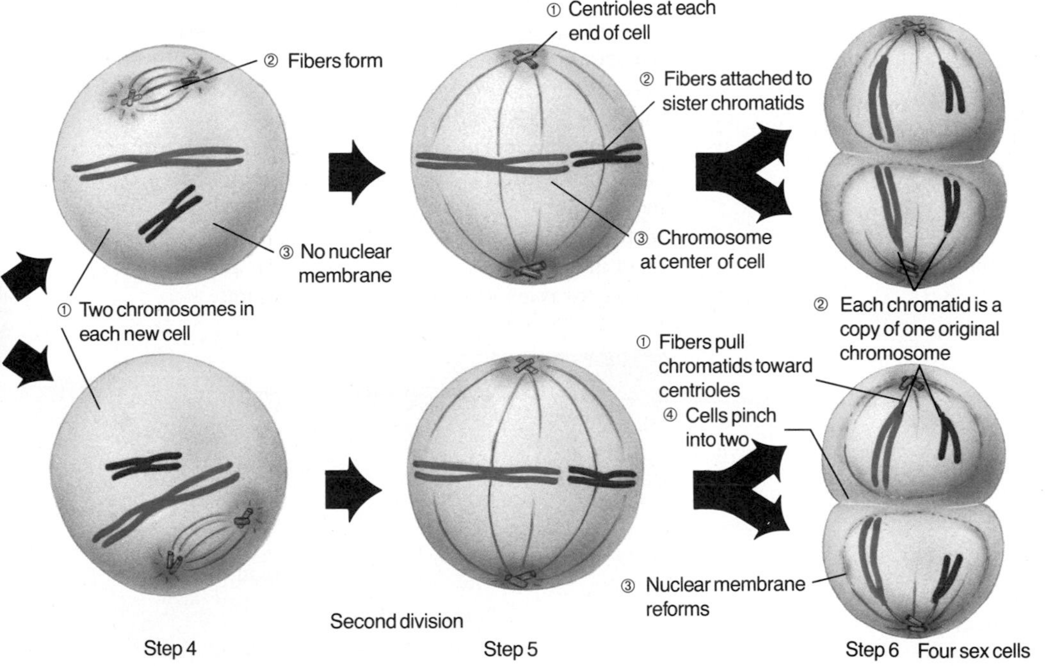

TEACH

Concept Development

▶ Point out that reduction in chromosome number occurs during steps one to three. At the end of meiosis I, each cell has only half the chromosome complement of the original cell.

▶ Step four is like mitosis beginning again. The important thing to stress here is that no new chromosome replication occurs.

Guided Practice

Have students write down their answers to the margin question: step three.

Guided Practice

Quiz students concerning mitosis and meiosis. Ask them to compare and contrast the following features: where and when the process happens, chromosome number before and after the process.

Independent Practice

Study Guide/*Teacher Resource Package*, p. 129. Use the Study Guide worksheet shown at the bottom of this page for independent practice.

STUDY GUIDE 129

STUDY GUIDE — CHAPTER 22

Name ______ Date ______ Class ______

MEIOSIS

In your textbook, read about mitosis and meiosis in Section 22:2.

4. The chart below shows the steps of mitosis and meiosis in the correct order. Complete the chart by answering the questions beside the diagrams.

a. Where are the chromosomes? in nucleus
b. How many are present in each cell? four
c. What happened to the chromosomes in each cell? They doubled forming sister chromatids.
d. Where are the sister chromatids? cell center
e. What is happening to the sister chromatids? They move apart. Pairs move apart in meiosis.
f. How many cells are formed in mitosis? two
g. Are the chromosomes single or double? single
h. Are the chromosomes single or double now in meiosis? double
i. What happens in meiosis now? Sister chromatids move to opposite ends of the cell.
j. How many cells are formed in meiosis? four

OPTIONS

Steps of Meiosis/*Transparency Package*, number 22c. Use color transparency number 22c as you teach the steps of meiosis.

TEACH

Concept Development

▶ You may wish to point out that no new cell formed by meiosis will have paired chromosomes.

▶ The fact that only one egg cell survives should not contradict all that has been learned regarding meiosis. Point out to students that the process of meiosis still formed four egg cells.

Guided Practice

Have students write down their answers to the margin question: testes.

Idea Map

Have students use the idea map as a study guide to the major concepts of this section.

Independent Practice

Study Guide/*Teacher Resource Package,* p. 130. Use the Study Guide worksheet shown at the bottom of this page for independent practice.

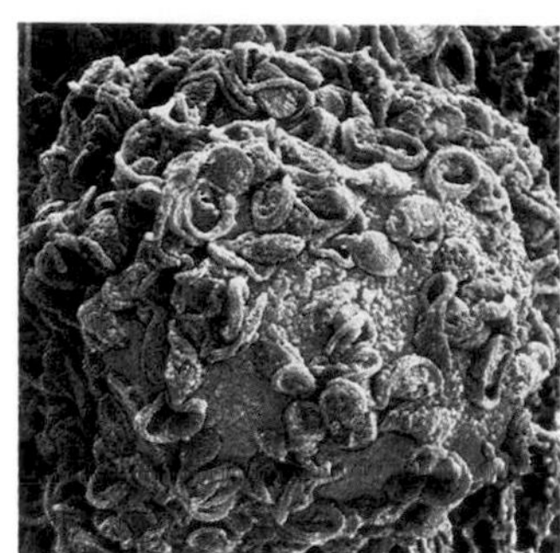

Figure 22-9 Human egg and sperm cells

Step Six

1. The fibers pull each strand of the sister chromatids apart and to opposite ends of the cell.
2. Each sister chromatid is an exact copy of just one of the original chromosomes.
3. The nuclear membrane begins to reform around each new set of chromosomes.
4. Cell membranes begin to pinch each cell in two along the center. The cytoplasm is divided between the new cells. The four new cells are sex cells.

Remember, that in our cell we started with four chromosomes. We now have two chromosomes in each of four cells. In a normal cell, there may be many more chromosomes. But, at the end of meiosis there will always be half the original number of chromosomes in each of four sex cells.

Skill Check

Understand science words: ovary. The word part *ovi* means egg. In your dictionary, find three words with the word part *ovi* in them. *For more help, refer to the **Skill Handbook**, pages 706-711.*

Sperm, Eggs, and Fertilization

Figure 22-9 shows a photograph of human egg and sperm cells. How are the cells alike? How are they different? The cells are alike in four ways. One, both are sex cells. Two, both formed during meiosis. Three, each has half the number of chromosomes found in body cells. Four, in humans, both cells begin to develop by meiosis at puberty (PEW bur tee). **Puberty** is the stage in life when a person begins to develop sex cells. It takes place between the ages of 10 and 15.

How are sperm and eggs different? Eggs are much larger than sperm. Each sperm has a tail. The tail helps it move. Sperm form in the testes (TES teez). In animals, **testes** are the male sex organs that produce sperm. Eggs form in the ovaries (OHV uh reez). In animals and some plants, **ovaries** are the female sex organs.

In which organs are sperm formed?

Study Tip: Use this idea map as a study guide for comparing eggs and sperm. Which sex cells are smaller?

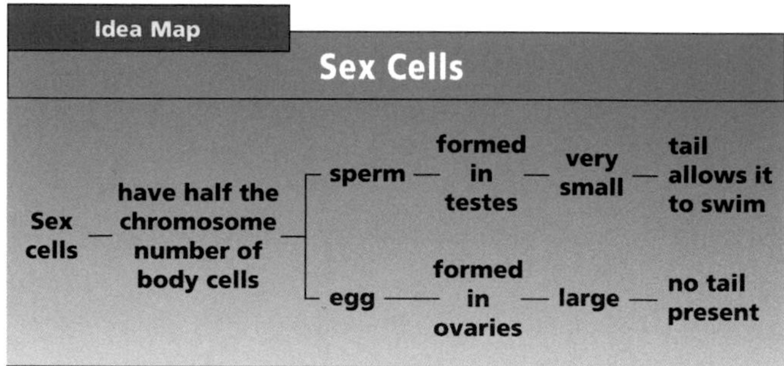

STUDY GUIDE 130

STUDY GUIDE — CHAPTER 22

Name ____ Date ____ Class ____

MEIOSIS

In your textbook, read about the steps of meiosis in Section 22:2.

5. Match each of the following steps of meiosis with the statements below. Letters may be used more than once. Write the correct letter on each blank. Note: The statements describing the steps of meiosis are not in the correct order.

A B C D E F G H

a. Matching chromosomes come together to form pairs. C
b. Each chromosome has two strands of sister chromatids. Pairs of sister chromatids are lined up near cell's center; original and copy still together. C
c. One cell division completed and two new cells formed. E
d. Each chromosome becomes doubled, forming sister chromatids. B
e. Original and copy chromosome move to opposite ends of cell. G
f. Centrioles move again to opposite ends of cells. E
g. Pairs of sister chromatids move to center of cell. C
h. Four new cells have formed from original. H
i. Nuclear membrane begins to fade away. B
j. Sister chromatid pairs move to opposite ends of cell. D
k. Four single chromosomes are present in cell. A
l. Each cell is now a sex cell. H
m. Nuclear membrane is reappearing. G

ENRICHMENT 24

ENRICHMENT — CHAPTER 22

Name ____ Date ____ Class ____

Use after Section 22:2.

MITOSIS, MEIOSIS, AND NUMBER OF CHROMOSOMES

Organisms differ in the number of chromosomes in their cells. The table below shows the number of chromosomes in the body cells of different organisms.

Use the table to help you answer the questions below. Refer to your textbook for the different steps of mitosis and meiosis.

Organism	Chromosome number	Organism	Chromosome number
alligator	32	amoeba	50
cat	32	chimpanzee	48
dog	78	eel	36
fly	12	human	46
lettuce	18	pigeon	80

1. How many chromosomes in the body cells of an alligator? 32 an amoeba? 50 a dog? 78 a human? 46 a pigeon? 80 lettuce? 18 a fly? 12
2. How many chromosomes in the sex cells of a dog? 39 a cat? 16 a chimpanzee? 24
3. During Step One of mitosis how many pairs of sister chromatids are in the body cell of a human? 46 a cat? 32 lettuce? 18 an alligator? 32
4. During Step Three of mitosis how many chromosomes are in the dividing body cell of a human? 92 a dog? 156 a pigeon? 160 an alligator? 64 a cat? 64 a fly? 24
5. After mitosis is complete, how many chromosomes are in the resulting body cells of a dog? 78 a cat? 32 a human? 46 a pigeon? 80 an amoeba? 50
6. During Step One of meiosis how many pairs of sister chromatids are present in the forming sex cell of an amoeba? 50 an eel? 36 lettuce? 18
7. At the end of Step Three of meiosis how many pairs of sister chromatids are present in each of the forming cells of a human? 23 a cat? 16 a dog? 39 a fly? 6
8. When meiosis is complete how many chromosomes are in each resulting sex cell of an alligator? 16 a human? 23 an eel? 18
9. After fertilization takes place, how many chromosomes are in the fertilized cell of a dog? 78 a cat? 32 a human? 46 an amoeba? 50 an alligator? 32

OPTIONS

Enrichment/*Teacher Resource Package,* p. 24. Use the Enrichment worksheet shown here to give students practice with determining chromosome number after meiosis.

Meiosis in Humans/*Transparency Package,* number 22d. Use color transparency number 22d as you teach meiosis.

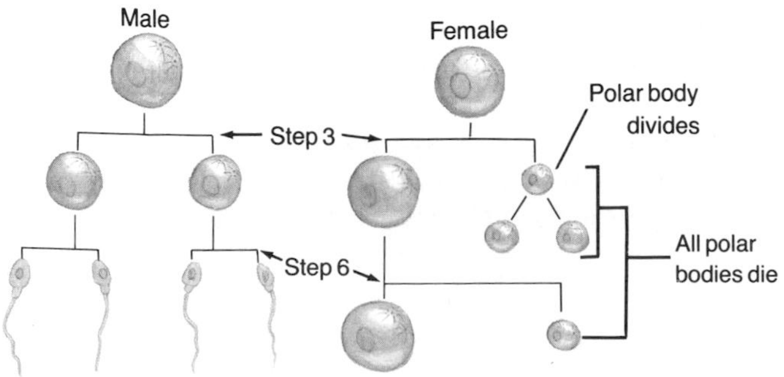

Figure 22-10 Compare the products of meiosis between human males and females.

During meiosis, each original male cell becomes four sperm, Figure 22-10. Meiosis in males occurs all the time from the beginning of puberty.

Now, look at how eggs are formed, Figure 22-10. When the cell first pinches in half at the end of the first division, one cell is smaller than the other. The smaller cell is called a polar body. A **polar body** is a small cell formed during meiosis in a female. This first polar body is formed every month in a female from the onset of puberty. The polar body divides and then dies. The large cell that remains forms another polar body when the cell pinches in half again. This third polar body also dies.

When sperm and egg join, the chromosomes from each cell also come together. The new organism has a complete set of chromosomes in each one of its body cells. Half the chromosomes in the organism come from the father, and half come from the mother.

Check Your Understanding

6. How do the number of chromosomes at the beginning and end of meiosis compare?
7. Describe changes in chromosomes during meiosis.
8. Compare the results of meiosis between human male and female sex cells.
9. **Critical Thinking:** What is the advantage of producing more sperm than eggs?
10. **Biology and Math:** If the body cells of an animal have 50 chromosomes, how many chromosomes would its sex cells have after meiosis?

RETEACHING 67

Reteaching — Chapter 22

Name ______ Date ______ Class ______

Use with Section 22:2.

Meiosis and Fertilization

Review the steps of meiosis in your textbook. Then draw the proper number of chromosomes in each diagram to show meiosis taking place. Use the same number and the same size of chromosomes as shown in Step 1 to complete the diagrams. You may want to use four different colored pencils to show the original and duplicated chromosomes.

Meiosis — Fertilization

Step 1, Step 2, Step 3, Step 4, Step 5, Step 6

sperm cell

fertilized egg

mitosis

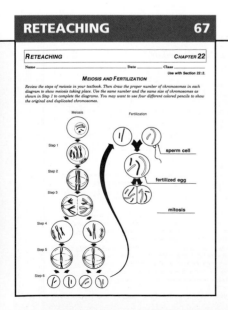

TEACH

Check for Understanding

Have students respond to the first three questions in Check Your Understanding.

Reteach

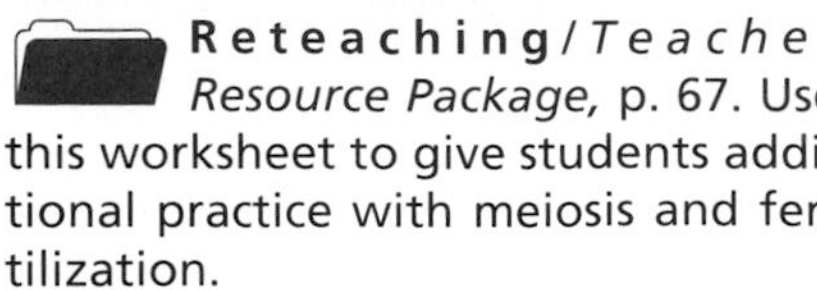

Reteaching/*Teacher Resource Package*, p. 67. Use this worksheet to give students additional practice with meiosis and fertilization.

Extension: Assign Critical Thinking, Biology and Math, or some of the **OPTIONS** available with this lesson.

3 APPLY

Divergent Question

Describe as many similarities and differences as you can between:
(a) sperm and egg cells
(b) mitosis and meiosis

4 CLOSE

Audiovisual

Show the videocassette *Meiosis*, Carolina Biological Supply, Co.

Answers to Check Your Understanding

6. The number is halved.
7. Chromosomes make copies of themselves, forming sister chromatids. Sister chromatids pair up with others of the same size. Sets of sister chromatids are moved to the center of the cell. Fibers separate sets of sister chromatids by moving them to opposite cell ends. Two cells then show fibers moving sister chromatids to the center of the cell. Sister chromatids are separated and move to opposite cell ends.
8. Female—one sex cell remains after meiosis. Male—four sex cells are formed.
9. More sperm are necessary because they leave the protection of the body and therefore have a lower chance of surviving.
10. 50/2 = 25

22:3 Changes in the Rate of Mitosis

PREPARATION

Materials Needed

Make copies of the Skill, Study Guide, Reteaching, and Lab worksheets in the *Teacher Resource Package.*

▶ Locate or purchase clear plastic sheets and marking pencils for Lab 22-2.

Key Science Words

cancer

Process Skills

In the Skill Check, students will classify. In the Lab 22-2, they will use numbers, make and use tables, form hypotheses, and interpret data.

1 FOCUS

▶ The objectives are listed on the student page. Remind students to preview these objectives as a guide to this numbered section.

MOTIVATION/Brainstorming

Students are familiar with the term *cancer.* Ask them to list for you facts they know about cancer. Write their ideas on the chalkboard.

Guided Practice

Have students write down their answers to the margin question: It slows down.

Objectives

7. Explain some effects of aging.

8. Describe the causes and effects of cancer.

Key Science Words

cancer

22:3 Changes in the Rate of Mitosis

Changes often occur in the growth of cells. The rate of mitosis can speed up or slow down. Let's look at two effects caused by a change in the rate of mitosis.

Aging

Aging is the process of becoming older. All living things age. Loss of hair, wrinkled skin, and loss of calcium in bones are some of the common signs of aging in humans.

Many changes that result from aging have something to do with mitosis. Let's take fingernail growth for example. Your fingernails grow by the process of mitosis. The new cells push out the old cells. Old cells harden, die, and form the fingernail. As a person ages, mitosis in cells of the fingernails slows down. Fingernail growth then slows down.

How does aging affect fingernail growth?

Changes in heart and body muscle also occur as you age. Muscle cells do not undergo mitosis. You are born with a certain number of muscle cells. As you grow, the muscle cells get bigger, but no new cells are made. As you become older, the muscle cells wear out, and no new ones replace them. This is why your heart weakens and cannot pump blood as well as you get older. Remember that your heart is made of muscle.

Table 22-1 shows a comparison between body functions at age 20 and age 70. Each difference may be the result of a slowing in the rate of cell mitosis. Mitosis is not a very well understood process. Scientists don't know why mitosis slows down with age.

TABLE 22–1. CHANGES THAT OCCUR IN THE HUMAN BODY WITH AGE

Body System	Trait	20-Year-Old	70-Year-Old
Skin/Nails	Rate of fingernail growth	1 mm/week	.6 mm/week
Nervous	Reaction time	.8 seconds	.95 seconds
Circulatory	Pumping action of heart	3.7 liters/minute	2.9 liters/minute
Nervous	Memory	14 of 24 words recalled	7 of 24 words recalled
Respiratory	Lung volume with deep breath	5.5 liters/ inhalation	3 liters/ inhalation
Muscular	% of body fat (male)	15%	30%

OPTIONS

Science Background

Tissues subjected to "wear and tear" have the highest mitotic rates. Cells lining the digestive tract are constantly scraped by passing food and are surrounded by acidic liquids. Skin cells are constantly abraded or drying out.

Skill/*Teacher Resource Package,* p. 23. Use the Skill worksheet shown here to help students learn the process of developing a hypothesis.

SKILL 23

SKILL: FORM A HYPOTHESIS — CHAPTER 22

Name ____ Date ____ Class ____

For more help, refer to the Skill Handbook, pages 704-705. *Use after Section 22:3.*

GROWTH PATTERNS IN TWO FISH

Joe and Rosa bought two goldfish that were the same color, size, and shape. They kept the fish in the same tank and fed them every day. They thought the fish were of the same species because they looked alike. Joe and Rosa had read that all cells in the body of a living thing go through mitosis at one rate. If the goldfish were of the same species, they thought the cells of both fish would all grow at the same rate. They made a hypothesis that the fish would grow at the same rate and would be about the same size a year later. To their surprise, one fish grew faster than the other. In six months, one fish was 2 cm longer than the other. What could be the explanation?

Answer the following questions to find out why the hypothesis about the growth of the fish was incorrect. Develop a hypothesis of your own about the growth shown by the goldfish.

1. What is mitosis? **cell reproduction in which two new cells are formed**
2. How does the size of the two new cells formed by mitosis compare with the size of the cell from which they were produced? **the new cells are smaller**
3. What happens to the size of each new cell soon after it has been formed? **Each cell grows in size.**
4. How does a living thing grow? **As cells reproduce by mitosis, the number of cells in a living thing increases. The increase results in growth.**
5. On what did the two students base their prediction about the growth of the two goldfish? **on the fact that the cells of the same kind of living thing go through mitosis at one certain rate**
6. State a hypothesis to explain why one fish grew faster than the other. **Answers will vary. Some possible answers are: the two goldfish may not be the same kind. One fish might have replaced more worn-out cells than the other fish. One fish might have eaten more than the other.**
7. Explain how you could test your hypothesis. **Answers will vary. A possible answer: Place two fish of the same kind and size in separate aquariums. Feed each fish the same amount of food each day. Measure both fish at least once a week. Record the measurements each time to keep track of any differences in length. Use a key to identify the species.**

Lab 22–2 Rate of Mitosis

Problem: Does mitosis occur in all cells all the time?

Skills

use numbers, make and use tables, form hypotheses, interpret data

Materials

clear plastic sheet
marking pencil
facial tissue
microscope

Procedure

1. Copy the data table.
2. Lay a plastic sheet over the diagrams of tissue cells in the figure.
3. **Use numbers:** Count the total number of cells in each diagram. Use a marking pencil to check off each cell as you count. Record the number of cells.
4. Wipe off the plastic with the facial tissue. Place it over the diagrams again.
5. **Form a hypothesis:** Read the table in Figure 22-1 on page 464 again. State which of the three tissues you think will show the most cells in mitosis. Write your **hypothesis** in your notebook.
6. Repeat steps 1 and 2, only this time count the numbers of cells reproducing and the numbers of cells not reproducing by mitosis. Record these numbers.

Data and Observations

1. **Interpret data:** Which tissue in the diagrams showed the most cells in mitosis?
2. Which tissue type in the diagrams showed the least number of cells in mitosis?

TISSUE	TOTAL NUMBER OF CELLS	NUMBER OF CELLS NOT IN MITOSIS	NUMBER OF CELLS IN MITOSIS
Liver	50	47	3
Stomach Lining	50	20	30
Skin	50	32	18

Analyze and Apply

1. Which tissue type would:
   (a) repair itself the fastest?
   (b) repair itself the slowest?
2. **Check your hypothesis:** Is your hypothesis supported by your data? Why or why not?
3. **Apply:** Root tip cells reproduce faster than skin cells, but slower than liver cells. Draw 50 root tip cells. Show how many you think would be reproducing.

Extension

Use numbers: Calculate the average number of dividing cells in one field of view of a prepared slide of onion root tip cells.

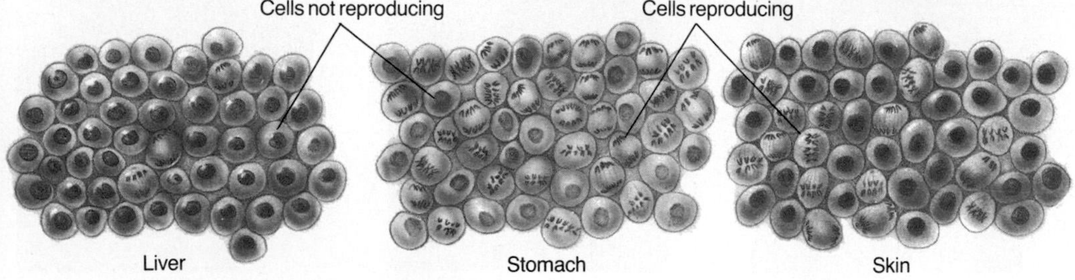

Lab 22-2 Rate of Mitosis

Overview

In this activity, students will recognize that different tissues undergo mitosis at different rates.

Objectives: Upon completion of this lab, students will be able to: (1) **distinguish** between cells not undergoing mitosis, (2) **correlate** mitosis rate with growth and repair rate.

Time Allotment: 30 minutes

Preparation

▶ **Alternate Materials:** Providing a photocopy of the diagrams to each student will eliminate the need for clear plastic sheets.

Lab 22-2 worksheet/*Teacher Resource Package,* pp. 85-86.

Lab 22-2 Computer Program/*Teacher Resource Package,* p. xx. Use the computer program shown at the bottom of this page as you teach this lab.

Teaching the Lab

▶ **Troubleshooting:** Review with students which cells in the diagrams represent cells undergoing mitosis.

Cooperative Learning: Divide the class into groups of three students. For more information, see pp. 22T-23T in the Teacher Guide.

COMPUTER PROGRAM XX

COMPUTER PROGRAM LAB 22-2 RATE OF MITOSIS

```
]POKE 33,33

]LIST

 10  GOSUB 390
 20  HOME
 30  PRINT "---------------------------------------";
 40  PRINT "!       ! TOTAL  ! NUMBER OF !NUMBER OF!";
 50  PRINT "!TISSUE ! NUMBER ! CELLS NOT !CELLS IN !";
 60  PRINT "!       !OF CELLS! IN MITOSIS!MITOSIS  !";
 70  PRINT "---------------------------------------";
 80  PRINT "!LIVER  !        !           !         !";
 90  PRINT "---------------------------------------";
 100  PRINT "!STOMACH!        !           !         !";
 110  PRINT "!LINING !        !           !         !";
 120  PRINT "---------------------------------------";
 130  PRINT "!SKIN   !        !           !         !";
 140  PRINT "---------------------------------------"
 150  FOR X = 1 TO 9
 160  VTAB V(X): HTAB H(X): FLASH : PRINT " ";: NORMAL
 170  VTAB 15: HTAB 1: CALL  - 958
 180  PRINT "ENTER YOUR VALUE FOR THIS SPACE";
 190  INPUT ": ";A
 200  VTAB V(X): HTAB H(X): PRINT A
 210  NEXT
 220  VTAB 15: HTAB 1: CALL  - 958
 230  PRINT "ARE THESE NUMBERS                        ENTERED CORRECTLY? (
    Y/N): ";: GET A$
 240  IF A$ = "N" OR A$ = "n" THEN  GOTO 20
 250  IF A$ <  > "Y" AND A$  <  > "y" THEN 220
 260  VTAB 15: HTAB 1: CALL  - 958: PRINT
 270  FLASH : PRINT "PRESS THE SPACE BAR TO SEE CORRECT DATA": GET A$
 278  NORMAL
 280  VTAB 16: HTAB 1: CALL  - 868
 290  FOR X = 1 TO 9
 300  VTAB V(X): HTAB H(X) + 3
 310  READ C: PRINT "(";C;")"
 320  NEXT
 330  INVERSE : PRINT
 340  PRINT : PRINT "DO YOU WANT THIS PRINTED (Y/N)? :";: GET A$
 345  NORMAL
 348  VTAB 15: HTAB 1: CALL  - 958
 350  IF A$ = "N" OR A$ = "n" THEN  END
 360  IF A$ <  > "Y" AND A$  <  > "y" THEN  GOTO 340
 370  GOSUB 2000
 380  END
 390  TEXT : HOME : PRINT "LAB 22-1                        MITOSIS RATE"
 400  PRINT : PRINT
 410  PRINT "YOU WILL BE ASKED TO TYPE IN YOUR        RESULTS FOR THE 3 TI
    SSUES ONTO A DATA   TABLE THAT IS EXACTLY LIKE THE ONE USED"
 420  PRINT "IN THE EXPERIMENT."
 430  PRINT
 440  PRINT "AFTER TYPING EACH NUMBER, PRESS THE      RETURN KEY. AFTER TY
    PING YOUR DATA, YOU WILL BE ASKED IF THE NUMBERS ARE ENTEREDCORRECTL
    Y.IF CORRECT TYPE THE LETTER Y.IF WRONG, TYPE THE LETTER N."
```

ANSWERS

Data and Observations

1. stomach
2. liver

Analyze and Apply

1. (a) stomach (b) liver
2. Students who hypothesized that the stomach would show the most cells in mitosis will answer yes.
3. The diagram will show about five to ten cells.

2 TEACH

MOTIVATION/Brainstorming

Ask students to explain the significance of the data in Table 22-1 and if each change with age might be the result of cell loss. Might these changes be associated with lack of strength or sensory abilities such as vision and hearing? With aging, the process of mitosis slows down.

Concept Development

▶ Make sure that students are correlating the events described on this page with Figure 22-5. The events are much more easily understood if this is done.

▶ The key concept in cancer is rapid cell mitosis in some tissue, which crowds out the tissue undergoing mitosis at a normal rate.

Guided Practice

Have students write down their answers to the margin question: Lung tissue becomes crowded by abnormal cells.

Independent Practice

Study Guide/*Teacher Resource Package*, pp. 131-132. Use the Study Guide worksheets shown at the bottom of this page for independent practice.

Bio Tip

Health: Exposure to radiation can affect the cell divisions in a person's sex cells. When you receive X rays at a hospital or dentist you should wear an apron made of lead for protection. X rays can't pass through lead.

How does cancer in the lungs affect lung tissue?

Cancer

Healthy cells have regular rates of reproducing. For example, a skin cell undergoes mitosis once every 20 days. During the other 19 days, it doesn't reproduce. A liver cell may undergo mitosis once every 200 days.

Cancer is a disease in which body cells reproduce at an abnormally fast rate. Follow the steps in Figure 22-11 that show cancer forming in the lungs. The cells are shown about 250 times their real size. Figure 22-11a shows normal lung cells. A thin layer of cells covers the lungs. Notice the changes in Figure 22-11b. The outer layer of cells has changed from one cell layer to many cell layers.

In Figure 22-11c, the outer layer of cells is no longer thin and even. Rapid mitosis has increased the number of cells. The shapes of the cells and their nuclei have also changed. The abnormal cells begin to crowd the lung tissues inside. The outer cells have become cancer cells. They will continue to increase in number until they crowd out all normal lung tissue.

Why do some cells start reproducing abnormally and become cancer cells? Three well-known causes include chemicals, radiation, and viruses. Cells may become cancer cells if they are in contact with poisonous chemicals for a long time. For example, it has been shown that chewing tobacco may cause cancer of the mouth. Skin cells may become cancer cells if a person spends too much time in the sun. High levels of X rays may cause cancer in bones. Even viruses cause certain cancers.

Figure 22-11 Follow the changes in lung tissue as the covering cells become cancer cells.

a

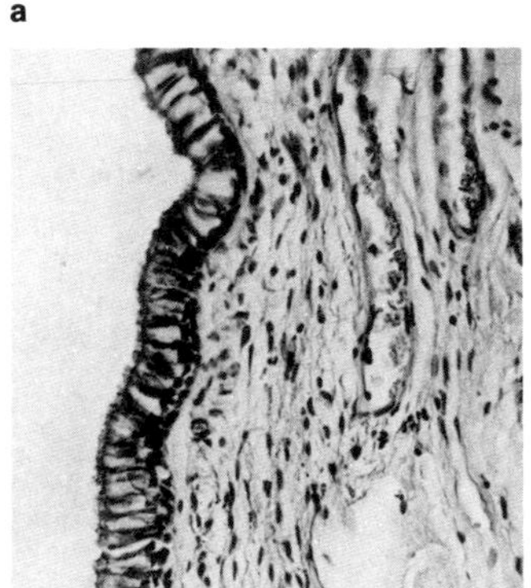

b

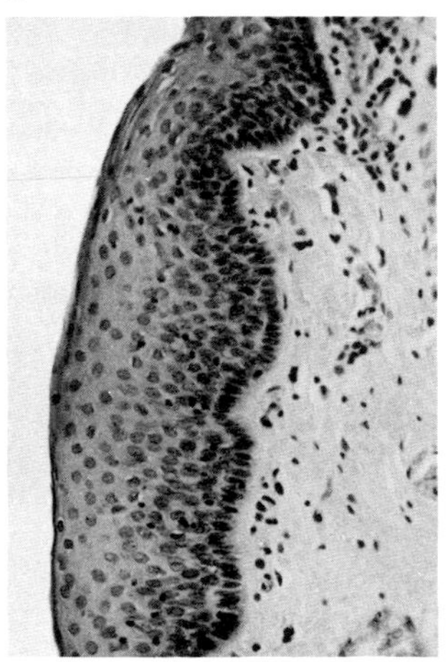

c

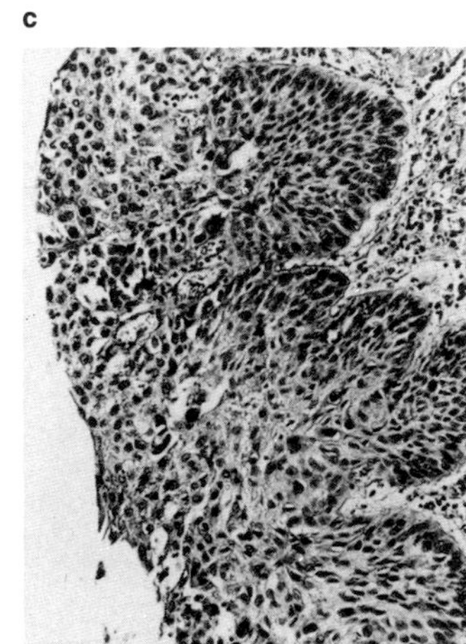

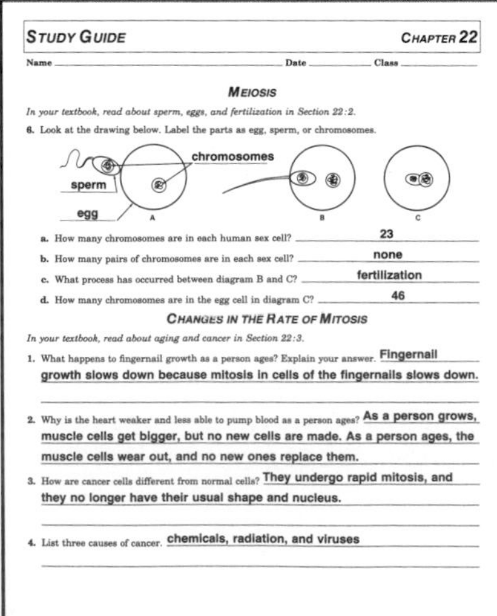

STUDY GUIDE 131

STUDY GUIDE — CHAPTER 22

Name ______ Date ______ Class ______

MEIOSIS

In your textbook, read about sperm, eggs, and fertilization in Section 22:2.

6. Look at the drawing below. Label the parts as egg, sperm, or chromosomes.

a. How many chromosomes are in each human sex cell? 23
b. How many pairs of chromosomes are in each sex cell? none
c. What process has occurred between diagram B and C? fertilization
d. How many chromosomes are in the egg cell in diagram C? 46

CHANGES IN THE RATE OF MITOSIS

In your textbook, read about aging and cancer in Section 22:3.

1. What happens to fingernail growth as a person ages? Explain your answer. Fingernail growth slows down because mitosis in cells of the fingernails slows down.
2. Why is the heart weaker and less able to pump blood as a person ages? As a person grows, muscle cells get bigger, but no new cells are made. As a person ages, the muscle cells wear out, and no new ones replace them.
3. How are cancer cells different from normal cells? They undergo rapid mitosis, and they no longer have their usual shape and nucleus.
4. List three causes of cancer. chemicals, radiation, and viruses

STUDY GUIDE 132

STUDY GUIDE — CHAPTER 22

Name ______ Date ______ Class ______

VOCABULARY

Review the new words used in Chapter 22 of your textbook. Then complete this exercise.

1. Match one of these choices to each of the following statements. Write the proper choice on each blank: mitosis, meiosis.
   a. Four new cells are formed from each original. meiosis
   b. This process makes sperm cells. meiosis
   c. Two new cells are formed from each original. mitosis
   d. New skin cells are made this way. mitosis
   e. This type of cell reproduction helps you grow. mitosis
   f. This type of cell reproduction makes egg cells. meiosis
   g. This makes cells with half the original cell chromosome number. meiosis
   h. This makes cells with the same chromosome number as the original. mitosis
2. Match one of the choices to each of the following phrases. Write the proper choice on each blank: testes, ovaries, cancer, polar body, puberty, sex cells, body cells, sister chromatids
   a. stage when person produces sex cells puberty
   b. organs that produce eggs ovaries
   c. small cell formed and then dies during meiosis in female polar body
   d. organs that produce sperm testes
   e. egg and sperm sex cells
   f. cells that make up the skin, blood, bones, and stomach body cells
   g. the two strands of a doubled chromosome sister chromatids
   h. a disease in which body cells reproduce faster than normal cancer

Figure 22-12 Chewing tobacco is a popular habit that may cause mouth cancer.

Cancer is caused by many things. There are probably many causes that scientists have not yet discovered. For these reasons, the problem of how to treat cancer is a very difficult one to solve. Over the past 30 years, regular medical treatment that includes doses of radiation has resulted in a doubling of the survival rates of cancer patients.

Skill Check

Classify: The following are possible causes of cancer. Classify them as chemical, radiation, or other: smoking, radon, asbestos, smog, AIDS virus, UV rays, and paint thinner. *For more help, refer to the **Skill Handbook,** pages 715-717.*

Check Your Understanding

11. What are some of the changes that take place as a person ages?
12. What is the effect of cancer on mitosis?
13. List four possible causes of cancer.
14. **Critical Thinking:** Your skin produces a dark protective pigment when exposed to the sun's burning rays. There are a variety of suntan lotions. Some help you tan faster, some block the rays of the sun. Which suntan lotion should you choose to protect you from developing skin cancer?
15. **Biology and Reading:** Some cancers are inherited. Retinoblastoma (REH tihn uh blah STOH muh) is a kind of eye cancer that is inherited by about 1 in 20 000 children. What does the word *inherited* mean as used in this description?

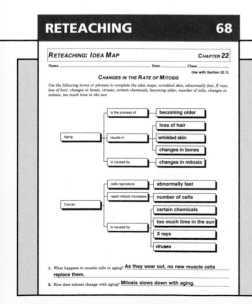

RETEACHING 68

RETEACHING: IDEA MAP — CHAPTER 22

Name ______ Date ______ Class ______

Use with Section 22:3.

CHANGES IN THE RATE OF MITOSIS

Use the following terms or phrases to complete the idea maps: wrinkled skin, abnormally fast, X rays, loss of hair, changes in bones, viruses, certain chemicals, becoming older, number of cells, changes in mitosis, too much time in the sun

Aging
- is the process of — becoming older
- results in — loss of hair; wrinkled skin; changes in bones
- is caused by — changes in mitosis

Cancer
- cells reproduce — abnormally fast
- rapid mitosis increases — number of cells
- is caused by — certain chemicals; too much time in the sun; X rays; viruses

1. What happens to muscle cells in aging? As they wear out, no new muscle cells replace them.
2. How does mitosis change with aging? Mitosis slows down with aging.

OPTIONS

Are There More Dividing Cells or Resting Cells in a Root Tip?/*Lab Manual,* p. 185. Use this lab as an extension to the rate of mitosis.

TEACH

Skill Check

Chemical: smoking, smog, paint thinner
Radiation: radon, UV rays
Other: asbestos, AIDS virus

Check for Understanding

Have students respond to the first three questions in Check Your Understanding.

Reteach

Reteaching/*Teacher Resource Package,* p. 68. Use this worksheet to give students additional practice with changes in the rate of mitosis.

Extension: Assign Critical Thinking, Biology and Reading, or some of the **OPTIONS** available with this lesson.

3 APPLY

Offer an explanation for the following: Warts are a type of tumor but are not cancerous. Explain why they are not harmful.

4 CLOSE

Audiovisual

Show the videocassette *Living with Cancer,* Films for the Humanities.

Answers to Check Your Understanding

11. loss of hair, wrinkled skin, changes in bones
12. Cancer causes abnormal mitosis in body cells.
13. contact with certain chemicals, X rays, viruses, too much sun
14. Suntan lotions that block the rays of the sun can help reduce the risk of skin cancer.
15. Inherited means that the disease is caused by chromosomes from the mother or father.

CHAPTER 22 REVIEW

Summary

Summary statements can be used by students to review the major concepts of the chapter.

Key Science Words

All boldfaced terms from the chapter are listed.

Testing Yourself

Using Words

1. meiosis
2. cancer
3. mitosis
4. ovary
5. puberty
6. polar body
7. testes

Finding Main Ideas

8. p. 478; Covering cells are usually two cells thick. They form a thin even layer over connective tissue. As cancer begins, the covering layer begins to thicken and crowds out connective tissue. Covering cells are no longer normal.
9. p. 469; In step two, the sister chromatids become attached to the spindle fibers and are pulled toward the center of the cell. In step three, the sister chromatids are pulled apart by the spindle fibers and become separated.
10. p. 474; Egg and sperm cells are made, four cells are formed from each original cell, the number of chromosomes is half the number in the original cell, and each new cell has only one of each type of chromosome.
11. p. 464; Mitosis allows us to grow and to replace damaged or worn-out cells.
12. p. 476; Mitosis slows down as we age. Muscle cells wear out and no new ones replace them. As a result, for example, your heart is not as strong as when you were younger.
13. p. 472; In mitosis, the chromosomes are not paired; in meiosis, the matching chromosomes are paired up.

Chapter 22 Review

Summary

22:1 Mitosis

1. Living things grow and repair themselves in a process of cell reproduction called mitosis.
2. Before mitosis begins, chromosomes become doubled and form sister chromatids. Each chromatid is an exact copy of the original chromosome.
3. During mitosis, two identical cells form from one original cell. Mitosis takes place in four steps. It results in two new body cells, each with the same number of chromosomes as in the original cell.

22:2 Meiosis

4. Sex cells form through a process called meiosis.
5. Meiosis involves two cell divisions. It results in four sex cells, each with half the number of chromosomes as the original cell.
6. In human males, four sperm result from meiosis. In females, only one egg results from meiosis. Egg and sperm join together at fertilization. Each supplies half the new cell's chromosomes. The new organism develops by mitosis.

22:3 Changes in the Rate of Mitosis

7. Aging is due to a slowing down of mitosis in some cells of the body.
8. Cancer is the result of abnormal mitosis. Cells reproduce too rapidly.
9. Cancer can be caused by chemicals, radiation or viruses.

Key Science Words

body cell (p. 464)
cancer (p. 478)
meiosis (p. 471)
mitosis (p. 464)
ovary (p. 474)
polar body (p. 475)
puberty (p. 474)
sex cell (p. 471)
sister chromatids (p. 466)
testes (p. 474)

Testing Yourself

Using Words

Choose the word from the list of Key Science Words that best fits the definition.

1. cell reproduction that forms sex cells
2. abnormal cell mitosis
3. cell reproduction in which two identical cells are made
4. female sex organ
5. stage in life when sex cells start to undergo meiosis

Using Main Ideas

14. step 6
15. The heart of an older person can't pump as much blood because some of the heart muscle cells have worn out and muscle cells are not replaced when worn out. It is therefore less efficient.
16. A cat would have 19 chromosomes in its sex cells.
17. (a) mitosis – two cells, meiosis – four cells; (b) mitosis – same as the original cell, meiosis – one-half the original cell; (c) mitosis – body cell, meiosis – sex cell.
18. Causes of cancer include chemicals, radiation, and viruses.

Review

Testing Yourself *continued*

6. small cell in the female that dies after being formed by meiosis
7. organs that produce sperm

Finding Main Ideas

List the page number where each main idea below is found. Then, explain each main idea.

8. changes that take place in lung tissue with cancer
9. the role of the fibers during Steps Two and Three of mitosis
10. what is accomplished during meiosis
11. what the benefits of mitosis are
12. specific changes that take place between age 20 and age 70
13. how the chromosome grouping in Step Two of mitosis differs from that in Step Two of meiosis

Using Main Ideas

Answer the questions by referring to the page number after each question.

14. In what step of meiosis do sister chromatids separate? (p. 474)
15. Why can't the heart of an older person pump as much blood as that of a younger person? (p. 476)
16. Cats have 38 chromosomes in their body cells. How many chromosomes would their sex cells have? (p. 471)
17. How do each of the following compare for mitosis and meiosis? (pp. 469, 474)
    (a) the number of cells formed
    (b) numbers of chromosomes in the new cells compared with number of chromosomes in the original cell
    (c) type of cell formed
18. What are three main causes of cancer? (p. 478)

Skill Review ✓

For more help, refer to the ***Skill Handbook,*** *pages 704-719.*

1. **Classify:** Compare the following traits of eggs and sperm: size, number of chromosomes, process that makes them, polar bodies formed, tail present.
2. **Sequence:** What changes take place in the cell membrane and nuclear membrane before or during mitosis?
3. **Measure in SI:** A student makes 500 new bone cells and each is 0.015 mm in size. Assuming they all form in the same direction, how much did this student grow?
4. **Observe:** Examine a prepared slide of a lily anther and count the number of chromosomes in the young pollen cells.

Finding Out More

Critical Thinking

1. Through an error, part of a chromosome within a fertilized egg cell is lost. Will every body cell within the new organism show the same error? Explain.
2. How might tanning parlors and cigarettes be related to cancer?

Applications

1. Demonstrate how rapidly a living thing increases in size by calculating the number of cells that result from 10 generations of mitosis.
2. Build models of a cell's chromosomes showing the changes that take place during mitosis and meiosis.

Skill Review

1. Traits of egg and sperm that are similar: number of chromosomes, process that makes them. Traits that are different: size, polar bodies formed, tail present.
2. During mitosis, the nuclear membrane breaks down, allowing the chromosomes to go to opposite ends of the cell. It then reforms around the nuclear material. The cell membrane pinches in two and separates the cell into two new identical cells.
3. 500 x 0.015 mm = 7.50 mm
4. Students should be able to see 12 chromosomes.

Finding Out More

Critical Thinking

1. Yes. All body cells within an organism have chromosomes that are exact duplicates of those in the original fertilized egg. If part of a chromosome is lost, this part cannot later be duplicated.
2. The tanning rays used in a tanning parlor and cigarettes are known to cause cancer.

Applications

1. There will be 1024 cells after 10 generations of mitosis.
2. Thin and thick yarn of different colors or colored plastic-coated wire can be used. The wire can be coiled to show thickening.

 **Chapter Review**/*Teacher Resource Package,* pp. 116-117.

 **Chapter Test**/*Teacher Resource Package,* pp. 118-120.

Chapter Test/*Computer Test Bank*

Plant Reproduction and Development

PLANNING GUIDE

CONTENT	TEXT FEATURES	TEACHER RESOURCE PACKAGE	OTHER COMPONENTS
(1 1/2 days) 23:1 Asexual Reproduction in Plants Asexual Reproduction by Roots Asexual Reproduction by Leaves Asexual Reproduction by Stems	Idea Map, p. 484 Check Your Understanding, p. 487	Reteaching: *Annual Reproduction in Plants,* p. 69 Focus: *Seeds That Sprouted After Hundreds of Years,* p. 45 Study Guide: *Asexual Reproduction in Plants,* p. 133	
(1 1/2 days) 23:2 Sexual Reproduction in Plants Flowers and Sexual Reproduction Pollination and Fertilization	Idea Map, p. 488 Idea Map, p. 490 Check Your Understanding, p. 491	Reteaching: *Fertilization in Flowers,* p. 70 Critical Thinking/Problem Solving: *Will Fertilization Take Place?* p. 23 Skill: *Recognize Spatial Relationships,* p. 24 Transparency Master: *Flower Anatomy and Pollination,* p. 113 Study Guide: *Sexual Reproduction in Plants,* pp. 134-135	**Laboratory Manual:** *What Are the Parts of a Flower?* p. 189 Color Transparency 23a: *Parts of a Flower*
(2 days) 23:3 Plant Development Seeds and Fruits Plant Development from Seeds Comparing Kinds of Reproduction	Skill Check: *Understand Science Words,* p. 494 Mini Lab: *Will Seeds Grow With Stored Food?* p. 492 Lab 23-1: *Germination,* p. 495 Lab 23-2: *Rooting,* p. 497 Technology: *Seed Banks,* p. 493 Check Your Understanding, p. 496 Problem Solving: *Flower Pollination,* p. 498	Application: *Flowers and Fruits,* p. 23 Enrichment: *Identifying Different Types of Fruits,* p. 25 Reteaching: *What Happens to Certain Flower Parts After Fertilization?* p. 71 Study Guide: *Plant Development,* pp. 136-137 Study Guide: *Vocabulary,* p. 138 Lab 23-1: *Germination,* pp. 89-90 Lab 23-2: *Rooting,* pp. 91-92	**Laboratory Manual:** *What Plant Part Are You Eating?* p. 193 Color Transparency 23b: *From Flower to Fruit* Color Transparency 23c: *Germination*
Chapter Review	Summary Key Science Words Testing Yourself Finding Main Ideas Using Main Ideas Skill Review	Chapter Review, pp. 121-122 Chapter Test, pp. 123-125	**Test Bank**

MATERIALS NEEDED

LAB 23-1, p. 495	LAB 23-2, p. 497	MARGIN FEATURES
metric ruler rubber band small beaker pencil tape permanent marker 2 milk cartons soil 20 corn seeds water stapler scissors	garlic bulb carrot labels water toothpicks small beaker metric ruler razor blade shallow dish	Skill Check, p. 494 dictionary Mini Lab, p. 492 soaked bean seeds paper towel petri dish

OBJECTIVES

SECTION	OBJECTIVE	OBJECTIVES CORRELATION			
		CHECK YOUR UNDERSTANDING	CHAPTER REVIEW	TRP CHAPTER REVIEW	TRP CHAPTER TEST
23:1	1. **Explain** how plants reproduce asexually from roots.	1	15, 23, 24	1, 33	26, 29, 30, 32, 34
	2. **Describe** how plants can reproduce asexually from leaves.	—	9, 26	6	29, 30, 31, 32, 33, 34
	3. **Compare** asexual reproduction from runners, tubers, bulbs, cuttings, and grafting.	2	2, 4, 10	3, 13,14, 18, 37	1, 4, 14, 25, 27, 28, 29, 30, 32, 33, 34
23:2	4. **List** the parts of a flower and their functions.	5, 6	5, 7, 18, 25	11, 22, 23, 24, 25, 26, 27, 28, 30, 31, 36	9, 10, 15, 16, 17, 18, 19, 21, 22, 23, 24, 38, 40, 41
	5. **Describe** two methods of pollination.	7	8, 13, 21	32, 35	8
	6. **Sequence** the steps that lead to fertilization in flowering plants.	—	16, 17, 22	8, 15, 19, 20, 29	5, 7, 20, 35
23:3	7. **Describe** how fruits and seeds develop.	10, 14	6, 11, 20	4, 7, 9	3, 11, 12, 36, 37, 39, 42
	8. **Explain** how seeds are scattered and grow into new plants.	11, 13	3, 14	2, 5, 34	6, 13
	9. **Compare** asexual and sexual reproduction in plants.	12	1, 12, 19	1, 10, 12, 16, 17, 38	2, 43, 44, 45, 46, 47, 48, 49, 50, 51, 52

Plant Reproduction and Development

CHAPTER OVERVIEW

Key Concepts

In this chapter students will study sexual and asexual reproduction by plants. These two processes are correlated with mitosis and meiosis. The advantages and disadvantages of sexual and asexual reproduction are also examined.

Key Science Words

bulb	petal
clone	pistil
cross pollination	pollination
cutting	runner
fruit	self pollination
germination	sepal
grafting	stamen
ovule	tuber

Skill Development

In Lab 23-1, students will **form a hypothesis, experiment,** and **observe** to see if soaked seeds germinate faster than unsoaked seeds. In Lab 23-2, they will **experiment, observe, measure in SI,** and **infer** whether or not plants can grow from roots and bulbs. In the Skill Check on page 494, students will **understand** the **science word** *germination.* In the Mini Lab on page 492, students will experiment, to see if seeds will grow without food.

CHAPTER PREVIEW

Chapter Content

Review this outline for Chapter 23 before you read the chapter.

Skills in this Chapter

The skills that you will use in this chapter are listed below.

- In **Lab 23-1,** you will form a hypothesis, experiment, and observe. In **Lab 23-2,** you will experiment, observe, measure in SI, and infer.
- In the **Skill Check,** you will understand science words.
- In the **Mini Lab,** you will experiment.

482

Bridging

Plants exhibit the same life functions as animals. These functions were established in Chapter 2. One life function listed at that time was the ability of living things to reproduce. This chapter enables students to look at the process of plant reproduction in great detail.

Chapter 22 dealt with the topics of mitosis and meiosis. How plants actually utilize these processes during asexual and sexual reproduction will be emphasized.

Chapter 23

Plant Reproduction and Development

You have read that two of the features of living things are that they grow and reproduce. How do flowering plants grow and reproduce? Look at the flower in the photo on the left. You may have noticed that insects are attracted to flowers. Insects have important relationships with many different flowering plants. Many insects help flowers reproduce.

Look at the photo below. This is a fruit that developed from the flower on the left. How did an insect help the flower turn into a fruit? The flower, the fruit, and the insect all play a role in the sexual reproduction of flowering plants. Flowering plants may also reproduce asexually from roots, stems, and leaves.

Try This!

Are fruits different from vegetables? Examine several different fruits and vegetables. Decide how these two plant parts differ. Form a definition of these two terms based on your observations.

A fruit develops from a flower.

Misconception

Ask students the major purpose of a plant's flower and they will reply that it supplies us with beauty. Few students realize that it is the flower that is involved with plant reproduction. The flower is actually the reproductive organ for flowering plants.

GETTING STARTED

Using the Photos

Have students look at the photos and try to determine the role of an insect in plant reproduction. Students should know that an egg must be fertilized by a sperm. They may know that the egg is present in the pistil and pollen is present in the anthers. Lead the discussion so students realize that the insect transfers the pollen, which contains sperm cells, to the pistil. A fruit is the mature ovary.

MOTIVATION/Try This!

Are fruits different from vegetables? Include several root examples (carrots, radish), stems (asparagus), and leaf parts (lettuce, brussel sprouts) as well as fruits (apples, cherry, squash). Students will **observe** on their own that all fruits contain seeds while other plant parts do not. They will resist calling a tomato or cucumber a fruit. However, if seeds are present within the plant part, it is a fruit.

Chapter Preview

Have students study the chapter outline before they begin to read the chapter. They should note the overall organization of the chapter, that the first topic described deals with asexual reproduction, and that the second topic is sexual reproduction. The chapter ends by covering the topic of plant development.

23:1 Asexual Reproduction in Plants

PREPARATION

Materials Needed

Make copies of the Focus, Study Guide, and Reteaching worksheets in the *Teacher Resource Package.*

▶ Obtain the various plants or bulbs needed for the demonstrations and activities.

Key Science Words

tuber
runner
bulb
cutting
grafting

1 FOCUS

▶ The objectives are listed on the student page. Remind students to preview these objectives as a guide to this numbered section.

Focus/*Teacher Resource Package,* p. 45. Use the Focus transparency shown at the bottom of this page as an introduction to plant reproduction.

ACTIVITY/Demonstration

Purchase a *Kalanchoe* plant from a garden or floral shop. Pass the plant around, asking students to note the small notches located in the leaves of the plant. Have them look carefully at what is seen in the notches. (Small plants are usually present.) Ask students to speculate as to the function of these "plantlets."

Objectives

1. **Explain** how plants reproduce asexually from roots.
2. **Describe** how plants can reproduce asexually from leaves.
3. **Compare** asexual reproduction from runners, tubers, bulbs, cuttings, and grafting.

Key Science Words

tuber
runner
bulb
cutting
grafting

23:1 Asexual Reproduction in Plants

As you have read before, roots, stems, and leaves are plant parts with a variety of different jobs. One job of these plant parts is reproduction. Plant reproduction from roots, stems, and leaves is asexual reproduction. Sometimes they are also helpful in plant reproduction. Recall from Chapter 4 that reproduction from one parent is called asexual reproduction.

Asexual Reproduction by Roots

Many plants have roots that can grow into whole new plants. The sweet potatoes that you buy in the grocery store are roots. If you place a sweet potato in water, it will soon grow many small, new plants. Figure 23-1 shows how these changes take place. Notice that each new plant has its own roots, stems, and leaves. Each small plant can be pulled off the sweet potato and planted.

The sweet potato plants formed in this way are produced by asexual reproduction. The new plants have grown by mitosis. The original plant part didn't produce eggs and sperm, and there was no fertilization.

Many flowering plants reproduce asexually from roots. Dandelions and morning glory roots can be cut into many small pieces. Each piece of root can be planted and in time will form a new plant. Many trees, such as poplars and magnolias, are not killed when they are cut down. If the roots are left in the ground, they will send up new shoots.

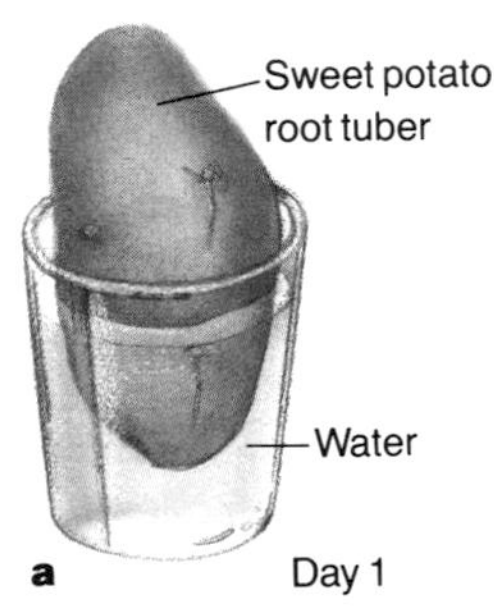

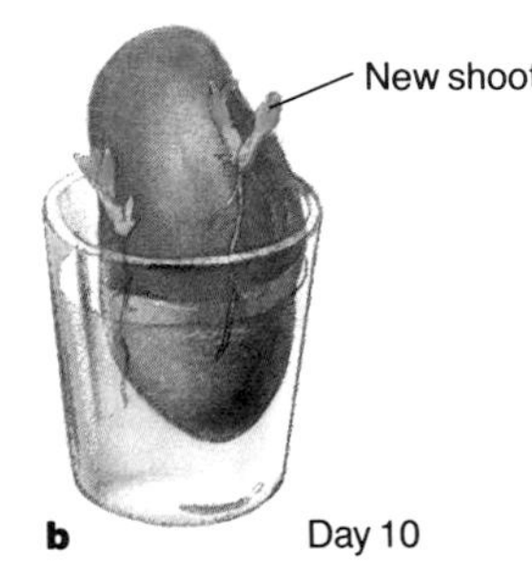

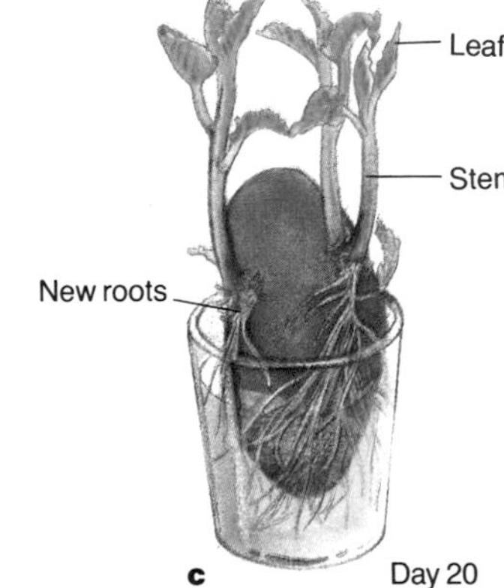

Figure 23-1 A sweet potato is placed in water (a). Small plants begin to grow (b). Each new plant has its own roots, stems, and leaves (c).

OPTIONS

Science Background

The emphasis in this section lies in the correlation between asexual reproduction and mitosis. During mitosis, body cells are formed. These cells are identical to all other cells within the plant in terms of chromosome number. These cells are not specialized gamete or sex cells.

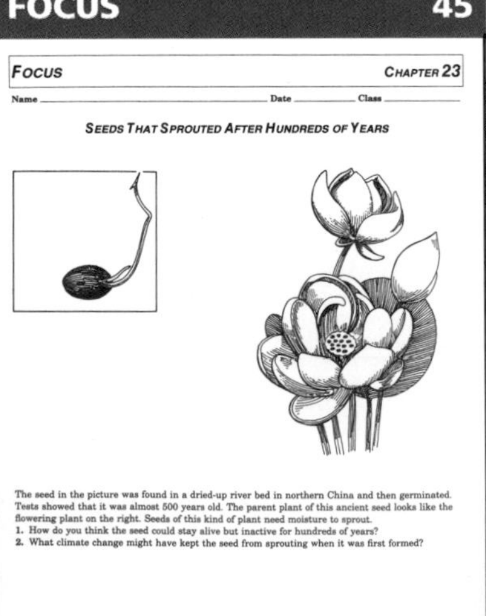

FOCUS 45

FOCUS CHAPTER 23

Name ______ Date ______ Class ______

SEEDS THAT SPROUTED AFTER HUNDREDS OF YEARS

The seed in the picture was found in a dried-up river bed in northern China and then germinated. Tests showed that it was almost 500 years old. The parent plant of this ancient seed looks like the flowering plant on the right. Seeds of this kind of plant need moisture to sprout.

1. How do you think the seed could stay alive but inactive for hundreds of years?
2. What climate change might have kept the seed from sprouting when it was first formed?

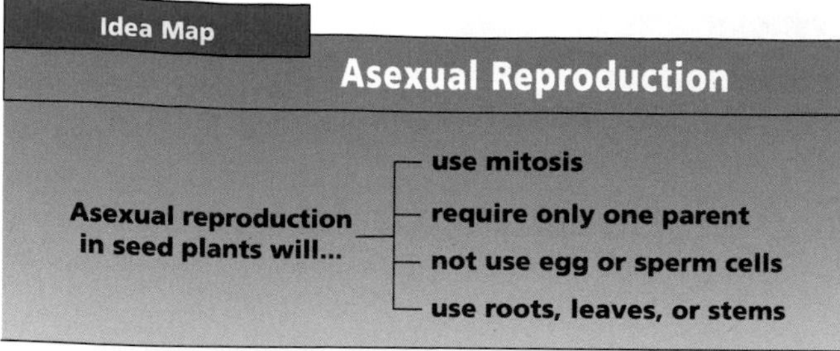

Idea Map
Asexual Reproduction
Asexual reproduction in seed plants will...
use mitosis
require only one parent
not use egg or sperm cells
use roots, leaves, or stems

Study Tip: Use this idea map as a study guide to asexual reproduction in plants. Which plant parts can reproduce asexually?

Other plants that reproduce asexually from roots include wild carrots, lilac bushes, rose bushes, and apple trees. They send up new shoots from their root systems underground. Many plants like the sweet potato have swollen roots called tubers. A **tuber** is an underground root or stem swollen with stored food. Begonias and dahlias, common garden flowers, also have root tubers. They grow new plants every year from the food stored in the tubers.

What kind of root is a sweet potato?

Asexual Reproduction by Leaves

Some plants can reproduce asexually from leaves. Some leaves, when removed from the main plant, will grow into an entire new plant. For example, a leaf of an African violet plant can be placed with its stalk in the soil. An entire new plant will grow from this single leaf. Figure 23-2 shows the steps in the growth of a new plant from the leaf of a snake plant.

How can an African violet reproduce asexually?

Remember that the process of making new plants from leaves, like roots, is asexual. There is only one parent. The new plants look just like the parent plants.

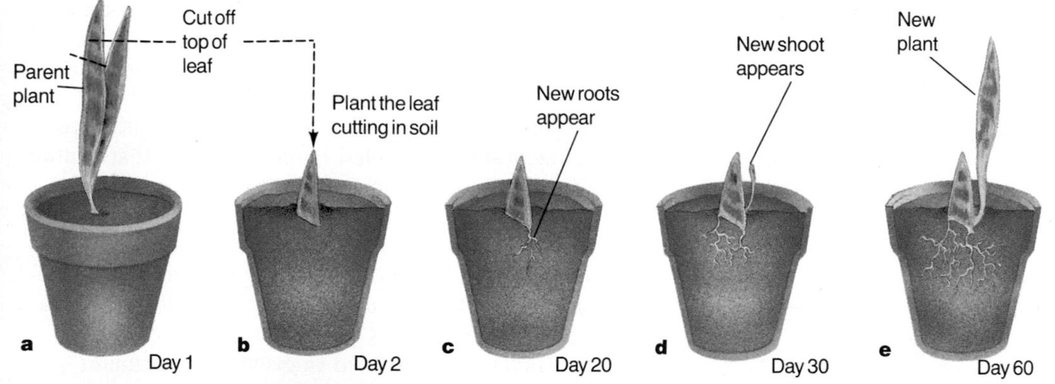

Figure 23-2 These are the steps for producing a new snake plant asexually from a leaf of a parent plant. Which plant part grows first? the roots

STUDY GUIDE 133

STUDY GUIDE — **CHAPTER 23**

Name ______ Date ______ Class ______

ASEXUAL REPRODUCTION IN PLANTS

In your textbook, read about reproduction by roots, leaves, and stems in Section 23:1.

1. Complete the table below.

Plants	Plant part being used	Egg or sperm cells needed? (yes or no)	Number of parents needed	Mitosis or meiosis occurring
African violet	leaf	no	1	mitosis
Tuber (white potato)	stem	no	1	mitosis
Tuber (Sweet Potato)	root	no	1	mitosis
Onion bulb	stem	no	1	mitosis
Delicious apple + Macintosh apple	stem	no	2	mitosis
Strawberry	stem	no	1	mitosis

2. Were sex cells or fertilization involved in any of the situations shown above? no

2 TEACH

MOTIVATION/Demonstration

Place some sweet potatoes in beakers of water as shown in Figure 23-1. Have students check them weekly and note how long it takes for new plants to appear. Allow students to remove the new plants and grow them in soil.

Concept Development

▶ Some common examples of plants that can be propagated from leaves are chrysanthemum, begonia, geranium, African violet, and piggy-back plant.

▶ In leaf cuttings, the leaf blade, or the leaf blade and petiole (leaf stalk) are used in starting the new plant. Adventitious roots and shoots form from the leaf cutting.

▶ A sweet potato is classified as a root because of its internal structures. Its similarity in appearance to the stem of the white potato is coincidental.

Idea Map

Have students use the idea map as a study guide to the major concepts of this section.

Independent Practice

Study Guide/*Teacher Resource Package,* p. 133. Use the Study Guide worksheet shown at the bottom of this page for independent practice.

Guided Practice

Have students write down their answers to the margin questions: root tuber; from its leaves.

TEACH

ACTIVITY/Demonstration

Bring a variety of plant stems such as white potato, onion, garlic, and shallot to class. Remind students that these are considered stem parts.

Guided Practice

Have students write down their answers to the margin question: by cuttings and grafting.

Check for Understanding

Have students explain the similarities and differences between:

- bulb and tuber
- cutting and runner
- asexual and sexual reproduction

Reteach

Ask certain students to read their answers to the Check for Understanding questions. Discuss any problem areas in their responses.

Guided Practice

Have students list examples of plants that reproduce asexually using the following parts: roots, leaves, stems.

a b

Figure 23-3 New spider plants form at the end of runners (a). Potatoes are stem tubers (b). Both plants are reproducing asexually from stems.

Asexual Reproduction by Stems

What are two ways that plants can be reproduced from stems?

There are several ways that stems of flowering plants reproduce asexually. Two natural ways are by runners and underground stems.

Clover, strawberry, and spider plants grow small, new plants at the end of runners. A **runner** is a stem that grows along the ground or in the air and forms a new plant at its tip. Figure 23-3a shows an example of runners forming on a spider plant. Each new plant is a copy of the parent. In the forests of South Africa, where the spider plant grows naturally, these new plants would eventually break away from the parent plant. As houseplants, the small plants can be removed from the parent and placed in their own pots. They will then grow into new adult spider plants.

Many new plants grow asexually from underground stems. A potato is a stem tuber and an onion is a bulb. Both are underground stems. Have you ever found small plants growing from the sides of a potato? What you might have seen is shown in Figure 23-3b. Other plants with stem tubers are water lilies and caladium, a common houseplant with two-colored leaves shaped like arrowheads.

Many spring wildflowers have bulbs. A **bulb** is a short, underground stem surrounded by fleshy leaves that contain stored food. Look at the onion bulb that is cut in half, Figure 23-4. Notice the young shoot already formed at the center of the bulb. Garden flowers such as tulips, daffodils, and hyacinths (HI uh sihnths) are grown from bulbs.

Gardeners use their knowledge of this ability of stems to grow new plants to grow plants from cuttings or graftings. Have you ever tried to grow new geranium

Figure 23-4 Notice the small stem at the base of an onion bulb.

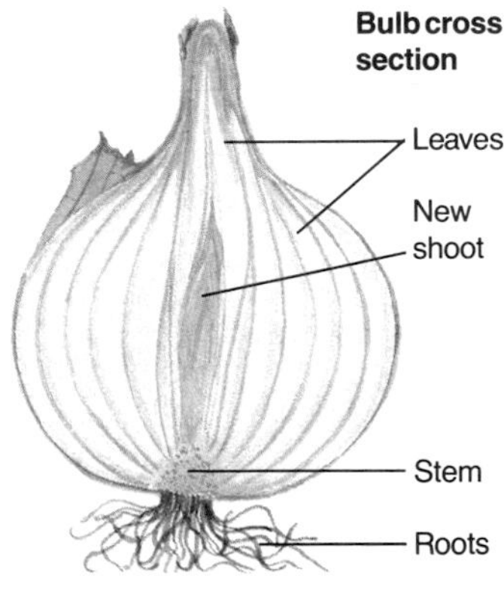

OPTIONS

ACTIVITY/Challenge

Snake plants and African violets are common species available in most plant stores. As a class project, have students asexually propagate these two plants. Plastic foam or paper cups make excellent inexpensive plant pots.

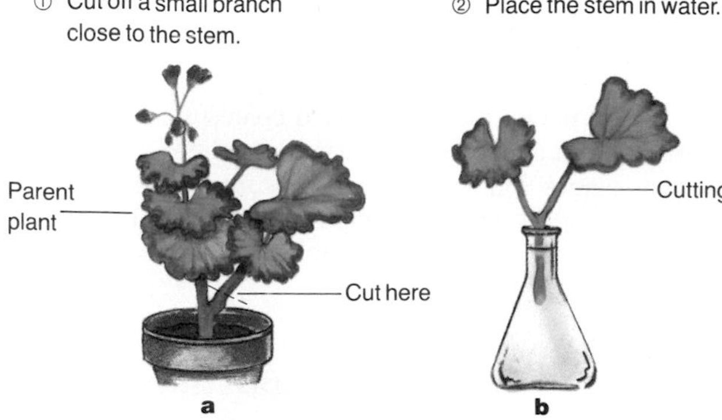

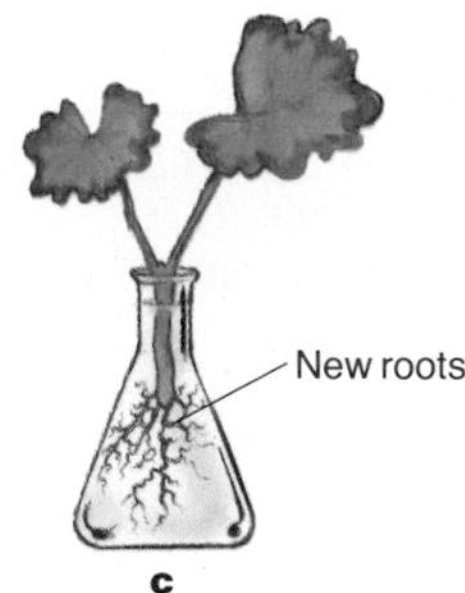

Figure 23-5 These are the steps for producing a new plant from a stem cutting.

plants using the method shown in Figure 23-5? If so, you have grown a plant from a cutting. A **cutting** is a small section of plant stem that has been removed from a parent plant and planted to form a new plant.

Grafting is a process of joining a stem of one plant to the stem of another plant. For example, the stem of a Delicious apple tree may be joined or grafted to the stem of a MacIntosh apple tree. The original Delicious apple stem will continue to form Delicious apples. The original MacIntosh stem will continue to form MacIntosh apples. The result is a tree that will form both kinds of apples.

Why is grafting important to gardeners, farmers, and plant scientists? A gardener can grow a variety of fruits from one tree. The most common reason for grafting is to protect a plant from disease. For example, some kinds of rose plants or apple trees are more resistant to disease than other kinds. The kinds that have better flowers or fruits are grafted onto the roots of similar kinds that are resistant to diseases, Figure 23-6.

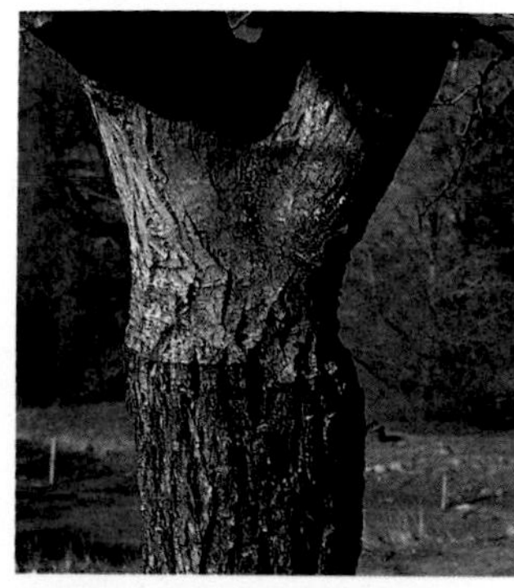

Figure 23-6 An old graft can be seen as a line where the two stems meet.

Check Your Understanding

1. How does a root tuber help a plant reproduce?
2. How can an African violet reproduce asexually?
3. Name five different ways that a plant stem can help in asexual reproduction and give an example of each.
4. **Critical Thinking:** How might asexual reproduction help a plant survive a forest fire?
5. **Biology and Reading:** What does the prefix *a-* mean when it is attached to the word *sexual*?

TEACH

Check for Understanding

Have students respond to the first three questions in Check Your Understanding.

Reteach

Reteaching/*Teacher Resource Package,* p. 69. Use this worksheet give students additional practice in asexual reproduction in plants.

Extension: Assign Critical Thinking, Biology and Reading, or some of the **OPTIONS** available with this lesson.

3 APPLY

ACTIVITY/Brainstorming

Do farmers use asexual reproduction methods in growing crops of corn, wheat, grapes, onions?

4 CLOSE

Summary

Obtain a plant catalog. Copy one or two pages and have students list the plants that are available that reproduce asexually.

Answers to Check Your Understanding

1. A tuber stores up food, which is used by the new plants that grow from it.
2. New plants can grow from a leaf.
3. cuttings–geranium; runners–strawberry; tubers–potato; bulbs– onion; grafting–apple trees
4. When all the plants in a forest have been burned to the ground, there would not be any flowers left to form seeds. Any underground plant parts that had a supply of stored food could grow and produce new plants.
5. The prefix *a-* means without or away from. *Asexual* means without sex.

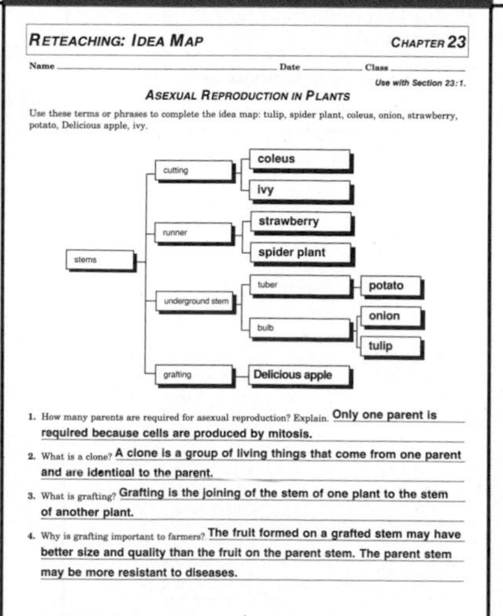

RETEACHING 69

RETEACHING: IDEA MAP — CHAPTER 23

Name ______ Date ______ Class ______

Use with Section 23:1.

ASEXUAL REPRODUCTION IN PLANTS

Use these terms or phrases to complete the idea map: tulip, spider plant, coleus, onion, strawberry, potato, Delicious apple, ivy.

1. How many parents are required for asexual reproduction? Explain. Only one parent is required because cells are produced by mitosis.
2. What is a clone? A clone is a group of living things that come from one parent and are identical to the parent.
3. What is grafting? Grafting is the joining of the stem of one plant to the stem of another plant.
4. Why is grafting important to farmers? The fruit formed on a grafted stem may have better size and quality than the fruit on the parent stem. The parent stem may be more resistant to diseases.

23:2 Sexual Reproduction in Plants

PREPARATION

Materials Needed

Make copies of the Study Guide, Transparency Master, Skill, Critical Thinking/Problem Solving, and Reteaching worksheets in the *Teacher Resource Package.*

▶ Flowers may be purchased from a floral shop for the demonstration.

Key Science Words

sepal	ovule
petal	pollination
stamen	cross pollination
pistil	self pollination

1 FOCUS

▶ The objectives are listed on the student page. Remind students to preview these objectives as a guide to this numbered section.

ACTIVITY/Demonstration

Obtain a flower from a floral shop (preserved flowers may also be used). Prepare a slide of pollen grains from the anther for microscopic viewing. Allow students to view the slide and ask them to describe what they see, estimate the size of the individual cells, and offer a possible explanation of what these cells are.

Idea Map

Have students use the idea map as a study guide to the major concepts of this section.

Guided Practice

Have students write down their answers to the margin question: stamen.

23:2 Sexual Reproduction in Plants

Objectives

4. **List** the parts of a flower and their functions.
5. **Describe** two methods of pollination.
6. **Sequence** the steps that lead to fertilization in flowering plants.

Key Science Words

sepal
petal
stamen
pistil
ovule
pollination
cross pollination
self pollination

Flowering plants make our world beautiful to live in. Flowers come in an enormous variety of colors, shapes, and sizes. But, plants don't produce flowers for our pleasure. Flowers are important to the survival of the plant. Without flowers, many plants wouldn't be able to reproduce sexually.

Flowers and Sexual Reproduction

Figure 23-7 is a diagram of a section through one kind of flower. Find the numbers on the diagram as you read the following statements that describe the different flower parts. In most flowers some flower parts are showy. These parts are neither male nor female. In most flowers some parts are female and other parts are male. Some flowers lack one or more of these parts. The flower in Figure 23-7 shows typical flower parts for a complete flower.

Parts 1 and 2 are sepals and petals. **Sepals** are often green, leaflike parts of a flower that protect the young flower while it is still a bud. **Petals** are often brightly colored and scented parts of a flower that attract insects to the flower.

What flower part forms pollen grains?

Part 3 is the male flower part. The **stamen** is the male reproductive organ of a flower. Usually there are one to many stamens in each flower. Each stamen has a saclike part at its top in which pollen grains are formed. Figure 23-8a shows pollen grains under an electron microscope. You read in Chapter 6 that pollen grains are male structures that contain sperm cells.

Study Tip: Use this idea map as a study guide to parts of a flower. Which structure in a flower contains ovules?

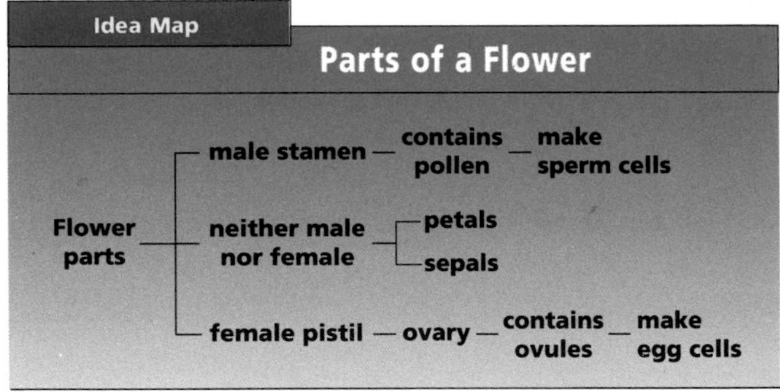

OPTIONS

Science Background

The emphasis within this section of the text lies in the correlation between sexual reproduction and meiosis. During meiosis, sex cells are formed. These cells differ from all other cells within the plant in terms of chromosome number. These cells are specialized gamete or sex cells.

Transparency Master/*Teacher Resource Package,* p. 113. Use the Transparency Master shown here to help students with flower anatomy.

TRANSPARENCY 113

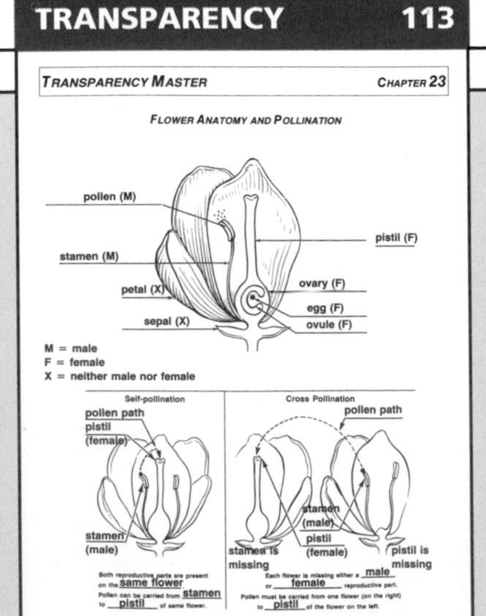

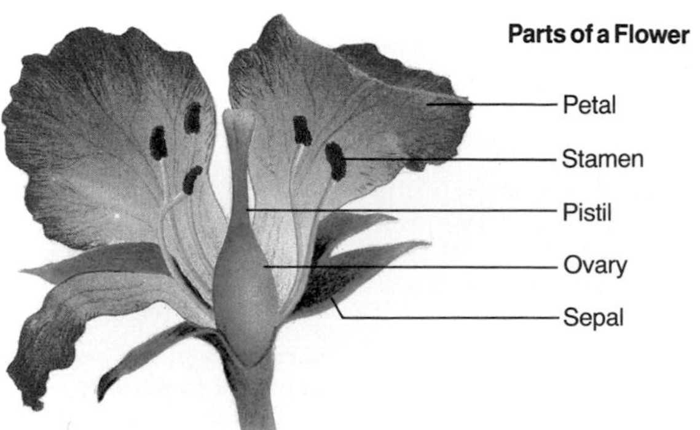

Figure 23-7 Follow the text to read the functions of each part of a flower.

Part 4 in Figure 23-7 is the female flower part. The **pistil** (PIH stul) is the female reproductive organ of a flower. Often there is only one pistil in the center of a flower. Each pistil has a large, round ovary at its base. In Figure 23-8b this is cut open so you can see the ovules inside. Above the ovary is a stalk with a sticky tip. The sticky tip helps to trap pollen grains. Inside the ovary are tiny, round parts called ovules. **Ovules** contain the egg cells of a seed plant.

If you ever looked closely at a flower, such as a dandelion, a rose, a carnation, or a daffodil, you may have noticed that none of these has the structure of our typical flower in Figure 23-7. Some flowers don't have sepals, some have petals that are fused to form a tube, some have many tiny flowers all clustered together in a head, and some don't have any stamens. Flowers, just like all other organisms, show an enormous range of variation.

Figure 23-8 Pollen grains under an electron microscope show wonderful surface patterns (a). A section through a pistil as seen under a light microscope shows the position of its ovules (b).

a

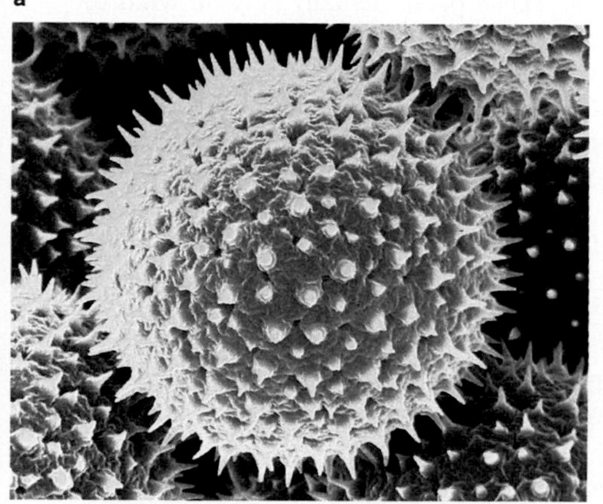

b

2 TEACH

MOTIVATION/Demonstration

Obtain a large flower for student observation and dissection. Avoid composite flowers such as daisies, sunflowers, or mums. Day lily and iris are suitable. If the anthers are mature, a fine yellow powder can easily be seen. Ask students what this powder is.

Independent Practice

Study Guide/*Teacher Resource Package,* p. 134. Use the Study Guide worksheet shown at the bottom of this page for independent practice.

SKILL 24

SKILL: RECOGNIZE SPATIAL RELATIONSHIPS — **CHAPTER 23**

Name ______ Date ______ Class ______

For more help, refer to the Skill Handbook, pages 706-711. *Use after Section 23:2.*

THE FLOWER

When you use a microscope, you often observe a cross section of an organism or a part of an organism. To understand what you observe, you need to know how the cross section relates to the whole specimen. Look at the drawings of three objects below. The lines through the objects show where the cross section was made. Next to each object is a diagram of the cross section. Object C has two cross sections, made at different levels of the object.

A — Cross section; B — Cross section; C — Cross section 1, Cross section 2

1. Draw cross sections of the objects below at levels 1, 2, and 3.

Cross section 1 — Cross section 2 — Cross section 3

2. On the left is a diagram of the ovary of a flower. A line through the ovary shows where a cross section was made. Fill in the diagram on the right to show what the cross section of the ovary looks like.

STUDY GUIDE 134

STUDY GUIDE — **CHAPTER 23**

Name ______ Date ______ Class ______

SEXUAL REPRODUCTION IN PLANTS

In your textbook, read about flowers and sexual reproduction in Section 23:2.

1. Label these four parts: pistil, petal, stamen, sepal.

(red) pistil; stamen (blue); petal (yellow); sepal (green)

2. Use the following colors to shade in the above drawing.
   a. yellow, for parts that attract insects
   b. green, for parts that protect flower in bud stage
   c. red, for parts that are female
   d. blue, for parts that are male
3. Label the parts shown here. Use these choices: sticky tip, pollen grains, pistil, ovary, stamen, ovule, saclike part, stalk.

saclike part; pollen grains; stamen; pistil; sticky tip; stalk; ovary; ovule

4. Name the part being described. Use these choices: saclike part, ovary, ovules, pollen grains, sticky tip, pistil, stamen.
   a. contains ovules — ovary
   b. male flower part — stamen
   c. contains pollen — saclike part
   d. will form sperm — pollen grains
   e. female flower part — pistil
   f. traps pollen grains — sticky tip
   g. hold female reproductive cells — ovules

OPTIONS

Parts of a Flower/*Transparency Package,* number 23a. Use color transparency number 23a as you teach the parts of a flower.

What Are the Parts of a Flower?/*Lab Manual,* pp. 189-192. Use this lab as an extension to flower anatomy.

Skill/*Teacher Resource Package,* p. 24. Use the Skill worksheet shown here to have students recognize sections of flower parts.

TEACH

Concept Development

▶ Advise students that the pollen that fertilizes the egg of a specific plant species must be of the same species. If the wrong species of pollen lands on a flower stigma, the egg cell will not be fertilized. The same is true in animals. Different animal species can mate but offspring will not result.

▶ Emphasize that self pollination involves one flower, and cross pollination involves two flowers.

Guided Practice

Have students write down their answers to the margin questions: pollination by pollen from the same flower or same plant; three.

Cooperative Learning: Divide the class into several groups. Assign the following task to all groups.

(a) draw two flowers that must undergo cross pollination. Show the transfer of pollen.

(b) draw a flower that depends on self pollination. Show the transfer of pollen.

One student should be assigned as recorder within each group.

Idea Map

Have students use the idea map as a study guide to the major concepts of this section.

Study Tip: Use this idea map as a study guide to sexual reproduction in plants. What kind of cell division is necessary for sexual reproduction?

Idea Map

Sexual Reproduction

Sexual reproduction in seed plants will...
- **use meiosis**
- **require two parents**
- **use pollen and ovaries**
- **use egg or sperm cells**
- **form new plants not identical to parents**

Pollination and Fertilization

You know that in sexual reproduction an egg and a sperm must join for fertilization. How does pollen get from the stamens of a plant to the pistil? Then, how do sperm cells inside the pollen reach the eggs within the ovules?

What is self pollination?

Pollen is transported from stamens to pistils by a process called pollination (pahl ih NAY shun). **Pollination** is the transfer of pollen from the male part of a seed plant to the female part.

In flowering plants, the design of the flower is very important in pollination. Many flowers with colorful petals have a strong scent that attracts insects. Insects climb over the flowers and pick up the pollen on their bodies. Many insects, such as bees, collect pollen for food. Some flowers also make a sugary chemical called nectar that bees and birds also use as food. Pollen catches on the hairs and feathers of their bodies while they feed on the nectar.

Some plants don't have large, colorful petals or attractive scents. These plants usually rely on wind to move the pollen from one plant to another. Grasses and many trees have this type of flower. Many trees, such as maples and willows, have long, hanging flowers that are yellow or green in color. These flowers are not attractive to insects. The pollen formed in these flowers is blown around by the wind.

Pollen is often carried by insects, birds, or wind between different plants. This is called cross pollination, Figure 23-9. **Cross pollination** is when pollen from the stamen of one flower is carried to the pistil of another flower on a different plant. Figure 23-9 also shows self pollination. **Self pollination** is when pollen moves from the stamen of one flower to the pistil of the same flower, or of another flower on the same plant.

Figure 23-9 Compare two types of pollination. How many plants are needed for self pollination? one

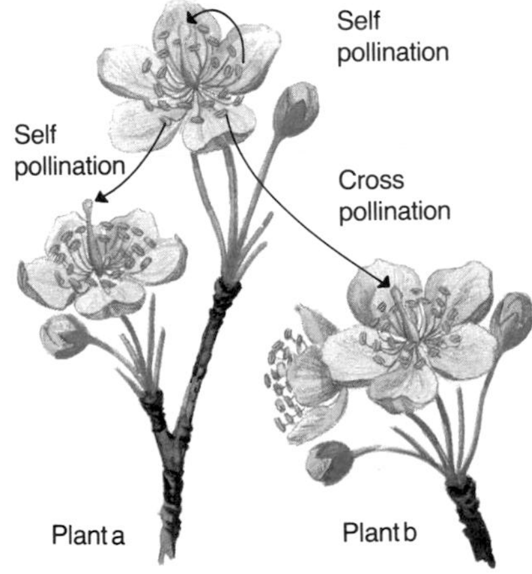

OPTIONS

ACTIVITY/Challenge

List the chromosome number of the cells that form these flower parts: petal, sepal, pollen, egg, sperm, ovule, stigma, style, anther. Assume that this plant has a body cell chromosome number of 12.

Critical Thinking/Problem Solving/ *Teacher Resource Package,* p. 23. Use the worksheet shown here to reinforce fertilization in plants.

CRITICAL THINKING 23

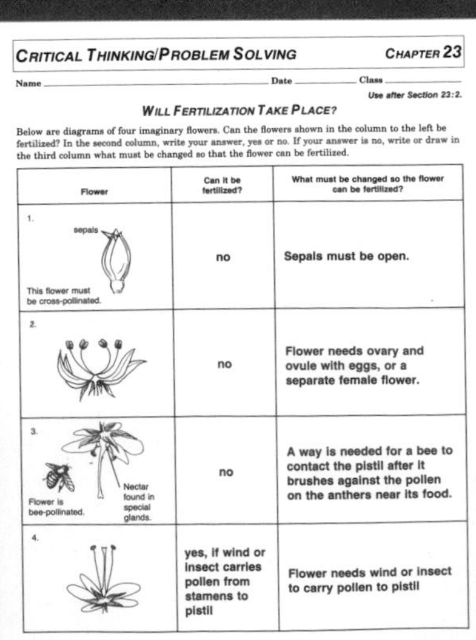

CRITICAL THINKING/PROBLEM SOLVING — CHAPTER 23

Name ______ Date ______ Class ______

Use after Section 23:2.

WILL FERTILIZATION TAKE PLACE?

Below are diagrams of four imaginary flowers. Can the flowers shown in the column to the left be fertilized? In the second column, write your answer, yes or no. If your answer is no, write or draw in the third column what must be changed so that the flower can be fertilized.

Flower	Can it be fertilized?	What must be changed so the flower can be fertilized?
1. sepals; This flower must be cross-pollinated.	no	Sepals must be open.
2.	no	Flower needs ovary and ovule with eggs, or a separate female flower.
3. Flower is bee-pollinated. Nectar found in special glands.	no	A way is needed for a bee to contact the pistil after it brushes against the pollen on the anthers near its food.
4.	yes, if wind or insect carries pollen from stamens to pistil	Flower needs wind or insect to carry pollen to pistil

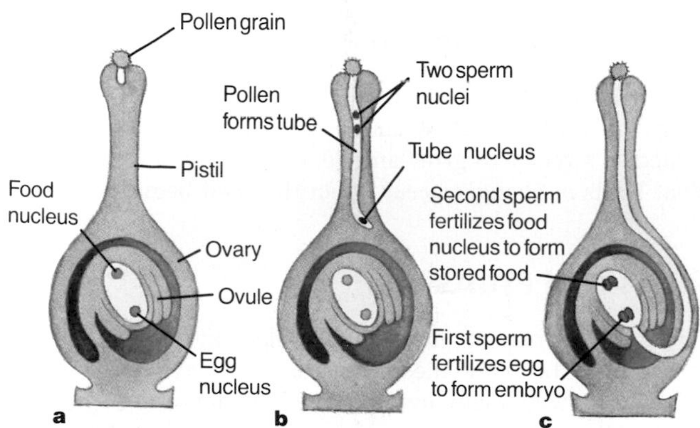

Figure 23-10 Follow the sequence of steps in plant fertilization as shown in these sections of a pistil. How many sperm are needed to fertilize one ovule?two

How does sperm inside a pollen grain reach the egg inside an ovary? Follow the steps in Figure 23-10.

1. A pollen grain lands on the sticky tip of the pistil. It must somehow reach the egg within the ovule.
2. The pollen grain begins to grow a tube into the stalk of the pistil. This pollen tube grows all the way down to the ovary. Inside each pollen grain are three nuclei. One nucleus leads the way down the tube. The other two nuclei are sperm nuclei and these follow the first nucleus.
3. The tube reaches the ovule. A sperm nucleus inside the tube can now pass into the ovule and join with the egg. Fertilization takes place. The other sperm from the pollen tube joins with another nucleus in the ovule to form a food supply for the new seed.
4. A new plant or embryo now grows inside the ovule. As the ovule grows, it becomes a seed.

How many nuclei pass down a pollen tube?

Bio Tip

Health: A person who is a vegetarian gets most of his or her needed protein from plant seeds.

Check Your Understanding

6. List flower parts that are male, female, or neither.
7. What are two types of pollination?
8. How many sperm are needed to fertilize one ovule?
9. **Critical Thinking:** Hummingbirds and moths both feed on nectar of flowers. A hummingbird has a very long, thin beak and a moth has a very long mouthpart for feeding. What kinds of flowers would they most likely visit?
10. **Biology and Writing:** Are petals and sepals sexual parts in plants? Why or why not?

TEACH

Independent Practice

Study Guide/*Teacher Resource Package,* p. 135. Use the Study Guide worksheet shown at the bottom of this page for independent practice.

Check for Understanding

Have students respond to the first three questions in Check Your Understanding.

Reteach

Reteaching/*Teacher Resource Package,* p. 70. Use the Reteaching worksheet shown at the bottom of this page to give students additional practice with fertilization in flowers.

Extension: Assign Critical Thinking. Biology and Writing, or some of the **OPTIONS** available with this lesson.

3 APPLY

ACTIVITY/Software

(1) *Plant Growth Simulator, Elementary Version;* (2) *Plant Growth Simulator, Secondary Version,* Focus Media, Inc.

4 CLOSE

ACTIVITY/Videocassette

Show the videocassette *Sexual Encounters of the Floral Kind,* Carolina Biological Supply Co.

Answers to Check Your Understanding

6. male–stamen; female–pistil; neither–petals and sepals
7. self pollination and cross pollination
8. two
9. flowers with very long tubular petals that contain a lot of nectar
10. Petals and sepals are not sexual parts in plants. Only those parts that produce sperm and egg are sexual.

STUDY GUIDE 135

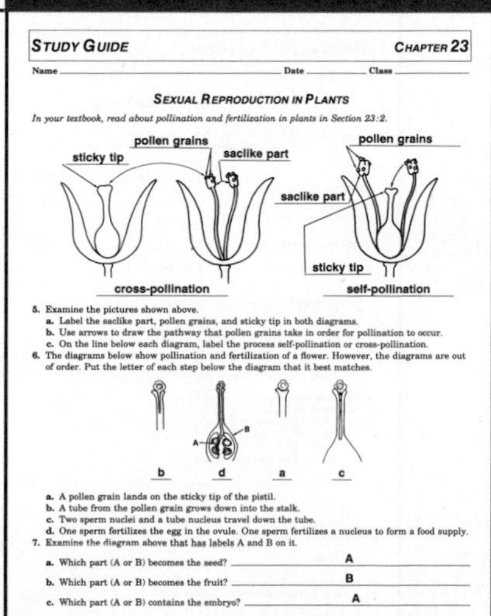

STUDY GUIDE — CHAPTER 23

Name ______ Date ______ Class ______

SEXUAL REPRODUCTION IN PLANTS

In your textbook, read about pollination and fertilization in plants in Section 23:2.

5. Examine the pictures shown above.
   a. Label the saclike part, pollen grains, and sticky tip in both diagrams.
   b. Use arrows to draw the pathway that pollen grains take in order for pollination to occur.
   c. On the line below each diagram, label the process self-pollination or cross-pollination.
6. The diagrams below show pollination and fertilization of a flower. However, the diagrams are out of order. Put the letter of each step below the diagram that it best matches.

   a. A pollen grain lands on the sticky tip of the pistil.
   b. A tube from the pollen grain grows down into the stalk.
   c. Two sperm nuclei and a tube nucleus travel down the tube.
   d. One sperm fertilizes the egg in the ovule. One sperm fertilizes a nucleus to form a food supply.
7. Examine the diagram above that has labels A and B on it.
   a. Which part (A or B) becomes the seed? ___A___
   b. Which part (A or B) becomes the fruit? ___B___
   c. Which part (A or B) contains the embryo? ___A___

RETEACHING 70

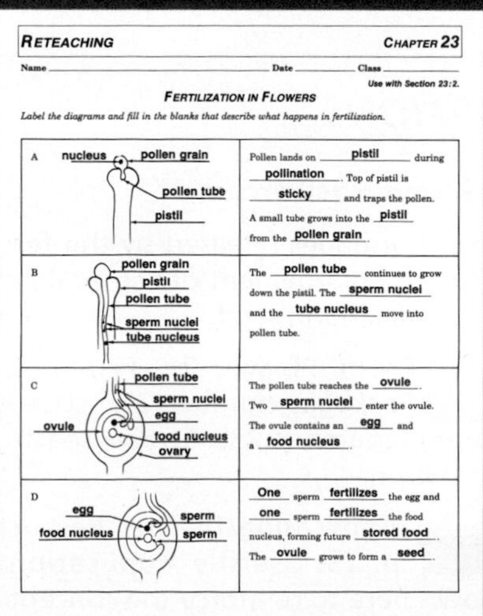

RETEACHING — CHAPTER 23

Name ______ Date ______ Class ______

Use with Section 23:2.

FERTILIZATION IN FLOWERS

Label the diagrams and fill in the blanks that describe what happens in fertilization.

A — nucleus; pollen grain; pollen tube; pistil	Pollen lands on ___pistil___ during ___pollination___. Top of pistil is ___sticky___ and traps the pollen. A small tube grows into the ___pistil___ from the ___pollen grain___.
B — pollen grain; pistil; pollen tube; sperm nuclei; tube nucleus	The ___pollen tube___ continues to grow down the pistil. The ___sperm nuclei___ and the ___tube nucleus___ move into pollen tube.
C — pollen tube; sperm nuclei; egg; ovule; food nucleus; ovary	The pollen tube reaches the ___ovule___. Two ___sperm nuclei___ enter the ovule. The ovule contains an ___egg___ and a ___food nucleus___.
D — egg; food nucleus; sperm; sperm	___One___ sperm ___fertilizes___ the egg and ___one___ sperm ___fertilizes___ the food nucleus, forming future ___stored food___. The ___ovule___ grows to form a ___seed___.

23:3 Plant Development

PREPARATION

Materials Needed

Make copies of the Application, Study Guide, Enrichment, Lab, and Reteaching worksheets in the *Teacher Resource Package.*

▶ Purchase corn seeds from a supply house (or popcorn from a grocery store) and collect milk cartons for Lab 23-1. Purchase carrots and garlic for Lab 23-2.

▶ Purchase beans for the Mini Lab.

▶ Obtain fruits and seeds for the demonstrations.

Key Science Words

fruit
germination
clone

Process Skills

In Lab 23-1, students will form hypotheses, experiment, and observe. In Lab 23-2, they will experiment, observe, measure in SI, and infer. In the Mini Lab, they will experiment. In the Skill Check, they will understand science words.

1 FOCUS

▶ The objectives are listed on the student page. Remind students to preview these objectives as a guide to this numbered section.

ACTIVITY/Brainstorming

Ask students the value to a plant of having a:
(a) very large seed containing much stored food.
(b) very large fruit containing much stored food.

Mini Lab

The process of removing the entire embryo from the seed will result in some embryos being broken or mutilated. Discard these damaged embryos.

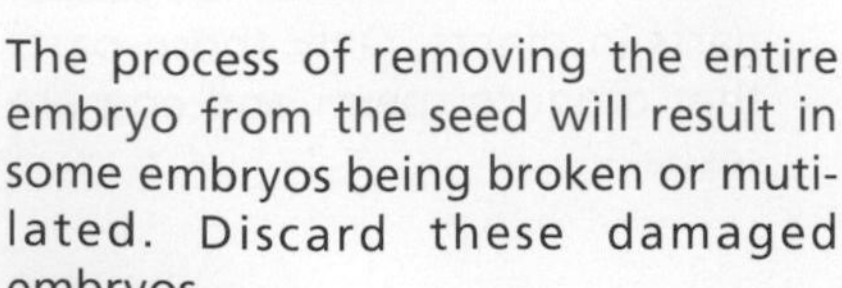

Objectives

7. **Describe** how fruits and seeds develop.
8. **Explain** how seeds are scattered and grow into new plants.
9. **Compare** asexual and sexual reproduction in plants.

Key Science Words

fruit
germination
clone

Mini Lab

Will Seeds Grow Without Stored Food?

Experiment: Remove only the embryo from several soaked bean seeds. Place the embryos on moist paper in a closed petri dish and wait to see if they grow. *For more help, refer to the* ***Skill Handbook,*** *pages 704-705.*

23:3 Plant Development

In addition to reproduction, two other features of living things are that they grow and develop. Once a seed is formed, it's ready to grow and develop into a new plant. What kinds of changes occur when the seed begins to grow?

Seeds and Fruits

After fertilization, changes take place in the flower. Use Figure 23-11 to follow these changes.
1. In this flower, many ovules have been fertilized by four sperm cells.
2. Shortly after fertilization, the petals, stamens, and stalk of the pistil wither and die.
3. At the same time, the ovules and the ovary begin to grow.
4. Finally, the ovules mature into seeds. A seed is a plant part that contains a plant embryo. Remember from Chapter 6 that the embryo of a plant has a new young plant and stored food. The young plant and the stored food came from the joining of egg and sperm nuclei in the ovule.

As the ovary matures it becomes a fruit. A **fruit** is an enlarged ovary that contains seeds. You may have noticed that almost all the fruits you have ever eaten have contained seeds. If you use this definition of a fruit, can a tomato be a fruit? Is a squash, a green pepper, a cucumber, or a pumpkin a fruit? You must answer yes, because they all grew from ovaries and all have seeds inside.

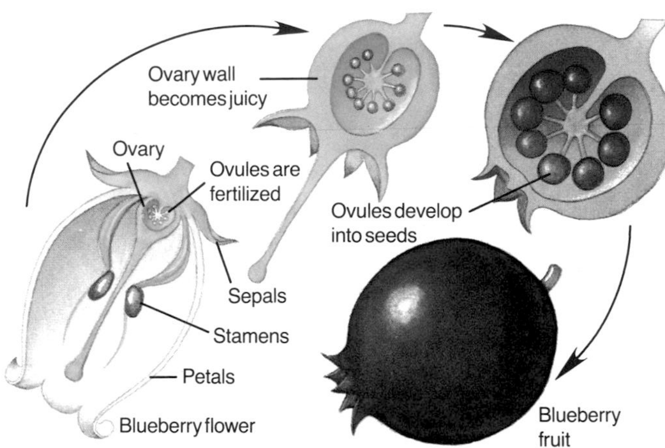

Figure 23-11 Follow the steps that occur after fertilization in the forming of seeds in a fruit.

OPTIONS

Science Background

Plant hormones released by the fertilized ovule result in enlargement of the ovary and ovule to form a fruit and seed.

From Flower to Fruit/*Transparency Package,* number 23b. Use color transparency number 23b as you teach about fruit formation.

Application/*Teacher Resource Package,* p. 23. Use the Application worksheet shown here to reinforce the concept of fruits

APPLICATION 23

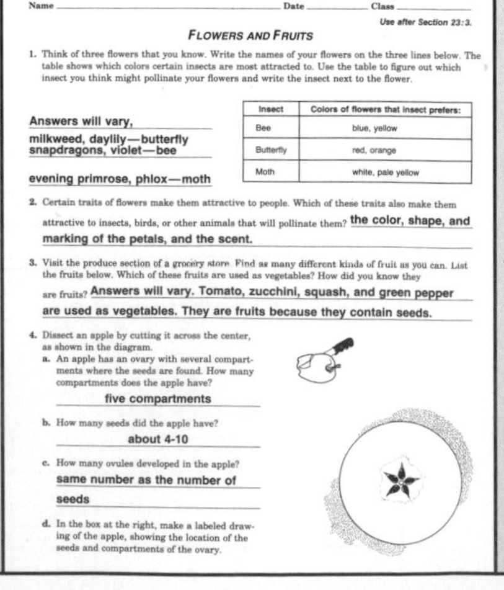

APPLICATION: CONSUMER — CHAPTER 23

Name ______ Date ______ Class ______

Use after Section 23:3.

FLOWERS AND FRUITS

1. Think of three flowers that you know. Write the names of your flowers on the three lines below. The table shows which colors certain insects are most attracted to. Use the table to figure out which insect you think might pollinate your flowers and write the insect next to the flower.

Answers will vary,
milkweed, daylily—butterfly
snapdragons, violet—bee
evening primrose, phlox—moth

Insect	Colors of flowers that insect prefers:
Bee	blue, yellow
Butterfly	red, orange
Moth	white, pale yellow

2. Certain traits of flowers make them attractive to people. Which of these traits also make them attractive to insects, birds, or other animals that will pollinate them? **the color, shape, and marking of the petals, and the scent.**

3. Visit the produce section of a grocery store. Find as many different kinds of fruit as you can. List the fruits below. Which of these fruits are used as vegetables? How did you know they are fruits? **Answers will vary. Tomato, zucchini, squash, and green pepper are used as vegetables. They are fruits because they contain seeds.**

4. Dissect an apple by cutting it across the center, as shown in the diagram.
   a. An apple has an ovary with several compartments where the seeds are found. How many compartments does the apple have? **five compartments**
   b. How many seeds did the apple have? **about 4-10**
   c. How many ovules developed in the apple? **same number as the number of seeds**
   d. In the box at the right, make a labeled drawing of the apple, showing the location of the seeds and compartments of the ovary.

TECHNOLOGY

Seed Banks

There are all kinds of banks. There are banks to hold your money, sperm banks, and even banks for body organs. Scientists also have formed a seed bank at a large laboratory in Fort Collins, Colorado. It is called the United States National Seed Storage Laboratory. The deposits made in this bank are exactly what you would expect from its name—seeds. In Fort Collins, seeds from all over the world are frozen in vats of liquid nitrogen. Someday, these living seeds will be removed from the vats and germinated.

Why do seeds need to be stored? Seeds are the link from one generation of plants to the next. One in 10 plant species is endangered. If a plant species becomes extinct, there is no way to get it back. Extinction is forever.

A seed bank is a means of saving plants that are endangered. Scientists of the future could cross-breed plants that have desirable traits with plants from the past.

Without plants for food, most living things can't survive. The "interest" the seed bank pays on seed deposits is that all living things benefit. The seed bank will help make the best seeds available for growing food plants for the future. Scientists will also be able to replace extinct plant species back into the wild when a new and suitable environment is found.

Seeds can be stored for a long time under controlled conditions.

If you could observe the development of a peanut or a walnut, you would conclude that they too were fruits. From these observations, it's clear that fruits are not just the juicy, fleshy fruits like oranges and grapes. Any plant part that develops from an ovary can be called a fruit. Fruits can also be nutty, and some aren't even edible by humans.

One seed develops from each fertilized ovule in an ovary. How many ovules were inside a cherry flower before fertilization? The answer is one. How do we know? Because a cherry fruit has only one seed. How many ovules are inside an orange flower? At least ten because there are about ten seeds in an orange, Figure 23-12. Have you ever counted the seeds in a watermelon? If you have, then you will know how many ovules were fertilized.

What is the ovule in a fruit?

Figure 23-12 The seeds of an orange develop from ovules. The juicy fruit and rind of the orange develop from the ovary.

TECHNOLOGY

Seed Banks

Background

Two thirds of harvested rice comes from only four species. Previously, over 100 different species of rice were grown. Those not being grown today are lost forever unless the seeds are saved in seed banks.

Discussion

Worldwide, plant species are disappearing at the rate of two a day. Discuss with students that this is a similar situation to that of endangered animal species.

Reference

Shell, E.R. "Seeds in the Bank Could Stave Off Disaster on the Farm." *Smithsonian,* Jan. 1990, pp. 94-100.

TEACH

Guided Practice

Have students write down their answers to the margin question: a seed.

Independent Practice

Study Guide/*Teacher Resource Package,* p. 136. Use the Study Guide worksheet shown at the bottom of this page for independent practice.

STUDY GUIDE 136

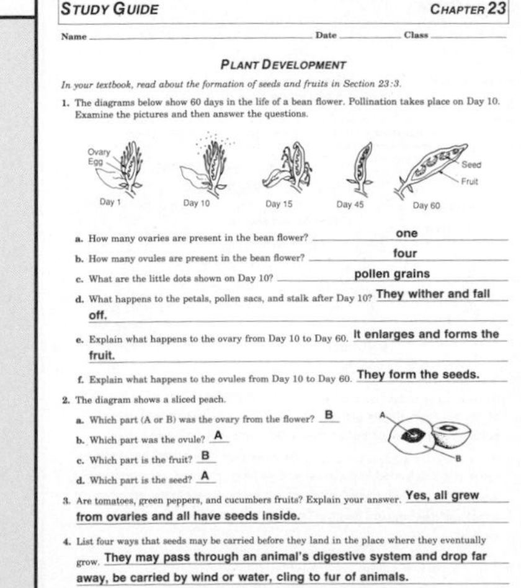

STUDY GUIDE — CHAPTER 23

Name ______ Date ______ Class ______

PLANT DEVELOPMENT

In your textbook, read about the formation of seeds and fruits in Section 23:3.

1. The diagrams below show 60 days in the life of a bean flower. Pollination takes place on Day 10. Examine the pictures and then answer the questions.

a. How many ovaries are present in the bean flower? **one**

b. How many ovules are present in the bean flower? **four**

c. What are the little dots shown on Day 10? **pollen grains**

d. What happens to the petals, pollen sacs, and stalk after Day 10? **They wither and fall off.**

e. Explain what happens to the ovary from Day 10 to Day 60. **It enlarges and forms the fruit.**

f. Explain what happens to the ovules from Day 10 to Day 60. **They form the seeds.**

2. The diagram shows a sliced peach.

a. Which part (A or B) was the ovary from the flower? **B**

b. Which part was the ovule? **A**

c. Which part is the fruit? **B**

d. Which part is the seed? **A**

3. Are tomatoes, green peppers, and cucumbers fruits? Explain your answer. **Yes, all grew from ovaries and all have seeds inside.**

4. List four ways that seeds may be carried before they land in the place where they eventually grow. **They may pass through an animal's digestive system and drop far away, be carried by wind or water, cling to fur of animals.**

OPTIONS

What Plant Part Are You Eating?/*Lab Manual,* pp. 193-196. Use this lab as an extension to fruits.

TEACH

ACTIVITY/Hands-On

Provide lima or pinto beans for the class to examine after soaking overnight. The next day students should be able to open the seeds with ease to observe the internal seed parts.

Guided Practice

Have students write down their answers to the margin question: it scatters them away from the parent plant.

Filmstrip

Show the filmstrip *Fruit and Seed Structure and Function,* Educational Images.

ACTIVITY/Demonstration

That seeds remain viable for long periods of time can be demonstrated by germinating seeds bought from grocery store shelves. What appear to be dead seeds are, in reality, seeds that will germinate if supplied with water.

Independent Practice

Study Guide/*Teacher Resource Package,* p. 137. Use the Study Guide worksheet shown at the bottom of this page for independent practice. Use Study Guide p. 138 for vocabulary review.

Skill Check

Understand science words: germination. The word *germ* means a small part of living matter that can develop into a living organism. In your dictionary, find three words with the word part *germ* in them. *For more help, refer to the* ***Skill Handbook,*** *pages 706-711.*

Plant Development from Seeds

What happens to the fruit and seeds after they are fully ripe? If the fruit is brightly colored and juicy it may be eaten by an animal. The seeds pass through the animal's digestive system and when they are dropped, they are often far from the parent plant. In most cases, however, the fruit remains on the parent plant and dries up as the seeds mature. Sometimes, the fruits eventually burst open and the seeds are thrown away from the parent plant. Some seeds are carried away by wind. Larger seeds may be carried away by water. Sometimes, the fruits are carried away with the seeds held inside. Dandelion seeds are scattered by the wind while still held in their tiny dried fruits. These one-seeded fruits have hairs that act like a parachute. Have you ever seen a sticky seed that clings to the fur of an animal? The wall of the fruit is covered with tiny hooks that catch in fur or clothing. These seeds are carried away in an animal's coat. The new plants can then grow far from the parent plant where there is more space, light, and water that they need to survive.

How is the wind important to some seeds?

What happens next? If a seed lands on soil that has moisture and proper temperature, it may germinate. **Germination** (jur muh NAY shun) is the first growth of a young plant from a seed. In many flowering plants, the stored food is the main part of the seed. This food is available for the growth of the new plant.

Let's look at a bean seed as it germinates. First the root and then the stem grow from the seed. In beans, the two seed halves are made mostly of stored food for the new plant. The stem that comes out of the seed has a small pair of leaves on it. Once out of the seed, the stem and leaves soon turn green and begin to make food by photosynthesis. When the food supply of the two seed halves is used up, they drop off the plant.

Figure 23-13 Follow the sequence of steps in the development of a bean plant from a seed.

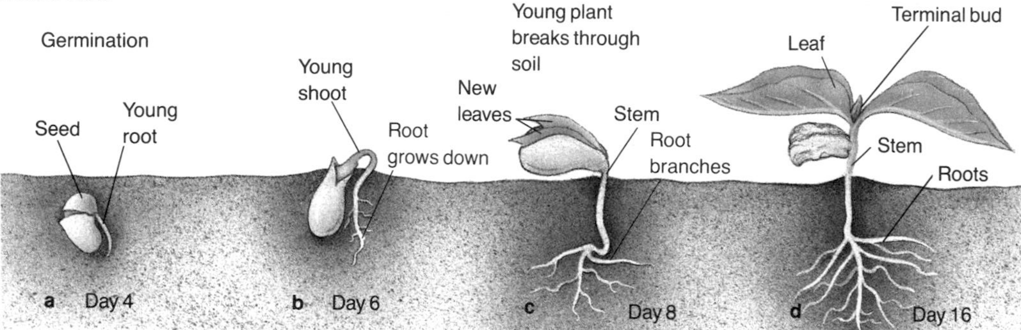

494

ENRICHMENT 25

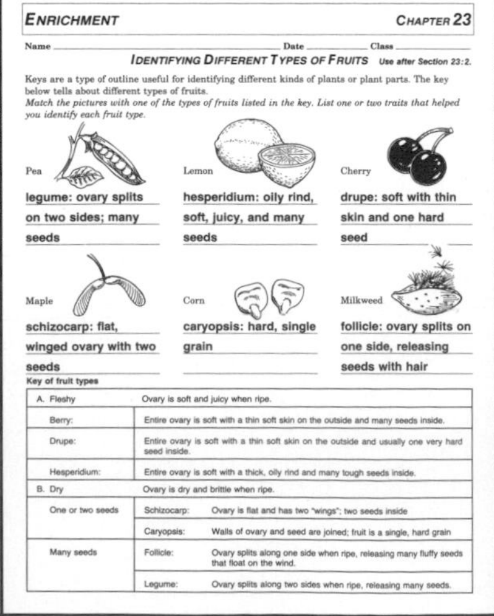

ENRICHMENT CHAPTER 23

Name ______ Date ______ Class ______

IDENTIFYING DIFFERENT TYPES OF FRUITS Use after Section 23:2.

Keys are a type of outline useful for identifying different kinds of plants or plant parts. The key below tells about different types of fruits.

Match the pictures with one of the types of fruits listed in the key. List one or two traits that helped you identify each fruit type.

Pea: legume: ovary splits on two sides; many seeds

Lemon: hesperidium: oily rind, soft, juicy, and many seeds

Cherry: drupe: soft with thin skin and one hard seed

Maple: schizocarp: flat, winged ovary with two seeds

Corn: caryopsis: hard, single grain

Milkweed: follicle: ovary splits on one side, releasing seeds with hair

Key of fruit types

A. Fleshy	Ovary is soft and juicy when ripe.	
Berry:	Entire ovary is soft with a thin soft skin on the outside and many seeds inside.	
Drupe:	Entire ovary is soft with a thin soft skin on the outside and usually one very hard seed inside.	
Hesperidium:	Entire ovary is soft with a thick, oily rind and many tough seeds inside.	
B. Dry	Ovary is dry and brittle when ripe.	
One or two seeds	Schizocarp:	Ovary is flat and has two "wings"; two seeds inside
	Caryopsis:	Walls of ovary and seed are joined; fruit is a single, hard grain
Many seeds	Follicle:	Ovary splits along one side when ripe, releasing many fluffy seeds that float on the wind.
	Legume:	Ovary splits along two sides when ripe, releasing many seeds.

STUDY GUIDE 137

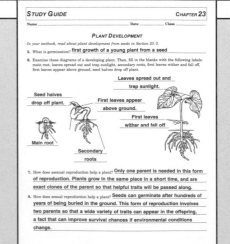

STUDY GUIDE CHAPTER 23

Name ______ Date ______ Class ______

PLANT DEVELOPMENT

In your textbook, read about plant development from seeds in Section 23:3.

5. What is germination? **first growth of a young plant from a seed**

6. Examine these diagrams of a developing plant. Then, fill in the blanks with the following labels: main root, leaves spread out and trap sunlight, secondary roots, first leaves wither and fall off, first leaves appear above ground, seed halves drop off plant.

Leaves spread out and trap sunlight.
Seed halves drop off plant.
First leaves appear above ground.
First leaves wither and fall off
Main root
Secondary roots

7. How does asexual reproduction help a plant? **Only one parent is needed in this form of reproduction. Plants grow in the same place in a short time, and are exact clones of the parent so that helpful traits will be passed along.**

8. How does sexual reproduction help a plant? **Seeds can germinate after hundreds of years of being buried in the ground. This form of reproduction involves two parents so that a wide variety of traits can appear in the offspring, a fact that can improve survival chances if environmental conditions change.**

OPTIONS

Germination/*Transparency Package,* number 23c. Use color transparency number 23c as you teach germination.

Enrichment/*Teacher Resource Package,* p. 25. Use the Enrichment worksheet shown here to help students understand fruits.

Lab 23–1 Germination

Problem: Will soaked seeds germinate faster than unsoaked seeds?

Skills

form a hypothesis, experiment, observe, interpret data

Materials

2 milk cartons
soil
20 corn seeds
water
stapler
scissors
metric ruler
rubber band
small beaker
pencil
tape
permanent marker

Procedure

1. Copy the data table.
2. Prepare milk carton planters as shown in the figure.
3. Fill each carton with moist soil.
4. Wrap a rubber band around a pencil exactly 2 cm from the end of the eraser. Using your pencil as a measuring stick, poke a row of ten holes exactly 2 cm deep in both cartons as shown.
5. **Experiment:** To the first carton, add one soaked corn seed to each hole. Use the marker to label the carton Soaked Corn Seeds. Add your name and the date.

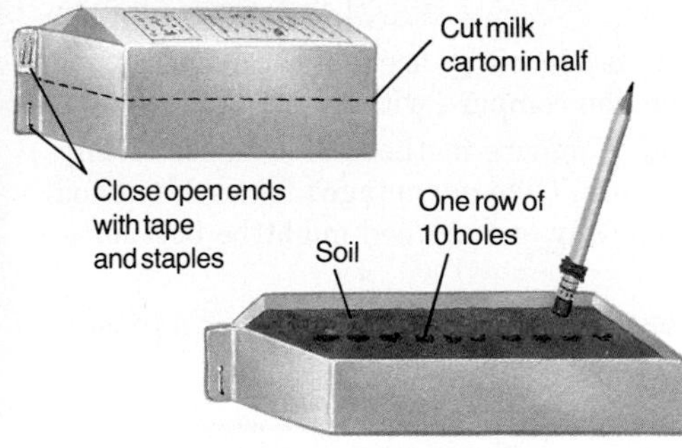

Cut milk carton in half
Close open ends with tape and staples
Soil
One row of 10 holes

6. To the second carton, add one unsoaked corn seed to each hole. Label the carton Unsoaked Corn Seeds.
7. Gently cover the seeds with moist soil.
8. Read the problem question and write a **hypothesis** about it in your notebook.
9. **Observe:** Check each carton every day. Record the total number of plants that germinate each day.

Data and Observations

1. How long did it take for the first unsoaked corn seed to germinate?
2. How long did it take for the first soaked seed to germinate?

	NUMBER OF SEEDS GERMINATED					
Days from planting	0	1	2	5	6	7
Soaked	0	0	1	6	8	9
Not soaked	0	0	0	2	3	5

Analyze and Apply

1. What is the purpose of this experiment?
2. (a) What is meant by a control?
   (b) Which group of seeds were the control?
3. (a) What is meant by a variable?
   (b) What was the variable?
4. **Check your hypothesis:** Is your hypothesis supported by your data? Why or why not?
5. **Apply:** How could you find out if your results would be the same using different kinds of seeds?

Extension

Design an experiment to test the effect of soaking the seeds for less than 24 hours.

ANSWERS

Data and Observations

1. about six days
2. about four days

Analyze and Apply

1. to determine if soaking a seed affects the rate of germination
2. (a) a procedure used during an experiment in which one group being tested is left unchanged (b) those that were not soaked
3. (a) some type of change or treatment made to one group (b) the soaking of the seeds
4. Students who hypothesized that soaked seeds would germinate faster than unsoaked seeds will answer, yes.
5. by repeating the experiment using different kinds of seeds

Lab 23-1 Germination

Overview

Seeds that are planted are usually watered to promote germination. This lab allows students to determine whether the presoaking of seeds in water will speed up the process of germination.

Objectives: Upon completion of this lab, students will be able to: (1) **compare** the speed of seed germination of a control group to that of an experimental group, (2) **explain** the meaning of the term variable, (3) **interpret** data regarding the influence of watering on speed of germination.

Time Allotment: Day 1 – 30 minutes; Day 2 - 8 – 5 minutes

Preparation

▶ **Alternate Materials:** Substitute polystyrene cups for milk carton and beakers, sand for soil. Substitute bean seeds for corn. Popcorn can be used in place of corn seeds.

Lab 23-1 worksheet/*Teacher Resource Package,* pp. 89-90.

Teaching the Lab

▶ **Troubleshooting:** Do not allow soil to dry out, but reduce watering to avoid molding of seeds and young plants. If mold appears, water should be restricted even further.

TEACH

Guided Practice

Have students write down their answers to the margin question: a group of living things that came from one parent.

Check for Understanding

Have Students respond to the first three questions in Check Your Understanding.

Reteach

Reteaching/*Teacher Resource Package*, p. 71. Use the Reteaching worksheet shown at the bottom of this page to give students additional practice in the events after fertilization.

Extension: Assign Critical Thinking. Biology and Reading, or some of the **OPTIONS** available with this lesson.

3 APPLY

Connection: Social Studies

Have students use maps to determine the major crops for a specific region or country.

4 CLOSE

ACTIVITY/Videocassette

Show the videocassette *Life Cycle of the Flowering Balsam,* Carolina Biological Supply Co.

Answers to Check Your Understanding

11. Petals die; ovules form seeds; ovary becomes a fruit; stamens die.
12. the root
13. asexual—new plants will have the same traits as the parent; sexual—new plants will have traits from each parent
14. wind—always present; water—has buoyancy to keep seeds afloat; animals—can probably carry seeds the farthest
15. a fruit, ripened ovary

Figure 23-14 Tulips of one variety all came from the same stock of bulbs and form a clone.

What is a clone?

Bio Tip

Leisure: You can make an indoor garden from kitchen wastes. Grow a pineapple plant from the leafy top of a pineapple, an orange tree from an orange seed, a carrot from a carrot top, and an avocado plant from an avocado seed.

Comparing Kinds of Reproduction

You have read about two ways a plant can reproduce. Let's now compare the advantages of both asexual and sexual reproduction in plants.

Asexual reproduction

1. In asexual reproduction only one parent is needed. A new plant can form from a root, stem, or leaf by mitosis. Reproduction by this method produces adult plants in a short time.
2. Some plants, like bananas, do not form seeds. Thus, the only way for them to reproduce is asexually.
3. All the new plants from asexual reproduction are clones of the parent plant. A **clone** (KLOHN) is a group of living things that come from one parent and are identical to the parent. This means that any trait or feature that is useful for survival will be kept in all offspring. Useful traits include large flowers, bright colors, or juicy fruits.

Sexual reproduction

1. Sexual reproduction requires two parents. Plants produced this way are made up of traits from both parents. No two plants will have the same combination of traits and so there will be a wide variety of traits in the offspring.
2. If proper growing conditions are not present, many seeds can survive for long periods of time. Some seeds have been known to germinate after hundreds of years of lying buried in the ground.
3. With a variety of traits, different plants will have a better chance to survive if conditions change.

Check Your Understanding

11. Describe what becomes of each of the following flower parts after fertilization: petals, ovules, ovary, stamens.
12. Which part of a plant grows first after a seed begins to germinate?
13. How will plants produced by asexual reproduction and sexual reproduction compare with their parents?
14. **Critical Thinking:** Compare methods of seed scattering from a parent plant. Give advantages for each method and give reasons why one method might be best for a plant's survival.
15. **Biology and Reading:** If you eat an orange or a tomato, which part of the plant are you eating?

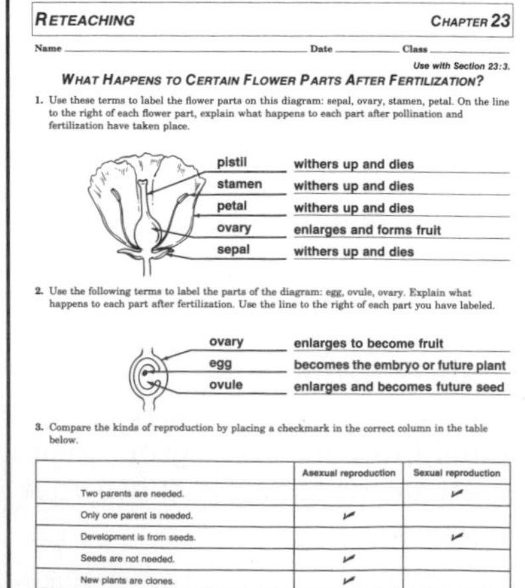

RETEACHING 71

RETEACHING CHAPTER 23

Name ______ Date ______ Class ______

Use with Section 23:3.

WHAT HAPPENS TO CERTAIN FLOWER PARTS AFTER FERTILIZATION?

1. Use these terms to label the flower parts on this diagram: sepal, ovary, stamen, petal. On the line to the right of each flower part, explain what happens to each part after pollination and fertilization have taken place.

pistil withers up and dies
stamen withers up and dies
petal withers up and dies
ovary enlarges and forms fruit
sepal withers up and dies

2. Use the following terms to label the parts of the diagram: egg, ovule, ovary. Explain what happens to each part after fertilization. Use the line to the right of each part you have labeled.

ovary enlarges to become fruit
egg becomes the embryo or future plant
ovule enlarges and becomes future seed

3. Compare the kinds of reproduction by placing a checkmark in the correct column in the table below.

	Asexual reproduction	Sexual reproduction
Two parents are needed.		✓
Only one parent is needed.	✓	
Development is from seeds.		✓
Seeds are not needed.	✓	
New plants are clones.	✓	
New plants have a variety of traits.		✓
Adult plants are produced in a short time.	✓	

Lab 23–2 Rooting

Problem: Can new plants be grown from roots and bulbs?

Skills

experiment, observe, measure in SI, infer

Materials

garlic bulb
carrot
labels
water
toothpicks
small beaker
metric ruler
razor blade
shallow dish

DATE				
garlic bulb	For	sample	data	
carrot	see	TRP	pages	91-92

Procedure

1. Copy the data table.
2. **Experiment:** Stick three toothpicks into a garlic bulb as shown in the figure.
3. Fill a small beaker with water. Label the beaker with your name and the date.
4. Balance the garlic in the water as shown. Make sure that the pointed end of the garlic is sticking up out of the water.
5. **Observe:** Use the data table to draw what the garlic looks like today. Mark the date on the table.
6. **Measure in SI:** Use a metric ruler to measure about 2 cm from the top of a carrot. Use a razor blade to cut off a slice of a carrot where you measured it.

CAUTION: *Always cut away from yourself when using a razor blade.*

7. Place the carrot section into a shallow dish. The cut end should be facing down.
8. Label your dish. Add water to the dish.
9. Use the data table to draw what the root looks like today. Write in the data.
10. Check the bulb and root every day. Make a labelled diagram every four days on your data table.

Data and Observations

1. What plant part of the garlic was used? Of the carrot?
2. Describe what formed on the garlic and carrot slice after several days.

Analyze and Apply

1. Define asexual reproduction.
2. **Infer:** What did the parent plants of the garlic and carrot look like?
3. Using your data, how fast do garlic and carrot plants reproduce asexually?
4. **Apply:** How does asexual reproduction help a garlic plant survive?

Extension

Design an experiment to test if garlic bulbs will grow better in the light than in the dark.

Lab 23-2 Rooting

Overview

Students will grow plants by asexual reproduction. This lab illustrates that new plants can be grown from plant parts such as bulbs or roots.

Objectives: Upon completion of this lab, students will be able to: (1) **observe** and record the events associated with asexual reproduction using a plant bulb, and root, (2) **compare** the rate at which asexual reproduction occurs when using different plant parts and different plants, (3) **determine** that new plants grown asexually are clones of the parent plant.

Time Allotment: Day 1 – 20 minutes
Days 2 to 3 – 5 minutes
Day 4 – 15 minutes
Days 5 to 7 – 5 minutes
Day 8 – 15 minutes

Preparation

▶ **Alternate Materials:** Substitute onions for garlic, radish or beets for carrots, and paper cups for beaker.

Lab 23-2 worksheet/*Teacher Resource Package,* pp. 91-92.

Teaching the Lab

▶ **Troubleshooting:** Garlic bulb and carrot root section must always be kept in water. On weekends, add sufficient water to dish and beaker, and cover with a plastic bag.

▶ Students must look carefully for new root growth occurring in garlic. Carrot tops must be cleared of original growth when first prepared so any new growth can be observed.

ANSWERS

Data and Observations

1. garlic—the bulb, which includes a stem and leaves; carrot—the root
2. garlic—roots from the base of the stem; carrot—roots from the top of the root

Analyze and Apply

1. production of offspring from one parent
2. The parent of the garlic bulb will be the same as the bulb in this experiment; it was probably formed by asexual reproduction. The parent of the carrot may have been grown from seed and therefore may have been a little different.
3. Answers will vary. The garlic and carrot parts will probably show new growth after four to ten days.
4. A bulb is an underground storage organ that can survive over winter. Without the bulb, the garlic plant would not survive the cold temperatures above ground.

PROBLEM SOLVING

Flowering Pollination

Problem–solving Strategies

The following strategies can be used to solve the problem in this feature: construct a table, list all possible solutions, look for a pattern, talk to an expert.

Hints

▶ Ask students which plants seem to advertise, and how do they advertise? Would you expect insects to be attracted more to color or smell? How about birds?

▶ Have students list all the different ways that flowers can be pollinated, and then have them list the requirements for each way. This information can be put into a table, or key. Have them look for clues like colored petals, tubular flowers, or a water environment. For example, a certain flower might be pollinated by moths. Moths only fly at night and have a good sense of smell and poor vision. So flowers pollinated by moths bloom at night, have a very strong odor, and are white so that they can be seen at night.

PROBLEM SOLVING

FLOWER POLLINATION

Many flowers are adapted to animals. Animals are important to flowers as carriers of sperm to eggs. You have read that the sperm of seed plants are produced inside pollen grains. Animals that carry pollen from flower to flower are called pollinators. Flowers have many traits that cause pollinators to notice them. The sweet or rotten smell of some flowers attracts bees or flies. Some

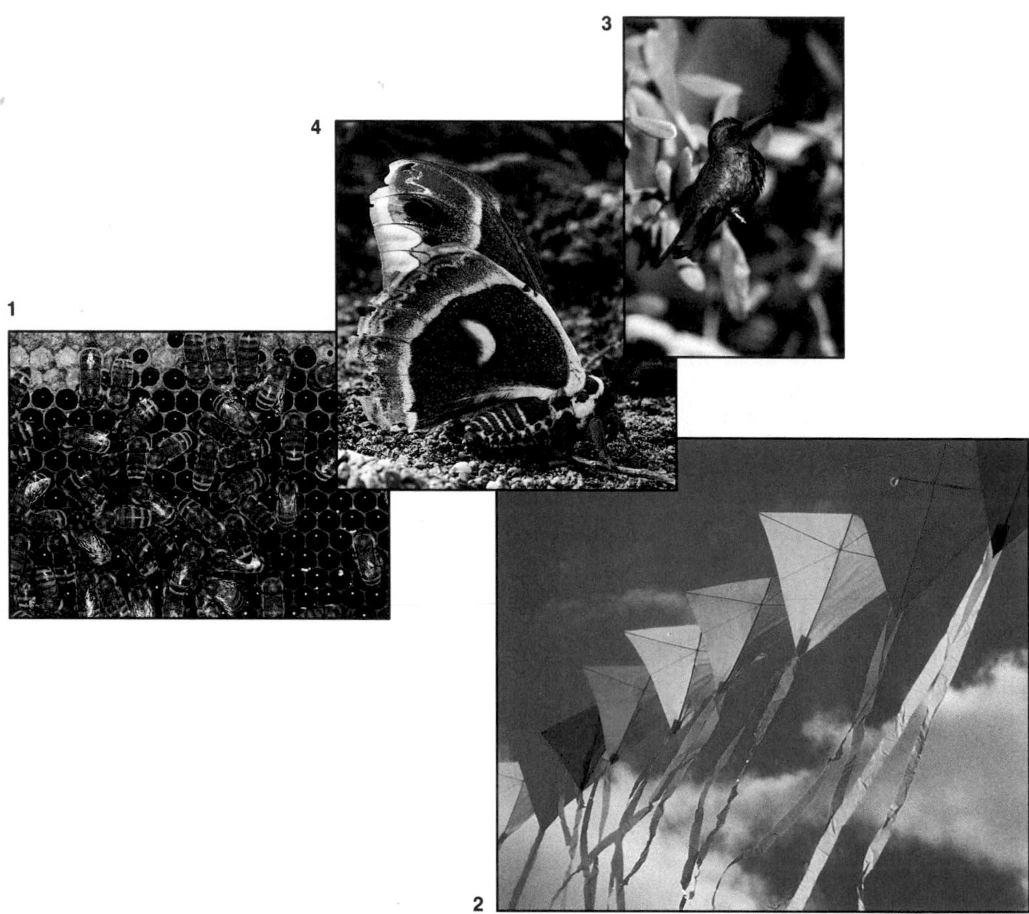

flowers also provide pollinators with food called nectar. Colors and patterns on the petals act as guides that lead the animal to the food source. Many flowers also have platforms for the animals to land on while they feed. The position of the flower on the plant may also make it easier for certain animals to feed from the flower as they are pollinated.

Your job is to match each flower shown with its pollinator. Keep in mind that some flowers that use wind for pollination don't need to be attractive to animals.

Solving the Problem

1. d
2. b
3. c
4. a

Discussing the Problem

▶ You can discuss with students how flowers and pollinators, in many cases, have evolved together, and how some plants have only one pollinator. If that pollinator were to become extinct, the plant would also become extinct. Discuss the advantages and disadvantages of the different kinds of pollination and whether it is better for a plant to be selectively pollinated or non-selectively pollinated.

Extension

Have selected students read parts of Darwin's book on orchids and fertilization and have them report to the class.

CHAPTER 23 REVIEW

Summary

Summary statements can be used by students to review the major concepts of the chapter.

Key Science Words

All boldfaced terms from the chapter are listed.

Testing Yourself

Using Words

1. clone
2. tuber
3. germination
4. grafting
5. stamen
6. fruit
7. pistil
8. self pollination

Finding Main Ideas

9. p. 485; Some leaves, when removed from the main plant, will grow into an entire new plant when the leaf stalk is placed in soil.
10. p. 487; Grafting is important in producing fruit crops and in protecting plants from disease.
11. p. 492; Squash, walnuts, and dandelion seeds are enlarged ovaries that contain seeds.
12. p. 496; Asexual reproduction is reproduction by mitosis alone, where only one parent is needed, and where the new plants are clones of the parent plant. Sexual reproduction is reproduction by meiosis, where two parents are required, and where the new plants will have a variety of traits different from the parent plants.
13. p. 490; Cross pollination is when pollen from the stamen of one flower is carried to the pistil of another flower on a different plant. Self pollination is when the pollen moves from the stamen of one flower to the pistil of the same flower or another flower on the same plant.
14. p. 494; After germination, the root and then the stem grow from the seed. The stem and first leaves on the stem turn green and begin to make food by photosynthesis.
15. p. 485; Root tubers grow new plants each year from the food stored in the tubers.
16. p. 489; The pistil is the female reproductive organ of a flower and produces the egg cells of a seed plant.
17. p. 491; The pollen grain lands on the pistil and grows a tube down into the stalk of the pistil. Three nuclei make their way down the tube to the ovule. One of the nuclei enters the ovule and joins with the egg.
18. p. 488; Sepals protect the young flower while it is still a bud. Petals attract insects.

Using Main Ideas

19. Sexual reproduction produces a variety of traits in the offspring and makes it possible for germination to take place when growing conditions are favorable. Asexual reproduction preserves favorable traits in offspring, and since only one parent is needed, new plants can be produced in a short period of time.
20. A seed containing a young root and a young shoot, along with stored food, are found in an ovary.
21. The color, structure, and scent of flowers help to attract pollinators.

Chapter 23 Review

Summary

23:1 Asexual Reproduction in Plants

1. Asexual reproduction uses only one parent and produces identical offspring. Some plants reproduce from roots and root tubers.
2. Some plants reproduce asexually from leaves.
3. Some plants reproduce by underground stems, such as tubers and bulbs, or by runners. Some plants can be reproduced from cuttings or by grafting.

23:2 Sexual Reproduction in Plants

4. Sexual reproduction uses two parents and produces different offspring. The female part of the flower is the pistil. The male part is the stamen.
5. Pollination is the transfer of pollen from male to female flower parts. The two methods of pollination are self and cross pollination.
6. Pollen tubes grow down to ovules in the pistil. Sperm nuclei join with egg nuclei in the ovules.

23:3 Plant Development

7. After fertilization, a fruit forms from the ovary, and seeds form from ovules.
8. Seeds germinate and form new plants.
9. Asexual reproduction requires only one parent. Useful traits are kept in offspring. Sexual reproduction requires two parents and results in a wide variety of traits.

Key Science Words

bulb (p. 486)
clone (p. 496)
cross pollination (p. 490)
cutting (p. 487)
fruit (p. 492)
germination (p. 494)
grafting (p. 487)
ovule (p. 489)
petal (p. 488)
pistil (p. 489)
pollination (p. 490)
runner (p. 486)
self pollination (p. 490)
sepal (p. 488)
stamen (p. 488)
tuber (p. 485)

Testing Yourself

Using Words

Choose the word from the list of Key Science Words that best fits the definition.

1. exact copies of a living thing
2. underground stem of potato
3. the growth of a young plant from a seed
4. joining a stem of one plant to the stem of another
5. male reproductive organ of flower
6. enlarged ovary with seeds
7. female reproductive organ of flower
8. carrying of pollen from stamen of one flower to pistil of same flower

500

Review

Testing Yourself *continued*

Finding Main Ideas

List the page number where each main idea below is found. Then, explain each main idea.

9. how to grow a new plant from a leaf
10. why grafting is important
11. why squash, walnuts, and dandelion "seeds" are fruits
12. the differences between asexual and sexual reproduction in plants
13. how self pollination and cross pollination differ
14. the changes or development that take place in a seed after germination
15. how plants reproduce from root tubers
16. what the function of a pistil is
17. how sperm in pollen reach the egg
18. the roles of petals and sepals in a flower

Using Main Ideas

Answer the questions by referring to the page number after each question.

19. What are two advantages of sexual and two advantages of asexual reproduction to a plant? (p. 496)
20. What are the parts that form inside an ovary? (p. 492)
21. How do the color, structure, and scent of flowers aid pollination? (p. 490)
22. What happens to sperm and egg nuclei at fertilization? (p. 491)
23. How may some trees reproduce asexually after they have been cut down? (p. 484)
24. How does a sweet potato reproduce asexually? (p. 484)
25. What is the job of a stamen? (p. 488)
26. What are two ways leaves produce new plants? (p. 485)

Skill Review ✓

*For more help, refer to the **Skill Handbook,** pages 704-719.*

1. **Understand science words:** Which terms don't fit the definition of asexual reproduction? Explain why. clone, egg germination, mitosis, one parent
2. **Experiment:** What part of an experiment could be the control if you compared the rates of germination of wheat seeds and bean seeds?
3. **Infer:** How do plants get onto islands?
4. **Form a hypothesis:** If you noticed lots of young oak seedlings beneath an old oak tree, what would you hypothesize about how they got there?

Finding Out More

Critical Thinking

1. *Aerodynamic* means designed for flight. What are some seeds that are carried away from the parent plant by wind with the help of aerodynamic fruits?
2. What is the advantage of a seed surviving for many years without germinating?

Applications

1. Examine pollen from different flowers under a microscope. Diagram what you see. How is pollen related to hay fever?
2. Prepare a list of 10 plants used by humans as food. Determine if these plants are grown by farmers using methods of asexual or sexual reproduction.

Applications

1. Pollen carried by wind lands in the nasal cavities and produces an allergic reaction.
2. Answers will vary. Examples are sexual—corn, apples, peaches, cherries, plums, cucumbers, tomatoes, pears, beans, peas; asexual—potatoes, sweet potatoes, apple trees, figs, strawberries, onions, artichoke, garlic, turnips, olive trees, plum trees.

Chapter Review/*Teacher Resource Package,* pp. 121-122.

Chapter Test/*Teacher Resource Package,* pp. 123-125.

Chapter Test/*Computer Test Bank*

Using Main Ideas

22. The sperm and egg nuclei form an embryo that grows inside the ovule.
23. After they are cut down, some trees will send up new shoots from the roots that will grow into a cluster of new trees.
24. A sweet potato reproduces asexually by growing new plants from the root tuber.
25. The stamen is the male reproductive organ of a flower and produces pollen grains that contain sperm cells.
26. A leaf can produce a new plant when the stalk is placed in soil. The leaves of some plants can form new leaves on the tips of each leaf. These new plants will drop off and become new plants.

Skill Review

1. egg—is the result of meiosis; germination—seeds are formed by sexual reproduction
2. The rate of germination of one of the seeds must be known and used as a control to compare with the rate of germination of the other seeds.
3. Seeds are carried onto the island by the wind or by birds.
4. The oak tree dropped its seeds (acorns) below the tree.

Finding Out More

Critical Thinking

1. Examples include milkweed, maple trees, cottonwood trees, dandelion, grasses, wheat, willow trees, ragweed, thistle, cattails
2. It can wait for the most favorable growing conditions and have a better chance of surviving as an adult plant.

Animal Reproduction

PLANNING GUIDE

CONTENT	TEXT FEATURES	TEACHER RESOURCE PACKAGE	OTHER COMPONENTS
(1/2 day) 24:1 Asexual Reproduction Review of Asexual Reproduction Methods of Asexual Reproduction	Mini Lab: *What Do Hydra Buds Look Like?* p. 505 Idea Map, p. 504 Check Your Understanding, p. 506	Reteaching: *Asexual Reproduction,* p. 72 Study Guide: *Asexual Reproduction,* p. 139	**Laboratory Manual:** *How Do Some Animals Reproduce Asexually?* p. 197
(2 1/2 days) 24:2 Sexual Reproduction Review of Sexual Reproduction External and Internal Fertilization Breeding Season	Mini Lab: *Are Sperm Attracted to Eggs?* p. 508 Lab 24-1: *Sex Cells,* p. 511 Idea Map, p. 507 Check Your Understanding, p. 510	Application: *Reproduction in Animals,* p. 24 Enrichment: *Types of Animal Reproduction,* p. 26 Reteaching: *Sexual Reproduction,* p. 73 Critical Thinking/Problem Solving: *How Are Some Mammals Able to Birth More Than One Young at a Time?* p. 24 Skill: *Sequence,* p. 25 Study Guide: *Sexual Reproduction,* p. 140 Lab 24-1: *Sex Cells,* pp. 93-94	**Laboratory Manual:** *How Do Internal and External Reproduction Compare?* p. 201
(2 days) 24:3 Reproduction in Humans Human Reproductive System Stages of Reproduction The Menstrual Cycle Diseases of the Reproductive System	Skill Check: *Sequence,* p. 518 Skill Check: *Understand Science Words,* p. 514 Lab 24-2: *Menstrual Cycle,* p. 512 Science and Society: *Sperm Banks,* p. 517 Check Your Understanding, p. 519	Reteaching: *Egg Release and Attachment,* p. 74 Focus: *How Fertilizing and Growing Tiger Embryos* In Vitro *Differs From Normal Reproduction,* p. 47 Transparency Master: *Human Reproductive System,* p. 121 Study Guide: *Reproduction in Humans,* pp. 141-143 Study Guide: *Vocabulary,* p. 144 Lab 24-2: *Menstrual Cycle,* pp. 95-96	**Laboratory Manual:** *What Are the Stages of the Menstrual Cycle?* p. 205 Color Transparency 24a: *Stages of Reproduction* Color Transparency 24b: *The Menstrual Cycle*
Chapter Review	Summary Key Science Words Testing Yourself Finding Main Ideas Using Main Ideas Skill Review	Chapter Review, pp. 126-127 Chapter Test, pp. 128-130	**Test Bank**

MATERIALS NEEDED

LAB 24-1, p. 511	LAB 24-2, p. 512	MARGIN FEATURES
microscope prepared slide of starfish eggs prepared slide of starfish sperm metric ruler petri dish for drawing circles	metric ruler graph paper colored pencils	Skill Check, p. 514 dictionary Skill Check, p. 518 pencil paper Mini Lab, p. 505 microscope prepared hydra slide Mini Lab, p. 508 microscope dropper sea urchin eggs sea urchin sperm

OBJECTIVES

		OBJECTIVES CORRELATION			
SECTION	OBJECTIVE	CHECK YOUR UNDERSTANDING	CHAPTER REVIEW	TRP CHAPTER REVIEW	TRP CHAPTER TEST
24:1	1. **Identify** the features of asexual reproduction.	1, 4	10, 20	10	1, 21, 28, 31, 32, 33
	2. **Describe** types of asexual reproduction.	2, 3, 5	10, 22	33	12, 15, 35, 37
24:2	3. **Describe** the features of sexual reproduction.	6, 10	21	2	5, 6, 19, 27, 28, 34
	4. **Compare** internal and external fertilization.	7, 9	15, 18	1, 5, 11, 12, 13, 14, 15, 16, 37	3, 4, 8, 11, 12, 14, 18, 29, 36
	5. **Discuss** ways animals improve chances of fertilization.	8	2, 5, 14, 20	6, 8	2, 17, 23, 30
24:3	6. **Identify** the reproductive parts of humans and the stages of human reproduction.	11	4, 7, 8, 12, 16	3, 4, 21, 22, 23, 24, 25, 26, 27, 28, 29, 30, 31, 34, 35, 36, 38	7, 16, 24, 39, 40, 41, 42, 43, 44, 45, 46, 47, 48, 49, 50, 51, 52, 53, 54, 55, 56, 57, 58
	7. **Compare** changes in the menstrual cycle with and without fertilization.	12, 15	3, 9, 13, 19	9, 7, 18, 19, 20, 32	9, 10, 20, 22, 26
	8. **Discuss** symptoms and problems of sexually transmitted diseases.	13, 14	17	7	25

Animal Reproduction

CHAPTER OVERVIEW

Key Concepts

In this chapter, students will study methods of both sexual and asexual reproduction. The major emphasis is on the human reproductive system. Events of the menstrual cycle are described, as well as sexually transmitted diseases of the reproductive system.

Key Science Words

estrogen	regeneration
estrous cycle	reproductive system
external fertilization	sexually transmitted disease
internal fertilization	scrotum
menstrual cycle	uterus
menstruation	vagina
oviduct	vas deferens
penis	

Skill Development

In Lab 24-1, students will **make and use tables, measure in SI, recognize and use spatial relationships,** and **make scale drawings** in comparing sperm and egg cells. In Lab 24-2, they will **make and use graphs, infer,** and **relate cause and effect** in observing changes during the menstrual cycle. In the Skill Check on page 518, students will **sequence** events that take place during the menstrual cycle. On page 514, students will **understand** the **science word** *oviduct.* In the Mini Lab on page 505, students will **use a microscope** to examine hydra buds. In the Mini Lab on page 508, students will **observe** whether sperm are attracted to eggs.

CHAPTER PREVIEW

Chapter Content

Review this outline for Chapter 24 before you read the chapter.

24:1 Asexual Reproduction
- Review of Asexual Reproduction
- Methods of Asexual Reproduction

24:2 Sexual Reproduction
- Review of Sexual Reproduction
- External and Internal Fertilization
- Breeding Season

24:3 Reproduction in Humans
- Human Reproductive System
- Stages of Reproduction
- The Menstrual Cycle
- Diseases of the Reproductive System

Skills in this Chapter

The skills that you will use in this chapter are listed below.

- In **Lab 24-1,** you will make and use tables, measure in SI, recognize and use spatial relationships, and make scale drawings. In **Lab 24-2,** you will make and use graphs, infer, and relate cause and effect.
- In the **Skill Checks,** you will sequence and understand science words.
- In the **Mini Labs,** you will use a microscope and observe.

502

Bridging

In Chapter 22, students learned about the processes of mitosis and meiosis in detail. The practical aspects of that chapter can now be applied to asexual and sexual reproduction occurring within the animal kingdom and especially within humans.

Chapter 24

Animal Reproduction

Look at the cloud of butterflies in the photo on the left. Where did they come from and where are they all going? The butterflies are migrating from Canada and the United States to Mexico. As the butterflies move southward, more and more butterflies join the flock. A flock of butterflies can number in the thousands. When the butterflies arrive in Mexico, they reproduce. In the spring, the butterflies will turn northward and head back to Canada and the United States.

How do butterflies reproduce? Like many other organisms, butterflies produce egg and sperm and have sexual reproduction. The joining together of the egg and sperm results in a new butterfly. In this chapter, you will study how different animals reproduce to form more of their own kind.

Try This!

How do fish eggs and chicken eggs compare? Examine some fish eggs and a chicken egg. What do fish eggs and chicken eggs have in common? How do they differ?

Adult monarch butterfly

GETTING STARTED

Using the Photos

In looking at the photos, students should note that butterflies are insects and, as do many organisms, they reproduce sexually in warm temperatures. Have students discuss why warm temperatures may be important for reproduction of some organisms.

MOTIVATION/Try This!

How do fish eggs and chicken eggs compare? In completing the chapter opening activity, students will **observe** that both eggs are quite large. They are the reproductive cells of a female animal, have formed by meiosis, and are chordate eggs. They differ in size and appearance. Explain that the actual egg cell is difficult, if not impossible, to see. What is seen is mainly stored food.

Chapter Preview

Have students study the chapter outline before they begin to read the chapter. They should note the overall organization of the chapter. The first topic deals with asexual reproduction in animals. This is followed with a discussion of sexual reproduction. The last part of the chapter covers human reproduction and sexually transmitted diseases.

Misconception

Students may not be aware of the fact that most higher animals will release eggs regardless of whether they are or are not fertilized. Example: most students will assume that a chicken will lay eggs only if it has mated with a rooster. Egg production and release by a chicken is the same as egg production and release of an egg by a human. Most of the time the eggs are not fertilized.

24:1 Asexual Reproduction

PREPARATION

Materials Needed

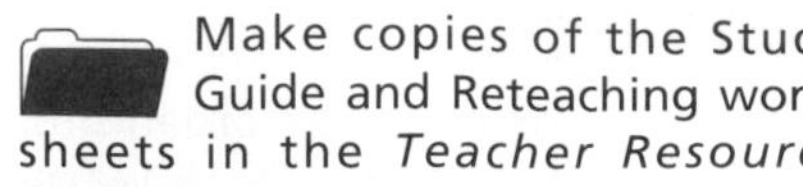
Make copies of the Study Guide and Reteaching worksheets in the *Teacher Resource Package.*

▶ Obtain prepared slides of hydra showing budding for the Mini Lab.

Key Science Words

regeneration

Process Skills

In the Mini Lab, students will use a microscope.

1 FOCUS

▶ The objectives are listed on the student page. Remind students to preview these objectives as a guide to this major section.

MOTIVATION/Story

Fishermen used to cut up starfish that they found in their fishing nets and throw them back into the sea. Each piece of starfish thrown back into the sea grew into another adult.

Guided Practice

Have students write down their answers to the margin question: mitosis.

Idea Map

Have students use the idea map as a study guide to the major concepts of the section.

24:1 Asexual Reproduction

Objectives

1. **Identify** the features of asexual reproduction.
2. **Describe** types of asexual reproduction.

Key Science Words

regeneration

All living things reproduce. Reproduction allows for the survival of different species of living things. For example, if butterflies didn't reproduce, there would be no more butterflies. The method or way in which living things reproduce differs from species to species. There are two main ways that animals reproduce. One of them is asexual reproduction.

Review of Asexual Reproduction

Sometimes only one parent is needed in order to have young. When reproduction requires only one parent, it is called asexual reproduction. You first studied asexual reproduction in Chapter 4 when you studied reproduction in bacteria. Let's review some features of asexual reproduction.

What type of cell reproduction occurs in asexual reproduction?

1. Egg and sperm cells are not used. Therefore, there is no meiosis.
2. Organs such as ovaries and testes are not used because no egg and sperm are produced in asexual reproduction.
3. Mitosis is the type of cell reproduction involved.
4. Since there are no egg or sperm certain body cells must undergo mitosis to form the offspring.
5. Offspring are identical to one another and the parent. They have the same kind of chromosome material and the same traits. The offspring are clones.

Study Tip: Use this idea map as you study asexual reproduction. Note the different forms of asexual reproduction—budding and regeneration.

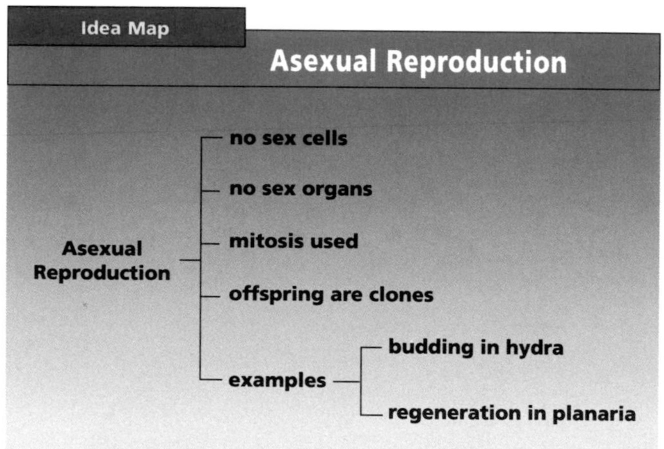

OPTIONS

Science Background

Asexual reproduction yields clones. All offspring produced by asexual reproduction are identical to the parent due to the fact that no genetic recombination takes place.

Asexual reproduction is sometimes said to be a simple form of reproduction. Since asexual reproduction is simple, do you suppose most animals use it? The answer is no. Simple animals, such as sponges, hydras, and flatworms, can reproduce this way. Complex animals, such as humans, birds, and fish, do not reproduce this way.

Methods of Asexual Reproduction

Animals are able to reproduce asexually by budding and regeneration (rih jen uh RAY shun). You learned about budding in Chapter 5. It is reproduction in which a small part of the body grows into a new organism. A hydra is a good example. Follow the steps in Figure 24-1 to see how budding works.

The new hydra, or bud, is at first smaller than the parent. Its other features, such as body shape and presence of tentacles, are the same as the parent's. This is an important feature of asexual reproduction. All offspring are exact copies, or clones, of the parent.

Figure 24-1 shows a photograph of a hydra forming a bud. The photo is enlarged about 50 times. Did the bud form by mitosis or meiosis? Why?

A few animals can reproduce asexually by regeneration. **Regeneration** is reproduction in which the parent separates into two or more pieces and each piece forms a new organism. A planarian, which is a flatworm, is an animal that undergoes regeneration.

Mini Lab

What Do Hydra Buds Look Like?

Use a microscope: Examine prepared slides of a hydra under low power. Diagram and label a hydra with buds. Does a hydra bud look like the parent? *For more help, refer to the **Skill Handbook**, pages 712-714.*

How is a bud of a hydra like the parent?

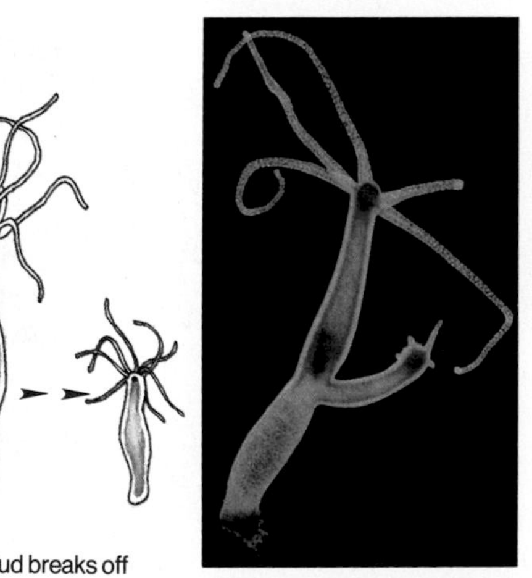

Figure 24-1 Hydra reproduce by budding.

2 TEACH

MOTIVATION/Audiovisual

Show the filmstrip *Asexual Reproduction,* Carolina Biological Supply Co.

Concept Development

▶ Make sure that students thoroughly understand the five key features of asexual reproduction.

▶ Point out that if mitosis is responsible for budding, then all cells must be identical to the original parent cells. This is the characteristic of a clone.

Mini Lab

Prepared slides of hydra are available from biological supply houses. Caution students to use only low power magnification with these slides.

Guided Practice

Have students write down their answers to the margin question: It is identical to the parent.

Check for Understanding

Ask students the following: (1) What is asexual reproduction? (2) What process of cell reproduction is used? (3) How do the offspring look when compared to the parent, and what term describes this condition?

Reteach

Use answers to Check for Understanding for class discussion.

OPTIONS

ACTIVITY/Enrichment

Planaria are available from biological supply houses. You may want to purchase some and have students watch them regenerate. Cut the animals in half and observe the two halves each day. About 1 week is needed for visible changes.

How Do Some Animals Reproduce Asexually?/*Lab Manual,* pp. 197-200. Use this lab as an extension to asexual reproduction.

TEACH

Independent Practice

Study Guide/*Teacher Resource Package,* p. 139. Use the Study Guide worksheet shown at the bottom of this page for independent practice.

Check for Understanding

Have students respond to the first three questions in Check Your Understanding.

Reteach

Reteaching/*Teacher Resource Package,* p. 72. Use this worksheet to give students additional practice with asexual reproduction.

Extension: Assign Critical Thinking, Biology and Reading, or some of the **OPTIONS** available with this lesson.

3 APPLY

Brainstorming

What would the world population look like if humans could only reproduce by asexual reproduction?

4 CLOSE

Ask students which of the five features of asexual reproduction apply to the healing of a cut finger and which do not.

Answers to Check Your Understanding

1. reproduction by one parent
2. reproduction in which the parent separates into two or more pieces and each piece forms a new organism
3. reproduction in which a small part of the body grows into a new organism
4. only one parent is needed
5. Starfish reproduce by regeneration, a kind of asexual reproduction.

Figure 24-2 Planarians can reproduce by regeneration.

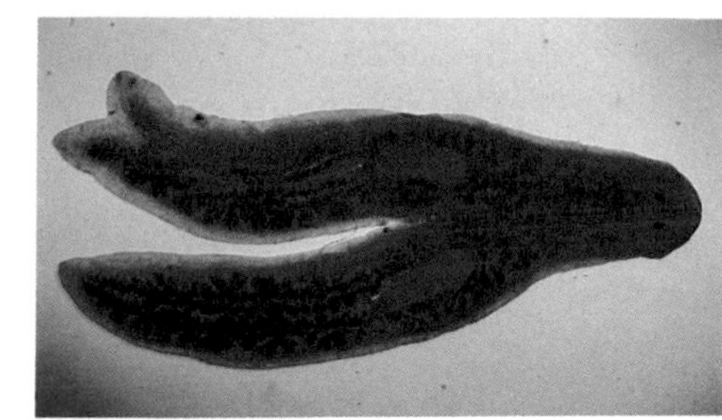

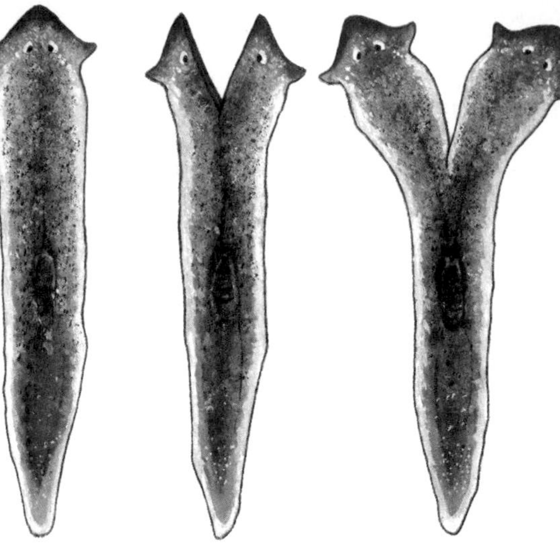

Figure 24-2 shows how a planarian regenerates. The planarian starts regenerating at its head end. Two heads form and then the animal begins to split along its body. Regeneration continues until what started out as a single animal ends up as two planarians.

The figure also shows a photograph of a planarian enlarged about 50 times. Note that the planarian appears to have two head ends. In time, the two heads will separate to form two whole planarians.

Check Your Understanding

1. What is asexual reproduction?
2. What is regeneration?
3. What is budding?
4. **Critical Thinking:** What would be an advantage of asexual reproduction?
5. **Biology and Reading:** People who fish for a living consider starfish pests. When starfish are caught in the fishing nets, they are sometimes cut up and tossed back into the water. Each piece grows into a new starfish. What kind of reproduction is this?

STUDY GUIDE 139

STUDY GUIDE — CHAPTER 24

Name ______ Date ______ Class ______

ASEXUAL REPRODUCTION

In your textbook, read about asexual reproduction in Section 24:1.

1. Identify the type of asexual reproduction shown in each picture.

a. regeneration b. budding

2. On each blank write T if the statement is true or F if the statement is false.

F a. During asexual reproduction animals reproduce by meiosis.
F b. A hydra forms buds in its ovaries.
F c. An offspring produced by sexual reproduction is identical to its parent.
T d. Complex animals reproduce by sexual reproduction.
T e. Regeneration occurs when an organism separates into pieces and each piece forms a new organism.
F f. Organisms produce eggs and sperm when they reproduce asexually.
T g. A planarian regenerates by mitosis.
T h. A hydra is a simple animal.
F i. Asexual reproduction requires two parents.
T j. When a planarian regenerates, it can form two heads.
F k. All the offspring of a hydra are different from each other.

3. Answer the question below.

What is a clone? A clone is an offspring that is an exact copy of its parent.

RETEACHING 72

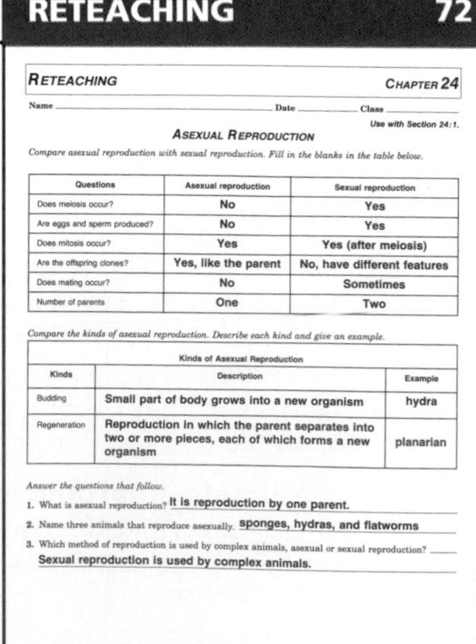

RETEACHING — CHAPTER 24

Name ______ Date ______ Class ______

Use with Section 24:1.

ASEXUAL REPRODUCTION

Compare asexual reproduction with sexual reproduction. Fill in the blanks in the table below.

Questions	Asexual reproduction	Sexual reproduction
Does meiosis occur?	No	Yes
Are eggs and sperm produced?	No	Yes
Does mitosis occur?	Yes	Yes (after meiosis)
Are the offspring clones?	Yes, like the parent	No, have different features
Does mating occur?	No	Sometimes
Number of parents	One	Two

Compare the kinds of asexual reproduction. Describe each kind and give an example.

Kinds of Asexual Reproduction		
Kinds	Description	Example
Budding	Small part of body grows into a new organism	hydra
Regeneration	Reproduction in which the parent separates into two or more pieces, each of which forms a new organism	planarian

Answer the questions that follow.

1. What is asexual reproduction? It is reproduction by one parent.
2. Name three animals that reproduce asexually. sponges, hydras, and flatworms
3. Which method of reproduction is used by complex animals, asexual or sexual reproduction? Sexual reproduction is used by complex animals.

24:2 Sexual Reproduction

Can you name five animals that use sexual reproduction? You might name dogs, cats, horses, humans, and cattle. What about birds, insects, frogs, or fish? These animals also use sexual reproduction.

Most animals use sexual reproduction in forming offspring. Some simple animals like hydra and planarians can use sexual reproduction in addition to asexual reproduction.

Objectives

3. **Describe** the features of sexual reproduction.
4. **Compare** internal and external fertilization.
5. **Discuss** ways animals improve chances of fertilization.

Key Science Words

external fertilization
internal fertilization
estrous cycle

Review of Sexual Reproduction

Let's review some of the features of sexual reproduction.

1. Sex cells, called egg and sperm, are used.
2. Organs are used to form the sex cells. Testes of the male form sperm cells. Ovaries of the female form egg cells.
3. Meiosis is the type of cell reproduction that forms the sex cells.
4. Mating may take place. Mating is the process of a male and female joining together to make sure that egg and sperm meet. Fertilization of egg by sperm is more likely to take place after mating.
5. Offspring formed by sexual reproduction will not look alike. They usually do not look exactly like either parent, although they may show some features of each parent.

Will offspring formed by sexual reproduction be clones? No. Sexual reproduction forms offspring with different features.

Sexual reproduction uses what kind of cell reproduction?

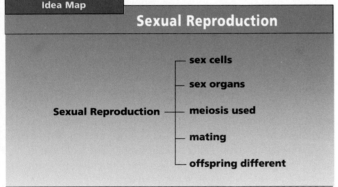

Idea Map

Sexual Reproduction

Sexual Reproduction
- **sex cells**
- **sex organs**
- **meiosis used**
- **mating**
- **offspring different**

Study Tip: Use this idea map as you study sexual reproduction. Note that in sexual reproduction, eggs can be fertilized outside the body or inside the body.

SKILL 25

SKILL: SEQUENCE CHAPTER 24

Name ______ Date ______ Class ______

For more help, refer to the Skill Handbook, pages 706-711. *Use after Section 24:2.*

SEXUAL MATURITY OF ANIMALS

When animals are old enough to reproduce, they are sexually mature. Table 1 shows that the age of sexual maturity varies in different animals. Does the time needed to reach sexual maturity depend on the group of the animal?

Look at the information in Table 1. Then, complete Table 2 by listing the animals from Table 1 in order of age of sexual maturity. Begin with the animal that takes the least amount of time. End with the one that takes the greatest amount of time. Then, answer the questions that follow the tables.

Table 1

Group	Animal	Age of sexual maturity
Soft-bodied	scallop	4 years
Jointed-leg	water flea	4 days
	cicada	17 years
Spiny-skin	starfish	1 year
Bony fish	eel	8 years
	bass	3 years
Amphibian	toad	2 years
Reptile	garter snake	2 years
	box turtle	4 years
Bird	sparrow	1 year
Mammal	whale	2 years
	deer	3 years
	elephant	12 years

Table 2

Animal	Age of sexual maturity
water flea	4 days
starfish	1 year
sparrow	1 year
toad	2 years
garter snake	2 years
whale	2 years
bass	3 years
deer	3 years
scallop	4 years
box turtle	4 years
eel	8 years
elephant	12 years
cicada	17 years

1. Which animal takes the shortest time to reach sexual maturity? **water flea**
   Which takes the longest time? **cicada**
2. Do mammals take more or less time than the other animals to reach sexual maturity? Explain. **Except for the elephant, most of the mammals reach sexual maturity in about the same time as the other animals.**
3. Does the time needed to reach sexual maturity depend on the animal's group? **no**

OPTIONS

Science Background

Some animal species have separate sexes, as in the case of humans. This is known as dioecious. Some animals, such as flatworms and segmented worms, have combined sexes. They are monoecious animals capable of self-fertilization, but they generally exhibit cross-fertilization.

Skill/*Teacher Resource Package*, p. 25. Use the Skill worksheet shown here to sequence the sexual maturity of animals.

24:2 Sexual Reproduction

PREPARATION

Materials Needed

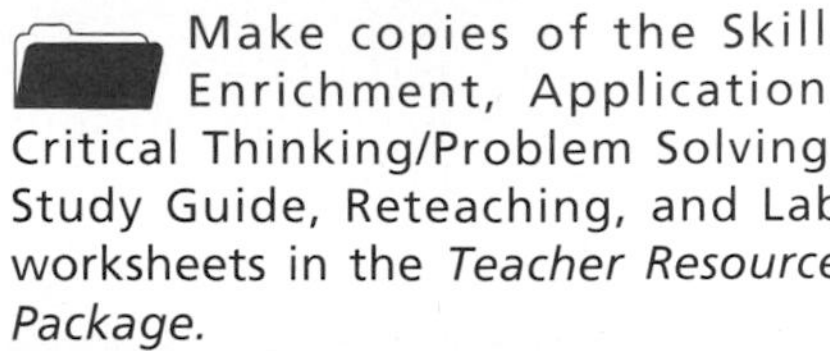

Make copies of the Skill, Enrichment, Application, Critical Thinking/Problem Solving, Study Guide, Reteaching, and Lab worksheets in the *Teacher Resource Package.*

▶ Purchase or collect sea urchin sperm and eggs for the Mini Lab.

▶ Obtain prepared slides of starfish egg and sperm for Lab 24-1.

Key Science Words

external fertilization
internal fertilization
estrous cycle

Process Skills

In the Mini Lab, students will observe. In Lab 24-1, students will make and use tables, measure in SI, recognize and use spatial relationships, and make scale drawings.

1 FOCUS

▶ The objectives are listed on the student page. Remind students to preview these objectives as a guide to this numbered section.

MOTIVATION/Audiovisual

Show 35-mm color slides of sperm from a variety of animals. Have students note similarities and differences.

Guided Practice

Have students write down their answers to the margin question: meiosis.

Idea Map

Have students use the idea map as a study guide to the major concepts of this section.

2 TEACH

Concept Development

▶ Point out how the five features of sexual reproduction differ from those of asexual reproduction.

▶ Suggest that fertilization is random and that breeding seasons increase chances for fertilization.

Independent Practice

Study Guide/*Teacher Resource Package,* p. 140. Use the Study Guide worksheet shown at the bottom of this page for independent practice.

Guided Practice

Have students write down their answers to the margin question: outside the body.

Mini Lab

Purchase sea urchin eggs and sperm from a biological supply house or obtain locally if possible.

Figure 24-3 After the female fish deposits her eggs, the male will fertilize them.

External and Internal Fertilization

In some animals the sex cells join outside the body. How is this possible? Animals like the female fish in Figure 24-3 release their eggs in water. Meanwhile, male fish also release their sperm in water. Then sperm and egg meet, and fertilization takes place.

Where does external fertilization take place?

The events just described are called external fertilization. **External fertilization** is the joining of egg and sperm outside the body. It's easy to remember because *external* means outside. The fertilized egg then forms a new animal. The young usually grow without care from their parents. This lack of care by the parents seems to be true for many animals that have external fertilization.

Most animals with external fertilization live in water or deposit their sex cells in water. Sperm must be able to swim to the egg. They could not do so unless they were in water.

How can animals with external fertilization make sure that egg and sperm meet? They can't always. They can, however, improve the chances in two ways. First, these animals give off thousands of sex cells at one time. The large number of sex cells increases the odds that one of the eggs will be fertilized. Second, these animals gather in large groups. You may have heard large groups of frogs croaking on a warm, rainy spring night. They gather in large groups to reproduce. When the sex cells are given off, the chance that they will meet is greater.

Mini Lab

Are Sperm Attracted to Eggs?

Observe: Add a dropperful of sea urchin sperm to some sea urchin eggs. Observe what happens under the microscope. *For more help, refer to the **Skill Handbook**, pages 704-705.*

OPTIONS

Enrichment/*Teacher Resource Package,* p. 26. Use the Enrichment worksheet shown here to help students learn types of animal reproduction.

STUDY GUIDE 140

STUDY GUIDE — CHAPTER 24

Name ________ Date ________ Class ________

SEXUAL REPRODUCTION

In your textbook, read about external and internal fertilization in Section 24:2.

1. Define external and internal fertilization.
   a. external fertilization: **External fertilization is the joining of egg and sperm outside the body.**
   b. internal fertilization: **Internal fertilization is the joining of egg and sperm inside the body.**
2. Where do most animals that have external fertilization live? **Most animals with external fertilization live in water.**
3. What would happen to sperm and eggs if land animals had external fertilization? **They would dry out.**
4. List two advantages of internal fertilization. **Internal fertilization increases the chance that an egg will become fertilized. It allows reproduction to take place out of water.**

In your textbook, read about breeding seasons in Section 24:2.

5. What is a breeding season? **A breeding season is a certain time of the year when animals reproduce.**
6. How does the breeding season of frogs help them? **The breeding season takes place when a lot of water is available and the temperature is warm enough for the young to survive.**
7. How does the breeding season of large mammals such as deer help them? **Since their young take longer to develop, the breeding season helps make sure that the young are born in the warm part of the year when they have a better chance to survive.**
8. What is an estrous cycle? **An estrous cycle is a time when a female is ready to mate.**

ENRICHMENT 26

ENRICHMENT — CHAPTER 24

Name ________ Date ________ Class ________

Use after Section 24:2.

TYPES OF ANIMAL REPRODUCTION

Read the descriptions below of how different types of animals reproduce. Then, decide which method of reproduction is being described: budding, regeneration, external fertilization, or internal fertilization. Label each method as a form of sexual or asexual reproduction.

1. A male dragonfly deposits its sperm in an opening near the female dragonfly's neck.
   internal fertilization; sexual reproduction
2. A sponge can reproduce by growing a miniature hollow cylinder along its side. This miniature cylinder can break off and form a new organism.
   budding; asexual reproduction
3. Male clams shed sperm into the water and female clams shed eggs into the water. Water currents bring the sperm and the eggs together.
   external fertilization; sexual reproduction
4. Earthworms mate, joining head to tail. Each exchanges sperm with the other. The sperm move into a pouch called the seminal receptacle (SEM un ul · ree SEP tih kul). A few days later the ovaries release eggs. The sperm join with the eggs inside the earthworm's body.
   internal fertilization; sexual reproduction
5. The female yellow perch lays eggs on the bottom of a lake. The male releases milt over the eggs. This is a fluid that contains sperm. Some of the eggs are fertilized by the sperm, and tiny fish hatch from the eggs.
   external fertilization; sexual reproduction
6. If a piece of a sponge breaks off from the main body of the sponge, the piece can grow into a new organism.
   regeneration; asexual reproduction
7. To attract a female, one kind of bird, the male vermillion flycatcher, dives in the air while singing a special song. Mating can take place in midair. The male presses his body near the female's so that the openings to their reproductive systems touch. Then, he releases sperm. The sperm travel into the female's body.
   internal fertilization; sexual reproduction
8. One of a starfish's five arms breaks off at the base. The arm can grow an entire new body.
   regeneration; asexual reproduction
9. Free-swimming, fully-formed jellyfish break away from the body of a stationary jellyfish.
   budding; asexual reproduction

Fish, starfish, sponges, and frogs are animals with external fertilization. These animals are found in or near water. Frogs can hop around on land, but they can reproduce only in water.

If *external* means outside, then what does *internal* mean? It means inside. Some animals have internal fertilization. **Internal fertilization** is the joining of egg and sperm inside the female's body.

When mating takes place during internal fertilization, sperm are released inside the female's body. Releasing the sperm this way increases the chance that an egg will become fertilized. It also allows reproduction to take place out of water. Animals with internal fertilization can reproduce on land. For example, insects, reptiles, birds, and mammals have internal fertilization. In addition to reproducing on land, animals with internal fertilization usually protect and care for their young.

What are two ways that animals improve chances for external fertilization?

Breeding Season

Most animals reproduce only during a certain time each year. For example, spring is the breeding season for frogs, Figure 24-4. A breeding season is a certain time of the year when particular kinds of animals reproduce.

The breeding season for frogs takes place when a lot of water is available and the temperature is warm enough. Why is water important for frog reproduction?

Figure 24-4 Frogs breed only at certain times of the year.

TEACH

Concept Development

▶ Stress that breeding seasons occur in animals showing both types of fertilization.

Guided Practice

Have students write down their answers to the margin question: by giving off many sex cells at one time and by gathering in large groups to mate.

Check for Understanding

Ask students the following:
(1) What is sexual reproduction? (2) What process of cell reproduction is used? (3) How do the offspring look when compared to the parent? (4) What special cell types are needed and where are they made?

Reteach

Use answers to Check for Understanding for class discussion.

CRITICAL THINKING 24

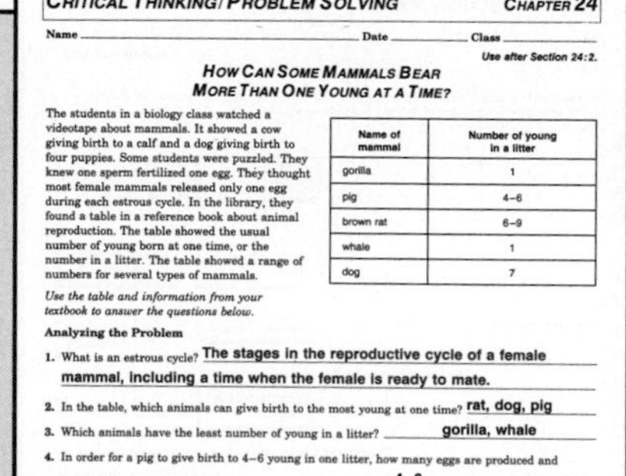

CRITICAL THINKING/PROBLEM SOLVING — CHAPTER 24

Name ______ Date ______ Class ______

Use after Section 24:2.

HOW CAN SOME MAMMALS BEAR MORE THAN ONE YOUNG AT A TIME?

The students in a biology class watched a videotape about mammals. It showed a cow giving birth to a calf and a dog giving birth to four puppies. Some students were puzzled. They knew one sperm fertilized one egg. They thought most female mammals released only one egg during each estrous cycle. In the library, they found a table in a reference book about animal reproduction. The table showed the usual number of young born at one time, or the number in a litter. The table showed a range of numbers for several types of mammals.

Name of mammal	Number of young in a litter
gorilla	1
pig	4–6
brown rat	6–9
whale	1
dog	7

Use the table and information from your textbook to answer the questions below.

Analyzing the Problem

1. What is an estrous cycle? The stages in the reproductive cycle of a female mammal, including a time when the female is ready to mate.
2. In the table, which animals can give birth to the most young at one time? rat, dog, pig
3. Which animals have the least number of young in a litter? gorilla, whale
4. In order for a pig to give birth to 4–6 young in one litter, how many eggs are produced and fertilized in an estrous cycle? 4–6

Solving the Problem

1. Suppose you were given one female and one male of the same species. How could you test how many eggs the female releases at one time? How could you know how many eggs were fertilized? Let the animals mate and count the offspring in one litter. The number of eggs and sperm that join to form fertilized eggs equals the number of offspring.
2. Using the same animals, how could you determine the range of number of young in a litter? Let the animals have several litters and calculate an average.

APPLICATION 24

APPLICATION: ENVIRONMENT — CHAPTER 24

Name ______ Date ______ Class ______

Use after Section 24:2.

REPRODUCTION IN ANIMALS

Different animals give birth to different numbers of offspring. Also, the time it takes for offspring to grow inside the mother varies for different animals. This period is called the gestation (je STAY shuhn) period. The number of offspring and gestation period for several animals is listed in the table below.

Animal	Average number of offspring at each birth	Length of gestation period (months)
Gray squirrel	9	1½
Dog	7	2
Red fox	6	2
Lion	3	3½
Black bear	2	7
Zebra	1	11½

Length of gestation period (months): 2 4 6 8 10 12 14 16 18 20 22
gray squirrel, dog, red fox, lion, black bear, zebra

Number of offspring: 1 2 3 4 5 6 7 8 9
gray squirrel, dog, red fox, lion, black bear, zebra

1. Use the information in the table to fill in the bar graphs.

Study the information in Section 24:2 of your text and the bar graphs above to answer the following questions.

2. How does the number of offspring relate to the length of the gestation period of the animal? The animals with fewer offspring have longer gestation periods, and the animals with many offspring have shorter gestation periods.
3. Which season would you expect to be the breeding season for a gray squirrel? Explain. Spring, because a squirrel's gestation period is only 1½ months long. If it breeds in the spring, the babies would be born in the spring or summer, when the weather is good for young animals to survive.
4. For a zebra to give birth in the spring, when would its breeding season have to be? Explain. It would have to breed in the spring, because its gestation period is 11½ months long. It would give birth in the next spring.

OPTIONS

Application/*Teacher Resource Package*, p. 24. Use the Application worksheet shown here to teach reproduction in animals.

Critical Thinking/Problem Solving/ *Teacher Resource Package*, p. 24. Use the Critical Thinking/Problem Solving worksheet shown here to help students understand how some mammals give birth to more than one young at a time.

Figure 24-5 Large mammals, such as the deer, breed in the fall and have their young the following spring.

Most fish, birds, and many small mammals breed in the spring of the year. The young hatch from eggs, or are born during the late spring or summer of that same year. Many large mammals, such as the deer shown in Figure 24-5, breed in the fall of the year. The unborn young take longer to develop. The young are born during early spring of the next year. This breeding season helps make sure that the young are born in the warm part of the year when they have a better chance to survive.

Another way that animals improve the chance of fertilization is by having an estrous (ES trus) cycle. An **estrous cycle** is a cycle in which a female will mate only at certain times. It is only at these times that the female's eggs can be fertilized.

Mammals have estrous cycles. For example, rats are ready to mate every five days. Most dogs have two estrous cycles per year. Cows have a 20-day cycle.

Check Your Understanding

6. Which cells are used in sexual reproduction?
7. What is meant by external fertilization?
8. What is the difference between a breeding season and an estrous cycle?
9. **Critical Thinking:** Which animals do you think produce more offspring, those with external fertilization or those with internal fertilization? Why?
10. **Biology and Reading:** What kind of reproduction is it when starfish release sperm and eggs into the water?

TEACH

Check for Understanding

Have students respond to the first three questions in Check Your Understanding.

Reteach

Reteaching/Teacher Resource Package, p. 74. Use this worksheet to give students additional practice with understanding sexual reproduction.

Extension: Assign Critical Thinking, Biology and Reading, or some of the **OPTIONS** available with this lesson.

3 APPLY

ACTIVITY/Challenge

Have students use references to determine (a) the frequency of estrous cycles in different animals and (b) what controls whether or not animals mate only in the spring.

4 CLOSE

Divergent Question

Ask students the following: What evidence can you provide to show that (a) humans do not have a breeding season and (b) dogs do have an estrous cycle?

Answers to Check Your Understanding

6. egg and sperm cells
7. joining of egg and sperm outside the body of an animal
8. A breeding season is a certain time of year when particular kinds of animals reproduce; an estrous cycle is a cycle in which a female will mate only at certain times.
9. external fertilization; since offspring get no protection from parents, many die; more must be produced
10. The starfish undergo meiosis to produce sperm and eggs and reproduce by sexual reproduction.

OPTIONS

How Do Internal and External Reproduction Compare?/*Lab Manual*, pp. 201-204. Use this lab as an extension to studying sexual reproduction.

RETEACHING 74

RETEACHING: IDEA MAP CHAPTER 24

Name ______ Date ______ Class ______

Use with Section 24:2.

SEXUAL REPRODUCTION

Use these terms and phrases to complete the idea map: may occur on land, must occur in water, outside of body, sperm released in female's body, animals gather in large groups, thousands of eggs, thousands of sperm, inside of body.

- Fertilization
  - external fertilization
    - outside of body
      - thousands of eggs
      - thousands of sperm
    - must occur in water
      - animals gather in large groups
  - internal fertilization
    - inside of body
      - sperm released in female's body
    - may occur on land

1. When is the breeding time for frogs? It occurs when there is a lot of water and the temperature is warm enough.
2. When is the breeding time for fish, birds, and small mammals? Explain how this is helpful to the animals. It occurs in the spring. The young hatch from eggs in late spring or summer of the same year, when weather is warm and they have a better chance to survive.
3. When do large mammals such as deer and bears breed? Explain why this is helpful to the animals. They breed in fall. The unborn take long to develop and are born in the early spring of the next year, when weather is milder.
4. What is the estrous cycle? The estrous cycle is the time when a female is ready to mate. It is the only time that mating occurs.

Lab 24–1 Sex Cells

Problem: How alike are egg and sperm cells?

Skills

make and use tables, measure in SI, recognize and use spatial relationships, make scale drawings

Materials

microscope
prepared slide of starfish eggs
prepared slide of starfish sperm
metric ruler
petri dish for drawing circles

Procedure

1. Copy the data table.
2. Use your microscope to look at a prepared slide of starfish eggs under low power and high power.
3. Fill out the top row in your table.
4. Repeat step 2 with a prepared slide of starfish sperm.
5. Fill out the bottom row in your data table.
6. To measure the actual size of an egg cell, draw a circle on a sheet of paper. Use the petri dish as a guide.
7. **Recognize and use spatial relationships:** Using high power, draw one egg in the circle. Draw it to scale as seen through the microscope. Label it "starfish egg."
8. **Measure in SI:** Measure the diameter of your diagram in millimeters. Record this number in your table.
9. Multiply the number in step 8 by 0.004 to get the actual size of the cell. Record this number in your table.
10. Repeat steps 6 to 9 with the slide of sperm. Label your diagram "starfish sperm." Note that there are two parts to a sperm. Label the small, oval end "head." Label the long, threadlike part "tail."

Data and Observations

1. Compare the actual sizes of egg and sperm.
2. Compare the shapes of egg and sperm.

Analyze and Apply

1. Compare the following for starfish and humans:
   (a) type of reproduction—sexual or asexual
   (b) type of fertilization—internal or external
2. **Apply:** Explain how the shape of a sperm cell helps it swim.

Extension

Make scale drawings: Prepare a wet mount of a small piece of magazine print. Locate a period at the end of a sentence. Using the same procedures as in the lab, measure the diameter of the period under high power. Compare the sizes of the starfish egg and sperm to that of the period.

*Answers will vary.

	SHAPE OF CELL	BODY OR SEX CELL	HAS A TAIL	SWIMS	NUMBER SEEN UNDER HIGH POWER	LENGTH OF DIAGRAM (mm)	MULTIPLY BY	SIZE OF CELL (mm)
Egg	round	sex	no	no	1	44 mm*	0.004	0.176 mm*
Sperm	round with tail	sex	yes	yes	30*	2 mm*	0.004	0.008 mm*

ANSWERS

Data and Observations

1. An egg is about 0.16 mm in diameter; a sperm head is 0.003 mm.
2. Eggs are round; sperm have an oval head and a tail.

Analyze and Apply

1. (a) both are sexual
   (b) starfish - external; human - internal
2. A sperm has a tail that moves back and forth to help the sperm swim.

Lab 24-1 Sex Cells

Overview

In this lab, students are given an opportunity to look at prepared slides showing typical animal sex cells, thus reinforcing their skills with a microscope. After students have actually measured the sizes of both egg and sperm cells, the vast difference in size and the difference in numbers of sex cells produced by a male and female will become evident.

Objectives: Upon completing this lab, students will be able to (1) **distinguish** an egg cell from a sperm cell, (2) **compare** the size difference between these two cells, (3) **measure** and record the actual cell size of starfish sex cells.

Time Allotment: 20 minutes

Preparation

▶ **Alternate Materials:** Sea urchin egg and sperm slides may be substituted. If petri dishes are not available, a circle with a diameter of 100 mm is all that is needed.

Lab 24-1 worksheet/*Teacher Resource Package*, pp. 93-94.

Teaching the Lab

▶ If slides are not available, the activity may still be performed by students. Use the two photos provided with the activity. They are close to the size seen when viewed under high power magnification. Have students use them for their drawings to be made to scale on the 100-mm circle.

Lab 24-2 Menstrual Cycle

Overview

In this lab, students are introduced to two of the female hormones responsible for controlling the events of the menstrual cycle. They will graph data presented in table form and will be able to correlate changes in uterus thickness with increasing or decreasing concentrations of these hormones.

Objectives: Upon completion of this lab, students will be able to (a) **construct a graph** on estrogen and progesterone hormone concentrations, (b) **construct a graph** on changes in uterus thickness, (c) **relate** the lowering and rising of hormone concentrations to a loss (menstruation) and thickening of uterus lining.

Time Allotment: 30 minutes

Preparation

▶ You may wish to review basic graphing techniques with your students prior to starting this activity.

Lab 24-2 worksheet/*Teacher Resource Package,* pp. 95-96.

Teaching the Lab

▶ The text describes estrogen but does not include any discussion of progesterone. You may wish to point out that both hormones influence uterine buildup.

▶ **Troubleshooting:** Check graphs to make sure that students have indeed used proper units and have prepared the graphs correctly.

Menstrual Cycle

Lab 24–2

Problem: What causes uterus thickness to change during the menstrual cycle?

Skills

make and use graphs, infer, relate cause and effect

Materials

graph paper
colored pencil
ruler

Procedure

1. Obtain a sheet of graph paper.
2. Draw and label two graphs as shown in the figure. *For more help, refer to the **Skill Handbook,** pages 715-717.*
3. Use the data in the table to complete the top graph.
   (a) Plot the estrogen units on the graph.
   (b) Connect the points for estrogen with a line and label the line "estrogen units."
   (c) Plot the progesterone units.
   (d) Use a colored pencil to connect the points for progesterone and label the line progesterone units.
4. Use the data in the table to complete the bottom graph.
   (a) Plot uterus thickness on the graph.
   (b) Connect the points on the graph with a line.

DAY	AMOUNT OF HORMONE		THICKNESS OF UTERUS LINING (mm)
	ESTROGEN	PROGESTERONE	
1	50	5	.5
5	65	5	1.5
10	200	5	2.25
15	75	40	3.0
20	100	150	4.0
25	50	100	5.0
27	50	30	4.75
1	50	5	.5

Data and Observations

1. How do the amounts of estrogen and progesterone change throughout the menstrual cycle?
2. How does the thickness of the uterus change throughout the menstrual cycle?

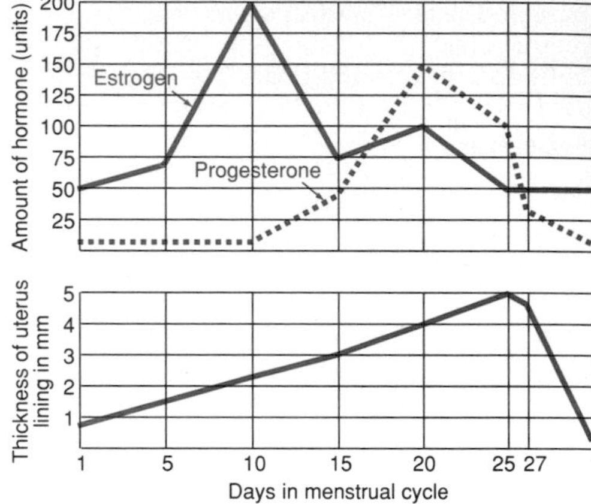

Analyze and Apply

1. **Infer:** How is the change in the thickness of the uterine lining related to the change in estrogen amount for days 1-10?
2. Compare the change in thickness of the uterine lining with the change in progesterone amount for days 10-27.
3. **Apply:** (a) What happens to the uterine lining between day 27 and day 1? (b) What is this process called?

Extension

Relate cause and effect: What happens to the egg on days 1-13, 14, and 15-27? How does this compare to the amounts of hormones and uterus thickness?

ANSWERS

Data and Observations

1. Estrogen increases until day 10, then decreases. Progesterone stays the same through day 10, then increases until day 20, then decreases.
2. The thickness of the uterus increases until day 25, then begins to decrease.

Analyze and Apply

1. As the amount of estrogen goes up and down, the thickness of the uterus continues to increase.
2. As the amount of progesterone goes up, the thickness of the uterus goes up, until day 20. The amount of progesterone then begins to drop, but the thickness continues to increase for about 5 more days.
3. (a) The uterus decreases in thickness because it is being shed. (b) menstruation

24:3 Reproduction in Humans

Humans have reproductive systems with many parts. The reproductive organs of males and females each do special jobs. Let's look at the human reproductive system to see how the different parts work.

Objectives

6. **Identify** the reproductive parts of humans and the stages of human reproduction.
7. **Compare** changes in the menstrual cycle with and without fertilization.
8. **Discuss** symptoms and problems of sexually transmitted diseases.

Key Science Words

reproductive system
scrotum
penis
vas deferens
oviduct
uterus
vagina
menstrual cycle
estrogen
menstruation
sexually transmitted disease

Human Reproductive System

The system used to produce offspring is called the **reproductive system.** What does this system look like in males and females?

Figure 24-6 shows the main parts of the male reproductive system. The job of each part is also listed. Study these jobs. Notice that this figure is a cut-away view from the side. Also notice that certain parts of the male reproductive system are also part of the excretory system studied in Chapter 13.

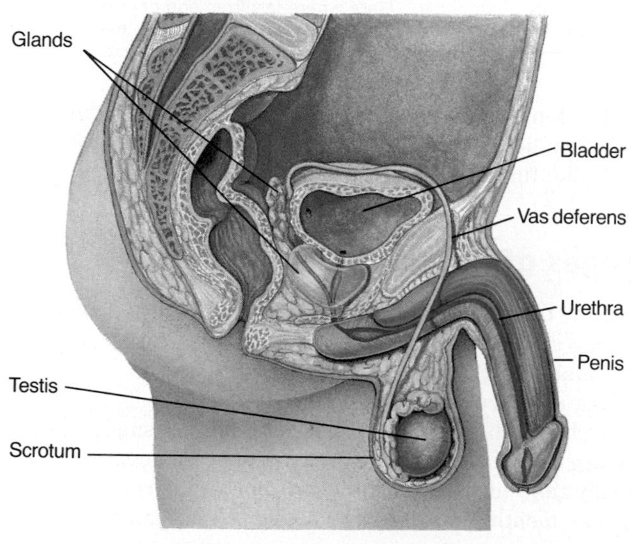

Figure 24-6 The male reproductive system is shown here in a cut-away view from the side.

PART	JOB
Testis	Produces sperm cells by meiosis
Scrotum (SKROH tum)	Sac that holds testes
Penis (PEE nus)	Places sperm in vagina during mating
Vas deferens (VAS·DEF uh runs)	Carries sperm from testes to urethra
Urethra (yoo REE thruh)	Carries sperm and urine out of body
Glands	Provides liquid in which sperm can swim

24:3 Reproduction in Humans

PREPARATION

Materials Needed

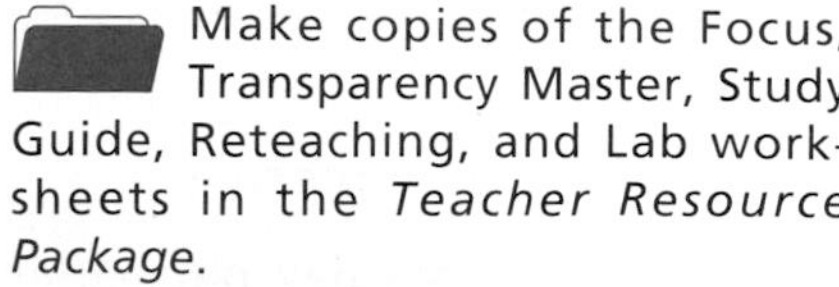

Make copies of the Focus, Transparency Master, Study Guide, Reteaching, and Lab worksheets in the *Teacher Resource Package*.

▶ Obtain graph paper and colored pencils for Lab 24-2.

Key Science Words

reproductive system
scrotum
penis
vas deferens
oviduct
uterus
vagina
menstrual cycle
estrogen
menstruation
sexually transmitted disease

Process Skills

In Lab 24-2, students will make and use graphs, infer, and relate cause and effect. In the Skill Checks, students will sequence and understand science words.

1 FOCUS

▶ The objectives are listed on the student page. Remind students to preview these objectives as a guide to this numbered section.

ACTIVITY/Audiovisual

Show the filmstrip *Human Body Series: Reproductive System*, Carolina Biological Supply Co.

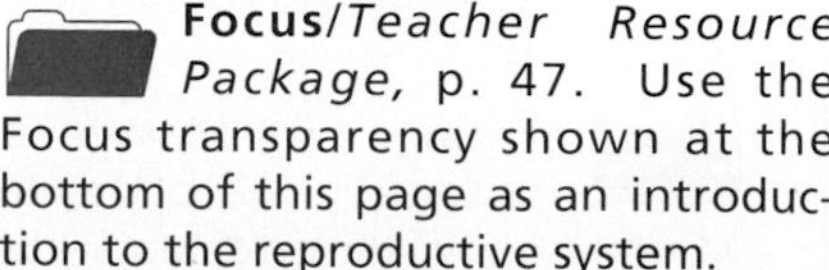

Focus/*Teacher Resource Package*, p. 47. Use the Focus transparency shown at the bottom of this page as an introduction to the reproductive system.

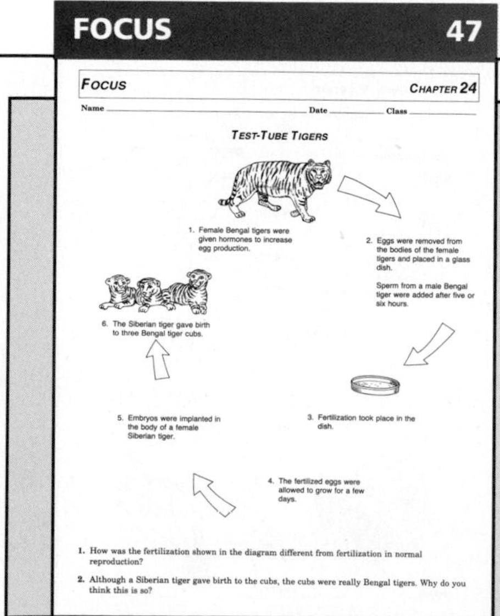

FOCUS 47

FOCUS CHAPTER 24

Name ____ Date ____ Class ____

TEST-TUBE TIGERS

1. Female Bengal tigers were given hormones to increase egg production.
2. Eggs were removed from the bodies of the female tigers and placed in a glass dish.
Sperm from a male Bengal tiger were added after five or six hours.
3. Fertilization took place in the dish.
4. The fertilized eggs were allowed to grow for a few days.
5. Embryos were implanted in the body of a female Siberian tiger.
6. The Siberian tiger gave birth to three Bengal tiger cubs.

1. How was the fertilization shown in the diagram different from fertilization in normal reproduction?
2. Although a Siberian tiger gave birth to the cubs, the cubs were really Bengal tigers. Why do you think this is so?

OPTIONS

Science Background

The menstrual cycle is under hormonal control. Hormones involved are gonadotropic releasing factor (stimulates anterior pituitary), follicle stimulating hormone (stimulates egg development), luteinizing hormone (stimulates egg release), and estrogen and progesterone (inhibit the release of FSH and LH, thus preventing more than one egg from maturing).

2 TEACH

MOTIVATION/Brainstorming

Ask students to speculate as to the possible outcome if sperm are present and two different eggs are released at the same time. (Fraternal twins are possible.)

Concept Development

▶ Ask students to pay particular attention to the information contained in Figure 24-6. It not only introduces several new terms but also identifies the functions of the parts of the male reproductive system.

▶ Be sure students study the functions of each part of the female reproductive system as shown in Figure 24-7.

▶ Review with students the nature of egg and sperm cells with regard to their chromosome number. Remind students that each human sex cell contains 23 pairs of chromosomes.

Independent Practice

Study Guide/*Teacher Resource Package*, p. 141. Use the Study Guide worksheet shown at the bottom of this page for independent practice.

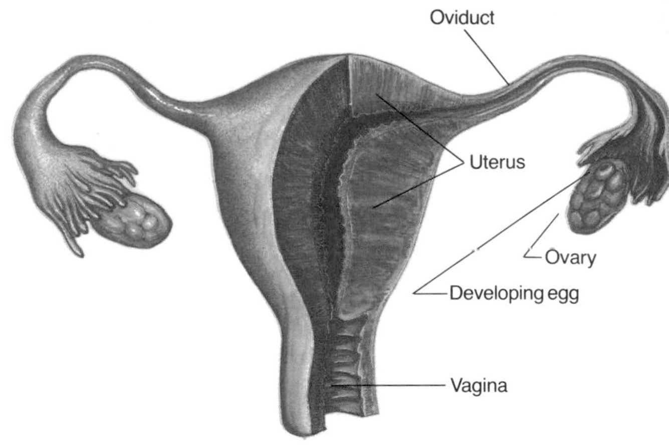

Figure 24-7 The female reproductive system is shown here in a cut-away view from the front.

PART	JOB
Ovary	Produces egg cells
Oviduct	Carries egg from ovary to uterus
Uterus	Place where fertilized egg develops
Vagina	Receives penis of male during mating

The female reproductive system is shown in Figure 24-7. This figure shows a cut-away view from the front. Study the function of each part.

Skill Check

Understand science words: oviduct. The word part *ovi* means egg. In your dictionary, find three words with the word part *ovi* in them. *For more help, refer to the **Skill Handbook,** pages 706-711.*

Stages of Reproduction

How does an egg become fertilized? What happens to the egg after it is fertilized? Look at Figure 24-8 and follow the numbers in the figure as you read.

1. Egg cells are formed in each ovary.
2. Each month, one ovary releases an egg. Usually, only one egg is released about every 28 days. The ovaries usually take turns releasing eggs. One ovary releases an egg one month, and the other ovary releases an egg the next month.

Figure 24-8 shows what happens next.

3. Once released from the ovary, the egg moves into a tube called an oviduct (OH vuh dukt). **Oviducts** are tubelike organs that connect the ovaries to the uterus. The **uterus** (YEWT uh rus) is a muscular organ in which the fertilized egg develops. The uterus is made of smooth muscle.

Figure 24-8 shows how fertilization takes place.

4. Sperm are released into the vagina during mating. The

OPTIONS

Stages of Reproduction/*Transparency Package*, number 24a. Use color transparency number 24a as you teach the stages of reproduction.

Transparency Master/*Teacher Resource Package*, p. 121. Use the Transparency Master shown here to teach the human reproductive system.

STUDY GUIDE 141

STUDY GUIDE — CHAPTER 24

Name ______ Date ______ Class ______

REPRODUCTION IN HUMANS

In your textbook, read about the human reproductive systems in Section 24:3.

1. Label the diagram below using these words: oviduct, ovary, uterus, egg, vagina.

(E) oviduct
(C) ovary
(B) egg
(A) uterus
(D) vagina

2. In each circle on the diagram, write the letter of the job listed below that the body part does.
   A. Muscular organ where fertilized egg develops.
   B. Cell formed in the ovary.
   C. A place where the egg is formed.
   D. Muscular tube that leads to uterus.
   E. Tubelike parts that connect ovary to uterus.
3. Fill in the blanks below with the correct numbers.
   a. Ovaries in a human female 2
   b. Testes in a human male 2
   c. Eggs usually produced by human at one time 1
4. Label the diagram below using these words: testes, penis, vas deferens, urethra, scrotum, glands.
5. In each circle on the diagram, write the letter of the job listed below that the body part does.
   A. Sperm pass out of the body here.
   B. Sperm are made here.
   C. Sperm move from the testes to the penis here.
   D. Provides liquid for sperm.
   E. Carries sperm out of body.
   F. Sac that holds testes.

(C) vas deferens
(D) glands
(E) urethra
(F) scrotum
(A) penis
(B) testes

TRANSPARENCY 121

TRANSPARENCY MASTER — CHAPTER 24

HUMAN REPRODUCTIVE SYSTEM

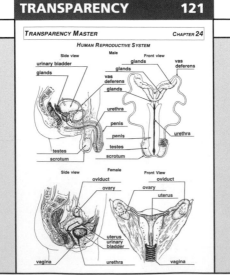

Male: Side view — urinary bladder, glands, testes, scrotum; Front view — glands, vas deferens, glands, vas deferens, glands, urethra, penis, penis, testes, scrotum, urethra

Female: Side view — oviduct, ovary, uterus, urinary bladder, vagina, urethra; Front View — oviduct, ovary, uterus, vagina

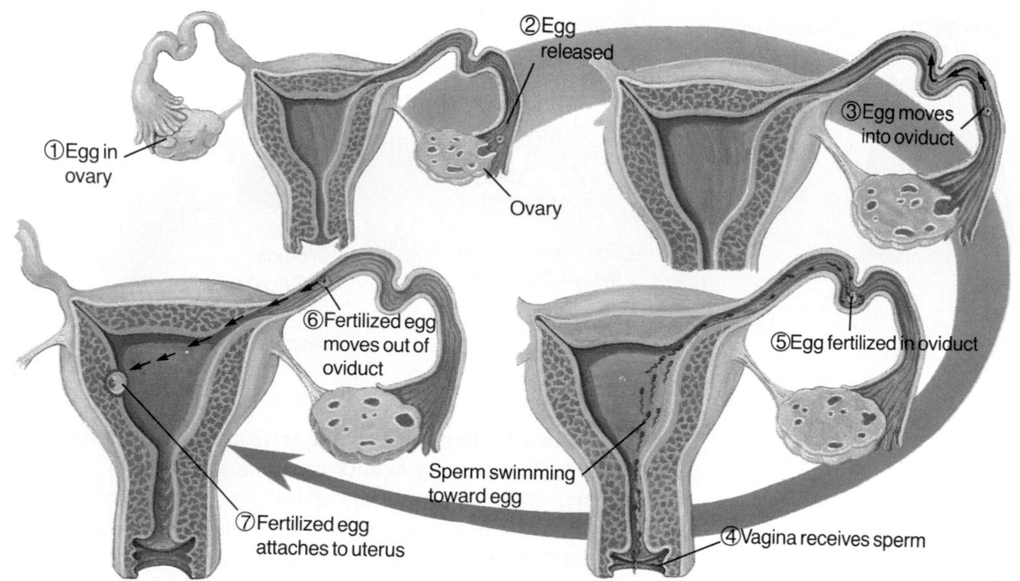

vagina (vuh JI nuh) is a muscular tube that leads from outside the female's body to the uterus. Sperm swim from the vagina into the uterus and then into the oviducts.
5. If an egg is present, fertilization takes place.
Figure 24-8 shows what happens after fertilization.
6. As the fertilized egg moves down the oviduct, it divides several times and becomes an embryo.
7. The embryo then attaches itself to the wall of the uterus. Once attached, it will remain there for nine months as it develops into a baby.

Figure 24-8 The stages of reproduction in the female are shown here. Where is the egg fertilized?in the oviduct

What happens to an egg after it is fertilized in the oviduct?

The Menstrual Cycle

You know that one egg is released by an ovary about every 28 days. What controls this timing? Many of the changes in the reproductive system are controlled by hormones. You learned in Chapter 15 that hormones are chemicals that affect certain body organs.

The monthly changes that take place in the female reproductive organs are called the **menstrual** (MEN struhl) **cycle.** The word *menstrual* comes from Latin and means monthly.

The menstrual cycle occurs about every month starting when a female is 10 to 13 years old. The monthly cycles continue for about 40 years.

Bio Tip

Science: Three billion human eggs would fill a small bucket. The same number of human sperm would fit into a thimble.

TEACH

Concept Development

▶ Point out that the events described illustrate the major ideas connected with internal fertilization.

▶ For ease in organization, the menstrual cycle can be divided into the three phases: days 1-14, days 14-24, and days 25-28.

Bridging

A review of Chapter 15 will refresh students' memories regarding hormones, their properties, where they are formed, and how they are carried through the body.

Misconception: Students usually are not aware of the fact that menstruation prepares the reproductive system to once again begin to form an egg and an environment conducive to fertilization and development of the fertilized egg.

Guided Practice

Have students write down their answers to the margin question: It divides into a mass of cells and travels to the uterus where it becomes embedded.

Independent Practice

Study Guide/*Teacher Resource Package,* p. 142. Use the Study Guide worksheet shown at the bottom of this page for independent practice.

STUDY GUIDE 142

STUDY GUIDE — CHAPTER 24

Name ______ Date ______ Class ______

REPRODUCTION IN HUMANS

In your textbook, read about stages of reproduction in Section 24:3.

6. Examine the diagrams below and label the parts. Then, answer the questions.

egg, uterus, ovary	a. Why will fertilization not take place in this diagram? **No sperm are present. Fertilization is the joining of egg and sperm.**
sperm, vagina	b. Why will fertilization not take place in this diagram? **No egg is present.**
embryo	c. Why will fertilization not take place in this diagram? (HINT: Note that an embryo is already present.) **Usually no eggs are released if fertilization and attachment within the uterus have occurred.**
oviduct	d. Why will fertilization not take place in this diagram? **There are no ovaries to produce eggs, and no eggs or sperm.**

OPTIONS

Challenge: Have students note changes occurring in the ovary and uterus during days 1 to 14 and compare them to changes during days 15 to 28.

The Menstrual Cycle/*Transparency Package,* number 24b. Use color transparency number 24b as you teach the menstrual cycle.

TEACH

Concept Development

▶ Explain that the ovary is an egg-forming structure and an endocrine gland.

▶ Point out changes that occur within the uterus during the menstrual cycle.

▶ The major job of the uterus during the last 14 days of the menstrual cycle is to prepare for a fertilized egg.

▶ Animals that have an estrous cycle do not have menstruation. The thickened uterus is absorbed internally and, as a consequence, no obvious blood loss is detected.

Independent Practice

Study Guide/*Teacher Resource Package*, p. 143. Use the Study Guide worksheet shown at the bottom of this page for independent practice.

Guided Practice

Have students write down their answers to the margin question: The lining of the uterus is shed.

Cooperative Learning: Divide the class into 8 or 9 groups. Have each group prepare a table similar to Table 24-1 to represent changes occurring in the female menstrual cycle if fertilization *does* occur. Ask the groups to record their tables onto a transparency and present their tables to the class.

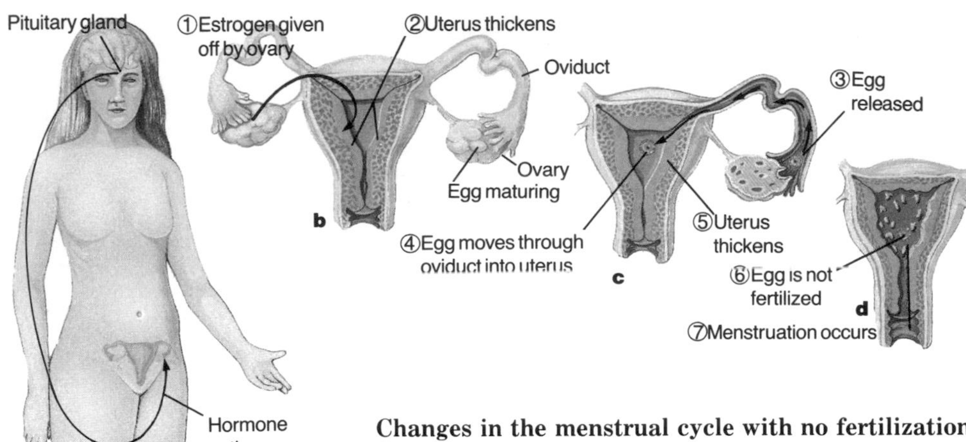

Figure 24-9 The changes shown here take place during the menstrual cycle if no egg is fertilized.

What happens in the uterus when an egg is not fertilized?

Changes in the menstrual cycle with no fertilization

Figure 24-9a shows events near the start of the menstrual cycle. The pituitary gland gives off a hormone. This hormone travels by way of the blood to the ovaries. It causes an egg in the ovaries to mature.

Figure 24-9b shows the changes that follow. The numbered steps in the diagram match the numbered statements.

1. The ovary itself forms estrogen (ES truh jun). **Estrogen** is a female hormone. It is responsible for the changes seen in a female as she enters puberty.
2. Estrogen also causes the lining of the uterus to increase in thickness. This increase in thickness makes it possible for a fertilized egg to attach to the uterine lining.

Figure 24-9c shows the next set of events. No sperm are present, so fertilization of the egg will not occur.

3. The ovary releases an egg. After the egg is released, the ovary begins to produce progesterone (pruh JES tuh rohn), a second female hormone.
4. The egg moves through the oviduct and enters the uterus.
5. Meanwhile, the uterine lining continues to thicken from the progesterone being made by the ovary.

Figure 24-9d shows what happens next.

6. The egg has not been fertilized. Therefore, it will not attach to the uterus.
7. The thick uterine lining is no longer needed. It begins to break apart. The cells of the thickened uterine lining break off and leave the body through the vagina along with the unfertilized egg and a small amount of blood. This loss of cells from the uterine lining, blood, and egg is called **menstruation** (men STRAY shun).

OPTIONS

Science Background

Onset of menstruation and sexual maturity is called menarche. Cessation of egg release and menstruation is called menopause.

STUDY GUIDE 143

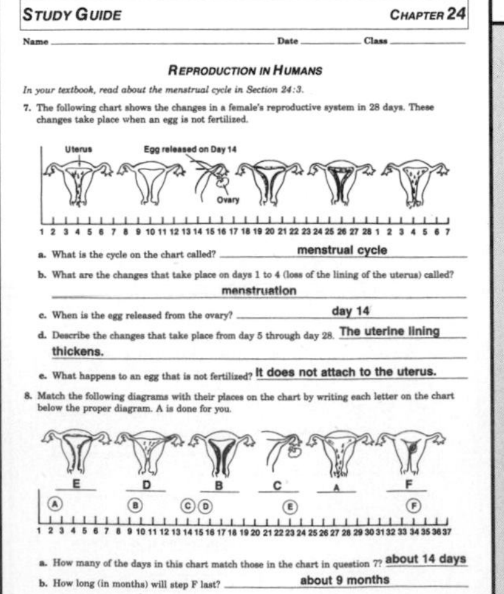
STUDY GUIDE CHAPTER 24

Name ______ Date ______ Class ______

REPRODUCTION IN HUMANS

In your textbook, read about the menstrual cycle in Section 24:3.

7. The following chart shows the changes in a female's reproductive system in 28 days. These changes take place when an egg is not fertilized.

a. What is the cycle on the chart called? menstrual cycle

b. What are the changes that take place on days 1 to 4 (loss of the lining of the uterus) called? menstruation

c. When is the egg released from the ovary? day 14

d. Describe the changes that take place from day 5 through day 28. The uterine lining thickens.

e. What happens to an egg that is not fertilized? It does not attach to the uterus.

8. Match the following diagrams with their places on the chart by writing each letter on the chart below the proper diagram. A is done for you.

a. How many of the days in this chart match those in the chart in question 7? about 14 days

b. How long (in months) will step F last? about 9 months

Science and Society

Sperm Banks

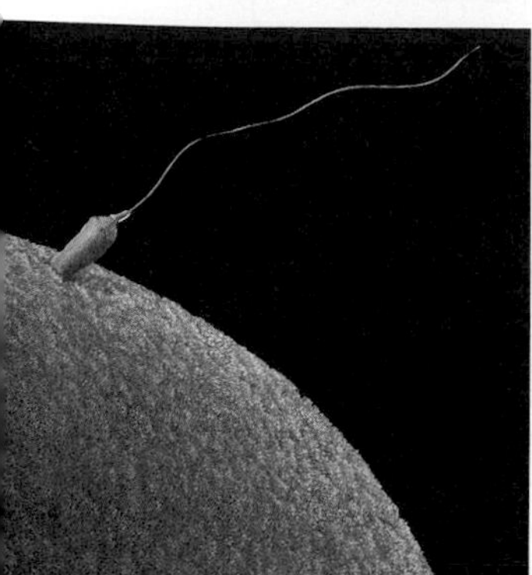

Technology has made it possible to store human sperm for years in sperm banks. Sperm are collected from donors and then frozen in liquid nitrogen. Chemicals are added to the liquid nitrogen to keep the sperm alive and prevent them from being damaged by the freezing temperatures. The sperm are kept frozen until they are needed.

How are the sperm banks used? For some couples, the husband is unable to produce sperm. These couples can receive sperm donated to the sperm bank by other males. Males who wish to donate sperm contact the sperm bank. The sperm is collected and stored. The stored sperm are used to fertilize one of the woman's eggs. The sperm are injected into the uterus with a syringe. This method of fertilizing eggs is called artificial insemination.

What Do You Think?

1. Couples who use sperm banks often don't know who donated the sperm. The name of the donor isn't revealed to them. Thus, the couple doesn't know who the biological father is. The donor also doesn't know who receives his sperm. How is keeping the identities of donors and couples who receive sperm a secret helpful? Would it be better to reveal the identities?

2. Couples who use sperm banks can look at catalogs that list the traits of different sperm donors. In this way, they can choose some of the genetic qualities of their future child. What if the couple wanted their child to be like Albert Einstein or Bruce Springsteen? Who would be responsible if the child were born with a genetic disorder instead of being like Einstein?

Sperm are stored in liquid nitrogen.

3. Imagine you could create a person with beautiful hair and eyes, a great personality, and lots of physical ability. Sperm bank technology makes it possible to create this "super person." Over time, a large group of "super people" could be produced. But, your friend likes blond hair and brown eyes. You prefer brown hair and blue eyes. Who decides which traits are the most desirable ones to have? What kinds of problems does society face with the ability to create "super people"?

Conclusion: Do the benefits of sperm banks outweigh the possible problems?

517

Sperm Banks

Background

The technique of freezing and thawing viable sperm has been around since 1938. The first successful artificial insemination of a female using sperm bank technology was reported in 1953.

A sample of donor sperm (typically the donors are screened and classified) is treated with glycerol to prevent ice crystals from forming. It is then cooled to -80°C for forty-five minutes. Then it is placed into a tank of liquid nitrogen for permanent storage (-196°C).

Teaching Suggestions

Many different scenarios can be created by students as to advantages and disadvantages of using artificial insemination. Have students discuss some of their own ideas about this technique. Scenarios may include: AIDS and other STDs being carried by the sperm, birth defects resulting, not knowing the donor, storing sperm prior to a vasectomy.

What Do You Think?

1. Genetic disease may be a major concern of parents.
2. and 3. Have students look up the meaning of the term *eugenics* to answer these questions.

Conclusion: Students may want to discuss the possibilities of a controlled population similar to something out of science fiction. Guide them to consider whether some couples would be happier with a child produced through artifical insemination or an adopted child. Have them consider that any child can be born with defects.

Suggested Readings

Baran, Annette. *Lethal Secrets.* New York, NY: Warner Books, Inc., 1989.

Noble, Elizabeth. *Having Your Baby by Donor Insemination.* Boston, MA: Houghton Mifflin, 1987.

TEACH

Concept Development

▶ Students should realize that a sperm cell that can swim on its own is needed for human fertilization. The trip through the female reproductive tract is rather long. Fertilization occurs in the oviducts, which are a distance from the vagina itself.

Connection: History

Ask students to research:

1. the derivation of (a) the term *venereal disease* (The term itself is now replaced by STD; however, students are still familiar with the term VD. The term stems from Venus, the Goddess of Love.) and (b) hermaphrodite (a person who is both male and female, derived from Hermes and Aphrodite)
2. figures in history who died of or who were considered to have contracted some form of STD

Check for Understanding

Have students compare the male and female reproductive systems by making these general comparisons: (1) names of parts and functions that are similar and different, (2) how sex cells are similar and different, (3) pathways that sperm and egg follow when leaving the reproductive system, and (4) main steps of the menstrual cycle and the reasons such a cycle is not needed in the male.

Reteach

Prepare diagrams of the human male and female reproductive systems and have students label the major organs.

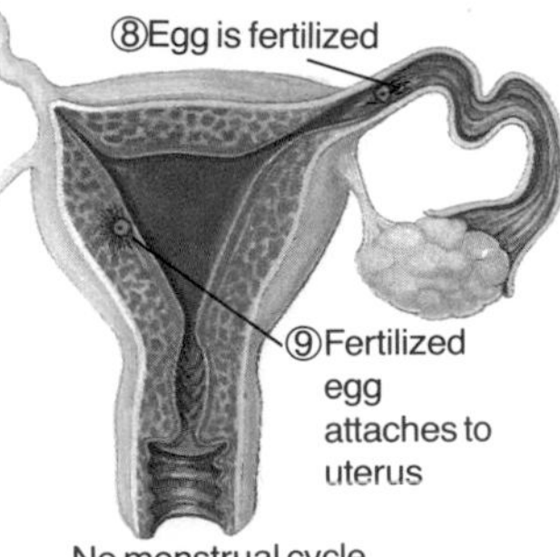

Figure 24-10 If fertilization occurs, the fertilized egg attaches to the uterus.

TABLE 24–1. MENSTRUAL CYCLE

Day in Cycle	Event Occurring if Egg Is Not Fertilized	Diagram
1-4	Menstruation—loss of egg, blood, uterus lining	24-9d
5-13	Thickening of uterus lining by estrogen	24-9a,b
14	Release of egg from ovary	24-9c
15-28	Continued thickening of uterus lining	24-9c
1-4	Menstruation if egg is not fertilized	24-9d

With menstruation, the cycle starts again. We could return to Figure 24-9a and follow the events for a second time. What event marks the beginning of a menstrual cycle? Table 24-1 shows you. It lists the days within the cycle when major events take place.

Changes in the menstrual cycle if fertilization occurs

What if fertilization does occur? Until step 5, the events are the same. After that, something different happens. Study Figure 24-10 as you read.

8. Sperm are present, and an egg is fertilized. Meanwhile, the uterine lining has thickened in preparation for receiving the embryo that develops from the fertilized egg.

9. The embryo attaches to the uterus. It remains attached for nine months while it develops into a baby. No new menstrual cycle will begin until the baby is born.

Skill Check

Sequence: Study Table 24-1 and Figure 24-9. Sequence the events that take place on days 5–14 of the menstrual cycle. *For more help, refer to the* ***Skill Handbook,*** *pages 706-711.*

Diseases of the Reproductive System

Like all other body systems, the human reproductive system can be invaded by microbes. This invasion can result in diseases being passed from person to person during sexual contact. Diseases transmitted through sexual contact are called **sexually transmitted diseases,** or STDs.

Some common STDs are listed in Table 24-2. These diseases can damage the reproductive system as well as other body systems. What kinds of microbes cause STDs? The diseases gonorrhea (gawn uh REE uh), chlamydia (kluh MIH dee uh), and syphilis (SIF uh lus) are caused by bacteria. AIDS and genital herpes are caused by viruses.

Gonorrhea, chlamydia, and syphilis can be treated and cured with antibiotics. Genital herpes and AIDS aren't curable.

OPTIONS

Science Background

The specific organism responsible for each STD is as follows: gonorrhea, *Neisseria gonorrhoea*; chlamydia, *Chlamydia trachomatis*; syphilis, *Treponema pallidum;* genital herpes, *Herpes genitalis* or Herpes simplex virus II (HSV II); AIDS, HIV or Human Immunodeficiency Virus.

TABLE 24–2. SEXUALLY TRANSMITTED DISEASES

Disease	Symptoms	Problems
Gonorrhea	females–puslike discharge from vagina, painful urination, no symptoms in many women males–pus discharge from penis, painful urination	females–sterility, passed to newborn from infected mother during birth males–infection of the testes
Chlamydia	(see gonorrhea), no symptoms in 70% of females, 10% of males	females–sterility, problem pregnancies males–sterility
Syphilis	sore on vagina or penis followed by rash, sore throat, swollen glands	damage to heart and brain, passed from mother to fetus
Genital Herpes	blisterlike cut or sore on vagina or penis, may look like a rash	passed to newborn from infected mother during birth
AIDS	fever, night sweating, dry cough, weight loss, swollen glands, constant tiredness	destruction of the immune system, pneumonia, cancer, fatal after long illness

How can a person reduce the chance of getting an STD? The best way is to avoid sexual contact. A second way is to use a condom during sexual contact. A third way is to have sexual contact with only one partner.

Which STDs can be cured?

In addition to sexually transmitted diseases, the reproductive system can be affected by other types of diseases. In males, the gland that supplies the liquid in which sperm swim can become swollen or develop tumors. In females, the tissue that surrounds the opening to the uterus can develop cancer. Both of these problems can be cured if they are detected early. Regular visits to a doctor are the best prevention.

Check Your Understanding

11. Name the functions of the ovary and testes.
12. At about what age does the menstrual cycle first begin?
13. What kinds of organisms cause STDs?
14. **Critical Thinking:** How is it possible for a person to have a sexually transmitted disease for a long time without knowing it?
15. **Biology and Reading:** If nonidentical twins are produced, how many eggs must have been produced at the same time in the mother's ovaries? Is this normal?

RETEACHING 74

RETEACHING CHAPTER 24

Name ______ Date ______ Class ______

Use with Section 24:3.

EGG RELEASE AND ATTACHMENT

Label the parts of the reproductive system and explain what is happening in each diagram.

oviduct

uterus

An egg is developing in the ovary.

ovary

vagina

A sperm is fertilizing an egg.

sperm

egg

Sperm are present but the egg cannot be fertilized.

implanted embryo

The egg has been implanted in the wall of the uterus.

STUDY GUIDE 144

STUDY GUIDE CHAPTER 24

Name ______ Date ______ Class ______

VOCABULARY

Review the new words used in Chapter 24 of your textbook. Then, fill in the blank next to each definition with the word or phrase it defines.

penis — 1. male reproductive organ that deposits sperm inside a female

scrotum — 2. sac that holds testes

uterus — 3. organ in which a fertilized egg will develop

vagina — 4. tube leading from outside the female's body to the uterus

oviducts — 5. tubelike organs that connect the ovaries to the uterus

regeneration — 6. reproduction in which parent separates into two or more pieces, each of which forms a new organism

menstruation — 7. loss of the uterine lining

estrous cycle — 8. cycle in which the female will mate only at certain times

external fertilization — 9. joining of egg and sperm outside the body

menstrual cycle — 10. monthly cycle that takes place in female reproductive organs

internal fertilization — 11. joining of egg and sperm inside the female's body

estrogen — 12. a female hormone

sexually transmitted diseases — 13. diseases transmitted through sexual contact

reproductive system — 14. system used to produce offspring

TEACH

Guided Practice

Have students write down their answers to the margin question: gonorrhea, chlamydia, and syphilis.

Independent Practice

Study Guide/*Teacher Resource Package,* p. 144. Use the Study Guide worksheet shown at the bottom of this page for independent practice.

Check for Understanding

Have students respond to the first three questions in Check Your Understanding.

Reteach

Reteaching/*Teacher Resource Package,* p. 74. Use this worksheet to give students additional practice with the movement of an egg.

Extension: Assign Critical Thinking, Biology and Reading, or some of the **OPTIONS** available with this lesson.

3 APPLY

ACTIVITY/Challenge

Ask students to research and report on various types of birth control.

4 CLOSE

Software

Reproduction Organs, Queue, Inc.

Answers to Check Your Understanding

11. Ovaries produce egg cells, and testes produce sperm cells.
12. 10-13 years old
13. bacteria and viruses
14. Many STDs have no symptoms or very mild symptoms.
15. two eggs; twins are not very common

CHAPTER 24 REVIEW

Summary

Summary statements can be used by students to review the major concepts of the chapter.

Key Science Words

All boldfaced terms from the chapter are listed.

Testing Yourself

Using Words

1. estrogen
2. breeding season
3. menstruation
4. uterus
5. estrous cycle
6. external fertilization
7. oviduct
8. vagina
9. menstrual cycle
10. regeneration

Finding Main Ideas

11. p. 504; Egg and sperm cells are not used, special organs are not used, mitosis takes place, certain body cells undergo mitosis to form offspring, and the offspring are clones of the parent.
12. p. 515; Sperm swim up through the vagina into the uterus.
13. pp. 515-516; The egg, under hormone control, begins to mature within the ovary. The uterus lining, also under hormone control begins to thicken. The production of hormones decreases and the uterus lining is shed if no fertilization occurs.
14. p. 508; Thousands of sex cells are released. Also, the animals gather in large groups before releasing their sex cells.

Chapter 24

Review

Summary

24:1 Asexual Reproduction

1. Asexual reproduction does not require sex cells, mating, or sex organs. It does use mitosis.
2. Budding and regeneration are two types of asexual reproduction.

24:2 Sexual Reproduction

3. Sexual reproduction uses mating and egg and sperm that are formed during meiosis.
4. In external fertilization, egg and sperm join outside the bodies of the parents. In internal fertilization, egg and sperm join inside the body of the female.
5. Having breeding seasons or an estrous cycle increases the chance of fertilization.

24:3 Reproduction in Humans

6. Eggs are formed in the ovaries and released into the oviducts. Fertilization of an egg occurs in the oviduct. The fertilized egg attaches itself to the uterine lining after it has divided several times.
7. The menstrual cycle prepares the uterus for a fertilized egg. If fertilization does not take place, menstruation occurs.
8. Sexually transmitted diseases are caused by bacteria and viruses and are spread by sexual contact.

Key Science Words

estrogen (p. 516)
estrous cycle (p. 510)
external fertilization (p. 508)
internal fertilization (p. 509)
menstrual cycle (p. 515)
menstruation (p. 516)
oviduct (p. 514)
penis (p. 513)
regeneration (p. 505)
reproductive system (p. 513)
sexually transmitted disease (p. 518)
scrotum (p. 513)
uterus (p. 514)
vagina (p. 515)
vas deferens (p. 513)

Testing Yourself

Using Words

Choose the word from the list of Key Science Words that best fits the definition.

1. hormone found in females
2. certain time of the year when animals reproduce
3. loss of egg, uterine lining, and blood
4. organ in which a fertilized egg develops
5. cycle in which a female will mate only at certain times
6. egg and sperm joining outside body
7. tubelike organ connecting ovary to uterus
8. where sperm are released in the female
9. monthly changes in the female reproductive system

Review

Testing Yourself *continued*

10. what it is called when the parent breaks into two or more pieces to reproduce

Finding Main Ideas

List the page number where each main idea below is found. Then, explain each main idea.

11. what the main features of asexual reproduction are
12. the pathway followed by sperm within the vagina
13. changes that take place during the different stages of the menstrual cycle
14. how animals with external fertilization improve the chances of fertilization
15. why animals with internal fertilization can reproduce on land
16. the roles of testes and ovaries

Using Main Ideas

Answer the questions by referring to the page number after each question.

17. What are three ways you can reduce the chances of getting an STD? (p. 519)
18. Why do animals with external fertilization almost always live or reproduce in water? (p. 508)
19. What happens on or about day 14 of the menstrual cycle? (p. 518)
20. How does mating help animals reproduce? (p. 509)
21. How does asexual reproduction compare to sexual reproduction in terms of (p. 504, p. 507):
    (a) the process of cell division used?
    (b) whether sex cells are needed?
22. How is budding different from regeneration? (p. 505)

Skill Review ✓

For more help, refer to the ***Skill Handbook,*** *pages 704-719.*

1. **Make and use tables:** Make a table that compares the features of asexual and sexual reproduction.
2. **Sequence:** Sequence the steps involved in regeneration of a planarian.
3. **Understand science words:** What does the prefix *ex* mean in the word *external?*
4. **Make scale drawings:** An egg viewed under high power (430x) measures 30 mm when drawn to scale in a circle that has a diameter of 100 mm. What is the actual size of the egg?

Finding Out More

Critical Thinking

1. As a hobby, you wish to grow identical planaria. Suggest a plan for carrying out your hobby.
2. Each ovary takes a turn releasing one egg every 28 days. Yet, people do have fraternal (unalike) twins. Explain how this is possible.

Applications

1. Explain how a condom, diaphragm, fertility awareness, birth control pill, vasectomy, and tubal ligation actually work as birth control methods.
2. Find out which mammals have menstrual or estrous cycles and how long these cycles are. Prepare a chart of your findings for room display.

Finding Main Ideas

15. p. 509; The sperm are released inside the female's body.
16. pp. 513-514; Testes produce sperm cells, and ovaries produce egg cells.

Using Main Ideas

17. Avoid sexual contact, use a condom, and have sexual contact with only one partner.
18. Sperm cells must be able to swim to the egg, and this can only be done in water.
19. A mature egg moves into the uterus.
20. It increases the chance that an egg will be fertilized, and it allows fertilization to take place out of the water.
21. a. In asexual, cells undergo mitosis; in sexual, cells undergo meiosis.
    b. In asexual, no sex cells are needed; in sexual, the sex cells, egg and sperm, are needed.
22. In budding, a new organism develops from a small part of the body. In regeneration, the parent can split into two or more pieces. Each piece forms a new organism.

Skill Review

1. List asexual and sexual as headings. List features in columns under each heading.
2. Sequence of steps is: regeneration begins at the head, two heads form; planarian continues to split along body, two separate planaria are formed.
3. *Ex* means out of or from
4. 0.0697 mm

Finding Out More

Critical Thinking

1. You could make a small vertical cut in the middle of the head of a planarian. It will then divide and form two identical planaria.
2. Two eggs are released.

Applications

1. Condom, diaphragm, and vasectomy are methods that prevent sperm from reaching an egg. Tubal ligation prevents an egg from reaching the uterus. Birth control pills prevent an egg from maturing; fertility awareness is knowing the time an egg can be fertilized.
2. Answers will vary depending on the mammals that are researched. Examples of animals having estrous cycles are dogs and cats.

Chapter Review/*Teacher Resource Package*, pp. 126-127.

Chapter Test/*Teacher Resource Package*, pp. 128-130.

Chapter Test/*Computer Test Bank*

Animal Development

PLANNING GUIDE

CONTENT	TEXT FEATURES	TEACHER RESOURCE PACKAGE	OTHER COMPONENTS
(2 days) 25:1 Development Inside the Female Early Stages of Development Needs of the Embryo Human Development	Skill Check: *Understand Digrams,* p. 526 Lab 25-1: *Development,* p. 531 Career Close-up: *Ultrasound Technician,* p. 527 Idea Map, p. 525 Check Your Understanding, p. 530	Enrichment: *Comparing Weight in Different Stages of Mammal Development,* p. 27 Reteaching: *Vocabulary Puzzle,* p. 75 Transparency Master: *Cleavage of a Fertilized Egg,* p. 127 Study Guide: *Development Inside the Female,* pp. 145-147 Lab 25-1: *Development,* pp. 97-98	**Laboratory Manual:** *How Does a Human Fetus Change During Development?* p. 211 **Laboratory Manual:** *What Changes Occur During Birth?* p. 215 Color Transparency 25a: *Cleavage*
(1/2 day) 25:2 Development Outside the Female Eggs That Are Laid Needs of the Embryo	Mini Lab: *What Can Pass Through an Egg Shell?* p. 533 Check Your Understanding, p. 533	Reteaching: *Development Outside the Female,* p. 76 Skill: *Predict,* p. 26 Study Guide: *Development Outside the Female,* p. 148	
(1 1/2 days) 25:3 Metamorphosis Frog Metamorphosis Insect Metamorphosis	Skill Check: *Understand Science Words,* p. 535 Lab 25-2: *Metamorphosis,* p. 534 Idea Map, p. 534 Check Your Understanding, p. 537	Application: *Metamorphosis,* p. 25 Reteaching: *Insect Metamorphosis,* p. 77 Critical Thinking/Problem Solving: *What Happens to Insects in the Winter?* p. 25 Focus: *Metamorphosis* p. 49 Study Guide: *Metamorphosis,* p. 149 Study Guide: *Vocabulary,* p. 150 Lab 25-2: *Metamorphosis,* pp. 99-100	Color Transparency 25b: *Frog Metamorphosis*
Chapter Review	Summary Key Science Words Testing Yourself Finding Main Ideas Using Main Ideas Skill Review	Chapter Review, pp. 131-132 Chapter Test, pp. 133-135 Unit Test, pp. 136-137	**Test Bank**

MATERIALS NEEDED

LAB 25-1, p. 531	LAB 25-2, p. 534	MARGIN FEATURES
metric ruler	metric ruler hand lens grasshopper stages of metamorphosis moth stages of metamorphosis	Skill Check, p. 535 dictionary Mini Lab, p. 533 beaker eggshell glucose

OBJECTIVES

SECTION	OBJECTIVE	OBJECTIVES CORRELATION			
		CHECK YOUR UNDERSTANDING	CHAPTER REVIEW	TRP CHAPTER REVIEW	TRP CHAPTER TEST
25:1	1. **Sequence** the changes that take place in a fertilized egg before it attaches to the uterus.	3, 5	6, 13	28	1, 29, 35
	2. **Explain** how the needs of an embryo are met as it develops.	2, 4	2, 7, 9, 15, 19	15, 16, 18, 19, 20, 21	6, 7, 9, 11, 17, 18, 22, 25, 34, 48, 49, 50, 53, 54
	3. **Describe** the stages of human development from the first month until birth.	1	1, 8, 14, 18, 20	3, 5, 17, 22, 23, 25	8, 12, 15, 23, 24, 27, 31, 32, 33, 36, 37, 38, 39, 40, 41, 42, 43, 44, 45, 46, 47, 51, 52
25:2	4. **Compare** development in frogs, birds, and reptiles.	6, 9, 10	13, 20	4	19, 20, 26, 30
	5. **Explain** how the needs of a chick embryo are met.	7, 8	12, 16, 23	1, 2, 6	4, 13, 16, 21
25:3	6. **Sequence** the stages of frog metamorphosis.	11, 13	3, 10, 17, 21	24, 28	3, 28
	7. **Explain** incomplete metamorphosis.	15	4, 10, 11, 22	12, 13, 14, 28	5, 14
	8. **Describe** complete metamorphosis.	12	5, 10, 22	7, 8, 9, 10, 11, 26, 28	2, 3, 10

Animal Development

CHAPTER OVERVIEW

Key Concepts

In this chapter, students will study the growth, development, and birth process of an embryo inside the body of a female animal. A human embryo is used as the representative example. Students will study growth and development outside the body using the chicken as an example. In the last sections, students will study both complete and incomplete animal metamorphosis.

Key Science Words

amniotic sac	larva
cleavage	metamorphosis
complete metamorphosis	navel
fetus	nymph
incomplete metamorphosis	placenta
labor	pupa
	umbilical cord

Skill Development

In Lab 25-1, students will **measure in SI, use numbers, infer,** and **make and use graphs** to judge the age of a human fetus. In Lab 25-2, students will **interpret data, measure in SI,** and **compare** complete and incomplete metamorphosis. In the Skill Check on page 526, students will **interpret diagrams** as they study the path of oxygen from mother to embryo. On page 535, students will **understand** the **science word** *metamorphosis.* In the Mini Lab on page 533, students will **design an experiment** to test whether substances can pass through an egg shell.

CHAPTER PREVIEW

Chapter Content

Review this outline for Chapter 25 before you read the chapter.

25:1 Development Inside the Female
- Early Stages of Development
- Needs of the Embryo
- Human Development

25:2 Development Outside the Female
- Eggs That Are Laid
- Needs of the Embryo

25:3 Metamorphosis
- Frog Metamorphosis
- Insect Metamorphosis

Skills in this Chapter

The skills that you will use in this chapter are listed below.

- In **Lab 25-1,** you will measure in SI, use numbers, infer, and make and use graphs. In **Lab 25-2,** you will interpret data, measure in SI, and compare.
- In the **Skill Checks,** you will understand diagrams and understand science words.
- In the **Mini Labs,** you will design an experiment.

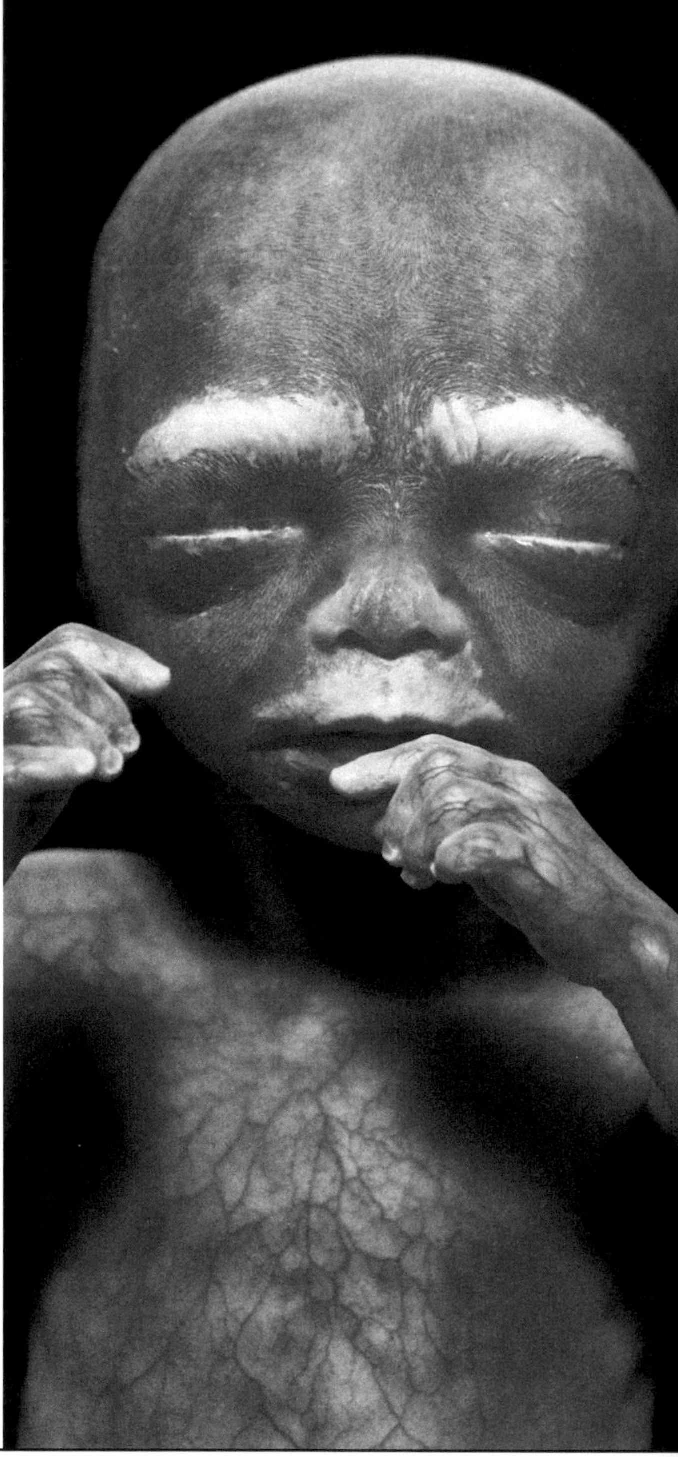

Six-month-old human fetus

522

Bridging

Chapter 24 covered the events leading to fertilization of an egg. This chapter continues the story by explaining the changes that occur to a fertilized egg as it undergoes development into a fetus.

Chapter 25

Animal Development

A human female carries an unborn child for about 266 days, approximately 9 months. Other animals carry their young different lengths of time. Rats carry their young for only 22 days. In cats and dogs, the length of time for carrying young is about 60 days. In horses, it is about 336 days. Some animals don't carry their young at all. The young develop outside the female's body. Birds, frogs, and insects are some animals that develop outside the female.

The photo on the left shows a six-month-old unborn human as it appears within the mother's body. Has it formed all the parts it will need at birth? How does it get food and oxygen? You will discover the answers to these questions as you read this chapter.

Try This!

What changes take place during birth? Use a compass to draw a circle 2 mm in diameter. This circle is the usual size of the opening to the uterus. Draw a circle 98 mm in diameter. This circle is the size of the opening to the uterus during birth. Why is this change in size needed?

GETTING STARTED

Using the Photos

In looking at the photos, students should try to identify the body parts that are visible in the embryo. Students may be surprised to find so many body parts already formed. Emphasize that body parts continue to grow and develop until birth.

MOTIVATION/Try This!

What changes take place during birth? Upon completing the chapter-opening activity, students will have **formulated models.** The opening of the uterus must enlarge to accommodate the fetus during birth. The uterus, being smooth muscle, slowly changes in size during labor.

Chapter Preview

Have students study the chapter outline before they begin to read the chapter. They should note the overall organization of the chapter, that the first topic described deals with development inside the body of a female animal. This is followed by development occurring outside the body of a female animal. Finally, the various changes taking place among frogs and insects during metamorphosis is covered.

Misconception

Blood between mother and fetus does not mix directly during development. The placenta does connect fetus to mother, and the placenta contains a rich supply of blood vessels as does the uterus. However, the capillary networks of both organs (uterus and placenta) do not connect directly. Transfer of materials between placenta and uterus or vice versa occurs via diffusion. Molecules of food, oxygen, and blood proteins such as antibodies can diffuse across this barrier but blood cells do not.

25:1 Development Inside the Female

PREPARATION

Materials Needed

Make copies of the Transparency Master, Reteaching, Study Guide, Enrichment, and Lab worksheets in the *Teacher Resource Package.*

▶ Obtain clay for the Focus activity.

Key Science Words

cleavage
amniotic sac
placenta
umbilical cord
fetus
labor
navel

Process Skills

In the Skill Check, students will understand diagrams. In Lab 25-1, students will measure in SI, use numbers, infer, and make and use graphs.

1 FOCUS

▶ The objectives are listed on the student page. Remind students to preview these objectives as a guide to this numbered section.

ACTIVITY/Hands-On

Provide each student with a small wad of clay about the size of a pea. Ask them to divide the clay into two equal halves, then each half into two equal halves, then again, and again so that they have sixteen pieces. The original wad of clay represents the mass of a fertilized egg. Each division into two equal halves represents the separation of cell contents during mitosis. Students will note that the number of cells increases but the mass of cellular material does not.

Guided Practice

Have students write down their answers to the margin question: when it undergoes mitosis to make two cells.

25:1 Development Inside the Female

Objectives

1. **Sequence** the changes that take place in a fertilized egg until it attaches to the uterus.
2. **Explain** how the needs of an embryo are met as it develops.
3. **Describe** the stages of human development from the first month until birth.

Key Science Words

cleavage
amniotic sac
placenta
umbilical cord
fetus
labor
navel

You began as a fertilized egg and are now a young adult. You have gone through many changes. Many of these changes took place while you were still in your mother's body.

Early Stages of Development

All living things go through development. You learned in Chapter 2 that development is all the changes that occur in a living thing as it grows. In humans, development begins when a single fertilized egg changes into many different body parts or tissues. Development results in the forming of bone, muscle, hair, nerve, and skin tissues.

What are the changes that can be seen in humans as they develop? In order to answer this question we must start with a single fertilized egg. The fertilized egg undergoes changes that take it from a one-celled stage to a many-celled stage. These changes are largely the result of mitosis.

Most of the early changes take place while the egg is still within the female's oviduct. Follow the numbered steps of Figure 25-1 as you continue to read. Also pay attention to how long it takes for each change to take place.

1. An egg is fertilized.
2. The fertilized egg undergoes mitosis to make two cells. It is now an embryo. How long did this step take?

When does a fertilized egg become an embryo?

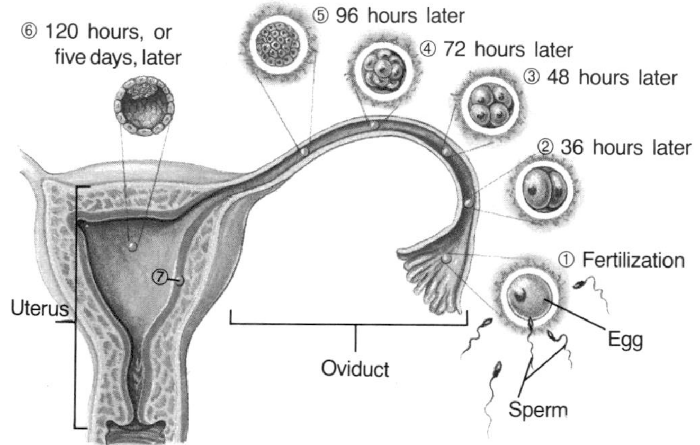

Figure 25-1 The fertilized egg goes through cleavage in the oviduct. How long does it take for the embryo to become a solid ball of cells? 96 hours

OPTIONS

Science Background

In humans, during the weeks of early development, the formation of the three embryonic germ layers has begun to form with ectoderm, endoderm, and mesoderm now being present. Ectoderm forms the skin, nervous system, retina, cornea, lens, and inner ear. Endoderm forms the liver, pancreas, thyroid, and linings of the digestive and respiratory systems. Mesoderm forms muscles, bone, connective tissue, blood and blood vessels, kidneys, and reproductive organs.

3. Mitosis continues and two cells form four cells. Four cells then form eight. Eight cells will form sixteen cells.
4. Three days later, the embryo is sixteen cells in size.
5. Next, the embryo forms a solid ball of cells. Has it left the oviduct yet?
6. Finally, after five days (120 hours), the embryo moves out of the oviduct into the uterus. By this time, it is a hollow ball of cells.
7. Next, the embryo attaches itself to the lining of the uterus. This is where it develops for the next 37 weeks.

These early changes are called cleavage (KLEE vihj). **Cleavage** is the series of changes that take place to turn one fertilized egg into a hollow ball of many cells. The number of cells increases from one to about one hundred in just five days. The word *cleave* means to chop or divide. What divides during cleavage?

All the changes that take place during cleavage occur within the body of the female. Many animals, such as humans, cats, and whales, show this type of development.

Needs of the Embryo

Embryos, just like adults or newborns, have certain needs. These needs include protection, food, oxygen, and getting rid of wastes. How are these needs met?

Protection

The embryo must be protected against injury. An amniotic (am nee AHT ik) sac forms around it as shown in Figure 25-2. An **amniotic sac** is a tissue filled with liquid that protects the embryo. The liquid around the embryo cushions it in the same way as packing material cushions the contents of a package.

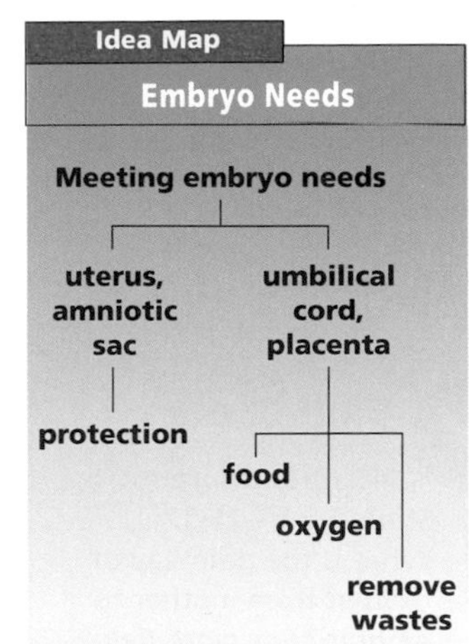

Study Tip: Use this idea map as a study guide to development inside the female. How are the needs of the embryo met?

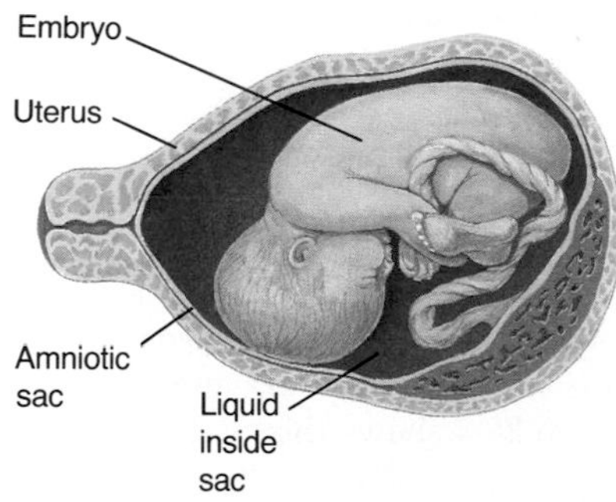

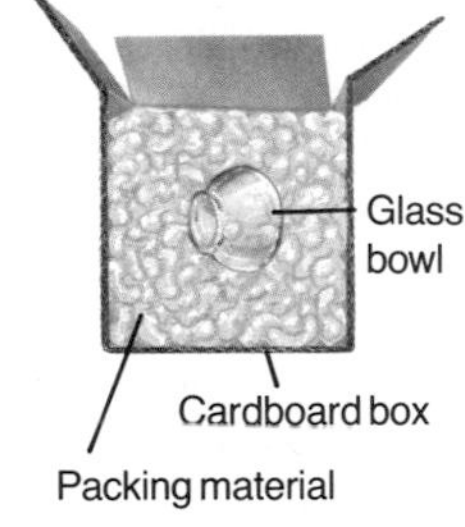

Figure 25-2 The amniotic sac protects the embryo, much like the packing material protects the bowl.

2 TEACH

MOTIVATION/Audiovisual

Show the video *The Course of Development*, Human Relations Media.

Concept Development

▶ Make sure that students read the numbered statements and match them with the numbers appearing in Figure 25-1.

▶ If Chapter 24 was not studied, it may be helpful to review the anatomy of the female human reproductive system. Emphasis should be placed on the ovary, oviducts, and uterus.

▶ Point out that growth results from an increase in cells. Development refers to the actual changes responsible for forming new tissues.

▶ You may want to preview the four needs by simply listing them on the chalkboard before studying each one in detail. Or, try to elicit them from your students by asking what the needs might be.

Using Science Words: The word *embryo* in Greek means to swell. When a female becomes pregnant, a new human begins to grow from a fertilized egg. As it grows, there is a swelling of the female.

Idea Map

Have students use the idea map as a study guide to the major concepts of this section.

TRANSPARENCY 127

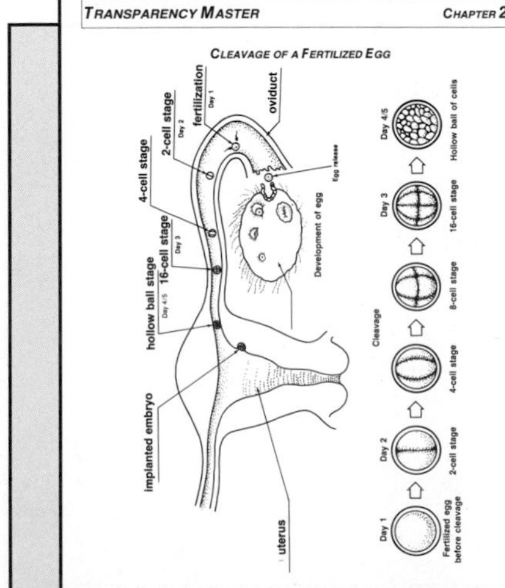

OPTIONS

Cleavage/*Transparency Package,* number 25a. Use color transparency number 25a as you teach early changes in a human embryo.

Transparency Master/*Teacher Resource Package,* p. 127. Use the Transparency Master shown here to teach cleavage of a fertilized egg.

TEACH

Concept Development

▶ Emphasize that no mixing of fetal and maternal blood occurs. Gases, food, and wastes pass through the placental barrier by means of diffusion.

▶ As a review, you may want to ask students why oxygen is needed by all cells. Terms such as *respiration, cellular respiration,* or *energy release* would be most acceptable.

▶ You may wish to relate ideas learned in Chapter 9 on nutrition to this section. Ask students the form of food as it passes through the placenta. (It is digested in the form of glucose, fatty acids, amino acids.)

Bridging

Remind students that certain drugs and disease-causing organisms can also pass from the blood of mother to their embryos. This is why children can be born with AIDS, drug addiction, or syphilis.

Skill Check

Students should follow the blue arrows in Figure 25-3 from the mother's blood in the uterus to the embryo.

MOTIVATION/Brainstorming

Ask students to speculate on the kinds of problems that a fetus or embryo would face if for some reason the placenta did not make proper contact with the mother's uterus.

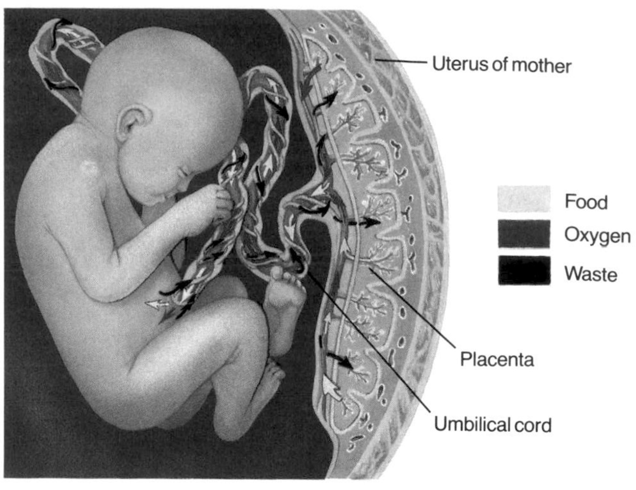

Figure 25-3 The embryo receives food and oxygen and gets rid of wastes through the placenta.

Skill Check

Interpret diagrams: Study Figure 25-3. What is the pathway of oxygen from mother to embryo? *For more help, refer to the **Skill Handbook,** pages 706-711.*

Food

How does an embryo get food? Certainly it doesn't eat while inside the amniotic sac. Yet, it must be supplied with food in order to grow.

Before a human is born, food is supplied by the mother. The embryo's food is in the mother's blood. This food comes from food that the mother eats.

How does the food get from the mother's blood to the embryo? Food passes from an organ called the placenta (pluh SENT uh) to the embryo. The **placenta** is an organ that connects the embryo to the mother's uterus. The placenta has many blood vessels in it. Food passes from the mother's blood through the placenta into a cord, called the umbilical (uhm BIL ih kuhl) cord. The **umbilical cord** is made of blood vessels that connect the embryo to the placenta.

Figure 25-3 shows the placenta and umbilical cord in a human embryo. Notice the yellow arrows. They show the direction of food from mother to embryo.

Oxygen

The embryo receives oxygen the same way as it receives food. Oxygen passes from the mother's blood in the uterus to the blood in the placenta. Once in the capillaries of the placenta, oxygen passes into the blood vessels of the umbilical cord. These blood vessels connect directly to the blood vessels of the embryo. Oxygen is then passed to the embryo. Figure 25-3 shows this pathway with blue arrows.

OPTIONS

Science Background

The umbilical cord consists of three blood vessels connecting fetus to placenta. These vessels include two veins and one artery. The vein brings oxygenated blood to the fetus, and the arteries carry away deoxygenated blood. The placenta provides a large surface area for exchange of materials between fetal and maternal circulatory systems.

Career Close-Up

Ultrasound Technician

A woman is pregnant and her doctor suggests an ultrasound of the fetus. What actually is ultrasound? Who will take the ultrasound?

An ultrasound technician operates a machine that can take pictures of any organ inside the body. The machine uses sound waves that reflect off body organs. These sound waves are changed into pictures that allow a doctor to see inside the body. Unlike X rays, ultrasound pictures show movement. Ultrasound is also safer than X rays.

Ultrasound pictures will show if a woman is carrying twins. They help the doctor judge the age of the fetus. In this way, the doctor can give a better prediction as to when the child will be born. Abnormal development or birth defects may also be detected. Finally, the sex of the fetus can be determined.

To be an ultrasound technician a person needs a high school education. Two or more years of special training may be needed. After the proper education and training, most ultrasound technicians work in hospitals.

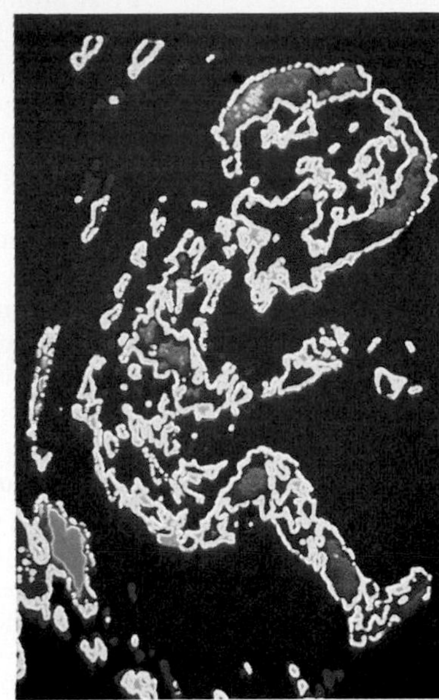

Ultrasound shows what a developing fetus looks like.

Wastes

The cells of the embryo produce wastes. Carbon dioxide and urea are two such waste chemicals. The cord and placenta help get rid of these wastes. The embryo's blood carries these wastes from the embryo to the placenta, where the wastes enter the mother's bloodstream. Figure 25-3 shows this pathway. In which direction are the black arrows that carry wastes going? Why?

How does an embryo get rid of wastes?

A pregnant female eats for herself and the developing embryo. She also breathes for herself and the embryo. She must get rid of her wastes and those of the embryo.

Now you see why proper nutrition is important during pregnancy. Good health is also very important at this time.

Career Close-Up

Ultrasound Technician

Background

The technician directs high frequency sound waves by way of a transducer to a patient's body. The sound waves create an echo when reflected from body tissue, providing an image on a video monitor.

Related Careers

Many ultrasound technicians may also be certified as X-ray technicians, nuclear medicine technologists, or radiation therapy technologists.

Job Requirements

A two- or three-year course of study is required after high school graduation. Certification is then given by the American Registry of Radiologic Technologists.

For More Information

Society of Diagnostic Medical Sonographers, 12225 Greenville Avenue, Suite 434, Dallas, TX 75234, (214)-235-7367; or American Medical Association, Department of Allied Health Education and Accreditation, 515 North State Street, Chicago, IL 60610, (312)-464-5000

TEACH

Guided Practice

Have students write down their answers to the margin question: The embryo's blood carries wastes from the embryo and the placenta by way of the umbilical cord.

Independent Practice

Study Guide/*Teacher Resource Package,* p. 145. Use the Study Guide worksheet shown at the bottom of this page for independent practice.

STUDY GUIDE 145

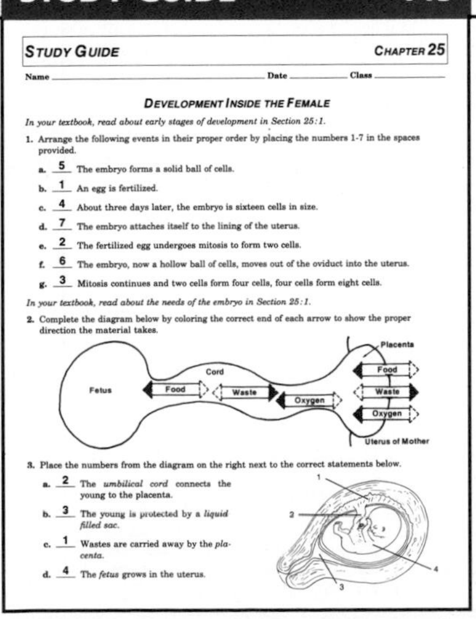

STUDY GUIDE — CHAPTER 25

Name ______ Date ______ Class ______

DEVELOPMENT INSIDE THE FEMALE

In your textbook, read about early stages of development in Section 25:1.

1. Arrange the following events in their proper order by placing the numbers 1-7 in the spaces provided.
   - a. 5 The embryo forms a solid ball of cells.
   - b. 1 An egg is fertilized.
   - c. 4 About three days later, the embryo is sixteen cells in size.
   - d. 7 The embryo attaches itself to the lining of the uterus.
   - e. 2 The fertilized egg undergoes mitosis to form two cells.
   - f. 6 The embryo, now a hollow ball of cells, moves out of the oviduct into the uterus.
   - g. 3 Mitosis continues and two cells form four cells, four cells form eight cells.

In your textbook, read about the needs of the embryo in Section 25:1.

2. Complete the diagram below by coloring the correct end of each arrow to show the proper direction the material takes.

3. Place the numbers from the diagram on the right next to the correct statements below.
   - a. 2 The *umbilical cord* connects the young to the placenta.
   - b. 3 The young is protected by a *liquid filled sac.*
   - c. 1 Wastes are carried away by the *placenta.*
   - d. 4 The *fetus* grows in the uterus.

TEACH

Analogy: Show objects having masses comparable to a fetus at the end of the second and third months. A small paper clip has a mass of about one gram. The length of the fetus from crown to rump after the third month is about the width of one's palm.

Connection: Math

Provide students with calendars and give them an opportunity to determine some expected birth dates by listing the dates of a mother's last menstrual period. Have them add 280 days (40 weeks) to the first day of the last menstrual period. A second method of calculating a birth date is to count back three calendar months from the first day of the last menstrual period and then add one week. You may want students to try both methods to see if they end with the same delivery date.

Guided Practice

Have students write down their answers to the margin question: two months.

Human Development

What changes occur as the embryo continues to develop? When do these changes take place? Let's look at the human embryo to help answer these questions.

First Month

Many changes take place during the first month. Figure 25-4a shows what the embryo looks like at one month. The stomach, brain, and heart start to form. Liver and ears begin to appear. The thyroid gland forms. The heart is already beating. It can be seen as a bulge just in front of the arms.

You can even see the start of eye development. The dark circle in the head will be the embryo's eye. Fingers can be seen. Can you see legs at this point in development?

How large is the embryo at this stage? To see how large the embryo is, measure the small figure in the box in millimeters. This figure is an embryo drawn to actual size. The embryo has a mass of 0.02 grams.

Second Month

During the second month, arms and legs form. Fingers and toes appear. The eyes have eyelids. The mouth has lips and the nose has nostrils. Figure 25-4b shows these parts. Muscles and bone form. The embryo can even move at this age.

Bio Tip

Health: A fetus born at 20 weeks of development has about a 5 percent chance of survival.

At what age does an embryo begin to move?

Figure 25-4 A one-month-old embryo (a) and a two-month-old embryo (b) are shown enlarged and actual size.

a

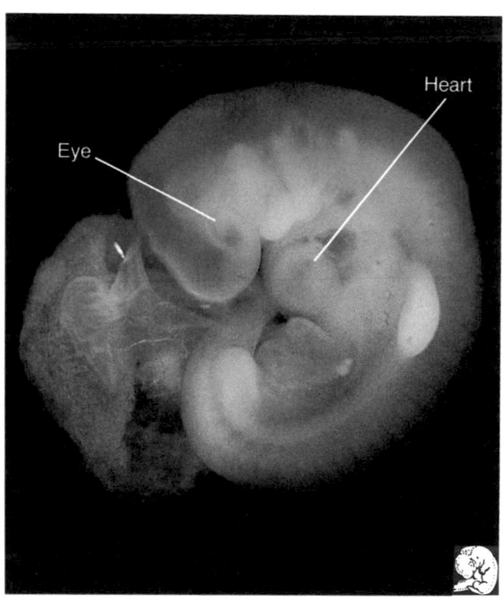

b

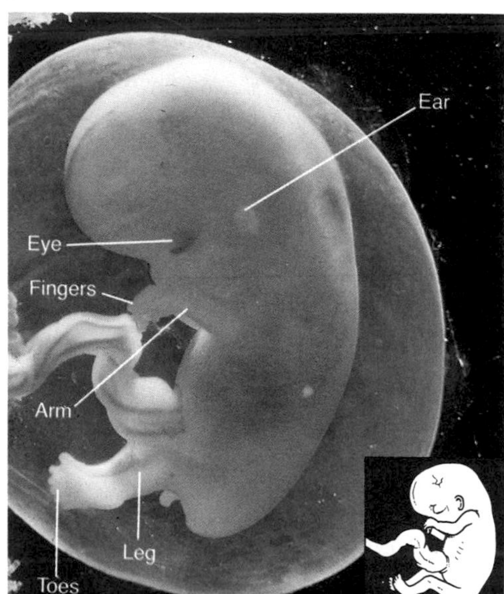

OPTIONS

Challenge: Have your students investigate at what age a fetus may live if born prematurely. An age of 22 weeks is usually given as the age after which there is some chance for survival. However, fetuses born during the 26th to 28th weeks of development still have a difficult time surviving.

Enrichment/*Teacher Resource Package*, p. 27. Use the Enrichment worksheet shown here for students to compare weight in different stages of mammal development.

ENRICHMENT 27

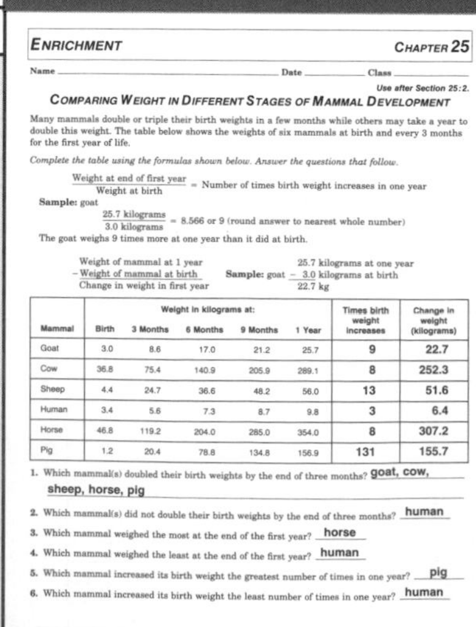

ENRICHMENT CHAPTER 25

Name ______ Date ______ Class ______

Use after Section 25:2.

COMPARING WEIGHT IN DIFFERENT STAGES OF MAMMAL DEVELOPMENT

Many mammals double or triple their birth weights in a few months while others may take a year to double this weight. The table below shows the weights of six mammals at birth and every 3 months for the first year of life.

Complete the table using the formulas shown below. Answer the questions that follow.

$$\frac{\text{Weight at end of first year}}{\text{Weight at birth}} = \text{Number of times birth weight increases in one year}$$

Sample: goat

$$\frac{25.7 \text{ kilograms}}{3.0 \text{ kilograms}} = 8.566 \text{ or } 9 \text{ (round answer to nearest whole number)}$$

The goat weighs 9 times more at one year than it did at birth.

Weight of mammal at 1 year
− Weight of mammal at birth
Change in weight in first year

Sample: goat
25.7 kilograms at one year
− 3.0 kilograms at birth
22.7 kg

Mammal	Weight in kilograms at: Birth	3 Months	6 Months	9 Months	1 Year	Times birth weight increases	Change in weight (kilograms)
Goat	3.0	8.6	17.0	21.2	25.7	9	22.7
Cow	36.8	75.4	140.9	205.9	289.1	8	252.3
Sheep	4.4	24.7	36.6	48.2	56.0	13	51.6
Human	3.4	5.6	7.3	8.7	9.8	3	6.4
Horse	46.8	119.2	204.0	285.0	354.0	8	307.2
Pig	1.2	20.4	78.8	134.8	156.9	131	155.7

1. Which mammal(s) doubled their birth weights by the end of three months? goat, cow, sheep, horse, pig
2. Which mammal(s) did not double their birth weights by the end of three months? human
3. Which mammal weighed the most at the end of the first year? horse
4. Which mammal weighed the least at the end of the first year? human
5. Which mammal increased its birth weight the greatest number of times in one year? pig
6. Which mammal increased its birth weight the least number of times in one year? human

You cannot tell yet whether the embryo is a boy or a girl. Its mass is 1.0 gram. Measure the small figure in the box in millimeters. Has the embryo doubled in size from the first month?

Third Month

At the start of the third month, the embryo is called a fetus (FEET us). The **fetus** is an embryo that has all of its body systems. The organs are not complete, but they are all present. You can tell whether the fetus is a boy or a girl. Its mass is 14 grams. Figure 25-5 shows a life-size fetus at three months. Measure the length of the fetus in millimeters.

Fourth Month to Birth

By the fourth month, the fetus is rather active. It kicks, bends, and turns. The mother begins to feel it moving. By the end of the fourth month, the fetus is 160 millimeters long and has a mass of 100 grams.

Development goes on for the next five months. After a total of 38 weeks, or about 266 days, birth will take place. The fetus will be about 500 millimeters and 3000 grams. How much larger is it than it was at one month?

Not all animals develop in 38 weeks. Table 25-1 lists how long certain animals take to develop before they are born. Dogs take nine weeks to develop. Elephants take 84 weeks. Does length of time needed for development appear to be related to animal size? In what way?

TABLE 25–1. TIME FOR DEVELOPMENT

Animal	Weeks for Development
Rat	3
Rabbit	4
Cat	9
Dog	9
Sheep	21
Bear	28
Gorilla	36
Human	38
Horse	48
Elephant	84

Amniotic sac

Placenta

Umbilical cord

Figure 25-5 This three-month-old fetus is shown actual size.

TEACH

Check for Understanding

Have students copy the following terms: cleavage, amniotic sac, placenta, umbilical cord, fetus, labor, and navel. Ask them to properly use each term in a sentence.

Reteach

Have students explain how a fertilized egg, embryo, and fetus differ in terms of stage of development, size, and the degree of change that has taken place.

Cooperative Learning: Divide the class into 4 groups. Have each group prepare a short oral report on one of the following topics: Early changes in development, Early needs of the developing embryo, Human development, or Human birth.

Each group should prepare any needed charts or diagrams to help with their presentation. These charts should be placed on a transparency for viewing by the entire class. There should be a spokesperson for each group who will present the report to the rest of the class.

Independent Practice

Study Guide/*Teacher Resource Package*, pp. 146-147. Use the Study Guide worksheet shown at the bottom of this page for independent practice.

STUDY GUIDE 146

STUDY GUIDE — CHAPTER 25

Name ______ Date ______ Class ______

DEVELOPMENT INSIDE THE FEMALE

4. Why are proper nutrition and good health important during pregnancy? **A pregnant female is living for two—eating, breathing, and getting rid of wastes for herself and the developing embryo.**
5. How does the amniotic sac help the developing embryo? **This tissue is filled with liquid that cushions and protects the embryo from injury.**

In your textbook, read about human development in Section 25:1.

6. Complete the following table by placing a checkmark in the column that tells when the traits listed form.

Trait	Month 1	2	3	4 to birth
Muscles and bones form.		✓		
Liver and ears appear.	✓			
Kicking, bending, and turning occurs.				✓
Embryo is 1.0 gram.		✓		
Arms and legs form.		✓		
Stomach starts to form.	✓			
Fetus is 3000 grams.				✓
Sex of child can be seen.			✓	
Eyes begin to develop.	✓			
Fingers and toes appear.		✓		
Brain and heart start to form.	✓			
Fetus is 100 grams.				✓
Eyes have eyelids.		✓		
Embryo is 0.02 grams.	✓			
Heart is beating.	✓			

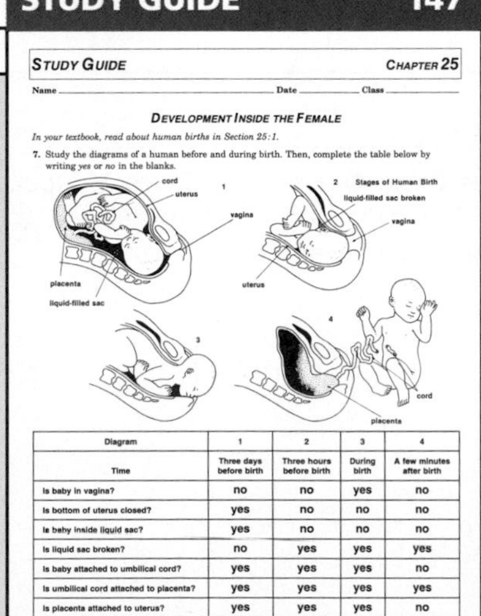

STUDY GUIDE 147

STUDY GUIDE — CHAPTER 25

Name ______ Date ______ Class ______

DEVELOPMENT INSIDE THE FEMALE

In your textbook, read about human births in Section 25:1.

7. Study the diagrams of a human before and during birth. Then, complete the table below by writing *yes* or *no* in the blanks.

Diagram	1	2	3	4
Time	Three days before birth	Three hours before birth	During birth	A few minutes after birth
Is baby in vagina?	no	no	yes	no
Is bottom of uterus closed?	yes	no	no	no
Is baby inside liquid sac?	yes	no	no	no
Is liquid sac broken?	no	yes	yes	yes
Is baby attached to umbilical cord?	yes	yes	yes	no
Is umbilical cord attached to placenta?	yes	yes	yes	yes
Is placenta attached to uterus?	yes	yes	yes	no

OPTIONS

How Does a Human Fetus Change During Development?/*Lab Manual*, pp. 211-214. Use this lab as an extension to studying early human development.

TEACH

Check for Understanding

Have students respond to the first three questions in Check Your Understanding.

Reteach

Reteaching/*Teacher Resource Package*, p. 75. Use this worksheet to give students additional practice with the vocabulary in this section.

Extension: Assign Critical Thinking, Biology and Reading, or some of the **OPTIONS** available with this lesson.

3 APPLY

Demonstration

Use an X ray of a female pelvis to point out the opening in the pelvis (pelvic inlet).

4 CLOSE

Software

The Reproductive System: A Baby Is Born, Queue, Inc.

Answers to Check Your Understanding

1. (a) a change in form or appearance
   (b) inside the oviduct
2. amniotic sac
3. (a) the start of the third month (b) by end of first month (c) by third month (d) by third month
4. CO binds with blood cells so that they can't carry oxygen. The embryo can suffer brain damage because of lack of oxygen to the brain.
5. The embryo is a hollow ball of cells that attaches itself to the lining of the uterus when it leaves the oviduct.

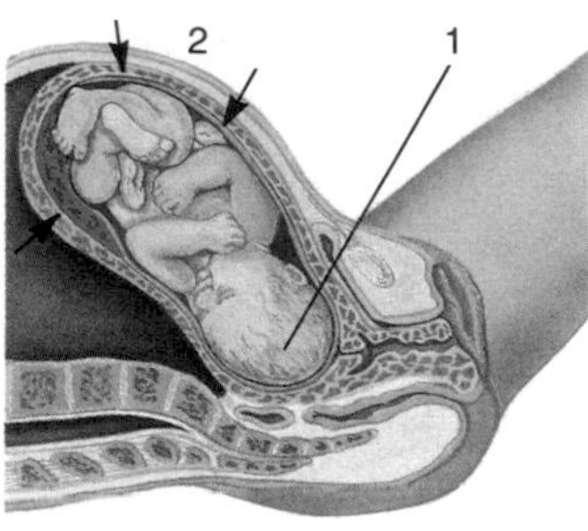

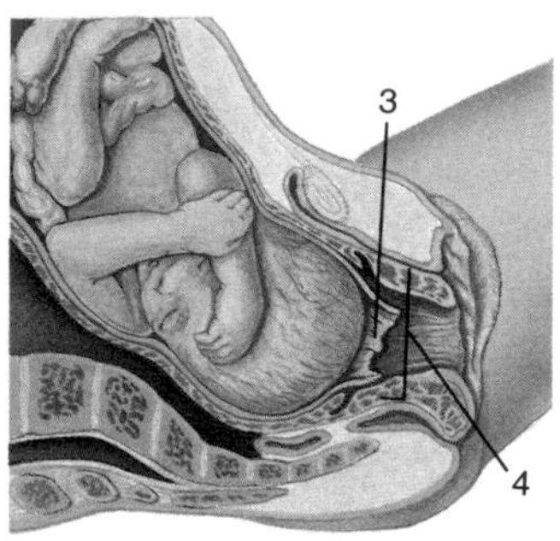

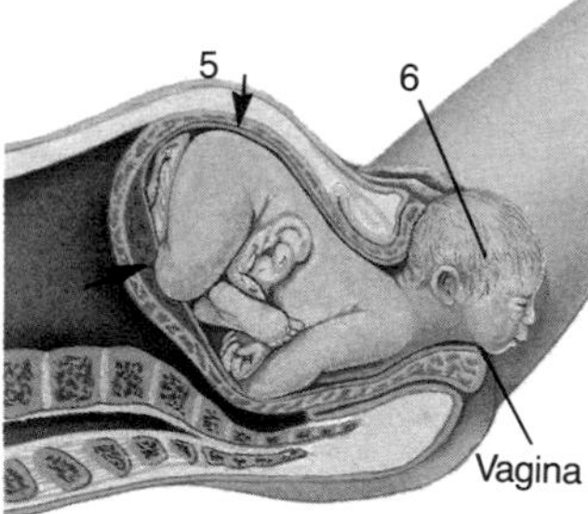

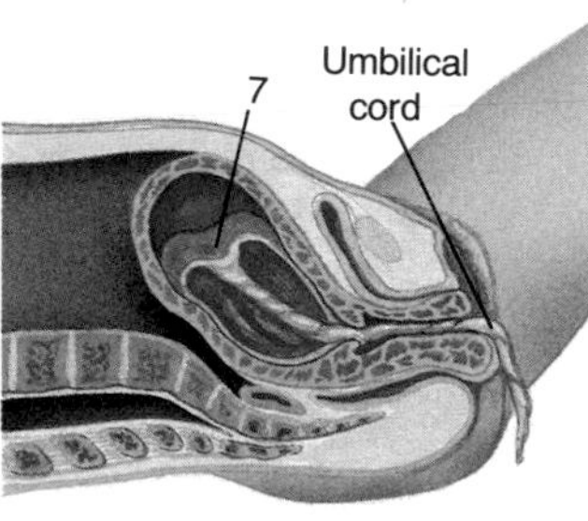

Figure 25-6 Study the steps of human birth shown here as you read the text.

Human Birth

Birth has one main purpose. It must push the fetus out of the uterus through the vagina. Follow the steps in Figure 25-6 as you read.

1. Before birth, the fetus usually turns head down. It will be born head first.
2. The uterus begins to contract. The uterus is smooth muscle. Is smooth muscle voluntary or involuntary? involuntary Contractions of the uterus are called **labor.**
3. The amniotic sac breaks. Liquid within the sac passes out through the mother's vagina.
4. The opening at the bottom of the uterus begins to widen. The fetus's head begins to move into this opening. Steps 2, 3, and 4 may take 8 to 12 hours.
5. More contractions take place. They help to push the fetus through the mother's vagina. Steps 4 and 5 might take several hours.
6. The fetus, or baby, is born.
7. The last step is getting rid of the placenta. The uterus contracts and pushes out the placenta and the amniotic sac. At this stage, the placenta is often called the afterbirth.

One evidence of your birth that still exists is your navel. Your **navel** is where the umbilical cord was attached to your body.

Check Your Understanding

1. (a) What is development?
   (b) Where does early development take place in humans?
2. What part protects the embryo?
3. At what age:
   (a) is an embryo called a fetus?
   (b) does the heart begin to beat?
   (c) can you tell if the embryo is male or female?
   (d) are all organs present?
4. **Critical Thinking:** If a pregnant woman smokes, carbon monoxide can pass through the placenta to the fetus. What effect would this have on the fetus? (HINT: In Chapter 13, you studied the effects of carbon monoxide on the body.)
5. **Biology and Reading:** What is the shape of the embryo at the time it moves out of the oviduct and into the uterus? What happens to the embryo after it leaves the oviduct?

OPTIONS

What Changes Occur During Birth?/*Lab Manual*, pp. 215-218. Use this lab as an extension to studying human development and birth.

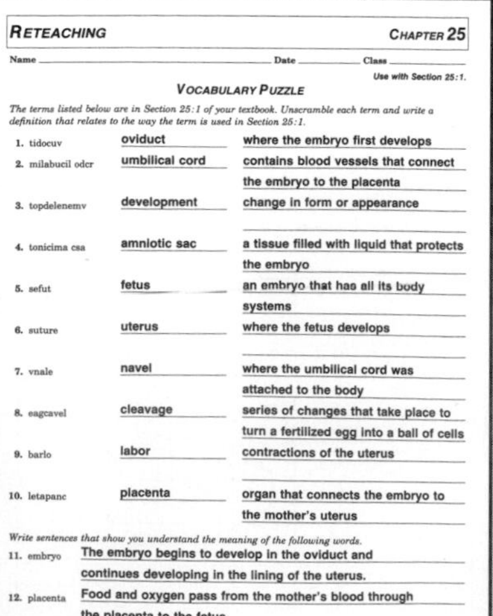

RETEACHING 75

RETEACHING CHAPTER 25

Name ________ Date ________ Class ________

Use with Section 25:1.

VOCABULARY PUZZLE

The terms listed below are in Section 25:1 of your textbook. Unscramble each term and write a definition that relates to the way the term is used in Section 25:1.

1. tidocuv — oviduct — where the embryo first develops
2. milabucil odcr — umbilical cord — contains blood vessels that connect the embryo to the placenta
3. topdelenemv — development — change in form or appearance
4. tonicima csa — amniotic sac — a tissue filled with liquid that protects the embryo
5. sefut — fetus — an embryo that has all its body systems
6. suture — uterus — where the fetus develops
7. vnale — navel — where the umbilical cord was attached to the body
8. eagcavel — cleavage — series of changes that take place to turn a fertilized egg into a ball of cells
9. barlo — labor — contractions of the uterus
10. letapanc — placenta — organ that connects the embryo to the mother's uterus

Write sentences that show you understand the meaning of the following words.

11. embryo — The embryo begins to develop in the oviduct and continues developing in the lining of the uterus.
12. placenta — Food and oxygen pass from the mother's blood through the placenta to the fetus.

Lab 25–1 Development

Problem: How do you judge the age of a human fetus?

Skills

measure in SI, use numbers, infer, make and use graphs

Materials

ruler

Procedure

1. Copy the data table below.
2. **Measure in SI:** The figure shows three fetuses 1/10 actual size. Measure the body length and foot length for each fetus in millimeters. Write the measurements in your data table.
3. Fill in all but the last column of your data table.
4. The data table on this page lists ages of a fetus. It also shows the average size of a fetus at each of these ages. Use the table and your measurements to determine the ages of fetuses A, B, and C.

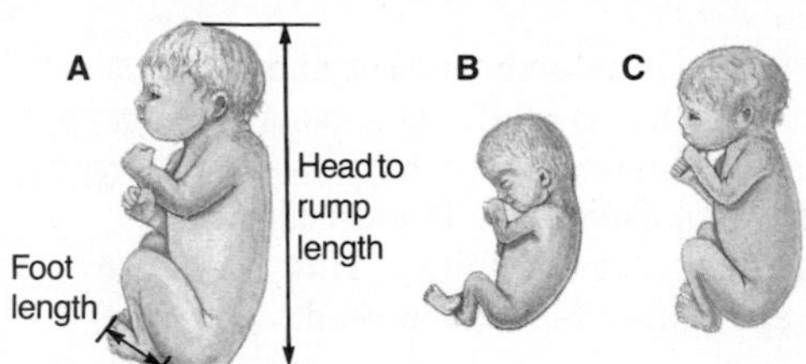

Data and Observations

1. At what age does the fetus open its eyes?
2. How much does the fetus grow between weeks 20 and 28?

AGE IN WEEKS	AVERAGE BODY LENGTH (mm)	AVERAGE FOOT LENGTH (mm)	EYES	HAIR
16	140	27	closed	none
20	210	40	closed	body, head
28	270	60	open	body, head
36	340	80	open	head

Analyze and Apply

1. How does a fetus obtain food and oxygen?
2. **Infer:** Could ultrasound tell you the sex of a fetus at six weeks of age? Why?
3. **Apply:** Assume you are an ultrasound technician and you report the age of fetus C to the doctor. The doctor tells you that the fetus should be 34 weeks old. The mother drinks a lot of alcohol. How would this affect the size of her fetus?

Extension

Make a line graph of the data for average body length.

FETUS	BODY LENGTH		FOOT LENGTH		EYES	HAIR	AGE OF FETUS (WEEKS)
	MEASURED	ACTUAL (×10)	MEASURED	ACTUAL (×10)			
A	33	330	7.2	72	open	head	36
B	21	210	3.6	36	closed	body, head	20
C	27	270	5.4	54	open	body, head	28

ANSWERS

Data and Observations

1. 28 weeks
2. 60 mm

Analyze and Apply

1. through the placenta
2. No, sex can't be determined until the third month.
3. Alcohol would prevent the fetus from growing as fast. Therefore, it would be smaller than normal.

Lab 25-1 Development

Overview

Students will determine the age of three fetuses by comparing their measurements to a table of standard sizes. They will also use traits such as presence of body hair and open or closed eyes.

Objectives: Upon completion of this lab, students will be able to (1) **determine** how data obtained from ultrasound can be used to judge the approximate age of a fetus, (2) **define** the role of the placenta, (3) **state** at what age in development one can establish the sex of the fetus.

Time Allotment: 20 minutes

Preparation

▶ Make copies of the data table for students.

▶ Show a transparent ruler on the overhead projector to remind students which units are millimeters.

▶ Explain to students that the data chart asks them to multiply their measurements by ten because the figures are 1/10th actual size.

Lab 25-1 worksheet/*Teacher Resource Package,* pp. 97-98.

Teaching the Lab

▶ **Troubleshooting:** Students will have to use their data and observations with information provided in order to determine age of diagrams. Measurements of head to rump and foot length will not match exactly with the data in the table. Students must match their values with the nearest values in the table.

25:2 Development Outside the Female

PREPARATION

Materials Needed

Make copies of the Skill, Study Guide, and Reteaching worksheets in the *Teacher Resource Package.*

▶ Purchase chicken eggs for the Focus activity.

Key Science Words

No new science words will be introduced in this section.

Process Skills

In the Mini Lab, students will design an experiment.

1 FOCUS

▶ The objectives are listed on the student page. Remind students to preview these objectives as a guide to this numbered section.

ACTIVITY/Hands-On

Provide students with a chicken egg to examine its outer shape, inner shell surface, and inner contents. Break the eggs open into shallow dishes.

Guided Practice

Have students write down their answers to the margin question: in water.

25:2 Development Outside the Female

Objectives

4. **Compare** development in frogs, birds, and reptiles.
5. **Explain** how the needs of a chick embryo are met.

All animals undergo development. The female, however, may not have a uterus. In this case, development must take place elsewhere.

Eggs That Are Laid

A female frog lays eggs outside her body. Birds and reptiles do the same thing. These eggs undergo development in a way similar to that in humans. One difference is that for frogs, birds, and reptiles, development takes place outside the female's body.

Where do frog eggs develop?

Fish, amphibians, and many invertebrates lay their eggs in water. These eggs undergo cleavage after they are fertilized, just as the fertilized human egg did. Figure 25-7 shows photos of cleavage taking place in a frog egg. Photo (a) is of one cell. Photo (b) is of two cells. How many cells can you see in photos (c) and (d)? 8 and 16

Bird and reptile eggs go through cleavage stages just as frog and human eggs do. Development in birds and reptiles takes place on land, not in water. Eggs of birds and reptiles can develop on land because they have shells. The shell keeps the embryo from drying out.

Needs of the Embryo

What are the needs of an embryo that undergoes development in an egg that is laid? Let's use a chicken egg as an example. A chick embryo must have food and oxygen. It must get rid of waste chemicals. It must also be protected against drying out and injury. How are these needs met? Look at Figure 25-8 as you read.

Figure 25-7 A frog egg undergoes cleavage.

a

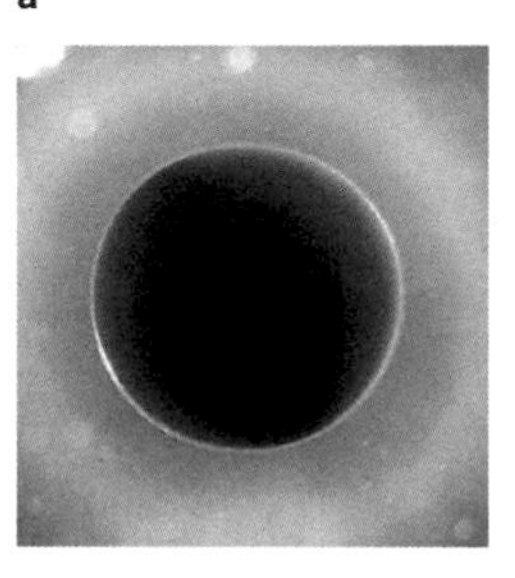

b

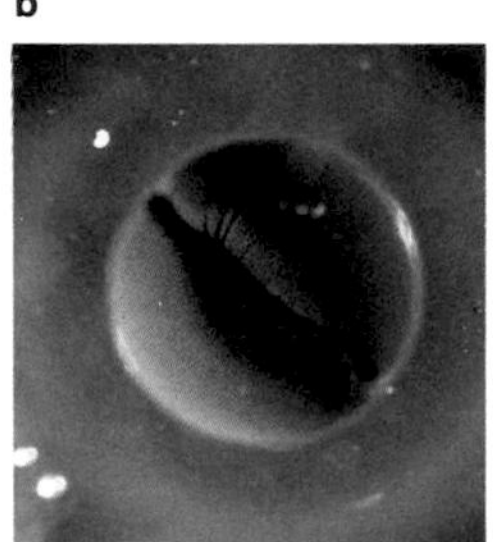

c

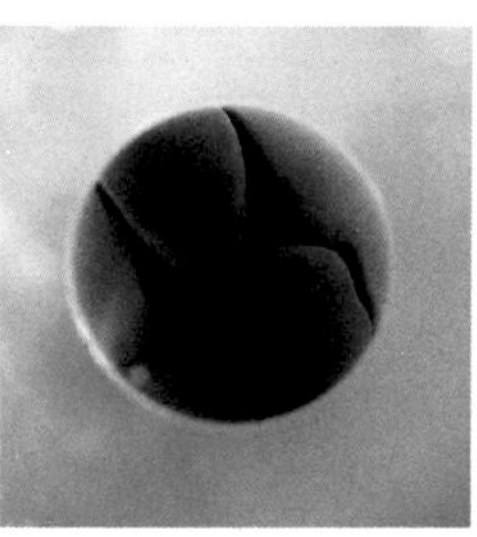

d

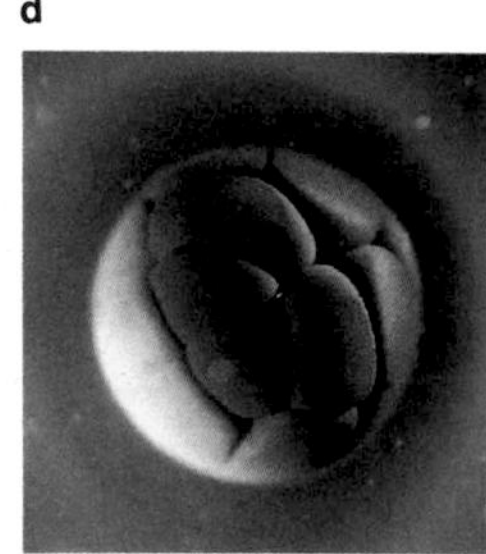

OPTIONS

Science Background

Egg size in animals varies from the very large ostrich egg (200 mm) to the chicken egg (50 mm) to the mammalian egg (0.05 mm). The relatively large sizes of bird eggs and reptile eggs are due to the large amounts of yolk and albumen.

Skill/*Teacher Resource Package*, p. 26. Use the Skill worksheet shown here for students to predict when organisms will hatch or be born.

SKILL 26

SKILL: FORM A HYPOTHESIS — CHAPTER 25

Name ______ Date ______ Class ______

For more help, refer to the Skill Handbook, pages 704-705. *Use after Section 25:2.*

INCUBATION AND GESTATION

After an egg is fertilized, the new organism has to go through a period of development either in the mother's uterus or inside the egg. The period of time that the young develops in the uterus before birth is called the gestation period. The period of time that the young develops in an egg before hatching is called the incubation period. The day that the young will be born or will hatch can be predicted if you know the time needed for gestation or incubation and if you know when mating of the parents took place.

Table 1 below shows the incubation or gestation periods for some animals. Use the data in the table to predict when the young of each animal will hatch or will be born. Write the date you predict in the last column of the table. You can refer to Table 2 for the number of days in each month. When you have completed the table, answer the questions that follow.

Table 1 Incubation or gestation time for some animals

Animal	Day of mating	Type of development	Time needed	Day of birth
Red fox	Jan. 20	Gestation	52 days	Mar. 13
Alligator	Jan. 25	Incubation	60 days	Mar. 26
Rabbit	Mar. 15	Gestation	28 days	Apr. 12
Opossum	Apr. 1	Gestation	13 days	Apr. 14
Sparrow	Apr. 10	Incubation	13 days	Apr. 23
Box turtle	Apr. 20	Incubation	88 days	July 17
Bullfrog	July 3	Incubation	5 days	July 8
Fin whale	Dec. 6	Gestation	360 days	Dec. 1

Table 2 Number of days in each month

Jan. 31	Mar. 31	May 31	July 31	Sept. 30	Nov. 30
Feb. 28	Apr. 30	June 30	Aug. 31	Oct. 31	Dec. 31

1. Which animal has the shortest period of development? bullfrog
2. Do the young of this animal develop inside or outside the female? outside
3. Which animal has the longest period of development? fin whale
4. Do the young develop inside or outside the female? inside

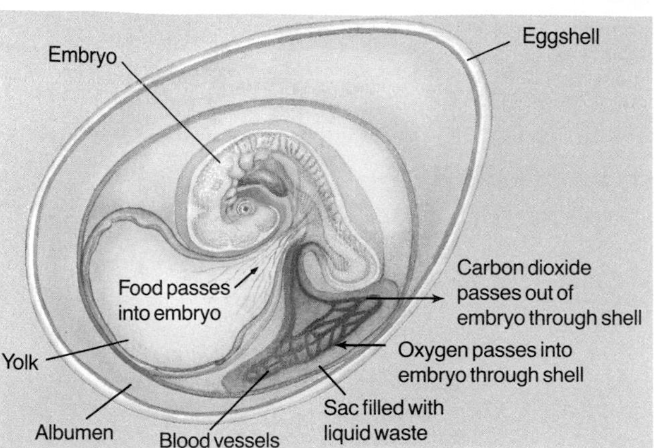

Figure 25-8 Chick embryo

Food Supply

You may not realize it, but you are familiar with the two parts that supply food to the embryo. They are the yolk and albumen (al BYEW mun). Yolk is the yellow part and is made up of protein and fat. Albumen is the white of the egg. Albumen also has protein in it. By hatching time, the chick has used up the yolk and albumen.

Oxygen Supply

Oxygen diffuses through the eggshell from the air outside. Blood vessels that lie just below the shell pick up the oxygen. The oxygen then passes to the embryo.

Waste Removal

Gas wastes leave the egg through the shell. Liquid wastes are stored in a sac within the egg until hatching.

Protection

The shell protects the chick embryo. It protects the embryo from water loss and injury.

Mini Lab

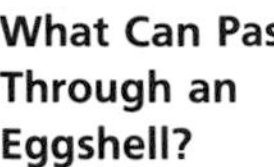

What Can Pass Through an Eggshell?

Design an experiment: Design an experiment to test if glucose can pass through an eggshell. What is the control in your experiment? *For more help, refer to the* ***Skill Handbook****, pages 704-705.*

How is a chick embryo supplied with oxygen?

Check Your Understanding

6. Where do frog and bird development take place?
7. What does egg yolk supply to a developing chick?
8. What happens to wastes as a chick develops?
9. **Critical Thinking:** What is an advantage of developing outside the female's body? What is a disadvantage?
10. **Biology and Reading:** Which vertebrates lay eggs in water? Which vertebrates lay eggs on land?

2 TEACH

Independent Practice

Study Guide/*Teacher Resource Package*, p. 148. Use the Study Guide worksheet shown at the bottom of this page for independent practice.

Check for Understanding

Have students respond to the first three questions in Check Your Understanding.

Reteach

Reteaching/*Teacher Resource Package*, p. 76. Use this worksheet to give students additional practice with development outside the female.

Extension: Assign Critical Thinking, Biology and Reading, or some of the **OPTIONS** available with this lesson.

3 APPLY

Divergent Question

Ask why a chicken egg is so much larger than a human egg.

4 CLOSE

Audiovisual

Show the filmstrip *Frog Development,* Carolina Biological Supply Co.

Answers to Check Your Understanding

6. outside the body; frog, in water; bird and reptile, on land
7. yolk–protein and fat
8. Gas wastes leave through the shell; liquids are stored in a sac.
9. Advantage: female produces more offspring; disadvantage: more offspring die without the protection of the female's body.
10. fish and amphibians, in water; reptiles and birds, on land.

RETEACHING 76

RETEACHING: IDEA MAP — CHAPTER 25

Name ______ Date ______ Class ______

Use with Section 25:2.

DEVELOPMENT OUTSIDE THE FEMALE

Use these terms and phrases to complete the idea map: from air through eggshell, yolk, eggshell prevents, water loss, albumen, injury, carbon dioxide, through eggshell, stored in sac in egg, liquid.

Needs of chick embryo
- food supplied by — yolk; albumen
- oxygen source — from air through eggshell
- waste removal — carbon dioxide — through eggshell; liquid — stored in sac in egg
- protection — eggshell prevents — water loss; injury

1. Where does development usually take place in frogs, birds, and reptiles? outside the female's body
2. Name two kinds of vertebrates that lay their eggs in water. fish and amphibians
3. What feature allows birds and reptiles to develop on land? Explain why this feature is helpful. Birds and reptiles have shells around their eggs that keep the embryo from drying out during development.

STUDY GUIDE 148

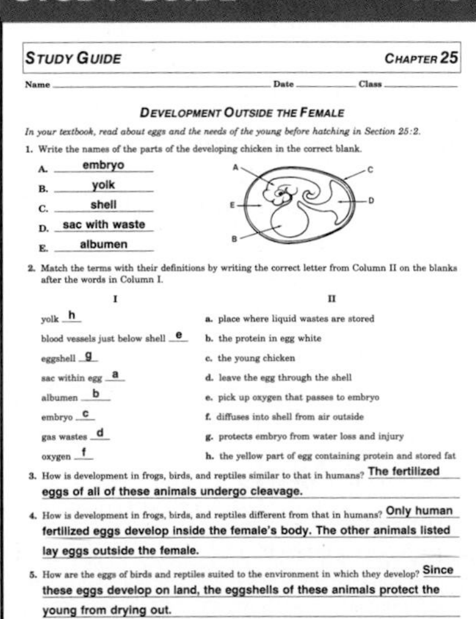

STUDY GUIDE — CHAPTER 25

Name ______ Date ______ Class ______

DEVELOPMENT OUTSIDE THE FEMALE

In your textbook, read about eggs and the needs of the young before hatching in Section 25:2.

1. Write the names of the parts of the developing chicken in the correct blank.
   A. embryo
   B. yolk
   C. shell
   D. sac with waste
   E. albumen
2. Match the terms with their definitions by writing the correct letter from Column II on the blanks after the words in Column I.

I	II
yolk h	a. place where liquid wastes are stored
blood vessels just below shell e	b. the protein in egg white
eggshell g	c. the young chicken
sac within egg a	d. leave the egg through the shell
albumen b	e. pick up oxygen that passes to embryo
embryo c	f. diffuses into shell from air outside
gas wastes d	g. protects embryo from water loss and injury
oxygen f	h. the yellow part of egg containing protein and stored fat

3. How is development in frogs, birds, and reptiles similar to that in humans? The fertilized eggs of all of these animals undergo cleavage.
4. How is development in frogs, birds, and reptiles different from that in humans? Only human fertilized eggs develop inside the female's body. The other animals listed lay eggs outside the female.
5. How are the eggs of birds and reptiles suited to the environment in which they develop? Since these eggs develop on land, the eggshells of these animals protect the young from drying out.

Lab 25-2 Metamorphosis

Overview

Students will observe and compare stages of complete and incomplete insect metamorphosis.

Objectives: Upon completion of the lab, students will be able to (1) **identify** stages of complete metamorphosis, (2) **identify** stages of incomplete metamorphosis, (3) **compare** stages of incomplete and complete insect metamorphosis.

Time Allotment: 30 minutes

Preparation

▶ Purchase insect stages as preserved specimens or plastic embedded mounts from a biological supply house.

▶ Collection of some insect stages may be undertaken by students.

Lab 25-2 worksheet/*Teacher Resource Package*, pp. 99-100.

Teaching the Lab

▶ **Troubleshooting:** Tell students which stage is capable of reproduction.

Cooperative Learning: Divide the class into groups of two to three students.

Metamorphosis

Lab 25–2

Problem: How do complete and incomplete metamorphosis compare?

Skills

interpret data, measure in SI, compare

Materials

hand lens
grasshopper stages of metamorphosis
moth stages of metamorphosis
metric ruler

Procedure

Part A

1. Copy the data table.
2. Using a hand lens, examine the eggs of a grasshopper.
3. Complete the data table for this stage.
4. Repeat steps 2 and 3 for the nymph and adult stages.

Part B

1. Using a hand lens, examine the eggs of a moth.
2. Complete the data table for this stage.
3. Repeat step 2 for the larva, pupa, and adult stages. Measure only body length for the adult. Do not include the wings.

Data and Observations

1. For the grasshopper, list two ways in which
   (a) the egg differs from the nymph or adult
   (b) the nymph and adult are alike
2. For the moth, list two ways in which
   (a) the pupa differs from the adult
   (b) the larva and adult differ

Analyze and Apply

1. **Interpret data:** Which type of metamorphosis do grasshoppers show—complete or incomplete?
2. Which type of metamorphosis do moths show–incomplete or complete?
3. **Apply:** Metamorphosis has made it possible for insects to live in almost every type of environment and use many different materials for food. Why do you think this is so?

Extension

Compare the stages of metamorphosis for a crayfish to those of a grasshopper.

	STAGE	BODY LENGTH (mm)	LEGS PRESENT	NUMBER OF LEGS	WINGS PRESENT	CAN IT FLY?	MOUTH‡ PARTS PRESENT?	CAN IT FEED?	CAN IT REPRODUCE?
Part A	Egg	3*	no		no	no	no	no	no
	Nymph	12*	yes	6	no	no	yes	yes	no
	Adult	25*	yes	6	yes	yes	yes	yes	yes
Part B	Egg	1*	no		no	no	no	no	no
	Larva	40*	yes	6(16)**	no	no	yes	yes	no
	Pupa	22*	no		no	no	no	no	no
	Adult	30*	yes	6	yes	yes	yes	yes	yes

*Answers will vary. **Only the first three pairs of legs are true legs. ‡Parts may be difficult to see.

ANSWERS

Data and Observations

1. (a) The egg does not have mouthparts, legs, or wings.
   (b) Both have legs and mouthparts.
2. (a) The pupa does not have legs, wings, or mouthparts.
   (b) The larva is larger than adult and does not have wings.

Analyze and Apply

1. incomplete
2. complete
3. The different stages of metamorphosis are adapted to withstanding different environmental conditions. Feeding on different materials prevents the adults and immature stages from using the same food sources and possibly not having enough food.

25:3 Metamorphosis

If you saw a puppy, you would be able to tell that it was a dog. If you saw a baby bird, you would be able to tell that it was a bird. Many young animals look like the adults, but some do not. These animals must go through another type of change before they look like an adult.

Objectives

6. **Sequence** the stages of frog metamorphosis.
7. **Explain** incomplete metamorphosis.
8. **Describe** complete metamorphosis.

Key Science Words

metamorphosis
larva
nymph
incomplete metamorphosis
complete metamorphosis
pupa

Frog Metamorphosis

Many animals hatch and go through a series of changes before they look like their parents. Changes in appearance and lifestyle that occur between the young and the adult stages are called **metamorphosis** (met uh MOR fuh sus).

You may have seen tadpoles swimming in a pond or stream. These tadpoles will undergo metamorphosis to become adult frogs. Follow the changes in Figure 25-9 to see how a young frog changes into an adult.

1. The adult female frog lays eggs in the water. Eggs are fertilized outside the body. Notice that frog eggs do not have shells. They have a jellylike covering that protects them.
2. Early development takes place for about 12 days.

Skill Check

Understand science words: metamorphosis. The word part *meta* means change. In your dictionary, find three words with the word part *meta* in them. *For more help, refer to the **Skill Handbook**, pages 706-711.*

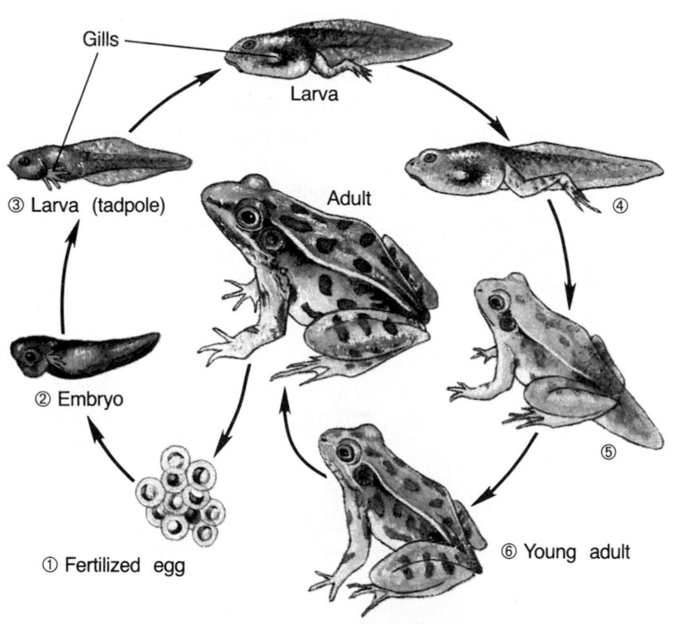

Figure 25-9 The stages of metamorphosis in a leopard frog are shown here.

STUDY GUIDE 149

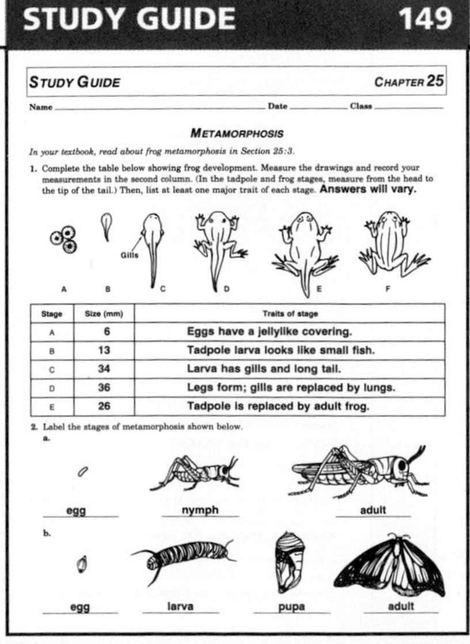

STUDY GUIDE CHAPTER 25

Name ______ Date ______ Class ______

METAMORPHOSIS

In your textbook, read about frog metamorphosis in Section 25:3.

1. Complete the table below showing frog development. Measure the drawings and record your measurements in the second column. (In the tadpole and frog stages, measure from the head to the tip of the tail.) Then, list at least one major trait of each stage. **Answers will vary.**

Gills

A B C D E F

Stage	Size (mm)	Traits of stage
A	6	Eggs have a jellylike covering.
B	13	Tadpole larva looks like small fish.
C	34	Larva has gills and long tail.
D	36	Legs form; gills are replaced by lungs.
E	26	Tadpole is replaced by adult frog.

2. Label the stages of metamorphosis shown below.

a. egg, nymph, adult

b. egg, larva, pupa, adult

FOCUS 49

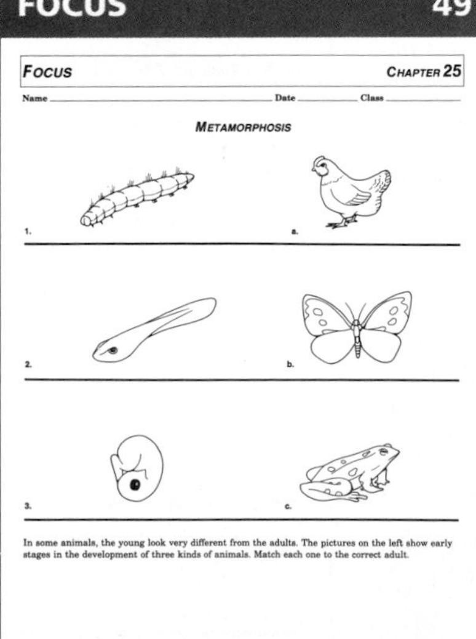

FOCUS CHAPTER 25

Name ______ Date ______ Class ______

METAMORPHOSIS

1. a.

2. b.

3. c.

In some animals, the young look very different from the adults. The pictures on the left show early stages in the development of three kinds of animals. Match each one to the correct adult.

25:3 Metamorphosis

PREPARATION

Materials Needed

Make copies of the Focus, Critical Thinking/Problem Solving, Study Guide, Application, Reteaching, and Lab worksheets in the *Teacher Resource Package.*

▶ Order preserved grasshopper and moth stages of metamorphosis for Lab 25-2.

Key Science Words

metamorphosis
larva
nymph
incomplete metamorphosis
complete metamorphosis
pupa

Process Skills

In Lab 25-2, students will interpret data, measure in SI, and compare. In the Skill Check, students will understand science words.

1 FOCUS

▶ The objectives are listed on the student page. Remind students to preview these objectives as a guide to this numbered section.

Convergent Question

Ask students to describe maggots, caterpillars, and tadpoles.

Focus/*Teacher Resource Package*, p. 49. Use the Focus transparency at the bottom of this page as an introduction to metamorphosis.

Independent Practice

Study Guide/*Teacher Resource Package*, p. 149. Use the Study Guide worksheet shown at the bottom of this page for independent practice.

2 TEACH

MOTIVATION/Display

Purchase a few tadpoles so that students can observe and watch these animals undergoing metamorphosis.

Concept Development

▶ Emphasize that the word *incomplete* suggests that something is missing. Incomplete metamorphosis lacks the larva and pupa stages.

Guided Practice

Have students write down their answers to the margin questions: A tadpole has gills for obtaining oxygen and a tail for swimming. Its mouth and body are shaped differently from adults.

Idea Map

Have students use the idea map as a study guide to the major concepts of this section.

How does a tadpole differ from an adult frog?

3. A tadpole appears from the embryo. This tadpole is a larva (LAR vuh). A **larva** is a young animal that looks completely different from the adult. If you didn't know that a tadpole was a frog, you might mistake it for a small fish.
4. Note how the larva differs from the adult. Look at its mouth, body, and tail shape. The larva has gills for obtaining oxygen. Does the adult have the exact same shape?
5. The larva continues to change. Front and hind legs form. Gills are replaced by lungs.
6. Finally the larva, or tadpole, no longer exists. It has changed into a young adult frog.

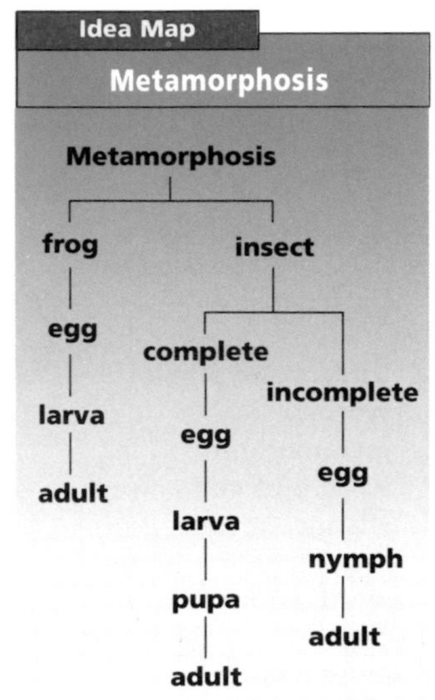

Study Tip: Use this idea map as a study guide to metamorphosis.

Insect Metamorphosis

Insects also undergo metamorphosis. Unlike frogs, insects have two types of metamorphosis. They are called incomplete and complete metamorphosis.

Incomplete metamorphosis

When some insects hatch from eggs, they almost look like miniature adults. There are many differences, however. These young are called nymphs (NIHMFS). A **nymph** is a young insect that looks similar to the adult. Note in Figure 25-10 that when a nymph first hatches, it does not have wings like the adult. It is also sexually immature.

The nymph grows and changes until it reaches adult size and appearance. This type of change is called incomplete metamorphosis. **Incomplete metamorphosis** is a series of changes in an insect from nymph to adult. Grasshoppers and crickets have incomplete metamorphosis.

Complete metamorphosis

Many insects, such as butterflies and moths, have complete metamorphosis. **Complete metamorphosis** is a series of changes in an insect in which the young do not look like the adult. Figure 25-11 shows these changes.

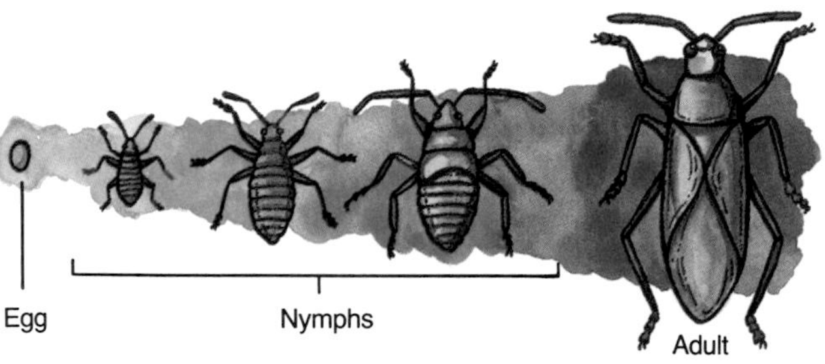

Figure 25-10 Incomplete metamorphosis in an insect includes egg, nymph, and adult stages.

OPTIONS

Frog Metamorphosis/*Transparency Package,* number 25b. Use color transparency number 25b as you teach frog metamorphosis.

Critical Thinking/Problem Solving/ *Teacher Resource Package,* p. 25. Use the worksheet shown here to explain what happens to insects in winter.

Application/*Teacher Resource Package,* p. 25. Use the Application worksheet to teach metamorphosis of cicadas.

CRITICAL THINKING 25

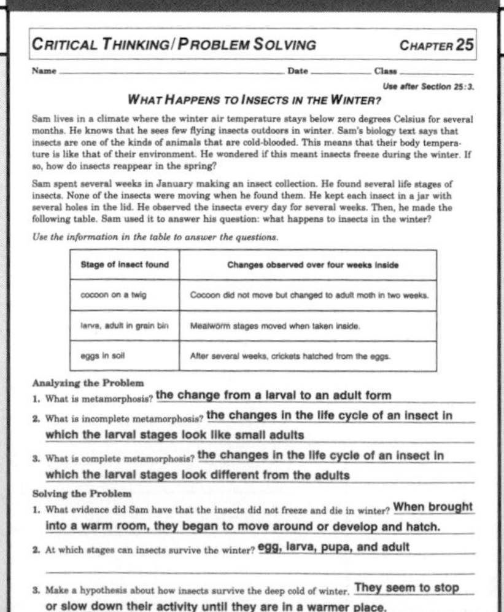

CRITICAL THINKING/PROBLEM SOLVING — CHAPTER 25

Name ______ Date ______ Class ______

Use after Section 25:3.

WHAT HAPPENS TO INSECTS IN THE WINTER?

Sam lives in a climate where the winter air temperature stays below zero degrees Celsius for several months. He knows that he sees few flying insects outdoors in winter. Sam's biology text says that insects are one of the kinds of animals that are cold-blooded. This means that their body temperature is like that of their environment. He wondered if this meant insects freeze during the winter. If so, how do insects reappear in the spring?

Sam spent several weeks in January making an insect collection. He found several life stages of insects. None of the insects were moving when he found them. He kept each insect in a jar with several holes in the lid. He observed the insects every day for several weeks. Then, he made the following table. Sam used it to answer his question: what happens to insects in the winter?

Use the information in the table to answer the questions.

Stage of insect found	Changes observed over four weeks inside
cocoon on a twig	Cocoon did not move but changed to adult moth in two weeks.
larva, adult in grain bin	Mealworm stages moved when taken inside.
eggs in soil	After several weeks, crickets hatched from the eggs.

Analyzing the Problem

1. What is metamorphosis? the change from a larval to an adult form
2. What is incomplete metamorphosis? the changes in the life cycle of an insect in which the larval stages look like small adults
3. What is complete metamorphosis? the changes in the life cycle of an insect in which the larval stages look different from the adults

Solving the Problem

1. What evidence did Sam have that the insects did not freeze and die in winter? When brought into a warm room, they began to move around or develop and hatch.
2. At which stages can insects survive the winter? egg, larva, pupa, and adult
3. Make a hypothesis about how insects survive the deep cold of winter. They seem to stop or slow down their activity until they are in a warmer place.

APPLICATION 25

APPLICATION: ENVIRONMENT — CHAPTER 25

Name ______ Date ______ Class ______

Use after Section 25:3.

METAMORPHOSIS

Some insects take a long time to complete their metamorphosis. Certain types of cicadas take 17 years! The cycle begins when the adults mate, and the females lay eggs in the twigs of trees. The eggs develop into tiny nymphs. Then, the nymphs drop to the ground and burrow about one foot into the soil. They bite into the roots of grasses or trees and feed on the sap. The nymphs stay underground, slowly growing, for 17 years. Then, the nymphs emerge from the ground, molt, and become adults with wings. They mate, and the cycle begins again.

All of the cicadas within several square miles have the same cycle. Millions of cicadas emerge over a period of a few days. Several weeks later, the nymphs burrow into the ground. Then, no cicadas will be seen in that area for another 17 years.

Adults mate, females lay eggs in tree twigs
Nymphs emerge, molt, become adults
Nymphs drop to ground, burrow in
Nymphs grow underground, feed on sap

Use this information along with the diagram to answer the following questions.

1. Does the 17-year cicada undergo complete or incomplete metamorphosis? Incomplete
   Explain. It is incomplete because the nymph grows and changes until it reaches adult size and appearance. A cicada does not go through stages that do not look like the adult.
2. Birds, cats, and other animals feed on cicadas when the cicadas emerge from the ground. Do you think cicadas make a reliable food source for these animals? Explain. No. The cicadas would provide a lot of food, but only once every 17 years.
3. What is the advantage to the cicada of a nymph stage that lives underground for so long? While it is underground, it is safer from predators.
4. Imagine that cicada nymphs burrowed into the ground under a tree in a vacant lot. What changes might happen in 17 years that would be harmful to the nymphs? The tree might be cut down; the lot could be paved over; a house could be built there.

Figure 25-11 Complete metamorphosis includes egg (upper left), larva (upper right), pupa (lower left), and adult (lower right) stages.

1. The adult female butterfly lays fertilized eggs that develop into embryos.
2. The embryo hatches into a small larva 10 to 15 days later. This larva is also called a caterpillar.
3. The larva moves about and feeds on plant matter.
4. The larva stops feeding and enters a pupa (PYEW puh) stage. A **pupa** is a quiet, non-feeding stage that occurs between larva and adult. The pupa is surrounded by a protective covering. Many changes take place in the pupa.
5. After about one week, the pupa opens and an adult butterfly emerges.

How do pupa and nymph stages differ?

Check Your Understanding

11. Name the stages of metamorphosis in a frog.
12. Arrange the following stages of development in their proper order: nymph, fertilized egg, adult.
13. How are frog eggs protected?
14. **Critical Thinking:** What form of a tapeworm is similar to the pupa stage of a butterfly? Why?
15. **Biology and Writing:** Is metamorphosis in a frog more like complete or incomplete metamorphosis? Write a paragraph that explains your answer.

TEACH

Guided Practice

Have students write down their answers to the margin questions: pupa—quiet, non-feeding stage; nymph—like a mini adult.

Independent Practice

Study Guide/*Teacher Resource Package,* p. 150. Use the Study Guide worksheet shown at the bottom of this page for independent practice.

Check for Understanding

Have students respond to the first three questions in Check Your Understanding.

Reteach

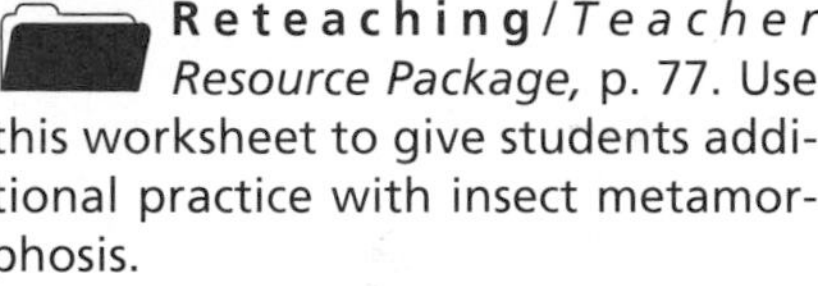

Reteaching/*Teacher Resource Package,* p. 77. Use this worksheet to give students additional practice with insect metamorphosis.

Extension: Assign Critical Thinking, Biology and Writing, or some of the **OPTIONS** available with the lesson.

3 APPLY

Convergent Question

Ask students what stage of the moth life cycle is most likely to damage wool clothing. (larva, because it is a feeding stage)

4 CLOSE

Bridging

Have students compare human development and metamorphosis.

Answers to Check Your Understanding

11. egg, embryo, larva, adult
12. fertilized egg, nymph, adult
13. They have a jellylike covering.
14. the cyst stage; both are quiet non-feeding stages
15. Answers will vary.

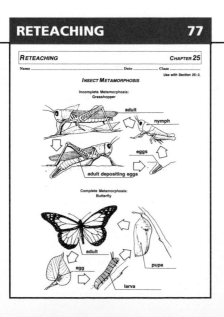

RETEACHING 77

RETEACHING CHAPTER 25

Name ______ Date ______ Class ______

Use with Section 25:3.

INSECT METAMORPHOSIS

Incomplete Metamorphosis:
Grasshopper

adult
nymph
eggs
adult depositing eggs

Complete Metamorphosis:
Butterfly

adult
pupa
egg
larva

STUDY GUIDE 150

STUDY GUIDE CHAPTER 25

Name ______ Date ______ Class ______

VOCABULARY

Review the new words in Chapter 25 of your textbook. Then, complete this puzzle.

Below are five tables. List the following words in every table in which they are correct. Some words are used more than once.

amniotic sac breaks, complete metamorphosis, fetus, cleavage, incomplete metamorphosis, labor, larva, metamorphosis, navel, nymph, placenta, pupa, umbilical cord

A change that takes place in all living things
cleavage

Changes or stages that take place in insects
nymph
larva
incomplete metamorphosis
pupa
complete metamorphosis

Changes or stages that take place in frogs
larva
metamorphosis

Parts or stages in humans
placenta
umbilical cord
fetus
navel

Changes that occur during a human birth
amniotic sac breaks
labor

CHAPTER 25 REVIEW

Summary

Summary statements can be used by students to review the major concepts of the chapter.

Key Science Words

All boldfaced terms from the chapter are listed.

Testing Yourself

Using Words

1. fetus
2. umbilical cord
3. larva
4. nymph
5. pupa
6. cleavage
7. placenta
8. labor
9. amniotic sac
10. metamorphosis

Finding Main Ideas

11. pp. 536-537; Both start from eggs and end with adult stages. In incomplete metamorphosis, a nymph stage appears. In complete metamorphosis, larva and pupa stages appear.
12. p. 533; The shell protects the embryo from water loss and injury.
13. pp. 524-525; Mitosis occurs in a fertilized egg to make 2 cells, then 4, then 8, then 16 cells; it forms a solid ball, then a hollow ball, and attaches to the uterus.
14. p. 532; The development of both takes place outside the female's body and both undergo cleavage. Frogs develop in water, and birds develop on land.
15. p. 530; They push the fetus out through the mother's vagina. They also push the placenta out after the fetus is born.
16. pp. 525-527; The embryo receives protection from amniotic sac, receives oxygen and food from placenta through umbilical cord, and gets rid of wastes through umbilical cord to the placenta.
17. p. 533; An eggshell allows oxygen and carbon dioxide to pass through the shell and protects the embryo.
18. pp. 535-536; It differs in body, mouth, and tail shape, and has gills for obtaining oxygen.

Using Main Ideas

19. At four months, the fetus is active. It continues to grow and develop until birth occurs at the end of the ninth month.
20. The uterus provides a place for development; the placenta connects the embryo to the uterus; the umbilical cord connects the embryo to the placenta.
21. Human development takes place inside the body, but birds, amphibians, and reptiles develop outside the body.

Chapter 25 Review

Summary

25:1 Development Inside the Female

1. Cleavage is a series of changes from a fertilized egg to a hollow ball of cells.
2. A human embryo receives protection, food, and oxygen, and gets rid of wastes while in the uterus.
3. Most major changes to the human embryo take place within the first three months. Development continues through the ninth month.

25:2 Development Outside the Female

4. Development occurs outside the female's body in frogs, birds, and reptiles.
5. The chicken egg supplies the chick embryo with protection, food, and a way of obtaining oxygen and getting rid of gas wastes.

25:3 Metamorphosis

6. During metamorphosis, frogs change from an egg to a larva to an adult.
7. Incomplete insect metamorphosis has nymph stages that look like the adult.
8. Complete metamorphosis has larva and pupa stages that don't look like the adult.

Key Science Words

amniotic sac (p. 525)
cleavage (p. 525)
complete metamorphosis (p. 536)
fetus (p. 529)
incomplete metamorphosis (p. 536)
labor (p. 530)
larva (p. 536)
metamorphosis (p. 535)
navel (p. 530)
nymph (p. 536)
placenta (p. 526)
pupa (p. 537)
umbilical cord (p. 526)

Testing Yourself

Using Words

Choose the word from the list of Key Science Words that best fits the definition.

1. name given to the embryo at the start of the third month
2. blood vessels connecting the embryo to the placenta
3. young frog that looks completely different from the adult
4. young insect that looks similar to the adult
5. quiet, non-feeding stage during metamorphosis
6. series of changes that turn an egg into a hollow ball with many cells
7. organ connecting the embryo to the uterus
8. contractions of the uterus
9. liquid-filled tissue that protects the embryo
10. change in appearance that occurs between young and adult stages

Review

Testing Yourself *continued*

Finding Main Ideas

List the page number where each main idea below is found. Then, explain each main idea.

11. how incomplete and complete metamorphosis are alike and how they differ
12. how the shell of an egg allows development out of water
13. the changes that take place during cleavage
14. how early development of a frog and bird are alike, how they differ
15. how contractions of the uterus help during birth
16. the four main needs of an embryo that develops inside the female and how each need is met
17. the main jobs of an eggshell
18. how a larva differs from an adult frog

Using Main Ideas

Answer the questions by referring to the page number after each question.

19. What changes happen to a human fetus from four months to birth? (p. 529)
20. What are the jobs of the uterus, placenta, and umbilical cord? (pp. 525, 526, 530)
21. How does human development compare with bird, amphibian, and reptile development? (pp. 524, 532)
22. How does a frog egg obtain protection? (p. 535)
23. What are the stages that take place during incomplete and complete metamorphosis? (pp. 536, 537)
24. What are the jobs of the shell, sac, and yolk in a bird egg? (p. 533)

Skill Review ✓

*For more help, refer to the **Skill Handbook,** pages 704-719.*

1. **Design an experiment:** Design an experiment to determine if flies will undergo metamorphosis faster if kept in the dark. What would be your control in this experiment?
2. **Infer:** An embryo measures 15 mm in length. Is it older or younger than 1 month in age?
3. **Make and use graphs:** Make a line graph that shows the number of cells in a human embryo after 36, 48, 72, 96, and 120 hours.
4. **Understand diagrams:** Study Figure 25-1. What changes does the fertilized egg undergo in the oviduct?

Finding Out More

Critical Thinking

1. Babies are often born with diseases that the mother had during pregnancy. AIDS is an example. How might such a disease be passed to the fetus?
2. During pregnancy, the placenta sometimes pulls loose from the uterus. How might this affect the embryo?

Applications

1. How does the organ used for respiration differ between tadpoles and adult frogs? Relate this to where the tadpole and adult live.
2. Match the parts of a bird embryo with the following human parts and their jobs: kidney, skin, mouth, lungs. Explain your answer.

Using Main Ideas

22. A jellylike covering protects the egg.
23. The stages in incomplete metamorphosis are egg, nymph, and adult. In complete metamorphosis, they are egg, larva, pupa, and adult.
24. The shell protects the embryo and keeps it from drying out, the sac holds liquid wastes, and the yolk provides protein and fat.

Skill Review

1. A control would be to keep the same number of flies in natural light as those kept in complete darkness and those kept in constant light.
2. older
3. after 36 hours, 2 cells; 48, 4 cells; 72, 16 cells; 96, solid ball of cells; 120, hollow ball of cells
4. It divides into 2 cells, then 4, then 8, then 16 to form a solid ball of cells. After 5 days, it leaves the oviduct as a hollow ball of cells.

Finding Out More

Critical Thinking

1. Diseases can pass from the mother's blood through the placenta to the umbilical cord and on to the embryo just as food does.
2. The placenta is the pathway between mother and embryo for food, oxygen, and waste removal. Without these, the embryo can't survive.

Applications

1. The tadpole lives in water and has gills to obtain oxygen from the water. The adult frog lives on land, has lungs, and obtains oxygen from the air.
2. The sac is analogous to the kidney; the shell is analogous to skin and lungs; the yolk supplies food, as a mouth does.

Chapter Review/*Teacher Resource Package,* pp. 131-132.

Chapter Test/*Teacher Resource Package,* pp. 133-135.

Chapter Test/*Computer Test Bank*

Unit Test/*Teacher Resource Package,* pp. 136-137.

Unit 6 Reproduction and Development

CONNECTIONS

Biology in Your World

Some organisms are close to extinction, and other organisms have outgrown their natural boundaries and threaten other forms of life. The more we know abut how organisms reproduce and develop, the better we can control populations and restore nature's balance.

Literature Connection

Aldous Huxley (1894-1963) came from a family of scientists. His grandfather and brothers made significant contributions to zoology, biology, and physiology. Huxley's satirical novel, *Brave New World,* is about a society that worships science and machines at the expense of individual dignity. The novel expresses his concern about scientific discoveries and their effect on society's values. Today, advances in the area of human reproduction pose difficult legal and ethical questions for the scientific community.

Art Connection

English sculptor Henry Moore (1898-1986) was influenced early in his career by Mexican and African art. His works in stone, wood, and bronze have simple lines and many look weathered. Several of his sculptures depict families or mothers with their children. Another favorite theme was reclining figures. One of his best-known sculptures, *Reclining Figure,* is on display at Lincoln Center in New York City.

CONNECTIONS

Biology in Your World

Growth, Development, Change

Development is not the same for all animals. Some animals undergo distinct stages, changing form entirely. Other animals just grow larger. The following examples compare human development with that of other organisms.

LITERATURE

A Crystal Ball?

In 1931, test-tube babies occurred only in science fiction. In *Brave New World,* author Aldous Huxley wrote about human eggs being fertilized outside the uterus. He also wrote about the eggs being made to divide into 96 identical embryos, or clones.

The process Huxley wrote about is a reality today. It is called *in vitro* fertilization. With *in vitro* fertilization, some childless couples are now able to have children. Huxley's prediction about clones has also come true. Animals such as frogs and mice have been cloned in the laboratory.

ART

Family Group, by Henry Moore

For all of history, our survival has depended on our ability to reproduce. However, just producing babies is not enough. Without care and attention, even well-fed babies will not gain weight.

Early artwork of females stressed fertility because of the importance of reproduction. Some artists have gone beyond just showing fertility. Henry Moore, a 20th century English sculptor, is one such artist. In 1949 he did a bronze sculpture called "Family Group," which shows a loving family environment. The parents are protecting and caring for the children. How does Moore's sculpture relate to what is known about growth and development?

540

LEISURE

See for Yourself!

In warm weather you can find frogs' eggs and tadpoles in ponds. The eggs look like small black beads surrounded by clear jelly. They can be collected using a long-handled dip net. The eggs will hatch in about one week at room temperature (don't leave them in the sun or near a heat source). Keep only eight tadpoles for each gallon of water. Use either pond water, bottled spring water, or tap water that has been sitting out for a few days. About a week after hatching, feed the tadpoles pond plants or boiled lettuce. In a few months, the tadpoles will develop hind legs. Front legs form later as the tails shorten. As the lungs develop, the young frogs will need a rock to rest on. If you plan to raise a frog, you must feed it live insects or mealworms. Good luck!

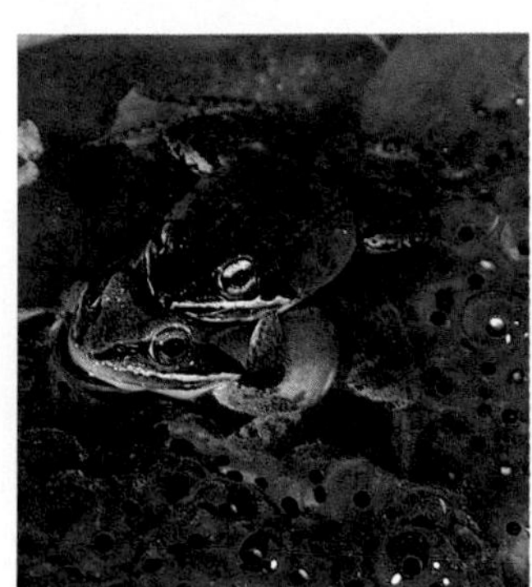

Return the frogs to the pond when you are finished observing them.

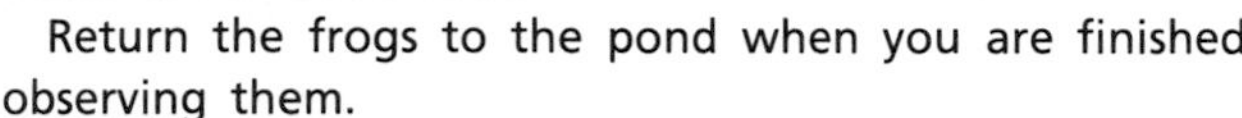

CONSUMER

The Luxury of Silk

As you learned in this unit, a moth does not hatch from an egg completely formed. Instead, a caterpillar hatches from the egg. The caterpillar eventually forms a cocoon around itself. A moth then emerges from the cocoon.

Over 4000 years ago, the Chinese discovered that the cocoons of silk moths could be unwound into silk threads. Today, the caterpillars and cocoons of these moths are grown in factories. The silk fibers are woven into shiny cloth that is lightweight, yet strong.

Silk is used to make upholstery and fashionable clothing. Silk garments are often more expensive than those made from synthetic fibers. Why do you think silk is more expensive?

CONNECTIONS

Leisure Connection

Frog eggs can be bought throughout the year from biological supply houses. Peeper eggs mature quickly.

An aquarium can provide an excellent environment for the eggs to develop. Aquatic plants provide oxygen and can be anchored in gravel at the bottom of the aquarium. If any frog eggs die, they will float to the surface. Be sure to remove dead eggs or animals. The best water temperature for development is 20°C. If the water is colder, the tadpoles take longer to develop.

Consumer Connection

When the silkworm moth breaks out of its cocoon, it breaks the long silk thread into many pieces. These pieces can be spun into silk yarn and used as a fabric filler, but they are not as valuable as unbroken fibers. As a result, most silkworms are killed while in their cocoons and silk farmers have fewer moths to lay eggs.

Silk fabric woven with fillers such as spun silk is less expensive than pure silk. Silk blends retain many of the desirable qualities of silk, but cost less.

References

Coldrey, Jennifer. *The Silkworm Story.* London: Andre Deutsch Limited, 1983.

Huxley, Aldous. *Brave New World.* New York: Harper & Row, 1932.

Lieber, James. "A Piece of Yourself in the World." *The Atlantic,* Vol. 263, No. 6, 1989, p. 76.

Moore, Henry, and John Hedgecoe. *Henry Moore.* San Francisco: Chronicle Books, 1986.

Parker, Steve. *Pond and River.* London: Alfred A. Knopf, Inc., 1988.

Unit 7
Traits of Living Things

UNIT OVERVIEW

Unit 7 focuses on how genetic continuity occurs in all living things. Chapter 26 deals with genes, chromosomes, and their relationship to traits of living things. Chapter 27 focuses on human genetics and covers sex-related traits, chromosome errors, and genetic diseases. Chapter 28 discusses the structure of DNA and how it works. Chapter 29 covers the topics of adaptation, natural selection, and isolation as they relate to the theory of evolution.

Advance Planning

Audiovisual and computer software suggestions are located within each specific chapter under the heading TEACH.

To prepare for:

Lab 26-1: Order corn seeds and gather petri dishes.
Lab 26-2: Provide 40 red and 40 white beans and 2 paper bags for each student team.
Mini Lab: Purchase various types of dried beans.
Lab 27-1: Put tape on 35 sets of coins in advance of this lab and use the coins for other classes.
Mini Lab: Purchase poster board and markers.
Lab 28-1: Purchase tracing paper, heavy paper, and red, blue, green, and yellow crayons.
Lab 28-2: Purchase or order *Coleus* plants, clear plastic cups, and aluminum foil.
Mini Lab: Purchase crayons and markers.
Lab 29-1: Using a paper punch, punch out 30 black and 30 white dots per student team. Collect white and black paper.
Lab 29-2: Order plastic powder and gather leaves.
Mini Labs: Order petrified wood and collect pieces of unpetrified wood. Purchase 10 pea pods per team.

Unit 7

CONTENTS

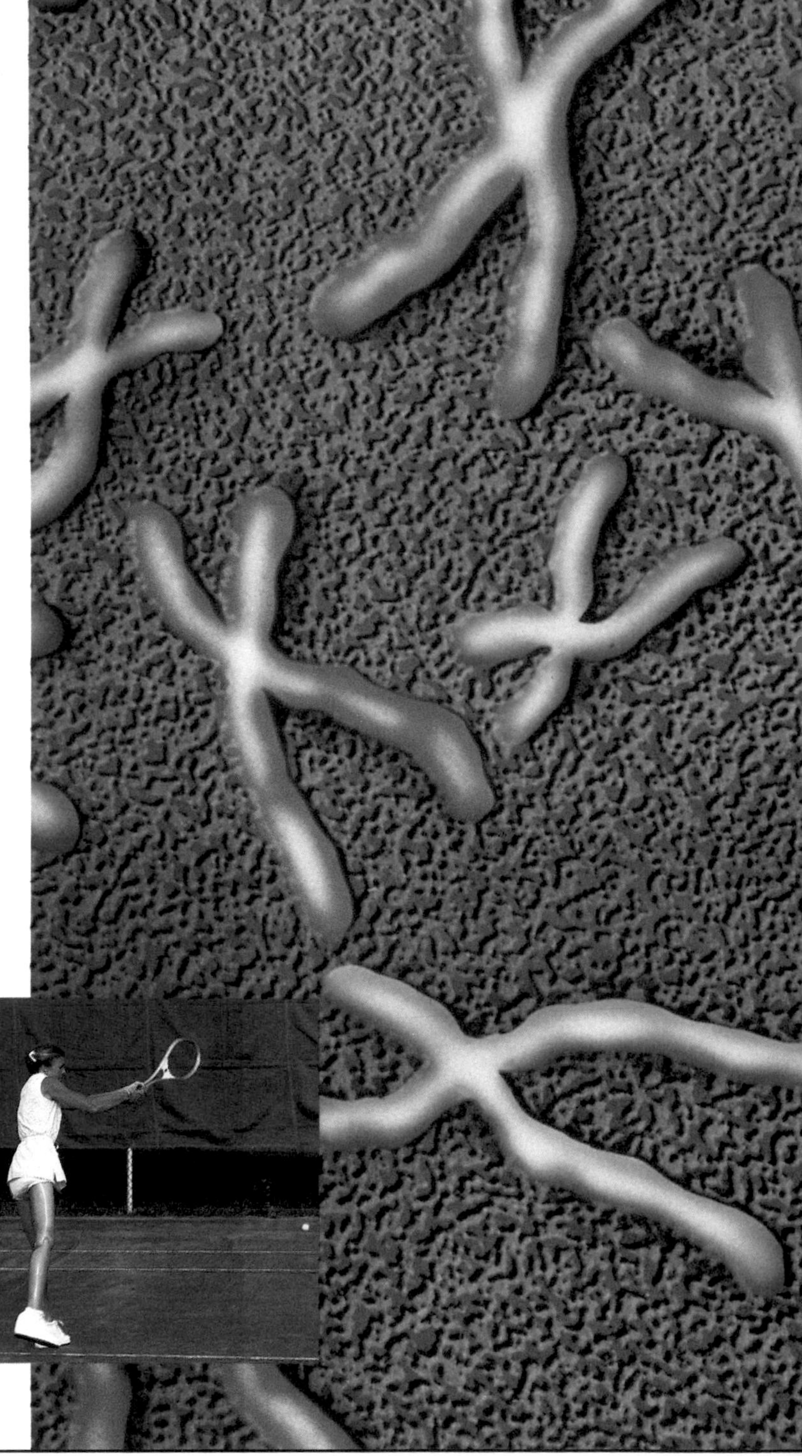

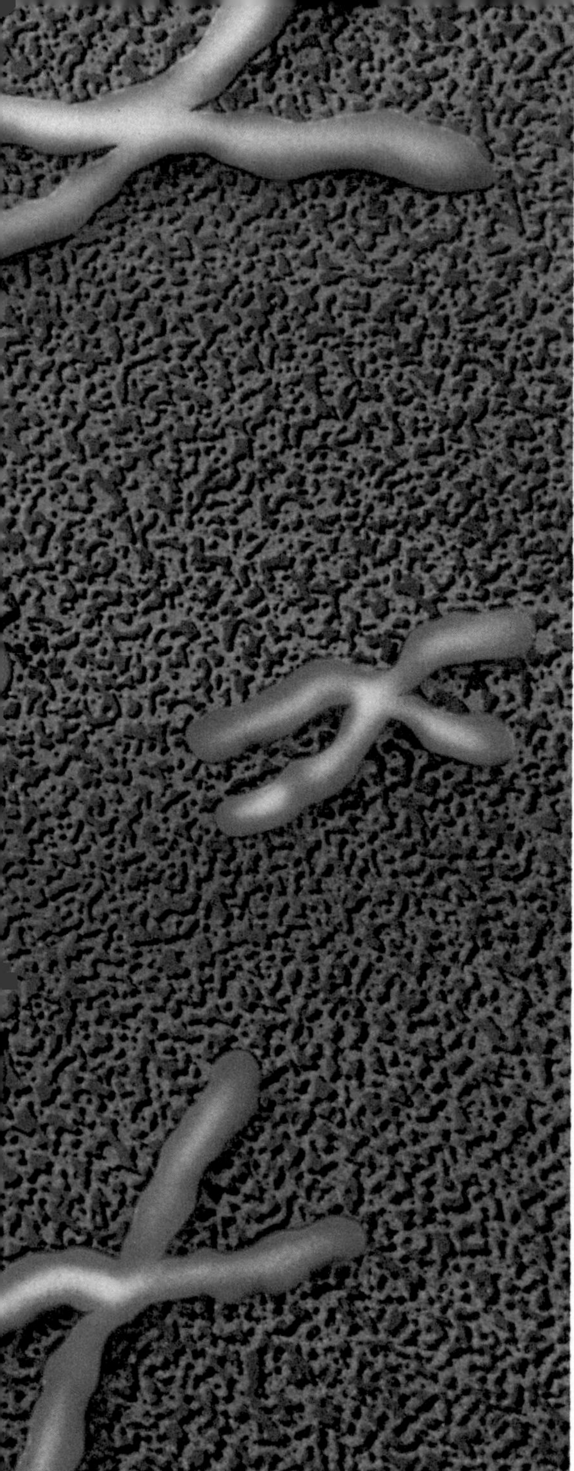

Traits of Living Things

What would happen if...

humans could regrow body parts that were damaged or cut off? People who lose a body part in an accident or during surgery would grow a replacement. An infected arm or leg could be removed to stop the spread of the infection. A new arm or leg would grow in its place.

The growing back of body parts is controlled by genes. In a young child, a finger tip could regrow if one were cut off. At your age, only the skin and a few other body tissues regrow. For some reason, most body tissues lose the ability to regrow as humans age.

Some organisms can regrow body parts. Scientists are studying them to learn how body parts regrow. Maybe they will learn how to make the genes that control the ability of body parts to regrow.

UNIT OVERVIEW

Photo Teaching Tip

Ask students to read the passage that accompanies the unit opening photographs and then discuss what it might be like to be without a hand, a foot, or another body part. Explain that the field of genetics is probably the fastest growing area of biology today. It is now possible to move parts of a chromosome from one cell to another. Explain that this modern technology is known as genetic engineering. Ask students what might be some of the consequences of this type of technology. What might be some benefits and what could be considered dangerous about changing the basic blueprint of an organism? Is genetic engineering the answer to all our disease or handicap problems?

Theme Development

Living things reproduce and pass traits to offspring. Students have studied in prior chapters how cells reproduce and how other living things reproduce and develop through their life cycles. Now, students will find out how the various traits of the parents will be passed to and expressed in their offspring. They will learn how DNA controls traits and makes proteins. They will find out how the changes in the traits of an organism help to explain how evolution occurs.

Inheritance of Traits

PLANNING GUIDE

CONTENT	TEXT FEATURES	TEACHER RESOURCE PACKAGE	OTHER COMPONENTS
(3 days) 26:1 Genetics, How and Why Chromosomes Genes on Chromosomes Passing Traits to Offspring Dominant and Recessive Genes When Both Parents Are Heterozygous	Skill Check: *Understand Science Words,* p. 549 Mini Lab: *What Traits Do Some Seeds Share?* p. 547 Mini Lab: *What Type of Earlobes Do Most Students Have?* p. 548 Check Your Understanding, p. 551 Idea Map, p. 547	Reteaching: *Traits of Plants and Animals,* p. 78 Study Guide: *Genetics: How and Why,* p. 151	**Laboratory Manual:** *How Can the Genes of Offspring Be Predicted?* p. 219
(2 days) 26:2 Expected and Observed Results The Punnett Square Expected Results Observed Results Mendel's Work	Skill Check: *Calculate,* p. 558 Lab 26-1: *Corn Genes,* p. 554 Lab 26-2: *Punnett Squares,* p. 556 Career Close-up: *Animal Breeder,* p. 555 Check Your Understanding, p. 561 Idea Map, p. 558	Application: *Genetics Problems in Agriculture,* p. 26 Enrichment: *Incomplete Dominance,* p. 28 Reteaching: *Using the Punnett Square to Solve Problems,* p. 79 Critical Thinking/Problem Solving: *How Can Plants Show Unexpected Traits?* p. 26 Skill: *Use Numbers,* p. 27 Focus: *What Might the Cross Between Two Different Kinds of Dogs Look Like?* p. 51 Transparency Master: *Punnett Square,* p. 133 Study Guide: *Expected and Observed Results,* pp. 152-155 Study Guide: *Vocabulary,* p. 156 Lab 26-1: *Corn Genes,* pp. 101-102 Lab 26-2: *Punnett Squares,* pp. 103-104	**Laboratory Manual:** *What Is a Test Cross?* p. 223 Color Transparency 26: *Offspring From Two Heterozygous Parents*
Chapter Review	Summary Key Science Words Testing Yourself Finding Main Ideas Using Main Ideas Skill Review	Chapter Review, pp. 138-139 Chapter Test, pp. 140-142	**Test Bank**

MATERIALS NEEDED

LAB 26-1, p. 554	LAB 26-2, p. 556	MARGIN FEATURES
20 corn seeds paper towels wax pencil petri dish water	40 white beans 40 red beans 2 paper bags	Skill Check, p. 549 dictionary Skill Check, p. 558 pencil paper Mini Lab, p. 547 various kinds of dried beans Mini Lab, p. 548 pencil paper

OBJECTIVES

		OBJECTIVES CORRELATION			
SECTION	OBJECTIVE	CHECK YOUR UNDERSTANDING	CHAPTER REVIEW	TRP CHAPTER REVIEW	TRP CHAPTER TEST
26:1	1. **Compare** the number of chromosomes in sex cells and body cells.	1, 5	5, 9, 14, 18, 22, 25, 26	1, 2, 4	1, 2, 35, 37
	2. **Distinguish** between dominant and recessive genes.	2	2, 7, 21	7, 9, 10, 13, 18, 19	4, 9, 18, 19, 20, 24, 25, 26, 28, 33
	3. **Describe** how different gene combinations result from fertilization and how traits are passed to offspring.	3, 4, 10	1, 3, 4, 8, 11, 12, 17, 23	3, 5, 6, 14, 16, 17	3, 5, 6, 8, 29, 32, 34, 36
26:2	4. **Discuss** the purpose of a Punnett square.	7	6, 10, 15, 19	11, 12, 20	10, 11, 14, 15, 17
	5. **Compare** expected results and observed results.	6, 9	16, 27	15	12, 13, 16, 17, 21, 22, 23, 27, 31, 38
	6. **Explain** the importance of Gregor Mendel's work.	8	13, 20	8	7, 30

Inheritance of Traits

CHAPTER OVERVIEW

Key Concepts

This chapter introduces genetics with a discussion and description of where chromosomes and genes are located and what their jobs are. This chapter also explains how traits are passed from parents to offspring and what dominant and recessive traits are. Students learn how to determine expected and observed results by using the Punnett square and will read about the accomplishments of Gregor Mendel.

Key Science Words

dominant gene	Punnett square
gene	pure dominant
genetics	pure recessive
heterozygous	recessive gene

Skill Development

In Lab 26-1, students will **observe, predict**, and **interpret data** with corn seeds that germinate into green plants. In Lab 26-2, students will **observe** and **formulate a model** of traits in heterozygous parents. They will **form hypotheses** to show possible combinations of traits in offspring. In the Skill Check on page 549, students will **understand** the **science word** *heterozygous.* In the Skill Check on page 558, students will **calculate** expected results of several coin tosses. In the Mini Lab on page 547, students will **classify** dried beans according to traits. In the Mini Lab on page 548, students will **make and use tables** to show numbers of students with particular traits.

CHAPTER PREVIEW

Chapter Content

Review this outline for Chapter 26 before you read the chapter.

26:1 Genetics, How and Why
- Chromosomes
- Genes on Chromosomes
- Passing Traits to Offspring
- Dominant and Recessive Genes
- When Both Parents Are Heterozygous

26:2 Expected and Observed Results
- The Punnett Square
- Expected Results
- Observed Results
- Mendel's Work

Skills in this Chapter

The skills that you will use in this chapter are listed below.
- In **Lab 26-1,** you will observe, predict, and interpret data. In **Lab 26-2,** you will observe, formulate a model, and form hypotheses.
- In the **Skill Checks,** you will calculate and understand science words.
- In the **Mini Labs,** you will classify and make and use tables.

Bridging

In Unit 6, students learned how reproduction occurs in cells and organisms. That unit also focused on plant and animal development. In this unit, students will learn how all organisms pass on their genetic traits and how living things change through time by evolution.

Chapter **26**

Inheritance of Traits

The small photo on this page shows two parent rabbits. The large photo on the opposite page shows some baby rabbits. Which of the baby rabbits do you think belong to the two parents? What traits did you use to help you answer the question? What traits did the parents pass to the offspring?

How about the all-white baby rabbit? Did someone who was caring for several litters of rabbits put the white rabbit in the wrong container? Probably not. Perhaps the parents passed the trait for white fur to the baby white rabbit. Can offspring show a trait that is not seen in the parents? You should be able to answer this question after you read this chapter.

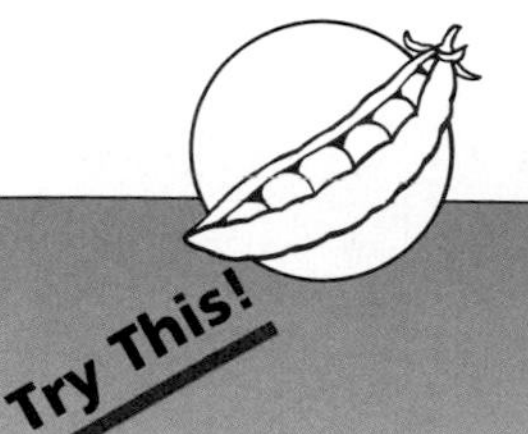

Try This!

Are two peas in a pod alike? Open a pea pod and look carefully at the peas. Make a list of ways the peas are the same and ways they are different. Each pea in a pod is like each child in a family. Children in a family show different traits.

Parent rabbits

GETTING STARTED

Using the Photos

Students will notice that the offspring of rabbits can be different in color, size, and other features when compared to the parents. Some students may assume that the white rabbit is from a different litter. Tell students they will learn why organisms can look different from either parent.

MOTIVATION/Try This!

Are two peas in a pod alike? Upon completing this chapter-opening activity, students will learn to **compare** traits. Students can relate differences and similarities among peas to those among children in the same family.

Chapter Preview

Have students study the chapter outline before they begin to read the chapter. Students should note that chromosomes are discussed first and then both dominant and recessive genes. The second section discusses the differences between expected and observed results of gene combinations.

Misconception

Explain to students that offspring of animals do not need to look like both parents. Some traits of parents do not show up in offspring and are called recessive.

26:1 Genetics, How and Why

PREPARATION

Materials Needed

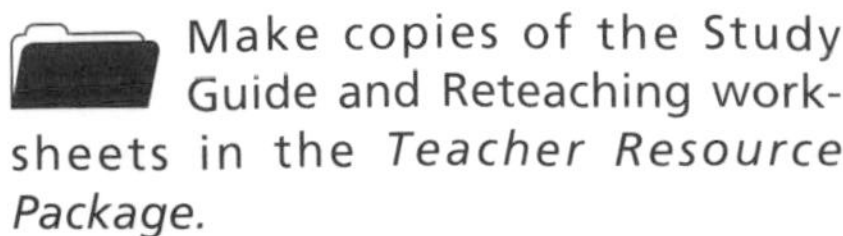

Make copies of the Study Guide and Reteaching worksheets in the *Teacher Resource Package.*

▶ Obtain different kinds of dried bean seeds for the Mini Lab.

Key Science Words

genetics
gene
dominant gene
recessive gene
pure dominant
pure recessive
heterozygous

Process Skills

In the Skill Check, students will understand science words. In the Mini Labs, students will classify and make and use tables.

1 FOCUS

▶ The objectives are listed on the student page. Remind students to preview these objectives as a guide to this numbered section.

MOTIVATION/Bulletin Board

Set up a bulletin board that shows pictures of wild and domestic animals and their young. Ask students why most wild young look like their parents while domestic young have traits very different from their parents. Discuss how and why humans selectively breed animals.

Objectives

1. **Compare** the number of chromosomes in sex cells and in body cells.
2. **Distinguish** between dominant and recessive genes.
3. **Describe** how different gene combinations result from fertilization and how traits are passed to offspring.

Key Science Words

genetics
gene
dominant gene
recessive gene
pure dominant
pure recessive
heterozygous

26:1 Genetics, How and Why

Genetics (juh NET ihks) is the study of how traits are passed from parents to offspring. Offspring usually show some traits of each parent. For a long time, scientists did not understand how this could happen. Later, they found that the traits of the parents were passed to offspring by sex cells.

Chromosomes

Before you learn how traits are passed from parents to offspring, let's review something about cells. Look at a cell in Figure 26-1. The large, round part in the center is the nucleus. It has two main jobs. One is to direct the actions of other cell parts. The other is to allow the cell to reproduce.

Inside the nucleus are long, threadlike parts called chromosomes. Chromosomes can be seen best when a cell is ready to reproduce. During cell reproduction, the chromosomes become short and thick.

Suppose we look closer at two kinds of cells. One kind is called a body cell. Remember that body cells are cells that make up most of the tissues and organs in your body. Look at Figure 26-1. Notice that the body cell has two of each kind of chromosome. The chromosomes in body cells are paired.

Another type of cell is a sex cell. The sex cell can be a sperm cell or an egg cell. Notice in Figure 26-1 that there is only one of each kind of chromosome present in the sex cell. Sex cells, then, have half as many chromosomes as body cells.

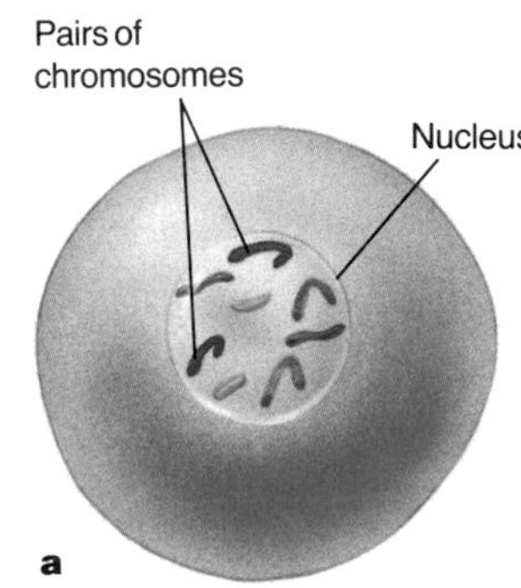

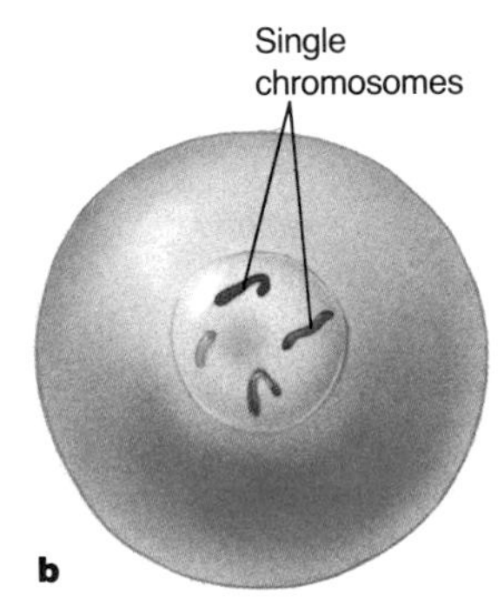

Figure 26-1 Chromosomes are found in the nucleus. Body cells have two copies of each chromosome (a). Sex cells have one copy of each chromosome (b).

OPTIONS

Science Background

Inheritance of traits in all living things is controlled by genes. Genes are located on chromosomes. The amount of space that each gene takes up is different. Chromosomes are found in all body and sex cells of living things. The chromosome number in a sex cell is half that of a body cell. Genes are of two types: dominant and recessive. Combinations of these two genes in an organism give rise to three genotypes and two phenotypes.

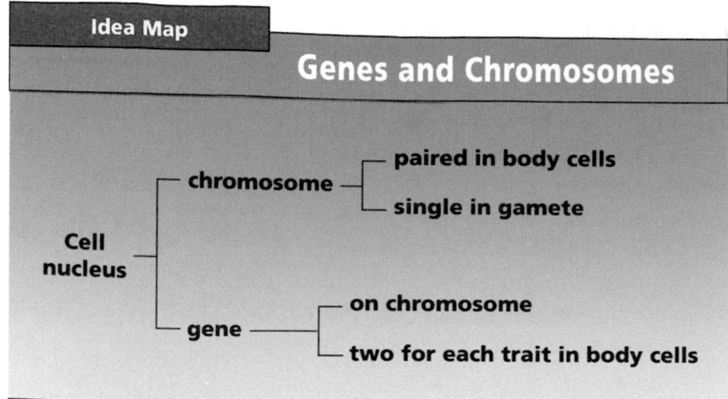

Study Tip: Use this idea map as a study guide to genes and chromosomes. Some features of each are shown.

Genes on Chromosomes

All chromosomes contain genes (JEENZ). A **gene** is a small section of chromosome that determines a specific trait of an organism. Examples of traits are eye color, hair color, and shape of body parts such as ears. Chemical processes inside the body, which cannot be seen, are also traits. Organisms have thousands of different traits. Genetics is really a study of the genes that control all of these traits. Note that the word *genetics* contains the word *gene.*

Genes are arranged on a chromosome, one next to another, much like beads on a necklace. Each chromosome has different kinds of genes that control different traits. Figure 26-2 shows drawings of human chromosomes. The locations of several genes are shown.

Remember that chromosomes in body cells are paired. The genes on chromosomes in body cells are paired, too. There is one gene of each gene pair on each chromosome of a chromosome pair. You can see this pairing in Figure 26-2. Each trait we study will have one gene pair, or two genes that represent it. The two genes representing the trait are located on chromosomes that make a pair.

Mini Lab

What Traits Do Some Seeds Share?

Classify: Look at the different dried beans found in the grocery store. Classify the beans into groups based on color, shape, and size. *For more help, refer to the **Skill Handbook,** pages 715-717.*

How many genes in a body cell represent each trait?

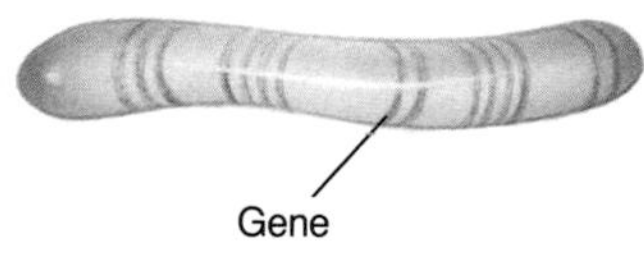

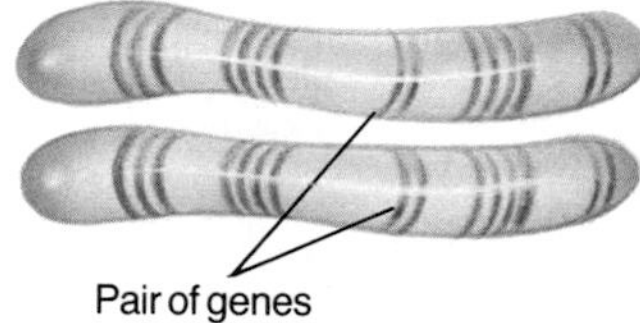

Figure 26-2 Genes are arranged next to each other on a chromosome. How many copies of a gene are in a sex cell? one

OPTIONS

Science Background

Point out that *chromosome* means color body. Before the turn of the 20th century, chromosomes were not thought to have any role in heredity. Explain that chromosomes were seen as dark bodies inside a cell when stain was added. Chromosomes absorbed more stain than other cell parts—hence the name chromosomes.

2 TEACH

MOTIVATION/Brainstorming

Show photos of some animals with their offspring–cats with kittens, etc.–and have students discuss traits the offspring have inherited from the parents. List the traits on the chalkboard. Ask how parents pass traits to their offspring.

Concept Development

▶ Remind students that in Chapter 24 they learned that the sex cells of two parents join during fertilization. Each one of the parents supplies one of each kind of chromosome to the fertilized egg. Because each parent supplies one of each type, the chromosomes occur in pairs.

▶ Explain that some traits in living things may not show in either parent but can appear in offspring.

Idea Map

Have students use the idea map as a study guide to the major concepts of this section.

Mini Lab

Get bags of several different kinds of bean seeds at the grocery store. Mix the beans together in a large container and give each student a small cup of beans. Have them compare the size, color, and shapes of the beans.

Analogy: Use the following analogy to compare chromosomes in body cells and sex cells: Have students imagine one closet with 23 pairs of shoes and a second closet with only 23 shoes, no pairs. A body cell is similar to the first closet; a sex cell is similar to the second closet.

Guided Practice

Have students write down their answers to the margin question: two genes or one pair.

TEACH

Concept Development

▶ Point out that all genes on a chromosome are not the same size. Some cover a smaller or larger section of a chromosome than others.

▶ Make sure students understand that each chromosome can contain several thousand genes.

▶ Point out that one of the chromosomes in each body cell is a maternal chromosome because it came from the person's mother; the other is a paternal chromosome because it came from the father.

▶ Review meiosis (Chapter 22) with students. Explain that when chromosomes double prior to division, the number of genes doubles, too. The parents can have four genes for the earlobe trait in each sex cell. After meiosis, each sex cell will have only one gene for the earlobe trait. Stress that each parent gives the child one gene for the earlobe trait.

▶ Explain that humans inherit thousands of traits from their parents.

▶ Emphasize that the genes in the egg and sperm of parents are passed to offspring at the time of fertilization.

▶ Point out that during fertilization any sperm cell can fertilize any egg cell.

Mini Lab

Make sure that students understand that a student with free earlobes can be pure dominant or heterozygous. Usually a class will have more students with the dominant trait because the recessive gene is hidden and not expressed in heterozygotes.

MOTIVATION/Overhead

Make a transparency of Figure 26-3 showing the kinds of sex cells parents can make. Go over the diagram with care so that students understand this concept.

Mini Lab

What Type of Earlobes Do Most Students Have?

Make and use tables: Make a table showing how many classmates have free or attached earlobes. Do more have the dominant or the recessive trait? *For more help, refer to the* ***Skill Handbook,*** *pages 715-717.*

Passing Traits to Offspring

How are traits passed from parents to their offspring? To answer this question, let's use the trait of earlobe shape in humans as an example. A person can have attached earlobes or free earlobes. Figure 26-3 shows what these traits look like. What genes would you expect to find in the body cells of each of these people?

Suppose the mother shows the attached earlobe trait. Suppose the father shows the free earlobe trait. Which trait would appear in their children?

Figure 26-3 shows what kinds of sex cells the parents can make. The mother has the gene pair for attached earlobes. She can make eggs that have this gene. The father has the gene pair for free earlobes. He can make sperm that have this gene. What genes for earlobe shape will their child have? The child will have one gene for each trait.

In fertilization, one sperm will join with one egg. Which sperm and egg will join? We don't know. We can see that it would make no difference in this example. Any child produced will have a gene for attached earlobes and a gene for free earlobes. From which parent did the child receive the gene for attached earlobes? From which parent did the child receive the gene for free earlobes?

Figure 26-3 Attached earlobe trait (a) and free earlobe trait (b). The trait for earlobe shape is passed from parents to their child.

a

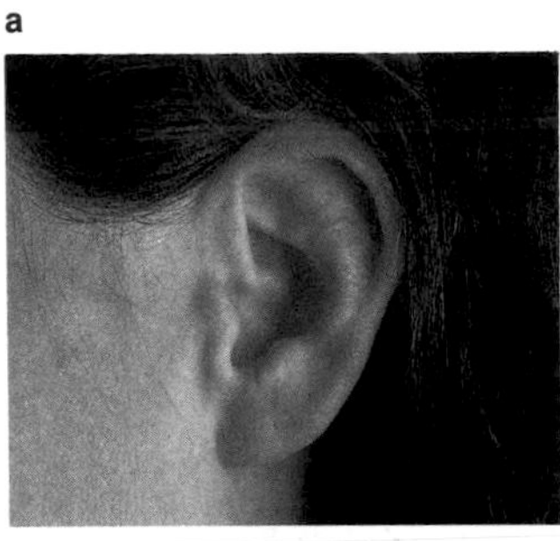

b

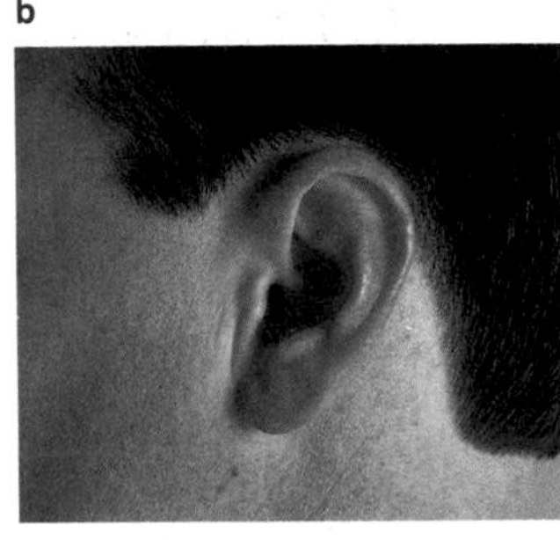

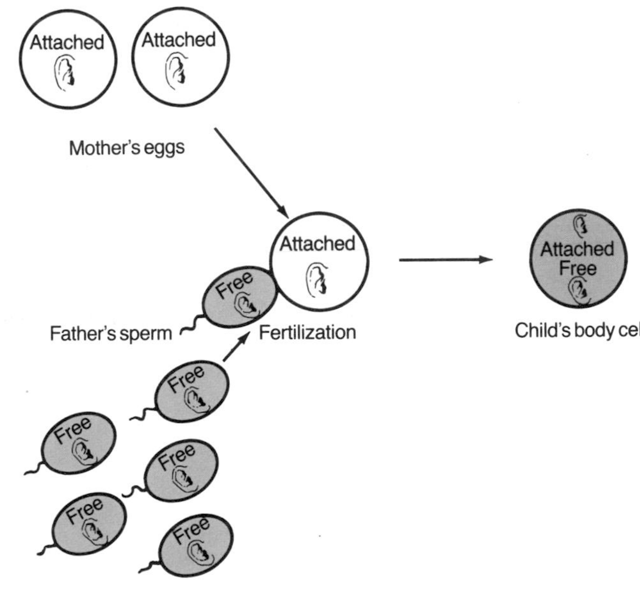

OPTIONS

ACTIVITY/Challenge

Have students cut out sperm and egg cells from construction paper and label one-half of them attached and one-half free. Have students show the different combinations that can occur during fertilization.

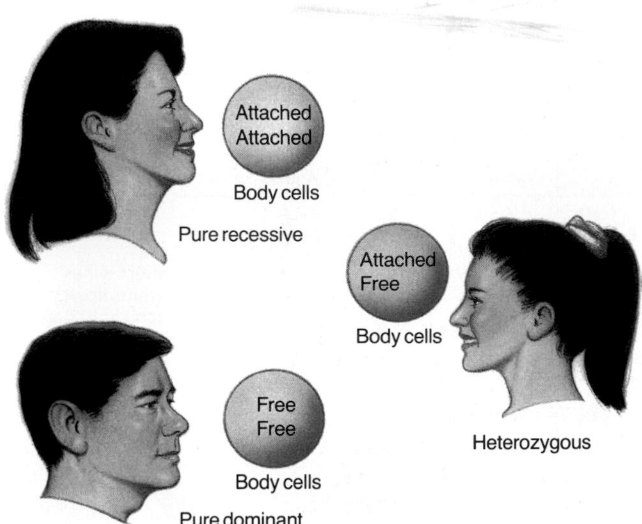

Figure 26-4 A child with one gene for attached earlobes and one gene for free earlobes will have free earlobes.

Dominant and Recessive Genes

What does a child with one gene for attached earlobes and one for free earlobes look like? Figure 26-4 shows you. Children born with both genes will have free earlobes. Why? Some genes can keep others from showing their traits. Genes that keep other genes from showing their traits are called **dominant** (DAHM uh nunt) **genes.** The genes that do not show their traits when dominant genes are present are called **recessive** (rih SES ihv) **genes.** In this example, the gene for free earlobes is dominant. The gene for attached earlobes is recessive.

An organism with two dominant genes for a trait is said to be **pure dominant.** Using the word *pure* means that both genes are the same. In our example, the father is pure dominant for free earlobes.

An organism with two recessive genes for a trait is said to be **pure recessive.** In our example, the mother is pure recessive for attached earlobes.

The child with a gene for attached earlobes and a gene for free earlobes has two different genes. The child is heterozygous (HET uh roh ZI gus). A **heterozygous** individual is one with a dominant and a recessive gene for a trait. Even though the heterozygous individual has the recessive gene, the recessive trait does not show. The trait of the dominant gene shows.

Skill Check

Understand science words: heterozygous. The word part *hetero* means different. In your dictionary, find three words with the word part *hetero* in them. *For more help, refer to the* ***Skill Handbook****, pages 706-711.*

What is a recessive gene?

TEACH

Concept Development

▶ Point out that alternate forms of a given gene are called alleles.

▶ Make sure students understand that a person having one dominant and one recessive gene for a trait does not show a trait that is intermediate between the two.

▶ Reinforce that a dominant trait completely blocks the appearance of a recessive trait.

▶ Point out to students that not all traits are inherited as either a dominant or recessive trait, as the earlobe trait is. Other patterns of inherited traits will be discussed in the next chapter.

ACTIVITY/Guest Speaker

Have a veterinarian come to your classroom to explain purebred animals.

Independent Practice

Study Guide/*Teacher Resource Package,* p. 151. Use the Study Guide worksheet shown at the bottom of this page for independent practice.

Guided Practice

Have students write down their answers to the margin question: genes that don't show their traits when dominant genes are present.

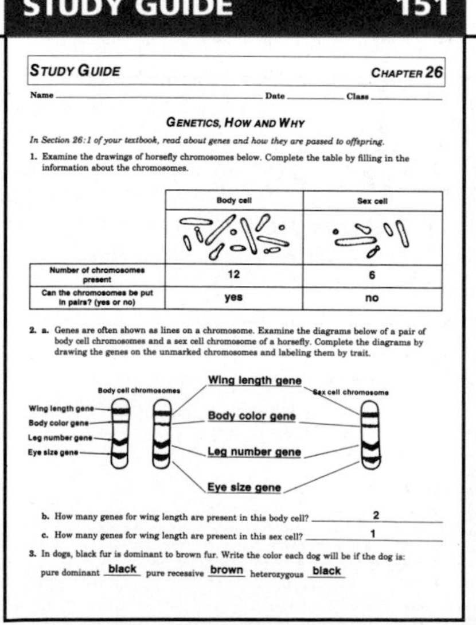
STUDY GUIDE 151

STUDY GUIDE CHAPTER 26

Name ______ Date ______ Class ______

GENETICS, HOW AND WHY

In Section 26:1 of your textbook, read about genes and how they are passed to offspring.

1. Examine the drawings of horsefly chromosomes below. Complete the table by filling in the information about the chromosomes.

	Body cell	Sex cell
Number of chromosomes present	12	6
Can the chromosomes be put in pairs? (yes or no)	yes	no

2. a. Genes are often shown as lines on a chromosome. Examine the diagrams below of a pair of body cell chromosomes and a sex cell chromosome of a horsefly. Complete the diagrams by drawing the genes on the unmarked chromosomes and labeling them by trait.

Body cell chromosomes — Sex cell chromosome
Wing length gene
Body color gene
Leg number gene
Eye size gene

b. How many genes for wing length are present in this body cell? 2

c. How many genes for wing length are present in this sex cell? 1

3. In dogs, black fur is dominant to brown fur. Write the color each dog will be if the dog is:
pure dominant black pure recessive brown heterozygous black

TEACH

Concept Development

▶ Stress that when fertilization does take place, it is usually random. The law of random fertilization states that any sperm cell can fertilize any egg cell.

▶ Emphasize that the dominant trait in a heterozygote is expressed over a recessive trait.

▶ Reinforce how gene combinations produce pure dominant, pure recessive, and heterozygous offspring.

Check for Understanding

Have students form teams of three for a discussion group. After students discuss the following questions in their group, pull all of the teams together for a final wrap-up. (1) Where would you find a gene in the sperm and egg? (in the nucleus) (2) Where would you find a chromosome in the sperm and egg? (in the nucleus) (3) How many pairs of chromosomes would you find in a human sperm? (none) (4) How many pairs of chromosomes would you find in a human egg? (none) (5) How are sperm and eggs different from body cells? (Sex cells have half the number of chromosomes that a body cell has.) (6) How many chromosomes do we get from each of our parents? (23 or one of each pair)

Reteach

Have students make models of a sperm and an egg using the following materials: cell–construction paper; chromosomes–string; and gene–piece of colored yarn glued to string. Tell them to put only three chromosomes in their model.

Guided Practice

Have students write down their answers to the margin question: two.

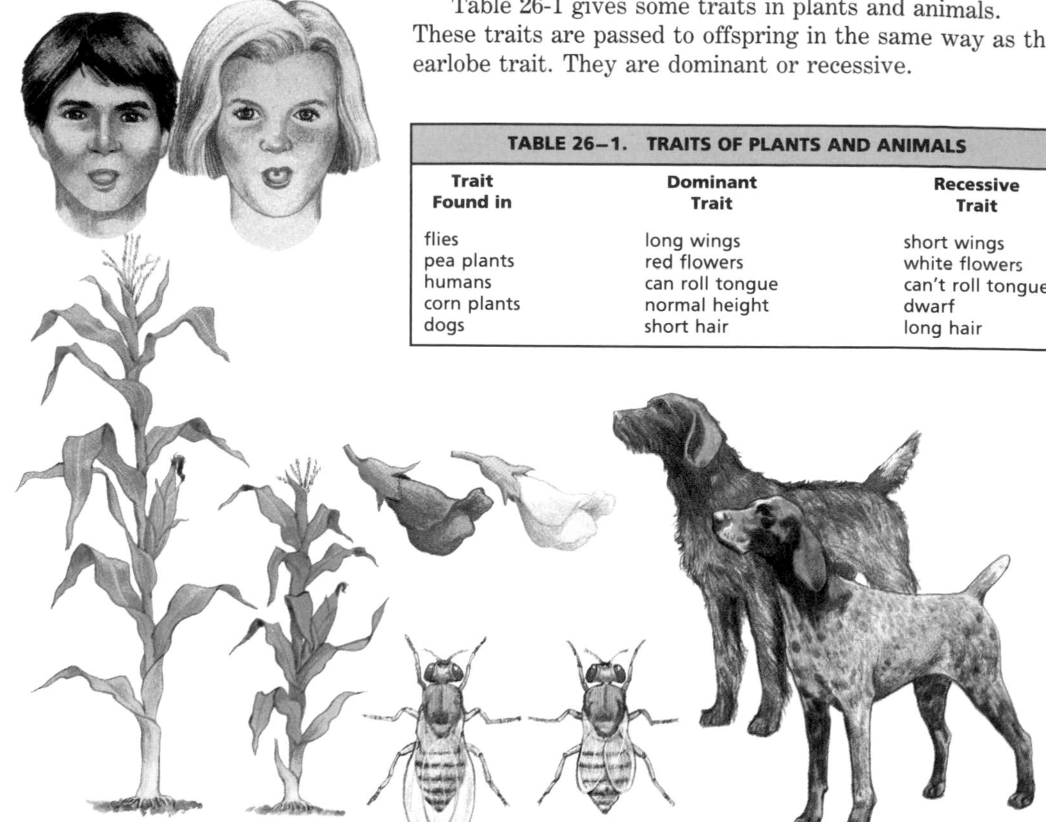

Table 26-1 gives some traits in plants and animals. These traits are passed to offspring in the same way as the earlobe trait. They are dominant or recessive.

TABLE 26–1. TRAITS OF PLANTS AND ANIMALS

Trait Found in	Dominant Trait	Recessive Trait
flies	long wings	short wings
pea plants	red flowers	white flowers
humans	can roll tongue	can't roll tongue
corn plants	normal height	dwarf
dogs	short hair	long hair

When Both Parents Are Heterozygous

When one parent had both genes for attached earlobes and the other parent had both genes for free earlobes, all of their children had a combination of genes. The children had free earlobes. Now, let's suppose both parents have a combination of genes. What could their children look like?

How many different kinds of sex cells can a heterozygous person make?

If the mother's body cells have both genes, she can make two kinds of eggs. Each egg will have a gene for attached earlobes or a gene for free earlobes, but not both. If the father's body cells have both genes, he can make two kinds of sperm. Each sperm will have the gene for attached earlobes or the gene for free earlobes, but not both. Figure 26-5 shows the possible combinations when egg and sperm join. There are four possible combinations.

OPTIONS

How Can the Genes of Offspring Be Predicted?/*Lab Manual*, pp. 219-222. Use this lab as an extension to predicting traits in offspring.

ACTIVITY/Enrichment

Explain that there are many different varieties of dogs, cats, horses, and cows. Have students try to find pictures of the different varieties of these animals and give a class report on their findings. Pet food companies have excellent color drawings of dogs and cats and their ancestral lineage.

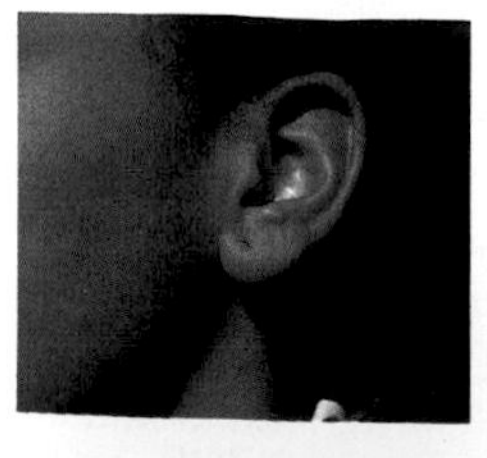

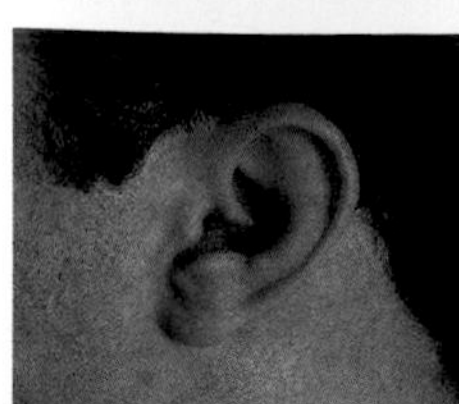

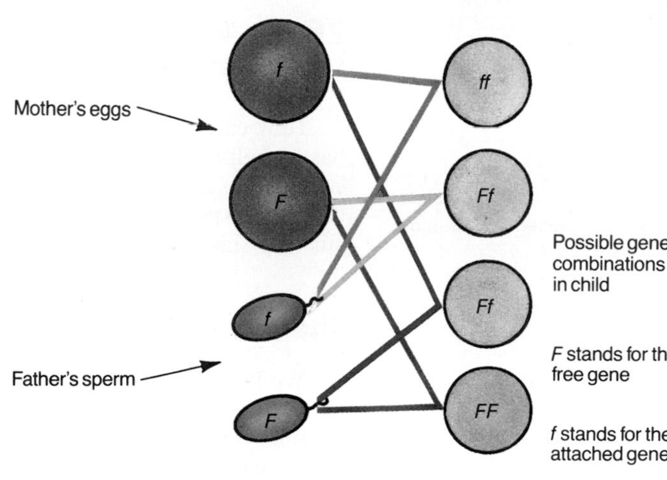

Figure 26-5 What genes can a child have if both parents are heterozygous? ***FF, Ff, Ff, ff***

Table 26-2 shows what a child with each combination would look like. There are three chances in four that a child would have free earlobes and one chance in four that a child would have attached earlobes. We call this a 3 to 1 ratio.

TABLE 26–2. GENE COMBINATIONS FOR EARLOBE TRAITS

With these genes from the egg:	sperm:	The child is:	The child has:
free	free	pure dominant	free earlobes
free	attached	heterozygous	free earlobes
free	attached	heterozygous	free earlobes
attached	attached	pure recessive	attached earlobes

Check Your Understanding

1. How are chromosomes in sex cells different from those in body cells?
2. One person is pure dominant for a trait while another is heterozygous. How are their genes different?
3. How many different kinds of offspring could result if one parent is pure dominant and the other parent is pure recessive? How many different kinds of offspring could result if both parents are heterozygous?
4. **Critical Thinking:** Why does an individual usually carry only two genes for a certain trait?
5. **Biology and Math:** Why do living organisms have an even number of chromosomes in their body cells?

TEACH

Check for Understanding

Have students respond to the first three questions in Check Your Understanding.

Reteach

Reteaching/*Teacher Resource Package*, p. 78. Use this worksheet to give students additional practice with traits of plants and animals.

Extension: Assign Critical Thinking, Biology and Math, or some of the **OPTIONS** available with this lesson.

3 APPLY

Audiovisual

Show the video *Genetics: Observing Patterns of Inheritance*, Insight Media.

4 CLOSE

Convergent Question

Pose the question: What would happen if all of the traits an organism inherited were recessive? (All of the organisms of the same type would have the same traits.)

Answers to Check Your Understanding

1. Chromosomes are in pairs in body cells but there is only one chromosome of each pair in a sex cell.
2. A pure dominant person has two dominant genes; a heterozygous person has one dominant and one recessive.
3. one; three
4. An individual receives only one gene from each parent for a trait.
5. Chromosomes are paired, and two of any number is an even number.

RETEACHING 78

RETEACHING: IDEA MAP — **CHAPTER 26**

Name ______ Date ______ Class ______

Use with Section 26:1.

TRAITS OF PLANTS AND ANIMALS

Use the following terms to complete the idea map: recessive, dominant, heterozygous, pure recessive, pure dominant. You may need to use some terms more than once. Then answer the questions that follow.

Genes
- dominant trait
  - pure dominant
    - dominant
    - dominant
  - heterozygous
    - dominant
    - recessive
- recessive trait
  - pure recessive
    - recessive
    - recessive

1. When is a living thing a pure dominant individual? **when it has two dominant genes for a trait**
2. What are dominant genes? **genes that keep other genes from showing their traits**
3. What are recessive genes? **genes that do not show their traits when dominant genes are present**
4. What is meant by a heterozygous individual? **A heterozygous individual has one dominant gene and one recessive gene for a trait.**
5. Could a child be born with a recessive trait if one parent is pure dominant for that trait? Explain. **No, the child would inherit a dominant gene from the parent who is pure dominant, so the recessive trait could not show.**
6. Could a child be born with a recessive trait if both parents are heterozygous for that trait? Explain. **Yes, there is one chance in four that the child will be born with the recessive trait.**

26:2 Expected and Observed Results

PREPARATION

Materials Needed

Make copies of the Focus, Transparency Master, Study Guide, Skill, Critical Thinking/Problem Solving, Enrichment, Application, Reteaching, and Lab worksheets in the *Teacher Resource Package.*

▶ Obtain corn seeds for Lab 26-1.

▶ Purchase white and red kidney beans and paper bags for Lab 26-2.

Key Science Words

Punnett square

Process Skills

In Lab 26-1, students will observe, predict, and interpret data. In Lab 26-2 students will observe, formulate a model, and form hypotheses. In the Skill Check, they will calculate.

1 FOCUS

▶ The objectives are listed on the student page. Remind students to preview these objectives as a guide to this numbered section.

MOTIVATION/Demonstration

To help students understand expected results, use a deck of 52 cards and have students predict how many times you could draw the following from the top of the deck: (a) an ace (4/52 or 1/13), (b) an ace of hearts (1/52), (c) a red ace (2/52 or 1/26).

Guided Practice

Have students write down their answers to the margin question: which genes can combine when egg and sperm join.

Focus/*Teacher Resource Package,* p. 51. Use the transparency shown at the bottom of this page as an introduction to crossing traits in organisms.

Objectives

4. **Discuss** the purpose of a Punnett square.
5. **Compare** expected results and observed results.
6. **Explain** the importance of Gregor Mendel's work.

Key Science Words

Punnett square

What does a Punnett square show?

26:2 Expected and Observed Results

How can knowing the types of genes that each parent has be helpful? You can predict what traits their children could have. Sometimes, however, the combinations of genes that you expect do not appear in the offspring. Let's find out why this is true.

The Punnett Square

We have seen how an egg and a sperm may combine to form an offspring. Each time, we figured out all the possible combinations of egg and sperm cells. There is an easier way to do this. This easy way is called the Punnett (PUH nuht) square. The **Punnett square** is a way to show which genes can combine when egg and sperm join. To make things easier, letters are used in place of genes. A large letter, such as ***F,*** is used for a dominant gene. The large ***F*** stands for free earlobe. A small letter, such as ***f,*** is used for a recessive gene. The small ***f*** stands for attached earlobe. A person with ***FF*** genes is pure dominant and has free earlobes. A person with ***Ff*** genes is heterozygous and has free earlobes. Notice that the large letter goes first in heterozygous organisms. A person with ***ff*** genes is pure recessive. What kind of earlobes does that person have?

Follow these six steps to determine the possible combinations of genes a child could have. In this example, both parents will be heterozygous. They will have a gene for free earlobes and a gene for attached earlobes. Use the letters ***Ff*** to stand for the gene pair in their body cells.

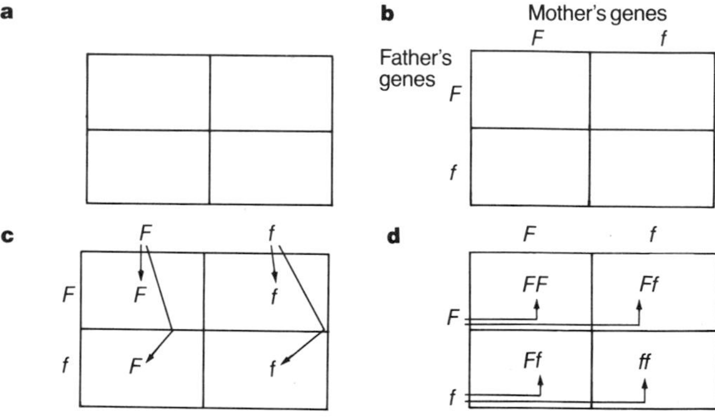

Figure 26-6 How to make and use a Punnett square

OPTIONS

Science Background

Geneticists use a Punnett square to calculate the results of a genetic cross. The Punnett square was developed by Reginald Punnett in the early 1900s. In the Punnett square, the known male gametes are placed along either the top or left edge of the square and the eggs along the remaining side. The expected offspring appear in the boxes inside the square when all of the possible male and female gametes have been combined.

FOCUS 51

FOCUS CHAPTER 26

Name ______ Date ______ Class ______

CROSSBREEDING DOGS

If a short-haired pointer is crossed with an Irish setter, what kind of hair do you think the puppies will have? On what are you basing your answer? How could you find out if you are not sure?

1. Draw a Punnett square as shown in Figure 26-6a. Each small box stands for one possible combination of genes that could show up in the offspring. Each combination of genes comes from a sperm cell fertilizing an egg cell.
2. Decide what kinds of genes will be in the sex cells of each parent. Write the letters that stand for the genes in the mother's egg cells across the top of the square. Figure 26-6b shows you how. In this case, put the two genes for eggs, ***F*** and ***f***, across the top.
3. Now, write the letters that stand for genes in the father's sperm along the side of the square. There are two possible genes for the sperm. They are ***F*** (free earlobes) and ***f*** (attached earlobes).
4. Copy the letters that appear at the top of the square into the boxes below each letter. Figure 26-6c shows how.
5. Copy the letters that appear at the side of the square into the boxes next to each letter. Figure 26-6d shows how.
6. Look at the small boxes in the Punnett square. They show the possible combinations of eggs and sperm. When egg and sperm combine, a new organism develops. The boxes also show what combinations of genes the organism could have. In our example, a child could have one of the following combinations: ***FF***, ***Ff***, or ***ff***.

The Punnett square in Figure 26-7 shows you how the child could look. Remember, ***F*** is dominant over ***f***. There are two different combinations of genes that would result in a child with free earlobes—***FF*** and ***Ff***. Notice that three out of the four boxes contain either ***FF*** or ***Ff***. Three out of four gene combinations of egg and sperm would result in a child with free earlobes.

There is only one combination of genes that would result in a child with attached earlobes—***ff***. Only one out of four boxes in the Punnett square has ***ff***. On average, one out of four gene combinations would result in a child with attached earlobes.

Expected Results

The Punnett square that you drew shows what kinds of traits offspring can have. It shows what to expect when the sperm and egg of two parents join. Expected results are what can be predicted in offspring based on the genetic traits of parents. We predicted that one out of four children would have attached earlobes. We could do this because we knew what genes the parents had.

Bio Tip

Consumer: Sometimes an ear of white corn contains a yellow kernel of corn. A pollen grain carrying the dominant yellow gene was carried by the wind from a nearby garden. It fertilized the egg in one of the kernels of the white ear of corn.

Figure 26-7 Three out of four gene combinations are for free earlobes.

	F	*f*
F	*FF* Free earlobes	*Ff* Free earlobes
f	*Ff* Free earlobes	*ff* Attached earlobes

2 TEACH

MOTIVATION/Demonstration

Make a transparency of a Punnett square to show the earlobe problem step-by-step. Make sure that students realize that for the pair of genes appearing in each box of the Punnett square, one gene is from each parent.

Concept Development

▶ Point out that when writing the genotype of a heterozygote, the capital letter is written first.

▶ Make sure students understand that the results shown here are only for the earlobe trait.

Independent Practice

Study Guide/*Teacher Resource Package,* p. 152. Use the Study Guide worksheet shown at the bottom of this page for independent practice.

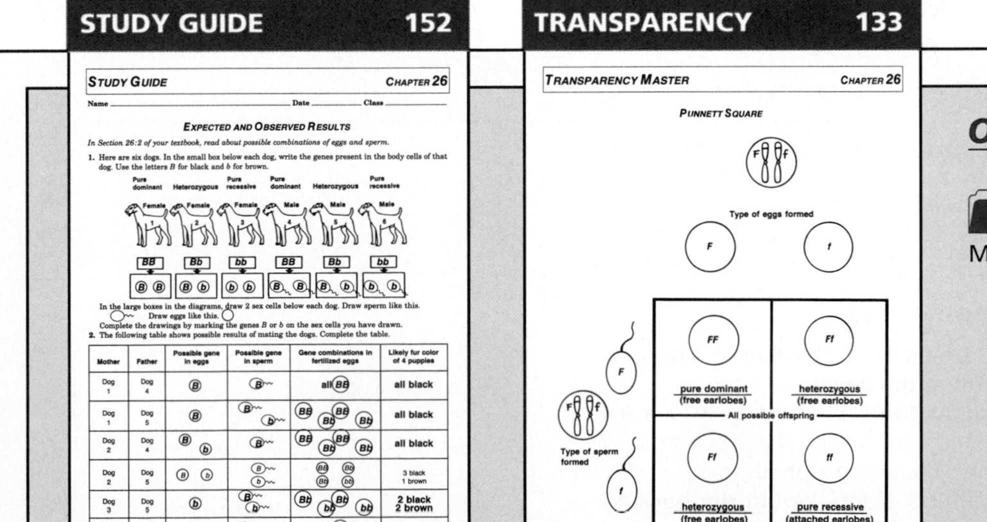

STUDY GUIDE 152

STUDY GUIDE — CHAPTER 26

Name ______ Date ______ Class ______

EXPECTED AND OBSERVED RESULTS

In Section 26:2 of your textbook, read about possible combinations of eggs and sperm.

1. Here are six dogs. In the small box below each dog, write the genes present in the body cells of that dog. Use the letters *B* for black and *b* for brown.

Pure dominant	Heterozygous	Pure recessive	Pure dominant	Heterozygous	Pure recessive
Female 1	Female 2	Female 3	Male 4	Male 5	Male 6
BB	Bb	bb	BB	Bb	bb
B B	B b	b b	B B	B b	b b

In the large boxes in the diagrams, draw 2 sex cells below each dog. Draw sperm like this. Draw eggs like this.
Complete the drawings by marking the genes *B* or *b* on the sex cells you have drawn.

2. The following table shows possible results of mating the dogs. Complete the table.

Mother	Father	Possible gene in eggs	Possible gene in sperm	Gene combinations in fertilized eggs	Likely fur color of 4 puppies
Dog 1	Dog 4	B	B	all BB	all black
Dog 1	Dog 5	B	B b	BB BB Bb Bb	all black
Dog 2	Dog 4	B b	B	BB BB Bb Bb	all black
Dog 2	Dog 5	B b	B b	BB Bb Bb bb	3 black 1 brown
Dog 3	Dog 5	b	B b	Bb Bb bb bb	2 black 2 brown
Dog 3	Dog 6	b	b	all bb	all brown

TRANSPARENCY 133

TRANSPARENCY MASTER — CHAPTER 26

PUNNETT SQUARE

OPTIONS

Transparency Master/*Teacher Resource Package,* p. 133. Use the Transparency Master shown here to teach the Punnett square.

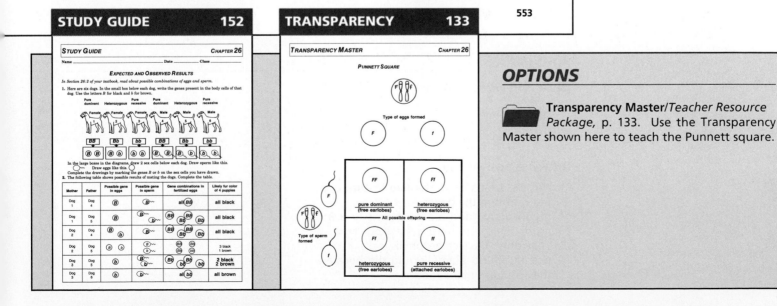

Lab 26-1 Corn Genes

Overview

Students will find that germinating corn seeds will either have green or white leaves. From their data, they will see that not all corn seeds have genes for green leaves. Until germination, they cannot tell which genes the seeds have because all the seeds look alike.

Objectives: Students will be able to (1) **classify** offspring by genetic traits, (2) **infer** which trait, green or albino, is dominant, and (3) **predict** what would happen to future generations of offspring with the albino trait.

Time Allotment: 30 minutes the first day; 10 minutes each day for 4 days after sprouting

Preparation

▶ Order the seeds in advance of the activity. Get petri dishes, towels, and light sources ready.

Lab 26-1 worksheet/*Teacher Resource Package*, pp. 101-102.

Teaching the Lab

▶ Review the terms *dominant*, *recessive*, and *hybrid* before beginning this lab. Have students use letters to represent possible gene combinations in green and albino corn plants.

▶ If you have small trays you could have students grow the seeds in soil.

Corn Genes

Lab 26–1

Problem: Do all corn seeds have genes for becoming green plants?

Skills

observe, predict, interpret data

Materials

20 corn seeds
paper towels
petri dish
water
wax marking pencil

Procedure

1. Copy the data table.
2. Look at the seeds carefully. Can you tell which seeds will grow into green plants and which will grow into white plants?
3. Moisten a paper towel with water.
4. Place the towel in the bottom half of the petri dish, Figure A. Fold it to fit.
5. Place the seeds on the towel. Cover the dish. Write your name on the cover.
6. Place the dish under a light and check it every day. Add more water if needed.
7. **Observe:** When the first seeds begin to sprout, record the leaf color. This is day 1.
8. Check your corn seeds for four more days. Record the numbers of new plants with green and with white leaves each day.

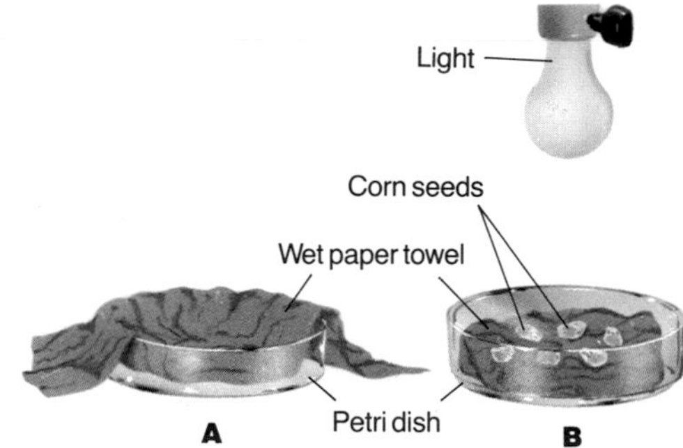

Data and Observations

1. What colors were the plants when they first sprouted?
2. Were there more green plants or white plants five days after sprouting?

	NUMBER OF CORN SEEDS SPROUTED	NUMBER WITH GREEN LEAVES	NUMBER WITH WHITE LEAVES
Day 1	1	1	0
Day 2	2	2	0
Day 3	6	4	2
Day 4	7	6	1
Day 5	3	2	1
Total	19	15	4

Analyze and Apply

Corn plants that remain white several days after sprouting have the albino trait. These plants soon die because they cannot make food. These plants are missing chlorophyll.

1. Could you tell before the seeds sprouted which would form green leaves? Explain.
2. **Predict:** What results would you see if the seeds came from heterozygous parents?
3. Why do albino plants not live as long as green plants?
4. **Apply:** Do you think most plants in fields and forests would be albino or green? Explain your answer.

Extension

Design an experiment to find out if the green corn plants in this lab carry the albino gene as a recessive trait.

ANSWERS

Data and Observations

1. white
2. green

Analyze and Apply

1. No, the trait was not visible in the seed; the trait is in the genes.
2. green plants and albino plants in a 3:1 ratio
3. They don't have chlorophyll.
4. Green; albino plants would die because they couldn't make food.

Career Close-Up

Animal Breeder

An animal breeder works with a veterinarian or animal breeding specialist to keep records on animals and record what offspring of animals look like. Egg and milk production, size, and coat color are but a few of the genetic traits that animals show. Records of the traits of parent animals can help the animal breeder predict what traits can show in the offspring.

Many animal breeders work for state universities. Others may work on large farms that specialize in breeding. For example, farms that raise hundreds of cows may use an animal breeder to follow weight gain of cattle or record milk production. Animal breeders may work on horse ranches that specialize in race horses. They can also work at kennels where dogs are bred to be sold.

Wherever an animal breeder works, much of the training is learned on the job. A knowledge of biology and genetics is useful in this career.

Some animal breeders record the milk production of cows.

The type of chin that a person has is also a genetic trait. A person with a cleft chin has a small indentation in the middle of the chin. A cleft chin is a dominant trait, Figure 26-8. A smooth chin is a recessive trait.

a

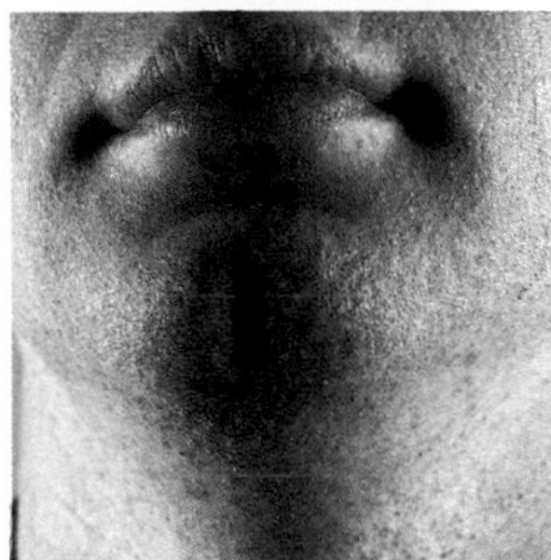

b

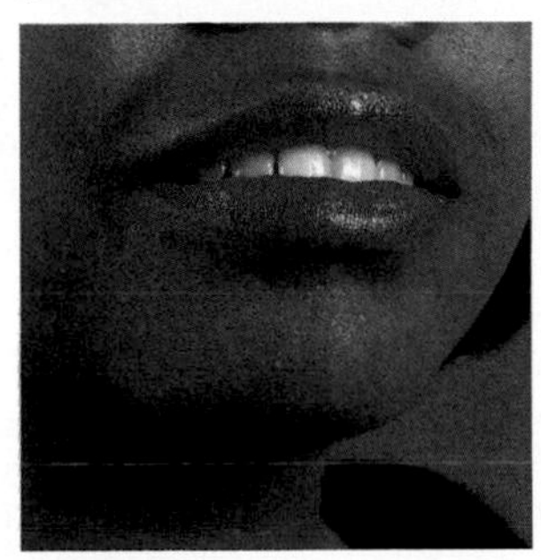

Figure 26-8 Person with cleft chin (a) and smooth chin (b)

Career Close-Up

Animal Breeder

Background

The animal breeder has to keep accurate records about expected and observed traits of offspring and their parents. Today, many of the records are placed in a computer file for ease of storage and access. The animal breeder is expected to be able to cross parents of known genotypes to get a specific number of offspring of desired genotypes and phenotypes.

Related Careers

animal caretaker and pet store clerk

Job Requirements

A high school diploma and an interest in genetics and animals are necessary requirements for becoming an animal breeder. On-the-job training by the employer and some courses at a community college are helpful.

For More Information

Check the library for government publications listing career opportunities and also with the state department of agriculture office in your state.

SKILL 27

SKILL: USE NUMBERS CHAPTER 26

Name ______ Date ______ Class ______

For more help, refer to the Skill Handbook, pages 718-719. *Use after Section 26: 2.*

FUR COLOR IN RABBITS

Mary and Jake are breeding rabbits to sell to a pet shop. They will be paid $20.00 for each white rabbit and $8.00 for each rabbit of any other color. They did not know how the trait for fur color is inherited in rabbits. To find out, they put many mating pairs of rabbits together and kept careful records of the offspring. Each pair of rabbits produced four offspring.

Use the table and your knowledge of heredity to answer the questions below.

Mating	Number of mating pairs	Fur color of parents	Fur color of offspring	
			White	Gray
A	10	white × white	40	0
B	10	gray × white	0	40
C	10	gray × gray	10	30
D	10	gray × gray	0	40
E	10	gray × white	20	20
Total	50		70	130

1. Complete the table above by filling in the numbers of mating pairs and the total number of offspring of each color.
2. How much money could Mary and Jake make by selling the white offspring? **$1400**
3. How much money could they make by selling the gray offspring? **$1040**
4. Suppose the pet shop changes its policy and will pay $20.00 for gray rabbits and $8.00 for white rabbits. How much money would Mary and Jake make by selling the offspring of the mating pairs? **$2600 for the gray rabbits and $560 for the white rabbits, for a total of $3160**
5. Which gene for fur color is dominant? **The gene for gray fur.**
6. Which mating will produce the most white rabbits? **white × white**

OPTIONS

Skill/*Teacher Resource Package*, p. 27. Use the Skill worksheet shown here for students to use numbers in understanding breeding.

Lab 26-2 Punnett Squares

Overview

Students will use beans of two colors to simulate two genes for a trait found in sperm and eggs. By selecting a bean at random from one bag (potential egg cell) and a bean from a second bag (potential sperm cell), they will simulate fertilization of the egg. The student will determine the "observed" genotype and phenotype of each potential offspring. Students will build a Punnett square to determine the expected offspring and compare these results to their observed results.

Objectives: Students will be able to: (1) **demonstrate** how random fertilization works, (2) **simulate** a genetic cross using beans as sperm and egg cells, and (3) **compare** expected and observed data.

Time Allotment: 45 minutes

Preparation

▶ Get the beans and paper bags for the activity.

Lab 26-2 worksheet/*Teacher Resource Package*, pp. 103-104.

Teaching the Lab

▶ Beans can be stored in zip-lock type plastic bags for future years.

▶ Red and white beans can be purchased at the grocery store.

▶ Optional: Paper bags can be marked male and female so that students can determine which gene comes from which parent.

Punnett Squares — Lab 26–2

Problem: What determines how offspring will look?

Skills

observe, formulate a model, form hypotheses

Materials

40 white beans
40 red beans
2 paper bags

Procedure

1. Copy the data table.
2. Place 20 white and 20 red beans into a paper bag. Label the bag female parent. These beans represent eggs.
3. Place 20 white and 20 red beans into a second paper bag. Label this bag male parent. These beans represent sperm.
4. Set up a Punnett square to show the parent gene types. Use ***R*** to stand for the dominant gene, red. Use ***r*** to stand for the recessive gene, white. Remember that each parent can produce sex cells carrying the red trait or the white trait. They are both heterozygous.
5. Complete your Punnett square to show the expected offspring of these parents.
6. Shake the bags.
7. Reach into each bag without looking and remove one bean. The two beans stand for the gene combination that results when sperm and egg join.
8. **Observe:** Look at the beans. Record the colors of the beans in your table next to trial 1. Use a check mark to record your results in the proper column.
9. Put the two beans back into the bags from which they came.
10. Write a **hypothesis** to show how many red/red ***(RR)***, red/white ***(Rr)***, and white/white ***(rr)*** pairs you will get in 40 trials. Use your Punnett square for help.
11. Repeat steps 6–9 for 39 more trials.
12. Using your table, find the totals of red/red (***RR***), red/white (***Rr***), and white/white (***rr***) combinations.

Data and Observations

1. What gene pairs result in red offspring?
2. What gene pairs result in white offspring?

TRIAL	FEMALE PARENT		MALE PARENT		GENE PAIRS
	RED BEANS	WHITE BEANS	RED BEANS	WHITE BEANS	
1	√		√		*RR*
2		√		√	*rr*
3		√		√	*rr*
4	√			√	*Rr*
5		√	√		*Rr*
40		√		√	*rr*

Analyze and Apply

1. Out of 40 offspring, how many did you expect to be pure dominant ***(RR)***, heterozygous ***(Rr)***, and pure recessive ***(rr)***?
2. Which of the three gene combinations did you expect in greatest number?
3. **Check your hypothesis:** Was your hypothesis supported by your data? Why or why not?
4. **Apply:** What determines how offspring will look?

Extension

Design an experiment to show that the more trials you do, the closer your observed results come to your expected results.

ANSWERS

Data and Observations

1. ***RR, Rr***
2. ***rr***

Analyze and Apply

1. 10 ***RR***; 20 ***Rr***; 10 ***rr***
2. ***Rr***
3. students who hypothesized that there will be 10 ***RR***, 20 ***Rr***, 10 ***rr*** in 40 trials will say that their hypotheses were supported.
4. the combination of genes that come together in the offspring

Let ***I*** stand for cleft chin and ***i*** stand for smooth chin. It might be easier to remember the symbols if you think of ***I*** standing for indentation. How might a child appear if one parent were ***Ii*** and the other were ***ii?*** Use the Punnett square in Figure 26-9 to get the answer. Two out of four gene combinations could be for children with cleft chins. Note that these children with cleft chins have ***Ii*** genes. The other two combinations could be for children with smooth chins, or children with ***ii*** genes. These results are what is expected. Would you expect these parents to have a pure dominant child? Why or why not?

	I	*i*
i	*Ii* Cleft chin	*ii* Smooth chin
i	*Ii* Cleft chin	*ii* Smooth chin

Figure 26-9 Children can have two possible chin types if one parent is heterozygous and the other is pure recessive.

Observed Results

We know that the results expected from the Punnett square do not always occur in every family. Look at Table 26-3. These data are from ten different families that show the cleft chin trait. In each family, one parent has the genes ***Ii*** and has a cleft chin. The other parent has the genes ***ii*** and has a smooth chin.

The table shows exactly what you would see if you looked at the children of these families. The traits actually seen in offspring when parents with certain genetic traits mate are the observed results. Using a Punnett square allows you to predict that half the children in these families could have cleft chins. Half the children could have smooth chins. The observed results, however, do not exactly match the expected results because you don't know which sperm and egg will join.

TABLE 26–3. OFFSPRING AND CHIN TYPES

Family	Number of Children in Family	Number with Cleft Chin	Number with Smooth Chin
A	2	0	2
B	1	1	0
C	5	3	2
D	4	2	2
E	2	1	1
F	3	1	2
G	1	1	0
H	6	4	2
I	2	1	1
J	3	1	2
Totals	29	15	14

TEACH

Concept Development

▶ Explain that each child born to two heterozygous parents has one out of four chances of having a smooth chin even though the first child has a smooth chin.

▶ Explain that observed results are not calculated.

▶ Point out that the expected offspring from each family shown in Table 26-3 is one child with cleft chin for each child having a smooth chin.

▶ Explain that the more data you have to look at, the closer the observed will be to the expected. (The totals on Table 26-3 show this.)

▶ Emphasize that families D and E are closer to expected results than other families.

Independent Practice

Study Guide/*Teacher Resource Package,* p. 153. Use the Study Guide worksheet shown at the bottom of this page for independent practice.

STUDY GUIDE 153

STUDY GUIDE CHAPTER 26

Name ________ Date ________ Class ________

EXPECTED AND OBSERVED RESULTS

In Section 26:2 of your textbook, read about solving genetics problems using the Punnett square.

3. Examine the diagrams below. Each is a step in the Punnett square method. Put the steps in order by writing the numbers 1 to 4 below them on the correct blanks.

2 3 1 4

4. What do the letters outside the Punnett square stand for? genes in eggs and sperm

What do the letters inside each box stand for? genes in offspring

5. Examine the following Punnett squares and circle those that are correct.

6. Complete the following to determine the expected offspring.

OPTIONS

ACTIVITY/Challenge

Have students use the Punnett squares to determine the offspring from the following crosses of people having cleft or smooth chin:

a. ***ii*** x ***II*** (all cleft chin)
b. ***ii*** x ***ii*** (all smooth chin)
c. ***Ii*** x ***II*** (1/2 ***Ii***: 1/2 ***II***; all cleft chin)

TEACH

Idea Map

Have students use the idea map as a study guide to the major concepts of this section.

Skill Check

They should get about 1/2 heads and 1/2 tails. They are able to predict expected results.

Guided Practice

Have students write down their answers to the margin question: The more results you observe, the closer observed results will be to expected results.

Check for Understanding

Review expected and observed results. Make sure students understand that expected results can be calculated, but observed results are actually seen. Set up some simple problems that students can do by using the Punnett square. Do one problem as a class so they can learn from any mistakes.

Reteach

Have students use their Punnett squares from Check for Understanding and write out the expected results.

Independent Practice

Study Guide/*Teacher Resource Package*, p. 154. Use the Study Guide worksheet shown at the bottom of this page for independent practice.

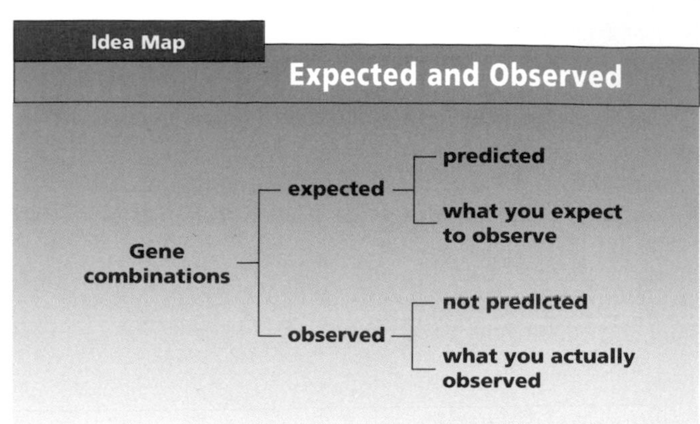

Study Tip: Use this idea map as a study guide to expected and observed results. The idea map shows how they are different.

A little more than half the children have cleft chins. Nearly half the children have smooth chins. Each family by itself may not show the results you expect to see. If you add the results together, they are close to what you expect to see in a Punnett square. In fact, the more results you observe, the closer the observed results will be to the expected results.

Think about what happens when you flip a coin. You expect the coin to come up heads or tails. If you flip a coin two times, does it come up heads once and tails once? It may. It may come up heads twice or tails twice. Two heads or two tails are not what you expect. In fact, if you flip the coin four times you may even see four heads or four tails. Why?

Each time you flip a coin, you are starting over. If you flip the coin once and see heads, it does not mean that the next flip must come up tails. The coin can land either way each time you flip it. With just a few flips, you are less likely to see the exact same number of heads as tails. If you flip the coin many, many times, the number of heads and tails should be about equal. The observed results will be closer to the expected results.

Skill Check

Calculate: Calculate how many heads and tails you would get if you were to flip a coin 10 times and then 50 times. Explain which you are able to calculate, expected or observed results. *For more help, refer to the* ***Skill Handbook****, pages 718-719.*

When are observed results similar to expected results?

Mendel's Work

Let's go back in time to 1865. An Austrian monk named Gregor Mendel saw certain traits in the garden pea plants he grew in his garden. Mendel counted and recorded the

OPTIONS

ACTIVITY/Challenge

Ask students to find out how many students in their neighborhood have a cleft chin and how many have a smooth chin. Ask which trait they expect to see more often and why.

Critical Thinking/Problem Solving/ *Teacher Resource Package*, p. 26. Use the worksheet shown here to teach inherited traits.

CRITICAL THINKING 26

CRITICAL THINKING/PROBLEM SOLVING — CHAPTER 26

Name ______ Date ______ Class ______

Use after Section 26:2.

HOW CAN PLANTS SHOW UNEXPECTED TRAITS?

A gardener saved some seeds from red tomatoes she grew one summer. The next spring, she and her friend planted the seeds. The plants grew and formed flowers. When the tomatoes formed, many were red but some were yellow. The gardeners counted the fruits. They found 148 red tomatoes and 52 yellow tomatoes. At the library, they used garden books and a genetics text to understand what had happened.

Analyzing the Problem

1. What was the ratio of red to yellow tomatoes? **148 to 52, or about three-fourths red and one-fourth yellow**
2. What are the expected results based on 200 tomatoes? **150 to 50, or three-fourths red and one-fourth yellow**

Solving the Problem

Use the information above and these Punnett squares to answer the questions that follow. Assume that the trait for red (R) is dominant to yellow (r).

A

	R	R
R	RR	RR
R	RR	RR

B

	R	R
r	Rr	Rr
r	Rr	Rr

C

	R	r
R	RR	Rr
r	Rr	rr

D

	R	r
r	Rr	rr
r	Rr	rr

1. Write the symbols for tomatoes that will look red. **RR, Rr**
2. Write the symbols for tomatoes that will look yellow. **rr**
3. Which Punnett square shows a cross between pure red tomatoes? **A**
4. Which Punnett square shows a cross between pure red and pure yellow tomatoes? **B**
5. Were the seeds that the gardener planted "pure" for red color? How can you tell? **No, some tomatoes in the offspring were yellow.**
6. Yellow tomato skin color is an inherited trait. How can you determine if the gene is dominant or recessive? **Cross yellow and pure red tomato plants. If the gene for yellow is recessive, there will be only red offspring.**

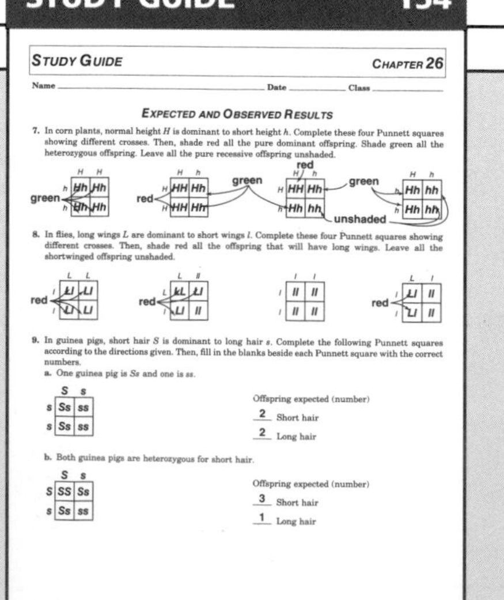

STUDY GUIDE 154

STUDY GUIDE — CHAPTER 26

Name ______ Date ______ Class ______

EXPECTED AND OBSERVED RESULTS

7. In corn plants, normal height H is dominant to short height h. Complete these four Punnett squares showing different crosses. Then, shade red all the pure dominant offspring. Shade green all the heterozygous offspring. Leave all the pure recessive offspring unshaded.

	H	H
h	Hh	Hh
h	Hh	Hh

	H	h
H	HH	Hh
H	HH	Hh

	H	h
H	HH	Hh
h	Hh	hh

	H	h
h	Hh	hh
h	Hh	hh

8. In flies, long wings L are dominant to short wings l. Complete these four Punnett squares showing different crosses. Then, shade red all the offspring that will have long wings. Leave all the shortwinged offspring unshaded.

	L	L
l	Ll	Ll
l	Ll	Ll

	L	ll
L	LL	Ll
l	Ll	ll

	l	l
l	ll	ll
l	ll	ll

	L	l
l	Ll	ll
l	Ll	ll

9. In guinea pigs, short hair S is dominant to long hair s. Complete the following Punnett squares according to the directions given. Then, fill in the blanks beside each Punnett square with the correct numbers.

a. One guinea pig is *Ss* and one is *ss*.

	S	s
s	Ss	ss
s	Ss	ss

Offspring expected (number)
2 Short hair
2 Long hair

b. Both guinea pigs are heterozygous for short hair.

	S	s
S	SS	Ss
s	Ss	ss

Offspring expected (number)
3 Short hair
1 Long hair

a

Figure 26-10 Gregor Mendel used a scientific method to study pea plants (a). Two of the traits he studied are shape and color of the seed (b).

traits he saw in the pea plants. He used a scientific method to do hundreds of experiments. Using the data he gathered and his knowledge of mathematics, he was able to explain some basic laws of genetics. Mendel explained what dominant and recessive traits were. He also showed how these traits passed from parent to offspring. How did he do it?

Why is Mendel's work important?

Mendel looked at several traits in the garden pea plant, Figure 26-10. One of those traits was height of the plant. He noticed that tall parent plants mated with short parent plants always produced tall plants, Figure 26-11. Remember that if ***T*** stood for the tall gene and ***t*** stood for the short gene, the parents would be ***TT*** and ***tt***. What genes would the offspring have? Would the offspring be heterozygous or pure?

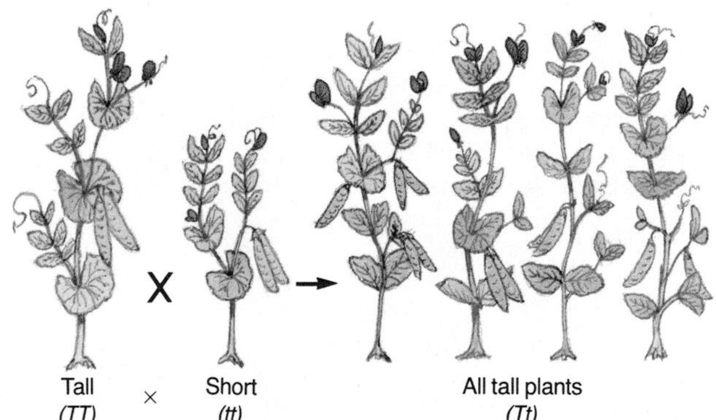

Figure 26-11 Mendel's results when he mated a tall parent plant with a short parent plant

TEACH

Concept Development

▶ Point out that Mendel did not know about meiosis but assumed that traits, which he called unit characters, separated from each other when gametes were formed.

Independent Practice

Study Guide/*Teacher Resource Package,* p. 155. Use the Study Guide worksheet shown at the bottom of this page for independent practice.

Guided Practice

Have students write down their answers to the margin question: He explained basic laws of genetics and dominant and recessive traits.

Connection: Social Studies

Have students give a report on the ideas of some scientists that extended Mendelian genetics. Suggest Carl Correns, Wilhelm Johannsen, W. E. Castle, or Hugo DeVries.

STUDY GUIDE 155

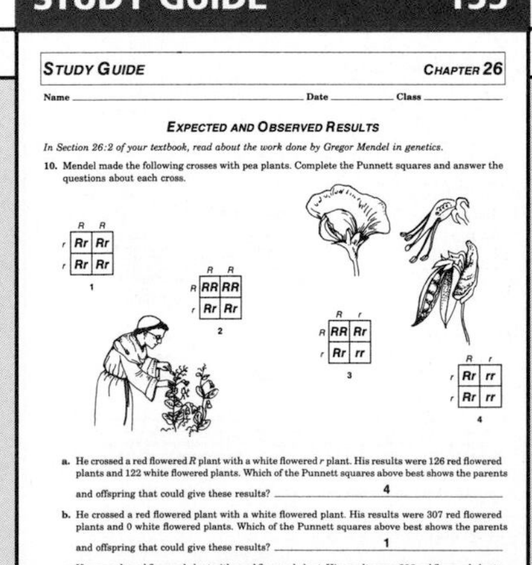

STUDY GUIDE — CHAPTER 26

Name ______ Date ______ Class ______

EXPECTED AND OBSERVED RESULTS

In Section 26:2 of your textbook, read about the work done by Gregor Mendel in genetics.

10. Mendel made the following crosses with pea plants. Complete the Punnett squares and answer the questions about each cross.

1

	R	R
r	Rr	Rr
r	Rr	Rr

2

	R	R
R	RR	RR
r	Rr	Rr

3

	R	r
R	RR	Rr
r	Rr	rr

4

	R	r
r	Rr	rr
r	Rr	rr

a. He crossed a red flowered *R* plant with a white flowered *r* plant. His results were 126 red flowered plants and 122 white flowered plants. Which of the Punnett squares above best shows the parents and offspring that could give these results? **4**

b. He crossed a red flowered plant with a white flowered plant. His results were 307 red flowered plants and 0 white flowered plants. Which of the Punnett squares above best shows the parents and offspring that could give these results? **1**

c. He crossed a red flowered plant with a red flowered plant. His results were 306 red flowered plants and 110 white flowered plants. Which of the Punnett squares above best shows the parents and offspring that could give these results? **3**

d. He crossed a red flowered plant with a red flowered plant. His results were 300 red flowered plants and 0 white flowered plants. Which of the Punnett squares above best shows the parents and offspring that could give these results? **2**

ENRICHMENT 28

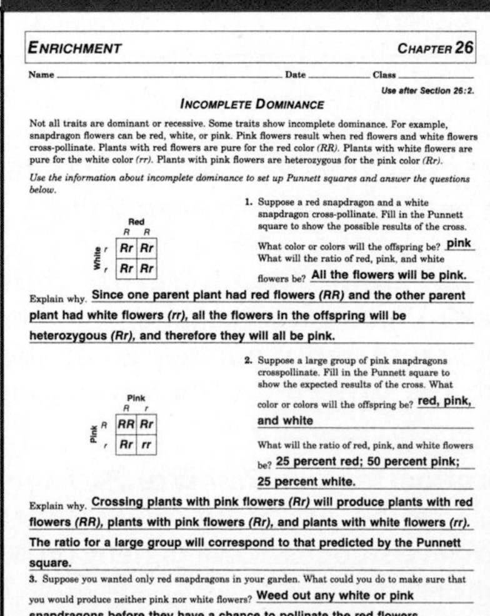

ENRICHMENT — CHAPTER 26

Name ______ Date ______ Class ______

Use after Section 26:2.

INCOMPLETE DOMINANCE

Not all traits are dominant or recessive. Some traits show incomplete dominance. For example, snapdragon flowers can be red, white, or pink. Pink flowers result when red flowers and white flowers cross-pollinate. Plants with red flowers are pure for the red color *(RR)*. Plants with white flowers are pure for the white color *(rr)*. Plants with pink flowers are heterozygous for the pink color *(Rr)*.

Use the information about incomplete dominance to set up Punnett squares and answer the questions below.

1. Suppose a red snapdragon and a white snapdragon cross-pollinate. Fill in the Punnett square to show the possible results of the cross.

White \ Red	R	R
r	Rr	Rr
r	Rr	Rr

What color or colors will the offspring be? **pink**
What will the ratio of red, pink, and white flowers be? **All the flowers will be pink.**

Explain why. **Since one parent plant had red flowers *(RR)* and the other parent plant had white flowers *(rr)*, all the flowers in the offspring will be heterozygous *(Rr)*, and therefore they will all be pink.**

2. Suppose a large group of pink snapdragons crosspollinate. Fill in the Punnett square to show the expected results of the cross. What color or colors will the offspring be? **red, pink, and white**

Pink \ Pink	R	r
R	RR	Rr
r	Rr	rr

What will the ratio of red, pink, and white flowers be? **25 percent red; 50 percent pink; 25 percent white.**

Explain why. **Crossing plants with pink flowers *(Rr)* will produce plants with red flowers *(RR)*, plants with pink flowers *(Rr)*, and plants with white flowers *(rr)*. The ratio for a large group will correspond to that predicted by the Punnett square.**

3. Suppose you wanted only red snapdragons in your garden. What could you do to make sure that you would produce neither pink nor white flowers? **Weed out any white or pink snapdragons before they have a chance to pollinate the red flowers.**

OPTIONS

Enrichment/*Teacher Resource Package,* p. 28. Use the Enrichment worksheet shown here to explain incomplete dominance.

TEACH

Cooperative Learning: Put students into teams of four and have them use reference materials to answer questions below. Have a member of each team report their findings to the class. Have them answer the following:

1. How might Mendel's father's occupation have influenced Mendel? (His father was an orchardist and worked in plant husbandry.)
2. Why did Mendel's laws sit on a shelf for over 30 years before anyone used them? (Most people did not understand what Mendel had done and did not understand what math had to do with the inheritance of traits.)
3. How did scientists of that time think traits were inherited? (Look up blood theory of inheritance.)
4. Other than the laws of genetics, what else did Mendel accomplish in science? (He developed several new varieties of fruits and vegetables.)
5. How did Mendel know that he had true breeding strains of peas for his experiments? (He bought them from a "seedsman" who would guarantee the "pure breeding" quality of the seeds.)

Mendel then took the tall offspring and mated them with each other. He noticed that about three-fourths of the plants they produced were tall and about one-fourth were short. Look at Figure 26-12. Can you see that Mendel's results came very close to what we now expect to see when heterozygous plants are mated? Mendel concluded that his plants were heterozygous after he saw the results of his experiments.

Remember that a heterozygous individual has a dominant gene and a recessive gene. Mendel's heterozygous plants would be ***Tt.*** Study the Punnett square in Figure 26-12 to see what happens when two heterozygous plants mate.

	T	*t*
T	*TT* Tall	*Tt* Tall
t	*Tt* Tall	*tt* Short

Figure 26-12 Mendel's results when he mated two heterozygous plants. How many gene combinations are possible? three

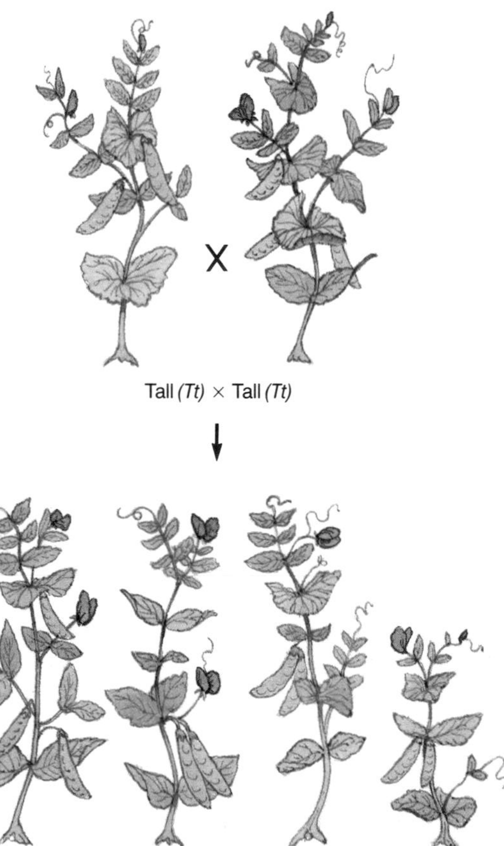

OPTIONS

What Is a Test Cross?/*Lab Manual*, pp. 223-226. Use this lab as an extension to crossing traits.

Offspring From Two Heterozygous Parents/*Transparency Package*, number 26. Use color transparency number 26 as you teach traits in the offspring of heterozygous parents.

Application/*Teacher Resource Package*, p. 26. Use the Application worksheet shown here to have students solve genetic problems in agriculture.

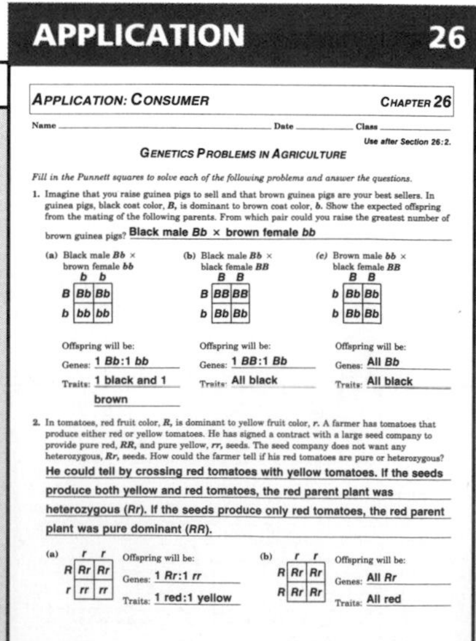

APPLICATION 26

APPLICATION: CONSUMER — **CHAPTER 26**

Name ______ Date ______ Class ______

Use after Section 26:2.

GENETICS PROBLEMS IN AGRICULTURE

Fill in the Punnett squares to solve each of the following problems and answer the questions.

1. Imagine that you raise guinea pigs to sell and that brown guinea pigs are your best sellers. In guinea pigs, black coat color, ***B,*** is dominant to brown coat color, ***b.*** Show the expected offspring from the mating of the following parents. From which pair could you raise the greatest number of brown guinea pigs? **Black male *Bb* × brown female *bb***

(a) Black male ***Bb*** × brown female ***bb***

	b	*b*
B	*Bb*	*Bb*
b	*bb*	*bb*

Offspring will be:
Genes: **1 *Bb*:1 *bb***
Traits: **1 black and 1 brown**

(b) Black male ***Bb*** × black female ***BB***

	B	*B*
B	*BB*	*BB*
b	*Bb*	*Bb*

Offspring will be:
Genes: **1 *BB*:1 *Bb***
Traits: **All black**

(c) Brown male ***bb*** × black female ***BB***

	B	*B*
b	*Bb*	*Bb*
b	*Bb*	*Bb*

Offspring will be:
Genes: **All *Bb***
Traits: **All black**

2. In tomatoes, red fruit color, ***R,*** is dominant to yellow fruit color, ***r.*** A farmer has tomatoes that produce either red or yellow tomatoes. He has signed a contract with a large seed company to provide pure red, ***RR,*** and pure yellow, ***rr,*** seeds. The seed company does not want any heterozygous, ***Rr,*** seeds. How could the farmer tell if his red tomatoes are pure or heterozygous? **He could tell by crossing red tomatoes with yellow tomatoes. If the seeds produce both yellow and red tomatoes, the red parent plant was heterozygous (*Rr*). If the seeds produce only red tomatoes, the red parent plant was pure dominant (*RR*).**

(a)

	r	*r*
R	*Rr*	*Rr*
r	*rr*	*rr*

Offspring will be:
Genes: **1 *Rr*:1 *rr***
Traits: **1 red:1 yellow**

(b)

	r	*r*
R	*Rr*	*Rr*
R	*Rr*	*Rr*

Offspring will be:
Genes: **All *Rr***
Traits: **All red**

TABLE 26-4. MENDEL'S RESULTS

Trait	Number of Offspring Observed		
	Dominant Trait	**Recessive Trait**	**Total**
Color of pea pod	green–428	yellow–152	580
Shape of pea	round–5474	wrinkled–1850	7324
Color of pea	yellow–6022	green–2001	8023
Flower color	red–705	white–224	929

Mendel studied seven traits in pea plants. Some traits that he looked at were the color of the pea pod, shape of the peas, color of the peas, and color of the flower. Table 26-4 shows that he got the same results whenever he mated heterozygous plants. About three-fourths of the offspring had the dominant trait and one-fourth had the recessive trait.

Check Your Understanding

6. Why are observed results sometimes different from expected results?
7. Draw a Punnett square to show what genes a child would be expected to have if each parent were heterozygous for long eyelashes. Use ***L*** to stand for the dominant trait, long eyelashes. Use ***l*** to stand for the recessive trait, short eyelashes.
8. What laws of genetics did Mendel explain?
9. **Critical Thinking:** You mate a red-flowered plant with a white-flowered plant. You expect all the offspring to be red, but you find that half of them are white. Explain why.
10. **Biology and Writing:** Being an albino is a recessive trait in which no color is produced in the skin or eyes. Could an albino child be produced by two normally-pigmented parents? Explain.

RETEACHING 79

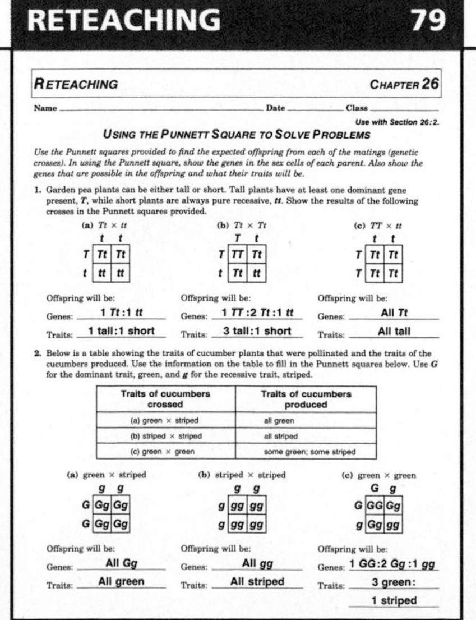

RETEACHING — CHAPTER 26

Name ______ Date ______ Class ______

Use with Section 26:2.

USING THE PUNNETT SQUARE TO SOLVE PROBLEMS

Use the Punnett squares provided to find the expected offspring from each of the matings (genetic crosses). In using the Punnett square, show the genes in the sex cells of each parent. Also show the genes that are possible in the offspring and what their traits will be.

1. Garden pea plants can be either tall or short. Tall plants have at least one dominant gene present, *T*, while short plants are always pure recessive, *tt*. Show the results of the following crosses in the Punnett squares provided.

(a) *Tt* × *tt*

	t	*t*
T	*Tt*	*Tt*
t	*tt*	*tt*

Offspring will be:
Genes: 1 *Tt* :1 *tt*
Traits: 1 tall:1 short

(b) *Tt* × *Tt*

	T	*t*
T	*TT*	*Tt*
t	*Tt*	*tt*

Offspring will be:
Genes: 1 *TT* :2 *Tt* :1 *tt*
Traits: 3 tall:1 short

(c) *TT* × *tt*

	t	*t*
T	*Tt*	*Tt*
T	*Tt*	*Tt*

Offspring will be:
Genes: All *Tt*
Traits: All tall

2. Below is a table showing the traits of cucumber plants that were pollinated and the traits of the cucumbers produced. Use the information on the table to fill in the Punnett squares below. Use ***G*** for the dominant trait, green, and ***g*** for the recessive trait, striped.

Traits of cucumbers crossed	Traits of cucumbers produced
(a) green × striped	all green
(b) striped × striped	all striped
(c) green × green	some green; some striped

(a) green × striped

	g	g
G	Gg	Gg
G	Gg	Gg

Offspring will be:
Genes: All Gg
Traits: All green

(b) striped × striped

	g	g
g	gg	gg
g	gg	gg

Offspring will be:
Genes: All gg
Traits: All striped

(c) green × green

	G	g
G	GG	Gg
g	Gg	gg

Offspring will be:
Genes: 1 GG:2 Gg :1 gg
Traits: 3 green: 1 striped

STUDY GUIDE 156

STUDY GUIDE — CHAPTER 26

Name ______ Date ______ Class ______

VOCABULARY

Review the new words used in Chapter 26 of your textbook. Then, answer these questions.

1. Below each of the following words are choices. Circle the choices that are examples of each of those words.
   a. Dominant gene
   (D) e k (L) (N) o (R) (S)
   b. Recessive gene
   M (n) (d) F G (i) (k) P
   c. Pure dominant
   (AA) Gg (KK) ll pp Rr (TT)
   d. Pure recessive
   (ee) Ff HH Oo (qq) Uu (ww)
   e. Offspring combinations in which dominant gene *must* show
   (AA) (Dd) (EE) ff (Jj) (RR) (Ss)
   f. Offspring combinations in which recessive gene *must* show
   (aa) Gg Ff KK Oo PP (ss) (tt)
2. Fill in the blanks below using these choices: dominant, genes, genetics, heterozygous, pure, recessive, chromosomes, Punnett square.
   a. Chromosomes have parts that determine traits. These parts are genes.
   b. A person having two genes that are alike is said to be pure.
   c. A gene that prevents others from showing is said to be dominant.
   d. A gene that may not show up even though it is there is said to be recessive.
   e. Long rod-shaped bodies inside a cell's nucleus are called chromosomes.
   f. One who studies how traits are passed on is studying genetics.
   g. A person with one dominant and one recessive gene for a trait is heterozygous.
   h. A way to show which genes can combine when an egg and sperm join is a Punnett square.

TEACH

Independent Practice

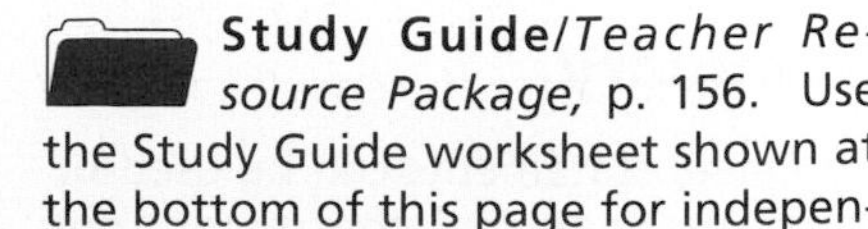

Study Guide/*Teacher Resource Package,* p. 156. Use the Study Guide worksheet shown at the bottom of this page for independent practice.

Check for Understanding

Have students respond to the first three questions in Check Your Understanding.

Reteach

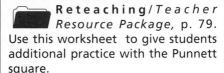

Reteaching/*Teacher Resource Package,* p. 79. Use this worksheet to give students additional practice with the Punnett square.

Extension: Assign Critical Thinking, Biology and Writing, or some of the **OPTIONS** available with this lesson.

3 APPLY

Convergent Question

Have students explain why some families in Table 26-3 do not have a 1:1 ratio of children with cleft and smooth chins.

4 CLOSE

Software

Genetics, Queue, Inc.

Answers to Check Your Understanding

6. because you don't know which sperm and egg will join
7. 1 ***LL***: 2 ***Ll***: 1 ***ll***
8. what dominant and recessive traits were and how these traits passed from parent to offspring
9. The red parent plant is heterozygous.
10. yes, if both parents are heterozygous and carry the recessive gene for albinism

CHAPTER 26 REVIEW

Summary

Summary statements can be used by students to review the major concepts of the chapter.

Key Science Words

All boldfaced terms from the chapter are listed.

Testing Yourself

Using Words

1. heterozygous
2. dominant gene
3. pure dominant
4. pure recessive
5. gene
6. Punnett square
7. recessive gene
8. genetics

Finding Main Ideas

9. p. 547; They are arranged one next to another, like beads on a necklace.
10. pp. 552-553; Letters stand for genes. Letters for one parent go across the top and letters for the other parent go along the side. The letters are copied into the boxes beside each to show how they can combine.
11. p. 549; Dominant genes prevent the recessive traits from showing.
12. p. 547; Genes determine the traits.
13. p. 559; Mendel used the scientific method to do hundreds of experiments.
14. p. 546; They are best seen when a cell is ready to reproduce.
15. p. 553; The boxes represent the possible combinations of genes.
16. p. 557; The traits that offspring have are observed results.
17. pp. 550-551; Each parent can make two kinds of egg or sperm, which can join in four possible combinations.
18. pp. 546-547; There is only one of each kind of chromosome present in a sex cell, and each chromosome has different kinds of genes.

Chapter 26

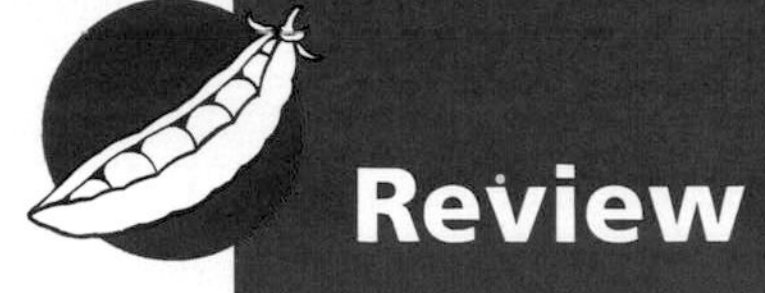

Review

Summary

26:1 Genetics, How and Why

1. Chromosomes are threadlike parts in the nuclei of body cells and sex cells. Body cells have twice as many chromosomes as sex cells.
2. Dominant genes keep recessive genes from showing their traits. An organism may have two dominant genes for a trait, two recessive genes, or one of each.
3. An individual that is pure for a trait can make one kind of sex cells for a certain trait. A heterozygous individual can make two kinds of sex cells for a certain trait. The kind of offspring produced depends on which sex cells combine.

26:2 Expected and Observed Results

4. The Punnett square helps to predict the combinations of genes offspring can receive.
5. Expected results are the predicted results. Observed results are what you actually see.
6. Mendel reported how traits were inherited in garden pea plants. He explained basic principles of genetics.

Key Science Words

dominant gene (p. 549)
gene (p. 547)
genetics (p. 546)
heterozygous (p. 549)
Punnett square (p. 552)
pure dominant (p. 549)
pure recessive (p. 549)
recessive gene (p. 549)

Testing Yourself

Using Words

Choose the word from the list of Key Science Words that best fits the definition.

1. has a dominant and a recessive gene for a trait
2. a gene that prevents a recessive gene from showing
3. has two dominant genes for a trait
4. having two recessive genes for the same trait
5. a small section of a chromosome that determines a trait
6. a way to show which genes combine when egg and sperm join
7. a gene that does not show when the dominant gene for the trait is present
8. study of how traits are passed from parents to offspring

Finding Main Ideas

List the page number where each main idea below is found. Then, explain each main idea.

9. how genes are arranged on a chromosome
10. how a Punnett square can be used to predict combinations of genes when sperm and eggs combine

Using Main Ideas

19. It predicts the possible combinations of egg and sperm cells.
20. Mendel performed experiments with pea plants.

Review

Testing Yourself *continued*

11. why recessive traits do not show in heterozygous individuals
12. what determines an organism's traits
13. how traits in the garden pea plant were studied
14. when chromosomes in a cell are seen best
15. what the four small boxes of a Punnett square represent
16. the traits that offspring actually have
17. that heterozygous parents can have children with a dominant or recessive trait
18. that each sex cell has one gene for a given trait

Using Main Ideas

Answer the questions by referring to the page number after each question.

19. What does a Punnett square predict? (p. 552)
20. Who discovered how garden pea plants inherit their traits? (p. 559)
21. What are genes that do not show even though they are present? (p. 549)
22. How are chromosomes and the nucleus related? (p. 546)
23. How is fertilization of an egg by a sperm like flipping a coin? (p. 558)
24. How are genes related to chromosomes? (p. 547)
25. What are two types of sex cells? (p. 546)
26. How do body cells and sex cells differ in chromosome number? (p. 546)
27. If Mendel crossed a heterozygous tall plant with a pure recessive short plant, what kinds of plants could he expect them to produce? (p. 553)

Skill Review ✔

For more help, refer to the ***Skill Handbook,*** *pages 704-719.*

1. **Calculate:** Use a calculator to find out how close Mendel's data (Table 26-4) are to showing a 3:1 ratio of dominant to recessive traits. Divide each trait by the total.
2. **Form hypotheses:** Form a hypothesis to explain why two offspring in a family have different traits.
3. **Interpret data:** Dogs with spots show a dominant trait and dogs without spots show a recessive trait. A dog breeder mates two spotted dogs. There are three dogs without spots in the first litter. Explain why.
4. **Classify:** Classify the following as cells or cell parts: sperm, gene, chromosome, egg, nucleus.

Finding Out More

Critical Thinking

1. Suppose you planted flower seeds. The package stated that the plants grow two feet tall. You noticed that 30 percent of the plants grew less than one foot tall. What does this tell you about the tallness trait?
2. Explain why some children can resemble one parent more than the other.

Applications

1. Find out which members of your family can roll their tongues and which can't.
2. Find out how seed companies produce flower seeds that will grow into plants with certain traits.

Using Main Ideas

21. Genes that don't show up are recessive.
22. Chromosomes are threadlike parts found inside the nucleus.
23. Each time you flip a coin you are starting over, and each time an egg and sperm join you do not know exactly what to expect.
24. Genes are small sections along a section of chromosome.
25. Sperm and egg are two types of sex cells.
26. A sex cell has one of each kind of chromosome; a body cell has two of each kind of chromosome.
27. He could expect a ratio of 1 tall plant to 1 short plant.

Skill Review

1. Students should see that all of Mendel's data shows a 3 dominant:1 recessive.
2. No two sperm or egg cells from the same person have the same gene combinations.
3. The dogs with spots are heterozygous and three dogs in the first litter received recessive traits from each parent.
4. Sperm and egg are cells; gene, chromosome, and nucleus are cell parts.

Finding Out More

Critical Thinking

1. The tallness trait is dominant, but the parent plants were heterozygous.
2. Children resemble the parent whose genes are dominant over the other's recessive genes.

Applications

1. Students could record their findings on a chart and then compare their charts.
2. Students could write to seed companies to ask for information, or they can inquire at local greenhouses.

Chapter Review/*Teacher Resource Package,* pp. 138-139.

Chapter Test/*Teacher Resource Package,* pp. 140-142.

Chapter Test/*Computer Test Bank*

Human Genetics

PLANNING GUIDE

CONTENT	TEXT FEATURES	TEACHER RESOURCE PACKAGE	OTHER COMPONENTS
(2 1/2 days) 27:1 The Role of Chromosomes Chromosome Number A Way to Tell Chromosome Number Sex—A Genetic Trait	Skill Check: *Understand Science Words,* p. 568 Lab 27-1: *Sex Determination,* p. 571 Science and Society: *Can Couples Choose the Sexes of Their Children?* p. 569 Idea Map, p. 566 Check Your Understanding, p. 570	Reteaching: *Chromosome Numbers,* p. 80 Focus: *What Do You Know About Human Genetics?* p. 53 Study Guide: *The Role of Chromosomes,* p. 157 Lab 27-1: *Sex Determination,* pp. 105-106	Color Transparency 27: *Sex Determination*
(2 1/2 days) 27:2 Human Traits Survey of Human Traits Incomplete Dominance Blood Types in Humans Genes on the X Chromosome	Mini Lab: *What Traits Do Humans Share?* p. 574 Lab 27-2: *Human Traits,* p. 577 Idea Map, p. 573 Check Your Understanding, p. 576	Application: *Knowing Your Blood Type,* p. 27 Reteaching: *Colorblindness,* p. 81 Critical Thinking/Problem Solving: *Could the Taylors' Son Be Colorblind?* p. 27 Study Guide: *Human Traits,* pp. 158-159 Lab 27-2: *Human Traits,* pp. 107-108 Transparency Master: *A Trait With Incomplete Dominance,* p. 137	**Laboratory Manual:** *What Do Normal and Sickled Cells Look Like?* p. 227 **Laboratory Manual:** *How Are Traits of the Sex Chromosomes Inherited?* p. 231
(2 days) 27:3 Genetic Disorders Errors in Chromosome Number Genetic Disorders and Sex Chromosomes Genetic Disorders and Autosomes Genetic Counseling	Skill Check: *Formulate Models,* p. 579 Idea Map, p. 579 Check Your Understanding, p. 579	Enrichment: *Tracing a Genetic Disorder in a Family,* p. 29 Reteaching: *Genetic Disorders,* p. 82 Skill: *Make a Line Graph,* p. 28 Study Guide: *Genetic Disorders,* pp. 160-161 Study Guide: *Vocabulary,* p. 162	
Chapter Review	Summary Key Science Words Testing Yourself Finding Main Ideas Using Main Ideas Skill Review	Chapter Review, pp. 143-144 Chapter Test, pp. 145-147	**Test Bank**

MATERIALS NEEDED

LAB 27-1, p. 571	LAB 27-2, p. 577	MARGIN FEATURES
2 coins paper cup masking tape	pencil paper	Skill Check, p. 568 dictionary Skill Check, p. 579 poster board markers paper Mini Lab, p. 574 pencil paper

OBJECTIVES

SECTION	OBJECTIVE	OBJECTIVES CORRELATION			
		CHECK YOUR UNDERSTANDING	CHAPTER REVIEW	TRP CHAPTER REVIEW	TRP CHAPTER TEST
27:1	1. **Compare** the chromosome numbers in body cells and sex cells.	1, 5	1, 16	1, 18	19, 20
	2. **Describe** methods that doctors use to study chromosomes of a fetus.	2	2, 11	20	21
	3. **Compare** the chromosomes of males and females.	3, 4	5, 6, 9, 15	3, 7, 12, 19	2, 11, 12, 17
27:2	4. **Compare** recessive and dominant traits with incomplete dominance.	6	7, 12	4, 6, 10, 15, 22	3, 4, 5, 7, 8, 10
	5. **Describe** different ways human traits can be inherited.	7, 8, 9	14, 17, 19, 20, 21	5, 11, 13, 14, 16, 17	1, 9, 13, 22, 23, 24, 25, 37, 38, 39, 40, 41
27:3	6. **Describe** some genetic disorders in humans.	12, 14	3, 8, 18	2, 8, 21	6, 16, 18
	7. **Give examples** of how genetic counseling can help families.	—	4, 10	9	14, 15, 26, 27, 28, 29, 30, 31, 32, 33

Human Genetics

CHAPTER OVERVIEW

Key Concepts

This chapter introduces students to the role of chromosomes in human genetics. Students will learn about several inherited traits and their patterns of inheritance. Students will also learn about health problems caused by chromosome errors.

Key Science Words

amniocentesis
autosome
color blindness
dyslexia
genetic counseling
incomplete dominance
pedigree
sex chromosome
sickle-cell anemia
X chromosome
Y chromosome

Skill Development

In Lab 27-1, students will **make and use tables, formulate a model, calculate,** and **design an experiment** to determine how many males and females could be expected in a family of four children. In Lab 27-2, students will **observe, make and use tables,** and **interpret data** to determine common traits. In the Skill Check on page 568, students will **understand** the **science word** *autosome.* On page 579, students will formulate a model to show how a dyslexic person sees letters. In the Mini Lab on page 574, students will **make and use tables** to show traits that they have inherited from their parents.

CHAPTER PREVIEW

Chapter Content

Review this outline for Chapter 27 before you read the chapter.

Skills in this Chapter

The skills that you will use in this chapter are listed below.

- In **Lab 27-1,** you will make and use tables, formulate a model, calculate, and design an experiment. In **Lab 27-2,** you will observe, make and use tables, and interpret data.
- In the **Skill Checks,** you will formulate a model, and understand science words.
- In the **Mini Labs,** you will make and use tables.

564

Bridging

Students will focus on the traits that humans inherit. The major concepts that students learned in Chapter 26 will be used to reinforce and learn patterns of genetics as applied to humans. They will learn that the way humans inherit most of their traits is similar to that of other living things.

Chapter 27

Human Genetics

Did you ever notice how often the children in a family look alike? This is because they share many of the same traits they inherited from their parents. Some traits may not be the same in all the children, however. How can you explain these differences?

The girls in the large photo are sisters. What traits do they have in common? What traits can you see that are different in the two sisters? Can you tell anything about the traits of the parents without actually seeing them?

The girl in the smaller photo is a cousin of the two sisters. The father of the two sisters and the father of the cousin are brothers. What traits do the sisters share with the cousin? Why do sisters share more traits than two cousins?

Try This!

Are human traits different from traits of other animals? Look at pictures of several animals. Make lists to show which traits or body parts are shared by humans and other animals and which are different.

GETTING STARTED

Using the Photos

Students should notice that all three girls share some common family features. Point out that two sisters will share more similar traits than two cousins. Explain that sometimes cousins resemble each other more than two sisters or a sister and brother because of the way chromosomes separate during meiosis.

MOTIVATION/Try This!

Are human traits different from traits of other animals? Upon completing the chapter-opening activity, students will have gained practice in learning to **classify.** Discuss the students' lists. Point out that geneticists think that humans inherit between 60 000 and 100 000 traits. Many of these traits control metabolic processes.

Chapter Preview

Have students study the chapter outline before they begin to read the chapter. They should note that they will study the role of chromosomes first. Next, they will learn about genetic traits in humans. In the last section, they will study chromosome errors and genetic disorders.

Misconception

Students are usually unaware of patterns of inheritance caused by traits other than Mendelian dominance or recessiveness. They also assume that they must show traits that are not different from either their mother or father.

27:1 The Role of Chromosomes

PREPARATION

Materials Needed

Make copies of the Focus, Study Guide, Reteaching, and Lab worksheets in the *Teacher Resource Package*.

▶ Have coins on hand for Lab 27-1.

Key Science Words

amniocentesis
X chromosome
sex chromosome
Y chromosome
autosome

Process Skills

In Lab 27-1, students will make and use tables, formulate models, calculate, and design an experiment. In the Skill Check, students will understand science words.

1 FOCUS

▶ The objectives are listed on the student page. Remind students to preview these objectives as a guide to this numbered section.

MOTIVATION/Bulletin Board

Construct a bulletin board of human races. Use the title Humans—One Species, Many Differences. Use photos to show differences in skin color, hair color, height, etc.

Focus/*Teacher Resource Package*, p. 53. Use the Focus transparency shown at the bottom of this page as an introduction to human genetics.

Guided Practice

Have students write down their answers to the margin question: in pairs.

Idea Map

Have students use the idea map as a study guide to the major concepts of this section.

Objectives

1. **Compare** the chromosome numbers in body cells and sex cells.
2. **Describe** methods that doctors use to study chromosomes of a fetus.
3. **Compare** the chromosomes of males and females.

Key Science Words

amniocentesis
X chromosome
sex chromosome
Y chromosome
autosome

How are chromosomes arranged in body cells?

27:1 The Role of Chromosomes

All living things can pass their traits to their offspring. You learned in Chapter 26 that these traits can be dominant or recessive. The genes that control the traits are found on sections of the chromosomes.

Chromosome Number

There are three things you should know about chromosome numbers in living things.
1. Each human sperm or egg has 23 chromosomes.
2. Each human body cell has 23 pairs of chromosomes. There are 46 chromosomes in each human body cell.
3. Different organisms have different numbers of chromosomes. The chromosomes in most living things are paired. A tomato plant has 12 chromosomes in each of its body cells. That's equal to six pairs per cell. Table 27-1 gives the numbers of chromosomes in some other living things.

TABLE 27–1. CHROMOSOME NUMBERS

Animal or Plant	Number of Chromosomes in Body Cells	Number of Chromosome Pairs in Body Cells
Red clover	12	6
Pea	14	7
Onion	16	8
Corn	20	10
White pine	24	12
Cat	38	19
Rabbit	44	22
Chicken	78	39

Study Tip: Use this idea map as a study guide to the chromosomes in human cells. The numbers of chromosomes in body and sex cells are shown.

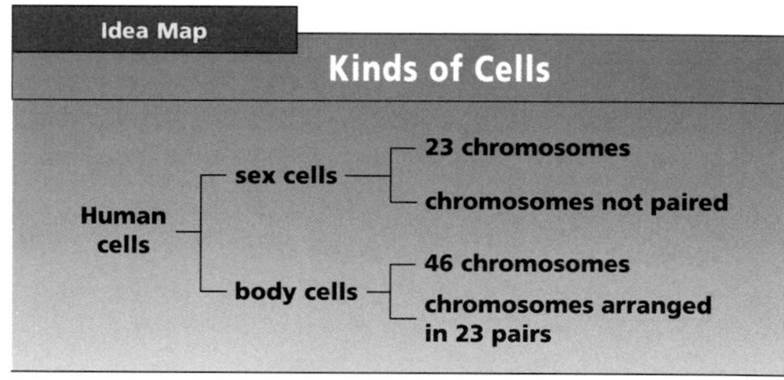

OPTIONS

Science Background

It was not known until the start of the 20th century that genes and chromosomes were important in the study of heredity. Geneticists found sex chromosomes in many animals to be XX in females and XY in males. In some animals, the male has XX sex chromosomes while the female has only one X. The arrangement of chromosomes in pairs from largest to smallest is called a karyotype, and this system of classification was developed in the late 1950s.

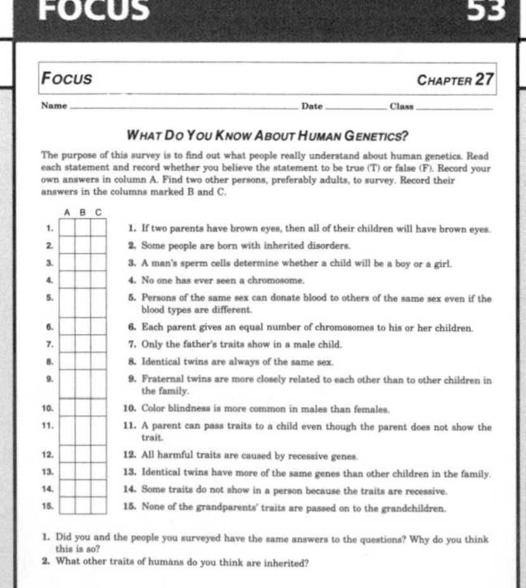
FOCUS 53

FOCUS CHAPTER 27

Name ____ Date ____ Class ____

WHAT DO YOU KNOW ABOUT HUMAN GENETICS?

The purpose of this survey is to find out what people really understand about human genetics. Read each statement and record whether you believe the statement to be true (T) or false (F). Record your own answers in column A. Find two other persons, preferably adults, to survey. Record their answers in the columns marked B and C.

	A	B	C	
1.				1. If two parents have brown eyes, then all of their children will have brown eyes.
2.				2. Some people are born with inherited disorders.
3.				3. A man's sperm cells determine whether a child will be a boy or a girl.
4.				4. No one has ever seen a chromosome.
5.				5. Persons of the same sex can donate blood to others of the same sex even if the blood types are different.
6.				6. Each parent gives an equal number of chromosomes to his or her children.
7.				7. Only the father's traits show in a male child.
8.				8. Identical twins are always of the same sex.
9.				9. Fraternal twins are more closely related to each other than to other children in the family.
10.				10. Color blindness is more common in males than females.
11.				11. A parent can pass traits to a child even though the parent does not show the trait.
12.				12. All harmful traits are caused by recessive genes.
13.				13. Identical twins have more of the same genes than other children in the family.
14.				14. Some traits do not show in a person because the traits are recessive.
15.				15. None of the grandparents' traits are passed on to the grandchildren.

1. Did you and the people you surveyed have the same answers to the questions? Why do you think this is so?
2. What other traits of humans do you think are inherited?

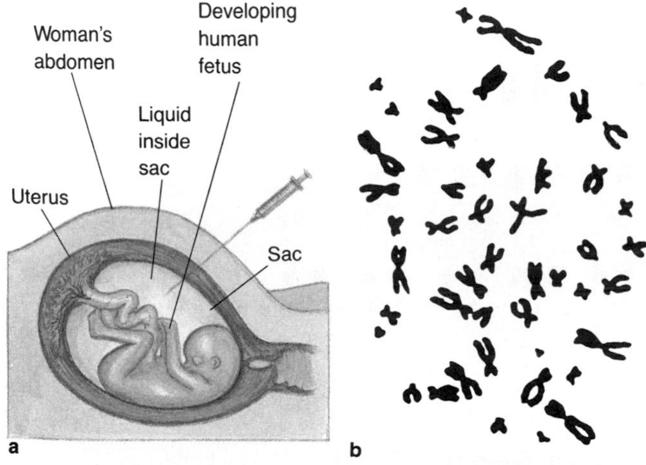

Figure 27-1 Amniocentesis (a). Chromosomes taken from the sac in which the fetus develops (b).

A Way to Tell Chromosome Number

Doctors today can tell if a child has the correct number of chromosomes even before it is born. They use a process called amniocentesis (am nee oh sen TEE sus). **Amniocentesis** is a way of looking at the chromosomes of a fetus.

Look at Figure 27-1a. A needle is inserted into the pregnant woman's abdomen. The needle enters the amniotic sac in which the fetus develops, and some liquid is removed through the needle. In this liquid are cells from the fetus's skin. The cells have rubbed off the fetus just as your skin cells do.

How does a doctor perform amniocentesis?

These cells are grown for about 10 days in a nutrient liquid that makes them divide. Remember that chromosomes can be seen best when the cell is dividing. The cells are then studied with a microscope and an enlarged photo like the one in Figure 27-1b is made. The chromosomes are cut out and the ones that match are arranged in pairs. A large chart is made showing the chromosome pairs. The lab technician looks at the chromosomes to make sure there are 46 of them and there are no missing or added parts.

Using a newer way to look at the chromosomes of a fetus, a doctor can take a small piece of the placenta surrounding the fetus. This area has cells with the same number and kind of chromosomes as the fetus. The chromosomes are counted and studied to see whether parts are missing or added.

2 TEACH

MOTIVATION/Display

Make a transparency of Table 27-1 and have students compare the number of chromosomes in plants and animals. This table shows animals having more chromosomes than plants. Explain that some plants have more chromosomes than animals. For example, fruit flies have only four pairs of chromosomes. Point out that chromosome number has nothing to do with how complex an organism is. Some protozoa have 60 to 100 chromosomes.

Concept Development

- Explain that sexual reproduction is important in that both parents contribute genetic material to their offspring. In this way the offspring shows some traits of each parent.
- Make sure students understand that amniocentesis is not a routine procedure, and is not given just to determine the sex of a child.
- Explain that amniocentesis is used to find out if an unborn baby has some abnormal chromosomes or some other genetic defect. A doctor can use amniotic fluid to test for certain genetic defects, such as Tay-Sachs disease.

Guided Practice

Have students write down their answers to the margin question: by removing liquid from the amniotic sac and examining the cells in it.

OPTIONS

Science Background

Taking a small piece from the placenta is called chorionic villi sampling. This technique takes very little time, and the patient is able to resume normal activity within an hour. Chorionic sampling, as well as amniocentesis, does not involve major surgery.

TEACH

Concept Development

▶ Point out that other mammals have sex chromosomes similar to humans—females have XX and males have XY.

▶ To help students remember that the male contains the Y chromosome, draw attention to the male as determining the sex of the offspring.

Check for Understanding

Have students set up a Punnett square with parents' sex chromosomes on the outside. Show each of the mother's sex cells by writing her X chromosomes across the top of the Punnett square. Show the father's sex cells by writing X and Y along the side of the Punnett square. Write the symbols for each parent's sex chromosomes in the small square. Each small square in the Punnett square stands for a way that the chromosomes could combine when the egg and sperm join.

Reteach

Have students write a short paragraph to explain how humans inherit sex as a genetic trait.

Guided Practice

Have students write down their answers to the margin question: female.

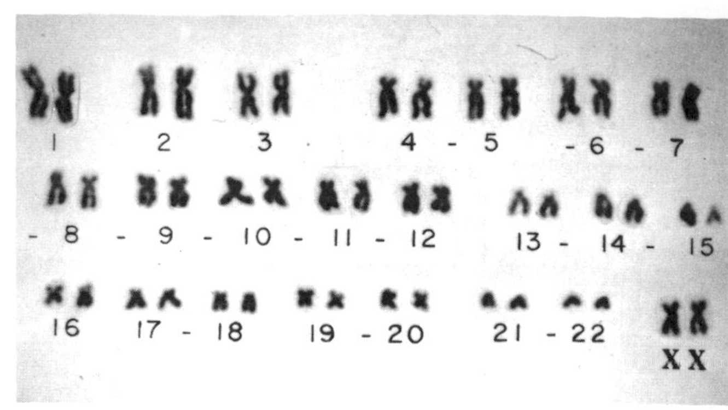

Figure 27-2 These photos of chromosomes have been cut out and arranged in pairs. How many chromosomes does a human body cell have? 46

Sex—A Genetic Trait

Whether you were born male or female depends on your chromosomes. In humans, a special pair of chromosomes determines sex.

What sex is a person with two X chromosomes?

Figure 27-2 shows the 23 pairs of chromosomes from a female. Notice that the chromosomes are numbered, except for those in the lower right corner. Those are marked XX. Each of the **X chromosomes** is a sex chromosome of the female. **Sex chromosomes** are chromosomes that determine sex. A human female has two X chromosomes in each body cell.

As you can see in Figure 27-3, the male's sex chromosomes are different from those of a female. The larger sex chromosome is an X chromosome. The smaller one is called a Y chromosome. The **Y chromosome** is a sex chromosome found only in males. A human male has one X and one Y chromosome in each body cell.

The numbered chromosomes in Figure 27-2 are called autosomes (AH toh sohmz). **Autosomes** are chromosomes that don't determine the sex of a person. They are also called nonsex or body chromosomes. The autosomes of a male are like those of a female.

Skill Check

Understand science words: autosome. The word part *auto* means self. In your dictionary, find three words with the word part *auto* in them. *For more help, refer to the **Skill Handbook**, pages 706-711.*

Figure 27-3 A female has two X chromosomes. A male has one X and one Y chromosome.

OPTIONS

Sex Determination/*Transparency Package*, number 27. Use color transparency number 27 as you teach how sex is determined.

Science and Society

Can Couples Choose the Sexes of Their Children?

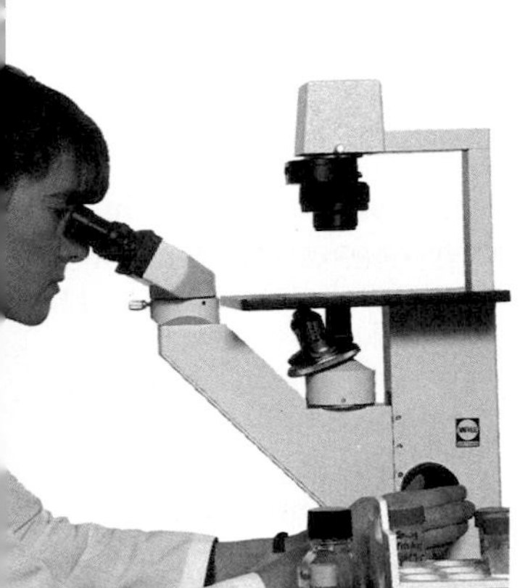

Suppose a couple had two girls and they wanted to have a boy. There is a 50 percent chance of having a baby boy. Is there any way to increase that chance? Researchers have found several ways to separate the sperm containing the Y chromosome from the sperm containing the X chromosome. Because the X chromosome is larger and heavier than the Y chromosome, these sperm can be separated by special filtering methods. When the sperm are separated, they are put into different tubes. Usually, one tube will have about three Y sperm for every X sperm. Thus, the chances of having a boy baby are increased from 50 percent to about 75 percent.
A doctor then inserts the sperm cells carrying the Y chromosome into the vagina of the female. If she becomes pregnant, she has a better chance of having a boy than a girl. However, she still has a 25 percent chance of having a girl.

What Do You Think?

1. About 200 genetic disorders are controlled by the X chromosome. Many of these are fatal or result in lifelong health problems. These disorders can be prevented if a couple has only girls. Is it acceptable for couples to choose the sex of their children to prevent health problems?

2. Certain cultures prefer children of one sex over children of the other sex. Suppose that over the next 10 years, all couples in Japan decided to have only boys. Predict some problems that could result in the country.

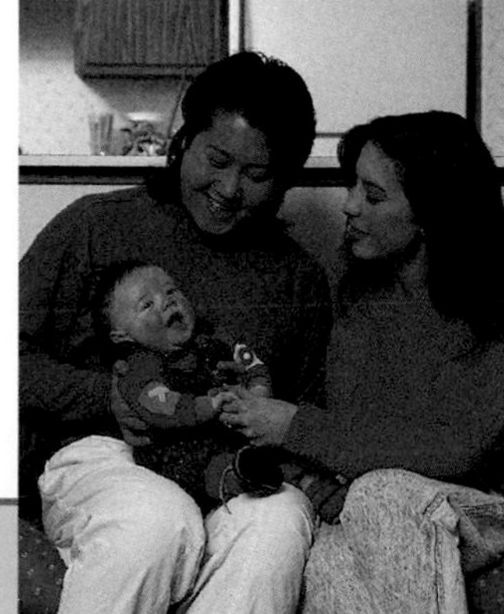

Some cultures prefer male children to female children.

3. Choosing the sex of a child can be very expensive. Not all people can afford to choose the sex of their children. If choosing the sex of children becomes popular, should the government or health insurance companies pay the medical costs of couples who cannot afford to pay?

Conclusion: Under what conditions, if any, should people be allowed to choose the sex of their children? If you knew that these methods guaranteed the sex of a child instead of just increasing the chances, how would you feel about them?

569

Suggested Readings

Maranto, Gina. "Choosing Your Baby's Sex." *Discover,* Oct. 1984, pp. 24-27.

Science and Society

Can Couples Choose The Sexes of Their Children?

Background

Scientists have placed X- and Y-bearing sperm cells in two different materials—serum albumin and a gel. They found that a larger number of Y-bearing sperm cells reached the bottom faster in the albumin. In the gel, a larger number of X-bearing sperm cells reached the bottom first. When artificially inseminated with cells from serum albumin, women conceived a larger number of male children. Those inseminated with the cells from the gel conceived a larger number of female children.

Teaching Suggestions

Point out that parents who have two girls or two boys and want another child of the opposite sex could benefit from this procedure.

Explain that parents who know of specific sex-linked traits in the family could select to have females who would be free of the harmful trait.

What Do You Think?

1. Some students will feel that this is a valid reason for choosing sex of offspring, but others may still feel it is not right.
2. Students may mention a decline in marriages and birth rates, or failure to fill some occupations or sports programs.
3. Those who are in favor of choosing the sex of a child will probably feel that there should be some help with the expense.

Conclusion: Some students may feel that these methods would be wrong for changing chance due to natural events. Others may even feel a bit repulsed by the idea of scientific control over reproduction. Some may feel that couples should have the right to make their own decisions. Students may feel, however, that the methods are acceptable for medical reasons.

TEACH

Independent Practice

Study Guide/*Teacher Resource Package*, p. 157. Use the Study Guide worksheet shown at the bottom of this page for independent practice.

Check for Understanding

Have students respond to the first three questions in Check Your Understanding.

Reteach

Reteaching/*Teacher Resource Package*, p. 80. Use this worksheet to give students additional practice with chromosome numbers.

Extension: Assign Critical Thinking, Biology and Math, or some of the **OPTIONS** available with this lesson.

3 APPLY

Convergent Question

Some members of royalty were known to divorce their wives because they gave birth to all girls. What could a study of genetics have told them?

4 CLOSE

Summary

Have the students summarize the pros and cons to using amniocentesis.

Answers to Check Your Understanding

1. A sex cell has 23 chromosomes; a body cell has 46.
2. a way to look at chromosomes in an unborn child
3. Each has one X chromosome. The female has a second X chromosome, while the male has a Y chromosome.
4. The number of chromosomes in the organism would double with each generation.
5. There is a 50 percent chance that her next child will be a boy.

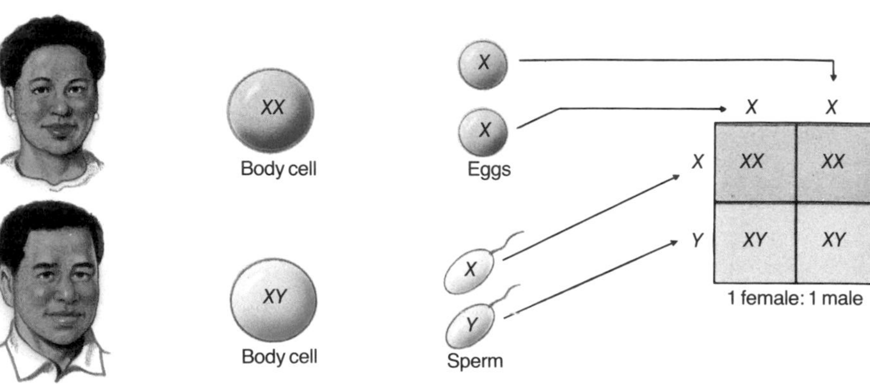

Figure 27-4 A child receives an X chromosome from the mother and an X or a Y chromosome from the father.

What kind of sex chromosomes, X or Y, are found in eggs and sperm? Because females have only one kind of sex chromosome, they can make only one kind of egg. Each egg of a female has one X chromosome. Males have two different sex chromosomes, so they can make two different kinds of sperm. Each sperm of a male has either an X chromosome or a Y chromosome. As you can see from Figure 27-4, a child can receive only an X chromosome from its mother. The child can receive an X or Y chromosome from its father.

Notice that the father determines the sex of the children. If the child receives the father's X chromosome, the child will be a girl. If the child receives the father's Y chromosome, what will be the sex of the child? This Punnett square shows that we can expect half the children to be females and the other half to be males.

Check Your Understanding

1. How do sex cells and body cells of humans differ in chromosome number?
2. What is amniocentesis?
3. How are the sex chromosomes of human males and females alike? How are they different?
4. **Critical Thinking:** What would happen if each sex cell had the same number of chromosomes as a body cell?
5. **Biology and Math:** Suppose a woman has three girls. What is the chance her next child will be a boy?

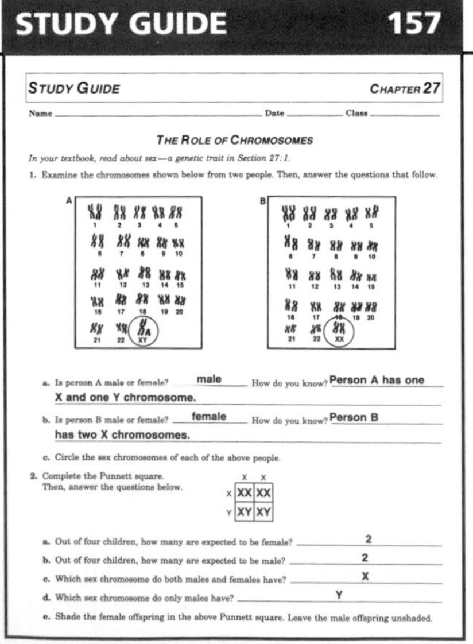

STUDY GUIDE 157

STUDY GUIDE CHAPTER 27

Name ______ Date ______ Class ______

THE ROLE OF CHROMOSOMES

In your textbook, read about sex—a genetic trait in Section 27:1.

1. Examine the chromosomes shown below from two people. Then, answer the questions that follow.

a. Is person A male or female? male How do you know? Person A has one X and one Y chromosome.

b. Is person B male or female? female How do you know? Person B has two X chromosomes.

c. Circle the sex chromosomes of each of the above people.

2. Complete the Punnett square. Then, answer the questions below.

	X	X
X	XX	XX
Y	XY	XY

a. Out of four children, how many are expected to be female? 2

b. Out of four children, how many are expected to be male? 2

c. Which sex chromosome do both males and females have? X

d. Which sex chromosome do only males have? Y

e. Shade the female offspring in the above Punnett square. Leave the male offspring unshaded.

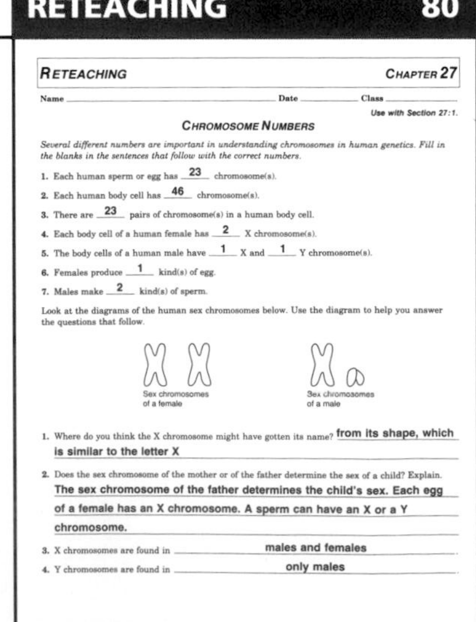

RETEACHING 80

RETEACHING CHAPTER 27

Name ______ Date ______ Class ______

Use with Section 27:1.

CHROMOSOME NUMBERS

Several different numbers are important in understanding chromosomes in human genetics. Fill in the blanks in the sentences that follow with the correct numbers.

1. Each human sperm or egg has 23 chromosome(s).
2. Each human body cell has 46 chromosome(s).
3. There are 23 pairs of chromosome(s) in a human body cell.
4. Each body cell of a human female has 2 X chromosome(s).
5. The body cells of a human male have 1 X and 1 Y chromosome(s).
6. Females produce 1 kind(s) of egg.
7. Males make 2 kind(s) of sperm.

Look at the diagrams of the human sex chromosomes below. Use the diagram to help you answer the questions that follow.

1. Where do you think the X chromosome might have gotten its name? from its shape, which is similar to the letter X
2. Does the sex chromosome of the mother or of the father determine the sex of a child? Explain. The sex chromosome of the father determines the child's sex. Each egg of a female has an X chromosome. A sperm can have an X or a Y chromosome.
3. X chromosomes are found in males and females.
4. Y chromosomes are found in only males.

Lab 27–1 Sex Determination 

Problem: In a family of four children, how many will be girls and how many will be boys?

Skills

make and use tables, formulate a model, calculate, design an experiment

Materials

2 coins
paper cup
masking tape

Procedure

1. Copy the data table 10 times.
2. Cover two coins with tape. Mark one coin with an X on each side. Mark the other coin with an X on one side and a Y on the other side.
3. Draw a Punnett square to show how many males and females you expect to see in one family with four children. Multiply the number of males by 10 and the number of females by 10. The totals are the numbers of males and females you would expect to see in ten families.
4. Put both coins in the paper cup. Shake the cup and drop the coins on your desk. Read the combination.
5. On table 1, make a check mark for your result on the first shake.
6. Shake, read, and mark your results three more times.
7. **Calculate:** Total the columns marked XX and XY.
8. Repeat steps 4 to 7 nine more times using a new table for each group of four shakes.
9. Add the number of females on all 10 tables. This is the total number of females you observed. Do the same for males.
10. Compare the observed totals in step 9 with the expected totals in step 3.

Data and Observations

1. How many male and female children do you expect in each family? Explain your answer using the words *chromosome, X, Y, sperm,* and *egg.*
2. How many males and how many females did you expect in 10 families?

	TABLE 1 RESULTS	
SHAKE	**XX**	**XY**
1		
2	Answers will	
3	vary.	
4		
Total		

Analyze and Apply

1. Was the total number of males and females observed different from what you expected? If so, how can you explain the difference?
2. If you had made tables for 20 families, how many male children and how many female children would you expect?
3. If you had made tables for 100 families, would the observed results have been closer to the expected results? Explain your answer.
4. **Apply:** Suppose a doctor told a couple with three girls that their next child would be a boy. Is the doctor correct? Explain.

Extension

Design an experiment to show how often families with four children will have two boys and two girls.

COMPUTER PROGRAM XXII

COMPUTER PROGRAM LAB 27-1 SEX DETERMINATION

```
]POKE 33,33

]LIST

10  TEXT : HOME
20  PRINT "READ LAB 27-1 IN YOUR TEXT BOOK."
28  PRINT : PRINT
30  PRINT "THE  COMPUTER WILL TOSS THE COINS FOR YOU AND WILL ALSO RECORD YOUR RES
ULTS ON A  TABLE"
40  DIM Z(40),A(10,4)
50 X =  INT ( RND (1) * 60) + 1
60 X =  INT (X / 10)
70  IF X < 1 OR X > 5 THEN 50
80  IF X = 1 THEN XX = 20:XY = 20
90  IF X = 2 THEN XX = 21:XY = 19
100  IF X = 3 THEN XX = 22:XY = 18
110  IF X = 4 THEN XX = 19:XY = 21
120  IF X = 5 THEN XX = 18:XY = 22
130  FOR X = 1 TO XX
140 P =  INT ( RND (1) * 40) + 1
150  IF Z(P) <  > 0 THEN 140
160 Z(P) = 1
170  NEXT X
180  FOR X = 1 TO XY
190 P =  INT ( RND (1) * 40) + 1
200  IF Z(P) <  > 0 THEN 190
210 Z(P) = 2
220  NEXT X
230 SS = 0
240  FOR X = 1 TO 10
250  FOR Y = 1 TO 4
260 SS = SS + 1
270 A(X,Y) = Z(SS)
280  NEXT Y,X
290  PRINT : PRINT : PRINT "PRESS ANY KEY TO START";: GET ER$
300  TEXT : HOME
310  VTAB (5): PRINT "TABLE              RESULTS"
320  PRINT "-----------------------"
330  PRINT "SHAKE             XX    XY"
340  POKE 34,8
350  PRINT "-----------------------"
360  FOR X = 1 TO 10
370 RI = 0:R2 = 0
380  FOR Y = 1 TO 4
390  VTAB (13): PRINT "-----------------------"
400  VTAB (5): HTAB (7): PRINT X
410  VTAB (21): PRINT "PRESS ANY KEY FOR EACH                  COIN TOSS OF TABL
E #";X;: GET ZZ$
420  VTAB (Y + 8): HTAB (3): PRINT Y;
430  IF A(X,Y) = 1 THEN  HTAB (17): PRINT "*":R1 = R1 + 1:RX = RX + 1
440  IF A(X,Y) = 2 THEN  HTAB (23): PRINT "*":R2 = R2 + 1:RY = RY + 1
450  IF R1 = 2 AND R2 = 2 THEN TB = TB + 1
460  NEXT Y
470  VTAB (14): PRINT "TOTAL";
480  HTAB (17): PRINT R1;
```

ANSWERS

Data and Observations

1. 2, There are 2 chances out of 4 that a sperm with a Y chromosome and an egg with an X chromosome will join.
2. 20 males; 20 females

Analyze and Apply

1. Answers will vary; differences are due to chance.
2. 40 males; 40 females
3. Yes, the more results you observe, the closer the observed results will be to the expected.
4. No, there is 1 chance out of 2 that the baby will be a boy, and 1 chance out of 2 that it will be a girl.

Lab 27-1 Sex Determination

Overview

In this lab, students will determine by simulation how often certain combinations of males and females can occur in a family. They will compare answers predicted from a Punnett square to answers obtained by flipping coins.

Objectives: Upon completing the lab, students will be able to (1) **predict** expected data, (2) **experiment** to get observed data, and (3) **compare** the expected to observed data in order to infer what happened in the experiment.

Time Allotment: 45 minutes

Preparation

▶ You may wish to put tape on the coins in advance of class.

Lab 27-1 worksheet/*Teacher Resource Package*, pp. 105-106.

Teaching the Lab

▶ Explain to students that the results they get each time they drop the coins are strictly chance happenings. In the same manner, the sex of a child is usually a chance happening.

Lab 27-1 Computer Program/*Teacher Resource Package*, p. xxii. Use the computer program shown at the bottom of this page as you teach this lab.

27:2 Human Traits

PREPARATION

Materials Needed

Make copies of the Study Guide, Transparency Master, Application, Critical Thinking/ Problem Solving, Reteaching, and Lab worksheets in the *Teacher Resource Package.*

Key Science Words

incomplete dominance
sickle-cell anemia
color blindness

Process Skills

In the Mini Lab, students will make and use tables. In Lab 27-2, students will observe, make and use tables, and interpret data.

1 FOCUS

▶ The objectives are listed on the student page. Remind students to preview these objectives as a guide to this numbered section.

Convergent Question

Ask students why humans are able to inherit traits as other living things do. Ask them what all living things share that enables them to pass on their traits.

Objectives

4. **Compare** recessive and dominant traits with incomplete dominance.
5. **Describe** different ways human traits can be inherited.

Key Science Words

incomplete dominance
sickle-cell anemia
color blindness

27:2 Human Traits

Have you ever gone "people watching"? The next time you are at a shopping center, movie theater, or football game, look at the people around you. They have many traits that you can see. These traits come from their parents. People also have many traits that you can't see. These traits direct things that go on inside the body.

Survey of Human Traits

The girl in Figure 27-5a has freckles. She also has dimples in her cheeks. Both traits are caused by dominant genes. In both of these traits, one or both of the parents shows the dominant trait. Remember, only one dominant gene is needed to make a dominant trait show up. Two recessive genes are needed to make a recessive trait show up.

What kinds of traits are recessive? Attached earlobes is a recessive trait. Neither of the parents needs to have attached earlobes for their child to show this trait. Set up a Punnett square to show why that is true.

Other recessive traits are straight hair and not being able to roll the sides of your tongue. Can you guess what the dominant traits are? The ability to roll your tongue is dominant. Curly hair is dominant to straight hair. Short eyelashes are recessive. What is the dominant trait?

a

b

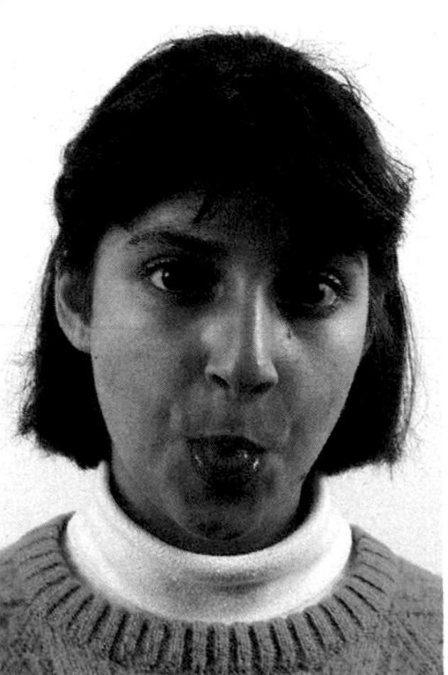

Figure 27-5 Freckles and dimples are dominant traits (a). The ability to roll the tongue is a dominant trait (b).

OPTIONS

Science Background

Between 8 and 13 percent of African Americans have the sickle-cell trait and are heterozygous with incomplete dominance. One out of every 500 African-American babies is born with sickle-cell anemia.

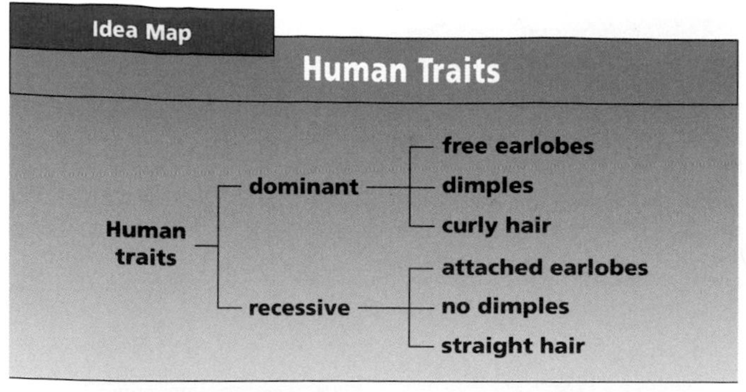

Study Tip: Use this idea map as a study guide to some human traits. How many other dominant and recessive traits can you think of?

Incomplete Dominance

Some traits are neither totally dominant nor totally recessive. Scientists know of several genes that don't show total dominance. A case in which neither gene is totally dominant to the other is called **incomplete dominance.** If you placed a piece of blue glass over a piece of yellow glass and held it up to the light, what would you see? Figure 27-6 shows that the glass would look green. If you took apart the pieces of glass, you would see that they were still blue and yellow.

The same kind of thing happens with incomplete dominance. Remember that when a dominant and a recessive gene are together in a heterozygous organism, only the dominant trait is usually seen. In incomplete dominance, we see a new trait that is a blend of the dominant and recessive traits. When pure dominant red snapdragons are mated with pure recessive white snapdragons, the heterozygous offspring are all pink. It is important to know that the genes themselves do not combine. When they are separated, we see the original traits again. If two pink snapdragons are mated, they produce red, white, and pink offspring.

What trait is seen in an individual that is heterozygous for an incompletely dominant trait?

Figure 27-6 In incomplete dominance, the combining of two genes gives a new trait.

2 TEACH

MOTIVATION/Filmstrip

Show the video *The Gene Machine,* Films for the Humanities and Science.

Concept Development

▶ Make sure that students understand that some of their own traits may not be seen in either of their parents. These traits may be recessive, and each parent may have contributed the same recessive genes.

▶ Point out that recessive genes can skip several generations before they show up in offspring.

▶ Explain that geneticists know which of the human traits are dominant and recessive.

▶ Point out that the traits produced by incomplete dominance are sometimes called "intermediate" traits because their phenotypic effect is intermediate between the two traits.

Idea Map

Have students use the idea map as a study guide to the major concepts of this section.

Guided Practice

Have students write down their answers to the margin question: a new trait that is a combination of dominant and recessive traits.

OPTIONS

How Are Traits on Sex Chromosomes Inherited?/*Lab Manual,* pp. 231-234. Use this lab as an extension to studying human traits.

TEACH

Concept Development

▶ Tell students that persons with sickle-cell anemia can be given medication to lessen the effect of the disease; however, it cannot be cured.

Independent Practice

Study Guide/*Teacher Resource Package,* p. 158. Use the Study Guide worksheet shown at the bottom of this page for independent practice.

Guided Practice

Have students write down their answers to the margin question: the shape of red blood cells.

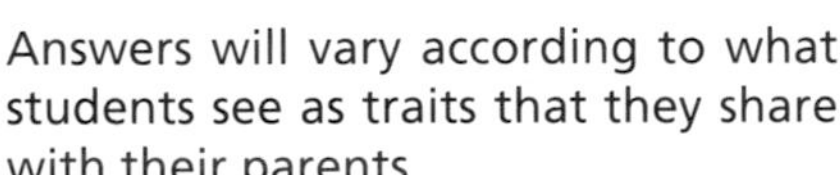

Mini Lab

Answers will vary according to what students see as traits that they share with their parents.

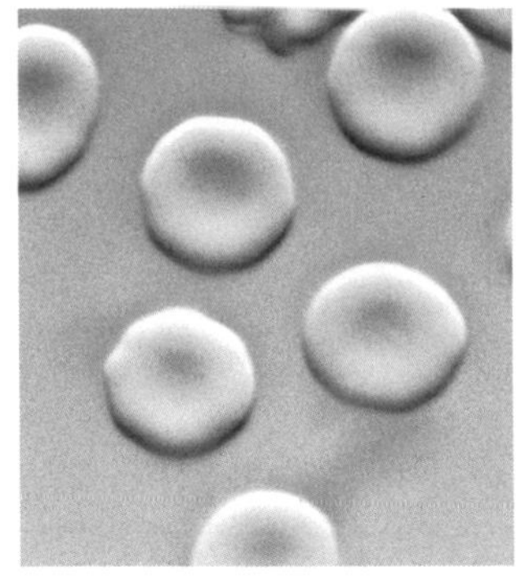

a

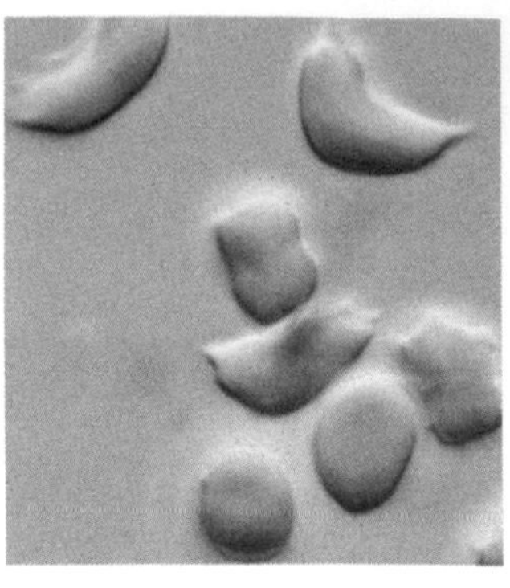

b

Figure 27-7 Normal round (a) and sickled (b) red blood cells. Which kind of cells does a heterozygous person have? both

What human trait shows incomplete dominance?

Some traits in humans show incomplete dominance. One of these is the shape of red blood cells. In most people, red blood cells are round. Some people have red blood cells shaped like those in Figure 27-7b. These cells are called sickle cells. They are shaped like a sickle that is used to cut grass. Some people have both shapes of blood cells.

Let the letter ***R*** stand for the gene for round blood cells. Let ***R′*** stand for the gene for sickle cells. In incomplete dominance, two different letters or symbols are used for the genes controlling the trait. The ***R*** gene is not totally dominant over the ***R′*** gene. The ***R′*** gene is not totally dominant over the ***R*** gene. Capital letters can stand for both. A person with round cells has ***RR*** genes. A person with all sickle cells has ***R′R′*** genes. A person with both kinds of cells has ***RR′*** genes.

Someone with ***RR′*** genes usually doesn't have serious health problems. People who have some sickle cells, however, may not be as active as those who have all round cells. As you know, red blood cells carry oxygen to body cells. Sickle cells do not carry oxygen as well as round blood cells.

People with ***R′R′*** genes have sickle-cell anemia. **Sickle-cell anemia** is a genetic disorder in which all the red blood cells are shaped like sickles. This disorder is much more common among African-Americans than among people of other races. People with sickle-cell anemia have serious health problems. Their lives may be shortened because of the disorder. The sickle cells cannot carry enough oxygen. Body tissues can be damaged because they don't receive enough oxygen. Sickle cells do not move easily through the blood capillaries because their shape causes the capillaries to become clogged.

Mini Lab

What Traits Do Humans Share?

Make and use tables: Make a table of traits inherited from your parents. Compare your list with that of a classmate. How many traits do you have in common? *For more help, refer to the* ***Skill Handbook,*** *pages 715-717.*

OPTIONS

What Do Normal and Sickled Cells Look Like?/*Lab Manual,* pp. 227-230. Use this lab as an extension to studying incomplete dominance.

Transparency Master/*Teacher Resource Package,* p. 137. Use the Transparency Master shown here to teach traits with incomplete dominance.

STUDY GUIDE 158

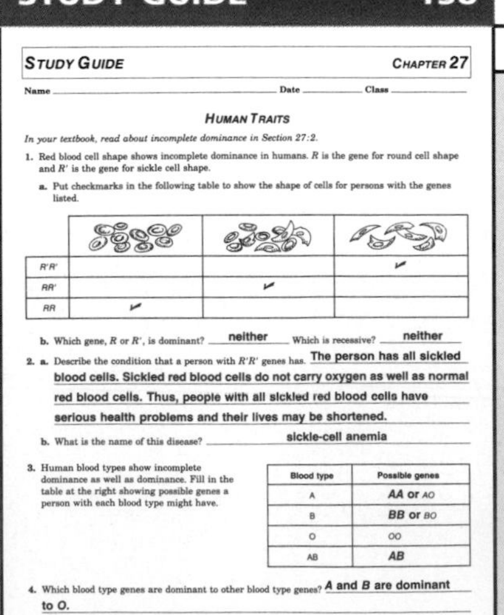

STUDY GUIDE — CHAPTER 27

Name ______ Date ______ Class ______

HUMAN TRAITS

In your textbook, read about incomplete dominance in Section 27:2.

1. Red blood cell shape shows incomplete dominance in humans. *R* is the gene for round cell shape and *R′* is the gene for sickle cell shape.
   a. Put checkmarks in the following table to show the shape of cells for persons with the genes listed.

	(round cells)	(round and sickle cells)	(sickle cells)
R′R′			✓
RR′		✓	
RR	✓		

   b. Which gene, *R* or *R′*, is dominant? **neither** Which is recessive? **neither**

2. a. Describe the condition that a person with *R′R′* genes has. **The person has all sickled blood cells. Sickled red blood cells do not carry oxygen as well as normal red blood cells. Thus, people with all sickled red blood cells have serious health problems and their lives may be shortened.**
   b. What is the name of this disease? **sickle-cell anemia**

3. Human blood types show incomplete dominance as well as dominance. Fill in the table at the right showing possible genes a person with each blood type might have.

Blood type	Possible genes
A	***AA*** **or** *AO*
B	***BB*** **or** *BO*
O	*OO*
AB	***AB***

4. Which blood type genes are dominant to other blood type genes? **A and B are dominant to O.**

5. Which blood type genes show incomplete dominance to each other? **A and B**

TRANSPARENCY 137

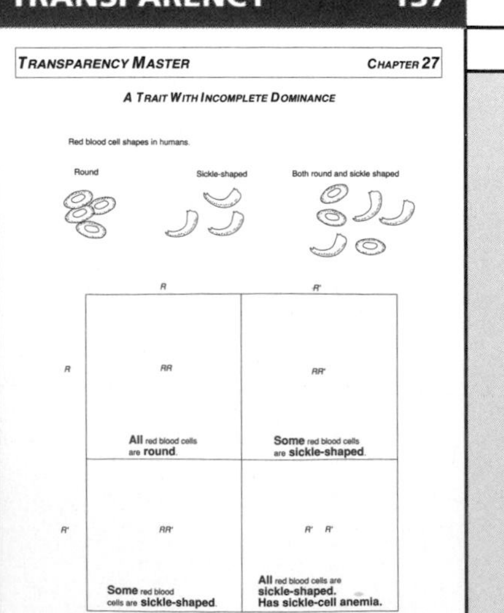

TRANSPARENCY MASTER — CHAPTER 27

A TRAIT WITH INCOMPLETE DOMINANCE

	R	*R′*
R	*RR* — **All** red blood cells are **round**.	*RR′* — **Some** red blood cells are **sickle-shaped**.
R′	*RR′* — **Some** red blood cells are **sickle-shaped**.	*R′ R′* — **All** red blood cells are **sickle-shaped. Has sickle-cell anemia.**

If two parents have ***RR'*** genes, what would we expect the children to have? Look at the Punnett square in Figure 27-8. One out of four children is expected to have all round cells. Two out of four children are expected to have both round and sickle cells. The fourth child is expected to have all sickle cells. That child would have sickle-cell anemia.

	R	R'
R	RR	RR'
R'	RR'	R'R'

Figure 27-8 How sickle-cell anemia can be inherited when both parents are heterozygous. How many children can be expected to have sickle-cell anemia? one-fourth of all the children

Blood Types in Humans

Remember from Chapter 12 that there are four blood types—A, B, AB, and O. Human blood type is controlled in part by dominance of genes. Although three genes control blood types, each person has only two of them. The two genes that you have control your blood type.

The three genes that control blood type are ***A, B,*** and ***O.*** Both ***A*** and ***B*** are dominant to ***O. A*** and ***B,*** however, are not dominant to each other. Look at Table 27-2 as you read the next three paragraphs.

If you have type O blood, you have ***OO*** genes. If you have type AB blood, you have one ***A*** gene and one ***B*** gene.

If you have type A blood, you have ***AA*** or ***AO*** genes. If you have ***AO*** genes, the ***A*** gene is dominant to the ***O*** gene.

If you have type B blood, you have ***BB*** or ***BO*** genes. If you have ***BO*** genes, the ***B*** gene is dominant to the ***O*** gene.

TABLE 27–2. BLOOD TYPES AND GENES

Blood Type	Genes
O	***OO***
AB	***AB***
A	***AA*** or ***AO***
B	***BB*** or ***BO***

Genes on the X Chromosome

Like other chromosomes, the sex chromosomes carry genes. Figure 27-9 shows some traits that are controlled by genes on the sex chromosomes. Notice that females have two genes for each of these traits. That is because females have two X chromosomes.

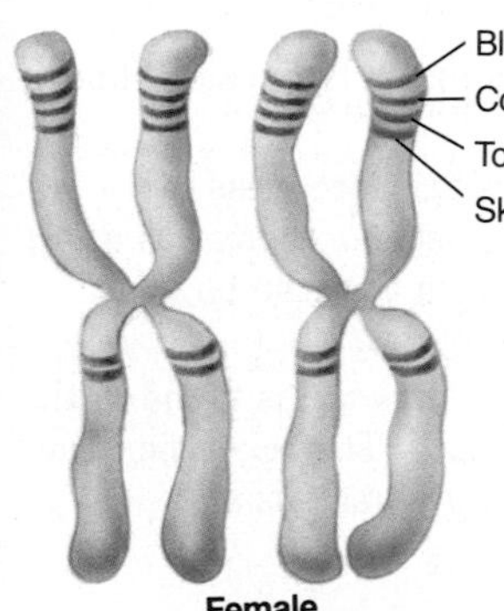

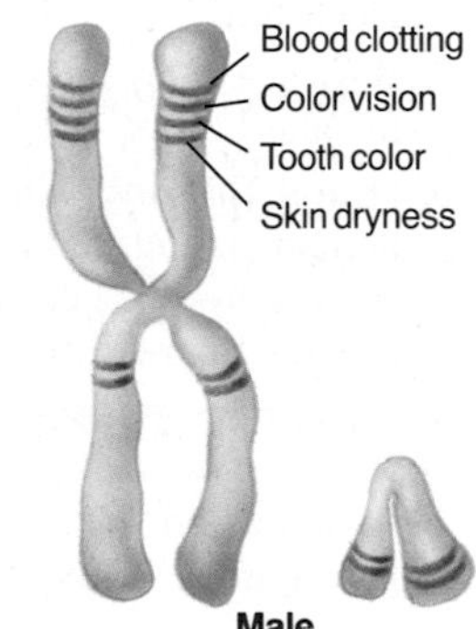

Figure 27-9 Certain genes on the X chromosome are missing from the Y chromosome.

TEACH

Concept Development

▶ Point out that even though there are three genes for blood type, a human can inherit any combination of two of the three genes.

▶ Emphasize that the blood type of a child can be different from that of the parents.

▶ Stress that not all genes on the sex chromosomes carry undesirable traits, such as color blindness.

▶ Point out that most states give a test for color blindness when people take the test for a driver's license.

Check for Understanding

Give students a short quiz in which they have to construct Punnett squares to solve at least two problems. Have transparencies with Punnett squares already drawn on them and ask some students to demonstrate how they got their answer.

Reteach

As students work on the problems and check their answers, work with groups of students who are still having difficulty with a certain problem. Setting up a difficult problem on an overhead projector can help students understand how genes combine.

Misconception: Students may think Rh + or Rh- factor is the same as the A, B, and O blood groups. Tell students that the Rh factors are controlled by other genes.

CRITICAL THINKING 27

CRITICAL THINKING/PROBLEM SOLVING — CHAPTER 27

Name ______ Date ______ Class ______

Use after Section 27:2.

COULD THE TAYLOR'S SON BE COLOR BLIND?

A genetic counselor had several appointments every morning. Today, he was asked an interesting question. The Taylors' son is going to take driving lessons. He has been having trouble seeing road signs clearly. The Taylors want to know if their son is color blind. They have several color blind relatives who see red and green objects in shades of gray. The counselor asked some questions and drew Punnett squares.

Use the information that follows to hypothesize what the counselor will say.

Mr. Taylor is not color blind. His father and his brother are color blind for red and green. His mother and his sister can see red and green. Mrs. Taylor and her relatives can see red and green. They are not color blind.

Analyzing the Problem

1. Would you hypothesize that the gene for color blindness might be on a sex chromosome? Why? Yes, females and males have different patterns of inheriting genes.
2. If the color vision gene is on the X chromosome, how many genes for color vision does a woman inherit? two From whom? one from each parent
3. If the color vision gene is on the X chromosome, how many genes for color vision does a man inherit? one From whom? one from his mother

Solving the Problem

1. Use the Punnett squares below to show the genes for color vision in Mrs. Taylor's family. Call the gene for color vision *C* and its color blind form *c*.

Mrs. Taylor's Family

Her mother \ Her father	C	Y
C	CC	CY
C	CC	CY

Mr. Taylor's Family

His mother \ His father	c	Y
C	Cc	CY
c	cc	cY

2. From which parent could Mr. Taylor's brother and sister inherit a *C* or *c* gene? mother
3. How can Mr. Taylor have normal color vision while his brothers cannot see red and green? His mother must be heterozygous, *Cc* for the gene. Mr. Taylor must be CY. He inherited a C from his mother and a Y chromosome from his father.
4. Is it likely that the Taylor's son is color blind? Explain. No, he would inherit a C gene from his mother and a Y chromosome from his father.

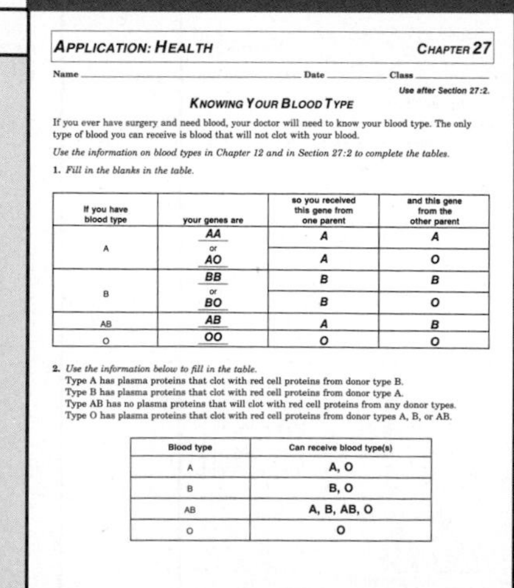

APPLICATION 27

APPLICATION: HEALTH — CHAPTER 27

Name ______ Date ______ Class ______

Use after Section 27:2.

KNOWING YOUR BLOOD TYPE

If you ever have surgery and need blood, your doctor will need to know your blood type. The only type of blood you can receive is blood that will not clot with your blood.

Use the information on blood types in Chapter 12 and in Section 27:2 to complete the tables.

1. *Fill in the blanks in the table.*

If you have blood type	your genes are	so you received this gene from one parent	and this gene from the other parent
A	*AA* or	*A*	*A*
	AO	*A*	*O*
B	*BB* or	*B*	*B*
	BO	*B*	*O*
AB	*AB*	*A*	*B*
O	*OO*	*O*	*O*

2. *Use the information below to fill in the table.*
Type A has plasma proteins that clot with red cell proteins from donor type B.
Type B has plasma proteins that clot with red cell proteins from donor type A.
Type AB has no plasma proteins that will clot with red cell proteins from any donor types.
Type O has plasma proteins that clot with red cell proteins from donor types A, B, or AB.

Blood type	Can receive blood type(s)
A	A, O
B	B, O
AB	A, B, AB, O
O	O

OPTIONS

Application/*Teacher Resource Package*, p. 27. Use the Application worksheet shown here to help students understand blood types.

Critical Thinking/Problem Solving/*Teacher Resource Package*, p. 27. Use the Critical Thinking/Problem Solving worksheet shown here for students to learn who could be colorblind.

TEACH

Independent Practice

Study Guide/*Teacher Resource Package,* p. 159. Use the Study Guide worksheet shown at the bottom of this page for independent practice.

Check for Understanding

Have students respond to the first three questions in Check Your Understanding.

Reteach

Reteaching/*Teacher Resource Package,* p. 81. Use this worksheet to give students additional practice with color blindness.

Extension: Assign Critical Thinking, Biology and Reading, or some of the **OPTIONS** available with this lesson.

3 APPLY

ACTIVITY/Challenge

Give students some simple genetics problems that deal with incomplete dominance, blood types, and sex-linked traits.

4 CLOSE

ACTIVITY/Guest Speaker

Ask a local airplane pilot to explain why pilots need excellent color vision.

Answers to Check Your Understanding

6. when neither gene is totally dominant over the other
7. AA or AO
8. The male doesn't have a second X chromosome to prevent recessive genes from being expressed.
9. No. He would get the nearsighted trait from his mother.
10. A male is hemizygous for traits on the X chromosome because he has only one X chromosome. The other sex chromosome of a male is the Y chromosome.

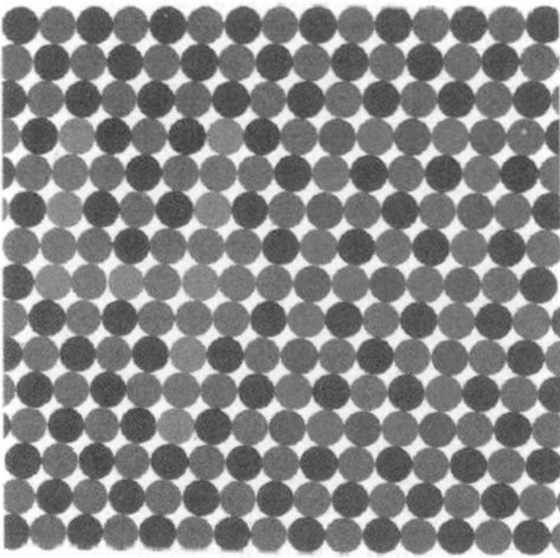

Figure 27-10 To be tested for red-green color vision, a person may be shown a figure like this one.

Males have only one gene for each of these traits. The Y chromosome does not have the genes that are on the X chromosome. When the X and Y chromosomes are together, genes on the X chromosome control the traits.

Let's look at color blindness. **Color blindness** is a problem in which red and green look like shades of gray or other colors. Look at Figure 27-10. Someone who is color blind for red and green can't see the numbers in it.

Being able to see red and green as two separate colors is a dominant trait. Let's use *C* for this gene. Not being able to see red and green is a recessive trait. A ***c*** will be used for this gene.

A female who has ***CC*** genes will be able to see red and green. If she has ***Cc*** genes, she still will be able to see red and green. If she has ***cc*** genes, she will be color blind. Two of the three gene combinations for the female allow her to see red and green.

A male is more likely to be color blind. Why? Think about what genes he could have. Remember that the Y chromosome will not have a gene for the trait.

A male who has the ***C*** gene on his X chromosome will be able to see red and green. If he has the ***c*** gene on his X chromosome, he will not be able to see red and green. There are only two possible gene combinations for the male. One of them will allow him to see red and green. What would happen if a woman with ***Cc*** genes and a man with a ***c*** gene on his X chromosome had children? See if you can answer this question. 1 normal male: 1 color blind male: 1 heterozygous normal female: 1 color blind female

Check Your Understanding

6. What is incomplete dominance?
7. What two gene combinations can a person with type A blood have?
8. Why are there more color blind males than color blind females?
9. **Critical Thinking:** The gene for nearsightedness in humans is found on the X chromosome. A boy has a nearsighted father. Does this mean that the boy will become nearsighted? Why or why not?
10. **Biology and Reading:** The word part *hemi* is found in the word *hemisphere. Hemi* means half. The scientific term for genes on the X chromosome in a male is hemizygous. Why?

STUDY GUIDE 159

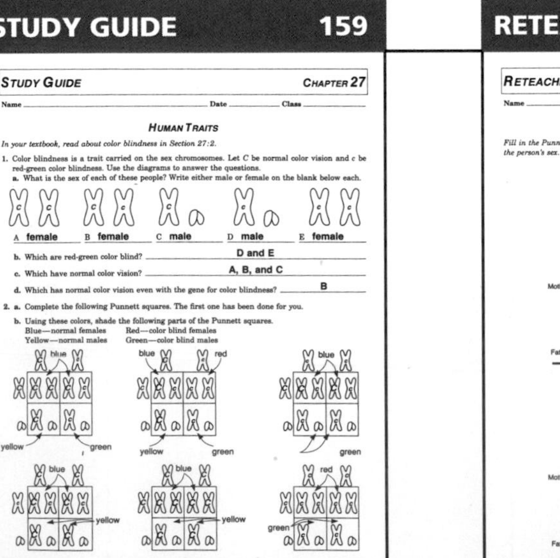

STUDY GUIDE — CHAPTER 27

Name ________ Date ________ Class ________

HUMAN TRAITS

In your textbook, read about color blindness in Section 27:2.

1. Color blindness is a trait carried on the sex chromosomes. Let *C* be normal color vision and *c* be red-green color blindness. Use the diagrams to answer the questions.
   a. What is the sex of each of these people? Write either male or female on the blank below each.
   A female B female C male D male E female
   b. Which are red-green color blind? D and E
   c. Which have normal color vision? A, B, and C
   d. Which has normal color vision even with the gene for color blindness? B
2. a. Complete the following Punnett squares. The first one has been done for you.
   b. Using these colors, shade the following parts of the Punnett squares.
   Blue—normal females Red—color blind females
   Yellow—normal males Green—color blind males

RETEACHING 81

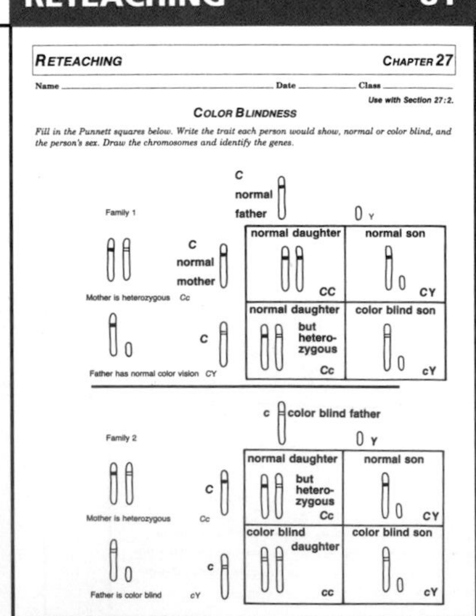

RETEACHING — CHAPTER 27

Name ________ Date ________ Class ________

Use with Section 27:2.

COLOR BLINDNESS

Fill in the Punnett squares below. Write the trait each person would show, normal or color blind, and the person's sex. Draw the chromosomes and identify the genes.

Lab 27–2 Human Traits

Problem: Which traits are most common?

Skills

observe, make and use tables, interpret data

Materials

pencil
paper

Procedure

1. Copy the data table.
2. **Make and use tables:** Have another student check you for each of the traits listed in the table. Record in your table with a check mark whether you show the dominant or recessive trait.
3. Reverse roles and check your partner for each trait.

TRAIT	DOMINANT	RECESSIVE
Skin color	Answers will	vary.
Extra fingers or toes		
Freckles		
Earlobe		
Tongue rolling		
Shape of hairline		
Hair on middle sections of fingers		
Chin shape		

Data and Observations

1. How many dominant traits do you have? How many recessive traits do you have?
2. How many other students in your class have the same traits as you?

Analyze and Apply

1. Which statement best explains this lab?
   (a) All students in the class show the same dominant and recessive traits.
   (b) A person may show some dominant and some recessive traits.
   (c) It is easier to recognize a dominant trait in someone than a recessive trait.
2. **Apply:** Were there more dominant or more recessive traits in your class? How can you explain this?

Extension

Design an experiment to determine if any of the traits are on the X chromosome.

TRAIT	DOMINANT	RECESSIVE
Skin color	Dark colors	Light colors
Extra fingers or toes	Six or seven fingers or toes	Five fingers and toes
Freckles	Freckles	No Freckles
Earlobe	Free	Attached
Tongue rolling	Can roll edges	Cannot roll edges
Shape of hairline	Pointed in middle	Not pointed in middle
Hair on middle sections of fingers	Hair	No hair
Chin shape	Indentation in middle	No indentation

ANSWERS

Data and Observations

1. Answers will vary.
2. Answers will vary.

Analyze and Apply

1. b
2. Answers will vary. Some recessive genes will be found more frequently than dominant genes.

Lab 27-2 Human Traits

Overview

Students will find out which inherited traits are most common among classmates by checking the phenotypes of another class member. Using their data, they will be able to determine whether there are more dominant or recessive traits visible in the members of the class. They will also find out that many members of the class have the same traits. Students will construct Punnett squares from a data table to determine why offspring in three families show certain traits.

Objectives: Upon completing the lab, students will be able to (1) **determine** the dominant and recessive traits found in a population of students, (2) **state** which dominant and recessive traits they have, and (3) **use numbers** to show which traits were found more and less often.

Time Allotment: 45 minutes

Preparation

Lab 27-2 worksheet/*Teacher Resource Package*, pp. 107-108.

Teaching the Lab

▶ Be sure students understand that neither dominant nor recessive traits in the table indicate normal or abnormal.

27:3 Genetic Disorders

PREPARATION

Materials Needed

Make copies of the Study Guide, Skill, Enrichment, and Reteaching worksheets in the *Teacher Resource Package.*

▶ Obtain poster board for the Skill Check.

Key Science Words

dyslexia
genetic counseling
pedigree

Process Skills

In the Skill Check, students will formulate models.

1 FOCUS

▶ The objectives are listed on the student page. Remind students to preview these objectives as a guide to this numbered section.

MOTIVATION/Brainstorming

Ask students what the difference is between a genetic disorder and genetic error.

Independent Practice

Study Guide/*Teacher Resource Package*, p. 160. Use the Study Guide worksheet shown at the bottom of this page for independent practice.

27:3 Genetic Disorders

Objectives

6. **Describe** some genetic disorders in humans.
7. **Give examples** of how genetic counseling can help families.

Key Science Words

dyslexia
genetic counseling
pedigree

Each day, nearly 600 babies are born in the United States with some type of disorder. Some of the disorders are inherited. Let's look at a few of them.

Errors in Chromosome Number

Some people are born with more or fewer than 46 chromosomes. This happens when the sperm or egg cell does not have 23 chromosomes. Figure 27-12 shows how this can come about.

During meiosis, the sister chromatids are supposed to pull apart from each other. Notice in Figure 27-12 that the sister chromatids of the short chromosome pulled apart and were separated into different cells. The sister chromatids of the longer chromosome stuck together. Both of them went into the same cell. That cell now has an extra chromosome.

If these cells were eggs, the one on the right would have one fewer chromosome, or 22. If this egg joined a sperm, a child with only 45 chromosomes would result. The egg on the left has an extra chromosome. If this egg joined a sperm, a child with 47 chromosomes would result.

Not pulling apart can happen to almost any pair of chromosomes. When it happens to the sex chromosomes, certain traits show up. Figure 27-11 shows sex chromosome patterns that sometimes show up in people. The O stands for a missing sex chromosome. Notice the boy and the girl who have only one sex chromosome. The sex chromosome from one parent is missing. What are some of the problems that result from having one of these chromosome patterns?

Female	Male
XO	YO
	XXY

Figure 27-11 Sex chromosome patterns

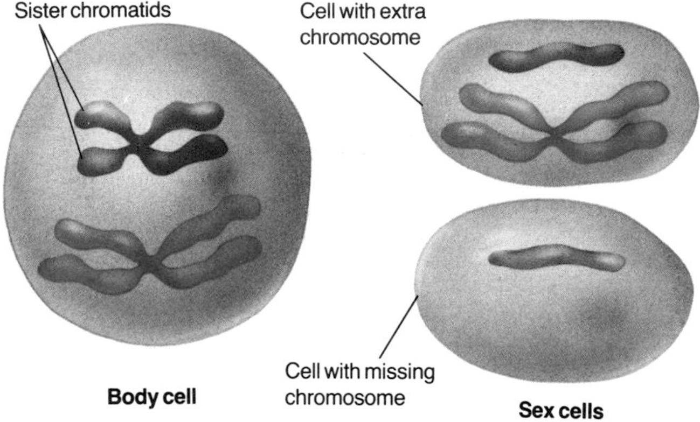

Figure 27-12 When sister chromatids do not pull apart during meiosis, there can be an error in chromosome number in the child.

OPTIONS

Science Background

Geneticists refer to the sticking together of homologous chromosomes during meiosis as nondisjunction. Nondisjunction means failure to separate from one another.

STUDY GUIDE 160

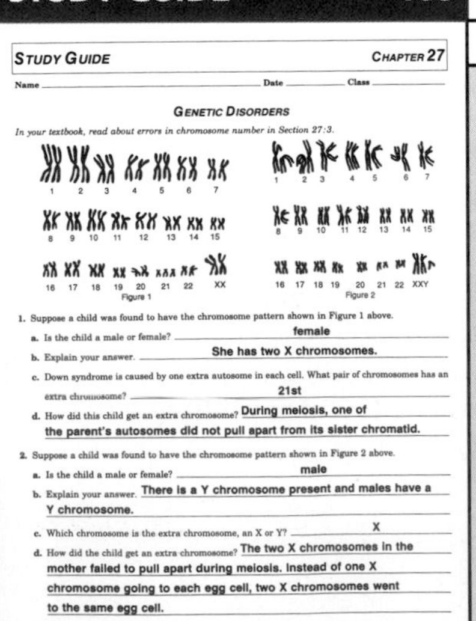

STUDY GUIDE — CHAPTER 27

Name ______ Date ______ Class ______

GENETIC DISORDERS

In your textbook, read about errors in chromosome number in Section 27:3.

1. Suppose a child was found to have the chromosome pattern shown in Figure 1 above.
   a. Is the child a male or female? **female**
   b. Explain your answer. **She has two X chromosomes.**
   c. Down syndrome is caused by one extra autosome in each cell. What pair of chromosomes has an extra chromosome? **21st**
   d. How did this child get an extra chromosome? **During meiosis, one of the parent's autosomes did not pull apart from its sister chromatid.**
2. Suppose a child was found to have the chromosome pattern shown in Figure 2 above.
   a. Is the child a male or female? **male**
   b. Explain your answer. **There is a Y chromosome present and males have a Y chromosome.**
   c. Which chromosome is the extra chromosome, an X or Y? **X**
   d. How did the child get an extra chromosome? **The two X chromosomes in the mother failed to pull apart during meiosis. Instead of one X chromosome going to each egg cell, two X chromosomes went to the same egg cell.**

A YO male will die before it is born. An XO female and an XXY male cannot make sex cells, but they can live.

The child in Figure 27-13 was born with an extra autosome. During meiosis, one of his autosomes did not pull apart from its copy. A doctor would say he has Down syndrome. The child learns more slowly than most children his age. Children with Down syndrome often have heart problems. Researchers are learning more about problems caused by having an extra chromosome.

Figure 27-13 Child with Down syndrome

Genetic Disorders and Sex Chromosomes

You have studied traits controlled by genes on the sex chromosomes. The ability to see red and green was one of them. There are also serious genetic disorders controlled by genes on the X chromosome.

A certain recessive gene on the X chromosome can cause a rare disorder called hemophilia. Remember that hemophilia is a disorder in which a person's blood does not clot. Bleeding from a cut or bruise may take hours to stop. Hemophilia almost always shows up in male children. How would it be possible for a female child to inherit hemophilia? by inheriting one recessive gene from each parent

Genetic Disorders and Autosomes

Genetic disorders can also be caused by genes found on the autosomes.

Dyslexia (dis LEHK see uh) is a genetic disorder that is also called word blindness. It is caused by a dominant gene. People with dyslexia see and write some letters of the alphabet or parts of words backward. They have trouble learning to read.

Skill Check

Formulate a model: Make a model of the alphabet on a poster board showing how a person with dyslexia might see these letters. *For more help, refer to the* ***Skill Handbook,*** *pages 706-711.*

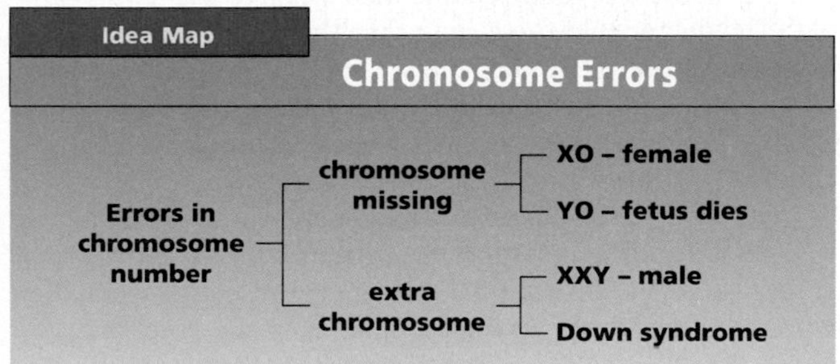

Study Tip: Use this idea map as a study guide to errors in chromosome number. Some examples of these errors are shown.

2 TEACH

Software

Genetics Counselor, Queue, Inc.

Concept Development

▶ Explain that scientists do not understand why the chromosomes fail to separate from each other.

▶ Explain that parts can be added or removed from a chromosome. This can cause a change in the traits a person inherits.

▶ Point out that viruses, chemicals, and radiation can cause a change in the structure of a chromosome.

Independent Practice

Study Guide/*Teacher Resource Package*, p. 161. Use the Study Guide worksheet shown at the bottom of this page for independent practice.

Skill Check

Tell students that some dyslexic people reverse the letters *b* for *d* and *p* for *q*. They also change the order of letters and numerals, such as was for saw, and 13 for 31.

Idea Map

Have students use the idea map as a study guide to the major concepts of this section.

Cooperative Learning: Have teams of 3-4 write a news report on Down syndrome. Have each team give an oral report.

SKILL 28

SKILL: MAKE A LINE GRAPH — CHAPTER 27

Name ______ Date ______ Class ______

For more help, refer to the Skill Handbook, pages 715-717. — *Use after Section 27:3.*

GENETIC DISORDERS IN NEWBORN BABIES

Genetic disorders can be caused by errors in chromosome number that occur during formation of sex cells. After fertilization, an embryo's body cells might contain more than the normal 46 chromosomes. A chromosome part might be missing, or an extra part might be attached. Down syndrome is a genetic disorder that usually is caused by an extra chromosome. Down syndrome is quite common. In one study of 1000 newborn babies, 53 babies had Down syndrome. Another 32 babies had other chromosome errors. The table below shows mothers with normal babies and with babies having genetic disorders.

Study the table. Then, answer the questions that follow it.

Age of mother (years)	Number of babies with Down syndrome	Number of babies with other chromosome errors	Number of babies without chromosome errors
15–19	1	1	142
20–24	1	1	141
25–29	2	1	140
30–34	3	2	138
35–39	4	3	136
40–44	11	8	123
45 and older	31	16	95
TOTAL	53	32	915

1. In what age group were most of the mothers of the babies with Down syndrome? **45 years and older**
2. In what age group were most of the mothers of babies with other chromosome disorders? **45 years and older**
3. On the grid, make a line graph to show the number of babies with Down syndrome. Then, use a different color pencil to show the number of babies with other chromosome errors.
4. At what ages are mothers more likely to have babies with chromosome errors? **from 40 years and older**

- - - = babies with Down syndrome
—— = babies with other chromosome errors
Number of babies: 0 5 10 15 20 25 30 35 40 45 50 55
Age of mother (years): 15 20 25 30 35 40 45 50

Note that graph lines coincide for mothers of ages 15 and 20 years.

STUDY GUIDE 161

STUDY GUIDE — CHAPTER 27

Name ______ Date ______ Class ______

GENETIC DISORDERS

In your textbook, read about hemophilia in Section 27:3.

1. In the boxes below each of these people, draw the sex chromosomes. Then, on the chromosomes write the genes they have for hemophilia. The dominant gene is *H*. The recessive gene is *h*.

Normal, pure dominant female	Female with hemophilia	Normal male	Male with hemophilia	Normal, heterozygous female
H H	h h	H	h	H h

2. Complete the following Punnett squares. Then, match the correct Punnett square with each one of the following expected results. Write the letter of the Punnett square on the line next to the expected result it matches.

Expected results	
2 normal females, 1 normal male, 1 male with hemophilia	B
1 normal female, 1 normal male, 1 female with hemophilia, 1 male with hemophilia	A
2 normal females, 2 males with hemophilia	C

A B C

3. Circle the Punnett squares that show individuals with hemophilia.

	H	h
H	HH	HH
h	Hh	hh

4. Describe the condition of hemophilia. **Hemophilia is a genetic disorder in which the person's blood will not clot.**

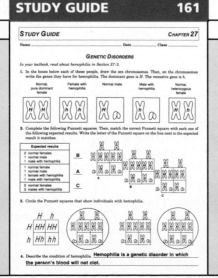

OPTIONS

Science Background

In 1910, Dr. Thomas Hunt Morgan discovered that traits governed by genes carried on the sex chromosomes showed a different pattern of inheritance than traits governed by autosomal genes.

Skill/*Teacher Resource Package*, p. 28. Use the Skill worksheet shown here to have students make a line graph on genetic disorders in newborn babies.

TEACH

Concept Development

▶ Genetic counselors are usually found in hospitals that do research in genetic diseases.

▶ Explain that geneticists collect data to predict how often these genes will show in a human population.

▶ Point out that one in twenty persons in the United States carries a recessive gene for cystic fibrosis.

Guided Practice

Have students write down their answers to the margin questions: a genetic disorder in which some chemicals don't break down as they should; a diagram that shows how a certain trait is passed along in a family.

Connection: Social Studies

Have students investigate which local and state agencies deal with health problems of genetic origin. Have them find out what these agencies do to help people and how much money is spent dealing with these kinds of health problems.

ACTIVITY/Speaker

The local chapter of the Association for Retarded Citizens usually has a speakers bureau that can provide a free speaker to speak to your class about genetic counseling.

What is PKU?

Twenty years ago, a child born with PKU would spend its life in a hospital. PKU is a genetic disorder in which some chemicals in the body do not break down as they should. These chemicals can harm the brain cells. Today babies are tested for PKU soon after birth. A child born with PKU can be given a special diet, starting within the first few weeks of life. This diet has only small amounts of the chemicals that will not break down properly. The child can grow normally with this diet.

Bio Tip

Health: Cystic fibrosis patients lose large amounts of salt from their bodies, resulting in very salty sweat. For many years, having very salty sweat was used as a test for this disorder.

Genetic Counseling

"It runs in the family." Have you heard this comment before? It means that many family members have a certain trait. The trait could be found in parents, grandparents, brothers, sisters, or other relatives. Family members can have the same hair color, eye color, or shape of nose.

Genetic disorders run in families, too. How can a couple find out whether a disorder in their family will show up in their children? They can seek genetic counseling. **Genetic counseling** is the use of genetics to predict and explain traits in children. A genetic counselor can tell whether a problem is caused by genes.

A genetic counselor asks a lot of questions about many members of a family. Then the counselor makes some conclusions. A genetic counselor can help answer the following questions:

1. How did their baby get the disorder?
2. If the baby is healthy, does it have a problem gene?
3. Is the trait dominant or recessive?
4. What will happen to the baby's health as it gets older?
5. What are the chances that future children will have the trait?

Figure 27-14 A couple receiving genetic counseling

The baby of a young couple died when it was two years old. The doctor told the couple that their baby had cystic fibrosis (sis tik • fi BROH suhs). This is a genetic disorder in which the lungs and pancreas don't work the way they should. There are very serious breathing problems. Many children with this disorder die at an early age.

The baby's parents went to a genetic counselor, who told them that the disorder was caused by having two recessive genes, ***ff***. Both parents appeared normal, but they were each heterozygous for the dominant and recessive genes, ***Ff***.

OPTIONS

Enrichment: Call the local chapter of the March of Dimes and request the booklet "A Guide to Human Chromosome Defects." This booklet gives good background information on karotypes and chromosome errors, and the drawings and charts can be made into overhead transparencies.

Enrichment/*Teacher Resource Package*, p. 29. Use the Enrichment worksheet shown here for students to trace a genetic disorder in a family.

ENRICHMENT 29

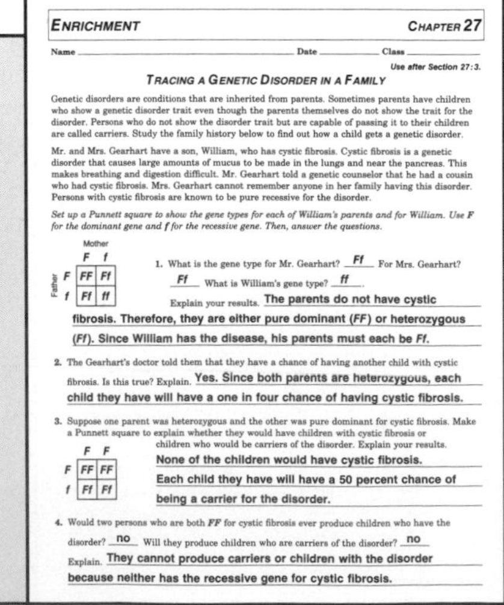

ENRICHMENT CHAPTER 27

Name ______ Date ______ Class ______

Use after Section 27:3.

TRACING A GENETIC DISORDER IN A FAMILY

Genetic disorders are conditions that are inherited from parents. Sometimes parents have children who show a genetic disorder trait even though the parents themselves do not show the trait for the disorder. Persons who do not show the disorder trait but are capable of passing it to their children are called carriers. Study the family history below to find out how a child gets a genetic disorder.

Mr. and Mrs. Gearhart have a son, William, who has cystic fibrosis. Cystic fibrosis is a genetic disorder that causes large amounts of mucus to be made in the lungs and near the pancreas. This makes breathing and digestion difficult. Mr. Gearhart told a genetic counselor that he had a cousin who had cystic fibrosis. Mrs. Gearhart cannot remember anyone in her family having this disorder. Persons with cystic fibrosis are known to be pure recessive for the disorder.

Set up a Punnett square to show the gene types for each of William's parents and for William. Use **F** *for the dominant gene and* **f** *for the recessive gene. Then, answer the questions.*

Father \ Mother	F	f
F	FF	Ff
f	Ff	ff

1. What is the gene type for Mr. Gearhart? *Ff* For Mrs. Gearhart? *Ff* What is William's gene type? *ff*. Explain your results. **The parents do not have cystic fibrosis. Therefore, they are either pure dominant (*FF*) or heterozygous (*Ff*). Since William has the disease, his parents must each be *Ff*.**

2. The Gearhart's doctor told them that they have a chance of having another child with cystic fibrosis. Is this true? Explain. **Yes. Since both parents are heterozygous, each child they have will have a one in four chance of having cystic fibrosis.**

3. Suppose one parent was heterozygous and the other was pure dominant for cystic fibrosis. Make a Punnett square to explain whether they would have children with cystic fibrosis or children who would be carriers of the disorder. Explain your results.

	F	F
F	FF	FF
f	Ff	Ff

None of the children would have cystic fibrosis. Each child they have will have a 50 percent chance of being a carrier for the disorder.

4. Would two persons who are both ***FF*** for cystic fibrosis ever produce children who have the disorder? **no** Will they produce children who are carriers of the disorder? **no** Explain. **They cannot produce carriers or children with the disorder because neither has the recessive gene for cystic fibrosis.**

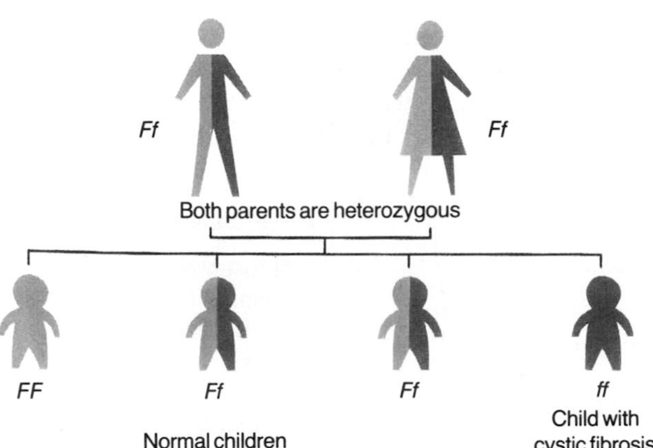

Figure 27-15 A family pedigree for cystic fibrosis

The counselor showed the parents a drawing of a family pedigree like the one in Figure 27-15. A **pedigree** is a diagram that can show how a certain trait is passed along in a family. A pedigree may be used to trace a family trait and to predict whether future generations will have the trait.

What is a pedigree?

The couple learned that there was a one in four chance of any of their children being born with the disorder and that tests such as amniocentesis can tell whether a fetus has the disorder. Talking to the counselor gave them an idea of what to expect if they decided to have more children.

Check Your Understanding

11. How can an error in meiosis cause a sex cell to have the wrong number of chromosomes?
12. Name three genetic disorders and tell how each one of them is controlled by genes.
13. How can a genetic counselor use a pedigree to help families with genetic disorders?
14. **Critical Thinking:** Why do you think an XO female can survive but a YO male will die before birth?
15. **Biology and Math:** A genetic counselor sees a couple who is worried that their unborn child may have hemophilia. Tests show that the fetus is female and that the mother is heterozygous for the recessive gene, which is on the X chromosome. Will the baby have hemophilia? Why or why not?

TEACH

Independent Practice

Study Guide/*Teacher Resource Package*, p. 162. Use the Study Guide worksheet shown at the bottom of this page for independent practice.

Check for Understanding

Have students respond to the first three questions in Check Your Understanding.

Reteach

Reteaching/*Teacher Resource Package*, p. 82. Use this worksheet to give students additional practice with genetic disorders.

Extension: Assign Critical Thinking, Biology and Math, or some of the **OPTIONS** available with this lesson.

3 APPLY

ACTIVITY/Skill

Give students several genetics problems to evaluate their understanding of genetic disorders.

CLOSE

Filmstrip

Show the video *Heredity, Health, and Genetic Disorders,* Human Relations Media.

Answers to Check Your Understanding

11. When sister chromatids both go into the same cell, the other cell will be missing a chromosome.
12. hemophilia—recessive gene on the X chromosome; dyslexia—dominant gene on autosome; cystic fibrosis—recessive gene on autosome
13. A pedigree traces how a trait is passed on in a family.
14. Some or all genes on the X chromosome are necessary for life.
15. No, only male children of this couple could have the disorder.

RETEACHING 82

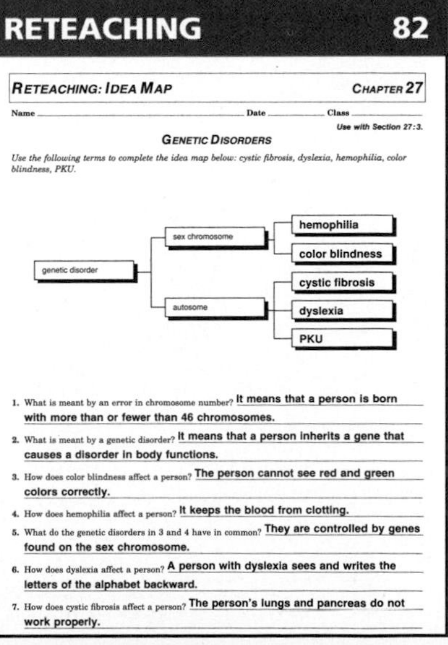

RETEACHING: IDEA MAP — CHAPTER 27

Name ______ Date ______ Class ______

Use with Section 27:3.

GENETIC DISORDERS

Use the following terms to complete the idea map below: cystic fibrosis, dyslexia, hemophilia, color blindness, PKU.

genetic disorder
- sex chromosome
  - hemophilia
  - color blindness
- autosome
  - cystic fibrosis
  - dyslexia
  - PKU

1. What is meant by an error in chromosome number? **It means that a person is born with more than or fewer than 46 chromosomes.**
2. What is meant by a genetic disorder? **It means that a person inherits a gene that causes a disorder in body functions.**
3. How does color blindness affect a person? **The person cannot see red and green colors correctly.**
4. How does hemophilia affect a person? **It keeps the blood from clotting.**
5. What do the genetic disorders in 3 and 4 have in common? **They are controlled by genes found on the sex chromosome.**
6. How does dyslexia affect a person? **A person with dyslexia sees and writes the letters of the alphabet backward.**
7. How does cystic fibrosis affect a person? **The person's lungs and pancreas do not work properly.**

STUDY GUIDE 162

STUDY GUIDE — CHAPTER 27

Name ______ Date ______ Class ______

VOCABULARY

Review the new words in Chapter 27 of your textbook. Then, complete this puzzle.

Across

5. Use of genetics to predict and explain traits in children
6. Condition in which neither gene is dominant
7. Chromosome that does not determine sex
8. Disorder in which red blood cells are not round
9. Sex chromosomes of the female
10. Chromosomes that determine if child is male or female
11. Diagram that can show how a trait is passed along in a family

Down

1. Genetic disorder called word blindness
2. Disorder in which some colors are not seen as they should be
3. Way of looking at chromosomes of a fetus
4. Sex chromosomes of a male

CHAPTER 27 REVIEW

Summary

Summary statements can be used by students to review the major concepts of the chapter.

Key Science Words

All boldfaced terms from the chapter are listed.

Testing Yourself

Using Words

1. autosome
2. amniocentesis
3. dyslexia
4. genetic counseling
5. sex chromosome
6. X chromosome
7. incomplete dominance
8. color blindness
9. Y chromosome
10. pedigree

Finding Main Ideas

11. p. 567; Amniocentesis is a way to look at cells of a fetus.
12. p. 573; A new trait in incomplete dominance is a combination of the dominant and recessive trait.
13. p. 578; A pair of chromosomes does not pull apart, and two chromosomes go into one cell.
14. p. 574; Body cells are damaged because sickle cells do not carry enough oxygen to them. Because of their shape, sickle cells clog articles.
15. p. 568; The X and Y chromosomes are chromosomes that determine sex.
16. p. 566; Human body cells contain 46 chromosomes, but sex cells have 23 chromosomes.

Using Main Ideas

17. The male determines the sex of a child.
18. The parents can be heterozygous and carry the recessive gene for cystic fibrosis.
19. The parents can be heterozygous and both carry the gene for type O blood. The child inherited a pure recessive trait.

Chapter 27 Review

Summary

27:1 The Role of Chromosomes

1. Each human sex cell has 23 chromosomes. Each human body cell has 46 chromosomes arranged in pairs.
2. Amniocentesis is a way to look at the chromosomes of a fetus.
3. The sex of a person is determined by a pair of sex chromosomes. Human females have two X chromosomes. Human males have one X and one Y chromosome.

27:2 Human Traits

4. If a person has a dominant trait, one or both of the parents will also have the trait. If a person has a recessive trait, both of the parents will also carry the gene for the trait. Traits in which neither gene is totally dominant over the other show incomplete dominance.
5. Three genes control blood types in humans but each person has only two genes for this trait. Males show recessive traits located on the X chromosome more often than females do.

27:3 Genetic Disorders

6. If chromosome pairs do not pull apart during meiosis, errors in chromosome number result. Hemophilia, cystic fibrosis, and dyslexia are genetic disorders.
7. A genetic counselor uses knowledge of genetics to predict and explain disorders in children.

Key Science Words

amniocentesis (p. 567)
autosome (p. 568)
color blindness (p. 576)
dyslexia (p. 579)
genetic counseling (p. 580)
incomplete dominance (p. 573)
pedigree (p. 581)
sex chromosome (p. 568)
sickle-cell anemia (p. 574)
X chromosome (p. 568)
Y chromosome (p. 568)

Testing Yourself

Choose the word from the list of Key Science Words that best fits the definition.

1. chromosome not related to sex
2. way to observe cells from a fetus
3. word blindness
4. the use of genetics to predict problem traits in children
5. chromosome that determines sex of a child
6. female sex chromosome

Review

Testing Yourself *continued*

7. trait in which neither gene is totally dominant over the other
8. vision problem related to sex chromosome
9. male sex chromosome
10. diagram used to trace a family trait

Finding Main Ideas

List the page number where each main idea below is found. Then, explain each main idea.

11. how to see cells of a fetus
12. how a new trait appears when there is incomplete dominance
13. how errors in chromosome number occur
14. why people with sickle-cell anemia have serious health problems
15. what the X and Y chromosomes are
16. that sex cells contain half the number of chromosomes as body cells

Using Main Ideas

Answer the questions by referring to the page number after each question.

17. Which parent determines the sex of a child? (p. 570)
18. How can a child have cystic fibrosis when the parents do not? (p. 580)
19. How can two parents with type A blood have a child with type O blood? (p. 575)
20. A color-blind female marries a normal male. What could the color vision of their children be? (p. 576)
21. One parent is heterozygous for blood type A. The other is heterozygous for blood type B. What might the children's blood types be? (p. 575)

Skill Review ✓

For more help, refer to the ***Skill Handbook,*** *pages 704-719.*

1. **Make and use tables:** Make a table to show the numbers of baby boys and girls born in a local hospital in one month. How does the ratio of boys to girls compare with what you expect?
2. **Observe:** Find out how many students can roll their tongue and how many cannot. Explain why there are more students showing one trait.
3. **Interpret data:** Two parents have four children, each of which has a different blood type. One child is type A, one is type B, one is type O, and one is type AB. How can you explain this?
4. **Calculate:** If the body cells of an animal contain 78 chromosomes, how many chromosomes does a sperm cell from that animal contain?

Finding Out More

Critical Thinking

1. Explain why geneticists would want to spend more time finding out about genetic disorders in humans rather than how height, hair color, and eye color are inherited.
2. Why do most states require that newborn babies be tested for PKU soon after they are born?

Applications

1. Find out how people with Down syndrome lead useful lives.
2. Find out the treatment for cystic fibrosis.

Using Main Ideas

20. They could have color-blind sons and normal-vision daughters.
21. They could have one with AB, one with BO, one with AO, and one with OO.

Skill Review

1. Depending on the source of the data, students may notice that one month more girls will be born and the next month more boys will be born. Point out that they should expect a 1:1 ratio.
2. Rolling the tongue is a dominant trait.
3. The parents are both heterozygous for blood type. One is AO and the other is BO.
4. 39

Finding Out More

Critical Thinking

1. Genetic disorders can cause serious problems and death.
2. If babies born with PKU are given a special diet within the first weeks of life, they can develop normally.

Applications

1. Students will find that many people with Down syndrome lead productive lives by attending school and holding jobs.
2. Those with cystic fibrosis require frequent breathing and lung treatments.

Chapter Review/*Teacher Resource Package*, pp. 153-154.

Chapter Test/*Teacher Resource Package*, pp. 155-157.

Chapter Test/*Computer Test Bank*

DNA—Life's Code

PLANNING GUIDE

CONTENT	TEXT FEATURES	TEACHER RESOURCE PACKAGE	OTHER COMPONENTS
(3 1/2 days) 28:1 The DNA Molecule DNA Structure DNA Chromosomes Proof That DNA Controls Traits How DNA Works Making Proteins How DNA Copies Itself	Mini Lab: *How Are Nitrogen Bases Paired?* p. 591 Lab 28-1: *DNA,* p. 588 Technology: *DNA Fingerprinting,* p. 593 Idea Map, p. 587 Idea Map, p. 589 Check Your Understanding, p. 594	Enrichment: *The DNA Code,* p. 30 Reteaching: *DNA Structure and How DNA Copies Itself,* p. 83 Skill: *Predict,* p. 29 Transparency Master: *DNA Controls Traits,* p. 141 Study Guide: *The DNA Molecule,* pp. 163-165 Lab 28-1: *DNA,* pp. 109-110	**Laboratory Manual:** *How Does DNA Make Protein?* p. 235 Color Transparency 28a: *The Relationship Between DNA and the Cell* Color Transparency 28b: *How DNA Copies Itself*
(2 1/2 days) 28:2 How The Genetic Message Changes Mutations Cloning Plant and Animal Breeding Splicing	Skill Check: *Understand Science Words,* p. 601 Mini Lab: *How Does a Mutation Occur?* p. 596 Lab 28-2: *Cloning, p.* 598 Idea Map, p. 591 Check Your Understanding, p. 601	Application: *Plant and Animal Breeding,* p. 28 Reteaching: *DNA Changes,* p. 84 Critical Thinking/Problem Solving: *How Can You Find Changes in the Genetic Code?* p. 28 Focus: *Twins,* p. 55 Study Guide: *How the Genetic Message Changes,* pp. 166-167 Study Guide: *Vocabulary,* p. 168 Lab 28-2: *Cloning,* pp. 111-112	**Laboratory Manual:** *How Can a Mutation in DNA Affect an Organism?* p. 239
Chapter Review	Summary Key Science Words Testing Yourself Finding Main Ideas Using Main Ideas Skill Review	Chapter Review, pp. 148-149 Chapter Test, pp. 150-152	**Test Bank**

MATERIALS NEEDED

LAB 28-1, p. 588	LAB 28-2, p. 598	MARGIN FEATURES
scissors tracing paper heavy paper tape blank sheet of paper red, blue, green, and yellow crayons	scissors clear plastic cup aluminum foil *Coleus* plant soil water label metric ruler	Skill Check, p. 601 dictionary Mini Lab, p. 591 markers paper Mini Lab, p. 596 crayons scissors paper

OBJECTIVES

SECTION	OBJECTIVE	OBJECTIVES CORRELATION			
		CHECK YOUR UNDERSTANDING	CHAPTER REVIEW	TRP CHAPTER REVIEW	TRP CHAPTER TEST
28:1	1. **Describe** the structure of DNA.	1, 5	3, 8, 18	1, 7, 8, 9, 16, 17, 19	1, 2, 4, 34, 35, 36, 37, 38, 39
	2. **Explain** how DNA controls genetic traits.	2	1, 16, 27	2, 12, 25, 27	3, 8, 40
	3. **Describe** how DNA copies itself and works to make proteins.	4	2, 9, 10, 14, 15, 21, 24	6, 10, 24	5, 6, 9, 12, 28, 41
28:2	4. **Describe** how mutations occur.	6	4, 12, 22	3, 28	7, 29, 42, 44
	5. **Describe** how cloning and breeding produce off-spring with desired traits.	7, 9	2, 7, 11, 17, 25	5, 18, 19, 20, 21, 22, 23, 26	10, 11, 13, 15, 16, 17, 19, 20, 21, 23, 24, 26, 30, 31, 32, 43
	6. **Explain** how recombinant DNA can help humans.	8, 10	5, 13, 20, 23	4, 11, 13, 14, 29	14, 18, 22, 25, 27, 33

DNA – Life's Code

CHAPTER OVERVIEW

Key Concepts

In this chapter, students will examine the appearance and function of DNA. They will study the experimental evidence that shows DNA is the genetic material of the cell. Students also will study errors that occur in the DNA code and their consequences. They will learn about the modern applications of DNA technology.

Key Science Words

breeding
DNA
fraternal twins
genetic code
identical twins
mutation
nitrogen base
radiation
recombinant DNA
RNA

Skill Development

In Lab 28-1, students will **formulate a model, interpret diagrams,** and **observe** to determine what a model of DNA looks like. In Lab 28-2, students will **observe, infer,** and **interpret data** to understand how a *Coleus* plant can be cloned. In the Skill Check on page 601, students will **understand** the **science word** *recombinant DNA*. In the Mini Lab on page 591, students will **formulate a model** of paired nitrogen bases. In the Mini Lab on page 596, students will **formulate a model** of normal DNA and a mutation.

CHAPTER PREVIEW

Chapter Content

Review this outline for Chapter 28 before you read the chapter.

28:1 The DNA Molecule
- DNA Structure
- DNA and Chromosomes
- Proof That DNA Controls Traits
- How DNA Works
- Making Proteins
- How DNA Copies Itself

28:2 How the Genetic Message Changes
- Mutations
- Cloning
- Plant and Animal Breeding
- Splicing Genes

Skills in this Chapter

The skills that you will use in this chapter are listed below.

- In **Lab 28-1,** you will formulate a model, interpret diagrams, and observe. In **Lab 28-2,** you will observe, infer, and interpret data.
- In the **Skill Checks,** you will understand science words.
- In the **Mini Labs,** you will formulate models.

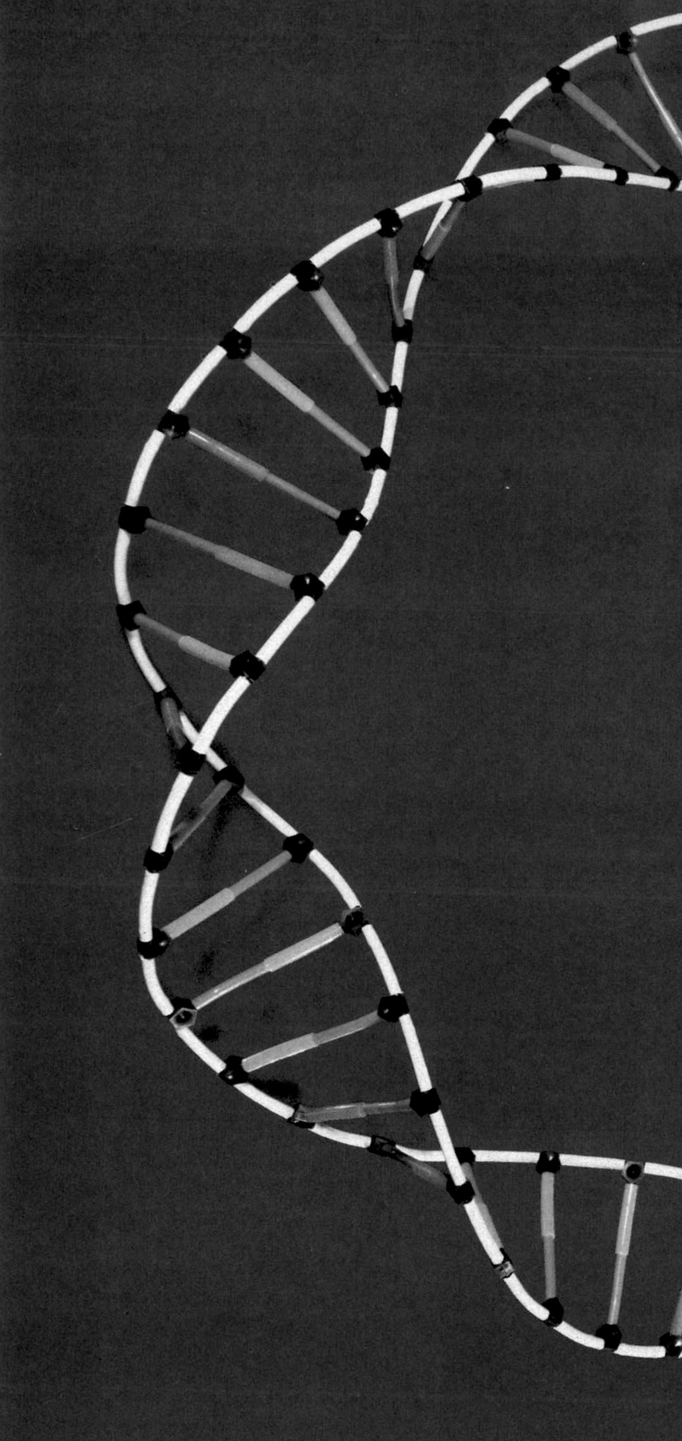

584

Bridging

Students learned in detail the steps of mitosis and meiosis in Chapter 22. This chapter will explain exactly how it is possible for a chromosome to copy itself during the forming of sister chromatids.

Chapter **28**

DNA—Life's Code

Many different kinds of codes are used for many different reasons. Braille is an example of a code. It is used by a visually impaired person to help him or her read. The photo on this page shows a book written in Braille. Another code is one that is found in each of your cells. It is a code that determines all of your traits. It directs your body to be you. What you see in the photo on the left is a model of a chemical molecule. How this molecule acts as a code to determine your body's traits is what this chapter is all about.

Try This!

How many words can you make with only four letters? Design an alphabet that has only four letters. Write as many words as possible using the four letters. You may use the same letter more than once.

Braille is a code.

GETTING STARTED

Using the Photos

Have students think of other codes they are familiar with or perhaps have used. Have them relate written codes to chemical codes.

MOTIVATION/Try This!

How many words can you make with only four letters? Upon completing the chapter-opening activity, students will demonstrate how only four major molecules in a cell code for all the variations in living things.

Chapter Preview

Have students study the chapter outline before they begin to read the chapter. They should note the overall organization of the chapter, that the first topic is a description of the DNA molecule. This is followed by information that describes how the DNA code may change and how these changes may now be put to beneficial use.

Misconception

Students have learned that the nucleus of a cell is the control center. In reality, the control of the cell lies not with the nucleus but with what is present within the nucleus. Chromosomes and their corresponding genes control the cell. Genes, in turn, are actually under the control of the DNA code.

28:1 The DNA Molecule

PREPARATION

Materials Needed

Make copies of the Study Guide, Skill, Transparency Master, Enrichment, Reteaching, and Lab worksheets in the *Teacher Resource Package*.

▶ Have crayons, scissors, and tracing paper on hand for Lab 28-1.

▶ Purchase suggested candies for Check for Understanding.

Key Science Words

DNA
nitrogen base
RNA
genetic code

Process Skills

In the Mini Lab, students will formulate a model. In Lab 28-1, students will formulate a model, interpret diagrams, and observe.

1 FOCUS

▶ The objectives are listed on the student page. Remind students to preview these objectives as a guide to this numbered section.

MOTIVATION/Convergent Question

Tell students that a certain chromosome has genes that control the following traits located on it: skin color, number of teeth, number of fingers, and blood type. Ask them what traits will be present on the sister chromatid when it is formed.

Objectives

1. **Describe** the structure of DNA.
2. **Explain** how DNA controls genetic traits.
3. **Describe** how DNA copies itself and works to make proteins.

Key Science Words

DNA
nitrogen base
RNA
genetic code

28:1 The DNA Molecule

Within each of your cells is a chemical that controls life. It is what we have been calling *genes* in the past few chapters. Now you will find out how this chemical makes up the genes, how it determines all your traits, and how it passes an organism's instructions from generation to generation. You will see why this chemical has been called the code of life.

DNA Structure

The model shown on page 584 is a computer drawing of a DNA molecule. The letters DNA stand for *d*eoxyribo*n*ucleic (dee AHK sih ri boh noo klay ik) *a*cid. We shall use only the letters DNA each time we talk about this molecule. What is DNA? **DNA** is a molecule that makes up genes and determines the traits of all living things. Humans, birds, mushrooms, plants, protozoans, and bacteria have DNA. All living things contain DNA in their cells.

Scientists often use models to explain things that are very complex. We shall use a model of DNA to explain what DNA looks like and how it does its job.

Figure 28-1a shows a ladder. It is made up of two upright side pieces and many rungs. Figure 28-1b shows a small part of the DNA model. Note that it looks something like the ladder. An actual DNA molecule is much longer

Figure 28-1 DNA is often compared to a ladder (a). A model of DNA is shown (b).

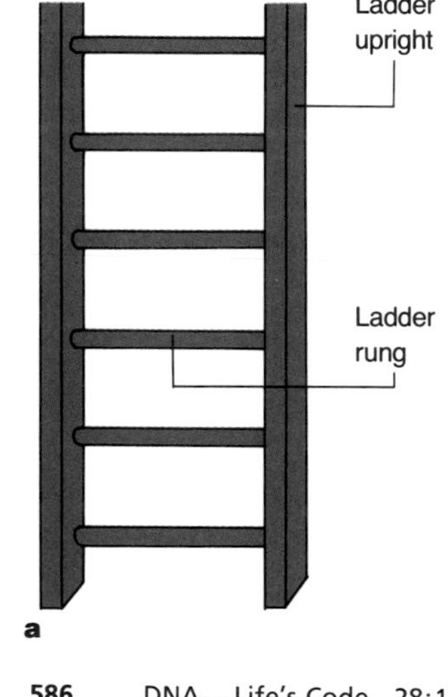

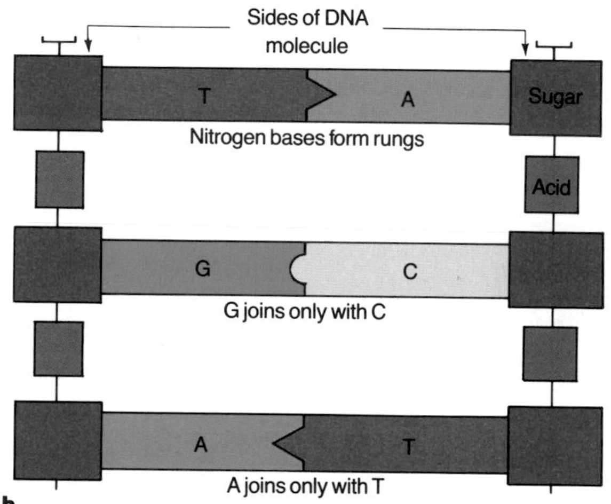

OPTIONS

Science Background

DNA is a molecule present in all life forms. Its function and structure (except for a few organisms such as viruses) always is the same. Thus, one can use this similarity as evidence for common evolutionary ancestry of all life forms.

than the model. Scientists have estimated that a single DNA molecule in a human cell may contain about 100 million rungs.

There are six features of the DNA model.

1. DNA has two main sides. These sides are like the upright parts of a ladder.
2. The sides are made of two different chemicals. One is a sugar. The other is an acid. These two chemicals alternate along each side.
3. There are parts that connect the two sides together. These parts look like the rungs of a ladder.
4. **Nitrogen bases** form the rungs of a DNA molecule.
5. There are four different nitrogen bases in DNA. The letters A, T, C, and G stand for the four bases.
6. The four bases join each other in certain ways to form the rungs. Like pieces of a puzzle, shape A will fit only shape T. Shape C will fit only shape G. As a result, base A joins only with base T. Base C joins only with base G.

You should know one more thing about the shape of DNA. Imagine holding each end of a ladder and twisting it. You would end up with a structure like the one in Figure 28-2. This figure shows that DNA is twisted into a spiral.

What are the parts of a DNA molecule?

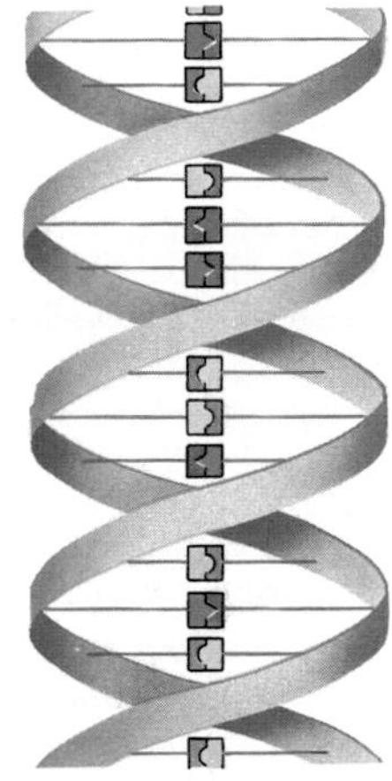

Figure 28-2 DNA is twisted into a spiral.

DNA and Chromosomes

DNA is in every cell in your body. It is also in every cell of all other living things. Where in these cells is it found? You probably know the answer already. DNA makes up parts of the chromosomes found in the nucleus.

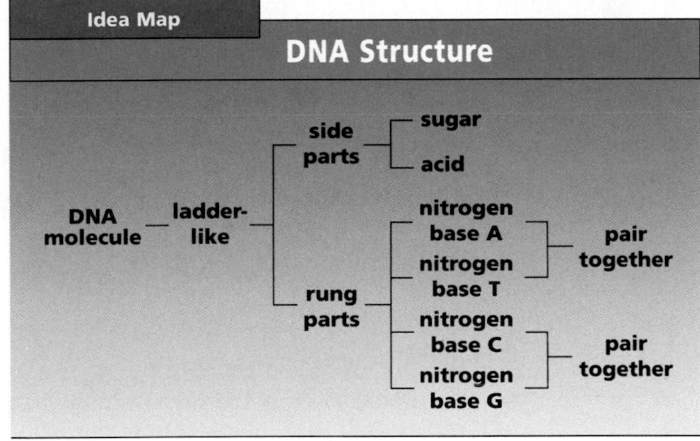

Study Tip: Use this idea map as a study guide to the structure of the DNA molecule. What is the shape of the DNA ladder?

OPTIONS

ACTIVITY/Enrichment

Use puzzle pieces to emphasize complementarity of base pairs A-T and C-G. Place four puzzle pieces on the overhead projector. Two of the pieces should fit each other and the remaining two should also fit each other.

The Relationship Between DNA and the Cell/*Transparency Package*, number 28a. Use color transparency 28a as you teach where DNA is located.

2 TEACH

/Software

DNA – The Basics, Queue, Inc.

Concept Development

▶ Sketch a ladder on the chalkboard and identify the upright sides of the ladder as well as the rungs. This will help students understand the terms *upright* and *rung.*

Guided Practice

Have students write down their answers to the margin question: two sides made of alternating sugar and acid molecules and cross rungs made of nitrogen bases.

Using Science Words

Show students where the initials *DNA* come from within the word *DeoxyriboNucleic Acid.* The *-nucleic* portion of the word is related to the part of the cell in which this chemical is located. *Deoxyribo-* is the stem for *deoxyribose,* the sugar molecule of DNA. *Acid* relates to phosphoric acid, another molecule of DNA.

Brainstorming

Ask students the significance of the fact that all life forms have the same chemical responsible for regulating gene traits. (From an evolutionary point of view, this strongly suggests common origin because of common chemical makeup.)

Idea Map

Have students use the idea map as a study guide to the major concepts of this section.

Lab 28-1 DNA

Overview

Students will construct a model of the DNA molecule that demonstrates its major components and shows how nitrogen bases are joined together in a specific pattern.

Objectives: Upon completion of this lab, students will be able to (1) **state** which nitrogen bases form pairs, (2) **recognize** that the DNA molecule is ladder-like in appearance, (3) **explain** the value of using models.

Time Allotment: 1 class period

Preparation

▶ Use manila folders or file cards for the heavy paper.

▶ Verify that students have four of each letter available.

▶ Suggest to the students that the nitrogen bases fit together like puzzle pieces.

▶ The completed DNA molecule from top to bottom should show this order of nitrogen bases: T-A, A-T, C-G, C-G, G-C, A-T, T-A, C-G.

Lab 28-1 worksheet/*Teacher Resource Package,* pp. 109-110.

Teaching the Lab

▶ **Troubleshooting:** Suggest to students that it is okay to turn nitrogen bases (models) upside down.

DNA

Lab 28–1

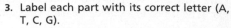

Problem: What does a model of DNA look like?

Skills

formulate a model, interpret diagrams, observe

Materials

tracing paper
scissors
blank sheet of paper
heavy paper
red, blue, green, and yellow crayons
tape

Procedure

1. Trace the four parts shown in Figure A with tracing paper.
2. Cut out the four tracings and copy each part onto heavy paper four times. You should have 16 model parts.
CAUTION: *Always be careful when using scissors.*
3. Label each part with its correct letter (A, T, C, G).
4. Cut out the 16 model parts. Label the other side of each part to match the first side.
5. Color only the parts on your figures that are nitrogen bases. Use this coloring code: A = red, T = blue, C = green, G = yellow. Color both sides of each part.
6. Arrange eight of the figures in any order on a blank sheet of paper. Use Figure B to help you.
7. Tape the eight figures in place.
8. Arrange the remaining eight figures according to how they fit the first eight figures. You can turn the parts in any direction. Tape these figures in place.
9. Compare your model with those of your classmates.

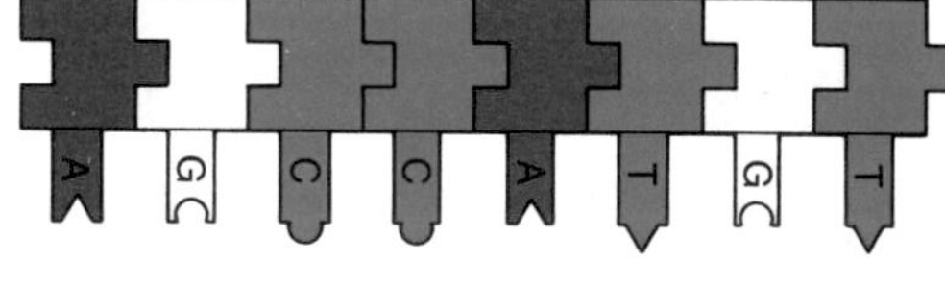

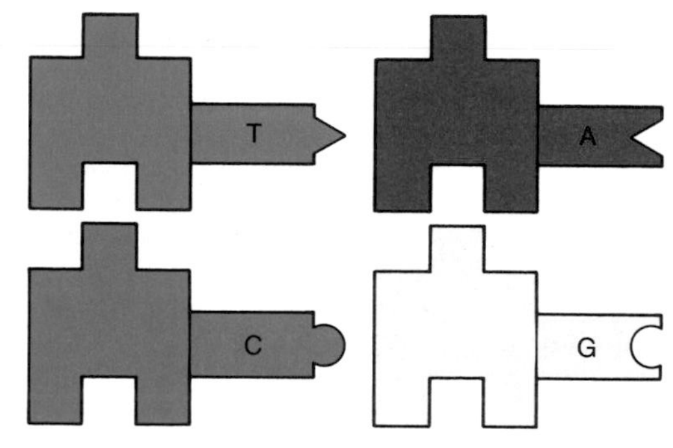

Data and Observations

1. What part, or letter, does the T fit? G? A? C? Explain these fits using your model.
2. In what ways is your model different from those of your classmates? In what ways is it alike?

Analyze and Apply

1. Where would you find this model if it were in a real cell?
2. Name the two chemicals that form the outer (uncolored) parts of your model.
3. **Interpret diagrams:** What chemical name describes the rungs that go across the middle?
4. **Apply:** Why do scientists use models?

Extension

Make a model to show the steps used by DNA as it copies itself. Use the parts from this lab.

ANSWERS

Data and Observations

1. A; C; T; G; In the model the pointed end of all Ts can only fit the matching triangle cut out of all As. The rounded end of all Cs can only fit the matching semicircular cut out of all Gs. They fit like puzzle pieces.
2. The sequence of bases will be different. The basic structure of the model, with the bases forming rungs, will be similar.

Analyze and Apply

1. in the nucleus, as part of chromosomes
2. a sugar and an acid
3. nitrogen bases
4. A model may help to better explain complex things.

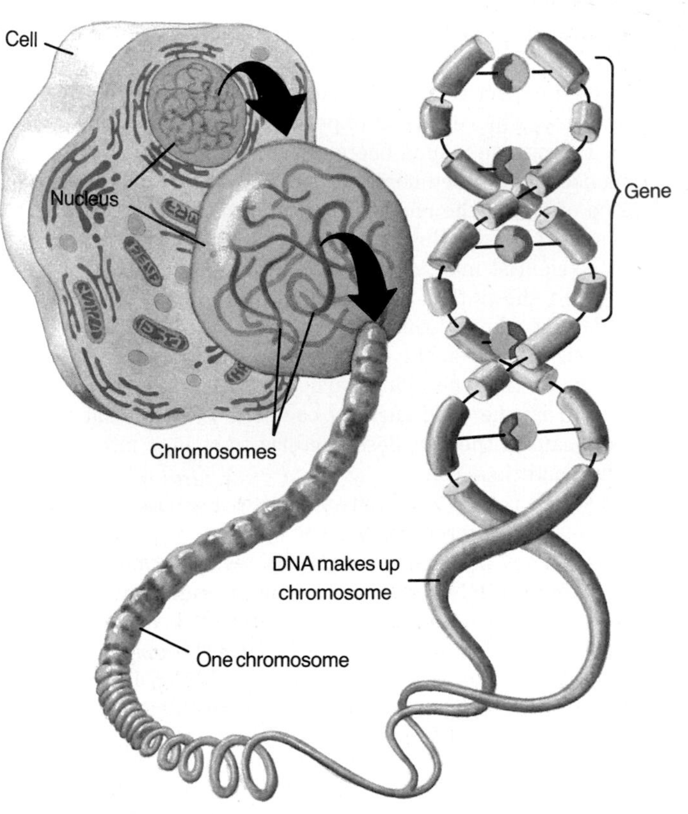

Figure 28-3 How the cell, nucleus, chromosomes, genes, and DNA are related

Look carefully at Figure 28-3. It shows how DNA is related to chromosomes. Keep in mind that this drawing is many times larger than the real thing.

Now think about this question. Where in the cell can we find genes? Genes are parts of chromosomes. We can describe a gene in two ways. First, it is a short piece of DNA. Second, it is a certain number of bases (rungs on the ladder) on the DNA molecule.

In Chapter 26, a gene was defined as a small section of chromosome that determines traits. All three definitions of a gene are correct.

Proof That DNA Controls Traits

How do scientists know that DNA controls our traits? To answer this question, let's look at some experiments done in 1928.

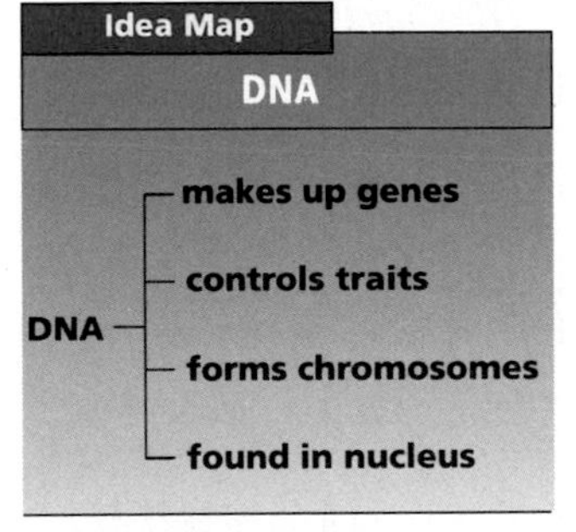

Idea Map
DNA
DNA
makes up genes
controls traits
forms chromosomes
found in nucleus

Study Tip: Use this idea map as a study guide to the DNA molecule. The features of DNA are shown.

TEACH

Concept Development

▶ Each twist of the DNA molecule comprises 10 base pairs.

▶ Have students study Figure 28-3 carefully. Until now, students have learned that the nucleus is the "control center" of the cell. Now they should be able to see that the nucleus controls the cell through its genes and the DNA code making up the chromosomes.

Independent Practice

Study Guide/*Teacher Resource Package*, p. 163. Use the Study Guide worksheet shown at the bottom of this page for independent practice.

Connection: Math

A scientist has calculated the size of one virus chromosome to be 1.6×10^5 nitrogen-base pairs long. It takes about 1000 base pairs to make up one gene. How many genes are present on the virus DNA? (Answer is 160: $1.6 \times 10^5 = 160\ 000$; $160\ 000 \div 1000 = 160$)

Note: you may have to review scientific notation to enable students to convert 1.6×10^5 to standard notation.

Idea Map

Have students use the idea map as a study guide to the major concepts of this section.

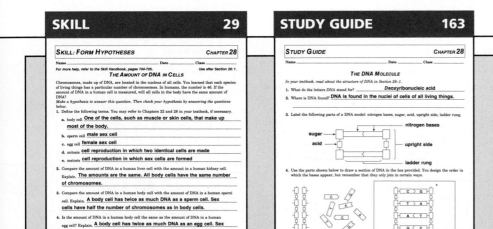

OPTIONS

Science Background

Skill/*Teacher Resource Package*, p. 29. Use the Skill worksheet shown here for students to predict the amount of DNA in cells.

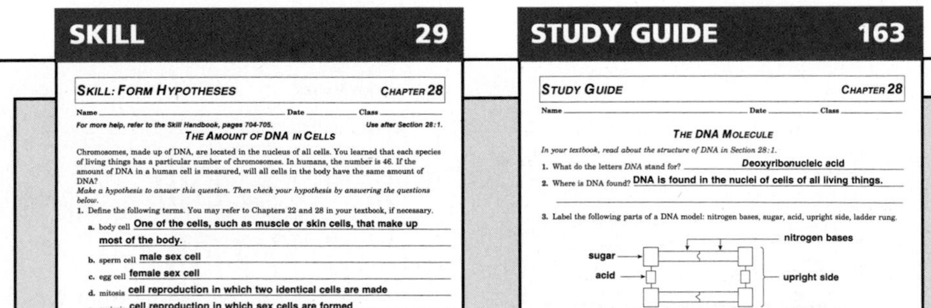

SKILL 29

SKILL: FORM HYPOTHESES — CHAPTER 28

Name ______ Date ______ Class ______

For more help, refer to the Skill Handbook, pages 704-705. *Use after Section 28:1.*

THE AMOUNT OF DNA IN CELLS

Chromosomes, made up of DNA, are located in the nucleus of all cells. You learned that each species of living things has a particular number of chromosomes. In humans, the number is 46. If the amount of DNA in a human cell is measured, will all cells in the body have the same amount of DNA?

Make a hypothesis to answer this question. Then check your hypothesis by answering the questions below.

1. Define the following terms. You may refer to Chapters 22 and 28 in your textbook, if necessary.
   a. body cell **One of the cells, such as muscle or skin cells, that make up most of the body.**
   b. sperm cell **male sex cell**
   c. egg cell **female sex cell**
   d. mitosis **cell reproduction in which two identical cells are made**
   e. meiosis **cell reproduction in which sex cells are formed**
2. Compare the amount of DNA in a human liver cell with the amount in a human kidney cell. Explain. **The amounts are the same. All body cells have the same number of chromosomes.**
3. Compare the amount of DNA in a human body cell with the amount of DNA in a human sperm cell. Explain. **A body cell has twice as much DNA as a sperm cell. Sex cells have half the number of chromosomes as in body cells.**
4. Is the amount of DNA in a human body cell the same as the amount of DNA in a human egg cell? Explain. **A body cell has twice as much DNA as an egg cell. Sex cells have half the number of chromosomes as in body cells.**
5. Is the amount of DNA in a human sperm cell the same as the amount of DNA in a human egg cell? Explain. **Yes, all sex cells have the same number of chromosomes.**
6. A cell is ready to undergo mitosis. Its chromosomes have doubled themselves. Compare the amount of DNA in this cell with a cell that is not undergoing mitosis. Explain. **The cell that is ready to undergo mitosis has double the amount of DNA as a cell not undergoing mitosis.**

STUDY GUIDE 163

STUDY GUIDE — CHAPTER 28

Name ______ Date ______ Class ______

THE DNA MOLECULE

In your textbook, read about the structure of DNA in Section 28:1.

1. What do the letters *DNA* stand for? **Deoxyribonucleic acid**
2. Where is DNA found? **DNA is found in the nuclei of cells of all living things.**
3. Label the following parts of a DNA model: nitrogen bases, sugar, acid, upright side, ladder rung.

   nitrogen bases
   sugar
   acid
   upright side
   ladder rung

4. Use the parts shown below to draw a section of DNA in the box provided. You design the order in which the bases appear, but remember that they only join in certain ways.

   C G A T A C T G

   C G
   T A
   A T
   G C

   ***The order of the bases will vary. However, C and G must join; A and T must join**

In your textbook, read about DNA and chromosomes in Section 28:1.

5. Define a gene in three ways. **A gene is a short piece of DNA. A gene is a certain number of bases on the DNA molecule. A gene is a small section of a chromosome that determines traits.**

TEACH

Concept Development

▶ Make sure students realize that as long as the harmful bacteria are killed, they cannot cause a disease.

▶ Explain that the practice of injecting dead bacteria into humans is quite common. It stimulates the body into producing antibodies against a foreign antigen.

▶ An understanding of experiment D is critical. Results are difficult to explain until the student reads on. The last part of the experiment shows that it is indeed DNA, and not other cellular components, that controls traits.

▶ Not all cells can transform or pick up pieces of other cells. This is a peculiarity of bacteria.

▶ Explain that biologists are able to separate different cell parts and then combine the different cell parts experimentally. This requires the use of the ultracentrifuge.

Independent Practice

Study Guide/*Teacher Resource Package*, p. 164. Use the Study Guide worksheet shown at the bottom of this page for independent practice.

Figure 28-4 shows what happened in these experiments. Look at the first experiment, **a.** These results make sense. You would expect that living harmless bacteria would not kill a mouse. The results in experiments **b** and **c** also make sense. Living pneumonia bacteria would be expected to kill the mouse. Dead pneumonia bacteria would be expected to have no effect on the mouse. Do the results in experiment **d** make sense? They didn't at first. Remember from Chapter 1 that a scientist may have to form a new hypothesis if the experiment shows that the old hypothesis is not supported. The scientist who did this experiment had to form a new hypothesis to explain the results of experiment **d.** He hypothesized that the living harmless bacteria picked up a cell part from the dead harmful bacteria. He said that this cell part caused the harmless bacteria to change into harmful bacteria.

What cell part did the harmless bacteria pick up? This question was answered years later by another group of scientists. They injected a mixture of living harmless bacteria and the DNA from pneumonia bacteria into a mouse. The mouse died. Then they injected living harmless bacteria mixed with other chemicals from the pneumonia bacteria. When the harmless bacteria picked up DNA from the harmful bacteria, they were changed into harmful bacteria. When the harmless bacteria picked up any other

Figure 28-4 How scientists proved that DNA controls traits

	Experiment a	Experiment b	Experiment c	Experiment d
Scientist injects mouse with	Living, harmless bacteria	Living pneumonia bacteria	Dead pneumonia bacteria	Mixture of living, harmless bacteria and dead pneumonia bacteria
Results	 Mouse lives	 Mouse dies	 Mouse lives	 Mouse dies
Meaning	Harmless bacteria cannot kill a mouse	Harmful bacteria can kill a mouse	Dead, harmful bacteria cannot kill a mouse	? This combination should not kill a mouse

OPTIONS

Science Background

In 1928, Fred Griffith conducted experiments in bacterial transformation. During transformation, the harmless form changed into the harmful form. In 1944, Avery, McCarty, and MacLeod showed that the chemical that changed the bacteria was DNA.

Transparency Master/*Teacher Resource Package*, p. 141. Use the Transparency Master shown here to show how DNA controls traits.

STUDY GUIDE 164

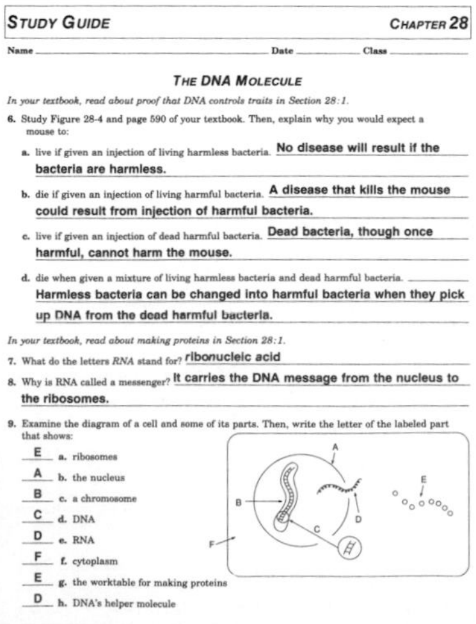

STUDY GUIDE — CHAPTER 28

Name ______ Date ______ Class ______

THE DNA MOLECULE

In your textbook, read about proof that DNA controls traits in Section 28:1.

6. Study Figure 28-4 and page 590 of your textbook. Then, explain why you would expect a mouse to:
   a. live if given an injection of living harmless bacteria. No disease will result if the bacteria are harmless.
   b. die if given an injection of living harmful bacteria. A disease that kills the mouse could result from injection of harmful bacteria.
   c. live if given an injection of dead harmful bacteria. Dead bacteria, though once harmful, cannot harm the mouse.
   d. die when given a mixture of living harmless bacteria and dead harmful bacteria. Harmless bacteria can be changed into harmful bacteria when they pick up DNA from the dead harmful bacteria.

In your textbook, read about making proteins in Section 28:1.

7. What do the letters *RNA* stand for? ribonucleic acid
8. Why is RNA called a messenger? It carries the DNA message from the nucleus to the ribosomes.
9. Examine the diagram of a cell and some of its parts. Then, write the letter of the labeled part that shows:
   E a. ribosomes
   A b. the nucleus
   B c. a chromosome
   C d. DNA
   D e. RNA
   F f. cytoplasm
   E g. the worktable for making proteins
   D h. DNA's helper molecule

TRANSPARENCY 141

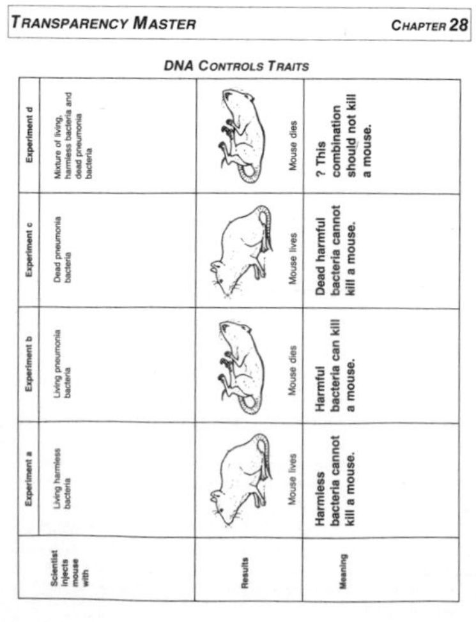

TRANSPARENCY MASTER — CHAPTER 28

DNA CONTROLS TRAITS

a. Person with normal blood cells	G	A	G	T	G	A	G	G	C	T	T	C
	|	|	|	|	|	|	|	|	|	|	|	|
	C	T	C	A	C	T	C	C	G	A	A	G

b. Person with sickle cells	G	A	G	T	G	A	G	G	C	T	A	C
	|	|	|	|	|	|	|	|	|	|	|	|
	C	T	C	A	C	T	C	C	G	A	T	G

Figure 28-5 A change in just one pair of DNA bases can change a living thing's traits.

chemical from the harmful bacteria, they did not change. The scientists concluded that only DNA caused the bacteria to change. DNA is the chemical that controls traits.

How DNA Works

How does DNA direct a plant to make chlorophyll? How does DNA direct the formation of sickle-shaped or round red blood cells? How does DNA direct all traits in all living things? Let's compare DNA and how it works to a computer. A computer reads electrical messages stored within its memory bank. These messages are stored in code form. DNA also has a code. The nitrogen bases in the DNA molecule spell out a message that is stored in code form.

What determines the coded message in DNA?

The order of the nitrogen bases, A, T, C, and G, is the coded message. Figure 28-5a shows the order of bases somewhere on a section of DNA. Let's suppose this order directs the formation of round red blood cells. Now, let's suppose we look at the same place on the DNA of another person. We see the message in Figure 28-5b. This order of bases directs the formation of sickle cells.

In this example, the orders of the bases in DNA are slightly different. This difference causes the traits to be very different. One person has normal round red blood cells. The other has sickle cells.

New orders of nitrogen bases can make new messages. Each message gives the cell instructions for a different trait. Think about our alphabet for a moment. The letters of the alphabet are always the same. We put the letters into different orders to form different words. The letters w, o, and l form the word *owl*. They also can form the word *low*. Each order codes for a different meaning. How many different letters are in the DNA alphabet?

Mini Lab

How Are Bases Paired?

Formulate a model: Mark each of 20 students with A, T, C, or G. Form a row of 10 students to show one side of DNA. Call up a student to pair with your letter. What pairs are possible? *For more help, refer to the **Skill Handbook**, pages 706-711.*

TEACH

Concept Development

▶ Explain that reading the dots and dashes of Morse code allows one to form words and sentences. The DNA code is similar. The order of nitrogen bases, rather than the sequence of dots and dashes, forms the code of our cells.

▶ Point out that *code of life* refers to the order of nitrogen bases in DNA.

Guided Practice

Have students write down their answers to the margin question: the order of the nitrogen bases.

Mini Lab

The only combinations between bases will be A + T, and C + G.

ENRICHMENT 30

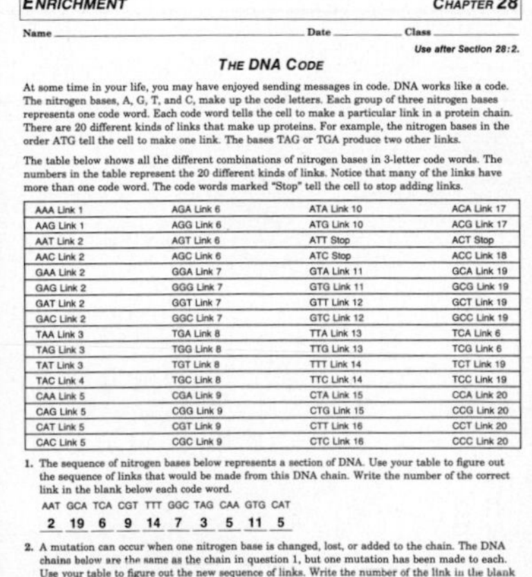

ENRICHMENT CHAPTER 28

Name ______ Date ______ Class ______

Use after Section 28:2.

THE DNA CODE

At some time in your life, you may have enjoyed sending messages in code. DNA works like a code. The nitrogen bases, A, G, T, and C, make up the code letters. Each group of three nitrogen bases represents one code word. Each code word tells the cell to make a particular link in a protein chain. There are 20 different kinds of links that make up proteins. For example, the nitrogen bases in the order ATG tell the cell to make one link. The bases TAG or TGA produce two other links.

The table below shows all the different combinations of nitrogen bases in 3-letter code words. The numbers in the table represent the 20 different kinds of links. Notice that many of the links have more than one code word. The code words marked "Stop" tell the cell to stop adding links.

AAA Link 1	AGA Link 6	ATA Link 10	ACA Link 17
AAG Link 1	AGG Link 6	ATG Link 10	ACG Link 17
AAT Link 2	AGT Link 6	ATT Stop	ACT Stop
AAC Link 2	AGC Link 6	ATC Stop	ACC Link 18
GAA Link 2	GGA Link 7	GTA Link 11	GCA Link 19
GAG Link 2	GGG Link 7	GTG Link 11	GCG Link 19
GAT Link 2	GGT Link 7	GTT Link 12	GCT Link 19
GAC Link 2	GGC Link 7	GTC Link 12	GCC Link 19
TAA Link 3	TGA Link 8	TTA Link 13	TCA Link 6
TAG Link 3	TGG Link 8	TTG Link 13	TCG Link 6
TAT Link 3	TGT Link 8	TTT Link 14	TCT Link 19
TAC Link 4	TGC Link 8	TTC Link 14	TCC Link 19
CAA Link 5	CGA Link 9	CTA Link 15	CCA Link 20
CAG Link 5	CGG Link 9	CTG Link 15	CCG Link 20
CAT Link 5	CGT Link 9	CTT Link 16	CCT Link 20
CAC Link 5	CGC Link 9	CTC Link 16	CCC Link 20

1. The sequence of nitrogen bases below represents a section of DNA. Use your table to figure out the sequence of links that would be made from this DNA chain. Write the number of the correct link in the blank below each code word.

AAT GCA TCA CGT TTT GGC TAG CAA GTG CAT
2 19 6 9 14 7 3 5 11 5

2. A mutation can occur when one nitrogen base is changed, lost, or added to the chain. The DNA chains below are the same as the chain in question 1, but one mutation has been made to each. Use your table to figure out the new sequence of links. Write the number of the link in the blank below each code word. Notice how the message changes.

nitrogen base T changed to A here
AAT GCA TCA CGT TTA GGC TAG CAA GTG CAT
2 19 6 9 13 7 3 5 11 5

nitrogen base G lost here
AAT CAT CAC GTT TTG GCT AGC AAG TGC AT
2 5 5 12 13 19 6 1 8

OPTIONS

ACTIVITY/Challenge

Have students list examples in which the changing of a three-letter sequence can alter the meaning of a word. Suggestions might be pin, nip; pat, tap, apt; or eat, ate, tea.

Enrichment/*Teacher Resource Package*, p. 30. Use the Enrichment worksheet shown here to help students understand the DNA code.

TEACH

Concept Development

▶ Use the example of hair color to explain that the kind of protein you make shows up as your traits. Explain that black hair color is due to a slightly different protein than is blond hair color.

▶ Figure 28-7 is critical to understanding the role of RNA in the process of protein formation and translation of the code located in DNA.

Cooperative Learning: Divide the class into five or six groups. Have each group compare and contrast DNA and RNA using Figure 28-7 as a guide plus any other diagrams or explanations within the chapter.

Guided Practice

Have students write down their answers to the margin question: It carries the DNA message from the DNA in the nucleus to the ribosomes in the cytoplasm.

Understand Science Words: The term *mRNA* is not used. If you feel it is important, explain that the letter *m* represents the word *messenger,* thus the term *messenger RNA.*

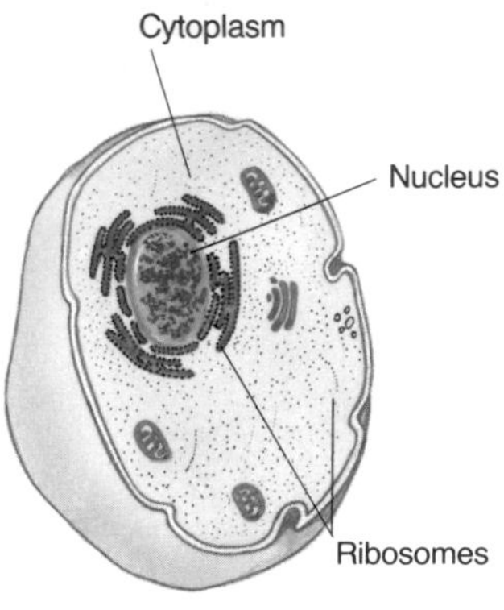

Figure 28-6 Ribosomes have a part in making proteins. Where are the ribosomes located? in the cytoplasm

What does RNA do in the making of proteins?

Making Proteins

DNA directs the making of proteins in cells. How do cells make proteins? Remember from Chapter 2 that ribosomes are the cell parts where proteins are made. Look at Figure 28-6. Notice that the ribosomes are in the cytoplasm, not in the nucleus.

How can DNA in the nucleus control what goes on at the ribosomes? It has a helper molecule called RNA. These letters are the initials for *r*ibo*n*ucleic (ri boh noo KLAY ik) *a*cid. **RNA** is a chemical that acts as a messenger for DNA. RNA carries the coded DNA message from the nucleus to the ribosomes. The ribosome acts as a worktable for making proteins. When RNA arrives at the ribosomes, it carries a message that must be decoded before it can direct the formation of a protein. Think of the coded DNA message as being written in a certain language. This is the language of the nitrogen bases A, T, C, and G. A protein is written in another language. Somehow, the DNA language must be translated into the protein language. The **genetic code** is the code that translates the DNA language into the protein language. Once the message has been translated, the protein can be made. Figure 28-7 shows how proteins are made. Traits show up in a cell because of the kinds of proteins being made at the ribosomes. Thus, the genes on the chromosomes have sent their messages to the ribosomes to make certain traits appear.

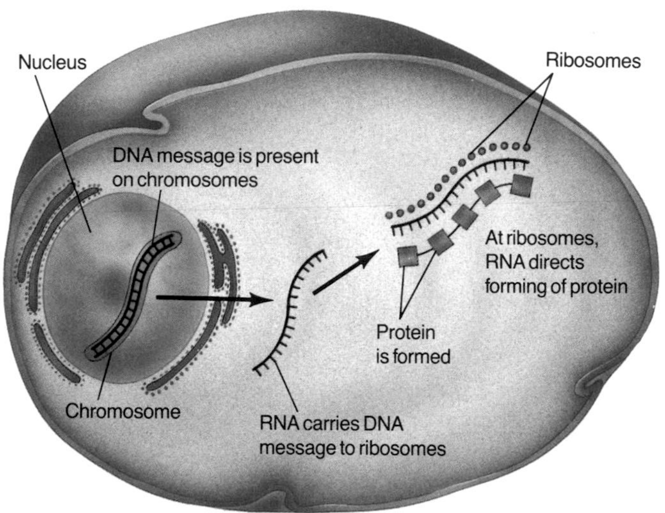

Figure 28-7 Steps needed in the cell to change the DNA message into a protein. Where are proteins made? in the ribosomes

OPTIONS

Science Background

The normal flow of information within a cell is: DNA → mRNA → tRNA → Protein. Certain viruses (the AIDS virus in particular) reverse the flow of information so that it is: RNA → DNA.

TECHNOLOGY

DNA Fingerprinting

In violent crimes such as rape or murder, physical evidence is often left at the scene. Blood, hair, or sperm cells may be the only evidence that the police have. A person can be arrested and found guilty long after a crime is committed. How do police know that this person is the rapist or murderer? They are able to identify the sperm or blood as his.

Every person has a special set of "fingerprints" from the moment he or she is born. These fingerprints are not on the fingertips. They are in each cell in the body. These fingerprints are the order of the bases in a person's DNA.

Today, it is possible to picture a person's DNA by using special laboratory tests. Any cell in the body can be used. In the case of a rapist, police are able to match the DNA of the sperm cells collected at the scene of the crime with the DNA of the arrested man's blood cells. Thus, police have proof that the sperm came from the man arrested. It is impossible for the sperm to have come from any other person because the order of the bases in DNA is different for each person. DNA fingerprinting will be used more and more in the future to solve crimes.

Mobile crime lab

How does the order of nitrogen bases in DNA fit into this story? The order of bases is the coded message that controls what kinds of proteins are made. The kinds of proteins you have determine what traits you have. Thus, all your traits and the traits of all living things result from the order of nitrogen bases in DNA.

How DNA Copies Itself

You have seen that DNA has many jobs. It carries the genetic messages for all living things. It controls the making of proteins. Remember that in cell reproduction, chromosomes make copies of themselves just before mitosis and meiosis. You know that chromosomes are made mostly of DNA. Now you know that DNA is what is copied. How does DNA copy itself? What is the story behind cell reproduction?

TECHNOLOGY

DNA Fingerprinting

Background

Scientists form a profile of chemicals by chopping DNA into short segments that form specific patterns for each person. These segments are then subjected to electrophoresis and can be "sorted out" and categorized according to their molecular weights. The odds of two people (not including identical twins) having the same DNA fingerprints are calculated at 30 billion to 1.

Discussion

Typically, sperm cells in a rape case are analyzed for DNA fingerprinting. Sperm cells contain only half the DNA of body cells, but they can still be used to identify a criminal. Sperm DNA will match with half the DNA in a body cell.

References

Lewis, Ricki. "DNA Fingerprints: Witness for the Prosecution." *Discover,* June 1988, pp. 44-52.

Moody, Mark D. "DNA Analysis in Forensic Science." *BioScience,* Jan. 1989, pp. 31-35.

TEACH

Concept Development

▶ Explain that each new molecule of DNA contains exactly one-half of the original DNA.

Check for Understanding

Have students build a model of DNA from common edible items. Have them use gum drops for bases, and miniature marshmallows for the sides. Use toothpicks to hold parts together.

Reteach

Have students tape their DNA molecule models to paper and label the parts.

OPTIONS

Science Background

Nitrogen bases are joined by hydrogen bonds. Hydrogen bonds are weak bonds in that they are easily broken. This property facilitates the unzipping of the DNA molecule for replication and protein synthesis.

How DNA Copies Itself/ *Transparency Package,* number 28b. Use color transparency number 28b as you teach the steps of DNA replication.

How Does DNA Make Protein?/*Lab Manual,* pp. 235-238. Use this lab as an extension to how DNA controls the making of protein.

TEACH

Independent Practice

Study Guide/*Teacher Resource Package*, p. 165. Use the study guide worksheet shown at the bottom of this page for independent practice.

Check for Understanding

Have students respond to the first three questions in Check Your Understanding.

Reteach

Reteaching/*Teacher Resource Package*, p. 83. Use this worksheet to give students additional practice with DNA structure and how DNA copies itself.

Extension: Assign Critical Thinking, Biology and Reading, or some of the **OPTIONS** available with this lesson.

3 APPLY

Brainstorming

Give students this scenario: You are a scientist in the late 1930s. Explain how you will prove that DNA controls our traits.

4 CLOSE

Convergent Question

Tell students that they are made up of half their father's and half their mother's DNA. Ask why brothers and sisters don't look exactly like them.

Answers to Check Your Understanding

1. It makes up the genes of all living things.
2. The order of bases controls the making of proteins in cells. The kind of protein made shows up as a trait.
3. RNA acts as a messenger and carries the DNA message from the nucleus to the ribosomes. Ribosomes act as worktables for making proteins.
4. the order of the nitrogen bases
5. T-T-C-G-A-G-G-A-C-G

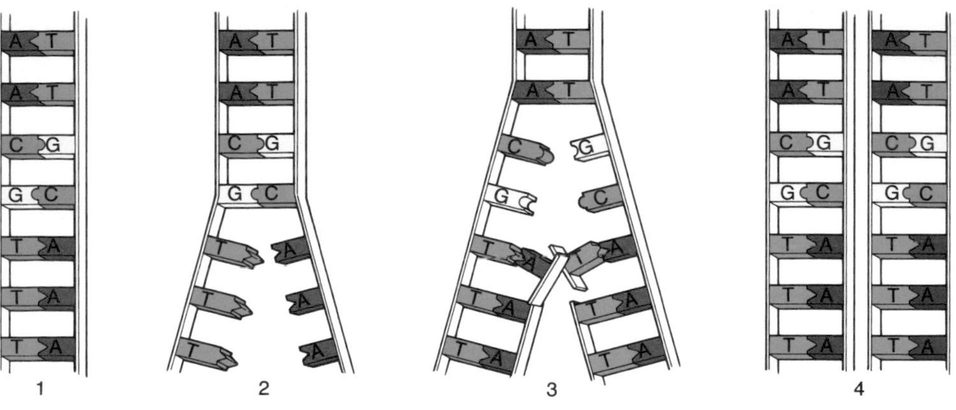

Figure 28-8 Steps used by DNA as it copies itself

Think about the ladder model of DNA again. Follow the steps in Figure 28-8 as you read how DNA copies itself.
1. DNA is ready to make a copy of itself.
2. The molecule begins to open up along its middle.
3. Loose nitrogen bases with the sugar and acid attached are present in the cell nucleus. These bases are not part of the DNA yet. They join the bases that are on the opened rungs. Look carefully and you will see that A joins only with T. C joins only with G. The loose nitrogen bases continue to join the bases on the DNA molecule.
4. Finally, two DNA molecules have formed.

Look closely at the two newly formed DNA molecules in step 4 of Figure 28-8. They are exactly alike. The order of nitrogen bases is also exactly the same as in the original molecule in step 1 of the figure. The genes on the two chromosomes are exactly the same. When a cell reproduces, the new cells that form have the same genetic message.

Check Your Understanding

1. Why is DNA important to all living things?
2. How does the order of nitrogen bases in DNA control traits?
3. How do RNA and ribosomes help DNA make proteins?
4. **Critical Thinking:** What features of the DNA structure are important if the genetic message is to be copied exactly?
5. **Biology and Reading:** Suppose one side of a piece of DNA has the bases A-A-G-C-T-C-C-T-G-C. What bases would the other side of the DNA molecule have?

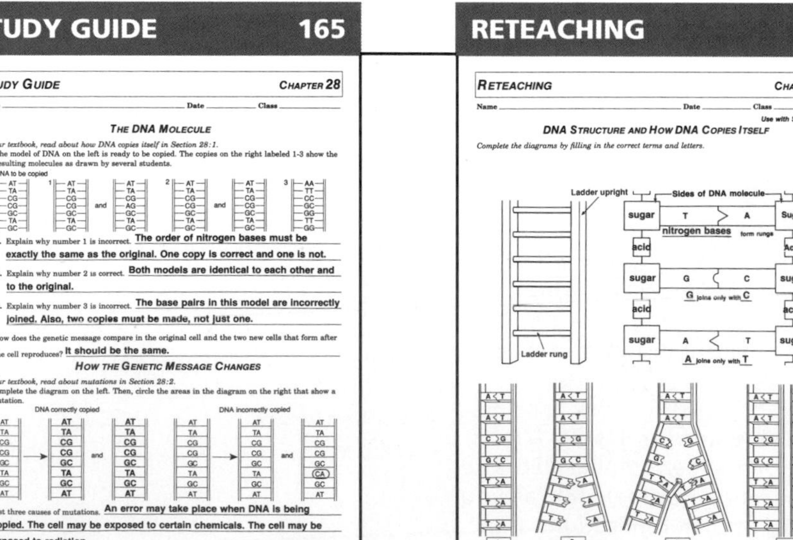

STUDY GUIDE 165

STUDY GUIDE — CHAPTER 28

Name ______ Date ______ Class ______

THE DNA MOLECULE

In your textbook, read about how DNA copies itself in Section 28:1.

10. The model of DNA on the left is ready to be copied. The copies on the right labeled 1-3 show the resulting molecules as drawn by several students.

DNA to be copied: AT TA CG CG GC TA GC
1: AT TA CG CG GC TA GC and AT TA CG AG GC TA GC
2: AT TA CG CG GC TA GC and AT TA CG CG GC TA GC
3: AA TT CC GC GG TT GG

a. Explain why number 1 is incorrect. **The order of nitrogen bases must be exactly the same as the original. One copy is correct and one is not.**

b. Explain why number 2 is correct. **Both models are identical to each other and to the original.**

c. Explain why number 3 is incorrect. **The base pairs in this model are incorrectly joined. Also, two copies must be made, not just one.**

11. How does the genetic message compare in the original cell and the two new cells that form after the cell reproduces? **It should be the same.**

HOW THE GENETIC MESSAGE CHANGES

In your textbook, read about mutations in Section 28:2.

1. Complete the diagram on the left. Then, circle the areas in the diagram on the right that show a mutation.

DNA correctly copied: AT TA CG CG GC TA GC AT → AT TA CG CG GC TA GC AT and AT TA CG CG GC TA GC AT

DNA incorrectly copied: AT TA CG CG GC TA GC AT → AT TA CG CG GC TA GC AT and AT TA CG CG GC (CA) GC AT

2. List three causes of mutations. **An error may take place when DNA is being copied. The cell may be exposed to certain chemicals. The cell may be exposed to radiation.**

RETEACHING 83

RETEACHING — CHAPTER 28

Name ______ Date ______ Class ______

Use with Section 28:1.

DNA STRUCTURE AND HOW DNA COPIES ITSELF

Complete the diagrams by filling in the correct terms and letters.

28:2 How the Genetic Message Changes

In Section 28:1 you read that newly formed cells have the same genetic message as the cell from which they came. Sometimes they do not. What happens when the message changes? Can scientists change the message of living things?

Objectives

4. **Describe** how mutations occur.
5. **Describe** how cloning and breeding produce offspring with desired traits.
6. **Explain** how recombinant DNA can help humans.

Key Science Words

mutation
radiation
identical twins
fraternal twins
breeding
recombinant DNA

Mutations

Sometimes errors happen when chromosomes are copied. The bases A, T, C, and G may join incorrectly. Joining incorrectly results in a change called a mutation (myew TAY shun). A **mutation** is any change in copying the DNA message.

What happens if you hit the wrong key on a computer keyboard? Doesn't the computer get the wrong message? Cells are like the computer. A wrong base in the DNA gives the cell the wrong message. The result is that the wrong type of protein is made. This change may cause a different trait to appear.

Hemophilia is a serious blood disease that can start from a mutation. Look at the pedigree in Figure 28-9. You

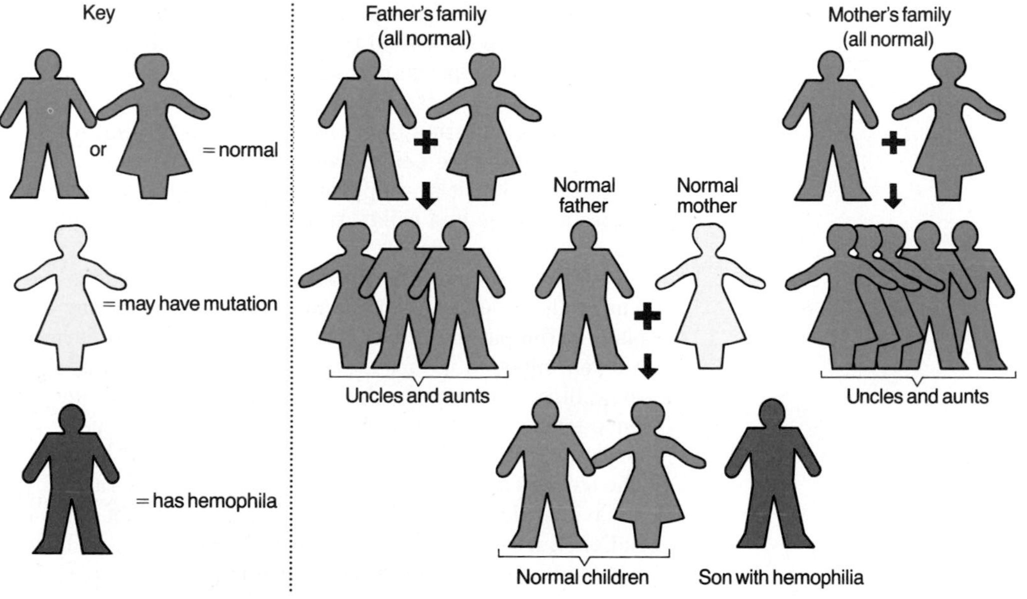

Figure 28-9 A family pedigree showing where a mutation for hemophilia may have occurred

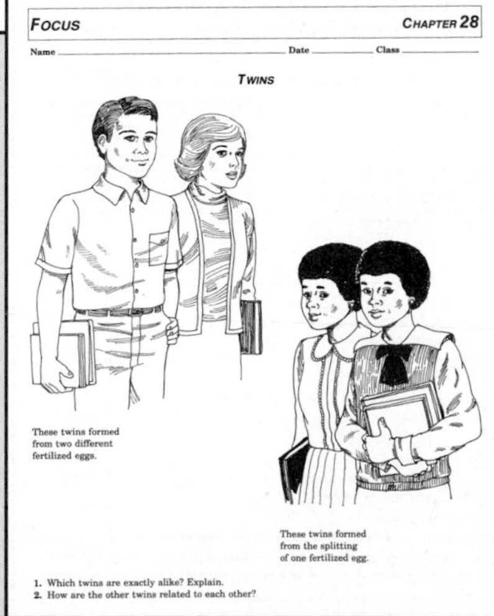
FOCUS 55

FOCUS — *CHAPTER* 28

Name ______ Date ______ Class ______

TWINS

These twins formed from two different fertilized eggs.

These twins formed from the splitting of one fertilized egg.

1. Which twins are exactly alike? Explain.
2. How are the other twins related to each other?

OPTIONS

Science Background

A point mutation is a mutation in which only one base pair is altered. It is also possible for a base pair to be added or deleted. Such a mutation causes a shift in the base sequence and is called a frameshift mutation. Somatic mutations take place in body cells during development. These mutations are not heritable and usually are not noticeable.

28:2 How the Genetic Message Changes

PREPARATION

Materials Needed

Make copies of the Focus, Critical Thinking/Problem Solving, Study Guide, Application, Reteaching, and Lab worksheets in the *Teacher Resource Package*.

▶ Gather *Coleus* plants, plastic cups, soil, and aluminum foil for Lab 28-2.

▶ Have materials like those in Lab 28-1 on hand for the Mini Lab.

Key Science Words

mutation	fraternal twins
radiation	breeding
identical twins	recombinant DNA

Process Skills

In the Mini Lab, students will formulate a model. In Lab 28-2, students will observe, infer, and interpret data. In the Skill Check, students will understand science words.

1 FOCUS

▶ The objectives are listed on the student page. Remind students to preview these objectives as a guide to this numbered section.

Bridging

The problem of skin cancer and radiation was touched upon in Chapter 22. Refer to that chapter and discuss how the development of skin cancer and changes in DNA caused by exposure to the sun might be related.

Focus/*Teacher Resource Package*, p. 55. Use the Focus transparency shown at the bottom of this page as an introduction to cloning.

2 TEACH

MOTIVATION/Brainstorming

Ask students to name mutation-causing agents. (List may include radiation from sunlight, X rays, atomic bomb explosions, certain drugs, industrial pollutants, insecticides, and even food additives.)

Concept Development

▶ Tell students that not all mutations are harmful. Some are helpful. The vast majority are probably neither helpful nor harmful and go unnoticed by life-forms.

▶ Alert students to the role that mutations play in evolution. Mutations that provide an organism with some slight advantage will increase that living thing's chances of survival.

Mini Lab

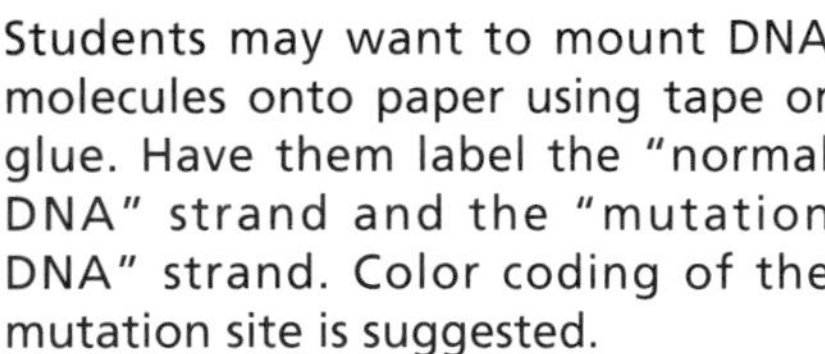

Students may want to mount DNA molecules onto paper using tape or glue. Have them label the "normal DNA" strand and the "mutation DNA" strand. Color coding of the mutation site is suggested.

Guided Practice

Have students write down their answers to the margin question: a change in the genetic message.

Figure 28-10 Sunscreens help protect the skin from the sun's radiation.

Mini Lab

How Does a Mutation Occur?

Formulate a model: Use parts like those in Lab 28-1 to build DNA as follows: AACGTA. Build a second model but show a mutation. Label the mutation. What can cause it? *For more help, refer to the **Skill Handbook**, pages 706-711.*

can see when the disease first appeared in this family. We expect traits to be passed from parents to children. In this family, the grandparents, uncles and aunts, and parents do not show the trait. It suddenly appears in the son. We can guess that a mutation took place when the sex cells of one of the parents were being made. It may have happened in the parents, but it first appears in their child. A mutation causes a change in a child's trait only when it takes place in the parent's sex cells.

What causes mutations?

What causes mutations to occur? Many mutations are simply the results of copying mistakes. An error may take place in the pairing of bases when DNA is copied during cell reproduction. Other mutations may be caused by something from outside the cell. Certain chemicals and some forms of radiation (rayd ee AY shun) can cause mutations. **Radiation** is energy that is given off by atoms. The sun releases a large amount of radiation. X rays, ultraviolet light, and visible light are examples of kinds of radiation from the sun. Very powerful radiation, such as X rays and ultraviolet light, can cause mutations.

OPTIONS

Critical Thinking/Problem Solving/ *Teacher Resource Package*, p. 28. Use the Critical Thinking/Problem Solving worksheet shown here to help students understand changes in the genetic code.

How Can a Mutation in DNA Affect an Organism?/*Lab Manual*, pp. 239-242. Use this lab as an extension to changes in the genetic message.

CRITICAL THINKING 28

CRITICAL THINKING/PROBLEM SOLVING CHAPTER 28

Name ____________ Date ________ Class ________

Use after Section 28:2.

HOW CAN YOU FIND CHANGES IN THE GENETIC CODE?

The students in biology looked at the model of DNA. They saw the two upright sides of sugar and acid wound around each other into a spiral. They saw the bases attached to the sides. The names of the most common bases in DNA are adenine (whose symbol is A), thymine (whose symbol is T), guanine (G), and cytosine (C). They saw how the bases pair to make a smooth spiral with no bulges.

The students learned that DNA copies itself when each base pairs with its opposite type. A always pairs with T, and G always pairs with C. In that way, two molecules of DNA are formed that are usually identical. A mistake in copying can cause a mutation.

The students did an exercise to test whether they could spot possible mutations. The teacher explained that a strand of DNA is one side of a DNA molecule. It has one upright side and unpaired bases. The teacher put these sequences of bases on the blackboard:

Strand A. A T T C A T G C A T
Strand B. T A A G T A C G T A
Strand C. A T A C A T G G A T
Strand D. A T T C A T G C A T
Strand E. T A A G T A C G T A
Strand F. T A G T A C G T A C
Strand G. T A A A G T A C G T

Then the teacher asked a series of questions. Answer the questions below that the teacher asked.

Analyzing the Problem

1. When strand A copies itself to make another DNA strand, will the order of the bases be like strand B, C, or D? strand B
2. When strand A was part of a molecule containing two strands, what was the sequence of bases in its opposite strand? Write the symbols here: T A A G T A C G T A like strand B.
3. How many copying errors, or mutations, are present in strand C, assuming it was copied from strand B? Write the number and the symbols for each error here: two—A T A instead of A T T and G G A instead of G C A

Solving the Problem

1. Sometimes errors occur by the loss (or deletion) or the addition of a base. Suppose that Strands E, F, and G are copied from strand D. Which strand shows a deletion error? Explain. Strand F; the third base, which should be A to pair with the T in strand D, is missing.
2. Which strand, E, F, or G, shows an addition mutation? strand G

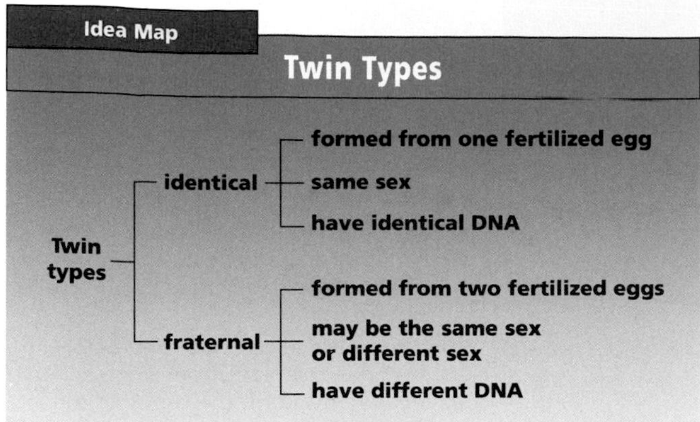

Study Tip: Use this idea map as a study guide to twin types. The features of identical and fraternal twins are shown.

Cloning

Do you have an identical twin? If you do, you have a clone. That's because **identical twins** are two children that form from the splitting of one fertilized egg. They have exactly the same genes. You know that two clones have the same genes. They are exact copies of each other. Since identical twins have the same genes, they must have the same DNA. See if you can tell which diagram in Figure 28-11 will result in identical twins. One of the diagrams shows how fraternal twins are formed. **Fraternal twins** are twins that form from two different fertilized eggs. They are not clones. Fraternal twins are no more alike than two other children in the same family would be. They don't even have to be the same sex.

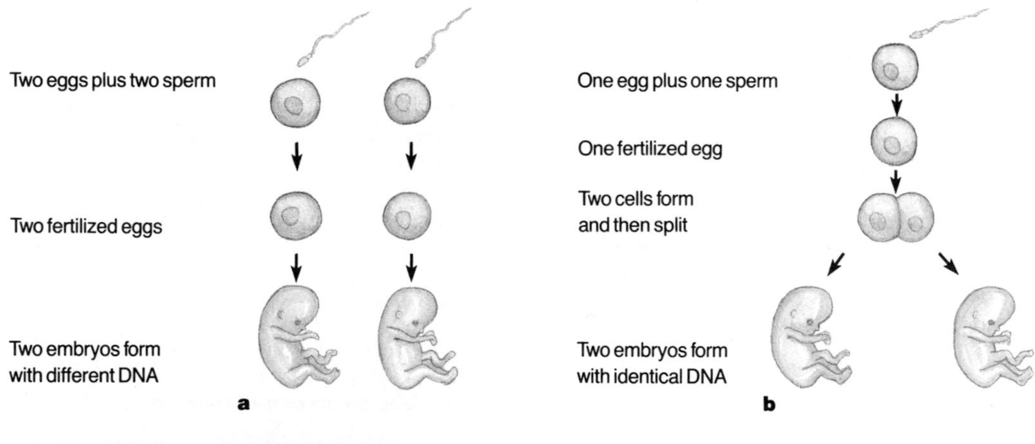

Figure 28-11 Differences between identical and fraternal twins. Which diagram shows identical twins? b

TEACH

Concept Development

▶ Identical twins will always be the same sex. Fraternal twins may or may not be the same sex.

▶ Students may want to know that twins occur about once in every 85 pregnancies. Two-thirds of these are fraternal. Triplets occur once in every 8000 pregnancies.

Idea Map

Have students use the idea map as a study guide to the major concepts of this section.

Independent Practice

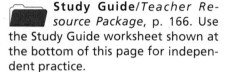

Study Guide/*Teacher Resource Package*, p. 166. Use the Study Guide worksheet shown at the bottom of this page for independent practice.

STUDY GUIDE 166

STUDY GUIDE **CHAPTER 28**

Name ______ Date ______ Class ______

HOW THE GENETIC MESSAGE CHANGES

In your textbook, read about cloning in Section 28:2.

3. A mother has four children. Children A and B were born at the end of her first pregnancy. Children C and D were born at the end of her second pregnancy. Which of her children:

Sperm, Egg, Fertilized egg — A (male), B (female), C (male) D (male)

a. are identical twins? C and D
b. were formed from two different eggs and sperm? A and B
c. are clones? C and D
d. have identical DNA? C and D
e. are fraternal twins? A and B
f. have different genes? A and B
g. were formed from one egg and one sperm? C and D

4. Use Figure 28-12 on page 599 of your textbook to answer the following questions.
a. In the cloning process shown, what cell part does the dark frog contribute? its nucleus
b. What does the light frog contribute? egg cell
c. Which frog is contributing its DNA? dark frog Explain your answer. Its DNA is in the nucleus.
d. Why does the cloned frog resemble the dark parent instead of the light parent? The DNA from the dark frog is responsible for all traits in the newly cloned frog.

Lab 28-2 Cloning

Overview

In this lab, students are introduced to the concept of cloning. *Coleus* will be used as the experimental organism.

Objectives: Upon completion of this lab, students will be able to (1) **demonstrate** the technique of plant cloning, (2) **explain** why the process of cloning yields so many offspring.

Time Allotment: first day – 20 minutes; days 2-8 – 10 minutes each

Preparation

▶ **Alternate Materials:** Plants such as *Geranium* or *Zebrina* may be used in place of *Coleus.* Polystyrene cups may be used instead of plastic cups.

▶ One *Coleus* plant could yield 5 to 8 cuttings.

 **Lab 28-2 worksheet**/*Teacher Resource Package*, pp. 111-112.

Teaching the Lab

▶ The term *asexual reproduction* or *asexual propagation* could be used to describe the process being used here. The correct term is *cloning.*

▶ Steps 11-12 are optional.

Cloning

Lab 28–2

Problem: Can a *Coleus* plant be cloned?

Skills

observe, infer, interpret data

Materials 

clear plastic cup	soil
aluminum foil	water
scissors	label
Coleus plant	metric ruler

Procedure

1. Copy the data table.
2. Label a clear plastic cup with your name. Fill it with water.
3. Cover the top of the cup with foil.
4. Use scissors to punch a small hole in the center of the foil. **CAUTION:** *Always be careful when using scissors.*
5. Use scissors to cut off a small branch from a *Coleus* plant. The figure shows where to make the cut.
6. Insert the cut end of the branch through the hole in the foil. The bottom of the branch must dip into the water.
7. In your table, write today's date. Draw what the end of the cut branch looks like.
8. Record the number of students who cut a branch from the same plant.
9. **Observe:** Check the branch each day for the next few days. Look for roots that appear at the cut end.
10. When you see roots beginning to appear on your branch, record the date in your table and draw the cut end. Continue to check your branch and draw its appearance.
11. When roots are about two centimeters long, remove the plant from the cup. Pour out the water and fill the cup with soil.
12. Place your plant into the soil, being careful not to break its new roots. Moisten the soil with water.

Data and Observations

1. How many branches were cut from your original plant?
2. How many days did it take for roots to appear on your branch?

NUMBER OF STUDENTS USING SAME PLANT _____

Date 4/16	Date 4/17	Date 4/18
Date 4/19	Date 4/20	Date 4/21

Analyze and Apply

1. Explain the advantage of cloning plants.
2. **Infer:** How would the DNA in plants grown from the same original plant compare? Why?
3. **Apply:** Was the cloning method you used sexual or asexual reproduction? Explain.

Extension

Garden stores sell chemicals that are supposed to speed up root growth from the cut ends of plants. **Design an experiment** to test this.

ANSWERS

Data and Observations

1. Answers will vary.
2. Answers will vary – possibly 3 to 6 days.

Analyze and Apply

1. All plants will be identical, and one can clone many plants from one original plant.
2. The DNA is exactly the same because the process is actually asexual reproduction.
3. asexual reproduction; only one parent was involved

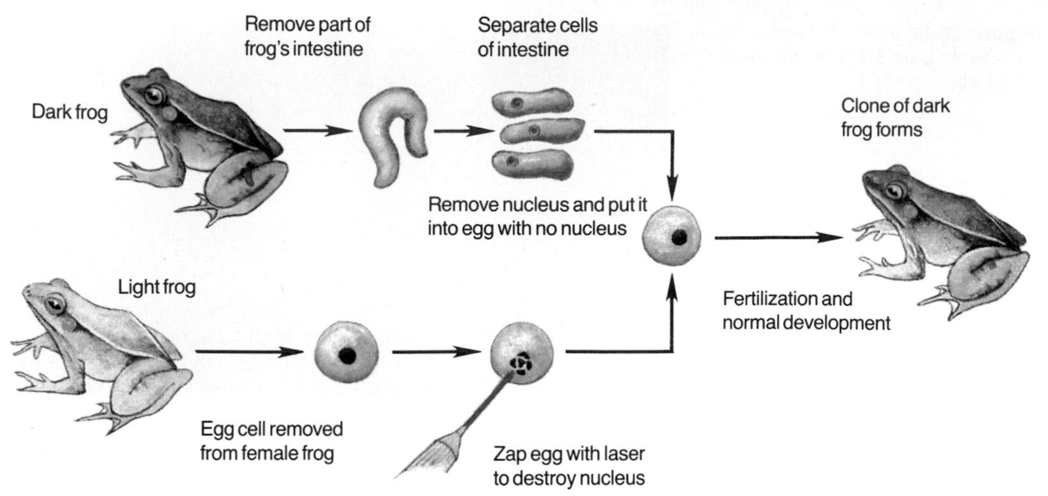
Remove part of frog's intestine
Separate cells of intestine
Dark frog
Clone of dark frog forms
Remove nucleus and put it into egg with no nucleus
Light frog
Fertilization and normal development
Egg cell removed from female frog
Zap egg with laser to destroy nucleus

Figure 28-12 Steps needed to clone a frog

Can humans clone animals? The answer is yes. Figure 28-12 shows how frogs are cloned. It is not science fiction. It has been done. Can humans be cloned in the laboratory? The technology makes it seem possible. A more important question is, should it be done?

Plant and Animal Breeding

Cloning is a way of producing living things with identical desirable traits. How do we get a living thing with the desired trait in the first place?

In Chapters 26 and 27 you worked many genetic problems. They showed what to expect with certain matings. Knowing what to expect tells us which living things to breed for certain traits. **Breeding** is the bringing together of two living things to produce offspring.

Selective breeding can bring out the desired traits of living things. If breeders bring together parents with different desired traits, the result can be offspring with the best traits of both parents.

An example of this can be seen in cotton plants. A certain type of cotton plant grew in Africa, but a plant disease was destroying it. Another type of cotton plant did not get the disease, but this plant could not grow in Africa. It grew only in Central America. The two plants were bred with each other. The result was a new type of cotton plant that would grow in Africa and did not get the disease.

Bio Tip

Consumer: Humans have been breeding dogs for hundreds of years. The evidence is seen in the many different varieties that exist today.

How has breeding produced better cotton plants?

TEACH

Concept Development

▶ A study of Figure 28-12 will help students understand the process of cloning in animals. Any body cell from within the dark frog could be used as a cell source. The egg cell from the light frog with its nucleus destroyed does not have to be fertilized because the nucleus being added to it from the dark frog already has the full chromosome number. All body cells have the full chromosome number.

▶ Discuss how breeeding has produced more robust varieties of plants and animals.

MOTIVATION/Brainstorming

Ask students why the new clone has the dark frog trait rather than the light frog trait. (DNA was contributed by the dark frog cell because its nucleus was used. The DNA code for dark skin protein is the code being used. The only thing being contributed by the light frog is the cytoplasm within its egg cell.)

Analogy: A signal within the genetic code turns gene action on and off just as a capital letter starts a sentence and a period stops a sentence.

Guided Practice

Have students write down their answers to the margin question: It has produced a cotton plant that is resistant to disease and that will grow in Africa.

APPLICATION 28

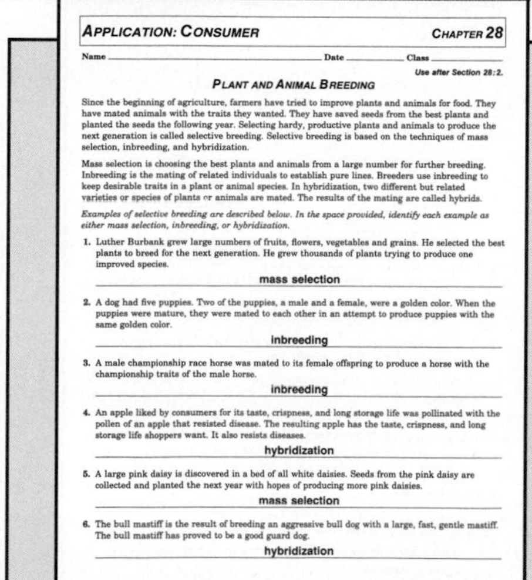
APPLICATION: CONSUMER — CHAPTER 28

Name ____ Date ____ Class ____

Use after Section 28:2.

PLANT AND ANIMAL BREEDING

Since the beginning of agriculture, farmers have tried to improve plants and animals for food. They have mated animals with the traits they wanted. They have saved seeds from the best plants and planted the seeds the following year. Selecting hardy, productive plants and animals to produce the next generation is called selective breeding. Selective breeding is based on the techniques of mass selection, inbreeding, and hybridization.

Mass selection is choosing the best plants and animals from a large number for further breeding. Inbreeding is the mating of related individuals to establish pure lines. Breeders use inbreeding to keep desirable traits in a plant or animal species. In hybridization, two different but related varieties or species of plants or animals are mated. The results of the mating are called hybrids.

Examples of selective breeding are described below. In the space provided, identify each example as either mass selection, inbreeding, or hybridization.

1. Luther Burbank grew large numbers of fruits, flowers, vegetables and grains. He selected the best plants to breed for the next generation. He grew thousands of plants trying to produce one improved species.
   mass selection
2. A dog had five puppies. Two of the puppies, a male and a female, were a golden color. When the puppies were mature, they were mated to each other in an attempt to produce puppies with the same golden color.
   inbreeding
3. A male championship race horse was mated to its female offspring to produce a horse with the championship traits of the male horse.
   inbreeding
4. An apple liked by consumers for its taste, crispness, and long storage life was pollinated with the pollen of an apple that resisted disease. The resulting apple has the taste, crispness, and long storage life shoppers want. It also resists diseases.
   hybridization
5. A large pink daisy is discovered in a bed of all white daisies. Seeds from the pink daisy are collected and planted the next year with hopes of producing more pink daisies.
   mass selection
6. The bull mastiff is the result of breeding an aggressive bull dog with a large, fast, gentle mastiff. The bull mastiff has proved to be a good guard dog.
   hybridization

OPTIONS

Application/*Teacher Resource Package*, p. 28. Use the Application worksheet shown here to give students practice with plant and animal breeding.

TEACH

Concept Development

▶ Explain that other applications of recombinant DNA research include: drug synthesis (insulin, interferon, vaccines) and development of crops that are resistant to heat, cold, disease, drought, and pestilence and have higher nutritional value.

Check for Understanding

Ask students to list several ways that humans have changed the gene code or altered traits of a living thing. Lists should include mutations, cloning, breeding, and gene splicing. Discuss whether the changes were helpful or harmful.

Reteach

Have students prepare a brief written report on one of their answers to Check Your Understanding.

Independent Practice

Study Guide/*Teacher Resource Package*, p. 167. Use the Study Guide worksheet shown at the bottom of this page for independent practice.

Guided Practice

Have students write down their answers to the margin question: because the genetic code for all living things is the same.

Figure 28-13 Scientists have selectively bred Brahmin bulls for small size.

Brahman cattle are usually raised for meat, Figure 28-13. Recently, scientists have been able to breed smaller Brahmans. Each cow produces less meat than a larger size cow, but it also does not eat as much. This is a real help to those farmers who don't have much land for cattle to graze. Ten mini cows can graze on the same amount of grass as one large cow and can produce almost three times as much beef.

Many crops and livestock are the result of careful selective breeding. The fruits and vegetables that you buy at the grocery store are the products of selective breeding. Breeders are producing cattle that have less fat, and they are trying to breed chickens that lay low-cholesterol eggs.

Figure 28-14 Steps needed to splice a wire

Wire is cut in half

New piece of wire is spliced, or inserted, between the two ends

Tape is used to hold ends together

Splicing Genes

Have you ever spliced a wire or broken film? If you have, then you know that the word *splice* means to insert, or join together. Figure 28-14 shows wires that have been joined together.

Today, scientists can splice genes. They join genes from one kind of living thing with the genes of a different kind of living thing. This splicing works because the genetic code for all living things is the same. They all have the same four bases, A, T, C, and G. All living things use the same genetic code to translate the DNA language into the protein language. What is different is the order in which the bases appear.

In gene splicing, a bacterium receives a section of DNA from another organism, such as a human. The new DNA combination that is formed in the bacterium is recombinant

OPTIONS

ACTIVITY/Challenge

Have some students prepare a debate to be presented to the rest of the class. The topic is the pros and cons of recombinant DNA technology (gene splicing).

STUDY GUIDE 167

STUDY GUIDE CHAPTER 28

Name ______ Date ______ Class ______

HOW THE GENETIC MESSAGE CHANGES

In your textbook, read about breeding of plants and animals and splicing genes between organisms in Section 28:2.

5. This diagram shows two bulls. Below each is a description of that bull's traits.

Bull A: Sleek, clean, solid-colored fur; Long tail, long legs; Milk production of his offspring is low.

Bull B: Rough, spotted fur; Short tail, short legs; Milk production of his offspring is high.

a. Which bull would you choose to breed with a cow to produce a herd of cows that would supply a lot of milk? **B** Why? **The milk production of bull B's offspring is high.**

b. Which bull would you choose for breeding to produce "beautiful" offspring? **A** Why? **Bull A has a sleek, clean, solid-colored fur.**

c. Which bull would you choose for breeding to produce offspring that would not jump over fences? **B** Why? **Bull B has shorter legs.**

d. Explain the value of plant and animal breeding. **The value of breeding is producing offspring with desired traits. It's been used to breed plants that won't get certain diseases and cattle that have less fat or greater milk production.**

6. What is recombinant DNA? **Recombinant DNA is the DNA that is formed when DNA from one organism is put into the DNA of another organism.**

7. Why does gene splicing work? **It works because the genetic code for all living things is the same.**

8. List four ways that gene splicing is of value to humans now or may be of value in the future. **Gene splicing can help make human insulin, growth hormone, and plants that are not harmed by chemical sprays. Someday, it may help to cure certain genetic diseases.**

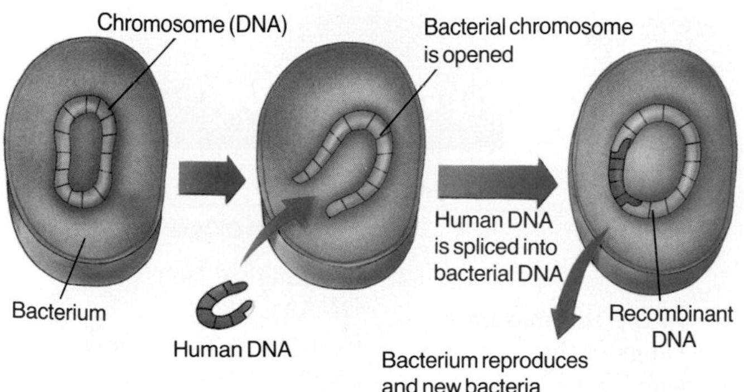

Chromosome (DNA)
Bacterial chromosome is opened
Human DNA is spliced into bacterial DNA
Bacterium
Human DNA
Recombinant DNA
Bacterium reproduces and new bacteria have the recombinant DNA

Figure 28-15 In gene splicing, a bacterium receives DNA from another organism.

(ree KAHM buh nunt) DNA. **Recombinant DNA** is the DNA that is formed when DNA from one organism is put into the DNA of another organism.

Gene splicing produces bacteria that can make certain chemicals. For example, scientists splice human genes that control the making of insulin into bacteria. The bacteria then make insulin in large amounts. Diabetics benefit because they can't make their own insulin.

Recombinant DNA has produced plants that are not harmed by chemical sprays. Some sprays kill weeds but also kill crop plants. By splicing spray-resistant genes into crop plants, the crop plant is unharmed by sprays.

Splicing of human genes into bacteria also has helped make human growth hormone. This hormone is given to children when their pituitary gland does not make enough of it. The real future of gene splicing may be in the ability to cure certain genetic diseases.

Skill Check

Understand science words: recombinant DNA. The word part *re* means again. In your dictionary, find three words with the word part *re* in them. *For more help, refer to the* ***Skill Handbook****, pages 706-711.*

Check Your Understanding

6. How does a mutation occur?
7. How could you produce an apple tree that was resistant to disease and produced large fruit?
8. What is being spliced to form recombinant DNA?
9. **Critical Thinking:** Could you breed an animal with exactly the combination of genes you wanted? Explain.
10. **Biology and Writing:** Do you think research on splicing genes should continue? Write a paragraph with at least three reasons that explain your answer.

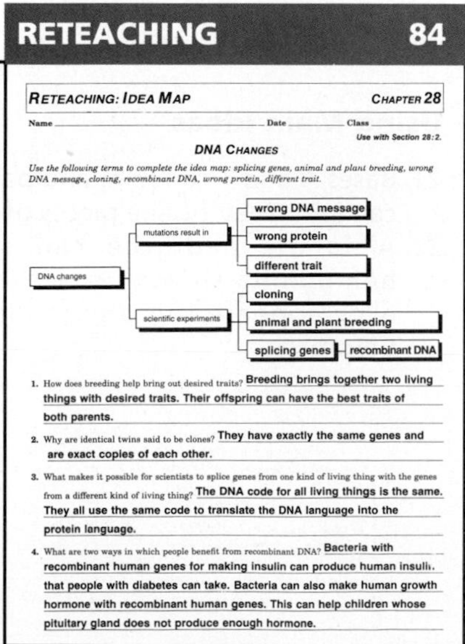

RETEACHING 84

RETEACHING: IDEA MAP CHAPTER 28

Name ______ Date ______ Class ______

Use with Section 28:2.

DNA CHANGES

Use the following terms to complete the idea map: splicing genes, animal and plant breeding, wrong DNA message, cloning, recombinant DNA, wrong protein, different trait.

DNA changes
- mutations result in
  - wrong DNA message
  - wrong protein
  - different trait
- scientific experiments
  - cloning
  - animal and plant breeding
  - splicing genes — recombinant DNA

1. How does breeding help bring out desired traits? Breeding brings together two living things with desired traits. Their offspring can have the best traits of both parents.
2. Why are identical twins said to be clones? They have exactly the same genes and are exact copies of each other.
3. What makes it possible for scientists to splice genes from one kind of living thing with the genes from a different kind of living thing? The DNA code for all living things is the same. They all use the same code to translate the DNA language into the protein language.
4. What are two ways in which people benefit from recombinant DNA? Bacteria with recombinant human genes for making insulin can produce human insulin that people with diabetes can take. Bacteria can also make human growth hormone with recombinant human genes. This can help children whose pituitary gland does not produce enough hormone.

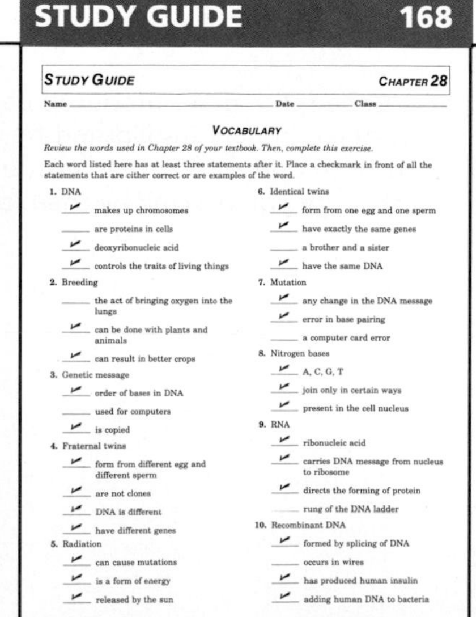

STUDY GUIDE 168

STUDY GUIDE CHAPTER 28

Name ______ Date ______ Class ______

VOCABULARY

Review the words used in Chapter 28 of your textbook. Then, complete this exercise.

Each word listed here has at least three statements after it. Place a checkmark in front of all the statements that are either correct or are examples of the word.

1. DNA
   - ✓ makes up chromosomes
   - ___ are proteins in cells
   - ✓ deoxyribonucleic acid
   - ✓ controls the traits of living things
2. Breeding
   - ___ the act of bringing oxygen into the lungs
   - ✓ can be done with plants and animals
   - ✓ can result in better crops
3. Genetic message
   - ✓ order of bases in DNA
   - ___ used for computers
   - ✓ is copied
4. Fraternal twins
   - ✓ form from different egg and different sperm
   - ✓ are not clones
   - ✓ DNA is different
   - ✓ have different genes
5. Radiation
   - ✓ can cause mutations
   - ✓ is a form of energy
   - ✓ released by the sun
6. Identical twins
   - ✓ form from one egg and one sperm
   - ✓ have exactly the same genes
   - ___ a brother and a sister
   - ✓ have the same DNA
7. Mutation
   - ✓ any change in the DNA message
   - ✓ error in base pairing
   - ___ a computer card error
8. Nitrogen bases
   - ✓ A, C, G, T
   - ✓ join only in certain ways
   - ✓ present in the cell nucleus
9. RNA
   - ✓ ribonucleic acid
   - ✓ carries DNA message from nucleus to ribosome
   - ✓ directs the forming of protein
   - ___ rung of the DNA ladder
10. Recombinant DNA
   - ✓ formed by splicing of DNA
   - ___ occurs in wires
   - ✓ has produced human insulin
   - ✓ adding human DNA to bacteria

TEACH

Check for Understanding

Have students respond to the first three questions in Check Your Understanding.

Independent Practice

Study Guide/*Teacher Resource Package*, p. 168. Use the Study Guide worksheet shown at the bottom of this page for independent practice.

Reteach

Reteaching/*Teacher Resource Package*, p. 84. Use this worksheet to give students additional practice with how DNA changes.

3 APPLY

ACTIVITY/Challenge

Have students use references to determine how humans breed dogs. Have them report on certain dog breeds.

4 CLOSE

Audiovisual

Show the video *Heredity and Mutation*, Films for the Humanities.

Answers to Check Your Understanding

6. When DNA copies itself, an error may take place in the pairing of bases.
7. You could breed a tree that produces large fruit with one that is resistant to disease.
8. genes
9. No; many genes are hidden in recessive form, so you would have to breed only for traits you can see.
10. Answers will vary. Example: Splicing genes should not continue because it is dangerous.

CHAPTER 28 REVIEW

Summary

Summary statements can be used by students to review the major concepts of the chapter.

Key Science Words

All boldfaced terms from the chapter are listed.

Testing Yourself

Using Words

1. DNA
2. breeding
3. nitrogen bases
4. mutation
5. recombinant DNA
6. identical twins
7. fraternal twins
8. RNA
9. genetic code
10. radiation

Finding Main Ideas

11. p. 599; Selective breeding can bring out the desired traits of living things.
12. p. 596; the incorrect pairing of bases, certain chemicals, and some forms of radiation
13. p. 600; The genetic code for all living things is the same.
14. p. 592; A helper molecule called RNA carries the DNA code to the ribosomes.
15. p. 594; First, the molecule opens along the nitrogen bases; second, new nitrogen bases in the nucleus join the bases on the opened rungs.
16. p. 591; The DNA message is determined by the order of the nitrogen bases A, C, G, and T.
17. p. 597; Identical twins have the same genes, the same DNA, and were formed from one egg and one sperm. Fraternal twins have different genes, different DNA, and were formed from two eggs and two sperm.
18. pp. 586-587; It resembles a stepladder that has been twisted.
19. p. 589; A gene is a short piece of DNA, a certain number of bases on the DNA molecule, and a small section of chromosome that determines traits.

Chapter 28

Review

Summary

28:1 The DNA Molecule

1. DNA is a molecule that makes up the chromosomes and genes of living things. The rungs of the ladder-shaped molecule are nitrogen bases.
2. Through experiments with bacteria, scientists showed that DNA controls traits.
3. The order of nitrogen bases A, T, C, and G forms a DNA message. RNA carries the DNA message to the ribosomes where specific proteins are formed. DNA is copied exactly to form new chromosomes just before mitosis and meiosis.

28:2 How the Genetic Message Changes

4. The DNA message may change if a mutation takes place. Mutations may be caused by some chemicals and radiation or by mistakes in copying.
5. Identical twins are clones. Clones have the same DNA and traits. Fraternal twins have different DNA. Selective breeding has produced new and better types of plants and animals.
6. Genes from one living thing can be spliced into the DNA of a different living thing. The result is recombinant DNA. Insulin and growth hormone have been made using gene splicing.

Key Science Words

breeding (p. 599)
DNA (p. 586)
fraternal twins (p. 597)
genetic code (p. 592)
identical twins (p. 597)
mutation (p. 595)
nitrogen base (p. 587)
radiation (p. 596)
recombinant DNA (p. 601)
RNA (p. 592)

Testing Yourself

Using Words

Choose the word from the list of Key Science Words that best fits the definition.

1. molecule that makes up genes
2. causing two living things to mate and produce desired offspring
3. form the rungs of the DNA molecule
4. a change in the DNA message
5. formed when DNA is spliced into the DNA of another organism
6. twins formed from the splitting of one fertilized egg
7. twins formed from two different fertilized eggs
8. molecule that acts as a cell messenger for DNA
9. translates the DNA language into the protein language
10. energy that is given off by atoms

20. p. 601; Gene splicing has produced bacteria that make human insulin and human growth hormone. It also has produced plants that are not affected by chemicals.

Using Main Ideas

21. Bases A and T can join, and bases C and G can join. They fit like pieces of a puzzle.
22. A family pedigree can show that hemophilia shows up without having ever appeared in any family member before.

Review

Testing Yourself *continued*

Finding Main Ideas

List the page number where each main idea below is found. Then, explain each main idea.

11. what is gained from selective breeding
12. what causes mutations to occur
13. why gene splicing works
14. how DNA in the nucleus can control what goes on at the ribosomes
15. the steps involved when DNA copies itself
16. what determines the DNA message
17. how identical and fraternal twins differ
18. what a model of DNA looks like
19. three ways to describe a gene
20. examples of how gene splicing has helped humans and improved plants

Using Main Ideas

Answer the questions by referring to the page number after each question.

21. Which DNA bases can join with one another? Why? (p. 587)
22. How can one show that hemophilia in a family may result from a mutation? (p. 595)
23. What are the steps in gene splicing? (p. 600)
24. What are the steps in making protein, starting with DNA in the nucleus? (p. 592)
25. How has plant breeding offered a solution to the problem of diseased cotton in Africa? (p. 599)
26. What is copied when new chromosomes form just before mitosis and meiosis? (p. 593)
27. Where would you find DNA in a pine tree? Why does a pine tree have DNA? (p. 589)

Skill Review ✓

*For more help, refer to the **Skill Handbook**, pages 704-719.*

1. **Observe:** Look at Figure 28-4. Why do dead harmful bacteria injected into a rat not cause any problem to the animal?
2. **Interpret diagrams:** What happens to the original DNA molecule when it copies itself? Look at Figure 28-8 for help.
3. **Interpret data:** What part of a bacterium carries the genetic message? What is the evidence for this, as shown by the scientists who did the experiments described on page 590?
4. **Infer:** Why is it important that mutations be prevented from occurring in testes and ovaries?

Finding Out More

Critical Thinking

1. Why would a mutation that appears in a person's body cell not appear in that person's offspring?
2. Should humans be cloned? Give reasons for your answer.

Applications

1. Write a report discussing the effects of the sun's radiation on the skin.
2. You wish to breed sheep in order to sell them as meat. What traits would you look for in the parents? Why?

Using Main Ideas

23. DNA within a bacterium is split open; a section of another organism's DNA is placed inside the bacterium; the bacterium closes back together, incorporating the new DNA as part of its DNA.
24. DNA in the nucleus contains a code of nitrogen bases; RNA carries the DNA code from the nucleus to ribosomes; the ribosomes make protein according to the code on the RNA.
25. A cotton plant that could grow only in Central America and did not get a disease was bred to a cotton plant that grew in Africa and did get the disease. The result was a plant that would grow in Africa and would not get the disease.
26. DNA is copied.
27. DNA is in the nucleus of each cell in a pine tree. All cells in living things have DNA.

Skill Review

1. Harmful bacteria that are dead will not kill the animal.
2. It opens along the middle, loose nitrogen bases join the bases on the DNA molecule, and finally two DNA molecules have formed.
3. Nitrogen bases in the DNA molecule carry the genetic message. Harmless bacteria change when they pick up DNA from harmful bacteria, but the offspring's traits are unaffected.
4. A mutation in the sex cells causes a change in the offspring's traits.

Finding Out More

Critical Thinking

1. Mutations cause a change only when they occur in the sex cells.
2. Answers will vary.

Applications

1. Reports should include reference to cancer and other skin problems.
2. Answers will vary, but should include large size, little fat, and lots of muscle since the sheep would be a source of food.

Chapter Review/*Teacher Resource Package, pp. 148-149.*

Chapter Test/*Teacher Resource Package*, pp. 150-152.

Chapter Test/*Computer Test Bank*

Evolution

PLANNING GUIDE

CONTENT	TEXT FEATURES	TEACHER RESOURCE PACKAGE	OTHER COMPONENTS
(2 1/2 days) 29:1 Changes In Living Things Adaptations An Example of Survival Natural Selection Mutations Species Formation Primate and Human Evolution	Skill Check: *Define Words in Context,* p. 609 Skill Check: *Understand Science Words,* p. 613 Lab 29-1: *Adaptations,* p. 608 Check Your Understanding, p. 614	Application: *Adaptations of Zoo Animals,* p. 29 Reteaching: *How Natural Selection Works,* p. 85 Critical Thinking/Problem Solving: *How Could Hollow Hip Bones Help Supersaurus?* p. 29 Focus: *Natural Selection,* p. 57 Study Guide: *Changes in Living Things,* pp. 169-171 Lab 29-1: *Adaptations,* pp. 113-114	**Laboratory Manual:** *How Do Some Living Things Vary?* p. 243 Color Transparency 29: *How Species Are Formed*
(3 1/2 days) 29:2 Explanations for Evolution Darwin's Work Fossil Evidence Other Evidence	Skill Check: *Interpret Diagrams,* p. 619 Mini Lab: *How Do Peas Vary?* p. 616 Mini Lab: *How Do Wood and Fossil Wood Compare?* p. 617 Lab 29-2: *Fossil Prints,* p. 618 Idea Map, p. 621 Check Your Understanding, p. 621 Problem Solving: *Solving the Primate Puzzle,* p. 622	Enrichment: *Human Evolution,* p. 31 Reteaching: *Evolution,* p. 86 Skill: *Outline,* p. 30 Study Guide: *Explanations for Evolution,* pp. 172-173 Study Guide: *Vocabulary,* p. 174 Lab 29-2: *Fossil Prints,* pp. 115-116 Transparency Master: *The Geologic Time Scale,* p. 147	**Laboratory Manual:** *How Do Fossils Show Change?* p. 247
Chapter Review	Summary Key Science Words Testing Yourself Finding Main Ideas Using Main Ideas Skill Review	Chapter Review, pp. 153-154 Chapter Test, pp. 155-157 Unit Test, pp. 158-159	**Test Bank**

MATERIALS NEEDED

LAB 29-1, p. 608	LAB 29-2, p. 618	MARGIN FEATURES
white paper black paper 30 white dots 30 black dots damp paper towel	plastic dish 100-mL graduated cylinder warm water metric ruler leaf plastic powder	Skill Check, p. 613 dictionary Skill Check, p. 619 pencil paper Mini Lab, p. 616 metric ruler pencil paper 10 pea pods Mini Lab, p. 617 graduated cylinder water piece of wood piece of petrified wood

OBJECTIVES

SECTION	OBJECTIVE	OBJECTIVES CORRELATION			
		CHECK YOUR UNDERSTANDING	CHAPTER REVIEW	TRP CHAPTER REVIEW	TRP CHAPTER TEST
29:1	1. **Give examples** of how adaptations help organisms survive.	1	1, 4, 5, 15, 16, 17	3, 7, 9	1, 2, 3, 21, 37, 39, 41, 43
	2. **Explain** how changes in life-forms occur.	2, 4	10, 18, 23	11	5, 10, 11, 22, 24, 26
	3. **Describe** the classification and evolution of primates and humans.	3	9, 13, 22	1, 24	27, 29
29:2	4. **Communicate** Darwin's main ideas.	6, 8	2, 12, 20	2, 10, 14, 15, 16, 17, 18, 21, 22, 25	4, 6, 7, 8, 9, 13, 14, 15, 16, 17, 18, 19, 20, 23, 25, 36, 38, 40, 42
	5. **Describe** evidence that supports evolution.	7, 9, 10	6, 7, 8, 11, 14, 19, 21	4, 5, 6, 8, 12, 13, 19, 20, 23	10, 12, 28, 30, 34, 35, 38, 39, 40, 41, 42

Evolution

CHAPTER OVERVIEW

Key Concepts

In this chapter, students will be introduced to natural selection through a series of events occurring between a predator and its prey. Mutations and species formation are covered. Primate and human evolution are discussed. The major statements by Darwin and the evidence supporting evolution are examined, including fossil, embryological, biochemical, and vestigial organ evidence.

Key Science Words

competition
evolution
extinct
fertile
fossil
natural selection
new-world monkey
old-world monkey
primate
sedimentary rock
species
variation
vestigial structure

Skill Development

In Lab 29-1, students will **form a hypothesis, experiment, interpret data, infer,** and **calculate** while studying color as an adaptation. In Lab 29-2, they will **formulate a model, observe,** and **infer** while making a fossil print. In the Skill Check on page 609, students will **define words in context** relating to natural selection. In the Skill Check on page 613, they will **understand** the **science word** *primate.* In the Skill Check on page 619, they will **interpret diagrams** of rock layers. In the Mini Lab on page 616, students will **make a bar graph** relating to variation in plants. In the Mini Lab on page 617, they will **infer** how petrified wood is formed.

CHAPTER PREVIEW

Chapter Content

Review this outline for Chapter 29 before you read the chapter.

29:1 Changes in Living Things
- Adaptations
- An Example of Survival
- Natural Selection
- Mutations
- Species Formation
- Primate and Human Evolution

29:2 Explanations for Evolution
- Darwin's Work
- Fossil Evidence
- Other Evidence

Skills in this Chapter

The skills that you will use in this chapter are listed below.

- In **Lab 29-1,** you will form hypotheses, experiment, interpret data, infer, and calculate. In **Lab 29-2,** you will formulate a model, observe, and infer.
- In the **Skill Checks,** you will understand science words, define words in context, and interpret diagrams.
- In the **Mini Labs,** you will infer and make a bar graph.

604

Bridging

In Chapter 28, students learned that all living organisms are composed of cells and that these cells contain the chemical DNA. This chapter will explain why life-forms are so similar in organization and in chemical composition.

Chapter 29

Evolution

There are millions of different kinds of living things on Earth. Each and every kind of living thing is well suited to where it lives. For example, there are many different kinds of cacti. The smaller photograph below shows a close-up view of a cactus plant. Cactus plants have spines instead of leaves. The spines are an adaptation that helps to reduce water loss. Cactus plants are well suited for growing in areas where there is little water available. How do scientists explain the great variety of living things on the face of Earth? How do they explain the fact that living things are well suited to where they live? This chapter will answer these questions.

Try This!

What Does Opposable Mean? Tape each thumb to the inside of your palm so that you can't use them. Try to write, button a shirt, pick up a piece of paper, and turn the pages of this book. Most primates have an opposable thumb. What does opposable mean? How helpful is this trait?

605

Misconception

The following statement is often heard from students, "Humans evolved from apes." Advise students that evolutionary evidence supports the theory that humans and apes evolved from a common early ancestor.

GETTING STARTED

Using the Photos

Discuss other ways that the cactus is adapted to a desert environment. The cells of the plant hold enormous volumes of water. The spines themselves help to reduce water loss through transpiration. Cacti are thick and fleshy, which helps them withstand the extremely dry conditions. Desert plants are widely spaced. This helps to reduce competition for water and nutrients. Have students try to think of adaptations of other desert organisms. Lizards have scaly skin for protection against drying out. Many desert animals are active at night when it is cooler. Many desert animals have larger extremities for getting rid of excess body heat.

MOTIVATION/Try This!

What does opposable mean? Students will observe the difficulty of being able to perform simple tasks when unable to use the thumb. An opposable thumb allows for contact between the thumb and other fingers. Without this trait, primates would not be able to develop such skills as tool making and use, tree climbing, etc.

Chapter Preview

Have students study the chapter outline before they begin to read the chapter. They should note the overall organization of the chapter, that the first topic describes the general changes in living things that occur over time. This is followed by a section that deals with the evidence that supports evolution.

29:1 Changes in Living Things

PREPARATION

Materials Needed

Make copies of the Focus, Application, Critical Thinking/Problem Solving, Enrichment, Reteaching, Study Guide, and Lab worksheets in the *Teacher Resource Package*.

▶ Gather black and white paper and prepare paper dots for Lab 29-1.

Key Science Words

natural selection
species
fertile
old-world monkey
primate
new-world monkey

Process Skills

In Lab 29-1, students will form a hypothesis, experiment, interpret data, infer, and calculate. In the Skill Checks, they will define words in context and understand science words.

1 FOCUS

▶ The objectives are listed on the student page. Remind students to preview these objectives as a guide to this numbered section.

MOTIVATION/Display

Gather pictures from nature magazines and display them for the class. In particular, use any animal that blends well with its surroundings or mimics objects in its environment. Ask students how each animal benefits from the coloration.

Focus/*Teacher Resource Package*, p. 57. Use the Focus transparency shown at the bottom of this page as an introduction to natural selection.

Objectives

1. **Give examples** of how adaptations help organisms survive.
2. **Explain** how changes in life-forms occur.
3. **Describe** the classification and evolution of primates and humans.

Key Science Words

natural selection
species
fertile
primate
new-world monkey
old-world monkey

29:1 Changes in Living Things

Living things are well suited to where they live. What exactly does this statement mean?

Adaptations

All the living things in the world have certain kinds of adaptations. An adaptation is a trait that makes a living thing able to survive in its surroundings. You first read about adaptations in Chapter 2.

Look at the foot of the bird shown in Figure 29-1a. The bird spends a great deal of its time perched on tree branches. Note the bird's long toes. The long toes curl around small branches and help the bird remain perched in the tree. The bird shown in Figure 29-1b spends a lot of time in water. How does the webbing between the toes help this bird swim?

An Example of Survival

How do traits help organisms survive in their environments? What is the outcome when an organism with a certain trait is able to survive? The following example will answer these questions.

Figure 29-1 Songbirds have feet adapted to perching on tree branches (a). Geese have feet adapted to swimming (b).

a

b

OPTIONS

Enrichment: Students can identify with the word *camouflage*. Ask if the term fits the idea of adaptation.

FOCUS 57

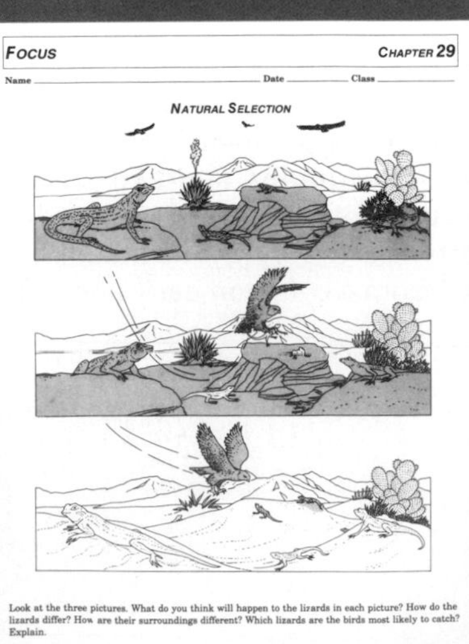

Focus CHAPTER 29

Name ______ Date ______ Class ______

NATURAL SELECTION

Look at the three pictures. What do you think will happen to the lizards in each picture? How do the lizards differ? How are their surroundings different? Which lizards are the birds most likely to catch? Explain.

A group of mice lives in an area that has dark soil. Owls that eat mice also live in this area. Because dark mice blend well with the dark soil, owls cannot see them easily. Thus, the dark mice are better protected because they blend with the soil color, Figure 29-2. Their color is an adaptation, a trait that helps them survive.

Figure 29-2 Owls can easily see light-colored mice on dark soil.

Dark mice do not always have offspring that are also dark in color. Every now and then they have light-colored offspring. The light-colored offspring, in turn, have other light-colored mice. Light-colored mice are easy to spot against the dark soil. As a result of their color, the light-colored mice are usually the first to be eaten by the owls. Light-colored mice living on dark soil are poorly adapted to their surroundings. Few light mice survive. As a result, few light mice reproduce. The number of light-colored mice tends to remain low. The dark mice, however, survive and reproduce. The dark mice will continue to outnumber the light mice.

How do adaptations help living things survive?

Suppose chemical changes take place in the soil and cause it to change color. The soil becomes lighter. Now owls can spot the dark mice on the ground more easily than they can spot the light mice. As a result, owls eat more dark mice than light mice.

Dark mice are no longer adapted to these surroundings. However, light mice are adapted to the light-colored soil. Dark color has become an unfavorable trait. The balance between the two mouse types begins to change. More light mice survive and reproduce. Any dark mice that are born are more likely to be eaten. Few of them get a chance to survive and reproduce.

2 TEACH

MOTIVATION/Brainstorming

Ask students for a list of animals that blend with their environments. Some examples would be snowshoe hare, tiger, walking stick, and chameleon. All of these animals have protective coloration.

Concept Development

▶ Point out how the environment determines which adaptation is protective.

Guided Practice

Have students write down their answers to the margin question: they make a living thing better suited to its environment.

Independent Practice

Study Guide/*Teacher Resource Package*, p. 169. Use the Study Guide worksheet shown at the bottom of this page for independent practice.

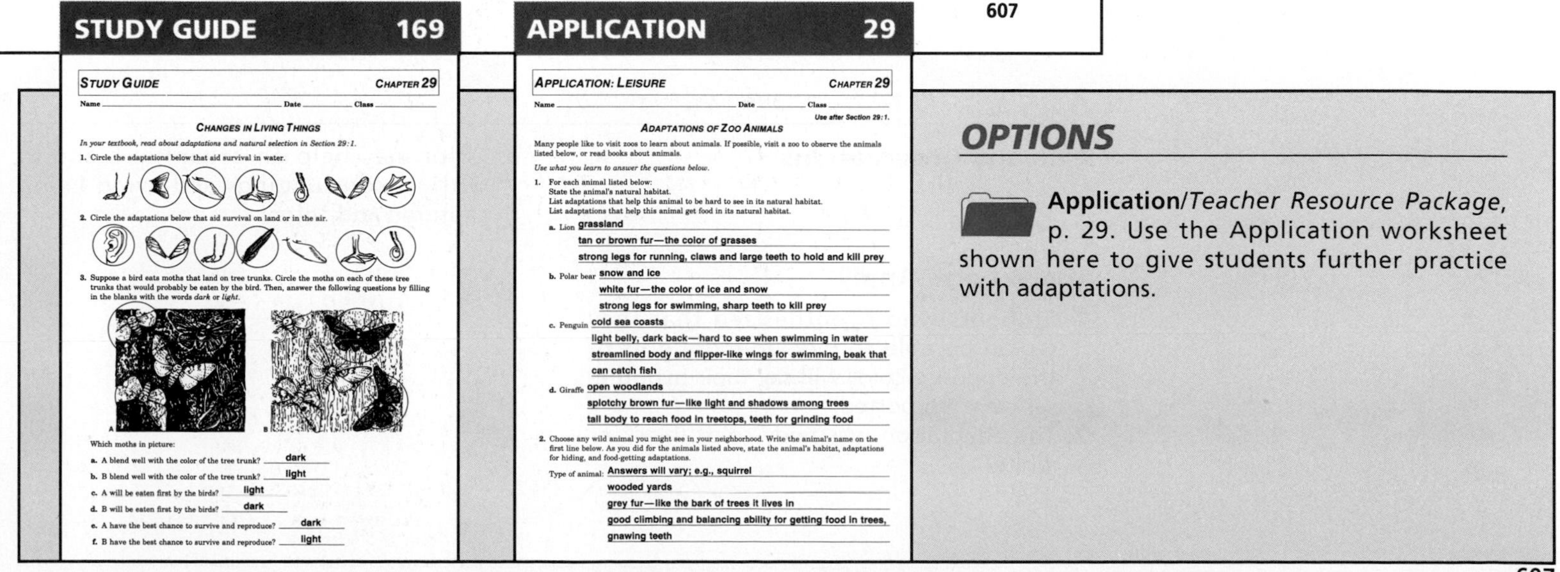

STUDY GUIDE 169

STUDY GUIDE — CHAPTER 29

Name ________ Date ________ Class ________

CHANGES IN LIVING THINGS

In your textbook, read about adaptations and natural selection in Section 29:1.

1. Circle the adaptations below that aid survival in water.
2. Circle the adaptations below that aid survival on land or in the air.
3. Suppose a bird eats moths that land on tree trunks. Circle the moths on each of these tree trunks that would probably be eaten by the bird. Then, answer the following questions by filling in the blanks with the words *dark* or *light*.

A B

Which moths in picture:

a. A blend well with the color of the tree trunk? dark
b. B blend well with the color of the tree trunk? light
c. A will be eaten first by the birds? light
d. B will be eaten first by the birds? dark
e. A have the best chance to survive and reproduce? dark
f. B have the best chance to survive and reproduce? light

APPLICATION 29

APPLICATION: LEISURE — CHAPTER 29

Name ________ Date ________ Class ________

Use after Section 29:1.

ADAPTATIONS OF ZOO ANIMALS

Many people like to visit zoos to learn about animals. If possible, visit a zoo to observe the animals listed below, or read books about animals.

Use what you learn to answer the questions below.

1. For each animal listed below:
   State the animal's natural habitat.
   List adaptations that help this animal to be hard to see in its natural habitat.
   List adaptations that help this animal get food in its natural habitat.
   a. Lion grassland
      tan or brown fur—the color of grasses
      strong legs for running, claws and large teeth to hold and kill prey
   b. Polar bear snow and ice
      white fur—the color of ice and snow
      strong legs for swimming, sharp teeth to kill prey
   c. Penguin cold sea coasts
      light belly, dark back—hard to see when swimming in water
      streamlined body and flipper-like wings for swimming, beak that can catch fish
   d. Giraffe open woodlands
      splotchy brown fur—like light and shadows among trees
      tall body to reach food in treetops, teeth for grinding food
2. Choose any wild animal you might see in your neighborhood. Write the animal's name on the first line below. As you did for the animals listed above, state the animal's habitat, adaptations for hiding, and food-getting adaptations.
   Type of animal: Answers will vary; e.g., squirrel
   wooded yards
   grey fur—like the bark of trees it lives in
   good climbing and balancing ability for getting food in trees, gnawing teeth

OPTIONS

Application/*Teacher Resource Package*, p. 29. Use the Application worksheet shown here to give students further practice with adaptations.

Lab 29-1 Adaptations

Overview

Through the use of modeling, students will learn that an organism can be protected from its prey by matching its background.

Objectives: Upon completion of this lab, students will be able to: (1) **demonstrate** that white dots on a white background are difficult to see, (2) **demonstrate** that black dots on a black background are difficult to see, (3) **conclude** that an organism matching its background can be an adaptation that helps in survival.

Time Allotment: 1 class period

Preparation

▶ Use a paper punch to make the dots prior to class. Store the dots in envelopes.

 **Lab 29-1 worksheet**/*Teacher Resource Package*, pp. 113-114.

Teaching the Lab

▶ Students should spread the dots out evenly but randomly on the paper backgrounds.

Cooperative Learning: Divide the class into groups of three students. For more information, see pp. 22T-23T in the Teacher Guide.

Adaptations

Lab 29–1

Problem: How is color an adaptation?

Skills

form hypotheses, experiment, interpret data, infer, calculate

Materials

white paper
black paper
30 white dots
30 black dots
damp paper towel

Procedure

1. Copy the data table. It should include space for 10 trials.
2. Spread 30 black and 30 white dots out on a page of white paper.
3. Write down a **hypothesis** as to whether you will be able to pick up more white dots or more black dots in 10 trials.
4. Moisten all your fingers with a damp paper towel. Quickly touch one dot with each finger. The dots should stick to your fingers. Do this as quickly as you can.
5. Count the number of black dots and white dots you picked up.
6. Record your totals as Trial 1.
7. Return all the dots to the white paper.
8. Repeat steps 4 through 7 nine more times.
9. Switch to the black background paper. Spread the dots on the black paper.
10. Write down a new **hypothesis.** Repeat steps 4 through / for ten trials.
11. Total each column in your table.

Data and Observations

1. Which color dots, black or white, were picked up more often on the white background?
2. Which color dots were picked up more often on the black background?

Analyze and Apply

1. **Check your hypotheses:** Are your hypotheses supported by your data? Why or why not?
2. **Infer:** What was the adaptation in this activity?
3. **Apply:** In nature, how does color help as an adaptation?

Extension

Calculate: Put the data for the class on the board. Calculate the averages for each category.

	WHITE BACKGROUND		BLACK BACKGROUND	
TRIAL	BLACK DOTS	WHITE DOTS	BLACK DOTS	WHITE DOTS
1	7	3	5	5
2	6	4	3	7
3	8	2	4	6
9	5	5	3	7
10	6	4	2	8
Total	70	30	42	58

ANSWERS

Data and Observations

1. black
2. white

Analyze and Apply

1. Students who hypothesized that they would be able to pick up more dots of the opposite color will say their hypotheses were supported.
2. The adaptation was body color (black or white).
3. Color may help an organism blend in with its surroundings and avoid being captured and eaten.

Natural Selection

We can now ask an important question using the mouse and owl story. What determined which mouse was better adapted to its surroundings? The owls determined, by eating certain mice, which color was an adaptation for survival. Only mice that are not eaten survive to reproduce. On the dark soil, more dark mice survived because owls did not see them. On the light soil, more light mice escaped the owls. **Natural selection** is the process in which something in a living thing's surroundings determines if it will or will not survive to have offspring. In natural selection, something in nature does the selecting. In our example, the owls did the selecting. When the soil became lighter, the group of mice changed from mostly dark to mostly light. The change was the result of natural selection.

Living things that are suited to their surroundings survive. They will be the ones most likely to reproduce. Their traits will be passed on to their offspring. Living things that are not suited to their surroundings won't survive. They won't reproduce, they won't have offspring, and their traits won't be passed on.

Why wouldn't a bright red frog survive in a muddy pond? Can you explain why more mud-colored frogs are likely to survive in muddy ponds than red frogs? How can web-toed frogs survive in water better than frogs with toe pads?

Skill Check

Define words in context: Read this statement: "The dinosaurs became extinct due to natural selection." What does natural selection mean as used in this sentence? *For more help, refer to the **Skill Handbook**, pages 706-711.*

Mutations

Adaptations are traits that help living things survive in their environments. Recall from Chapter 26 that traits are controlled by genes. Thus, adaptations are controlled by genes.

What is a source for new traits that help living things survive? Many new traits come from mutations. Remember, a mutation is a change in the DNA code. Mutations may supply living things with sources of new traits. Thus, they may supply new adaptations.

Are all mutations helpful for survival? No, some are harmful. For example, a mutation caused the deer in Figure 29-3 to have white fur. The deer no longer blends in with its surroundings. It can be seen more easily by its enemies and may be eaten.

Figure 29-3 A mutation caused this deer to have white fur.

TEACH

Videocassette

Show the videocassette *Natural Selection*, Films for the Humanities and Sciences.

Bridging

Propose these questions to your class: How do you explain a dark-colored mouse producing offspring that are light-colored? Can the dark-colored mouse control the type of coloration in its offspring? These two questions will begin to set the stage for ideas regarding natural selection. An answer to the first question is that genes control mouse coloration. Thus, a certain gene combination in the offspring can result in light color. *Genetic variation* is a term you may want to introduce. The second question will help students realize that living things cannot control the genetic traits that their offspring will inherit. The sorting out of traits is a random event occurring at meiosis.

ACTIVITY/Brainstorming

Ask students: If few light-colored mice survive, will the genes for this trait be as plentiful in the population as the genes for dark-colored fur?

Bridging

Ask students to review Section 28:2, which deals with mutations from a genetic perspective. Point out that in this section, mutations are being examined as potential sources of new adaptations.

CRITICAL THINKING 29

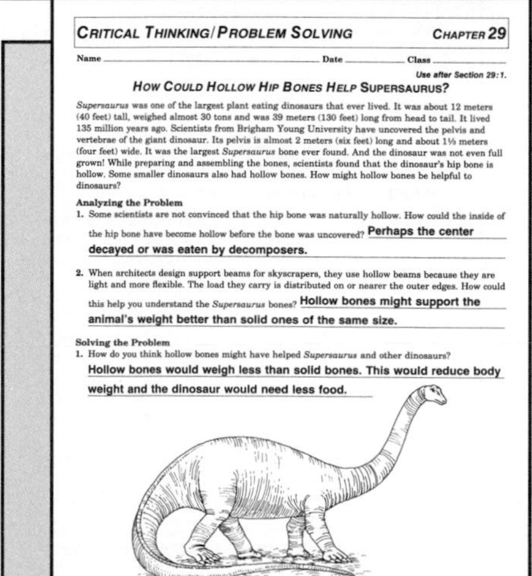

CRITICAL THINKING/PROBLEM SOLVING — CHAPTER 29

Name ______ Date ______ Class ______

Use after Section 29:1.

HOW COULD HOLLOW HIP BONES HELP SUPERSAURUS?

Supersaurus was one of the largest plant eating dinosaurs that ever lived. It was about 12 meters (40 feet) tall, weighed almost 30 tons and was 39 meters (130 feet) long from head to tail. It lived 135 million years ago. Scientists from Brigham Young University have uncovered the pelvis and vertebrae of the giant dinosaur. Its pelvis is almost 2 meters (six feet) long and about 1⅓ meters (four feet) wide. It was the largest *Supersaurus* bone ever found. And the dinosaur was not even full grown! While preparing and assembling the bones, scientists found that the dinosaur's hip bone is hollow. Some smaller dinosaurs also had hollow bones. How might hollow bones be helpful to dinosaurs?

Analyzing the Problem

1. Some scientists are not convinced that the hip bone was naturally hollow. How could the inside of the hip bone have become hollow before the bone was uncovered? **Perhaps the center decayed or was eaten by decomposers.**
2. When architects design support beams for skyscrapers, they use hollow beams because they are light and more flexible. The load they carry is distributed on or nearer the outer edges. How could this help you understand the *Supersaurus* bones? **Hollow bones might support the animal's weight better than solid ones of the same size.**

Solving the Problem

1. How do you think hollow bones might have helped *Supersaurus* and other dinosaurs? **Hollow bones would weigh less than solid bones. This would reduce body weight and the dinosaur would need less food.**

OPTIONS

How Do Some Living Things Vary?/*Lab Manual*, pp. 243-246. Use this lab as an extension to variation in living things.

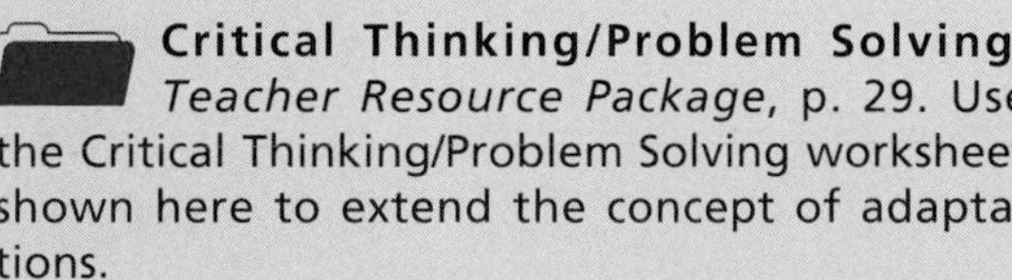

Critical Thinking/Problem Solving/ *Teacher Resource Package*, p. 29. Use the Critical Thinking/Problem Solving worksheet shown here to extend the concept of adaptations.

TEACH

Concept Development

▶ Mutations are sometimes said to be the "raw material" of adaptations. Ask students if they can explain this idea.

ACTIVITY/Brainstorming

What kinds of adaptations are seen in animals such as penguins, seals, or whales? Students may describe the long, slim body as an adaptation, enabling these animals to swim easily through the water. They may also describe the adaptation of front legs modified into finlike parts to help with swimming.

MOTIVATION/Display

Prepare a large diagram of the following fictitious animal. Ask students to describe the adaptations shown that help the animal with (a) food capturing (b) swimming (c) protection from predators. You may wish to point out that the animal feeds on fish and that its underside is gray while its top side is a deep blue except for the green sprigs on its head and tail.

Guided Practice

Ask students to design an animal that is adapted to blending in with plant branches. They may either: (a) list the desirable traits that would aid in the animal's survival, or (b) make a drawing of the animal and plant. Supply the following hints if necessary: size and color of the animal, location of plant branch, leaf size, and leaf shape.

Independent Practice

Study Guide/*Teacher Resource Package*, p. 170. Use the Study Guide worksheet shown at the bottom of this page for independent practice.

Bio Tip

Consumer: Wearing a lead apron when you have dental X rays helps prevent mutations of your reproductive cells.

What if the deer had a mutation that gave it extra long legs? The long legs might help it run faster from its enemies and escape being eaten. This new trait would probably help the deer in its surroundings. The trait could be passed to the offspring, thus increasing the number of individuals with the trait.

Mutations are natural events. Mutations appear in every living thing. These changes in genes may be helpful, harmful, or have no effect at all.

Species Formation

Chapter 3 described a species as the smallest group of living things in classification. There is another way to describe a species. A **species** is a group of living things that can breed with others of the same species and form fertile offspring. **Fertile** means being able to reproduce by forming egg or sperm cells. For example, the plants shown in Figure 29-4c are very similar in appearance. Yet, they can't produce fertile offspring if they breed with one another. Another example is shown in Figures 29-4a and 4b. These macaws look very much alike. They belong to different species, however. If they breed with each other, they won't form fertile offspring.

Figure 29-4 The macaws (a,b) are different species, as are the plants (c).

a

b

c

STUDY GUIDE 170

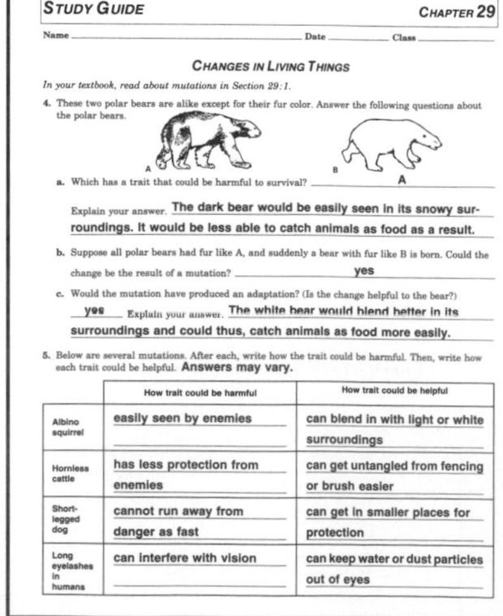

STUDY GUIDE — CHAPTER 29

Name ______ Date ______ Class ______

CHANGES IN LIVING THINGS

In your textbook, read about mutations in Section 29:1.

4. These two polar bears are alike except for their fur color. Answer the following questions about the polar bears.

A B

a. Which has a trait that could be harmful to survival? **A**

Explain your answer. **The dark bear would be easily seen in its snowy surroundings. It would be less able to catch animals as food as a result.**

b. Suppose all polar bears had fur like A, and suddenly a bear with fur like B is born. Could the change be the result of a mutation? **yes**

c. Would the mutation have produced an adaptation? (Is the change helpful to the bear?) **yes** Explain your answer. **The white bear would blend better in its surroundings and could thus, catch animals as food more easily.**

5. Below are several mutations. After each, write how the trait could be harmful. Then, write how each trait could be helpful. **Answers may vary.**

	How trait could be harmful	How trait could be helpful
Albino squirrel	easily seen by enemies	can blend in with light or white surroundings
Hornless cattle	has less protection from enemies	can get untangled from fencing or brush easier
Short-legged dog	cannot run away from danger as fast	can get in smaller places for protection
Long eyelashes in humans	can interfere with vision	can keep water or dust particles out of eyes

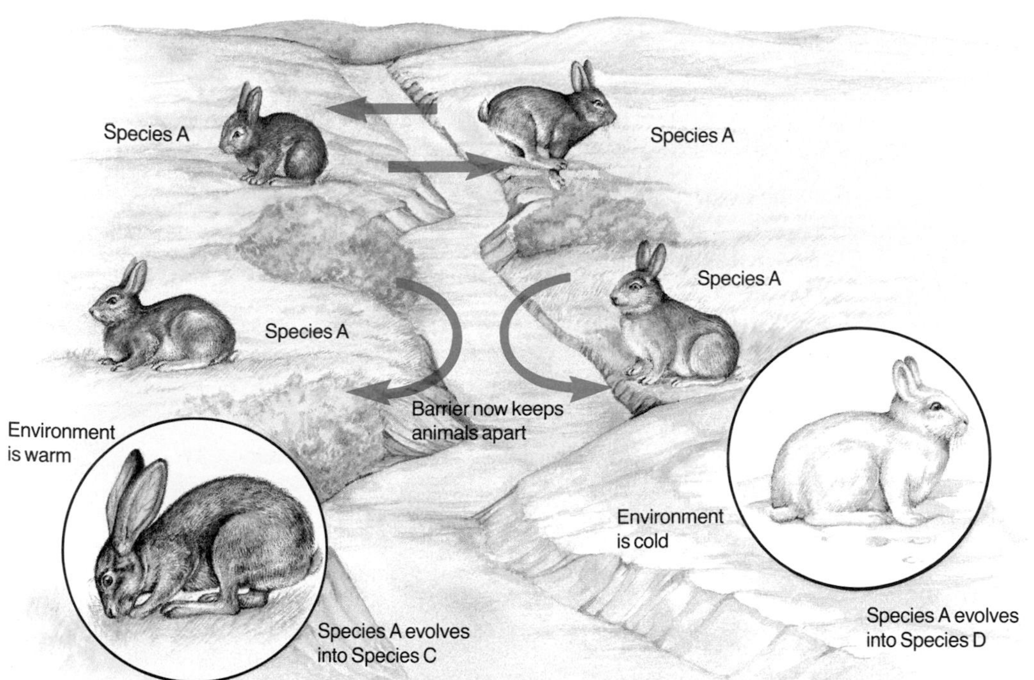
Species A
Species A
Species A
Species A
Environment is warm
Barrier now keeps animals apart
Environment is cold
Species A evolves into Species C
Species A evolves into Species D

Figure 29-5 A barrier can lead to the formation of new species.

Now we have a problem. Only members of the same species can breed and form offspring. Yet, new species are constantly appearing on Earth. How can new species appear? Follow the events shown in Figures 29-5 to see how this is possible. Let's start with a group of animals living on either side of a shallow stream. The animals at the top of Figure 29-5 are all of the same species. They can wade across the stream easily, but they are unable to swim. Due to a flood, the stream becomes a very wide river. It remains that way. The animals become separated into two groups. Being unable to swim, they are unable to cross the river. They continue to live apart for thousands of years. Note that the living conditions on each side of the river are different. During the time of separation, natural selection has taken place in each group. In each group, individuals lacking traits favorable for the new environment have died. Individuals with the favorable traits have survived and reproduced. The two groups gradually become different because their environments are different. In time, each group may become a different species.

How does the formation of a barrier lead to new species?

TEACH

Filmstrip

Show the filmstrip *Evolution III: Speciation,* Carolina Biological Supply Co.

Guided Practice

Have students write down their answers to the margin question: a barrier separates organisms. If conditions on either side of the barrier are different, new species may evolve.

OPTIONS

Challenge: Locate information on the Abert and Kaibab squirrel species. They live in different regions of the Grand Canyon. Report on: (a) how they are alike (b) how they differ (c) why they might have originally been the same species (d) how the canyon separated them into different groups (e) why they evolved into different species once separated by a canyon barrier.

Science Background

The forming of new species via a physical barrier is known as allopatric speciation. Barriers can be formed by volcanic eruptions, glaciers, or new mountain ranges. The term *allopatric* means other (allo) homeland (patric).

 **How Species Are Formed**/*Transparency Package,* number 29. Use color transparency number 29 as you teach species information.

TEACH

Check for Understanding

Provide students with the following scenario: Lions will chase their prey at very high speeds. Their prey can escape only if they are faster than the lions. Which of the prey will survive, those with stronger muscles for running or those with weaker muscles? Lions will also give up the chase after a few minutes of pursuing their prey. Which prey will survive, those with short endurance or those with long endurance? Which traits will be passed to future offspring of the prey?

Reteach

Ask certain students to explain their answers to the questions asked in Check for Understanding. Discuss students' answers and make any corrections or comments.

ACTIVITY/Field Trip

Visit the produce section of a large grocery store. Note the number of "new" plants available for human use that you did not see several years ago. Explain: (a) why these plants may not have been available a few years ago and what has allowed them to appear now, and (b) what the role of humans has been in making these new plants available.

Independent Practice

Study Guide/*Teacher Resource Package*, p. 171. Use the Study Guide worksheet shown at the bottom of this page for independent practice.

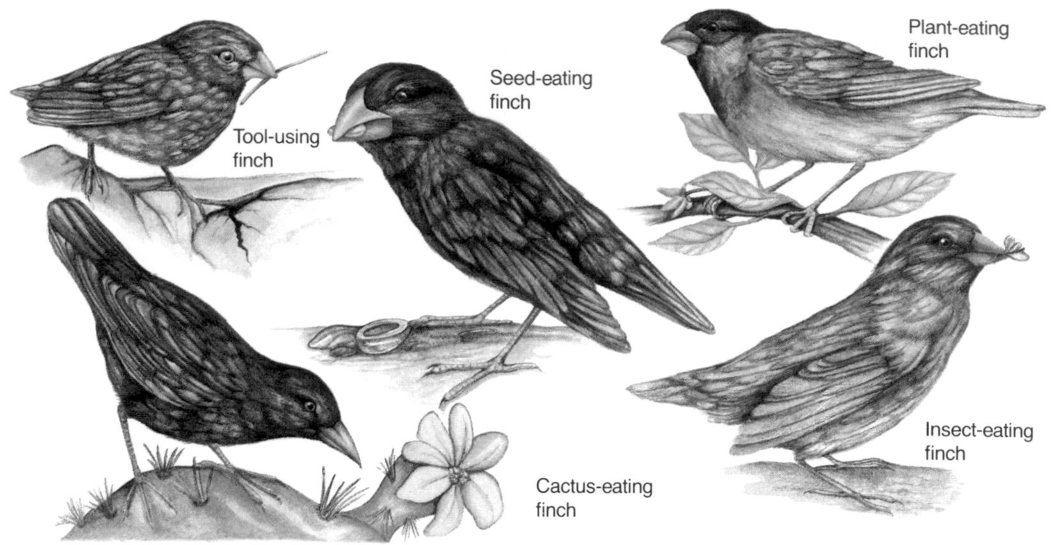

Figure 29-6 The finches on the Galapagos Islands are adapted to eating different kinds of food.

In the example just given, three events led to the development of two new species. First, a barrier formed that separated members of a species. The barrier could have been a river, ocean, new mountain, glacier, or a lava flow. Second, the animals found themselves living in different environments. Third, the groups began to show different traits as a result of natural selection. The two groups in time became two different species. As a result, they would not be able to breed and form fertile offspring if brought back together.

The finches that live on the Galapagos Islands are a well-known example of the forming of new species. On the Galapagos are several species of finch. Each species has a different beak shape. Some finches have thick beaks and are adapted to eating seeds. Some have small beaks and are adapted to eating insets. How did the finches come to live on the islands? The ancestor of the Galapagos finches probably flew to the islands from the mainland of South America. New species began to evolve when the finches spread out over the islands. The different groups of finches didn't come into contact with one another for a long time. Over time, the different groups became adapted to their new environments. They also became less like one another. A single finch ancestor had evolved into many different species.

OPTIONS

Challenge: The Galapagos Islands have a number of different finch species. Have students research the mechanism that led to the formation of these different bird species.

STUDY GUIDE 171

STUDY GUIDE CHAPTER 29

Name ______ Date ______ Class ______

CHANGES IN LIVING THINGS

In your textbook, read about species formation in Section 29:1.

6. a. How can the word *species* be defined as it relates to the classification of living things? **A species is the smallest group of living things.**

   b. How can the word *species* be defined as it relates to breeding? **A species is a group of living things that can breed with others of the same species and form fertile offspring.**

7. Use Figure 29-5 on page 611 of your textbook to help you do this exercise. The following statements involve events that can result in the formation of a new species. Number them from 1-6 in the proper order. Number one is done for you.

   3 a. animals are separated into two groups and must now live apart
   4 b. environments on either side of the river change with time
   1 c. animals of the same species living on either side of a stream can move from one side to the other
   2 d. the stream changes into a river
   5 e. animals, due to natural selection, undergo change
   6 f. after thousands of years, two different species of animals form

8. In the example in Figure 29-5, what three events led to the formation of new species? **A barrier formed that separated members of the species. Members of the species found themselves living in different environments. The groups began to show different traits as a result of natural selection.**

9. How do the finches of the Galapagos Islands differ? **Each has a differently shaped beak.**

10. Describe how a single finch ancestor probably evolved into many different species. **The ancestor probably flew to the islands from the mainland of South America. New species began to evolve when the finches spread out over the islands and became adapted to their new environments. Without contact with one another, the groups became less alike.**

Primate and Human Evolution

Fossils are very important when it comes to tracing the evolution of humans. They provide us with evidence of past life. Before looking at human evolution, a brief review of human classification will help. Some of the categories for humans are as follows: Phylum Chordate, Class Mammal, Order Primate.

The primate order is the one in which monkeys, apes, and humans are classified. **Primates** are mammals with eyes that face forward, a well-developed cerebrum, and thumbs that can be used for grasping. About 45 million years ago, primates evolved into two main groups, new-world monkeys and a second group. **New-world monkeys** have a tail that can grasp like a hand and nostrils that open upward. Howler and spider monkeys are examples of new-world monkeys. The second group that evolved is the ancestor of the old-world monkeys. It is also the ancestor of the group that evolved into apes and humanlike life-forms. **Old-world monkeys** can't grasp with their tails, if they have one, and their nostrils open downward. Baboons are old-world monkeys. Apes don't have tails and include gorillas and chimpanzees. Figure 29-7 shows the old-world monkeys, new-world monkeys, apes, and how they are related.

Skill Check

Understand science words: primate. The word *primate* comes from the word *prime* meaning first. In your dictionary, find three words with the word *prime* or word part *prima* in them. *For more help, refer to the* ***Skill Handbook****, pages 706-711.*

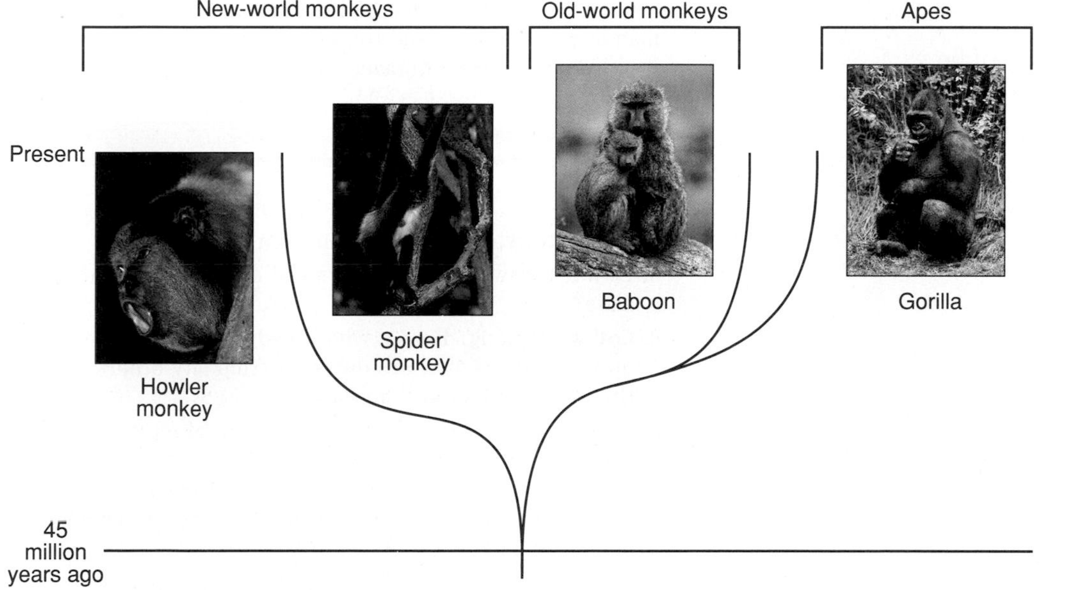

Figure 29-7 Primate groups include new-world monkeys, old-world monkeys, and apes.

TEACH

Concept Development

▶ Lesser known primates include lemurs, tarsiers, marmosets, and galagos (prosimians). More common are monkeys, apes, and humans (anthropoids).

Videocassette

Show the videocassette *Retracing Man's Steps,* Films for the Humanities and Sciences.

Bridging

Review the characteristics of each classification category with your students. Phylum chordate–having a chord along the dorsal side sometime during development, dorsal hollow nerve cord, gill slits. Class mammal–body usually covered with hair, constant body temperature, diaphragm, females with mammary glands that secrete milk to nourish young. Order primates–five digits on hand and foot, opposable thumb, usually one young at birth, eyes face forward and are surrounded and protected by bone.

Connection: English

Ask students to read the play *Inherit the Wind* or rent the video version of the film. Have them report their impressions to the class.

ENRICHMENT 31

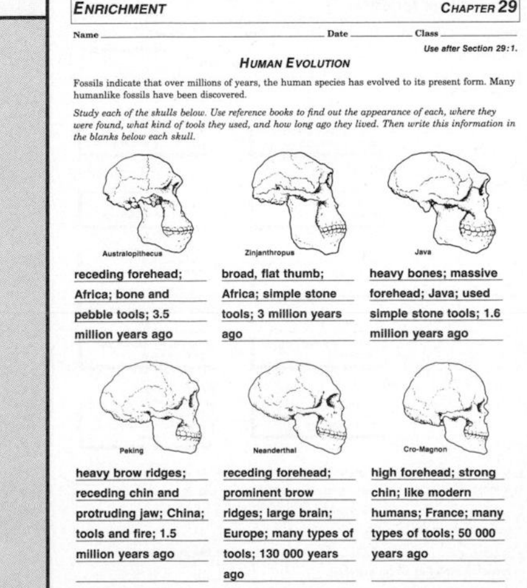

ENRICHMENT — CHAPTER 29

Name ______ Date ______ Class ______

Use after Section 29:1.

HUMAN EVOLUTION

Fossils indicate that over millions of years, the human species has evolved to its present form. Many humanlike fossils have been discovered.

Study each of the skulls below. Use reference books to find out the appearance of each, where they were found, what kind of tools they used, and how long ago they lived. Then write this information in the blanks below each skull.

Australopithecus: receding forehead; Africa; bone and pebble tools; 3.5 million years ago

Zinjanthropus: broad, flat thumb; Africa; simple stone tools; 3 million years ago

Java: heavy bones; massive forehead; Java; used simple stone tools; 1.6 million years ago

Peking: heavy brow ridges; receding chin and protruding jaw; China; tools and fire; 1.5 million years ago

Neanderthal: receding forehead; prominent brow ridges; large brain; Europe; many types of tools; 130 000 years ago

Cro-Magnon: high forehead; strong chin; like modern humans; France; many types of tools; 50 000 years ago

OPTIONS

ACTIVITY/Challenge

Ask students to use references to report on the appearance of early humans. Ask them to describe their traits, social structures, areas on Earth where they lived, advancements such as development of tools or use of fire. Diagrams would also be helpful.

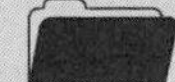

Enrichment/*Teacher Resource Package*, p. 31. Use the Enrichment worksheet shown here to extend knowledge of human evolution.

TEACH

Guided Practice

Have students write down their answers to the margin question: humans have thumbs for grasping, eyes that face forward, and well-developed cerebrums.

Check for Understanding

Have students respond to the first three questions in Check Your Understanding.

Reteach

Reteaching/*Teacher Resource Package*, p. 85. Use this worksheet if students are having trouble understanding natural selection.

Extension: Assign Critical Thinking, Biology and Math, or some of the **OPTIONS** available with this lesson.

3 APPLY

Software

Evolution, Queue, Inc.

4 CLOSE

Videocassette

Show the videocassette *The Human Influence,* Films for the Humanities and Sciences.

Answers to Check Your Understanding

1. Mice are protected from their enemies when they blend in with their surroundings.
2. If a barrier splits a population into two groups and the two groups have different environments, natural selection may eventually lead to the formation of two new species.
3. Both have eyes that face forward, a well developed cerebrum, and thumbs that can be used for grasping.
4. No. They can breed with other dog breeds to produce offspring.
5. The probability is about 1, or about 100 percent.

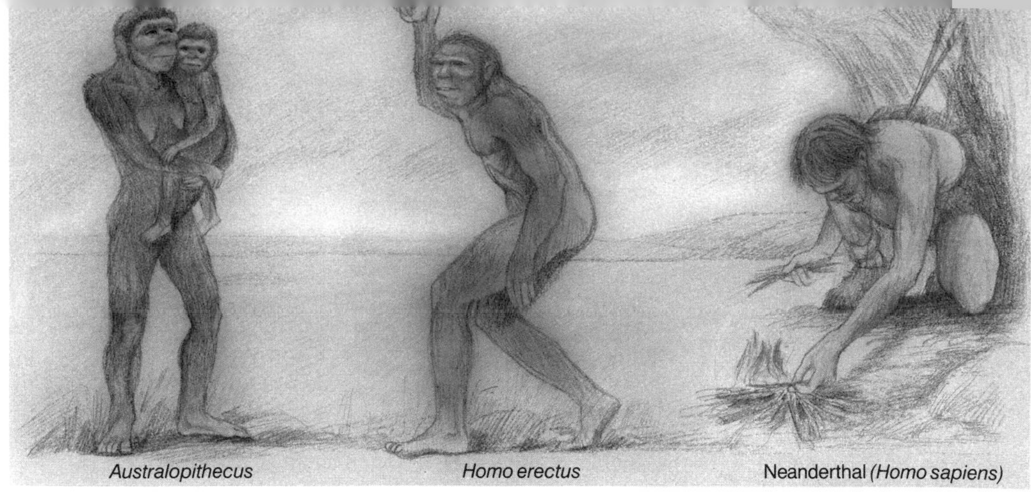

Figure 29-8 Australopithecus (ah stray loh PITH uh cus) is one of the earliest known humanlike forms. Then came *Homo erectus,* "upright man," and Neanderthals.

How are humans primates?

Humanlike ancestors first appeared around three million years ago. These ancestors walked upright, just as modern humans do. However, they were much shorter than modern humans. Several different humanlike groups evolved, but they all became extinct. Figure 29-8 shows these humanlike groups. Two groups of *Homo sapiens* have lived on Earth. *Homo sapiens* is the only human life-form alive today. One of the *Homo sapiens* groups was known as Neanderthal (nee AN dur thawl) man. Neanderthal man was shorter than modern humans and had thicker bones. Neanderthal man became extinct, and the second *Homo sapiens* group evolved into modern humans.

Check Your Understanding

1. How does color of a mouse affect its survival?
2. How can two species develop from one species?
3. How are new-world monkeys and old-world monkeys alike?
4. **Critical Thinking:** People who breed dogs sometimes end up with breeds that are different from any others. Are these dog breeds new species?
5. **Biology and Math:** In humans, the rate of mutation is about 1 in 100 000. You have about 100 000 genes. What is the chance that you have a gene that has a mutation and is, therefore, different from any of the genes your mother or father have?

OPTIONS

Challenge: Ask students to explain, on the basis of mutations and natural selection, how the brain size of humans has increased over time.

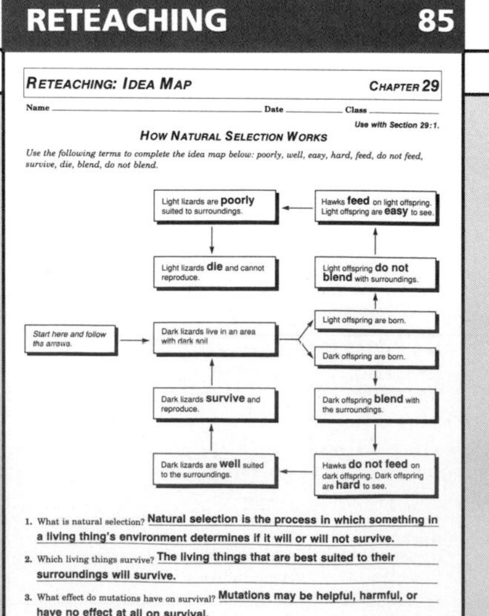

RETEACHING 85

RETEACHING: IDEA MAP — CHAPTER 29

Name ______ Date ______ Class ______

Use with Section 29:1.

HOW NATURAL SELECTION WORKS

Use the following terms to complete the idea map below: poorly, well, easy, hard, feed, do not feed, survive, die, blend, do not blend.

Start here and follow the arrows.
Dark lizards live in an area with dark soil.
Light offspring are born.
Light offspring **do not blend** with surroundings.
Hawks **feed** on light offspring. Light offspring are **easy** to see.
Light lizards are **poorly** suited to surroundings.
Light lizards **die** and cannot reproduce.
Dark offspring are born.
Dark offspring **blend** with the surroundings.
Hawks **do not feed** on dark offspring. Dark offspring are **hard** to see.
Dark lizards are **well** suited to the surroundings.
Dark lizards **survive** and reproduce.

1. What is natural selection? **Natural selection is the process in which something in a living thing's environment determines if it will or will not survive.**
2. Which living things survive? **The living things that are best suited to their surroundings will survive.**
3. What effect do mutations have on survival? **Mutations may be helpful, harmful, or have no effect at all on survival.**

29:2 Explanations for Evolution

How can we explain that life-forms have changed with time? What is the evidence that life-forms had a common beginning?

Objectives

4. **Communicate** Darwin's main ideas.
5. **Describe** evidence that supports evolution.

Key Science Words

variation
competition
evolution
fossil
extinct
sedimentary rock
vestigial structure

Darwin's Work

Much of what we have stated so far about adaptations and natural selection is not new. It was said over 100 years ago by Charles Darwin. When he was young, Darwin made a voyage around the world on a ship. During the trip, he observed many kinds of plants and animals and gathered examples of them. On some islands he collected living things not found anywhere else on Earth. Darwin saw that these living things were similar to life present in other parts of the world. For 20 years after his trip, Darwin studied the material he had collected. Finally, in 1859, he wrote a book explaining evolution (ev uh LEW shun) and his theory of natural selection.

Darwin made a number of important points in his book. We shall summarize several of his more important ideas.

1. **Living things overproduce.** More offspring are produced than survive. A single cottonwood tree forms thousands of seeds, Figure 29-9a. Frog eggs, shown in Figure 29-9b, are produced in the hundreds.

a

b

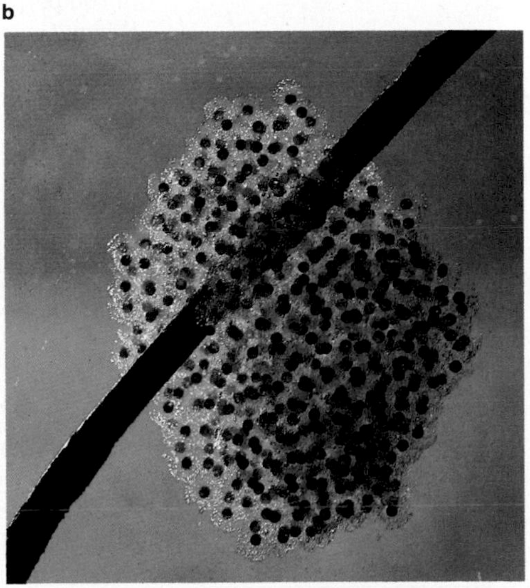

Figure 29-9 Cottonwood trees (a) and frogs (b) are examples of living things that produce more offspring than can survive.

OPTIONS

Challenge: Ask students how bacteria becoming resistant to certain antibiotics is an example of Darwin's principles. More bacteria are produced than can survive. There is variation among bacteria. Some are resistant to antibiotics. Some aren't. Bacteria compete for resources. Selection is always taking place. In this case, resistant bacteria survive. Nonresistant bacteria die. Over time, only resistant bacteria will be present in the population.

29:2 Explanations for Evolution

PREPARATION

Materials Needed

Make copies of the Transparency Master, Skill, Reteaching, Study Guide, and Lab worksheets in the *Teacher Resource Package*.

▶ Gather pea pods, rulers, wood blocks, petrified wood samples, balances, and graduated cylinders for the Mini Labs.

▶ Purchase the powder needed to form fossil imprints and gather leaves needed for Lab 29-2.

Key Science Words

variation
competition
evolution
fossil
extinct
sedimentary rock
vestigial structure

Process Skills

In Lab 29-2, students will formulate a model, observe, and infer. In the Skill Check, they will interpret diagrams. In the Mini Labs, they will make a bar graph and infer.

1 FOCUS

▶ The objectives are listed on the student page. Remind students to preview these objectives as a guide to this numbered section.

MOTIVATION/Brainstorming

Ask students whether living things change because they want to or because they need to. Neither idea is correct. Living things change as a result of natural selection.

2 TEACH

Convergent Question

Ask students to provide examples of variation in humans, dogs, or trees.

Cooperative Learning: Divide the class into 6 to 8 groups. Present the following: The giraffe today has a long neck that makes it well adapted for reaching its food. Have students explain how a change from short- to long-necked giraffes may have taken place over time using the four major themes of Darwin's work as a guide.

Guided Practice

Have students write down their answers to the margin question: there aren't enough resources to go around, and living things must compete for them.

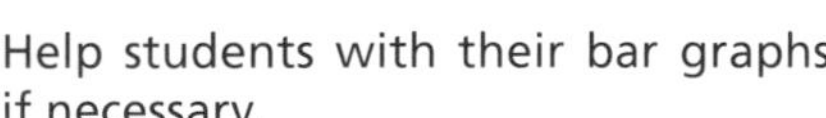

Mini Lab

Help students with their bar graphs if necessary.

Independent Practice

Study Guide/*Teacher Resource Package*, p. 172. Use the Study Guide worksheet shown at the bottom of this page for independent practice.

Figure 29-10 Tiger moths show variation in their wing patterns.

What does it mean that living things struggle to survive?

2. **There is variation (ver ee AY shun) among the offspring.** A **variation** is a trait that makes an individual different from others of its species. Each living thing does not appear exactly like all the others. Some of the differences between individuals are inherited. Figure 29-10 shows variations in color and pattern of tiger moth wings.
3. **There is a struggle to survive.** There are more living things than there are resources to go around. This results in competition. **Competition** is the struggle among living things to get their needs for life. Young pine trees compete for light, water, and soil nutrients. Rabbits compete with other rabbits for food, shelter, and mates.
4. **Natural selection is always taking place.** Individuals that have less desirable traits are less fit. They reproduce fewer offspring. Individuals that have desirable traits are more fit. They reproduce more offspring. The organisms alive today are the ones that are better suited to their surroundings. The traits, or variations, that make them more fit are the ones they inherited and will, in turn, pass to their offspring.

Darwin realized that species of organisms are always changing. He knew that the changes in species do not occur quickly. Darwin's studies led him to form the theory of natural selection to explain evolution. **Evolution** is a change in the hereditary features of a group of organisms over time. When a species changes through time, it is said to have evolved.

Mini Lab

How Do Peas Vary?

Make a bar graph: Find the average diameter of the peas in 10 pea pods. Make a bar graph of your data. How do your data relate to Darwin's statement about variation? *For more help, refer to the* ***Skill Handbook****, pages 715-717.*

OPTIONS

Enrichment: Ask students to provide examples of how term *evolution* is used in a nonbiological sense. That is, how is the term used to describe other events of change? Students may suggest evolving hair styles, clothing trends, auto design, etc.

STUDY GUIDE 172

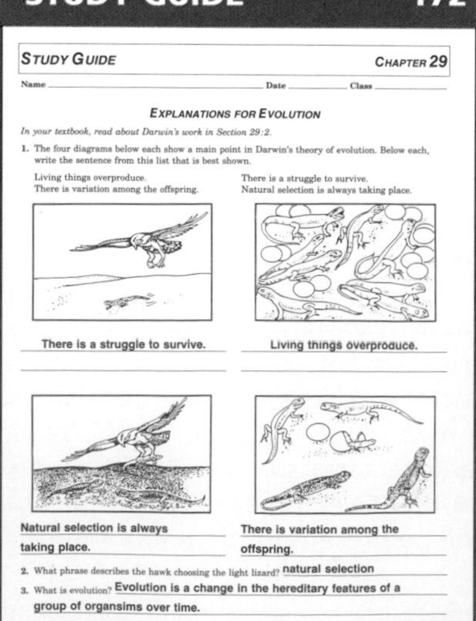

STUDY GUIDE — CHAPTER 29

Name ______ Date ______ Class ______

EXPLANATIONS FOR EVOLUTION

In your textbook, read about Darwin's work in Section 29:2.

1. The four diagrams below each show a main point in Darwin's theory of evolution. Below each, write the sentence from this list that is best shown.

Living things overproduce.
There is variation among the offspring.
There is a struggle to survive.
Natural selection is always taking place.

There is a struggle to survive.

Living things overproduce.

Natural selection is always taking place.

There is variation among the offspring.

2. What phrase describes the hawk choosing the light lizard? natural selection
3. What is evolution? Evolution is a change in the hereditary features of a group of organsims over time.

Fossil Evidence

What evidence supports evolution? Some evidence of evolution comes from fossils. **Fossils** are the remains of once-living things from ages past.

A fossil may be a print of a leaf. It may be a footprint of an animal. It could even be a skeleton. A fossil could be an animal trapped and frozen in ice. Or a fossil could be an insect trapped in hardened plant sap.

When living things from the past are compared to living things today, we can see that change has occurred. For example, Figure 29-11 shows the fossil remains of an extinct (ihk STINGT) animal. An **extinct** life-form is one that no longer exists.

Fossils are found in Earth's crust. They are present in sedimentary rocks. **Sedimentary rocks** form from layers of mud, sand, and other fine particles. The mud, sand, and fine particles are called sediments. These sediments form at the bottom of seas. Many animals and plants die and settle to the bottoms of oceans, lakes, or ponds with the sediments. These sediments change into rock over millions of years. Fossils form within these sediment layers. Fossils give us a record of what types of living things were on Earth in the past. Scientists can tell how old fossils are by dating them. Being able to date fossils gives scientists an idea of the history of life on Earth.

Mini Lab

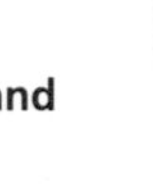

How Do Wood and Fossil Wood Compare?

Infer: Compare the density of a piece of wood with the density of a piece of fossil wood. Which has higher density? Why? *For more help, refer to the **Skill Handbook**, pages 706-711.*

Figure 29-11 This wooly mammoth is extinct. What present-day animal does it resemble?

TEACH

Demonstration

To illustrate the formation of sedimentary rocks, do the following: Place several spoonfuls of loose soil into an empty mayonnaise jar. Add several spoonfuls of clay soil and several spoonfuls of small stones. Add enough water to fill the jar two-thirds full. Cover the jar and shake several times. Allow the soil, clay, and stones to settle. To further illustrate how a fossil is formed, place a clam or oyster shell into the same jar. Remix the contents and allow it to settle once again.

Mini Lab

Purchase fossils from a biological supply house or from a local rock shop. Ask the industrial shop teacher to supply you with small cubes of wood that fit into a graduated cylinder or beaker. Procedure: (a) Design a suitable data table. (b) Mass the wood and fossil using a balance. (c) Determine fossil and wood volume by measuring displacement. (d) Review the formula for determining density (density = mass divided by volume).

ACTIVITY/Project

Ask students to prepare a time line that illustrates the appearance of different life-forms on Earth. Students may divide their charts into the different eras or periods. The information can be found in most college textbooks.

TRANSPARENCY 147

TRANSPARENCY MASTER — CHAPTER 29

GEOLOGIC TIME SCALE

Era	Period	Epoch	Age (years ago)	Representative life forms
Cenozoic	Quaternary	Recent	100 000	Humans; modern forms of plants and animals
		Pleistocene	1 000 000	Extinction of many mammals; primitive humans; grasslands
	Tertiary	Pliocene	10 000 000	Early humans; other mammals; herbs
		Miocene	30 000 000	Mammals; grasses
		Oligocene	40 000 000	Primates and other mammals; forests common
		Eocene	60 000 000	Primitive horse; other mammals; flowering plants
		Paleocene	75 000 000	Mammals predominant; more modern flowering plants
Mesozoic	Cretaceous		135 000 000	Extinction of giant reptiles; birds and insects; flowering plants
	Jurassic		165 000 000	Dinosaurs dominant; primitive birds and mammals; earliest flowering plants
	Triassic		205 000 000	Dinosaurs and other reptiles; early mammals; primitive seed plants
Paleozoic	Permian		230 000 000	Rise of insects; early reptiles
	Carboniferous		280 000 000	Insects and amphibians; mosses and ferns
	Devonian		325 000 000	Age of fishes; early amphibians; early bryophytes; ferns
	Silurian		360 000 000	Club mosses; insects and other invertebrates
	Ordovician		425 000 000	Primitive mollusks and fish; algae
	Cambrian		500 000 000	Protists; sponges, jellyfish; spore-producing plants
Precambrian			4 500 000 000	Monerans; simple protists; fungi; simple invertebrates

OPTIONS

Science Background

The oldest known fossils are deposits of cyanobacteria in sedimentary rock. Their age is estimated to be between 3 and 3.5 billion years.

How Do Fossils Show Change?/*Lab Manual*, pp. 247-250. Use this lab as an extension to fossil evidence.

Transparency Master/*Teacher Resource Package*, p. 147. Use the Transparency Master shown here to explain the geologic time scale.

Lab 29-2 Fossil Prints

Overview

Students will simulate the formation of a fossil in sedimentary rock. A rapid-setting dental powder is used.

Objectives: Upon completion of this lab, students will be able to: (1) **define** what a fossil is, (2) **model** the steps involved in forming a fossil, (3) **identify** the steps involved in forming a real fossil.

Time Allotment: 30 minutes

Preparation

▶ Plastic dishes may be cottage cheese containers.

▶ Order the plastic powder from: L.D. Caulk Co., Division of Dentsply, Milford, DE 19963. Request Type 2 Jeltrate or substitute. Another source is: Coe Labs, 3737 W. 127 St., Chicago, IL 60658. Request Type 2 alginate or substitute.

▶ The powder may also be ordered or purchased from your local dentist.

▶ Note: The exact amount of water to powder may vary with each brand used. Adjust accordingly.

Lab 29-2 worksheet/*Teacher Resource Package*, pp. 115-116.

Teaching the Lab

▶ Students can remove the solidified powder by simply flexing the sides of the container. The powder should pop out.

▶ Review the markings on the graduated cylinder with students as part of the prelab.

Cooperative Learning: Divide the class into groups of two students. For more information, refer to the Teacher Guide, pp. 22T-23T.

Fossil Prints — Lab 29–2

Problem: How is a fossil print made in rock?

Skills

formulate a model, observe, infer

Materials

plastic dish
100 mL graduated cylinder
leaf
warm water
plastic powder
metric ruler

Procedure

1. Copy the data table.
2. List as many traits as you can for the actual leaf. You may want to measure certain leaf parts with a ruler.
3. Measure 60 mL of plastic powder with a graduated cylinder. Pour the powder into a small dish as in the figure.
4. Slowly add 36 mL of warm water to the powder. Use your hands to mix the water and powder until it is claylike. The claylike substance represents soft rock.
5. Flatten the soft rock so that it covers the dish bottom. Smooth out the top surface.
6. Place a leaf onto the soft rock's surface.
7. Gently press the leaf into the soft rock.
8. Wait five minutes. Then remove the leaf.
9. Allow the soft rock to harden for a few more minutes.

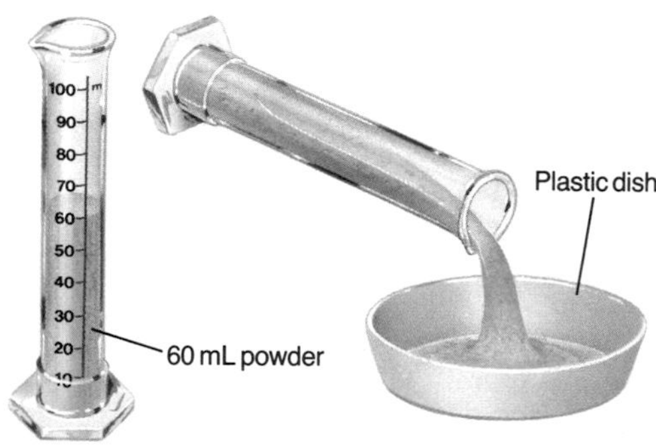

10. Examine the leaf "fossil" print. Compare it to the original leaf.
11. **Observe:** List as many traits as you can for the leaf "fossil" in your data table.
12. Clean and return your materials to their proper place.

Data and Observations

1. How are the actual leaf and leaf "fossil" alike? How do they differ?
2. Match the following steps with the numbered steps in the procedure.
   (a) A soft soil such as clay is present.
   (b) A leaf falls onto the clay surface.
   (c) The leaf gets pressed down into the clay.
   (d) The clay hardens. The leaf breaks down and disappears.
   (e) A print of the leaf remains on the hard rock.

TRAITS	
Actual leaf	Leaf "fossil"

Analyze and Apply

1. How do fossils give information about past ages?
2. **Infer:** List several examples of what may become a fossil.
3. **Apply:** How long would steps 8 and 9 take if this were happening in nature?

Extension

Observe: Examine pieces of marble for fossils. How did the fossils get into the marble?

ANSWERS

Data and Observations

1. margin of the leaf, vein pattern; different color, thickness, and more detail in the live organism
2. (a) 4 (b) 6 (c) 7 (d) 8, 9 (e) 10

Analyze and Apply

1. They show the imprint of a living thing from that age.
2. leaf, skeleton of an animal, entire plant, insect
3. millions of years

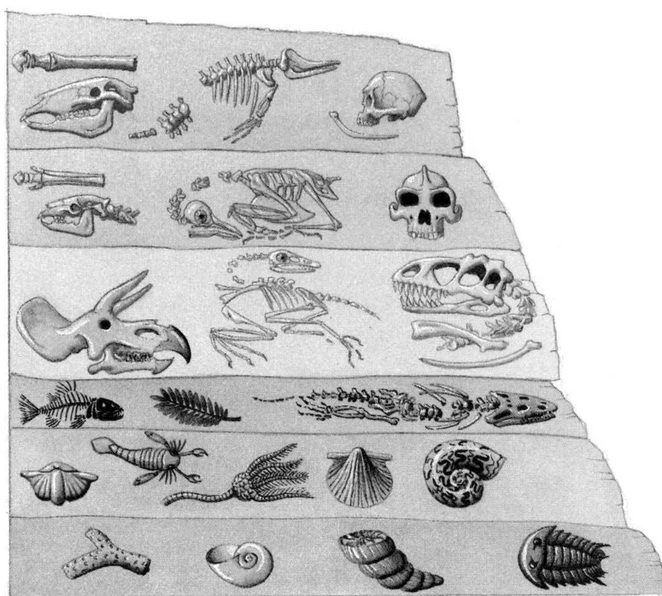

Figure 29-12 Fossils in the lower layers of sedimentary rock are older than those found near the top layers.

Figure 29-12 is a side view of sedimentary rocks in Earth's crust. Where is the oldest layer of rock located? Because it was the first layer to form, it is on the bottom. Younger layers settle on top of the oldest layer. So, as you move up the layers, the rocks get younger. This is similar to stacking newspapers. Suppose you always put the most recent newspaper on top of the stack. As long as the stack is left alone, the oldest paper will always be on the bottom. The newest paper will be on top. Fossils found in the lower layers of rock are older than those found in the upper layers.

Compare the fossils in the bottom layers to those near the top. How many fossil forms found toward the bottom and middle layers are still alive today? Not too many. How many fossil forms found in the top layers are still alive today? Certainly more than in the middle and bottom layers.

Other Evidence

In Chapter 3, you studied that comparing the origins of body structures and comparing body chemistries are ways to determine relationships among different species. Each of these comparisons is evidence of evolution.

Skill Check

Interpret diagrams: Study Figure 29-12. In which rock layers are the more simple fossils found? *For more help, refer to the **Skill Handbook**, pages 706-711.*

TEACH

Videocassette

Show the videocassette *The Record of the Rocks,* Films for the Humanities and Sciences.

Bridging

Ask students who have had a course in earth science the following question: Why does one not find fossil evidence in igneous or metamorphic rocks?

Filmstrip

Show the filmstrip *The Fossil History of Man,* Carolina Biological Supply Co.

Independent Practice

Study Guide/*Teacher Resource Package*, p. 173. Use the Study Guide worksheet shown at the bottom of this page for independent practice.

STUDY GUIDE 173

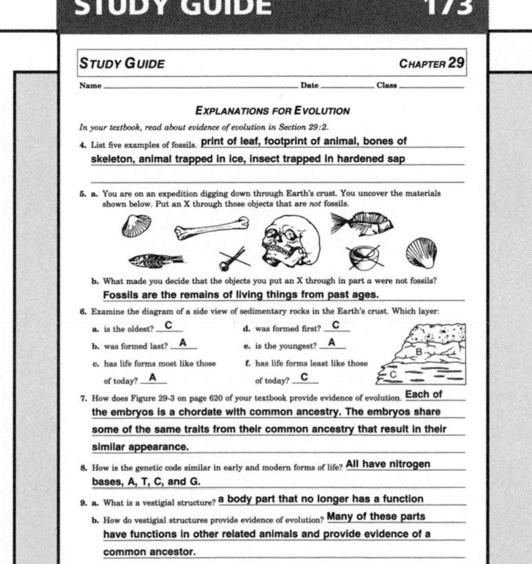

STUDY GUIDE CHAPTER 29

Name _____ Date _____ Class _____

EXPLANATIONS FOR EVOLUTION

In your textbook, read about evidence of evolution in Section 29:2.

4. List five examples of fossils. **print of leaf, footprint of animal, bones of skeleton, animal trapped in ice, insect trapped in hardened sap**

5. a. You are on an expedition digging down through Earth's crust. You uncover the materials shown below. Put an X through those objects that are *not* fossils.

b. What made you decide that the objects you put an X through in part *a* were not fossils? **Fossils are the remains of living things from past ages.**

6. Examine the diagram of a side view of sedimentary rocks in the Earth's crust. Which layer:

a. is the oldest? **C**
b. was formed last? **A**
c. has life forms most like those of today? **A**
d. was formed first? **C**
e. is the youngest? **A**
f. has life forms least like those of today? **C**

7. How does Figure 29-3 on page 620 of your textbook provide evidence of evolution. **Each of the embryos is a chordate with common ancestry. The embryos share some of the same traits from their common ancestry that result in their similar appearance.**

8. How is the genetic code similar in early and modern forms of life? **All have nitrogen bases, A, T, C, and G.**

9. a. What is a vestigial structure? **a body part that no longer has a function**

b. How do vestigial structures provide evidence of evolution? **Many of these parts have functions in other related animals and provide evidence of a common ancestor.**

SKILL 30

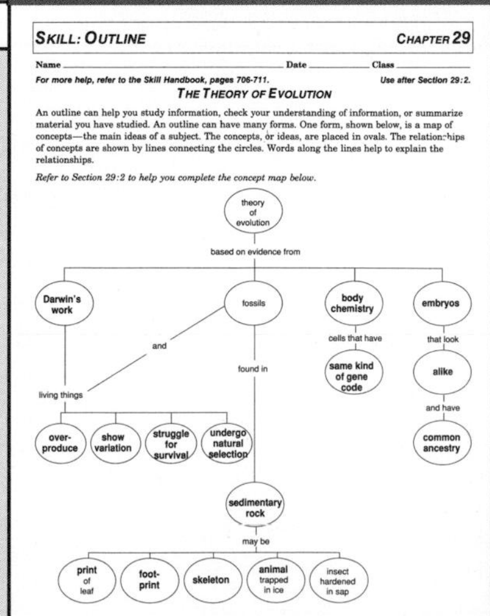

SKILL: OUTLINE CHAPTER 29

Name _____ Date _____ Class _____

For more help, refer to the Skill Handbook, pages 706-711. *Use after Section 29:2.*

THE THEORY OF EVOLUTION

An outline can help you study information, check your understanding of information, or summarize material you have studied. An outline can have many forms. One form, shown below, is a map of concepts—the main ideas of a subject. The concepts, or ideas, are placed in ovals. The relationships of concepts are shown by lines connecting the circles. Words along the lines help to explain the relationships.

Refer to Section 29:2 to help you complete the concept map below.

OPTIONS

Skill/*Teacher Resource Package*, p. 30. Use the Skill worksheet shown here to reinforce the concept of evolution.

TEACH

Concept Development

▶ Structures with similar origins and functions are called *homologous structures.* Structures with similar functions but different origins are called analogous structures.

▶ Plant-eating animals typically have a rather long caecum (cecum) along with the appendix that aids in the breakdown and digestion of cellulose.

ACTIVITY/Demonstration

Ask if any students can wiggle their ears. Ear muscles are considered to be vestigial structures.

Bridging

Ask how it is possible for human DNA placed within a bacterial cell to work. All living things contain DNA. This is very strong evidence of a common origin.

Guided Practice

Have students write down their answers to the margin question: a vestigal structure is evidence of a common ancestor.

Independent Practice

Study Guide/*Teacher Resource Package*, p. 174. Use the Study Guide worksheet shown at the bottom of this page for independent practice.

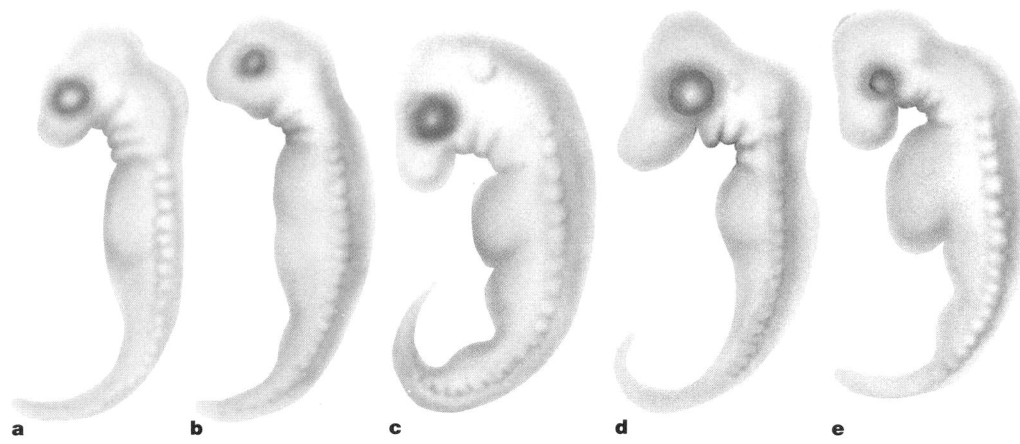

Figure 29-13 Embryos of a fish (a), frog (b), turtle (c), bird (d), and rabbit (e) look similar.

Another comparison also provides evidence of evolution. Figure 29-13 shows five different animal embryos. Fish, frog, turtle, bird, and rabbit embryos are shown. Which embryo is which? You really can't tell. They all look very much alike at this stage in their development. As they get older, you will be able to tell which embryo is which. How is the similar appearance of embryos evidence of evolution? All five animals are chordates. They have a common ancestry. The embryos share some of the same traits from their common ancestry. These traits result in all the embryos looking similar.

What other evidence is there of evolution? If later life-forms evolved from earlier ones, wouldn't the later forms have something in common with the earlier forms? Read the following examples for the answer to this question. Early life-forms are made of cells. So are later life-forms. Early life-forms have DNA as part of their chromosomes. So do later life-forms. The gene code in early life-forms is made of nitrogen bases, A, T, C, and G. Later life-forms have the same kind of gene code.

Have you ever wondered what that little pink lump is in the corner of your eye? What does it do? What does your appendix do? Both of these body parts are called vestigial (vuh STIJ ee ul) structures. A **vestigial structure** is a body part that no longer has a function. How is a vestigial body part evidence of evolution? Most of these body parts do have jobs in other animals. For example, in many mammals the appendix helps digest food. Rabbits are examples of animals with an appendix that still works to digest food.

How are vestigial structures evidence of evolution?

OPTIONS

Science Background

The small pink lump in the corner of the eye is called the nictitating membrane. Other vestigial structures in humans are: third molars, muscles that move the ears, body hair, coccyx vertebrae (tailbone), appendix.

STUDY GUIDE 174

STUDY GUIDE CHAPTER 29

Name ______ Date ______ Class ______

VOCABULARY

Review the new words in Chapter 29 of your textbook. Then, write a sentence defining each word.

1. species — a group of living things that can breed with others of the same species and form fertile offspring
2. old-world monkeys — monkeys that can't grasp with their tails and that have nostrils that open downward
3. natural selection — process in which something in the surroundings determines if a living thing survives to have offspring
4. vestigial structure — a body part that no longer has a function
5. sedimentary rocks — rocks that form from layers of mud, sand, and other fine particles
6. primate — mammal with eyes that face forward, a well-developed cerebrum, and grasping thumbs
7. evolution — change in the hereditary features of a group of organisms over time
8. new-world monkeys — monkeys that have a grasping tail and nostrils that open upward
9. extinct — a life-form that no longer exists
10. competition — a struggle among living things to get their needs for life
11. fossils — remains of once-living things from ages past
12. fertile — able to reproduce by forming egg or sperm cells
13. variation — trait that makes an individual different from others in its species

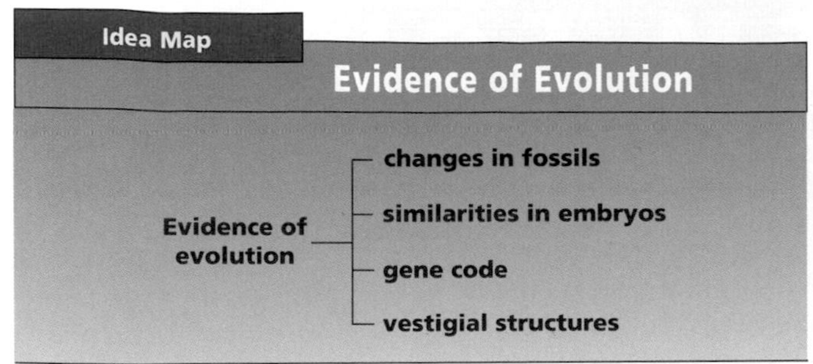

Study Tip: Use the idea map as a study guide to the kinds of evidence that show that species evolve over time.

This part of a rabbit intestine helps to break down plant material, the rabbit's chief source of food. The pink lump in your eye is all that is left of a third eyelid. In other animals the third eyelid is usually very thin and covers the entire eye. Frogs and turtles are examples of animals with third eyelids. The third eyelid of these animals protects the eye while the animal is under water. Birds, fish, and reptiles also have third eyelids that protect the eye.

We may not have any use for our appendixes or what remains of our third eyelid. These structures, however, are still useful to related animals. Thus, the presence of vestigial structures is evidence of a common ancestor for us and related animals. We still have the genes for appendixes and third eyelids, even though we don't use these structures. Animals that are related to us also have the genes for these traits.

Check Your Understanding

6. List and describe the four major points of Darwin's theory of natural selection.
7. Give several examples of fossils and tell where they are formed.
8. Describe how the embryos shown in Figure 29-13 are alike.
9. **Critical Thinking:** An athlete breaks her leg in a high jump. Years later, she has a son who walks with a slight limp. Is this an example of evolution? Why or why not?
10. **Biology and Reading:** What kinds of evidence do scientists have for evolution?

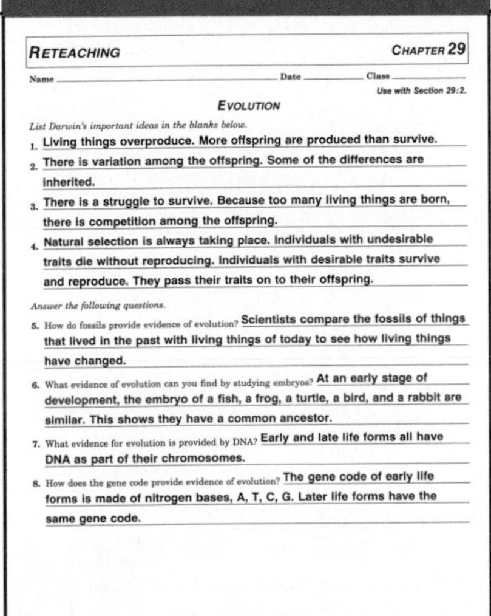

RETEACHING 86

RETEACHING CHAPTER 29

Name ______ Date ______ Class ______

Use with Section 29:2.

EVOLUTION

List Darwin's important ideas in the blanks below.

1. Living things overproduce. More offspring are produced than survive.
2. There is variation among the offspring. Some of the differences are inherited.
3. There is a struggle to survive. Because too many living things are born, there is competition among the offspring.
4. Natural selection is always taking place. Individuals with undesirable traits die without reproducing. Individuals with desirable traits survive and reproduce. They pass their traits on to their offspring.

Answer the following questions.

5. How do fossils provide evidence of evolution? Scientists compare the fossils of things that lived in the past with living things of today to see how living things have changed.
6. What evidence of evolution can you find by studying embryos? At an early stage of development, the embryo of a fish, a frog, a turtle, a bird, and a rabbit are similar. This shows they have a common ancestor.
7. What evidence for evolution is provided by DNA? Early and late life forms all have DNA as part of their chromosomes.
8. How does the gene code provide evidence of evolution? The gene code of early life forms is made of nitrogen bases, A, T, C, G. Later life forms have the same gene code.

TEACH

Idea Map

Have students use the idea map as a study guide to the major concepts of this section.

Check for Understanding

Have students respond to the first three questions in Check Your Understanding.

Reteach

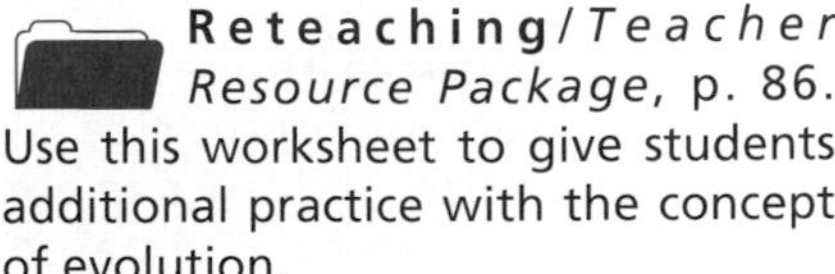

Reteaching/*Teacher Resource Package*, p. 86. Use this worksheet to give students additional practice with the concept of evolution.

Extension: Assign Critical Thinking, Biology and Reading, or some of the **OPTIONS** available with this lesson.

3 APPLY

ACTIVITY/Brainstorming

Why would you expect the following traits *not* to be passed to offspring: muscle building, tatoos, and plastic surgery to reshape a person's nose?

4 CLOSE

Convergent Question

Have students suggest how the dinosaurs may have become extinct.

Answers to Check Your Understanding

6. (1) Living things tend to overproduce. (2) Over production leads to competition. (3) Variation occurs among living things. (4) Living things with favorable variations will survive and reproduce more offspring.
7. a leaf print formed in sediments, an animal trapped in ice, a skeleton trapped in sediments
8. The embryos have tails, eyes, slits at the base of the neck.
9. No. There must be a change in the genes of the sex cell.
10. fossils, embryos, chemical evidence, and vestigial structures

PROBLEM SOLVING

Solving the Primate Puzzle

Problem-solving Strategies

The following strategies can be used to solve the problem: making a table to summarize similar traits and looking for a pattern.

Hints

▶ How far forward the jaw protrudes, number of teeth, size of canines, brain size, and jaw size are all traits that can be compared directly from the diagrams.

▶ An animal that walks on all fours would form footprints as well as handprints. Have students picture how a chimpanzee walks.

Solving the Problem

a) chimp and early human
b) all three
c) chimpanzee
d) chimp and early human
e) chimp and early human
f) modern human
g) chimpanzee
h) early human and modern human

1. Both have jaws that jut forward, about the same brain size, brow ridges.
2. Both walk upright.
3. All have 16 teeth on one side.
4. Chimps have large canines and walk on all fours.
5. Humans have a small lower jaw.

PROBLEM SOLVING

SOLVING THE PRIMATE PUZZLE

Picture yourself digging in an area known for its fossils of humans. You uncover some fossils, but you don't know if they are of a modern human, an early human, or a chimpanzee. You decide to compare your find with what is already known about modern humans, early humans, and chimpanzees. For example, you wish to compare jaw shape, number and size of teeth, and brain size. Read the statements that follow and study the diagrams on these two pages. Decide which skull or skulls are being described. Then, answer the questions.

a. This skull has a jaw that juts forward.
b. This skull has 16 teeth on one side.
c. This skull has large canine teeth (marked with an X).
d. These skulls have almost the same size brain.

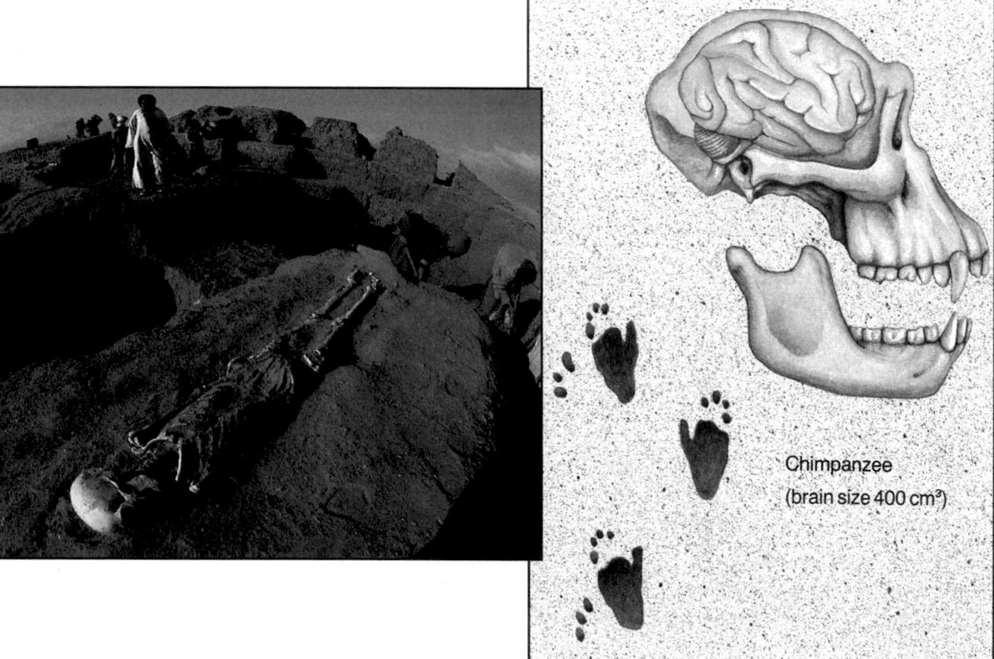

e. These skulls have thick bones (brow ridges) above the eye.
f. This skull has the smallest lower jaw.
g. These footprints show that the animal walked on all four legs.
h. These footprints show that the animal walked upright on two legs.

1. What traits are shared by chimpanzees and early humans?
2. What traits are shared by early humans and modern humans?
3. What traits are shared by all three animals?
4. What traits are present only in chimpanzees?
5. What traits are present only in modern humans?

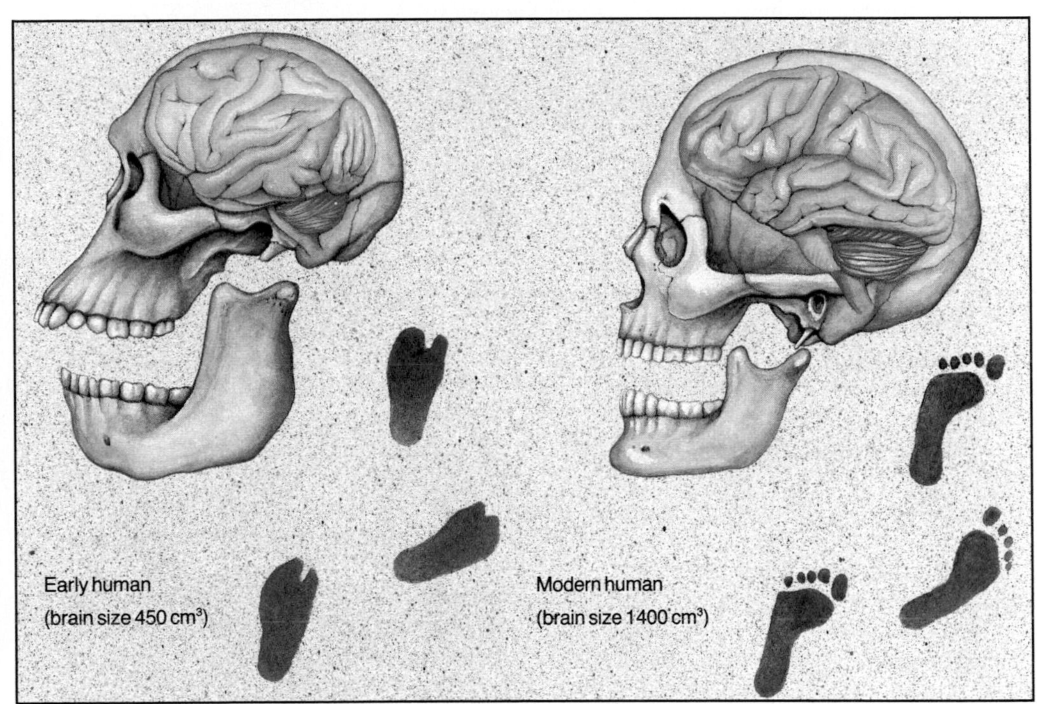

Discussing the Problem

▶ Students will recognize traits that help to identify chimpanzee, early human, and modern human skull fossils. These traits can be used to identify unknown fossils and determine if they are chimpanzee, early human, or modern human.

Extension: Using the skull outline as a guide, have students draw the skin and muscle layers onto the faces in an attempt to reconstruct the actual appearance of each animal. Note: you may wish to provide students with enlarged diagrams of the three skull outlines.

CHAPTER 29 REVIEW

Summary

Summary statements can be used by students to review the major concepts of the chapter.

Key Science Words

All boldfaced terms from the chapter are listed.

Testing Yourself

Using Words

1. evolution
2. competition
3. extinct
4. natural selection
5. variation
6. sedimentary rock
7. fossil
8. vestigial structure
9. primate
10. fertile

Finding Main Ideas

11. p. 619; The oldest layer is at the bottom because it was the first layer to form. Newer layers settle on top of the oldest layer.
12. p. 615; More offspring are produced than can survive. They aren't able to survive because resources are limited.
13. p. 613; Humans are Homo sapiens. They belong to the Phylum Chordate, the Class Mammal, and the Order Primate. Primates are mammals with eyes that face forward, a well-developed cerebrum, and thumbs that can be used for grasping.
14. p. 620; Since chordate embryos share similar traits, they must share a common ancestry.
15. p. 607; If the color of the background soil changes, the survival of the two different colored mice changes.
16. p. 609; Because of natural selection, some individuals are better adapted to their environment than others. These individuals will survive and produce more offspring than less well adapted individuals.

Chapter 29 Review

Summary

29:1 Changes in Living Things

1. All living things have adaptations that help them survive.
2. Changes in life-forms are the result of natural selection, mutations, and changes in the environment.
3. Primates evolved about 45 million years ago into two main groups. One of these groups was the ancestor of apes and humans. Humans evolved about three million years ago.

29:2 Explanations for Evolution

4. Darwin described his ideas about evolution over 100 years ago. His four main points were: living things overproduce, variation occurs in living things, there is a struggle to survive, and those that survive to reproduce are the ones that have traits best suited for their surroundings.
5. Evidence of evolution comes from fossil remains, similarity of embryos, similarity between chemical makeup of early and present-day life-forms, and from the presence of vestigial structures.

Key Science Words

competition (p. 616)
evolution (p. 616)
extinct (p. 617)
fertile (p. 610)
fossil (p. 617)
natural selection (p. 609)
new-world monkey (p. 613)
old-world monkey (p. 613)
primate (p. 613)
sedimentary rock (p. 617)
species (p. 610)
variation (p. 616)
vestigial structure (p. 620)

Testing Yourself

Using Words

Choose the word from the list of Key Science Words that best fits the definition.

1. a change in hereditary features of a group over time
2. struggle among living things for their needs
3. species that is no longer living
4. when something in the environment determines whether or not a living thing survives
5. a trait that makes a living thing different from others in its species
6. a type of rock formed from layers of mud and sand
7. remains of any once-living thing
8. the appendix or the third eyelid of humans
9. mammal that has eyes that face forward and grasping thumbs
10. being able to reproduce by forming egg or sperm cells

624

Using Main Ideas

17. Dark-colored mice are well adapted to living in areas with dark soil because they can hide more easily from their enemies.
18. First, a barrier forms that separates members of a species. The environment on either side of the barrier changes. Individuals that are well adapted to the new environments will survive and reproduce. Over time new species may evolve.
19. (a) Fossils show that extinct life-forms are related to present-day life-forms.
(b) Earlier and later life-forms have the same DNA code and, therefore, have something in common.
20. Some individuals have inherited adaptations that allow them to survive and reproduce better than individuals without those adaptations.
21. Animals and plants die and settle at the bottom of oceans, lakes, or ponds with sediments of mud, sand, and other fine particles. They are covered with more sediments, and over millions of years, the sediments change into rock. The animal or plant parts covered by the sediment form permanent imprints in the rock.

Review

Testing Yourself *continued*

Finding Main Ideas

List the page number where each main idea below is found. Then, explain each main idea.

11. why the oldest layer of sedimentary rock is found on the bottom
12. what Darwin meant when he said that living things overproduce
13. human classification and traits of the order to which they belong
14. the importance of chordate embryos looking alike
15. what may cause the balance to change in favor of the survival of light-colored or dark-colored mice
16. how natural selection works

Using Main Ideas

Answer the questions by referring to the page number after each question.

17. Why are dark-colored mice well adapted or not well adapted to living in areas with dark soil? (p. 607)
18. What are three events that lead to the formation of new species? (p. 612)
19. How are the following used as evidence of evolution?
    (a) comparison of fossil life-forms to present day life-forms (p. 617)
    (b) the DNA codes of all life-forms being made up of the same nitrogen bases (p. 620)
20. What did Darwin mean when he indicated that some individuals are more fit than others? (p. 616)
21. How are fossils formed? (p. 617)
22. How do monkeys and apes differ? (p. 613)
23. What are the three effects of mutations? (p. 609)

Skill Review ✔

*For more help, refer to the **Skill Handbook,** pages 704-719.*

1. **Infer:** Which flower would have the best chance of being pollinated by a moth, one that opens during the day or one that opens during the night? Why?
2. **Define words in context:** During the evolution of the horse, the number of toes decreased from four to three to one. What does the word evolution mean as used in this sentence?
3. **Interpret data:** During an experiment, a student reported the following distances that the frogs she was raising were able to jump: 1.2 m, 0.5 m, 0.9 m, 1.0 m, 0.6 m, 1.1 m. Are her data evidence of variation?
4. **Interpret diagrams:** Study Figure 29-13. How are the embryos alike?

Finding Out More

Critical Thinking

1. How might being white help a rabbit survive in Alaska?
2. Assume the trait in question 1 is a genetic trait. Will it be passed to future generations? Explain.

Applications

1. You wish to breed a chicken that produces many large eggs. Outline a breeding program that could accomplish this goal.
2. Use references to determine what the brain size, general appearance, and method of walking (two or four legs) were for early humanlike species.

625

Chapter Review/*Teacher Resource Package*, pp. 153-154.

Chapter Test/*Teacher Resource Package*, pp. 155-157.

Chapter Test/*Computer Test Bank*

Unit Test/*Teacher Resource Package*, pp. 158-159.

Using Main Ideas

22. Monkeys have tails, and apes don't have tails.
23. Mutations change the DNA code, are a source for new traits, and may supply new adaptations.

Skill Review

1. night; Moths fly at night.
2. At one time, horses had more toes than presently. However, some horses were born that had fewer toes. These horses were able to survive better and produce more young. Over time, horses with fewer toes became more numerous and eventually were the only kind of horse.
3. yes
4. tails, eyes, slits at base of neck, the beginnings of the spine

Finding Out More

Critical Thinking

1. It would blend in with the snowy background and could easily hide from enemies.
2. Yes. Rabbits with this trait are more likely to survive and produce offspring. Their offspring will, in turn, have the trait because it is genetically controlled.

Applications

1. Select the chickens that produce the most eggs and the largest eggs and only breed them. Do this each generation.
2. Brain size was generally smaller. Early humans were generally shorter. However, all humanlike species (hominids) walked upright.

Unit 7 Traits of Living Things

CONNECTIONS

Biology in Your World

The traits of an organism are determined by its genetic makeup. Scientists have learned to manipulate genetic material to produce desirable traits in plants and animals. Studying fossils helps us to understand the natural evolution of certain traits in all forms of life.

Literature Connection

Jack Horner was the first person to discover a dinosaur nest. Some nests contained only eggs, but others held the remains of hatched shells and babies. A few nests held larger babies than the other nests. This suggests that the babies stayed in the nest until they reached a certain size.

Horner concluded that the babies were cared for by a parent. Before, scientists thought dinosaurs laid their eggs and abandoned their young. Horner also concluded that the babies must have grown quickly to the size at which they could leave the nest. This fast growth made him wonder if the dinosaurs could have been warm-blooded.

History Connection

Charles Willson Peale (1741-1827) of Maryland painted many portraits of Revolutionary War heroes. He also founded the first major American museum. The Peale Museum opened in Philadelphia's Independence Hall and contained his paintings, technological gadgets, and stuffed animals. Its most famous exhibit was the complete mastodon skeleton. Peale recorded the excavation in his painting *Exhuming the Mastodon*.

CONNECTIONS

Biology in Your World

Variety: The Spice of Life

In this unit, you learned that variations in plants and animals are due to changes in the genetic material. Studying fossils reveals the variety of living things from the past. Today, scientists can use the variations in living things to breed crops and animals with certain traits.

LITERATURE

Looking for Baby Dinosaurs

John Horner's interest in baby dinosaurs began with a can full of tiny dinosaur bones. He got the bones from the owners of a rock shop in Montana in 1978.

Horner spent the next six years looking for more bones at a site in Montana.

He found the bones of baby dinosaurs in what appeared to be nests. The nests were close together and the babies were all the same age. Horner believes that these dinosaurs lived in groups and took care of their young.

Horner wrote *Digging Dinosaurs* about his findings. He also discusses why dinosaurs succeeded for 140 million years.

HISTORY

Putting the Pieces Together

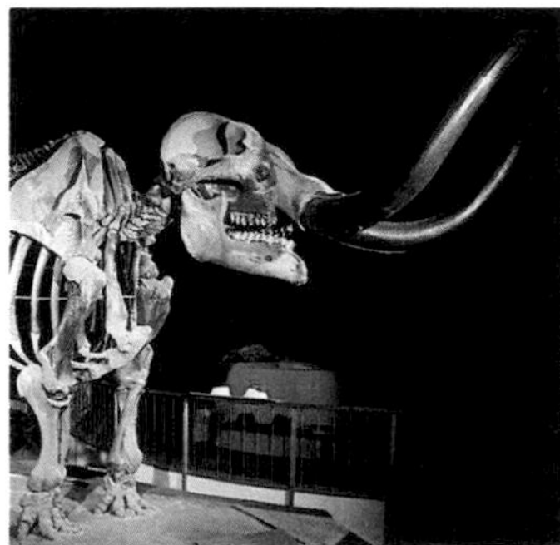

In 1801, farmers found some large bones in swamps near New York City. The bones were those of a mastodon. A mastodon is an extinct relative of the elephant. Mastodons lived in North America until about 10 000 years ago.

Charles Willson Peale was an artist and museum owner from Philadelphia who studied natural history. Hoping to find a complete mastodon skeleton, Peale organized an excavation at one of the sites. Most of the bones of an entire mastodon were found. In order to complete the skeleton, missing bones were carved from wood. The skeleton was displayed in Peale's museum.

626

LEISURE

Breeding Guppies

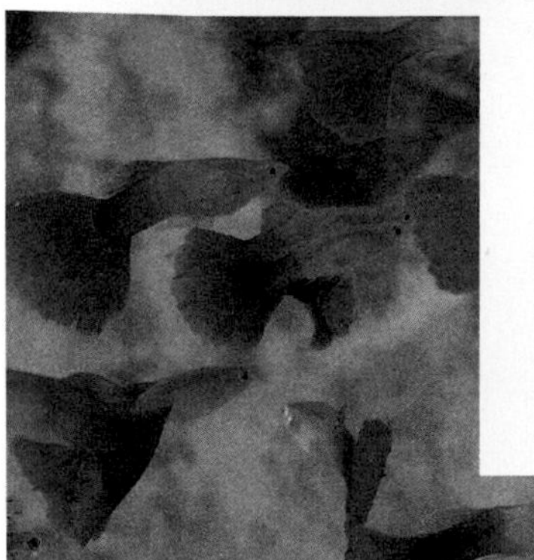

Female guppies are gray, ordinary-looking tropical fish. However, male guppies can be brightly colored. If you would like to see genetics in action, consider breeding guppies. You will need a tank and large jars to use as maternity wards. Check at a library or pet store for books on aquariums and breeding guppies. After each group is born, choose the largest and liveliest fish as the parents of the next generation. You can expect interesting results within a few generations. Keep records—you may succeed in producing a new strain of guppies!

CONSUMER

Delicious, Nutritious Bananas

Bananas are a very nutritious type of fruit. They are a good source of carbohydrates, phosphorus, and potassium. They are also a natural source of vitamins A and C. Bananas have very little fat.

Bananas grow in the tropics, where the plants produce fruit almost continuously. Thus, fresh bananas are almost always available.

The banana we eat is the Cavendish variety. It is being threatened by a fungus called black sigatoka (sihg uh TOH kuh). The fungus attacks the leaves of banana plants and can spread to the fruits. If not stopped, the fungus can kill the plants. At one time, chemical sprays were able to kill the fungus. But now, some of the fungi have become resistant to the chemicals.

Plant breeders are trying to develop a new hybrid banana that is resistant to black sigatoka. Some wild varieties of bananas are resistant to the fungus. The breeders are crossing these wild, nonedible varieties with the edible varieties.

Maybe in a few years you will see a new banana on your grocery store shelf.

CONNECTIONS

Leisure Connection

Guppies are prolific breeders, reproducing 30 to 50 live young every four to six weeks. The young guppies are only 3 millimeters long and are often eaten by the larger fish. Therefore, the baby guppies should be separated from the adult fish until they are too big to be eaten.

In the wild, guppies feed on worms, shellfish, and insect larvae. They are sometimes released in warm waters to control mosquitoes. If students breed too many fish, guppies can be released in ponds or lakes that are around 20°C. Sometimes, pet stores will buy surplus fish.

Consumer Connection

Consumers in the United States eat about 11 billion bananas yearly. Most of these varieties have thick yellow skins like the Cavendish. However, there are other varieties available. Red Jamaicas are small red bananas that have thin skins. Plantains are hard and starchy, and they are usually cooked and eaten as a vegetable.

When creating a new hybrid, some bananas have to be pollinated by hand. Therefore, producing a Cavendish hybrid resistant to black sigatoka will be difficult. In the meantime, consumers may see more Red Jamaicas and Plantains at the grocery store.

References

Brownless, Shannon. "Agriculture: The Best Banana Bred." *The Atlantic,* Vol. 264, No. 3, 1989, p. 22.

Horner, John R. *Digging Dinosaurs.* New York: Workman Publishing, 1988.

Sellers, Charles Coleman. "Unearthing the Mastodon." *American Heritage,* Vol. 30, Number 5, 1979, pp. 16-23.

Whitern, Wilfred A. *Guppies.* Neptune, NJ: T.F.H. Publications, Inc., 1980.

Unit 8 Relationships in the Environment

UNIT OVERVIEW

Unit 8 focuses on the various levels of ecological relationships. Chapter 30 deals with populations as the basic unit of ecology, and communities as the places where interrelationships occur between populations. Chapter 31 discusses the ecosystem and biome levels of ecological relationships. Chapter 32 focuses on some ecological problems today, such as pollution, acid rain, and endangered species.

Advance Planning

Audiovisual and computer software suggestions are located within each specific chapter under the heading TEACH.

To prepare for:

- Lab 30-1: Have graph paper and rulers ready for each team of students.
- Lab 30-2: Order owl pellets and get cardboard and glue for students to mount their skeletons.
- Lab 31-1: Order 2 *Elodea* sprigs for each team. Prepare the bromthymol blue solution (blue and green) several days in advance.
- Lab 31-2: Order brine shrimp eggs. Make the salt solutions a day in advance so all of the salt dissolves.
- Mini Lab: Collect dead leaves, jars, and plastic wrap.
- Lab 32-1: Prepare the bromthymol blue solution. Prepare the live and dead yeast mixtures on the day of the lab.
- Lab 32-2: Collect rainwater and household chemicals several days prior to the lab.
- Mini Lab: Collect jars with lids.

Unit 8

CONTENTS

628

Relationships in the Environment

What would happen if...

there were no mosquitoes? You may have memories of hot, itchy summers when you thought the world would be better off without mosquitoes. But, would it? The fish in the photo depend on mosquito larvae for food. Many birds, in turn, depend on the fish. Without the mosquito, many fish would starve to death. Many birds would then starve. The balance of nature would be upset by the lack of mosquitoes.

What is the effect of spraying chemicals to kill mosquitoes? In many communities, trucks that spray to kill mosquitoes are a regular sight. The spray that kills mosquitoes kills honeybees, too. What would be the effect of killing honeybees? What is the cost to the environment of getting rid of mosquitoes? Is the cost too high?

UNIT OVERVIEW

Photo Teaching Tip

Have students read the passage and examine the photographs on these unit opening pages. Ask students to make a list of all the animals and plants they consider to be a nuisance. Put this list on the chalkboard and ask students to brainstorm for a list of reasons why each of these so-called pests is valuable to the balance of nature. Begin the discussion by reviewing the connection between mosquitoes and fish as described in the passage. You may wish to lead the discussion to the importance of protecting species from extinction.

Theme Development

Living things interact with their environment. Students have studied the different kingdoms of living things and found out how their body parts work. Now, students will go beyond an individual living thing and study how similar and different populations interface with each other and the environment. They should understand that each species of living thing is an important part of the community because other living things may depend on its members for food or even for their habitat. They will learn how living things, humans included, can cause changes in the environment that make it unhealthy for other living things.

Populations and Communities

PLANNING GUIDE

CONTENT	TEXT FEATURES	TEACHER RESOURCE PACKAGE	OTHER COMPONENTS
(2 days) 30:1 Populations Population Size and Arrangement Population Changes Limits on Population Size	Skill Check: *Understand Science Words,* p. 632 Skill Check: *Make a Line Graph,* p. 634 Lab 30-1: *Competition,* p. 637 Science and Society: *Problems With an Increasing Human Population,* p. 635 Check Your Understanding, p. 636	Reteaching: *Limiting Factors,* p. 87 Study Guide: *Populations,* pp. 175-176 Lab 30-1: *Competition,* pp. 117-118 Focus: *Interfering With Fish Populations,* p. 59	
(2 days) 30:2 Communities Parts of a Community Producers Consumers Decomposers	Mini Lab: *What's in a Community,* p. 640 Check Your Understanding, p. 640 Idea Map, p. 639	Reteaching: *Populations and Communities,* p. 88 Skill: *Infer,* p. 31 Study Guide: *Communities,* p. 177	
(1 1/2 days) 30:3 Energy in a Community Food Chains Energy Flow in a Community	Check Your Understanding, p. 643	Enrichment: *A Salt Marsh Food Web,* p. 32 Transparency Master: *Pyramid of Numbers,* p. 151 Reteaching: *Energy in a Community,* p. 89 Study Guide: *Energy in a Community,* p. 178	**Laboratory Manual:** *What Are Some Parts of a Food Chain and a Food Web?* p. 251 Color Transparency 30: *Food Web*
(1 1/2 days) 30:4 Relationships in a Community Mutualism Commensalism Parasitism Predation	Skill Check: *Observe,* p. 646 Lab 30-2: *Predation,* p. 649 Check Your Understanding, p. 648	Application: *Predators and Prey,* p. 30 Reteaching: *Relationships in a Community,* p. 90 Critical Thinking/Problem Solving: *What Do Predators Do in a Community?* p. 30 Focus: *Interfering With Fish Populations,* p. 59 Study Guide: *Relationships in a Community,* p. 179 Study Guide: *Vocabulary,* p. 180 Lab 30-2: *Predation,* pp. 119-120	**Laboratory Manual:** *How Do Predator and Prey Populations Change?* p. 255
Chapter Review	Summary Key Science Words Testing Yourself Finding Main Ideas Using Main Ideas Skill Review	Chapter Review, pp. 160-161 Chapter Test, pp. 162-164	**Test Bank**

MATERIALS NEEDED

LAB 30-1, p. 637	LAB 30-2, p. 649	MARGIN FEATURES
metric ruler graph paper	light microscope microscope slide coverslip bowl forceps cardboard glue owl pellet water	Skill Check, p. 632 dictionary Skill Check, p. 634 pencil graph paper Mini Lab, p. 640 pencil paper

OBJECTIVES

		OBJECTIVES CORRELATION			
SECTION	OBJECTIVE	CHECK YOUR UNDERSTANDING	CHAPTER REVIEW	TRP CHAPTER REVIEW	TRP CHAPTER TEST
30:1	1. **Relate** the importance and methods of counting populations.	1	10, 11, 17, 24	12, 14, 25	1, 50
	2. **Discuss** why populations change size.	2, 5	6, 8, 25	7, 9, 15, 16	4, 10, 23, 49, 52
	3. **Explain** how limiting factors affect a population.	3, 4	3, 18, 22	8, 24, 26	5, 11, 13, 20
30:2	4. **Describe** the different parts of a community.	6, 9	4, 9, 19	3, 19, 21, 28	9, 16
	5. **Explain** the importance of producers, consumers, and decomposers.	7, 8, 10	12, 15, 23	18, 20	8, 19, 33, 34, 35, 36, 37, 38, 39, 40, 41, 42, 43, 44, 45, 46, 47, 48
30:3	6. **Trace** the path of energy and materials through a community.	11	1, 5	11, 13, 17	7, 12, 24, 51
	7. **Explain** how food chains are connected.	13, 14	13, 16	10, 22	3, 15
30:4	8. **Give examples** of mutualism.	16, 20	14	23	18, 26, 29, 31
	9. **Describe** commensalism.	18, 19	26	1, 4, 6	22, 27, 32
	10. **Compare** parasitism with predation.	17, 20	2, 7, 21	2, 5, 27	2, 6, 14, 17, 21, 25, 28, 30

Populations and Communities

CHAPTER OVERVIEW

Key Concepts

In this chapter, students will focus on the basic unit of ecology—the population. Next, the three basic parts of the community—plants, animals, and decomposers—are discussed as to how each fits into food chains and food webs. Mutualism, parasitism, and commensalism are examined.

Key Science Words

commensalism
community
emigration
energy pyramid
food chain
food web
habitat
immigration
limiting factor
niche
parasitism
population
predation
predator
prey
primary consumer
secondary consumer

Skill Development

In Lab 30-1, students will **form hypotheses, interpret data, infer,** and **design an experiment** relating to species competition. In Lab 30-2, they will **observe, infer,** and **design an experiment** regarding predation. On page 632, students will **understand** the **science word** *population.* In the Skill Check on page 634, students will **make a line graph** of population size. In the Skill Check on page 646, they will **observe** a lamprey to determine how it gets food. In the Mini Lab on page 640, students will **make and use a table** of producers, consumers, and decomposers.

CHAPTER PREVIEW

Chapter Content

Review this outline for Chapter 30 before you read the chapter.

Skills in this Chapter

The skills that you will use in this chapter are listed below.

- In **Lab 30-1,** you will form hypotheses, interpret data, infer, and design an experiment. In **Lab 30-2,** you will observe, infer, and design an experiment.
- In the **Skill Checks,** you will understand science words, make a line graph, and observe.
- In the **Mini Labs,** you will make and use tables.

630

Bridging

In Unit 2, students learned how all organisms were classified into kingdoms by structure and function of body parts. In this chapter, students will learn how the organisms in the different kingdoms are grouped into populations and how they interact in a community.

Chapter **30**

Populations and Communities

Some animals, like the caribou (KAR uh boo) on the left, live together in large groups called herds. There may be 50 to several hundred caribou in a herd. Each year the caribou migrate to a better feeding area. During migration, smaller herds combine to form a larger herd that may number in the thousands. What benefit might there be to living in a herd? What disadvantage is there to living in a herd?

Animals like the wolves shown below live together in small groups called packs. There may be 6 to 10 wolves in one pack. The pack may roam over an area of 25 to 50 square kilometers. Sometimes the wolves follow the caribou on their migration. How do wolves benefit from living in small packs? What might happen if the pack increased to 50 or 60 wolves?

Try This!

How important is each organism in a community? Write down the name of a plant. Now write the name of an organism that eats the plant. Continue to name an organism that eats the last organism you named. Your list shows relationships among living things.

GETTING STARTED

Using the Photos

Most grazing animals travel in large herds. The benefit of a large herd is that the young are protected and cared for by the entire herd. Point out that some herds of grazing animals may number in the thousands. Explain that predators travel in small packs and kill the sick or injured animals in the herd. Point out that if there were as many wolves in a pack as there were caribou in a herd, the wolves would have to kill a large number of caribou to survive. This would eventually destroy the food supply of the wolves.

MOTIVATION/Try This!

How important is each organism in a community? Students will **recognize and use spatial relationships** among living things. They should realize that most relationships form not a linear chain, but a web. Point out to students that some of the organisms may feed at several different levels.

Chapter Preview

Have students study the chapter outline before they begin to read the chapter. They should note the overall organization of the chapter, that each kind of living thing is a part of a population of a given area. Next, they will study how one population interacts with other populations to form a community. They will then learn how members of each population fit into the food chains and food web of a community and how energy flows through a food web in a community. Last, they will study relationships in a community.

Misconception

Students may not understand that all living things in a community are important in the food web. They may regard mice and snakes as undesirable or useless animals. Point out that mice supply many predators such as the snake with food, and snakes are food for larger predators.

30:1 Populations

PREPARATION

Materials Needed

Make copies of the Focus, Study Guide, Reteaching, and Lab worksheets in the *Teacher Resource Package.*

▶ Collect and arrange the pictures for the Focus activity.

▶ Have graph paper and rulers ready for Lab 30-1.

Key Science Words

population
emigration
immigration
limiting factor

Process Skills

In Lab 30-1, students will form hypotheses, interpret data, infer, and design an experiment. In the Skill Checks, they will understand science words and make a line graph.

1 FOCUS

▶ The objectives are listed on the student page. Remind students to preview these objectives as a guide to this numbered section.

MOTIVATION/Bulletin Board

Have pictures of plant and animal populations that show clumped, random, and uniform populations. A good example of a uniform population is trees that were planted in rows by humans. Have students discuss the advantages and disadvantages of the three types of populations in terms of competition for space, water, and sun.

MOTIVATION/Videocassette

Show the videocassette *Populations, Communities and Biomes,* Insight Media.

Focus/*Teacher Resource Package,* p. 59. Use the Focus transparency shown at the bottom of the page as an introduction to populations.

30:1 Populations

Objectives

1. **Relate** the importance and methods of counting populations.
2. **Discuss** why populations change in size.
3. **Explain** how limiting factors affect a population.

Key Science Words

population
emigration
immigration
limiting factor

On your way to school each day, you see different kinds of living things. If you stopped to take a closer look, you might see many individuals of the same kind of organism. There could be dozens or hundreds of one kind of living thing in one place. These living things make up a population. A **population** is a group of living things of the same species that live in an area.

Population Size and Arrangement

Suppose you counted all of the daisies in the field in Figure 30-1. They would make up the daisy population of that field. You can't see the populations of spiders, earthworms, or field mice in the photo, but they are there as well.

A change in the size of one population often causes a change in the size of another population. For this reason, scientists usually want to know of any increases or decreases in populations they study. Finding the size of a population is not always easy. It may be hard to count the number of mice or earthworms in a population because these animals move. Some animals may be counted twice. Some may not be counted at all.

Counting the number of daisies in the small field would be easier because they do not move and the size of the field is small. Sometimes the area where the members of a population are found is very large. Finding out the size of the spruce tree population of Yellowstone National Park would be much harder due to the park's large size.

Skill Check

Understand science words: population. The word part *popula* means a group of people. In your dictionary, find three words with the word part *popula* in them. *For more help, refer to the* ***Skill Handbook****, pages 706-711.*

Figure 30-1 Some populations are easier to see and count than others.

OPTIONS

Science Background

Animal population size can be influenced by the amount of food and space available. Natural populations cannot increase forever; population size is also controlled by environmental and biological factors. Animals immigrating to one area are emigrating from another area. A chief factor influencing the size of a plant population is the amount of daily sunlight and the space available in which roots can grow and spread.

FOCUS 59

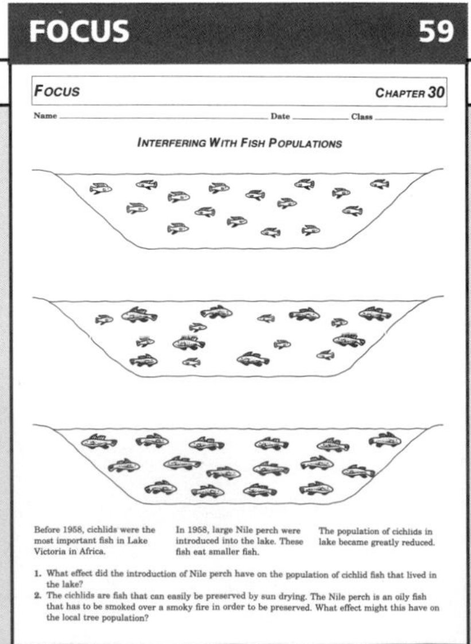

FOCUS CHAPTER 30

Name ______ Date ______ Class ______

INTERFERING WITH FISH POPULATIONS

Before 1958, cichlids were the most important fish in Lake Victoria in Africa.

In 1958, large Nile perch were introduced into the lake. These fish eat smaller fish.

The population of cichlids in lake became greatly reduced.

1. What effect did the introduction of Nile perch have on the population of cichlid fish that lived in the lake?
2. The cichlids are fish that can easily be preserved by sun drying. The Nile perch is an oily fish that has to be smoked over a smoky fire in order to be preserved. What effect might this have on the local tree population?

a

b

c

Figure 30-2 Ear tags (a), leg bands (b), and radio transmitters (c) are ways of marking animals for population counts.

Populations are counted in different ways. Animals such as mountain goats can be marked with ear tags, Figure 30-2. Birds are marked by leg bands. Sometimes radio transmitters are put on animals. The animals are then followed to their nesting places and their offspring are counted. Trees may be marked with paint or ribbons. How is the human population in the United States counted?

How can an animal population be counted?

Populations are not spread out evenly. Figure 30-3 shows that the population of the United States is clumped in cities. Is there a high or low population where you live?

A clumped population can be a useful plan. Members of the population may help one another find food or shelter. Many species of animals live in groups for protection. What kinds of animals live in groups called herds, flocks, and packs? Plants may be helped by living in clumps. Trees may be protected from strong winds if they grow close together. deer, birds, wolves

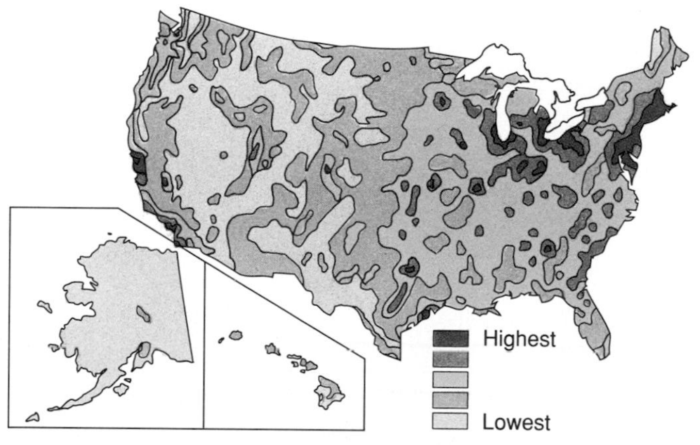

Figure 30-3 The human population in the United States is clumped. Which area has most people? the eastern half of the country, especially the east coast

2 TEACH

MOTIVATION/Audiovisual

Show about ten 35-mm color slides that depict populations of plants and animals. Some slides may show several different populations. A slide of a wooded area might show an oak tree population or a maple tree population. Explain that two or more interacting populations form a community.

Concept Development

▶ Explain that populations too large to count are estimated using sampling techniques in which the organisms in a unit area are counted and then this number is multiplied by the total area in which the organisms live. Explain that some populations of plants are uniform in their arrangement because humans plant them. Crop fields and sections of forests may show this uniform arrangement.

Guided Practice

Have students write down their answers to the margin question: by marking the animals with tags, bands, or transmitters.

Independent Practice

Study Guide/*Teacher Resource Package,* p. 175. Use the Study Guide worksheet shown at the bottom of this page for independent practice.

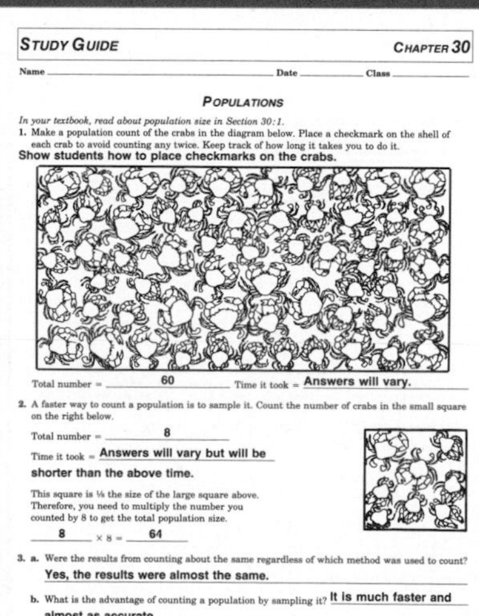

STUDY GUIDE 175

STUDY GUIDE — CHAPTER 30

Name ____ Date ____ Class ____

POPULATIONS

In your textbook, read about population size in Section 30:1.

1. Make a population count of the crabs in the diagram below. Place a checkmark on the shell of each crab to avoid counting any twice. Keep track of how long it takes you to do it.
Show students how to place checkmarks on the crabs.

Total number = **60** Time it took = **Answers will vary.**

2. A faster way to count a population is to sample it. Count the number of crabs in the small square on the right below.

Total number = **8**

Time it took = **Answers will vary but will be shorter than the above time.**

This square is ⅛ the size of the large square above. Therefore, you need to multiply the number you counted by 8 to get the total population size.

8 × 8 = **64**

3. a. Were the results from counting about the same regardless of which method was used to count? **Yes, the results were almost the same.**

b. What is the advantage of counting a population by sampling it? **It is much faster and almost as accurate.**

OPTIONS

ACTIVITY/Challenge

Have students determine how many trees are in the school yard or, if there is a fence row, how many trees are along the fence row. Point out that finding the size of a plant population is easier than finding that of an animal population because plants do not move around.

TEACH

Concept Development

▶ Explain that the greatest possible increase in population occurs under ideal conditions. Under these conditions, the birth rate is usually much higher than the death rate.

Skill Check

Data for making the line graph can be found in the *World Almanac and Book of Facts* published by the New York Times. Ask students to find out what factors are causing the human population to increase in their state.

Cooperative Learning: Divide students into several teams. Have the teams find out when the greatest number of immigrants came to the United States and why people immigrated. Have them make graphs and charts showing their data.

Guided Practice

Have students write down their answers to the margin question: it increases the population.

ACTIVITY/Filmstrip

Show the filmstrip *Population Ecology,* Carolina Biological Supply Co.

Independent Practice

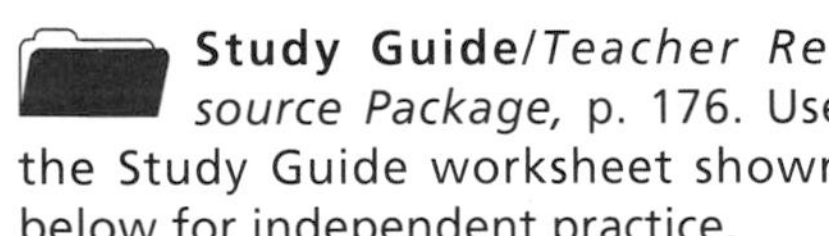

Study Guide/*Teacher Resource Package,* p. 176. Use the Study Guide worksheet shown below for independent practice.

Skill Check

Make a line graph: Find out what the population size was for your state in 1950, 1960, 1970, 1980, and 1990. Plot the data on a line graph. Make a point showing where you think the population for 2000 will be. *For more help, refer to the* ***Skill Handbook,*** *pages 715-717.*

Population Changes

Let's examine how the human population has changed in the United States in the last forty years. You can see from the figures in Table 30-1 that the population is increasing.

TABLE 30–1. UNITED STATES POPULATION

Year	Number of People
1950	152 271 000
1960	180 671 000
1970	205 052 000
1980	227 757 000
1989	248 239 000

The graph in Figure 30-4 shows the growth in world population since the year 1500. Several things can cause a population to change in size. If the number of births goes up or the number of deaths goes down, a population will increase. The population will decrease if there are more deaths than births. Animal populations can increase or decrease in other ways. Animals move from place to place. The movement of animals out of an area is called **emigration** (em uh GRAY shun). Emigration causes a decrease in population numbers.

How does immigration affect a population?

Animals that move out of one population usually enter another population. The movement of animals into a population is called **immigration** (ihm uh GRAY shun). Immigration causes an increase in population numbers.

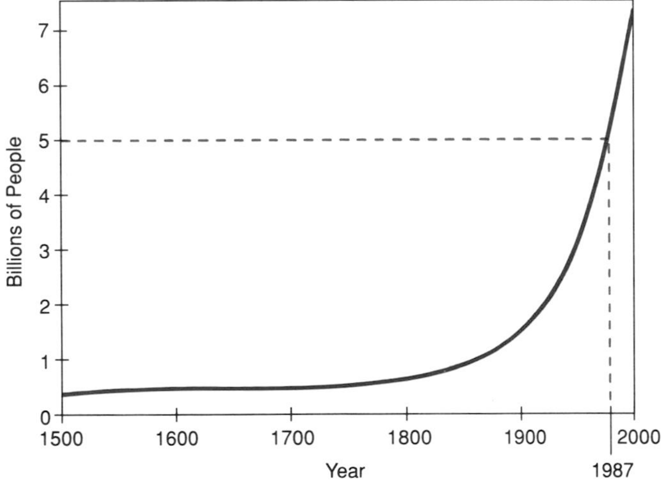

Figure 30-4 This graph shows how the human population in the world has grown since 1500. What is the population expected to be in the year 2000? about 7 billion

OPTIONS

Enrichment: Explain to students that the change in size of a plant population is dependent on the number of seeds that sprout and grow into new plants and how many plants are destroyed by insects and environmental factors.

ACTIVITY/Project

Ask students to investigage why the human life span has increased. Booklets are available from life insurance companies that explain why humans are living longer. Survivor charts that show which age groups have higher death rates, and why, are also available.

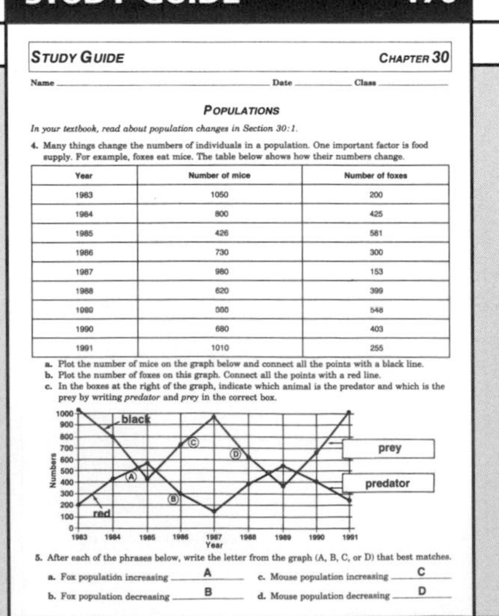

STUDY GUIDE 176

STUDY GUIDE — CHAPTER 30

Name ______ Date ______ Class ______

POPULATIONS

In your textbook, read about population changes in Section 30:1.

4. Many things change the numbers of individuals in a population. One important factor is food supply. For example, foxes eat mice. The table below shows how their numbers change.

Year	Number of mice	Number of foxes
1983	1050	200
1984	800	425
1985	426	581
1986	730	300
1987	980	153
1988	620	399
1989	[illegible]	548
1990	680	403
1991	1010	255

a. Plot the number of mice on the graph below and connect all the points with a black line.
b. Plot the number of foxes on this graph. Connect all the points with a red line.
c. In the boxes at the right of the graph, indicate which animal is the predator and which is the prey by writing *predator* and *prey* in the correct box.

5. After each of the phrases below, write the letter from the graph (A, B, C, or D) that best matches.

a. Fox population increasing A
b. Fox population decreasing B
c. Mouse population increasing C
d. Mouse population decreasing D

Science and Society

Problems with an Increasing Human Population

In 1975 the human population on Earth was four billion, or double its size in 1930. By 2020 the human population will probably double its size again, to almost 8.1 billion. Many countries today face food shortages each year. In the countries that lack food, one-half of the humans who die each year are children under the age of five. Some of these deaths are caused by diseases, but many of the deaths are caused by starvation.

Much of the land in the United States that was available for growing food crops is no longer available. Many farms have been sold, and the land is used for building homes and new industrial sites. Due to improved farming methods and better fertilizers, however, farmers can now grow more food on less land.

What Do You Think?

1. Thirty years ago, most countries produced their own food. Now, the United States and six other countries are the only ones in the world that produce enough food to feed all of their people. These countries have extra food that they store or sell to other countries.

Some people think that a country with extra food should give it to countries that do not have enough. If they give it away, who will pay the farmer?

In some countries, people have trouble raising enough food to eat.

2. The populations of different countries are growing at different rates. In 1988, the world population grew at a rate of 1.7 percent. In many developing countries in South America, Asia, and Africa, however, the growth rate was over 3 percent. These countries are the least able to feed their increasing populations. Should the government control family size? If so, who should decide who should have children and how many they should have?

3. Certain sprays that kill weeds and insects are banned in the United States because they are harmful. These sprays are sold to farmers in countries that have trouble raising enough food. If the sprays are not used, food production will decrease because some of the crops will be destroyed by insects or weeds. Should all countries pass laws banning the use of such sprays? Should the companies that make the chemicals be prevented from selling them?

Conclusion: Is it better to control population growth or to increase the amount of food produced?

Suggested Readings

Satter, D. "Why Russia Can't Feed Itself." *Reader's Digest,* Oct. 1989, pp. 61-66.

Steingarter, J. "A Taste of Things to Come." *Vogue,* Oct. 1989, pp. 410-411.

Sudo, P. "Why the Long Food Lines?" *Scholastic Update,* Oct. 1989, pp. 16-17.

Science and Society

Problems with an Increasing Human Population

Background

By the year 2020 there will be eight billion people living on Earth. It has been estimated that food production on farms and ranches will have to increase to two or three times what it is today in order to feed everyone. In some non-industrialized nations, humans spend most of their waking hours gathering food for their families. Even though food production has increased in the past forty years in most of the world, the rate of food production has not increased fast enough to keep up with the human population increase.

Teaching Suggestions

Have students find out: (a) which countries produce enough food to feed their people, (b) what natural disasters have occurred to keep food production down, and (c) what agricultural practices enable some countries to produce enough food. Students can work in cooperative groups for this assignment.

What Do You Think?

1. Countries that give away surplus food often end up paying for the food through taxes. Surplus grains often end up not being used at all.
2. Some countries, in fact, do have government-controlled limits on family size. In other countries, infant and child mortality is high, so couples have more children to compensate.
3. Discuss the possibilities of using biological controls instead of pesticides.

Conclusion: Allow students to discuss different means of controlling population, from government-controlled limits to voluntary cooperation. Encourage students to discuss increasing crop yields through better farming techniques, fertilizer, and irrigation.

TEACH

Connection: Math

Students can get the wind speed and temperature from the local paper and calculate the wind chill for a week. Wind chill charts are found in most encyclopedias.

Guided Practice

Have students write down their answers to the margin question: it slows down.

Check for Understanding

Have students respond to the first three questions in Check Your Understanding.

Reteach

Reteaching/*Teacher Resource Package*, p. 87. Use this worksheet to give students additional practice with limiting factors.

Extension: Assign Critical Thinking, Biology and Math, or some of the **OPTIONS** available with this lesson.

3 APPLY

ACTIVITY/Software

Population Concepts, Queue, Inc.

4 CLOSE

ACTIVITY/Software

Ecology, Queue, Inc.

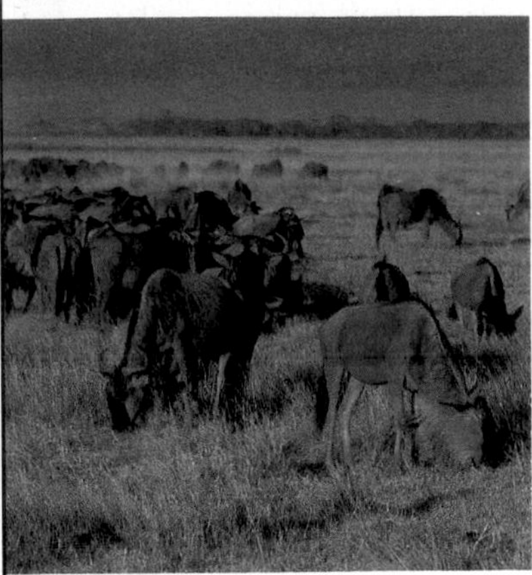

Figure 30-5 Competition affects the size of a population. What is the limiting factor in this photo? food

What happens to plant growth when space is limited?

Limits of Population Size

Why don't populations increase forever? What prevents the world from being overrun with all kinds of living things? Any condition that keeps the size of a population from increasing is called a **limiting factor.** Almost anything that affects the lives of organisms can be a limiting factor. Lack of light, space, water, or food are all limiting factors.

A population uses more sunlight, space, water, and food as it increases in size. Members of the same and similar species have the same needs. Remember from Chapter 29 that the struggle among organisms to get their needs for life is called competition. An increase in the population size causes more competition for the same materials. Some organisms may not get enough of these materials. The lack of needed materials causes population growth to slow down by decreasing the number of births and increasing the number of deaths.

Plant roots growing close to each other compete for nutrients, water, and space. The stems and leaves of different plants compete for light. A decrease in the amount of space and light causes the growth of plants to slow down. Why do gardeners pull out some of their lettuce seedlings?

Look again at the human population graph in Figure 30-4. The line slants upward showing a rapid increase in population. What does this tell you about the limiting factors in a human population? Could you make a prediction about the population size in the year 2000? Do you think human populations are affected by limiting factors? not yet

Check Your Understanding

1. Explain which is easier to count, plant populations or animal populations.
2. There are very few deaths in a deer population, yet the population is decreasing. Explain what might be happening to cause the decrease.
3. How can limiting factors cause a population change?
4. **Critical Thinking:** What might become limiting factors in a country whose population becomes too large?
5. **Biology and Math:** If there are 10 wolves in one pack roaming over an area of 20 square kilometers, what is the average density of wolves per square kilometer?

Answers to Check Your Understanding

1. plants, because they do not move about
2. Some of the deer could be emigrating to a new area, there could be fewer births, or limiting factors could be decreasing the population.
3. Living things compete for resources. When these resources are scarce, the population size may decrease. When these resources are abundant, population size may increase.
4. food, space, water, mates, shelter, jobs
5. 1/2 wolf per km^2

RETEACHING 87

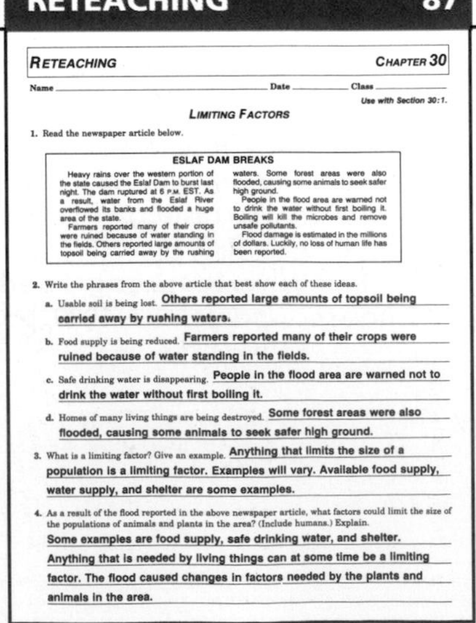

RETEACHING CHAPTER 30

Name ______ Date ______ Class ______

Use with Section 30:1.

LIMITING FACTORS

1. Read the newspaper article below.

ESLAF DAM BREAKS

Heavy rains over the western portion of the state caused the Eslaf Dam to burst last night. The dam ruptured at 6 P.M. EST. As a result, water from the Eslaf River overflowed its banks and flooded a huge area of the state.

Farmers reported many of their crops were ruined because of water standing in the fields. Others reported large amounts of topsoil being carried away by the rushing waters. Some forest areas were also flooded, causing some animals to seek safer high ground.

People in the flood area are warned not to drink the water without first boiling it. Boiling will kill the microbes and remove unsafe pollutants.

Flood damage is estimated in the millions of dollars. Luckily, no loss of human life has been reported.

2. Write the phrases from the above article that best show each of these ideas.
   a. Usable soil is being lost. **Others reported large amounts of topsoil being carried away by rushing waters.**
   b. Food supply is being reduced. **Farmers reported many of their crops were ruined because of water standing in the fields.**
   c. Safe drinking water is disappearing. **People in the flood area are warned not to drink the water without first boiling it.**
   d. Homes of many living things are being destroyed. **Some forest areas were also flooded, causing some animals to seek safer high ground.**
3. What is a limiting factor? Give an example. **Anything that limits the size of a population is a limiting factor. Examples will vary. Available food supply, water supply, and shelter are some examples.**
4. As a result of the flood reported in the above newspaper article, what factors could limit the size of the populations of animals and plants in the area? (Include humans.) Explain. **Some examples are food supply, safe drinking water, and shelter. Anything that is needed by living things can at some time be a limiting factor. The flood caused changes in factors needed by the plants and animals in the area.**

Lab 30–1 Competition

Problem: What happens when two animal species compete?

Skills

form hypotheses, interpret data, infer, design an experiment

Materials

graph paper
ruler

Procedure

In 1973, there were no houses in a large, old field. By 1988, there were 250 houses. A biologist found a population of dusky field mice living in the field. The biologist sampled this population from 1977 to 1992. Write a **hypothesis** in your notebook about what you think happened to the mouse population between 1977 and 1992.

1. Prepare a sheet of graph paper as follows. Mark the horizontal axis with the years 1977 to 1994. Label the horizontal axis "Years Sampled."
2. Mark the vertical axis from 0 to 90. Label the vertical axis "Size of Mouse Population per 1000 Square Meters."
3. Study the information in the table.
4. Plot the data for the field mouse population on the graph.
5. Connect the data points with a ruler to make a line graph. Continue the line to the right so you can estimate the size of the mouse population in 1994.

YEAR	NUMBER OF MICE PER 1000 SQUARE METERS	YEAR	NUMBER OF MICE PER 1000 SQUARE METERS
1977	89	1985	47
1978	85	1986	45
1979	82	1987	36
1980	79	1988	29
1981	78	1989	26
1982	51	1990	17
1983	48	1991	14
1984	42	1992	7

Data and Observations

1. Did the number of mice increase or decrease between 1977 and 1988?
2. Between which two years was the greatest change in population seen?

Analyze and Apply

1. **Infer:** What limiting factors are affecting the population size of the dusky field mouse?
2. With what other living thing do you think these mice are competing?
3. What might be happening to the birthrate of mice?
4. Suppose in 1984, 17 mice emigrated. What do you think would happen to the mouse population?
5. Predict what will happen to the number of mice in 1994.
6. List two factors that can increase the mouse population.
7. What effect would immigration have on the mouse population?
8. **Check your hypothesis:** Was your hypothesis supported by the data? Why or why not?
9. **Apply:** What happens when two animal species compete?

Extension

Design an experiment that would show how a limiting factor, such as size of habitat, affects a plant population.

Lab 30-1 Competition

Overview

This simulation gives the student a chance to see how the size of one population (mouse) can decrease because of an increase in the size of another population (human). The concepts of limiting factor, competition, and population change are reinforced.

Objectives: Students will be able to: (1) **demonstrate** how a population changes in size over time, (2) **interpret** a graph, and (3) **explain** the cause and effect of competition.

Time Allotment: 45 minutes

Preparation

▶ Have graph paper and a ruler for each student.

Lab 30-1 worksheet/*Teacher Resource Package*, pp. 117-118.

Teaching the Lab

▶ Be sure students use sharp pencils when plotting their data. Many students will not know how to set up the graph. Review graphing techniques during the prelab.

▶ **Troubleshooting:** Give students an idea of how big an area 1000 square meters is: about 1/5 the size of a football field.

Cooperative Learning: Divide the class into groups of two students. For more information, see pp. 22T-23T in the Teacher Guide.

ANSWERS

Data and Observations

1. decrease
2. between 1981 and 1982

Analyze and Apply

1. space and food
2. humans
3. decreasing
4. The population would sharply decrease. There would be less competition for space, food, and shelter.
5. The mice will probably disappear from the field.
6. immigration and increased birthrate
7. It would increase the size of the mouse population and cause competition for food, space, and shelter.
8. Students who hypothesized that the mouse population would decrease and probably disappear from the field will say that their hypotheses were supported.
9. The species that is more successful in obtaining its needs is able to increase in population size.

30:2 Communities

PREPARATION

Materials Needed

Make copies of the Skill, Reteaching, and Study Guide worksheets in the *Teacher Resource Package.*

Key Science Words

community
habitat
niche
primary consumer
secondary consumer

Process Skills

In the Mini Lab, students will make and use tables.

1 FOCUS

▶ The objectives are listed on the student page. Remind students to preview these objectives as a guide to this numbered section.

Divergent Question

Ask students to describe some interactions they have observed between two living things. Ask them to tell which of the two living things depended on the other.

Guided Practice

Have students write down their answers to the margin question: the job of an organism in its community.

30:2 Communities

Objectives

4. **Describe** different parts of a community.
5. **Explain** the importance of producers, consumers, and decomposers.

Key Science Words

community
habitat
niche
primary consumer
secondary consumer

The different populations in an area depend on each other. How can this be true? Look again at Figure 30-1. The daisies in the field can provide shelter for the spiders. The mice can eat the seeds of the daisy. What do you think the earthworm depends on? How do the mice and the earthworms help the daisies?

Parts of a Community

The populations of daisies, mice, and earthworms in Figure 30-1 make up a community. A **community** is all of the living things in an area that depend upon each other. Some communities, like the field of daisies, may be easy to see. Other communities may be harder to see. Is there a pond or lake near your home? What living things make up the pond community? Communities can be identified by the kinds of living things found there. What types of communities can you identify?

What is a habitat?

In a community, every living thing has a place to live that best suits it. You know that birds live in trees, fish live in ponds, and people live in houses. The place where a plant or animal lives is its **habitat** (HAB uh tat). A squirrel may use several different trees in the forest as its habitat, while a skunk may use one hollow log and the surrounding area as its habitat. Your skin is the habitat for the millions of bacteria that live there. Figure 30-6 shows a lichen attached to a rock. What do you think the lichen's habitat is?

Figure 30-6 Some lichens can grow on rocks.

Every living thing in a community also has a function, or job. The job of the organism in the community is its **niche** (NITSH). The job of most green plants is to produce food from sunlight, water, and carbon dioxide by photosynthesis. Animals have jobs, too. Earthworms help break up the soil so that plant roots can get water and nutrients. Bees pollinate flowers when they collect nectar to make honey.

You live in the community, too. Your habitat is your home, your school, and other places where you spend time. Your job is to study and learn. Your niche is that of a student. Think about other niches in your community. What do you think is the niche of an auto mechanic? How do other people depend on the mail carrier or the bus driver? How does your teacher depend upon you? How do you depend on your teacher?

OPTIONS

Science Background

The differences between environmental factors in two bordering communities tend to keep organisms from spreading to a new community. Communities are named after the dominant living thing or land feature, for example, a grassland or pond.

Skill/*Teacher Resource Package*, p. 31. Use the Skill worksheet shown here to reinforce the concept of community dynamics.

SKILL 31

SKILL: INFER — CHAPTER 30

Name ______ Date ______ Class ______

For more help, refer to the Skill Handbook, pages 706-711. *Use after Section 30:2.*

A MEADOW COMMUNITY

A three-year study of the South Fork Meadow showed that 36 kinds of animals lived in the community. Of these, 6 kinds of animals made up the largest populations. These animals are shown in the table below. Grasses and weeds made up the plant populations of the community.

The Most Abundant Animals at South Fork Meadow

Animal	Mouse	Rabbit	Hawk	Deer	Snake	Cricket
Food source in meadow	seeds	plant parts	mice, birds, snakes	plant parts	mice, birds, rabbits	plant parts

In the summer of the second year of the study, the populations of the crickets, mice, deer, and rabbits increased in size. In contrast, the hawk and snake populations stayed nearly the same sizes as the first year's populations. By the middle of the second summer, the meadow had developed many bare spots where the soil could be seen. By the middle of the third year, the cricket, rabbit, and mouse populations had decreased to about the population sizes of the first year. But, the hawk and snake populations had nearly doubled. The amount of bare soil had decreased.

1. Which organisms are the primary consumers in the meadow? **mouse, rabbit, deer, and cricket**
2. Which organisms are the secondary consumers in the meadow? **hawk and snake**
3. Which organisms are the producers in the meadow? Explain. **grasses and weeds, because they make their own food**
4. In which of the three years do you think there was a better balance in the meadow community? Why? **The first year because there were enough producers to feed the primary consumers**
5. Which populations do you think caused the balance in the community to change for the worse? Why do you think this change came about? **The primary consumers caused the balance to change. Their populations increased more quickly than their food, the plants, could reproduce.**
6. Why did the hawk and snake populations increase during the third year? **Because their food supply was so plentiful, they could grow and reproduce quickly.**

a

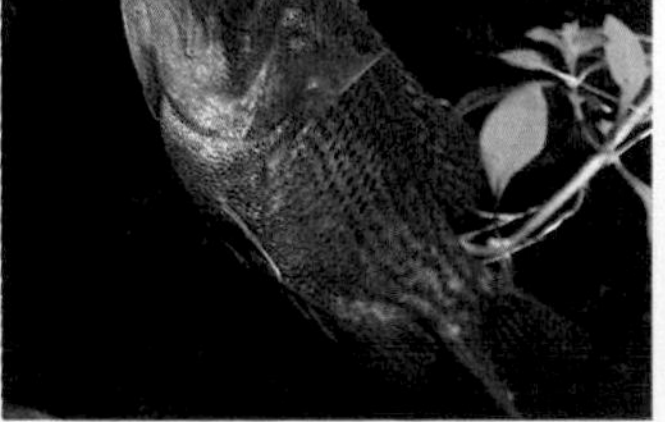

b

c

Figure 30-7 In a pond community, water plants (a) may be the producers, fish (b) may be the primary consumers, and turtles (c) may be the secondary consumers.

Producers

All of the organisms in a community are related to each other through their jobs. These jobs may be divided into three types: producers, consumers, and decomposers.

Producers are the organisms that make food in a community. In almost all communities, green plants, algae, or blue-green bacteria are the producers. Producers use some of the food for themselves. The food they make will also help to feed all the animals in the community. Producers also make oxygen during photosynthesis. Other organisms need the oxygen to live.

What do producers do for a community?

Consumers

The animals in a community must have food. Animals can't make their own food, so they are consumers. Consumers are organisms that eat other organisms.

Many animals, such as mice and deer, get food by eating plants. Animals that eat only plants are **primary consumers.**

Some animals eat other animals. Owls eat mice, and turtles eat fish. These animals are secondary consumers. **Secondary consumers** are animals that eat other animals.

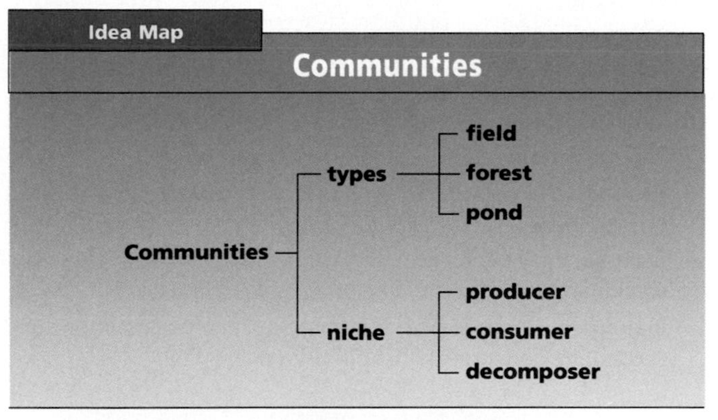

Study Tip: Use this idea map as a study guide to communities. Can you think of other types of communities?

2 TEACH

MOTIVATION/Videocassette

Show the videocassette *Matter, Energy, and Ecosystems,* Insight Media.

Concept Development

▶ Point out that some protists are producers in aquatic communities.

Guided Practice

Have students write down their answers to the margin question: They make food from the sun for the community.

Idea Map

Have students use the idea map as a study guide to the major concepts of this section.

Cooperative Learning: Have student teams make charts and posters of animals that are primary consumers and animals that are secondary consumers. Provide *National Geographic, Audubon,* and *National Wildlife* magazines for their use. Have each team report on their findings. Have them point out the features that each group of animals has, i.e., hooves on some primary consumers and claws on many secondary consumers.

Misconception: Students think that mushrooms get their food from the soil in the same way trees get their minerals from the soil. Point out that mushrooms are using dead matter in the soil as food. Explain that they absorb organic matter by secreting enzymes to break down the dead matter into nutrients.

ACTIVITY/Videocassette

Show the videocassette *To Know a Pond*, Insight Media.

Independent Practice

Study Guide/*Teacher Resource Package*, p. 177. Use the Study Guide worksheet shown at the bottom of this page for independent practice.

STUDY GUIDE 177

STUDY GUIDE — CHAPTER 30

Name ________ Date ________ Class ________

COMMUNITIES

In your textbook, read about the parts of a community in Section 30:2.

1. This picture of a community shows many different kinds of living things. Using these colors, shade the following parts.

Green—producers
Red—primary consumers
Yellow—secondary consumers
Blue—decomposers

green, green, green, yellow, red, red, green, red, yellow, blue

2. What is the habitat of the deer? **the field**
3. What is the niche of the deer? **primary consumer**
4. List two decomposers in this community. **bacteria, fungi (mushrooms and molds)**
5. What producers are present in this community? **grass, trees, plants**
6. List two secondary consumers and tell what they eat. **bird—worm; large member of cat family—cattle or deer**

OPTIONS

ACTIVITY/Challenge

Ask students to design a space station community and to list all the organisms that would be needed to sustain life.

TEACH

Mini Lab

Make a chart so each student has the same data. Use the headings Organisms Seen, Producers, Consumers, Decomposers.

Check for Understanding

Have students respond to the first three questions in Check Your Understanding.

Reteach

Reteaching/Teacher Resource Package, p. 88. Use this worksheet to give students additional practice with the parts of a community.

Extension: Assign Critical Thinking, Biology and Reading, or some of the **OPTIONS** available with this lesson.

3 APPLY

ACTIVITY/Software

Ecosystems; Coexist: Population Dynamics; Compete: Plant Competition, Queue, Inc.

4 CLOSE

ACTIVITY/Field Trip

Take a field trip to observe organisms in their environment. Have students list the producers, consumers, and decomposers they find.

Answers to Check Your Understanding

6. The earthworm's habitat is the soil. Its niche is to break up soil so plants can grow.
7. Producers make their own food from light, while consumers depend on others for food.
8. They recycle nutrients and break down dead matter.
9. producers and decomposers
10. When humans eat only plants, they are primary consumers. When humans eat other animals, they are secondary consumers.

Figure 30-8 A forest community has many different producers, consumers, and decomposers.

Mini Lab

What's in a Community?

Make and use tables: Make a table listing 10 organisms you see in your area and whether each is a producer, consumer, or decomposer. Which appears in the largest number? *For more help, refer to the* ***Skill Handbook,*** *pages 715-717.*

Decomposers

In the pond and many other communities, decomposers form another group. Remember from Chapter 4 that decomposers are living things that get their food from breaking down dead matter. Bacteria and fungi, such as molds and mushrooms, are decomposers. Decomposers break down dead matter into simpler chemicals. Decomposers are very important to a community. They recycle nutrients so other organisms can use them. Without decomposers, Earth would soon be covered by dead material.

The forest community shown in Figure 30-8 has many different populations of producers, consumers, and decomposers. There are populations of ferns, oak trees, squirrels, and mushrooms. The upper left-hand corner of the figure shows a section of soil from the forest community. This soil section has been enlarged about 2000 times to show the small organisms found there. Bacteria, fungi, and protozoan populations fill the soil. Many of these organisms are decomposers.

Check Your Understanding

6. What is the habitat and niche of an earthworm?
7. How are producers different from consumers?
8. Why are decomposers important to a community?
9. **Critical Thinking:** Which of the following groups are necessary to life on Earth: producers, primary consumers, secondary consumers, decomposers?
10. **Biology and Reading:** Are humans primary consumers or secondary consumers? Explain your answer.

OPTIONS

ACTIVITY/Project

Have students bring in articles from newspapers and magazines that report on producers, consumers, and/or decomposers. Have them report on the articles and explain how useful these organisms are.

RETEACHING 88

RETEACHING: IDEA MAP CHAPTER 30

Name ______ Date ______ Class ______

Use with Section 30:2.

POPULATIONS AND COMMUNITIES

Use the following terms to help you complete the idea map: beneath logs, consumers, decomposers, soil, producers, trees.

Forest community
- niches: producers, consumers, decomposers
- habitats: trees, soil, beneath logs

1. What would you call a group of living things of the same species in a community? **a population**
2. What two things does an organism obtain from its habitat? **shelter and food**
3. What are the habitats of some of the living things that live in a forest? **trees, soil, and beneath logs**
4. What are three niches in every community? **producers, consumers, and decomposers**
5. How do consumers depend on producers? **Consumers eat the food and use the oxygen made by producers.**
6. What is the niche of a decomposer? **A decomposer breaks down dead matter into simpler chemicals.**

30:3 Energy in a Community

Recall that energy is the ability to do work. You learned in Chapter 2 that organisms get energy from food. This food energy can be traced back to the sun. How?

Producers, or green organisms, use light energy to make food. This light energy comes from the sun. To make food, green organisms change energy from the sun into chemical energy (sugar). This chemical energy is, in turn, used by consumers. A community's energy source is the sun.

Objectives

6. Trace the path of energy and materials through a community.

7. Explain how food chains are connected.

Key Science Words

food chain
food web
energy pyramid

Food Chains

When an animal eats a plant and is then eaten by another animal, you have a food chain. A **food chain** is a pathway of energy and materials through a community. Grass→grasshopper→bird is an example of a simple food chain. Each of the living things in it is a link in the food chain. Each depends on the other living things in the food chain. Figure 30-9 shows several important steps in a food chain.

What is an example of a simple food chain?

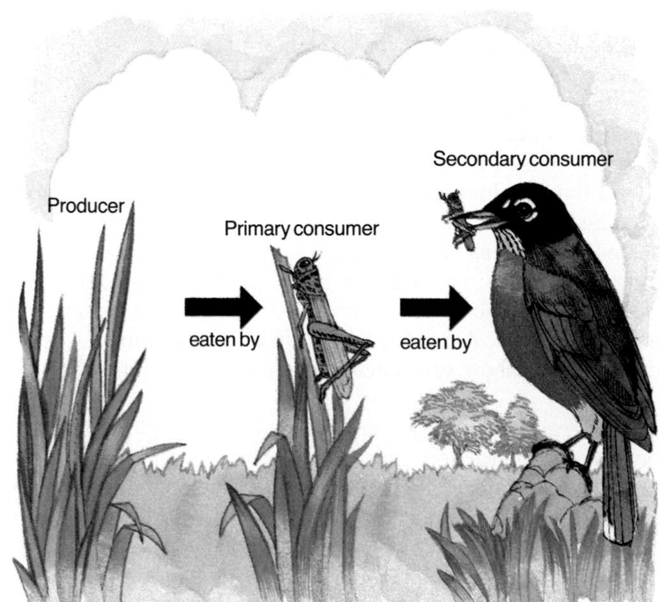

Figure 30-9 A food chain is a pathway of food through a community.

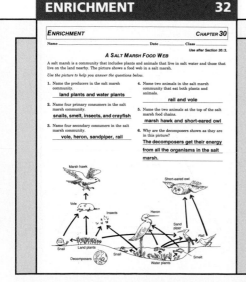

30:3 Energy in a Community

PREPARATION

Materials Needed

Make copies of the Enrichment, Transparency Master, Reteaching, and Study Guide worksheets in the *Teacher Resource Package*.

Key Science Words

food chain
energy pyramid
food web

1 FOCUS

▶ The objectives are listed on the student page. Remind students to preview these objectives as a guide to this numbered section.

Convergent Question

Ask students where they think they get their energy for their body activities. Students should conclude that their energy comes from the food they eat. They should recognize that their energy ultimately comes from the sun.

Guided Practice

Have students write down their answers to the margin question: grass–grasshopper–toad.

ENRICHMENT 32

ENRICHMENT CHAPTER 30

Name ______ Date ______ Class ______

Use after Section 30:3.

A SALT MARSH FOOD WEB

A salt marsh is a community that includes plants and animals that live in salt water and those that live on the land nearby. The picture shows a food web in a salt marsh.

Use the picture to help you answer the questions below.

1. Name the producers in the salt marsh community. land plants and water plants
2. Name four primary consumers in the salt marsh community. snails, smelt, insects, and crayfish
3. Name four secondary consumers in the salt marsh community. vole, heron, sandpiper, rail
4. Name two animals in the salt marsh community that eat both plants and animals. rail and vole
5. Name the two animals at the top of the salt marsh food chains. marsh hawk and short-eared owl
6. Why are the decomposers shown as they are in this picture? The decomposers get their energy from all the organisms in the salt marsh.

Marsh hawk, Short-eared owl, Vole, Insects, Heron, Sand piper, Rail, Snail, Land plants, Snail, Decomposers, Water plants, Smelt

OPTIONS

Science Background

Organisms store some energy for their body processes, but most is lost as heat. Short food chains are more efficient in transferring energy than longer food chains.

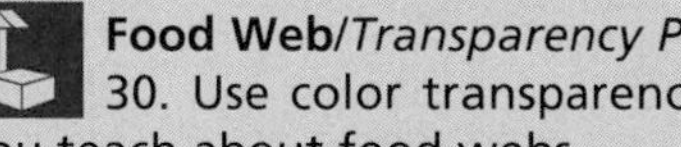

Food Web/*Transparency Package*, number 30. Use color transparency number 30 as you teach about food webs.

Enrichment/*Teacher Resource Package*, p. 32. Use the Enrichment worksheet shown here as an extension to food webs.

2 TEACH

MOTIVATION/Filmstrip

The Ecosystem II: Energy, Carolina Biological Supply Co.

Check for Understanding

Have students make a single food chain of local organisms and list producers, primary and secondary consumers, and decomposers.

Reteach

List several food chains on an overhead transparency. Connect the food chains into food webs.

Guided Practice

Have students write down their answers to the margin question: interconnected food chains in a community.

Independent Practice

Study Guide/*Teacher Resource Package,* p. 178. Use the Study Guide worksheet shown at the bottom of this page for independent practice.

Figure 30-10 This food web shows the relationships among living things in a meadow community.

Bio Tip

Consumer: On a farm, it takes 16 kilograms of plants to produce one kilogram of beef, but only five kilograms of plants to produce one kilogram of chicken. Think about this the next time you help with the shopping.

1. Food chains start with producers such as plants or other green organisms. They are the only organisms able to make their own food.
2. The next links in the food chain are the primary consumers (plant-eating animals).
3. Above the primary consumers are the secondary consumers (meat-eating animals). These animals eat primary consumers.
4. All living things die. They are food for the decomposers.

The arrows in the diagram show the direction in which the energy moves. In our example, plant leaves are eaten by grasshoppers, so an arrow points from the plant to the grasshopper. The next arrow shows that the grasshopper is eaten by a bird. Arrows going from all living things to the decomposers show that decomposers feed on all dead material.

What is a food web?

Several different primary consumers can eat the same producer. Several secondary consumers can eat the same primary consumer. The same producer or consumer may be part of several different food chains. Several food chains may be connected. Figure 30-10 shows how. Food chains connected in a community are called a **food web.** A food web shows how energy is moved through a community.

OPTIONS

ACTIVITY/Challenge

Set up a jar of pond water with protozoans, algae, water fleas, and other micro-invertebrates. Have the students make drawings of the organisms they see and use the drawings to make several food chains.

Transparency Master/*Teacher Resource Package,* p. 151. Use the Transparency Master shown here to show the relationship between energy pyramids and pyramids of numbers.

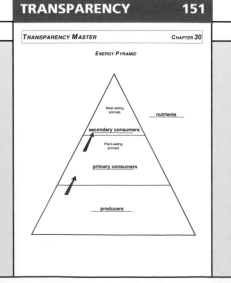

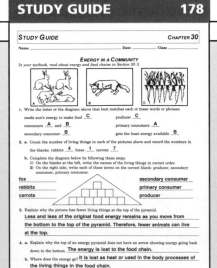

STUDY GUIDE 178

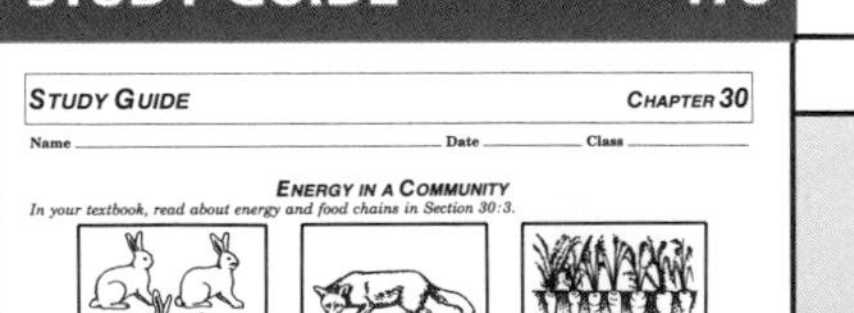

STUDY GUIDE — CHAPTER 30

Name ______ Date ______ Class ______

ENERGY IN A COMMUNITY

In your textbook, read about energy and food chains in Section 30:3.

1. Write the letter of the diagram above that best matches each of these words or phrases.

needs sun's energy to make food C — producer C
consumers A and B — primary consumers A
secondary consumer B — gets the least energy available B

2. a. Count the number of living things in each of the pictures above and record the numbers in the blanks. rabbits 4 foxes 1 carrots 7

b. Complete the diagram below by following these steps.
1) On the blanks at the left, write the names of the living things in correct order.
2) On the right side, write each of these terms on the correct blank: producer, secondary consumer, primary consumer.

fox — secondary consumer
rabbits — primary consumer
carrots — producer

3. Explain why the picture has fewer living things at the top of the pyramid. Less and less of the original food energy remains as you move from the bottom to the top of the pyramid. Therefore, fewer animals can live at the top.

4. a. Explain why the top of an energy pyramid does not have an arrow showing energy going back down to the bottom. The energy is lost to the food chain.

b. Where does the energy go? It is lost as heat or used in the body processes of the living things in the food chain.

TRANSPARENCY 151

TRANSPARENCY MASTER — CHAPTER 30

ENERGY PYRAMID

Meat-eating animals
nutrients
secondary consumers
Plant-eating animals
primary consumers
producers

Energy Flow in the Community

A producer gets energy from the sun and uses it to produce food and oxygen. Much of the food made through photosynthesis is used by the producer for growth and other cell processes. A large amount of the energy is lost as heat. Only a small amount of the food energy produced is available to the primary consumer that eats the producer. Therefore, primary consumers must eat large numbers of plants to get the energy they need for their cell processes and growth. When a secondary consumer eats a primary consumer, again only some of the food energy is available. The secondary consumer must eat several animals to get enough energy. You can see that each step of the food chain has fewer organisms than the step before it.

At each step of the food chain, from producers to primary consumers to secondary consumers, the amount of available energy becomes less and less. This loss of energy through a food chain can be shown in the shape of a pyramid. An **energy pyramid** is a diagram that shows energy loss in the food chain. Figure 30-11 shows an energy pyramid. The pyramid is wider at the bottom than at the top. There is more available energy at the bottom of the pyramid than at the top. Notice in Figure 30-11 that the number of primary consumers is smaller than the number of producers. Notice also that the number of secondary consumers is smaller than the number of primary consumers. There are fewer organisms at the top of the pyramid because less energy is available to them. Figure 30-11 also shows that all living things lose heat to their surroundings.

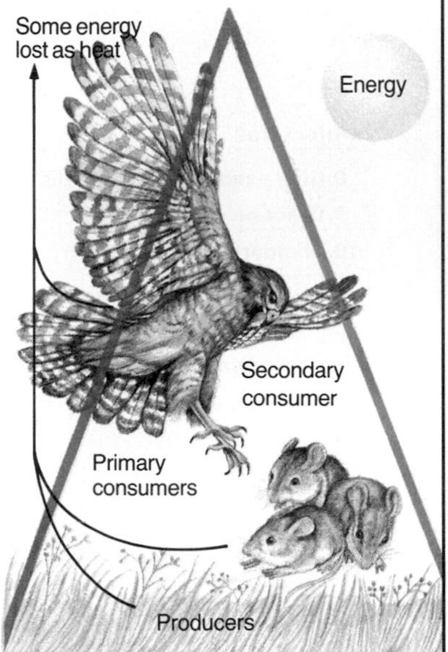

Figure 30-11 An energy pyramid shows energy loss in a food chain.

Check Your Understanding

11. Why must primary consumers eat large numbers of plants?
12. Which would be affected more by the loss of a species—a food chain or a food web? Why?
13. Why are plants necessary to the path of energy through a community?
14. **Critical Thinking:** What would happen to the food chains in an area if all plants were to die?
15. **Biology and Reading:** What happens to most of the energy at each level of a food chain?

TEACH

Check for Understanding

Have students respond to the first three questions in Check Your Understanding.

Reteach

Reteaching/*Teacher Resource Package,* p. 89. Use this worksheet to give students additional practice with energy flow in a community.

Extension: Assign Critical Thinking, Biology and Reading, or some of the **OPTIONS** available with this lesson.

3 APPLY

ACTIVITY/Hands-On

Have pictures of plants, animals, and fungi from magazines mounted on construction paper. Give each team of four students seven to ten pictures. Have them develop a food chain using the pictures. Have them present their food chain to the class. When the teams have presented their food chains, have several teams use their food chains to make a food web to present to the class.

4 CLOSE

ACTIVITY/Software

Food Chains, Queue, Inc.

Answers to Check Your Understanding

11. because only a small amount of the energy in the producers is available to the primary consumer
12. a food chain; The species that is lost represents a significant portion of the food chain, and its consumers will not be likely to have other food sources.
13. Plants are the only organisms that can convert sunlight energy into food energy.
14. The consumers and decomposers would die because they would have no food.
15. At each level of the food chain, most of the energy is lost as heat.

RETEACHING 89

RETEACHING: IDEA MAP CHAPTER 30

Name ______ Date ______ Class ______

Use with Section 30:3.

ENERGY IN A COMMUNITY

Use the following words or phrases to complete the idea map: secondary consumers, decomposers, producers, cell processes, primary consumers, growth. You may use a word or phrase more than once.

Energy → transfer of food in a food chain → secondary consumers → decomposers; primary consumers → decomposers; producers → decomposers
Energy → used up as food → cell processes; growth

1. What is the beginning source of energy in a community? the light from the sun
2. Which group of organisms are able to use this energy in the community? producers
3. What does this group of organisms do with the energy they receive? They make food and oxygen.
4. Which groups of organisms in a community cannot make food? consumers and decomposers
5. What is the source of energy for these organisms in the community? living or dead animals and plants
6. What do all organisms need energy for? growth and cell processes
7. How does light energy from the sun eventually reach the decomposers? Plants use the light from the sun to make food, and this is passed on to the consumers. When the producers and consumers die, the decomposers use these organisms for energy.

OPTIONS

What Are Some Parts of a Food Chain and a Food Web?/*Lab Manual,* pp. 251-254. Use this lab as an extension to food webs.

30:4 Relationships in a Community

PREPARATION

Materials Needed

Make copies of the Application, Critical Thinking/Problem Solving, Reteaching, Study Guide, and Lab worksheets in the *Teacher Resource Package.*

▶ Get owl pellets, cardboard, and glue ready for Lab 30-2. The cardboard may be cut from large cartons.

Key Science Words

commensalism
parasitism
predation
predator
prey

Process Skills

In Lab 30-2, students will observe, infer, and design an experiment.

1 FOCUS

▶ The objectives are listed on the student page. Remind students to preview these objectives as a guide to this numbered section.

Divergent Question

Ask students to explain some ways in which two organisms can be helpful or harmful to one another. Have them list the names of specific organisms. You could start with the example of a hawk and a mouse. List answers on the chalkboard.

Guided Practice

Have students write down their answers to the margin question: a relationship in which two organisms live together and depend on each other for survival.

30:4 Relationships in a Community

Objectives

8. **Give examples** of mutualism.
9. **Describe** commensalism.
10. **Compare** parasitism with predation.

Key Science Words

commensalism
parasitism
predation
predator
prey

There are many types of relationships within a community. Each relationship shows a different way that one living thing affects another. The relationship of one kind of organism to another may be helpful to both. In other relationships, one organism benefits while the second is harmed. There are still other cases where one organism is helped and the other is neither harmed nor helped. Communities could not exist without these different relationships.

Mutualism

Suppose there is a good rock concert in town and you would like to go. Right now, you do not have enough money for a ticket. Your best friend offers to buy you a ticket for this concert if you will give her a ride to the concert. It sounds like a good deal. Both you and your friend benefit from the arrangement.

What is mutualism?

This is an example of mutualism. Remember from Chapter 5 that mutualism is a relationship in which two organisms live in a community and depend on each other. Both organisms benefit from the relationship. Mutualism occurs among members of all five kingdoms. You first read about this kind of relationship in Chapter 5 when you read about lichens.

An example of a relationship between an animal and a protist can be seen in a dead log that contains termites, Figure 30-12. Termites are insects that eat wood. They are

Figure 30-12 The relationship among protists (a) living in the intestines of termites (b) is an example of mutualism.

OPTIONS

Science Background

Sometimes, two populations have very little effect on each other. Some of the relationships between two populations can be helpful to both populations while some are harmful to one of the populations. In some cases, only one population benefits while the other is unaffected. These relationships between populations can cause one of the populations in the community to increase or decrease in size over a period of time.

Figure 30-13 The relationship between orchid plants and trees is an example of commensalism.

not able to digest wood. They could not use it for energy if it weren't for a protist that lives inside the termite's intestine. The protist can digest the wood for the termite so that the termite can use it for energy. The protist has a home inside the termite and uses some of the wood for its own energy.

Humans can show mutualism with other organisms. An example is the bacterium that lives in the human intestine. The bacterium makes vitamin B_{12} for the human, who provides a home and food for the bacterium.

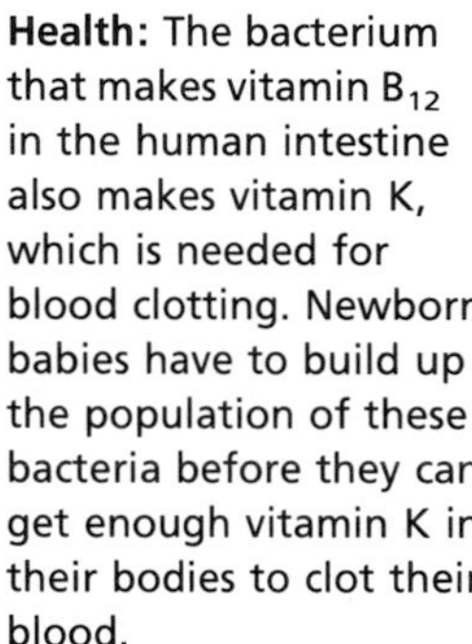

Bio Tip

Health: The bacterium that makes vitamin B_{12} in the human intestine also makes vitamin K, which is needed for blood clotting. Newborn babies have to build up the population of these bacteria before they can get enough vitamin K in their bodies to clot their blood.

Commensalism

Let's return to the example of the rock concert tickets. Suppose your friend has a free ticket, but can't go to the concert. She gives the ticket to you. You benefit from the free ticket. Whether or not you use the ticket doesn't matter to your friend, does it? She got the ticket free. She won't lose anything whether you use the ticket or not.

What is commensalism?

Commensalism (kuh MEN suh lihz um) is seen in this example. **Commensalism** is a relationship in which two organisms live in a community, and one benefits while the other gets no benefit and is not harmed.

Commensalism occurs between many living things. For example, orchid plants and trees have this kind of relationship. Orchids receive more sunlight for photosynthesis if they grow high on tree branches rather than close to the ground, Figure 30-13. The orchid plants are helped by the tree. The tree gets nothing in return from the orchids.

2 TEACH

MOTIVATION/Filmstrip

Show the filmstrip *Symbiosis,* Carolina Biological Supply Co.

Concept Development

▶ Explain to the students that *mutual* means having something in common.

▶ Make sure students understand that one organism benefits and the other is not harmed in a commensal relationship.

Audiovisual

Make an overhead transparency listing the organisms that live as mutualists.

Analogy: The analogy of the rock concert will be discussed with the topics of mutualism, commensalism, and parasitism. In each section, the analogy of the ticket and two friends should help to reinforce these three community relationships.

Guided Practice

Have students write down their answers to the margin question: a relationship in which one organism benefits and the other is unaffected.

Independent Practice

Study Guide/*Teacher Resource Package,* p. 179. Use the Study Guide worksheet shown at the bottom of this page for independent practice.

STUDY GUIDE 179

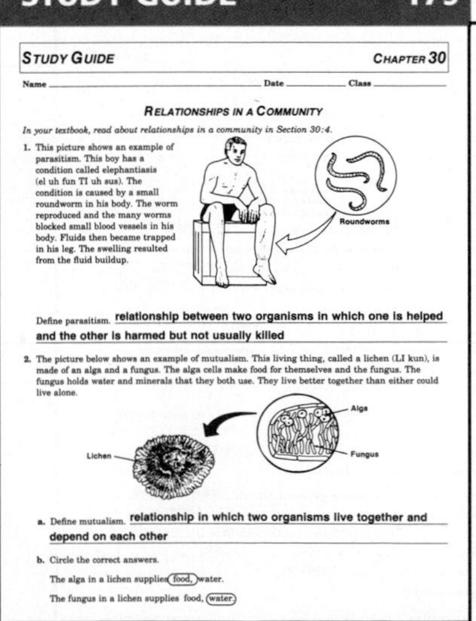

STUDY GUIDE CHAPTER 30

Name ______ Date ______ Class ______

RELATIONSHIPS IN A COMMUNITY

In your textbook, read about relationships in a community in Section 30:4.

1. This picture shows an example of parasitism. This boy has a condition called elephantiasis (el uh fun TI uh sus). The condition is caused by a small roundworm in his body. The worm reproduced and the many worms blocked small blood vessels in his body. Fluids then became trapped in his leg. The swelling resulted from the fluid buildup.

Define parasitism. relationship between two organisms in which one is helped and the other is harmed but not usually killed

2. The picture below shows an example of mutualism. This living thing, called a lichen (LI kun), is made of an alga and a fungus. The alga cells make food for themselves and the fungus. The fungus holds water and minerals that they both use. They live better together than either could live alone.

a. Define mutualism. relationship in which two organisms live together and depend on each other

b. Circle the correct answers.

The alga in a lichen supplies (food,) water.

The fungus in a lichen supplies food, (water.)

TEACH

Concept Development

▶ Explain to students that the organism a parasite attaches to is called a host.

▶ Point out that parasites can be monerans, protists, fungi, plants, or animals.

▶ Ask students why it is important that parasites not kill their hosts. Have them predict what would happen to the parasites if all of their hosts were to die.

Audiovisual

Make an overhead transparency listing the organisms that are parasites.

Skill Check

The lamprey has a mouth that is adapted to piercing flesh and sucking the body fluids of its host.

Independent Practice

Study Guide/*Teacher Resource Package*, p. 180. Use the Study Guide worksheet shown at the bottom of the page for independent practice.

Skill Check

Observe: A lamprey is a parasitic fish. Look at the photo of a lamprey on this page and see if you can tell how the lamprey gets its food. Does it have any body parts that are adapted to its way of life? *For more help, refer to the* ***Skill Handbook,*** *pages 704-705.*

Parasitism

Let's return to the rock concert tickets one more time. Suppose your friend offers to sell you some concert tickets. Later, you find out that she has charged you much more money than the tickets were worth. Your friend is making a profit at your expense.

This is an example of parasitism (PAR uh suh tihz um). **Parasitism** is a relationship between two organisms in which one is helped and the other is harmed. Remember that a parasite lives at the expense of another living thing. The living thing on which the parasite lives is called the host. The host is rarely killed in this kind of relationship. What would happen to the parasite if it killed its host?

Many organisms are parasites. Fleas are parasites with which you may be familiar. Fleas use the blood of dogs or other animals for food. The flea benefits and the host animal is harmed in the relationship.

There are other common examples of parasitism. When you get sick, chances are that bacteria or viruses are using your body as a host. At some time you may have had strep throat. This disease is caused by bacteria living in your throat and using your body as a host. The bacteria grow and reproduce. They give off chemicals that irritate your throat tissues and interfere with the function of other body systems.

Figure 30-14 The relationship between a flea (a) and a rabbit, or between a lamprey (b) and other fish is an example of parasitism.

a

b

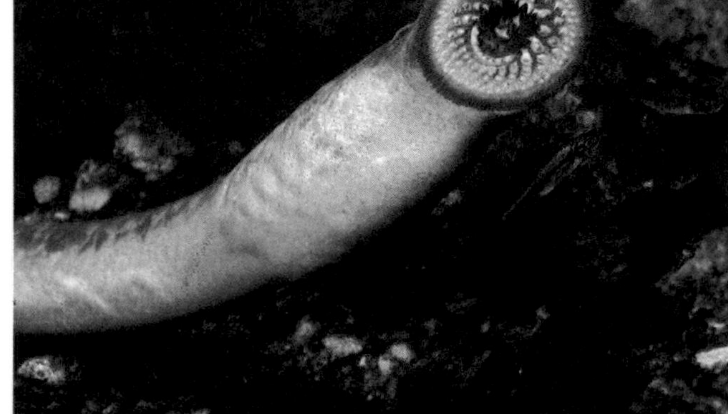

OPTIONS

Challenge: Have students research and present a report to the class on parasites that are harmful to humans.

STUDY GUIDE 180

STUDY GUIDE — CHAPTER 30

Name ______ Date ______ Class ______

VOCABULARY

Review the new words used in Chapter 30 of your textbook. Then complete this puzzle. Use the words listed below to fill in the blanks in the sentences that follow.

commensalism	population	immigration
energy pyramid	habitat	emigration
niche	community	limiting factor
primary consumers	food chain	secondary consumers
prey	food web	predator
predation	parasitism	

A group of organisms of the same species make up a ___population___.

The size of this group of organisms can change because new organisms enter and leave. This is called ___immigration___ and ___emigration___.

A condition that keeps the size of a population from increasing is a ___limiting factor___.

Living things of different kinds live together in a ___community___. The place where a plant or animal lives is its ___habitat___. The job of the organism is its ___niche___. Animals that eat only plants are ___primary consumers___. Animals that eat other animals are ___secondary consumers___.

Energy and materials are passed from one living thing to another in a community through a ___food chain___. A ___food web___ shows how food chains are connected in a community. An ___energy pyramid___ is a diagram that shows energy loss in the food chain.

Living things depend on each other in several ways. In ___commensalism___, one organism is helped and the other is not affected. In ___parasitism___, one organism is helped and the other is harmed but not usually killed. In ___predation___, one animal hunts and kills another animal. The ___prey___ is the animal that is eaten. The ___predator___ is the animal that hunts and kills the other animal.

Figure 30-15 A predator hunts and kills other animals for food.

Predation

There is another relationship in a community in which one organism benefits and the other is harmed. This is **predation,** or the predator-prey relationship. An animal that hunts, kills, and eats another animal is a **predator.** The **prey** is the animal that the predator kills and eats. Unlike parasitism, in predation the predator actually kills the prey.

What is a predator?

Predators are secondary consumers. They can limit the sizes of some populations. Rabbits living near a field of clover become prey for owls that live in the same area. Look at the graph of the rabbit population in Figure 30-16. The graph shows sudden increases and decreases in population size. What are some things that might cause the population to decrease?

Rabbit population in a field

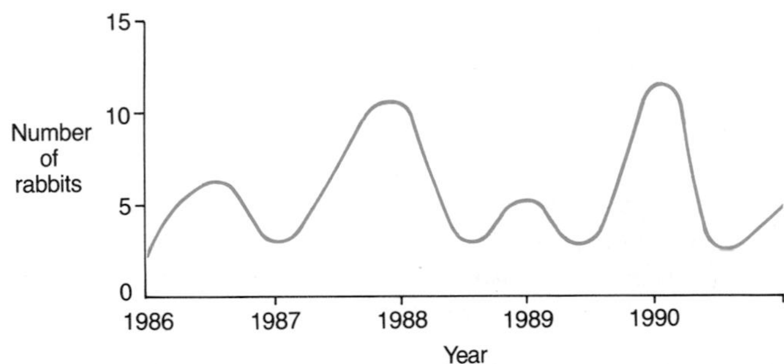

Figure 30-16 Predators can be a limiting factor for a prey population.

TEACH

Concept Development

▶ Explain that plants like the Venus flytrap, pitcher plant, and sundew are called carnivorous plants because they capture insects for food.

▶ Explain that the members of a predator population are competing among themselves for prey. If the prey population decreases rapidly, the decrease becomes a limiting factor for the predators. This discussion will help reinforce the concepts of limiting factors and competition learned earlier in this chapter.

Guided Practice

Have students write a short paragraph to explain whether a predator is a producer, a primary consumer, or a secondary consumer. Have them give a reason for their answer.

Check for Understanding

Have students use Table 30-2 on page 648 to explain how the four relationships in a community are alike and how they are different.

Reteach

Divide the students into teams and have them use the library to find several examples of each type of community relationship. Have student teams report their findings to the class.

Guided Practice

Have students write down their answers to the margin question: An animal that kills and eats another animal.

CRITICAL THINKING 30

CRITICAL THINKING/PROBLEM SOLVING — CHAPTER 30

Name ________ Date ________ Class ________

Use after Section 30:4.

WHAT DO PREDATORS DO IN A COMMUNITY?

The game warden in a county noticed many foxes in the woods. She knew that foxes were predators and she thought the foxes were eating too many rabbits. The game warden decided to catch some of the foxes and release them somewhere else. During the following summer, the game warden moved four foxes. She trapped and moved the same number of foxes each year for three more years. During that time, she noticed that the populations of owls and mice increased in size. She was surprised to find there were no more rabbits than before. What is happening to the balance in this community?

Analyzing the Problem

1. Which animals are predators? foxes and owls
2. Which animals are prey? rabbits and mice
3. Which of the animals compete with each other? Explain. The foxes and owls may compete with each other for mice and rabbits as food.

Solving the Problem

1. How could removal of foxes be related to the increase of mice? Trapping and removing the foxes removed a predator of mice. More mice could reproduce and grow to be adults, who also reproduce.
2. Why do you suppose the rabbit population did not increase, even though foxes were removed? Owls are another predator and must be eating the rabbits.
3. Do the results suggest that a predator can have more than one prey? Give an example. Yes, owls seem to eat both mice and rabbits.
4. Do the results suggest that a prey can be food for more than one predator? Yes, rabbits seem to be food for both owls and foxes.
5. Why do some people think predators are harmful and should be removed from an area? Some people want to keep the prey for human uses.
6. Why do some people think predators have a helpful role in a community? Predators eat prey and keep a balance of animals in the area. If not eaten, the population of prey animals might grow larger and eat plants that humans need.

APPLICATION 30

APPLICATION: ENVIRONMENT — CHAPTER 30

Name ________ Date ________ Class ________

Use after Section 30:4.

PREDATORS AND PREY

Many prey animals have behaviors that help them escape from their predators. One way that prey animals protect themselves is to stay together in a group.

1. Give three examples of animals that live, feed, or travel together in groups. Answers might include flocks of geese, schools of fish, or herds of zebras.

Do the experiment described below. You will need a partner and 8-10 table tennis balls. You and your partner should stand about 2 meters apart in an open area, facing each other. One of you will act as the predator. The other person will toss 8-10 balls to the predator. The balls will represent the prey. The balls should be tossed gently, but also quickly, all at once, and without warning. The balls would represent a group of prey animals running past a predator. The predator will try to catch as many balls (prey) as possible. Record on the table below how many balls the predator catches. Repeat the experiment five times.

Now do another experiment. This time, toss only one ball to the predator. The ball would represent what it is like for a predator to try to catch a single prey animal. Repeat this experiment five times. On the table, record whether one or zero balls was caught each time.

Number of balls (prey) caught when many balls are tossed:	Answers will vary but students should catch				
Number of balls (prey) caught when one ball is tossed:	more balls when only one is thrown.				

Refer to your table to answer the following questions.

2. Which do you think is harder, catching a ball when it is tossed as part of a group or when it is tossed separately? Explain. It is harder to catch a ball when it is tossed in a group, because it is harder to focus your attention on any single ball.
3. How do you think a prey animal is protected from predators by being part of a group? It might be hard for the predator to catch any single animal due to the movement of all the animals together; animals in the middle of the group would be less likely to be caught than those on the outside: one animal might warn the group if predators are sighted.
4. How would you change the experiment to find out what happens if one member of the prey group is sick or old? All but one of the balls could be thrown at once, and then the last ball could be thrown separately.

OPTIONS

Application/*Teacher Resource Package,* p. 30. Use the Application worksheet shown here as an extension to predator-prey relationships.

Critical Thinking/Problem Solving/*Teacher Resource Package,* p. 30. Use the Critical Thinking/Problem Solving worksheet shown here to give additional practice with problems involving predator-prey interactions.

TEACH

Idea Map

Have students use the idea map as a study guide to the major concepts of this section.

Check for Understanding

Have students respond to the first three questions in Check Your Understanding.

Reteach

Reteaching/*Teacher Resource Package,* p. 90. Use this worksheet to give students additional practice with relationships in a community.

Extension: Assign Critical Thinking, Biology and Reading, or some of the **OPTIONS** available with this lesson.

3 APPLY

Brainstorming

Have student teams discuss the following question and report to the class on their findings. A shopping center is going to be built in an area that is now a forest. What concern should the developer and citizens of the community have for the plants and animals in the forest?

4 CLOSE

Guest Speaker

Have a veterinarian come to your class to speak about parasites in pets and farm animals.

Answers to Check Your Understanding

16. The bacteria that make Vitamin B_{12} in the human intestine have a mutualistic relationship with humans.
17. The orchids get more light.
18. parasitism
19. If too many orchid plants cover the tree, the tree might not be able to make food. The tree would be weakened and harmed.
20. (a) mutualism, (b) parasitism, (c) commensalism

Study Tip: Use this idea map as study guide to community relationships. Can you give an example of each kind of relationship?

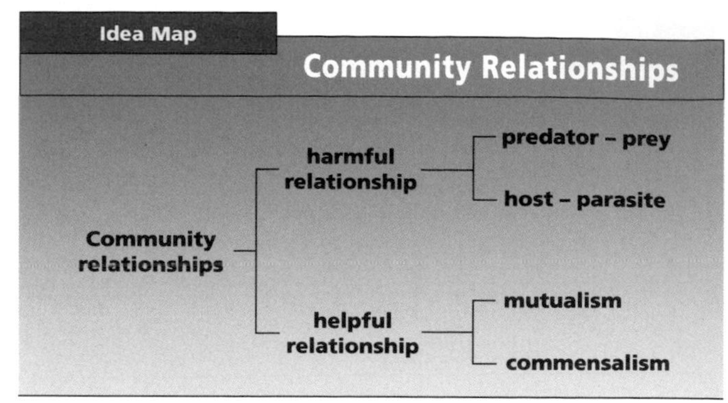

TABLE 30–2. RELATIONSHIPS		
Type of Relationship	**Organism 1**	**Organism 2**
Mutualism	helped	helped
Commensalism	helped	unaffected
Parasitism	helped	harmed
Predation	helped	harmed (killed)

Table 30-2 is a summary of the relationships that may occur among populations in a community. Now you can see why the statement "no living thing lives alone" is true.

Check Your Understanding

16. Give an example of mutualism involving humans.
17. How do orchid plants benefit by living high in trees?
18. What word describes the relationship between fleas and their hosts?
19. **Critical Thinking:** Explain how the relationship between orchid plants and a tree might change from commensalism to parasitism.
20. **Biology and Reading:** For each of the pairs of organisms below, write the word that best describes their community relationship.
    a. Ants protect a tree, which provides food for ants.
    b. A liver fluke lives inside a sheep, which develops liver disease.
    c. An insect eats the hairs that fall out of a deer's skin, but the deer is not affected.

OPTIONS

ACTIVITY/Project

Have a group of students research the predator/prey relationship between the lynx and the snowshoe hare. Ask them to prepare a poster illustrating how this relationship results in population cycles.

How Do Predator and Prey Populations Change?/*Lab Manual,* pp. 255-258. Use this lab as an extension to population dynamics involving predator-prey interactions.

RETEACHING 90

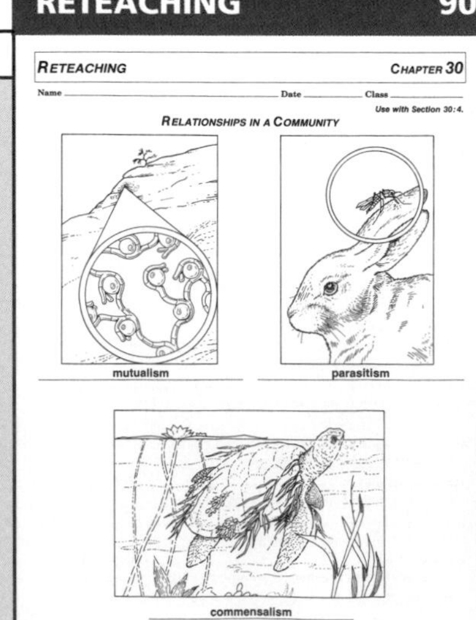

Lab 30–2 Predation

Problem: What do owls eat?

Skills

observe, infer, design an experiment

Materials

water	coverslip
bowl	light microscope
forceps	owl pellet
glue	cardboard
glass slide	

Procedure

Owl pellets are made of food, bones, and fur an owl has eaten but has not been able to digest. An owl forms pellets in its stomach and then coughs them up. Examining an owl pellet will give you some ideas about what an owl eats.

1. Copy the data table.
2. Place an owl pellet in the bowl. Add some water.
3. Use the forceps to remove the outside covering of the pellet.
4. Place a small piece of this covering on a glass slide and add a coverslip.
5. **Observe:** Examine the covering of the pellet on low power of your microscope. Make a drawing of what you see.
6. Continue to break the pellet open. Save all the parts present in the pellet.
7. Place the parts on a sheet of paper. Try to figure out how many living things the owl ate. Examine the bones and record your observations.
8. Try to assemble the bony parts into a skeleton. You can do this by gluing them to cardboard.

Data and Observations

1. What was the outside covering of the pellet? Where do you suppose it came from?
2. What types of things did you see in the pellet?

Analyze and Apply

1. An owl coughs up one pellet a day. How many animals did your owl eat each day?
2. Judging from the size of the remains in the owl pellet, name the kinds of living things that the owl ate.
3. Do owls eat plants or animals?
4. Is an owl a producer or a consumer? Explain your answer.
5. Is an owl a primary consumer or a secondary consumer?
6. **Apply:** Suppose an owl population increases from three to eight. What can happen to the population of organisms eaten by the owls? Why?

Extension

Design an experiment to show what happens to a predator population when the size of the prey population decreases.

Answers will vary.

NUMBERS OBSERVED				
Leg Bone	Rib	Mammal Skull	Bird Skull	Mammal Jawbone
3	8	0	2	4

ANSWERS

Data and Observations

1. feathers or fur from the animals eaten by the owl
2. feathers, fur, bones

Analyze and Apply

1. Answers will vary. Sometimes 5 or 6 skulls are easily seen.
2. Answers will vary. Owls eat small mammals, such as mice, voles, rabbits, and squirrels. They also eat birds.
3. animals
4. consumer; Owls eat other animals and do not make their own food.
5. secondary consumer
6. They will begin to decrease because more owls are present to prey on the animals.

Lab 30-2 Predation

Overview

Students will find out what owls eat by examining an owl pellet.

Objectives: Students will be able to (1) **determine** what an owl eats, (2) **classify** an owl as an herbivore or carnivore, and (3) **assemble** the bones from an owl pellet to make a skeleton.

Time Allotment: 45 minutes

Preparation

▶ Obtain zoology reference books that show the skeletons of birds and small mammals.

▶ Cut 10 cm x 10 cm squares for students to use in assembling the skeleton from the owl pellet.

▶ Owl pellets can be found under trees, ordered from a biological supply house, or obtained from a local zoo.

Lab 30-2 worksheet/*Teacher Resource Package,* pp. 119-120.

Teaching the Lab

Cooperative Learning: Divide the class into groups of two students. For more information, see pp. 22T-23T in the Teacher Guide.

CHAPTER 30 REVIEW

Summary

Summary statements can be used by students to review the major concepts of the chapter.

Key Science Words

All boldfaced terms from the chapter are listed.

Testing Yourself

Using Words

1. food chain
2. parasitism
3. limiting factor
4. habitat
5. energy pyramid
6. immigration
7. prey
8. emigration
9. niche
10. population

Finding Main Ideas

11. p. 633; Animal herds and flocks are clumped populations.
12. p. 640; Decomposers recycle nutrients for reuse by a community.
13. p. 641; A food chain shows how energy is passed through a community.
14. p. 644; The relationship is called mutualism.
15. p. 639; Plants are the producers, organisms that make food in a community.
16. p. 642; The second link in a food chain is a plant eater.
17. p. 633; Animals are sometimes marked with ear staples, birds with bands on their legs, and trees with paint or ribbons. Animals with radio transmitters can be followed to their homes, where their young can be counted.
18. p. 636; Limiting factors are the amount of food, space, and water.
19. p. 639; Animals that eat only plants are primary consumers. Animals that eat other animals are secondary consumers.
20. p. 643; An energy pyramid shows energy loss in a food chain.

Chapter 30

Review

Summary

30:1 Populations

1. There are many methods for counting the living things in a population.
2. A change in population size can be caused by a change in birth or death rates.
3. Limiting factors keep populations from increasing forever.

30:2 Communities

4. Each kind of organism in a community has its own habitat and niche.
5. Green organisms supply food in a community. Animals are consumers. Bacteria and fungi are decomposers.

30:3 Energy in a Community

6. The energy in a community comes originally from the sun. It is passed through the community as food.
7. Food chains are connected to form food webs.

30:4 Relationships in a Community

8. In mutualism, two living things depend on each other.
9. Commensalism is a relationship in which one organism benefits and the other is unaffected.
10. In parasitism, the host is harmed but not killed. A predator kills its prey.

Key Science Words

commensalism (p. 645)
community (p. 638)
emigration (p. 634)
energy pyramid (p. 643)
food chain (p. 641)
food web (p. 642)
habitat (p. 638)
immigration (p. 634)
limiting factor (p. 636)
niche (p. 638)
parasitism (p. 646)
population (p. 632)
predation (p. 647)
predator (p. 647)
prey (p. 647)
primary consumer (p. 639)
secondary consumer (p. 639)

Testing Yourself

Using Words

Choose the word from the list of Key Science Words that best fits the definition.

1. simple pathway of energy and materials through a community
2. relationship in which one member is helped and the other is harmed
3. keeps a population from increasing
4. place where an organism lives
5. a diagram that shows energy loss
6. animals moving into a population
7. eaten by a predator

Using Main Ideas

21. It could increase.
22. The sun is used as energy by producers to make food.
23. Bacteria and fungi are decomposers.
24. Radio transmitters allow animals to be followed to their homes, where the offspring can be counted.
25. Birth increases a population by adding new offspring; immigration increases a population by adding new adults.
26. commensalism

Review

Testing Yourself *continued*

8. animals moving out of a population
9. an organism's job in a community
10. a group of the same kind of living things in an area

Finding Main Ideas

List the page number where each main idea below is found. Then, explain each main idea.

11. examples of clumped populations
12. the job of decomposers in a community
13. what a food chain shows
14. a relationship in which two organisms depend on each other
15. the importance of plants to a community
16. what the second link of a food chain is
17. what methods are used to count populations
18. what the limiting factors for animal populations are
19. the difference between primary consumers and secondary consumers
20. what an energy pyramid shows

Using Main Ideas

Answer the questions by referring to the page number after each question.

21. If a predator population in an area decreases, what could happen to the size of the prey population? (p. 647)
22. What role does the sun play in a community? (p. 643)
23. What are two examples of decomposers? (p. 640)
24. Why are radio transmitters sometimes used to count a population? (p. 633)
25. What factors can increase a population? (p. 634)
26. What relationship is shown by orchids growing on a tree? (p. 645)

Skill Review ✓

*For more help, refer to the **Skill Handbook**, pages 704-719.*

1. **Make a line graph:** Find out from the school office how many students have been in your school each year during the past ten years. Make a line graph to show these data. Is the school population increasing or decreasing?
2. **Infer:** Infer what happens to two different organisms in a community if they have the same needs for food.
3. **Form hypotheses:** Form a hypothesis to explain how you could tell if owls eat small plant-eating animals.
4. **Make and use tables:** Make a table listing 10 organisms as producers, primary consumers, and secondary consumers. List how each organism gets food.

Finding Out More

Critical Thinking

1. What causes a prey population to increase again after it has been decreased by predators?
2. What would happen in a food web if one kind of organism in the web were all killed by a disease?

Applications

1. Make a list of 6 to 10 different organisms that live near your school or home. Construct a food web using the organisms on your list.
2. Find out why fungi and bacteria are useful organisms in a farm field.

651

Skill Review

1. Students can also plot the number of students in each grade for ten years to see which grades show an increase or decrease.
2. Students should be able to explain how organisms compete for the same food and that one or both of the populations may show a decrease in number.
3. By examining owl pellets and identifying the skulls of plant eaters and animal eaters, students could form a hypothesis as to the importance of plant eaters to owls.
4. Do this as an in-class assignment and give each student a chart. You may have some magazine and newspaper articles that will help them make their list of organisms.

Finding Out More

Critical Thinking

1. When a prey population decreases, the predators do not have enough to eat. Food becomes a limiting factor and the predator population decreases. A decrease in the predator population eventually allows the prey population to increase.
2. The web would be disrupted. Secondary consumers would have to find new prey species.

Applications

1. Students should show a web that depicts animals feeding at more than one level.
2. Students should realize that these organisms are decomposers and are necessary for recycling materials.

Chapter Review/*Teacher Resource Package,* pp. 160-161.

Chapter Test/*Teacher Resource Package,* pp. 162-164.

Chapter Review/*Computer Test Bank*

Ecosystems and Biomes

PLANNING GUIDE

CONTENT	TEXT FEATURES	TEACHER RESOURCE PACKAGE	OTHER COMPONENTS
(2 days) 31:1 Parts of an Ecosystem Soil and Nitrogen Cycle Water Oxygen-Carbon Dioxide Cycle	Skill Check: *Understand Science Words,* p. 655 Mini Lab: *What Are the Parts of the Water Cycle?* p. 657 Lab 31-1: *Carbon Dioxide,* p. 659 Check Your Understanding, p. 658 Career Close-up: *Wildlife Technician,* p. 656	Application: *Space Invaders,* p. 31 Enrichment: *How Fast Can Change Take Place in an Ecosystem,* p. 33 Reteaching: *The Water Cycle,* p. 91 Critical Thinking/Problem Solving: *How Can a Nonliving Factor Affect Animals in an Ecosystem?* p. 31 Study Guide: *Parts of an Ecosystem,* p. 181 Lab 31-1: *Carbon Dioxide,* pp. 121-122	**Laboratory Manual:** *How Much Water Will Soil Hold?* p. 259 **Laboratory Manual:** *How Can a Nonliving Part of an Ecosystem Harm Living Things?* p. 263 Color Transparency 31a: *The Nitrogen Cycle* Color Transparency 31b: *The Water Cycle*
(1 1/2 days) 31:2 Succession Succession in a Land Community Succession in a Water Community	Mini Lab: *How Do Leaves Decay?* p. 661 Check Your Understanding, p. 662	Reteaching: *Succession,* p. 92 Focus: *Changes in a Community,* p. 61 Transparency Master: *Succession—Bare Land to Forest,* p. 155 Study Guide: *Succession,* pp. 182-184	**Laboratory Manual:** *How Can a Nonliving Part of an Ecosystem Help Living Things?* p. 265
(1 1/2 days) 31:3 How Living Things Are Distributed Climate Land Biomes Water Biomes	Skill Check: *Sequence,* p. 664 Lab 31-2: *Brine Shrimp,* p. 667 Idea Map, p. 666 Check Your Understanding, p. 666 Problem Solving: *Biomes and Their Living Things,* p. 668	Reteaching: *Climates in Biomes,* p. 93 Skill: *Interpret Diagrams,* p. 32 Study Guide: *Biomes,* p. 185 Study Guide: *Vocabulary,* p. 186 Lab 31-2: *Brine Shrimp,* pp. 123-124	
Chapter Review	Summary Key Science Words Testing Yourself Finding Main Ideas Using Main Ideas Skill Review	Chapter Review, pp. 165-166 Chapter Test, pp. 167-169	**Test Bank**

MATERIALS NEEDED

LAB 31-1, p. 659	LAB 31-2, p. 667	MARGIN FEATURES
4 test tubes wax pencil 4 stoppers lamp blue test liquid green test liquid 2 *Elodea* sprigs 2 test-tube racks	3 small plastic cups marking pen hand lens flat toothpick distilled water brine shrimp eggs strong salt solution weak salt solution	Skill Check, p. 655 dictionary Skill Check, p. 664 pencil paper Mini Lab, p. 657 pencil paper Mini Lab, p. 661 jar plastic wrap soil water dead leaves

OBJECTIVES

SECTION	OBJECTIVE	OBJECTIVES CORRELATION			
		CHECK YOUR UNDERSTANDING	CHAPTER REVIEW	TRP CHAPTER REVIEW	TRP CHAPTER TEST
31:1	1. **Describe** the parts of an ecosystem.	1	2, 3, 8, 11, 14	2, 26, 28	2, 25, 26, 30
	2. **Describe** how the water cycle affects an ecosystem.	3, 4	1, 10, 19, 21	4, 30	1, 22, 47, 48, 49, 50
	3. **Explain** the nitrogen cycle and the oxygen-carbon dioxide cycle.	2, 5	7, 13, 19, 20, 22	1, 5, 7, 8, 31	3, 4, 6, 9, 10, 13, 16, 17, 20, 21, 23, 24, 27, 31, 42, 43, 44, 45, 46
31:2	4. **Describe** succession in a land community.	7, 9	4, 9, 16	3, 6, 23, 24, 28, 29	5, 11, 12, 14, 29, 32, 33, 34, 35, 36
	5. **Describe** succession in a water community.	8, 10	4, 9, 18, 24	12, 25	5, 8, 37, 38, 39, 40, 41
31:3	6. **Explain** how climate helps determine what living things live in an area.	11, 14	5, 6	11, 12, 13, 14, 15, 16, 33, 34	18, 19, 28
	7. **Describe** the major land biomes and water ecosystems.	12, 13, 15	12, 15, 23, 25	9, 17, 18, 19, 20, 21, 22, 32	7, 15

Ecosystems and Biomes

CHAPTER OVERVIEW

Key Concepts

This chapter deals with the interaction between the community and the nonliving parts of the environment to form an ecosystem. The major nonliving factors that affect the community are discussed. Changes over a long time (succession) in both aquatic and terrestrial communities are covered. Biomes are discussed as large land areas encompassing numerous ecosystems.

Key Science Words

biome
climate
climax community
ecology
ecosystem
nitrogen cycle
precipitation
succession
water cycle

Skill Development

In Lab 31-1 on page 659, students will **observe, form hypotheses, interpret data, infer,** and **design an experiment** to show that plants give off carbon dioxide. In Lab 31-2 on page 667, they will **observe, form hypotheses, interpret data,** and **design an experiment** to see how different concentrations of salt water affect brine shrimp. In the Skill Check on page 655, students will **understand** the **science word** *ecology.* In the Skill Check on page 664, they will **sequence** the climates of the major land biomes. In the Mini Lab on page 657, students will **interpret a diagram** of the water cycle. In the Mini Lab on page 661, they will **experiment** to find out how decomposers break down leaves.

CHAPTER PREVIEW

Chapter Content

Review this outline for Chapter 31 before you read the chapter.

Skills in this Chapter

The skills that you will use in this chapter are listed below.

- In **Lab 31-1,** you will observe, form hypotheses, interpret data, infer, and design an experiment. In **Lab 31-2,** you will observe, form hypotheses, interpret data, and design an experiment.
- In the **Skill Checks,** you will understand science words and sequence.
- In the **Mini Labs,** you will interpret diagrams and experiment.

652

Bridging

Chapter 30 develops the concept of living factors making up populations and communities and how these living factors interact with each other in the community. Chapter 31 discusses how nonliving factors interact with the living factors in an ecosystem and biome.

Chapter **31**

Ecosystems and Biomes

Look at the photo on the left. What part of the environment is causing the trees to bend toward one side? Why are the limbs growing more on one side than on the other? The photo on this page shows a field. Do you see any animals in the field? Where could they be? What happened to the green plants in the field?

In the last chapter, you learned that populations of living things interact with each other in a community. Within a community, living things also interact with their environment. In this and the next chapter, you will see how living things interact with their environments.

Try This!

How do you interact with your environment? Make a list of all the living and nonliving things in your environment. All of the living things interact with each other and with each nonliving thing. How does each thing affect you? How do you interact with each thing?

Winter field

GETTING STARTED

Using the Photos

After students tell you that wind and temperature have affected the organisms shown in the photo, point out that these factors make up the nonliving environment that surrounds an organism. Explain to students that the nonliving factors described in their text are the major factors that interact with living things in an ecosystem.

MOTIVATION/Try This!

How do you interact with your environment? Show 5-6 color slides or frames from a filmstrip that show environments in which organisms live (wet, dry, hot, cold, windy). Ask students to identify what effect the environment can have on the organisms not seen in the pictures.

Chapter Preview

In this chapter, students will learn how living factors interact with nonliving factors to form ecosystems and biomes. They will find out how specific factors such as minerals, water, and gases are recycled through organisms and the environment. They will learn how succession occurs in both land and water communities and compare the types of ecosystems and biomes in the world.

Misconception

Students may think that all minerals are recycled rapidly through the living and nonliving world. Point out that some minerals end up in rock strata and sediment layers for centuries.

31:1 Ecosystems

PREPARATION

Materials Needed

Make copies of the Critical Thinking/Problem Solving, Application, Enrichment, Study Guide, Reteaching, and Lab worksheets in the *Teacher Resource Package*.

▶ Gather rocks for the Focus activity.

▶ Prepare the bromthymol blue and green solutions for Lab 31-1.

Key Science Words

ecosystem
ecology
nitrogen cycle
water cycle

Process Skills

In Lab 31-1, students will observe, form hypotheses, interpret data, infer, and design an experiment. In the Skill Check, students will understand science words. In the Mini Lab, students will interpret diagrams.

1 FOCUS

▶ The objectives are listed on the student page. Remind students to preview these objectives as a guide to this numbered section.

ACTIVITY/Hands-On

Rub two rocks, either hard or soft, over a white piece of paper. Let students use a hand lens to examine the small particles that come from the rocks. Have students describe the particles as to size, color, and shape. Tell them that these particles are minerals and are important parts of soil.

Guided Practice

Have students write down their answers to the margin question: living and nonliving parts.

31:1 Ecosystems

Objectives

1. **Describe** the parts of an ecosystem.
2. **Describe** how the water cycle affects an ecosystem.
3. **Explain** the nitrogen cycle and the oxygen-carbon dioxide cycle.

Key Science Words

ecosystem
ecology
nitrogen cycle
water cycle

A community interacting with the environment is an **ecosystem.** An ecosystem can be as small as a roadside ditch or as large as one of the Great Lakes.

Parts of an Ecosystem

What two parts make up an ecosystem?

How do communities differ from ecosystems? A community includes the living things in an area. When you study a community, you study only how the living things affect each other. An ecosystem includes the nonliving parts as well as the living parts in an area. When you study an ecosystem, you study how the nonliving and living parts affect each other.

Scientists study ecosystems to find out how the different parts interact. To do this, they have built a closed laboratory in Arizona called Biosphere II, Figure 31-1a. Biosphere II is about the size of 1 1/2 football fields and is made of glass. It contains a small forest, desert, ocean, and streams. Eight scientists will live in this laboratory and remain sealed from outside life for two years. They will produce all their own food and drink the water in the streams. The scientists will study ecology (ih KAHL uh jee) and the living and nonliving things in this laboratory. **Ecology** is the study of how living things interact with each other and with their environment.

Look at the seashore ecosystem in Figure 31-1b. The living parts of this ecosystem are the plants, animals, and algae you see, as well as the bacteria, protozoans, and fungi that are too small to be seen. All these organisms are the producers, consumers, and decomposers you read about in Chapter 30. Suppose you could remove the living parts

Figure 31-1 Biosphere II (a) is a closed laboratory built for the study of ecosystems. A seashore (b) is an ecosystem.

a

b

OPTIONS

Science Background

Nutrients are passed through living and nonliving parts of an ecosystem as minerals. Since these chemicals pass through living things (bio) and soil and rocks (geo), the cycle is called a biogeochemical cycle.

Critical Thinking/Problem Solving/ *Teacher Resource Package*, p. 31. Use the Critical Thinking/Problem Solving worksheet shown here as an extension to parts of an ecosystem.

CRITICAL THINKING 31

CRITICAL THINKING/PROBLEM SOLVING — CHAPTER 31

Name ______ Date ______ Class ______

Use after Section 31:1.

HOW CAN A NONLIVING FACTOR AFFECT ANIMALS IN AN ECOSYSTEM?

As students walked past a meadow near the school, they heard crickets chirping. The crickets were noisier in the afternoon than in the morning and were chirping more quickly. What could be the cause?

In their biology class, the students learned that crickets are cold-blooded animals. They become more active as the temperature rises. Warm-blooded animals, such as humans, have the same body temperature all day long. Their cycles of activity are not so sensitive to temperature.

One student read that the temperature of the air can be estimated by measuring the activity of a cold-blooded animal and using a mathematical formula. The formula for crickets is: number of chirps per second divided by 2, plus 8, equals air temperature in degrees Celsius.

The students decided to test the formula by doing an experiment with cricket calls.
Each student listened to a cricket and noted the air temperature with a thermometer at a certain time during the day. Students put their results into a table:

Calculated air temperature			Measured air temperature °C
Chirps per second	Divided by 2	Plus 8 = result	
45	22.5	30.5	30
30	15	23	25
43	21.5	29.5	31
38	19	27	26

Analyzing the Problem

1. What is a cold-blooded animal? an animal whose body temperature and activity is affected by the temperature of its environment
2. What nonliving part of the ecosystem affected the chirping activity of the crickets? air temperature

Solving the Problem

1. Do the data show that air temperature can be estimated by cricket chirps? Yes, the numbers are not exactly the same, but they are close.
2. Suppose you have a tape of crickets chirping at different times of day. How could you tell if the air temperature is increasing or decreasing? Count the chirps at each time. The temperature is increasing if the rate of chirping increases.

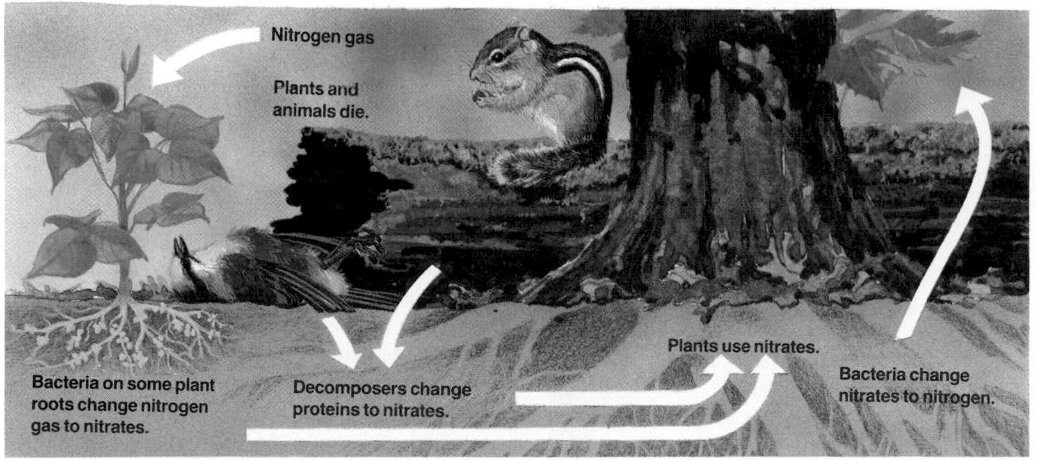

Figure 31-2 The nitrogen cycle. How is nitrogen gas returned to the air?

from Figure 31-1b. What would you see? You would see the nonliving parts. The nonliving parts of an ecosystem include the soil, air, water, light, and temperature. Nonliving parts help to determine where organisms can live.

Soil and the Nitrogen Cycle

The soil is an important nonliving part of an ecosystem. Soil comes from rocks that have broken down. It has many jobs. Soil serves as a place for plants to anchor their roots. Soil serves as a home for many living things. Ants and earthworms moving through the soil make holes for air and water. Moles, shrews, and other animals that burrow help mix and loosen the soil as they tunnel in all directions.

Soil holds other nonliving parts such as water, nutrients, and gases. Some of the most important soil nutrients needed by plants are called nitrates (NI trayts). Nitrates are chemicals that contain nitrogen. The way that nitrates get into soil is an example of the way living and nonliving parts of the ecosystem work together. Use Figure 31-2 to trace how nitrogen moves through an ecosystem.

1. Plants and animals need nitrogen to make protein. Air is mostly nitrogen, but most living things can't make protein from the nitrogen in the air. Bacteria living on the roots of some plants change the nitrogen in air to a form that plants can use to make protein.
2. When living things die, they are decomposed by bacteria and fungi. Some of the nitrogen in their bodies is changed into nitrates.

Skill Check

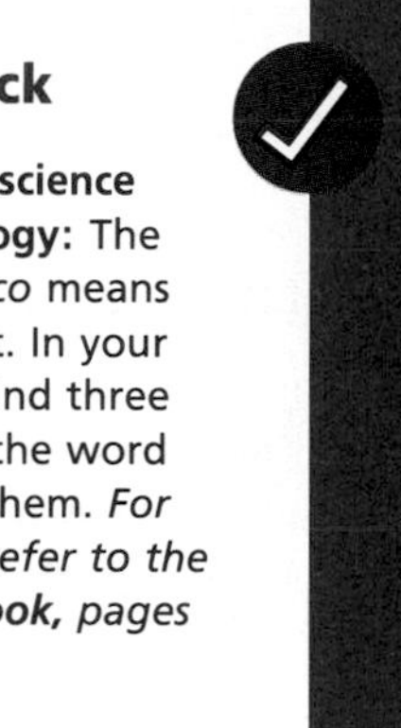

Understand science words: ecology: The word part *eco* means environment. In your dictionary, find three words with the word part *eco* in them. *For more help, refer to the* ***Skill Handbook****, pages 706-711.*

2 TEACH

MOTIVATION/Demonstration

Demonstrate how water evaporates by boiling water in a beaker as you are discussing the water cycle. Hold a beaker containing a little ice over the beaker of boiling water. Some water should condense on the cold beaker.

Concept Development

- ▶ Explain that nonliving factors can be called environmental or physical factors.
- ▶ Explain that nitrogen is but one of the many chemical elements that are cycled in an ecosystem.
- ▶ Point out that all living things, not just animals, need chemical elements to carry on their body processes. Tell students that the chemicals important to living things in an ecosystem are called nutrients or minerals.
- ▶ Point out that when living things die, they decompose and become nutrients that are recycled. Even bacteria and fungi die and are recycled.

Independent Practice

Study Guide/*Teacher Resource Package*, p. 181. Use the Study Guide worksheet shown at the bottom of this page for independent practice.

Audiovisual

Make a list on the chalkboard or an overhead transparency of the organisms that live in the soil. Point out some of their special features, such as burrowing parts.

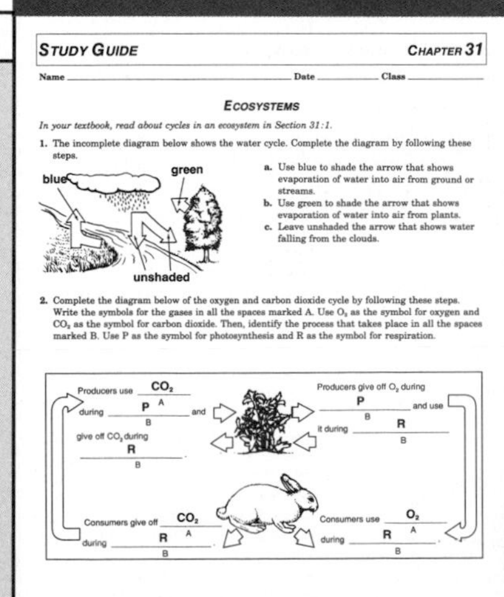

STUDY GUIDE 181

STUDY GUIDE — CHAPTER 31

Name ______ Date ______ Class ______

ECOSYSTEMS

In your textbook, read about cycles in an ecosystem in Section 31:1.

1. The incomplete diagram below shows the water cycle. Complete the diagram by following these steps.

a. Use blue to shade the arrow that shows evaporation of water into air from ground or streams.
b. Use green to shade the arrow that shows evaporation of water into air from plants.
c. Leave unshaded the arrow that shows water falling from the clouds.

2. Complete the diagram below of the oxygen and carbon dioxide cycle by following these steps. Write the symbols for the gases in all the spaces marked A. Use O_2 as the symbol for oxygen and CO_2 as the symbol for carbon dioxide. Then, identify the process that takes place in all the spaces marked B. Use P as the symbol for photosynthesis and R as the symbol for respiration.

OPTIONS

How Can a Nonliving Part of an Ecosystem Harm Living Things?/*Lab Manual*, pp. 263-264. Use this lab as an extension to living and nonliving parts of an ecosystem.

The Nitrogen Cycle/*Transparency Package*, number 31a. Use color transparency number 31a as you teach the nitrogen cycle.

Career Close-Up

Wildlife Technician

Background

Throughout the year, wildlife technicians are doing population counts, checking on the health of game animals, building shelters for wildlife, doing age and growth studies, and talking to hunting groups. A wildlife technician must also know about the plants in the area, as most game animals are plant eaters. If specific food plants in the area are depleted or overbrowsed, the wildlife technician sets up a program for reseeding or replanting these plants.

Related Careers

fisheries biology technician, animal caretaker in laboratories and zoos

Job Requirements

A high school diploma with on-the-job training and some course work at a local community college are required. A general interest in plants and animals is also helpful.

For More Information

Check the library for government publications that list opportunities in the field.

TEACH

Concept Development

▶ Point out that water not only serves as a habitat for some living things, such as fish, but also makes up over 90% of the body weight of living things.

▶ Reinforce the importance of water in photosynthesis. Explain that energy becomes available to all living things by way of food chains and that plants are the first step of a food chain.

▶ Point out how important evaporation and condensation are in the water cycle.

Career Close-Up

Wildlife Technician

Wildlife technician observing animal populations

A wildlife technician is a person who usually assists a wildlife biologist. Wildlife technicians count the numbers of animals in populations such as deer, turkeys, squirrels, and rabbits.

A wildlife technician may be expected to speak to people about wildlife management. During the hunting season, he or she may examine the animals killed by hunters to check for diseases and determine the ages of the animals. These data are used to predict how many surviving animals of each type are in the area. This information will tell if the number of hunting permits issued must be changed or if an area must be restocked.

A wildlife technician usually works for a state wildlife agency. The individual must have an interest in all kinds of living things and some knowledge of populations, communities, and ecosystems. Some wildlife technicians get an Associate of Arts degree to prepare for their jobs.

Bio Tip

Consumer: Manure rebuilds soil better than chemical fertilizers do. Manure broken down by decomposers provides nitrogen for plants, becomes part of the soil, and helps retain water in the soil. Dry manure can be bought in garden shops.

3. The nitrates are left in the soil. They can be used by plants as a source of nitrogen for making protein. Some plants are then eaten by animals. These animals can use nitrogen compounds found in plants to make proteins. When the plants or animals die, the nitrogen in their bodies is again returned to the soil.
4. Some nitrates in the soil are changed back into nitrogen gas by bacteria. The nitrogen gas is released into the air. The cycle repeats itself over and over again. The reusing of nitrogen in an ecosystem is called the **nitrogen cycle.**

The nonliving parts of the nitrogen cycle are nitrogen and soil. The living parts are the plants, animals, bacteria, and fungi. In every ecosystem, the nonliving and living parts interact with each other. Many other chemical materials are cycled through the ecosystem just as nitrogen is cycled.

OPTIONS

Application/*Teacher Resource Package*, p. 31. Use the Application worksheet shown here to give additional practice with balance in ecosystems.

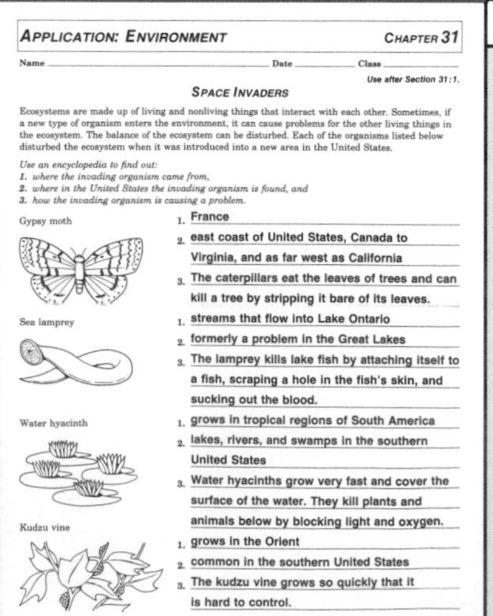

APPLICATION 31

APPLICATION: ENVIRONMENT — **CHAPTER 31**

Name ______ Date ______ Class ______

Use after Section 31:1.

SPACE INVADERS

Ecosystems are made up of living and nonliving things that interact with each other. Sometimes, if a new type of organism enters the environment, it can cause problems for the other living things in the ecosystem. The balance of the ecosystem can be disturbed. Each of the organisms listed below disturbed the ecosystem when it was introduced into a new area in the United States.

Use an encyclopedia to find out:
1. where the invading organism came from,
2. where in the United States the invading organism is found, and
3. how the invading organism is causing a problem.

Gypsy moth
1. France
2. east coast of United States, Canada to Virginia, and as far west as California
3. The caterpillars eat the leaves of trees and can kill a tree by stripping it bare of its leaves.

Sea lamprey
1. streams that flow into Lake Ontario
2. formerly a problem in the Great Lakes
3. The lamprey kills lake fish by attaching itself to a fish, scraping a hole in the fish's skin, and sucking out the blood.

Water hyacinth
1. grows in tropical regions of South America
2. lakes, rivers, and swamps in the southern United States
3. Water hyacinths grow very fast and cover the surface of the water. They kill plants and animals below by blocking light and oxygen.

Kudzu vine
1. grows in the Orient
2. common in the southern United States
3. The kudzu vine grows so quickly that it is hard to control.

Water

Water is a nonliving part of an ecosystem that is needed by all living things. The cells of all living things are mostly water. Without water, the cells would die. Plants can't make food without water. What would happen to an ecosystem if plants couldn't make food?

Water, like nitrogen, is cycled through the ecosystem. The path that water takes through an ecosystem is called the **water cycle.** Use Figure 31-3 to help you understand the steps of the water cycle.

1. Water in the air falls to Earth as rain or snow.
2. Some water runs off the land into rivers, ponds, lakes, or oceans.
3. Water from rain may soak into the soil. Some of this water is taken up by plants through their roots. The rest of the water flows into underground lakes and rivers.
4. Animals may drink some of the water on the ground.
5. Excess water passes out of plants through their leaves. Animals lose water through body openings or as wastes are removed. The water evaporates (ee VAP uh raytz) into the air. Evaporate means to change from a liquid to a gas. Water is present in the air as a gas.
6. Water from lakes, rivers, and oceans also evaporates into the air.

Mini Lab

What Are the Parts of the Water Cycle?

Interpret diagrams: Look at Figure 31-3. What parts of an ecosystem are important in the water cycle? What role does each part play? Are all living things part of the water cycle? *For more help, refer to the **Skill Handbook**, pages 706-711.*

In what form is water found in the air?

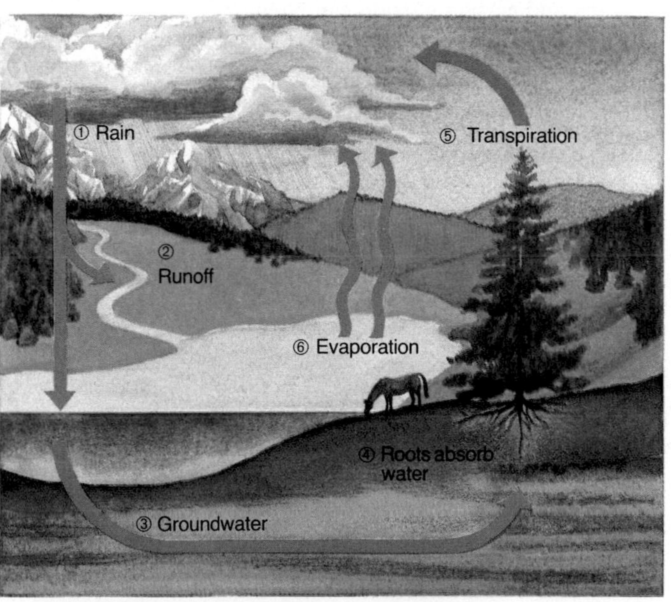

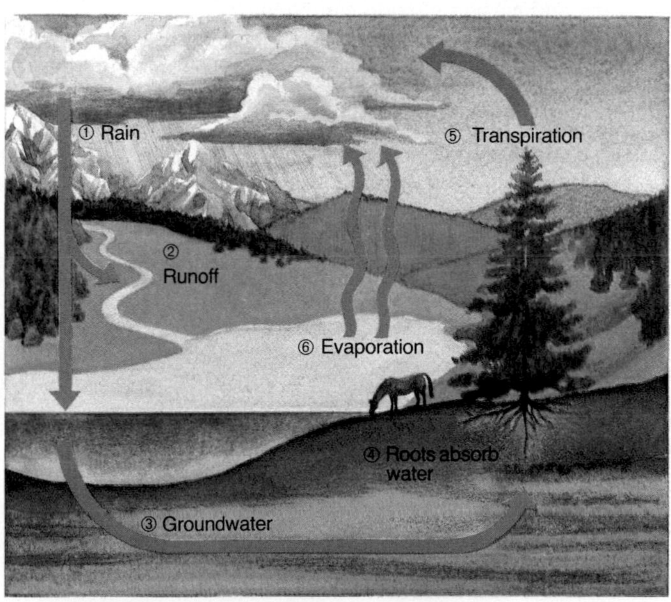

Figure 31-3 The water cycle. How is water returned to the air? it evaporates

TEACH

Concept Development

▶ Make sure that students understand that carbon dioxide dissolved in water in aquatic ecosystems is an important raw material for photosynthesis.

Mini Lab

As students are making their diagrams, make a list of the living and nonliving parts of the community on the chalkboard and have students pick out the most important factors for their water cycle diagram.

Guided Practice

Have students write down their answers to the margin question: gas.

Check for Understanding

Have students write a paragraph explaining how the organisms in a community are affected by nonliving factors. Have them list examples they have seen in the area where they live.

Reteach

Make a list of the nonliving factors that you discussed with the students. Ask them to explain how each one or several interact with the members of a community. Make a list of the student responses on the chalkboard. At the end of the discussion, have students decide which of the nonliving factors may be the most important to organisms.

ENRICHMENT 33

ENRICHMENT — CHAPTER 31

Name ______ Date ______ Class ______

Use with Section 31:1.

HOW FAST CAN CHANGE TAKE PLACE IN AN ECOSYSTEM?

Suppose an animal enters an ecosystem where it has never lived before. A small population of gray grass mice entered the tall grasslands area of a state park in the fall of 1984. From 1984 to 1990 a study took place to find out the new places the gray mice moved into each year. The graph below shows how many acres of tall grasslands the mice lived in during each year of the study. The mice continued to live in the places where they had lived in the years before, but as the population grew larger, they spread out into new places.

Answer the questions that follow based on the information above and in the graph.

1. On how many acres of grassland did the mouse population live in 1984? **1** in 1985? **5** in 1988? **40** in 1990? **80**
2. The gray mouse eats grass seeds. It also kills the roots of grass plants. What will happen to the grasslands if the gray mice stay there for a number of years? **The grassland will be destroyed.**
   What might happen to the mouse population after a number of years? **It will decrease.**
3. What can happen to the soil after the mice have destroyed the roots of the grass? **Seeds of different plants can begin to grow in the area.**
4. What is the name of the change that is occurring in this ecosystem? **succession**

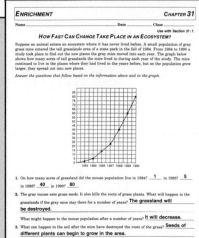

OPTIONS

Enrichment/*Teacher Resource Package*, p. 33. Use the Enrichment worksheet shown here as an extension to structure of ecosystems.

The Water Cycle/*Transparency Package*, number 31b. Use color transparency number 31b as you teach the water cycle.

TEACH

Guided Practice

Have students write down their answers to the margin question: for respiration and photosynthesis.

Check for Understanding

Have students respond to the first three questions in Check Your Understanding.

Reteach

Reteaching/*Teacher Resource Package*, p. 91. Use this worksheet to give students additional practice with the water cycle.

Extension: Assign Critical Thinking, Biology and Reading, or some of the **OPTIONS** available with this lesson.

3 APPLY

ACTIVITY/Field Trip

Use the school yard, fence row, or wooded area for a field trip. Have students record on a chart the nonliving factors that affect the organisms they see. Discuss the findings with the class.

4 CLOSE

Convergent Question

Have students answer the question: In what way would the nonliving factor(s) have to be changed so a ________ could live in this area? Fill in the blank with names like polar bears, tropical fish, orchids, etc.

Answers to Check Your Understanding

1. living and nonliving factors
2. Refer to Figure 31-3.
3. to make proteins
4. Water would not be recycled through the trees, so the amount of precipitation would be less; less oxygen would be produced; less carbon dioxide would be used.
5. It means a recurring series of events. The elements can be used over and over again.

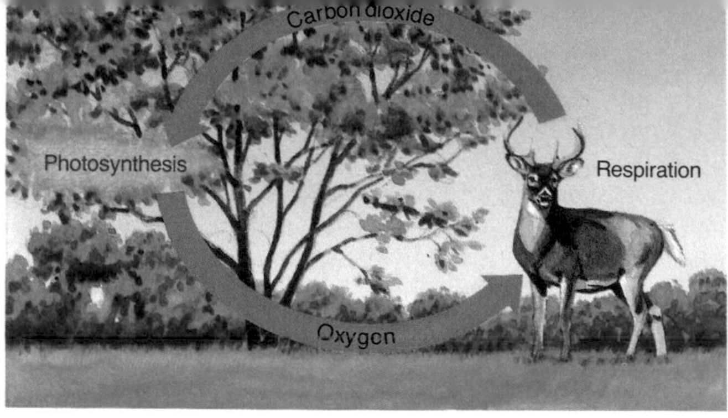

Figure 31-4 The oxygen-carbon dioxide cycle. What is given off during photosynthesis?

Oxygen-Carbon Dioxide Cycle

Why do living things need oxygen?

Air is needed in an ecosystem. Air is made up of several gases that are important to living things. You have learned about nitrogen. Two other gases in the air are oxygen and carbon dioxide. Why are these gases important? Without oxygen and carbon dioxide, respiration and photosynthesis can't take place.

Trace the path of oxygen and carbon dioxide through the ecosystem in Figure 31-4. Oxygen given off by producers during photosynthesis is needed by all living things for cellular respiration. Carbon dioxide given off during respiration is used by producers for making food. Oxygen and carbon dioxide can be cycled.

Producers and consumers in a water ecosystem, such as a lake, also have an oxygen-carbon dioxide cycle. Water has air mixed into it. Oxygen in the water is used by fish, plants, and other water life for respiration. Carbon dioxide in the water is used by water plants, blue-green bacteria, and algae for photosynthesis.

Check Your Understanding

1. What two parts make up an ecosystem?
2. Draw a diagram of the water cycle.
3. Why do plants and animals need nitrogen?
4. **Critical Thinking:** If a large forest was destroyed, how would cycling of materials be affected?
5. **Biology and Reading:** What is meant by the word *cycle* when discussing the nitrogen, water, and oxygen–carbon dioxide cycles?

OPTIONS

Enrichment: Construct a bulletin board that shows some of the nutrient cycles. Show pictures of plants, animals, rocks, streams, and the atmosphere as components of various cycles. Set up a separate section for each cycle.

How Much Water Will Soil Hold?/*Lab Manual*, pp. 259-262. Use this lab as an extension to cycles.

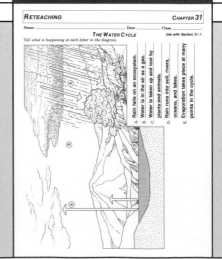

RETEACHING CHAPTER 31

THE WATER CYCLE

A. Rain falls on an ecosystem.
B. Water is in the air as a gas.
C. Water is taken up and lost by plants and animals.
D. Rain runs into soil, rivers, oceans, and lakes.
E. Evaporation takes place at many points in the cycle.

Lab 31–1 Carbon Dioxide

Problem: Do plants use carbon dioxide or give off carbon dioxide?

Skills

observe, form hypotheses, interpret data, infer, design an experiment

Materials

4 test tubes
marking pencil
4 stoppers
lamp
blue test liquid
green test liquid
2 *Elodea* sprigs
2 test-tube racks

Procedure

1. Read the problem. In your notebook, write a **hypothesis** that answers the question.
2. Copy the data table.
3. Number the tubes 1 to 4 with the marking pencil.
4. Fill tubes 1 and 2 nearly full with green test liquid. Put an *Elodea* sprig in tube 2. Stopper both tubes. Place them in a rack.
5. Record the color of the liquid in each tube.
6. Place both tubes in front of the lamp and turn the lamp on.
7. Keep both tubes in the light overnight.
8. Fill tubes 3 and 4 nearly full with blue test liquid. Put an *Elodea* sprig in tube 4. Stopper both tubes. Place them in a rack.
9. Record the color of the liquid in each tube.
10. Place both tubes in the dark overnight.
11. **Observe:** Record the color of the liquids in all tubes the next day.
12. Dispose of the materials as directed by your teacher.

Data and Observations

1. In which tubes, 1 or 2, did the green test liquid change color?
2. In which tubes, 3 or 4, did the blue test liquid change color?

TUBE	PLANT ADDED?	WHERE PLACED (DARK OR LIGHT)	COLOR OF TUBE FIRST DAY	COLOR OF TUBE SECOND DAY
1		light	green	green
2	√	light	green	blue
3		dark	blue	blue
4	√	dark	blue	green

Analyze and Apply

1. What was the purpose of tube 1?
2. What was the purpose of tube 3?
3. If the green liquid turns blue, carbon dioxide was used in the tube. Which tube, 1 or 2, showed evidence that carbon dioxide was used overnight?
4. If the blue liquid turns green, carbon dioxide was given off in the tube. Which tube, 3 or 4, showed evidence that carbon dioxide was given off overnight? Explain.
5. Do plants use or give off carbon dioxide?
6. **Check your hypothesis:** Was your hypothesis supported by your data? Why or why not?
7. **Apply:** What process occurs in green plants that gives off carbon dioxide? What process in plants uses carbon dioxide?

Extension

Design an experiment to test whether other water plants, such as hornwort, use and give off carbon dioxide.

ANSWERS

Data and Observations

1. tube 2–color changed from green to blue
2. tube 4–color changed from blue to green

Analyze and Apply

1. as a control; to see if the green test liquid would turn blue without the plant
2. as a control; to see if the blue test liquid would turn green without the plant
3. tube 2 because the green test liquid turned blue
4. tube 4 because the blue test liquid turned green
5. both; Carbon dioxide is used during photosynthesis and given off during respiration.
6. Students who hypothesized that plants both use and give off carbon dioxide will say that their hypotheses were supported.
7. respiration; photosynthesis

Lab 31-1 Carbon Dioxide

Overview

Students learn that carbon dioxide is used by plants in photosynthesis.

Objectives: Upon completing this lab, students will be able to: (1) **demonstrate** the test for CO_2, (2) **infer** when a plant uses or gives off CO_2, and (3) **separate and control variables** in an experiment.

Time Allotment: 45 minutes on day 1 and 10-15 minutes on day 2

Preparation

▶ For the blue liquid, add 0.1 g bromthymol blue powder to 2 L distilled water.

▶ For the green liquid, crush a seltzer tablet and add small amounts of it to the blue liquid until the liquid turns green.

▶ *Elodea* can be maintained in a gallon jar nearly full of water, with 5 cm of sand in which to anchor the plants. Put the jar in a lighted area.

Lab 31-1 worksheet/*Teacher Resource Package*, pp. 121-122.

Teaching the Lab

▶ Explain that CO_2 is constantly produced by plants. However, during photosynthesis, the amount of CO_2 used outweighs the amount produced, resulting in a net loss to the environment.

Cooperative Learning: Divide the class into groups of two students. For more information see pp. 22T-23T in the Teacher Guide.

31:2 Succession

PREPARATION

Materials Needed

Make copies of the Focus, Transparency, Study Guide, and Reteaching worksheets in the *Teacher Resource Package*.

▶ Gather two plastic shoe boxes, sand, and soil for the Focus Demonstration.

▶ Have glass jars, soil, dead leaves, and plastic wrap available for the Mini Lab.

Key Science Words

succession climax community

Process Skills

In the Mini Lab, students will experiment.

1 FOCUS

▶ The objectives are listed on the student page. Remind students to preview these objectives as a guide to this numbered section.

MOTIVATION/Demonstration

Fill a plastic shoe box with one inch of sand and add tap water until nearly full. Fill a second plastic shoe box with several inches of soil. Ask the students to imagine that the shoe box with water is a large pond and the shoe box with soil is a recently plowed field. Ask them how long it would take for organisms to appear in each. Ask them to explain what kinds of organisms could appear over a period of time.

Focus/*Teacher Resource Package*, p. 61. Use the Focus transparency shown at the bottom of this page to introduce succession.

Guided Practice

Have students write down their answers to the margin question: changes that take place in a community as it ages.

31:2 Succession

Objectives

4. **Describe** succession in a land community.
5. **Describe** succession in a water community.

Key Science Words

succession
climax community

What is succession?

The living and nonliving parts of an ecosystem may change over a period of time. For example, as trees grow taller in a forest ecosystem, they change the amounts of light, temperature, and water in the forest. Forests that have large trees are cooler, darker, and wetter than forests made up of small trees. Decaying leaves make the soil more acid. Some forest organisms cannot live in these new conditions. They are replaced by organisms that can live in the new conditions. When we refer to the changes in an ecosystem, we often refer just to the changes in the living part, the community. The changes that take place in a community as it gets older are called **succession.** All communities go through succession. You might not notice the changes unless you observe the community for many years, because they happen slowly.

Succession in a Land Community

To understand the stages of succession in one type of land community, we will start with a plowed field. In Figure 31-5a, there is nothing but bare soil.

After a few weeks or months, weed seeds are carried to the field by wind and animals. Weeds begin to grow over the soil. Worms and grasshoppers may be among the first animals to arrive. Beetles and ants arrive soon after. Figure 31-5b shows the changes that have occurred in the community.

As plants and animals die and decompose, their remains add nutrients to the soil. The soil becomes better suited to a greater variety of larger plants. Bushes and small trees begin to grow. Animal populations also change. Rabbits,

a

b

Figure 31-5 The first stage of succession on land is bare soil (a). The next stage is the growth of producers (b).

OPTIONS

Science Background

Climax communities can be changed by unusual conditions such as earthquakes, volcanoes, and erosion, or human activities such as lumbering, clearing land, or pollution.

How Can a Nonliving Part of an Ecosystem Help Living Things?/*Lab Manual*, pp. 265-266. Use this lab as an extension to relationships between living and nonliving parts of the environment.

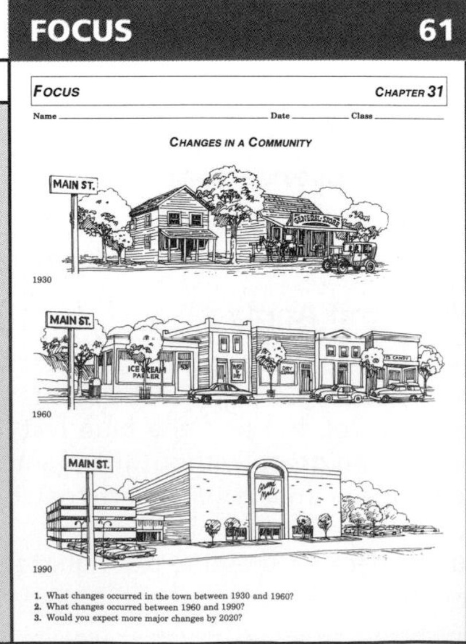

FOCUS 61

FOCUS CHAPTER 31

Name ______ Date ______ Class ______

CHANGES IN A COMMUNITY

1. What changes occurred in the town between 1930 and 1960?
2. What changes occurred between 1960 and 1990?
3. Would you expect more major changes by 2020?

a

b

Figure 31-6 A wide variety of plants provide food for many different animals (a). A climax community is usually a forest (b).

mice, foxes, skunks, and hawks may be found in the community shown in Figure 31-6a.

As more plants and animals die in the community, more nutrients are added to the soil. The soil itself becomes looser and better suited to the growth of larger plants. Now large trees are able to grow. If the community is not disturbed, a forest begins to develop. There are more kinds of animals in the forest than there are in a vacant field.

The last stage in the succession of this community is a forest like the one in Figure 31-6b. We call the forest the climax community. A **climax community** is the last or final stage of succession in a community. It is the final stage because it is stable and can replace itself with little change from then on. It may take 150 years or more for an area to become a climax community.

Mini Lab

How Do Leaves Decay?

Experiment: Fill a jar half full with dead leaves and soil. Moisten with water and cover with plastic wrap. Punch holes in the wrap. Record the odor weekly. What causes the change? *For more help, refer to the* ***Skill Handbook,*** *pages 704-705.*

Succession in a Water Community

Could the place you are sitting right now have been a pond or lake a few hundred years ago? It may seem impossible when you think of the living things that make up a water community. Once, however, there might have been a water community where you are sitting.

Let's look at the stages of succession for a pond that changes into a land community. The bottom and sides of a new pond are bare. The only green organisms in the pond are algae floating on the water surface. Snails and a few small fish can be found. After several years, the pond becomes more shallow because dead plants and algae have piled up on the bottom. Larger fish, tadpoles, crayfish, and frogs are now present.

Why does a pond become more shallow over time?

2 TEACH

MOTIVATION/Demonstration

Show students pictures of a Civil War battle field area, both current and from Civil War time. Gettysburg would work well. Ask students to identify any changes they notice.

Mini Lab

The odor will have a "moldy earth" smell. This odor is caused by fungi and bacteria decomposing the leaves.

Guided Practice

Have students write down their answers to the margin question: dead plants and algae pile up on the bottom, filling the pond.

Independent Practice

Study Guide/*Teacher Resource Package*, pp. 182-184. Use the Study Guide worksheet shown at the bottom of the page for independent practice.

TRANSPARENCY 155

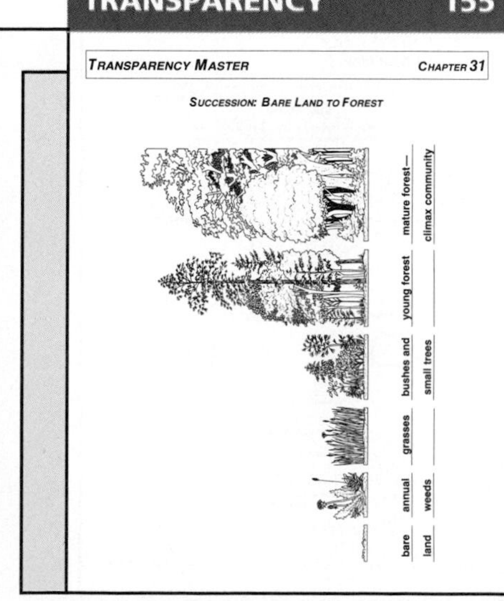

Transparency Master — *Chapter 31*

Succession: Bare Land to Forest

STUDY GUIDE 182

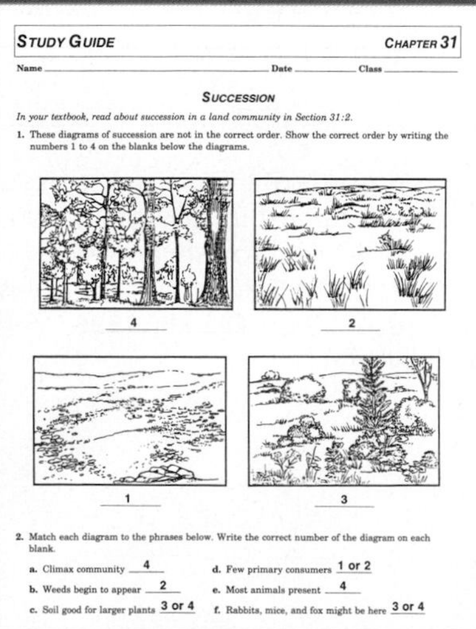

Study Guide — *Chapter 31*

Name ______ Date ______ Class ______

Succession

In your textbook, read about succession in a land community in Section 31:2.

1. These diagrams of succession are not in the correct order. Show the correct order by writing the numbers 1 to 4 on the blanks below the diagrams.

4   2   1   3

2. Match each diagram to the phrases below. Write the correct number of the diagram on each blank.

a. Climax community 4
b. Weeds begin to appear 2
c. Soil good for larger plants 3 or 4
d. Few primary consumers 1 or 2
e. Most animals present 4
f. Rabbits, mice, and fox might be here 3 or 4

OPTIONS

Enrichment: Living things change the environment and bring about succession. For example, as small plants fill a meadow they enrich the soil, thus making it more hospitable for shrubs. The shrubs add more nutrients to the soil as they die and decompose, allowing growth of trees. As trees in a forest grow larger, they provide shade and the smaller plants in their shadow may fail to thrive.

Transparency Master/*Teacher Resource Package*, p. 155. Use the Transparency Master shown here as you teach land succession.

TEACH

Check for Understanding

Have students respond to the first three questions in Check Your Understanding.

Reteach

Reteaching/Teacher Resource Package, p. 92. Use this worksheet to give students additional practice with succession.

Extension: Assign Critical Thinking, Biology and Reading, or some of the **OPTIONS** available with this lesson.

3 APPLY

ACTIVITY/Project

Have student teams build a model to show ecological succession in a plowed field. Have them fill a plastic box with two inches of soil, sprinkle with a cup of mixed seeds (grass, bird seed, dried beans) and cover with 1/4 inch of soil. Add water until moist. Students should notice that grass seeds sprout and grow rapidly only to be replaced by the beans and larger seeds.

4 CLOSE

Divergent Question

Ask students to describe areas around their home that are undergoing succession. How do they know that succession is occurring?

Answers to Check Your Understanding

6. the series of changes a community goes through as it gets older
7. primary consumers
8. frogs and turtles because they can live out of water
9. Since animals contribute nutrients to the soil when they die, plant succession will not proceed. A climax community will never develop, and the environment will remain unstable
10. No, the climax community for any body of water is a land community. That is because the body of water is filled in by soil.

Figure 31-7 Succession in a pond leads to dry land.

Over the years, more dead plants pile up and soil washes into the pond. The pond becomes more shallow and plants begin to grow around the edge of the pond, Figure 31-7c. Eventually, there will not be enough water for the fish to survive. Animals that can live out of water part of the time, such as turtles and frogs, will increase in number.

A hundred years later, the ground looks nothing like a pond. It may look like what you see in Figure 31-7d. Grass, shrubs, and small trees grow where the old pond was. Much of the animal life is completely different from when there was a young pond. Some day the area the pond occupied may contain a hardwood forest. A forest is not the only type of climax community that can develop. Depending upon soil, water, air, and sunlight, the climax community for an area might be a prairie or grassland, a desert, or a tropical rain forest. What kind of climax community can you identify where you live?

Check Your Understanding

6. What is succession?
7. If weeds are the first things to appear in a land community, what will the first animals probably be?
8. What animals are found in an older pond that is very shallow? Why?
9. **Critical Thinking:** How would succession be affected if animals did not return to an area after a fire?
10. **Biology and Reading:** Is the climax community for a lake a watery environment? Why or why not?

OPTIONS

Enrichment: Have students set up a closed ecosystem in a gallon jar using aquatic organisms. They can observe this for several weeks. Use the article "Sealed-Jar Ecosystem" by John Zuke in *The Science Teacher,* March, 1986: Vol. 53, pp. 46-47 as a reference.

RETEACHING 92

RETEACHING: IDEA MAP — CHAPTER 31

Name ______ Date ______ Class ______

Use with Section 31:2.

SUCCESSION

Use the following terms to complete the idea map: add nutrients to soil, forest climax community, small mammals and birds, die and decompose, bushes and small trees. Some terms may be used more than once.

Succession in a Plowed Field
bare soil
weeds
worms and insects
die and decompose
add nutrients to soil
needed by
needed by
bushes and small trees
small mammals and birds
die and decompose
add nutrients to soil
forest climax community

1. What is meant by succession? changes in a community as it gets older
2. What is a climax community? the last stage of succession in a community
3. Why is a climax community stable? because it can replace itself with little change

31:3 How Living Things Are Distributed

The nonliving parts of an ecosystem usually control what organisms can live in a certain area. Temperature, sunlight, and water are very important factors in determining which organisms live in a place.

Climate

Light and temperature are two nonliving parts of an ecosystem that are not cycled. Light from the sun is used by plants to make food. Producers transfer energy to other living things through food chains.

Temperature and light are often related. The soil in a field is warmed by the sun. The soil in a forest is cool because the leaves of trees prevent most of the sun's light from warming the ground.

The temperature of an ecosystem helps determine what organisms live there. Polar bears can live in very cold ecosystems, while lions, elephants, and palm trees live only in warmer ecosystems. Temperatures that are too low for some living things are just right for others.

The water cycle is also related to temperature and light. The amount of sunlight can affect the rate of evaporation. Water evaporates faster at warm temperatures. The temperature of the air affects the type of precipitation (prih sihp uh TAY shun) falling to Earth. **Precipitation** is water in the air that falls to Earth as rain or snow. Figure 31-8 shows temperatures and precipitation for the land biomes. You will learn about biomes on the next page.

Objectives

6. **Explain** how climate helps determine what living things live in an area.
7. **Describe** the major land biomes and water ecosystems.

Key Science Words

precipitation
climate
biome

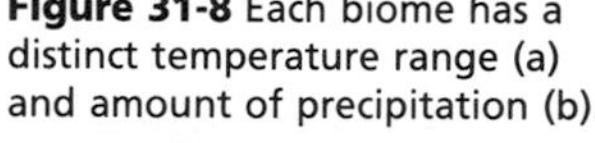

Figure 31-8 Each biome has a distinct temperature range (a) and amount of precipitation (b).

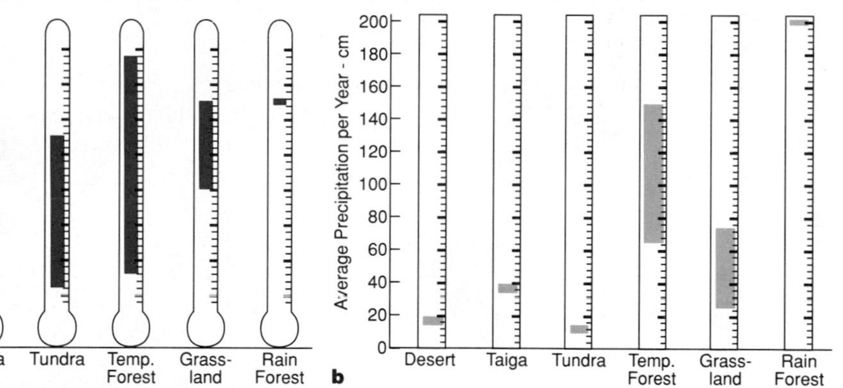

31:3 Biomes

PREPARATION

Materials Needed

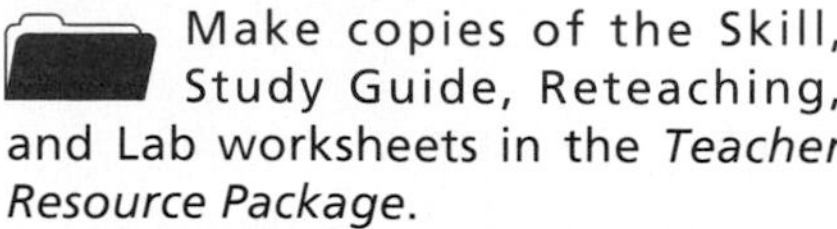

Make copies of the Skill, Study Guide, Reteaching, and Lab worksheets in the *Teacher Resource Package*.

▶ Have on hand a large world map for the Focus activity.

▶ Order brine shrimp eggs for Lab 31-2. Make the salt solutions a day in advance so all of the salt dissolves.

Key Science Words

precipitation
climate
biome

Process Skills

In Lab 31-2, students will observe, form hypotheses, interpret data, and design an experiment. In the Skill Check, students will sequence.

1 FOCUS

▶ The objectives are listed on the student page. Remind students to preview these objectives as a guide to this numbered section.

Divergent Question

Have students identify the following areas of the world on a map: polar, temperate, and equatorial. Ask them to identify the types of climate and living things they would expect to find in each area.

SKILL 32

SKILL: INTERPRET DIAGRAMS — CHAPTER 31

Name ______ Date ______ Class ______

For more help, refer to the Skill Handbook, pages 706-711. *Use after Section 31:3.*

BIOMES

The world has many kinds of biomes. You would have to travel hundreds of kilometers across North America to see just a few of them. A faster way of seeing what these biomes look like would be to climb a high mountain. As you travel up the mountain, you would notice that the average temperature and precipitation change. As a result, the different areas on the mountain resemble different biomes.

The diagram below shows the areas found on a particular mountainside at different elevations. Study the diagram, and then answer the questions.

Snow and Ice — 4750 meters
Tundra — 4500 meters
Taiga — 4000 meters
Temperate Forests

1. At what elevations would you pass through an area that resembles a taiga? **4000 meters to 4500 meters**
2. If you climbed to an elevation of 3000 meters, what biome-like area would you see? **temperate forests**
3. At what elevations would you see mostly small shrubs and lichens? **4500 meters to 4750 meters**
4. Why do you think there is no desert-like area on the mountain? **The mountain gets too much precipitation.**
5. Above what elevation would you expect not to see any plants? **4750 meters**
6. What could you conclude about the areas on the mountain if the west side of the mountain received much more precipitation than those on the east side? **The areas on the west side of the mountain might have different climate, plants, and animals from the areas on the east side.**

OPTIONS

Science Background

Many ecosystems in the same area having the same climate and organisms make up a biome. There are six basic biomes in the world.

Skill/*Teacher Resource Package*, p. 32. Use the Skill worksheet shown here to teach climate variations among biomes.

2 TEACH

MOTIVATION/Filmstrip

Show the filmstrip *Biomes Collection,* Carolina Biological Supply, Co.

Guided Practice

Have students write down their answers to the margin question: the amounts of light and precipitation and the average temperature of an area over a period of years.

ACTIVITY/Software

Self-Help: Ecology, Queue.

Skill Check

Students should give the following answers:

a. tundra, desert, taiga, grassland, temperate forest, tropical rain forest (in this order)

b. tundra, taiga, temperate forest, grassland, desert, tropical rain forest (in this order)

wettest/warmest–tropical rain forest

coldest/driest–tundra

Independent Practice

Study Guide/*Teacher Resource Package*, p. 185. Use the Study Guide worksheet shown at the bottom of this page for independent practice.

What is climate?

All of these factors—light, temperature, and precipitation—taken over many years is called the **climate** of an area. Some climates are wet while others are dry. Some are cold while others are warm or hot. The climate of an area helps determine what kinds of plants and animals can live there. You can see how living and nonliving factors act together to make an ecosystem.

> **Skill Check**
>
> **Sequence:** List the six major land biomes in order from (a) least to most precipitation and (b) from the lowest to highest temperature. Which biome is the wettest and warmest? Which biome is coolest and driest? *For more help, refer to the* ***Skill Handbook****, pages 706-711.*

Land Biomes

There are large areas on Earth that have similar climates and climax communities. A land area with a distinct climate and with specific types of plants and animals is called a **biome** (BI ohm). Each biome has its own distinct producers, consumers, and decomposers. A biome is made up of all the ecosystems on Earth that have similar climates and organisms. For example, there are many deserts on Earth. They all have very dry climates and similar organisms. All the deserts together make up the desert biome. Figure 31-10 shows the major biomes and some of the living things found in each one. Biomes include tropical rain forests, grasslands, deserts, temperate forests, taiga (TI guh), and tundra (TUN druh).

A biome usually covers parts of several continents. Each continent has several biomes. Look at the map in Figure 31-9. How many different biomes are there in the continent of North America?

Figure 31-9 The major land biomes

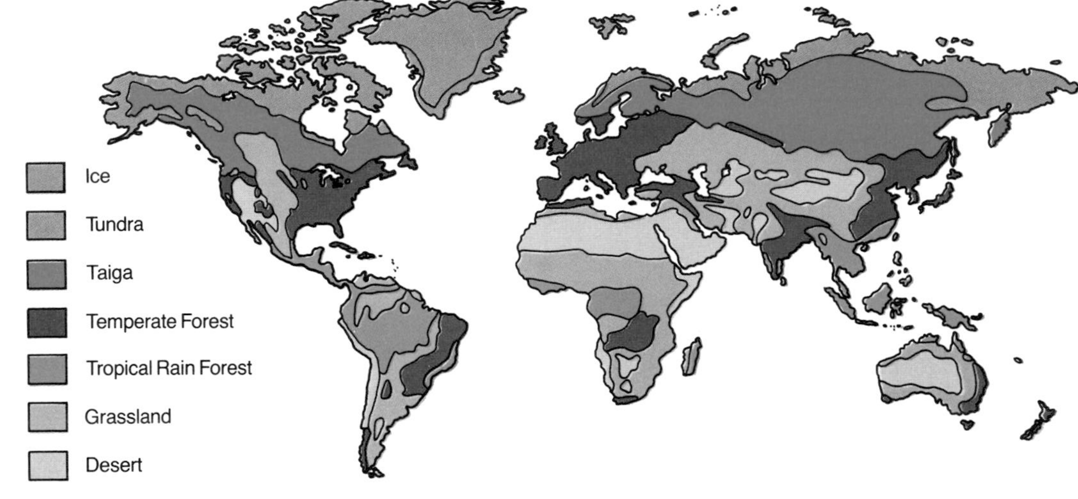

STUDY GUIDE 185

STUDY GUIDE **CHAPTER 31**

Name ______ Date ______ Class ______

HOW LIVING THINGS ARE DISTRIBUTED

In your textbook, read about biomes in Section 31:3.

1. The picture below shows the major world biomes. Using colored pencils, shade in the biomes described.
   a. Use blue for the biome that has an almost constant temperature.
   b. Use brown for the biome that has temperatures from −28° to 15°C.
   c. Use green for the biome that has evergreen trees, moose, weasels, and mink.
   d. Use purple for the biome that has grasses.
   e. Use yellow for the biome that has less than 25 cm of rainfall each year and whose common plants are cacti and small bushes.
   f. Use red for the biome that has trees such as hickory, maple, beech, and oak.

Refer to corresponding map on page 664 of text for key to biomes.

2. In which biome do you live? **Answers will vary.**
3. Which biome makes up most of the United States? **temperate forest**
4. a. Which two biomes have the least amount of rainfall? **desert and tundra**
   b. Why do no trees grow in these two biomes? **Trees require more water for growth than is present in these biomes.**

Figure 31-10 Biomes found on land

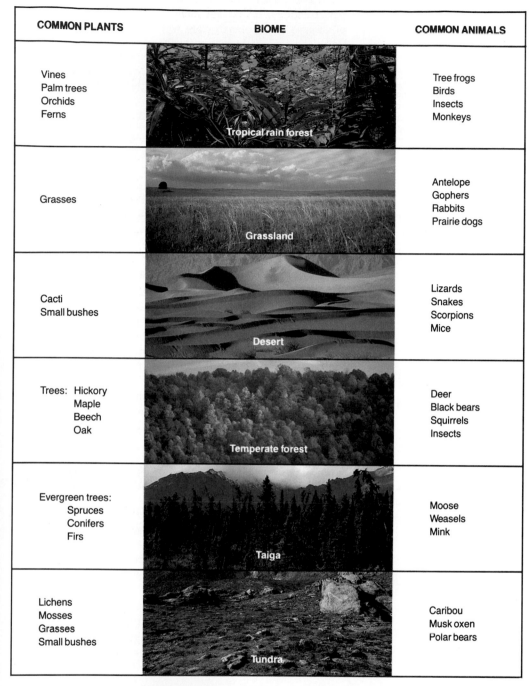

COMMON PLANTS	BIOME	COMMON ANIMALS
Vines Palm trees Orchids Ferns	Tropical rain forest	Tree frogs Birds Insects Monkeys
Grasses	Grassland	Antelope Gophers Rabbits Prairie dogs
Cacti Small bushes	Desert	Lizards Snakes Scorpions Mice
Trees: Hickory Maple Beech Oak	Temperate forest	Deer Black bears Squirrels Insects
Evergreen trees: Spruces Conifers Firs	Taiga	Moose Weasels Mink
Lichens Mosses Grasses Small bushes	Tundra	Caribou Musk oxen Polar bears

TEACH

Concept Development

▶ Point out that several biomes may be found in one country.

▶ Explain that at one time one-half of the land on Earth was grassland biome and today that land is used by humans to grow crops, raise animals, or for housing.

Audiovisual

Show the videocassette *Populations, Communities, and Biomes,* Insight Media.

Connection: Geography

Have students find pictures of other countries showing different biomes. The student can glue these pictures to construction paper and list the name of the country, the continent on which the country is found, and the biome in the picture. Note that some countries may have more than one biome.

Independent Practice

Study Guide/*Teacher Resource Package*, p. 186. Use the Study Guide worksheet shown at the bottom of this page for independent practice.

STUDY GUIDE 186

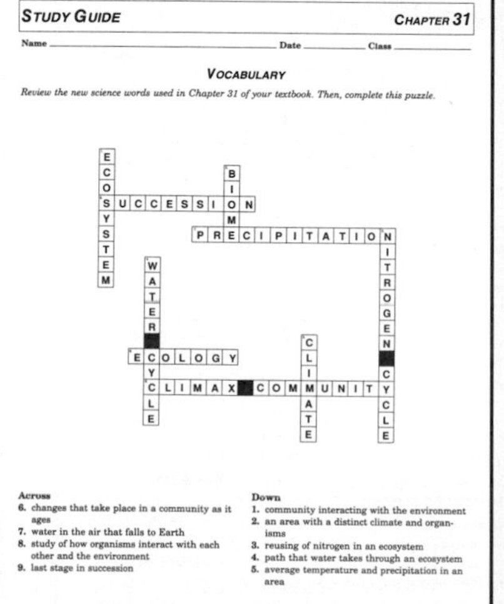

STUDY GUIDE — CHAPTER 31

Name ______ Date ______ Class ______

VOCABULARY

Review the new science words used in Chapter 31 of your textbook. Then, complete this puzzle.

Across
6. changes that take place in a community as it ages
7. water in the air that falls to Earth
8. study of how organisms interact with each other and the environment
9. last stage in succession

Down
1. community interacting with the environment
2. an area with a distinct climate and organisms
3. reusing of nitrogen in an ecosystem
4. path that water takes through an ecosystem
5. average temperature and precipitation in an area

Idea Map

Have students use the idea map as a study guide to the major concepts of this section.

Guided Practice

Have students write down their answers to the margin question: the ocean.

Check for Understanding

Have students respond to the first three questions in Check Your Understanding.

Reteach

Reteaching/Teacher Resource Package, p. 93. Use this worksheet to give students additional practice with the climates of different biomes.

Extension: Assign Critical Thinking, Biology and Writing, or some of the **OPTIONS** available with this lesson.

3 APPLY

Guest Speaker

Invite a wildlife biologist to speak to your class about working with communities and ecosystems.

4 CLOSE

Ask students to use the words population, community, ecosystem, and biome to explain how each word is related to the others.

Answers to Check Your Understanding

11. There is too little rainfall, and the temperatures are too cold.
12. tundra; caribou, musk oxen, polar bears
13. The saltwater ecosystem contains a large amount of mineral salts; a freshwater ecosystem does not.
14. The current biomes would change into different biomes as the climate changed. The regions most affected would be ice, tundra, and taiga.
15. Answers will vary.

Study Tip: Use this idea map as a study guide to biomes and ecosystems. Give an example of an animal that lives in each one.

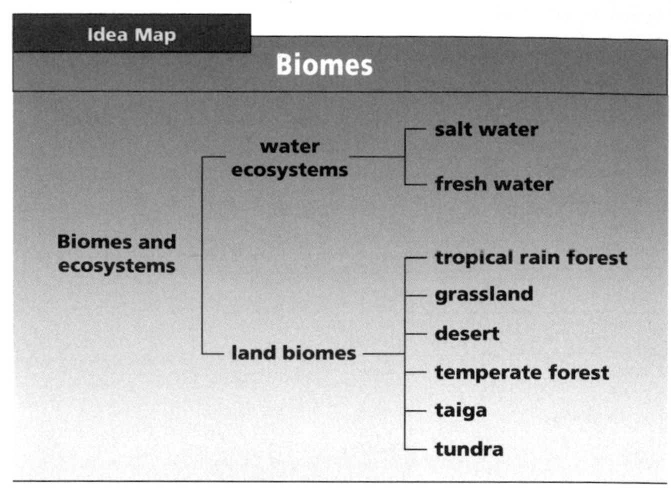

Water Ecosystems

Water ecosystems are divided into fresh water and salt water. Streams, rivers, and lakes make up the freshwater ecosystem. Streams and rivers may start as water draining from a pond or lake and eventually flow into an ocean. The oceans make up the saltwater ecosystem because they contain large amounts of salts. Most freshwater organisms would die if placed in an ocean.

What is Earth's largest ecosystem?

The ocean ecosystem is Earth's largest ecosystem. It can be divided into smaller ecosystems. These include tidal pools, salt marshes, seashores, coral reefs, and the open ocean.

Check Your Understanding

11. Why can't palm trees live in the tundra?
12. What biome has the lowest average precipitation? Name three organisms that live there.
13. What major difference between freshwater and saltwater ecosystems determines what organisms will live there?
14. **Critical Thinking:** What might be an effect on today's biomes if all climates became warmer?
15. **Biology and Writing:** Write a paragraph of at least five sentences that describes the biome you live in.

OPTIONS

Challenge: Have students locate the biome in which they live and make a list of the smaller ecosystems within this biome. It may include swamps, rivers, streams, fields, fence rows, etc. Make sure they understand the difference between an ecosystem and a biome. Have students identify the biome(s) that border(s) the biome in which they live.

RETEACHING 93

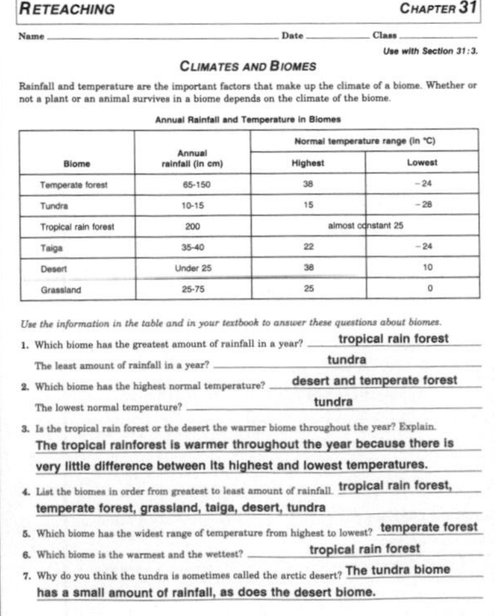

RETEACHING CHAPTER 31

Name ______ Date ______ Class ______

Use with Section 31:3.

CLIMATES AND BIOMES

Rainfall and temperature are the important factors that make up the climate of a biome. Whether or not a plant or an animal survives in a biome depends on the climate of the biome.

Annual Rainfall and Temperature in Biomes

Biome	Annual rainfall (in cm)	Normal temperature range (in °C)	
		Highest	Lowest
Temperate forest	65-150	38	−24
Tundra	10-15	15	−28
Tropical rain forest	200	almost constant 25	
Taiga	35-40	22	−24
Desert	Under 25	38	10
Grassland	25-75	25	0

Use the information in the table and in your textbook to answer these questions about biomes.

1. Which biome has the greatest amount of rainfall in a year? tropical rain forest
   The least amount of rainfall in a year? tundra
2. Which biome has the highest normal temperature? desert and temperate forest
   The lowest normal temperature? tundra
3. Is the tropical rain forest or the desert the warmer biome throughout the year? Explain. The tropical rainforest is warmer throughout the year because there is very little difference between its highest and lowest temperatures.
4. List the biomes in order from greatest to least amount of rainfall. tropical rain forest, temperate forest, grassland, taiga, desert, tundra
5. Which biome has the widest range of temperature from highest to lowest? temperate forest
6. Which biome is the warmest and the wettest? tropical rain forest
7. Why do you think the tundra is sometimes called the arctic desert? The tundra biome has a small amount of rainfall, as does the desert biome.

Lab 31–2 Brine Shrimp

Problem: How does salt affect the growth of brine shrimp?

Skills

observe, form hypotheses, interpret data, design an experiment

Materials

flat toothpick
brine shrimp eggs
weak salt solution
strong salt solution
distilled water
3 small plastic cups
marking pen
hand lens

Procedure

1. Copy the data table.
2. Label three cups 1, 2, and 3 with a marking pen.
3. Fill the cups nearly full with the following:
   cup 1—distilled water
   cup 2—weak salt solution
   cup 3—strong salt solution
4. Dip a toothpick into the brine shrimp eggs. Brine shrimp are tiny animals that live in salt water. Place the eggs that cling to the toothpick into cup 1.
5. Repeat step 4 with cups 2 and 3. The eggs will float on the water.
6. Place the cups on a shelf in the classroom.

CUP	AMOUNT OF SALT	DAY WHEN MOST SHRIMP HATCHED	CUP WITH MOST BRINE SHRIMP
1	none	did not hatch	
2	weak solution	day 3	
3	strong solution	day 2	√

7. Write a **hypothesis** in your notebook to explain which cup will have the most brine shrimp at the end of 3 days.
8. **Observe:** Observe the cups for the next three days. Use the hand lens to look for small orange-colored animals swimming in a jerking motion. These objects are the brine shrimp that hatched from the eggs. Note the cup in which you see the first shrimp and the number of shrimp that hatch in each cup on each day. Record your data in the data table.

Data and Observations

1. How many days did it take for you to see the first brine shrimp?
2. In which of the three cups did they hatch first?
3. In which of these three cups did the most brine shrimp hatch? In which did they grow best?
4. In which of the three cups did the brine shrimp not hatch at all?

Analyze and Apply

1. What would you call the ecosystems in which you were trying to grow brine shrimp?
2. In which type of ecosystem do you think brine shrimp hatch and grow best?
3. **Check your hypothesis:** Was your hypothesis supported by your data? Why or why not?
4. **Apply:** How does salt affect the growth of brine shrimp?

Extension

Design an experiment to find out if there is a maximum strength of salt water at which brine shrimp will grow.

Lab 31-2 Brine Shrimp

Overview

Students will determine how salt affects the growth of brine shrimp eggs by placing the eggs in distilled water and two different concentrations of salt water.

Objectives: Students will be able to (1) **infer** which solution grows brine shrimp best, (2) **form a hypothesis** to explain which solution will have the most brine shrimp hatch, and (3) **determine** the type of ecosystem in which brine shrimp grow.

Time Allotment: Day 0: 45 minutes; days 1, 2, 3: 15 minutes.

Preparation

▶ Weak salt solution: add a teaspoon of noniodized salt to a quart of water and stir until dissolved.

▶ Strong salt solution: add four teaspoons of noniodized salt to a quart of water and stir until dissolved.

Lab 31-2 worksheet/*Teacher Resource Package*, pp. 123-124.

Teaching the Lab

▶ Students will notice that the stronger salt solution will hatch the most eggs. This salt solution is nearly the same as ocean water.

Cooperative Learning: Divide the class into groups of two or three students. For more information, see p. 22T-23T in the Teacher Guide.

ANSWERS

Data and Observations

1. Answers may vary. Students should see the first shrimp on day 1 or 2.
2. cup 3
3. cup 3; cup 3
4. cup 1

Analyze and Apply

1. saltwater
2. the ocean or a saltwater ecosystem
3. Students who hypothesized that brine shrimp hatch best in strong salt solution will say that their hypotheses were supported.
4. The greater the salt concentration, the greater the hatching and growth of brine shrimp.

Biomes and Their Living Things

Problem-solving Strategies

The following strategies can be used to solve the problem in this feature: look for a pattern, guess and check, work backwards, list all possible solutions, solve a similar problem.

Hints

▶ Students should concentrate on how these animals are adapted to their environments. Some examples are color, outer covering or skin, amount of water needed, amount of light or shade needed.

Solving the Problem

1. desert biome: c, d, e
2. tropical rain forest biome: a, b, f, g

Students should be able to tell why the plant or animal they chose is particularly suited to its biome.

PROBLEM SOLVING

BIOMES AND THEIR LIVING THINGS

There are large areas on Earth, called biomes, that have similar climates and climax communities. Each biome has distinct plants and animals that live there. Photo 1 shows a desert biome. Deserts are usually very hot during the day and cold at night. The soil has few nutrients. Few living things are found in deserts because there is very little precipitation. Photo 2 shows a tropical rain forest. There are more living things here than in any other biome. Rain forests are hot and have large amounts of rainfall.

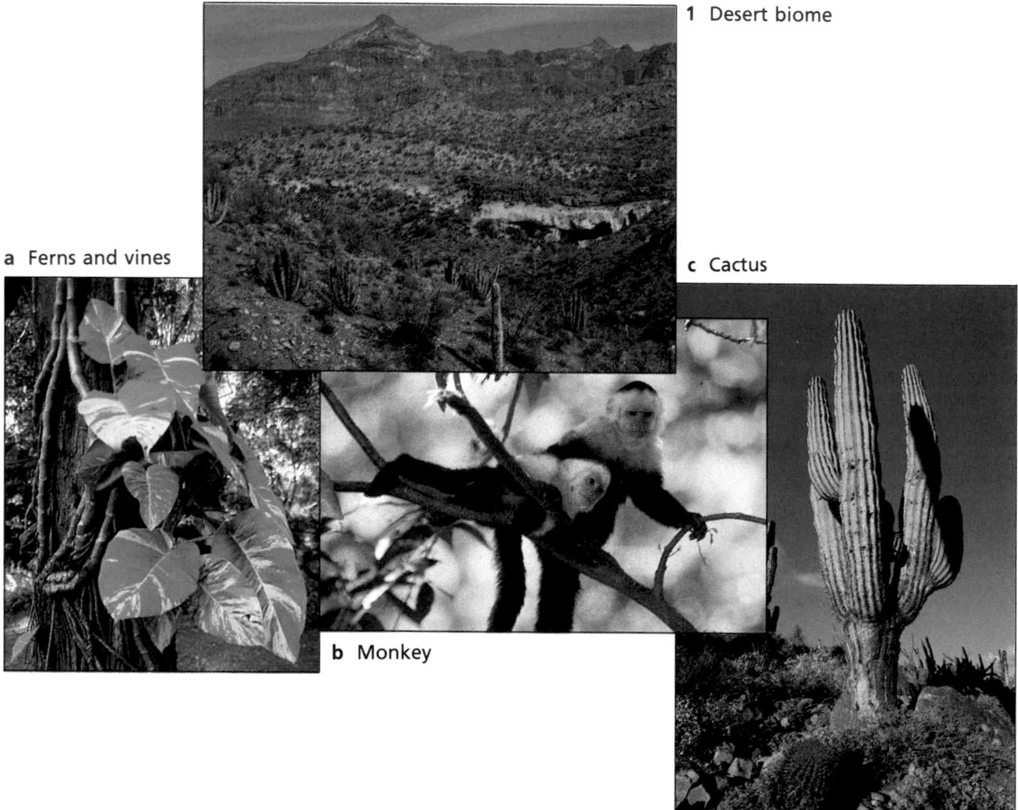

1 Desert biome

a Ferns and vines

c Cactus

b Monkey

668

Photos a through g show some plants and animals that can be found either in a desert biome or in a tropical rain forest biome. Match each plant and animal with its correct biome. Use Figure 31-10 to help you. Then, write a short paragraph describing one of the two biomes.

2 Tropical rain forest biome

d Scorpion

e Tree frog

g Toucan

f Lizard

Discussing the Problem

▶ Discuss with students how plants and animals in a desert biome require a lot of sunlight and little water, and often have drab coloring. Plants have root systems adapted to getting what water is there out of the sandy soil. Plants also grow very slowly and store what water they get. Evaporation is minimal. Very few plants and animals can survive in this biome. A tropical rain forest has a great abundance of plant and animal species. These species are well-suited to life in a hot, humid climate. Vegetation is lush and green, flowers are colorful. Plants grow rapidly and the water cycle repeats itself quickly. Animals are adapted to living in trees, or on the damp forest floor, or in the many streams or rivers that wind through the forest.

Extensions

Ask students to describe how other biomes relate to the desert or tropical rain forest. In what ways are they similar; in what ways, different? For example, how do tundra and desert relate? Students should be able to say that both have little precipitation, vegetation, and animal life. The main differences are nonliving factors: amount of sunlight and temperature. What would happen if plants from one biome were transplanted into another biome, for example an oak tree sapling in taiga?

CHAPTER 31 REVIEW

Summary

Summary statements can be used by students to review major concepts of the chapter.

Key Science Words

All boldfaced terms from the chapter are listed.

Testing Yourself

Using Words

1. water cycle
2. biome
3. ecosystem
4. climax community
5. precipitation
6. climate
7. nitrogen cycle
8. ecology
9. succession

Finding Main Ideas

10. p. 657; Water falls to Earth as rain. Some evaporates and some soaks into the ground. Water from the ground, oceans, lakes, plants, and animals, evaporates into the air.
11. p. 654; Ecosystems can be found on land or water.
12. p. 660; Trees in a forest absorb the heat of the sun and shade the soil.
13. p. 658; producers and consumers
14. p. 655; Soil is nonliving.
15. p. 664; tundra, taiga, temperate forest, grassland, and desert
16. p. 660; bare soil
17. p. 658; Respiration and photosynthesis cannot take place without these gases.
18. p. 662; The pond becomes shallower.

Using Main Ideas

19. Oxygen, water, nitrogen, and carbon dioxide are recycled through an ecosystem.
20. Oxygen is respired by all organisms and carbon dioxide is used by producers for photosynthesis.
21. It controls what kinds of plants and animals can live in an area.
22. Their remains add nutrients to the soil.
23. an ocean
24. Dead plants pile up and soil washes into the pond.
25. Each biome is different in its climate, plants, and animals.

Chapter 31 Review

Summary

31:1 Ecosystems

1. Ecosystems are made up of living and nonliving parts.
2. Water is a nonliving part that is cycled through the ecosystem and is necessary for all living things.
3. The nitrogen cycle returns nitrates to the soil so they can be used for plant growth. The oxygen-carbon dioxide cycle provides carbon dioxide for plant photosynthesis and oxygen for plant and animal respiration.

31:2 Succession

4. The changes that take place in the living parts of a community as it gets older are called succession. Each stage of succession is represented by different plants and animals.
5. Succession in a water community results in formation of dry land.

31:3 How Living Things Are Distributed

6. Light, temperature, and precipitation make up an area's climate. Climate determines what living things live in an area.
7. Biomes are large land areas with distinct climate and living things. Water ecosystems include fresh water and salt water.

Key Science Words

biome (p. 664)
climate (p. 664)
climax community (p. 661)
ecology (p. 654)
ecosystem (p. 654)
nitrogen cycle (p. 656)
precipitation (p. 663)
succession (p. 660)
water cycle (p. 657)

Testing Yourself

Using Words

Choose the word from the list of Key Science Words that best fits the definition.

1. path of water through an ecosystem
2. has a distinct climate and certain plants and animals
3. community interacting with the environment
4. the last stage of succession
5. one factor that makes up the climate of an area
6. the average of temperature and precipitation over many years
7. the reusing of nitrogen in an ecosystem
8. the study of how living things interact with each other and their environment
9. changes in a community over time

Review

Testing Yourself *continued*

Finding Main Ideas

List the page number where each main idea below is found. Then, explain each main idea.

10. how water is recycled in an ecosystem
11. where ecosystems can be found
12. why the soil in a vacant field has a different temperature than the soil in a forest
13. what uses oxygen in an ecosystem
14. whether soil is a living or a nonliving part of an ecosystem
15. what the different biomes are in North America
16. what the first stage of succession on land is
17. why oxygen and carbon dioxide are important gases in an ecosystem
18. what happens to the depth of a pond as the community changes

Using Main Ideas

Answer the questions by referring to the page number after each question.

19. Which of the following are recycled through an ecosystem: oxygen, water, light, nitrogen, carbon dioxide? (pp. 655, 657, 658, 663)
20. How is the oxygen-carbon dioxide cycle important to an ecosystem? (p. 658)
21. How does climate affect plants and animals? (p. 663)
22. How can the soil be affected by the death of plants and animals? (p. 655)
23. Which has more salts, an ocean or river? (p. 666)
24. Why does a pond become more shallow as it ages? (p. 662)
25. What kinds of things separate one biome from another? (p. 664)

Skill Review ✓

*For more help, refer to the **Skill Handbook,** pages 704-719.*

1. **Sequence:** List 5 ecosystems in the area where you live. Sequence these ecosystems from smallest to largest.
2. **Infer:** How can boiling water become part of the water cycle?
3. **Infer:** Explain why leaves that fell on the forest floor in autumn disappear during the next summer.
4. **Design an experiment:** Design an experiment to show how you could tell if you are giving off carbon dioxide when you breathe out.

Finding Out More

Critical Thinking

1. Suppose you set up a terrarium with plants, soil, decomposers, and water. You sealed it so it was air-tight. Could the plants live in this sealed environment? What is the one factor you would have to supply?
2. Use the map of biomes on page 664 to find out which biome you live in. What would happen if your biome got half the amount of precipitation it now gets?

Applications

1. Visit a park or area near your school. Record evidence for how nonliving things affect the living things.
2. Find out more about Biosphere II. Describe some of the problems scientists had to solve while planning and building this project.

671

Skill Review

1. Answers might include ponds, forests, meadows, and so on. The size of the ecosystem will vary with the area in which the students live.
2. Boiling water condenses and forms water droplets when it cools. These water droplets become heavier than air and form precipitation.
3. Leaves are decomposed by fungi and bacteria over a period of time.
4. Blow into a jar containing blue liquid. If the blue liquid changes to green or yellow, you are breathing out CO_2.

Finding Out More

Critical Thinking

1. The sealed environment could recycle its materials such as water, nitrogen, oxygen, and carbon dioxide, as long as it was supplied with light as an energy source.
2. The types of plants and animals in the biome would change. Plants that need a lot of moisture would not be able to survive with half the amount of moisture.

Applications

1. Temperature in autumn causes leaves to change and fall. Plants become dormant. Animals become less active or hibernate in winter. Some plants need more light or moisture (or less) than others. For example, ferns would get scorched in bright sun.
2. Some of the problems have been keeping a balance in the water, oxygen, carbon dioxide, and nitrogen so that cycles would be stable. Producing enough food for the scientists also was a problem, so that food would not need to be brought in. Scientists also needed to find a way to regulate the temperature.

Chapter Review/*Teacher Resource Package*, pp. 165-166.

Chapter Test/*Teacher Resource Package*, pp. 167-169.

Chapter Test/*Computer Test Bank*

Solving Ecological Problems

PLANNING GUIDE

CONTENT	TEXT FEATURES	TEACHER RESOURCE PACKAGE	OTHER COMPONENTS
(1 1/2 days) 32:1 Resources and Human Activities Wildlife and Plants Soil Waste Fossil Fuels	Skill Check: *Calculate,* p. 677 Mini Lab: *How Could You Protect a Species?* p. 675 Mini Lab: *What Does Sediment Look Like?* p. 676 Check Your Understanding, p. 677	Application: *How Humans Affect Animal and Plant Resources,* p. 32 Reteaching: *Resources and Human Activities,* p. 94 Critical Thinking/Problem Solving: *Can Pollution Change Succession?* p. 32 Skill: *Use Numbers,* pp. 33-34 Study Guide: *Resources and Human Activities,* p. 187	
(2 1/2 days) 32:2 Problems From Pollution Air Pollution Water Pollution Acid Rain Land Pollution	Skill Check: *Experiment,* p. 679 Skill Check: *Understand Science Words,* p. 681 Technology: *The Greenhouse Effect—A Computer Model,* p. 680 Lab 32-1: *pH,* p. 682 Lab 32-2: *Pollution,* p. 686 Idea Map, p. 685 Check Your Understanding, p. 685	Enrichment: *Acid Rain and Aquatic Organisms,* pp. 34-35 Reteaching: *Air Pollution,* p. 95 Focus: *Lichens Monitor Air Pollution,* p. 63 Transparency Master: *Acid Rain,* p. 161 Study Guide: *Problems From Pollution,* pp. 188-190 Lab 32-1: *pH,* pp. 125-126 Lab 32-2: *Pollution,* pp. 127-128	**Laboratory Manual:** *How Do Chemical Pollutants Affect Living Things?* p. 267 **Laboratory Manual:** *How Does Thermal Pollution Affect Living Things?* p. 271 Color Transparency 32: *How Pesticides Are Concentrated in a Food Chain*
(2 days) 32:3 Working Toward Solutions Conserving Our Resources Keeping Our Environment Clean	Check Your Understanding, p. 689	Reteaching: *Solutions to Environmental Problems,* p. 96 Study Guide: *Working Toward Solutions,* p. 191 Study Guide: *Vocabulary,* p. 192	
Chapter Review	Summary Key Science Words Testing Yourself Finding Main Ideas Using Main Ideas Skill Review	Chapter Review, pp. 170-171 Chapter Test, pp. 172-174 Unit Test, pp. 175-176	**Test Bank**

MATERIALS NEEDED

LAB 32-1, p. 682	LAB 32-2, p. 686	MARGIN FEATURES
pH paper pH chart forceps marking pencil 7 glass slides 7 droppers ammonia baking soda cola vinegar 2 samples of rainwater distilled water	4 test tubes marking pencil test-tube rack 5 droppers blue test liquid dead yeast mixture live yeast mixture detergent hydrogen peroxide distilled water	Skill Check, p. 677 pencil paper Skill Check, p. 679 plastic cup distilled water Skill Check, p. 681 dictionary Mini Lab, p. 675 pencil paper Mini Lab, p. 676 jar with lid soil water

OBJECTIVES

SECTION	OBJECTIVE	OBJECTIVES CORRELATION			
		CHECK YOUR UNDERSTANDING	CHAPTER REVIEW	TRP CHAPTER REVIEW	TRP CHAPTER TEST
32:1	1. **Explain** how wildlife and plants are affected by humans.	1, 4	5, 20	11	3, 29, 35, 49
	2. **Describe** how water and soil can be lost to the environment.	2	4, 11, 17	6, 22, 23, 24	8, 20, 24, 42, 43
	3. **Explain** why fossil fuels are being used up.	3	14, 21, 22	5, 29	5
32:2	4. **Discuss** the causes of air pollution and acid rain.	6	1, 8, 10, 15, 16, 25	1, 3, 7, 9, 12, 13, 14, 16, 18, 19	1, 4, 6, 7, 10, 12, 13, 14, 15, 18, 19, 21, 28, 30, 32, 34, 36, 38, 46, 47, 51, 52
	5. **Discuss** problems that come from nonbiodegradable chemicals that pollute water.	7, 8, 9	2, 3, 6, 7, 23, 26, 27	2, 8, 17, 19, 21, 28	9, 11, 16, 17, 22, 23, 25, 26, 27, 33, 39, 40, 41, 50
32:3	6. **Explain** methods of conserving resources.	11, 13	13, 18, 19	4	31, 44
	7. **Discuss** ways to keep the environment clean.	12, 14, 15	9, 24	10, 15	2, 37, 45, 48

Solving Ecological Problems

CHAPTER OVERVIEW

Key Concepts

In this chapter, students will learn about the major ecological problems in the world today. They will learn how plants, animals, soil, water, and air can be damaged. They will find out about the damage caused by air and water pollution. The chapter closes with ways humans can conserve natural resources and keep the environment clean.

Key Science Words

acid	ozone
acid rain	pesticide
base	pollution
biodegradable	radon
endangered	recycling
erosion	sediment
fossil fuel	smog
greenhouse effect	threatened
natural resource	toxic

Skill Development

In Lab 32-1, students will **observe, experiment, interpret data,** and **classify** to compare the pH of rainwater with that of household chemicals. In Lab 32-2, students will **observe, form hypotheses, interpret data,** and **design an experiment** to determine the effects of pollutants on yeast. In the Skill Check on page 677, students will **calculate** the world population. In the Skill Check on page 679, students will **experiment** with rainwater. On page 681, students will **understand** the **science word** *pesticide.* In the Mini Lab on page 675, students will **outline** protection for an endangered species. In the Mini Lab on page 676, students will **classify** sediment found in soil.

CHAPTER PREVIEW

Chapter Content

Review this outline for Chapter 32 before you read the chapter.

Skills in this Chapter

The skills that you will use in this chapter are listed below.

- In **Lab 32-1,** you will observe, experiment, interpret data, and classify. In **Lab 32-2,** you will observe, form hypotheses, interpret data, and design an experiment.
- In the **Skill Checks,** you will calculate, experiment, and understand science words.
- In the **Mini Labs,** you will outline and classify.

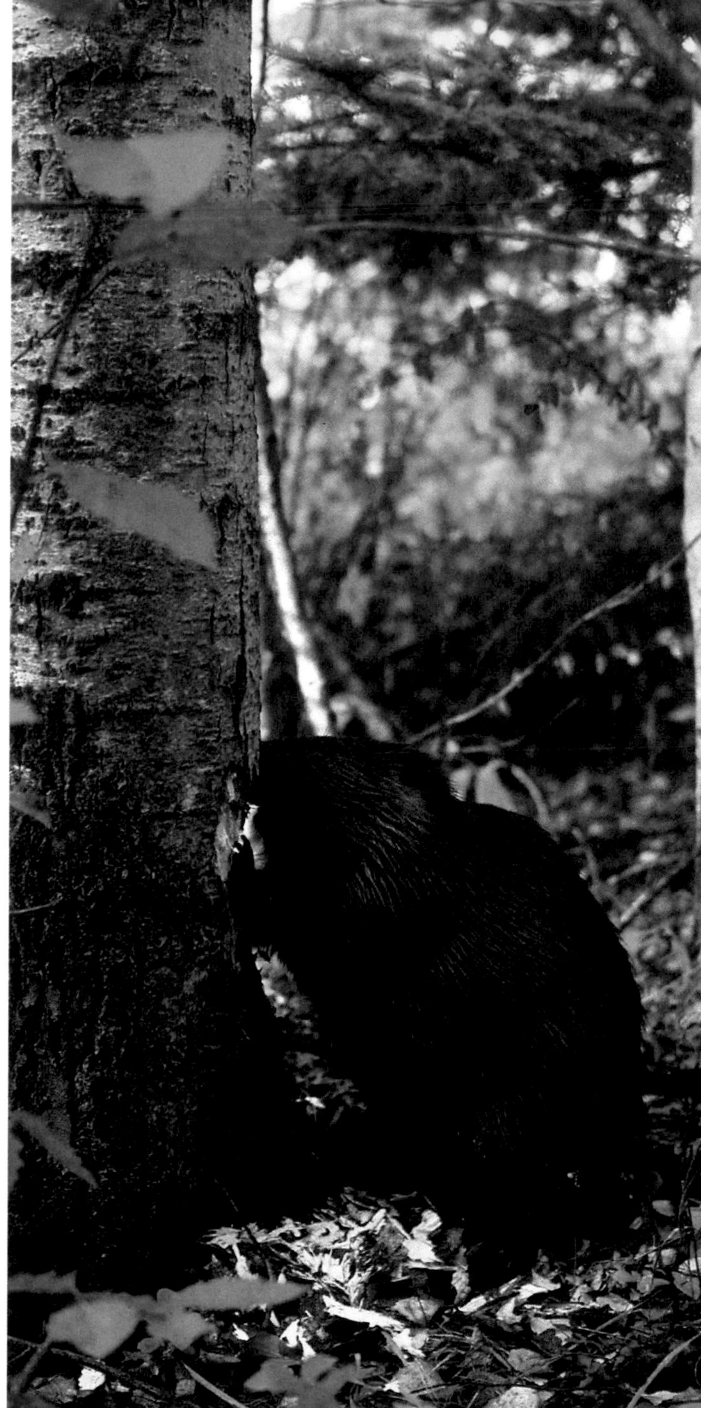

Bridging

Students learned about the different levels of ecological relationships in populations, communities, ecosystems, and biomes in Chapters 30 and 31. Throughout these two chapters the interrelationships between organisms and their environments is the central theme. Chapter 32 explores problems that exist in the environment today and gives suggestions as to how they can be solved.

Chapter **32**

Solving Ecological Problems

The increasing human population has brought about vast changes in the environment. Humans have changed their environment by building factories, parks, shopping malls, and by farming. Other living things change the environment, too, but not as fast as humans do. The beavers on the opposite page cut down trees and dam up streams. This activity creates ponds where the beavers can build their dens. The river in the photo on this page has been littered with trash thrown away by humans. Both of these activities have changed the environment.

In this chapter, you will read about the changes humans have made to the environment. Think about some of the ways you may have changed your environment.

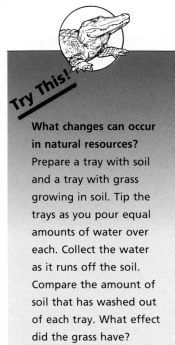

Try This!

What changes can occur in natural resources? Prepare a tray with soil and a tray with grass growing in soil. Tip the trays as you pour equal amounts of water over each. Collect the water as it runs off the soil. Compare the amount of soil that has washed out of each tray. What effect did the grass have?

Humans change the environment when they discard trash.

GETTING STARTED

Using the Photos

In looking at the photos, students should think of other ways humans have changed the environment. They should think of helpful as well as harmful changes to the environment. They should also think of ways that they could improve their environment.

MOTIVATION/Try This!

What changes can occur in natural resources? Upon completing the chapter-opening activity, students will have **experimented.** They will discover that grass protects soil from washing away.

Chapter Preview

Have students study the chapter outline before they begin to read the chapter. They should note that the chapter begins with a discussion of endangered species and possible solutions to this problem. The next broad topic is damage to our environment by various types of pollution. The last section focuses on possible ways to solve pollution problems.

Misconception

Students usually assume that damage to natural resources happens somewhere other than where they live. Point out a few local problems involving damage to natural resources in the community where the students live.

32:1 Resources and Human Activities

PREPARATION

Materials Needed

Make copies of the Skill, Application, Critical Thinking/Problem Solving, Study Guide, and Reteaching worksheets in the *Teacher Resource Package*.

▶ Obtain soil and jars for the Mini Lab.

Key Science Words

natural resource
endangered
threatened
erosion
sediment
pollution
fossil fuel

Process Skills

In the Skill Check, students will calculate. In the Mini Labs, students will outline and classify.

1 FOCUS

▶ The objectives are listed on the student page. Remind students to preview these objectives as a guide to this numbered section.

MOTIVATION/Bulletin Board

Display pictures of natural resources. *National Wildlife* and *International Wildlife* have excellent photos. Discuss problems that occur when natural resources are not protected.

Guided Practice

Have students write down their answers to the margin question: one that can be replaced during a lifetime.

32:1 Resources and Human Activities

Objectives

1. **Explain** how wildlife and plants are affected by humans.
2. **Describe** how water and soil can be lost to the environment.
3. **Explain** why fossil fuels are being used up.

Key Science Words

natural resource
endangered
threatened
erosion
sediment
pollution
fossil fuel

Air, water, soil, plants, and animals are some of our natural resources. A **natural resource** is any part of the environment used by humans. If these resources are used unwisely, the lives of many things can be harmed. For instance, cutting down a forest will destroy many of the animal populations that live there. See Figure 32-1.

Wildlife and Plants

What is a renewable resource?

Wildlife and plants are important resources for humans. They provide food, fibers, and building materials. Nearly half the medicines being used today come from living things. Plants make oxygen, which all living things use during respiration. Soil that is covered with plants absorbs and holds water from precipitation. Thus, the soil is not worn away. Animals may be considered a renewable resource. A renewable resource is a resource that can be replaced within a person's lifetime. Animals can reproduce, keeping the population stable. Plants are a renewable resource, too. A field can regrow in about five years. A forest may take 25 to 100 years or more to regrow.

As the human population gets bigger, it needs more space to grow food and to build homes and factories. Where do we get the space? We use the land around us. As we take over this land, we use more natural resources, make more trash, and take away habitats of animals and plants.

Figure 32-1 Cutting down a forest destroys many of the plant and animal populations that live there.

OPTIONS

Science Background

There are over 227 animals and 62 plants on the threatened and endangered lists.

a

b

c

Figure 32-2 The green pitcher plant (a) and whooping crane (b) are endangered species. Elephants (c) are killed illegally so their tusks can be carved into jewelry.

What happens to animal populations that are forced from their habitats? They must find new places to live. If they can't find enough space or food, they die. Unlike animals, plants can't move to a new area when their habitats are used for land development. These plants usually die. When a species of living thing no longer exists anywhere on Earth, it is extinct. Over the past three and one-half centuries, nearly 200 animal species have become extinct in the United States alone!

In the world today, over 1000 animal and plant species are endangered. **Endangered** means that a species is in danger of becoming extinct. Two endangered species are shown in Figure 32-2. Some living things are threatened. **Threatened** means that a species of living thing is close to being endangered. There are over 1200 threatened species of plants in the world.

How do animals and plants become threatened or endangered? Illegal hunting is one way. For example, African elephants are killed for their ivory tusks. Reptiles such as alligators and crocodiles are hunted illegally so their skins can be made into shoes, belts, and purses.

The rain forests of South America, Africa, and Asia are being cut down at an extremely high rate to make room for farmland. Every year, 100 000 square kilometers of rain forest are destroyed. This is an area equal to 38 football fields being destroyed every minute! Decreasing the forests means there are fewer plants releasing oxygen into the air and more carbon dioxide building up in the air. The ecological balance is upset. Why is this a problem for humans and other living things?

Scientists estimate that over 100 species of plants in these forests are becoming extinct each day. Extinction has always happened as a part of evolution, but by cutting down the rain forests, we speed up the process.

Mini Lab

How Could You Protect a Species?

Outline: Pick a plant or animal and assume that it has become endangered. Make an outline showing what you would do to protect this species. What needs does this species have? *For more help, refer to the **Skill Handbook,** pages 706-711.*

2 TEACH

MOTIVATION/Display

Write the word *humans* on the chalkboard and then write the words *wildlife, plants, soil, water,* and *fossil fuels* around it. Discuss how humans depend on each of these things, and how they are all interrelated.

Concept Development

▶ Explain that legal hunting of some animals helps control animal populations that no longer have natural predators.

▶ Discuss how some human needs are causing loss of habitat for animals.

Mini Lab

This open-ended activity will give students a chance to report on a favorite living thing. Have students compare their ideas in small groups.

APPLICATION 32

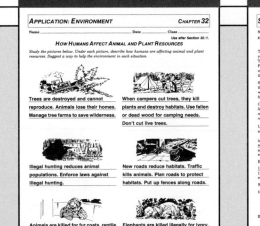

APPLICATION: ENVIRONMENT CHAPTER 32

Name ______ Date ______ Class ______

Use after Section 32:1.

HOW HUMANS AFFECT ANIMAL AND PLANT RESOURCES

Study the pictures below. Under each picture, describe how humans are affecting animal and plant resources. Suggest a way to help the environment in each situation.

Trees are destroyed and cannot reproduce. Animals lose their homes. Manage tree farms to save wilderness.

When campers cut trees, they kill plants and destroy habitats. Use fallen or dead wood for camping needs. Don't cut live trees.

Illegal hunting reduces animal populations. Enforce laws against illegal hunting.

New roads reduce habitats. Traffic kills animals. Plan roads to protect habitats. Put up fences along roads.

Animals are killed for fur coats, reptile skin shoes, and purses. Use manufactured fabrics or leather from farm animals.

Elephants are killed illegally for ivory. Enforce laws against killing elephants. Do not buy ivory products.

SKILL 33

SKILL: USE NUMBERS, CALCULATE CHAPTER 32

Name ______ Date ______ Class ______

For more help, refer to the Skill Handbook, pages 718-719. *Use with Section 32:1.*

DISAPPEARANCE OF TROPICAL RAIN FORESTS

Tropical rain forests of the world are being cut down at the rate of 116 500 square kilometers each year. The forests are cut down to make way for farming, or the cut trees are used for fuel or lumber. To understand the rate at which the forests are being destroyed, think about the size of the state of Pennsylvania. The state has a land area of about 117 000 square kilometers. If Pennsylvania were covered with forests, and the forests were destroyed at the rate of 117 000 square kilometers a year, the forests would be gone at the end of one year.

Suppose a tropical rain forest covered all the land of the United States. Then suppose the trees in this forest were being cut down at the same rate as those in the world's rain forests. How long would it take for the forest to disappear completely from the United States? How long would it take for the forest to disappear in particular states?

Calculate the number of years and days it would take to remove the forest from each of the states listed in Table 2 on the next page. Use Formula A or Formula B below. You can use Table 1 on the next page to change decimal parts of a year into days. For example, 0.2 year equals 73 days. Write the results of your calculations in the last column of Table 2. Two have been done for you.

Use Formula A for states larger than 100 000 square kilometers

$$\frac{\text{land area in square kilometers}}{\text{square kilometers removed yearly}} = \text{number of years to remove forest}$$

Example: Alabama

$$\frac{132\ 000 \text{ square kilometers}}{117\ 000 \text{ square kilometers removed yearly}} = 1.1 \text{ years (1 year and 36 days)}$$

Use Formula B for states smaller than 100 000 square kilometers

$$\frac{\text{land area in square kilometers}}{\text{square kilometers removed yearly}} \times 365 \text{ days} = \text{number of days to remove forest}$$

Example: Delaware

$$\frac{5200 \text{ square kilometers}}{117\ 000 \text{ square kilometers removed yearly}} \times 365 \text{ days} = 16 \text{ days}$$

When you have completed Table 2, answer the following questions.

1. How many square kilometers of tropical forests in the world are being destroyed each day? (Divide the number of square kilometers destroyed each year by 365 days.) 320 square kilometers each day

2. What problems can you think of that may be caused by destruction of the world's tropical rain forests? Answers will vary. Habitats of organisms will be destroyed and organisms might become extinct. Bare land might cause serious erosion. Loss of forests might cause climate changes.

OPTIONS

Skill/*Teacher Resource Package*, p. 33. Use the Skill worksheet shown here for students to use numbers to understand the disappearance of tropical forests.

Application/*Teacher Resource Package*, p. 32. Use the Application worksheet shown here to teach students how humans affect animal and plant resources.

TEACH

Mini Lab

Water that is not clear after 3 days may have fine clay and silt particles suspended in it. Have students compare the layers of sediment with a hand lens.

Guided Practice

Have students write down their answers to the margin question: Wind separates small particles and blows them away.

Independent Practice

Study Guide/*Teacher Resource Package*, p. 187. Use the Study Guide worksheet shown at the bottom of the page for independent practice.

Mini Lab

What Does Sediment Look Like?

Classify: Add soil to a jar of water. Cover and shake. Let the soil settle for three days. How many layers of sediment do you see? Describe the layers. Is the water clear? *For more help, refer to the* ***Skill Handbook,*** *pages 715-717.*

Soil

Soil is an important natural resource. The roots of plants hold soil in place. When plants are removed and the soil is not protected, erosion can take place. **Erosion** is the wearing away of soil by wind and water. When soil erodes, it is carried away faster than it can be replaced.

Soil that washes into streams and rivers can cause problems. As the current in a stream slows, the floating soil particles settle to the bottom. Material that settles on the bottom of the stream is called **sediment.** Sediment covers the habitats of water plants and animals. Fish eggs on the river bottom die because they don't get enough oxygen.

How does dry soil erode?

When bare soil dries out, it can erode quickly. Why? The wind easily separates the small particles of soil and blows them away. Erosion carries away good topsoil. The subsoil layer under the topsoil is exposed. Plants don't grow well in subsoil because it is packed down, contains little oxygen, and lacks the nutrients found in topsoil.

Water

Water is the most abundant resource on Earth. It is a renewable resource because it is cycled in the environment and can be reused. Water covers over 70 percent of Earth's surface. Over 70 percent of your body is water. You could not go without water for more than a few days at a time.

Water in the air is an important factor in climate and weather. The more water there is in the air, the wetter the climate will be in an area. Water is used to irrigate crops, for industry, and for cooling in electric power plants.

Figure 32-3 Soil washes into streams and becomes sediment (a). Wind can erode soil by blowing it away (b). Water is used to irrigate crops (c).

a

b

c

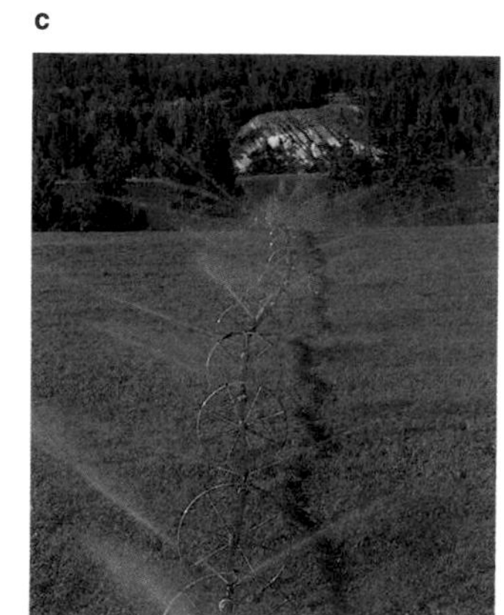

OPTIONS

Critical Thinking/Problem Solving/*Teacher Resource Package*, p. 32. Use the Critical Thinking/Problem Solving worksheet shown here to teach how pollution can change succession.

CRITICAL THINKING 32

CRITICAL THINKING/PROBLEM SOLVING — CHAPTER 32

Name ______ Date ______ Class ______

Use after Section 32:1.

CAN POLLUTION CHANGE SUCCESSION?

The students in a biology class went on a field trip in a rural area. They studied the ecology of two ponds about 50 meters apart. Both received good water supplies from underground springs. Both received about the same amount of runoff from rain.

The appearance of the ponds was quite different. Pond 1 was covered with green and brown pond scum. It had an unpleasant odor. When students took a water sample and looked at it with a microscope, they saw many kinds of single-celled and hairlike algae. This pond was near a cow pasture and near a field of growing crops. The field had been heavily fertilized. Its wire fence was rusty and broken through.

Pond 2 stood farther away from the pasture, on a hill near a pine-hardwood forest. The students could see the bottom of the pond through its clear brownish water. Under the microscope, the students saw a few algae and a few swimming protozoa.

The teacher said, "Each pond is proceeding through its natural succession. However, environmental conditions affect the rate of changes. Pollution can be caused by too much of a good thing, or by harmful substances." What conditions speed up changes in the pond environment?

Analyzing the Problem

1. What is succession? the natural process by which a pond ages, or changes over time
2. What is pollution? any factor that causes undesirable changes in the environment
3. What materials flow into Pond 1? wastes from cows and from fertilizers
4. What materials flow into Pond 2? rainwater, pine needles, and leaves

Solving the Problem

1. What effect did the runoff have on pond 1? It caused rapid heavy growth of algae.
2. What effect did the runoff have on pond 2? It supported growth of a mixed community of plants and animals.
3. Which pond is more polluted? pond 1
4. Which pond shows a faster rate of succession? pond 1
5. How could succession be slowed in the polluted pond? Decrease the flow of cow wastes and excess fertilizer into the pond.

STUDY GUIDE 187

STUDY GUIDE — CHAPTER 32

Name ______ Date ______ Class ______

RESOURCES AND HUMAN ACTIVITIES

In your textbook, read about natural resources in Section 32:1.

1. Each year during the five years from 1986 through 1990, millions of square kilometers of rain forests were cut down and cleared in Africa and Asia to make room for farmland. Use the information in the table below to help you answer the questions that follow.

	Number of square kilometers of forest removed	
Year	Africa	Asia
1990	24 000	16 000
1989	24 000	16 000
1988	24 000	16 000
1987	24 000	16 000
1986	24 000	16 000

2. a. How many square kilometers of forests were destroyed in Africa during the last five years? 120 000
   b. How many square kilometers of forests were destroyed in Asia during the last five years? 80 000
3. What happens to the soil when all of the plants are removed from the forests? The soil is not protected and erosion occurs. The soil is worn away by wind and water.
4. What happens to this soil when it is washed into a stream? It settles to the bottom and covers the habitats of plants and animals.
5. How does clearing the forests affect the level of gases in the air? There will be a decrease of oxygen and an increase of carbon dioxide.
6. How does the removal of the forest environments affect the extinction of organisms? It speeds up the process of extinction.

A major problem with lakes and ponds is rapid aging. Remember that lakes and ponds normally go through succession and become dry land. Producers living in the ponds and lakes need nutrients to live. Sometimes more nutrients are added to the water than are needed by these producers. The extra nutrients are in fertilizers washed from nearby farms, and in untreated sewage. These nutrients cause the pond or lake to go through succession faster than normal. Review the stages of aging in a lake as shown in Figure 31-7 on page 662. Aging is normally a slow, natural process, but it is speeded up because of pollution. **Pollution** is anything that makes the surroundings unhealthy or unclean.

Skill Check

Calculate: The United States has 1/20 of the world's population, but uses 1/3 of the world's energy resources. If the population of the United States is 250 million, what is the world population? *For more help, refer to the* ***Skill Handbook****, pages 718-719.*

Fossil Fuels

Coal, oil, and natural gas are all fossil fuels that humans use to run their cars, heat their homes, and produce electricity. A **fossil fuel** is the remains of organisms that lived millions of years ago. These remains were compressed over long periods of time at tremendous pressure. Because they take so long to form, fossil fuels are not renewable.

Why are fossil fuels not renewable?

Americans use fossil fuels for about 89 percent of our energy needs. As the human population continues to grow, more energy is needed to run larger cities and more cars, homes, and factories. The supply of fossil fuels is being used up at an alarming rate. When coal, oil, and natural gas supplies are gone, there will be no more. New energy sources must be found. Governments must help to save our fossil fuel supply by passing laws limiting their use.

Check Your Understanding

1. What is the difference among extinct, endangered, and threatened species?
2. How is aging of ponds and lakes affected by pollution?
3. Why must new sources of energy be found?
4. **Critical Thinking:** Why should people who live in cities be concerned about rain forests being destroyed?
5. **Biology and Math:** It is estimated that 100 species of plants become extinct in rain forests each day. How many plant species become extinct in rain forests in a year?

RETEACHING 94

RETEACHING CHAPTER 32

Name ______ Date ______ Class ______

Use with Section 32:1.

RESOURCES AND HUMAN ACTIVITIES

Below each picture, write whether the natural resource shown is renewable or nonrenewable.

renewable resource — renewable resource — nonrenewable resource

nonrenewable resource — renewable resource — renewable resource

Plants protect the soil from erosion by holding the soil in place. The steps below describe the erosion of soil by the wind. Number the steps in their correct order.

3 Wind carries away the topsoil.
1 Plants are removed from the soil.
5 Plants are not able to grow in the subsoil.
2 Bare soil dries out.
4 Subsoil layer is exposed.

1. What is a natural resource? A natural resource is any part of the environment used by humans.
2. What is the difference between renewable resources and nonrenewable resources? Renewable resources can be replaced within a person's lifetime, whereas nonrenewable resources cannot.
3. How did fossil fuels form? Fossil fuels formed from the remains of organisms that lived millions of years ago. The compression of the remains over many years changed them into fossil fuels.

TEACH

Skill Check

5000 million

Guided Practice

Have students write down their answers to the margin question: They take so long to form.

Check for Understanding

Have students respond to the first three questions in Check Your Understanding.

Reteach

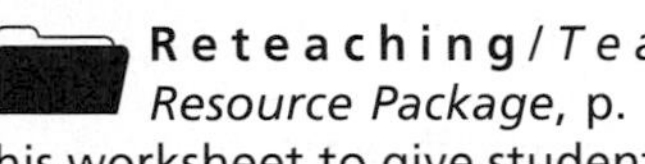

Reteaching/*Teacher Resource Package*, p. 94. Use this worksheet to give students additional practice with air pollution.

Extension: Assign Critical Thinking, Biology and Math, or some of the **OPTIONS** available with this lesson.

3 APPLY

ACTIVITY/Project

Have each student report on an endangered species and explain how to protect it.

4 CLOSE

Summary

Discuss how living things depend on the quality of their environment.

Answers to Check Your Understanding

1. Extinct means a species no longer exists; endangered means a species is in danger of becoming extinct; threatened means a species is close to being endangered.
2. It increases the rate at which ponds and lakes age.
3. Fossil fuels are not renewable and are being used up.
4. There will be less oxygen and more carbon dioxide.
5. 100 x 365 = 36 500

32:2 Problems from Pollution

PREPARATION

Materials Needed

Make copies of the Focus, Study Guide, Transparency Master, Enrichment, Reteaching,and Lab worksheets from the *Teacher Resource Package*.

▶ Obtain balloons and iron filings for the Focus motivation.

▶ Gather ammonia, baking soda, cola, vinegar, and rainwater for Lab 32-1.

Key Science Words

toxic
smog
greenhouse effect
ozone
radon
pesticide
biodegradable
acid
base
acid rain

Process Skills

In Lab 32-1, students will observe, experiment, interpret data, and classify. In the Skill Checks, students will experiment and understand science words.

1 FOCUS

▶ The objectives are listed on the student page. Remind students to preview these objectives as a guide to this numbered section.

MOTIVATION/Demonstration

Fill a balloon with air to show how a normal alveoli sac looks as air is taken in. Fill a second balloon with air but first add 5-10 mL of water and some iron filings. The fluid shows how emphysema prevents oxygen from entering the blood cells. The iron filings represent particulates taken in during breathing.

Focus/*Teacher Resource Package*, p. 63. Use the Focus transparency shown at the bottom of this page as an introduction to studying air pollution.

32:2 Problems from Pollution

Objectives

4. **Discuss** the causes of air pollution and acid rain.
5. **Discuss** problems that come from nonbiodegradable chemicals that pollute water.

Key Science Words

toxic
smog
greenhouse effect
ozone
radon
pesticide
biodegradable
acid
base
acid rain

What is the effect of pollution on our bodies and on our environment? A number of health problems are now known to be caused by pollutants in our environment. Plants and animals are dying from pollutants. Humans are affected by pollution, too.

Air Pollution

Most air pollution is caused by burning coal, oil, gasoline, or natural gas. In North America, cars, lawn mowers, and other gasoline engines burn a total of 12.5 million gallons of fuel each hour. Gasoline produces several harmful gases when burned in an engine. These pollutants are given off in toxic amounts. **Toxic** means poisonous.

Many large cities, such as New York and Los Angeles, suffer from smog emergencies. **Smog** is a combination of smoke and fog. It is made thicker by chemical fumes. Most of the smog that blankets our cities is produced when the harmful gases from industry and auto exhausts react with the energy in sunlight. Trace how smog develops, using Figure 32-4b. This reaction produces new chemicals that are irritating to the eyes, nose, lungs and throat. A smog emergency occurs when the air is very still for a long time, allowing dangerous amounts of these gases to build up.

Factories and power plants that burn coal also make a lot of air pollution. Coal contains a small amount of sulfur.

Figure 32-4 Air pollution is caused by the burning of fossil fuels in engines (a). Smog is formed when harmful gases from burning fossil fuels react with sunlight (b).

a

b

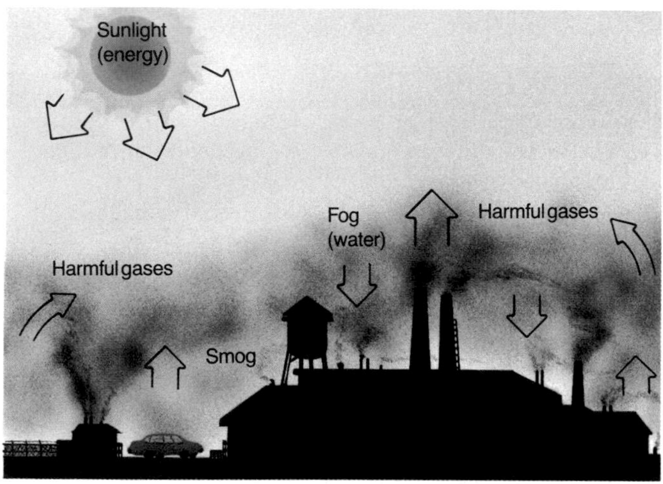

OPTIONS

Science Background

Mercury from industrial waste enters food chains through freshwater and saltwater ecosystems. When humans eat contaminated fish, the mercury travels to the brain and becomes toxic.

FOCUS 63

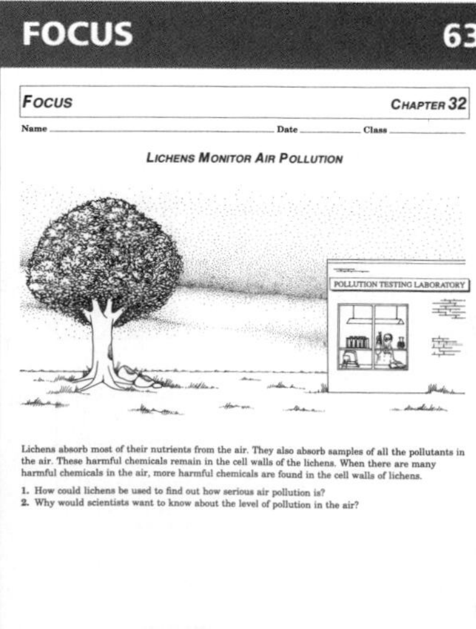

FOCUS — *CHAPTER 32*

Name ________ Date ________ Class ________

LICHENS MONITOR AIR POLLUTION

Lichens absorb most of their nutrients from the air. They also absorb samples of all the pollutants in the air. These harmful chemicals remain in the cell walls of the lichens. When there are many harmful chemicals in the air, more harmful chemicals are found in the cell walls of lichens.

1. How could lichens be used to find out how serious air pollution is?
2. Why would scientists want to know about the level of pollution in the air?

a

b

Figure 32-5 Factories and power plants that burn coal cause air pollution (a). Chemicals from spray cans and plastic foam containers (b) destroy Earth's ozone layer.

When coal burns, the sulfur combines with oxygen in the air to form sulfur dioxide. Sulfur dioxide can kill humans. Power plants that burn coal also give off tiny particles of soot or dust. These particles block sunlight and get into our lungs when we breathe.

When fossil fuels are burned by factories and power plants, large amounts of carbon dioxide are made and released into the air. We don't usually think of carbon dioxide as being a pollutant, but in large amounts it can be. This carbon dioxide forms a layer around Earth and traps heat so it can't escape into the atmosphere. The trapped heat may cause temperatures on Earth to rise slowly, a process know as the **greenhouse effect.** If temperatures on Earth rise even a few degrees, polar ice may melt and the habitats of plants and animals may change. Deserts can form in areas that were once forests.

You may have heard or read that Earth's ozone layer is getting thinner. **Ozone** is a molecule made of three oxygen atoms. It forms a layer high above Earth's surface that keeps harmful radiation from reaching Earth.

Scientists have learned that ozone is being destroyed by certain chemicals found in spray cans, refrigerators, and air conditioners. The same chemicals are used to make plastic foam food containers. The chemicals destroy ozone, and harmful radiation can reach Earth's surface.

Some air pollution problems can be found inside your home. You may have heard of **radon**, a gas that gives off radiation. Radon is found naturally in the ground. In large amounts, radon may cause cancer. Radon can build up to dangerous levels in some buildings. Fans can be added to these buildings to blow the polluted air outside.

Skill Check

Experiment: Wash and rinse a plastic cup in distilled water. Use the cup to collect rain water, then evaporate the water. Look for a film of tiny particles on the side of the cup. How do particles get into the cup? *For more help, refer to the* ***Skill Handbook****, pages 704-705.*

How is ozone destroyed?

2 TEACH

MOTIVATION/Software

Pollute, Opportunities for Learning.

Concept Development

▶ Explain that some pollutants enter the water cycle from the atmosphere. When it rains, these pollutants enter water systems and can enter plants through the soil.

▶ Remind students they learned about carbon monoxide in Chapter 13.

▶ Point out that over 70 percent of the sulfur in our atmosphere comes from burning coal. Explain that some sulfur enters the atmosphere during decomposition.

Skill Check

Many particulates in the air dissolve in precipitation. Dissolved solids reappear when the precipitation evaporates.

Guided Practice

Have students write down their answers to the margin question: by certain chemicals.

OPTIONS

ACTIVITY/Challenge

Have students explain how the pollution control devices on an automobile work.

How Does Thermal Pollution Affect Living Things? *Lab Manual,* pp. 267-270. Use this lab as an extension to studying pollution problems.

TECHNOLOGY

The Greenhouse Effect—A Computer Model

Background

Climatologists have predicted a warming trend that some say is caused by the greenhouse effect. They claim that gases like carbon dioxide, methane, and ozone accumulate in the atmosphere as a result of human activity and agricultural practices and block the exit of heat energy. They claim that temperatures have been rising slowly over the past several decades. Scientists use data to make inferences, predictions, and hypotheses. By looking at increases in temperature around the world they have noticed that warmer temperatures have drifted toward the poles.

Discussion

Point out that some fertile areas could become deserts if the climatologists are correct. Explain that scientists have predicted that the melting of glaciers and polar ice would raise the sea level of the world by six feet. Show students a topographical map of towns near the seashore to help them understand how much land could be underwater. Point out that one benefit of increased carbon dioxide could be more photosynthetic activity, thus, more food for humans. This is possible only if enough water is available.

References

Revkin, Andrew. "Endless Summer." *Discover,* Oct. 1988, pp. 50-54.

Lemonick, Michael. "Feeling the Heat." *Time,* Jan. 2, 1989, pp. 36-38.

TECHNOLOGY

The Greenhouse Effect — A Computer Model

Many scientists are certain that the hotter than usual weather of 1988 was due to the greenhouse effect. They say that the gases from factories, home fuels, and car exhaust are causing the temperature on Earth to rise. These gases trap the heat energy from the sun. Any increase in the amounts of these gases allows more heat to be trapped in the atmosphere.

People who study weather and climate patterns have developed a computer model to explain the hot, dry summer of 1988. Worldwide climate data from several years were placed into the computer, which showed what climate patterns had looked like in the past.

The scientists added more atmospheric gases to the computer model. The gases were added in the amount in which they had been increasing. The computer showed the expected changes for the next 30 years.

What changes were predicted based on the increase in gases? These changes included warmer winters around the world, increased melting of glaciers and polar ice, a six-foot rise in sea level, some desert biomes becoming wetter, and rain forests becoming drier.

Not all scientists agree on the results of the computer model. Some say that the model has not included the effects of plants, clouds, soil moisture, and mountains on global weather. They also claim that it is too difficult to predict weather for more than a few weeks at a time. They agree that Earth is warming, but not as fast or as much as the model shows. Which group of scientists is correct? More work using the models to predict weather patterns may give us the answers.

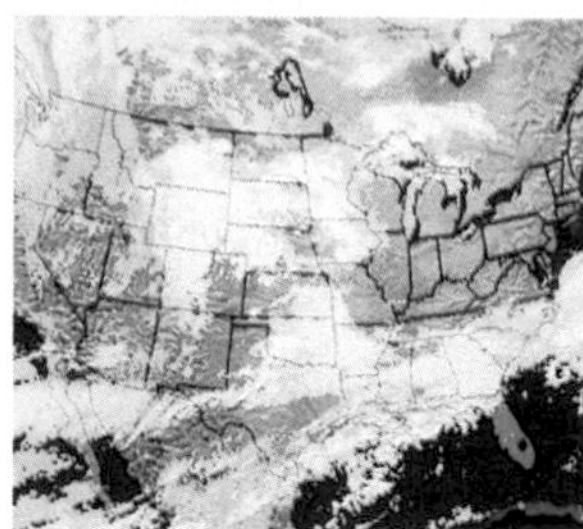

Scientists can use computers to model weather patterns.

Water Pollution

Why are pesticides a problem to the environment?

Water from streams and rivers supplies this country with about half of its drinking water. However, much of it contains toxic wastes. Our water also contains untreated sewage, and fertilizers and pesticides washed from farmlands. **Pesticides** are chemicals used to kill unwanted pests such as rodents or insects. When pesticides are washed off farmlands into rivers and streams, they pollute the water. Pesticides can cause damage to soil and wildlife. Because pesticides are so dangerous, many of them are no longer allowed to be used in this country.

TEACH

Guided Practice

Have students write down their answers to the margin question: They cause damage to soil and wildlife.

OPTIONS

How Pesticides Are Concentrated in a Food Chain/*Transparency Package*, number 32. Use color transparency number 32 as you teach pollution from chemicals.

The best known of all pesticides is DDT. DDT is a chemical spray used to kill insects. It has been shown to cause cancer. DDT also affects the shells of bird eggs. The shells of birds that have eaten DDT in their food are thin and break easily. These eggs don't hatch, so no offspring are produced. Because of DDT, some bird species have become endangered. DDT is so harmful that the Environmental Protection Agency (EPA) ruled in 1973 that DDT could no longer be used in the United States. However, it is still widely used in other countries.

A serious problem today is that other pesticides similar to DDT are still being used. Many of these chemicals are not biodegradable (bi oh duh GRAYD uh bul.) **Biodegradable** means that something can be broken down by microbes into harmless chemicals and used by other living things. Because many pesticides are not biodegradable, they remain in an ecosystem. DDT, other pesticides, and weed killers also move through food chains. This means that humans and other meat-eating animals can have very high amounts of these chemicals in their bodies.

We use chemicals to rid our crops of pests, to wash our clothes, and to manufacture the many products we use. Many dangerous wastes are left over when chemicals are made. The waste products from chemical manufacturing are often toxic. These wastes may cause pollution.

A big problem with toxic wastes is how to get rid of them. One solution has been to bury them at dump sites. We now know that buried chemical wastes can escape into the air, the surrounding soil, and nearby water. When these wastes escape into the water, the water is polluted. Therefore, burying wastes is not a good solution.

Skill Check

Understand science words: pesticide. The word part *pest* means something that annoys. In your dictionary, find three words with the word part *pest* in them. *For more help, refer to the **Skill Handbook**, pages 706-711.*

a

b

c

Figure 32-6 Toxic wastes are put into drums and buried in dump sites (a). Chemicals on the shelves of many homes are toxic (b). Pesticides are sprayed on crops (c).

TEACH

Concept Development

▶ Emphasize that pollutants on soil surfaces can percolate down and contaminate underground water. This water may be the water supply for many humans.

▶ Explain that many pesticides are applied as sprays. Those not broken down by microorganisms end up in food chains. Here, they block certain physiological processes in living things.

Independent Practice

Study Guide/*Teacher Resource Package*, p. 188. Use the Study Guide worksheet shown at the bottom of this page for independent practice.

STUDY GUIDE 188

STUDY GUIDE CHAPTER 32

Name ____________ Date ________ Class ________

PROBLEMS FROM POLLUTION

In your textbook, read about air and water pollution in Section 32:2.

1. Fill in the boxes of the pollution table below with the correct words or phrases: burning coal, oil, gasoline, and natural gas; PCBs; harmful gases; heavy metals; pesticides and weed killers; tiny particles; sulfur dioxide. Several are already done for you.

Pollution
- Water → toxic wastes, untreated sewage, fertilizer runoff → PCBs, heavy metals, pesticides and weed killers
- Air → burning coal, oil, gasoline, and natural gas → harmful gases, sulfur dioxide, tiny particles

2. How is smog produced? Smog is produced when harmful gases react with the energy in sunlight to produce new, irritating chemicals.

3. What is the greenhouse effect? The carbon dioxide formed by burning fossil fuels forms a layer around Earth and traps heat so it can't escape into the atmosphere. The trapped heat may eventually cause Earth's temperature to rise.

4. Why are chemicals such as PCBs and DDT so harmful to the environment? Because they are not biodegradable and cannot be excreted by animals, they accumulate in the environment and in the bodies of animals.

OPTIONS

Science Background

When DDT was developed over 40 years ago, it was called a "miracle" chemical because it killed disease-carrying and crop-destroying insects. Only a few scientists suspected that DDT could also be harmful to other living things. Not only did DDT enter the food chains, it also entered the water cycle. This particular pesticide sometimes becomes concentrated in food eaten by humans.

Lab 32-1 pH

Overview

Students will determine whether several household solutions are acidic, basic, or neutral. Students find the pH of the solutions by using the pH (number) scale and their data. They will compare the pH of solutions with that of samples of rain water.

Objectives: Students will be able to (1) **determine** the pH of several household chemicals and rainwater, (2) **demonstrate** the use of pH paper, (3) **classify** the solutions as acids or bases by using pH paper.

Time Allotment: 45 minutes

Preparation

▶ Have the known solution in dropper bottles, beakers, or flasks for easy dispensing. Prepare several sets. Place each kind of solution at a different spot in the room so the various solutions do not get mixed together.

▶ Cut the pH paper into 3-cm strips prior to class.

Lab 32-1 worksheet/*Teacher Resource Package*, pp. 125-126.

Teaching the Lab

▶ Have student teams put their data on a class chart on the chalkboard or a transparency so that they can compare their data with that of other teams.

▶ Freshly distilled water, free of carbon dioxide, has a pH of 7. If CO_2 is present, the water will have a slightly acidic pH.

▶ Acid rain will have a pH between 1 and 5.5

pH

Lab 32–1

Problem: How does the pH of rainwater compare with that of some household products?

Skills

observe, experiment, interpret data, classify

Materials

- pH paper
- pH chart
- forceps
- marking pencil
- 7 glass slides
- 7 droppers
- ammonia
- baking soda
- cola
- vinegar
- 2 samples of rainwater
- distilled water

Procedure

1. Copy the data table.
2. Label 5 glass slides 1 to 5.
3. Put a drop of liquid on each slide, as listed below. **CAUTION:** *If solutions are spilled on skin, rinse with water at once and notify your teacher.*
   Slide 1—baking soda Slide 4—cola
   Slide 2—distilled water Slide 5—ammonia
   Slide 3—vinegar
4. Pick up a piece of pH paper with the forceps.
5. Touch the pH paper to the liquid on slide 1 and remove the paper.
6. **Observe:** Compare the color of the wet end of the paper with the pH color chart.
7. Record the pH of the liquid on slide 1.
8. Discard the pH paper and rinse the forceps in tap water.
9. Test the liquids on slides 2 through 5 by repeating steps 4 through 8.
10. Put a drop of the first rainwater sample on a clean slide. Put a drop of the second rainwater sample on a second slide.
11. Test the pH of each sample of rainwater. Follow steps 4 through 8.
12. Record the pH of each sample.

SLIDE	CHECK CORRECT ANSWER			
	pH	ACID	NEUTRAL	BASE
1. Baking soda	8			√
2. Distilled water	7		√	
3. Vinegar	2.5–3.5	√		
4. Cola	6	√		
5. Ammonia	11			√
6. Rainwater	Answers	will vary.		
7. Rainwater	Answers	will vary.		

13. **Classify:** Finish filling in the data table by checking the correct column.

Data and Observations

1. Which of the materials tested was the strongest acid? How do you know?
2. Which of the materials tested was the strongest base? How do you know?

Analyze and Apply

1. Were your rainwater samples acidic or basic?
2. Why did you handle the pH paper with forceps?
3. What household product had a pH closest to your rainwater samples?
4. **Apply:** Why is acid rain a problem?

Extension

Experiment: Sample several bodies of water in your community and determine if the pH of the water is above or below 5.5.

ANSWERS

Data and Observations

1. Vinegar; the lower the pH, the stronger the acid.
2. Ammonia; it had the highest pH.

Analyze and Apply

1. Answers will vary, but the pH should be between 1 and 6.
2. so substances on the hands did not affect the pH paper
3. Answers will vary. Most students will answer either cola or vinegar.
4. It kills trees and other plants, destroys buildings, and makes lakes too acid to support life.

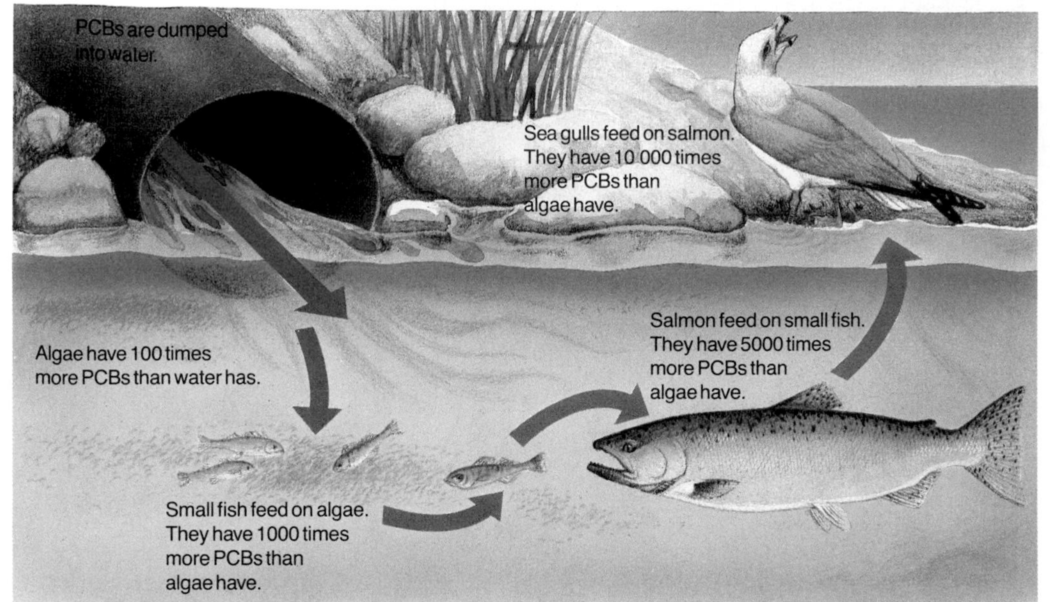

Figure 32-7 PCBs increase in the bodies of animals at every step of a food chain. Why does this happen?

One class of dangerous chemicals present in water is PCBs. PCBs are toxic wastes produced when paints and inks are made. PCBs cause many serious health problems in people. Many lakes polluted with PCBs have signs posted around them warning people not to eat fish taken from the lake. Fish have large amounts of PCBs in their bodies because of their place in the food chain. Figure 32-7 shows what happens to PCBs in a food chain. Animals can't excrete PCBs from their bodies. At every step up in a food chain, the amount of PCBs in each animal increases.

Other pollutants found in water are heavy metals such as lead and mercury. These metals come from factories that dump their wastes into rivers or lakes. These chemicals, too, can build up in fish and the animals that eat fish. Lead is also a problem in paint found in old houses. Sometimes small children eat this paint and get sick.

Acid Rain

A very serious problem related to pollution is acid rain. A substance can be an acid, a base, or neutral. Scientists have devised a scale called the pH scale to measure how strong an acid or a base is. The pH scale is numbered from 0 to 14. See Figure 32-8.

Figure 32-8 pH scale

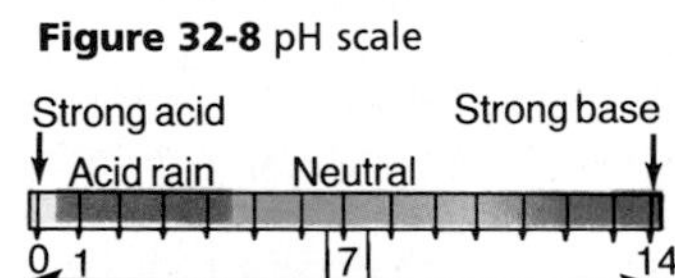

TEACH

Concept Development

▶ Explain that some aquatic animals develop tumors and ulcers when they are exposed to chemical pollutants in the water. When scientists find animals in this condition, they know that harmful chemicals are present.

▶ Explain to students that lead in the environment comes mostly from automobile exhaust, and mercury comes from industrial waste. These heavy metals enter food chains and become more concentrated as they move up the chain.

Guided Practice

Have students diagram an aquatic food chain using algae, water fleas, small fish, and humans to show how PCBs pass through food chains and cause problems for humans.

ENRICHMENT 34

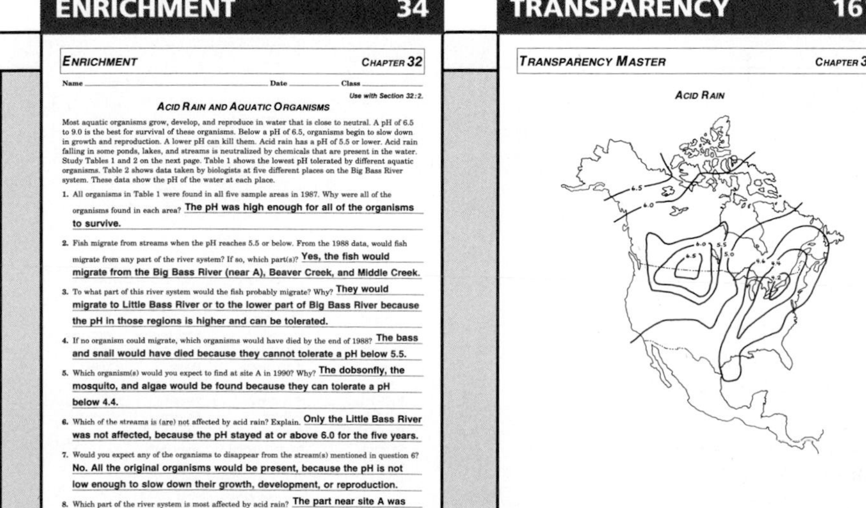

ENRICHMENT CHAPTER 32

Name ______ Date ______ Class ______

Use with Section 32:2.

ACID RAIN AND AQUATIC ORGANISMS

Most aquatic organisms grow, develop, and reproduce in water that is close to neutral. A pH of 6.5 to 9.0 is the best for survival of these organisms. Below a pH of 6.5, organisms begin to slow down in growth and reproduction. A lower pH can kill them. Acid rain has a pH of 5.5 or lower. Acid rain falling in some ponds, lakes, and streams is neutralized by chemicals that are present in the water. Study Tables 1 and 2 on the next page. Table 1 shows the lowest pH tolerated by different aquatic organisms. Table 2 shows data taken by biologists at five different places on the Big Bass River system. These data show the pH of the water at each place.

1. All organisms in Table 1 were found in all five sample areas in 1987. Why were all of the organisms found in each area? **The pH was high enough for all of the organisms to survive.**
2. Fish migrate from streams when the pH reaches 5.5 or below. From the 1988 data, would fish migrate from any part of the river system? If so, which part(s)? **Yes, the fish would migrate from the Big Bass River (near A), Beaver Creek, and Middle Creek.**
3. To what part of this river system would the fish probably migrate? Why? **They would migrate to Little Bass River or to the lower part of Big Bass River because the pH in those regions is higher and can be tolerated.**
4. If no organism could migrate, which organisms would have died by the end of 1988? **The bass and snail would have died because they cannot tolerate a pH below 5.5.**
5. Which organism(s) would you expect to find at site A in 1990? Why? **The dobsonfly, the mosquito, and algae would be found because they can tolerate a pH below 4.4.**
6. Which of the streams is (are) not affected by acid rain? Explain. **Only the Little Bass River was not affected, because the pH stayed at or above 6.0 for the five years.**
7. Would you expect any of the organisms to disappear from the stream(s) mentioned in question 6? **No. All the original organisms would be present, because the pH is not low enough to slow down their growth, development, or reproduction.**
8. Which part of the river system is most affected by acid rain? **The part near site A was most affected, because it showed the largest drop in pH over the five years.**

TRANSPARENCY 161

TRANSPARENCY MASTER CHAPTER 32

ACID RAIN

OPTIONS

Transparency Master/*Teacher Resource Package*, p. 161. Use the Transparency Master shown here to teach acid rain.

Enrichment/*Teacher Resource Package*, p. 34. Use the Enrichment worksheet shown here to teach how acid rain affects aquatic organisms.

TEACH

Concept Development

▶ Explain that acids in solution taste sour and release hydrogen gas when reacted with certain metals.

▶ Point out that normal rainfall is not pure water. The water in rain combines with carbon dioxide to form carbonic acid. Normal rain has a pH of 5.5 or above. Tell students that soda water is a weak solution of carbonic acid.

▶ You can show the relationship between acid rain and soil pollution by explaining that acidic soil can be harmful to many plants. Explain that plants cannot take in nutrients as well when the pH of the soil is low. Without nutrients, the plants will die. Point out that there are some plants, such as mosses and some conifers, that thrive in acid soil.

Independent Practice

Study Guide/*Teacher Resource Package*, p. 189. Use the Study Guide worksheet shown at the bottom of this page for independent practice.

Check for Understanding

Have students make a chart relating pollutants to the problems they cause. Tell them to use the following pollutants for their chart: carbon monoxide, sulfur dioxide, smog, particulates, heavy metals, and pesticides. Help students locate the sections of the text that explain these problems.

Reteach

Give a short matching quiz using the pollutants and problems from the chart in Check for Understanding.

Figure 32-9 Acid rain damages buildings (a) as well as forests (b). What gas causes acid rain? sulfur dioxide

a

Acids, such as vinegar and lemon juice, are liquids that have pH values lower than 7. The stronger an acid is, the lower its pH. Pure water is neutral, neither acid nor base, and has a pH of 7. **Bases,** such as ammonia and lye, are liquids that have pH values greater than 7. The stronger a base is, the higher its pH. The pH of rain is normally above 5.5, or almost neutral. **Acid rain** is rain that has a pH between 1 and 5.5.

b

How is it possible for rain (or fog or snow) to be acid? Acids form in the air when gases such as sulfur dioxide react with sunlight and water. Remember that these gases are formed by burning fossil fuels. As acid rain falls onto Earth, it damages forests, crops, soil, and buildings. See Figure 32-9. Acid rain has turned lakes and ponds into bodies of water with a pH value below 4.5. It has been estimated that 15 percent of all Minnesota lakes are now too acid for most living things. Over 200 lakes in New York State are dead due to acid rain. Nothing can live in them.

Acid rain seems to be worse for the east coast of the United States and Canada. Much of the countries' industry is in the east. Winds also carry acid rain from the western and central parts of these countries toward the east.

Bio Tip

Ecology: Each person in the United States produces 3.5 pounds of garbage each day. Eighty percent of this garbage can be recycled by using modern technology.

Land Pollution

We live in a plastic and chemical age. Think about all the items we use each day that are made of plastic. You probably have heard that plastic is not biodegradable . Plastics can't be broken down.

OPTIONS

How Do Chemical Pollutants Affect Living Things?/*Lab Manual*, pp. 271-274. Use this lab as an extension to studying pollution from chemicals.

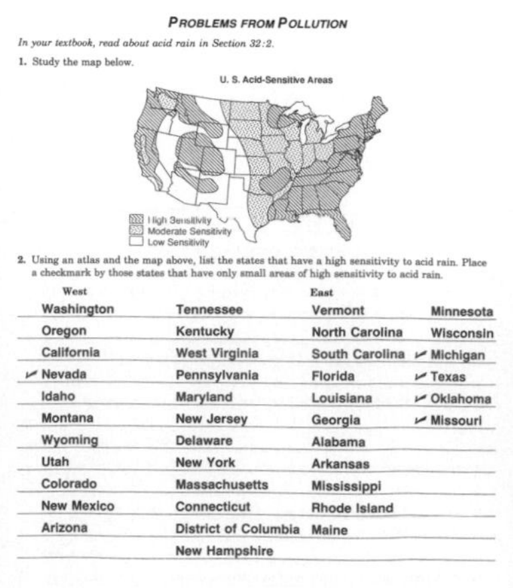

STUDY GUIDE 189

STUDY GUIDE — CHAPTER 32

Name ______ Date ______ Class ______

PROBLEMS FROM POLLUTION

In your textbook, read about acid rain in Section 32:2.

1. Study the map below.

2. Using an atlas and the map above, list the states that have a high sensitivity to acid rain. Place a checkmark by those states that have only small areas of high sensitivity to acid rain.

West		East	
Washington	Tennessee	Vermont	Minnesota
Oregon	Kentucky	North Carolina	Wisconsin
California	West Virginia	South Carolina	✓ Michigan
✓ Nevada	Pennsylvania	Florida	✓ Texas
Idaho	Maryland	Louisiana	✓ Oklahoma
Montana	New Jersey	Georgia	✓ Missouri
Wyoming	Delaware	Alabama	
Utah	New York	Arkansas	
Colorado	Massachusetts	Mississippi	
New Mexico	Connecticut	Rhode Island	
Arizona	District of Columbia	Maine	
	New Hampshire		

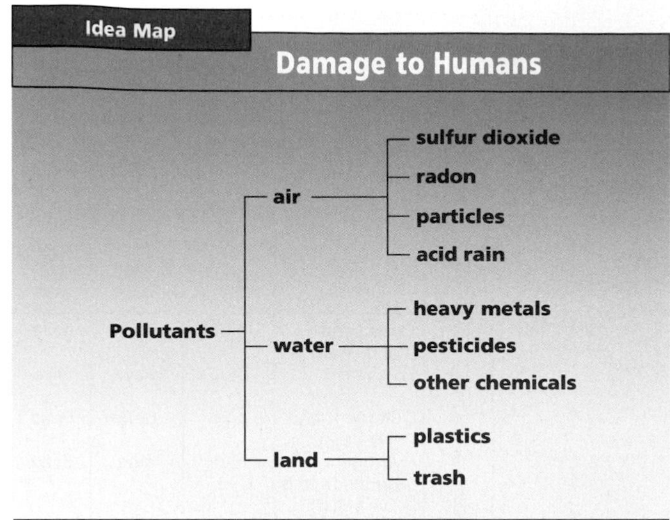

Study Tip: Use this idea map as a study guide to pollutants. Can you think of any other pollutants?

Suppose you set a bag filled with bits of food, paper scraps, and plastic jugs and bottles on the curb. The trash collectors forget to come to your house. In a few days, the bits of food begin to rot. The plastic containers, however, remain unchanged. After several weeks, the food and paper have rotted away. The plastic is still there. In fact, if you were to move away and then return in a few years, the plastic would still be unchanged. Think of all the plastic items people throw away each day. None of them are biodegradable. Dumps and landfills are becoming filled with these items. We are running out of places to put them.

Check Your Understanding

6. What is a major source of air pollution?
7. In what parts of the food chain do pesticides build up?
8. What problems arise from the use of plastics?
9. **Critical Thinking:** Bald eagles almost became extinct because DDT prevented their eggs from hatching. The eagles got the DDT from the fish they ate. How did the fish get the DDT?
10. **Biology and Writing:** In this section, you learned about damage to humans from air, water, and land pollution. Tell about another kind of pollution that damages humans.

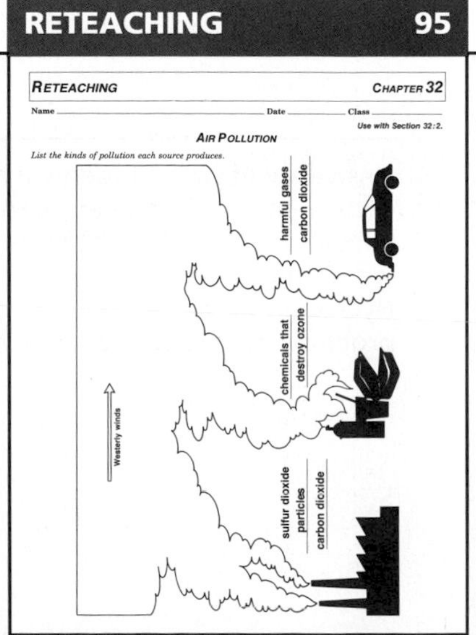
RETEACHING 95

Reteaching — Chapter 32

Name ______ Date ______ Class ______

Use with Section 32:2.

Air Pollution

List the kinds of pollution each source produces.

STUDY GUIDE 190

Study Guide — Chapter 32

Name ______ Date ______ Class ______

Problems from Pollution

3. What are two reasons that the eastern part of the United States has a greater acid rain problem than other parts?
   a. Winds carry acid rain from the western and central parts of the United States toward the east.
   b. Most of the industry in the United States is located in the east.
4. What does the pH scale measure? The pH scale measures how strong an acid or base a substance is.
5. What are some examples of acids? vinegar, lemon juice
6. What are some examples of bases? ammonia, lye
7. What pH do acids have? Acids have pH values lower than 7.
8. What pH do bases have? Bases have pH values higher than 7.
9. What is the pH of pure water? The pH of pure water is 7.
10. What is the pH of normal rain? The pH of normal rain is above 5.5.
11. What is the pH of acid rain? The pH of acid rain is between 1 and 5.5.
12. How is acid rain formed? Harmful gases such as sulfur dioxide react with sunlight and water to form acid rain.
13. List three results of acid rain in the United States.
   a. It has been estimated that 15% of all Minnesota lakes are now too acid for life.
   b. Over 200 lakes in the state of New York are "dead".
   c. Some lakes and ponds have a pH value below 4.5.
14. What things other than lakes does acid rain damage? Acid rain damages forests, crops, soil, and buildings.
15. Why must countries work together to solve the acid rain problem? The gases that cause acid rain are carried by the wind from one area to another.

TEACH

Idea Map

Have students use the idea map as a study guide to the major concepts of this section.

Independent Practice

Study Guide/*Teacher Resource Package*, p. 190. Use the Study Guide worksheet shown at the bottom of this page for independent practice.

Check for Understanding

Have students respond to the first three questions in Check your Understanding.

Reteach

Reteaching/*Teacher Resource Package*, p. 95. Use this worksheet to give students additional practice with how pollution causes damage.

Extension: Assign Critical Thinking, Biology and Writing, or some of the **OPTIONS** available with this lesson.

3 APPLY

Divergent Question

Ask students which pollutants can be found in the rivers and streams where they live.

4 CLOSE

Audiovisual

Show the video *Acid Rain: No Simple Solution*, Insight Media.

Answers to Check Your Understanding

6. burning of fossil fuels
7. secondary consumers
8. They don't break down, so they fill up landfills.
9. They ate smaller fish or protists that were contaminated with DDT that washed off fields.
10. Answers may include noise pollution, pollution of food sources from pesticides, and so on.

Lab 32-2 Pollution

Overview

Students will find out how certain pollutants affect yeast cells.

Objectives: Students will be able to (1) **describe** how some pollutants affect yeast cells, (2) **test** for the presence of carbon dioxide as a by-product of respiration, (3) **separate and control** variables in an experiment.

Time Allotment: 45 minutes on the first day, and 10-15 minutes on the next day

Preparation

▶ For bromthymol blue, add 0.1 g bromthymol blue powder to 2 L of distilled water.

▶ For live yeast mixture, add 1 tablespoon each of dry yeast and sugar to 200 mL of water.

▶ For dead yeast mixture, boil 100 mL of live yeast mixture for at least 5 minutes on a hot plate.

Lab 32-2 worksheet/*Teacher Resource Package*, pp. 127-128.

Teaching the Lab

▶ Students will notice that detergent and hydrogen peroxide will kill yeast cells. Evidence that yeast cells are alive is the color change from blue to green in tube 2. This is caused by the release of carbon dioxide gas by yeast cells.

Pollution

Lab 32–2

Problem: What is the effect of pollutants on yeast?

Skills

observe, form hypotheses, interpret data, design an experiment

Materials

4 test tubes
marking pencil
test-tube rack
5 droppers
blue test liquid
dead yeast mixture
live yeast mixture
detergent
hydrogen peroxide
water

Procedure

Yeast cells are living organisms. In this lab, they will be treated with different pollutants to see if they are killed.

1. Copy the data table.
2. Number four test tubes 1 to 4.
3. Add the following to each tube: Tube 1—10 drops of dead yeast mixture and 10 drops of water; Tube 2—10 drops of live yeast mixture and 10 drops of water; Tube 3—10 drops of detergent and 10 drops of live yeast mixture; Tube 4—10 drops of hydrogen peroxide and 10 drops of live yeast mixture.
4. Fill all tubes almost full with blue test liquid.
5. **Observe:** Record the color in each tube. This is day 1.
6. Write a **hypothesis** to state whether the yeast will be killed by detergent or hydrogen peroxide.
7. Leave the tubes in the rack overnight.
8. Record the color in each tube on day 2.
9. Dispose of your materials as directed by your teacher.

TUBE	CONTENTS	COLOR IN TUBE DAY 1	COLOR IN TUBE DAY 2	YEAST ALIVE OR DEAD
1	Dead yeast and water	blue	blue	dead
2	Live yeast and water	blue	green	alive
3	Detergent and live yeast	blue	blue	dead
4	Hydrogen peroxide and live yeast	blue	blue	dead

Data and Observations

1. What color was each tube on day 1?
2. What color was each tube on day 2?

Analyze and Apply

If the tube contents change from blue to green overnight, the yeast cells are alive. If the tube contents stay blue, the yeast cells are dead. Complete the last column of the data table, then answer the questions.

1. Which tubes contained live organisms the first day? Which tubes contained live organisms the second day?
2. **Interpret data:** The blue liquid changes to green if carbon dioxide gas is present. How is this gas related to living things?
3. What was the purpose of tubes 1 and 2?
4. **Check your hypothesis:** Did your data support your hypothesis? Why or why not?
5. **Apply:** From this lab, what would you say might be the effect of hydrogen peroxide and detergent on some other living things?

Extension

Design an experiment to test the effect of an acid and a base on yeast.

ANSWERS

Data and Observations

1. All tubes were blue on day 1.
2. Tube 2 was green. Tubes 1, 3, and 4 were blue.

Analyze and Apply

1. tubes 2, 3, 4; tube 2
2. All living things give off carbon dioxide during respiration.
3. as controls to see if dead yeast would change the color of the test liquid and to see what changes live yeast would make
4. Answers will vary. Students who said that detergent and hydrogen peroxide would kill yeast will report that their hypotheses were supported.
5. Hydrogen peroxide and detergent would probably harm or kill other living things.

32:3 Working Toward Solutions

Our environment is in trouble. It is being damaged by pollutants in the air, soil, and water. We are using up our resources and making more and more wastes as our population increases. Many resources can't be replaced.

Look at the area where you live. You probably can find examples of water, land, and air pollution. What can be done to solve pollution problems before they begin to limit population growth? How can we use resources wisely?

Objectives

6. **Explain** methods of conserving resources.
7. **Discuss** ways to keep the environment clean.

Key Science Words

recycling

Conserving Our Resources

There are several solutions to the problem of endangered plants and animals. One depends on the United States government. Another is up to you as an active, caring individual.

Today, the government has set aside 428 areas called National Wildlife Refuges. A refuge is an area that protects or shelters living things from being harmed by humans.

In 1973, the United States Congress passed the Endangered Species Act. This law states that anyone found guilty of killing, capturing, or removing any endangered species from its environment can be fined up to $20 000 and jailed for one year. The law also protects the habitat of any endangered species. In order for government refuges and laws to work, everyone must cooperate. This means that everyone must obey the law and make every effort not to reduce our wildlife populations.

What is the Endangered Species Act?

Erosion of soil can be slowed by planting crops across the slope of the land, rather than up and down, as shown in Figure 32-10. Strips of grass can be planted between fields to hold the soil. Rows of trees can be planted as windbreaks so the wind doesn't blow away dry soil.

Figure 32-10 Erosion of soil can be slowed by planting crops across a slope.

Water can be reused if wastes and harmful chemicals are first removed. Conserving water would also guard the supply of this precious resource. Each time an average-size lawn is watered, up to 2000 gallons of water is used. That's enough water to fill your bathtub 40 times! Now, imagine thousands of people watering their lawns daily. You can see that a lot of water is used on lawns.

Do you allow the water to run as you brush your teeth? If you do, you are sending about five gallons of water down the drain each time you brush. Turning off the tap is a simple solution to this problem.

OPTIONS

Science Background

No new water is being made on Earth today. All of the water used by living things is recycled through the water cycle.

32:3 Working Toward Solutions

PREPARATION

Materials Needed

Make copies of the Study Guide, Reteaching, and Lab worksheets in the *Teacher Resource Package*.

▶ Prepare bromthymol blue solution for Lab 32-2. Prepare live and dead yeast mixtures on the day of the Lab.

▶ Have students bring in magazine or newspaper articles on solutions to pollution problems for the Focus activity.

Key Science Words

recycling

Process Skills

In Lab 32-2, students will observe, form hypotheses, interpret data, and design an experiment.

1 FOCUS

▶ The objectives are listed on the student page. Remind students to preview these objectives as a guide to this numbered section.

Cooperative Learning: Have teams of students bring in newspaper or magazine articles that deal with solutions to pollution problems. Have each team choose one article, tell what pollutant is being discussed, and explain the proposed solution to the problem. When all teams have reported, close with a discussion about the cost of solving these problems.

Guided Practice

Have students write down their answers to the margin question: a law that makes it a crime to kill endangered species.

2 TEACH

MOTIVATION/Brainstorming

Ask students to name things that can be recycled.

Concept Development

▶ Point out that more and more pesticides are being replaced by animals, plants, protists, monerans, or fungi that serve as parasites or predators on unwanted organisms.

▶ Explain that it costs money to recycle materials, but if materials are not recycled, raw materials may not be available in the future.

▶ Explain that each citizen in a community is responsible for keeping the environment clean.

Guided Practice

Have students write down their answers to the margin question: to remove sulfur dioxide and particles from smoke.

Connection: Social Studies

Have students find out what local and state laws govern pollution. Have them also find out what state and local agencies are responsible for enforcement and how rigidly the laws are being enforced.

Independent Practice

Study Guide/*Teacher Resource Package*, p. 191. Use the Study Guide worksheet shown at the bottom of this page for independent practice.

Keeping Our Environment Clean

Why do some power plants use scrubbers?

How can we clean up our environment and keep it clean? Many steps have been taken to improve our air and water. New power plants that use coal must have scrubbers in their smokestacks. The scrubbers help to remove sulfur dioxide and particles from the smoke before it is released into the air. More improvements in air quality could be made if cleaner sources of energy were used. Solar and nuclear energy can be used to make electricity, instead of using coal or oil.

How has water quality improved? Several large bodies of water in the United States have been cleaned up in the last 20 years. Parts of Lake Erie were once so polluted with chemicals that people could not eat Lake Erie fish. Today people can swim and fish in Lake Erie again.

Wise use of technology also can help solve the pollution problem. Scientists have found that insect pests can be destroyed by their natural enemies. Aphids are tiny insects that suck the juices from plants. The ladybird beetle is a natural predator of aphids. Ladybird beetles can be released in an area where there are aphids. The aphids will be destroyed in a natural way without the use of pesticides.

Bacteria and viruses also can destroy some kinds of insects without hurting other living things. For example, bacteria can be used to control gypsy moths. The gypsy moth caterpillar has destroyed many oak forests. A bacterium found in the soil is able to kill this caterpillar. Biologists grow this type of bacterium in large tanks. The bacteria are then sprayed on tree leaves. The gypsy moth caterpillars die several hours after eating leaves with bacteria on them. Biologists are discovering ways to solve problems in our environment without creating new ones.

Figure 32-11 Soil bacteria can interrupt the life cycle of the gypsy moth (a). A ladybird beetle eats aphids (b).

a

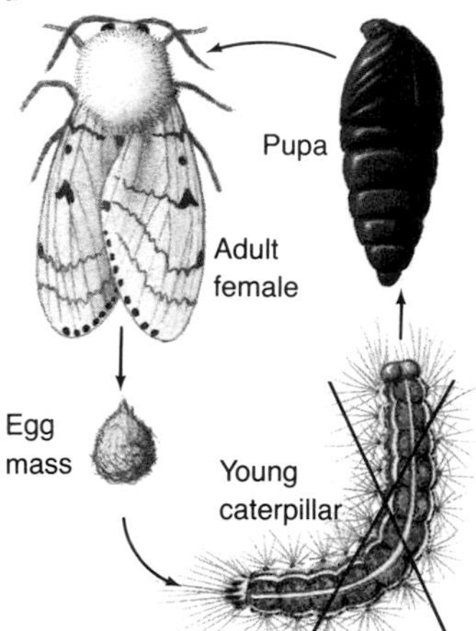

b

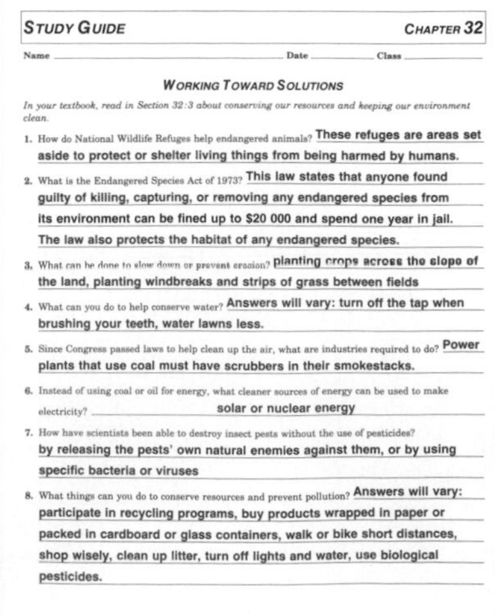

STUDY GUIDE 191

STUDY GUIDE CHAPTER 32

Name ______ Date ______ Class ______

WORKING TOWARD SOLUTIONS

In your textbook, read in Section 32:3 about conserving our resources and keeping our environment clean.

1. How do National Wildlife Refuges help endangered animals? **These refuges are areas set aside to protect or shelter living things from being harmed by humans.**
2. What is the Endangered Species Act of 1973? **This law states that anyone found guilty of killing, capturing, or removing any endangered species from its environment can be fined up to $20 000 and spend one year in jail. The law also protects the habitat of any endangered species.**
3. What can be done to slow down or prevent erosion? **planting crops across the slope of the land, planting windbreaks and strips of grass between fields**
4. What can you do to help conserve water? **Answers will vary: turn off the tap when brushing your teeth, water lawns less.**
5. Since Congress passed laws to help clean up the air, what are industries required to do? **Power plants that use coal must have scrubbers in their smokestacks.**
6. Instead of using coal or oil for energy, what cleaner sources of energy can be used to make electricity? **solar or nuclear energy**
7. How have scientists been able to destroy insect pests without the use of pesticides? **by releasing the pests' own natural enemies against them, or by using specific bacteria or viruses**
8. What things can you do to conserve resources and prevent pollution? **Answers will vary: participate in recycling programs, buy products wrapped in paper or packed in cardboard or glass containers, walk or bike short distances, shop wisely, clean up litter, turn off lights and water, use biological pesticides.**

a

b

Figure 32-12 Recycling (a) can reduce the amount of trash that goes into landfills. Over-packaged products (b) cause landfills to fill up. Why? The packaging is not biodegradable.

There are many things that people can do to help prevent pollution. **Recycling** is the reusing of resources. There are recycling centers for glass, plastic, and aluminum. Used paper and cardboard can be made into new paper. Over 500 000 trees could be saved every week if everyone recycled just the Sunday newspapers.

Being a wise consumer can also help. You can buy products wrapped in paper or packed in cardboard or glass. You can avoid buying individually wrapped items such as cheese slices. Every item that is packed in something other than plastic will help to reduce landfills.

How can you help reduce pollution? You can walk or bike short distances instead of driving, shop wisely and carefully for items that won't pollute the environment, recycle, clean up litter, turn off lights and water, and use natural pesticides. The answers to pollution problems are neither easy nor inexpensive. To have a good quality of life, everyone must work to keep the environment clean.

Bio Tip

Ecology: Using one metric ton of recycled paper for printing is equal to cutting down 17 trees to make into paper pulp.

Check Your Understanding

11. List one way to conserve each of the following: animals, water, trees.
12. How have laws helped in cleaning up our environment?
13. How can gypsy moths be controlled naturally?
14. **Critical Thinking:** How can producing more fuel-efficient cars help reduce air pollution?
15. **Biology and Reading:** What are at least two steps that have been taken to keep the air clean?

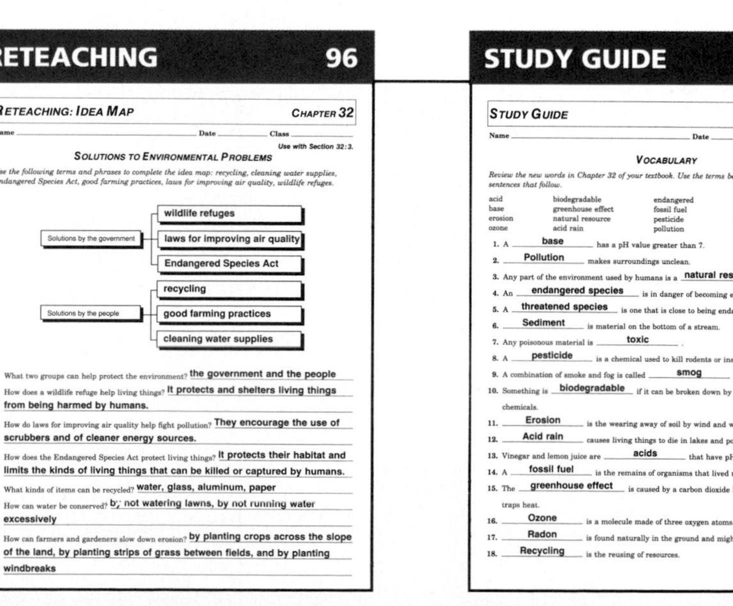

RETEACHING 96

RETEACHING: IDEA MAP — CHAPTER 32

Name ______ Date ______ Class ______

Use with Section 32:3.

SOLUTIONS TO ENVIRONMENTAL PROBLEMS

Use the following terms and phrases to complete the idea map: recycling, cleaning water supplies, Endangered Species Act, good farming practices, laws for improving air quality, wildlife refuges.

Solutions by the government
- wildlife refuges
- laws for improving air quality
- Endangered Species Act

Solutions by the people
- recycling
- good farming practices
- cleaning water supplies

1. What two groups can help protect the environment? the government and the people
2. How does a wildlife refuge help living things? It protects and shelters living things from being harmed by humans.
3. How do laws for improving air quality help fight pollution? They encourage the use of scrubbers and of cleaner energy sources.
4. How does the Endangered Species Act protect living things? It protects their habitat and limits the kinds of living things that can be killed or captured by humans.
5. What kinds of items can be recycled? water, glass, aluminum, paper
6. How can water be conserved? by not watering lawns, by not running water excessively
7. How can farmers and gardeners slow down erosion? by planting crops across the slope of the land, by planting strips of grass between fields, and by planting windbreaks

STUDY GUIDE 192

STUDY GUIDE — CHAPTER 32

Name ______ Date ______ Class ______

VOCABULARY

Review the new words in Chapter 32 of your textbook. Use the terms below to fill in the blanks of the sentences that follow.

acid	biodegradable	endangered	radon	smog
base	greenhouse effect	fossil fuel	recycling	threatened
erosion	natural resource	pesticide	sediment	toxic
ozone	acid rain	pollution		

1. A base has a pH value greater than 7.
2. Pollution makes surroundings unclean.
3. Any part of the environment used by humans is a natural resource
4. An endangered species is in danger of becoming extinct.
5. A threatened species is one that is close to being endangered.
6. Sediment is material on the bottom of a stream.
7. Any poisonous material is toxic .
8. A pesticide is a chemical used to kill rodents or insects.
9. A combination of smoke and fog is called smog .
10. Something is biodegradable if it can be broken down by microbes into harmless chemicals.
11. Erosion is the wearing away of soil by wind and water.
12. Acid rain causes living things to die in lakes and ponds.
13. Vinegar and lemon juice are acids that have pH values lower than 7.
14. A fossil fuel is the remains of organisms that lived millions of years ago.
15. The greenhouse effect is caused by a carbon dioxide layer around Earth that traps heat.
16. Ozone is a molecule made of three oxygen atoms.
17. Radon is found naturally in the ground and might cause cancer.
18. Recycling is the reusing of resources.

TEACH

Independent Practice

Study Guide/*Teacher Resource Package*, p. 192. Use the Study Guide worksheet shown at the bottom of this page for independent practice.

Check for Understanding

Have students respond to the first three questions in Check Your Understanding.

Reteach

Reteaching/*Teacher Resource Package*, p. 96. Use this worksheet to give students additional practice with solutions to environmental problems.

Extension: Assign Critical Thinking, Biology and Reading, or some of the **OPTIONS** available with this lesson.

3 APPLY

Cooperative Learning: Set up student teams to research how garbage, sewage, and litter are handled in your area.

4 CLOSE

Summary

Have students explain how they can help improve the environment.

Answers to Check Your Understanding

11. animals–don't wear reptile shoes, bags, or belts; water–turn off water when brushing teeth; trees–recycle paper
12. New power plants must have scrubbers.
13. by spraying trees with bacteria that kill gypsy moths
14. More efficient cars use less gasoline, so less poisonous gas and carbon dioxide are produced.
15. New power plants must have scrubbers; alternate energy sources, such as solar energy, are being explored.

CHAPTER 32 REVIEW

Summary

Summary statements can be used by students to review the major concepts of the chapter.

Key Science Words

All boldfaced terms from the chapter are listed.

Testing Yourself

Using Words

1. acid
2. toxic
3. sediment
4. erosion
5. threatened
6. pesticide
7. radon
8. smog
9. biodegradable
10. greenhouse effect

Finding Main Ideas

11. p. 677; The pond goes through succession faster than normal.
12. p. 681; They can escape into the air, soil, and nearby water.
13. p. 687; It protects endangered species and their habitats.
14. p. 677; The remains of organisms were compressed under tremendous pressure for long periods of time.
15. p. 679; Certain chemicals found in spray cans, refrigerators, and air conditioners destroy ozone.
16. p. 684; Acid rain forms when certain gases react with sunlight and water.
17. p. 676; It dries out, and wind easily separates small soil particles and blows them around.
18. p. 674; Plants and animals can be replaced within a person's lifetime.
19. p. 687; Water can be conserved by not watering lawns and by turning off water while brushing teeth.

Using Main Ideas

20. People have destroyed the habitats of other living things, hunted illegally, and used animal parts for jewelry, shoes, and purses.

Chapter 32

Review

Summary

32:1 Resources and Human Activities

1. Wildlife and plants are natural, renewable resources. They become endangered when they die faster than they can renew themselves.
2. Soil erosion occurs when soil is carried away by wind and water faster than it can be replaced. Water is a valuable resource. Pollution can cause ponds and lakes to go through a rapid aging process.
3. Fossil fuels are a nonrenewable source of energy. They are rapidly being used up.

32:2 Problems from Pollution

4. Air pollution is caused by burning fossil fuels in large amounts.
5. Heavy metals and pesticides can pollute water and build up in fish and other animals. Plastics and other materials that are not biodegradable fill up landfills and pollute Earth's surface.

32:3 Working Toward Solutions

6. Resources can be conserved by effective laws and by each person using resources wisely and carefully.
7. Keeping the environment clean depends on industry, government enforcement of laws, the development of clean energy sources, and the actions of all people.

Key Science Words

acid (p. 684)
acid rain (p. 684)
base (p. 684)
biodegradable (p. 681)
endangered (p. 675)
erosion (p. 676)
fossil fuel (p. 677)
greenhouse effect (p. 679)
natural resource (p. 674)
ozone (p. 679)
pesticide (p. 680)
pollution (p. 677)
radon (p. 679)
recycling (p. 689)
sediment (p. 676)
smog (p. 678)
threatened (p. 675)
toxic (p. 678)

Testing Yourself

Using Words

Choose the word from the list of Key Science Words that best fits the definition.

1. has a pH value less than 7
2. poisonous or harmful
3. particles deposited in a stream
4. wearing away of soil
5. close to being endangered
6. a chemical that kills unwanted organisms
7. a gas that gives off radiation
8. a combination of smoke and fog
9. ability of a chemical to be broken down by microbes
10. process that causes heat to be trapped near Earth's surface

Review

Testing Yourself *continued*

Finding Main Ideas

List the page number where each main idea below is found. Then, explain each main idea.

11. what happens to a pond when extra nutrients are washed into it
12. what can happen to toxic waste buried in dump sites
13. what the purpose of the Endangered Species Act is
14. how fossil fuels are formed
15. why the ozone layer is being destroyed
16. how acid rain is formed
17. why bare soil is easily moved about by the wind
18. why plants and animals are renewable resources
19. how water can be conserved

Using Main Ideas

Answer the questions by referring to the page number after each question.

20. What are two ways that people make living things endangered or threatened? (p. 675)
21. What are two energy sources that are cleaner than fossil fuels and are renewable? (p. 688)
22. What is radon? (p. 679)
23. What effects does DDT have on living things? (p. 681)
24. How can bacteria be used to control plant pests naturally? (p. 688)
25. Where does sulfur dioxide in the air come from? (p. 679)
26. How do pollutants get into our water supply? (p. 680)
27. Why do you suppose water at a water treatment plant is checked for mercury and lead? (p. 683)

Skill Review ✓

For more help, refer to the ***Skill Handbook****, pages 704-719.*

1. **Outline:** Make an outline of the different kinds of pollution discussed in this chapter.
2. **Calculate:** Assume there are 4800 species of animals in your state. Pollution is causing 30 species to die each week. Calculate how many years it will be before all animals are gone.
3. **Classify:** Classify the following items as to whether each is biodegradable: banana peel, plastic bottle, newspaper, DDT, plastic foam container, sandwich.
4. **Design an experiment:** Design an experiment to show whether newspapers are biodegradable.

Finding Out More

Critical Thinking

1. Marigolds produce chemicals that drive away insect pests. How could you use this knowledge to protect your garden?
2. Some people think that zoos and refuges are a waste of time and money. Give reasons for and against this statement.

Applications

1. Tape cardboard coated with a thin layer of vaseline to various locations in your community. After a few days, remove the cards and examine the particles trapped in the vaseline. Try to find out where they came from.
2. Write a report describing why Love Canal in New York State caused problems in the environment.

Using Main Ideas

21. Solar and nuclear energy can be used.
22. Radon is a natural gas that gives off radiation.
23. It can cause cancer and prevent offspring from being produced.
24. It can be used to destroy some insects without harming other living things.
25. Sulfur from burning coal combines with oxygen in the air to form sulfur dioxide.
26. Pesticides and fertilizers can wash off farmland into streams and rivers.
27. Mercury and lead are pollutants that can build up in animals.

Skill Review

1. Students will find the second section of the chapter helpful in making their outlines.
2. It will take a little over three years.
3. Banana peel, newspaper, and sandwich are biodegradable. Plastic bottle, DDT, and plastic foam are not.
4. Students should suggest using water, sunlight, and moving air.

Finding Out More

Critical Thinking

1. You can plant marigolds around the edge.
2. An argument for would be the protection of species; an argument against would be the large amount of land used.

Applications

1. Students may choose the front and back doors of a house or apartment, a wall of the school, or perhaps a room in their home.
2. Toxic materials were dumped into the canal. After a period of time, it was noticed that certain cancers appeared in the residents at a higher rate than average. Subsequently, the residents were evacuated and their homes boarded up.

 **Chapter Review**/*Teacher Resource Package*, pp. 170-171.

 **Chapter Test**/*Teacher Resource Package*, pp. 172-174.

Chapter Test/*Computer Test Bank*

 **Unit Test**/*Teacher Resource Package*, pp. 175-176.

Unit 8 Relationships in the Environment

CONNECTIONS

Biology in Your World

Human behavior is interconnected with and makes an impact on all other organisms. Students must make decisions about their own behavior and decide what is most practical for themselves and the rest of the world.

Literature Connection

Rachel Carson (1907-1964) was a marine biologist and author who worked for the U.S. Fish and Wildlife Service. Her controversial book, *Silent Spring,* sparked debate over the impact of pesticides on the environment.

Carson emphasized that all life is interrelated and that the extermination of one organism has repercussions on other organisms. For example, bald eagles came close to extinction because of loss of habitat and DDT. They ate fish containing DDT residues, which caused the birds to lay eggs with fragile shells. Since the restriction of DDT, successful breeding programs have increased the bald eagle population.

History Connection

In May 1990, the Environmental Protection Agency declared Love Canal safe. The government spent twelve years and $250 million to contain 22 000 tons of toxic waste and seal the site. The homes closest to the dump were destroyed.

In August 1990, the remaining 236 homes went up for sale. Resettlement officials attracted many prospective buyers with low prices and studies showing the area to be habitable. Environmental groups and some former residents disagree with the government about the safety of the area.

C O N N E C T I O N S

Biology in Your World

Disrupting a Delicate Balance

As you have seen in this unit, relationships are important in a community. If the survival of a single species is threatened, it may result in a chain reaction. We live in a rather fragile environment. Even well-meaning interference can be disastrous.

LITERATURE

Environmental Awakening

In 1962, biologist Rachel Carson wrote about the dangers of spraying with pesticides in her book, *Silent Spring.* She pointed out that robins died after eating earthworms that had picked up DDT residues. DDT had been sprayed on the leaves of elm trees. It was used to kill the beetles carrying the fungus that caused Dutch Elm disease. Carson also warned that pesticides could contaminate human food supplies.

Because of Carson's book, the use of certain pesticides was restricted in the United States.

HISTORY

A Ticking Time Bomb

In the 1920s, Love Canal was a partly-dug canal in the city of Niagara Falls, New York. It became a disposal site for household trash. Nearby chemical plants also dumped wastes in it. When the site was covered in 1958, about 20 000 metric tons of waste had been buried. A school was built on one edge of the canal. Homes were built on the other side. After very heavy rains in the mid 1970s, chemicals seeped out of the canal. These chemicals have been known to cause cancer, birth defects, miscarriages, and liver damage. Dangerous levels of these chemicals were found in the basements of many homes. In 1978-79, families were told to move from their homes. The soil had been damaged too much to be fixed.

LEISURE

Making Your Own Paper

Recycle old newspapers yourself. First, tear the paper into small pieces. Put the pieces into a blender with five cups of water. Blend until you get a watery pulp. Put a piece of window screen into a dishpan with about three centimeters of water. Pour one cup of the paper pulp over the screen and spread it evenly with your fingers. Lift the screen and drain. Put the screen and pulp between several sheets of newspaper, and press with a board to squeeze out the extra water. Remove the pulp from the screen and leave it on dry newspaper overnight. When the pulp is dry, carefully peel off your handmade paper.

CONSUMER

Stop the Throw-away Lifestyle

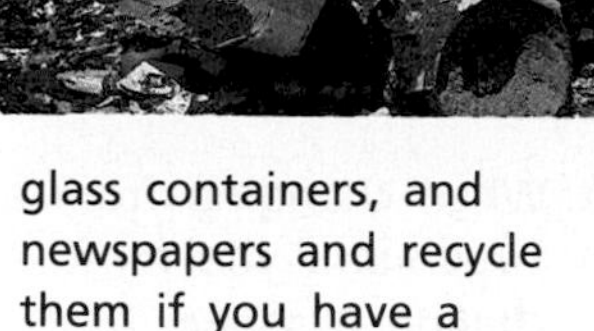

Landfills are overflowing. Some resources are being used up. What can you do to help? Instead of creating more waste, you can make some smart choices as a consumer.

Try not to buy products that are packaged in single-serving sizes or in unnecessary plastic. Whenever you can, buy things in large containers or in bulk. If possible, take your own containers and bags with you when you shop.

Set up a system that encourages recycling. Separate aluminum cans, glass containers, and newspapers and recycle them if you have a recycling center near you.

When you buy a new sweater to replace one that does not fit anymore, do not put the old one in the trash. Give it to someone who can use it or add it to the rag bag.

Substitute paper for plastic whenever you can. The plastic rings connecting a six-pack of canned soft drinks take a long time to decay in a landfill. Also, birds can get caught in the plastic rings and be strangled. Some types of plastic give off toxic fumes when they are burned.

Do Earth a favor. Think of the long-term effects before you buy something.

CONNECTIONS

Leisure Connection

Students may be interested in products made from or packaged in recycled paper. If the back of cardboard packaging is gray, it was made from recycled paper. For more information on recycled paper products, write to Seventh Generation at 10 Farrell St., South Burlington, VT 05403.

Consumer Connection

In order to cut down on waste, students may need to make decisions about what not to buy. Landfills are brimming with bags of grass clippings and leaves. Organic matter in plastic bags doesn't break down quickly. Grass clippings can be left on the lawn or composted with leaves and kitchen scraps. These alternatives don't require purchasing plastic bags.

References

Brown, Michael H. "Environment: A Toxic Ghost Town." *The Atlantic,* Vol. 263, No. 1, 1986, p. 23.

Carson, Rachel. *Silent Spring.* Boston: Houghton Mifflin Co., 1962.

De Bruin, Jerry. *Creative, Hands-On Science Experiences.* Carthage, IL: Good Apple, Inc., 1986.

The Earth Works Group. *50 Simple Things Kids Can Do to Save the Earth.* Kansas City, MO: Andrews and McMeel, 1990.

Levine, Adeline Gordon. *Love Canal: Science, Politics, and People.* Lexington, MA: Lexington Books, 1982.

Measuring in SI

Careful measurement is an important part of science. But even if you measure very carefully, your figures will have no meaning if your measuring unit means something different each time you use it. To be practical, a measurement unit must always mean the same thing to everybody. A *standard* unit is a definite amount used by everyone when measuring.

Most people in the world and all scientists use the International System (SI) of units. This is a modern form of the metric system.

In SI, all of the units are related to each other by the same set of prefixes. It is easy to change to smaller or larger units simply by multiplying or dividing by ten.

The main units used for measuring are the meter—for distance, gram—for mass, and liter—for volume.

Below is a table of the SI prefixes, their meanings, and rules for changing from one unit to another.

I. Rules for expressing units of measurement

A. Changing meters
   1. Meters can be changed into smaller units such as decimeters (dm), centimeters (cm), or millimeters (mm).
   2. Meters can be changed into larger units such as dekameters (dam), hectometers (hm), or kilometers (km).

B. Changing grams
   1. Grams can be changed into smaller units such as decigrams (dg), centigrams (cg), or milligrams (mg).
   2. Grams can be changed into larger units such as dekagrams (dag), hectograms (hg), or kilograms (kg).

C. Changing liters
   1. Liters can be changed into smaller units such as deciliters (dL), centiliters (cL), or milliliters (mL).
   2. Liters can be changed into larger units such as dekaliters (daL), hectoliters (hL), or kiloliters (kL).

II. Rules for changing from one unit to another

A. When changing from a *smaller unit to a larger unit* you must *divide.* (This type of change is shown by the arrow that points upward in the table.)

SI UNITS

Prefixes	Symbol	Meaning			
kilo	k	1000	thousand	Larger unit to Smaller unit ↓	↑
hecto	h	100	hundred		
deka	da	10	ten		
gram, meter, liter	g,m,L		main unit		
deci	d	0.1	tenth		
centi	c	0.01	hundredth		
milli	m	0.001	thousandth		Smaller unit to Larger unit

1. If you move up the table from any prefix to
   one above it, then divide by 10.
   two above it, then divide by 100.
   three above it, then divide by 1000.
   four above it, then divide by 10 000.
   five above it, then divide by 100 000.
   six above it, then divide by 1 000 000.
2. Examples
   Change 13.2 grams (g) to hectograms (hg). (*Hecto* is two places above gram in the table. Divide by 100.)
   13.2 g ÷ 100 = 0.132 hg

   Change 2.6 decimeters (dm) to kilometers (km).
   (*Kilo* is four places above *deci* in the table. Divide by 10 000.)
   2.6 dm ÷ 10 000 = 0.00026 km

   Change 14 milliliters (mL) to liters (L). (Liter is three places above *milli* in the table. Divide by 1000.)
   14 mL ÷ 1000 = 0.014 L

B. When changing from a *larger unit to a smaller unit* you must *multiply.* (This type of change is shown by the arrow that points downward in the table.)

1. If you move down the table from any prefix to
   one below it, then multiply by 10.
   two below it, then multiply by 100.
   three below it, then multiply by 1000.
   four below it, then multiply by 10 000.
   five below it, then multiply by 100 000.
   six below it, then multiply by 1 000 000.

2. Examples
   Change 25 hectograms (hg) to dekagrams (dag). (*Deka* is one place below *hecto* in the table. Multiply by 10.)
   25 hg × 10 = 250 dag

   Change 126 meters (m) to millimeters (mm). (*Milli* is three places below meter in the table. Multiply by 1000.)
   126 m × 1000 = 126 000 mm

   Change 0.08 kiloliters (kL) to dekaliters (daL).
   (*Deka* is two places below *kilo* in the table. Multiply by 100.)
   0.08 kL × 100 = 8.0 daL

Classification of Living Things

Scientists recognize five kingdoms of living things: the Moneran Kingdom, Protist Kingdom, Fungus Kingdom, Plant Kingdom, and Animal Kingdom. These five kingdoms are divided into smaller groups. Scientists do not always agree about the grouping of living things within a kingdom, or that there should be five kingdoms. This appendix lists the classification groups that are generally accepted by most scientists. Use this appendix as you study Chapters 3-8.

MONERAN KINGDOM
One-celled; no nucleus; cell wall and cell membrane present.

TRUE BACTERIA
Includes several phyla; may be round, rod-shaped, or spiral-shaped; cannot make food. Example: bacteria that cause sore throats.

Blue-green Bacteria Phylum
Contain colored pigments, usually blue-green; can make food. Example: *Anabaena.*

PROTIST KINGDOM
Nucleus present; one-celled or multicellular.

ANIMAL-LIKE PROTISTS
One-celled; most move about; classification based on type of movement; cannot make food.

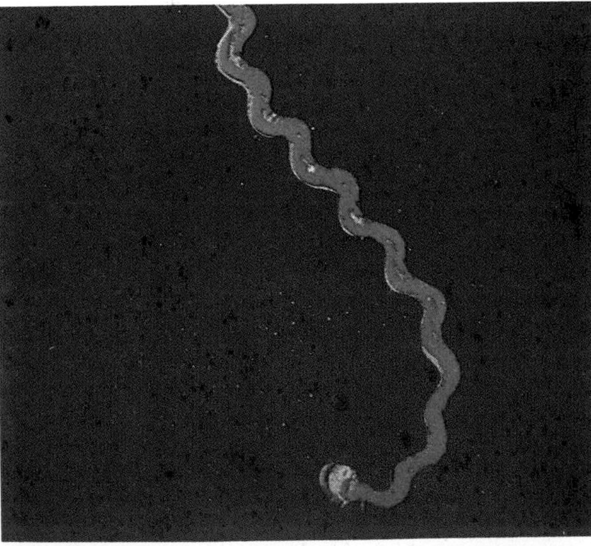

Amoeba Phylum
Move with false feet. Example: *Amoeba proteus.*

Ciliate Phylum
Move with cilia. Example: *Paramecium.*

Flagellate Phylum
Move with flagella. Example: *Trypanosoma.*

Sporozoan Phylum
Do not move. Example: *Plasmodium.*

PLANTLIKE PROTISTS
Some can move about; one-celled or multicellular; can make food.

Euglena Phylum
Move with flagella; one-celled; no cell wall. Example: *Euglena gracilus.*

Diatom Phylum
One-celled; golden-brown color; has two-part glass covering. Example: *Navicula.*

Dinoflagellate Phylum
One-celled; red or brown color. Example: *Gongaulax.*

Green Algae Phylum
One-celled or multicellular. Example: *Spirogyra* (spi ruh GI ruh).
Red and Brown Algae Phyla
Multicellular. Example: kelp.

FUNGUSLIKE PROTISTS
Have a life cycle that includes a moving, slimy mass, an amoebalike stage, and a spore-forming stage; cannot make food. Examples: two phyla that include the slime molds.

FUNGUS KINGDOM
Body consisting of hyphae; reproduce by spores.
Sporangium Fungus Phylum
Cannot make food; spores formed in sporangia. Example: bread mold.
Club Fungus Phylum
Cannot make food; spores formed in club-shaped structures. Examples: mushrooms, smuts.
Sac Fungus Phylum
Cannot make food; spores formed in saclike structures. Examples: yeast, *Penicillium.*
Lichens
Can make food; combination of fungus and organism with chlorophyll. Examples: British soldier lichen, reindeer moss.

PLANT KINGDOM
Green; chlorophyll in cells; can make food; cell walls present.

NONVASCULAR PLANTS
No tubes for carrying materials throughout plant; reproduce by means of spores; no roots, stems, leaves; includes several phyla (botanists use the term *division* instead of *phylum*). Examples: mosses and liverworts.

VASCULAR PLANTS
Tubes for carrying materials throughout plant; roots, stems, and leaves present; includes several phyla.
Fern Phylum
Reproduce with spores. Example: Boston fern.
Conifer Phylum
Reproduce with seeds; seeds in cones. Examples: pines, firs.
Flowering Plant Phylum
Reproduce with seeds; seeds in flowers. Examples: maple tree, daisy, wheat.

ANIMAL KINGDOM
Cannot make food; can move about; multicellular.

INVERTEBRATES
Animals without backbones; includes several phyla.
Sponge Phylum
Two cell layers; no symmetry; body with pores and canals; no tissues or organs; reproduce sexually and asexually. Examples: glass sponges, bath sponges.
Stinging-cell Animal Phylum
Two cell layers; radial symmetry; one opening (mouth) leading into a hollow body; mouth surrounded by tentacles; stinging cells; first phylum to show tissues. Examples: coral, sea anemone, *Hydra.*

Flatworm Phylum
Three cell layers and body organs; flattened body; bilateral symmetry; parasitic or free living; one opening (mouth) if present; first phylum to show a nervous system. Examples: *Planaria,* tapeworms.
Roundworm Phylum
Round body; bilateral symmetry; parasitic or free living; mouth and anus; sexual reproduction only. Examples: hookworm, *Ascaris.*
Segmented Worm Phylum
Segmented body; bilateral symmetry; free living; mouth and anus; heart and circulatory system. Examples: earthworm, clamworm, leech.
Soft-bodied Animal Phylum
Soft body covered by a fleshy mantle; movement by a muscular foot; bilateral symmetry; free living; mouth and anus; reproduce sexually.
Snail Class
Large muscular foot; one shell or no shell on outside of body. Examples: snails, slugs.
Clam Class
Large muscular foot; two shells. Examples: clams, oysters, scallops.
Squid Class
Muscular foot divided into tentacles and arms; shell (if present) inside body. Examples: squid, octopus.

Jointed-leg Animal Phylum
Body in sections; bilateral symmetry; free living; mouth and anus; first phylum to show a skeletal system (exoskeleton).
Crayfish Class
Body in two sections; five pairs of legs; two pairs of antennae. Examples: crabs, crayfish, shrimp.
Spider Class
Body in two sections; four pairs of legs; no antennae. Examples: spiders, scorpions.
Centipede Class
Body in two sections; one pair of poisonous claws; body segmented with one pair of legs per body segment. Example: centipedes.
Millipede Class
Body in two sections; body segmented with two pairs of legs per body segment. Example: millipedes.
Insect Class
Body in three sections; three pairs of legs; one pair of antennae; wings usually present. Examples: bees, ants, moths, beetles.
Spiny-skin Animal Phylum
Body with five part design; radial symmetry; covered with spines; tube feet. Examples: sea urchin, starfish.

VERTEBRATES
Animals with backbones; includes several phyla.
Chordate Phylum
Tough, flexible rod along the back sometime during life; skeleton inside body (endoskeleton); sexual reproduction; bilateral symmetry.
Jawless Fish Class
No scales or jaw; skeleton of cartilage; fins not paired; no gill covering; cold blooded; parasitic or free living. Example: lamprey.
Cartilage Fish Class
Toothlike scales; jaw; skeleton of cartilage; paired fins; no gill covering; cold blooded. Examples: sharks, rays.
Bony Fish Class
First to show bony skeleton; bony scales; paired fins; covered gills; most have a swim bladder; cold blooded. Examples: trout, salmon, goldfish.
Amphibian Class
Moist, scaleless skin; young live in water, adults on land; four legs; cold blooded. Examples: frog, toad, salamander.
Reptile Class
Dry, scaly skin; first to show ability to lay eggs outside of water; egg with shell and protective membranes; four legs (except snakes); cold blooded. Examples: turtle, snake, alligator.
Bird Class
Feathers; wings; scales and claws on legs; beak present; no teeth; warm blooded. Examples: swan, robin, sparrow, owl.
Mammal Class
Hair; mammary glands for nursing young; young develop within body of mother; warm blooded. Examples: human, dog, lion, whale.

Rootwords, Prefixes, and Suffixes

Many words can be broken down into root words, prefixes, and suffixes. A prefix is a word part that, when added to the beginning of a word, changes the meaning of the word. A suffix is a word part that, when added to the end of a word, changes the meaning of the word. Knowing the meanings of certain root words, prefixes, and suffixes can help you understand biology words, and therefore, biology better. Use the table on these two pages to help you understand words used in biology.

P = prefix
R = root
S = suffix

Word Part	Word	Meaning	Word Example	Definition
R	amphi	double	amphibian	double life
P	anti	against	antibiotic	against life
P	arthro	join/joint	arthritis	disease of joints
R	atrium	entrance	left atrium	entrance to heart
R	bio	life	biodegradable	change by life forms
			biology	study of life
R	carb	carbon	carbohydrate	having carbon and water
			carbon dioxide	having carbon and oxygen
P	cardio	heart	cardiac muscle	muscle found in heart
R	chloro	green	chlorophyll	green pigment in leaf
			chloroplast	green body in plant cell
R	chromo	colored	chromosome	colored body in cell nucleus
P	cyto	cell	cytoplasm	liquid within cell
R	dermis	covering	dermis	skin
			epidermis	outer skin covering
P	dia	through	diaphragm	through the middle of body
P	endo	inside	endoskeleton	skeleton inside body
			endospore	spore formed inside bacteria
P	epi	upon	epidermis	outer skin covering
			epiglottis	upon the glottis, or throat
P	ex	out of	exhaling	push air out of lungs
			extinct	life forms no longer on Earth
P	exo	outer	exoskeleton	skeleton on outside of body
R	fertile	to bear	fertilization	process that occurs before bearing young
			fertilizer	helps soil bear better plants
R	flagellum	whip	flagellum	cell part that looks like a whip
P	gen	create	genetics	how life traits are created
R	genos	race	genus	classification group

Word Part	Word	Meaning	Word Example	Definition
P	hemo	blood	hemophilia	disease in which the blood does not clot properly
			hemoglobin	protein in red blood cells
R	herb	grass	herb	small grass-like plant
			herbivore	plant-eating animal
R	hydr	water	hydroponics	growing plants in water
P	hypo	below	hypothesis	to put under or suppose
S	logy	study of	biology	study of life
			ecology	study of where life forms live
P	micro	small	microscope	instrument used to look at small objects
P	mito	thread	mitochondrion	thread-like parts in cytoplasm
			mitosis	changes in cell chromosomes (threads) during reproduction
R	morph	shape	metamorphosis	changes in body shape
P	multi	many	multicellular	having many cells
R	nephros	kidney	nephron	filter unit of kidney
R	neuro	nerve	neuron	nerve cell
P	non	not	noncommunicable	disease that is not catching
R	ov	egg	ovary	organ that makes egg cells
			oviduct	organ that carries egg from ovary
R	para	beside or near	parasite	living beside or inside
R	pherein	to carry	pheromone	carries insect messages
P	photo	light	photosynthesis	use of light by plants to make food
			phototropism	plants turning toward light
R	phyl	tribe	phylum	group name used to classify
R	phyll	leaf	chlorophyll	cell part that gives leaves their green color
R	pneuma	breath	pneumonia	disease of lungs that makes breathing difficult
P	post	after	posterior	hind part of animal
P	pre	before	prenatal	before birth
			prescription	writing before
P	re	back	regenerate	to grow back again
P	semi	half	semilunar	half moon-shaped valve
R	scop	to look	microscope	instrument you look through
S	soma	body	chromosome	colored body in cells
R	spor	seed	spore	cell that acts like a seed in reproduction
			sporozoan	protozoan that forms spores during reproduction
R	stoma	mouth	stomate	pore in leaves like a mouth
			stomach	sac connected to mouth
S	trop	turning	phototropism	turning toward light
			thigmotropism	turning toward something that touches
P	zoo	animal	zoology	study of animals

Safety in the Laboratory

The biology laboratory is a safe place to work if you are aware of important safety rules and if you are careful. You must be responsible for your own safety and for the safety of others. The safety rules given here will protect you and others from harm in the lab. While carrying out procedures in any of the **Labs,** notice the safety symbols and caution statements. The safety symbols are explained in the chart on the next page.

1. Always obtain your teacher's permission to begin a lab.
2. Study the procedure. If you have questions, ask your teacher. Be sure you understand all safety symbols shown.
3. Use the safety equipment provided for you. Goggles and a safety apron should be worn when any lab calls for using chemicals.
4. When you are heating a test tube, always slant it so the mouth points away from you and others.
5. Never eat or drink in the lab. Never inhale chemicals. Do not taste any substance or draw any material into your mouth.
6. If you spill any chemical, wash it off immediately with water. Report the spill immediately to your teacher.
7. Know the location and proper use of the fire extinguisher, safety shower, fire blanket, first aid kit, and fire alarm.
8. Keep all materials away from open flames. Tie back long hair.
9. If a fire should break out in the classroom, or if your clothing should catch fire, smother it with the fire blanket or a coat, or get under a safety shower. **NEVER RUN.**
10. Report any accident or injury, no matter how small, to your teacher.

Follow these procedures as you clean up your work area.

1. Turn off the water and gas. Disconnect electrical devices.
2. Return materials to their places.
3. Dispose of chemicals and other materials as directed by your teacher. Place broken glass and solid substances in the proper containers. Never discard materials in the sink.
4. Clean your work area.
5. Wash your hands thoroughly after working in the laboratory.

FIRST AID IN THE LABORATORY

Injury	Safe response
Burns	Apply cold water. Call your teacher immediately.
Cuts and bruises	Stop any bleeding by applying direct pressure. Cover cuts with a clean dressing. Apply cold compresses to bruises. Call your teacher immediately.
Fainting	Leave the person lying down. Loosen any tight clothing and keep crowds away. Call your teacher immediately.
Foreign matter in eye	Flush with plenty of water. Use eyewash bottle or fountain.
Poisoning	Note the suspected poisoning agent and call your teacher immediately.
Any spills on skin	Flush with large amounts of water or use safety shower. Call your teacher immediately.

SAFETY SYMBOLS

DISPOSAL ALERT
This symbol appears when care must be taken to dispose of materials properly.

BIOLOGICAL HAZARD
This symbol appears when there is danger involving bacteria, fungi, or protists.

OPEN FLAME ALERT
This symbol appears when use of an open flame could cause a fire or an explosion.

THERMAL SAFETY
This symbol appears as a reminder to use caution when handling hot objects.

SHARP OBJECT SAFETY
This symbol appears when a danger of cuts or punctures caused by the use of sharp objects exists.

FUME SAFETY
This symbol appears when chemicals or chemical reactions could cause dangerous fumes.

ELECTRICAL SAFETY
This symbol appears when care should be taken when using electrical equipment.

PLANT SAFETY
This symbol appears when poisonous plants or plants with thorns are handled.

ANIMAL SAFETY
This symbol appears whenever live animals are studied and the safety of the animals and the students must be ensured.

RADIOACTIVE SAFETY
This symbol appears when radioactive materials are used.

CLOTHING PROTECTION SAFETY
This symbol appears when substances used could stain or burn clothing.

FIRE SAFETY
This symbol appears when care should be taken around open flames.

EXPLOSION SAFETY
This symbol appears when the misuse of chemicals could cause an explosion.

EYE SAFETY
This symbol appears when a danger to the eyes exists. Safety goggles should be worn when this symbol appears.

POISON SAFETY
This symbol appears when poisonous substances are used.

CHEMICAL SAFETY
This symbol appears when chemicals used can cause burns or are poisonous if absorbed through the skin.

1 Practicing Scientific Method

Scientists use orderly methods to learn new information and solve problems. The methods used in this process of understanding the world include observing, forming a hypothesis, separating and controlling variables, interpreting data, and designing an experiment. Practice scientific methods by following the examples explained below.

Skill: Observing

When you use your senses, you are observing. What you observe can give you a lot of information about events or things. This information helps you make sense of the world around you.

Learning the Skill
There are two kinds of observations, qualitative and quantitative.

(a) Qualitative observations describe something without using numbers. You might use words such as sweet or sour, good or poor.
(b) In quantitative observations, numbers are used to describe something. Measurements are often made. Your height, age, and mass are quantitative observations.

Example
1. Qualitative observations for an animal may be any of the following: large or small, tall or short, smooth or furry, brown or black, long ears or short ears, naked or hairy tail.
2. Quantitative observations for the same animal may be: mass–459 g; height–27 cm; ear length–14 mm; age–283 days.

Skill: Forming a Hypothesis

A hypothesis is a possible explanation.

Learning the Skill
1. First, you need to recognize the problem or event that needs explaining. You can then begin to form a hypothesis to explain it.
2. You make a hypothesis in the form of a statement that contains the words *if* and *then.*

Example
You are raising African violets and want to know if salt water will kill them. A possible hypothesis is: *If* I give salt water to my African violets, *then* they will continue to grow as usual. Another hypothesis could be: *If* I give salt water to my African violets, *then* they will die.

Skill: Separating and Controlling Variables

To be sure you know which variable caused a particular outcome in your experiment, you must test only one variable at a time.
1. Determine what variables can affect the outcome of an experiment.
2. Make sure that only one variable is allowed to change during the experiment.
3. Set up an experimental group and a control group. The experimental group is the one in which you expect to see a change. The control group is the one in which you don't expect to see a change.

Example
1. You wish to know whether or not caffeine increases heart rate. First, you must find out what other things (variables) might increase heart rate. Is activity important? Is amount of caffeine consumed or time of day important?

2. Keep all variables but one constant. For example, you could:
   (a) have all your subjects sit during the entire experiment.
   (b) give all your subjects the same amount of caffeine.
   (c) collect your data the same time each day.

   The variable that remains constant is the giving of caffeine to all the subjects. Changing any other variable can cause misleading results. For example, you allow your subjects to walk around as they wish. You won't be able to tell if any changes in heart rate are due to the caffeine or the different activities.
3. Compare your results with those from a control group. In the control group, all variables are identical to those in the experimental group with one exception. The members of the control group drink plain water.

Skill: Interpreting Data

The word *interpret* means to explain the meaning of something. When you interpret data, you explain what the data mean.

Learning the Skill

Check the data:

(a) Compare the control group and the experimental group. Compare them for qualitative and quantitative differences.

(b) Decide if the variable being tested had any effect. If there is no difference between the control group and the experimental group, then the variable being tested probably had no effect.

Example

1. You wish to find out if fertilizer affects plant growth. Your hypothesis is: If I add fertilizer to the soil, then my plants will grow larger.
2. The table shows the data you collect.
3. You compare group A (control group) to groups B and C (experimental groups). In groups B and C, the plants are taller.
4. You decide that adding fertilizer to the soil did have an effect on plant growth. It caused the plants in groups B and C to grow taller. Also, the amount of fertilizer had an effect because the plants in group C grew taller than the plants in group B.

EFFECT OF FERTILIZER ON PLANTS

GROUP	TREATMENT	HEIGHT	AFTER 3 WEEKS
A	no fertilizer added to soil	16.5 cm	17 cm
B	3 g fertilizer added to soil	16.5 cm	31 cm
C	6 g fertilizer added to soil	16.5 cm	48 cm

Skill: Designing an Experiment

A successful experiment follows the steps of the scientific method.

Learning the Skill

1. Make observations. You observe that your neighbor fertilizes her chrysanthemums and that they are taller than yours.
2. Recognize the problem. Does fertilizer cause plants to grow larger?
3. Research the problem to see what kinds of things could cause plants to grow larger.
4. Form a hypothesis: If I fertilize my plants, then they will grow larger.
5. Run the experiment.
   (a) Gather your materials. For this experiment, you would need fertilizer, water, plants, soil, a ruler, and a light source.
   (b) Set up the procedure. The only difference between the control group and the experimental group should be whether or not fertilizer is received.
   (c) Collect the data in a table.
6. Interpret the data. Decide if the fertilizer had an effect on plant growth.
7. Reach a conclusion. Is your original hypothesis supported by your data?
8. If your original hypothesis is not supported, form another hypothesis and test it.

2 Reading Science

As you use this textbook, you will find it useful to practice the following reading skills. Processes in nature generally occur in particular sequences. Learning the skill of sequencing will help you remember these processes. The skills of outlining and summarizing main ideas, understanding science words, and interpreting diagrams will help you study the major concepts in this text. As you learn about biology, you will find the skills of inferring and making models will help you apply your knowledge.

Skill: Sequencing

Sequencing is the arranging of facts or ideas into a series. The order in which the facts or ideas are arranged is important because one fact must lead to the next in the series.

Learning the Skill
1. List all items to be sequenced.
2. Decide which item is the first in the series.
3. Continue to list all items in their proper order.

Examples
Place the following steps of sharpening a pencil in their proper sequence. Remember that the steps must be in the proper order for the activity to be carried out successfully. Each item must lead to the next.

(a) Turn the handle of the sharpener several times.
(b) Locate the pencil sharpener.
(c) Insert the pencil into the opening of the sharpener.
(d) Check the pencil point to see if it is properly sharpened.
(e) Remove the pencil from the sharpener.

In this example, the correct sequence is (b), (c), (a), (e), (d).

Skill: Outlining and Summarizing Main Ideas

Being able to outline the material in your textbook will help you learn and understand it and to see how ideas are connected.

Learning the Skill

1. Look over the material to be outlined and summarized. Locate the major headings or ideas. These are the numbered sections in each chapter. Use a Roman numeral for each numbered section and write the title of the section next to the Roman numeral.
2. Write a capital letter for each subsection. Subsections are indicated by the headings that follow each numbered section in a chapter.
3. Write the main idea of the subsection next to the capital letter. Leave several lines between all capital letters for supporting ideas.
4. List several supporting ideas below each main idea. These ideas should be in the form of numbered statements.
5. To summarize the main ideas, write the outline in the form of complete sentences.

Example

1. Outline numbered Section 22:1.

I. Mitosis (title of numbered section)
   A. Body Growth and Repair (title of subsection)
      1. cell reproduction is called mitosis (supporting idea)
      2. body growth occurs because of mitosis (supporting idea)
      3. body repair occurs because of mitosis (supporting idea)
   B. An Introduction to Mitosis (title of subsection)
      1. one cell forms two during mitosis (supporting idea)
      2. mitosis can be compared to making a photocopy (supporting idea)

2. Summarize the information in the outline. Mitosis is the process of cell reproduction that occurs as our bodies grow and repair themselves. During this process, one cell reproduces to form two. Mitosis can be compared to the making of a photocopy.

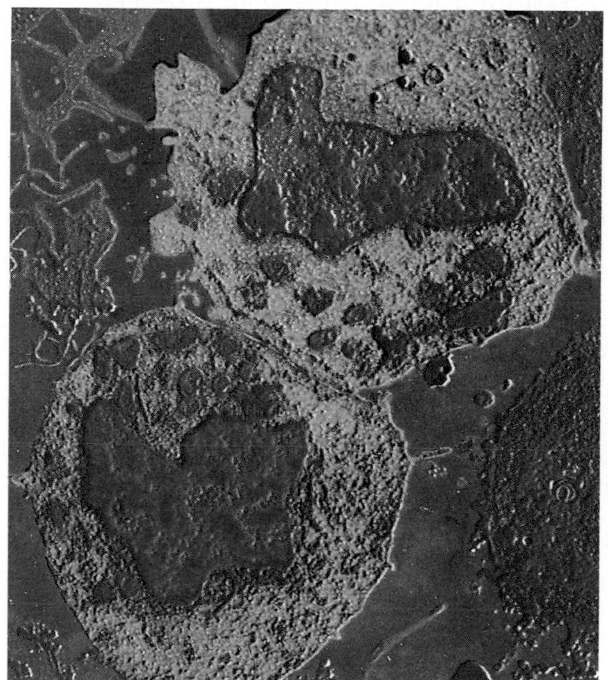

Skill: Understanding Science Words

There are two ways you can understand science words better. One way is to define the word in context. The way the word is used gives you a clue as to its meaning. A second way to understand science words is to look at the parts that make up the word. Each word part can give you a clue as to the meaning of the whole word.

Learning the Skill: Defining Words in Context

1. First, read to see if the word is defined directly in the sentence.
2. If the word is not defined directly, read several sentences beyond the one in which the word first appears. These sentences may provide information about the definition of the word.
3. If possible, define the word based on your own past knowledge. You may have learned the word in an earlier chapter, or you may be familiar with it because you hear it day to day.
4. Figure out the meaning of the word by how it is used in the sentence and by the sentences around it.

Examples

Find the definitions of the underlined words.

1. *Biology* is the study of life. The word *is* gives you a clue that the word is defined directly in the sentence.
2. A cat is a *mammal.* A mammal is an animal that has body hair, provides its young with milk from mammary glands, and is warm-blooded. The second sentence contains the definition of mammal.
3. All living things can *reproduce. Reproduce* is a familiar word. It is defined in Chapter 2. It is also one you probably hear from day to day.
4. Green plants carry out *photosynthesis.* Thus, they are able to make their own food. These sentences tell you that photosynthesis is the ability of a plant to make food.

Learning the Skill: Understanding Word Parts

1. Look at the word to see how many word parts you think it has. The word may have one or more word parts.
2. You may recognize parts of the word from previous lessons. Or, you may recognize parts of the word from other familiar words. Try to define each word part if you can. Then define the whole word.
3. Look for root words and prefixes or suffixes. A root word is the main part of the word. A prefix is a word part added to the front of a root word to change its meaning. A suffix is a word part added to the end of a root word to change its meaning.

Examples

1. What does the word *microorganism* mean? The word *microorganism* has two word parts, *micro* and *organism.* You remember the word *microscope* and that *micro* means small. You also remember that the word *organism* means a living thing. Therefore the word *microorganism* means a small living thing.
2. Examples of root words are:
   emia—blood
   vertebrate—animal with a backbone
   bio—life
   zoo—animal
3. The prefixes *an* and *in* mean without. What do the words *anemia* and *invertebrate* mean?
   anemia—having too little blood
   invertebrate—animal without a backbone
4. The suffix *logy* means the study of. What is biology? Zoology?
   biology—the study of life
   zoology—the study of animals

Skill: Interpreting Diagrams

When you look at a diagram, note first the orientation and symmetry of the organism. Knowing the orientation tells you where the front end is, where the tail end is, where the front side is, and where the back side is. Knowing the symmetry tells you how many sides the organism has. If it is an inside view of an organism, note whether it shows the whole organism or only part of one. Usually, inside views, also called sections, show only parts of organisms. If the diagram is of a process, note the order in which steps of the process occur.

Learning the Skill: Orientation

1. First, note whether the diagram, as in Figure 1, shows an internal or external view.
2. Locate the anterior, or head end, posterior, or tail end, dorsal, or back side, ventral, or belly side.

FIGURE 1

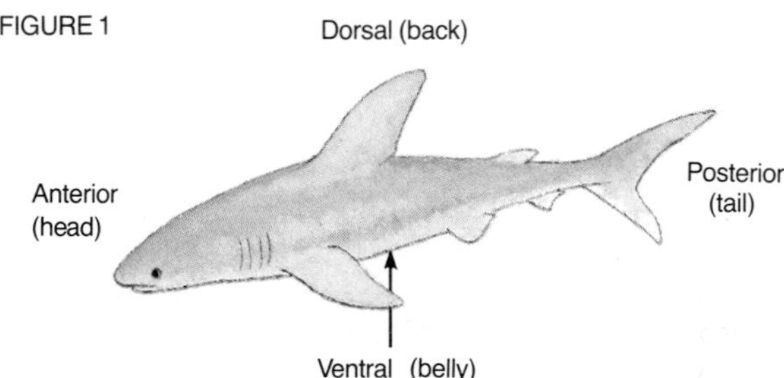

Learning the Skill: Symmetry

There are two types of symmetry, radial and bilateral. Bilateral means having two sides alike. Radial means spreading out from the center.

1. Draw an imaginary line through the center of the animal from its anterior end to its posterior end.
2. If the animal forms two mirror images, it probably has bilateral symmetry. You must do step 3 to find out for sure.
3. Draw a second line at right angles to the first. If the animal forms four equal parts, it has radial symmetry. If it doesn't, it has bilateral symmetry.

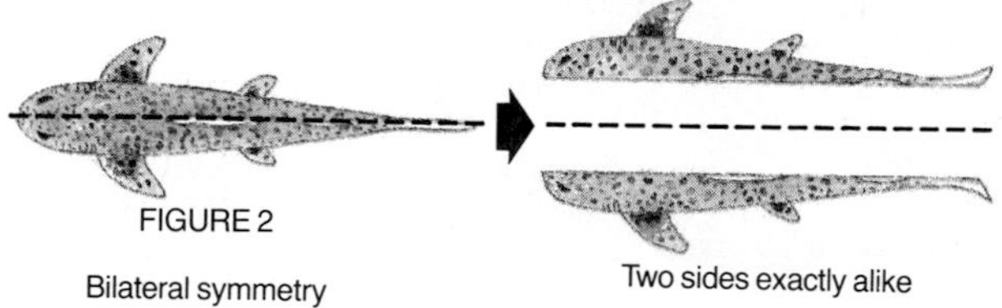

FIGURE 2

Bilateral symmetry

Example

1. Study the figure of the shark. A shark has bilateral symmetry. Note that the two sides are mirror images of one another.
2. Study the figure of the bicycle wheel and the sea anemone. A sea anemone has radial symmetry. The parts of the animal spread out from the center, much like the spokes of a wheel.

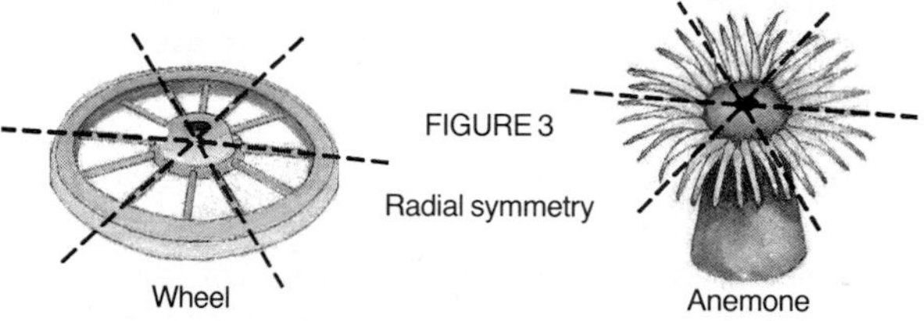

FIGURE 3

Radial symmetry

Learning the Skill: Sections

There are two kinds of sections, long sections and cross sections.

1. Cross sections are slices made at right angles to the axis. A slice through your waist would give a cross section of you.
2. Long sections are slices that run along the axis. A slice from the top of your head to the floor would give a long section of you.

Example

Study the figure of the squash. This figure shows a cross section of the squash. A cross section across the top part shows only the fleshy part of the squash. A cross section across the lower part of the squash shows an interior chamber filled with seeds.

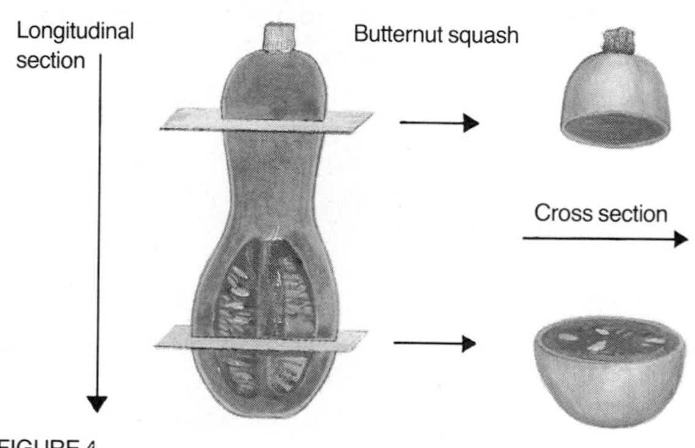

FIGURE 4

Skill: Inferring

To infer means to make an assumption based on facts, observations, or experimental data. You make an inference each time you say "I'll bet the school cafeteria is serving pizza for lunch because I can smell it."

Learning the Skill

1. Define the question. Sometimes you infer something without thinking about the question behind the inference. In the pizza example, what is the question? The question might be "what are we having for lunch today?" Sometimes, the question is asked directly, as in the example that follows.
2. Study the available information. In the pizza example, the available information is the odor of pizza in the air.
3. Look for connecting ideas. Make comparisons. Again in the pizza example, what else could you be smelling? Could it be sub sandwiches? The odor is similar, but your cafeteria has never served subs before.
4. Answer the question. Based on your responses to steps 2 and 3, you infer that pizza is on the menu.
5. Support your answer using the available information.

Example

1. The following information is about human population growth. One question that might come up regarding this information is "which country might have a food shortage by 2100?"
2. Study the table. What information does it give? It gives information about expected population growth in Japan and Pakistan.
3. Compare the expected increase in population for Japan with the expected increase in population for Pakistan.
4. Based on the data, you could infer that Pakistan will have a food shortage by 2100.
5. Supporting evidence is that the population of Pakistan is increasing at a much faster rate than the population of Japan. The larger a population becomes, the more food it requires. What additional information could change your inference? If Japan had to import most of its food, and Pakistan was the largest producer of grain in the world, you might infer that Japan would have a food shortage, or that neither country would have a food shortage.

POPULATION GROWTH

COUNTRY	1987	2100 (ESTIMATED)
JAPAN	122 million	127 million
PAKISTAN	104 million	315 million

Skill: Formulating Models

In a model, ideas in biology are represented by familiar objects. Models help to simplify processes or structures that are often difficult to understand.

Learning the Skill

1. Recognize the process or structure that is to be modeled.
2. Research the process or structure before you start your model. Find out how a structure such as an artery is put together. Find out what takes place during a process, such as breathing in and out.
3. Think of a simple way of showing this same process or structure using materials that are readily available.
4. Construct your model. Note if it operates correctly and shows the idea you wish it to show.

Example

1. Formulate a model that shows how the sizes of arteries, veins, and capillaries differ.
2. Read what you can about arteries, veins, and capillaries. Arteries are usually round and are the thickest of the three blood vessel types. Veins are flat and thinner than arteries. Capillaries are very small in size. All three vessels are hollow tubes.
3. Materials that you could use include straws to represent capillaries, mostaccioli noodles to represent veins, and manicotti noodles to represent arteries.
4. To construct the model, you might want to cook the noodles first. Cooking will make them softer, and make their texture more like that of arteries and veins. Cut the noodles and straws into short sections and glue them to thick paper so that the openings are facing outward. Label each structure appropriately.

3 Using a Microscope

There are many opportunities in this biology text for you to make your own observations and experimentations. In many labs, you will be able to practice your skills of using a compound microscope, making a wet mount, calculating magnification, and making scale drawings.

Skill: Using a Compound Microscope

The compound microscope allows you to magnify objects 100, 400, and 1000 X (times) their natural size. The word *compound* refers to the fact that a compound microscope has several lenses for magnifying objects.

Steps Needed to Acquire Skill

1. Review the parts of the compound microscope shown in Figure 1.
2. Place the glass slide and object to be viewed onto the stage. Hold the slide in place with the stage clips.
3. Move the slide so that the object to be viewed is directly over the stage opening.
4. Turn the low-power objective into place until you hear a click. Look to the side and turn the coarse adjustment until the low-power objective is almost touching the slide.
5. Turn on the microscope (if electric) or adjust the mirror toward a light source. Never use direct sunlight.
6. Look through the eyepiece and adjust the diaphragm until you see a bright light. The mirror may also have to be readjusted.
7. Use the coarse adjustment to raise the body tube until you can see the object.
8. Use the fine wheel adjustment to bring the object into sharp focus.
9. To see the object under high power, rotate the objectives until you hear another click. Use only the fine adjustment to sharpen the focus.

Troubleshooting

Problem: Object can't be seen clearly or found under low or high power.

Solution: Make sure that the eyepiece, objectives, slide, and coverslip are clean. Check to be sure that the water is not covering the coverslip and if it is, make a new wet mount. If the objective or eyepiece lens is dirty, clean it with lens paper. Check the coarse adjustment. Check the diaphragm opening. If there is too much light, transparent objects, such as amoebas, will be washed out.

Problem: Object can't be found under high power.

Solution: Check to be sure the object is centered over the stage opening. You may need to return to low power first.

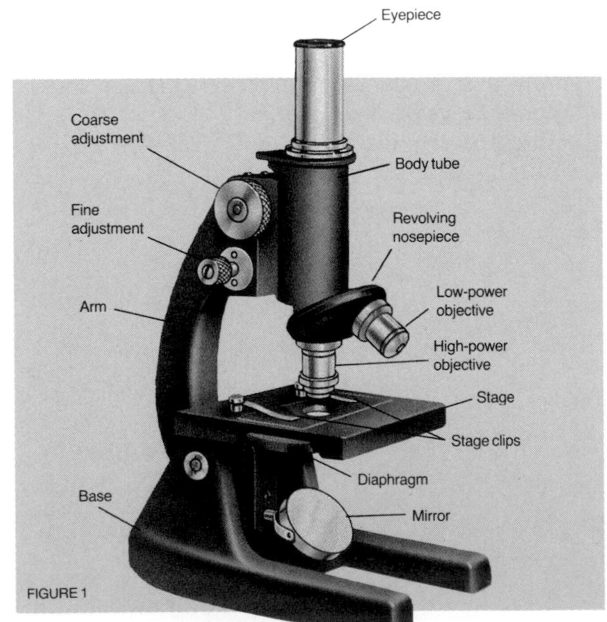

FIGURE 1

Skill: Making a Wet Mount

All the slides you prepare for observing under the microscope are called wet mounts. They are called wet mounts because the object to be viewed is prepared or mounted in water.

Learning the Skill

1. Add a drop or two of water to the center of a clean microscope slide.
2. Place the object to be viewed in the drop of water as shown in Figure 1.
3. Pick up a coverslip by its edges. Do not touch the surface of the coverslip. Stand the coverslip on its edge next to the drop of water.
4. Slowly lower the coverslip over the drop of water and the object to be viewed as shown in Figure 2.
5. Make sure that the object is totally covered with water. If it is not, remove the coverslip, add more water, and replace the coverslip.

Troubleshooting

1. Figures 3 and 4 show correctly prepared wet mounts.
2. The directions that follow tell you what to do if problems occur when you are making wet mounts.
   (a) Figure 5 shows what happens when there is not enough water on the wet mount or the coverslip is lowered too quickly. The water doesn't cover the entire object, or air bubbles may form.
   (b) Figure 6 shows what happens when too much water is used or the coverslip is dirty. If too much water is on the slide, place the tip of a paper towel at the edge of the coverslip to absorb some of the excess water. If there is dirt on the coverslip, replace it. If these steps don't work, clean the slide, dry the slide and coverslip, and make a new wet mount.
   (c) Figure 7 shows what happens when the object being viewed is too thick. Prepare a thinner object for viewing and make a new wet mount.

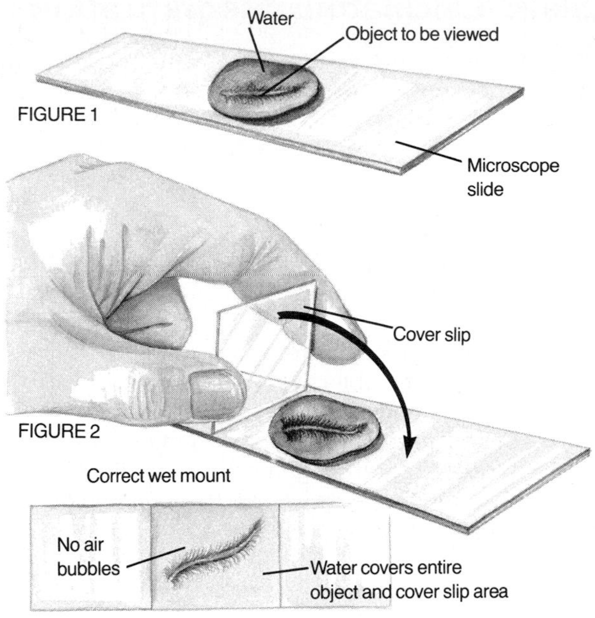

FIGURE 1

FIGURE 2

FIGURE 3

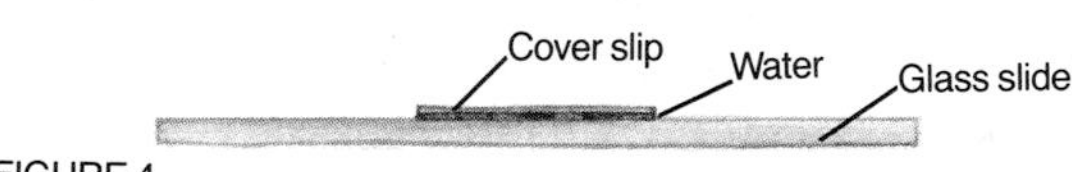

FIGURE 4

Incorrect wet mounts

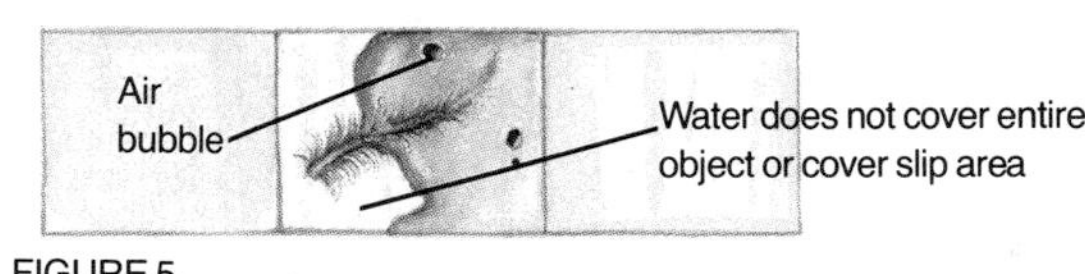

FIGURE 5

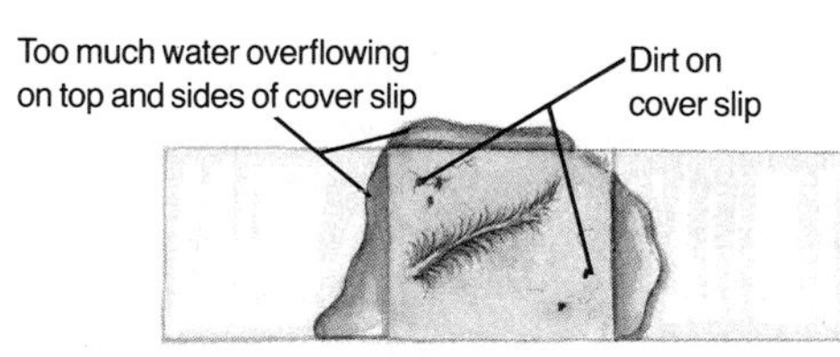

FIGURE 6

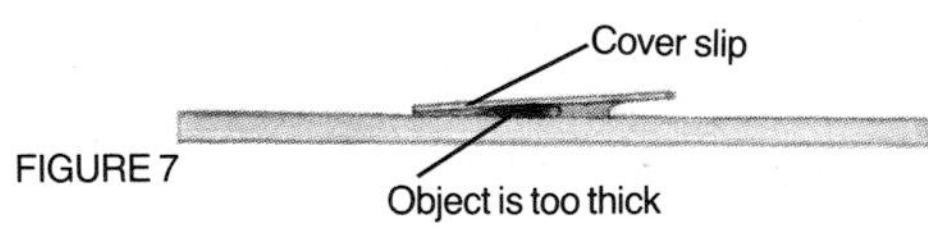

FIGURE 7

Skill: Calculating Magnification

Objects viewed under the microscope appear larger than normal because they are magnified. Total magnification describes how much larger an object appears when viewed through the microscope.

Learning the Skill

1. Look for a number marked with an X on the following:
   (a) eyepiece
   (b) low-power objective
   (c) high-power objective
   The X stands for how many times the lens of the microscope part magnifies an object.
2. To calculate *total* magnification, multiply the number on the eyepiece by the number on the objective.

Example

If the eyepiece magnification is 7×, the low-power objective magnification is 10×, and the high-power objective magnification is 40×:

(a) then total magnification under low power is 7× for the eyepiece × 10× for the low-power objective = 70× (7 × 10 = 70).

(b) then total magnification under high power is 7× for the eyepiece × 40× for the high-power objective = 280× (7 × 40 = 280).

Skill: Making Scale Drawings

When you draw objects seen through the microscope, the size that you make your drawing is important. Your drawing should be in proportion to the size the object appears to be when viewed through the microscope. This is called drawing to scale. Drawing to scale allows you to compare the sizes of different objects. It also allows you to form an idea of the actual size of the object being viewed, Figure 1.

Learning the Skill

1. Draw a circle on your paper. The circle may be any size.
2. Imagine the circle divided into four equal sections, as in Figure 2.

FIGURE 1

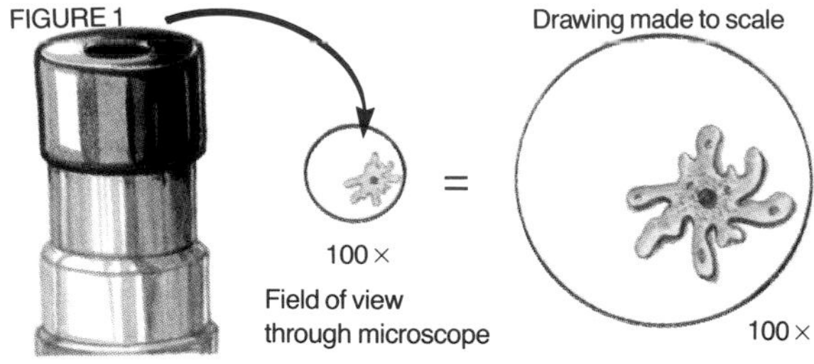

3. Locate an object under low or high power of the microscope. Imagine the field of view also divided into four equal sections.
4. Note how much of the field of view is taken up by the object. Also note what part of the field of view the object is in.
5. Draw the object in the circle. Position the object in about the same part of the circle as it appears in the field of view. Also, draw the object so that it takes up about the same amount of space within the circle as it actually takes up in the field of view, Figure 2.

FIGURE 2

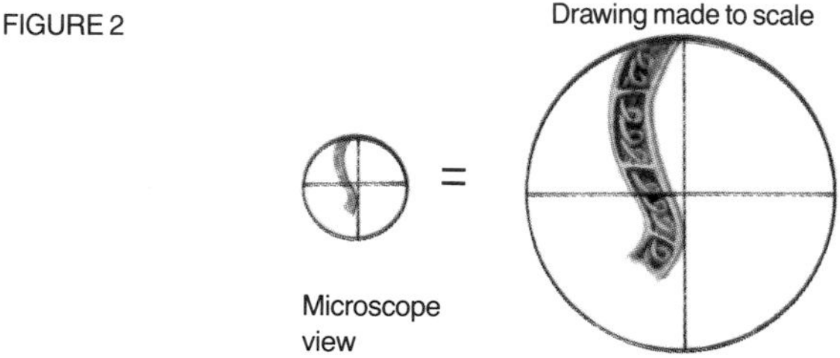

Troubleshooting

Figure 3 shows objects that haven't been drawn to scale correctly. One object has been drawn too small. One object has been drawn too large. The object in Figure 2 is drawn to the correct size and in the correct position.

FIGURE 3

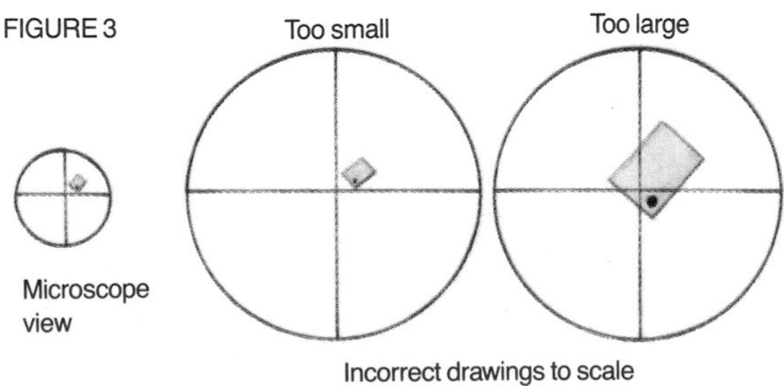

4 Organizing Information

As a scientist, you will be expected to collect data and draw conclusions. The skills of classifying, making and using tables, making line graphs, and making bar graphs will help you organize and interpret the information that you gather.

Skill: Classifying

Everyone, including scientists, groups or classifies to show similarities and differences among things and to put things in order.

Learning the Skill

1. Study the things to be classified.
2. Look at their traits and note traits that are similar and those that are different.
3. Pick out one major trait that can be used to separate the objects into at least two (or even three) separate groups.
4. Separate the things to be classified into these two groups. Then, taking each group at a time, look for other traits that can be used to separate each of the two groups into subgroups.
5. Continue to separate each subgroup into smaller and smaller groups until each group contains only one object.

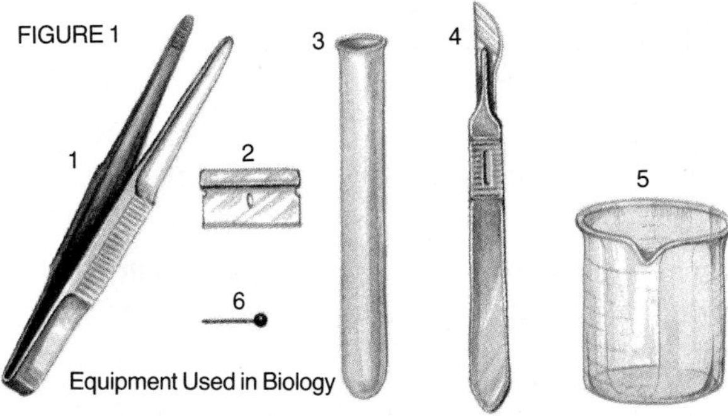

FIGURE 1 Equipment Used in Biology

Example

1. Classify equipment used in biology labs.
2. First, separate the equipment into two groups, possibly glass and metal.
3. Separate the glass items into subgroups. Separate metal items into subgroups. The diagram shows some possible subgroups for classifying the equipment.

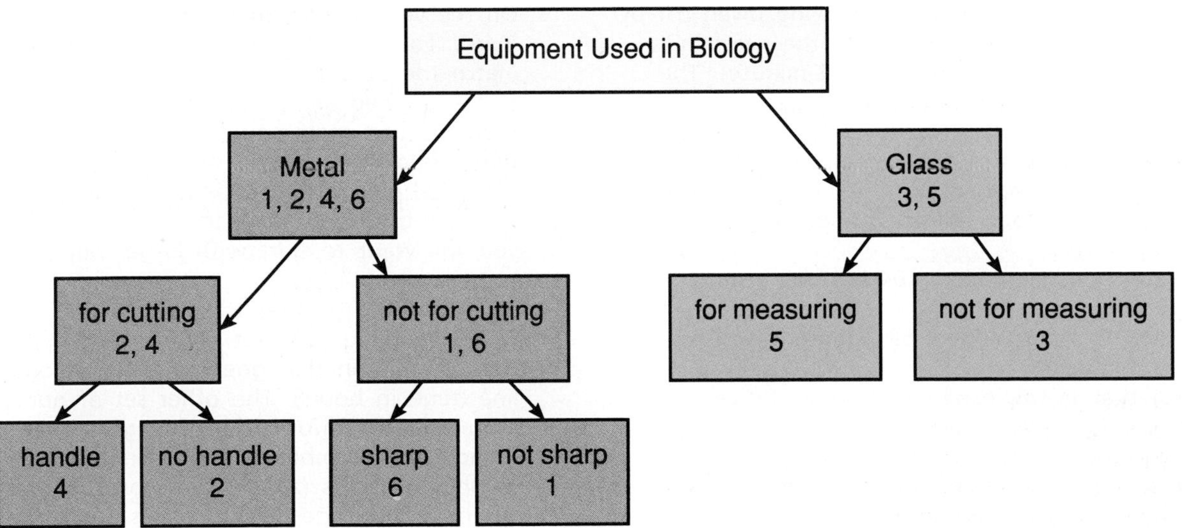

Skill: Making and Using Tables

Tables organize information in a way that makes it easy to read and interpret. Tables may be used to show qualitative information or quantitative information. (See page 704 of the Skill Handbook.) Tables have two uses. One, they are used to record data. Two, they provide information.

Learning the Skill
Tables have the following characteristics:
1. a title that tells what kind of information appears in the table
2. columns that run up and down
3. rows that run left to right
4. a heading for each column that tells what type of information is in that column

Example
An experiment was run to see if yeast cells give off different amounts of carbon dioxide gas when provided with different kinds of food. Starch, a food source, was put into a test tube containing yeast. Sugar, a second food source, was put into another test tube containing yeast. A third test tube that contained yeast, the control, had no food added. The test tubes were labeled A (no food), B (sugar added), and C (starch added). For the next 20 minutes, the experimenter counted the number of bubbles given off in each test tube. The number of bubbles was used as a measurement of the amount of carbon dioxide gas being given off by the yeast. The results were that the yeast in tube A gave off 3 bubbles in 20 minutes. The yeast in tube B gave off 104 bubbles. The yeast in tube C gave off 58 bubbles.

The results of this experiment could be summarized as follows:

Tube A, no food added, 3 bubbles given off in 20 minutes.

Tube B, sugar added, 104 bubbles given off in 20 minutes.

Tube C, starch added, 58 bubbles given off in 20 minutes.

Note that in this experiment, quantitative observations were made.

Another way to summarize the results is in a table. Study the table. Note how the information gathered in the yeast experiment is organized.

BUBBLES GIVEN OFF BY YEAST USING DIFFERENT FOOD TYPES

TUBE	FOOD ADDED	BUBBLES GIVEN OFF IN 20 MINUTES
A	none	3
B	sugar	104
C	starch	58

Skill: Making Line Graphs

A line graph is used to show how quantities of things change. It shows these changes in picture form. Very often, the data that are shown in a line graph are collected in a table first. Then, the data in the table are graphed.

Learning the Skill
1. Look at Figure 1 as you follow these directions. On a piece of graph paper draw two lines, one horizontal (A) and one vertical (B). The lines must meet in the lower left corner.
2. On the horizontal line, make regularly spaced marks (C). Label the marks. For example, if data were gathered every hour, then the first mark on the horizontal line would be labeled 1 hour, the second mark 2 hours, and so on.
3. On the vertical line, make regularly spaced marks. Label the marks. These labels must also match the data to be graphed. If the numbers to be graphed are the numbers of yeast cells, then the first mark could be labeled 1 cell, the second mark 2 cells, and so on. The way you label your graph depends on the data. If the quantities you want to graph are large, you will want to start with larger numbers on your graph.
4. Plot the data. Look at the data in the following table. One set of numbers represents the information that goes on the horizontal line (time in hours). The other set of numbers represents the information that goes on the vertical line (number of cells). First, plot the number of hours (zero). Place your pencil on the horizontal line at zero hours. Next plot

REPRODUCTION IN YEAST	
NUMBER OF YEAST CELLS	TIME IN HOURS
5	0
10	1
18	2
45	3
30	4
8	5

the number of cells. Move your pencil up to the mark labeled 5. Make a dot (D). Continue to plot the data until all the rows of numbers have been plotted.

5. If you have trouble determining where to place your dot, draw dotted lines from the horizontal and vertical lines. Where the dotted lines intersect is where you place your dot (E).
6. Connect each dot with a smooth line (F).
7. If you are graphing two sets of data, be sure to make the two lines different colors so you can tell them apart. Or, you can use a solid line for one and a dashed line for the other. Include a key that tells which color or line represents which set of data (G).

Example
Let's see how the data in the table would look in a line graph.

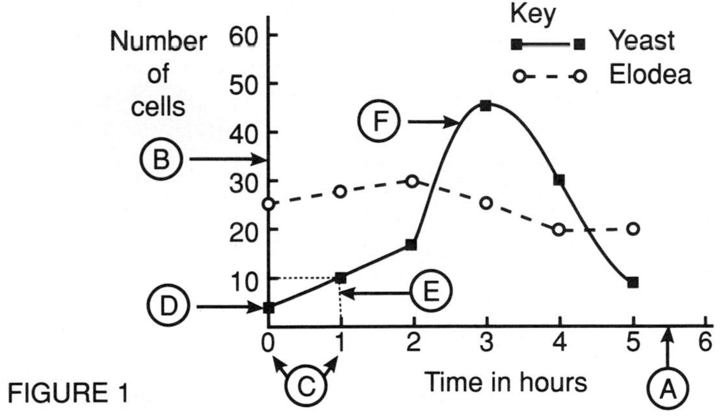

FIGURE 1

Skill: Making Bar Graphs

A bar graph is used to compare quantities of different kinds of things. It shows these comparisons in picture form.

Learning the Skill

1. Repeat steps 1-3 under Making Line Graphs. Label the horizontal and vertical lines with the appropriate labels.
2. Plot the data from the table below.

BREATH HOLDING ABILITY	
AMOUNT OF TIME ABLE TO HOLD BREATH (MINUTES)	ANIMAL
20	Gray Seal
10	Walrus
50	Blue Whale
15	Beaver

Place your pencil on the horizontal line where it is marked gray seal. Plot the number of minutes a gray seal can hold its breath by moving your pencil up to the appropriate mark on the vertical line. Place a small mark there. Then, draw a vertical bar up to the mark. Continue to plot the data until the values for all animals have been plotted.

Example

1. Let's see how the data in the table would look in a graph.

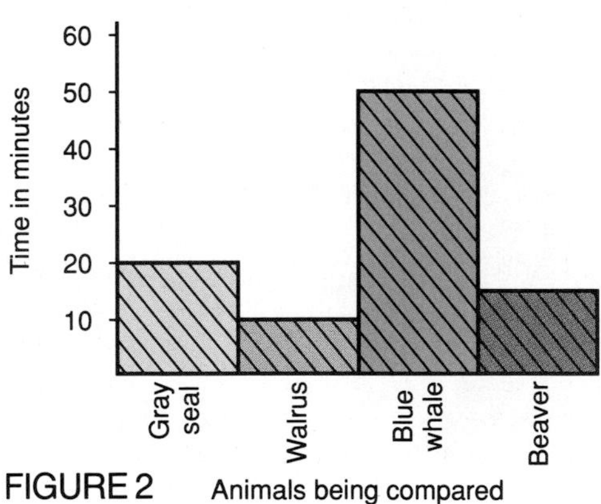

FIGURE 2

5 Using Numbers

Two important methods of science are the comparing of information and the repeating of experiments. All scientists use the skills of measuring volume, length, and mass in SI, and calculating in order to confirm hypotheses, results, and conclusions.

Skill: Measuring in SI—Volume

Volume measurements are made in milliliters (mL) or liters (L). 1000 milliliters = 1 liter. The equipment used for measuring volume is a graduated cylinder.

Learning the Skill

1. Locate the units on the graduated cylinder in Figure 1.
2. To read the volume of liquid in a graduated cylinder, do the following:
   (a) Place the cylinder on a flat surface.
   (b) Make sure you read the volume of liquid at eye level.
   (c) The surface of the liquid will form a curve. Find the lowest point of the curve and read the volume.

Troubleshooting

1. Figure 1 shows a correct volume reading.
2. The reading in Figure 2 is incorrect because:
   (a) The cylinder is not on a flat surface.
   (b) The top of the liquid is not at eye level.
   (c) The lowest point of the curve is not being used to read the volume.

Skill: Measuring in SI—Length

Measurements of length, distance, and height are made in millimeters (mm), centimeters (cm), and meters (m). The equipment used for measuring length is a metric ruler.

Learning the Skill

1. First decide which units you want to measure in. The units you choose will depend on the size of the object or distance being measured.
2. Note the divisions on the ruler. Figure 3 shows these divisions. One meter is divided into 100 centimeters. Each centimeter is divided into 10 millimeters.
3. Place one end of the object you are measuring next to the zero mark on the ruler. Note where the other end stops and read the number of units shown there.

Example

1. Measure the length of a leaf.
2. Place one end of the leaf at the zero mark as shown in Figure 2.
3. The leaf in the figure is 35 mm.

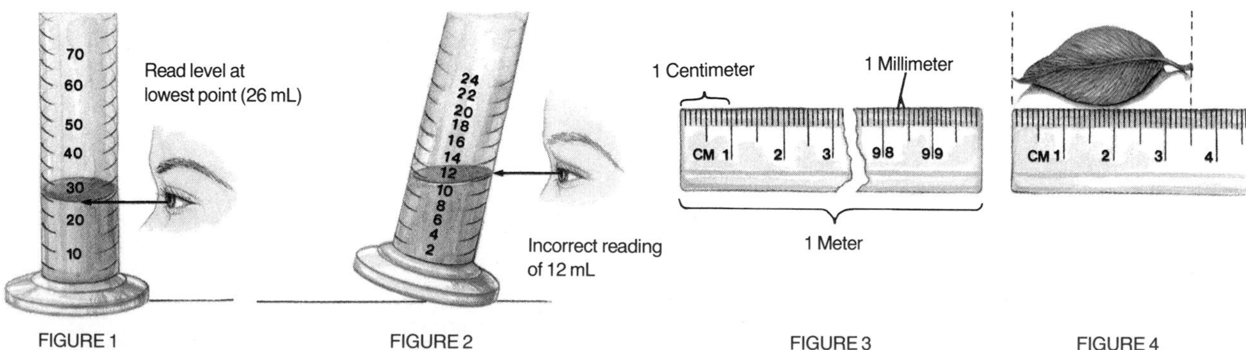

FIGURE 1 FIGURE 2 FIGURE 3 FIGURE 4

Skill: Measuring in SI—Mass

Mass measurements are made in grams (g), milligrams (mg), or kilograms (kg). The equipment used is a balance.

Learning the Skill

1. Place the object to be massed onto the pan. Note: liquids must be in a container; powders or solids must be placed on paper. The mass of the container or paper must later be subtracted from the total mass.
2. Slide all the riders to the left and release the locking mechanism.
3. Figure 1 shows that the back beam measures mass in 10 gram units. The middle beam measures mass in 1 gram units. The front beam measures mass in 0.1 and 0.01 gram units.
4. Starting with the rider on the back beam, move the rider to the right until the pointer drops below the zero point. Then move it back one notch. Repeat this process with the rider on the middle beam. Move the front rider until the pointer lines up with the zero point (center line).
5. The mass of the object will be the total of all the numbers indicated by the riders of the three beams.

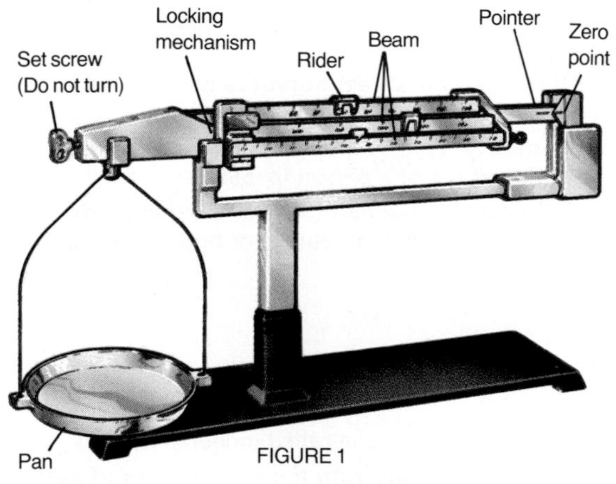

FIGURE 1

Example

The mass of the object measured on the balance in Figure 1 would be 47.52 g.

Skill: Calculating

Calculations may involve averaging numbers, comparing sets of numbers, or calculating area or volume.

Learning the Skill: Averaging

1. Add together the numbers to be averaged.
2. Divide the total by the number of figures used. The resulting number is the average.

Learning the Skill: Comparing Numbers

1. To find out how many times larger something is, *divide the smaller number into the larger.*
2. To find out how many times smaller something is than something else, *divide the larger number into the smaller.*

Learning the Skill: Calculating Area

1. Multiply the length times the width.
2. The result is the area in *square* units, for example, square meters or square centimeters.

Example

1. Calculate the area of the rectangle shown below.

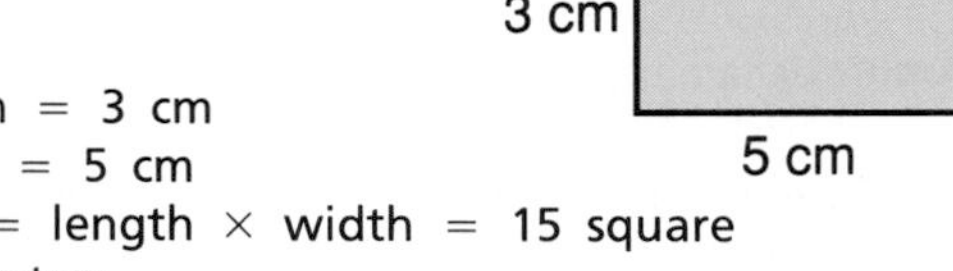

2. Length = 3 cm
   Width = 5 cm
   Area = length × width = 15 square centimeters
   Square units may be written cm^2, m^2, or mm^2.

Learning the Skill: Calculating Volume

1. Multiply length times width times height.
2. The result is the volume in *cubic* units, such as cubic meters or cubic centimeters.

Example

1. Calculate the volume of the cube shown below.

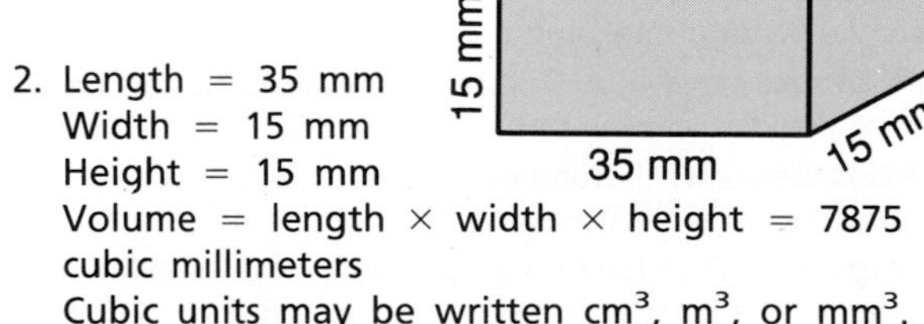

2. Length = 35 mm
   Width = 15 mm
   Height = 15 mm
   Volume = length × width × height = 7875 cubic millimeters
   Cubic units may be written cm^3, m^3, or mm^3.

GLOSSARY

PRONUNCIATION KEY

a . . . b**a**ck (bak)
ay . . . d**ay** (day)
ah . . . f**a**ther (fahth ur)
ow . . . fl**ow**er (flow ur)
ar . . . c**ar** (car)
e . . . l**e**ss (les)
ee . . . l**ea**f (leef)
ih . . . tr**i**p (trihp)
i(i+con+e) . . . **i**dea, l**i**fe (i dee uh, life)

oh . . . g**o** (goh)
aw . . . s**o**ft (sawft)
or . . . **or**bit (or but)
oy . . . c**oi**n (coyn)
oo . . . f**oo**t (foot)
ew . . . f**oo**d (fewd)
yoo . . . p**ur**e (pyoor)
yew . . . f**ew** (fyew)
uh . . . comm**a** (cahm uh)
u(+con) . . . flow**er** (flow ur)

sh . . . **sh**elf (shelf)
ch . . . na**t**ure (nay chur)
g . . . **g**ift (gihft)
j . . . **g**em (jem)
ing . . . s**ing** (sing)
zh . . . vi**si**on (vihzh un)
k . . . ca**k**e (kayk)
s . . . **s**eed, **c**ent (seed, sent)
z . . . **z**one, rai**s**e (zohn, rayz)

A

Acids: liquids that have pH values lower than 7 (p. 684)

Acid rain: rain that has a pH between 1 and 5.5 (p. 684)

Acquired Immune Deficiency Snydrome, or **AIDS:** a disease of the immune system (p. 259)

Adaptation: a trait that makes a living thing better able to survive (p. 29)

Algae (AL jee): plantlike protists (p. 97)

Alveoli (al VEE uh li): the tiny air sacs of the lungs (p. 268)

Amniocentesis (am nee oh sen TEE sus): a way of looking at the chromosomes of a fetus (p. 567)

Amniotic (am nee AHT ik) **sac:** a tissue filled with liquid that protects the embryo (p. 525)

Amphibian (am FIHB ee un): an animal that lives part of its life in water and another part of its life on land (p. 169)

Anemia: a condition in which there are too few red blood cells in the blood (p. 248)

Animals: organisms that have many cells, can't make their own food, and can move (p. 62)

Annual (AN yul): a plant that completes its life cycle within one year (p. 447)

Annual ring: each ring of xylem in a woody stem (p. 423)

Antacid (ant AS ud): a drug that changes acid into water and a salt (p. 382)

Antennae (an TEN ee): appendages of the head that are used for sensing smell and touch (p. 159)

Antibiotics (an ti bi AHT iks): chemical substances that kill or slow the growth of bacteria (p. 84)

Antibodies (ANT ih bohd eez): chemicals that help destroy bacteria or viruses (p. 257)

Antigens (ANT ih junz): foreign substances, usually proteins, that invade the body and cause diseases (p. 257)

Antihistamine (ANT i HIHS tuh meen): a drug that reduces swelling of tissues by stopping the leaking of blood plasma from capillaries (p. 380)

Anus (AY nus): an opening through which undigested food leaves the body (p. 145)

Aorta (ay ORT uh): the largest artery in the body (p. 230)

Appendage (uh PEN dihj): a structure that grows out of an animal's body (p. 158)

Appendix (uh PEN dihks): a small, fingerlike part of the digestive system found where the small and large intestines meet (p. 212)

Artery (ART uh ree): a blood vessel that carries blood away from the heart (p. 226)

Arthritis (ar THRIT us): a disease of bone joints (p. 299)

Asexual (ay SEK shul) **reproduction:** the reproducing of a living thing from only one parent (p. 80)

Atria (AY tree uh): the small top chambers of the heart (p. 225)

Auditory (AHD uh tor ee) **nerve:** a nerve that carries messages of sound to the brain (p. 341)

Autosomes (AH toh sohmz): chromosomes that do not determine the sex of a person (p. 568)

Axon (AK sahn): the part of a neuron that sends messages to surrounding neurons or body organs (p. 313)

B

Bacteria: very small, one-celled monerans (p. 79)

Balanced diet: a diet with the right amount of each nutrient (p. 192)

Ball-and-socket joint: a joint that allows you to twist and turn the bones in a circle where they meet (p. 291)

Bases: liquids that have pH values greater than 7 (p. 684)

Behavior: the way an animal acts (p. 352)

Bicuspid (bi KUS pud) **valve:** the valve between the left atrium and the left ventricle (p. 227)

Biennial (bi EN ee ul): a plant that produces seeds at the end of the second year of growth and then dies (p. 447)

Bile: a green liquid that breaks large fat droplets into small fat droplets (p. 210)

Biodegradable (bi oh duh GRAYD uh bul): something that can be broken down by microbes into harmless chemicals and used by other living things (p. 681)

Biology: the study of living and once-living things (p. 5)

Biome (BI ohm): a land area with a distinct climate and with specific types of plants and animals (p. 664)

Biotechnology (bi oh tek NAHL uh jee): the use of living things to solve practical problems (p. 85)

Blade: the thin, flat part of a leaf (p. 398)

Blood pressure: the force created when blood pushes against the walls of vessels (p. 232)

Blue-green bacteria: small, one-celled monerans that contain chlorophyll and can make their own food (p. 87)

Body cells: cells that make up most of the body, such as the skin, blood, bones, and stomach (p. 464)

Bone marrow: the soft center part of the bone (p. 248)

Bony fish: fish that have skeletons made mostly of bone (p. 168)

Brain: the organ that sends and receives messages to and from all body parts (p. 314)

Breeding: the bringing together of two living things to produce offspring (p. 599)

Bronchi (BRAUN ki): two short tubes that carry air from the trachea to the left and right lung (p. 267)

Budding: reproduction in which a small part of the parent grows into a new organism (p. 106)

Bulb: a short, underground stem surrounded by fleshy leaves that contain stored food (p. 486)

C

Caffeine: a stimulant found in coffee and tea, cocoa, chocolate, and some soft drinks (p. 385)

Calorie: a measure of the energy in food (p. 193)

Cambium: a thin layer of cells that divide to form new phloem on the outside and new xylem on the inside (p. 421)

Cancer: a disease in which body cells reproduce at an abnormally fast rate (p. 478)

Capillary: the smallest kind of blood vessel (p. 234)

Capsule: a sticky outer layer produced by bacteria (p. 80)

Carbohydrates (kar boh HI drayts): nutrients that supply you with energy (p. 185)

Carbon monoxide (CO): an odorless, colorless gas sometimes found in the air (p. 272)

Cardiac (KAR dee ac) **muscle:** the muscle that makes up the heart (p. 294)

Cartilage (KART ul ihj): a tough, flexible tissue that supports and shapes the bodies of some fish and some animal parts (p. 167)

Cartilage fish: jawed fish in which the entire skeleton is made of cartilage (p. 167)

Cell: the basic unit of all living things (p. 27)

Cell membrane: the cell part that gives the cell shape and holds the cytoplasm (p. 32)

Cell wall: the thick, outer covering outside the cell membrane (p. 35)

Cellular respiration: the process by which food is broken down and energy is released (p. 27)

Celsius (SEL see us): a scale with which scientists measure temperature (p. 14)

Centrioles (SEN tree ohlz): cell parts that help with cell reproduction (p. 35)

Cerebellum (ser uh BEL uhm): the brain part that helps make your movements smooth and graceful, rather than robotlike (p. 317)

Cerebrum (suh REE brum): the brain part that controls thought, reason, and the senses (p. 316)

Chemical change: turns food into a form that cells can use (p. 206)

Chlorophyll (KLOHR uh fihl): a chemical that gives plants their green color and traps light energy (p. 114)

Chloroplasts (KLOR uh plasts): cell parts that contain the green pigment, chlorophyll (p. 35)

Cholesterol (kuh LES tuh ral): a fatlike chemical found in certain foods (p. 237)

Chordate (KOR dayt): an animal that, at some time in its life, has a tough, flexible rod along its back (p. 165)

Chromosomes (KROH muh sohmz): cell parts with information that determines what traits a living thing will have (p. 32)

Cilia: short, hairlike parts on the surface of a cell (p. 96)

Circulatory system: the body system made up of your blood, blood vessels, and heart (p. 222)

Class: the largest group within a phylum (p. 54)

Classify: to group things together based on similarities (p. 48)

Cleavage (KLEE vihj): the series of changes that take place to turn one fertilized egg into a hollow ball of many cells (p. 525)

Climate: the average light, temperature, and precipitation in an area taken over many years (p. 664)

Climax community: the last or final stage of succession in a community (p. 661)

Clone (KLOHN): a living thing that comes from one parent and is identical to the parent (p. 496)

Club fungi: fungi with club-shaped parts that produce spores (p. 105)

Cocaine: a controlled drug used for its stimulant effects (p. 384)

Cochlea (KAHK lee uh): a liquid-filled, coiled chamber in the ear that contains nerve cells (p. 341)

Cold-blooded: having a body temperature that changes with the temperature of the surroundings (p. 166)

Colony: a group of similar cells attached to each other (p. 79)

Color blindness: a problem in which red and green are not seen as they should be (p. 576)

Commensalism (kuh MEN suh lihz um): a relationship in which two organisms live together, and one benefits while the other gets no benefit and is not harmed (p. 645)

Communicable (kuh MYEW nih kuh bul) **diseases:** those that can be passed from one organism to another (p. 83)

Community: all of the living things in an area that depend upon each other (p. 638)

Competition: the struggle among living things to get their needs for life (p. 616)

Complete metamorphosis: a series of changes in an insect in which the young do not look like the adult (p. 536)

Compound eyes: eyes with many lenses (p. 159)

Cones: nerve cells that can detect color (p. 336)

Conifer (KAHN uh fur): a plant that produces seeds in cones (p. 124)

Consumers: living things that eat, or consume, other living things (p. 27)

Control: a standard for comparing results (p. 18)

Cork: the outer layer of a woody stem (p. 421)

Cornea (KOR nee uh): the clear outer covering at the front of the eye (p. 335)

Coronary (KOR uh ner ee) **vessels:** the blood vessels that carry blood to and from the heart itself (p. 237)

Cortex: a food storage tissue in plants (p. 420)

Courting behaviors: behaviors used by males and females to attract one another for mating (p. 359)

Cross pollination: when pollen from the stamen of one flower is carried to the pistil of a flower on a different plant (p. 490)

Cutting: a small section of plant stem that has been removed from a parent plant and planted to form a new plant (p. 487)

Cyst (SIHST): a young worm with a protective covering (p. 143)

Cytoplasm (SITE uh plaz um): the clear, jellylike material between the cell membrane and the nucleus that makes up most of the cell (p. 32)

D

Data: the recorded facts or measurements from an experiment (p. 18)

Day-neutral plants: plants in which flowering doesn't depend on day length (p. 441)

Decomposers: living things that get their food from breaking down dead matter into simpler chemicals (p. 81)

Dendrites: parts of the neuron that receive messages from nearby neurons (p. 313)

Dependence: needing a certain drug in order to carry out normal daily activities (p. 383)

Depressant (dih PRES unt): a drug that slows down messages in the nervous system (p. 377)

Dermis: a thick layer of cells that form in the inner part of the skin (p. 343)

Development: all the changes that occur as a living thing grows (p. 26)

Diabetes mellitus (di uh BEET us · MEL uht us): a disease that results when the pancreas doesn't make enough insulin (p. 324)

Diaphragm: a sheetlike muscle that separates the inside of your chest from the intestines and other organs of your abdomen (p. 270)

Diffusion (dif YEW zhun): the movement of a substance from where there is a large amount of it to where there is a small amount of it (p. 38)

Digestion: the changing of food into a usable form (p. 205)

Digestive system: a group of organs that take in food and change it into a form the body can use (p. 204)

DNA: a molecule that makes up genes and determines the traits of all living things (p. 586)

Dominant (DAHM uh nunt) **genes:** those that keep other genes from showing their traits (p. 549)

Dosage: how much and how often to take a drug (p. 372)

Drug: a chemical that changes the way a living thing functions when it is taken into the body (p. 370)

Drug abuse: the incorrect or improper use of a drug (p. 383)

Dyslexia (dis LEHK see uh): a genetic disorder in which the person sees and writes some letters or words backward (p. 579)

E

Eardrum: the membrane that vibrates at the end of the ear canal (p. 340)

Ecology (ih KAHL uh jee): the study of how living things interact with each other and with their environment (p. 654)

Ecosystem: a community interacting with the environment (p. 654)

Egg: a female reproductive cell (p. 118)

Embryo (EM bree oh): an organism in its earliest stages of growth (p. 124)

Emigration (em uh GRAY shun): the movement of animals out of an area (p. 634)

Emphysema (em fuh SEE muh): a lung disease that results in the breakdown of alveoli (p. 273)

Endangered: a species of living thing that is in danger of becoming extinct (p. 675)

Endocrine (EN duh krin) **system:** the body system made up of small glands that make chemicals that carry messages through the body (p. 320)

Endodermis: a ring of waxy cells that surrounds the xylem in roots (p. 429)

Endoskeleton (EN doh skel uht uhn): a skeleton on the inside of the body (p. 165)

Endospore (EN duh spor): a thick-walled structure that forms inside a bacterial cell (p. 81)

Energy pyramid: a diagram that shows energy loss in the food chain (p. 643)

Enzymes (EN zimes): chemicals that speed up the rate of chemical change (p. 206)

Epidermis (ep uh DUR mus): the outer layer of cells of a plant (p. 401)

Epiglottis (ep uh GLAHT uhs): a small flap that closes over the windpipe when you swallow (p. 267)

Erosion: the wearing away of soil by wind and water (p. 676)

Esophagus (ih SAHF uh gus): a tube that connects the mouth to the stomach (p. 209)

Estrogen (ES truh jun): a female hormone (p. 516)

Estrous (ES trus) **cycle:** a cycle in which a female will mate only at certain times (p. 510)

Ethyl (ETH ul) **alcohol:** a drug formed from sugars by yeast that is found in all alcoholic drinks (p. 386)

Evolution (ev uh LEW shun): a change in the hereditary features of a group of organisms over time (p. 616)

Excretory (EK skruh tor ee) **system:** the body system made up of those organs that rid the body of liquid wastes (p. 274)

Exoskeleton (EK soh skel uht uhn): a skeleton on the outside of the body (p. 159)

Experiment: testing a hypothesis using a series of steps with controlled conditions (p. 16)

External fertilization: the joining of egg and sperm outside the body (p. 508)

Extinct (ihk STINGT): a life-form that no longer exists (p. 617)

F

Family: the largest group within an order (p. 54)

Farsighted: being able to see clearly far away but not close up (p. 345)

Fats: nutrients that are stored by your body and used later as a source of energy (p. 185)

Fern: a vascular plant that reproduces with spores (p. 121)

Fertile: being able to reproduce by forming egg or sperm cells (p. 610)

Fertilization: the joining of the egg and sperm (p. 118)

Fertilizer: a substance made of minerals that improves soil for plant growth (p. 449)

Fetus (FEET us): an embryo that has all of its body systems (p. 529)

Fibrous roots: many-branched roots that grow in clusters (p. 428)

Fission (FIHSH un): the process of one organism dividing into two organisms (p. 80)

Fixed joints: joints that don't move (p. 291)

Flagellum (fluh JEL um): a whiplike thread used for movement by bacteria (p. 80)

Flatworms: the simplest worms, they have flattened bodies (p. 142)

Flower: the reproductive part of a flowering plant (p. 128)

Flowering plant: a vascular plant that produces seeds inside a flower (p. 128)

Food chain: a pathway of energy and materials through a community (p. 641)

Food web: food chains connected in a community (p. 642)

Fossil fuel: the remains of organisms that lived millions of years ago (p. 677)

Fossils: the remains of once-living things from ages past (p. 617)

Fraternal twins: twins that form from two different fertilized eggs (p. 597)

Fruit: an enlarged ovary that contains seeds (p. 492)

Fungi: organisms that have cell walls and absorb food from their surroundings (p. 61)

G

Gallbladder: a small, baglike part located under the liver that stores bile (p. 210)

Gene (JEEN): a small section of chromosome that determines a specific trait of an organism (p. 547)

Genetic code: the code that translates the DNA language into the protein language (p. 592)

Genetic counseling: the use of genetics to predict and explain traits in children (p. 580)

Genetics (juh NET ihks): the study of how traits are passed from parents to offspring (p. 546)

Genus (JEE nus): the largest group within a family (p. 55)

Germination (jur muh NAY shun): the first growth of a young plant from a seed (p. 494)

Gill: a structure used by fish and some other animals to breathe in water (p. 166)

Grafting: the process of joining a stem of one plant to the stem of another plant (p. 487)

Gravitropism (grav uh TROH pihz um): the response of a plant to gravity (p. 444)

Greenhouse effect: the trapping of heat near Earth's surface by a layer of carbon dioxide (p. 679)

Guard cells: green cells that change the size of the stomata in a leaf (p. 402)

H

Habitat (HAB uh tat): the place where a plant or animal lives (p. 638)

Heart attack: the death of a section of heart muscle (p. 237)

Hemoglobin (HEE muh gloh bun): a protein in red blood cells that joins with oxygen and gives the red cells their color (p. 248)

Hemophilia (hee muh FIHL ee uh): a disease in which a person's blood won't clot (p. 252)

Herbaceous (hur BAY shus) **stems:** soft, green stems (p. 420)

Heterozygous (HET uh roh ZI gus): an individual with a dominant and a recessive gene for a trait (p. 549)

Hibernation: the state of being inactive during cold weather (p. 170)

Hinge joints: joints that allow bones to move only back and forth (p. 291)

Hookworm: a roundworm that is a parasite of humans (p. 145)

Hormones: chemicals made in one part of an organism that affect other parts of the organism (p. 320)

Host: an organism that provides food for a parasite (p. 73)

Hydrochloric (hi druh KLOR ik) **acid:** a chemical often called stomach acid (p. 210)

Hypertension (HI pur ten chun): occurs when blood pressure is extremely high (p. 236)

Hyphae (HI fee): threadlike structures that make up the bodies of most fungi (p. 102)

Hypothesis (hi PAHTH uh sus): a statement that can be tested (p. 16)

I

Identical twins: two children that form from the splitting of one fertilized egg (p. 597)

Immigration (ihm uh GRAY shun): the movement of animals into a population (p. 634)

Immune system: the body system made up of proteins, cells, and tissues that identify and defend the body against foreign chemicals and organisms (p. 256)

Immunity: the ability of a person who once had a disease to be protected from getting the same disease again (p. 258)

Incomplete dominance: a case of inheritance in which neither gene is totally dominant over the other (p. 573)

Incomplete metamorphosis: a series of changes in an insect from nymph to adult (p. 536)

Inhalant: a drug breathed in through the lungs in order to cause a behavior change (p. 379)

Innate behavior: a way of responding that does not require learning (p. 353)

Instinct: a complex pattern of behavior that an animal is born with (p. 353)

Insulin (IHN suh lun): a hormone that lets your body cells take in glucose, a sugar, from your blood (p. 323)

Interferon (ihnt ur FIHR ahn): a chemical substance that interferes with the way viruses reproduce (p. 77)

Internal fertilization: the joining of egg and sperm inside the female's body (p. 509)

International System of Units: a measuring system based on units of 10 (p. 11)

Invertebrates (in VERT uh brayts): animals without backbones (p. 134)

Involuntary muscles: muscles you can't control (p. 294)

Iris: a muscle that controls the amount of light entering the eye (p. 334)

J

Jawless fish: fish that have no jaws and are not covered with scales (p. 167)

Jointed-leg animal: an invertebrate with an outside skeleton, bilateral symmetry, and jointed appendages (p. 158)

K

Kilogram (kg): an SI unit of mass (p. 14)

Kingdom: the largest group of living things (p. 53)

Koch's postulates (KAHKS · PAHS chuh lutz): steps for proving that a disease is caused by a certain microscopic organism (p. 82)

L

Labor: contractions of the uterus (p. 530)

Large intestine: a tubelike organ at the end of the digestive tract (p. 212)

Larva (LAR vuh): a young animal that looks completely different from the adult (p. 536)

Lateral buds: buds along the sides of a stem that give rise to new branches, leaves, or flowers (p. 423)

Learned behaviors: behaviors that must be taught (p. 356)

Lens: a clear part of the eye that changes shape as you view things at different distances (p. 335)

Lens muscle: a muscle that pulls on the lens and changes its shape (p. 335)

Leukemia (lew KEE mee uh): a blood cancer in which the number of white blood cells increases at an abnormally fast rate (p. 250)

Lichen (LI kun): a fungus and an organism with chlorophyll that live together (p. 107)

Ligaments (LIGH uh munts): tough fibers that hold one bone to another (p. 289)

Light microscope: light passes through the object being looked at and then through two or more lenses (p. 7)

Limiting factor: any condition that keeps the size of a population from increasing (p. 636)

Liver: the largest organ in the body, it makes a chemical called bile (p. 210)

Long-day plants: plants that flower when the day length rises above 12 to 14 hours (p. 441)

M

Mammal (MAM ul): an animal that has hair and feeds milk to its young (p. 173)

Mammary (MAM uh ree) **glands:** body parts that produce milk (p. 173)

Mantle: a thin, fleshy tissue that covers a soft-bodied animal (p. 149)

Medulla (muh DUL uh): the brain part that controls heartbeat, breathing, and blood pressure (p. 317)

Meiosis (mi OH sus): a kind of cell reproduction that forms eggs and sperm (p. 471)

Menstrual (MEN struhl) **cycle:** the monthly changes that take place in the female reproductive organs (p. 515)

Menstruation (men STRAY shun): a loss of cells from the uterine lining, blood, and egg (p. 516)

Metamorphosis (met uh MOR fuh sus): the changes in appearance and lifestyle that occur between the young and the adult stages (p. 535)

Meter: an SI unit of length (p. 11)

Midrib: the main vein of a leaf (p. 399)

Migration: a kind of behavior in which animals move from place to place in response to the season of the year (p. 363)

Minerals: nutrients needed to help form different cell parts (p. 190)

Mitochondria (mite uh KAHN dree uh): cell parts that produce energy from food that has been digested (p. 34)

Mitosis (mi TOH sus): cell reproduction in which two identical cells are made from one cell (p. 464)

Molting: shedding an exoskeleton (p. 159)

Monerans: one-celled organisms that don't have a nucleus (p. 61)

Moss: a small, nonvascular plant that has both stems and leaves but no roots (p. 117)

Mucus (MYEW kus): a thick, sticky material that protects the stomach and intestinal linings from enzymes and stomach acid (p. 216)

Multicellular: an organism having many different cells that do certain jobs for the organism (p. 97)

Muscular dystrophy (MUS kyuh lur · DIHS truh fee): a disease that causes the slow wasting away of skeletal muscle tissue (p. 300)

Muscular system: all the muscles in your body (p. 292)

Mutation (myew TAY shun): any change in copying the DNA message (p. 595)

Mutualism: a living arrangement in which both organisms benefit (p. 107)

N

Natural resource: any part of the environment used by humans (p. 674)

Natural selection: the process in which something in a living thing's surroundings determines if it will or will not survive to have offspring (p. 609)

Navel: where the umbilical cord was attached to the body (p. 530)

Nearsighted: being able to see clearly close up but not far away (p. 344)

Nephron (NEF rahn): a tiny filter unit of the kidney (p. 276)

Nerve: many neurons bunched together (p. 312)

Nervous system: the body system made up of cells and organs that let an animal detect changes and respond to them (p. 310)

Neurons (NOO rahnz): nerve cells (p. 312)

New-world monkeys: those that have a tail that can grasp like a hand and nostrils that open upward (p. 613)

Niche (NITSH): the job of the organism in the community (p. 638)

Nicotine: a stimulant found in tobacco (p. 385)

Nitrogen bases: the chemicals that form the rungs of a DNA molecule (p. 587)

Nitrogen cycle: the reusing of nitrogen in an ecosystem (p. 656)

Nonvascular (nahn VAS kyuh lur) **plants:** plants that don't have tubelike cells in their stems and leaves (p. 116)

Nuclear membrane: a structure that surrounds the nucleus and separates it from the rest of the cell (p. 32)

Nucleolus (new KLEE uh lus): the cell part that helps make ribosomes (p. 32)

Nucleus (NEW klee us): the cell part that controls most of the cell's activities (p. 32)

Nutrients (NEW tree unts): the chemicals in food that cells need (p. 184)

Nutrition (new TRISH un): the study of nutrients and how your body uses them (p. 184)

Nymph (NIHMF): a young insect that looks similar to the adult (p. 536)

O

Old-world monkeys: those that can't grasp with their tail, if they have one, and whose nostrils open downward (p. 613)

Olfactory (ohl FAK tree) **nerve:** a nerve that carries messages from the nose to the brain (p. 339)

Optic (AHP tihk) **nerve:** a nerve that carries messages from the retina to the brain (p. 336)

Order: the largest group within a class (p. 54)

Organ: a group of tissues that work together to do a job (p. 41)

Organ system: a group of organs that work together to do a certain job (p. 41)

Organism: a living thing (p. 41)

Osmosis (ahs MOH sus): the movement of water across the cell membrane (p. 39)

Ovaries (OHV uh reez): the female sex organs that produce eggs (p. 474)

Over-the-counter drug: one that you can buy legally without a prescription (p. 371)

Overdose: the result of too much of a drug in the body (p. 374)

Oviducts (OH vuh dukts): tubelike organs that connect the ovaries to the uterus (p. 514)

Ovules: tiny, round parts of a seed plant that contain the egg cells (p. 489)

Ozone: a molecule made of three oxygen atoms that forms a layer high above Earth's surface (p. 679)

P

Palisade layer: the layer of long, green cells below the upper epidermis of a leaf (p. 402)

Pancreas (PAN kree us): an organ located below the stomach that makes three different enzymes (p. 210)

Parasite (PAR uh site): an organism that lives in or on another living thing and gets food from it (p. 73)

Parasitism (PAR uh suh tihz um): a relationship between two organisms in which one is helped and the other is harmed (p. 646)

Parental care: a behavior in which adults give food, protection, and warmth to eggs or young (p. 365)

Pasteurization (pas chuh ruh ZAY shun): the process of heating milk to kill harmful bacteria (p. 85)

Pedigree: a diagram that can show how a certain trait is passed along in a family (p. 581)

Penis (PEE nus): places sperm in vagina during mating (p. 513)

Perennial (puh REN ee ul): a plant that doesn't die at the end of one or two years of growth (p. 448)

Pesticides: chemicals used to kill unwanted pests (p. 680)

Petals: often brightly colored and scented parts of a flower that attract insects to the flower (p. 488)

Pheromones (FER uh mohnz): chemicals that affect the behavior of members of the same species (p. 360)

Phloem (FLOH em): cells that carry food that is made in the leaves to all parts of the plant (p. 121)

Photosynthesis (foht oh SIHN thuh sus): the process in which plants use water, carbon dioxide, and energy from the sun to make food (p. 114)

Phototropism (foh toh TROH pihz um): the growth of a plant in response to light (p. 443)

Phylum (FI lum): the largest group within a kingdom (p. 54)

Physical change: occurs when large food pieces are broken down into smaller pieces (p. 205)

Pistil (PIH stul): the female reproductive organ of a flower (p. 489)

Pituitary (puh TEW uh ter ee) **gland:** an endocrine gland that forms many different hormones (p. 321)

Placenta (pluh SENT uh): an organ that connects the embryo to the mother's uterus (p. 526)

Planarian (pluh NAIR ee un): a common freshwater flatworm that is not a parasite (p. 144)

Plants: organisms that are made up of many cells, have chlorophyll, and can make their own food (p. 62)

Plasma (PLAZ muh): the nonliving, yellow liquid part of blood (p. 247)

Platelets (PLAYT lutz): cell parts that aid in forming blood clots (p. 251)

Pneumonia (noo MOH nyuh): a lung disease caused by bacteria, a virus, or both (p. 273)

Polar body: a small cell formed during meiosis in a female (p. 475)

Pollen: the tiny yellow grains of seed plants in which sperm develop (p. 125)

Pollination (pahl ih NAY shun): the transfer of pollen from the male part of a seed plant to the female part (p. 490)

Pollution: anything that makes the surroundings unhealthy or unclean (p. 677)

Population: a group of living things of the same species that live in an area (p. 632)

Pore: a small opening in a sponge through which water enters (p. 137)

Precipitation (prih sihp uh TAY shun): water in the air that falls to Earth as rain or snow (p. 663)

Predation: the predator-prey relationship (p. 647)

Predator: an animal that hunts, kills, and eats another animal (p. 647)

Prescription drug: one that a doctor must tell you to take (p. 371)

Prey: the animal that the predator kills and eats (p. 647)

Primary consumers: animals that eat only plants (p. 639)

Primates: mammals with eyes that face forward, a well-developed cerebrum, and thumbs that can be used for grasping (p. 613)

Producers: living things that make, or produce, their own food (p. 27)

Proteins (PROH teenz): nutrients that are used to build and repair body parts (p. 185)

Protists: mostly single-celled organisms that have a nucleus and other cell parts (p. 61)

Protozoans (proht uh ZOH uhnz): one-celled animal-like organisms with a nucleus (p. 94)

Psychedelic (si kuh DEL ihk) **drug:** one that alters the way the mind works and changes the signals we receive from our sense organs (p. 378)

Puberty (PEW bur tee): the stage in life when a person begins to develop sex cells (p. 474)

Pulmonary (PUL muh ner ee) **artery:** an artery that carries blood away from the heart to the lungs (p. 229)

Pulmonary veins: veins that carry blood from the lungs to the left side of the heart (p. 229)

Punnett (PUH nuht) **square:** a way to show which genes can combine when egg and sperm join (p. 553)

Pupa (PYEW puh): a quiet, non-feeding stage that occurs between larva and adult (p. 537)

Pupil: an opening in the center of the iris through which light enters the eye (p. 334)

Pure dominant: an organism with two dominant genes for a trait (p. 549)

Pure recessive: an organism with two recessive genes for a trait (p. 549)

R

Radiation: energy that is given off by atoms (p. 596)

Radon: a gas found in the ground that gives off radiation (p. 679)

Recessive (rih SES ihv) **genes:** those that do not show their traits when dominant genes are present (p. 549)

Recombinant DNA: the DNA that is formed when DNA from one organism is put into the DNA of another organism (p. 601)

Recommended daily allowance: the amount of each vitamin and mineral a person needs each day to stay in good health (p. 189)

Recycling: the reusing of resources (p. 689)

Red blood cells: cells in the blood that carry oxygen to the body tissues (p. 247)

Reflexes: quick, protective reactions that occur within the nervous system (p. 318)

Regeneration (rih jen uh RAY shun): reproduction in which the parent separates into two or more pieces and each piece forms a new organism (p. 505)

Reproduce: to form offspring similar to the parents (p. 26)

Reproductive system: the body system used to produce offspring (p. 513)

Reptile: an animal that has dry, scaly skin and can live on land (p. 170)

Respiratory (RES pruh tor ee) **system:** the body system made up of body parts that help with the exchange of gases (p. 264)

Retina (RET nuh): a structure at the back of the eye made of light-detecting nerve cells (p. 335)

Ribosomes (RI buh sohmz): cell parts where proteins are made (p. 34)

RNA: a chemical that acts as a messenger for DNA (p. 592)

Rods: nerve cells that detect motion and help us to tell if an object is light or dark (p. 336)

Root hairs: threadlike cells of the epidermis that absorb water and minerals for a plant (p. 429)

Roundworms: worms that have long bodies with pointed ends (p. 145)

Runner: a stem that grows along the ground or in the air and forms a new plant at its tip (p. 486)

S

Sac fungi: fungi that produce spores in saclike structures (p. 106)

Saliva: a liquid that is formed in the mouth and contains an enzyme (p. 208)

Salivary (SAL uh ver ee) **glands:** three pairs of small glands located under the tongue and behind the jaw (p. 208)

Saprophytes (SAP ruh fites): organisms that use dead materials for food (p. 81)

Scientific method: a series of steps used to solve problems (p. 15)

Scientific name: the genus and species names together (p. 59)

Sclera (SKLER uh): the tough, white outer covering of the eye (p. 334)

Scrotum (SKROH tum): the sac that holds the testes (p. 513)

Secondary consumers: animals that eat other animals (p. 639)

Sediment: material that settles on the bottom of a body of water (p. 676)

Sedimentary rocks: those that form from layers of mud, sand, and other fine particles (p. 617)

Seed: a part of a plant that contains a new, young plant and stored food (p. 124)

Segmented worms: worms with bodies divided into sections called segments (p. 146)

Self pollination: when pollen moves from the stamen of one flower to the pistil of the same flower or of another flower on the same plant (p. 490)

Semicircular canals: inner ear parts that help us keep our balance (p. 341)

Semilunar (sem ih LEW nur) **valves:** valves located between the ventricles and their arteries (p. 227)

Sense organs: parts of the nervous system that tell an animal what is going on around it (p. 332)

Sepals: often green, leaflike parts of a flower that protect the young flower while it is still a bud (p. 488)

Sex cells: reproductive cells produced in sex organs (p. 471)

Sex chromosomes: chromosomes that determine sex (p. 568)

Sexual reproduction: the forming of a new organism by the union of two reproductive cells (p. 118)

Sexually transmitted diseases: those transmitted through sexual contact (p. 518)

Short-day plants: plants that flower when the day length falls below 12 to 14 hours (p. 441)

Sickle-cell anemia: a genetic disorder in which all the red blood cells are shaped like sickles (p. 574)

Side effect: a change other than the expected change caused by a drug (p. 372)

Sister chromatids (KROH muh tidz): two strands of a doubled chromosome (p. 466)

Skeletal muscles: muscles that move the bones of the skeleton (p. 293)

Skeletal system: the framework of bones in your body (p. 286)

Slime molds: funguslike protists that are consumers (p. 99)

Small intestine: a long, hollow, tubelike organ where most of the chemical digestion of food takes place (p. 210)

Smog: a combination of smoke and fog (p. 678)

Smooth muscle: involuntary muscle that makes up the intestines, arteries, and many other body organs (p. 295)

Social insects: insects that live in groups, with each individual doing a certain job (p. 362)

Soft-bodied animals: animals with a soft body that is usually protected by a hard shell (p. 149)

Solid bone: the very compact or hard part of a bone (p. 289)

Species: the smallest group of living things (p. 55); a group of living things that can breed with others of the same species and form fertile offspring (p. 610)

Sperm: a male reproductive cell (p. 118)

Spinal cord: the body part that carries messages from the brain to body nerves or from body nerves to the brain (p. 315)

Spiny-skin animal: an invertebrate with a five-part body design, radial symmetry, and spines (p. 163)

Sponges: simple invertebrates that have pores (p. 137)

Spongy bone: the part of a bone that has many empty spaces, much like those in a sponge (p. 289)

Spongy layer: the layer of round, green cells directly below the palisade layer of a leaf (p. 402)

Sporangia: structures, found on the tips of hyphae, that make spores (p. 104)

Sporangium (spuh RAN jee uhm) **fungi:** fungi that produce spores in sporangia (p. 104)

Spores: special cells that develop into new organisms (p. 96)

Sporozoans (spor uh ZOH uhnz): protozoans that reproduce by forming spores (p. 96)

Sprains: injuries that occur to your ligaments at a joint (p. 300)

Stamen: the male reproductive organ of a flower (p. 488)

Stereomicroscope (STER ee oh MI kruh skohp): used for viewing large objects and things through which light cannot pass (p. 8)

Stimulant (STIHM yuh lunt): a drug that speeds up body activities that are controlled by the nervous system (p. 376)

Stimulus: something that causes a reaction in an organism (p. 353)

Stinging-cell animals: animals with stinging cells and hollow, sock-shaped bodies that lack organs (p. 139)

Stoma (STOH muh): a small pore or opening in the lower epidermis of a leaf (p. 402)

Stomach: a baglike, muscular organ that mixes and chemically changes protein (p. 209)

Succession: the changes that take place in a community as it gets older (p. 660)

Symmetry (SIH muh tree): the balanced arrangement of body parts around a center point or along a center line (p. 134)

Synapse (SIN aps): a small space between the axon of one neuron and the dendrite of a nearby neuron (p. 313)

T

Taproot: a large, single root with smaller side roots (p. 428)

Tapeworm: a kind of flatworm that has a flattened, ribbonlike body divided into sections (p. 142)

Taste buds: nerve cells in the tongue that detect chemical molecules (p. 339)

Technology: the use of scientific discoveries to solve everyday problems (p. 20)

Tendon (TEN duhn): a tough, fibrous tissue that connects muscle to bone (p. 295)

Tentacles (TENT ih kulz): armlike parts of stinging-cell animals (p. 139)

Terminal bud: the bud at the tip of a stem (p. 423)

Testes (TES teez): the male sex organs that produce sperm (p. 474)

Theory: a hypothesis that has been tested again and again by many scientists, with similar results each time (p. 19)

Thigmotropism: a plant growth response to contact (p. 444)

Threatened: a species of living thing that is close to being endangered (p. 675)

Thyroid (THI royd) **gland:** an important endocrine gland that is found near the lower part of your neck and produces thyroxine (p. 322)

Thyroxine (thi RAHK sun): the hormone that controls how fast your cells release energy from food (p. 322)

Tissue: a group of similar cells that work together to carry out a special job (p. 40)

Toxic: poisonous (p. 678)

Trachea (TRAY kee uh): a tube about 15 centimeters long that carries air to two shorter tubes called the bronchi (p. 267)

Trait: a feature that a thing has (p. 48)

Transpiration (trans puh RAY shun): the process of water passing out through the stomata of leaves (p. 403)

Tricuspid (tri KUS pud) **valve:** the valve between the right atrium and the right ventricle (p. 227)

Tropism (TROH pihz um): a movement of a plant caused by a change in growth as a response to a stimulus (p. 443)

Tube feet: parts of a starfish that are like suction cups and help the starfish move, attach to rocks, and get food (p. 163)

Tuber: an underground root or stem swollen with stored food (p. 485)

U

Umbilical (uhm BIL ih kuhl) **cord:** made of blood vessels that connect the embryo to the placenta (p. 526)

Urea (yoo REE uh): a waste that results from the breakdown of body protein (p. 274)

Ureter (YOOR ut ur): a tube that carries wastes from a kidney to the uninary bladder (p. 276)

Urethra (yoo REE thruh): a tube that carries liquid wastes from the urinary bladder to outside the body (p. 276)

Urinary bladder: a sac that stores liquid wastes removed from the kidneys (p. 276)

Urine: the waste liquid that reaches the ureter (p. 277)

Uterus (YEWT uh rus): a muscular organ in which the fertilized egg develops (p. 514)

V

Vaccines: substances made from weakened or dead viruses that protect you against certain diseases (p. 78)

Vacuole (VAK yuh wol): a liquid-filled space that stores food, water, and minerals (p. 35)

Vagina (vuh JI nuh): a muscular tube that leads from outside the female's body to the uterus (p. 515)

Valves: flaps in the heart that keep blood flowing in one direction (p. 227)

Variable: something that causes the changes observed in an experiment (p. 18)

Variation (ver ee AY shun): a trait that makes an individual different from others of its species (p. 616)

Vas deferens (VAS · DEF uh runs): carries sperm from testes to urethra (p. 513)

Vascular (VAS kyuh lur) **plants:** plants that have tubelike cells in their roots, stems, and leaves to carry food and water (p. 116)

Vein: a blood vessel that carries blood back to the heart (p. 226)

Vena cava (VEE nuh · KAY vuh): the largest vein in the body (p. 229)

Ventricles (VEN trih kulz): the large bottom chambers of the heart (p. 225)

Vertebrates (VERT uh brayts): animals with backbones (p. 134)

Vestigial (vuh STIJ ee ul) **structure:** a body part that no longer has a function (p. 620)

Villi (VIHL i): the fingerlike parts on the lining of the small intestine (p. 214)

Virus: a chromosome-like part surrounded by a protein coat (p. 72)

Vitamins: chemical compounds needed in very small amounts for growth and tissue repair of the body (p. 188)

Vitreous (VI tree us) **humor:** a jelly-like material inside the eye (p. 335)

Volume: the amount of space a substance occupies (p. 13)

Voluntary muscles: muscles you can control (p. 294)

W

Warm-blooded: having a body temperature that is controlled so that it stays about the same no matter what the temperature of the surroundings (p. 171)

Water cycle: the path that water takes through an ecosystem (p. 657)

White blood cells: the cells in the blood that destroy harmful microbes, remove dead cells, and make proteins that help prevent disease (p. 249)

Wilting: when a plant loses water faster than it can be replaced (p. 403)

Woody stem: a nongreen stem that grows to be thick and hard (p. 421)

X

X chromosomes: sex chromosomes of the female (p. 568)

Xylem (ZI lum): cells that carry water and dissolved minerals from the roots to the leaves (p. 121)

Y

Y chromosome: a sex chromosome found only in males (p. 568)

INDEX

A

B

C

D

E

F

G

H

I

J

K

L

M

736

N

O

P

Q

R

S

T

U

V

W

X

Y

PHOTO CREDITS

Cover photo: Claude Steelman/Tom Stack & Associates
iv, Walter Cunningham; **v**(t) Larry Lefever/Grant Heilman, (inset) Rod Plank/Tom Stack & Associates, (c) Alvin Staffan, (b) Steve Lissau; **vi**(tl) Johnny Johnson/Animals, Animals, (tc) Walt Anderson/Tom Stack & Associates, (b) Aaron Haupt/Glencoe; **vii**(t) David Dennis, (c) a,Larry Lipsky/Tom Stack & Associates, b,Hans Pfletschin/Peter Arnold, Inc., c, National Audubon Society/Photo Researchers, d, Fred Bavendam/Peter Arnold, Inc., e, Spencer Swanger/Tom Stack & Associates, f, Aaron Haupt/Glencoe, g, Tim Courlas, h, H. Gritscher/Peter Arnold, Inc., (b) Lynn Stone; **ix**(tr) a, Donald Dietz/Stock Boston, b, Tim Davis/Photo Researchers, (tr), Hank Morgan/Science Source/Photo Researchers, (bl) a, John Radcliffe Infirmary/SPL/Photo Researchers, b, Lennart Nilsson, (br) First Image; **x**(t) Cobalt Productions, (b) Alan Carey; **xi**(t) R. Feldman/Dan McCoy/Rainbow, (b) Harris Biological Supply Company; **xii**(b) W. Gregory Brown/Animals, Animals, (t) Lynn Stone; **xiii**(b) Gerard Photography, (t) Dr Tony Brian/SPL/Photo Researchers; **xiv**(t) David Brownell, (b) Pictures Unlimited; **xv**(b) Grant Heilman/Grant Heilman, (t) Elaine Shay; **xvi**, James Westwater; **xvii**(t) Pictures Unlimited, (b)Alan Carey; **xviii**(t) William Weber, (b) John Giannicchi/SPL/Photo Researchers; **xix**(t) Elaine Shay, (b) David Frazier; **xx**(t) Frank Balthis, (b) Ted Rice; **xxi**, David Dennis; **xxii**(t) Comstock, (b) Bob McKeever/Tom Stack & Associates; **xxiii**(t) Larry Lefever/Grant Heilman, (b) G.C. Lockwood; **xxiv**, Pictures Unlimited; **1**, M. Woodbridge Williams/National Park Service; **2-3**, JPL/NASA, (inset)NASA; **4**, Bob Daemmrich; **5**, Tim Courlas; **6**(l) USDA, (r) Doug Martin; **8**(l) E. Herzog/Photo Researchers, (c) Michael Abbey/Photo Researchers, (r) Martin Rodgers/Taurus Photos; **11**(t) David Dennis, (b) Tim Courlas; **13**, NASA; **20**, Hank Morgan/Photo Researchers; **21**(t) F. Stuart Westmorland/Tom Stack & Associates, (b) Lionel Deleingne/Stock Boston; **24**, Johnny Johnson/Animals, Animals; **25**, Walt Anderson/Tom Stack & Associates; **27**(l) David M. Dennis/Tom Stack & Associates, (r) Dwight Kuhn; **29**(t) John Kaprieliam/Photo Researchers, (b) Larry Hamill; **31**, Oxford Scientific Films/Earth Scenes; **35**(l) K.R. Porter/Photo Researchers, (r) Robert Warmbrodt/Ohio State University; **37**(tl) John Shaw/Tom Stack & Associates, (bl) Oxford Scientific Films/Animals, Animals, (tr) Fritz Prenzel/Animals, Animals, (br) Juan M. Renyito/Animals, Animals; **42**(tr) Thomas Kitchin/Tom Stack & Associates, (bl)First Image, (tl)Brian Parker/Tom Stack & Associates, (br)Doug Martin; **43**(tl) Richard Kolar/Earth Scenes, (tr),(br) First Image; (br) Tim Courlas; **46**, Brian Parker/Tom Stack & Associates; **47**, Peter Parks/Oxford Scientific Films/Animals, Animals; **48**, Bud Fowle; **50**, First Image; **54**(l) Jeffery W. Lang/Photo Researchers, (tr) John Serrao/Photo Researchers, (br) Soames Summerhay/Photo Researchers; **56**, First Image; **57**(t) Comstock, (c) Lynn Stone, (b) Dave R. Fleetham/Tom Stack & Associates; **59**(l) Anup Shah/Animals, Animals, (c) Ralph A. Beinhold/Animals, Animals, (r) Rod Planck/Tom Stack & Associates, (tr) Jerry L. Ferrana/Photo Researchers; **60**(l) Alan Carey, (c) Michael Collier, (r) David Zosel; **61**, Woods Hole Oceanographic Institution; **66**, Steve Schapiro/Sygma; **67**, Doug Martin; **68-69**, Roger & Donna Aitkenhead/Animals, Animals, (inset) Runk-Schoenberger/Grant Heilman; **70**, Dr. Gopal Murti/Science Photo Library/Custom Medical Stock Photo; **71**, CNRI/Science Photo Library/Photo Researchers; **72**(l) Omikron/Science Source/Photo Researchers, (c) CNRI/SPL/Photo Researchers, (r) R. Feldman-Dan McCoy/Rainbow; **73**, Omnikon/Photo Researchers; **74**(t) Prof. Luc Montagnier/CNRI/Science Photo Library/Photo Researchers, (b) James E. Lloyd/Animals, Animals; **78**(l) Pictures Unlimited, (r) Martin Rodgers/Stock Boston; **79**(tl) Dr. Tony Brain & David Parker/Science Photo Library/Photo Researchers, (bl) CNRI/Science Photo Library/Photo Researchers, (r) CNRI/Science Photo Library/Photo Researchers; **81**, John Kohout/Root Resources; **83**(l) NIH/Science Photo Library/Photo Researchers, (r) CNRI/Science Photo Library/Photo Researchers; **84**(l) Doug Martin, (c),(r) First Image; **85**, First Image; **86**(t) Ken W. Davis/Tom Stack & Associates, (b) First Image; **88**, Brian Parker/Tom Stack & Associates; **89**(l) Biophoto Associates-Science Source/Photo Researchers, (r) Arthur M. Siegelman; **92**, Rod Planck/Tom Stack & Associates; **93**, Ward's Natural Science Establishment; **94**(l) Eric Grave/Science Source/Photo Researchers, (c) Oxford Scientific Films/Animals, Animals, (r) John Shaw/Tom Stack & Associates; **96**, Eric Grave/Photo Researchers; **98**(t) Jan Hinsch/SPL/Photo Researchers, (b) Ward's Natural Science Establishment; **99**, Joyce Photographics/Photo Researchers; **102**(r) David M. Dennis/Tom Stack & Associates, (l) Jack Swenson/Tom Stack & Associates; **105**, Cary Wolinsky/Stock Boston; **106**(l) A. McClenaghan/Photo Researchers, (r) Biophoto Associates/Photo Researchers; **107**, Breck Kent; **112**, Ray Bishop/Stock Boston; **113**, Al Staffan; **114**, Courtesy: Ray F. Everett; **117**(l) Rod Planck/Tom Stack & Associates, (r) Jack Wilburn/Earth Scenes; **118**, Aaron Haupt/Glencoe; **122**, Breck P. Kent/Earth Scenes; **124**(l) Rich Brommer, (c) John Gerlach/Tom Stack & Associates, (r)Doug Sokell/Tom Stack & Associates; **126**(t) Eric Carle/Stock Boston, (b) Bob Daemmrich; **127**(t) Donald Dietz/Stock Boston, (b) Tim Davis/Photo Researchers; **128**(t) Kodansha/Science Software System, (bl) Jack Wilburn/Earth Scenes, (br) Zig Leszczynski/Earth Scenes; **129**(t) Patti Murray/Earth Scenes, (b) First Image; **132**, Nancy Sefton/Photo Researchers; **133**, Brian Parker/Tom Stack & Associates; **137**, Cindy Garoutte/Tom Stack & Associates; **139**(l) William Curtsinge/Photo Researchers, (c) Dave Fleetham/Tom Stack & Associates, (r) Lynn Funkhouser/Peter Arnold, Inc.; **142**, Michael Klein/Peter Arnold, Inc.; **146**(l) Alvin Staffan, (r) Breck Kent; **149**(l) George Holton/Photo Researchers, (r) Garry G. Gibson/Photo Researchers; **150**(t) F.E. Unverhav/Animals, Animals, (b) Ed Robinson/Tom Stack & Associates; **152**(l) Larry Lipsky/Tom Stack & Associates, (lc) Hans Pfletschinger/Peter Arnold, Inc., (rc) National Audubon Society/Photo Researchers, (r) Fred Bavendam/Peter Arnold, Inc.; **153**(rc) Tim Courlas, (r) H. Gritscher/Peter Arnold, Inc., (l) Spencer Swanger/Tom Stack & Associates, (lc) Aaron Haupt/Glencoe; **156**, Mark Newman/Tom Stack & Associates; **157**, Colin Milkens/Oxford Scientific Films/Animals, Animals; **158**, Jack Swenson/Tom Stack & Associates; **159**(t) George Harrison/Grant Heilman, (b) Donald Specker/Animals, Animals; **160**, Tom McHugh/Photo Researchers; **163**(t) Ed Robinson/Tom Stack & Associates, (c) Larry Tackett/Tom Stack & Associates, (r) Runk-Schoenberger/Grant Heilman, (b) Ed Robinson/Tom Stack & Associates; **164**, Brian Parker/Tom Stack & Associates; **165**, Animals, Animals; **168**(t) Fred McConnaughey/Photo Researchers, (b) Al Staffan; **169**, Breck Kent/Animals, Animals; **170**(t) Alvin Staffan, (b) David Dennis; **173**, Wendy Neefus/Animals, Animals; **174**(l) Dave Watts/Tom Stack & Associates, (r) Dave Watts/Tom Stack & Associates; **175**(t) Tom McHugh/Photo Researchers, (b)P.F. Gero/Sygma; **178**(t) Peter Veit/DRK Photo, (b)Jim Zuckerman/Stock Concepts; **179**(t) Runk-Schoenberger/Grant Heilman, (b) Bud Fowle; **180-181**, Doug Martin, (inset) Bob Daemmrich; **182,183**, ML Uttermohlen; **184**, Pictures Unlimited; **185**, Tim Courlas; **189**, **190**, File; **191**, Studiohio; **192**(A-D) National Dairy Council, (E) Cobalt Productions; **196**, Light Source; **197**, Bob Daemmrich; **198,199**, ML Uttermohlem; **202**, Calvin Larsen/Photo Researchers; **203**, Davis Scharf/Peter Arnold, Inc.; **211**, Doug Martin; **217**, ML Uttermohlen; **220**, Steve Elmore/Tom Stack & Associates; **221**, Lennart Nilsson; **225**, David Gifford/SPL/Photo Researchers; **237**, Randy Schieber; **238**, Dan McCoy/Rainbow; **239**(l) Sygma, (r) Dan McCoy/Rainbow; **242**, CNRI/SPL/Photo Researchers; **243**, Aaron Haupt/Glencoe; **244**, Doug Martin; **245**, Geri Murphy; **246**, Carolina Biological Supply Co.; **247**(l) Doug Martin, (r) E.R. Degginger/Bruce Coleman; **249**(l) Runk-Schoenberger/Grant Heilman, (r) Lennart Nilsson; **250**(t) John Radcliffe Infirmary/SPL/Photo Researchers, (r) Lennart Nilsson; **251**(rt) Hickson-Bender, (rc) S.I.U./

742

Bruce Coleman, (l) Lennart Nilsson, (rb) L. Moskowitz/Medichrome; **252**, Doug Martin; **259**, Lennart Nilsson; **262**, Dave B. Fleetham/Tom Stack & Associates; **263**, Doug Martin; **272**, Young/Hoffhines; **273**, Susan McCartney/Photo Researchers; **280**, Owen Franklin/Stock Boston; **281**(t) Doug Martin, (b) Hank Morgan/Science Source/Photo Researchers; **284**, Roy Bishop/Stock Boston; **285,288**, First Image; **292,293** Bob Daemmrich; **294**, M. Huberland/Science Source/Photo Researchers; **299**, Comstock, (inset) Alexander Tsiaras/Stock Boston; **300**, Julie Simon/Discover Magazine; **301**, First Image; **308**, Aaron Haupt/Glencoe; **309**, SPL/Science Source/Photo Researchers; **304**(t) Doug Martin, (b)Scala/Art Resource; **305**, Doug Martin; **306-307**, David Parker/SPL/Photo Researchers, (insert)Sheila Terry/SPL/Photo Researchers; **326**, MRI-Cross section of body; **327**, Washington University School of Medicine; **330**, Holt Studios, Ltd/Animals Animals; **331**, Thomas Eisner; **333**, W. Perry Conway/Tom Stack & Associates; **334**, Tim Courlas; **336**, Ralph Eagle, Jr. MD/Science Source/Photo Researchers; **339**, Omnikron/Science Source/Photo Researchers; **342**, Doug Martin; **350**, ML Uttermohlen; **351**, Anthony Mercieca/Photo Researchers; **356**, David Frazier; **359**(l) Nik Kleinberg/Stock Boston, (r) J.H. Robinson/Photo Researchers; **361**(l) Cary Wolinsky/Stock Boston, (r) Stephen Krasemann/Peter Arnold, Inc.; **362**, Gary Milburn/Tom Stack & Associates; **363**(l) Stephen Krasemann/Peter Arnold, Inc., (r) K. Brink/Vireo; **364**, John David Brandt/Animals, Animals; **365**, Mac Albin; **368**, Pictures Unlimited; **369**, Aaron Haupt/Glencoe; **370**, Doug Martin; **371**(l) Tim Courlas, (r) Aaron Haupt/Glencoe; **378**, Tom HcHugh/Photo Researchers; **380**, Doug Martin; **381**, ML Uttermohlen; **382**, Pictures Unlimited; **383**, Scott Camazine/Photo Researchers; **384**(l) Christopher Brown/Stock Boston, (r) Hugh Patrick Brown/Sygma; **385**(l) Norm Thomas/Photo Researchers, (r) Pictures Unlimited; **386**, ML Uttermohlen; **388**, Larry Kolvoord/The Image Works; **389**(t) Bob Daemmrich/Stock Boston, (b) Bob Daemmrich/The Image Works; **392**(t) Historical Picture Service, (b)Tate Gallery/Art Resource; **393**, Doug Martin; **394-395**, Michael P. Gadomsli/Photo Researchers, (inset)Sam Bryan/Photo Researchers; **396**, Randy Schieber; **397**, Aaron Haupt/Glencoe; **399**(l) Jack Fields/Photo Researchers, (r) G.I. Bernard/Earth Scenes; **403**(t) Jerry Bauer, (b) Studiohio; **404**, Steve Lissau; **408**, Pictures Unlimited; **411**(l),(c) G.R. Roberts, (r) John Gerlack/Tom Stack & Associates,; **412**, Aaron Haupt/Glencoe; **413**(t) G.I. Bernard/Earth Scenes, (b) Aaron Haupt/Glencoe; **414**(l) Pictures Unlimited, (r) John Shaw/Tom Stack & Associates; **418**, H. Reinhard/Okopia/Photo Researchers; **419**, Doug Martin; **421**, Jeff Lepore/Photo Researchers; **422**, Doug Martin; **426**, Kjell B. Sandved/Photo Researchers; **427**, First Image; **428**(l) John Kaprielian/Photo Researchers, (r) Michael P. Gadomski/Photo Researchers; **431**(l) Bob Daemmrich, (r) Alan & Sandy Carey; **433**(l) G.R. Roberts, (r) Dwight Kuhn; **435**(l) Breck P. Kent/Earth Scenes, (r) Elaine Braithwaite/Peter Arnold, Inc.; **438**, Lefever-Grushow/Grant Heilman; **439**, Norm Thomas/Photo Researchers; **440**, Pat Lynch/Photo Researchers; **443**, G.R. Roberts; **444**, John Colwell/Grant Heilman; **446**(l) Charles C. Johnson, (r) Nuridsany et Perennou/Photo Researchers; **447**(l) Richard Kolar/Earth Scenes, (r) Richard Schiell/Earth Scenes; **449**(l) David M. Dennis, (c) Greg Vaughn/Tom Stack & Associates, (r) First Image; **450**(l) First Image, (c) Rod Planck/Tom Stack & Associates, (r) Kenneth Murray/Photo Researchers; **451**(l) Alan & Sandy Carey, (r) Bob Daemmrich; **452**(l) Michael S. Thompson/Comstock, (c) Kathy Merrifield/Photo Researchers, (r) G.R. Roberts; **453**(l) Patti Murray/Animals, Animals, (r) John Gerlach/Tom Stack & Associates; **454**(l) Patrick Grace/Photo Researchers, (c) G.R. Roberts, (r) Larry Hamill; **455**(l) Ed & Chris Kumler/Glencoe, (lc) John Shaw/Tom Stack & Associates, (rc) Richard Shiell/Earth Scenes, (r) Scott Camazine/Photo Researchers; **458**(t) Zig Leszczynski/Earth Scenes, (b)Illustrated London News; **459**(t) USDA, (b)David Frazier; **460-461**, Grant Heilman/Grant Heilman, (inset)Jeff Heger/Houston Convention & Visitor Bureau; **462**, IFA/Peter Arnold, Inc.; **463**, D.R. Specker/Earth Scenes; **465**, ML Uttermohlen; **467**, Grant Heilman/Grant Heilman; **470**, Photo Researchers; **474**, David Scharf/Peter Arnold, Inc.; **478**, Oscar Auerbach, M.D.; **479**(l) Aaron Haupt/Glencoe, (r) Brian Yablonsky/duomo; **482**, Breck Kent/Animals, Animals; **483**, Frank Cezus; **486**, Pictures Unlimited; **487**, Biological Photo Service; **489**(l) Dr. Jeremy Burgess/SPL/Photo Researchers, (r) Runk-Schoenberger/Grant Heilman; **493**(t) Agricultural Research Service/USDA, (b) First Image; **496**, LLT Rhodes/Earth Scenes; **498**(l) John Cancelosi/Tom Stack & Associates, (lc) Tom Edwards/Animals, Animals, (rc) Craig K. Lorenz/Photo Researchers, (r) Ron Rovtar; **499**(l) Al Staffan, (lc) Patti Murray/Earth Scenes, (rc) Rod Planck/Tom Stack & Associates, (r) Grant Heilman/Grant Heilman; **502**, Peter Menzel/Stock Boston; **503**, John Gerlach/Animals, Animals; **505**, Walker England/Photo Researchers; **506**, Carolina Biological Supply Company; **508**, Mark Stouffer/Animals, Animals; **509**, David M. Dennis; **510**, John Shaw/Tom Stack & Associates; **517**(t) Francis Leroy/Biocosmos/Science Photo Library/Photo Researchers, (b) Hank Morgan/Science Source/Photo Researchers; **522**, Lennart Nilsson; **523**, Studiohio; **527**, Howard Sochurek/Medical Images, Inc.; **528**(l) Lennart Nilsson, (r) Hans Pfletschinger/Peter Arnold, Inc.; **529**, Lennart Nilsson; **532**, Hans Pfletschinger/Peter Arnold, Inc.; **537**(tl), (bl) John Shaw/Tom Stack & Associates, (tr) Michael Fogden/Animals, Animals, (br) Don and Pat Valenti/Tom Stack & Associates; **540**(t) Latent Image, (b)David Frazier; **541**(t) Zig Leszczynski/Animals, Animals; **542-543**, Omnikon/Science Source/Photo Researchers, (inset)Catherine Ursillo/Photo Researchers; **544,545**, Studiohio; **548**, Aaron Haupt/Glencoe; **551**(t) Mavournea Hay/Daemmrich Associates, (b) Aaron Haupt/Glencoe; **555**(t) Doug Martin, (b) First Image; **559**, Bettmann Archives; **564,565**, Tim Courlas; **567**, American Cancer Society; **568**(t) File Photo, (b) Biophoto Associates/Photo Researchers; **569**, Doug Martin; **572**(l) Studio Productions, (r) First Image; **573**, Tim Courlas; **574**(l) Biological Photo Service, (r) Murayama/Biological Photo Service; **576**, First Image; **579**, Richard Hutching/Science Source/Photo Researchers; **580**, Doug Martin; **584**, Runk-Schoenberger/Grant Heilman; **585,593**, First Image; **596**(t) Aaron Haupt/Glencoe, (b) First Image; **600**, John Colwell/Grant Heilman; **604**, D. Cavagnaro/Peter Arnold, Inc.; **605**, First Image; **606**(l) Richard R. Hansen/Photo Reseachers, (r) Cary Wolinsky/Stock Boston; **609**, Richard P. Smith/Tom Stack & Associates; **610**(l) Tom McHugh/Photo Researchers, (r) Kenneth W. Fink/Photo Researchers; **613**(l) Tom McHugh/Photo Researchers, (lc) Tom McHugh/Photo Researchers, (rc) Stephen J. Krasemann/Photo Researchers, (r) Tom McHugh/Photo Researchers; **615**(l) Aaron Haupt/Glencoe, (r) John Shaw/Tom Stack & Associates; **616**(l) Ray Coleman/Photo Researchers, (r) Jeff Lepore/Photo Researchers; **619**, National Museum of Natural History; **619**, Bohdan Hrynewych/Stock Boston; **622**, Georg Gerster/Comstock; **626**(t) E.R. Degginger/Earth Scenes, (b)National Museum of Natural History; **627**(t) Studiohio, (b)Bud Fowle; **628-629**, Larry Lefever/Grant Heilman, (inset)Rod Plank/Tom Stack & Associates; **630**, Stephen J. Krasemann/Photo Researchers; **631**, Thomas Kitchin/Tom Stack & Associates; **632**, Tim Cullinan; **633**(l) Joe McDonald/Animals, Animals, (c) Larry Brock/Tom Stack & Associates, (r) Richard P. Smith/Tom Stack & Associates; **635**(t) Bruno J. Zehnder/Peter Arnold, Inc., (r) Eugene Gilliam; **636**, John Shaw/Tom Stack & Associates; **638**, Gerald Corsi/Tom Stack & Associates; **639**(l) C.C. Lockwood/Earth Scenes, (c) E.R. Degginger/Animals, Animals, (r) Zig Leszczynski/Animals, Animals; **640**, David Thompson/Oxford Scientific Films/Earth Scenes; **644**(l) Eric V. Grave/Photo Researchers, (r) Dwight R. Kuhn; **645**, Jacques Jangoux/Peter Arnold, Inc.; **646**(l) Animals, Animals/G.I. Bernard, (r) Zig Leszczynski/Animals, Animals; **647**, Charles G. Summers, Jr/Tom Stack & Associates; **652**, Kevin Schafer/Tom Stack & Associates; **653**, Sydney Thomson/Earth Scenes; **654**(l) Space Biospheres Ventures, (r) David C. Fritts/Animals, Animals; **656**, Bob Daemmrich; **660**(l) Doug Martin, (r) Pictures Unlimited; **661**(l) Michael P. Gadomski/Photo Researchers, (r) Michael P. Gadomski/Photo Researchers; **665**(a) Brian Parker/Tom Stack & Associates, (b) Richard R. Thom/Tom Stack & Associates, (c) Michael & Barbara Reed/Earth Scenes, (d) Michael P. Gadomski/Photo Researchers, (e) Charlie Ott/Photo Researchers, (f) Tom Stack/Tom Stack & Associates; **668**(lc) Charlie Ott/Photo Researchers, (rc) Jack Swenson/Tom Stack & Associates, (l) Doug Martin/Glencoe, (r) Jeff Foott/Tom Stack & Associates; **669**(tr) F. Stuart Westmorland/Tom Stack & Associates, (br)Tom McHugh/Photo Researchers, (bl) Zig Leszczynski/Animals, Animals, (tl) Joe DiStefano/Photo Researchers, (c) Dr.

Paul Zahl/Photo Researchers; **672,** Pat & Tom Leeson/Photo Researchers; **673,** David Dennis; **674,** Richard Kolar/Earth Scenes; **675**(l) Jeff Lepore/Photo Researchers, (c) Cary Wolinsky/Stock Boston, (r) Sven-Oloflinblad/Photo Researchers; **676**(l) Gregory G. Dimijian, MD/Photo Researchers, (c) Owen Franken/Stock Boston, (r) Tom Kitchin/Tom Stack & Associates; **678,** Doug Martin; **679**(l) Fredrick D. Bodin/Stock Boston, (r) ML Uttermohlen; **670,** Doug Martin; **681**(l) Tom Kitchin/Tom Stack & Associates, (c) Pictures Unlimited, (r) David Frazier; **684**(l) Don & Pat Valenti/Tom Stack & Associates, (r) John Shaw/Tom Stack & Associates; **687,** Cary Wolinsky/Stock Boston; **688,** Dr. Jeremy Burgess/SPL/Photo Researchers; **689,** ML Uttermohlen; **692**(t) Arthur C. Twomey/Photo Researchers, (b)Michael J. Philippot/Sygma; **693**(t) Studiohio, (b) Thomas Kitchin/Tom Stack & Associates; **696**(b) Omnikon/Science Source/Photo Researchers, (t)Manfred Kage/Peter Arnold, Inc.; **697**(t) Richard Kessel, (b)Stephen J. Krasemann/DRK Photo; **698,** Pictures Unlimited; **699**(t) Geri Murphy, (b)Lynn Stone; **706,** Doug Martin; **707,** CNRI/SPL/Photo Researchers; **710,711,** Aaron Haupt/Glencoe.

744

At what point shall we expect the approach of danger? By what means shall we fortify against it? Shall we expect some transatlantic military giant, to step the Ocean, and crush us at a blow? Never! All the armies of Europe, Asia and Africa combined, with all the treasure of the earth . . . could not by force, take a drink from the Ohio, or make a track on the Blue Ridge, in a trial of a thousand years. . . . If destruction be our lot, we must ourselves be its author and finisher. As a nation of freemen, we must live through all time, or die by suicide.

ABRAHAM LINCOLN, 1838

Narrative by

Geoffrey C. Ward

Based on a documentary filmscript by

Geoffrey C. Ward,
Ric Burns, and Ken Burns

With contributions by

Don E. Fehrenbacher
Barbara J. Fields
Shelby Foote
James M. McPherson
C. Vann Woodward

The Bodley Head
London

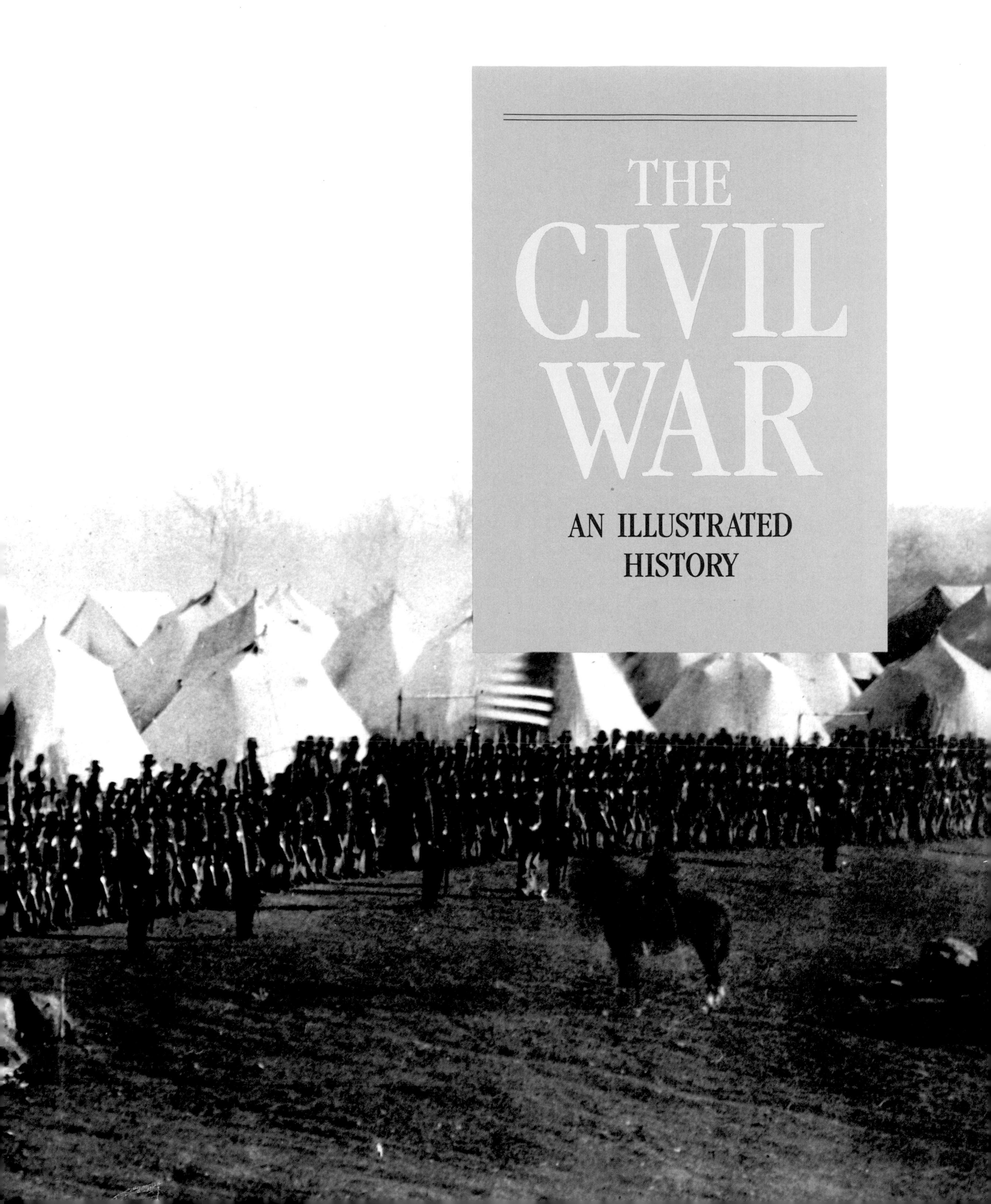
THE
CIVIL
WAR
AN ILLUSTRATED
HISTORY

First published 1991
Reprinted 1991

The Bodley Head, 20 Vauxhall Bridge Road,
London SW1V 2SA

A CIP catalogue record for this book is
available from the British Library

ISBN 0-370-31550-2

Manufactured in the United States of
America

Overleaf: The 5th Vermont at Camp Griffin, Virginia, at the beginning of the war. Its men would see action at Yorktown, Savage's Station, Antietam, Fredericksburg, Gettysburg, the Wilderness, Spotsylvania, in the Shenandoah, and at Petersburg—and 338 of them would not return when the fighting had ended.

Front endpaper: The 2nd Rhode Island Infantry drills by company near Washington in the summer of 1861.

Back endpaper: Survivors of the same regiment relive the Battle of Gettysburg at an 1886 reunion in Devil's Den.

SILVER STA

CONTENTS

Preceding pages:
Abraham Lincoln, 1865.
Ulysses S. Grant, about 1863.
Robert E. Lee, 1865.
Frederick Douglass, about 1850.
John Bell Hood, after the war.
Confederate volunteers, 1861.
General Winfield Scott Hancock (seated) and his division commanders (left to right): Francis C. Barlow, David B. Birney, and John Gibbon at Cold Harbor, Virginia, 1864.
Artillery limbers and caissons meant for U. S. Grant's army at Petersburg line the ordnance wharf at City Point, Virginia, 1864.
Ruins of Richmond, 1865.
Disinterring the dead at Cold Harbor for reburial after the war.

INTRODUCTION

THE CROSSROADS OF OUR BEING

At 4:30 a.m. on the 12th of April, 1861, General Pierre Gustave Toutant Beauregard directed his Confederate gunners to open fire on Fort Sumter, at that hour only a dark shape out in Charleston harbor. Thirty-four hours later a white flag over the fort ended the bombardment. The only casualty was a Confederate horse. It was a bloodless opening to the bloodiest war in American history.

No one could have predicted the magnitude of the explosion that rocked America following that opening shot. Until then America had been, as Bruce Catton wrote, "small enough to carry in the mind and in the heart, and a young man's fatherland was what he could see from his bedroom window." Yet most of what America was before the Civil War went into sparking that explosion, and most of what the nation became resulted from it. Entirely unimaginable before it began, the war was the most defining and shaping event in American history—so much so that it is now impossible to imagine what we would have been like without it.

Shortly after Appomattox, Walt Whitman, a Brooklyn journalist and sometime poet who worked in the appalling Union hospitals, warned posterity of what he had seen. "Future years," he wrote, "will never know the seething hell and the black infernal background, the countless minor scenes and interiors of the secession war; and it is best they should not. The real war," Whitman insisted, "will never get in the books."

The writers and historians of future years have not been scared off by Whitman's admonition. In the century and a quarter since the war's conclusion, more than fifty thousand books have been published on the Civil War: countless personal diaries and regimental histories, biographies and military narratives, pictorial essays, social analyses, works that have treated causes and effects, demographics, crop statistics, even the weather. There have been books of maps, books of letters, books of orders, books of books, slim philosophical essays and multi-volume narratives, novels, poems, and music. Each year dozens of new titles appear, again offering to revisit the war, to reinterpret or rearrange those strange days and hard events—faint traces and distant signals now—looking still for the coherent, the conclusive explanation.

And yet Whitman's words retain their force. The "real war" stays there, outside all the books, beckoning to us. Why *did* Americans kill each other? How *did* it happen? Who *were* these people who fought and killed, marched and sang, wrote home, skedaddled, deserted, died, nursed and lamented, persevered and were defeated? What was it like to be in that war? What did it do to America and Americans? What happened to the movement that freed blacks from slavery? Why have succeeding generations obscured the war with bloodless, gallant myth, blurring the causes of the war and its great ennobling outcome—the freeing of four million black people and their descendants from bondage? What did it mean that the Union won? What does it mean to be a Union? Why are we still so drawn to this tale of suffering, catastrophe, valor, and death?

Some events so pervasively condition the life of a culture that they retain the power to fascinate permanently. They become the focus of myth and the anchor of meaning for a whole society. The Civil War was such an event. Indeed, as Robert Penn Warren once wrote, "the Civil War is, for the American imagination, the great single event of our history. Without too much wrenching, it may, in fact, be said to *be* American history. Before the Civil War we had no history in the deepest and most inward sense. Or as Shelby Foote, author of the classic three-volume narrative history *The Civil War,* put it in a recent interview for our film series:

Any understanding of this nation has to be based, and I mean really based, on an understanding of the Civil War. I believe that firmly. It defined us. The Revolution did what it did. Our involvement in European wars, beginning with the First World War, did what it did. But the Civil War defined us as what we are and it opened us to being what we became, good and bad things. And it is very necessary, if you're going to understand the American character in the twentieth century, to learn about this enormous catastrophe of the nineteenth century. It was the crossroads of our being, and it was a hell of a crossroads: the suffering, the enormous tragedy of the whole thing.

Like so many others, we were drawn to that crossroads: brought back to the words and images those who lived through it left behind, to the mire of questions and myths, to the brutality and heroism of the four-year struggle that defines us as a people.

This book was born and raised in the midst of the making of a ten-hour documentary film series on the Civil War, produced for public television between 1985 and 1990. The series took us some five years—only a little longer than the war itself lasted—to plan, research, write, shoot, edit; rewrite, reshoot, research, and reedit. Twenty-four scholars, five editors, four researchers, innumerable librarians and archivists, and two helicopter pilots were among the scores of people who helped us prepare the series. It represents, we believe, the most comprehensive treatment of the Civil War ever committed to film. To us, as historical-film makers, it was the most challenging, arduous, compelling, and mysterious task imaginable, and as with all such tasks, it was enormously transforming.

The historical documentarian's vocation, whether in a film series or a book of this kind, is not precisely the same as the historian's, although it shares many of the aims and much of the spirit of the latter. Historians delight in telling us what our history is and what it means. The documentarian, on the other hand, as often delights in recording and conveying the simple fact that we have had a history at all: that there was once a time when people looked like this, or sounded like that, or felt these ways about such things. The historical documentary is often more immediate and more emotional than history proper because of its continual joy in making the past present through visual and verbal documents.

It is our belief that, so far as possible, the documents of the past must be allowed to speak for themselves, to convey meanings and emotions and stories on their own. In the course of producing the film series, we went to more than eighty museums and libraries, and filmed some 16,000 photographs, paintings, lithographs, broadsides, and newspapers of the period. From those thousands we have culled 475 images—in our opinion some of the most eloquent, compelling, amusing, curious, and beautiful images of the war—and included them in this book.

The America that went to war in 1861 was perhaps the most literate nation on earth. Soldiers at the front and civilians at home left an astonishingly rich and moving record of what they saw and felt. From the voluminous writings of those witnesses, and with the help of a truly extraordinary team of scholars and consultants, we gleaned a stockpile of quotations to accompany our stockpile of images: descriptions, reflections, opinions, cries of outrage, cynicism, sorrow, laughter, and triumph.

As best we could, we have told the story of the war—both in the film series and in the pages that follow—in the voices of the men and women who actually lived it. They include not only Robert E. Lee, Frederick Douglass, and Abraham Lincoln but the South Carolina diarist Mary Chesnut; the New York lawyer George Templeton Strong; a private from Pawtuxet, Rhode Island, Elisha Hunt Rhodes; an escaped slave from Glasgow, Missouri, Spotswood Rice—and Horace Greeley, Clara Barton, Nathaniel Hawthorne, and Julia Ward Howe; and in the end, literally hundreds of voices from across the spectrum of American experience, men and women whose lives were touched or destroyed or permanently changed by the war.

Our intention has been to put an arm around the whole war, to embrace happenings large and small, to convey the drama of epochal events alongside the color and life that lay in minute details and daily happenings. Somehow, the fact that Stonewall Jackson sucked constantly on lemons in the midst of battle adds to the chilling mystery of his military triumphs in the Shenandoah Valley in 1862. A photograph of citizens scanning the casualty lists to see which of their sons, brothers, and fathers would be coming home and which would not speaks volumes about the grief and horror that washed over the country—becoming part of domestic routine without ever quite being domesticated. In this book as in our film, we wanted to hear what Lincoln sounded like. We wanted to know what an embalming table looked like. We wanted to see an aerial reconnaissance balloon, and a soldier having his hair cut, and what Chambersburg, Pennsylvania, looked like after the Confederates burned it to the ground, and how men drilled, ate, fought, suffered, and died.

By the summer of 1861, Wilmer McLean had had enough. Two great armies were converging on his farm, and what would be the first major battle of the Civil War—Bull Run, or Manassas as the Confederates called it—would soon rage across the aging Virginian's farm, a Union shell going so far as to tear through his summer kitchen. Now McLean moved his family away from Manassas, far south and west of Richmond—out of harm's way, he prayed—to a dusty little crossroads town called Appomattox Court House.

After Bull Run, luckless Wilmer McLean moved his family from his farmhouse near Manassas Junction, Virginia (right), to the handsome brick home at Appomattox Court House (below), where he confidently hoped "never to see another soldier."

And it was there in his living room three and a half years later that Lee surrendered to Grant, and Wilmer McLean could rightfully say, "The war began in my front yard and ended in my front parlor."

The Civil War was fought in 10,000 places, from Valverde, New Mexico, and Tullahoma, Tennessee, to St. Albans, Vermont, and Fernandina on the Florida coast. More than 3 million Americans fought in it, and over 600,000 men, 2 percent of the population, died in it.

American homes became headquarters. American churches and schoolhouses sheltered the dying, and huge foraging armies swept across American farms, burned American towns. Americans slaughtered one another wholesale, right here in America, in their own cornfields and peach orchards, along familiar roads and by waters with old American names.

In two days at Shiloh, on the banks of the Tennessee River, more American men fell than in all previous American wars combined. At Cold Harbor, some 7,000 Americans fell in twenty minutes. Men who had never strayed twenty miles from their own front doors now found themselves soldiers in great armies fighting epic battles hundreds of miles from home. They knew they were making history, and it was the greatest adventure of their lives.

The Civil War has been given many names: the War Between the States, the War Against Northern Aggression, the Second American Revolution, the Lost Cause, the War of the Rebellion, the Brothers' War, the Late Unpleasantness. Walt Whitman called it the War of Attempted Secession. Confederate General Joseph Johnston called it the War *Against* the States. By whatever name, it was unquestionably the most important event in the life of the nation. It saw the end of slavery and the downfall of a southern planter aristocracy. It was the watershed of a new political and economic order, and the beginning of big industry, big business, big government. It was the first modern war and, for Americans, the costliest, yielding the most American casualties and the greatest domestic suffering, spiritually and physically. It was the most horrible, necessary, intimate, acrimonious, mean-spirited, and heroic conflict the nation has known.

Inevitably, we grasp the war through such hyperbole. In so doing, we tend to blur the fact that real people lived through it and were changed by the event. One hundred eighty-five thousand black Americans fought to free their people. Fishermen and storekeepers from Deer Isle, Maine, served bravely and died miserably in strange places like Baton Rouge, Louisiana, and Fredericksburg, Virginia. There was scarcely a family in the South that did not lose a son or brother or father.

As with any civil strife, the war was marked by excruciating ironies. Robert E. Lee became a legend in the Confederate army only after turning down an offer to command the entire Union force. Four of Lincoln's own brothers-in-law fought on the Confederate side, and one was killed. The little town of Winchester, Virginia, changed hands seventy-two times during the war, and the state of Missouri sent thirty-nine regiments to fight in the siege of Vicksburg: seventeen to the Confederacy and twenty-two to the Union.

Few people have expressed the meaning of these ironies, anomalies, and divisions better than Robert Penn Warren:

> *A civil war is, we may say, the prototype of all war, for in the persons of fellow citizens who happen to be the enemy we meet again with the old ambivalence of love and hate and with all the old guilts, the blood brothers of our childhood. In a civil war—especially one such as this when the nation shares deep and significant convictions and is not a mere handbasket of factions huddled arbitrarily together by historical happen-so—all the self-divisions of conflicts within individuals become a series of mirrors in which the plight of the country is reflected, and the self-division of the country a great mirror in which the individual may see imaged his own deep conflicts, not only the conflicts of political loyalties, but those more profoundly personal.*

Between 1861 and 1865, Americans made war on each other and killed each other in great numbers—if only to become the kind of country that could no longer conceive of how that was possible. What began as a bitter dispute over Union and States' Rights, ended as a struggle over the meaning of freedom in America. At Gettysburg in 1863, Abraham Lincoln said perhaps more than he knew. The war was about a "new birth of freedom."

KEN BURNS

RIC BURNS

Walpole, New Hampshire

In 1860, most of the nation's 31 million people lived peaceably on farms and in small towns.

At Sharpsburg, Maryland, a German pacifist sect, the Dunkers tended their whitewashed church in a sea of wheat and corn.

At a small college in Gettysburg, Pennsylvania, population 2,400, young men studied Latin and mathematics.

Steamboats filled with cotton came and went at Vicksburg, high on a bluff overlooking the Mississippi.

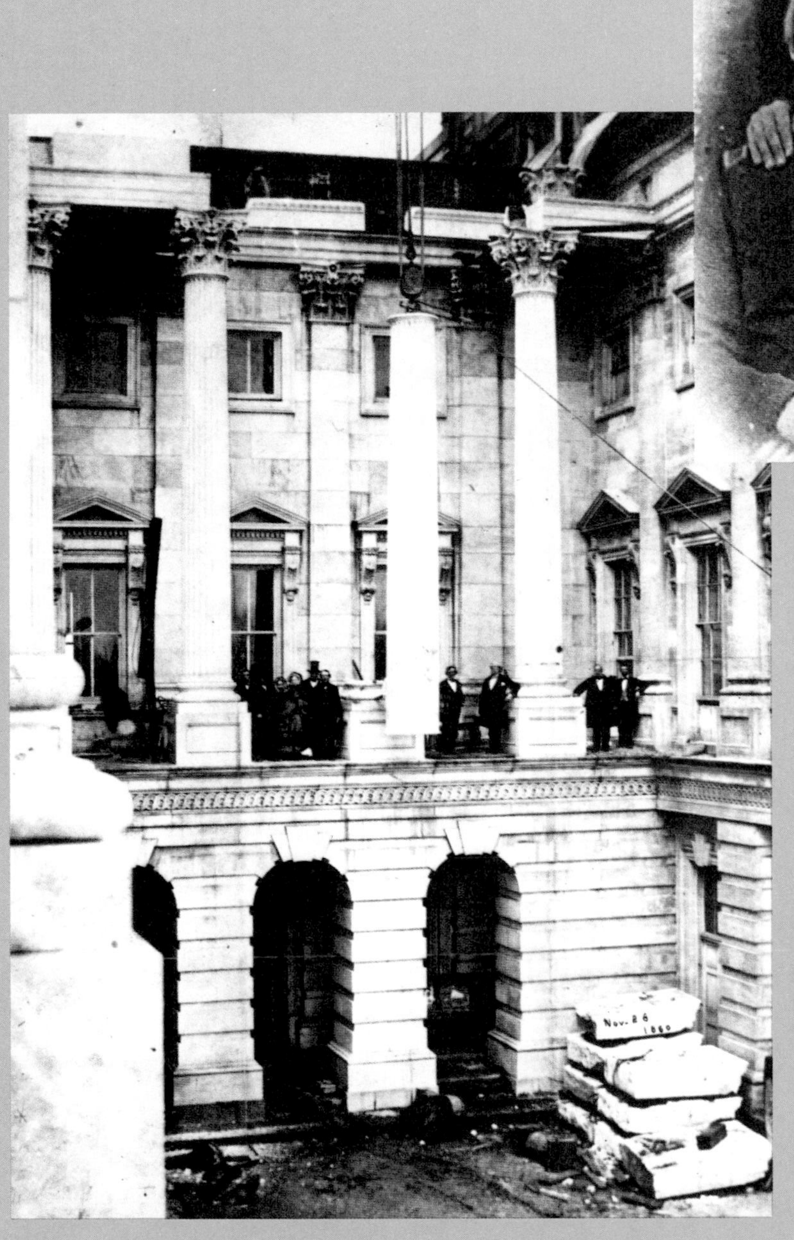

In Washington, Senator Jefferson Davis reviewed plans for remodeling the Capitol.

At West Point on the Hudson, officers (including Phillip Sheridan, center) trained, and formed friendships they thought would last a lifetime.

By 1865, everything had changed.

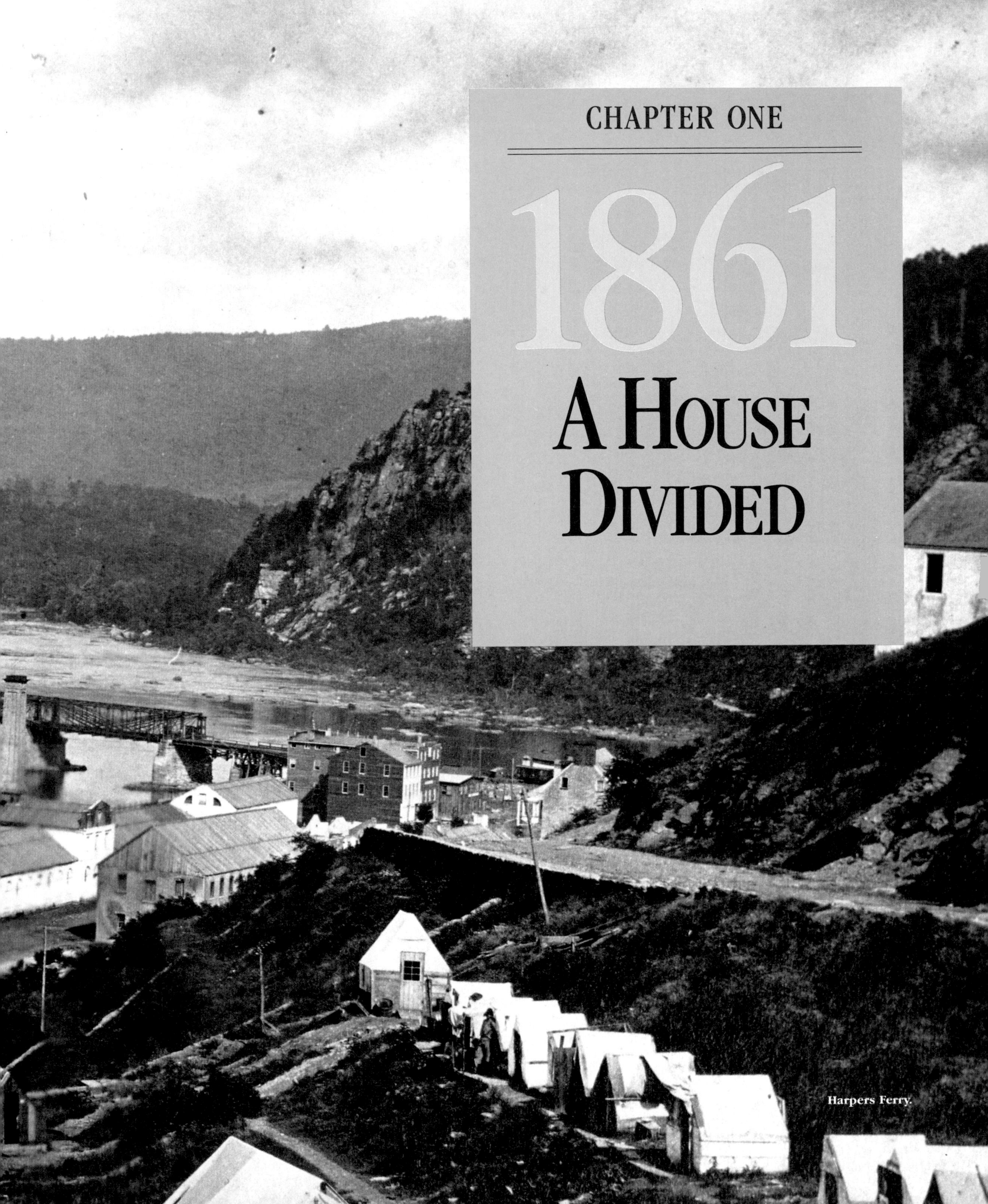

CHAPTER ONE

1861 A HOUSE DIVIDED

Harpers Ferry.

THE METEOR

On the clear moonlit night of November 7, 1837, two hundred men, some carrying torches, surrounded a brick warehouse on the east bank of the Mississippi at Alton, Illinois. It housed a weekly newspaper, the *Observer,* whose editor, the Reverend Elijah P. Lovejoy, had already been driven out of St. Louis, just across the river, for his violent denunciations of slavery. Three times mobs had seized his presses and hurled them into the Mississippi, and Lovejoy and a small group of supporters were now determined not to let it happen again.

The crowd shouted for the editor to surrender. Rocks shattered the upstairs windows. Several men in the crush waved guns. Lovejoy had one, too. He, or one of his allies, took aim and fired out the window. One man fell, and was lifted above the heads of his friends out of harm's way. But it was too late: the wound was mortal and the men surged toward the warehouse, shouting for revenge.

One man started up a ladder toward the roof, carrying a blazing brand. The editor ran downstairs, pistol in hand, threw open the door, and ordered him to stop. The mob shot Lovejoy five times.

News of his death spread fast. A white man had been killed in a quarrel over black slavery, and that quarrel seemed now to threaten every American's right to speak his mind. In Massachusetts, ex-President John Quincy Adams felt "a shock, as of an earthquake." Protest meetings were held throughout the North, and, as one abolitionist wrote, "thousands of our citizens who lately believed that they had nothing to do with slavery, now begin to discover their error."

"The question now before us," a clergyman told a gathering in the Congregational Church at Hudson, Ohio, "is no longer, 'Can the Slaves be made free?' but 'Are *we* free or are we slaves under mob law?'"

In the back of the church, a strange, gaunt man rose to his feet and raised his right hand. "Here, before God," he said, "in the presence of these witnesses, I consecrate my life to the destruction of slavery." He was John Brown.

"In firing his gun, John Brown has merely told what time of day it is. It is high noon, thank God.*"*

WILLIAM LLOYD GARRISON

Twenty-one years later, on Sunday evening, October 16, 1859, that same John Brown, bearded now like an Old Testament prophet, led a tiny army of five black and thirteen white men into the village of Harpers Ferry, Virginia. He brought along a wagon filled with two hundred rifles, two hundred pistols, and a thousand pikes with which to arm the slaves he was sure were going to rally to him. Once they had, he planned to lead them southward along the crest of the Appalachians and destroy slavery. "I expect to effect a mighty conquest," he said, "even though it be like the last victory of Samson."

The sight of a white man beating a slave boy with a shovel had first made Brown hate slavery, but, inconsistent in everything except that hatred, he zealously lashed most of his own twenty children for transgressions as trivial as telling fibs or being too slow at their chores. He was an inept businessman,

John Brown, 1856. "Had I interfered in the manner which I admit in behalf of the rich, the powerful, the intelligent, the so-called great, or in behalf of any of their friends," he said at his trial, "it would have been all right, and every man in this court would have deemed it an act worthy of reward rather than punishment."

John Brown's slave rebellion ended inside the little Harpers Ferry engine house at the left, at the hands of United States Marines under the command of Lieutenant Colonel Robert E. Lee.

who had failed twenty times in six states, and routinely defaulted on his debts, yet believed himself God's agent on earth. He and four of his sons had already slipped up to a cluster of cabins on Pottawatomie Creek in Kansas Territory, called five proslavery men and boys outside, and hacked them to death with broadswords, all in the name of defeating "Satan and his legions."

Brown's favorite Biblical passage was Hebrews 9:22—"Without shedding of blood is no remission [of sin]"—and his willingness to risk the shedding of his own blood in that cause won him the ardent but clandestine support of a small network of northern abolitionists who could not bring themselves actually to take up arms against the institution they loathed. Among them were Dr. Thomas Wentworth Higginson, a Unitarian minister in Boston; Professor Samuel Gridley Howe, an educator of the blind and a veteran of the Greek revolt against the Turks; and Frederick Douglass, himself a former slave, who had declined Brown's personal invitation to take part in his raid, believing it suicidal, and who would blame himself often in later years for his decision. "His zeal in the cause of freedom was infinitely superior to mine," Douglass wrote of Brown. "Mine was as the taper light; his was as the burning sun. I could live for the slave; John Brown could *die* for him."

At Harpers Ferry, Brown and his men quietly seized the federal armory, arsenal, and engine house, and rounded up hostages, including George Washington's great-grand-nephew, who was made to bring with him a sword given to the general by Frederick the Great of Prussia. Brown strapped it on.

After that, nothing went right. The first man Brown's men killed was the town baggage master, a free black. The slaves did not rise, but angry townspeople did, surrounding the engine house and picking off its defenders. The first of Brown's followers to fall was Dangerfield Newby, a former slave who had hoped by joining Brown to liberate his wife and children from a Virginia plantation. Someone in the crowd cut off his ears as souvenirs.

Before the one-sided battle was over, nine more of Brown's men would die, including two of his own sons.

On Tuesday morning, ninety United States Marines arrived from Washington. In command was Lieutenant Colonel Robert E. Lee of Virginia, a cavalry officer on leave when the call for Federal help reached the capital; he had hurried to the scene so swiftly that he had no time to put on his uniform.

Robert E. Lee, about 1852.

Lee's men easily stormed the engine house. Brown was slashed with an officer's dress sword and turned over to Virginia to be tried for treason against the state. He lay on the floor of the courtroom, too weak from his wounds to stand. An "Old Lion tangled in the net," wrote William Dean Howells, ". . . a captive but a lion yet."

Brown's guilt was impossible to deny. "The miserable old traitor and murderer belongs to the gallows," said the Richmond *Whig.* There could be only one outcome to his trial. "I have been *whipped,* as the saying is," Brown acknowledged to his wife, "but I am sure I can recover all the lost capital occasioned by that disaster; by only hanging a few moments by the neck; and I feel quite determined to make the utmost possible out of a defeat."

Brown was right: Herman Melville would call him "the meteor of the war." "This day will be a great day in our history," Henry Wadsworth Longfellow noted in his diary on the morning of Brown's execution, "the date of a new Revolution—quite as much needed as the old one." Henry David Thoreau saw Brown's hanging and the crucifixion of Christ as "two ends of a chain which is not without its links. He is not old Brown any longer; he is an angel of light."

Southerners might have expected sentiments like these from such committed public opponents of slavery, but the widespread admiration for Brown's courage among ordinary northerners not known for their antislavery feeling was astonishing and unprecedented—evidence of how deeply antislavery sentiment had penetrated northern thinking.

Most northerners tempered their praise for Brown's zeal and courage with disapproval of his methods: the raid on Harpers Ferry was the act of a madman, said the religious weekly *The Independent,* but "the controlling motive of [Brown's] demonstration was sublime."

But such distinctions were lost on the South, shaken first by the raid and now horrified that so many of their fellow countrymen in the North seemed sympathetic to the actions of a fanatic bent on sowing slave insurrections. "The day of compromise is passed," said the Charleston *Mercury;* even "the most bigoted Unionist" was now convinced that "there is no peace for the South in the Union." "I have always been a fervid Union man," wrote a wealthy North Carolinian, "but I confess the endorsement of the Harpers Ferry outrage . . . has shaken my fidelity and . . . I am willing to take the chances of every possible evil that may arise from disunion, sooner than submit any longer to Northern insolence."

Fifteen hundred troops guarded the scene of Brown's hanging at Charles Town, among them a contingent of cadets from the Virginia Military Institute led by Thomas J. Jackson, an eccentric instructor in military tactics whom the boys called "Tom Fool" behind his back. One of the militiamen present, a private in the Richmond Grays, was a young actor, John Wilkes Booth; he detested abolition but had to admit that "Brown was a brave old man . . . a man inspired . . . the greatest character of this century."

The brave old man disappointed everyone by saying nothing from the gallows. But he had handed one of his guards a note:

> I, John Brown, am now quite *certain* that the crimes of this *guilty* land will never be purged *away* but with Blood.

"In all social systems there must be a class to do the menial duties, to perform the drudgery of life. . . . Fortunately, for the South she found a race adapted to the purpose. . . . The difference between us is that our slaves are hired for life and well-compensated. Yours are hired by the day, not cared for, and scantily compensated."

SENATOR JAMES HENRY HAMMOND
of South Carolina

THE MOMENTOUS QUESTION

There was little guilt to be seen on the gentle surface of that land. Most Americans spoke the same language, tilled the same soil, worshiped the same Protestant God. They also shared a common pride in first having wrested independence from the mightiest power on earth, Great Britain, and then for having carved an energetic, fast-growing country out of a wilderness. Above all, they were boastful about the republican institutions they had devised and with which they had governed themselves for seventy-one years, institutions which, nearly all Americans agreed, were the envy of every other people on earth.

Few citizens, North or South, would have argued with the recent declaration of Senator Stephen R. Mallory of Florida that "it was no more possible for this country to pause in its career than for the free and untrammeled eagle to cease to soar." Yet within a year Mallory himself would be Secretary of the Navy in a new government at war with that country.

What had happened? There were many answers, so many that it sometimes seemed as if no two people went to war for precisely the same reason: economics played a part in it; so did questions of politics and culture and sectional power. "We are separated because of incompatibility of temper," one southern woman explained. "We are divorced . . . because we *hated* each other so. . . ."

But from the first there was one issue that more than any other divided North from South. "There was never a moment," during the earliest years of our national history, wrote the essayist John Jay Chapman, "when the slavery issue was not a sleeping serpent. That issue lay coiled up under the table during the deliberations of the Constitutional Convention in 1787. It was, owing to the cotton gin, more than half awake at the time of the Louisiana Purchase in 1803. . . . Thereafter, slavery was on everyone's mind, though not always on his tongue."

In 1619, a year before the *Mayflower* landed at Plymouth, a Dutch frigate stopped at the port of Jamestown, Virginia, and sold twenty black Africans to the English colonists there. Soon there were hundreds of thousands of slaves in the colonies, many in the North but most in the South, where they worked tobacco, indigo, and rice.

Slaves at work on Pope's Plantation near Hilton Head, South Carolina.

The American Revolution, which began in 1775, was animated by the belief that "all men are created equal," yet slavery was still legal in every one of the thirteen colonies. By the time of the Constitutional Convention in 1787, slavery had been banished in five northern states, but fifteen of the fifty-five delegates in Independence Hall that summer were slaveowners, and at least fifteen more derived personal profit from the South's "peculiar institution." No delegate bothered even to suggest an end to slavery; when the Pennsylvania Antislavery Society formally presented old Benjamin Franklin with a resolution calling upon him to propose its abolition, he pocketed it rather than antagonize his colleagues by speaking up. Nor did any delegate oppose the clause that called upon citizens to return fugitive slaves to their masters; such a law was every bit as logical, said Roger Sherman of Connecticut, as one that made it a crime to steal a horse.

Yet again and again, in discussions of apparently unrelated concerns—interstate commerce, the protection of private property, congressional apportionment—the paradox of slavery crept into the debates. In the argument over apportionment, the practicalities of politics even reversed the

"In thinking of America, I sometimes find myself admiring her bright blue sky—her grand old woods—her fertile fields—her beautiful rivers—her mighty lakes and star-crowned mountains. But my rapture is soon checked when I remember that all is cursed with the infernal spirit of slave-holding and wrong; When I remember that with the waters of her noblest rivers, the tears of my brethren are borne to the ocean, disregarded and forgotten; That her most fertile fields drink daily of the warm blood of my outraged sisters, I am filled with unutterable loathing."

FREDERICK DOUGLASS

Former slaves sorting cotton on a southern plantation, not long after the war.

subsequent roles of North and South: delegates from northern states without slaves to be tallied argued that slaves were mere property, unworthy of being counted, while the southern states insisted—in this instance, at least—that slaves were human beings, and therefore deserved to be included. The resulting compromise—that each slave was to be counted as three-fifths of a man—was the first of a long, increasingly threadbare series of compromises designed to head off open confrontation between the sections.

"Nothing is more certainly written in the book of fate than that these people are to be free," said Thomas Jefferson of the slaves, and it seemed to him and many others then that slavery was on its way out even in the South, where the once-rich tobacco lands worked by slaves were nearly exhausted. Northern and southern members of the first Congress alike had voted together to abolish the international slave trade by 1808.

But things had not gone as the framers planned, for by that year, the domestic slave trade was flourishing as never before. The savior of southern slavery had been a shrewd and inventive Yankee. In 1792, Eli Whitney, a young Yale graduate, traveled south to Savannah, Georgia, where he hoped to find employment as a tutor. He did not take the job, but on his way he met Mrs.

ALL NIGHT, FOREVER

"No day ever dawns for the slave," a freed black man wrote, "nor is it looked for. For the slave it is all night—all night, forever." One white Mississippian was more blunt: "I'd rather be dead than be a nigger on one of these big plantations."

A slave entered the world in a one-room dirt-floored shack. Drafty in winter, reeking in summer, slave cabins bred pneumonia, typhus, cholera, tuberculosis. The child who survived to be sent to the fields at twelve was likely to have rotten teeth, worms, dysentery, malaria. Fewer than four out of one hundred slaves lived to be sixty.

"It is expected," a planter wrote, "that [slaves] should rise early enough to be at work by the time it is light. . . . While at work, they should be brisk. . . . I have no objection to their whistling or singing some lively tune, but no *drawling* tunes are allowed . . . for their motions are almost certain to keep time with the music." Slaves worked till dark, unless there was a full moon that permitted them to be kept at it still longer.

On the auction block, blacks were made to jump and dance to demonstrate their sprightliness and good cheer, were often stripped to show how strong they were, how little whipping they needed. "The customers would feel our bodies," an ex-slave recalled, "and make us show our teeth, precisely as a jockey examines a horse." Since slave marriages had no legal status, preachers changed the wedding vows to read, "Until death *or distance* do you part."

"We were no more than dogs," a slave woman recalled. "If they caught us with a piece of paper in our pockets, they'd whip us. They was afraid we'd learn to read and write, but I never got the chance."

Slave quarters on a small Georgia plantation (above), and a gathering of slaves on a more prosperous establishment near Baton Rouge, Louisiana (below).

"Them days was hell," another woman remembered. "Babies was snatched from their mother's breast and sold. . . . Chilrens was separated from sisters and brothers and never saw each other agin. Course they cried. You think they not cry when they was sold like cattle?"

Violence, flight, and insanity sometimes followed forced separations. "O, that I were free!" a slave wrote. "I will run away: I had as well be killed running as die standing."

Slave resistance took many forms. Some risked flogging—or worse—and fled. Many more malingered, performing as little as possible of the labor from which they derived no benefit. Some maimed themselves. A few were still more openly defiant.

In 1800, a slave named Gabriel Prosser massed an army of several hundred slaves outside Richmond, planning to kill all the whites and proclaim himself king of Virginia. "I have nothing more to offer than what George Washington would have had to offer," he told his followers. "I have ventured my life in endeavoring to obtain the liberty of my countrymen." A torrential rain delayed the attack and Prosser and many others were seized, tried, and hanged—after suitable financial compensation was paid to their owners.

The four daguerreotypes at the right were commissioned in 1850 by the Swiss-born scientist Louis Agassiz, as part of an effort to demonstrate that the races of man were somehow separate species. Despite the absurd purpose for which they were made, the images represent a unique legacy—the earliest surviving portraits of slaves whose names and African origins are known. The name of the man at upper left has been lost, but his abdomen clearly shows tribal scars; next to him is Renty, an elderly field hand said to have been a "Congo" slave; below him are his daughter Delia, and Jack, a slavedriver with scarified cheeks, born on the Guinea coast.

A slave auction in Richmond, Virginia, painted by Eyre Crowe.

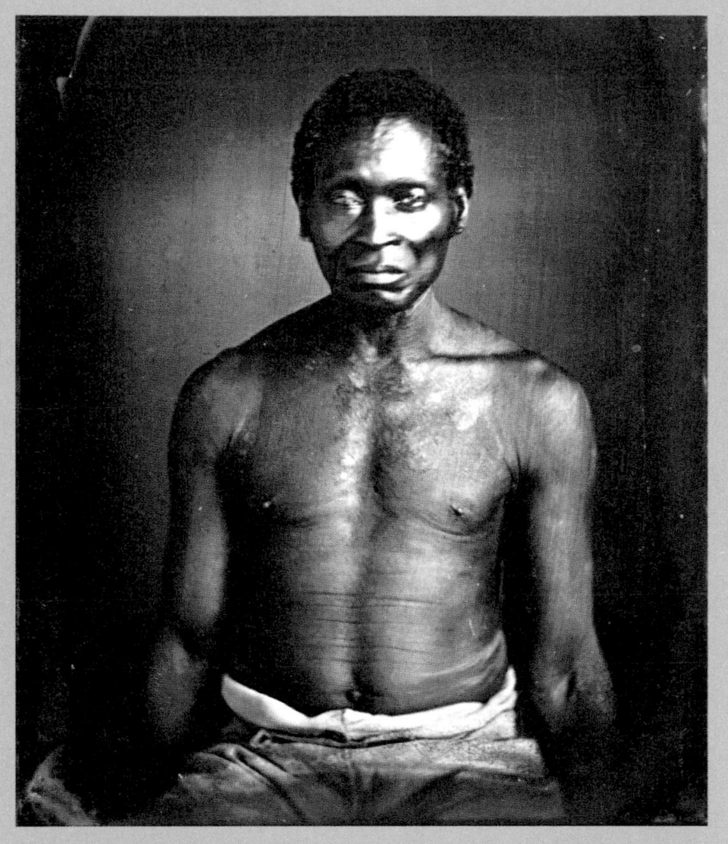

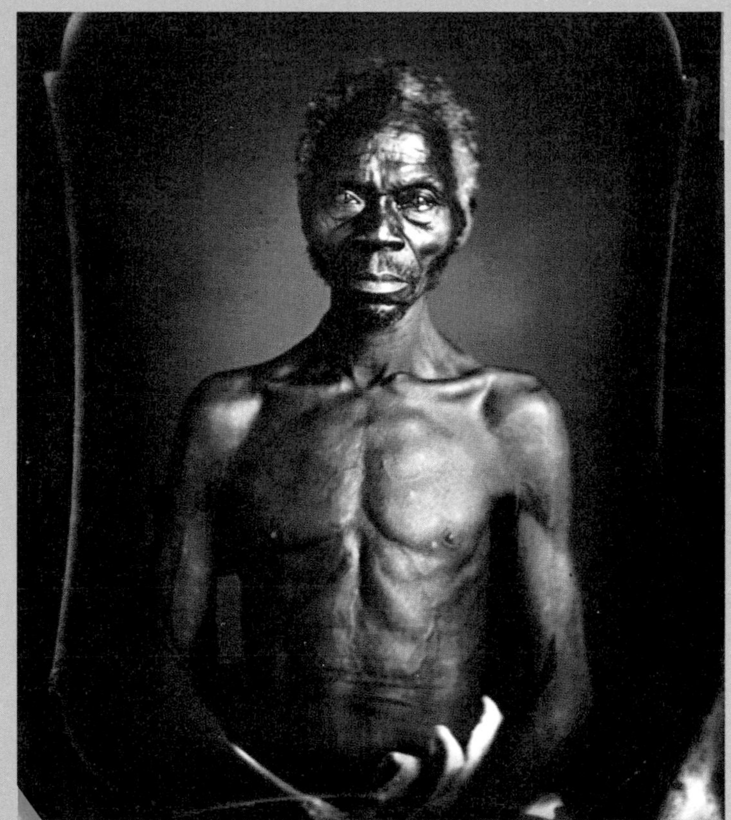

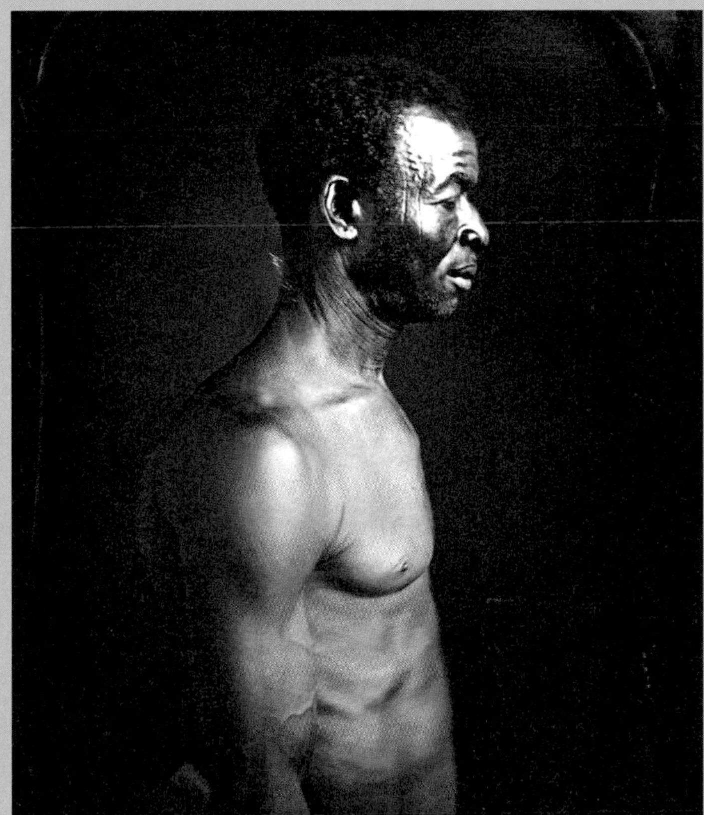

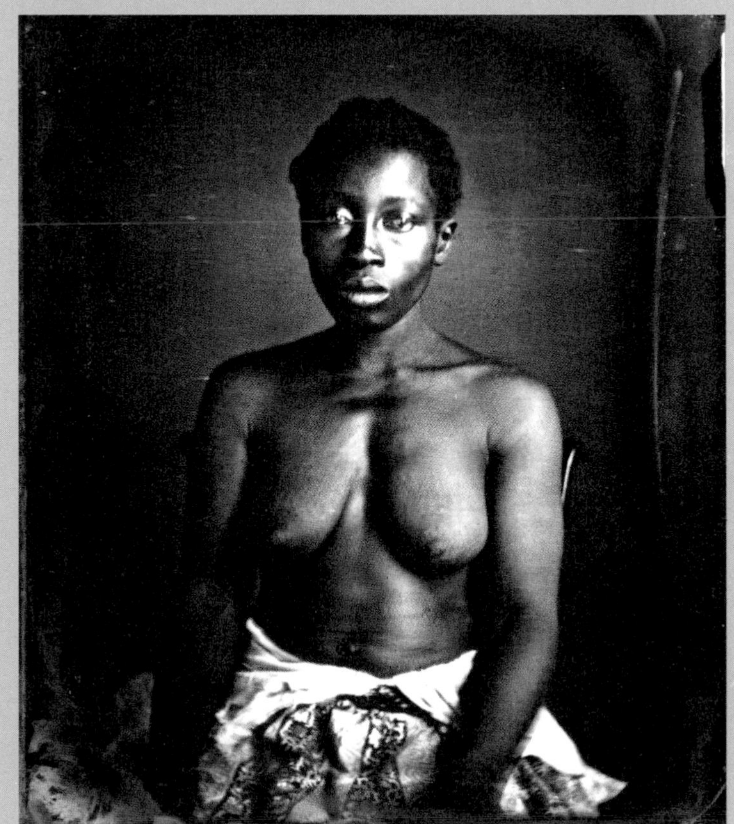

Nathaniel Greene, the widow of a Revolutionary War general. Business was bad for her and her fellow planters because there was no fast or economical way to separate from its seed the upland, short-staple cotton that grew so well across the Deep South. "There were a number of very distinguished Gentlemen at Mrs. Greene's," Whitney remembered, "who all agreed that if a *machine* could be invented . . . it would be a great thing, both to the Country and the inventor."

Ten days later, Whitney had the answer—a cotton engine, or "gin," a simple device that used toothed cylinders to snag the lint through a wire screen, leaving the seeds behind. Whereas it had taken one slave ten hours, no matter how hard he was driven, to produce a single pound of lint, an improved version of Whitney's gin could eventually crank out 300 to 1,000 pounds a day. Within two years, the cotton states were exporting 1,601,000 pounds of cotton to the new spinning frames and power looms of England, twelve times the 1792 total. By 1850, that figure had risen to more than a million tons.

By 1860, the last year of peace, one of every seven Americans would belong to another. Four million men, women, and children were slaves. More than three million of them worked the fields of the Deep South, where "Cotton is King," said Senator James Henry Hammond of South Carolina, "and the African must be a slave, or there's an end of all things, and soon."

Having tied much of the South to slavery, Eli Whitney helped transform the North. He made no money from his cotton gin—the device was pirated almost before he had finished designing it—but he went on to make a great fortune at his firearms factory outside New Haven, one of the first entrepreneurs to employ the system of interchangeable parts that revolutionized American manufacturing and would one day help make the North's industrial might irresistible.

While southerners tended their fields, the North grew. In 1800, half the nation's five million people lived in the South. By 1850, only a third lived there. Of the nine largest cities, only New Orleans was located in the lower South. Meanwhile, a tenth of the goods manufactured in America came from southern mills and factories. There were one hundred piano makers in New York alone in 1852. In 1846, there was not a single book publisher in New Orleans; even the city guidebook was printed in Manhattan.

Northerners invented the steamboat, the clipper ship, the steel plow, the telegraph, the mechanical reaper, the revolver, the sewing machine, the lead pencil, the friction match, the safety pin, the typewriter, the straw hat, the rubber ball.

"Every day [the North] grows more wealthy and densely populated," wrote a French visitor, "while the South is stationary or growing poor. . . . The first result of this disproportionate growth is a violent change in the equilibrium of power and political influence. Powerful states become weak, territories without a name become states. . . . Wealth, like population, is displaced. These changes cannot take place without injuring interests, without exciting passions."

To calm those passions, Congress had acceded to Missouri's request for

Slaves who fled their masters, photographed at Follie's Farm near Cumberland Landing, Virginia, in 1862.

admission as a slave state in 1820, but was careful at the same time to draw a line through the rest of the old Louisiana Purchase and bar slavery north of it in the wistful hope that a permanent border would thereby be created between freedom and slavery. That compact would hold for a quarter of a century.

But slavery would not be compromised. "This momentous question," wrote the aged Jefferson, "like a firebell in the night, awakened and filled me with terror. I considered it at once the knell of the Union." President John Quincy Adams agreed: "I take it for granted that the present question is a mere preamble—a title page to a great tragic volume."

In 1829 David Walker, the free black proprietor of a secondhand-clothing store in Boston, published his *Appeal,* an incendiary pamphlet that called upon the slaves to rise against their masters.

> I speak, Americans, for your good. We must and shall be free, I say, in spite of you. You may do your best to keep us in wretchedness and misery, to enrich you and your children; but God will deliver us from under you. And woe, woe, will be to you if we have to obtain our freedom by fighting.

The mayor of Savannah demanded that the mayor of Boston arrest Walker and outlaw the pamphlet; it was already illegal in Georgia to teach a slave to read. Boston's mayor refused.

William Lloyd Garrison battled slavery for almost four decades: "The success of any great moral enterprise," he wrote, "does not depend upon numbers."

In 1831, William Lloyd Garrison began publishing in that same city a militant antislavery newspaper, *The Liberator.* Few causes failed to excite Garrison; he was as enthusiastic about phrenology, clairvoyance, and spiritualism as he was about pacificism, temperance, and women's rights. But it was the plight of the slaves that obsessed him.

> I am aware that many object to the severity of my language; but is there not cause for severity? I *will* be as harsh as truth, and as uncompromising as justice. On this subject I do not wish to think, or speak, or write, with moderation. . . . I am in earnest—I will not equivocate—I will not excuse—I will not retreat a single inch—and *I will be heard.*

The abolitionists, believing not only that slavery was wrong but that the Federal Government must act to abolish it, were always a small minority, but Garrison quickly became their most implacable spokesman. *The Liberator* never had more than three thousand subscribers, never made a profit. Garrison wrote and printed and mailed it with a single helper, working twelve-hour days, fueled by fruit and stale cake bought at the bakery beneath his office. But he *was* heard, his stories were picked up by other newspapers, North and South, and his message was clear: slavery was sin, and to demand anything less than its immediate, unconditional abolition was to acquiesce in evil. "The Southern planter's career," he said, "is one of unbridled lust, of filthy amalgamation, of swaggering braggadocio, of haughty domination, of cowardly ruffianism, of boundless dissipation, of matchless insolence, of infinite self-conceit, of unequalled oppression, of more than savage cruelty."

In this rare daguerreotype made at Syracuse, New York, sometime during the 1840s, Frederick Douglass is seated to the left of the table, surrounded by fellow members of the American Anti-Slavery Society.

Garrison had a small but growing army of allies, white and black. Wendell Phillips was his closest lieutenant, a brilliant orator known to his admirers as the "Knight-Errant of Unfriended Truth" and so unswerving in his devotion to his cause that neither sugar nor cotton was permitted in his home because they were produced by slaves. Frederick Douglass, the son of a slave and a white man, had twice run away from his owner. "I appear this evening as a thief and robber," he liked to tell audiences. "I stole this head, these limbs, this body from my master, and ran off with them." Douglass became so eloquent an antislavery orator that skeptics charged he could never have been a slave. He wrote an autobiography in part to prove them wrong, then purchased his own freedom with $600 obtained from English admirers, and returned to the struggle, to publish his own journal, the *North Star*.

The same year Garrison began publishing his newspaper, Nat Turner led a slave uprising in Virginia, killing fifty-seven whites and terrifying much of the South. Southerners blamed northern abolitionists for inspiring the uprising rather than admit that slaves might have thought it up on their own. Turner and his followers were hunted down, some were killed outright, others tried and executed. The South Carolina legislature offered $5,000 for Garrison's arrest.

Senator John C. Calhoun of South Carolina.

Southern voices that had once urged an eventual end to slavery were silenced now, and those that defended it did so with a new ferocity: "I hold that in the present state of civilization," said Senator John C. Calhoun of South Carolina, "the relation now existing in the slave-holding states between the two [races] is, instead of an evil, a good—a *positive* good."

Differences over slavery were now at the heart of the unending American argument over free speech. Laws against teaching slaves to read were stiffened. In Georgetown, in the District of Columbia, free black subscribers were forbidden to pick up their copies of *The Liberator* at the post office; punishment included twenty-five lashes. President Andrew Jackson proposed to Congress that antislavery literature be barred from the southern mails. Congress imposed a gag rule on itself, expressly forbidding members to speak of slavery on the floor. A Boston mob nearly lynched Garrison, and not far from Independence Hall in Philadelphia another mob burned down a hall newly built by abolitionists and consecrated to the principle of free speech. "All classes must be invoked to abstain from discussion," said Edward Everett, the Governor of Massachusetts, "which by exasperating the master, can have no effect other than to render more oppressive the condition of the slave." Still, the discussion would not stop.

"Let us show at least as much spirit in defending our rights as the Abolitionists have evinced in denouncing them."

JOHN C. CALHOUN

In 1846, a young Whig lawyer from Springfield, Illinois, was elected to Congress. For Abraham Lincoln, the Declaration of Independence was to be taken literally, at least so far as white men were concerned. All had the right to rise as far as talent would take them, just as he had. He was opposed to slavery, too; if it was not wrong, he said, then nothing was wrong, and whenever he heard anyone argue in its favor, he felt a strong impulse to see it tried on the man personally. But since the Constitution did not authorize Congress to interfere with slavery in states where it already existed, agitation for its abolition would accomplish nothing, except to arouse the dangerous passions of the people and make the South more stubbornly determined never to give it up. The wrong of slavery would be righted with time, he believed. So long as the northern states forbade slavery and Congress continued to bar it from new western territories north of the Missouri Compromise line of 1820, the institution would die a "natural death." Slavery was a vexing but "minor question," he said, "on its way to extinction."

Former President Andrew Jackson.

"Our Federal Union: it must be preserved!"

ANDREW JACKSON

That same year, the United States went to war with Mexico. When it was over, President James K. Polk of Tennessee, with the aid of two southern-born generals, Winfield Scott and Zachary Taylor, and an army two-thirds of whose soldiers were southerners, had added a million and a quarter square miles of new territory to his country, almost half of it south of the line drawn in 1820.

Already outvoted in the House, where the rapid growth of the northern population had long since overwhelmed their representatives, the South still held parity in the Senate. Now they saw the spread of slavery into that great western emptiness as essential to their survival: unless the new states to be carved from it were to permit slavery, the South would find itself at the mercy of northern senators interested only in exploiting it.

"What do you propose, gentlemen of the Free-Soil party?" Senator Jefferson Davis of Mississippi once challenged his northern colleagues. "Do you propose to better the condition of the slave? Not at all. . . . You say that you are opposed to the expansion of slavery . . . is the slave to be benefited by it? Not at all. It is not humanity that influences you . . . it is that you may have an opportunity of cheating us that you want to limit slave territory . . . it is that you may have a majority in the Congress of the United States and convert the Government into an engine of Northern aggrandizement . . . you want by an unjust system of legislation to promote the industry of the United States at the expense of the people of the South."

Only the most militant Garrisonians had ever argued that Congress was empowered to bar slavery from the states. But for many northerners, these vast new western territories were another matter; for them, it was unthinkable that the American flag should impose the South's "peculiar institution" on new lands hard won by Americans from every part of the country.

"There are grave doubts," Henry Adams now wrote, "at the hugeness of the land," whether "one government can *comprehend* the whole." Slavery seemed to be at the center of every argument. Thomas Hart Benton, Missouri's first senator and one of Manifest Destiny's most fervid prophets, compared its maddening ubiquity to the Old Testament plague of frogs: "You could not look upon the table but there were frogs, you could not sit down at the banquet but there were frogs, you could not go to the bridal couch and lift the sheets but there were not frogs!"

Increasingly, too, there began to be talk of southern secession if southern demands were not met. The idea of secession was at least as old as the Union, and from time to time spokesmen for one aggrieved section or another had angrily threatened to withdraw their states from the Union rather than coexist within it with those who they believed had betrayed the principles of the framers.

There was a tempting symmetry to their argument. The sovereign states had created the Union for their mutual benefit, secessionists said, and they had freely granted to it all its power. Therefore, if any state or section felt

Senator Henry Clay of Kentucky (left) had owned slaves himself since the age of five but hated the institution and, despite criticism from many of his constituents, argued for gradual emancipation. Senator Daniel Webster of Massachusetts (above) opposed slavery, too. But neither man believed differences over it should be allowed to shatter the Union, and the Compromise of 1850, for which they helped win passage, helped stave off crisis for a decade.

itself injured by the Federal Government it had helped create, it had a perfect right to withdraw rather than submit. The use of Federal force to stop a state from seceding would be unconstitutional "coercion," since such force could never rightfully be brought to bear on those who had tendered it to the central government in the first place.

Secession was never an exclusively southern notion—the first American secessionists, in fact, had been disgruntled New Englanders who had threatened to leave the Union rather than continue to participate in the War of 1812 because of the damage it was doing to their economy. But it had always burned brightest in the South.

Unionists countered that the American people as a whole—not the thirteen original states—had forged the Union, and therefore they alone could dissolve it. Meanwhile, its constituent parts could not be allowed to ignore laws enacted by Congress, which represented all the people, or to depart from the Union at will. It was that belief that led President Jackson, himself a southerner, to threaten to lead troops into South Carolina in 1832 if that state persisted in claiming the right to nullify a Federal tariff of which it did not approve. No democratic republic could survive if a minority could thwart the majority's desires. "The Union must be preserved at all hazards and any price," Jackson warned the people of South Carolina. "Those who told you that you might peaceably prevent the execution of the laws deceived you. The object is disunion. Disunion by armed force is treason. Are you really ready to incur its guilt?" They had not been ready then, but the most resolute among them never abandoned the doctrine, and nearly three decades later another President would consult Jackson's words before delivering his own inaugural.

In 1850, a gingerly new compromise, brokered by Senator Henry Clay of Kentucky, permitted California to enter the Union as a free state, while simultaneously strengthening the Fugitive Slave Law; Federal agents were now ordered to assist in the seizure of runaways, and ordinary citizens who helped a slave escape were subject to a fine of $2,000 and six months in jail. "The Union stands firm," said Senator Daniel Webster of Massachusetts, who had supported the new arrangement, but to those more resolutely opposed to slavery than he, the American government itself now seemed to be shifting to the side of the enemy. "I confess, I hate to see the poor creatures hunted down . . ." said former Congressman Lincoln, "but I bite my lip and keep quiet."

Harriet Beecher Stowe.

Others did not. "Let the President drench our land of freedom in blood," said the abolitionist congressman Joshua Giddings of Ohio, "but he will never make us obey *that* law." In Chicago, the city council passed a resolution declaring the Fugitive Slave Act in violation of both the Constitution and the laws of God. At Oberlin College in Ohio, students freed a captured runaway from jail in nearby Wellington. In Boston, federal troops and an outlay of nearly $100,000 were needed to send a single fugitive slave, Anthony Burns, back to his master. Church bells tolled in mourning. The American flag was lowered to half-staff. "We went to bed one night old-fashioned, conservative, Compromise Union Whigs," one Bostonian wrote after Burns and his captors had sailed South, "and waked up stark mad abolitionists."

UNCLE TOM'S CABIN;

OR,

LIFE AMONG THE LOWLY.

BY

HARRIET BEECHER STOWE.

VOL. I.

BOSTON:
JOHN P. JEWETT & COMPANY.
CLEVELAND, OHIO:
JEWETT, PROCTOR & WORTHINGTON.
1852.

So powerful an antislavery weapon was *Uncle Tom's Cabin* that within three years of its publication some thirty southern novels had been published seeking to refute its charges.

"Are the great principles of political freedom and of natural justice, embodied in [the] Declaration of Independence, extended to us?" Frederick Douglass asked a mostly white Fourth of July gathering at Rochester, New York, in 1852. "This Fourth of July is *yours* not *mine. You* may rejoice, I must *mourn.* To drag a man in fetters into the grand illuminated temple of liberty, and call upon him to join you in joyous anthems, were inhuman mockery and sacrilegious irony."

That same year, Harriet Beecher Stowe published *Uncle Tom's Cabin, or Life Among the Lowly.* "If there had been a grand preparatory blast of trumpets or if it had been announced that [I] would do this or that," she remembered, "I think it likely that I could not have written; but nobody expected anything, and so I wrote freely." It was sentimental, sometimes patronizing, implausible in many of its details (Simon Legree, the villainous overseer, is a New Englander). Most of the book was written in Brunswick, Maine; its author had spent precisely one weekend in a slave state. The climactic scene, the tragic death of the noble Uncle Tom, came to her, she said, in a vision while she sat in church.

But her portrayal of slavery's cruelty moved readers as nothing else had. More than 300,000 books were sold in the United States within the year, and a million and a half pirated copies were in print worldwide. The novel spawned songs, plays, a card game played by northern children that "showed the continual separation of [slave] families." Mrs. Charles Dickens wept over it. So did Queen Victoria.

By 1854, Calhoun, Clay, and Webster were all gone from the Senate, and its most prominent figure was Stephen A. Douglas, Democrat of Illinois. Known to his admirers as "the Little Giant," Douglas was short, shrewd, and ambitious. He owned 140 slaves himself but said he did not care whether slavery was voted up or down. He now sought to promote a transcontinental railroad along a route that would enrich both his state and himself through the enactment of still another compromise: this one proposed to ignore the old border between slave and free soil mandated by Congress in 1820 and let settlers in the new territories of Kansas and Nebraska decide for themselves whether slavery was to be barred. "If the people of Kansas want a slaveholding state," he said, "let them have it, and if they want a free state they have a right to it, and it is not for the people of Illinois, or Missouri, or New York, or Kentucky, to complain, whatever the decision of the people of Kansas may be."

Much of the North felt betrayed; with the Kansas-Nebraska Act, Congress

Six members of the Kansas Free State battery stand ready with a cannon left over from the Mexican War, photographed at Topeka in 1856.

"We are organizing. We will be compelled to shoot, burn & hang, but the thing will soon be over."

SENATOR DAVID ATCHISON of Missouri to SENATOR JEFFERSON DAVIS of Mississippi

seemed to have given up the power to speak for the whole nation on a matter in which the whole nation had an abiding interest. Slavery's progress toward extinction, in which Lincoln and many others had been so confident, seemed suddenly to have stopped. Thousands of northern Democrats deserted their party. The old Whig party disintegrated. Douglas complained that his way home to Illinois that spring was lit by the light of his own burning effigies.

On July 4, William Lloyd Garrison held up a copy of the Federal Constitution before a large crowd at Framingham, Massachusetts, branded it "a covenant with death, and an agreement with hell" and set it afire, exclaiming, "So perish all compromises with tyranny! And let all the people say, Amen!" The crowd roared its assent as the flames rose.

"The spirit of Seventy-Six and the spirit of Nebraska are utter antagonists . . ." said former Congressman Lincoln. "Little by little . . . we have been giving up the old for the new faith . . . we began by declaring that all men are created equal, but now from that beginning we have run down to the other declaration, that for some men to enslave others is 'a sacred right of self-government.'"

A new political organization grew out of northern protests against the Kansas-Nebraska Act, a curious amalgam of nativists and temperance advocates, disillusioned free-soil Democrats and disaffected Whigs, but united now in their opposition to seeing slavery extended into hitherto forbidden territory. They were first called simply the "Anti-Nebraska men," then the Republican party; their enemies called them the "Black Republicans." "Come on then, Gentlemen of the Slave States," said Senator William Seward of New York. "We will engage in competition for the virgin soil of Kansas, and God give the victory to the side which is stronger in numbers and is in the right."

Five thousand proslavery Missourians crossed into Kansas illegally, seized polling places, and installed a legislature that made even speaking against slavery a crime. Antislavery settlers set up their own government, backed by northerners who sent in reinforcements and crates of Sharps rifles—called "Beecher's Bibles" after the Brooklyn clergyman Henry Ward Beecher, Harriet Beecher Stowe's brother, who had pledged that his congregation would buy and ship twenty-five of them to Kansas. There were shootings, stabbings. A proslavery sheriff was killed at Lawrence. Eight hundred southerners raided the town to search out the assassin, got drunk, and instead burned down the hotel that had been antislavery headquarters.

Echoes of the Kansas violence reached the floor of the United States Senate itself. After the abolitionist senator Charles Sumner of Massachusetts had finished a two-day denunciation of proslavery Missourians as "hirelings picked from the drunken spew and vomit of an uneasy civilization," Congressman Preston S. Brooks of South Carolina caned him into unconsciousness. "I gave him about thirty first-rate stripes," Brooks told reporters proudly. "Towards the last, he bellowed like a calf. I wore my cane out completely but saved the head—which is gold." Admirers sent him new canes. Northern and southern senators alike began to carry knives and pistols into the chamber. It was the news of Sumner's beating that had first driven John Brown to murder in Kansas; it had caused him to become "crazy," his eldest son remembered, "*crazy.*"

RIVAL PRESIDENTS

Abraham and Mary Todd Lincoln.

"A house divided against itself cannot stand. I believe this government cannot endure, permanently half slave *and half* free. *I do not expect the Union to be dissolved. I do not expect the house to fall. But I do expect it will cease to be divided. It will become* all *one thing, or all the* other.*"*

ABRAHAM LINCOLN, 1858

Abraham Lincoln was born in Kentucky in 1809, the son of a mostly unsuccessful farmer, who could barely sign his name. Lincoln hated farming and, driven by an ambition one close friend called "a little engine that knew no rest," left home at twenty-two, settled in the tiny struggling town of New Salem, Illinois, and was running for the legislature as a Whig just seven months later.

He held a host of jobs to support himself—rail-splitter, store clerk, store owner, field worker, captain of militia in the Black Hawk War, postmaster, surveyor, newspaper subscription agent, operator of a whiskey still.

There were few blacks, slave or free, along the western border, where Lincoln grew to manhood, and his only documented contact with them was not calculated to make him sympathetic to their plight. Twice, he helped pole flatboats of farm produce down the Mississippi to New Orleans. Tied up along the riverbank near Baton Rouge on one of those journeys, Lincoln and a companion were attacked by seven slaves seeking to steal their cargo. The young flatboatmen had to fight for their lives to get away. Nonetheless, he seems always to have thought slavery wrong.

Lincoln moved to the state capital at Springfield in 1837 and began to practice law. Five years later, he married Miss Mary Todd, a short, vivacious woman who spoke fluent French and came from a prominent slaveowning Lexington, Kentucky, family that thought so well of itself, Lincoln is supposed to have said, that while God made do with one *d,* the Todds demanded two.

FROM A SINGLE STATE

"In the next four years is . . . locked up the fate of the Union. If the issues are boldly and properly met my hope is that the Constitution will prevail; if the attempt is made to postpone them the next Presidential election will . . . bring us to the alternative of resistance to oppressive usurpation or the tame surrender of our birthright."

JEFFERSON DAVIS, 1857

Jefferson and Varina Davis.

Like Abraham Lincoln, Jefferson Davis was born in a Kentucky log cabin, the son of a farmer. But Davis's father soon moved his family to the Mississippi cotton kingdom and prospered. He sent his son first to Transylvania University at Lexington and then to West Point, where he graduated twenty-third in a class of twenty-three. He served in the Black Hawk War—during which he may have sworn in recruits who included Abraham Lincoln—then married the daughter of his commander, Colonel Zachary Taylor, against her father's wishes, and left the army. His wife died three months later, and for ten lonely years he lived as a planter at Brierfield, a plantation near Vicksburg, Mississippi, given to him by his elder brother. He was a gentle, patriarchal master: punishments were meted out to his slaves by a black judge and jury—Davis reserving for himself only the right to reduce any sentence he thought too harsh.

In 1845, he entered Congress and married Varina Howell of Natchez, half his age—"Would you believe it," she wrote her mother on first meeting her future husband, "he is refined and cultivated and yet . . . a Democrat."

During the Mexican War, Davis commanded the Mississippi Rifles and helped win the Battle of Buena Vista by forming his men into a V and breaking a cavalry charge. Hailed as "the Gamecock of the South," he served in the Senate and as Secretary of War under Franklin Pierce, displaying great erudition, unwavering devotion to the unlimited expansion of slavery, and an abiding dislike for the give-and-take of politics. "Sir," he told a Senate colleague who had simply asked him if he could see his way clear to voting for an appropriations bill, "I make no terms. I accept no compromises."

In the next three months, more than two hundred men were killed in "Bleeding Kansas." The killing along the Missouri border would not stop for ten years.

Worse news for the antislavery forces was still to come. Every new state that had entered the Union since 1819 had disfranchised the blacks within its borders. In 1857, the United States Supreme Court handed down a decision that disfranchised them in the territories as well. A decade earlier, a slave named Dred Scott had sued for his freedom, on the grounds that he had lived on the free soil of Missouri Territory for several years. The Supreme Court now turned him down. Chief Justice Roger B. Taney of Maryland, so long in office that he had sworn in seven presidents, wrote the majority opinion. Taney had liberated all his own slaves, had even bought the freedom of others, but according to his reading of the Constitution, Scott was still a slave and neither slaves *nor their descendants* could ever have standing in court, could ever be American citizens. "They had . . . been regarded as beings of an inferior order" by the founders of the republic," Taney wrote, "and altogether unfit to associate with the white race . . . so far inferior that they had no rights which a white man was bound to respect." Moreover, since the Constitution had recognized slavery, Congress had no power to exclude it from the territories as it had tried to do under the Missouri Compromise.

Indignation over the Dred Scott decision, written by Chief Justice Roger B. Taney (above), helped persuade Abraham Lincoln (above right) to challenge Stephen A. Douglas (right) for the Senate in 1858. When the two men faced one another again for the presidency two years later, Lincoln's running mate (far right) was Senator Hannibal Hamlin of Maine, whose sallow complexion suggested to some in the opposition that he was secretly a mulatto.

Abraham Lincoln, about to return to politics and challenge the celebrated Stephen Douglas for his Senate seat, denounced the decision as a planters' plot, politically motivated to prepare the way for a *second* court decision that might make it unconstitutional to bar slavery even from a state.

> All the powers of earth seem rapidly combining against [the slave]. Mammon is after him, ambition follows, philosophy follows, and the theology of the day is fast joining the cry. They have him in his prison house; they have searched his person, and left no prying instrument with him. One after another they have closed the heavy doors upon him; and now they have him . . . bolted in with a lock of a hundred keys, which can never be unlocked without the concurrence of every key—the keys in the hands of a hundred different men, and they scattered to a hundred different and distant places.

Lincoln lost narrowly to Douglas, and John Brown's raid the following year would fail to unlock the slave's prison house, but North and South continued to move apart, each deeply riven within itself.

Many southerners opposed slavery, and thought talk of secession madness. There were whole regions of the South where cotton was not king, where poor upcountry farmers, who owned no slaves, had nothing but contempt for the prosperous lowland planters who did. "All they want is to get you to fight for their infernal Negroes," said a farmer from Winston County, Alabama, "and after you do their fightin', you may kiss their hin' parts for all they care."

Some in the North hated slavery because it was wrong; others opposed it because they thought it threatened the jobs of white wage earners; still others condoned it because there was money to be made. "The business of the North as well as the South has become adjusted to it," wrote a New York merchant. "There are millions upon millions of dollars due from Southerners to the

merchants and mechanics of this city alone, the payment of which would be jeopardized by any rupture between the North and South. We cannot afford to let [the abolitionists] succeed in [their] endeavor to overthrow slavery. It is not a matter of principle with us. It is a matter of business necessity."

Free blacks enjoyed little freedom in much of the North. Only four states—Maine, New Hampshire, Vermont, and Massachusetts—permitted them to vote; in no state could they serve on a jury; not even the five thousand blacks who had fought for American freedom in the Revolution had been allowed to serve in any state militia. The legislatures of Ohio, Indiana, Oregon, and Abraham Lincoln's own Illinois had all enacted statutes called "Black Laws," discouraging or entirely excluding blacks from settling within their borders. And in much of the North there was little sympathy for the slaves themselves. "If they were not such a race of braggarts and ruffians I should be sorry for our fire-eating brethren [in the South]," another wealthy New Yorker wrote, "weighted down, suffocated and paralyzed by a Nigger incubus four million strong of which no one knows how they are to get rid."

By the presidential election of 1860, the Democratic party, which had held the White House for most of the past forty years, had splintered over slavery. Stephen Douglas was the nominee of the northern wing. Southern Democrats had split away to nominate Senator John C. Breckinridge of Kentucky. To further complicate things, the tattered remnant of the old Whig party nominated John Bell of Tennessee, his only platform, "the Constitution," whatever that might mean to an agitated electorate.

The Republicans saw their chance, and chose as their nominee the former congressman of moderate antislavery views who had lost the Senate race to Douglas just two years earlier, Abraham Lincoln. He was a compromise candidate, everyone's second choice in a convention dominated by more

Tradition dictated that Lincoln, here seen standing head and shoulders above his constituents in the doorway of his home at Springfield, Illinois, not actively campaign for the presidency. But he did greet the delegations of supporters who flocked to see him.

celebrated politicians, a moderate from the center of a moderate middle-western state without which the new party stood little chance of victory. Persuaded that the Constitution forbade presidential action against slavery where it already existed, Lincoln was nonetheless pledged to halt its further spread. "On that point," he told his supporters, "hold firm, as with a chain of steel. The tug has to come, and better now than any time hereafter."

South Carolina warned that she would secede from the Union if a President so pledged were elected.

Douglas conducted a strenuous stump campaign—the first in presidential history—while his rivals remained discreetly silent, but his party was hopelessly divided. Lincoln won on election day with just 40 percent of the popular vote, carrying every free state—but not a single slave state.

The election of Lincoln, said the Richmond *Whig,* "is undoubtedly the greatest evil that has ever befallen this country. But the mischief is done, and the only relief for the American people is to shorten sail . . . send down the top masts, and prepare for a hurricane." "The tea has been thrown overboard," echoed the Charleston *Mercury,* "the revolution of 1860 has been initiated."

Republicans celebrated Lincoln's victory in northern cities—and across the South he was burned in effigy in front of county courthouses. The South Carolina legislature called for a convention to consider seceding from the Union.

George Templeton Strong.

A conservative and wealthy New York lawyer and civic leader, little known beyond his immediate circle and chronically shy, George Templeton Strong confided his forceful opinions largely to the diary he began at fifteen and kept up daily for forty years. Strong deplored the immigrant poor and the vulgar rich of his city with equal vehemence and had always found it easier to denounce abolitionism than slavery.

But as early as 1848 he was worried over a "possible rupture over the slavery question," and after the Dred Scott decision he grew increasingly indignant about what he called the "retrograde civilization of the South," dominated by what he called "nigger-breeders" and "women-floggers." When the fighting began he donated money to help equip a regiment and sought other ways in which a middle-aged and badly nearsighted patriot could serve his country.

SECESSIONITIS

When Lincoln was elected, there were thirty-three states in the Union and a thirty-fourth, free Kansas, was about to join. By the time of his inauguration in March of 1861, just twenty-seven remained, and from the Executive Mansion rebel flags could be seen across the Potomac on Arlington Heights.

South Carolina had led the way on December 20, and five days later the handful of Federal troops still stationed at Fort Moultrie in Charleston withdrew to Fort Sumter, far out in the harbor. Their commander, Major Robert Anderson, said he had moved his men in order "to prevent the effusion of blood."

On January 9, 1861, Mississippi seceded. Florida left the Union on the tenth. Then, Alabama, Georgia, Louisiana.

In Austin, Texas, Governor Sam Houston was deposed when he tried to stop his state from joining the Confederacy. He warned his people:

> Let me tell you what is coming. . . . Your fathers and husbands, your sons and brothers, will be herded at the point of the bayonet. . . . You may, after the sacrifice of countless millions of treasure and hundreds of thousands of lives, as a bare possibility, win Southern independence. . . . But I doubt it. I tell you that, while I believe with you in the doctrine of States Rights, the North is determined to preserve this Union. They are not a fiery, impulsive people as you are, for they live in colder climates. But when they begin to move in a given direction . . . they move with the steady momentum and perseverance of a mighty avalanche.

Texas left the Union anyway. Virginia, the most populous southern state, birthplace of seven Presidents of the United States, seemed likely to follow.

All the indications are," wrote a Wall Street attorney, George Templeton Strong, "that this treasonable inflammation—*secessionitis*—keeps on making steady progress, week by week."

On the afternoon of February 10, 1861, former Senator Jefferson Davis and his wife, Varina, were in the garden of Brierfield, their plantation just below Vicksburg, Mississippi, pruning rosebushes.

A slave hurried across the lawn and handed him a piece of paper. "Reading that telegram," Varina Davis remembered, "he looked so grieved that I feared some evil had befallen our family. After a few minutes, he told me [what it contained], as a man might speak of a sentence of death." He had been elected President of the Provisional Government of the Confederate States of America.

Davis was tall and gaunt; a brittle, nervous, dyspeptic man with a twitching cheek, a symptom of the neuralgia that would eventually blind him in one eye. He was often unable to sleep and so formal that he disliked using first names even when speaking to his slaves. He had a reputation for aloof obstinacy. Sam Houston, for one, thought him "cold as a lizard" and his own admiring wife admitted that "he did not know the arts of a politician and would not practice

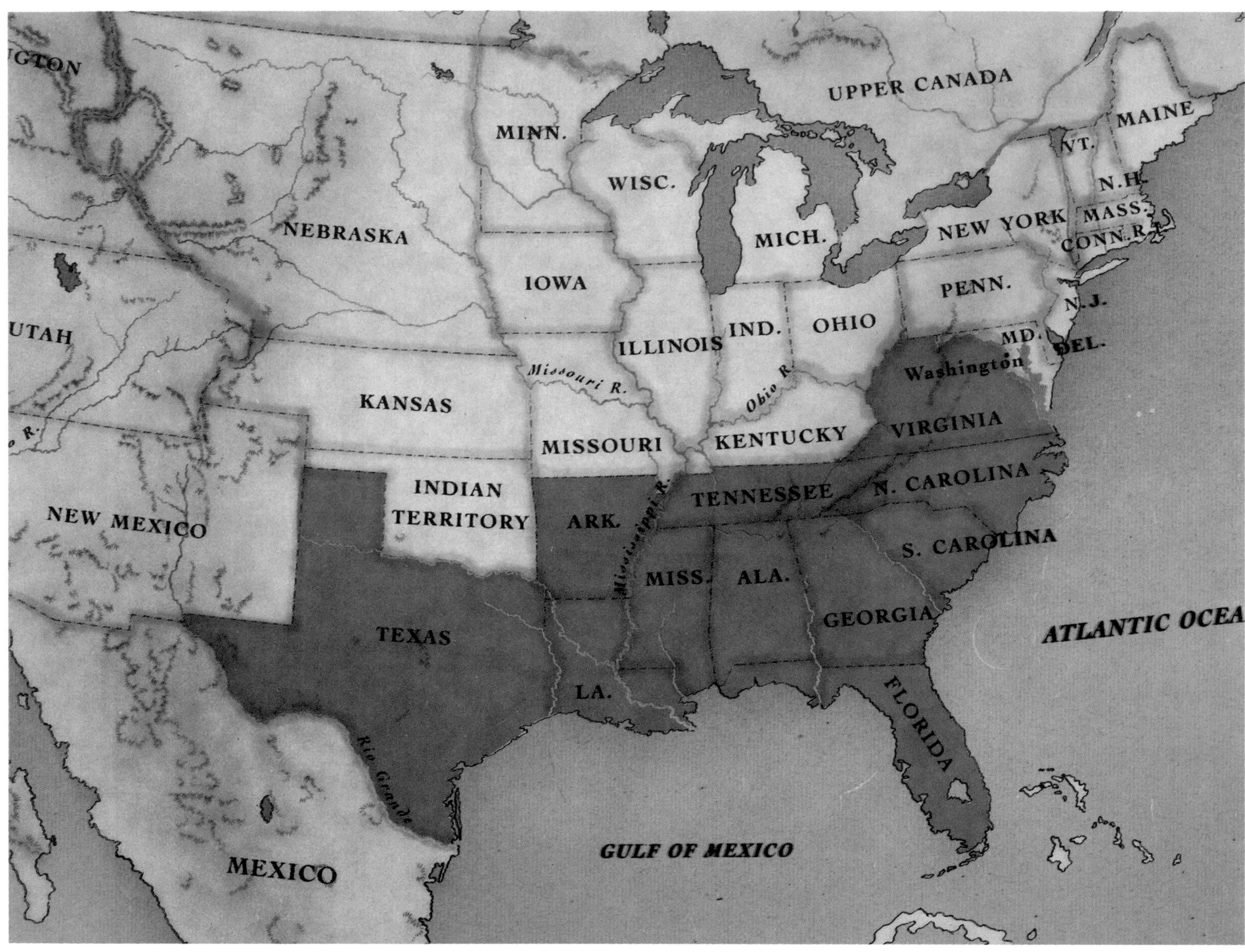

The Confederate States of America: South Carolina led the way out of the Union on December 20, 1860, and by March 1861, six more states, outraged over Lincoln's election to the presidency and emboldened by South Carolina's example, had seceded: Mississippi, Florida, Alabama, Georgia, Louisiana, and Texas. After the bombardment of Fort Sumter and Lincoln's call for troops to put down the rebellion in April, Virginia, Arkansas, Tennessee, and North Carolina followed suit, bringing the number of states in the new Confederacy to eleven.

them if understood"—but friends and family also testified to his private warmth and cordiality. Since the secession of his state he had been unsure of what role he might play in the new Confederacy: it was his fondest hope that he would be asked to lead its armies in the field.

The government he was now to head was just two days old, framed by a brand-new Constitution very like the old one, except that it explicitly guaranteed the right to own slaves, granted the President a six-year term, and provided each member of the cabinet a seat on the floor of Congress. The capital of the new nation was to be Montgomery, Alabama, and Davis agreed to start for it the next day, the eleventh.

The next morning a steady, cold rain fell on Springfield, Illinois, as Abraham Lincoln, about to depart for his capital at Washington, stood hatless at the Great Western Depot, saying good-bye to his neighbors.

Neither Jefferson Davis (right), the Provisional President of the Confederacy, nor the Provisional Vice President, Alexander H. Stephens (above), had initially favored secession, and Stephens had actually argued in his state's convention against dissolving the Union. Nor did the two men much like each other. But they had the respect of moderates and fire-eaters alike in the Provisional Congress that chose them to direct the fortunes of their new nation.

> Here I have lived a quarter of a century, and have passed from a young to an old man. Here my children have been born, and one is buried. I now leave, not knowing when, or whether ever, I may return, with a task before me greater than that which rested upon Washington. Without the assistance of that Divine Being, who ever attended him, I cannot succeed. With that assistance I cannot fail. Trusting in Him, who can go with me, and remain with you and be everywhere for good, let us confidently hope that all will yet be well. To His care commending you, as I hope in your prayers you will commend me, I bid you an affectionate farewell.

On February 18, Jefferson Davis took his oath of office on the steps of the state capitol at Montgomery, then addressed the big, festive crowd.

> Our present political position has been achieved in a manner unprecedented in the history of nations. It illustrates the American idea that governments rest on the consent of the governed, and that it is the right of the governed, and that it is the right of the people to alter or abolish them at will whenever they become destructive of the ends for which they were established.... Obstacles may retard, but they can not long

> prevent, the progress of a movement sanctified by its justice and sustained by a virtuous people.

His listeners cheered, wept, sang "Farewell to the Star-Spangled Banner," and "Dixie's Land," a popular minstrel song composed by Dan Emmett, a northerner.

The new Confederate Vice President, Alexander H. Stephens, a wispy, tubercular former congressman from Georgia, was more blunt than the new President had been.

> Our new government is founded on the opposite idea of the equality of the races. . . . Its corner stone rests upon the great truth that the Negro is not equal to the white man. This . . . government is the first in the history of the world, based upon this great physical and moral truth.

That government seemed to Mary Chesnut, the wife of former Senator James Chesnut of South Carolina, to be off to a somewhat shaky start. To make sure that all seven states of the Confederacy were treated equally, Davis appointed to his cabinet a man from each. Most of its members had originally opposed secession; three were foreign-born. "There is a perfect magazine of discord and discontent in that cabinet," she noted. "It only wants a hand to apply a torch and up they go."

Everything at Montgomery had to be improvised. The cabinet met for the first time in a hotel room. A sheet of stationery pinned to the door marked the President's office. The Secretary of the Treasury had to buy his own desk and chair. The first Confederate currency was jobbed out to a New York firm; the South had no press up to the task. "Where will I find the State Department?" a visitor asked Robert Toombs, the Confederate Secretary of State. "In my hat, sir," he answered, "and the archives in my coat pocket."

"*Republics,*" wrote Mary Chesnut, "everybody jawing, everybody putting their mouths in, nothing sacred, all confusion of babble, crimination and *re*crimination—republics can't carry on war. . . . Hurrah for a strong one-man government." No issue seemed too insignificant not to be debated by the relentlessly independent-minded creators of the Confederacy. A South Carolina judge told his fellow guests at a dinner party less than a week after Davis's inauguration that the Provisional Congress had already "trampled the [new] Constitution under foot [because they] have provided President Davis with a house." Then there were those who argued that the Confederacy should continue to fly the Stars and Stripes, since their new country was truest to authentic American principles; let the Yankees go to all the trouble and expense of designing a new banner. But they were finally overruled, and the honor of raising the first Confederate flag would be conferred upon Miss Letitia Tyler, the granddaughter of the former President of the United States John Tyler, a Virginian, and soon to become a member of the Provisional Congress of the Confederacy.

"Thank God!" said former Congressman Lucius Quintus Lamar of Mississippi, "we have a country at last, to live for, to pray for, and, if need be, to die for!"

Mary Chesnut.

The first United States senator to resign his post and offer his services to the new Confederacy was James Chesnut, Jr., of South Carolina; he became a member of the new Provisional Congress.

His wife, Mary, came to Montgomery with him to act as his hostess. The Chesnuts were good friends of Jefferson Davis and his wife, and moved easily among the highest circles of the new government, though Mary privately missed her many friends in Washington and felt slavery wrong, in part because it bred hypocrisy and undermined the sanctity of marriage. "God forgive us," she wrote, "but ours is a monstrous system."

She was childless and subject to depressions and nightmares, for which she sometimes took opium. She began to keep a daily journal in the spring of 1861, seeking to pin to paper some of the history now swirling around her. "This journal is intended to be entirely *objective,*" she wrote. "My subjective days are over. No more *silent* eating into my own heart, making my own misery, when without these morbid fantasies I could be so happy."

"This Southern Confederacy must be supported now by calm determination and cool brains. We have risked all and we must play our best, for the stake is life or death."

MARY CHESNUT

Jefferson Davis was sworn in on the steps of the Alabama state capitol at Montgomery on February 18, 1861. "Upon my . . . head were showered smiles, plaudits and flowers," Davis remembered, "but beyond them I saw troubles innumerable."

There were now two rival North American republics. The incumbent President of the United States, James Buchanan, who believed both secession and coercion unconstitutional, felt powerless to act. Federal installations throughout the South were turned over to the Confederate states, one after another, without a shot being fired.

What would Lincoln do? For nearly four months he had held his silence as the Union he had pledged to maintain fell apart. Now, making his own twelve-day journey by rail toward the northern capital at Washington, the President-elect offered few hints. Unable to act until Inauguration Day and known to most of

"The Eagle's Nest," lithograph published by E. B. and E. C. Kellog in 1861.

the country outside of Illinois only as a one-time congressman who owed his election to the fact that the national debate over slavery's expansion had fragmented the Democrats, he confined himself largely to platitudes. He made jokes about his height and homeliness: "*Ladies* and gentlemen," he said. "I am glad to see you; I suppose you are to see me; but I certainly think I have the best of the bargain," and he had tried to improve his appearance at least a little by growing a new beard. "Last night I saw the new President . . . ," wrote a man who had attended a reception for him. "He is a clever man, and *not so bad looking as they say,* while he is no great beauty. He is tall, 6 feet and 4 inches, has a commanding figure, bows pretty well, is not stiff, has a pleasant face, is amiable and *determined.*"

But it was still not clear exactly what he was determined to do. He told the crowds that it was their duty as much as his to preserve the Union. Wherever

"The bird of our country is a debilitated chicken, disguised in eagle feathers. We have never been a nation; we are only an aggregate of communities, ready to fall apart at the first serious shock."

GEORGE TEMPLETON STRONG

they lived, whatever their political differences in the past, all Americans were "bound together . . . and are attached to our country and to our whole country."

Not even the defiant ceremonies at Montgomery seemed to alarm him. Again and again, he blandly assured those who came out to hear him that the secession crisis was "artificial": "*there is no crisis* excepting such a one as may be gotten up at any time by designing politicians"; "There is nothing going wrong . . . nobody is suffering anything . . . there shall be no blood shed unless it be forced upon the Government."

"If Mr. Lincoln has nothing better to offer upon this fearful crisis," said the New York *Herald,* "let him say nothing at all." Edward Everett, the former Governor of Massachusetts, spoke for a good many disappointed easterners: "He is evidently a person of very inferior cast of character."

In fact, Lincoln had gravely miscalculated. Secession, he still believed, was a plot by a small but powerful band of wealthy planters. Most white southerners had no stake in slavery and, if only he held firm, they were sure to resist the stampede toward disunion.

Washington's Birthday, February 22, was still celebrated as a national holiday, North and South. Lincoln raised a flag in front of Independence Hall at Philadelphia that morning, telling the crowd, "I would rather be assassinated on this spot" than surrender the idea of equality embodied in the Declaration of Independence.

His misunderstanding of what had happened in the South was now compounded by what in a later day would have been called a public-relations disaster. His journey was to have ended with a big, noisy parade through Baltimore and a grand welcome at Washington itself. But at Philadelphia, a Scottish-born railroad detective named Allan Pinkerton warned him of a plot to kill him at Baltimore. Assassination threats were nothing new to Lincoln; they had been arriving steadily since Election Day, and he was inclined to ignore this one, too, until a similar rumor reached him from a second, independent source. His advisors prevailed upon him to skip the Maryland capital. Should assassins prove successful, they argued, the Union cause itself might not survive.

He agreed to take the night train to Washington and slip into the city anonymously, accompanied only by Pinkerton and an old Illinois friend, Ward Hill Lamon. The trip was uneventful except for the presence of a cheerful drunk in a nearby berth, whom Lamon could not dissuade from singing "Dixie" off and on all night, and when Lincoln arrived at six the next morning, friends whisked him off to Willard's Hotel, where he was to live until he moved into the Executive Mansion.

Hostile newspapers delighted in his ignominious arrival. A cartoonist would draw him skulking into town, muffled in a cape, a cap pulled low over his eyes. "Everybody here," said the Charleston *Mercury,* "is disgusted at this cowardly and undignified entry." "The cold shoulder is given to Mr. Lincoln," reported William Howard Russell, Washington correspondent for the London *Times.* "People take particular pleasure in telling how he came towards the seat of his Government disguised."

March 4, Inauguration Day, was cold and windy in Washington. A large, tense crowd gathered before the Capitol to see and hear the new President. Southern sentiment was strong in the city. Two riflemen watched from every window, more lined the roofs of nearby buildings, and cannon stood on the Capitol grounds, ready to be touched off should there be trouble. General Winfield Scott, the venerable hero of the Mexican War and general-in-chief of the army, may have been too fat and gouty even to mount a horse, but his resolve was undiminished at seventy-five, and he threatened to "manure the slopes of Arlington" with the blood of anyone who dared disrupt the proceedings.

Things went off peaceably enough. Chief Justice Taney administered the oath, and the new President proved both firm and conciliatory. He promised not to interfere with slavery where it already existed, but he also denied the right of any single state to secede from the Union all the states had made, and he vowed to "hold, occupy and possess" Federal installations. Then he spoke directly to the South:

> In your hands, my dissatisfied countrymen, and not in mine is the momentous issue of civil war. The government will not assail you. You can have no conflict, without being yourselves the aggressors. . . . We are not enemies but friends. We must not be enemies. Though passion may have strained, it must not break our bonds of affection. The mystic chords of memory, stretching from every battle-field and patriot grave, to every living heart and hearthstone, all over this broad land, will yet swell the chorus of the Union, when again touched, as surely they will be, by the better angels of our nature.

The Capitol remained unfinished, its rotunda still lacking its dome, and there was some sentiment for suspending construction until the crisis had passed. Lincoln insisted that the work continue. "I take it as a sign," he said, "that the Union will continue."

"The 4th of March has come and gone," a young patent office clerk named Clara Barton told a friend a few days after the inauguration, "and we have a *live Republican* President, and, what is perhaps singular, during the whole day we saw no one who appeared to manifest the least dislike to his living." Preoccupied by the actions of his opponents, Lincoln now also had to contend with the importuning of his friends. For the first time, Republicans had a chance at the thousands of Federal jobs that had once gone to Democrats. "The city is full of western chaps . . ." wrote the humorist Robert Henry Newell. "Every soul of them knew old Abe when he was a child, and one old boy can even remember going for a doctor when his *mother* was born."

Two lines of office seekers snaked along the drive to the Executive Mansion, one going in, the other coming out, all day, every working day. One man, turned down first for a Federal judgeship, then for postmaster of his hometown, came back again to see if he might be made a lighthouse keeper; anyplace on the Atlantic coast would do, he said. Another chased after the President's carriage, waving his papers, until Lincoln turned him away, saying, "No! no! I won't open shop in the street."

"Plainly, the central idea of secession is the essence of anarchy. A majority, held in restraint by constitutional checks, and limitations . . . is the only true sovereign of a free people."

ABRAHAM LINCOLN, March 4, 1861

Abraham Lincoln delivers his inaugural address beneath the portico of the unfinished Capitol. "People differ about Lincoln's inaugural . . ." George Templeton Strong wrote, but "I think there's a clink of metal in it. It's unlike any message or state paper of any class that has appeared in my time. . . . It doesn't run in the ruts of Public Documents, number one to number ten million and one, but seems to introduce one to a *man* and to dispose one to like him."

STRIKING THE HORNET'S NEST

The sixty-eight Union men of Major Anderson's command had remained huddled together within the walls of Fort Sumter in Charleston Harbor since the day after Christmas, cut off from reinforcement or resupply, besieged by six thousand eager South Carolina militiamen and a semicircle of artillery batteries. Anderson was a career soldier from Kentucky, sympathetic to slavery—he had once owned slaves himself—and certain that arms alone could never force the seceding states back into the Union, but unshakable in his devotion to duty and to his flag.

General Scott advised Lincoln to abandon the fort; it was now impossible to resupply without a big fleet and 25,000 troops. Most members of Lincoln's cabinet agreed. Nearly all were now privately sure they could do a better job than their new chief. Four had been his serious rivals for the presidential nomination. Simon Cameron, a Pennsylvania politician with a reputation so unsavory, one acquaintance said, that the only thing he would *not* steal was a red-hot stove, was Secretary of War. Salmon P. Chase, the Secretary of the Treasury, thought Lincoln altogether too timid in opposing slavery and may already have been dreaming of supplanting him as President in 1864. Edward Bates of Missouri, the Attorney General, believed his chief entirely too outspoken against slavery and was certain that reprovisioning Fort Sumter would lead not only to civil war but to "social war, & . . . servile war, the horrors of which need not be dwelt upon."

But no member of the cabinet was more initially sure of his superiority to the President who appointed him than the Secretary of State, William H. Seward of New York, who had been the front-runner for the Republican nomination Lincoln had won. He first muddied the difficult debate over Fort Sumter's fate by sending private and unauthorized assurances to the South that the island fort would be peacefully abandoned, then sent Lincoln an extraordinary document called "Some Thoughts for the President's Consideration." Firm policies were needed, it said, and Seward was more than ready to formulate and execute them; the fort should be given up, he argued, while a war with Spain or France might be stirred up to reunite North and South against a common enemy. Lincoln, who valued Seward's ability and intelligence while deploring his tactics and discounting his ambition, politely declined; he would be his own President.

As the weeks dragged by, sympathy for Major Anderson and his besieged garrison spread across the North. "The Administration must have a policy of action," said *The New York Times.* "Better almost anything than additional suspense. The people want *something* to be decided on [to] serve as a rallying point for the abundant but discouraged loyalty of the American heart."

Finally, on April 6, Lincoln drew the line. Half a year had passed since his election, and there were no signs that further delay would improve the prospects of reuniting the sundered Union. He would provision Fort Sumter, he told the Governor of South Carolina, but he would not attempt to reinforce or rearm it provided neither the fort nor the fleet was attacked.

He still hoped for peace but was willing now to risk war. For him,

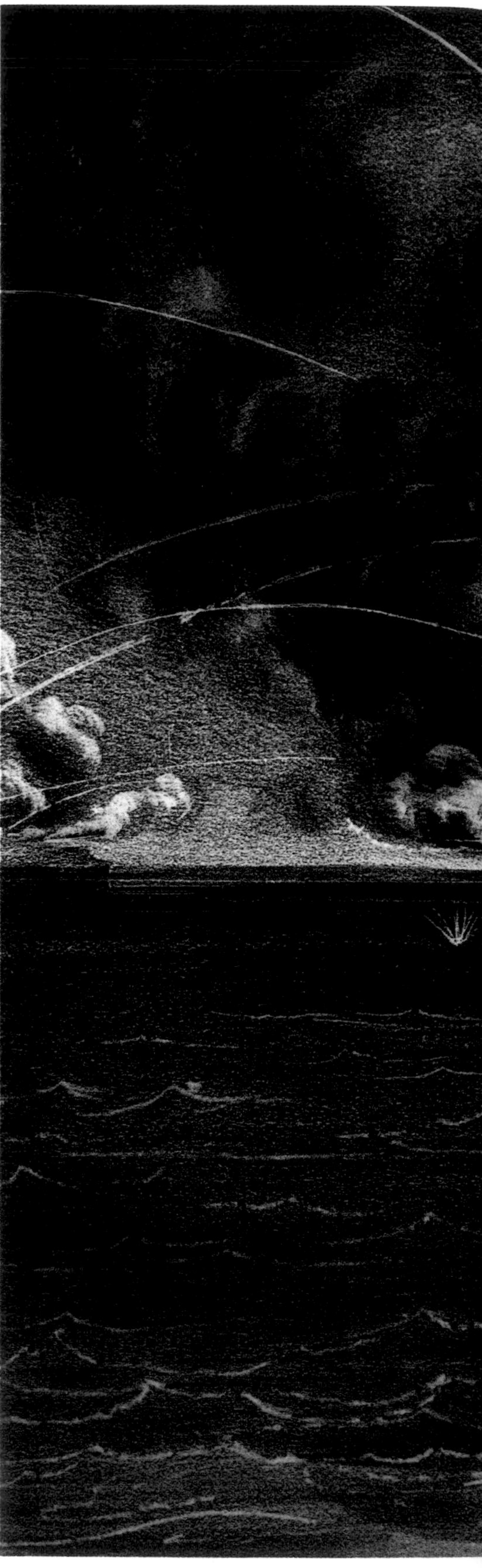

"All the pent-up hatred of the past months and years is voiced in the thunder of these cannon, and the people seem almost beside themselves in the exultation of a freedom they deem already won."

WILLIAM MERRICK BRISTOL

Confederate batteries fire on Fort Sumter, April 12, 1861.

VOL. X.....NO. 2984.

FORT SUMPTER FALLEN.

PARTICULARS OF THE BOMBARDMENT.

The Fort on Fire and the Garrison Exhausted.

NO ATTEMPT AT REINFORCEMENT.

The Cessation of Firing and the Capitulation.

NO LIVES LOST ON EITHER SIDE.

Major Anderson and his Men Coming to New-York.

How the News was Received in

preserving the Union was far more than a question of mere geography, more than a northern cause, more even than a national cause: it was mankind's. If the Union was allowed to dissolve, the great experiment in self-government begun by the founders of the republic would fail; the promise of the Declaration of Independence that "the weights should be lifted from the shoulders of all men, and that all should have an equal chance" would have been betrayed.

The Confederate government was not sure how to react. Secretary of State Toombs wanted no part of firing on the fort. "Mr. President," he told Davis, "at this time it is suicide, murder, and will lose us every friend at the North. You will wantonly strike a hornet's nest which extends from mountain to ocean, and legions now quiet will swarm out and sting us to death. It is unnecessary; it puts us in the wrong; it is fatal."

But those more impatient for action finally prevailed, men like the Alabama secessionist J. G. Gilchrist, who told the Secretary of War, Leroy P. Walker, that "unless you sprinkle blood in the face of the people of Alabama, they will be back in the old Union in less than ten days." Not only would an attack strengthen the resolve of the states already in the Confederacy, such men were certain, but it would bring Virginia into the Confederacy as well. "If you want us to join you," Congressman Roger Pryor of Virginia told a cheering Charleston crowd, "*strike a blow!*"

After midnight on April 12, Pryor, James Chesnut, and two other Confederate emissaries were rowed out to Fort Sumter to deliver to Major Anderson an ultimatum from the Confederate Secretary of War. The Union commander had until 4 a.m. to surrender; otherwise the South Carolina batteries would open fire.

"Our Southern brethren have done grievous wrong," wrote Major Robert Anderson after surrendering Fort Sumter (shown above left, shortly afterward) to General P. G. T. Beauregard. "They have rebelled and have attacked their father's house and their loyal brothers. They must be punished and brought back but this necessity breaks my heart."

Major Robert Anderson, U.S.A.

General Pierre Gustave Toutant Beauregard, C.S.A.

Anderson refused to surrender. "If we never meet in this world again," he said as he escorted his official visitors back to their boat, "God grant that we may meet in the next."

He and his men could do nothing but hunker down and wait for the inevitable.

Mary Chesnut heard it come: "April 12 . . . The heavy booming of a cannon—I sprang out of bed, and on my knees, prostrate, I prayed as I have never prayed before."

The Civil War began at 4:30 a.m. on the 12th of April, 1861, when the Confederate commander, a dapper, showy Creole from Louisiana named General Pierre Gustave Toutant Beauregard, ordered his men to open up on Fort Sumter. Beauregard was himself a gunner, so skilled as an artillery student at West Point that his instructor there had broken with tradition to keep him on as his assistant for another year. Major Anderson, commander of the helpless Federal outpost upon which his guns were now trained, had been that instructor.

General States Rights Gist of South Carolina was in charge of the Confederate batteries that morning, but the honor of firing the first shot was offered first to a civilian from Virginia, Congressman Pryor. Until that moment he had been a fire-eating secessionist, but now, suddenly, he found himself unable "to fire the first shot of the war"; the enormity of what that shot was likely to set loose had proved too much for him. Other willing hands were found, among them those of old Edmund Ruffin, also a Virginian and an advocate of secession for twenty years. "Of course, I was highly gratified by the compliment," he said, "and delighted to perform the service."

A Union sergeant remembered watching as "the burning fuse which marked the course of the [first] shell . . . mounted among the stars," and a young Charleston girl recalled the "perfect sheet of flame" that followed as battery after battery joined in, making "a rumbling, deadening sound . . . the war was on."

Charleston civilians gathered on rooftops to cheer both the Confederate batteries and the courage of the Union defenders, who held out for a day and a half despite the impact of 3,341 shells on their little manmade island. Mary Chesnut noted that although she was herself unable to take more than tea for fear and excitement during the whole bombardment, "not by one word or look can we detect any change in the demeanor of [the] negro servants. . . . They make no sign. Are they stolidly stupid or wiser than we are, silent and strong, biding their time?"

No one was seriously hurt during the shelling—a horse was the only fatality—and the Union men managed to fire back from time to time, but Fort Sumter's situation was clearly hopeless. After thirty-four hours, Anderson called for a truce.

When he and his men sailed north to the United States after their surrender, Beauregard permitted his old teacher to take with him the shot-torn American flag that had flown above the fort. The Union commander intended someday to be buried in it.

The Confederate flag flies within Fort Sumter's battered walls while victorious rebels play at manning Federal guns abandoned the day before.

"Woe to those who began this war if they were not in bitter earnest."

MARY CHESNUT

"So Civil War is inaugurated at last. God defend the right."

GEORGE TEMPLETON STRONG

AN ARM'D RACE IS ADVANCING!

"The intelligence that Fort Sumter has surrendered to the Confederate forces," wrote the editor of the Montgomery *Advertiser*, ". . . sent a thrill of joy to the heart of every true friend of the South. The face of every southern man was brighter, his step lighter, and his bearing prouder than it had been before."

That same intelligence galvanized the North as well. "All the past we leave behind," Walt Whitman wrote. Here, the shot-torn Sumter flag waves from the statue of George Washington in New York's Union Square on April 20, 1861, surrounded by 100,000 New Yorkers demanding vengeance.

North and South, men flocked to join their respective armies. "War!" wrote Whitman. "An arm'd race is advancing! The welcome for battle, no turning away; War! Be it weeks, months or years, an arm'd race is advancing to welcome it."

"April 15. Events multiply. The President is out with a proclamation calling for 75,000 volunteers. . . . It is said 200,000 more will be called within a few days."

George Templeton Strong

"The streets of Charleston present some such aspect as those of Paris in the last revolution. Crowds of armed men singing and promenading the streets, the battle blood running through their veins—that hot oxygen which is called 'the flush of victory' on the cheek. . . . Sumter has set them distraught; never such a victory. It is a bloodless Waterloo."

William Russell, London *Times*

"Send me your picture" was a common refrain in soldiers' letters from home. The *carte de visite* photographs—so called because they were the size of visiting cards—of Union volunteers on these and the following pages never got there, piling up instead at the dead-letter department of the Post Office during the course of the war.

"Father and I were husking out . . . corn . . . when William Corry came across the field. He was excited and said, 'Jonathan, the Rebels have fired upon Fort Sumter.' Father got white, and couldn't say a word."

Theodore F. Upson, Lima, Indiana

"So impatient did I become for starting that I felt like a thousand pins were pricking me in every part of my body and started off a week in advance of my brothers."

Frank P. Peak, Arkansas

"Dear Brother. They are a'volunteering right smartly here. If you want to join a company, come down here and let's go together. I have a notion of trying a while."

James Jackson
Covington County, Alabama

"The New Orleans Zouaves was composed of the most lawless and desperate material which that city could send forth. It is said that its colonel, with the approval of the Mayor of New Orleans, established recruiting booths in the different jails there."

Mrs. Sallie Putnam

"Students have all gone to war. College suspended. And God help the right."

Registrar's journal
Centenary College

"One thing, as regards this matter, I regret, and one thing I am glad of; the regrettable thing is that I am too old to shoulder a musket myself, and the joyful thing is that [my son] Julian is too young."

Nathaniel Hawthorne

"I feel that I would like to shoot a Yankee, and yet I know that this would not be in harmony with the spirit of Christianity."

William L. Nugent, Mississippi

"We was treated as good as company could be at every station. . . . We got kisses from the girls at a good many places and we returned the same to them."

Private Hercules Stannard

"I have got the best suit of clothes that I [ever] had in my life."

Private Peter Wilson
1st Iowa Volunteers

"If a fellow wants to go with a girl now he had better enlist. The girls sing 'I am Bound to be a Soldier's Wife or Die an Old Maid.'"

Private Theodore Upson
100th Indiana

TRAITORS AND PATRIOTS

When word of Sumter's fall reached Washington, the regular United States Army consisted of fewer than 17,000 men, most of them stationed in the far West. Just two of its generals had ever commanded an army in the field, Winfield Scott and another, still more venerable, hero of the Mexican War, John Wool, age seventy-seven.

Lincoln called upon the governors of the states and territories to furnish Washington with 75,000 militiamen, each to serve for just ninety days. The response was instantaneous and heartening. Six months of anxious waiting were over. The time had come for action.

"War! and volunteers are the only topics of conversation or thought," wrote a student at Oberlin College in central Ohio. "The lessons today have been a mere form. I cannot study. I cannot sleep, and I don't know as I can write." Ohio had been asked for thirteen regiments, but so many men volunteered, the Governor wrote the Secretary of War, that "owing to an unavoidable confusion in the first hurry and enthusiasm of our people," he could not "without seriously repressing [their ardor] . . . stop short of twenty regiments. The lion in us is thoroughly roused."

Still without weapons and wearing civilian clothes, Vermont volunteers struggle to master the intricacies of drill at Camp Baxter, just outside St. Johnsbury, in the early weeks of the war.

The Sumter Light Guards—Company K of the 4th Regiment of the Georgia Volunteers—display their bright new uniforms in April 1861.

Ulysses S. Grant, West Point 1843, was back home in Galena, Illinois, clerking in his father's tannery after drink and boredom had driven him from the peacetime army. When he heard that fighting had started, he tried to obtain a commission, got no reply, and finally went to Springfield to see if the army still had a place for him. It did, as mustering officer, handling the flood of volunteers, at $4.20 a day. "There are but two parties now," he said, "traitors and patriots, and I want hereafter to be ranked with the latter."

The same sentiment was evident all across the North. At a special church service in Auburn, New York, wrote the pastor's wife, "the great audience rose, clapping and applauding, as the soldiers filed into the pews reserved for them. The sermon was a radical discourse, and recognized slavery as the underlying cause. . . . The choir sang patriotic odes, the audience joining with one voice in the exultant refrain, 'It is sweet, it is sweet, for one's country to die!'"

In Manhattan streets, men wore postage stamps on their hats as impromptu emblems of their patriotism; their wives and daughters ran up Union bonnets with red, white, and blue ribbons. "In our own little circle . . ." wrote a New York matron to a friend abroad, "one mother has sent away an idolized boy; another, two; *another, four.* One boy, just getting over diphtheria, jumps out of bed and buckles his knapsack on. One sweet young wife is packing a regulation valise for her husband today, and doesn't let him see her cry."

The 6th New York Regiment included so many Bowery toughs it was said a man had to have served time in prison just to get in, while the élite 7th set out for Washington with sandwiches made at Delmonico's and a thousand velvet-covered campstools on which to sit and eat them.

Whole towns signed up. The 10th Michigan Volunteers was comprised entirely of Flint men; their commander was the mayor; their regimental doctor had been caring for them since they were boys.

Immigrants marched off, too—Irishmen in the fighting 69th, the Irish Zouaves, Irish Volunteers, and St. Patrick Brigade; Italians in the Garibaldi Guards and Italian Legion; Germans in the Steuben Volunteers, German Rifles, Turner Rifles, and DeKalb Regiment. Many immigrant volunteers could neither give nor receive orders in English.

On June 5, Elisha Hunt Rhodes, age nineteen, the son of a Yankee sea captain, left his job as a harness-maker's clerk in Pawtuxet, Rhode Island, and joined the 2nd Rhode Island Volunteers. He would have joined earlier had his widowed mother not begged him to stay home. "Sunday was a sorrowful one at our home," he recalled. "My mother went about with tears in her eyes, while I felt disappointment that I could not express and therefore nursed my sorrow in silence." Finally, she came to his room after he had gone to bed, and "with a spirit worthy of a Spartan mother of old said, 'My son, other mothers must make sacrifices and why should not I? If you feel that it is your duty to enlist, I will give my consent.'"

The following morning, Rhodes and his best friend from school were waiting on the steps of the Providence armory two hours before the recruiting office opened for business. Rhodes signed on as a private. "We drilled all day and night," he confided to the diary he began to keep. "Standing before a long mirror, I put in many hours of weary work and soon thought myself quite a soldier. . . . I was elected First Sergeant, much to my surprise. Just what a First Sergeant's duties might be, I had no idea."

Two weeks later, the 2nd Rhode Island moved toward the war. "Today," Rhodes wrote, "we have orders to pack up and be ready to leave . . . for Washington. . . . My knapsack was so heavy that I could scarcely stagger under the load. At the wharf an immense crowd had gathered and we went on board our steamer with mingled feelings of joy and sorrow."

Washington was a southern city, entirely surrounded by slave states, and its streets and corridors were alive with talk of treason. Southern-born government clerks hurried south, telling their friends they would be back in a week or two, when the Confederates had taken the city.

One out of three regular army officers went south, too. "I must go with the South," wrote Joseph E. Johnston of Virginia, the Quartermaster General, "though the action is in the last degree ungrateful. I owe all that I am to the government of the United States. It had educated and clothed me with honor. To leave the service is a hard necessity, but I must go. Though I am resigning my position, I trust I may never draw my sword against the old flag."

The most promising officer in the United States Army was another Virgin-

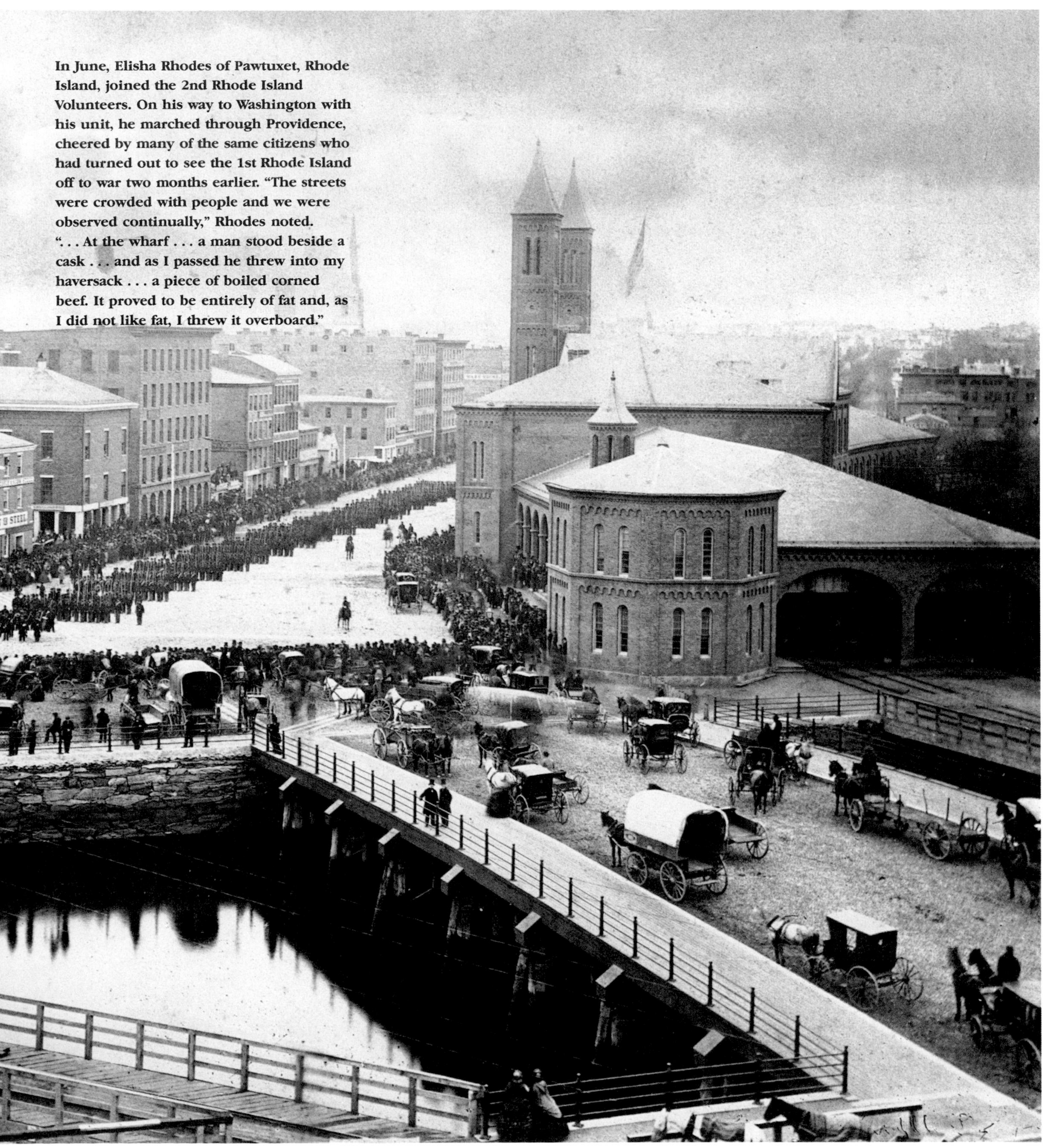

In June, Elisha Rhodes of Pawtuxet, Rhode Island, joined the 2nd Rhode Island Volunteers. On his way to Washington with his unit, he marched through Providence, cheered by many of the same citizens who had turned out to see the 1st Rhode Island off to war two months earlier. "The streets were crowded with people and we were observed continually," Rhodes noted. ". . . At the wharf . . . a man stood beside a cask . . . and as I passed he threw into my haversack . . . a piece of boiled corned beef. It proved to be entirely of fat and, as I did not like fat, I threw it overboard."

ian, Robert E. Lee, who had been a hero in the Mexican War. "If . . . the President of the United States would tell me that a great battle was to be fought for the liberty or slavery of the country," said his old commander, Winfield Scott, "and asked my judgment as to the ability of the commander, I would say with my dying breath, 'Let it be Robert E. Lee!'"

Lee believed the Union "perpetual," thought talk of secession "idle" and dangerous because it might drag the South "into the Gulf of Revolution." "As an American citizen," he had written before the shelling at Sumter began, "I take great pride in my country, her prosperity and institutions, and would defend any state if her rights were invaded. But I can anticipate no greater calamity for the country than the dissolution of the Union. It would be an accumulation of all the evils we complain of, and I am willing to sacrifice everything but honor for its preservation."

"Made my first detail . . . for guard duty to which most men objected because they said they did not enlist to do guard duty but to fight the Yankees—all fun and frolic."

ORDERLY SERGEANT A. L. P. VAIRIN
2nd Mississippi Volunteers

Four days after Sumter fell, Lee was offered field command of the entire Union army at Lincoln's behest. He deferred his decision, waiting to see what his native state would do.

The next day, Virginia voted to secede. That afternoon, Lee confided to a pharmacist that he "was one of those dull creatures that cannot see the good of secession." But in the end he went with his state, and on April 23 accepted command of the Army of Virginia. He wrote a farewell note to a northern friend:

> I cannot raise my hand against my birthplace, my home, my children. I should like, above all things, that our difficulties might be peaceably arranged. . . . Whatever may be the result of the contest I foresee that the country will have to pass through a terrible ordeal, a necessary expiation for our national sins. May God direct all for our good, and shield and preserve you and yours.

Lincoln's call for troops had roused the South as well as the North, but not in the way he had intended. "The militia of Virginia will *not* be furnished to the powers at Washington," the Governor of that state wrote Lincoln. ". . . Your object is to subjugate the Southern States. . . . You have chosen to inaugurate civil war."

When Virginia left the Union, Richmond became the new capital of the Confederacy. Tennessee left, too. So did Arkansas and North Carolina. There were now eleven Confederate states to stand off the Union's twenty-three. So many southerners volunteered, from places like Hiawassee, Georgia, Hushpuckena, Mississippi, Moonsville, Alabama, that a third of them—twenty thousand men—had to be sent back home. Some refused to go.

John B. Gordon, a Georgia attorney and businessman who believed slavery "the Mightiest Engine in the world for the civilization, education and refinement of mankind," raised a company of mountaineers who insisted on wearing coonskin caps and called themselves the "Raccoon Roughs." When they reached Atlanta and were told they were not yet needed, they stayed put while Gordon sent telegrams offering their services to all the southern governors. Alabama finally found room for them, and they boarded the train for Montgomery. Gordon recalled the greetings they received along the way:

During the first giddy weeks after Fort Sumter, Confederate volunteers like these men of the 1st Virginia Militia—the "Richmond Grays"—were confident that their next encounter with the enemy would bring the same effortlessly happy result.

The relaxed self-confidence of the men of the Washington Artillery of New Orleans was at least partially justified; established in 1838 and commanded by the leaders of creole society, their unit had seen action during the Mexican War and looked forward to more.

"Bonfires blazed from the hills at night, and torch-light processions with drums and fifes paraded the streets of towns. In the absence of real cannon, blacksmith's anvils were made to thunder our welcome."

Among the Tennesseans who answered the call was twenty-one-year-old Sam Watkins of Columbia. He joined the Maury Grays, 1st Tennessee Regiment, at Nashville. Like most rebel soldiers, he had no personal stake in slavery. He was willing to fight because he believed in States' Rights, he said, and because "the South is our country, the North is the country of those who live there."

In July, his regiment was sent to Virginia.

> The bugle sounded to strike tents and place everything aboard the cars.... We went bowling along [at] ... thirty miles an hour, as fast as steam could carry us. At every town and station, citizens and ladies were waving their handkerchiefs and hurrahing for Jeff Davis and the Southern Confederacy.... Ah, it is worth soldiering to receive such welcomes as this.

"Lincoln may bring his 75,000 troops against us," said Vice President Stephens. "We fight for our homes, our fathers and mothers, our wives, brothers, sisters, sons and daughters! . . . We can call out a million of peoples if need be, and when they are cut down we can call another, and still another."

In fact, the odds against a southern victory seemed long. There were nearly 21 million people in the North, just 9 million in the Confederacy, and 3.5 million of them were slaves, whom their masters did not dare arm. The North had more than twice as many miles of railroad track as the South. The value of all the manufactured goods produced in all the Confederate states added up to less than one-fourth of those produced in New York alone.

None of this mattered to the men who joined the Tallapoosa Thrashers and Chickasaw Desperadoes and Cherokee Lincoln Killers.

It was an article of southern faith that while southerners were invincible, northerners were avaricious weaklings. The Yankees' "most bloodthirsty achievements," said the New Orleans *Crescent,* "consist of harpooning whales and eviscerating codfish."

The Raleigh *Banner* agreed:

> The army of the South will be composed of the best material that ever yet made up an army; while that of Lincoln will be gathered from the sewers of the cities—the degraded, beastly outscoring of all the quarters of the world, who will serve for pay and will run away as soon as they can when danger threatens.

Private Sam Watkins of Company H, the 1st Tennessee.

"The die was cast; war was declared . . . every person, almost, was eager for the war, and we were all afraid it would be over and we not be in the fight."

SAM WATKINS

Mobile was "boiling over with enthusiasm" for war, said Raphael Semmes, a former U.S. naval officer based in Alabama, who had resigned his commission and headed South to put on a new uniform. "The young merchants had dropped their ledgers and were forming and drilling companies by night and day."

Charleston was "crowded with soldiers," said Mary Chesnut. "These new ones are running in, fairly. They fear the war will be over before they get a sight of the fun. Every man from every little country precinct wants a place in the picture."

"The young men carry dress suits with them," a Rome, Georgia, woman noted. "Every soldier, nearly, has a servant with him, and a whole lot of spoons and forks, so as to live comfortably and elegantly in camp, and finally to make a splurge in Washington when they shall arrive there, which they expect will be very soon."

Each side thought the other would collapse within ninety days, and both sides agreed that it was to be a white man's fight. Blacks who tried to sign up were turned away.

HURRY UP AND WAIT

The first few days after Fort Sumter's fall were a desperately anxious time in Washington. The Richmond *Examiner* reported

> one wild shout of fierce resolve to capture Washington City, at all and every human hazard. The filthy cage of unclean birds must and will be

Civilian volunteers patrol the lawn of the Executive Mansion in April 1861, waiting for the northern army to arrive.

> purified by fire. . . . Our people can take it, and Scott the arch-traitor, and Lincoln the Beast, combined cannot prevent it. The just indignation of an outraged and deeply injured people will teach the Illinois Ape to retrace his journey across the borders of the Free negro states still more rapidly than he came.

Some 15,000 rebels were already said to be within striking distance of Alexandria, another 8,000 were at Harpers Ferry, and more were believed to be on the way.

All that stood between them and the nation's capital in the first days after Fort Sumter were a few regular troops and a scattering of neighborhood militia units, including the Silver Grays Home Guard, made up of loyal if unsteady veterans of the War of 1812.

Maryland secessionists burned railroad bridges, stopped the mails, cut off Washington's telegraph communication with the North. Frightened citizens

"April 19. There has been a serious disturbance in Baltimore. Regiments from Massachusetts assailed by a mob that was repulsed by shot and steel.... It's a notable coincidence that the first blood in this great struggle is drawn by Massachusetts men on the anniversary of Lexington. This is a continuation of the war that Lexington opened—a war of democracy against oligarchy."

GEORGE TEMPLETON STRONG

fled into the countryside. The streets were deserted. Government departments struggled with skeleton staffs. "Disaffection lurked, if it did not openly avow itself," Seward remembered, "in every department and every bureau . . . in the post office and in the custom house." The nervous Union commandant of the big Federal navy yard at Norfolk abandoned his post to the Confederates, burning five warships to the waterline rather than hand them over to the rebels.

A Voluntary Guard now patrolled the White House grounds, commanded by Senator James H. Lane, a veteran of the guerrilla warfare in Bleeding Kansas, and the Kentucky abolitionist Cassius Marcellus Clay, wearing "three pistols and an Arkansas tooth pick." General Scott drew up a last-ditch defense plan. In case of attack, the President and his cabinet were to retreat to the basement of the thick-walled Treasury building and try to survive on water and 2,000 barrels of flour. At night, Confederate campfires could be seen across the Potomac from the White House.

On April 19, a Baltimore mob opened fire on the 6th Massachusetts as it passed through the streets on its way to Washington, and the Massachusetts men fired back; four soldiers and nine civilians were killed and others were wounded. A Maryland delegation demanded that Lincoln send no more soldiers through their state. "I must have troops," the President answered, ". . . our men are not moles, and can't dig under the earth. They are not birds, and can't fly through the air. There is no way but to march across, and that they must do." But privately he made sure that no more troops would come through Baltimore, fearing their unwanted presence might drive the state out of the Union and into the Confederacy.

Ten days after Lincoln issued his call for troops, the bulk of his army had still not arrived. He came close to despair, pacing his office and muttering, "Why don't they come? Why don't they come?" When some of the Massachusetts men wounded at Baltimore were brought to see him at the White House, he told them, "I don't believe there *is* a North.... *You* are the only northern realities."

Then, around noon on April 25, a train whistle announced that the troops had made it through at last. The 7th New York arrived first, stepping past the White House singing an old Methodist hymn with brand-new lyrics—"John Brown's Body." Lincoln, a friend remembered, "was all smiles."

"Hurrah! we are in Washington, and what a city!" wrote Elisha Rhodes after the 2nd Rhode Island arrived. "Mud, pigs, negroes, palaces, shanties everywhere. Today we brushed up . . . and were reviewed by the President. As we passed the White House I had my first view of Abraham Lincoln. He looks like a good, honest man, and I trust that with God's help he can bring our country safely out of its peril."

Rhode Islanders set up their bunks among the cases of curiosities at the Patent Office. New Yorkers slept on the carpeted floor of the chamber of the House of Representatives, and amused themselves making speeches from the Speaker's chair. Massachusetts boys camped in the rotunda and cooked their bacon on the furnaces in the cellar.

Southern sympathizers were appalled: "You would not now know this God-forsaken city," wrote Mrs. Phillip Phillips, "our beautiful capital, with all its artistic wealth, desecrated, *disgraced* with Lincoln's low soldiery. The *respectable* part [of the soldiers] view it also in the same spirit, for one of the Seventh [New York] Regiment told me that never in his life had he seen such ruin going on as is now enacted in the halls of our once honored Capitol!"

But those who remained loyal saw things differently. " 'Washington City' was no longer a name to the mother waiting and praying in the distant hamlet," Mary Clemmer Ames remembered. "Her *boy* was camped on the floor of the rotunda. . . . Never, till that hour, did the Federal city become to the heart of the American people . . . truly the capital of the nation."

Union camps encircled the District. Washington would soon become the most heavily fortified city on earth, ringed by 22 batteries and 74 forts.

Colonel Elmer Ellsworth in civilian dress: "In the untimely loss of your noble son," Abraham Lincoln wrote Ellsworth's parents after his death, "our affliction here, is scarcely less than your own. So much of promised usefulness to one's country, and of bright hopes for one's self and friends, have rarely been so suddenly dashed as in his fall."

Mrs. Elizabeth Lindsay Lomax was an army officer's widow whose son had commanded the militia unit that escorted Lincoln to his inauguration. Now he had gone south to serve his native Virginia and she had decided to stay on in Washington. "This afternoon," she wrote that spring, "Virginia Tayloe came to take me for a drive." On their return they stopped at the 7th New York's encampment. "They have a charming military band and are a wonderful looking body of men. We stayed to see them drill, but oh, to think they are drilling to kill—and to kill my own people."

That killing began on May 23, the day after the voters of Virginia officially ratified their state's ordinance of secession by a margin of better than three to one. The people of Virginia having "thus allowed this giant insurrection to make its nest within her borders . . ." Lincoln declared, "this government has no choice but to deal with it, where it finds it" and sent troops across the Potomac to seize Arlington Heights, occupy Alexandria, and establish a buffer zone for the capital.

In the vanguard was Colonel Elmer Ellsworth, once an apprentice lawyer in Lincoln's law office and close to the President's whole family, a celebrity soldier at just twenty-four as captain of the dashing New York Fire Zouaves, recruited from the New York City Fire Department. When Ellsworth saw the rebel flag flying above an Alexandria hotel, he charged inside and up the stairs to cut it down. On the colonel's way back down with the rebel banner, the hotelkeeper killed him with a shotgun. Ellsworth's aide instantly cut down his killer, but the North had its first martyr.

Souvenir hunters carved up the staircase on which Ellsworth died. Flags flew at half-staff all across the North. The body lay in state in the East Room of the White House, then in City Hall at New York, where a new volunteer unit was instantly formed—Ellsworth's Avengers.

Lincoln could do nothing to force Virginia back into the Union, but the independent-minded farmers of the state's upland western counties showed signs of resisting the new secessionist government. To encourage them, Lincoln dispatched an army commanded by General George Brinton McClellan, a handsome thirty-four-year-old West Point graduate from a fine Philadelphia family. McClellan had little trouble driving out the small force of Confederates stationed in the Alleghenies—though some of his aides worried privately that he seemed overly cautious in following up his victories—and at

Thirty-seven miles of fortifications would soon ring Washington, including the intricate earthworks within Battery Rogers at Alexandria, Virginia, to the south (above), and the rifled parrot gun at Fort Totten, to the north (right), here being tended by men of the 3rd Massachusetts Heavy Artillery.

Philippi, in a pouring rain, his men caught a Confederate force sound asleep and forced it to flee in panic with only a single Union fatality. Not even Robert E. Lee, of whom everyone had thought so highly, seemed able to inspire his outnumbered army to hold back the Union advance. In the fall he would be sent farther south, lampooned in southern newspapers as "Evacuating Lee" and "Granny Lee" for having failed to hold his ground.

The western counties would eventually secede from Virginia—and rejoin the Union as the new state of West Virginia.

In March, weeks before the shelling of Fort Sumter began, eight runaway slaves had slipped into the Federal garrison at Fort Pickens, in Florida, "entertaining the idea," the commander reported, that Union troops had been sent there "to protect them and grant them their freedom." The fort's commander sent them back to their owners under armed guard, acting in accordance with the policy set by the President himself in his inaugural address and since echoed by Congress: The North was waging a war "to defend and maintain the supremacy of the Constitution and to preserve the Union"; since that Constitution legitimized slavery, there was no thought "of overthrowing or interfering with the rights or established institutions" of any state. Lincoln would not make war on slavery.

But slaves in growing numbers continued to risk their owners' wrath and come over to the Union side, and many northern officers found turning them away increasingly distasteful. It fell to an unlikely New England commander to force a change in that policy: General Benjamin F. Butler, a Massachusetts Democrat with crossed eyes and mixed motives, who had once backed Jefferson Davis for President of the United States. Stationed first in Maryland, Butler had sought to placate loyal slaveowners there by grandiloquently promising to provide troops should their slaves rise against them. But once in

command of Fortress Monroe in Tidewater Virginia in May, he reversed himself. Three slaves who had been laboring on Confederate fortifications managed to make it to his lines, closely pursued by their master, who angrily demanded their return. Butler asked Washington for permission to turn the indignant planter down. His slaves were "contraband of war," he argued, and, like any other property helpful to the enemy cause, should be returned only if their owner took an oath of loyalty.

"Major Cary of Virginia asked if I did not feel myself bound by my constitutional obligations to deliver up fugitives under the Fugitive-Slave Act," Butler wrote. "To this I replied that the Fugitive-Slave Act did not affect a foreign country, which Virginia claimed to be, and she must reckon it one of the infelicities of her position that in so far at least she was taken at her word."

By late spring, there were almost a thousand black men, women, and children at Fortress Monroe, and hundreds more were crossing into the Union lines wherever they could. In August, Congress would officially endorse Butler's stand, passing a cautiously worded confiscation act, which authorized commanders to liberate only those slaves being directly employed by the Confederate army. It said nothing about the status of those slaves once they had been taken from their masters and asserted no congressional right to free any other slaves.

"Contrabands"—former slaves who had come over to the Union army—at work on the Union Quartermaster's Wharf at Alexandria.

"The American people and the Government at Washington may refuse to recognize it for a time," Frederick Douglass said, "but the 'inexorable logic of events' will force it upon them in the end; that the war now being waged in this land is a war for and against slavery."

"Teach the rebels and traitors that the price they are to pay for the attempt to abolish this government must be the abolition of slavery."

FREDERICK DOUGLASS

On June 3, Lincoln's old rival Stephen A. Douglas died in Chicago. Lincoln had asked him to tour the border states after Fort Sumter, appealing to his followers to stay loyal to the Union. Secessionists had jeered and pelted him with eggs, but he had kept at it until exhaustion drove him home. His final words for his two sons were: "Tell them to obey the laws and support the Constitution of the United States."

In order to preserve the Constitution, Douglas's old adversary was now edging beyond it. He waged war without congressional assent until the summer, seized northern telegraph offices to ensure the wires were not used for subversion, and suspended the writ of *habeas corpus,* at first only "at any point on or in the vicinity of the military line . . . between the City of Philadelphia and the City of Washington," but later "throughout the United States."

In this, Chief Justice Taney ruled, the President had exceeded his power. Only Congress could suspend the writ. (In fact, while the Constitution affirms that the writ may be withdrawn "in Cases of Rebellion or Invasion," it fails to say who may do the suspending.) Lincoln toyed with the idea of having the Chief Justice arrested, then chose simply to ignore his ruling, asking, ". . . are all the laws, *but one,* to go unexecuted, and the Government itself go to pieces, lest that one be violated?" (In 1863, Congress would empower the President to suspend the writ "during the present rebellion," thereby belatedly reasserting its own authority over actions he had long since taken.)

No one knows precisely how many Americans were seized and held without trial during the war, but the total was well above 13,500. Most of those imprisoned were genuine Confederates or their sympathizers in or near the war zone, but men were also locked up whose only crimes were drunkenly "hurrahing for Jeff Davis" or omitting the traditional prayer for the President from church services.

Lincoln also declared a blockade of southern ports. The Confederates countered by withholding exports, confident that an England starved of cotton would eventually come in on the side of the South.

ALL GREEN ALIKE

The rival American capitals continued to glare at one another across a hundred miles of rolling Virginia countryside. Civilians on both sides grew impatient.

No one was more impatient—or inconsistent—than Horace Greeley, the Republican editor of the New York *Tribune,* the influential newspaper he had founded in 1841. And no one was more patient with him than the President he hectored so hard. Greeley had first demanded that the South be allowed to leave the Union unmolested, then asked Lincoln to surrender Fort Sumter, and finally praised him for holding it. When the Baltimore rioters fired on Union troops, he had urged that "the city be burned with fire and leveled to the earth and made an abode for owls and satyrs and a place for fishermen to dry their nets."

Now, he wanted Richmond taken, right away: "THE NATION'S WAR CRY: FORWARD TO RICHMOND! THE REBEL CONGRESS MUST NOT BE ALLOWED TO MEET THERE ON THE 20TH OF JULY. BY THAT DATE THE PLACE MUST BE HELD BY THE NATIONAL ARMY."

Lincoln was growing impatient, too. The fighting in western Virginia had made headlines but resolved little.

Thirty-five thousand Confederate troops under the conqueror of Sumter, General Beauregard, had moved north to defend Virginia against the invasion they now expected daily.

Irvin McDowell, the Union field commander, did not yet want to fight. He was an oddly prim soldier. He drank no coffee or tea, did not smoke or chew tobacco, and was especially proud that once, when his horse fell on him and knocked him unconscious, he had still managed to keep his teeth clamped shut against the restorative brandy a surgeon had tried to pour down his throat.

"This is not an army," he warned the President. "It will take a long time to make an army."

"You are green, it is true," Lincoln answered, "but they are green, also; you are all green alike." His army's three-month enlistment was almost up. McDowell was to get on with it.

William Howard Russell of the London *Times* had seen a lot of fighting while reporting the Crimean War and the 1857 mutiny in India. Now he was convinced he was about to see some more: "The great battle which is to arrest rebellion, or . . . make it a power in the land is no longer distant or doubtful." But he also doubted that the Union army was ready for it. "They think that an army is like a round of cannister," he said of Lincoln and his new administration, "which can be fired off whenever the match is applied."

"It begins to look warlike," wrote Elisha Rhodes, "and we shall probably have a chance to pay our southern brethren a visit upon the sacred soil of Virginia very soon. Well, I hope we shall be successful and give the rebels a good pounding."

On July 18, the volunteer Union army, 37,000 strong, marched south into Virginia. A reporter for the Washington *Star* described the spectacle:

> The scene from the hills was grand . . . regiment after regiment was seen coming along the road and across the Long Bridge, their arms gleaming in the sun. . . . Cheer after cheer was heard as regiment greeted regiment, and this with the martial music and sharp clear orders of commanding officers, made a combination of sounds very pleasant to the ear of a Union man.

The northern troops had a good time despite the fierce heat. "They stopped every moment to pick blackberries or get water," General McDowell remembered, "they would not keep in the ranks, order as much as you pleased. . . .

A Union encampment.

"July 9, 1861. Our battle summer. May it be our first and last. So-called. After all, we have not had any of the horrors of war."

MARY CHESNUT

"July 16, 1861. We have orders to be ready to move, but where no one can tell. Rations are being cooked and we expect to march very soon."

ELISHA RHODES

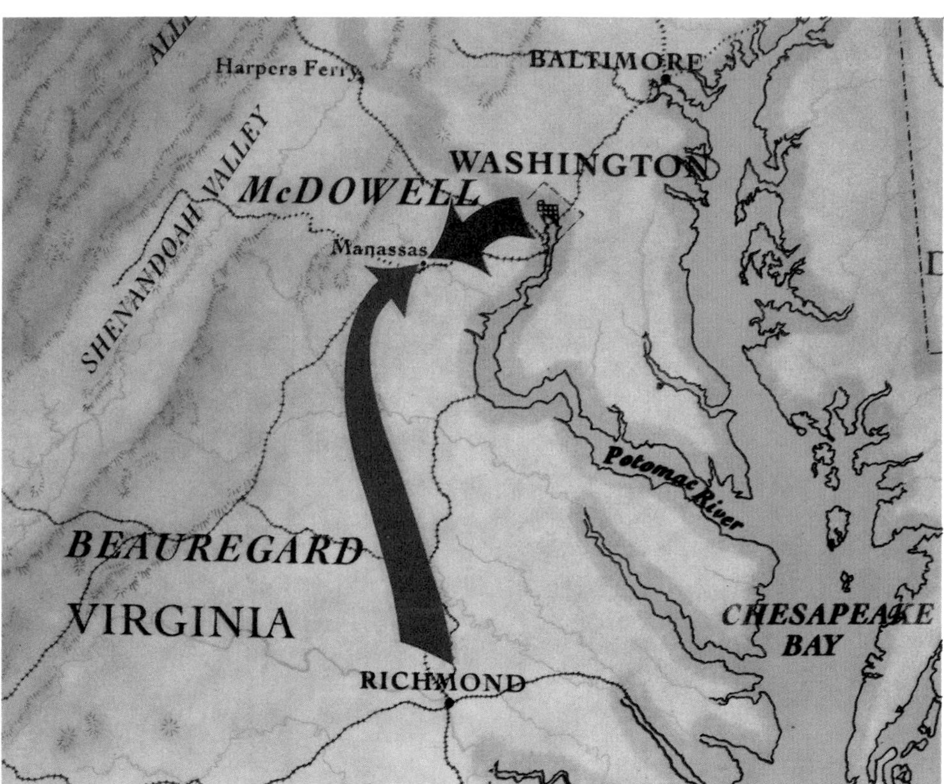

First Blood: The Union and Confederate armies move toward their first serious clash, near Manassas Junction, Virginia, just twenty-five miles from Washington. All of the maps in this book are based upon those in the atlas accompanying the 128-volume *War of the Rebellion: A Compilation of the Official Records of the Union and Confederate Armies,* published between 1880 and 1901. Red indicates Confederate forces, blue indicates Union forces; colored bars and arrows are meant to represent only general troop movements and approximate troop positions.

They were not used to denying themselves much; they were not used to journeys on foot." It took them two and a half days to march twenty-five miles, a stretch seasoned troops would routinely cover in half the time later in the war.

Elisha Rhodes had a good time, too. "Our regiment stacked arms in a large meadow," he wrote. "Rail fences were plenty and we soon had fires burning and coffee cooking in our cups. . . . I enjoyed the evening by the fire and speculating on what might happen on the morrow."

Hundreds of Washington civilians rode out to join the advancing army, hoping to see a real battle. Some brought binoculars, picnic baskets, bottles of champagne. "The French cooks and hotel-keepers," William Howard Russell wrote, "by some occult process of reasoning, have arrived at the conclusion that they must treble the prices of their wines and of the hampers of provisions which the Washington people are ordering to comfort themselves at their bloody derby."

Some of the troops rather liked the notion of fighting their first battle in front of illustrious spectators. "We saw carriages and barouches which contained civilians who had driven out from Washington to witness the operations," a Massachusetts volunteer remembered. "A Connecticut boy said, 'There's our Senator!' and some of our men recognized . . . other members of Congress. . . . We thought it wasn't a bad idea to have the great men from Washington come out to see us thrash the Rebs."

Beauregard knew the northerners were coming. Mrs. Rose O'Neal Greenhow, a prominent society leader in Washington and the aunt of Stephen A.

Union General Irvin McDowell (sixth from left) and staff on the front steps of his headquarters—Robert E. Lee's commandeered home at Arlington, Virginia.

Douglas, was one of those who had seen to that, sending him word of the advance, her coded note concealed in the hair of a sympathetic southern girl. And he had ordered his men to form a meandering eight-mile line along one side of Bull Run Creek near a railroad center called Manassas Junction.

McDowell moved first on Sunday morning, July 21, sending his men across the creek a little after nine. An onlooker remembered that the advancing Union army looked like "a bristling monster lifting himself by a slow, wavy motion up the laborious ascent."

Elisha Rhodes recalled the first serious shooting he ever heard:

> On reaching a clearing separated from our left flank by a rail fence, we were saluted by a volley of musketry, which, however, was fired so high that all the bullets went over our heads. . . . My first sensation was . . . astonishment at the peculiar *whir* of the bullets, and that the Regiment immediately laid down without waiting for orders. Colonel Slocum gave the command: "By the left flank—MARCH" and we commenced crossing the field. One of our boys by the name of Webb fell off the fence and

"Richmond, July 23, 1861. I have seen the great and glorious battle of Manassas which brought a nation into existence, and the scene was grand and impressive beyond the power of language . . . no red fox ever made tracks so fast as did these cowardly wretches." DR. J. C. NOLT

Ignoring Confederate fire, New England troops charge rebel positions in this rendering of the early fighting on the Bull Run battlefield, painted by a soldier who lived through it, Captain James Hope of the 2nd Vermont.

broke his bayonet. This caused some amusement, for even at this time we did not realize that we were about to engage in battle.

Not far away, Union cavalrymen, wearing crisp new uniforms and waiting to be ordered to the front, tried not to look as the first bloody, wounded men were carried past them to a surgeon's tent. Some, who failed to avert their gaze fast enough, vomited from their saddles.

Still, at first it all seemed to be going just as McDowell had planned. His divisions tore at the Confederate left and began to turn it, driving the rebels from one position after another. "We . . . fired a volley," a Massachusetts private wrote, "and saw the Rebels running. . . . The boys were saying

constantly, in great glee, 'We've whipped them.' 'We'll hang Jeff Davis to a sour apple tree.' 'They are running.' 'The war is over.'"

On a green hillside three miles away, civilian onlookers waved their hats and fluttered their handkerchiefs. It was not yet noon.

"General McDowell rode up," a Union lieutenant recalled, "dressed in full uniform, including white gloves, and told us we had won a great victory. . . . We cheered him vociferously and felt like veritable heroes."

Northern victory seemed so sure, an officer remembered, that on one part of the battlefield some of the Union men stopped to gather souvenirs among the rebel troops who had fallen on the slope.

> What a horrible sight it was! Here a man, grasping his musket firmly in his hands, stone dead; several with distorted features, all horribly dirty. Many were terribly wounded, some with legs shot off; others with arms gone. . . . So badly wounded they could not drag themselves away . . . slowly bleeding to death. We stopped many times to give some a drink and soon saw enough to satisfy us with the horrors of war, and so, picking up some swords and bayonets, we . . . retraced our steps.

But holding a hill at the center of the southern line was a Virginia brigade commanded by Thomas J. Jackson, who believed the southern cause literally sacred and was able to convey that religious certitude to his men. While other southern commands wavered, his held firm. General Bernard Bee of South Carolina, trying to rally his own frightened men early that afternoon, shouted, "Look, there is Jackson with his Virginians, standing like a stone wall!" Bee himself was killed a little later, but the rebel lines held and the nickname stuck.

It was the turning point. The fighting seesawed back and forth across the hillside from two to four in the afternoon. Between the armies stood a farmhouse, the home of Judith Henry, an elderly widow too ill to move. Union shells ripped through the wall of her bedroom, tearing off the old woman's foot and riddling her body.

Confederate reinforcements began to arrive, led by General Joseph E. Johnston, who had now found it within him to draw his sword against his old flag. The first came on horseback, led by Colonel Jubal Early. Many more arrived by train, something new in war.

The Union men, most of whom had now been marching and fighting in brutal heat without food or water for fourteen hours, were demoralized to see fresh rebels pouring onto the field. "Where are *our* reserves?" some were heard to ask.

At about four, Beauregard ordered a massive counterattack. Jackson urged his men to "yell like furies!" The high-pitched rebel yell first heard that afternoon—half exultant shout, half foxhound's yelp—would eventually echo from a thousand battlefields. "There is nothing like it this side of the infernal region," a Union veteran remembered many years after the war. "The peculiar corkscrew sensation that it sends down your backbone under these circumstances can never be told. You have to feel it, and if you say you did not feel it, and heard the yell, you have *never* been there."

To Beauregard's delight, the northerners began to edge backward. "I dispatched orders to go forward in a common charge," he recalled. "Before the full advance of the Confederate ranks the enemy's whole line irretrievably broke, fleeing across Bull Run by every available direction."

The retreat became a rout, McDowell admitted, "and this degenerated still further into a panic." Frightened civilians and frightened soldiers alike pushed and shoved to get away from the battlefield. "They plunged through Bull Run wherever they came to it," a rebel officer wrote, "regardless of fords or bridges, and there many were drowned. . . . We found . . . along the road, parasols and dainty shawls lost in their flight by the frail, fair ones who had seats in most of the carriages of this excursion."

General Thomas J. Jackson got his nickname "Stonewall" at First Manassas. "Whilst great credit is due to other parts of our gallant army," he told his wife when it was over, "God made my brigade more instrumental than any other."

Albert G. Riddle, an Ohio congressman, and two or three of his colleagues tried to turn the soldiers back.

> We called to them, tried to tell them there was no danger, called them to stop, implored them to stand. We called them cowards, denounced them in the most offensive terms, put out our heavy revolvers and threatened to shoot them, but all in vain; a cruel, crazy, mad, hopeless panic possessed them, and communicated to everybody about in front and rear. The heat was awful, although it was now about six; the men were exhausted—their mouths gaped, their lips cracked and blackened with the powder of the cartridges they had bitten off in the battle, their eyes starting in frenzy; no mortal ever saw such a mass of ghastly wretches.

Elisha Rhodes found himself among those demoralized men.

> I . . . struggled on, clinging to my gun and cartridge box. Many times I sat down in the mud determined to go no further, and willing to die to end my misery. But soon a friend would pass and urge me to make another effort, and I would stagger a mile further. At daylight we could see the spires of Washington, and a welcome sight it was. . . . The loss of the regiment in this disastrous affair was ninety three killed, wounded or missing.

The Union army remembered it as "the great skedaddle."

No one knows what might have happened had the southern army pursued them. "A friend in the federal capital," Mary Chesnut noted later, "writes me that we might have walked into Washington any day for a week after Manassas, such was the consternation and confusion there." But in fact the southern army was nearly as unprepared for its victory as its foes had been for their defeat, and a heavy downpour the next morning turned the roads to mud and made the question academic.

The Confederates discovered Congressman Albert Ely of New York hiding behind a tree and carried him off to Richmond. "The Yankee Congressman came down to see the fun," one rebel soldier said, "came out for wool and got shorn." President Davis himself sent the distinguished prisoner a pair of blankets to demonstrate to his people how southern gentlemen treated those whom they had defeated in battle.

"Where are the vaunts, and the proud boasts with which you went forth? Where are your banners, and your bands of music, and your ropes to bring back prisoners? The sun rises, but shines not."

WALT WHITMAN

Davis, who had ridden out to see the fighting for himself, was jubilant. "Your little army," he told his people, "derided for its want of arms, derided for its lack of all the essential material of war, has met the grand army of the enemy, routed it at every point, and it now flies, inglorious in retreat before our victorious columns. We have taught them a lesson in their invasion of the sacred soil of Virginia."

Manassas had been *"one of the decisive battles of the world,"* wrote a prominent Georgia secessionist. It "has secured our independence." Persuaded that they had already won the war, that the North would now have no choice but to sue for peace, some Confederate volunteers left the army, eager to get home for the autumn harvest.

Sam Watkins, who arrived with his Tennesseans at Manassas Junction after the shooting had stopped, recalled the letdown he and his friends felt:

> We felt that the war was over, and that we would have to return home without even seeing a Yankee soldier. Ah, how we envied those that were wounded. We . . . would have given a thousand dollars . . . to have had our arm shot off, so we could have returned home with an empty sleeve. But the battle was over and we left out.

Some 4,500 men were killed, wounded, or captured on both sides in the battle that the North called Bull Run and the South remembered as Manassas.

William Howard Russell watched the northern army stagger back into Washington.

> I saw a steady stream of men, covered with mud, soaked through with rain, who were pouring irregularly . . . up Pennsylvania Avenue toward the Capitol. A dense stream of vapor rose from the multitude; but looking closely . . . I perceived they belonged to different regiments, New Yorkers, Michiganders, Rhode Islanders, Massachusettsers, Minnesotians, mingled pell-mell together.

Russell asked one pale young man who "looked exhausted to death" whether the whole army had been defeated. "That's more than I know," the soldier answered. "I know I'm going home. I've had enough fighting to last my lifetime."

"Today will be known as BLACK MONDAY," wrote George Templeton Strong when the bad news reached New York. "We are utterly and disgracefully routed, beaten, whipped by secessionists."

Horace Greeley, who had urged Lincoln to launch the premature drive on Richmond that had resulted in the defeat at Bull Run, now demanded that the President consider abandoning the entire struggle for the Union: "On every brow sits sullen, scorching, black despair . . ." he wrote. "If it is best for the country and for mankind that we make peace with the rebels, and on their own terms, do not shrink even from that."

Lincoln did not take Greeley's new advice: instead, he signed bills calling for the enlistment of 100,000 additional troops to serve for three years instead of three months. No one now believed this would be a ninety day war. The President vowed to hold his ground, strengthen the blockade, replace the three-month volunteers with men enrolled for longer service, and then launch expeditions into Virginia, the loyal area of east Tennessee, and down the Mississippi.

And he put a new man in charge of the Union forces at Washington. George McClellan seemed just what the North needed. Second in his class at West Point, hero of the Mexican War, he was a skilled engineer, author of manuals on military tactics, enthusiastic admirer of Napoleon, and was said to be able to bend a quarter between thumb and forefinger and heave a 250-pound man above his head. Fresh from a series of small but well-publicized victories in western Virginia, McClellan brought with him to the stunned capital what one observer called "an indefinable *air of success.*"

He would need all his strengths and skills to rebuild the shattered Union army. "Tonight not 200 men are in camp," a New York soldier confided to his diary. "Captain Catlin, Captain Hulburt, Lieutenant Cooper and one or two other officers are under arrest. A hundred men are drunk, a hundred more are at houses of ill fame, and the balance are everywhere.... Colonel Alford is very drunk all the time now."

After Bull Run, Horace Greeley (opposite, above), the erratic but influential editor of the New York *Tribune,* called for a quick peace. But throughout the rest of the North, wrote Charles Coffin of the Boston *Journal,* "village drums were beating, soldiers marching," including the men and boys of Momence, Illinois (opposite below), still short on weaponry but long on patriotism and eager for revenge. The general who would soon command them, George Brinton McClellan (right), had few apparent doubts about his ability to bring it about. "When I . . . found those old men flocking around me; when I afterwards [looked over] the Capitol of our great nation, and saw the crowd gathering around to stare at me," he wrote from Washington to his wife, "I began to feel how great the task committed to me. . . . Who would have thought, when we were married, that I should so soon be called upon to save my country?"

"I found no preparations whatever for defense . . ." McClellan wrote. "Not a regiment was properly encamped, not a single avenue or approach guarded. All was chaos and the streets, hotels and barrooms were filled with drunken officers and men absent from their regiments without leave—a perfect Pandemonium."

McClellan devoted the summer to bringing order out of that chaos. "I spent long days in my saddle and my nights in the office," he remembered, "—a very fatiguing life, but one which made my power felt everywhere and by *everyone.*" He imposed discipline—"Let an honest pride be felt," he told his troops, "in possessing that high virtue of a soldier, *obedience*"—replaced inept officers with regulars, saw that the men drilled for up to eight hours a day, and laid out tidy camps around the city to incorporate the ten thousand new volunteers now arriving each week by rail.

When he staged grand reviews to improve morale, a newspaperman noted, "each regiment tried to outdo all others in its appearance and its marching, . . . bands playing national airs, drums beating, flags waving. . . . The ground shook beneath the steady marching." Lincoln and his wife, Mary, and their two youngest sons, Willie and Tad, often watched from a carriage. But even the Lincolns were bit players in McClellan's drama. "It was to be observed that the eyes of the people were not on the President of the Republic . . ." an officer wrote. "All the attention was upon that young general with the calm eye, with the satisfied air, who moved around followed by an immense staff, to the clanking of sabers and the acclamation of the spectators."

Even McClellan's officer corps was glamorous. It included three representatives of deposed French royalty; Philip Kearny, a one-armed adventurer and millionaire who had fought for France against Austria, winning the Legion of Honor for charging enemy positions with his reins between his teeth; and a still richer amateur soldier, Colonel John Jacob Astor III, who went to war with his own chef, steward, and valet.

A hundred thousand untrained volunteers had become an army—the Army of the Potomac, *McClellan's* army. His men, who loved him for having made them proud of themselves again, called him "Little Mac." The newspapers called him "Young Napoleon," and he actively encouraged the comparison. "Soldiers!" he had proclaimed to his troops in western Virginia in true Napoleonic fashion. "I have heard that there was danger here. I have come to place myself at your head and to share it with you. I fear now but one thing—that you will not find foemen worthy of your steel."

Nathaniel Hawthorne witnessed the soldiers' enthusiasm for their new commander: "They received him with loud shouts, by the eager uproar of which—now near, now in the center, now on the outskirts of the division—we could trace his progress through the ranks . . . they believed in him, and *so did I.*" So did McClellan himself. "You have no idea how the men brighten up when I go among them," he told his wife. "I can see every eye glisten. Yesterday they nearly pulled me to pieces in one regiment. You never *heard* such yelling."

"The boys are happy as clams at high water," wrote a Massachusetts artilleryman after a visit by his commander. "The rank and file think [McClellan] is just the man to lead us on to victory when *he* gets ready and not when Horace Greeley says to go."

The defeat at Bull Run and the appalling rout that followed it were bad enough in themselves, but Lincoln also feared they would make the job of keeping the slaveholding border states within the Union still more difficult. Delaware, with barely two out of every hundred residents a slave, never seriously considered seceding, but Kentucky, Missouri, and Maryland all remained dangerously undecided. "I think to lose Kentucky is nearly the same as to lose the whole game," Lincoln explained to a friend. "Kentucky gone, we cannot hold Missouri, nor, as I think, Maryland. These are all against us, and the job on our hands is too large for us."

While a secessionist governor and a Unionist legislature wrestled for

Led by its regimental band, the 96th Pennsylvania marches by column of companies, the formation in which they would rush into battle once their new commander gave the word. "Nothing but drill and guard duty," Elisha Rhodes wrote that autumn. "Even the late battle has become an old story. Some of our men actually became crazy from the excitement. I have recovered my strength and feel that I could make another campaign without much trouble."

control, Union volunteers in Louisville marched on one side of a street while Confederates drilled on the other. Two of Senator John Crittenden's sons became major generals, one for the North and one for the South. Mary Lincoln's youngest brother joined the Confederate army, as did three of her half-brothers and a brother-in-law, even after Lincoln personally offered him a major's commission in the Union army.

The balance of power in Kentucky was so precarious that Lincoln was willing to respect what he called the "conditional Unionism" of the state in which he had been born, provided it did not seem about to tip toward the South, and even agreed to turn a blind eye for a time to the steady stream of weapons and supplies passing through the state to the Confederacy. But in the fall, when Confederates commanded by an Episcopal bishop, General Leonidas Polk, moved to seize Kentucky, Union troops under a new commander, Brigadier General Ulysses S. Grant, were ordered to seize Paducah and Smithland at the mouths of the strategically important Cumberland and Tennessee rivers. Two months later, Grant's undisciplined recruits were almost destroyed, looting a captured rebel camp instead of preparing for a Confederate counterattack, and their commander was returned temporarily to desk duty. But Union troops now occupied three-quarters of Kentucky, and although secessionists formed a provisional government and the Confederate Congress solemnly accepted the state into the Confederacy, Kentucky remained loyal.

Maryland was still more crucial to the Union, for if it fell, Washington would be encircled by hostile states. Bull Run had emboldened its secessionist legislators, and in September, on the eve of a special legislative session that Lincoln feared would vote to secede, he sent troops to occupy Baltimore, locked the mayor and thirty-one legislators in jail, and kept them there without trial for more than two months until a new and safely Unionist legislature was elected in November. Maryland, too, held for the Union.

In Missouri, Governor Claiborne Fox Jackson, who favored secession and had denounced Lincoln's call for troops as "illegal, unconstitutional, revolutionary, inhuman, diabolical," commanded the state militia. To oppose him, Congressman Frank Blair, Jr., the younger brother of Lincoln's Postmaster General, Montgomery Blair, organized a Unionist Home Guard, made up largely of antislavery Germans, and resolved to hold the state. Under red-bearded Captain Nathaniel Lyon, a veteran of the Bloody Kansas border war, he spirited 21,000 Union muskets out of town before the rebels could seize them, then surrounded the southern militiamen, forced their peaceful surrender, and marched them through St. Louis. There, a secessionist mob pelted his men with stones, then shot and killed a captain. Lyon's men shot back, killing twenty-eight people, including a baby in its mother's arms.

Secession sentiment rose; Sterling Price, a hero of the Mexican War, volunteered his services to Governor Jackson; and guerrilla warfare burst out again along the Kansas border. It would not stop for almost four years and it would take decades before the hatreds it engendered began to fade.

Nathaniel Lyon, now a brigadier general, chased Price and a growing secessionist army two hundred miles across Missouri until he caught up with them at Wilson's Creek in the southwest corner of the state in August. Lyon was killed there, and the Union army driven back to St. Louis. Lexington fell to the rebels. Half of Missouri was now in Confederate hands.

Lincoln's overall commander in the West was John Charles Frémont, "the Pathfinder," a sometime explorer and soldier and full-time politician. He was a magnetic man, handsome and energetic, but overly fond of pomp. His staff was top-heavy with lesser European nobility in glittering uniforms, and his headquarters was surrounded by a hand-picked personal guard of thirty Kentuckians, all of them taller than five foot eleven. He was also recklessly ambitious: he had been the first Republican candidate for President five years earlier and was already planning to displace Lincoln in 1864. Lincoln once privately called him "the damndest scoundrel that ever lived, but in the infinite mercy of Providence . . . also the damndest fool."

After the Union defeat at Wilson's Creek—and without consulting Washington—Frémont issued a proclamation threatening with death all guerrillas captured behind Union lines and proclaiming free all the slaves owned by Missouri secessionists. The President was furious: generals did not make policy; the threat of emancipation would unnecessarily alienate the border states. Lincoln rescinded the order when his request that it be

William Tecumseh Sherman.

After South Carolina seceded, William Tecumseh Sherman, West Point, class of 1840, resigned as head of the Louisiana Academy and came north. A red-haired, agitated, rail-thin Ohioan, he had many friends in the South and saw little wrong with slavery. "You [politicians] have got things in a hell of a fix," he told his brother, Senator John Sherman of Ohio, "and you may get them out as best you can. . . . I am going to St. Louis to take care of my family, and will have no more to do with it."

But when the shooting started he signed on anyway, reentering the army as a colonel rather than accept higher rank because he did not wish to be a "political general." His command fought with more discipline than most during the retreat from Bull Run, and he was made Union commander in Kentucky. But he quailed in November 1861, when ordered to invade eastern Tennessee in support of Unionist partisans, insisting that he would require at least 200,000 men. He grew melancholy, prone to fits of anxiety and rage. "Sherman," McClellan said, "is gone in the head." The end of the year found him at home in the care of his wife, contemplating suicide.

modified was ignored, and in November replaced his flamboyant commander with Henry Wager Halleck, an aloof West Point tactician and former attorney, whose military scholarship and inbred caution earned him the nickname "Old Brains." Halleck promptly assured the President that further action against the enemy would now be inadvisable until spring.

Brigadier General Ulysses S. Grant photographed in the first year of the war: "As we approached the brow of the hill . . ." he recalled of one of his earliest engagements, "my heart kept getting higher and higher until it felt to me it was in my throat. I would have given anything then to have been back in Illinois, but I kept right on. When the valley below was in full view I halted. The enemy's troops were gone. My heart resumed its place, and it occurred to me at once that he had been as much afraid of me as I of him. This was a view of the question I had never taken before, but it was one I never forgot afterwards."

"The true course in conducting military operations," George McClellan declared from Washington, "is to make no movement until the preparations are complete." On paper, McClellan's projected movements looked promising. The Union forces were to mount a three-pronged assault on the Confederacy: one army would drive into Virginia and take Richmond; another would secure Kentucky and Tennessee for the Union, then push into the heart of the Confederacy and occupy Mississippi, Alabama, Georgia, while the navy cleared the Mississippi, surrounded the Confederacy by sea, and choked off supplies.

But as summer turned to autumn, it became increasingly clear that, having made a magnificent army, George McClellan had no immediate plans to lead it anywhere.

Republicans in Congress grew impatient. If the Union did not soon avenge Bull Run, they feared, Europe would see it as a sign that northern resolve was weakening and recognize the Confederacy. Even Horace Greeley again began to clamor for action.

From the first, George McClellan had demonstrated an apparent self-confidence that bordered on vainglory. "I find myself in a new and strange position here," he had told his wife upon arriving in the capital. "President, cabinet, General Scott and all deferring to me—by some strange operation of magic I seem to have become *the* power of the land. I almost think that were I to win some small success now, I could become *Dictator,* or anything else that might please me. . . . But nothing of that kind would please me—therefore I won't be Dictator. Admirable self-denial!"

Now, as the pressure built for him to move against the enemy and the newspapers began to make fun of the daily bulletins of "All quiet on the Potomac" that had once seemed so reassuring, he responded to President, cabinet, and Congress alike with arrogant contempt. "I am becoming daily more disgusted with these wretched politicians," he told his wife. "They are a most despicable set of men. . . . Seward [is a] meddling, officious, incompetent little puppy. . . . The President is nothing more than a well-meaning baboon . . . 'the original gorilla.'"

For his part, Lincoln was patient with his commander, even when he called at his home late one evening and waited in his parlor until McClellan returned from a wedding party, only to be told by the butler that the general could not see him; he had retired for the night. The President's secretary was outraged at this insult, and urged that McClellan be dismissed immediately. Lincoln forbore: he would gladly hold the general's horse, he said, if it meant victories, and when the general insisted that it was General Scott, not he, who was responsible for all the delay—he alleged that the old hero was either "a *dotard* or a *traitor*"—the President allowed Scott to retire and made Mc-

Clellan general-in-chief as well as commander of the Army of the Potomac. "I can do it all," McClellan assured him

McClellan did nothing. Allan Pinkerton, now his personal secret operative, reinforced his chief's natural caution, assuring him that a Confederate army of at least 150,000 men under Joseph E. Johnston was within striking distance of Washington—three times as many troops as were actually anywhere near the capital. Others told McClellan that Pinkerton was wrong, but it was Pinkerton he wanted to believe. He would not move, he said, until he had 270,000 men of his own.

In September, when rebel pickets withdrew from an exposed position a few miles southwest of Washington, Union troops found that the great cannon that McClellan's spies had assured him were trained on the city were nothing but

The Union grand strategy for defeating the rebellious states: As envisioned by General George McClellan, it called for three simultaneous overland assaults, combined with a blockade of southern ports and naval thrusts up and down the Mississippi.

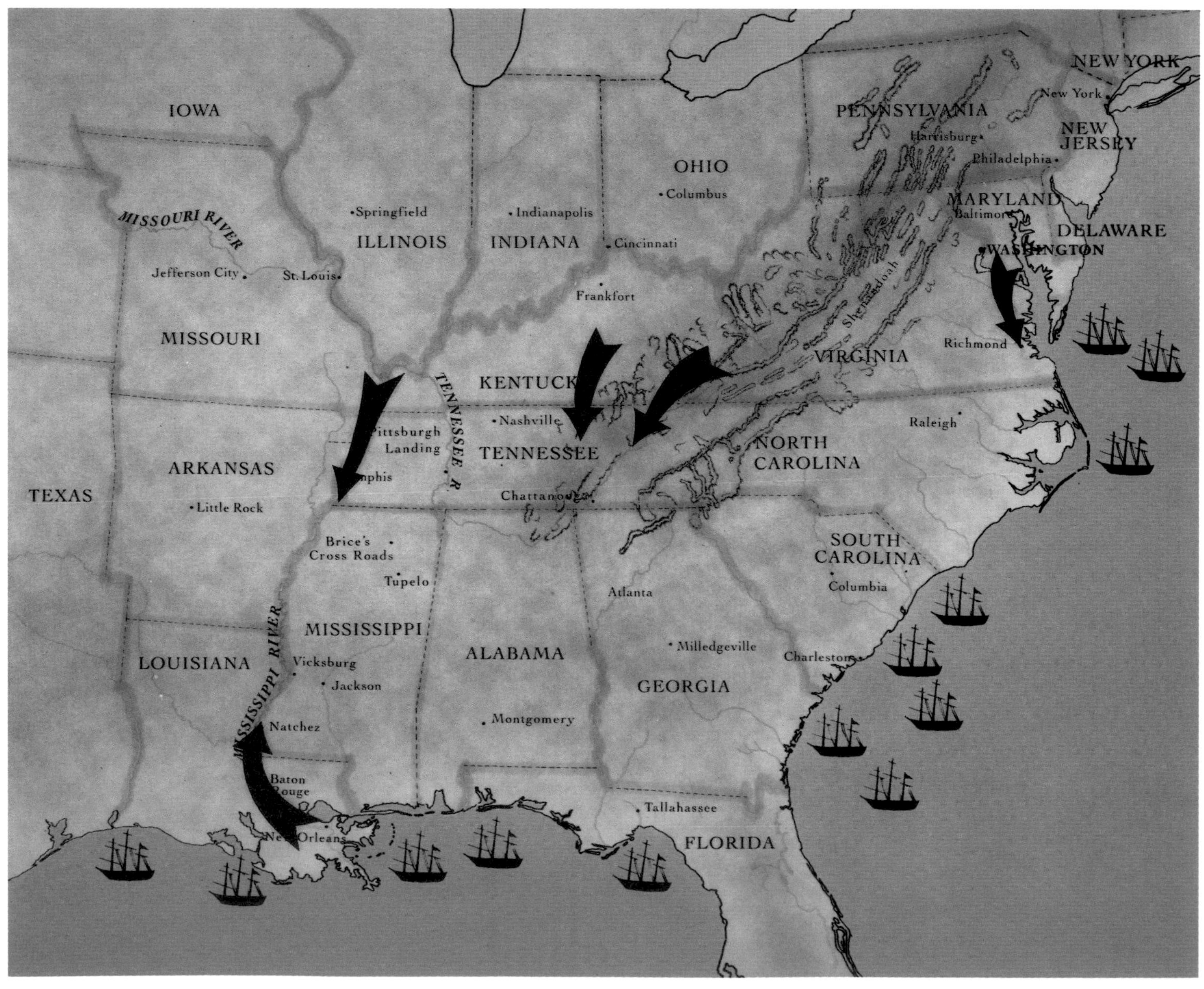

PHOTOGRAPHING THE WAR

Photographers would follow the armies almost everywhere, not only to make portraits for the men to send home, but also to document as much of the war as they could for a civilian public eager to see at least something of what their sons and husbands, fathers and sweethearts were seeing.

Best known was Mathew Brady, a fashionable portrait artist who set off from Washington for the Bull Run battlefield because, he said, "a spirit in my feet said 'Go' and I went." Secretly almost blind, he took few photographs himself; the highly prized "Photographs by Brady" were mainly the work of his assistants, including Alexander Gardner and Timothy O'Sullivan.

Workers in a London photographer's studio (above) cut mats for the stereoscopic views popular in parlors on both sides of the Atlantic.

Sam A. Cooley (above left), his camera and wagons, accompanied Federal troops to the South Carolina coast; the unknown photographer (left) was with them in Tennessee.

G.G. WALKER'S
PHOTOGRAPHIC GALLERY.

The logistics of photography in the field were daunting. The art itself was only twenty-two years old when the war began, and lenses were still incapable of stopping movement. To make a successful exposure, the photographer set up his big, clumsy camera—originally intended for use in a studio—while back in his specially built photographer's wagon, his assistant gingerly removed an 8-by-10-inch glass plate from its wooden, dust-proof box, sensitized it in total darkness, then rushed it to the camera, waited until the shutter was tripped, then hurried the plate back into the wagon for developing.

Men like "G. W. H.," who accompanied the 47th Pennsylvania (opposite above), and G. G. Walker, whose log gallery (opposite, below left), stood in the Great Dismal Swamp near Suffolk, Virginia, in the winter of 1863, were largely content to turn out inexpensive portraits of men like those on this page. (The four Confederates at top right appear with the body servants who went with them into the field.) Other photographers served the army more formally: the man at the bottom right of the opposite page applied his giant camera to photographing maps for the Topographical Engineers Corps.

Impatience with McClellan's caution had already begun to grow by October 1861, when it was revealed that he had been held at bay at Centreville, Virginia, by sham artillery (above). Soon, his early fondness for comparing himself to Napoleon would backfire, as in the drawing above left, made when excessive prudence again seemed to overtake him the following year.

mammoth logs, painted black to look like artillery; a scornful reporter called them "Quaker Guns."

McClellan was embarrassed by the discovery, but his confidence was not bolstered. And he was genuinely unsettled in October, when a Union force ordered to probe Confederate defenses at Ball's Bluff, Virginia, was trapped on the bank of the Potomac and shot to pieces. Among the wounded carried from the field was a young Massachusetts lieutenant, fresh from Harvard, with two musket balls in his chest, Oliver Wendell Holmes, Jr. Colonel Edward D. Baker, an Oregon senator for whom the Lincolns had named their second son, was killed.

Lincoln wept and his eight-year-old son, Willie, wrote a memorial poem and sent it to the editor of the *National Republican:*

There was no patriot like Baker
So noble and so true;
He fell as a soldier in the field,
his face to the sky of blue.

In December, in the wake of this second Union disaster so dangerously close to the capital, Congress established a Joint Committee on the Conduct of the War to search out those responsible and ensure that the administration prosecute the war with suitable vigor. Its chairman was Senator Benjamin Wade of Ohio, a Radical Republican eager to get on with the struggle—and deeply distrustful of conservative Democrats like George McClellan. General Charles P. Stone, another Democrat, who had already angered the Radicals because they thought he had been overly eager to return runaway slaves to their owners in Maryland, was blamed for the Ball's Bluff defeat. He was falsely accused of disloyalty, given no opportunity to defend himself, and imprisoned for 189 days in New York Harbor, not far from Bedloe's Island, on which he would one day build the pedestal for the Statue of Liberty.

McClellan took his great army into winter quarters, continuing to blame others for his own inactivity. He had been "thwarted and deceived by . . . incapables at every turn . . . ," he assured his wife. "It now begins to look as if we are condemned to a winter of inactivity. If it is so the fault will not be mine."

"You might as well attempt to put out the flames of a burning house with a squirt-gun. I think this is to be a long war—very long—much longer than any politician thinks."

WILLIAM TECUMSEH SHERMAN

Northern morale had ebbed again, when an open confrontation at sea with Britain made matters still worse for the Union. The American warship *San Jacinto,* patrolling off Cuba, stopped a British steamer, the *Trent,* and arrested two Confederate envoys on their way to England. The two agents—James Murray Mason of Virginia and John Slidell of Louisiana—were well-known secessionist firebrands, and when they arrived at Boston their captor, the Antarctic explorer Captain Charles Wilkes, was welcomed as a conquering hero. The *New York Times* urged a second Independence Day declared in his honor; Congress voted him a special gold medal.

Jefferson Davis denounced the seizure as beneath the dignity even of "barbarians." Britain was no less outraged. "Captain Wilkes is an ideal Yankee," said the London *Times.* "Swagger and ferocity, built on a foundation of vulgarity and cowardice, these are his characteristics . . . the most prominent marks by which his countrymen . . . are known all over the world." "*You* may stand for this," the Prime Minister, Lord Palmerston, told his cabinet, "but damned if I will." He demanded the immediate release of the two Confederates, and backed his threat by dispatching eleven thousand British troops to Canada, ready for action.

Charles Darwin wrote Asa Gray, an American friend and fellow scientist: "When you receive this we may be at war, and we two be bound, as good patriots, to hate each other. How curious it is to see two countries, just like two angry and silly men, taking so opposite a view of the same transaction."

Lincoln's cabinet opposed surrendering the Confederate agents. Seward, Lincoln remembered, arrived at one meeting "loaded to the muzzle" with reasons to defy Britain. Nonetheless, on Christmas Day the President decided to free his captives: they had become "white elephants," he said; besides, one war at a time was enough.

Abraham Lincoln had begun the year persuaded that the secession crisis was "artificial" and would simply go away once the people of the South saw the dangers of the foolish path down which scheming and heedless politicians had led them. By the year's end he knew the crisis was real enough, and was frankly fearful that Britain would recognize the legitimacy of the rebellion before he could persuade his own general-in-chief to take the offensive against it.

"Little did I conceive," William Howard Russell wrote of Bull Run and its impact toward the end of the year, "of the greatness of the defeat, the magnitude of the disaster which it had entailed upon the United States. . . . So short-lived has been the American Union, that men who saw it rise may live to see it fall."

HONORABLE MANHOOD

A week before Manassas, Major Sullivan Ballou of the 2nd Rhode Island wrote home to his wife in Smithfield:

July 14, 1861
Camp Clark, Washington

My very dear Sarah:

The indications are very strong that we shall move in a few days—perhaps tomorrow. Lest I should not be able to write again, I feel impelled to write a few lines that may fall under your eye when I shall be no more. . . .

I have no misgivings about, or lack of confidence in the cause in which I am engaged, and my courage does not halt or falter. I know how strongly American Civilization now leans on the triumph of the Government, and how great a debt we owe to those who went before us through the blood and sufferings of the Revolution. And I am willing—perfectly willing—to lay down all my joys in this life, to help maintain this Government, and to pay that debt. . . .

Sarah my love for you is deathless, it seems to bind me with mighty cables that nothing

Before they went off to war, soldiers often had themselves photographed alongside the wife or sweetheart they had to leave behind.

but Omnipotence could break; and yet my love of Country comes over me like a strong wind and bears me unresistibly on with all these chains to the battle field.

The memories of the blissful moments I have spent with you come creeping over me, and I feel most gratified to God and to you that I have enjoyed them so long. And hard it is for me to give them up and burn to ashes the hopes of future years, when, God willing, we might still have lived and loved together, and seen our sons grown up to honorable manhood, around us. I have, I know, but few and small claims upon Divine Providence, but something whispers to me—perhaps it is the wafted prayer of my little Edgar, that I shall return to my loved ones unharmed. If I do not my dear Sarah, never forget how much I love you, and when my last breath escapes me on the battle field, it will whisper your name. Forgive my many faults, and the many pains I have caused you. How thoughtless and foolish I have often times been! How gladly would I wash out with my tears every little spot upon your happiness. . . .

But, O Sarah! if the dead can come back to this earth and flit unseen around those they loved, I shall always be near you; in the gladdest days and in the darkest nights . . . *always, always,* and if there be a soft breeze upon your cheek, it shall be my breath, as the cool air fans your throbbing temple, it shall be my spirit passing by. Sarah do not mourn me dead; think I am gone and wait for thee, for we shall meet again. . . .

Sullivan Ballou was killed at the first battle of Bull Run.

The names of the soon-to-be-separated couples on these pages are unknown.

WHY THE WAR CAME

DON E. FEHRENBACHER

TWO WEEKS BEFORE ABRAHAM LINCOLN TOOK THE oath of office as President of the United States of America on March 4, 1861, Jefferson Davis was sworn in as President of a new republic that extended from South Carolina to Texas. Nothing in the history of the Civil War is more remarkable than the speed with which secession proceeded and the Confederacy took shape, once the outcome of the presidential contest was known. The rush to action reflected an intensity of feeling also expressed in much southern rhetoric. Political leaders, editors, and other spokesmen denounced the election of Lincoln as an outrage amounting virtually to a declaration of war on the slaveholding states. "Let the consequences be what they may," said an Atlanta newspaper, "whether the Potomac is crimsoned in human gore, and Pennsylvania Avenue is paved ten fathoms in depth with mangled bodies . . . the South will never submit to such humiliation and degradation as the inauguration of Abraham Lincoln."

Why did the lawful election of a new President provoke such fury and lead so promptly to dissolution of the Union? First of all, no one at the time seems to have doubted that the secession crisis was a crisis over slavery. To be sure, there were other reasons for southern disaffection, such as a sense of having been reduced to economic vassalage by the commercial and industrial interests of the Northeast. Nevertheless, the grievances listed by the seceding states concentrated almost entirely on slavery. So did efforts in Congress to produce a compromise. So did the outpouring of public discussion. "The institution of African Slavery produced the Secession of the Cotton States," declared another Atlanta newspaper soon after Davis's inauguration. "If it had not existed, the Union of the States would, to-day, be complete." Lincoln had already said about the same thing in a letter to a southern leader: "You think slavery is *right* and ought to be extended; while we think it is *wrong* and ought to be restricted. That I suppose is the rub. It certainly is the only substantial difference between us."

The dynamic force at work in the crisis was southern perception of the Republican party, not merely as a political opposition, but as a hostile, revolutionary organization bent on total destruction of the slaveholding system. Fearful predictions filled the air. The Lincoln administration, it was said, would seek to repeal the fugitive-slave laws, abolish slavery in the territories and the District of Columbia, prohibit interstate trade in slaves, and reverse the Dred Scott decision through a reorganization of the Supreme Court. More than that, Republican control of the government would break down southern defenses against abolitionist propaganda and subject the slaveholding society to a mounting threat of internal disorder. The platform of the Republican party, according to an Alabama senator, was "as strong an incitement and invocation to servile insurrection, to murder, arson, and other crimes, as any to be found in abolition literature." Republicans must be dealt with as enemies, said a North Carolina newspaper; their policies would "put the torch to our dwellings and the knife to our throats."

Actually, Republican leaders were something considerably less than revolutionaries. Their party platform, which repudiated the kind of violence associated with John Brown and affirmed "the right of each state to order and control its own domestic institutions," did not have the ring of an incendiary document. Indeed, Republican antislavery doctrine amounted to a moral compromise with slavery that abolitionists were disposed to treat with scorn. Why, then, did so many southerners take an apocalyptic view of Lincoln's election? And on the other hand, why did so many northerners vote for Lincoln, knowing that his election would be disturbing to the peace of the nation? These are simple questions that soon lead one deep into historical complexities.

Slavery had been a troublesome but marginal problem in the founding of the Republic and in national politics for three decades thereafter. Sectional discord in those years had been centered primarily on other public issues, such as the Hamiltonian financial program of the 1790s and the Jeffersonian Embargo of 1807. As late as 1832, it was federal tariff policy that provoked South Carolina's belligerent experiment in nullification. Furthermore, southerners of the early national period, if they defended slavery at all, had usually done so in qualified and con-

tingent terms, portraying it as a regrettable legacy that was ineradicable in their own time, but not for all time. The Federal Constitution, while acknowledging the presence of slavery in the nation, seemed to treat it implicitly as an impermanent feature of American society. A generation imbued with the spirit of the Enlightenment found it easy to believe that the disturbing problem of human servitude would eventually yield to the benevolent forces of social progress.

By the middle decades of the nineteenth century, however, accumulating changes of great magnitude were dissolving such optimism and placing the American Union chronically at risk. The rise of the cotton kingdom had enhanced the value of slave labor and its importance in the national economy. Despite some northern efforts to restrict it, the slaveholding system had expanded westward as far as Missouri, Arkansas, and Texas. The nation's slave population tripled between 1800 and 1840. Yet, although slavery flourished, the slaveholding class suffered from a growing sense of insecurity as it came under fierce attack from a new breed of abolitionists and as the South settled ever deeper into the status of a minority section.

Slaveholders felt both physically threatened and morally degraded by the antislavery crusade. What they sought with increasing passion was not only security for their social system but vindication of their social respectability and personal honor. The defense of slavery accordingly lost its earlier strain of ambivalence and became more emphatic, with elaborate appeals to history, the scriptures, and racial theory. More and more, the South came to resemble a fortress under siege, expelling or silencing its own critics of slavery and barricading itself against abolitionist oratory and literature. Southerners in Congress closed ranks against even mild antislavery proposals, such as termination of slave trading in the District of Columbia. They argued that any concession to the spirit of abolitionism would denigrate the South and serve as an entering wedge for further attacks on the slaveholding system. During the final stages of the sectional controversy, many southern leaders compromised their own states' rights principles by demanding a Federal policy unreservedly protective of slavery. Some of them even insisted that all northern criticism of the institution must cease or be suppressed by the states in which it originated. One consequence of these and other proslavery excesses was the enlistment in the antislavery movement of a good many northerners who felt little sympathy for the slave but had developed a strong aversion to the "slave power."

From 1846 onward, the sectional issue that inflamed national politics was the status of slavery in the western territories. Apparently resolved by the Compromise of 1850, the problem arose again in a bitter struggle over Kansas, where for several years intermittent violence foreshadowed the great conflict that lay ahead. By the summer of 1858, it had become clear that Kansas would never be a slave state and that slavery was not taking root in any other territory. Yet the controversy grew in intensity, even as it seemed to be declining in relevance, perhaps because of a deepening awareness on both sides that the territories were just the skirmish line of a larger conflict over the future of slavery and the regional balance of power in an expanding nation. Ever more ominously in this unremitting quarrel there loomed the threat of disunion.

Talk of secession was almost as old as the Republic, but

only in the 1850s did the idea crystallize into a definite movement for southern independence. Until near the end of that decade, the out-and-out secessionists (or "fire-eaters") remained a relatively small group, except in South Carolina and one or two other states. But a much larger number of southerners were tempted by the idea and partly converted. They tended, for instance, to uphold the right of secession, while pondering its feasibility. Often they retained a strong attachment for the Union while at the same time yearning to cut loose from its antislavery elements. The election of Lincoln galvanized such men, and most of them were ready, when the time came, to be caught up in the excitement of establishing a new nation.

But secession, although it sprang from an impetuous spirit, was a complicated and highly formal enterprise, very difficult to set in motion. Earlier threats of disunion had nearly all arisen because of proceedings in Congress, which meant that a sectional crisis could always be defused by legislative compromise. In any case, the problem of slavery in the territories had ceased to be an urgent matter (except as it affected presidential politics within the Democratic party), and there was no other sectional issue with which Congress seemed likely to provoke a major crisis. Meanwhile, however, the South found itself facing a different kind of menace that might well become the trigger for disunion, and this was something over which Congress had no control—namely, the increasing possibility that antislavery forces would capture the presidency.

Historians once explained the birth of the Republican party in rather simple terms as the response of outraged northerners to the Kansas-Nebraska Act of 1854, which opened up those two territories to slavery. Later scholarship indicates, however, that a fundamental realignment of the party system was already under way when the Kansas question arose. The change began at the local level and reflected concern about certain ethnocultural issues, such as nativism and temperance, to which the old parties seemed to be paying too little attention. Out of this local unrest there arose the Know-Nothing movement, organized politically as the American party, which for a time seemed likely to replace the failing Whig organization as the principal opposition to the Democrats. But the anti-Nebraska coalition of 1854, soon to take the name Republican, superimposed its political revolution upon that of the nativists and in the end absorbed much of the American party's membership. The emergence of Republicanism as a major political force was in fact a very complex event that cannot be attributed solely to antislavery zeal or to any other single cause. Nevertheless, what proved to be crucial in 1860 was not the true nature of the Republican party, whatever that may have been, but rather, southern perception of the party as a thinly disguised agency of abolitionist fanaticism.

For many southerners, the prospect of a Republican administration summoned up visions of a world in which slaveholding would be officially stigmatized as morally wrong, in which slaves would be encouraged to rise up against their masters, and in which national policy would move inexorably toward emancipation and racial equality. But to understand fully the reaction of the South to Lincoln's election, one must take into account not only the antislavery complexion of Republicanism but also the proslavery character of the Federal government before

1861. For nearly three-quarters of a century, southern slaveholders, along with northerners deferential to the slaveholding interest, had predominated in the presidency, the executive departments, the foreign service, the Supreme Court, the higher military echelons, and the Federal bureaucracy. Cabinet posts and other important positions were frequently entrusted to proslavery militants like John C. Calhoun, but no antislavery leader was appointed to high Federal office before Lincoln became President. The nation's foreign policy was conducted habitually and often emphatically in a manner protective of slavery. The presence of slaveholding in the national capital testified to its official respectability. In 1857, the Chief Justice of the United States awarded slavery a privileged status under the Constitution when he declared that the Federal government had no power to regulate the institution but did have "the power coupled with the duty of guarding and protecting the owner in his rights." When the secession crisis arose, James Buchanan, the Pennsylvania Democrat in the White House, blamed it entirely on "the incessant and violent agitation of the slavery question throughout the North." Is it any wonder that most southerners viewed the election of Lincoln as a revolutionary break with the past?

The danger of disunion apparently did not deter a great many persons from voting Republican in 1860. For one thing, the threat to secede had been heard so often that it was widely regarded as mere bluster, aimed at extracting concessions from fainthearted "Union-savers." Furthermore, many northerners persuaded themselves that the secessionists, even if serious, were just a noisy minority whose plot would be smothered by the stronger forces of southern unionism. The New York editor William Cullen Bryant spoke for perhaps a majority of Republicans when he remarked soon after the election: "As to disunion, nobody but silly people believe it will happen."

Lending encouragement to such mistaken expectations was the amount of dissension in the South on the question of immediate withdrawal from the Union. Besides the many outright unionists, there were "cooperationists," who argued that secession should be preceded by a general southern convention, and there were conditional disunionists who wanted to wait until the Lincoln administration had committed an "overt act" of aggression against the South. But secessionist leaders knew that for their purposes delay was more dangerous than lack of full support. The shocking antislavery capture of the presidency provided a clear signal for disunion such as might never be sounded again, and its mobilizing effect would soon be wasted if action bogged down in debate. Cooperationist strategy had time and again proved unsuccessful. Therefore, the hour had come, said the fire-eaters, for secession to be undertaken in single file. One bold state must lead the way, drawing the rest of the South after it, state by state. As the movement proceeded, it would presumably gather momentum and eventually force even the border slave states to leave the Union.

When a South Carolina convention unanimously approved an ordinance of secession on December 20, 1860, it did so with full assurance that other states would follow. Sure enough, Mississippi seceded on January 9, 1861, then Florida and Alabama in the next two days, then Georgia, Louisiana, and finally Texas on February 1. At that point, however, the parade of departures came to a halt, as secession met defeat everywhere in the upper South. Later, of course, four more states seceded, but theirs was a different kind of decision that amounted to joining one side in a war already begun. The crucial determination to dissolve the Union in response to the election of Lincoln was made by just seven state governments, representing less than one-third of the free population of the entire South. Those same seven states of the lower South created the Confederacy, framed its constitution, and elected its President. Furthermore, it was men from the lower South who eventually made the fateful decision to open fire on Fort Sumter. Virginians, by way of contrast, lived for four years under a government that they had no part in establishing and fought for four years in a war that they had no part in initiating.

Driven by fear, anger, and pride into preemptive action against what appeared to be an intolerable future, the secessionist majorities in the lower South seized the initiative after Lincoln's election and forced a battery of hard choices on the rest of the country. The decisiveness of these men enabled them to shape the course of events to their liking for a time, although it served them badly at Fort Sumter. Their decisive behavior is the heart of the matter in any explanation of the outbreak of the Civil War, just as slavery is the heart of the matter in any explanation of that behavior.

CHAPTER TWO

1862
FOREVER FREE

Winter camp of the 1st Connecticut Artillery at Ford Richardson, Virginia, just outside Washington.

CHAMPAGNE AND OYSTERS

"For months past (and lately more pressingly)," wrote Attorney General Edward Bates on New Year's Eve, "I have urged upon the President to have some military organization about his person. . . . I insisted that, being 'commander in chief' by law, he *must* command—especially in such a war as this."

Lincoln was willing enough. He even toyed with the notion of leading the army into the field himself, pored over books on military strategy, asked officers for advice. His generals would not move. When he urged his commanders in the West, Henry Halleck in Missouri and Don Carlos Buell in Kentucky, to make a concerted advance against the enemy, Halleck begged off. "I am not ready to cooperate," he wrote Lincoln on New Year's Day. "Too much haste will ruin everything." "It is exceedingly discouraging," Lincoln scrawled across the top of Halleck's letter, "As everywhere else, nothing can be done." To Buell he wrote, "Delay is ruining us."

Nearer at hand, George McClellan's well-fed, splendidly equipped Army of the Potomac still outnumbered the nearest Confederate forces three to one, but the general's chronic reluctance to risk failure by taking the field against them was now compounded by typhoid fever, which kept him confined to his bed for three weeks, during which he refused to divulge his plans for a spring offensive or even allow a visit by the President.

"General, what shall I do?" the President asked the Quartermaster General, Montgomery Meigs, on January 10. "The people are impatient; Chase has no money and he tells me he can raise no more; the General of the Army has typhoid fever. The bottom is out of the tub. What shall I do?"

Meigs had no ready answer. Meanwhile, the Joint Committee on the Conduct of the War continued to urge that McClellan be replaced and that something be done about the rampant corruption everywhere evident in the awarding of War Department contracts. Lincoln stuck by his commander, although he privately shared the committee's impatience with him. "If General McClellan does not want to use the Army," the President told one White House war council, "I would like to *borrow* it for a time, provided I could see how it could be made to do something." But he did replace Secretary of War Cameron with Edwin McMasters Stanton, an able and incorruptible War Democrat from Ohio who had served as Attorney General under James Buchanan. Stanton had become a friend of McClellan's—and privately shared his belief in Lincoln's "painful imbecility"—but he, too, grew unhappy with his general. "*The champagne and oysters on the Potomac must be stopped,*" he wrote. "I will *force* this man McClellan to fight."

In order to make that happen, the President issued General War Order Number One on January 27, calling for a general movement by all land and naval forces on Washington's Birthday, February 22. Four days later, McClellan was specifically ordered to move against Joseph E. Johnston's army at Manassas Junction by that same date, then proceed overland to take Richmond.

"He who does something at the head of one regiment, will eclipse him who does nothing at the head of a hundred."

ABRAHAM LINCOLN, 1862

Abraham Lincoln, photographed at Mathew Brady's gallery by Anthony Berger: "I see the president almost every day . . ." Walt Whitman wrote from Washington. "I see very plainly Abraham Lincoln's dark brown face with its deep-cut lines, the eyes always to me with a deep latent sadness in the expression. . . . None of the artists or pictures has caught the deep, though subtle and indirect expression of this man's face. There is something else there. One of the great portrait painters of two or three centuries ago is needed."

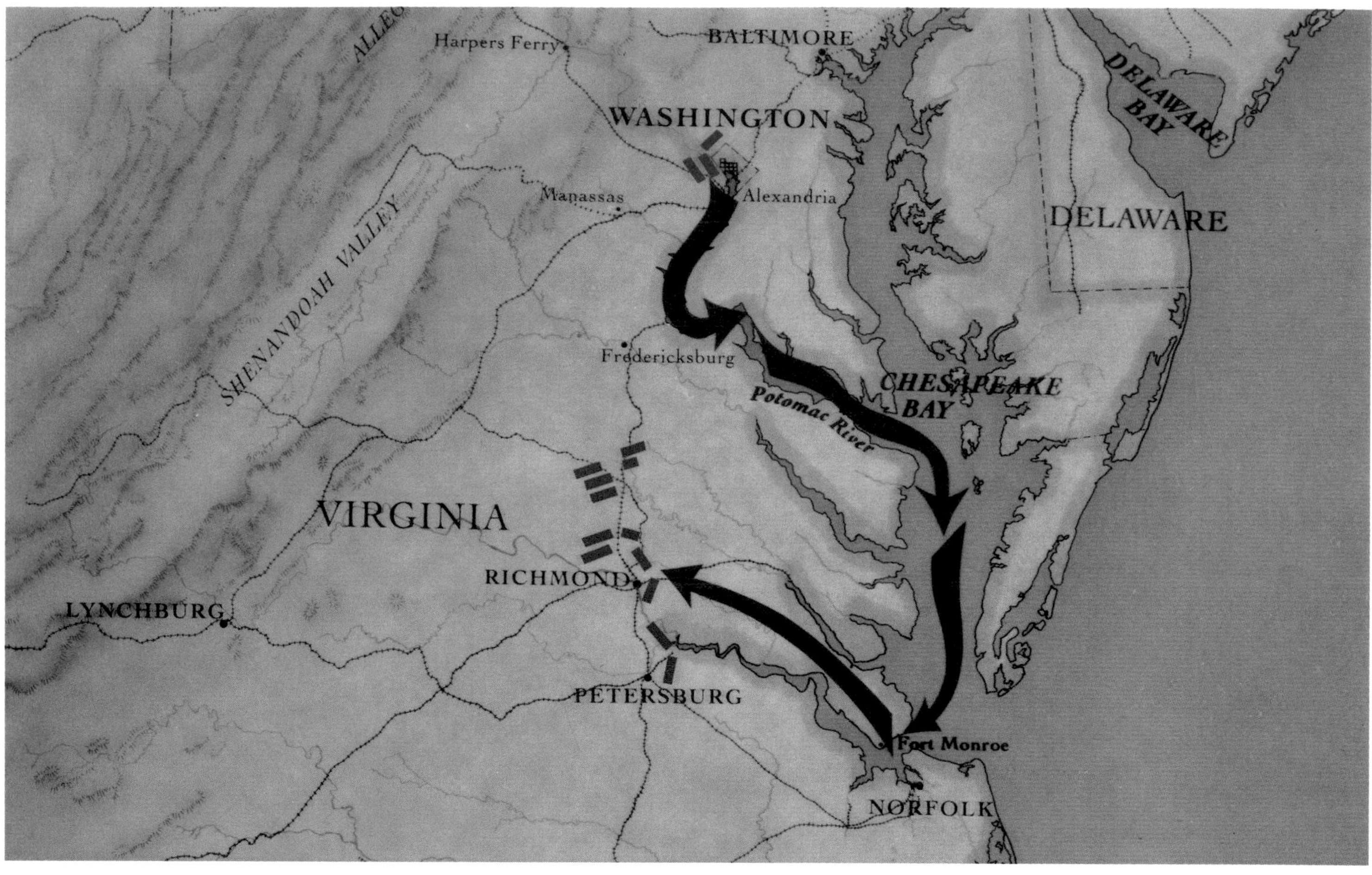

McClellan's Peninsular Campaign: Instead of advancing through northern Virginia, where he was sure huge rebel armies lurked, the Union commander proposed instead to ship his 121,500-man Army of the Potomac to the tip of the York-James Peninsula by sea, then fight his way west to Richmond. The Peninsular Campaign began in March 1862—more than seven months after McClellan took command.

McClellan's own soldiers were anxious to get on with it, Elisha Rhodes among them.

> January 31, 1862. Mud, mud, mud. I am thinking of starting a steamboat line to run on Pennsylvania Avenue.... If I was owner of this town, I would sell it very cheap. Will the mud never dry up so the army can move? I want to see service and I want the war over so that I can go home.

Finally, McClellan offered a counterplan of his own. Rather than make a frontal attack on the huge Confederate force he was convinced lay in wait for him at Manassas Junction, he proposed to circumvent it, float his army down Chesapeake Bay to Urbanna, near the mouth of the Rappahannock River, and then march overland to Richmond before the Confederate commander could block him. The Virginia roads were good all year round, he assured the President.

Lincoln did not much like McClellan's plan: it would leave a large rebel army between Washington and the Army of the Potomac for one thing, but when he was assured that sufficient forces would be left behind to protect the capital, he acquiesced. "I don't care, gentlemen, what plan you have," he confessed to his generals, "all I ask is for you to just pitch in!"

"Just don't let them hurry me is all I ask," General McClellan (top right, second from left, with members of his staff) told Lincoln. Among those whose impatience he feared most were Edwin M. Stanton, the new Secretary of War (top), and the Secretary of State, William H. Seward.

But the campaign began badly. When, as part of the buildup for his advance, McClellan sent a force on February 27 to break the rebel grip on the Potomac, the boats provided to carry his men through a lock on the Chesapeake and Ohio Canal proved six inches too wide.

"It means that it is a damned fizzle," Stanton said when he got the news. "It means that he doesn't intend to do anything." Lincoln himself was uncharacteristically angered. "Why in the Nation . . ." he asked a member of McClellan's staff, "couldn't the General have known whether a boat would go through that lock before spending a million dollars getting them there? I am no engineer but it seems to me that if I wished to know whether a boat would go through a hole . . . common sense would teach me to go and measure it."

Chairman Ben Wade of the Senate Committee on the Conduct of the War now told the President *anybody* would be better than McClellan. "Wade, anybody will do for you," Lincoln said, "but I must have somebody."

Still more embarrassment followed. Anticipating McClellan's imminent move, Joseph E. Johnston promptly withdrew his army from Manassas Junction—leaving behind defenses nowhere near so formidable as McClellan had said they were—and shifted it to a stronger position behind the Rappahannock River, making McClellan's intended landing place unsafe. "We have been humbugged by the rebels," wrote George Templeton Strong. After a whole battery of Quaker guns was discovered at Centerville, Senator William P. Fessenden of Maine wrote to his family:

> You will have heard of the wooden guns at Centerville. It is true and we are smarting under the disgrace which this discovery has brought upon us. We shall be the scorn of the world. It is no longer doubtful that General McClellan is utterly unfit for his position. . . . And yet the President will keep him in command and leave our destiny in his hands. . . . Well, it cannot be helped. We went for a rail-splitter, and we have got one.

On March 11, McClellan was relieved of his post as general-in-chief of the Federal armies so that he could concentrate all his attention on the task at hand, and begin his move toward a new landing place, Fortress Monroe, Virginia, at the eastern tip of the finger of land between the James and York rivers, just seventy miles from Richmond.

TOO GOOD FOR THIS EARTH

Robert Lincoln, the President's eldest son, was away at Harvard, but Lincoln delighted in his youngest boys, Willie, eleven, and eight-year-old Thomas, known as Tad. They had the run of the Executive Mansion, racing their goats across the grounds, training a toy cannon on cabinet meetings, setting off the alarm system just to see the staff scurry. "Mr. Lincoln . . . was very exceedingly indulgent to his children . . ." his wife remembered. "He always said: 'It is my pleasure that my children are free, happy and unrestrained by parental tyranny. Love is the chain whereby to bind a child to its parents.'"

Tad was high-strung but slow, still unable to read. Willie was his parents' favorite, especially loved perhaps because he had been conceived shortly after the death of a fourth son back in Springfield. He was a studious child, liked to compose verse and memorize railroad timetables, and had raised a boys' battalion from among his schoolmates. Once he and Tad told their father that their doll had been found asleep on guard duty.

> **The doll Jack is pardoned.**
> **By order of the President.**
> **A. Lincoln**

Early in February, Willie developed what the doctor then called "bilious fever." His parents sat up night after night to nurse him, but, at 5:30 on the twentieth, he died. Lincoln was desolated. "I never saw a man so bowed down in grief," said the White House seamstress, "murmuring, 'My poor boy, he was too good for this earth. . . . It is hard, hard to have him die!' "

Nothing could console Mary Lincoln. Willie's death, she believed, was divine punishment for having been "so wrapped up in the world, so devoted to our own political advancement." She could never again bear to enter the room in which he died, veered wildly between loud weeping and silent depression for three months, and desperately sought to communicate with her dead children through spiritualists. Finally, a servant remembered, Lincoln led her to the window and pointed to the mental hospital. "Mother, do you see that large white building on the hill, yonder? Try and control your grief, or it will drive you mad, and we may have to send you there." She did her best to steel herself. "If I had not felt the spur of necessity urging me to cheer Mr. Lincoln, whose grief was as great as my own," she said later, "I could never have smiled again."

The war left the President little time to mourn, and he was soon back at the office working eighteen-hour days.

Willie Lincoln.

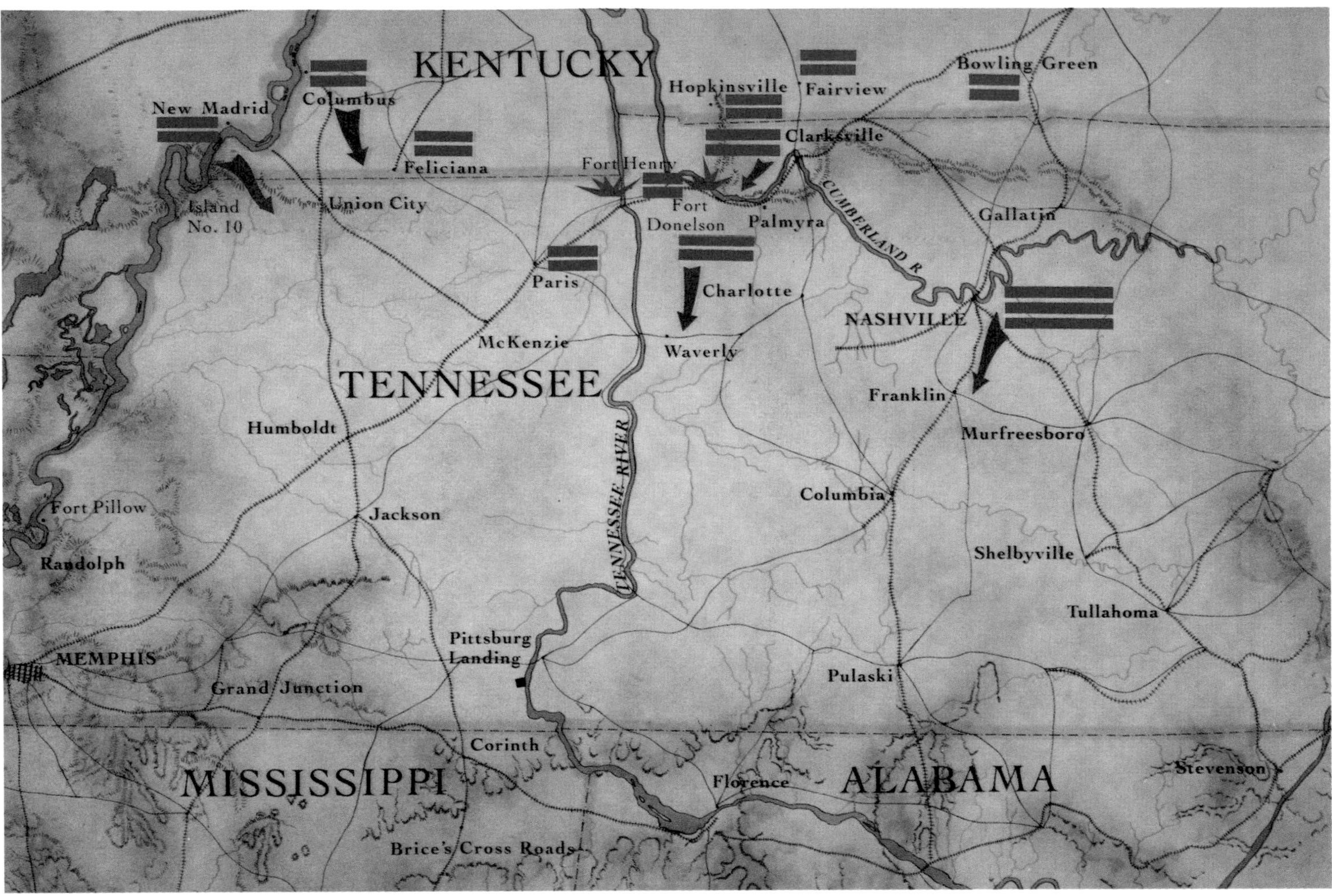

Federal victories at Fort Henry on the Tennessee and Fort Donelson on the Cumberland ensured that both Kentucky and western Tennessee remained within the Union. With these twin triumphs, General Ulysses S. Grant's star began to rise, and northern armies could start moving south in the spring of 1862.

UNCONDITIONAL SURRENDER

Meanwhile, there had been good news from the West. "Whatever nation gets . . . control of the Ohio, Mississippi, and Missouri Rivers," wrote William Tecumseh Sherman, "will control the continent." Flowing north to south, broad enough to carry invading armies, the western rivers plunged into the heart of the Confederacy.

U. S. Grant had already seized Paducah, Kentucky, which controlled access to the Tennessee and Cumberland, in 1861. Now, in the winter of 1862, he won two still more important victories. The first was at Fort Henry, on the Tennessee, which he took easily on February 6 with fifteen thousand men, aided by a fleet of Union gunboats under Commodore Andrew Foote that hammered its walls from almost point-blank range.

Fort Donelson, on the Cumberland, twelve miles to the east, proved a more difficult challenge. The rebel forces within its walls were equal to Grant's own, having been reinforced by most of the Fort Henry garrison, and the fort itself stood high on a bluff, so that when the Federal gunboats came in close their shells arced harmlessly over it, while the rebel guns smashed into them from above. After two of six Union vessels were sunk, the rest were damaged, and Foote himself was badly wounded, Grant called off the assault by water and settled in for a siege. The weather was bitterly cold and, lying in the snowy woods all night, the shivering Union men burrowed under blankets of frozen leaves to try to keep warm.

In command within the fort were two men for whom the Union commander had little but scorn: John Floyd, "no soldier," according to Grant, but Buchanan's former Secretary of War, who had once been charged with malfeasance in office and now lived in fear of being captured by Union forces and tried for having scattered the regular army just when it was to be needed most; and his second-in-command, Gideon Pillow, a gray-bearded Tennessean best known for having quarreled noisily with his commander in the midst of the Mexican War; Grant simply thought Pillow "conceited."

At first light on February 15, while Grant was conferring with Foote downstream from Donelson, Pillow led a rebel column out of the fort, intending to cut an escape route through the Federal besiegers and open a road to Nashville.

Confederate cavalry led the way, under Nathan Bedford Forrest, a blacksmith's son who had made himself a millionaire selling land, cotton, and slaves. When word of Sumter reached Memphis, he had put up posters calling upon anyone who wanted to kill Yankees to come and ride with him, and had equipped an entire battalion of cavalry out of his own pocket.

"War means fighting. And fighting means killing," Forrest liked to say.

Now he and his men had their chance to do both, tearing at the Union's right flank in a battle that raged back and forth across the bloody snow all morning. A Confederate escape route lay open at last, when, shortly after noon, Pillow grew anxious and pulled most of his men back, leaving only a thin line of troops under Simon Bolivar Buckner of Kentucky to hold their hard-won position.

Meanwhile, Grant had galloped back to the battlefield along an icy forest road, to find his officers in confusion, unclear as to who was in command or what to do next. He took instant charge and ordered his old West Point commandant, Charles F. Smith, to launch a counterattack. "Second Iowa," Smith told his men, "you must take that fort," and ordered his line forward.

Smith himself led the way: "Come on, you volunteers, come on," he shouted. "This is your chance. You volunteered to be killed for love of your country and now you can be. You are only damned volunteers. I am only a soldier and don't want to be killed, but you came to be killed and now you can be."

"I was nearly scared to death," a Union soldier remembered, "but I saw the old man's white moustache over his shoulder, and went on." Buckner's men fell back. Union gunboats returned to shell the fort. The Confederate breakout had failed; the rebels were trapped.

Their commanders now conferred. General Floyd said he could not bring himself to surrender—he had sworn an oath never to do so—and asked Pillow if he would do it if command was passed to him. Pillow said no. Buckner, an old friend of Grant's, who had loaned him money in hard times, said that he would be willing to give up rather than shed more useless blood.

Oblivious of the dead and wounded men lying in the snow around him, General Ulysses S. Grant (mounted, at center) watches his men sweep toward Fort Donelson.

Forrest was outraged. He was sure the fort's defenders could fight their way out and, when his superiors overruled him, said, "I did not come here for the purpose of surrendering my command," and stormed from the council. While Pillow and Floyd slipped away from the fort by boat under cover of darkness, leaving behind their entire garrison, Forrest ordered his seven hundred men to saddle up, then led them out of the fort, across an icy, shoulder-deep backwater of the Cumberland, and through the snowy woods seventy-five miles to sanctuary at Nashville. Bedford Forrest would return again and again to haunt the Union.

A little past midnight, Grant received a note from Buckner asking surrender terms. "What answer shall I send to this?" Grant asked Smith. "No terms with traitors, by God!" the old man said. Grant shared the sentiment but softened the language: "No terms except an unconditional and immediate surrender can be accepted. I propose to move immediately upon your works."

Buckner thought this "ungenerous and unchivalrous" but was not foolish enough to fight on: he surrendered his garrison—fifteen thousand men, the largest number ever to surrender on the American continent up to that time.

Despite the escape of Forrest and his men, the Tennessee and Cumberland rivers were now in Union hands. Within a week, so was Nashville. The Confederates had been forced out of Kentucky, and in just eleven months Grant had gone from harness maker's clerk to Union hero. Eager for news of a Union victory, the North was ecstatic. "Chicago reeled mad with joy," said the Chicago *Tribune.* At Cincinnati, "Everybody was shaking hands with everybody else, and bewhiskered men embraced each other as if they were lovers."

The delighted northern public now thought they knew what Grant's initials stood for, and the newspapers took to calling him "Unconditional Surrender Grant." Stories that described him coolly smoking under fire brought him barrels of cigars from admirers all over the North. In fact, he had always preferred a pipe, but, never able to turn away good tobacco in any form, he now took up cigars, smoking twenty a day.

Ulysses S. Grant in 1862: He "habitually wears an expression," a soldier said, "as if he had determined to drive his head through a brick wall and was about to do it."

IRONCLADS

"I regard the possession of an iron-armored ship as a matter of the first necessity," wrote the Confederate Secretary of the Navy, Stephen R. Mallory, the former United States Senator from Florida who had served before the war as chairman of the Commission on Naval Affairs and, just two years earlier, had confidently predicted the perpetuity of the Union. He would be the only member of the Confederate cabinet to serve in the same post until the end.

The Confederacy began the war with no navy at all, but by the fall of 1861 Mallory was on the way to getting what he wanted: a small fleet of iron ships that could splinter wooden vessels at will and take on the whole Federal navy. On the hull of the steam frigate *Merrimack,* scuttled when the Union abandoned Norfolk, Confederate engineers were bolting together iron plates, building a warship more powerful than anything the Union had. News of the monster quickly reached the North: "Who," asked Gustavus Fox, the Assistant Secretary of the northern navy, "is to prevent her dropping her anchor in the Potomac . . . and throwing her hundred-pound shells into [the White House] or battering down the halls of the Capitol?"

There was probably only one man in America who could stop the *Merrimack,* and he was mad at the navy. The Swedish-born inventor John Ericsson, proud, vain, cranky, brilliant, felt he had been cheated out of payment for services to the fleet years before. But when Secretary of the Navy Gideon Welles begged him to do something to stop the *Merrimack,* he came up with the most original design in the history of naval architecture. His ship would have only two guns to the *Merrimack*'s ten, but they would be mounted in a revolving turret, and despite the fact that Ericsson's vessel

Federal sailors row for their lives after the apparently unstoppable Confederate ironclad *Merrimack* has crippled the twenty-four-gun Federal sloop *Cumberland* off Hampton Roads, Virginia, and is about to turn her relentless attention to the *Congress* and *Minnesota*.

would be made entirely of iron, he assured a panicky Navy Department, "the sea shall ride over her and she shall live in it like a duck."

Professional navy men were unconvinced. Lincoln overruled them. "All I can say," he told a friend, "is what the girl said when she put her foot in the stocking—'I think there's *something* in it.'" He and Welles were taking a chance. Ericsson was plagued with bad luck: during a public demonstration of his propeller-driven warship, the *Princeton,* in 1844, an experimental gun had blown up, killing six people, including the Secretaries of State and the Navy.

But on January 30, 1862, Ericsson's revolutionary ship slid into Manhattan's East River, just 101 days after he agreed to build her. He called his creation the *Monitor,* and there had never been anything like her: the single vessel contained forty-seven patented devices.

It was an awful trip. "Our hawsers were cast loose & we were on our way . . . in the midst of a terrible snow storm," the paymaster remembered. "We ran first to the New York side and then to Brooklyn & so back and forth across the river . . . like a drunken man on a sidewalk. . . . We found she would not answer her rudder at all."

It was no better at sea. Freezing water spilled in, ventilators failed, the ship filled with gas, and her crew began to faint. But four hundred miles away, off the coast of Virginia, the *Merrimack* was waiting. The *Monitor* kept limping south.

Meanwhile, Saturday, March 8, was washday for the blockading Union fleet in Hampton Roads, and laundry was drying on the rigging of all the Union warships when the Confederate *Merrimack* came out to fight. She headed straight for the fifty-gun frigate *Cumberland,* the most powerful conventional ship in the Federal squadron. The *Cumberland*'s pilot never forgot her approach: "As she came ploughing through the water . . . she looked like a huge, half-submerged crocodile. Her side seemed of solid iron, except where the guns pointed from the narrow ports. . . . At her prow I could see the iron ram projecting straight forward."

The *Cumberland* opened fire, but her shots bounced harmlessly off the *Merrimack*'s side, "like India rubber balls," a horrified officer said. The Confederate rammed the *Cumberland,* then stood in so close the two ships' cannon muzzles almost touched.

The *Cumberland*'s guns were still firing when her deck was awash. She sank in shallow water. The *Merrimack* went on to set the *Congress* afire, then drove the *Minnesota* aground. But now it was getting dark. The marauding Confederate ship drew back for the night. She would finish off the *Minnesota* in the morning.

"The *Merrimack* will change the whole character of the war," Edwin Stanton told a White House cabinet meeting. "She will destroy, *seriatim,* every naval vessel. She will lay all the cities on the seaboard under contribution."

For one day the Confederate navy ruled the sea. Two hundred and fifty Union sailors were dead. Aboard the battered *Minnesota,* the men boiled up coffee and ate some crackers and cheese. "We enjoyed ourselves," a sailor remembered, "for none cared to look forward to the morrow, as there was but one termination possible as far as we knew then."

But at one o'clock in the morning the wakeful crew saw another vessel draw up alongside them in the darkness. The *Monitor* had arrived.

The *Merrimack* (left) trades fire with the *Monitor*: "Gun after gun was fired by the *Monitor*," recalled the captain of the helpless *Minnesota*, who watched from the sidelines, "which was returned with whole broadsides from the rebels, with no more effect, apparently, than so many pebble-stones thrown by a child . . . clearly establishing the fact that wooden vessels cannot contend successfully with iron-clad ones, for never before was anything like it dreamed of by the greatest enthusiast in maritime warfare."

The men who went to sea: A photographer sought out the young powder monkey (above) aboard the U.S.S. *New Hampshire*; the bearded seaman (right) took time out from shore leave to have his picture made.

Sunday, March 9, began early. The *Merrimack* was under way by seven o'clock, heading for the helpless *Minnesota.*

Now it was the Confederates who were baffled. "Close alongside [the *Minnesota*] there was a craft such as the eyes of a seaman never looked upon before," wrote a southern lieutenant, "an immense shingle floating on the water, with a gigantic cheese box rising from its center; no sails, no wheels, no smokestack, no guns. What could it be?"

The two ships hammered away at each other, hull to hull, fighting at such close range that five times the two vessels collided as the men inside, half-blind with smoke, loaded and fired, loaded and fired. "We went . . . as hard as we could," a Union lieutenant aboard the *Monitor* remembered. "The shot, shell, grape, cannister, musket, and rifle balls flew about in every direction, but did us no damage. Our [gun turret] was struck several times and though the noise was pretty loud, it did not affect us any. Stodder & one of the men were carelessly leaning against the tower, when a shot struck [it] exactly opposite to them, and disabled them for an hour or two."

After four and a half hours, the *Merrimack* drew off.

It was her only fight. The Confederates blew her up two months later when they were forced out of Norfolk. The Union set to work building more *Monitor*s, while Europe watched in worried fascination. From the moment the two ships opened fire that Sunday morning, every other navy on earth was obsolete.

In London, Henry Adams cheered the Union triumph, but also saw in it an ominous portent:

> About a week ago [the British] discovered that their whole wooden navy was useless. . . . These are great times. . . . Man has mounted science, and is now run away with. . . . Before many centuries more . . . science may have the existence of mankind in its power, and the human race commit suicide by blowing up the world.

Even with the menace of the *Merrimack* now behind him, Lincoln's blockade of southern ports was easier to declare than enforce. The Confederate coastline, broken by numberless inlets and 189 rivers, stretched from the Potomac to the Rio Grande—3,500 miles. When the war began, one-quarter of the navy's regular officers had defected to the South, and Secretary of the Navy Welles was left with just 41 vessels in commission—half of them officially obsolete—to patrol it all.

Welles was an ex-Democrat and newspaper publisher from New England, with little experience of naval affairs and a notably unpersuasive wig; Lincoln called him "Father Neptune." But he was able and tireless: under his direction, scores of ships—sailboats, yachts, ferryboats, tugs—were built, bought, or fitted out with guns. By 1862, Union naval forces had established footholds at Port Royal, Beaufort, the Sea Islands, Roanoke Island, and New Bern, and 427 Federal ships rode at anchor off southern ports.

Life aboard ship was rugged and monotonous. An officer suggested that his mother would have some inkling of what blockade duty was like if she would "go to the roof on a hot summer day, talk to a half-dozen degenerates, descend to the basement, drink tepid water full of iron rust, climb to the roof again, and repeat the process until . . . fagged out, then go to bed with everything shut tight."

Crews included old salts, immigrants who spoke no English, country boys who'd never seen the ocean before, let alone sailed on it. Blacks served at sea long before they were allowed to fight on land, but only in the lowest ranks. Each day was devoted to scrubbing, painting, drilling, repairing, coaling, target practice—day after day, week after week. Food was often limited to two dishes: pickled beef and "dogs' bodies"—dried peas, boiled in a cloth. Too many weeks at sea produced a condition one naval surgeon called "*land* sickness"—a morbid longing to go ashore.

Secessionist gospel held that the South had nothing to fear from a blockade. Neither the British nor the French economies could survive for long without southern cotton, Davis and his advisors believed; one or both nations would surely intervene on behalf of the Confederacy. "The cards are in our hands!" said the Charleston *Mercury,* "and we intend to play them out to the bankruptcy of every cotton factory in Great Britain and France for the acknowledgement of our independence." And, as *Punch* implied, there were a good many Britons who agreed:

Gideon Welles, Secretary of the Navy.

The building of ironclads proceeded by trial and error: The U.S.S. *Carondelet* (top right), one of the first of the so-called "Pook Turtles," built by Samuel M. Pook, outran rebel shelling during the struggle for Island No. 10 on the Mississippi; John Ericsson himself built the U.S.S. *Passaic* (right), whose battered turret withstood heavy fire off Charleston in 1863; but the iron sheathing of the U.S.S. *Galena* (far right) proved too thin to stand up to rebel batteries on the James in July 1862.

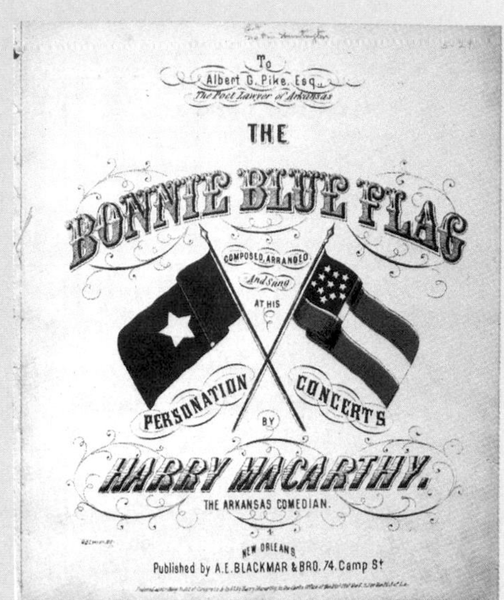

AFFECTION'S CLOUDLESS SKY

"I invited my comrades to assist me in emptying three canteens of 'Oh! Be Joyful,'" a Confederate soldier wrote home, "then spent the balance of the evening singing—until Tattoo, then we parted in good spirits."

It was a singing war. Sentimental songs were popular with both armies—"Lorena," "Just Before the Battle, Mother," "The Vacant Chair," "Tenting Tonight," "All Quiet Along the Potomac," "When This Cruel War Is Over," "Home, Sweet Home," "Somebody's Darling." (When soldiers on the march came across a dead body, some liked to jerk a thumb at the corpse and say, "That's Somebody's Darlin' there.")

On the way to battle, Confederates favored "I Wish I Was in Dixie's Land," better known as "Dixie," and "The Bonnie Blue Flag," which Ben Butler thought so inspirational to southerners that he arrested its New Orleans publisher and threatened to fine anyone singing it twenty-five dollars. But the North had the best marching songs—"We're Coming, Father Abraham," "Tramp, Tramp, Tramp, the Boys Are Marching," "Rally Round the Flag, Boys," "John Brown's Body." A southern major who listened to a northern officer sing some of them after the war admitted, "Gentlemen, if we'd had your songs, we'd have licked you out of your boots."

The words to the most stirring of all the songs to which the Union men marched were written by a woman, Julia Ward Howe. An abolitionist, poet, and suffragist, married to the reformer Samuel Gridley Howe, who had helped arm John Brown and his raiders, she wanted to contribute something of her own to the cause she believed holy. "My husband was beyond the age of military service, my eldest son but a stripling. I could not leave my nursery to follow the march of our armies."

She visited Washington in the autumn of 1861, watched one of McClellan's stirring grand reviews, and returned to her room at Willard's Hotel with "John Brown's Body" ringing in her head. She woke in the middle of the night, she remembered, and "as I lay waiting for the dawn, the long lines of the desired poem began to twine themselves in my mind." She got out of bed and scribbled them out in the dark with a broken pen, thinking to herself, "I like this better than most things I have written." She sold her poem for four dollars to the *Atlantic Monthly*, which published it in February 1862. Its title was "The Battle Hymn of the Republic," and it swept the Union camps.

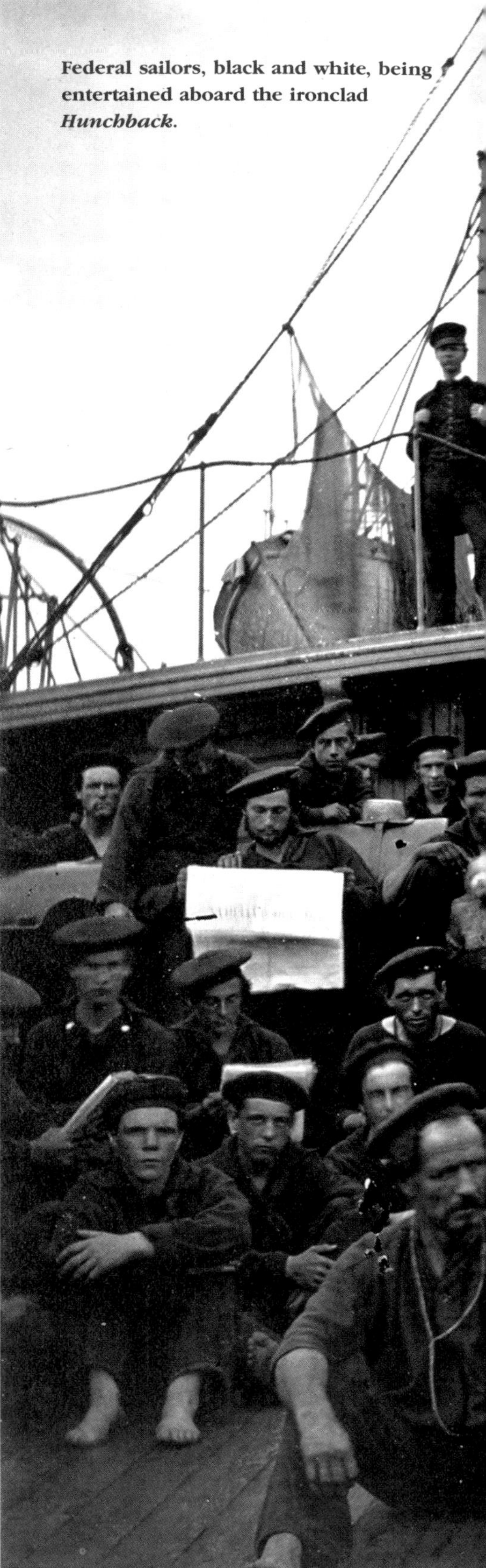

Federal sailors, black and white, being entertained aboard the ironclad *Hunchback*.

LORENA

I

The years creep slowly by, Lorena,
The snow is on the grass again;
The sun's low down the sky, Lorena,
The frost gleams where the flow'rs have been.
But the heart throbs on as warmly now,
As when the summer days were nigh;
Oh! The sun can never dip so low,
A-down affection's cloudless sky.
The sun can never slip so low,
A-down affection's cloudless sky.

II

A hundred months have passed since, Lorena,
Since last I held that hand in mine,
And felt the pulse beat fast, Lorena,
Though mine beat faster far than thine.
A hundred months, 'twas flowery May,
When up the hilly slope we climbed,
To watch the dying of the day,
And hear the distant church bells chime.
To watch the dying of the day,
And hear the distant church bells chime.

III

We loved each other then, Lorena,
More than we ever dared to tell;
And what we might have been, Lorena,
Had but our loving prospered well—
But then, 'tis past, the years are gone,
I'll not call up their shadowy forms;
I'll say to them, "Lost years, sleep on!
Sleep on! nor heed life's pelting storms."
I'll say to them, "Lost years, sleep on!
Sleep on! nor heed life's pelting storms."

IV

The story of that past, Lorena,
Alas! I care not to repeat,
The hopes that could not last, Lorena,
They lived, but only lived to cheat.
I would not cause e'en one regret
To rankle in your bosom now;
For "if we try, we may forget,"
Were words of thine long years ago.
For "if we try, we may forget,"
Were words of thine long years ago.

V

Yes, these were words of thine, Lorena,
They burn within my memory yet;
They touched some tender chords, Lorena,
Which thrill and tremble with regret.
'Twas not thy woman's heart that spoke;
Thy heart was always true to me:
A duty, stern and pressing, broke
The tie which linked my soul with thee.
A duty, stern and pressing, broke
The tie which linked my soul with thee.

VI

It matters little now, Lorena,
The past is in the eternal past,
Our heads will soon lie low, Lorena,
Life's tide is ebbing out so fast.
There is a future! O, thank God!
Of life this is so small a part!
'Tis dust to dust beneath the sod!
But up there, up there, 'tis heart to heart.
'Tis dust to dust beneath the sod!
But there, up there, 'tis heart to heart.

"I don't believe," said Robert E. Lee after listening to a band concert, "we can have an army without music." Northern troops were no less enthusiastic about the serenades played by their regimental bands, such as that of the 97th Indiana (opposite above): "I don't know that we should have done without our band . . ." a Massachusetts man wrote home. "Every night about sundown Gilmore gives us a splendid concert, playing selections from the operas and some very pretty marches, quicksteps, waltzes and the like." The men also enjoyed singing songs like "Lorena" (whose lyrics are given above) and the others shown here.

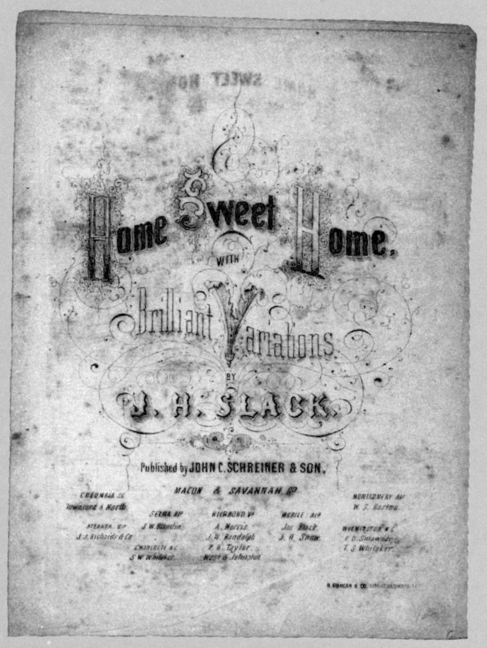
Home Sweet Home.
with
Brilliant Variations
by
J. H. Slack.
Published by JOHN C. SCHREINER & SON.
MACON & SAVANNAH, GA.

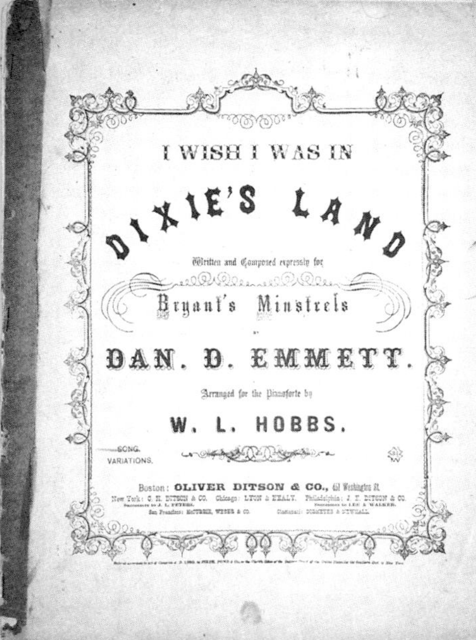
I WISH I WAS IN
DIXIE'S LAND
Written and Composed expressly for
Bryant's Minstrels
BY
DAN. D. EMMETT.
Arranged for the Pianoforte by
W. L. HOBBS.
SONG.
VARIATIONS.
Boston: OLIVER DITSON & CO.

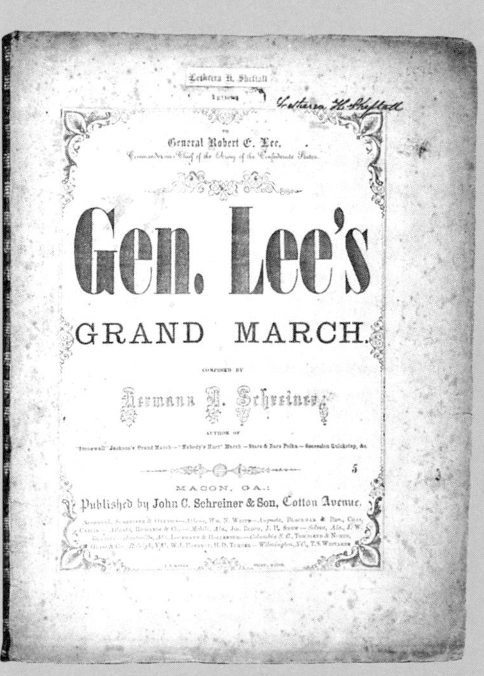
General Robert E. Lee,
Gen. Lee's
GRAND MARCH.
COMPOSED BY
Hermann L. Schreiner
MACON, GA.:
Published by John C. Schreiner & Son, Cotton Avenue.

C S Army—R N Andrews.
J B Jackson, Albany—Fla. Conference.
J W Traywick, Chaplain C S Army.

TERRIBLE EFFECTS OF THE COTTON FAMINE IN ENGLAND.

Quarter of a Million of People in one District out of Work, and Living on Charity.

We give herewith, from our latest English files, some information concerning the nature and extent of the suffering in the cotton man-

Southern wharves—like these at Charleston, photographed shortly after the war—were kept free of cotton by the Confederacy in hopes of encouraging foreign intervention. "Keep every bale of cotton on the plantation," the Memphis *Argus* urged its readers. "Don't send a thread to New Orleans or Memphis till England and France have recognized the Confederacy—not one thread."

Though with the North we sympathize,
It must not be forgotten
That with the South we've stronger ties,
Which are composed of cotton,
Whereof our imports mount unto
A sum of many figures
And where would be our calico
Without the toil of niggers?

To create a still greater scarcity—and to encourage southern farmers to produce the food the North now denied them—the Confederates cut back on growing cotton and burned two and a half million bales to keep it from falling into Federal hands. A young Louisiana woman watched the conflagration on the docks at New Orleans.

April 26 . . . We went this morning to see the cotton burning—a sight never before witnessed and probably never again to be seen. Wagons, drays—everything that can be driven or rolled—were loaded with the bales and taken to burn on the commons. Negroes were running around, cutting them open, piling them up, and setting them afire. All were as busy as though their salvation depended on disappointing the Yankees.

Eventually, 400,000 British mill workers were driven from their jobs, starved of southern cotton.

Union officers enjoy the well-kept grounds of John E. Seabrook's abandoned plantation on Edisto Island.

Federal treasury agents (above) supervise the sorting of confiscated cotton at Hilton Head, while Miss Kate Foote (right), a Connecticut volunteer sent south by the New England Freedman's Aid Society, tutors former slaves.

NOBLE WORK

"Here I am," Lieutenant Charles Francis Adams, Jr., wrote home from the Sea Islands in 1862, "surrounded by troopers, missionaries, contrabands, cotton fields and serpents, in a summer climate, disgusted with all things military and fighting off malaria with whiskey and tobacco. No man seems to realize that here, in this little island, all around us, has begun the solution of the tremendous 'nigger' question. . . . Some ten thousand former slaves are thrown upon the hands of the unfortunate government; they are the forerunners of hundreds of thousands more."

When Union forces seized parts of the South Carolina coast, plantation owners fled, leaving behind empty houses and thousands of slaves. Missionaries, teachers, and other volunteers soon arrived to help the newly liberated make their first adjustments to freedom. "We have come to do anti-slavery work," one teacher wrote. "We think it noble work, and will do it nobly."

"Although the war has not been waged against slavery," Secretary of State William Seward noted in the spring of 1862, "yet the army acts . . . as an emancipating crusade."

THE PENINSULA

"I will bring you now face to face with the rebels . . ." George McClellan told his great army before setting out at last for the Peninsula on March 17. "I am to watch over you as a parent over his children; and you know that your general loves you from the depths of his heart. It shall be my care . . . to gain success with the least possible loss."

Montgomery Meigs organized the great flotilla of 400 vessels that took three weeks to ferry the Army of the Potomac to Fortress Monroe: 121,500 men, 14,592 horses and mules, 1,150 wagons, 44 batteries of artillery, 74 ambulances, pontoon bridges, tons of provisions, tents, telegraph wire.

Once ashore, McClellan made slow progress. Maps proved inadequate. Roads he was sure would be bone-dry turned out to be bogs. Rivers supposed to run parallel to his columns cut across them and had to be forded.

On April 5, the Union advance guard reached Yorktown, where the Confederates had built earthworks on top of positions abandoned eighty years before, when the British surrendered to George Washington and ended the Revolution that North and South now each claimed as its own. "How many pleasing recollections crowd upon the mind of each soldier as he walks over these grounds," a Texas chaplain wrote. "The patriots of the Revolution were struggling for Liberty, and so are we."

There were just eleven thousand southern troops dug in at Yorktown, no match for McClellan's mighty army. But the Confederate commander was John Bankhead Magruder, a showy Virginian whose expensive tastes had earned him the nickname "Prince John," and who loved amateur theatrics—during the Mexican War he had staged a performance of *Othello* in which young Ulysses S. Grant, dressed in crinolines, had tried out for Desdemona.

He now outdid himself as an impresario. To convince McClellan that his small force was enormous, he kept up a sporadic, widely scattered artillery barrage, ordered his bandsmen to play loudly after dark, and paraded one battalion in and out of a clearing in an endless circle until it seemed to Union observers a mighty host. "This morning we were called out by the 'Long Roll,'" a weary Alabama corporal wrote that night, "and have been traveling most of the day, seeming with no other view than to show ourselves to the enemy at as many different points of the line as possible. I am pretty tired."

The charade worked. "It seems clear that I shall have the whole force of the enemy on my hands," McClellan telegraphed Washington, "probably not less than 100,000 men, and possibly more." He called for reinforcements and proposed to conduct "the more tedious but sure operations of siege."

Lincoln urged him to press forward: "I think you had better break the enemy's line . . . at once. By delay the enemy will relatively gain on you. . . . It is indispensable to you that you strike a blow. . . . The country will not fail to note—is now noting—that the present hesitation to move upon an entrenched enemy is but the story of Manassas repeated. . . . I have never written you . . . in greater kindness of feeling than now, nor with a fuller purpose to sustain you. . . . *But you must act.*"

McClellan ignored him: "The President very coolly telegraphed me . . . that

"The whole region seems literally filled with soldiery. One of the finest armies ever marshalled on the globe now wakes up these long stagnant fields and woods. General McClellan is here, and commands in person."

THE REVEREND A. M. STEWART
102nd Pennsylvania

Federal ordnance meant for McClellan's army on the Peninsula piles up at Ship Point near Yorktown. An Englishman who watched the Union fleet ferry men and supplies for the invasion of Virginia pronounced it "the stride of a giant."

Federal troops employ two of Professor Thaddeus Lowe's horse-drawn hydrogen generators to inflate his observation balloon, the *Intrepid* (above left); then, firmly tethered against errant winds, Lowe himself rises to survey enemy positions.

he thought I had better break the enemy's lines at once," he told his wife. "I was much tempted to reply that he had better come and do it himself."

McClellan dug in instead, urging his men to build ever more impressive earthworks, sending Professor Thaddeus Lowe into the sky to peer over the Confederate ramparts from his observation balloon, complaining to his wife, defending himself to his superiors. "Do not misunderstand the apparent inaction. Not a day, *not an hour,* has been lost. Works have been constructed that may almost be called gigantic."

"All talk and no fight," a rebel soldier wrote. "*Ditching* all the time. I think if we had fewer ditches and more stonewalls it would be better for us, though I'd rather dig ditches than fight in them. I don't see the sense of piling up earth to keep us apart. If we don't get at each other some time, when will the war end? My plan would be to quit ditching and go to fighting."

Confederate General Joseph E. Johnston, whose army had now had time to move onto the Peninsula, rode down from Richmond and could not believe his luck. "*No one* but McClellan could have hesitated to attack," he said.

SHILOH

On Sunday morning, April 6, 1862, as the ditching continued in front of Yorktown, 42,000 Union troops under U. S. Grant were encamped in wooded ravines on the west side of the Tennessee River near Pittsburg Landing, Tennessee. They had been there almost a month, waiting for General Don Carlos Buell and his Army of the Ohio to join them. Then, together, the two armies were to plunge into the heart of Mississippi.

It had been cold and wet at first, and there had been a good deal of dysentery in the Union camp; the men called it "the Tennessee Two-Step."

Twenty-two miles inland, at Corinth, where rebel troops suffering from the same malady called it "the evacuation of Corinth," the commander of the western department of the Confederate army saw no reason to wait for Grant's reinforcements to arrive. He was Albert Sidney Johnston, the handsome fifty-eight-year-old Kentuckian whom Jefferson Davis and U. S. Grant

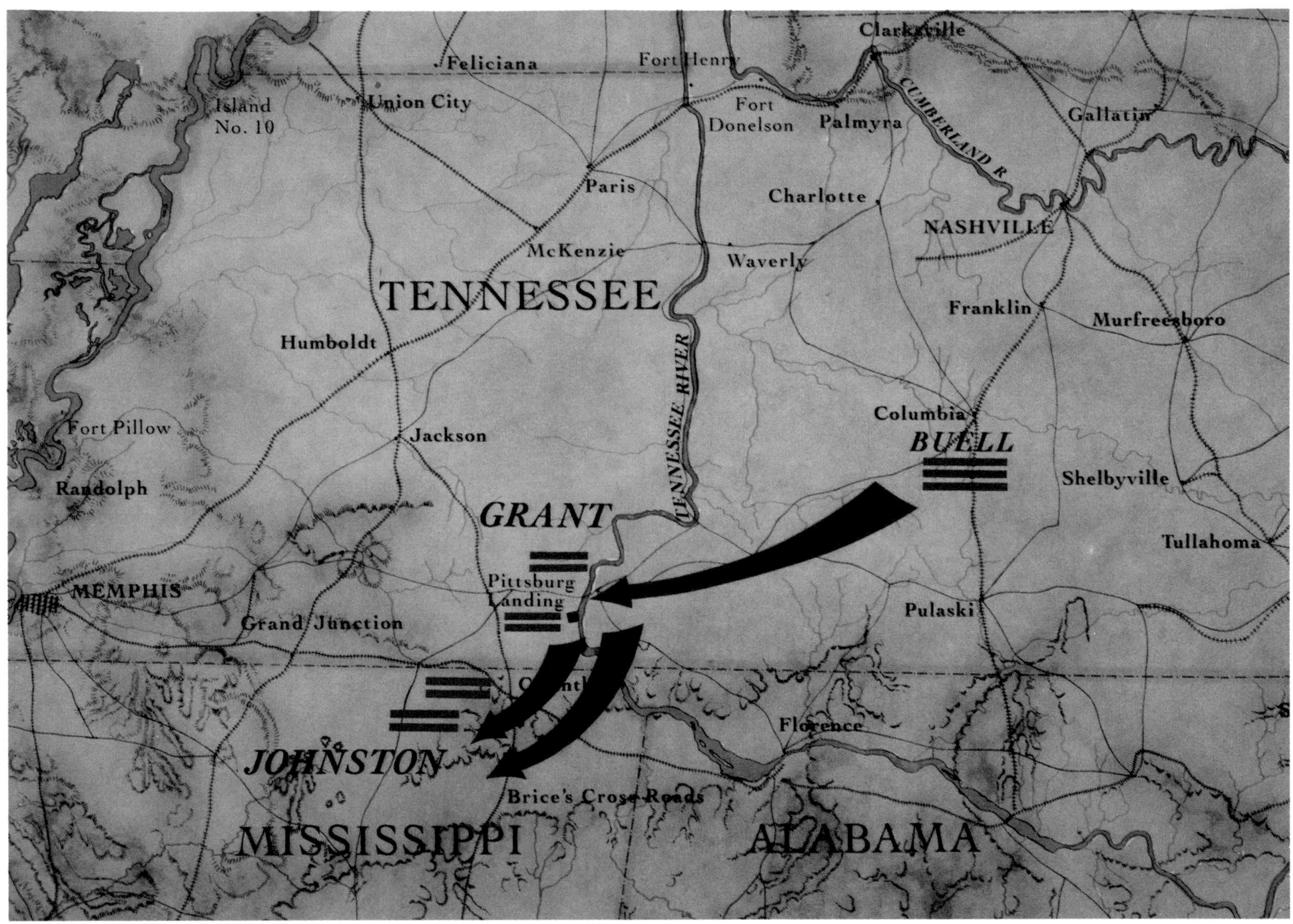

U. S. Grant deploys at Pittsburg Landing in southern Tennessee: By late March 1862, Grant was waiting for Don Carlos Buell and his Army of the Ohio so that their two armies could advance together into Mississippi. But Albert Sidney Johnston and his Confederates were at Corinth, just twenty-two miles away.

both believed the ablest soldier in the Confederacy. The thing to do, Johnston said, was attack Grant before Buell got there.

He moved his army north, over the objections of his second-in-command, General Beauregard, the victor of Fort Sumter and Bull Run, who worried that Grant would see and hear them coming. Johnston scoffed: "I would fight them if they were a million," he said.

Beauregard reluctantly drew up a plan of divided attack, based upon Napoleon's advance on Waterloo, and the Confederate army began to move.

"Tonight we will water our horses in the Tennessee River," Johnston told his staff officers on the morning of April 6, only a mile or so from the unsuspecting Federal camps.

"It was a most beautiful morning . . ." Private Leander Stilwell of the 100th Indiana remembered. "It really seemed like Sunday in the country at home. The boys were scattered around [camp] . . . polishing and brightening their muskets and brushing up and cleaning their shoes, jackets, [and] trousers."

At about 9:30, the Confederates opened fire, then charged into the advance Union camps. Sam Watkins was among them: "The order was given for the

Federal artillerymen and the battery of twenty-four-pound siege guns with which they helped stave off federal disaster in front of Pittsburg Landing at the end of the first day at Shiloh.

whole army to advance," he recalled. "The fire opened—a ripping, roaring, boom bang! The air was full of balls and deadly missiles. The litter corps was carrying off the dead and wounded. . . . 'Well, boys, we are *driving* 'em.'"

"As I rose from the comfortable log from behind which a bunch of us had been firing," Private Stilwell wrote later, "I saw men in gray and brown clothes, running through the camp on our right, and I saw something else, too . . . a gaudy sort of thing with red bars . . . a Rebel flag."

Brigadier General William Tecumseh Sherman, who had shaken off the melancholy that had sent him home that winter, was encamped with his Ohioans on a hill not far from a little Methodist church built of logs and named Shiloh. The 6th Mississippi rushed at them up that hill: of the 425 men who started up only 100 made it to the top. But the Union soldiers fell back along most of their line.

The Confederates had not eaten for twenty-four hours, and when they reached the northern camps, they stopped their advance long enough to paw through knapsacks, loot tents, and eat abandoned breakfasts. After they had moved on, thousands of dollars in Federal greenbacks were left blowing across the encampments; the rebels thought them worthless.

Beauregard, wearing a bright red cap, moved his personal effects into Sherman's own deserted tent, then stepped onto a nearby stump to see the fighting better. It extended along a three-mile front.

Eight out of ten men on both sides had never before been in combat. A veteran of Fort Donelson tried to rally his Illinois farm boys: "Why, it's just like shooting squirrels, only these squirrels have guns, that's all."

Beauregard's own men, the Orleans Guards, wore bright blue uniforms. At one point, thinking they were Union troops, their fellow Confederates fired on them, and they returned the fire. When ordered to stop shooting at their friends, the colonel of the Guards only reluctantly agreed: "Damn it, sir, we

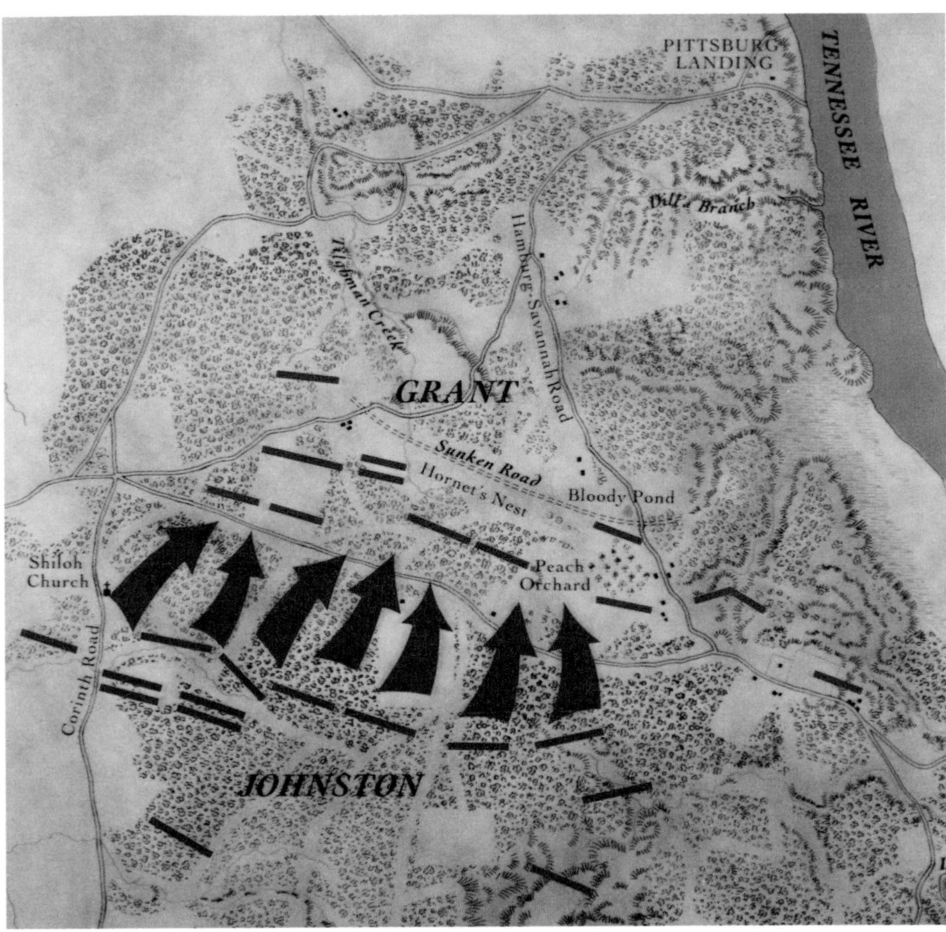

The Battle of Shiloh begins: On the morning of April 6, 1862, Confederates commanded by Albert Sidney Johnston (above) roared into Grant's encampment around Pittsburg Landing, beginning the bloodiest battle of the war. It would be remembered by the name of the little whitewashed church around which some of the fiercest early fighting swirled—Shiloh, a Hebrew word meaning "place of peace." Johnston was a special favorite of the Confederate President: "I hoped and expected that I had others who would prove generals," Jefferson Davis remembered, "but I knew I had one, and that was Sidney Johnston."

fire upon *everybody* who fires on us!" (Later, when they wore their jackets inside out to show the white lining, their own commander would mistake them for someone else's brigade.)

"I reckon this is going to be a great battle, such as I have been anxious to see for a long time," one of Sherman's men remembered thinking as the rebels came on, "and I think I have seen *enough* of it." Thousands of green Federal troops did see enough—and ran. A disgusted sergeant from Iowa recalled a soldier who fled past him, shouting, "'Give them hell, boys. *I* gave them hell as long as I could.' Whether he really had given them any of *the sulphurous* . . . I cannot say, but assuredly he had given them everything else he possessed, including his gun, cartridge-box, coat and hat."

One officer was found hiding with two of his men inside a big hollow log. Most stragglers did not stop running until they reached the river, and a few even tried to swim to safety on the other side. The rest—perhaps five thousand men before the day had ended—cowered beneath the bluff. When an officer exhorted a group of them to return to the fight, they applauded his eloquence—and ducked still lower. Grant believed that "most of them would have been shot where they lay, without resistance, before they would have taken muskets and marched to the front."

Confederates ran, too, and Sam Watkins remembered seeing a private named Smith step deliberately out of the ranks and shoot his finger off to keep out of the fight.

Still, by late morning, Johnston believed victory was his: "We are sweeping the field," he told Beauregard, "and I think we shall press them to the river."

But a thin Federal line was still holding in the center, Illinois and Iowa farmers mostly, lying behind the thickets that grew along a sunken road. A dozen massive Confederate assaults were launched against them and were hurled back. One Union man remembered the Confederates who kept coming at them as "maddened demons"; another said it had "seemed almost barbarous to fire on brave men pressing forward so heroically to the mouth of hell." Survivors of the fighting here would remember it as "the Hornets' Nest."

More hard fighting took place in a peach orchard to the left of the Sunken Road, where the Federals lay flat beneath the blossoming trees, firing as the rebels came, soft pink petals raining down on the living and the dead.

Johnston himself led the last charge into the orchard, riding his horse Fire-Eater. The Union men broke, and an exultant Johnston returned to his lines; several bullets had nicked his uniform and one had cut his boot sole in half. "They didn't trip me up that time," he told an aide. But another Union bullet had cut an artery behind his knee and his boot filled with blood. He was too absorbed in the fighting to pay attention until he suddenly reeled in the saddle. Aides lifted him gently down. An officer bent over him, asking if Johnston recognized him. He did not, and died at about 2:30 in the afternoon. His aides did their best to conceal what had happened. "Advancing a little further," Sam Watkins recalled, "we saw General Albert Sidney Johnston surrounded by his staff and Governor Harris of Tennessee. We saw some little commotion among those who surrounded him, but we did not know at the time that he was dead. The fact was kept from the troops."

The loss would grieve Jefferson Davis. "Without doing injustice to the living," he would tell his people, "it may safely be asserted that our loss is irreparable; and that among the shining hosts of the great and good who now cluster around the banner of our country, there exists no purer spirit, no more heroic soul, than that of the illustrious man whose death I join you in lamenting."

Command at Shiloh passed to Beauregard.

The Union men still defending the Hornets' Nest were under an Illinois politician, General Benjamin Prentiss, who took with deadly seriousness Grant's order to "maintain that position at all costs." His line bent back upon itself but did not break. Confederates now surrounded his men on three sides. Sixty-two guns were brought to bear upon the sunken road, the largest concentration of artillery yet assembled in an American war, and the order to fire was given. The rain of shells splintered trees, boulders, men; an Iowa lieutenant remembered it as "a mighty hurricane sweeping everything before it."

Finally, at 5:30, Prentiss and the 2,200 survivors of his division surrendered. They had held up the center of the southern advance for nearly six hours.

It was growing dark. The Confederates had been on the move for twelve hours and had pushed the Yankees back two miles. Beauregard wired President Davis that he had won "a complete victory." "I had General Grant

Drummer boy John Clem of the 12th Michigan, just ten years old, became celebrated as "Johnny Shiloh" after an artillery shell smashed his instrument during that battle. During the Federal retreat at Chickamauga in 1863, he would shoot a Confederate who dared try to take the artillery caisson upon which he was riding, and win himself new headlines as "the Drummer Boy of Chickamauga." He remained in the army all his active life and retired as a major general shortly before the First World War.

The meandering path (right) led to the Hornets' Nest, where Union troops (above) under Brigadier General Benjamin M. Prentiss held out for six hours, withstanding a dozen rebel assaults and point-blank artillery fire before surrendering—and thereby turned near-certain defeat into a standoff. "Captain, give me a gun!" shouted a wounded Union soldier who had returned to the fighting after being ordered to the rear. "This durn fight ain't got any rear!"

Union steamboats at Pittsburg Landing a few days after they had arrived with the reinforcements that saved Grant's army from disaster. At right is the *Tycoon,* dispatched by the Cincinnati Sanitary Commission to help care for the wounded. Tied up next to her is the *Tigress,* Grant's floating headquarters.

"Now those Yankees were whipped, fairly whipped, and according to all the rules of war they ought to have retreated. But they didn't."

SAM WATKINS

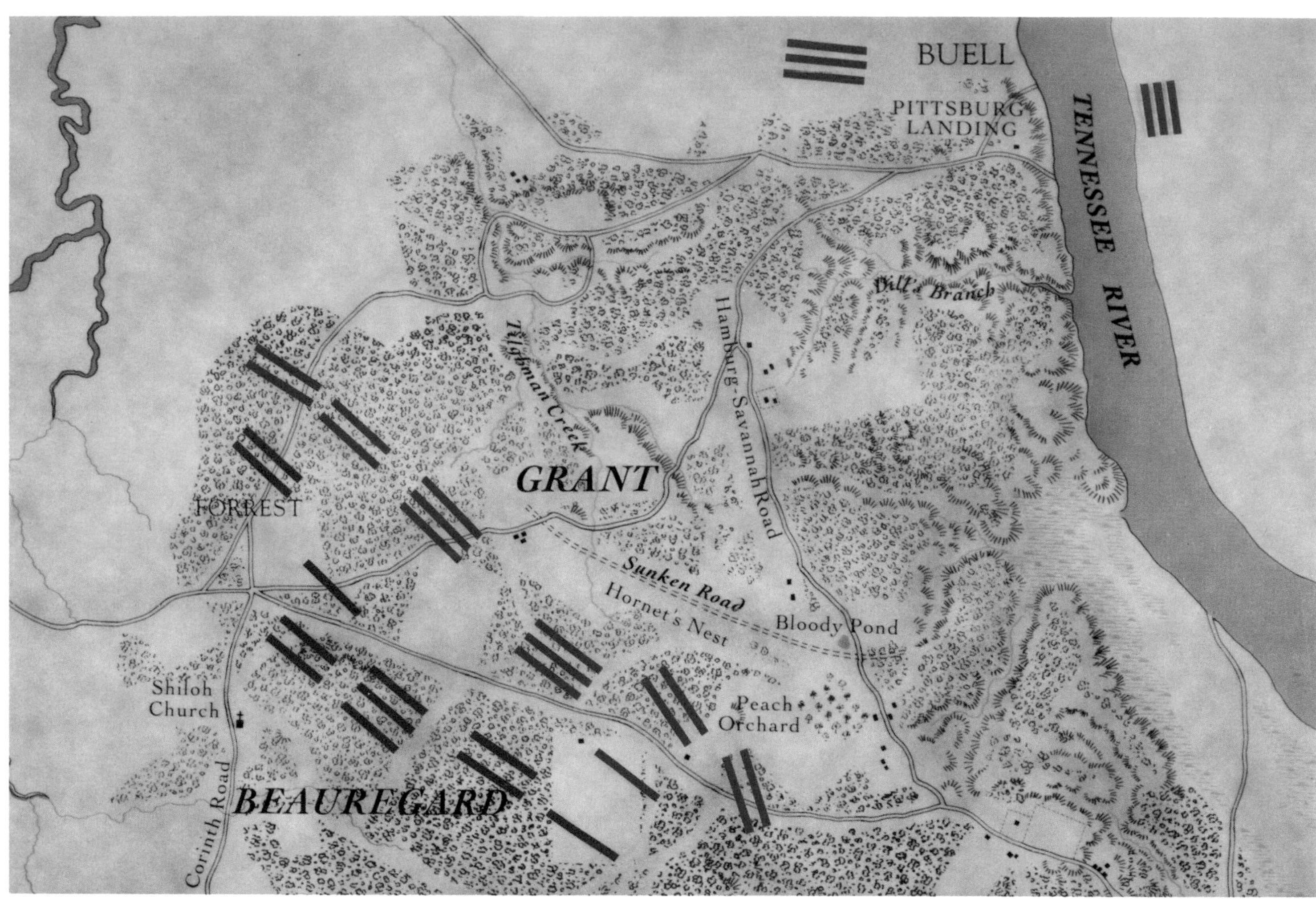

The tide turns on the second day at Shiloh: On April 7, Grant's army—now heavily reinforced by the last-minute arrival of Don Carlos Buell's fresh troops—counterattacked, driving the weary, outnumbered Confederates from the field.

just where I wanted him," he remembered thinking, "and could finish him up in the morning."

"Now those Yankees were whipped, fairly whipped," Sam Watkins said, "and according to all the rules of war they ought to have retreated. But they didn't."

Federal gunboats lobbed shells into the Confederate camps all night. Wounded men lay everywhere; neither army yet had a system for gathering or caring for them in the field. "Some cried for water," a Union veteran remembered years later, "others for someone to come and help them. I can hear those poor fellows crying for water. . . . God heard them, for the heavens opened and the rain came." Scores of wounded men collapsed and died while drinking from a mud hole near the Peach Orchard, reddening its water and giving it the name Bloody Pond.

Flashes of lightning showed hogs feeding on the ungathered dead.

That night Sherman, who had been wounded twice and had had three horses shot from under him, came upon the Union commander taking shelter from the rain under a tree. Grant planned to sleep there, rather than listen to the screams of the wounded who filled his headquarters.

"Well, Grant," Sherman said. "We've had the devil's own day, haven't we?"

"Yes," Grant answered. "Yes. Lick 'em tomorrow."

Finally, Buell's Army of the Ohio began to arrive, 25,000 fresh Union troops. "Never to me was the sight of reinforcing legions so . . . welcome," wrote Private Stilwell, "as on that Sunday evening when . . . Buell's advance column deployed on the bluffs of Pittsburg Landing." The first northern units disembarked to "Dixie."

General Henry Wager Halleck, commander of the Department of Missouri, of whom Ulysses S. Grant once said, "It was very much easier for him to excuse a favor than to grant one."

At dawn the next day, the Federal force, now some 50,000 strong, attacked Beauregard's 30,000 weary troops. The Confederates fell back, counterattacked, fell back, firing as they went. By late afternoon, Beauregard decided to withdraw to Corinth.

Confederate cavalry was assigned to cover the retreat, led by Bedford Forrest, and when Sherman spotted Forrest's men he sent skirmishers scrambling after them, into a belt of fallen trees. Forrest ordered one last charge, swinging his saber and galloping headlong into the Union troops, only to discover that his men were not following him. Caught in a swarm of blue uniforms, Forrest whirled, slashing at the Yankees who tried to stop him, and was hit in the back by a musket ball. Despite the shock and pain, he managed to lean down and haul a trooper across his saddle to serve as a shield as he galloped away. Once out of range, he hurled his terrified protector aside and rode on toward Corinth.

The battlefield was littered with corpses, laid so thickly in some places, Grant remembered, "it would have been possible to walk across the clearing in any direction stepping on dead bodies without a foot touching the ground." A Union captain found a wounded rebel "covered with clotted blood, pillowing his head on the dead body of a comrade. The first thing he said to me was, '. . . Oh, God! What made you come down here to fight us? We never would have come up there.'"

Hastily organized burial details set to work. "When the grave was ready," a member of one recalled, "we placed the bodies therein, two deep. All the monument reared to those brave men was a board upon which I cut with my pocket knife the words '125 rebels.' We buried our Union boys in a separate trench and on another board cut '35 Union.'"

One hundred thousand men fought at Shiloh. Nearly one in four was a casualty. Three thousand four hundred and seventy-seven men died, more than all the Americans who died in all the battles of the Revolution, the War of 1812, and the war with Mexico, combined.

Grant, who would now be denounced as a butcher, understood the terrible meaning of those losses.

> Up to the battle of Shiloh I, as well as thousands of other citizens, believed that the rebellion against the Government would collapse suddenly and soon if a decisive victory could be gained over any of its armies . . . but [afterward] I gave up all idea of saving the Union except by *complete conquest.*

Grant's reward for this costly triumph was the loss of his command. His earlier victory at Fort Donelson had already earned him the jealous enmity of his superior, General Halleck, who spread the rumor that he had been drinking. Now, Halleck had Grant reassigned, assumed field command of the

A Union cavalry trooper.

OUR BOY

"A man's conceit dwindles," a Maine private wrote, "when he crawls into an unteasled shirt, trousers too short and baggy behind, coat too long at both ends and a cap as shapeless as a feedbag. . . . A photograph of any one of them, covered with yellow dust or mosaics of mud, could ornament [any mantel, North or South] as a true picture of 'Our Boy.'"

The average age of a soldier in either army was twenty-five. The minimum age for enlistment was eighteen, but recruiting officers were not particular. Drummer boys as young as nine signed on. Charles E. King, musician in Company F, 49th Pennsylvania Volunteers, was twelve when he enlisted, and thought to be the youngest combat soldier in the war. He would be killed at Antictam.

Two out of three Confederate soldiers were farmers or farmers' sons. So were half the Union men, and a quarter of them were foreign-born.

A New York chaplain wrote home about his unit:

Almost every known trade, profession or calling has its representatives in our regiment, tailors, carpenters, masons, and plasterers, moulders and glassblowers, puddlers and rollers, machinists and architects, printers, bookbinders, and publishers, gentlemen of leisure, politicians, merchants, legislators, judges, lawyers, doctors, preachers. Some malicious fellow might ask the privilege of completing the catalogue by naming jailbirds, idlers, loafers, drunkards, and gamblers—but we beg his pardon and refuse the license.

The average soldier was 5 feet, 8¼ inches tall and weighed 143½ pounds. A third of the southern soldiers could neither read nor write. The chance of dying in combat was one in 65. One in 10 would be wounded. One in 13 would die of disease.

"War," wrote Lieutenant Oliver Wendell Holmes, Jr., "is an organized bore." A Pennsylvania private agreed: "The first thing in the morning is drill. Then drill, then drill again. Then drill, drill, a little more drill, then drill, lastly drill."

The soldiers' diet was no more appealing. Union troops were issued beans, bacon, pickled beef—called "salt horse" by the

A regimental cook feeds bandsmen of the 3rd New Hampshire.

The drum corps of the 93rd New York Infantry.

men—"desiccated compressed mixed vegetables," a dried cake that yielded a thin soup when crumbled into boiling water. And, inevitably, hardtack—square flour-and-water biscuits so hard, some said, they could stop bullets. "It was no uncommon occurrence," a Union veteran remembered, "for a man to find the surface of his pot of coffee swimming with weevils after breaking up hardtack in it . . . but they were easily skimmed off and left no distinctive flavor behind."

In the southern army, the men favored something called "sloosh," cornmeal swirled in bacon grease, then wrapped around a ramrod and cooked over the campfire. "Tell Ma that I think of her beans and collards often and wish for some," a southern private wrote to his sister. "But wishing does no good."

Coffee was the preferred drink of both armies. Union troops crushed the beans with their rifle butts, drank four pints of it a day, "strong enough to float an iron wedge," and when they could not build a fire were content to chew the grounds. Southerners often made do with substitutes brewed from peanuts, potatoes, chicory.

The American talent for improvisation turned quickly to improving camp life. "All the appliances of home life which are possible . . . are being introduced into our encampment," a New York chaplain reported. ". . . A weekly newspaper, a photographic establishment . . . a temperance league [and a] Christian Association. . . . We have a post office, letter box, postmaster and mail carrier. Our boys write vastly more letters than they receive. . . . You can hardly imagine the eagerness with which the mailman . . . is looked for, the delight on the reception of a letter, the sadness, sometimes even to tears, with which those who are disappointed turn away."

Regiments ran their own lending libraries, staged theatricals, built churches, kept menageries of pets and mascots, bought delicacies from licensed sutlers, whose tents were often known as "Robbers Row." They debated the great issues of the day: "Resolved: That we should Support the Union as It is and as It Will Be," and "Which Has the Most Influence on Men, to Wit: Money or Women?"

A Confederate private.

Federal troops line up for a rare delicacy.

A Union barber sets up shop outdoors.

army himself, and started for Corinth, just twenty-two miles away. It took him a full month to cover that distance—stopping early every day to throw up giant fortifications against rebel attacks that never came. When the Union troops finally reached the town, Beauregard and his men had gone. "Corinth was not captured," wrote General Lew Wallace, "it was abandoned to us. At dawn of May 30th we marched into its deserted works, getting nothing— . . . not a sick prisoner, not a rusty bayonet, not a bite of bacon—nothing but an empty town and some Quaker guns."

Following this dubious victory, Halleck was named general-in-chief of the Federal armies. Grant, disgusted, decided to resign and go home. Sherman talked him out of it. "You could not be quiet at home for a week," he said, "when armies are moving." Grant and Sherman trusted each other. They were both Ohio men and West Pointers, who relished cigars and scorned pomp and politics. Grant enjoyed Sherman's rapid-fire brilliance and was grateful for the dispatch with which he carried out every order. Sherman admired his friend's cool temper, his steadiness in the midst of crisis, and what he called Grant's "simple faith in success."

When fellow southerners tried to persuade David G. Farragut before the war that his duty lay with the Confederacy, he was unmoved: "Mind what I tell you," he said. "You fellows will catch the devil before you get through with this business."

NEW ORLEANS

No success of the sort in which Grant stubbornly believed would be possible unless the North could seize the Mississippi and cut the Confederacy in two. In the spring of 1862, Union fleets attacked southern strongholds on the river, north and south.

On April 7, the second day of Shiloh, Union gunboats and twenty thousand troops under John Pope together took the Confederate fortress at Island Number 10, near New Madrid, Missouri, leaving the river open as far south as Memphis. On June 6, Union vessels blasted their way through a Confederate fleet and subdued that city, too, as thousands of spectators watched from shore.

Meanwhile, another fleet of twenty-four ships, commanded by a sixty-year-old flag officer, David G. Farragut, was ordered to sail up the river and seize New Orleans, the South's largest city and busiest port. Farragut had been a sailor all his life. Adopted as a boy by David Porter, the naval hero of the War of 1812, he had been placed in command of a captured British ship at twelve. But because he had lived in Virginia before the war and had a southern wife, his loyalty to the Union had been questioned. The New Orleans assignment was a personal vindication. "I have now attained what I have been looking for all my life," he said, "—a flag—and having attained it, all that is necessary to complete the scene is a victory. If I die in the attempt it will only be what every officer has to expect."

The Confederates did all they could to make things hard for him. To reach the city, Farragut's ships had to get past Forts Jackson and St. Philip, thick-walled structures with a line of hulks stretched across the river between them, meant to stall northern ships within range of southern guns. "Nothing afloat could pass the forts," a New Orleans citizen remembered believing, and "Nothing that walked could get through our swamps."

Commander David Dixon Porter, Farragut's ambitious younger foster

Farragut's fleet storms past Forts Jackson (left) and St. Phillip: "[T]hey opened a tremendous fire on us . . ." a lieutenant aboard the Federal gunboat *Cayuga* remembered. "The air was filled with shells and explosions which almost blinded me as I stood on the forecastle, trying to see my way."

brother, thought he had the answer. He proposed that a flotilla of small sailing vessels, each bearing a huge mortar capable of firing a thirteen-inch shell, be anchored below the forts to pound them into dust in advance of the fleet.

But when, after six days of steady battering, the first fort remained intact, Farragut decided on a more daring scheme. Under cover of darkness he would run past the forts, smash through the barricade and head for New Orleans itself.

Two Union gunboats slipped below the forts at night to cut loose some of the hulks that blocked the passage. Then, at two o'clock in the morning of April 24, Farragut's warships started past the forts. The moon rose and the Confederates opened fire. The first vessel was hit forty-two times. Porter's guns answered as best they could.

"The passing of the forts . . ." Farragut remembered, "was one of the most awful sights and events I ever saw or expect to experience . . . [it] seemed as if all the artillery of heaven were playing upon the earth." His flagship, the *Hartford,* was set ablaze and ran aground beneath the Confederate guns. "It looked that only a miracle could save her," a sailor remembered. "The engines, backing with all their power, could not relieve her, in flames from water to masthead . . . the crew in a death struggle with the flames, heat and smoke."

Farragut's crew managed finally to put out the fire and get the *Hartford* moving again, and within an hour and a half all but four of his ships made it past the forts.

BENJAMIN BUTLER AT NEW ORLEANS

Lincoln named Benjamin F. Butler military governor of occupied New Orleans. Butler had already subdued Baltimore for the Union, and saw no need to be gentler with New Orleans. "[T]hey shall fear the stripes if they do not reverence the stars in our banner," he said.

Butler hanged a man suspected of having desecrated the American flag, from the window of the U.S. mint from which he had torn it down. He closed a secessionist newspaper, confiscated the property of citizens who refused to swear allegiance to the Union—and earned the scornful nickname "Spoons" for allegedly pocketing silverware in the process.

New Orleans women insulted Butler's troops in the street, calling them names and disdainfully pulling their skirts aside. When a woman in the French Quarter leaned out her window and emptied the contents of her chamber pot over Admiral Farragut's head, Butler issued General Order Number 28.

As the Officers and Soldiers of the United States have been subject to repeated insults from the women calling themselves ladies of New Orleans, in return for the most scrupulous non-interference and courtesy on our part, it is ordered that hereafter when any female shall, by word, gesture, or movement, insult or show contempt for any officer or soldier of the United States, she shall be regarded and held liable to be treated as a woman of the town, plying her avocation.

Southern chivalry was aroused: "Men of the South!" demanded General Beauregard, himself a proud Louisianan. "Shall our mothers, our wives, our daughters and our sisters be thus outraged by the ruffianly soldiers of the North, to whom is given the right to treat, at their pleasure, the ladies of the South as common harlots?" Confederate sympathizers in Britain were equally offended. "Any Englishman," declared the British Prime Minister, Lord Palmerston, "must blush to think that such an act has been committed by one belonging to the Anglo-Saxon race."

Butler was given a new nickname—"Beast"—but he refused to back down. The harassment of his men stopped, and no woman was ever arrested.

In New Orleans, just as he had in Maryland, Ben Butler swiftly turned the friction between masters and slaves to Union advantage, declaring the planters disloyal to the Union and their slaves therefore "manumitted & emancipated." Blacks thronged off the plantations and into the Union lines. "The Yankees have taken Negroes off all the places below Omega," a planter's wife wrote, "the Negroes generally going most willingly, being promised their freedom by the vandals." "Go to the Yankees," another slaveholder told his slaves. "They are kings here now."

"I was always a friend of southern rights," Butler said, "but an enemy of southern wrongs."

This equestrian statue of Andrew Jackson had already been standing for six years in Jackson Square at New Orleans, the city Old Hickory had saved from the British in 1815, when Benjamin Butler (right) became military governor, but he felt compelled to order carved into its pedestal a fresh Jacksonian slogan, calculated to enrage the citizenry: "The Union must and shall be preserved."

"I have been hearing so much about the Yankees I was very anxious to see them. The whites would tell their colored people not to go to the Yankees for they would harness them to carts and make them pull the carts around in place of horses. I asked Grandmother one day if this was true. She replied, 'Certainly not!' That the white people did not want slaves to go over to the Yankees, and told them these things to frighten them. I wanted to see those wonderful Yankees so much, as I heard my parents say that the Yankees were going to set all the slaves free."

SUSIE KING TAYLOR

As they approached New Orleans, a makeshift Confederate squadron of eight ships sailed out to meet them. Farragut sank six of them, and the city surrendered without firing a shot.

"New Orleans gone—and with it the Confederacy?" Mary Chesnut wrote. "Are we not cut in two? That Mississippi *ruins* us, if lost." The impact of the city's fall was felt across the Atlantic, too. "People here," wrote Henry Adams from London, "are quite struck aback at Sunday's news of the capture of New Orleans. It took them three days to make up their minds to believe it. The division of America had become an idea so fixed that they had about shut out all the avenues to the reception of any other."

Farragut became a northern hero and America's first rear admiral. The North now controlled the southern Mississippi and had a base from which to launch expeditions into the Deep South, but it did not yet possess the whole river. Vicksburg, high on a bluff four hundred miles to the north, remained in Confederate hands. Farragut pushed part of his fleet as close to it as he could, taking Baton Rouge and Natchez as he went, but he quickly realized the pretty little town was impregnable from the river: "Ships . . . cannot crawl up hills 300 feet high," he reported. An army would be required.

"Vicksburg," said Jefferson Davis, whose plantation was only a few miles upriver, "is the nailhead that [holds] the South's two halves together."

It would be U. S. Grant's next assignment to pull that nail.

QUESTIONS OF MONEY

"War is not a question of valor, but a question of money . . ." Congressman Roscoe Conkling of New York had said just eleven days after the Bull Run disaster. "It is not regulated by the laws of honor, but by the laws of trade. I understand [that] the practical problem to be solved in crushing the rebellion of despotism against representative government is who can throw the most projectiles? Who can afford the most iron or lead?"

To help ensure that it was the North that could, Congress enacted the first income tax, established the first national banking system, and began printing up the first national currency—called "greenbacks." It also passed an Internal Revenue Act, said to be a tax on "everything."

By the end of 1862, the Federal Government was spending $2.5 million a day on the war.

Meanwhile, Congress awarded public lands to homesteaders, and to railroaders seeking to lay track for a transcontinental line—Lincoln hoped to take the train west to California himself, once he had left the presidency. The Morrill Act gave states Federal lands on which to build colleges and universities.

Before the war, a trip to the local post office was the sole contact most Americans had with their national government; now it was becoming an increasingly important part of their daily lives.

Northern business grew alongside government, and government contracts provided businessmen with the quickest profits. Philip Armour gave up gold mining to strike it rich packing pork for the army. Jay Cooke, acting as government agent, sold war bonds, raised more than $400 million for the

Union—and got rich on the commissions. Samuel Colt of New Haven, Connecticut, continued to ship hundreds of his revolvers to the Confederacy until after the first battle of Bull Run, while maintaining contracts with the Union for 146,840 more. "Run the armory night and day with double sets of hands," he told his men. "I had rather have an accumulation of arms than to have money lying idle."

"Besides the army formed to act against the enemy, there was another army—of lobbyists, contractors, speculators, which was continually renewed and never exhausted."

GENERAL RÉGIS DE TROBRIAND

Unscrupulous contractors sold the War Department rusty rifles, boats that leaked, caps that melted in the rain—all at inflated prices. When one manufacturer was asked why the soles of the shoes he had supplied fell off after a few minutes' marching, he explained that they had been meant for the cavalry. "The world has seen its iron age, its silver age, its golden age and its [bronze] age," said the New York *Herald.* "This is the age of shoddy."

Southern industry grew, too, driven by necessity, and the Confederate government, established on the principle of decentralization, soon found itself supervising everything from the daily output of the women who spun cloth for uniforms in their parlors to the forging of cannon at the big Tredegar Iron Works at Richmond.

The man in charge was the chief of the Confederate Ordnance Bureau, General Josiah Gorgas, a West Pointer from a tiny Pennsylvania town called Running Pumps, who had married a wealthy Virginian and adopted his wife's state as his own. More than any other man, he kept the Confederate armies armed and supplied during four long years of war. Gorgas sent agents north to buy up and smuggle back what arms they could, dispatched others to Europe aboard blockade runners, and ensured that rebel soldiers collected Union arms from every battlefield on which they fought. One hundred thousand Union rifles were harvested in 1862 alone, an achievement hailed in the Macon *Daily Telegraph:*

> Want a weapon? Why capture one!
> Every Doodle has got a gun,
> Belt and bayonet, bright and new;
> Kill a Doodle, and capture two!

But Gorgas knew that smuggling and scavenging were not enough: if the Confederacy was to survive, it would have to find ways to arm itself. He supervised construction of arsenals, foundries, rolling mills; sought out supplies of pig iron, sulfur, saltpeter, and other materials needed for railroad track and weaponry; encouraged entrepreneurs to manufacture rifles and pistols. The Tredegar works alone managed to turn out 2,200 cannon.

The Confederacy's overseas sympathizers were suitably impressed. "There is no doubt," said William E. Gladstone, Britain's Chancellor of the Exchequer, "that Jefferson Davis and other leaders of the South have made an army; they are making, it appears, a navy, and they have made what is more than either—they have made a *nation.* We may anticipate with certainty the success of the Southern states."

But while the Confederate war machine expanded, the army it was supplying shrank. The term of enlistment of the earliest volunteers was up in the spring of 1862, and most men planned to go home.

The South's economy was traditionally based on the products of its fields and forests, such as the kegs of turpentine (above) here heaped on the dock at Wilmington, North Carolina, after the war. But by 1865 Confederate factories were capable of producing guns so large they required the giant sling-cart (right)—and a full complement of a dozen mules and 150 men—just to haul them into place.

And so, in April—with McClellan's vast army on Virginia soil and after the Confederate defeats at Donelson and Shiloh and New Orleans, and at Pea Ridge in Arkansas, where Union forces effectively ended southern hopes of taking Missouri—the Confederate Congress passed two laws at the insistence of Jefferson Davis: one extended all enlistments for the duration; the other required all able-bodied white men between the ages of eighteen and thirty-five to serve in the army for three years. It was the first draft in American history.

"From this time on till the end of the war," Sam Watkins wrote, "a soldier was simply a machine, a *conscript*. . . . All our pride and valor had gone, and we were sick of war and cursed the Southern Confederacy." Veterans like Watkins were especially resentful because wealthy draftees were allowed to pay substitutes to serve in their place, and men who owned twenty slaves or more were altogether exempt. "A law was made . . . about this time allowing every person who owned twenty negroes to go home," Watkins remembered. "It gave us the blues. We wanted twenty negroes. There was raised the howl of 'rich man's war, poor man's fight.'"

The Governors of Georgia and North Carolina vowed simply to ignore the law. "The Conscription Act," said Joseph E. Brown of Georgia, "at one fell swoop, strikes down the sovereignty of the States, tramples upon the constitutional rights and personal liberty of the citizens, and arms the President with imperial power."

To preserve itself, the South seemed to some to be destroying the principles that had propelled it out of the Union. Nearly half of those eligible for the new draft failed to sign up.

BEANPOLES AND CORNSTALKS

McClellan's army was the best-equipped in history. The productive capacity and technical ingenuity of America was now focused on weapons, and the Civil War would see the first railroad artillery, the first military telegraph and military railroads, the first land mines and telescopic sights and trench warfare.

The most important single innovation, however, was a French refinement—Captain Claude Minié's new bullet, an inch-long slug that expanded into the barrel's rifled grooves and spun at great speed from the muzzle. The spin allowed the ball to travel farther and far more accurately than musket balls fired from the smooth-barreled weapons with which many soldiers started off to war. The minié ball could kill at half a mile and was accurate at 250 yards—five times as far as any other one-man weapon—and it made defense five times as safe as assault.

Nine out of ten infantry assaults would fail during the Civil War. More than 90 percent of battle wounds were caused by bullets. The age of the bayonet had ended, though most officers did not yet know it when the war began—and some had still not learned it when the war was over.

General James W. Ripley, the Union Chief of Ordnance, was an old-fashioned artilleryman who thought most new weapons just made the problems of supply and standardization needlessly difficult. Abraham Lincoln disagreed. He was himself an amateur inventor, holder of a patent on a device to float boats that had run aground, and he was fascinated with gadgetry. If someone's scheme promised to shorten the war, he wanted to hear about it.

He was not universally receptive, however, passing up a plan to manufacture canoe-shaped footwear that was supposed to allow Federal troops to walk on water, tactfully turning down an offer from the King of Siam for a herd of war elephants, and quickly losing interest in one man's claims to being able to forecast the weather.

April 28. It seems to me Mr. Capen knows nothing about the weather in advance. He told me three days ago that it would not rain again till the 30th of April or the 1st of May. It is raining now & has been for ten hours. I can not spare any more time to Mr. Capen.

Lincoln encouraged the use of balloons for battlefield observation, personally tested new rifles at the War Department, and ordered up several "coffee-grinder" machine guns—though they never caught on in combat because line officers feared they would overheat and explode. And he delighted in the big splash eleven-inch shells made when fired into the Potomac by the great bottle-shaped Dahlgren guns at the navy yard.

Lincoln, who had been a railroad lawyer, also understood the crucial importance of railroads in moving men and matériel to and from the front. When railroad executives balked at cooperating with the war effort, he pushed through Congress a bill that authorized him to assume control of any line if the war warranted it.

Daniel McCallum, a dour sometime poet and engineer who had run the Erie Railroad, was made superintendent of captured southern lines; he began with just seven miles of Virginia track to oversee and ended the war with better

To arm, feed, clothe, supply, and transport hundreds of thousands of northern soldiers like these demanded prodigies of energy, ingenuity, and organization.

than 2,000—plus 419 locomotives, 17,000 railroad workers, and no one knows how many thousand captured cars.

Herman Haupt, an engineer trained at West Point, was McCallum's tireless assistant in the East, in charge of construction and repair. Cutting red tape and building bridges fast were his specialties. "That man Haupt has built a bridge across Potomac Creek," Lincoln said in wonder, "about four hundred feet long and nearly a hundred feet high, over which loaded trains are running every hour, and . . . there is nothing in it but beanpoles and cornstalks." Generals complained that Haupt was insufficiently obsequious, but his civilian superiors admired his ability to get things done. "Be as patient as possible with the generals," Secretary Stanton told him. "Some of them will trouble you more than they do the enemy."

Brigadier General Herman Haupt.

Machinery of war: Army engineers built the railroad bridge at top right across Potomac Creek in under forty hours. The roundhouse and workshop in the Baltimore & Ohio yards at Martinsburg, Virginia (center right), would soon be razed by Stonewall Jackson's Confederates, but nothing could stop northern factories from turning out ordnance for the Union (bottom right).

ON TO RICHMOND

On the Peninsula, the siege of Yorktown continued to drag on for almost a month, enlivened only by the occasional sharpshooter and a dozen Confederate artillery shells or so a day, lobbed at the Union observation balloon. One day, according to a northern reporter, "When about one hundred feet above the ground, the rope . . . broke and general [Fitz-John Porter] sailed off . . . toward Richmond at a greater speed than the Army of the Potomac is moving. He . . . had sufficient calmness to pull the valve rope, and gradually descended . . . about three miles from camp."

It rained two out of every three days. Hundreds fell ill. "Under the dry leaves where we encamp," a Union chaplain wrote, "a great secesh army of wood ticks have wintered. . . . Few [are] so happy as not to find half a dozen of these villainous bloodsuckers sticking in his flesh [every morning]."

By May 3, nearly a hundred Federal guns were at last in place before Yorktown, some so massive that it had taken a hundred horses to haul them into place. McClellan planned to begin his bombardment on the fifth. But that night the southern batteries suddenly intensified their fire. "From one end of

A Union soldier surveys Federal ships anchored in the York River from the summit of the Water Battery, the most formidable of the defenses abandoned by Joseph Johnston's Confederate army at Yorktown.

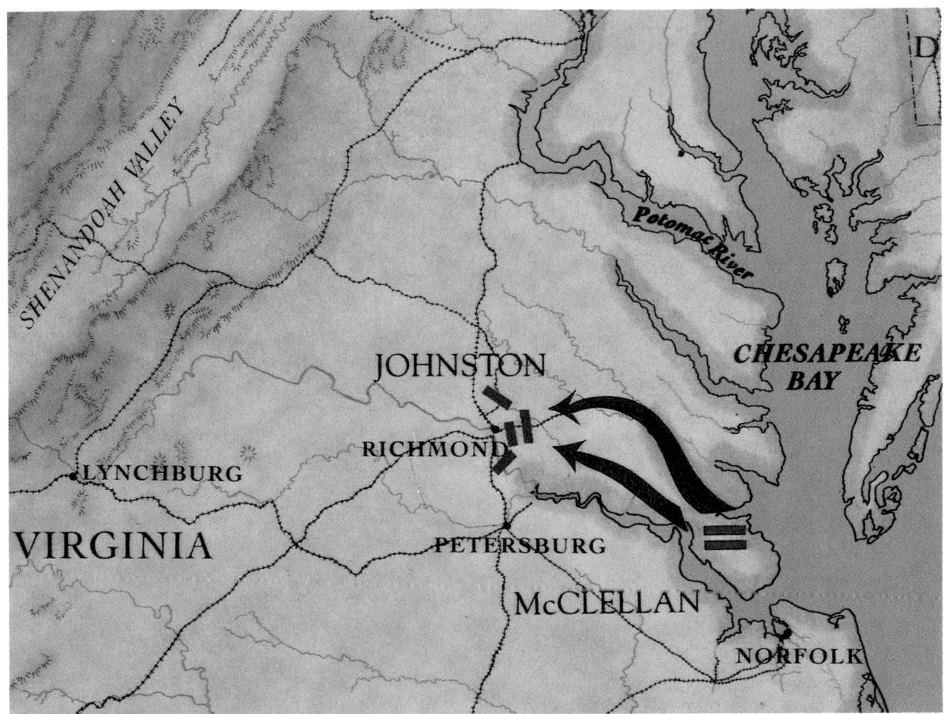

Cautious pursuit on the Peninsula: Outwitted at Yorktown, George McClellan warily follows the Confederate army as it withdraws west toward Richmond. Among those who followed him was Elisha Rhodes (above), who wrote that "all that we have to eat is the cattle killed by the way. No bread or salt in the Regiment and I am most starved. But it is all for the Union and we do not complain."

the line to the other, the shells and shot poured into our camps," a Union surgeon recalled, "and the arches of fire that marked the course of the shells, with flame spouting from the mouths of the guns, created a magnificent pyrotechnic display."

The next morning the Confederates had vanished. Disbelieving Federal troops edged into the deserted southern camps. "The whole place is strewed with heaps of oyster shells, empty bottles and cans of preserved fruit and vegetables. . . . Their exit was so sudden that their bread was left in the kneading troughs, their pork over the fire, and biscuits half-baked."

Lincoln had been right: McClellan's chronic "hesitation" had caused "the story of Manassas" to be repeated. McClellan declared a victory, nonetheless: "Our success is brilliant, and you may rest assured that its effects will be of the greatest importance. There shall be no delay in following up the rebels."

Joseph Johnston withdrew in a steady downpour to Williamsburg, the old colonial capital of Virginia. The Confederates fought a savage holding action there before moving on; it was the first real fighting McClellan's new Army of the Potomac had had to endure. After southern troops captured a Federal battery, one-armed General Phil Kearny led the muddy charge that took it back, riding into the guns and shouting, "Don't flinch, boys! They're shooting at me, not at you!"

Elisha Rhodes was among the survivors: "The field presented a horrible appearance, and in one small spot I counted sixty dead bodies. . . . Thank God for this victory and may we have many more and so end the war."

The two armies continued on toward Richmond. At White House Landing, Union men came upon the site of the home where George Washington had once courted Martha Custis. A note was nailed to the door:

Northern soldiers who profess to reverence Washington forebear to desecrate the home of his first married life, the property of his wife, now owned by her descendants.

A grand-daughter of Mrs. Washington

The signer was Mary Custis Lee, the wife of Robert E. Lee. McClellan set up his tent on the front lawn rather than occupy the historic house, posted guards to keep away souvenir hunters, and permitted Mrs. Lee to pass through his lines under a white flag. (After McClellan had moved on, a Federal straggler set the old house on fire.)

Elisha Rhodes recorded the Federal advance:

May 20. Richmond is just nine miles off. Our advance has been slow. . . . The Negroes are delighted to see us, but the whites look as if they would like to kill us.

May 24. From a hill nearby we can see the spires of the churches in Richmond.

The final southern line of defense was just five miles east of the Confederate capital. Richmond prepared for disaster. A woman remembered the panic evident throughout the city:

Baggage wagons, heaped with trunks, boxes and baskets, were constantly rattling through the streets. Houses were left deserted . . . but a more alarming feature was noticeable in the ominous-looking boxes . . . containing the archives of the government and marked for Columbia, South Carolina.

The Confederate Congress fled. So did Varina Davis, taking with her the

In Richmond, on February 22, 1862, Jefferson Davis was reinaugurated President of the Confederacy for a six-year term beneath this statue of George Washington in Capitol Square (above left, shown filled with paroled rebels in 1865). The city of Richmond purchased the home of Dr. John Brockenbrough (above), then rented it to the Confederate Government as a home for the President and his family. Mary Chesnut thought it "really a handsome establishment." It became a scene of tragedy in 1864 when the President's five-year-old son, Joseph, fell to his death from a rear balcony. "I have said all the prayers I know how," his older brother Jefferson Davis, Jr., told a neighbor who came rushing, "but God will not wake Joe."

President's four children. The Confederate gold supply was placed on a flatcar coupled to a locomotive kept under a constant head of steam.

But again McClellan stalled. Although his army still outnumbered Johnston's three to two, he remained convinced the opposite was true and demanded that another forty thousand men under Irvin McDowell be sent to reinforce him before he mounted his final assault. Secretary Stanton was livid. "If he had a *million* men," he said, "he would swear the enemy had two millions, and then he would sit down in the mud and yell for three."

Phil Kearny began calling his commander "the Virginia Creeper."

Stonewall Jackson's Valley Campaign in April and May 1862: To keep Union forces from reinforcing McClellan on the Peninsula, Jackson and the fast-moving infantrymen he called his "foot cavalry" ranged up and down the Shenandoah Valley in northern Virginia, despite the best efforts of three Federal commanders—John Charles Frémont, Nathaniel Banks, and Irvin McDowell—to stop him. Banks lost so many supplies to Jackson's lightning raiders that Confederates took to calling him "Commissary Banks."

STONEWALL

McDowell would not come. He was to be fully occupied in the Shenandoah Valley, west of the Blue Ridge, where Stonewall Jackson was already keeping two Federal forces busy.

Jackson was a pious, blue-eyed killer, reluctant on Sundays even to read a letter from his wife—whom he called "my little dove"—but utterly untroubled by the likelihood of death. Once, when an officer protested that if he followed Jackson's orders his men would be annihilated, Stonewall reassured

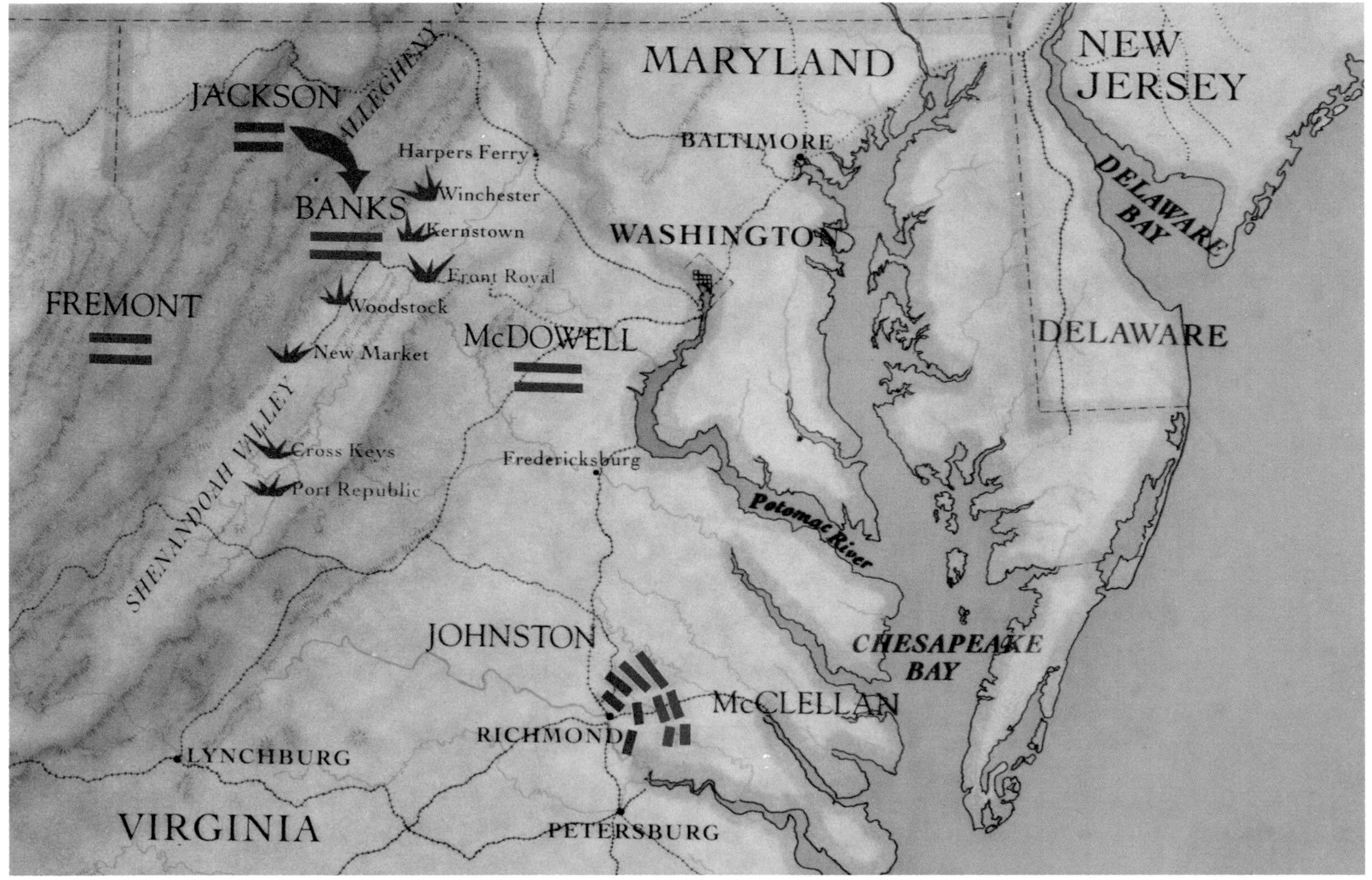

Federal teamsters struggle down a rutted track in the Shenandoah Valley, in this painting by Johannes A. Oertel. For such men, the beauty of the valley was more than offset by the poor roads and the constant, nagging fear that Jackson—who "would fight for a wheelbarrow," a southern officer said—might be lurking somewhere nearby.

him. "I always endeavor to take care of my wounded and bury my dead. You have heard my order—*obey it.*" It was man's "entire duty," he said, "to pray and fight."

"He would have a man shot at the drop of a hat," Sam Watkins recalled, "and he'd drop it himself." His men did not love him. He was too grim, too remote for that, and he demanded too much. "All old Jackson gave us was a musket, a hundred rounds and a gum blanket," one of his veterans remembered, "and he druv us so like Hell."

Some thought him mad. He used no pepper because, he said, it made his left leg ache; he believed that only by keeping one hand in the air could he stop himself from going "out of balance"; preferred to stand rather than sit for fear of putting his internal organs "out of alignment"; and sucked constantly on lemons, even in the heat of battle. Others worried that his religious certitude would cloud his judgment. His command, Jackson believed, was "*an army of the living God,* as well as of its country."

But his men admired him, were willing to endure the regular, twenty-five-mile-a-day marches he demanded, because he brought them victories.

Jackson had his own unique way of fighting. "Always mystify, mislead and surprise the enemy . . ." he said, "and when you strike and overcome him, never let up in the pursuit. . . . Never fight against heavy odds if . . . you can hurl your own force on only a part . . . of your enemy and crush it. . . . A small army may thus destroy a large one . . . and repeated victory will make it *invincible.*"

It was Jackson's charge in the Shenandoah to unsettle the Union and keep Washington from reinforcing McClellan. John C. Frémont and Nathaniel Banks, whose combined forces far outnumbered Jackson's seventeen thousand, had been pursuing him up and down the valley and back again for weeks. At Winchester, Front Royal, Cross Keys, Port Republic, and half a dozen other places, they thought they had him. Armed with a detailed map that stretched eight and a half feet, he was able to surprise them, slash at their flanks, then get away clean. Once, he managed to slip a seven-mile-long train of wagons filled with booty between two pursuing Federal columns without even being detected.

After routing Banks's division at the battle of Winchester—an unoffending little town that would change hands seventy-two times before the war was over—Jackson chased it all the way to the Potomac.

"Stop, men!" Banks shouted to some of his retreating troops. "Don't you love your country?" "Yes, by God," one answered, "and I'm trying to get back to it just as fast as I can!"

Panicky officials in Washington feared Jackson would attack the Federal capital. McDowell's corps was sent to block him.

Jackson's valley campaign was a triumph. In just over a month, his men had marched almost 400 miles, inflicted 7,000 casualties, seized huge quantities of badly needed supplies, kept almost 40,000 Federal troops off the Peninsula—frightened the North and inspired the South.

"He who does not see the hand of God in this," Jackson told an aide, "is *blind,* sir, blind!" Then he led his sunburned army onto the Peninsula to join the defense of Richmond.

"You appear much concerned at my attacking on Sunday. *I was greatly concerned, too; but . . . so far as I can see, my course was a wise one . . . though very distasteful to my feelings; and I hope and pray to our Heavenly Father that I may never again be circumstanced as on that day."*

STONEWALL JACKSON to his wife, after defeating Nathaniel Banks at Winchester

After Seven Pines, Robert E. Lee (above) replaced Joseph E. Johnston (right) in command of the defense of Richmond. "His name might be 'Audacity,'" a southern officer said of the new commander. "He will take more chances and take them quicker, than any other General in this country, North or South."

THE SEVEN DAYS

On Friday, May 30, in Virginia, the rains came heavily, inundating the bottomlands of the Peninsula. Along the roads outside Richmond, McClellan's force was divided in two by the flooded Chickahominy.

Joseph E. Johnston attacked the smaller force south of the river on May 31. The two-day battle was a bloody draw. The Confederates, who did best near a crossroads called Seven Pines, chose to remember that name; Union soldiers called it Fair Oaks after the scene of their most successful fighting.

The North lost 5,000 men, the South 6,000. Joseph Johnston himself was severely wounded, but it was McClellan who was intimidated. "I am tired of the sickening sight of the battlefield," he wrote home, "with its mangled corpses and poor wounded. Victory has no charms for me when purchased at such cost."

Richmond was still in danger, but a new commander now took over its defense—Robert E. Lee. "The shot that struck me down," General Johnston said, "was the best ever fired for the Confederacy, for I possessed in no degree the confidence of the government, and now a man who does enjoy it will succeed me and be able to accomplish what I never could."

Since March, Lee had been in Richmond, advising the President. Now, for the first time, he was placed at the head of a major army. McClellan professed to be pleased: "I prefer Lee to Johnston—[Lee] is too cautious and weak under grave responsibility—personally brave and energetic to a fault, he yet is wanting in moral firmness when pressed by heavy responsibility and is likely to be timid and irresolute in action."

But in writing of Lee, McClellan had perfectly described himself. Lee was, in fact, a fighter, anxious to "get at" the Union men who had dared invade his state. He renamed his force the Army of Northern Virginia, seized the initiative and refused to let it go.

The Confederate President asked him where he thought the South's next defense line should be drawn, once Richmond was taken. Lee suggested the Taunton River one hundred miles to the south. But then he added, "Richmond must not be given up. It *shall* not be given up."

To help ensure that it was not, he first sent his cavalry chief, Brigadier General Jeb Stuart, to reconnoiter McClellan's forces. Stuart was not a handsome man—his West Point classmates called him "Beauty" in derision—but he made up for it with his charm, his gallantry, and the gaudy uniforms he

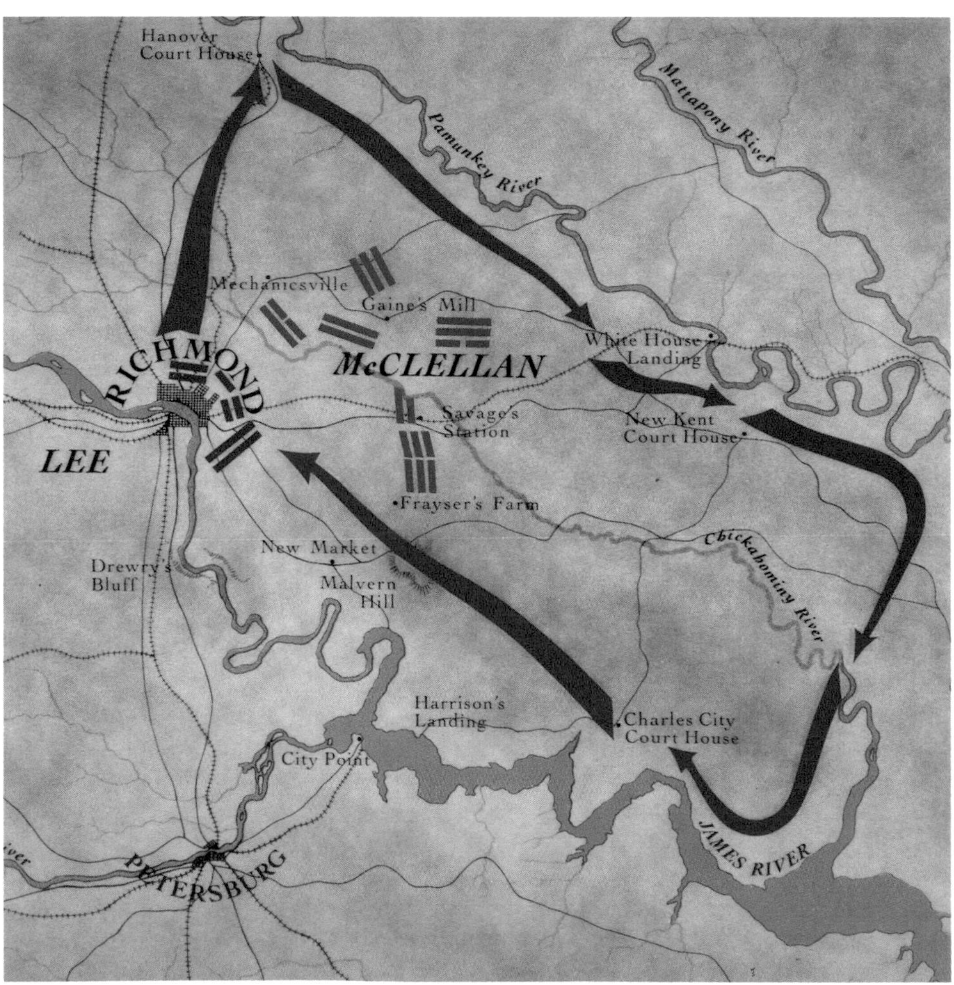

Jeb Stuart's ride: In order that Lee might understand what Federal troops such as these men of the 5th New Hampshire and the 64th New York, building a bridge over the Chickahominy, were up to (right), Stuart led his cavalry on a spectacular reconnoitering ride around McClellan's encampments east of Richmond. He returned to a hero's welcome in the Confederate capital—and the warm praise of his commander.

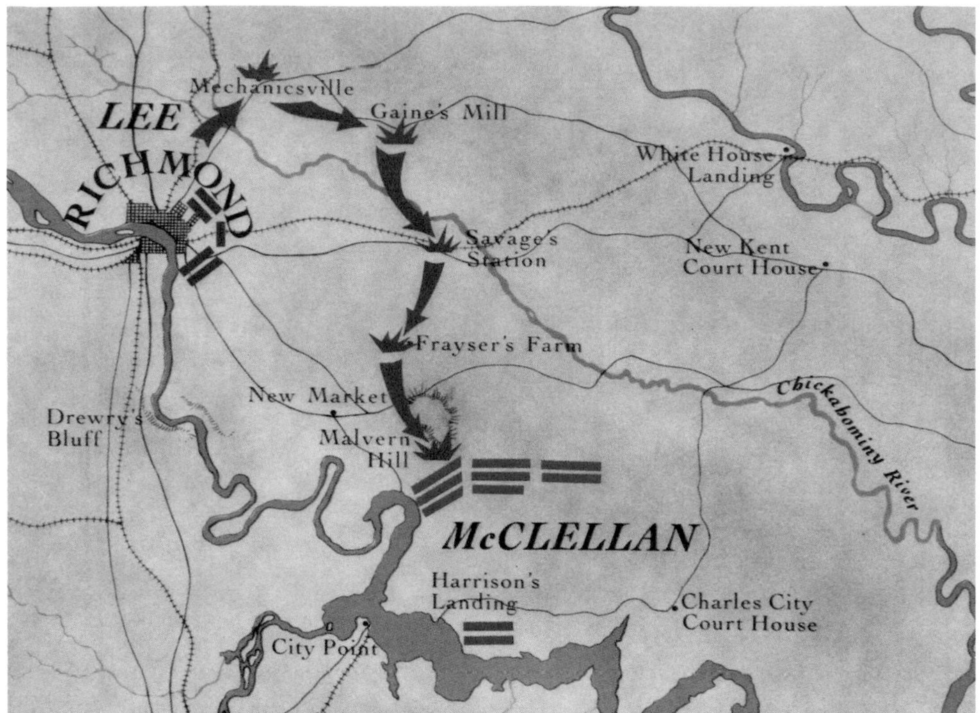

The Seven Days: The bloody sequence of battles around Richmond began on June 26, 1862, and lasted for a week. Determined to hurl McClellan back from the Confederate capital, Lee attacked him again and again—at Mechanicsville, Gaines' Mill, Savage's Station, Frayser's Farm, and Malvern Hill. McClellan won four out of the five battles, but proved as fearful in victory as he was in defeat, backing steadily away until he reached Harrison's Landing on the James. The Peninsula Campaign, begun with such bright hope, had ended in defeat.

designed for himself. "We must substitute *esprit* for numbers," he said. "Therefore, I strive to inculcate in my men the spirit of the chase."

He now led 1,200 troopers on a pounding, three-day, 150-mile ride around McClellan's huge army. When the war began, his father-in-law, Philip St. George Cooke, had stayed loyal to the Union and become a general, a decision Stuart said he would "regret . . . but once, and that will be *continuously.*" As commander of McClellan's cavalry, it became Cooke's task to catch his son-in-law.

"It was neck or nothing, do or die," said one of Stuart's men. "We had one chance of escape against ten of capture or destruction." They cut their way through northern pickets, burned Federal camps, and sawed down telegraph poles, took 170 prisoners and 300 horses and mules, and slowed only to accept bouquets and kisses from admiring women. "A Union sutler's store was remorselessly ransacked and the edibles consumed," a rebel cavalryman remembered. "*This* historian ate in succession figs, beef-tongue, pickle, candy, tomato catsup, preserves."

When they found their way blocked by the flooded Chickahominy, they banged together a bridge, clattered across it, then set it ablaze, leaving Stuart's father-in-law's men cursing on the other side.

McClellan was at last getting ready to mount his barrage of Richmond when Lee hit him first, at Mechanicsville on the Union right, on June 26. "In Richmond," a citizen remembered, "the sounds of the battle were so sharp and clear . . . that it seemed the fight must be on the very edge of town . . . windows rattled at every discharge."

Paying the price: Private Edwin Jennison, killed in action at Malvern Hill (above), and men of the 3rd Vermont visiting the newly dug graves of comrades killed on the Peninsula (right). "I am tired of the sickening sight of the battlefield, with its mangled corpses and poor suffering wounded," McClellan wrote, though in fact he rarely ventured close to actual combat. "Victory has no charms for me when purchased at such cost."

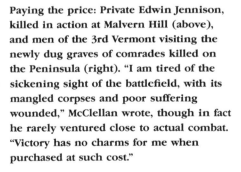

Ambrose P. Hill, a Virginian and one of Lee's sturdiest lieutenants, had once proposed marriage to Ellen Marcy, the woman who became McClellan's wife, and when Hill's men stormed into the northern lines, one Union officer was heard to mutter, "God's sake, Nelly, why didn't you marry him?"

The attack cost Lee fifteen hundred men, but he would not let up. He continued to move forward, determined to drive McClellan off the Peninsula, and McClellan fell back steadily before him.

The fighting went on for a full week—at Gaines' Mill, Savage's Station, Frayser's Farm, and at Malvern Hill, where on July 1 Federal artillery and rifle fire blew to pieces the Confederates who came at them up the long slope. A Union colonel never forgot what he saw at dawn the next day:

> Our ears had been filled [all night] with agonizing cries from thousands before the fog was lifted, but now our eyes saw [that] five thousand dead or wounded men were on the ground. A third of them were dead or dying, but enough of them were alive and moving to give the field a singular *crawling* effect.

"It was thought to be a great thing to charge a battery of artillery or an earthworks lined with infantry . . ." a Confederate general remembered of the Seven Days' battles. "We were very lavish of blood in those days."

At least fifteen thousand bleeding men were carried into Richmond that week. "Every house was open for the wounded," a local woman who volunteered to nurse them remembered.

> They lay on verandas, in halls, in drawing rooms of stately mansions. I used to veil myself closely as I walked to and from my hotel, that I might shut out the dreadful sights—the squads of prisoners and, worst of all, the open wagons in which the dead were piled. Once I did see one of those dreadful wagons! In it, a stiff arm was raised, and it shook as it was driven down the street, as though the dead owner appealed to Heaven for vengeance.

A Federal encampment on the Peninsula: "The weather is very hot," Elisha Rhodes wrote on Independence Day, "but we have moved our camp to a wood where we get the shade. This is a queer 4th of July, but we have not forgotten that it is our national birthday, and a salute has been fired. We expect to have something to eat before long."

All but one of the battles of the Seven Days had been Union victories, yet McClellan treated them as defeats, continuing to back down the Peninsula until by July 3 he had reached the safety of Federal gunboats at Harrison's Landing on the James. Union officers urged him to counterattack: Lee had lost twenty thousand men. McClellan refused. During the fighting he had seldom actually come closer than two miles to combat; one officer suggested privately that his commander was motivated by either "cowardice or treason."

In just one week, Lee had unnerved McClellan, forced his huge army down the Peninsula, and demonstrated for the first time the strengths that would make him a legend: surprise, audacity, and an eerie ability to read his opponents' minds.

On Independence Day, one southern private noted:

> There are blackberries in the fields so our boys and the Yanks made a bargain not to fire at each other, and went out in the field, leaving one man on each post with the arms, and gathered berries together and talked over the fight, and traded tobacco and coffee and newspapers as peacefully and kindly as if they had not been engaged for . . . seven days in butchering one another.

Three days later, Lincoln sailed down to see his commanding general. McClellan insisted that he had not lost; he had merely "*failed to win* only because overpowered by superior numbers." He needed 50,000 more men; 100,000 perhaps.

No such numbers were available, Lincoln told his commander. If McClellan did not feel he could resume the offensive, he should return to the defense of Washington. Meanwhile, his men would be withdrawn from the Peninsula.

"Today we took a steamer," Elisha Rhodes noted in his diary on September 3, "and went up the Potomac past Washington . . . and landed at Georgetown. . . . It is hard to have reached the point we started from last March, and Richmond is still the Rebel Capital."

BACK TO BULL RUN

Lincoln replaced McClellan at last, turning to two commanders who had won victories in the West. Henry Halleck was made general-in-chief of the United States Army, and John Pope, who had taken Island Number 10, was named to command all Federal troops north and west of Richmond.

Tall and bombastic, Pope was not popular among his fellow officers: one of

them once declared that he did "not care a pinch of owl dung" for John Pope, and Pope so often declared that his headquarters were in the saddle that his many enemies liked to say he had his headquarters where his hindquarters should have been. His inveterate boasting managed to alienate the men of his new army even before he led them into battle.

> Let us understand each other. I have come to you from the West, where we have always seen the backs of our enemies; from an army whose business it has been to seek the adversary and to beat him when he was found. . . . Dismiss from your minds certain phrases, which I am sorry to find much in vogue amongst you. I hear constantly of "taking strong positions and holding them," of "lines of retreat" and "bases of supplies." Let us discard such ideas. . . . Let us look before us and not behind. Success and glory are in the advance, disaster and shame lurk in the rear!

Southerners hated him for the harshness with which he treated civilians. He encouraged his men to seize food and supplies from Virginia farms and threatened to hang without trial anyone suspected of aiding the Confederacy.

Lee thought Pope "a miscreant" who needed to be "suppressed," and when it became clear that McClellan was no longer a threat to Richmond, he divided his army into two commands and started north to attack him.

On August 9, Stonewall Jackson fought Pope to a standoff at Cedar Mountain, near Culpeper Courthouse.

THE ANGEL OF THE BATTLEFIELD

"[W]hile our soldiers stand and fight," said Clara Barton in 1861, "I can stand and feed and nurse them." Barely five feet tall and unmarried in a time when that was thought unnatural for any woman, she was a clerk in the Patent Office at Washington in 1861 and began her war work among homesick troops from her native Massachusetts by collecting and distributing brandy and tobacco and lemons, soaps and sewing kits and homemade jellies.

But in the bloody aftermath of Bull Run she realized much more was needed. She stayed behind the lines for a time, fearful that if she went to the battlefield she might be thought a camp follower, but her place, she eventually came to see, was "anywhere between the bullet and the battlefield." Her face sometimes blue from gunpowder, she followed the fighting, brewing gruel over open fires to aid the sick, dispensing bandages and kind words, sometimes digging bullets out of flesh with her pen-knife. She ministered to the wounded and dying at Cedar Mountain, Second Bull Run, Chantilly, South Mountain, and at Antietam, where, when rebel artillery seemed sure to hit the field hospital and all the male surgical assistants scurried for cover, she stood her ground, holding the rolling operating table steady so the surgeon could complete his work. "Now what do you think of Miss Barton?" the surgeon wrote his wife after describing her courage under fire. "In my feeble estimation, General McClellan, with all his laurels, sinks into insignificance beside the true heroine of the age, the angel of the battlefield."

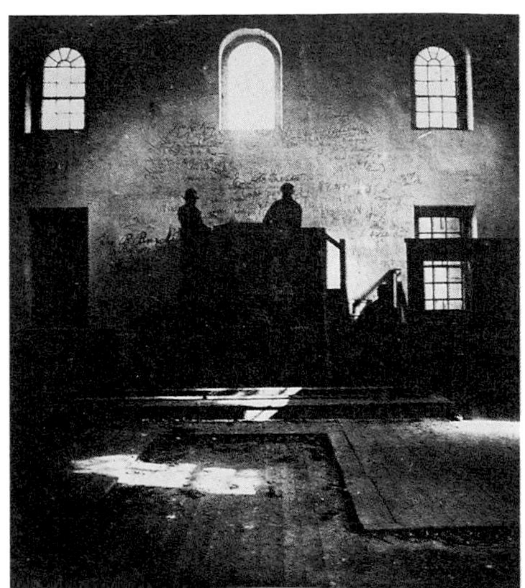

Federal troops marked their frequent passing of this little house of worship at Falls Church, Virginia, by inscribing their names and regiments on its walls.

Jeb Stuart hit him next, raiding his headquarters and getting away with $35,000 in cash, Pope's dress coat, and a notebook outlining the disposition of the Union forces.

Then Jackson led 25,000 men on a two-day, fifty-six-mile march around Pope's right flank to cut his rail line to Washington and loot his supply depot at Manassas Junction. One of Jackson's lean marchers remembered the special savor of that afternoon:

> It makes an old soldier's mouth water now just to think of it. Some filled their haversacks with cakes, some with candy, others with oranges, lemons, canned goods. . . . I know one that took nothing but French mustard; it turned out to be the best thing taken, as he traded it for bread and meat, it lasting him for days.

Then Jackson seemed again to disappear. It took two days for Pope to find him, dug in on Stony Ridge, overlooking the same Bull Run battlefield where he had helped defeat the Union army the year before.

Announcing that he would now "bag the whole crowd," Pope attacked Jackson on August 29. The Confederates held, their men hurling rocks at the Federal troops when ammunition ran low, their commander confident that he had "the blessing and protection of Providence."

Pope was convinced the battered rebels would now flee, and promised a relentless pursuit the next day. Meanwhile, the other wing of Lee's army had arrived, and at two in the afternoon Major General James Longstreet sent five divisions storming into the Union flank along a two-mile front.

Twenty-five thousand men were killed, wounded, or missing at Second Bull Run, five times the figure that had so horrified the country the first time the North and South fought there.

Clara Barton was among those who cared for the maimed survivors. "The men were brought down from the field . . ." she wrote, "till they covered acres." She helped split open bales of hay upon which to lay the wounded. "By midnight there must have been *three thousand* helpless men lying in that hay. . . . All night we made compresses and slings—and bound up and wet wounds, when we could get water, fed what we could, traveled miles in that dark over these poor helpless wretches, in terror lest some one's candle fall *into* the hay and consume them all."

"*I* am not stampeded," a furious Phil Kearny told a fellow officer that night. "*You* are not stampeded. That is about all, sir, by God, that's about all." The next day, Kearny himself was killed, shot in the back after accidentally riding into the rebel lines. Confederate General A. P. Hill, who had known him before the war, mourned, "Poor Kearny! He deserved a better death than that." Lee called for a truce so that his body could be escorted back to the Union lines.

Lincoln sent Pope west to Minnesota to deal with an uprising among the Sioux and, with Lee advancing north and no one else to whom to turn, reluctantly put George McClellan back in command of the Grand Army of the Potomac. "We must use the tools we have," Lincoln told his cabinet.

"Again," McClellan told his wife, "I have been called upon to save the country."

SHE RANKS ME

"The suffering of men in battle," a Union relief worker wrote, "is nothing next to the agony that women feel sending forth their loved ones to war." North and South, women struggled to fill in for missing men as best they could, working in mills and factories, running the family farm. "Our hired man left to enlist just as corn planting commenced," wrote an Iowa woman, "so I shouldered my hoe and have worked out ever since. I guess my services are just as acceptable as his."

Women also looked for other ways to further the war effort. In Concord, Massachusetts, Louisa May Alcott begged a friend to forgive her for not writing sooner—"too occupied violently sewing patriotic blue shirts." So many socks were knitted in Charleston, Mary Chesnut noted, that "one poor man said he had dozens of socks and just one shirt. He preferred more shirts and fewer stockings."

In the North, the United States Sanitary Commission and other private relief agencies provided ways by which women's efforts could be efficiently channeled. When the war began, Mary Livermore, a Chicago minister's wife, left her children in the care of a housekeeper and went to work full-time for the commission, organizing midwestern volunteers into three thousand chapters and, when Grant's army was threatened with scurvy, sending so much food south, one reporter wrote, "that a line of vegetables connected Chicago and Vicksburg."

Mary Ann Bickerdyke, a widow and Sanitary Commission agent, traveled with the Union army through four years and nineteen battles, assisting at amputations, brewing barrels of coffee, washing clothes, rounding up cattle and chickens and eggs to feed the grateful men whom she called her boys, and who called her "Mother Bickerdyke." When a surgeon asked her on whose authority she acted, she answered, "On the authority of Lord God Almighty, have you anything that outranks that?" She was the only female visitor William Tecumseh Sherman allowed in his camps;

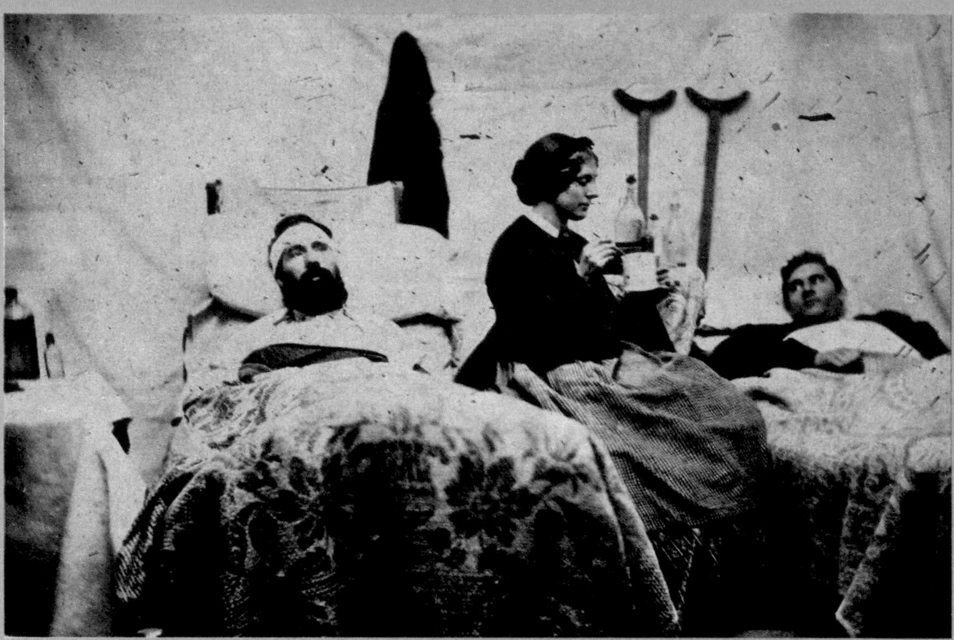

A nurse (above) tends her wounded charges in a Federal hospital at Nashville, Tennessee, while Manhattan women (below), belonging to the Women's Central Association of Relief, tally shipments to the field in their office at Cooper Union.

Mary Ann Bickerdyke.

Dorothea Dix.

asked why he made an exception in her case, he answered simply, "She ranks me."

Southerners, too, tried to care for their soldiers, but "we had no Sanitary Commission . . ." a Confederate veteran remembered. "We were too poor; we had no line of rich and populous cities closely connected by rail, all combined in the good work of collecting and forwarding supplies and maintaining costly and thoroughly equipped charities. With us, every house was a hospital."

Only four Confederate states managed to organize formal relief organizations—and each of them was careful to provide only for its own sons: Georgians looked out exclusively for Georgians, Alabama blankets warmed only Alabamians.

More than three thousand northern women served as army nurses, despite bad pay, worse conditions, and the frequent hostility of the men with whom they worked. Just five days after Sumter fell, Dorothea Dix, fifty-nine-year-old crusader for the mentally ill, volunteered her services to the Union. She was put in charge of all female nurses employed by the armies.

Tireless, unbending, and so autocratic that one woman called her "Dragon Dix," she barred any applicant she thought interested only in romantic adventure—even nuns were sometimes turned down. "No woman under thirty years need apply to serve in government hospitals," she insisted. "All nurses are required to be very plain-looking women. Their dresses must be brown or black, with no bows, no curls, no jewelry and no hoop skirts."

"Working on her own hook she does good," George Templeton Strong wrote after one stormy meeting with her, "but no one can cooperate with her, for she belongs to the class of comets." Nevertheless, under her relentless guidance, the standard of care was improved and, despite the bitter rivalry of male colleagues, she stayed at her post throughout the war without pay.

Southern women worked as nurses, too, despite criticism that it was unladylike for them to care for "ruffians." "A woman's respectability must be at a low ebb," wrote one southern nurse, "if it can be endangered by going into a hospital."

Frances Clalin in uniform as a trooper in the cavalry of the Missouri militia.

Sally Tompkins of Richmond and a staff of only 6 nursed 1,333 wounded men in her private hospital—and kept all but 73 of them alive, a record unmatched by any other Civil War hospital, North or South.

Some northern women took a still more active role. It has been suggested that as many as four hundred of them disguised themselves as men and became soldiers. Patriotism moved many; some simply could not bear to be away from husbands or sweethearts; still others enlisted for more complex psychological reasons. After Chickamauga, Confederates sent a disguised and wounded woman captive back to her unit with a note: "As the Confederates do not use women in war, this woman, wounded in battle, is returned to you."

SHARPSBURG

The northern armies were stymied, but the North seemed to be edging toward emancipation anyway. In March 1862, with the fate of Missouri and the other border states still in doubt, Congress—now controlled by the Republicans—had forbidden the army to return slaves to their masters.

In April, with McClellan still mired on the Peninsula, Congress abolished slavery in the District of Columbia.

In June, it forbade slavery in the western territories, settling the issue that for so long had disturbed the public peace.

"Only the damndest of 'damned abolitionists' *dreamed* of such [things] a year ago," wrote George Templeton Strong. "John Brown's soul is marching on, with the people after it."

Still, Lincoln refused to move against slavery itself. "I would do it," he said, "if I were not afraid that half the officers would fling down their arms and three more States would rise." Fearful of driving off the border states, he continued to back a plan that would have paid $400 for every slave freed, then shipped the freedmen off to a colony in Africa or Central America. It was an old idea, popular among whites, unpopular with blacks. The *Anglo-African,* a New York black newspaper, suggested that recalcitrant *slaveowners* be colonized.

"We are *Americans,*" Frederick Douglass reminded the country, "speaking the same language, adopting the same customs, holding the same general opinions . . . and shall rise and fall with Americans."

In August, Horace Greeley addressed an open letter to the President: "We think you are unduly influenced by the counsel of certain fossil politicians hailing from Border Slave states. . . . We ask you to consider that Slavery is everywhere the inciting cause and sustaining base of treason. . . . It seems to us the most obvious truth that whatever strengthens or fortifies Slavery . . . drives home the wedge intended to divide the Union."

Lincoln offered a no less public answer: "My paramount object in this struggle *is* to save the Union, and is *not* either to save or to destroy slavery. If I could save the Union without freeing *any* slave, I would do it; if I could save it by freeing *all* the slaves, I would do it; and if I could save it by freeing some and leaving others alone, I would also do that."

In fact, Lincoln had already secretly decided to free those slaves held captive in the rebellious states. Emancipation would damage the Confederate economy at home, he believed, and aid the Union cause abroad. But Secretary of State Seward had talked him out of a public declaration while McClellan's newly battered army was regrouping. It would have seemed then, Seward said, like "the last *shriek,* on our retreat . . . the government stretching forth its hands to Ethiopia, instead of Ethiopia stretching forth her hands to the government."

Lincoln needed a victory, and victory still seemed very far away. The Union was being invaded on two fronts.

That same month, a Confederate army under Braxton Bragg had invaded Kentucky from Tennessee, seized Lexington, and sworn in a secessionist governor. That had been the signal for Lee to open a second front. The

"January the 12 1862

"My Dear Wife

"it is with grate joy i take this time to let you know Whare I am i am now in Safety in the 14th Regiment of Brooklyn this Day i can Adress you thank god as a free man I had a little truble in giting away But as the lord led the Children of Isrel to the land of Canon So he led me to a land Whare Fredom Will rain in spite Of earth and hell. . . . My Dear i cant express my Grate desire that i Have to See you i trust the time Will Come When We Shal meet again And if We dont met on earth We Will Meet in heven Whare Jesas ranes . . .

"Wife I must Close rest yourself Contented i am free . . . Kiss Daniel For me"

JOHN BOSTON
Maryland fugitive slave

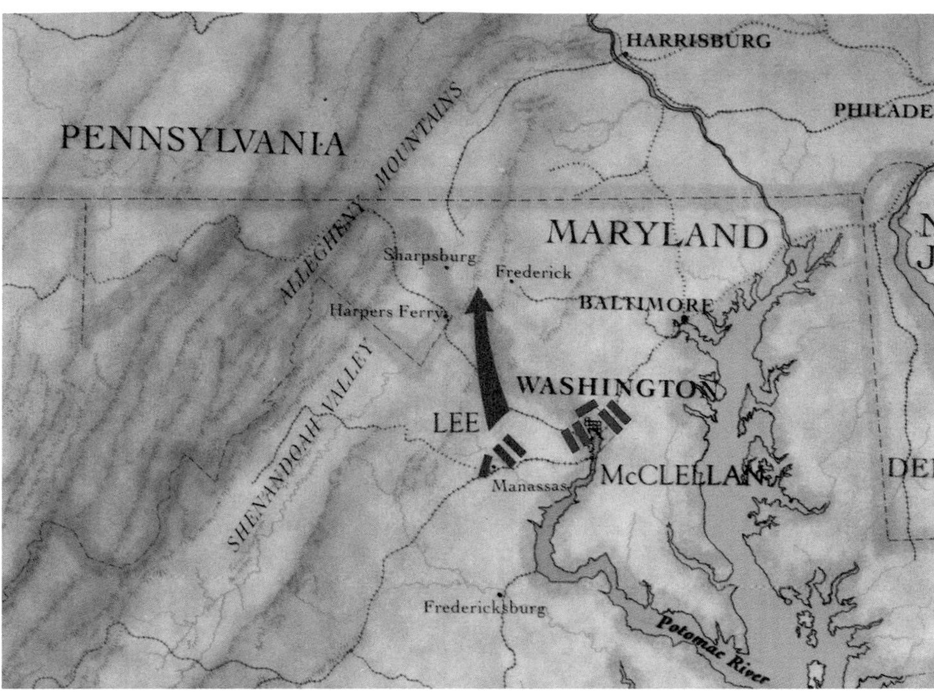

Lee invades Maryland: "The present," Robert E. Lee wrote to Jefferson Davis on September 3, 1862, "seems to be the most propitious time since the commencement of the war for the Confederate army to enter Maryland." Davis agreed. Both men hoped that having driven one northern army from southern soil, the Confederacy might be able to persuade England and France to recognize it by winning another victory in the North. As his army stepped off, Lee's objective was Harrisburg, Pennsylvania, but McClellan was pursuing him, and on September 15 he came to a halt at Sharpsburg, Maryland.

southern victories of spring and summer had brought Lee and his army international renown. One more successful campaign, he wrote Jefferson Davis, would likely force Europe to recognize the Confederacy.

In September he led forty thousand soldiers across the Potomac into Maryland. Lee's men "were the dirtiest . . . I ever saw," a Maryland woman remembered, "a most ragged, lean and hungry set of wolves. Yet there was a dash about them that the northern men lacked." Watching from her doorstep, another woman wrote: "This body of men moving along with no order, their guns carried in every fashion, no two dressed alike, their officers hardly distinguishable from the privates . . . Were *these* the men that had driven back again and again our splendid legions?"

The Confederate field commanders were not in much better shape. Lee had both hands bandaged and splinted from a fall. Jackson had badly injured his back. Two of the bravest generals—John Bell Hood and A. P. Hill—were riding at the rear of their men, under arrest after quarreling with superiors. Lee would have to suspend their arrests when the fighting started.

He hoped to inspire Marylanders to rise against the Union, and instructed his men to sing "Maryland, My Maryland" as they marched. It didn't work: most residents of the small towns through which he rode stayed fearfully behind closed doors.

McClellan assumed Lee would march on either Washington or Baltimore, but his real target was the Federal rail center at Harrisburg, Pennsylvania. Before he reached it, he wanted to ensure that his supply line remained open, and sent half his command under Jackson to capture the twelve-hundred-man Union garrison at Harpers Ferry, while he concentrated the rest of his army at Hagerstown, twenty miles to the north.

McClellan pursued the rebel force with his customary caution. Then on

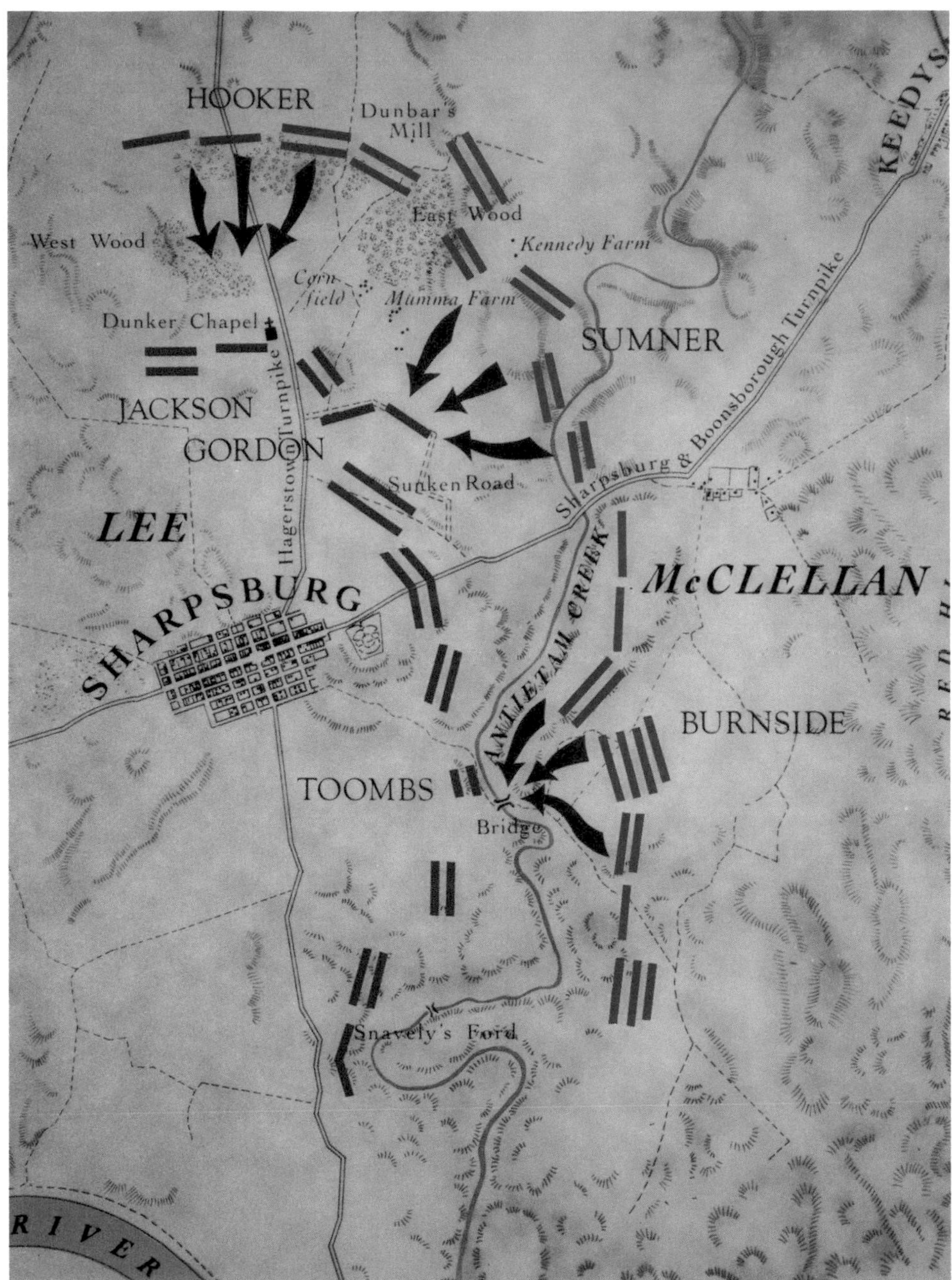

The Battle of Antietam: The bloodiest single day of the war began just outside Sharpsburg early on the morning of September 16, 1862, when Union troops under General Joseph Hooker (above)—who insisted on riding a massive white horse so that his men could easily see him despite the smoke of battle, even though it meant that rebel sharpshooters could find him easily, too—attacked the Confederates near the Dunker church. Later, the fighting would move to the Sunken Road, and then to a bridge over Antietam Creek, across which troops under General Ambrose Burnside managed to fight their way only to be withdrawn again when rebel reinforcements arrived at the end of the day.

September 13, in a meadow near Frederick where the Confederates had camped, a Union corporal found three cigars wrapped in a piece of paper. It turned out to be a copy of Lee's special orders.

The Union commander now knew Lee had divided his army. "Here is a paper," he told his aides, "with which, if I cannot whip Bobbie Lee, I will be willing to go home." And he eagerly wired the President: "I have all the plans of the rebels, and will catch them in their own trap if my men are equal to the emergency. My respects to Mrs. Lincoln. Received most enthusiastically by the ladies. Will send you trophies."

But even armed with the precious paper, McClellan did nothing for sixteen

The men of Independent Battery E of the Pennsylvania Light Artillery saw savage fighting near the Dunker church at Antietam. Here they pose for Alexander Gardner between the East and West Woods after the battle.

crucial hours, convinced again that he was outnumbered by an army actually less than half the size of his.

On September 15, Lee and the 18,000 Confederates with him took up positions along the crest of a three-mile ridge just east of the town of Sharpsburg, Maryland, the Potomac at their back. In front ran a little creek called Antietam. McClellan and his army of 95,000 soon began arriving across the creek.

Major General James Longstreet of Georgia watched them come.

> On the forenoon of the 15th, the blue uniforms of the Federals appeared among the trees that crowned the heights on the eastern bank of the Antietam. The number increased, and larger and larger grew the field of blue until it seemed to stretch as far as the eye could see, and from the tops of the mountains down to the edges of the stream gathered the great army of McClellan.

Had McClellan hurled his great army at the Confederates that day or the next, the war might have ended. But he did not, pausing instead to draw up

"By George, this is a magnificent field, and if we win this fight it will cover all our errors and misfortunes forever!"

GEORGE B. MCCLELLAN

Dead Confederate artillerymen grouped near one of their limbers in front of the Dunker church. Colonel Stephen D. Lee of Virginia, who commanded some of the rebel guns here, remembered Antietam as "artillery hell."

plans and get everything ready, giving Jackson's corps time to rejoin Lee and double his force.

"There was a single item in our advantage," an aide to Lee remembered, long after the fighting was over, "but it was an important one." McClellan had brought superior forces to Sharpsburg, but he had also brought himself.

The battle that began on September 17 was really three battles.

The first started at 6 a.m. on Lee's left, where a Federal force charged along the Hagerstown Pike to attack Jackson's men hidden in two clumps of woods and beyond the big cornfield that lay between them. The Union objective was a plateau edged with artillery on which stood a squat whitewashed church, built by the austere German Baptist pacifist sect called Dunkers, who thought even a steeple immodest.

"The Federals in apparent double battle line were moving toward us at charge bayonets, common time," a member of the Stonewall Brigade recalled, "and the sunbeams falling on their well-polished guns and bayonets gave a glamor and a show at once fearful and entrancing."

The Union commander in this part of the field was Major General Joseph Hooker, a profane and prickly hard-drinking Massachusetts soldier whose men called him "Fighting Joe." Batteries from both sides opened up on the cornfield. "Every stalk of corn in the greater part of the field was cut as closely as could have been done with a knife," Hooker remembered, "and the slain lay in rows precisely as they had stood in their ranks a few moments before."

Elisha Rhodes remembered it, too. "I have never in my soldier's life seen such a sight," he wrote. "The dead and wounded covered the ground. In one spot a Rebel officer and 20 men lay near a wreck of a Battery. It is said Battery 'A' 1st Rhode Island Artillery did this work."

The rebels fired back. In a matter of minutes, the 12th Massachusetts alone

General John B. Gordon of the 6th Alabama (above) was shot through the left cheek as he and his men tried to hold the narrow Sunken Road (above right) that became Bloody Lane—still filled with Confederate dead two days after the battle (below right). "In this road there lay so many dead rebels that they formed a line which one might have walked upon as far as I could see," remembered a New Hampshire lieutenant who had fought his way over them. "They lay there just as they had been killed apparently, amid the blood which was soaking the earth."

General Ambrose Burnside (inset) commanded the Union force that braved fierce Confederate fire to storm across the little stone bridge over Antietam Creek, shown here in a painting by a survivor, Captain James Hope of the 2nd Vermont Volunteers.

"We heard all through the war that the army was eager to be led against the enemy," wrote another soldier who managed to make it across that afternoon. "It must have been so, for truthful correspondents said so, and editors confirmed it. But when you came to hunt for this particular itch, it was always the next regiment that had it. The truth is, when bullets are whacking against tree trunks and solid shots are cracking skulls like egg-shells, the consuming passion in the breast of the average man is to get out of the way. Between the physical fear of going forward and the moral fear of turning back, there is a predicament of exceptional awkwardness from which a hidden hole in the ground would be a wonderfully welcome outlet."

lost 224 of 334 men. Hooker himself was carried from the field, shot through the foot. Eighteen generals would be killed or wounded that day, nine Union, nine Confederate.

But Hooker's men were closing in on the Dunker church, "loading and firing with demoniacal fury and shouting and laughing hysterically," a Wisconsin soldier said, "and the whole field before us is covered with rebels fleeing for life, into the woods."

At that moment, Jackson sent in his last reserves—a division of Texans under John Bell Hood, fierce fighters at any time but now enraged at having missed breakfast, which had promised to be their first real meal in days. Their first volley was "like a scythe running through our line," one Union survivor remembered, and then the Confederate counterattack came on.

Federal gunners battered this Lutheran church in Sharpsburg because rebel flag signalmen occupied its tower. Later, it provided sanctuary for the wounded.

The northern troops ran and Hood's men ran after them into the cornfield—where first Federal artillery and then Federal reinforcements caught them. Hood had broken the Union assault but at a terrible cost. Sixty percent of the men he led into the cornfield never left it. When the survivors finally withdrew, an officer asked Hood where his division was. "Dead on the field," he answered.

Two more massive assaults were mounted against the Confederate left. Captain Oliver Wendell Holmes, Jr., only recently recovered from his wounds at Ball's Bluff, was shot again, through the neck this time, the bullet just missing the windpipe and jugular and cutting the seams of his coat collar as it exited.

The battle surged back and forth across the cornfield fifteen times. By 10 a.m., eight thousand men lay dead or wounded.

At about the same time, the struggle shifted to the center of Lee's line, a sunken country road that in peaceful times had divided one farmer's fields from another's. Now it served as a ready-made rifle pit for two Confederate brigades.

Lee ordered the center to hold at all costs. Colonel John B. Gordon, commander of the 6th Alabama stationed there, assured him: "These men are going to stay here, General, till the sun goes down or victory is won." Gordon watched the Federal assault force form, four lines deep: "The brave Union commander, superbly mounted, placed himself in front, while his band cheered them with martial music. I thought, 'What a pity to spoil with bullets such a scene of martial beauty!'"

Gordon let the blue line get within a few rods, then gave the order to fire. The Union commander was killed instantly, his men wavered, retreated, but came back at the Confederates five times.

During the fighting, Gordon was hit twice in the right leg, once in the left arm, a fourth time through the shoulder. He refused all aid, limping along the line to steady his men as the Federals kept coming. "I was [finally] shot down by a fifth ball which struck me squarely in the face," he remembered. "I fell forward and lay unconscious with my face in my cap; and [might] have smothered [in] blood . . . but for [a Yankee bullet hole] which let the blood run out."

"O, why did we not attack them and drive them into the river? I do not understand these things. But then I am only a boy."

ELISHA RHODES

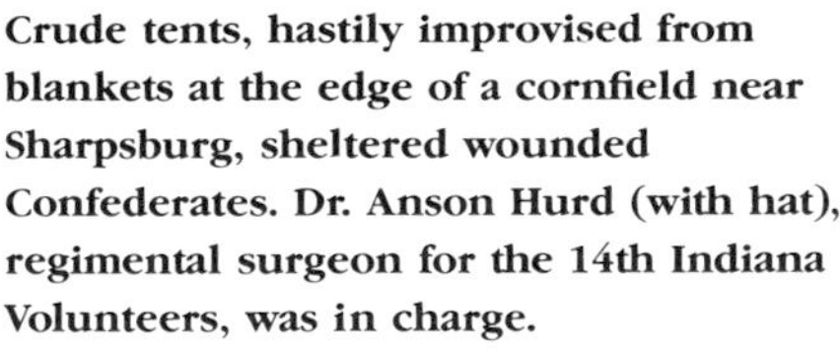

Crude tents, hastily improvised from blankets at the edge of a cornfield near Sharpsburg, sheltered wounded Confederates. Dr. Anson Hurd (with hat), regimental surgeon for the 14th Indiana Volunteers, was in charge.

The Federals kept trying to overrun the sunken road, unit after unit falling back from the sheets of southern fire, until some New Yorkers managed to find a spot from which they could shoot down upon the road's defenders. Then, one wrote, "We were shooting them like sheep in a pen. If a bullet missed the mark at first it was liable to strike the further bank, angle back and take them secondarily."

The sunken road—remembered now as Bloody Lane—rapidly filled with bodies, two and three deep, and the triumphant Federals knelt on top of what one called "this ghastly flooring" to fire at the fleeing survivors. "A frenzy seized each man," one New Yorker recalled, "and impatient with their [empty rifles] they tore the loaded ones from the hands of the dead and fired them with fearful rapidity, sending ramrods along with the bullets for double execution."

The Confederate center had splintered. One more push might have broken it apart, but McClellan decided it "would not be prudent" to attack again.

The third battle took place on the Confederate right, where General Ambrose Burnside's corps tried to fight its way across a strongly defended stone bridge over Antietam Creek.

Burnside was a tall, imposing man—his spectacular whiskers set a style that became known, by a play upon his name, as "sideburns"—but "[h]e shrank from responsibility," a friendly fellow officer said, "with sincere modesty," and he owed his position to his old friend McClellan, who now promised to support his assault across the bridge.

He had 12,500 men, against barely 400 Georgians. But the rebels commanded the bluff overlooking the bridge and their commander was Brigadier General Robert A. Toombs, who had wanted to be President of the Confederacy and had finally joined the army rather than abide the boredom of being Secretary of State. The southerners held Burnside up for three hours, fighting off four bloody charges before the Union army managed to cross the creek and began pressing the last Confederate line in front of Sharpsburg.

In the forefront of the struggle that afternoon were the flamboyant 9th New York Volunteers, the Fire Zouaves. "I was lying on my back," one recalled, "supported on my elbows, watching the shells explode overhead and speculating as to how long I could hold up my finger before it would be shot off. . . . When the order to get up was given I turned over to look at Colonel Kimball . . . thinking he had become suddenly insane."

The Zouaves charged into the guns, chanting "Zou! Zou! Zou!" Eight of them were blown to pieces by a single shell. Seven successive color bearers were hit, but the Confederates finally broke, racing back toward Sharpsburg. "Oh, how I ran!" one Virginian remembered. "I was afraid of being struck in the *back,* and I frequently turned around in running, so as to avoid if possible so disgraceful a wound."

The southern line of retreat to the Potomac was nearly severed. Union victory again seemed certain. "The Yankees appeared to think they had performed wonders," the Virginian wrote, "for instead of pursuing us and shooting us down, they began to give some regular methodical cheers, as if they had gained a game of baseball."

Watching from a hilltop, even Lee seemed to despair. Then, far to the south, he saw a dusty column coming up.

"Whose troops are those?" he asked an aide peering through a telescope.

"They are flying the Virginia and Confederate flags, sir."

It was the Confederate Light Division, arriving from Harpers Ferry: three thousand men, footsore from their rapid seventeen-mile march, but ready to fight, and commanded by A. P. Hill in the bright red shirt he always wore in battle. Many of those with him were wearing captured blue jackets, and, rather than shoot at men who seemed to be Union troops, the Federals held their fire until it was too late.

Now, as the fresh rebel army smashed into his flank, Burnside begged McClellan to send up the reinforcements he had promised. McClellan refused: "It would not be prudent," he said again.

As night fell, Burnside withdrew to the stone bridge his men had fought so hard to seize. The fighting died away.

It had been the bloodiest single day of the war. The Union lost 2,108 dead, 10,293 more wounded or missing—double those of D-Day eighty-two years later.

Lee lost fewer men—10,318—but that number represented a quarter of his army. "It was heart-rending," James Longstreet recalled, "to see how Lee's army had been slashed by the day's fighting. . . . Ten thousand fresh [Union] troops could have come in and taken Lee's army and everything it had."

"The wounded filled every building and overflowed into the country

"Before the sunlight faded, I walked over the narrow field. All around lay the Confederate dead, clad in butternut. As I looked down on the poor pinched faces all enmity died out. There was no 'secession' in those rigid forms nor in those fixed eyes staring at the sky. Clearly, it was not their *war."*

PRIVATE DAVID L. THOMPSON
9th New York

THE TERRIBLE REALITY

In late September 1862, Mathew Brady opened an exhibition entitled "The Dead of Antietam" at his New York gallery. The photographs were made by Brady's assistants, Alexander Gardner and James F. Gibson. Nothing like them had ever been seen in America before.

"The dead of the battle-field come up to us very rarely, even in dreams," wrote a reporter for *The New York Times.*

We see the list in the morning paper at breakfast, but dismiss its recollection with the coffee.

There is a confused mass of names, but they are all strangers; we forget the horrible significance that dwells amid the jumble of type. . . .

We recognize the battle-field as a reality, but it stands as a remote one. It is like a funeral next door. It attracts your attention, but it does not enlist your sympathy. But it is very different when the hearse stops at your own door and the corpse is carried over your own threshold. . . .

Mr. Brady has done something to bring to us the terrible reality and earnestness of the war. If he has not brought bodies and laid them in our door-yards and along [our] streets, he has done something very like it.

These rebel dead (above right), sprawled along the Hagerstown Pike, and the Confederate horse (below right), killed nearby along with its owner, Colonel Henry B. Strong of the 6th Louisiana, were photographed by Alexander Gardner on September 19, 1862.

Alexander Gardner made all three of these photographs: Confederates gathered for burial (above left); a southern soldier, still unburied, lies next to a northern lieutenant's fresh grave (below left); and the headboard of Private John Marshall, 28th Pennsylvania, not far from the Dunker church.

"It is so nearly like visiting the battlefields to look over these views," wrote Dr. Oliver Wendell Holmes, who saw them after visiting the battlefield in search of his wounded son, "that all the emotions excited by the actual sight of the stained and sordid scene . . . came back to us, and we [bury] them in the recesses of our cabinet as we buried the mutilated remains of the dead they too vividly represent."

round," a farmer's wife recalled, "into farm-houses, barns, corn-cribs, cabins—wherever four walls and a roof were found together."

While waiting for the surgeon who was to see to his shattered shoulder, a Union officer remembered, "Every few minutes an attendant would bring past me, to the open window, an arm, a leg, or a mangled hand, which he pitched into a little trench dug under the window for the purpose."

"I [had to wring] the blood from the bottom of my clothing before I could step, for the weight about my feet," Clara Barton wrote. She had come so close to the fighting that afternoon that as she bent over a wounded man a Confederate bullet clipped her sleeve and killed him.

Still, for all the carnage, the Union commander could finally claim a victory: Lee's invasion had been stopped. McClellan might have gone on to finish the war, as well. He had plenty of reserves waiting outside Sharpsburg, and Lee, now outnumbered three to one, braced for the attack he was certain would come the next day. "God bless you and all with you," Lincoln wired his commander. "Destroy the rebel army if possible." But McClellan did not attack, and on the 18th, the Confederate army slipped back south across the Potomac.

Lee's attack had been halted. He had suffered terrible losses. But his army had not been destroyed.

On October 1, Lincoln traveled to Sharpsburg to see his commander. His object, again, was to get McClellan to follow Lee's army. The general seemed to agree, as Lincoln remembered it: "I came back thinking he would move at once. But when I got home he began to argue why he ought *not* to move. I peremptorily *ordered* him to advance. It was nineteen days before he put a man over the river [and] nine days longer before he got his army across, and then he stopped again."

On October 8, the second Confederate invasion of the North that had begun that summer was also halted, as Federal forces under Don Carlos Buell beat back Braxton Bragg's Confederates at Perryville, Kentucky.

With both enemy invasions checked, Lincoln could breathe a little more easily—and give way a little to the impatience with his general that he had struggled to control all spring and summer. "I have just read your dispatch about sore-tongued and fatigued horses," Lincoln telegraphed McClellan on October 25. "Will you pardon me for asking what the horses of your army have done since the Battle of Antietam that fatigues anything?"

Lee's army continued to retreat back across the Blue Ridge Mountains with McClellan following along too far behind to close with him. On November 5, Lincoln relieved George McClellan of command; he was no longer willing, he told a friend, "to bore with an auger too dull to take hold." The general was sure he had been wronged. "They have made a great mistake," he said. "Alas, for my poor country!"

On November 10, McClellan reviewed his army for the last time. The men were "thunderstruck," an officer noted. "There is but one opinion among the troops, and that is that the government has gone mad."

Weeping color bearers hurled their regimental banners at McClellan's feet. Others silently watched him ride by, a soldier noted, "as a mourner looks down into the grave of a dearly loved friend." Elisha Rhodes mourned, too.

"We could see the deep sadness in [the President's] face, and feel the burden on his heart thinking of his great commission to save this people, and knowing that he could do this no otherwise than as he had been doing—by and through the manliness of these men."

COLONEL JOSHUA CHAMBERLAIN
20th Maine

Lincoln and McClellan confer in the general's headquarters tent at Antietam on October 4, 1862. Although McClellan told his wife that the President "was very affable & I really think he does feel very kindly towards me personally," the two men would never meet again.

"It was no longer a question of the Union as it was that was to be re-established. It was the Union as it should be—that is to say, washed clean from its original sin.... We were no longer merely the soldiers of a political controversy... were now the missionaries of a great work of redemption, the armed liberators of millions.... The war was ennobled; the object was higher."

GENERAL RÉGIS DE TROBRIAND

> This has been a sad day for the Army of the Potomac. General McClellan has been relieved from command and has left us.... This change produces much bitter feeling and some indignation. McClellan's enemies will now rejoice, but the Army loves and respects him. Like loyal soldiers, we submit.

The general returned to his home in New Jersey "to await further orders" that never came.

Lincoln believed that if Lee's army was driven from Union soil, it would be a sign that "God had decided the question in favor of the slaves." Antietam gave him the opportunity for which he had been waiting. On September 22—five days after the battle—the President issued his Emancipation Proclamation. "If my name ever goes into history," he said, "it was for this act."

> On the first day of January, in the year of our Lord one thousand eight hundred and sixty three, all persons held as slaves within any State, or designated part of a State, the people whereof shall then be in rebellion against the United States, shall be then, thenceforth, and forever free.

Jefferson Davis called Lincoln's proclamation the "most execrable measure recorded in the history of guilty man," even though it promised freedom only to those slaves living in regions still unoccupied by the Federal armies that might have made that freedom a reality. Slaves in the border states of Maryland, Missouri, and Tennessee remained in bondage. "The Government liberates the enemy's slaves as it would the enemy's cattle," said the London *Spectator,* "simply to weaken them in the coming conflict.... The principle asserted is not that a human being cannot justly own another, but that he cannot own him *unless he is loyal to the United States.*"

Emancipation: Lincoln reads his draft of the proclamation to his cabinet (above left). "I have got you together to hear what I have written down," Secretary of the Treasury Salmon P. Chase, shown standing at the left, remembered Lincoln saying before he began. "I do not wish your advice about the main matter, for that I have determined for myself.... I must do the best I can and bear the responsibility of taking the course which I feel I ought to take."

A Federal agent (far right) declares "thenceforth and forever free" a gathering of slaves on a Sea Island plantation. Once black recruitment began, "Contraband" Jackson (above right) could be transformed into "Drummer" Jackson of the 79th U.S. Colored Troops (right).

Abolitionists were not entirely satisfied either, but they were also not unduly discouraged: In his exemptions, Wendell Phillips said confidently, Lincoln "is only stopping on the edge of Niagara, to pick up and save a few chips. He and they will go over together." Most northerners now believed that slavery was doomed.

At a Washington dinner attended by cabinet members, John Hay, the President's secretary, noted that "everyone seemed to feel a new sort of exhilarating life. The President's proclamation had freed them as well as the slaves. They gleefully . . . called each other abolitionists and seemed to enjoy the novel accusation of appropriating that horrible name."

Many considerations kept Europe out of the conflict in America—not least among them the fact that the Union had the largest army in the world in 1862. (The second largest was the Confederate.) But the proclamation had just the effect Lincoln had hoped for abroad. Neither England nor France was willing openly to oppose a United States pledged to end slavery. "The triumph of the Confederacy would be a victory of the powers of evil," wrote John Stuart Mill, "which would give courage to the enemies of progress and damp the spirits of friends all over the civilized world. [The American civil war] is destined to be a turning point, for good or evil, of the course of human affairs."

"If anything can reconcile *me* to the idea of a horrid failure after all our efforts to make good our independence of Yankees," Mary Chesnut confided to her diary, "it is Lincoln's proclamation freeing the Negroes. . . . Three hundred of Mr. Walter Blake's negroes have gone to the Yankees."

THE NORTHERN LIGHTS

Ambrose Burnside, George McClellan's successor, led his grumbling army south through a cold rain toward Richmond in late November, determined to display the aggressive spirit that his predecessor had so conspicuously

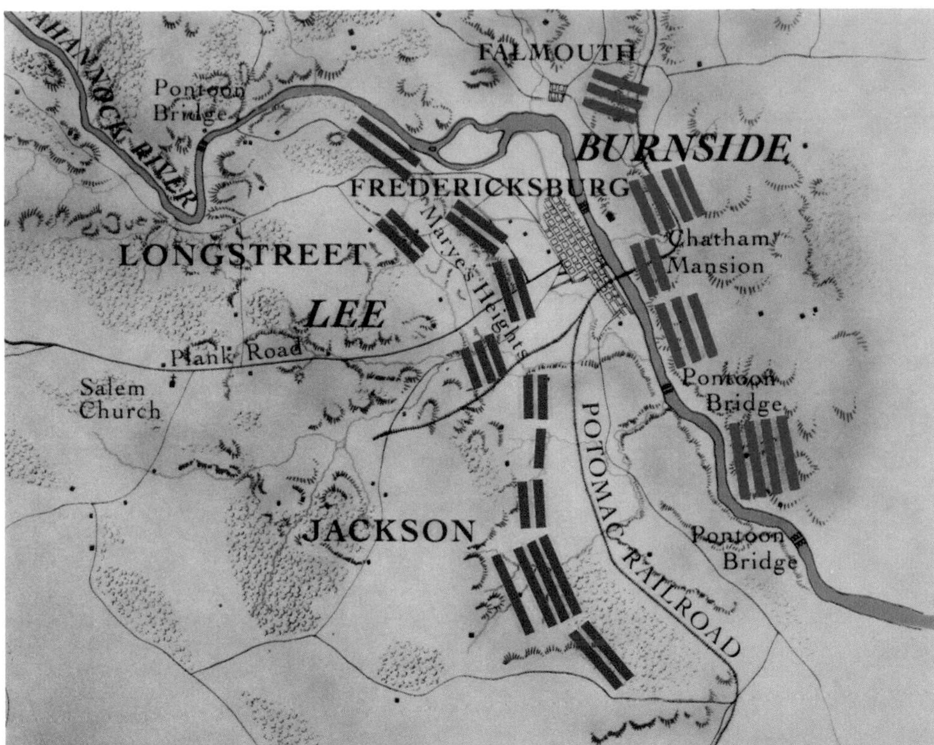

The Battle of Fredericksburg: On December 13, almost three months after Robert E. Lee began his withdrawal from Sharpsburg, McClellan's successor, Ambrose Burnside, managed to bring him to battle again, at Fredericksburg, Virginia. From the top of Marye's Heights, east of town, Lee could see the Chatham Mansion, where thirty years before he had courted his wife. It was Burnside's headquarters now, and from it the Union commander ordered his men to assault the impregnable center of Lee's line.

lacked. Bold action did not come naturally to Burnside. He was, for all his impressive looks and dignified air, an indecisive and anxious man, unpersuaded of his own competence, who had twice turned down overall command. "Few men . . ." a Massachusetts colonel wrote, "have risen so high upon so slight a foundation as [Burnside]."

A line of hills overlooked Fredericksburg, Virginia, and the gently sloping plain on either side of it. Burnside's plan was to cross the Rappahannock, occupy the town, and seize and fortify the hills before Lee could react. But when his 120,000 men arrived, the War Department let him down; seventeen days would pass before the pontoon bridges he needed to get across the river arrived, time enough for Lee to stretch his 75,000 men six and a half miles along the crests of the hills. Stonewall Jackson commanded the right of the rebel line, with A. P. Hill. James Longstreet oversaw the left.

The Confederates urged the people of Fredericksburg to abandon their town before the Federals attacked it. Six thousand civilians were suddenly without homes. "I never saw a more pitiful procession than they made trudging through the deep snow . . ." wrote a Virginia artilleryman, "little children tugging along with their doll babies . . . women so old and feeble that they could carry nothing and could barely hobble themselves. . . . Some had a Bible and a toothbrush in one hand, a picked chicken and a bag of flour in the other. Where they were going we could not tell, and I doubt if they could."

While the armies waited, they traded with each other, sending back and forth across the narrow river little fleets of makeshift boats loaded with Union sugar and coffee and newspapers to be swapped for southern papers and tobacco.

The 114th Pennsylvania Zouaves lunge forward to check a rebel counterattack during the initial Union assault on the Confederate left at Fredericksburg. "My men went in *beautifully,*" General George Gordon Meade remembered, "but finding themselves unsupported on either right or left, and encountering an overwhelming force of the enemy, they were . . . finally driven back."

Picket lines were so close to one another that the men could eavesdrop on one another's conversations. A Union veteran recalled: "The Confederates are said to have repeatedly remarked, 'Before you Yanks can get to Richmond you will have to get up Early, go up a Longstreet, get over the Lee of a Stonewall, and climb two Hills.' *I* never heard them say anything so allegorical."

"We were attracted by one . . . of the enemy's bands playing . . . their national airs," a Confederate officer remembered, "—the 'Star Spangled Banner,' 'Hail Columbia,' and others once so dear to us all. It seemed as if they expected some response from us; but none was given until, finally, [they] struck up 'Dixie,' and then both sides cheered, with much laughter."

Finally, on December 11, the Union forces began to shell Fredericksburg itself, setting much of the town on fire, then started to cross the river on six bridges under cover of their own artillery. "We had nearly two hundred cannon in position," Elisha Rhodes said. "The roar was tremendous. [As we crossed] the air was filled with shot and shell flying over our heads into Fredericksburg. The rebels did not often reply but would at times land a shot over onto our side."

Some wondered why the Confederates did not make it harder for them to cross. "They want to get us in," one veteran said. "Getting out won't be quite so smart and easy. You'll see if it will." While they awaited orders to move toward the hills, the Union men looted what was left of Fredericksburg.

The Union assault, when it finally came on the morning of December 13, was in two parts. Four divisions under General William Franklin attacked Jackson on the left. "Jackson appeared that day in a bright new uniform instead of his familiar rumpled dress . . ." General Fitzhugh Lee recalled. "It was a most remarkable metamorphosis . . . and his men did not like it, fearing,

as some of them said, that 'Old Jack would be afraid of soiling his clothes and would not get down to his work.'"

They need not have worried. "My men," he told an anxious aide, "have sometimes failed to *take* a position, but to *defend* one—never." The fighting seesawed back and forth for a time, and a Union division commanded by George Gordon Meade momentarily pierced Jackson's line, but artillery eventually drove the Federal forces back.

Meanwhile, the main assault force under Joseph Hooker was ordered to take Marye's Heights. Here, Confederate artillery was massed to cover all the approaches, and a four-foot-high stone wall ran along the bottom of the hill, behind which four lines of infantry were stationed to pour unbroken volleys on those who managed to survive the cannonading. "General," an artilleryman assured Longstreet, "a chicken could not live in that field when we open on it."

Lee could not believe the enemy would be so foolish as to attack Marye's Heights. Neither could some Union generals, who warned Burnside that to do so would be "murder, not warfare." Burnside pressed ahead regardless, and Hooker's men massed in and around the battered town. Then the signal was given. "The [Union men] . . . pour out upon the plain in a stream which seems to come from an inexhaustible fountain," wrote a reporter for the Richmond *Enquirer,* crouched down among the rebel defenders. "The meadows are black with them, tens of thousands in solid columns. We can only conjecture at this distance the number. Old soldiers think there are sixty thousand."

Joshua Lawrence Chamberlain.

The 20th Maine was made up of farmers and lumbermen, seamen and storekeepers and trappers, but its colonel was a thirty-three-year-old college professor, Joshua Lawrence Chamberlain. When Bowdoin College, where he taught rhetoric, oratory, and modern languages, refused him a leave of absence to enlist in 1861, he applied for a sabbatical to study in Europe, then volunteered.

On paper, his only qualification for command was that he was "a gentleman of the highest moral, intellectual and literary worth." But he seemed to have an inborn gift for inspiring men. "I wish you could hear [Joshua] give off a command and see him ride along the battalion on his white horse," his brother Tom wrote home. "He looks so splendidly. He told me last night that he never felt so well in his life."

Chamberlain's well-being was not the product of his diet: "What makes it strange," he wrote home, "is that I should have gained twelve pounds living on worms." Nor was he attracted by war's pageantry or glamour. Rather, he saw combat as "a test of character." "It makes bad men worse," he believed, "and good men better," and he resolved to be as good a soldier as he was a man.

Marye's Heights: The rebels stood behind the stone wall (opposite, far left) to shoot down the Union troops that Burnside sent running toward them. On May 3, 1863—a little less than five months after Fredericksburg—the Union would have its sweet but short-lived revenge on Marye's Heights. During the Chancellorsville campaign (above), Union troops under General John Sedgwick stormed over the stone wall that had earlier stopped their comrades, leaving behind these dead Mississippians belonging to General William Barksdale's brigade. The next day, the Confederates hurled them back again.

William Owen of the Washington Artillery of New Orleans watched from Marye's Heights as the Union line advanced toward his guns.

> How beautifully they came on! Their bright bayonets glistening in the sunlight made the line look like a huge serpent of blue and steel. . . . We could see our shells bursting in their ranks, making great gaps; but on they came, as though they would go straight through us and over us. Now we gave them cannister, and that staggered them. A few more paces onward and the Georgians in the road below us rose up, and, glancing an instant along their rifle barrels, let loose a storm of lead into the faces of the advancing brigade. This was too much; the column hesitated, and then, turning, took refuge behind the bank. . . . But another line appeared from behind the crest and advanced gallantly, and again we opened our guns upon *them.*

Among the attackers was the Irish Brigade, shouting "Erin go bragh!" and waving their green banners. They got within twenty-five paces of the stone wall. The men of the 24th Georgia who shot them down were Irish, too.

Longstreet compared the Union men falling before his guns to "the steady dripping of rain from the eaves of a house." A Union officer watched from a church steeple as brigade after brigade charged the stone wall. They seemed to "melt," he said, "like snow coming down on warm ground."

Fresh troops waited in the streets of Fredericksburg, trying not to look at the field hospitals, now filled with mangled men in agony but safe for the moment from the terrible fire. "I will never forget the joy of the wounded when they were brought into our lines," wrote General Regis de Trobriand. "One of them cried out, trying to raise himself from his litter, 'All right now! I shall not die like a dog in the ditch!'"

The 20th Maine, commanded by a former college professor, Joshua Lawrence Chamberlain, was among the last units to fight its way across the river. "The air was thick with the flying, bursting shells," Chamberlain wrote. "Whooping solid shot swept lengthwise our narrow bridge . . . driving the compressed air so close to our heads that there was an unconquerable instinct to shrink beneath it. . . . The crowding, swerving column set the pontoons swaying, so that the horses reeled and men could scarcely keep their balance."

Their advance on Marye's Heights was remembered by one of the Union men who had gone in earlier and now lay pinned down under enemy fire. "The 20th Maine . . . coming across the field in line of battle, as upon parade, the great gaps . . . plainly visible as the shot and shell tore through. . . . It was a grand sight and a striking example of what discipline will do for *such* material in *such* a battle."

The Maine men, too, soon found themselves hugging the ground.

Fourteen assaults were beaten back from Marye's Heights before Burnside decided it could not be taken. Nine thousand men fell under the Confederate guns.

Lee watched it all happen from above: "It is well that war is so terrible," he said, "we should grow too fond of it."

Night brought quiet, as Chamberlain recalled:

> But out of that silence . . . rose new sounds more appalling still . . . a strange ventriloquism, of which you could not locate the source, a smothered moan . . . as if a thousand discords were flowing together into a key-note weird, unearthly, terrible to hear and bear, yet startling with its nearness; the writhing concord broken by cries for help . . . some begging for a drop of water, some calling on God for pity; and some on friendly hands to finish what the enemy had so horribly begun; some with delirious, dreamy voices murmuring loved names, as if the dearest were bending over them; and underneath, all the time, the deep bass note from closed lips too hopeless, or too heroic to articulate their agony.

The temperature fell below freezing and a stiff wind blew across the battlefield. Men now froze as well as bled to death. Chamberlain tried to sleep: "It seemed best to bestow myself between two dead men among the many left there by earlier assaults, and to draw another crosswise for a pillow out of the trampled, blood-soaked sod, pulling the flap of his coat over my face

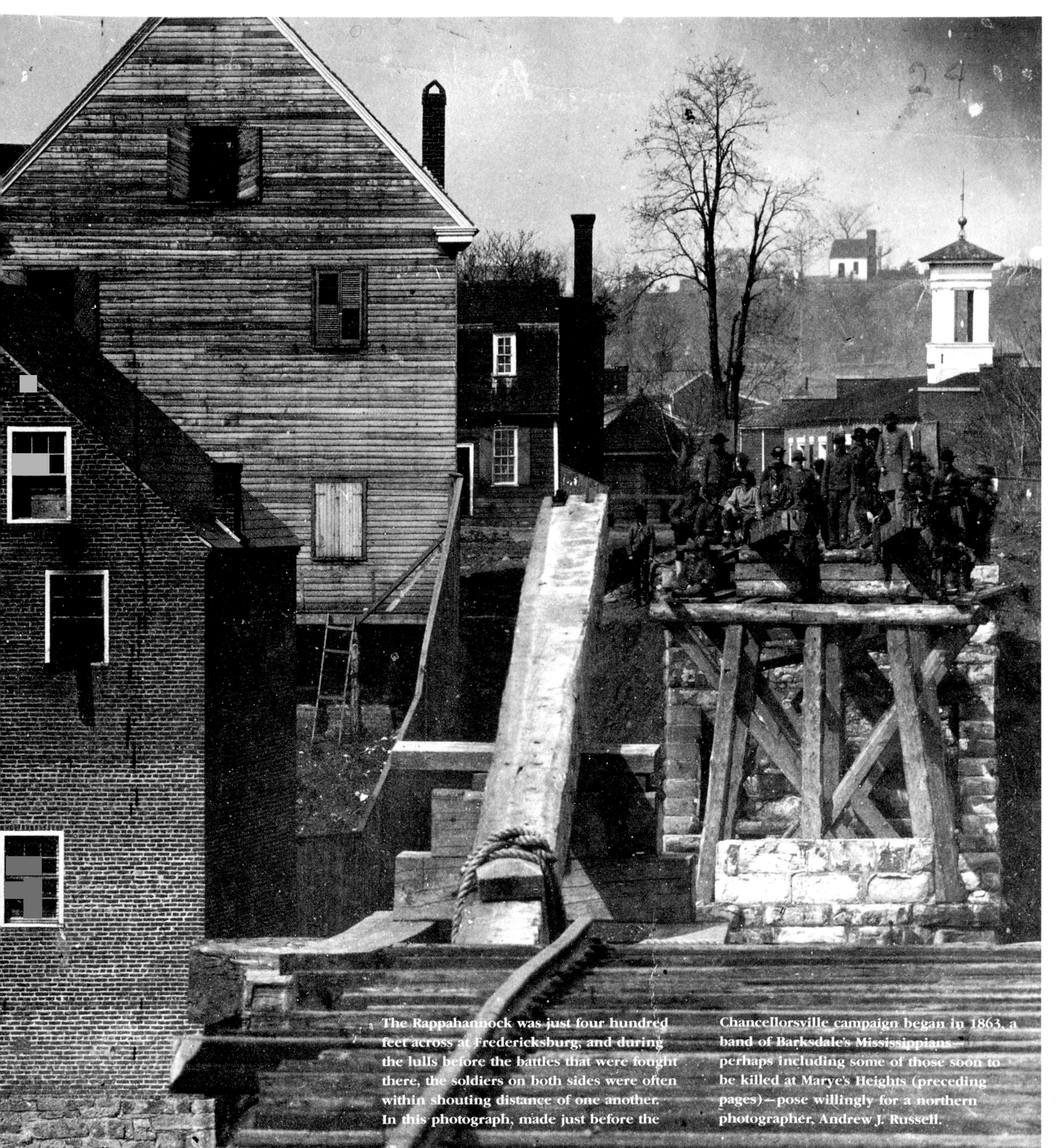

The Rappahannock was just four hundred feet across at Fredericksburg, and during the lulls before the battles that were fought there, the soldiers on both sides were often within shouting distance of one another. In this photograph, made just before the Chancellorsville campaign began in 1863, a band of Barksdale's Mississippians—perhaps including some of those soon to be killed at Marye's Heights (preceding pages)—pose willingly for a northern photographer, Andrew J. Russell.

to fend off the chilling winds, and still more chilling, the deep, many voiced moan that overspread the field."

The men from Maine remained trapped there all that night and all the next day, crouching behind a wall of their own dead, trying not to hear the Confederate bullets smack into the corpses of their friends.

Burnside, weeping openly, declared that he would lead a new attack himself; his subordinates talked him out of it and he decided to withdraw back across the Rappahannock. As he rode past his men, an aide called for three cheers for the general. Not one voice responded.

That night, Chamberlain and his men scraped out shallow graves for their dead. They had planned to give them "a starlight burial," Chamberlain remembered, and as they worked, the northern lights began to dance in the winter sky. "Who would not pass on as they did," he asked, "dead for their country's life, and lighted to burial by the meteor splendors of their native sky?"

Seeing the same display, some Confederates believed it a heavenly sign of their victory.

The Union lost 12,600 men. "Our poppycorn generals," wrote a Massachusetts private, "kill men as Herod killed the innocents." The Confederates lost 5,300, most of them missing, gone home for Christmas.

Rebel troops drifted down into what was left of Fredericksburg after the Union soldiers had finished burning and ransacking it. Stonewall Jackson came down, too, and when a member of his staff asked him what should be done with the sort of men who could do such things, he answered, "Kill 'em. Kill 'em all."

Salmon P. Chase was the most radical member of Lincoln's cabinet and burned with the desire to supplant his chief as President in 1864. The President would accept his resignation that year, explaining that their relations had reached a "point of mutual embarrassment" impossible to "overcome."

MY COUNTRY 'TIS OF THEE

"If there is a worse place than hell," Lincoln told a visitor that winter, "I am in it." The fall state and congressional elections had not gone well. Radical Republicans, angered that the President had remained loyal to McClellan so long and disappointed by the limited scope of the Emancipation Proclamation, failed to campaign wholeheartedly, leaving the field to the Democrats, who accused the administration of incompetence on the battlefield and of unconstitutional abuse of its power, both in curbing dissent and in daring to speak of freeing slaves. The Democrats took New York, Pennsylvania, Ohio, Indiana, and Lincoln's own Illinois, all of which had been in the President's column in 1860, as well as the governorship of New York.

Asked for his reaction to all this bad news, Lincoln said he felt like the boy who stubbed his toe—he was too big to cry, and it hurt too much to laugh.

The Fredericksburg disaster only made matters worse. The people of the United States, said *Harper's Weekly,* "have borne, silently and grimly, imbecility, treachery, failure, privation, loss of friends and means, almost every suffering which can affect a brave people. But they cannot be expected to suffer that such massacres as this at Fredericksburg shall be repeated."

"The fact is that the country is done for unless something is done at once . . ." said Senator Zachariah Chandler. "The President is a weak man, too weak for the occasion, and those fool or traitor generals are wasting time and

The U.S. Capitol, its dome still unfinished, dominated official Washington, but real power often lay elsewhere. "Of all detestable places," wrote George Templeton Strong after the briefest possible visit, "Washington is the first. Crowd, heat, bad quarters, bad fare, bad smells, mosquitoes and a plague of flies transcending everything within my experience. Beelzebub surely reigns here and Willard's Hotel is his temple."

yet more precious blood in indecisive battles and delays." Rumors circulated that Lincoln would resign in favor of Vice President Hannibal Hamlin, that McClellan would somehow be recalled to Washington to assume dictatorial power, that Radicals in the Senate planned to force the reorganization of the cabinet.

The Radicals did blame Secretary of State Seward for Union defeats and political losses. He was, one said, "the evil genius" of the administration, too willing to compromise with the South, too reluctant to move boldly against slavery. On December 16 and 17, Senate Republicans caucused and, with only a single dissenting vote, demanded that Lincoln dismiss Seward and reorganize his cabinet in the interest of "unity of purpose and action."

In this, they had the enthusiastic if clandestine support of Secretary of the Treasury Chase, who hoped to rid the cabinet of his chief rival and improve his own chances for the Republican nomination for President in 1864. This attack on his leadership by men of his own party at such a critical time deeply distressed Lincoln: "We are now on the brink of destruction," he told an aide. "It appears to me that the Almighty is against us."

"Christmas December 25, 1862. We have passed a very quiet day and except that we have been excused from drill, the day has been like others. . . . In the evening . . . we had a sing. I should like to be at home on this Christmas night."

ELISHA RHODES

A Union mess hall, tricked out with evergreens for Christmas dinner.

But in the end his old political shrewdness prevailed. Seward offered his resignation. The President held on to it, telling no one. Then, he brought a Senate delegation before his entire cabinet, minus Seward, and forced every Secretary—including Chase—publicly to affirm that the Secretary of State was a valuable member of the administration. Confronted with such apparent unanimity, the senators withdrew in confusion. Chase then tendered *his* resignation. Now, the Senate could no longer force Seward from the cabinet without losing Chase as well. Both men stayed on. "Now I can ride," Lincoln told an aide. "I have a pumpkin in each end of my bag."

On New Year's Eve, Elisha Rhodes took stock of the year just past:

> December 31. Well, the year 1862 is drawing to a close. As I look back I am bewildered when I think of the hundreds of miles I have tramped, the thousands of dead and wounded that I have seen. . . . The year has not amounted to much as far as the War is concerned, but we hope for the best and feel sure that in the end the Union will be restored. Goodbye, 1862.

That same evening, as midnight approached, a large crowd of black and white abolitionists gathered in the Music Hall in Boston to await the moment when Emancipation would become a reality. On the stage, Frederick Douglass wept with joy next to William Lloyd Garrison. The cheering crowd called for Harriet Beecher Stowe and she rose from her seat in the balcony, grateful tears in her eyes. A black minister, the Reverend Charles Bennet Ray, sang "Sound the loud timbrel of Egypt's dark sea, Jehovah hath triumphed, his people are free."

At a contraband camp near Washington former slaves testified. One remembered the sale of his daughter. "Now no more of that," he said. "They can't sell my wife and children any more, bless the Lord." Another former slave remembered:

> I was a young gal, about ten years old, and we . . . heard that Lincoln gonna turn [us] free. Ol' Missus say there wasn't nothin' to it. Then a Yankee soldier told someone . . . that Lincoln done signed the 'Mancipation. Was wintertime and mighty cold that night, but everybody commenced getting ready to leave. Didn't care nothin' 'bout Missus—was going to the Union lines.

On the Sea Islands off the South Carolina coast, Federal agents read the proclamation aloud to groups of former slaves; at Camp Saxton, the 1st South Carolina Volunteers, a new, all-black regiment commanded by a Boston abolitionist, Thomas Wentworth Higginson, held its own celebration. The chaplain read the proclamation, which was "cheered to the skies." Then, as Higginson unfolded a new American flag but before he could deliver his prepared remarks, the black troops broke spontaneously into song. "It seemed the choked voice of a race at last unloosed," Higginson wrote. The song they sang was "My Country 'Tis of Thee."

WHO FREED THE SLAVES?

BARBARA J. FIELDS

IN AUGUST 1862, ANSWERING THOSE WHO URGED him to proclaim emancipation a goal of the war, Abraham Lincoln bluntly summarized his policy: "If I could save the Union without freeing *any* slave, I would do it; if I could save it by freeing *all* the slaves, I would do it; and if I could save it by freeing some and leaving others alone, I would also do that." Although Lincoln privately believed that slavery was wrong and wished it might be abolished, his public policy faithfully reflected the standpoint of those for whom the war was an issue between free, white citizens: between unionists and secessionists, between right judged by free-soil northerners and rights claimed by slaveholding southerners. Those appointed or self-appointed as spokesmen for "respectable" opinion in the loyal states agreed on that premise even when they disagreed heatedly on the conclusion to be drawn from it. Some might believe that property rights, including rights to human property, must be held inviolable, others that slavery must not be allowed to spread, yet others that neither goal mattered compared to preserving the Union undisturbed. Nevertheless, as respectable citizens of sound and practical sense, all concurred that the aggrieved parties in the struggle of North against South were white citizens, and that the issue should be decided on the basis of what would best promote such citizens' desires and interests.

But wars, especially civil wars, have a way of making respectability scandalous and scandalousness respectable, and that is just what the American Civil War did. Abruptly, people whose point of view had never been respectable became the voice not just of morality but of practical common sense as well: abolitionists, black and white, calling not just for the containment of slavery but for its eradication; free black people demanding the right to take an active part in the war; and especially the slaves themselves, insisting on the self-evident truth that their liberty, like everyone else's, was an inalienable gift of God.

A black soldier in Louisiana, born a slave, dismissed with contempt those northerners, including Abraham Lincoln, who proposed to save the Union without disturbing slavery: "Our union friends Says the[y] are not fighting to free the negroes we are fighting for the union and free navigation of the Mississippi river very well let the white fight for what the[y] want and we negroes fight for what we want . . . liberty must take the day nothing Shorter." By the time that anonymous soldier's defiant manifesto, discarded on a street in New Orleans, was found by a policeman, Lincoln had been forced to recognize the truth it expressed. In issuing his final Emancipation Proclamation on January 1, 1863, Lincoln himself conceded that liberty must take the day, nothing shorter. Preserving the Union—a goal too shallow to be worth the sacrifice of a single life—had become a goal impossible in any event to achieve in that shallow form.

In truth, it had been impossible from the beginning. Once the Federal Union was breached, with its delicately wrought and euphemistically phrased constitutional protections for slaveholders, slavery could never again be safe. The wisest minds on both sides of the battle lines understood that perfectly. Wendell Phillips, the great abolitionist and campaigner against human oppression in all forms, reminded secessionists that "the moment you tread outside of the Constitution, the black man is not three fifths of a man,—he is a whole one." Brigadier General Daniel Ullmann, commander of a brigade of black soldiers in the Union Army, put the matter with vivid precision: "The first gun that was fired at Fort Sumter sounded the death-knell of slavery. They who fired it were the greatest practical abolitionists this nation has produced." Perhaps Ullmann had specifically in mind the white-haired veteran secessionist from Virginia, Edmund Ruffin, who claimed for himself the symbolic honor of firing the first shot at Fort Sumter (and who would later take his own life, unable to reconcile himself to the defeat of the Confederacy). Certainly conservative slaveholders had foreseen the danger and warned their fellow slaveholders that secession would unleash a revolution that must end with the destruction of slavery.

What was true from the beginning—and clear to the wise—was not immediately clear to everyone, however. Shortsighted rebels expected to preserve slavery while fighting for independence. Equally shortsighted unionists believed that they could forever compromise the issue of the slaves' freedom to suit the convenience of white citizens. Abraham Lincoln carefully tailored his policies and his public pronouncements to protect such unionists from the truth. In December 1862, three months after

announcing his intention to free slaves in the rebellious Confederacy, Lincoln proposed an unamendable amendment to the Constitution that would have postponed the final abolition of slavery in the United States until the year 1900.

Unlike Lincoln, the slaves harbored no illusion that a war to defeat secession could be anything but a war to end slavery. They knew ahead of Lincoln himself that he would have to take on the role of emancipator, and they acted on that knowledge before there was anything but blind faith to sustain it. Right after Lincoln's election, before even South Carolina had seceded, slaves deep in the South celebrated the coming jubilee. In April 1861, as Federal troops made their way through Maryland on their way to defend the nation's capital, a former slave told soldiers that he was sorry he had already paid his owner for his freedom. "If I had known you gun men was acoming," he observed dryly, "I'd a saved my money." A farmer in Monroe County, Alabama, wrote in distress to Jefferson Davis in May 1861—before the war had fairly begun—that "the Negroes is very Hiley Hope up that they will soon Be free."

At times the slaves' faith was not just blind, but mistaken. In August 1864, a slave in Maryland—who had heard, no doubt, of Lincoln's Emancipation Proclamation—wrote confidently to ask Lincoln's help in forcing her mistress to let her go free. Annie Davis believed, incorrectly, that the proclamation freed slaves everywhere. She did not realize that, in the loyal slave states of Maryland, Delaware, Missouri, and Kentucky, as well as in Tennessee and in the portions of Louisiana and Virginia held by the Federal army, Lincoln was more determined to retain the goodwill of the slaveowners than to secure the liberty of the slaves.

Even inevitable lessons do not necessarily come easy or cheap. Only gradually and at great cost did the nation at large learn that the slaves were more than property to be haggled over or offered as payment for the compromises of others. They were people: people whose will and intentions were as much a fact of the war as terrain, supplies, and the position of the enemy; people whose point of view must therefore be taken into account. The burden of teaching that lesson fell upon the slaves. Their stubborn actions in pursuit of their faith gradually turned faith into reality. It was they who taught the nation that it must place the abolition of slavery at the head of its agenda.

Officers and men of the armed forces were among the first to acknowledge practical reality, because it was they to whom the slaves first gained access. The deceptively simple first step in the process came when slaves ran away to seek sanctuary and freedom behind Federal lines, something they began doing as soon as Federal lines came within reach. And, unfortunately for Lincoln's plan to keep the question of union separate from the question of slavery, Federal lines first came within the slaves' reach in the border slave states that Lincoln was determined to keep in the Union at all costs. Slaves from loyal Maryland as well as rebellious Virginia fled to the Federal army during the Battle of Bull Run, the first engagement of the war. While unionists and secessionists fought openly for control in Missouri, slaves escaping from owners of both types made their way to Federal positions. In Kentucky, whose attempted neutrality both armies promptly challenged, slaves escaping from soldiers of the invading Confederate army joined slaves escaping from local owners in seeking refuge with Federal troops.

Once the slaves arrived, something had to be done about them. Deciding just what proved a ticklish matter, since every possible course—taking them in, sending them away, returning them to their owners, or looking the other way—threatened to offend some group whose goodwill the administration needed. Sheltering the fugitives would antagonize the loyal slaveholders, whose support underpinned Lincoln's strategy for holding the border slave states in the Union and perhaps wooing back to the Union some slaveholders within the Confederacy itself. But handing fugitives over to their pursuers would infuriate abolitionists. On principle, soldiers of abolitionist or free-soil leaning resisted orders to return fugitives; and even soldiers who held no strong convictions one way or the other resented being ordered to perform a menial chore—slave-catching—at the behest of arrogant masters and mistresses whom they suspected of feigning loyalty while secretly favoring the rebellion. Looking the other way and doing nothing could not resolve the problem either: each side would interpret any such attempt as a maneuver to help the other. Moreover, purely military considerations suggested that some slaves ought not to be returned to their owners: those assigned to work for the Confederate army and those who offered valuable intelligence or served as pilots and guides for Federal troops.

Lincoln did his best to evade the whole question, ordering his commanders not to allow fugitives within the lines in the first place. But orders could not stop the slaves from seeking refuge with Union forces; nor could orders prevent Union forces—out of altruistic sympathy with the fugitives' desire for freedom, pragmatic pursuit of military advantage, or a selfish desire to obtain willing servants—from granting the refuge sought. Whatever action military officials then took committed the government, visibly, to a definite policy concerning slaves and their owners. However politicians might strive to separate the war from the question of slavery, military men learned at first hand that the two were inextricably linked.

Eventually, the lesson learned in the field must impress itself as well upon politicians. Aggrieved slaveholders took their complaints to the press, to local officials, to their congressional delegations, to the War Department, or to Lincoln himself. Aggrieved soldiers and abolitionists did the same. Somewhere within the political system, someone would sooner or later have to act. Lincoln's first Secretary of War, Simon Cameron, acted too forthrightly. His public proposal that the Union free the slaves of rebels and enlist slave men as soldiers ensured his ouster from the cabinet. Cameron's successor, Edwin M. Stanton, knew better than to run his head into a hornets' nest. He carefully refrained from general pronouncements and, in answering inquiries from commanders in the field about how to deal with fugitives, perfected the art of the reply that contained no answer. Left without political guidance, some commanders fretted and floundered. Others took initiatives that enveloped the government in public controversy and turned the heat back onto the political officials who had hoped to escape it.

Twice Lincoln's commanders embarrassed him publicly by moving ahead of him on the question of emancipation. In August 1861, General John C. Frémont proclaimed martial law in Missouri and declared free all slaves of secessionist owners. Frémont refused Lincoln's order that he amend the proclamation. Accordingly, Lincoln amended it himself and, after a decent interval, relieved Frémont of command and appointed General David Hunter to replace him. Frémont's proclamation enraged unionist slaveholders but stirred the enthusiasm of abolitionists: audiences on the lecture circuit interrupted Wendell Phillips with wild applause and would not permit him to continue, once he mentioned the magic name of Frémont. In May 1862, General Hunter himself, by then transferred to command of the Department of the South (which included South Carolina, Georgia, and Florida), put Lincoln on the spot once more—and for higher stakes—by declaring slavery abolished throughout his department. This time the slaves at issue belonged not to loyal owners in loyal states but to unquestionably rebellious owners in the Confederacy itself. Upon Lincoln fell the onus—the disgrace, many believed—of abolishing Hunter's abolition, as he had abolished Frémont's.

While Lincoln, pursuing his own delicate political calculations, permitted himself the luxury of temporizing on the question, Congress took decisive action. In July 1861, responding to the many complaints it had received, the House of Representatives resolved that it was "no part of the duty of the soldiers of the United States to capture and return fugitive slaves." In August, Congress passed an act confiscating slaves whose owners had knowingly required or permitted them to labor on behalf of the rebellion. The language of the act left unsettled whether or not such slaves became free: the Union general Benjamin F. Butler popularized the term "contraband" to cover the uncertainty, and eventually "contraband" came to apply to virtually any slave the Union army or navy encountered. But for all its equivocation, the first confiscation act opened a door through which slaves fleeing military labor with the Confederate army could take the first step toward freedom; and it established a precedent for less equivocal actions to follow.

Before long, Congress proceeded from cautious first steps to much bolder ones. In March 1862, it adopted a new article of war that forbade military personnel—upon pain of court-martial—to return fugitive slaves to their owners. That key act provided runaways with useful military accomplices, especially after the Confederate invasion of Kentucky during the fall of 1862 swept large numbers of free-soil midwesterners into the ranks of the Union army. Shortly after adopting the new article of war, Congress abolished slavery in the District of Columbia and, later, in all the territories. In July 1862, over Lincoln's objections, Congress passed a second confiscation act that did what Frémont had tried to do in Missouri: it declared free all slaves whose owners supported the rebellion. In the same month, Congress authorized the enlistment of "persons of African descent" into military service. Above all else, it was military recruitment that doomed slavery in the loyal slave states. So far ahead of Lincoln had Congress traveled on the road to emancipation that, at the moment of its issuance, the final Emancipation Proclamation freed not a single slave who was not already entitled to freedom by act of Congress.

The initiative of the slaves forced Congress to act. Slaves could not vote, hold office, or petition for redress of grievances. They were not, in fact, citizens at all. But the war provided them a port of entry into the political system, a transmission belt to carry their demand for freedom from military lines to the highest levels of government, whether officials seated at the heights wanted to hear it or not. By touching the government at its most vulnerable point, the point at which its military forces were fighting for its life, the slaves were able to turn their will to be free into a political problem that politicians had to deal with politically.

Still, freedom did not come to the slaves from words on paper, either the words of Congress or those of the President. In an especially ugly episode, officials in Kentucky seized hundreds of refugees from Tennessee and Alabama who had followed the Union army north. Free in the Confederacy under the confiscation act and the Emancipation Proclamation, the refugees found themselves imprisoned and sold as slaves in the Union state of Kentucky, where slavery remained legal until the ratification of the Thirteenth Amendment eight months after the war was over.

Only a minority of slaves could free themselves by enlistment or escape, usually at the cost of leaving behind friends, family members, and painfully accumulated property. Spiteful owners took vicious reprisals against the families of those who left, especially if they left to become soldiers. And although the second confiscation act and the Emancipation Proclamation turned the armed forces of the Union into an engine of liberation within the Confederacy, nothing but the unarmed force of the slaves themselves could prevent owners from seizing them again once the troops moved on. After all, the main business of the army and navy was fighting the war, not protecting the freedmen.

Whether in the loyal slave states of the Union or in the heart of the Confederacy, the slaves themselves had to make their freedom real. Thousands of slave men gained freedom for themselves and their families by enlisting for military service. Others, temporarily assigned by Confederate authorities to perform military labor away from home, returned to spread subversive news—about the progress of the war or about the Union's emancipation edicts—among slaves hitherto insulated from events in the outside world. When rebel owners fled, fearing the approach of the Federal army, many slave men and women refused to be dragged along. Instead they stayed behind to welcome the Union forces, taking over and dividing the abandoned plantation property and setting up their own households and farms. Deep in the Confederacy, where they could expect no help from Union forces, slaves forced concessions from mistresses left to manage plantations on their own. Mistresses were ardent Confederate patriots and the bedrock upon which slavery rested. But with routine disrupted and able-bodied white men away at war, many had no choice but to make terms when the slaves slowed the pace of work or demanded wages before they would work at all.

The slaves decided at the time of Lincoln's election that their hour had come. By the time Lincoln issued his Emancipation Proclamation, no human being alive could have held back the tide that swept toward freedom. How far the slaves' freedom would extend and how assiduously the government would protect it were questions to which the future would provide a grim answer. But, for a crucial moment, the agenda of the slaves merged with that of the government. The government discovered that it could not accomplish its narrow goal—union—without adopting the slaves' nobler one—universal emancipation. That is what Spotswood Rice, an ex-slave soldier from Missouri, meant when he taunted his daughters' mistress with the boast that "this whole Government gives chear to me and you cannot help your self."

CHAPTER THREE

1863

THE UNIVERSE OF BATTLE

A Union encampment near Washington, D.C.

THE FIRE IN THE REAR

New Year's Day, 1863, found the Army of the Potomac miserably encamped at Falmouth, Virginia, on the northern bank of the frozen Rappahannock. The men had not been paid for six months, and while army warehouses at Washington were filled with food, little of it got to the winter camp. "I do not believe I have ever seen greater misery from sickness," wrote the Union medical Inspector General Thomas F. Perly, "than now exists in our Army of the Potomac."

"This morning," Elisha Rhodes wrote, "we found ourselves covered with snow that had fallen during the night. It is too cold to write. How I would like to have some of those 'On to Richmond' fellows out here with us in the snow." One Wisconsin officer called the winter of 1863 "the Valley Forge of the war."

The camps were filthy, a Sanitary Commission inspector reported, "littered with refuse, food and other rubbish, sometimes in an offensive state of decomposition; slops deposited in pits within the camp limits or thrown out broadcast; heaps of manure and offal close to the camp."

Hundreds died from scurvy, dysentery, typhoid, diphtheria, pneumonia. Disease was the chief killer in the war. Two soldiers died of it for every one killed in battle. Farm boys, crowded together with other men for the first time in their lives, were especially susceptible to every sort of ailment; there were epidemics of measles, mumps, and other childhood diseases. In one year, 995 of every thousand men in the Union army contracted diarrhea and dysentery. Medical care was primitive, at best, in both armies.

"All complainants were asked the same question," a Confederate physician remembered. " 'How are your bowels?' If they were open, I administered a plug of opium, if they were shut, I gave a plug of blue mass." "One of the wonders of these times was the army cough . . ." a Union soldier recalled. "[It] would break out . . . when the men awoke, and it is almost a literal fact that when one hundred thousand men began to stir at reveille, the sound of their coughing would drown that of the beating drums."

"Homesickness, too, set in," a Boston war correspondent wrote that winter, "and became a disease." The desertion rate grew to two hundred a day. By late January, a quarter of the men were absent without leave.

Eager to redeem himself after the terrible defeat at Fredericksburg the month before, General Ambrose Burnside now resolved to march his men north along the Rappahannock and try to get around the Confederate left. He promised to strike "a great and mortal blow to the rebellion." But as the army moved out, a steady, icy rain began to fall.

"Virginia mud," a Union officer explained later, "is a clay of reddish color and sticky consistency which does not appear to soak water, or mingle with it, but simply to hold it, becoming softer and softer."

"Men, horses, artillery, pontoons and wagons were stuck . . ." Elisha Rhodes noted in his journal. "The wagons began to turn over and mules actually drowned in the mud and water. . . . [Across the river] the Rebels put up a sign marked 'Burnside stuck in the mud.' We can *fight* the rebels but not in mud."

"January 11, 1863.

"Martha . . . I can inform you that I have Seen the Monkey Show at last, and I don't Waunt to see it no more I am satsfide with Ware Martha I Cant tell you how many ded I did see . . . one thing Shore I dont Waunt to see that site no more."

PRIVATE THOMAS WARRICK, C.S.A.

Confederate pickets struggle to stay warm near Fredericksburg, Virginia.

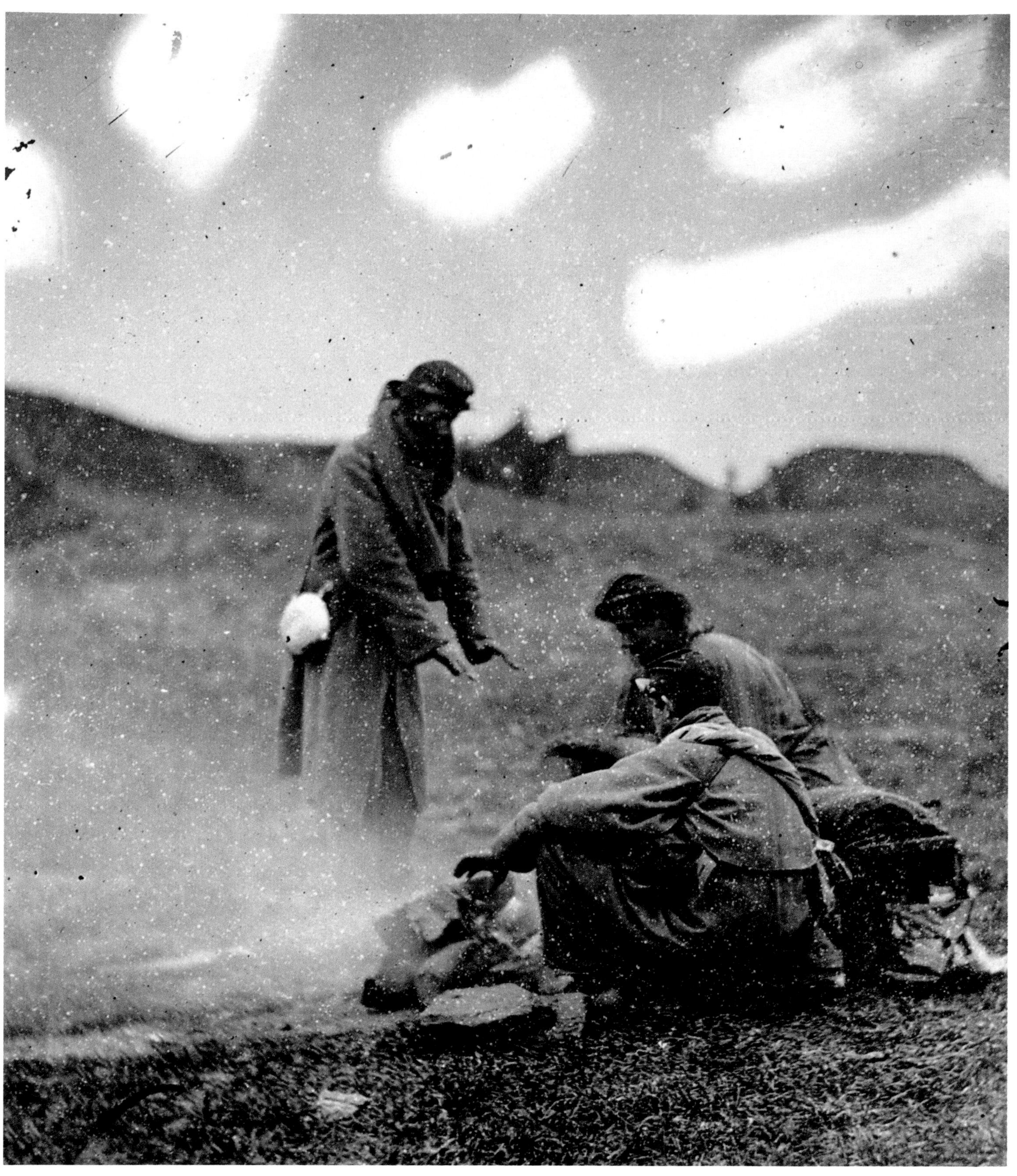

SENSATION PREACHERS . . . AND STRONG-MINDED WOMEN

Not long after Fort Sumter, northern citizens formed the United States Sanitary Commission to organize private relief and see that the rampant diseases that had caused four of five British deaths in the Crimean War that ended in 1856 were not visited on northern boys. Over the protests of army officers like the surgeon who dismissed them as "sensation preachers, village doctors and strong-minded women," Sanitary commissioners prowled the Union camps and hospitals, demanding that they be cleaned up, insisting on better food, making sure blankets and shoes and medicines and packages from home were distributed fairly. Their efforts paid off: the Crimean disease rate was halved.

Prominent men ran the commission. Frederick Law Olmsted, a designer of Central Park and an organizational genius, was general secretary; George Templeton Strong became treasurer. But hundreds of thousands of women in seven thousand local auxiliaries all over the North did much of the work: knitting, baking, wrapping bandages, organizing rallies, raising funds.

In September 1863, the Chicago headquarters of the commission sponsored a fair in the hope of raising $25,000 for relief. Few believed such a vast sum possible.

A gold watch was offered for the largest contribution and donations poured in. President Lincoln sent his personal copy of the Emancipation Proclamation. "I had some desire to retain the paper," he confessed, "but if it shall contribute to the relief and comfort of the soldiers, that will be better." In the end, the proclamation sold for $3,000 and Lincoln won the watch. When the fair closed two weeks later, its stunned organizers had brought in over $100,000.

The Brooklyn chapter then staged its fair—and raised $300,000 more. Soon, cities and towns all over the North were competing to see who could raise the most money to improve the lives of the men in the field.

Copies of this *carte de visite* portrait of young women dressed as nurses were sold to benefit the Sanitary Commission. The Philadelphia Sanitary Fair (right) realized more than $1 million for the welfare of Union troops.

"As to the politics of Washington, the most striking thing is the absence of personal loyalty to the President. It does not exist. He has no admirers, no enthusiastic supporters, none to bet on his head."

RICHARD DANA

Federal infantrymen guard the Chain Bridge across the Potomac, three miles upriver from Georgetown; it was one of the city's most heavily guarded—and frequently photographed—approaches to the capital.

After three days of this, Burnside called a halt to his "Mud March," and returned to camp.

The government at Washington was mired down, too, plagued by politics and rumor. Military failures and appalling casualties had fueled a growing peace movement. "Party spirit has resumed its sway," Seward wrote. "The president tells me that he now fears 'the fire in the rear'—meaning the [Democrats], especially at the Northwest—more than our military chances."

Opposition to the war was indeed spreading, notably among the Democrats in the heartland—Michigan, Ohio, Iowa, and especially Indiana and Illinois, where the new Democratic legislatures officially called for an armistice and repeal of the Emancipation Proclamation.

Southern sympathy was strong in the region; so was fear of free black labor. Democratic state conventions pledged to oppose Lincoln's "wicked abolition crusade against the South" and "*resist* to the *death* all attempts to draft any of our citizens into the army." Newspapers called openly for soldiers to desert.

"I am sorry," a midwestern father wrote his soldier son, "[that] you are engaged in this unholy, unconstitutional and hellish war . . . which has no other purpose but to free the negroes and enslave the whites. Come home. If you have to desert, you will be protected." All but thirty-five men of the 128th Illinois did desert over emancipation, declaring that they would "lie in the woods until moss grew on their backs rather than help free the slaves." Others allowed themselves to be captured and paroled.

Clement Vallandigham (center) and some of the admirers who hailed him as "Valiant Val." "Money you have expended without limits," he told House Republicans, "and blood poured out like water. Defeat, debt, taxation, and sepulchers—these are your only trophies."

The administration's decision to suspend habeas corpus continued to anger Peace Democrats. Lincoln had "swapped the Goddess of Liberty for the pate and wool of a nigger," said the editor of the Lacrosse, Wisconsin, *Democrat.* "[He] is the fungus from the corrupt womb of bigotry and fanaticism . . . a worse tyrant and more inhuman butcher than has existed since the days of Nero." "Not one of the many hundreds illegally arrested and locked up for months has been publicly charged with any crime," George Templeton Strong confided to his diary. "All this is very bad—imbecile, dangerous, unjustifiable." Resentment focused especially on Secretary of State Seward, who openly relished the power Lincoln's decision gave him. "If I tap that little bell," he told one visitor, "I can send you to a place where you will never hear the dogs bark."

Groups with names like Knights of the Golden Circle, Order of American Knights, and Sons of Liberty began to meet in secret and mutter about forcing an end to the war. Their enemies compared them to venomous copperheads, and some bore the name proudly, wearing on their lapels the heads of liberty, snipped from copper pennies.

The most flamboyant Copperhead spokesman was forty-two-year-old Congressman Clement Vallandigham, an Ohio preacher's son married to a Maryland planter's daughter, whose fondest dream was to restore what he called "the Federal Union as it was forty years ago." In the spring, he campaigned for

"Thair is a great controversy out hear about the nigger Question. . . . if they go to Sending them out hear to fight thay will get Enough of it for it Will raise a rebellion in the army that all the abolitionist this side of Hell could not Stop The Southern Peopel are rebels to government but they are White and God never intended a nigger to put White People Down."

SERGEANT ENOCH T. BAKER
Pennsylvania

Union soldiers under guard for some infraction of the rules: "We are bound up pretty tight here . . ." one Federal wrote home in 1863. "The military law is quite different from the Common law. We have to toe the mark."

the Democratic nomination for Governor of Ohio on a peace platform, calling upon soldiers to desert, declaring the South invincible, warning New England that if it persisted in supporting the war the western states might separate from it and rejoin the South. "You have not conquered the South," he said. "You never will. War for the Union was abandoned; war for the Negro openly begun and with stronger battalions than before. With what success? Let the dead at Fredericksburg . . . answer."

Under orders from the commander of the Department of the Ohio, the army arrested and tried Vallandigham for treason, finding him guilty and sentencing him to prison for disloyal utterances aimed at "weakening the power of the Government [to put down] an unlawful rebellion."

Democrats protested throughout the North. "[This arrest] is cowardly, brutal, infamous," said Governor Horatio Seymour of New York. "It is not merely a step toward Revolution, it *is* revolution . . . our liberties are overthrown." Even some Republicans were appalled that a civilian had been tried and sentenced by a military court merely for making speeches.

Lincoln had little sympathy for Vallandigham. "Must I shoot a simple-minded soldier boy who deserts, while I must not touch a hair of the wily agitator who induces him to desert?" he asked. "I think that in such a case to silence the agitator and save the boy is not only constitutional but withal a great mercy." But he did not wish to make a martyr of his political foe, and commuted his sentence to banishment in the South.

Ohio Democrats did nominate the absent Vallandigham for Governor and he eventually made his way to Canada by blockade runner, issuing campaign statements from a hotel room in Windsor.

OH! BE JOYFUL

"Is it possible that God will bless a people as wicked as our soldiers?" a Mississippi soldier asked. "I fear not. One unceasing *tide* of blasphemy & wickedness, coarseness and obscenity." The men bet on anything—boxing matches, horse races, cockfights, baseball games in which the bat was a barrel stave and the ball a walnut wound with twine. Sam Watkins remembered another kind of contest:

The boys would frequently have a louse race. There was one fellow [named Dornin] who was winning all the money. We could not understand it. If some fellow happened to catch a fierce-looking louse, he would call on Dornin for a race. Dornin would come and always win the stake. The lice were placed in plates—this was the race course—and the first that crawled off was the winner. At last we found out Dornin's trick; he always heated his plate.

There were 450 brothels in Washington alone, known to steady customers as "Fort Sumter," "Madame Russell's Bake Oven," "Headquarters USA." The men called visiting them "going down the line." An Illinois private reported to a hometown friend on the fun he was having: "I had a good time in Washington. . . . Lager beer and a horse and buggy, and in the evening 'Horizontal Refreshments,' or in plainer words, riding a Dutch gal—had a good time generally, I tell you."

The women trooped after both armies, taking up temporary residence in any town where soldiers seemed likely to be stationed for a while. Chicago, Cincinnati, Memphis, Louisville, Norfolk, New Orleans, St. Louis, soon all had thriving red-light districts. So did scores of small towns. At Richmond, prostitutes solicited on the grounds of the Confederate Capitol, and dared set up shop directly across from a hospital run by the Young Men's Christian Association. "I will state as a matter of history that female virtue, if it ever existed in this country, now seems almost a perfect wreck," a Confederate major wrote. "Prostitutes are thickly crowded through mountain and valley, hamlet and city."

One in ten Federal soldiers was treated for venereal disease during the war, and thousands more cases went unreported. The figures for southern soldiers were probably about the same. There was no effective treatment.

Liquor flowed freely, too: "No one agent so much obstructs this army . . . as the degrading vice of *drunkenness,*" McClellan thought. Total abstinence "would be worth 50,000 men to the armies of the United States."

If a soldier couldn't buy it, he made it. One Union recipe called for "bark juice, tar-water, turpentine, brown sugar, lamp-oil and alcohol." Southerners sometimes dropped in raw meat and let the mixture ferment for a month or so to add what one veteran remembered as "an old and mellow taste." The men called their home brews "Nockum Stiff," "Bust-Head," "Pop Skull," "Tanglefoot," and "Oh! Be Joyful."

Killing time: Officers of the 114th Pennsylvania at the poker table (left); Colonel S. W. Owen of the 3rd Pennsylvania (right) sleeps off a long night with his friends; those found in obvious violation of army rules appeared before the Provost Marshal (far right). The men at the top of the opposite page, stationed in Fort Pulaski in Savannah Harbor, play baseball, which was fast becoming the national pastime, North and South.

OFFICE OF THE
Provost Marshal

U.S.
Bordin
ANd
No Licker
Sold to
Soljers.
MEELS
AT ALL
OURS
Salt

"The army is the worst place in the world to learn bad habbits of all kinds. there is several men in this Regt. when they enlisted they were nice respectable men and belonged to the Church of God, but now where are they? they are ruined men."

PRIVATE DELOS W. LAKE
19th Michigan

The "U.S. Hotel D'Grub" was a storehouse run by the man in the cap and vest, Quartermaster William Jaquim of the 159th New York. The reassuring sign that liquor was not sold to the enlisted men may or may not have been accurate.

THE KINGDOM OF JONES

"If we are defeated," said the Atlanta *Southern Confederacy,* "it will be by the people at home." The new nation was showing signs of ancient strains.

"[President Davis] is ready for any quarrel with any and everybody, at any time and at all times; and the suspicion grows that rather than not have a row on hand with an enemy, he would make one with the best friend he had on earth."

Richmond Daily Whig

The Confederate Congress was quarrelsome and unpopular. It frequently met in secret, members elected from areas occupied by northern armies often failed to show up, there were no parties to impose discipline, and members routinely failed to reach consensus even on important matters. "They sat with closed doors," said Vice President Stephens. "It was well they did, and so kept from the public some of the most disgraceful scenes ever enacted by a legislative body."

Benjamin H. Hill of Georgia bloodied William L. Yancey of Alabama with an inkstand. The journal clerk of the House shot and killed the chief clerk. Henry S. Foote of Tennessee was attacked by colleagues at various times with fists, a Bowie knife, a revolver, and an umbrella. "Pardon me," a South Carolinian wrote his representative, "is the majority *always* drunk?"

The congressmen's dislike for one another was exceeded only by their dislike of Jefferson Davis. "The state of feeling between the President and Congress is bad—could not be worse . . ." said General Thomas R. R. Cobb of Georgia. "The embodiment and concentration of cowardly littleness, he garnishes it over with pharisaical hypocrisy. How can God smile upon us while we have such a man [to] lead us?"

Davis continued to make enemies more easily than friends. He quarreled with his commanders and agonized over minutiae. "From his uncontrollable tendency to digression," said Secretary of the Navy Mallory, "[cabinet meetings] consumed four or five hours without determining anything."

The Confederate President refused to unbend in public, or to curry favor with the press. He commuted nearly every death sentence for desertion that reached his desk, explaining that "the poorest use of a soldier" was "to shoot him," but kept his compassion a secret.

There was high turnover among the six offices in the Confederate cabinet—three Secretaries of State during the course of the war, and six Secretaries of War. The ablest cabinet member, Judah P. Benjamin of Louisiana, who served successively as Attorney General, Secretary of War, and Secretary of State, was mistrusted by much of the public because he was a Jew.

Davis's three most implacable enemies were all Georgians: ex-General Robert Toombs, who had wanted to be President himself; Governor Joseph Brown, who thought Davis a tyrant, trampling upon the States' Rights he was supposed to be upholding; and Vice President Alexander Stephens, who objected to conscription and the repeal of habeas corpus and believed Davis so "weak and vacillating, timid, petulant, peevish, obstinate" that he left Richmond in 1862, rarely to return.

Jefferson Davis, in one of his best-known photographic portraits. Once, walking in Richmond, he was stopped by a Confederate soldier on leave, who asked, "Sir, Mister, be'nt you Jefferson Davis?" Davis said he was. He had thought so, the soldier said. "You look so much like a Confederate postage stamp."

Davis was trying to win a war while forging a nation out of eleven states suspicious of even the most trivial move toward centralized government. The Governor of South Carolina professed to be appalled because troops from his state were sometimes commanded by officers from another. When Davis called for a day of national fasting, Georgia's Governor Brown ignored it, then

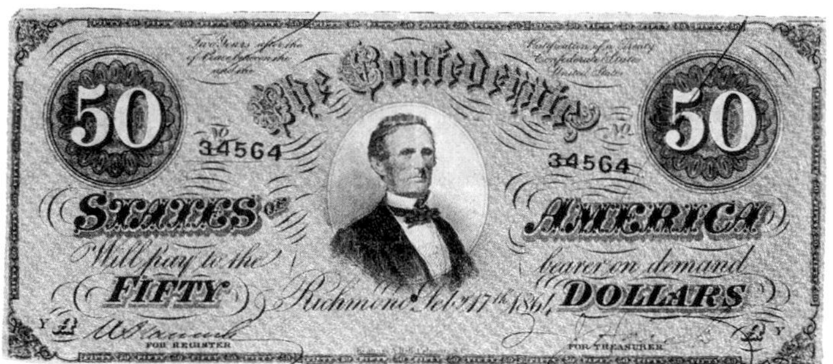

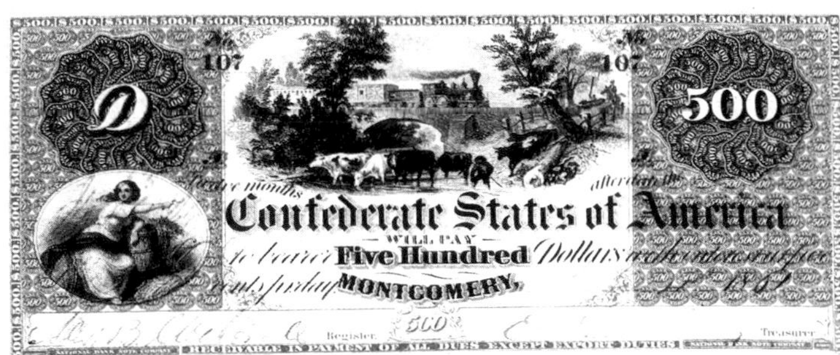

Currency circulating in the South was a confusing welter of notes issued variously by the Confederate Treasury (left) and the separate states (above), as well as by private companies, banks, railroads. "Great God, what a people—" wrote a Mississippi editor, "two hundred and fifty different sorts of shinplasters, and not one dime in silver to be seen."

named a different fast day of his own, explaining, "My position is the position of the old States' Rights leaders of the days of 1787. I entered into this Revolution to contribute my mite to sustain the rights of states and prevent the consolidation of the Government, and I am *still* a rebel . . . no matter who may be in power."

To pay for the war, Treasury Secretary Christopher Memminger cranked out millions of dollars in notes unbacked by gold; southern printing was so bad that counterfeiters were sometimes caught because their products looked so much better than the real thing. Congress finally worked out a formula for taxing personal possessions—gold watches, pianos, carriages—but not slaves, thanks to effective lobbying by the big planters.

Farmers were called upon to contribute one-tenth of their produce. Large landowners complained loudly about that, too, although they could afford the loss far better than the small producers already suffering most. A poor North Carolina farmer complained to his Governor: "The slaveowner has the plantations & the hands to raise the breadstuffs & the common people is drove off in the war to fight for the big man's Negro & he at home making nearly all the corn that is made . . . puts the price on his corn so as to take all the soldier's wages for a few bushels. . . . It seems that all hearts is turned to gizzards."

An impressment act empowered the army to seize crops and livestock in exchange for increasingly valueless scrip. "Beardless and senseless boys," wrote the Richmond *Market,* "who do not know how many bushels of wheat it takes to make a barrel of flour, are sent through the country with authority to impress supplies for the army without knowing what is needed." Poor farmers hid their grain and drove their herds into the woods rather than give them up. In one Louisiana parish, a farmer told an officer he would "prefer seeing Yankees to our cavalry." "There are soldiers' families in my neighborhood," wrote a resident of Calhoun County, Florida, "that the last head of cattle have been taken from them, and drove off, and they left to starve."

The army was also authorized to impress male slaves as laborers, paying a monthly fee to their often resentful masters. "Patriotic planters would willingly put their own flesh and blood into the army," said Senator Louis T. Wigfall of Texas, but when they were asked for a slave it was like "drawing an eyetooth." Impressment interfered with the smooth operation of big planta-

A plantation at Beaufort, South Carolina, photographed during the Federal occupation that began in 1862.

tions, often spread disease among the slaves, and by introducing local slaves to slaves from elsewhere, encouraged running away. A black "infected with strange philosophies," warned Senator James Hammond of South Carolina, "[might] demoralize a dozen negro settlements."

Captured runaways were brutally punished. "They are traitors of the worst kind," a slaveowner wrote, "and spies also, who may pilot the enemy into your bedchamber . . . and [should] no doubt be *treated* as spies." To hold on to their slaves, some planters drove them inland to backwaters "remote from all excitement." One hundred and fifty thousand were marched all the way to Texas. Hundreds, perhaps thousands, died along the way.

Still, the flight of slaves toward Union lines steadily accelerated. "Negro property is a most unmanageable property," one abandoned master said, "and has been our ruin." "Fifty-one slaves have already gone from this county," a Georgia planter told his son. "Your Uncle John has lost *five. Three* are said to have left from your Aunt Susan's and Cousin Laura's; one was captured, two not. . . . The temptation of *cheap goods, freedom* and *paid labor* cannot be withstood."

"If hell has any . . . particular corner especially heated, my prayer to God is that every man (or pretended man) shall be consigned to that department who speculates in food or clothing, and the necessaries of life in these troublous times."

Southern Watchman,
Athens, Georgia

Meanwhile, misery had begun to reach from the countryside into southern towns and cities. A Confederate clerk noted in his journal:

> Richmond. February 11th. Some idea may be formed of the scarcity of food in this city from the fact that, while my youngest daughter was in the kitchen today, a young rat came out of its hole and seemed to beg for something to eat; she held out some bread which it ate from her hand and seemed grateful. Several others soon appeared and were as tame as kittens. Perhaps we shall have to eat them!

Richmond fishmongers hiked their prices, and hired thugs to ensure they were not undersold. Merchants filled warehouses with barrels of flour, then held them for the highest possible price. On the eve of one major battle, speculators bought up all the coffins and mourning crepe in town, then jacked up the prices. "Had these contemptible wretches the power," said the Richmond *Examiner,* "they would bottle the universal air and sell it at so much a bottle."

Some—including many of the region's wealthiest planters—also traded more or less openly with the North, bribing troops on both sides of the line to look the other way while bales of cotton moved north, and gold and Federal currency made their way south. When the wife of one Mississippi planter objected, he told her, "I wish to fill my pockets. I can in five years make a larger fortune than ever."

Nothing embittered soldiers at the front more than the knowledge that comfortable civilians were further enriching themselves at their expense. "The fact is," an officer wrote home, "that . . . Yankee gold is fast accomplishing what Yankee arms could never achieve—the subjugation of our people."

The average family food bill rose from $6.65 per month before Fort Sumter to $68 dollars by mid-1863, and a single cake of soap cost $1.10—a tenth of a soldier's monthly pay. Northern greenbacks were worth four times as much as Confederate bills throughout the South, and northern gold pieces were especially sought after—even in economic terms, it was hard for the South to remain truly independent.

Prices continued to rise 10 percent a month. "You take your money to the market in the market basket," wrote a South Carolina judge, "and bring home what you buy in your pocketbook." By autumn, a barrel of flour at Richmond would cost $70. By year's end it would cost $250, a pair of shoes between $200 and $800, and an officer's uniform *$2,000.*

A soldier wrote home that with soaring liquor prices "it would cost about fifty dollars [just] to get tight here." Beggars who had once asked for a nickel now demanded a dollar.

While the northern blockade remained in place, the low, sleek, gray-painted Confederate blockade runners—the *Banshee, Let Her Be, Let Her Rip, Leopard, Lynx, Stonewall Jackson, Jeff Davis, Lady Davis*—continued to slip through the Union cordon, carrying cotton to Bermuda or Nassau and bringing back precious manufactured goods, luxury items—and some 600,000 rifles.

A Confederate sergeant from Virginia with his brother and sister. "Diere Sisteer," an Alabama soldier wrote home, "So fur I have cum out Saft . . . [they] Shot a hole throw my Sacel an I had hit on my back but a mis is as good as a mile Dear Sisteer I want you to write to me and giv me all the nus I can Say to you that brother James got woned in the thy."

Fifteen hundred blockade runners were seized, sunk, or burned by Federal ships during the war, but hundreds more made it through; one vessel, the *Hattie,* did so sixty times. Mary Chesnut noted the lift to civilian spirits their arrival gave: "An iron steamer has run the blockade at Savannah. We raise our wilted heads like flowers after a shower."

Still, Union patrols probably kept hundreds more ships from ever setting out for southern ports. Demand quickly overwhelmed the supply of smuggled goods, and scarcity made southerners inventive. Women saved their family's urine from which to make niter for gunpowder. "Confederate needles" were made from hawthorn bushes, paint brushes from hog bristles, rope from Spanish moss, red dye from figs, tea from raspberry leaves. Substitutes for coffee included ground parched peas, corn, chicory, beets, okra and pumpkin seeds, acorns. "In fact, all that is wanted is something to color the water," said the Macon *Daily Telegraph.* "It is coffee or dirty water, just as you please."

The Confederate medical department urged people to gather snakeroot, pokeweed, skunk cabbage, dandelions as medicines. Even wealthy young ladies learned to make do, as an anonymous poet wrote:

My homespun dress is plain, I know.
My hat's palmetto, too.
But then it shows what Southern girls
For Southern rights will do.
We have sent the bravest of our land
To battle with the foe
And we will lend a helping hand—
We love the South, you know.

Colleges and universities shut their doors; their students were off at the front. Many country public schools closed down, too, because local communities were no longer able to pay teachers or provide approved Confederate textbooks. "If one Confederate soldier kills 90 Yankees," asked one of these, "how many Yankees can 10 Confederate soldiers kill?"

On April 2, 1863, hundreds of women, infuriated by soaring prices, stormed through downtown Richmond shops, smashing windows and gathering up armfuls of food and clothing. Troops ordered them to halt. Jefferson Davis himself came out and spoke to them. "You say you are hungry and have no money," he shouted. "Here is all *I* have." He flung a handful of coins among the angry women, begged them to blame the Yankees, "who are the authors of

Farm women take a moment from their sewing at Cedar Mountain, Virginia.

all our troubles," not his government, and warned that troops would open fire in five minutes. The crowd did not move as four long minutes ticked by. Davis consulted his pocket watch. "My friends," he said, "you have one minute left." The women straggled home. Davis had the ringleaders arrested and briefly jailed.

Similar incidents took place in Augusta, Columbus, Milledgeville, Mobile, and half a dozen other towns. From a North Carolina farm a desperate woman wrote to her governor: "A crowd of we Poor women went to Greenesborough yesterday for something to eat as we had not a mouthful of meet nor bread in my house what did they do but put us in gail in plase of giving us aney thing to

"You kiss Soo for me and tell Soo to kiss you and by manageing the thing that way, I will get two kisses, and tell Feb if he possibly can steal a kiss from Miss Bettie and after he kisses her tell her it was for me I would be very glad indeed, I would."

PRIVATE WILLIAM H. PHILLIPS, C.S.A.
to his cousin

eat. . . . I have 6 little children and my husband is in the armey and what am I to do?" There was no answer, and, fearful of further damaging morale, the government urged southern newspapers not to report such incidents.

Class divisions remained intact. A well-to-do Georgia planter scorned poor white recruits as "not the men upon whom a brave leader would rely for energetic, heroic action, [but] they will answer as food for powder and understand how to use the spade." And a South Carolina woman who nursed the wounded professed to see innate differences even in the hospital wards: "The better-born, that is, those born in the purple, the gentry, were the better patients: *they* endured in silence."

Wealthy soldiers found it easy to get passes to visit home from time to time. The poor were expected to stay at the front. "This damned ginral won't give you a furlough or a discharge till you are dead ten days," a Georgia private complained, "and *then* you have to prove it."

Many men were driven to desert by bleak letters from home. "Our son is lying at death's door," a woman known to history only as "Louisa" wrote her husband. "He cannot live long for the fix he is in. He is raving distracted. His earnest calls for Pa almost breaks my heart. John, come if you can. If they will not let you off, I don't know the reason."

"I saw a site today that made me feel mity Bad," an Alabama private wrote home. "I saw a man shot for deserting there was twenty fore Guns shot at him thay shot him all to pease . . . he went home and thay Brote him Back and then he went home again and so they shot him for that Martha, it was one site that I did hate to see it. But I could not helpe my self I had to do Jest as thay sed for me to doo."

By the end of the year, and despite the threat of such punishments, two-fifths of the southern army would be absent, with or without leave.

A Confederate officer, dispatched into the South Carolina hills to persuade another band of deserters to return to the army, explained his failure: "The people there are poor, ill-informed, and but little identified with *our* struggle. They have been easily seduced from their duty."

Deserters sometimes banded together in remote areas, driving off with rifle fire the troops sent to round them up. Union supporters supplied them with food and clothing.

From a Mississippi cave called "Devil's Den" on an island in the Leaf River, a unionist guerrilla band led by a former shoemaker named Newton Knight controlled most of Jones County. He and his men ran off tax collectors, burned bridges, and ambushed Confederate columns for nearly three years. Newspapers called their region "the Kingdom of Jones."

By the war's end, unionists in every state in the Confederacy except South Carolina had sent regiments of white troops to fight for the North.

UNDER THE SHADE OF THE TREES

Shortly after the Mud March, Lincoln replaced Ambrose Burnside with Joseph Hooker, the Massachusetts soldier who had demonstrated his tenacious courage on the Peninsula and at Antietam, but who also drank and talked too much for his own good. After Fredericksburg he had confided to a newspaperman that a dictator was needed to win the war. Lincoln had heard such talk before, and wrote to tell him so:

> General: I have placed you at the head of the Army of the Potomac. I have heard, in such a way as to believe it, of your recently saying that both the Army and the Government needed a dictator. Of course it was not for this, but in *spite* of this, that I have given you the command. Only those generals who gain successes can set up dictators. What I now ask of you is military success and I will risk the dictatorship. . . . Give us victories.
>
> Yours very truly,
> A. Lincoln

Hooker professed to be grateful for this letter; it was, he said, just the sort of letter a loving father would write to an errant son, and he vowed to prove worthy of it. The general cleaned up the camps, made sure his men were paid and fed, tightened discipline, and devised insignia badges for the men of each corps to boost morale. "Under Hooker," a soldier recalled, "we began to *live.*"

"My plans are perfect," Hooker said. "May God have mercy on General Lee, for *I* will have none." His plans called for one part of his enormous army under

Joseph Hooker's strategy to outsmart Robert E. Lee: While part of his army kept Lee pinned down at Fredericksburg, Hooker (opposite) planned to swing his main force to the north and west of the rebels and come upon them from behind. On paper, the plan looked masterful.

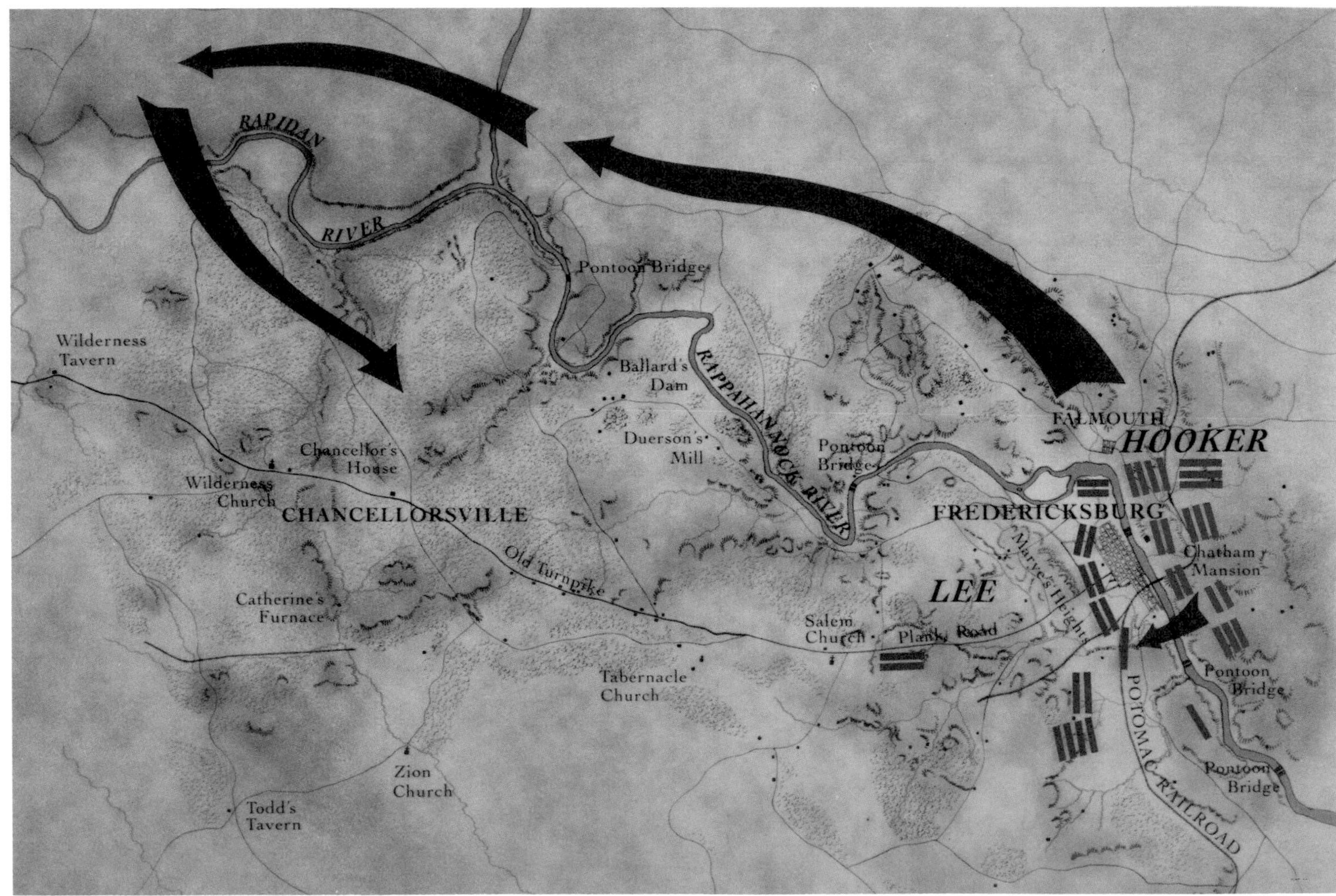

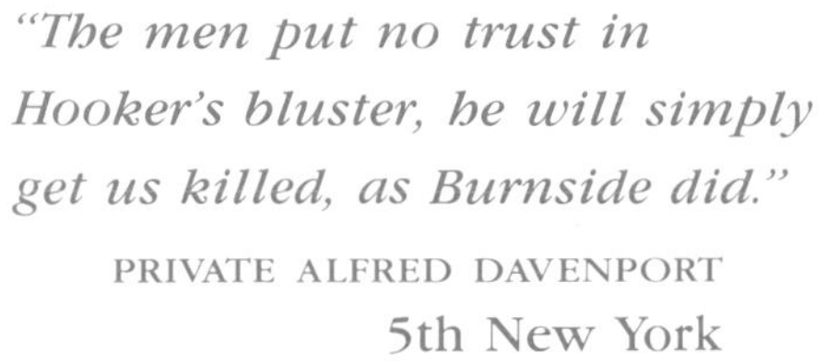

"The men put no trust in Hooker's bluster, he will simply get us killed, as Burnside did."

PRIVATE ALFRED DAVENPORT
5th New York

General John Sedgwick to demonstrate against Lee's front, still at Fredericksburg, while the main body was to march up the Rappahannock, cross the river, attack him from the rear, destroy his army, and move on to seize Richmond.

"Everyone repeated 'Lee is in our power!'" a Union officer remembered. "Nobody doubted that before two days all our past reverses would be effaced by the annihilation of [his] Army." Lincoln was hopeful, too, but also wary. "The hen is the wisest of all the animal creation," he said, "because she never cackles until *after* the egg is laid."

On April 27, Hooker began moving toward Chancellorsville, ten miles west of Fredericksburg. Chancellorsville was not a town but a solitary house in the midst of a cultivated clearing, surrounded on all sides by woods. "The house," an Iowa private remembered, was "of the Southern type, belonging to a well-known family of the neighborhood, still occupied by the women. Upon the upper porch was quite a bevy of ladies in light, dressy, attractive spring costumes. They scolded [us] audibly and reviled [us] bitterly. [Before] another day was over they would pitifully plead to be carried to a place of safety."

Hooker and his officers moved in downstairs, confident that within forty-eight hours they would destroy Lee's army. "The enemy must either ingloriously fly," Hooker said, "or come out from behind his defences and give us battle upon our own ground, where certain destruction awaits him."

Lee was again outnumbered nearly two to one: he had fewer than 60,000 men to Hooker's 115,000. But he was not fooled by Hooker's feint at Fredericksburg, and now defied military convention and split his smaller force, leaving just 10,000 men there and rushing the others west to shore up his flank.

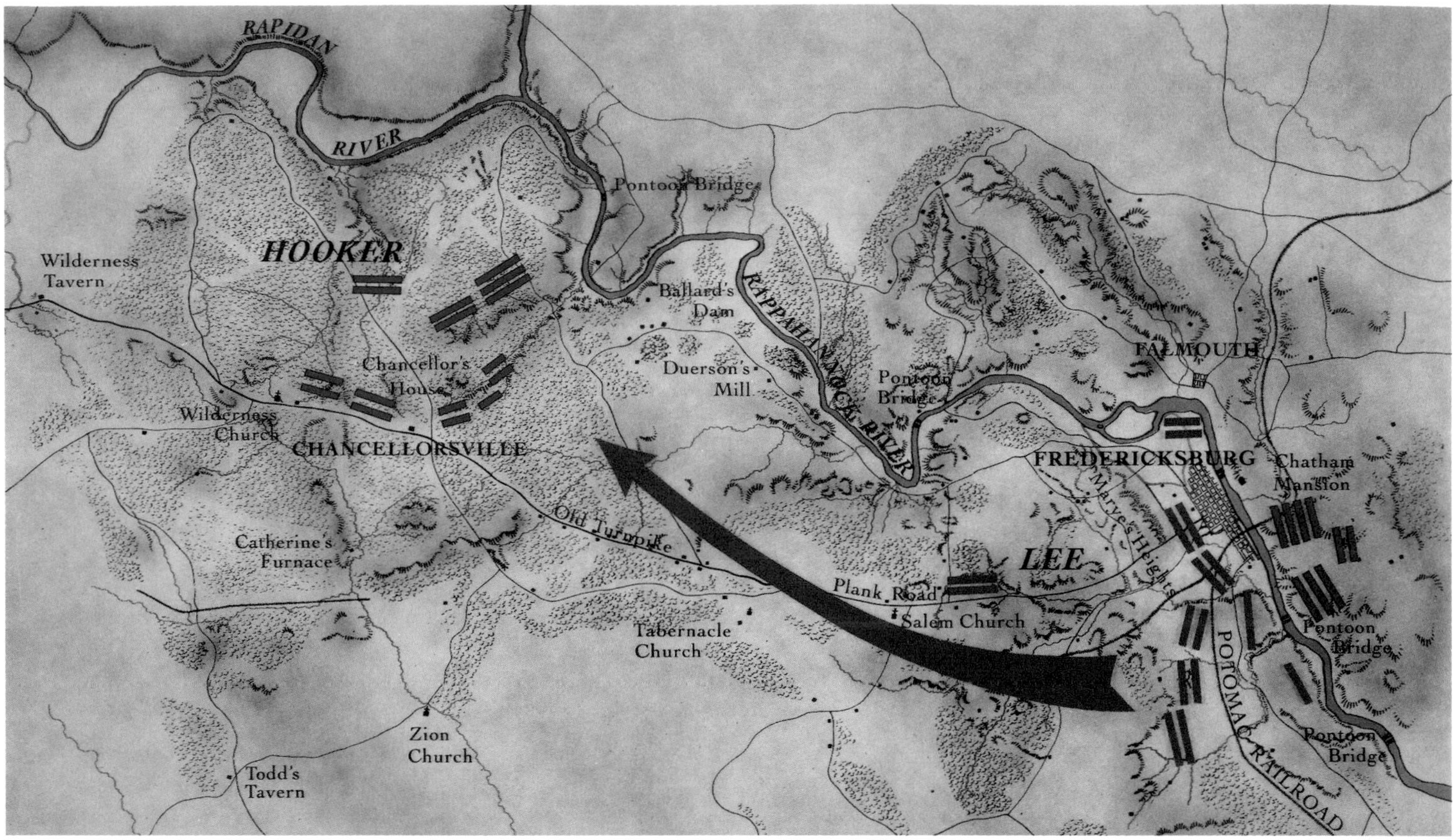

On May 1, Hooker's men began moving south toward the Confederate lines. The woods were so dense and tangled that the local people called them the Wilderness. It was slow going but they had nearly made it out of the thickets when the Confederates opened fire. Then, inexplicably, Hooker ordered his forces back to Chancellorsville, leaving the woods—and the initiative—to the Confederates. "To tell the truth," Hooker later said, "I just lost confidence in Joe Hooker."

That night, Stonewall Jackson persuaded Lee to divide his army a second time, and the next day led 26,000 men on a fourteen-mile march to attack the Union's right flank. Hooker, warned of their approach, somehow persuaded himself that Jackson was retreating.

All day long came reports from terrified Union pickets of rebel forces moving just beyond the screen of trees to the west. They were ignored. At about 5:30 that afternoon, the men on the Union right were boiling coffee and playing cards when deer suddenly came bounding through their camp. Jackson's men were right behind them. "It was a perfect whirlwind of men," a survivor said. "The enemy seemed to come from every direction." The Federals fell back two miles before Union artillery and falling darkness stopped the Confederate sweep just short of the Chancellor House.

Eager to continue the fight, Jackson and several of his officers rode out

Robert E. Lee's daring counterstroke: Seeing Hooker coming, he defied all military convention and divided his outnumbered force, rushing most of his men west to halt the Federal advance on May 1, 1863.

The Chancellor House, in which Hooker made his headquarters and around which he concentrated his army at the end of the first day's fighting, to the astonishment of his own officers and the delight of the enemy.

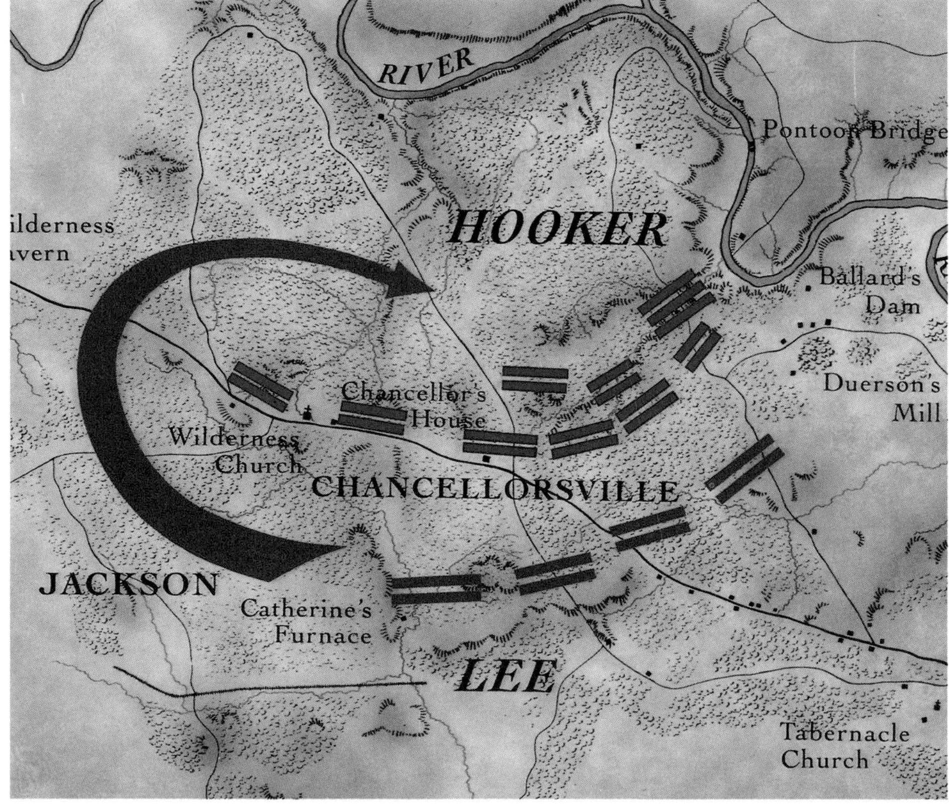

Stonewall Jackson moves in for the kill: Dividing his army yet again, Lee sent Jackson and 28,000 men—guided by a local civilian who knew the way through the dense Wilderness—marching around Hooker's lines to attack the Union right on the morning of May 2.

Robert E. Lee and Stonewall Jackson met for the last time shortly before midnight on May 1 (left) to discuss the strategy by which the Confederates would drive Hooker's army all the way back to the Chancellor House by the end of the following day.

between the lines to reconnoiter for a night attack. Union pickets fired at them, and when Jackson wheeled back toward his own lines, jumpy Confederate pickets mistook his shadowy party for northerners and also opened fire. Two of Jackson's aides fell dead from their saddles; Jackson himself was hit once in the right hand and twice in the left arm.

He was carried to a field hospital, where his shattered arm was amputated the next morning. Lee was horrified. "He has lost his left arm," he said, "but I have lost my right."

Meanwhile, Union troops again advanced across the Fredericksburg plain, where nine thousand of their comrades had fallen just five months before. This time, they overwhelmed the defenders, jumped over the stone wall at the foot of the hill and swarmed to the summit—only to be pushed off again the next day by Confederate troops under Jubal Early.

By then, the Union defeat was nearly total. Hooker had continued to bumble: he abandoned a hilltop, allowing Confederate artillery to fire down on his troops, and refused to send in reinforcements when they were needed. While he watched the fighting from the porch of the Chancellor House, a Confederate shell split the pillar against which he was leaning, and knocked

Determined Federals such as these men of the Vermont Brigade, shown holding off an attack by Jubal Early's Confederates, kept the Union withdrawal from Chancellorsville from becoming a rout.

"Thus ended the campaign which Hooker opened as with a thunderbolt from the hand of Mars, and ended as impotently as an infant who has not learned to grasp its rattle."

PRIVATE WARREN GOSS
Massachusetts

Return to Fredericksburg: The New Jersey men above were waiting for orders to go into action at Marye's Heights. Brigadier General Herman Haupt (leaning on the stump) and the dead Confederate artillery horses and smashed caissons at right were photographed by Andrew Russell on May 3, 1863, not long before the Federal forces were driven off again after the Battle of Salem Church.

him senseless. He remained groggy all day but would not turn over command to his subordinates.

Finally, he ordered his men to fall back. The Confederates followed, lobbing shells among them. One hit the Chancellor House, setting it ablaze. Others landed in the Wilderness, dry as tinder and filled with wounded men. A survivor remembered the horrors that followed:

> I was among the [Union] wounded. Using my musket for a crutch, I began to pull away the burning brushwood, and got some of them out. One of the wounded Johnnies . . . began to help. . . . We were trying to rescue a young fellow in gray. The fire was all around him. The last I saw of that fellow was his face. . . . His eyes were big and blue, and his hair like raw silk surrounded by a wreath of fire. I heard him scream "O, Mother! O, God!" It left me trembling all over, like a leaf. After it was over my hands were blistered and burned so I could not open or shut them; but me and them rebs tried to shake hands.

On May 6, the Union army again retreated back across the Rappahannock. Hooker had lost seventeen thousand men. "Thus," wrote a disgusted private, "ended the campaign which Hooker opened as with a thunderbolt from the hand of Mars, and ended as impotently as an infant who has not learned to grasp its rattle."

"My God! My God!" Lincoln said when he got the news of Chancellorsville. "What will the country say?"

For Lee, it had been a brilliant but costly victory—thirteen thousand of his men were dead or out of action, almost a quarter of those engaged. But it was the loss of one man that concerned him most.

After the amputation of his arm, Stonewall Jackson was moved to a small farmhouse near a place called Guiney's Station, where he seemed at first to be recuperating. Then, suddenly, he developed pneumonia and began to lapse in and out of fevered consciousness.

His wife arrived to soothe him, and when he saw her concern, he rallied to ask her "not to wear a long face. I love cheerfulness and brightness in a sick room." Lee said Jackson could not possibly die: "God will not take him from us now that we need him so much." And Jackson himself agreed. He was willing

The crows were taken off by our skiff and brought here.

Later from the Rappahannock.

OUR VICTORY COMPLETE.

STONEWALL JACKSON LOST HIS LEFT ARM BUT DOING WELL.

RICHMOND, May 5—No official despatches were received last night or this morning from Gen. Lee's headquarters, but a private telegram represents our victory complete.

Gen. Jackson's left arm was skillfully amputated below the shoulder by Dr. McGuire, of Winchester. The General was removed to a country house about fifteen miles distant from the battle field, and is *doing well*. (Glory be to God.—ED.)

Direct railroad communication with our army is not yet re-established.

The guide of the raiders was captured yesterday at Lunstall's Station, York River Railroad, where a skirmish occurred between the Yankees and a few Confederate infantry.

The Approach on Rome, Georgia

As the confident newspaper story above suggests, when Stonewall Jackson was carried into the farmhouse (above left) near Guiney Station, Virginia, to recuperate from the amputation of his arm, everyone assumed he would soon be back in command of his men. His death plunged much of the South into mourning, and groups of grieving men and women (opposite page) had themselves photographed around his grave at the Virginia Military Institute, where he had taught before the war.

to abide by God's decision, of course, but "I do not believe I shall die at this time. I am persuaded the Almighty has yet a work for me to perform."

On the morning of Sunday, May 10, however, the surgeon told Jackson's wife the general would not last the day, and she gently broke the news to her husband. "Doctor," Jackson said, "Anna informs me that you have told her I am to die today. Is it so?"

The doctor nodded that it was.

Jackson brightened a little. "Very good, very good," he said. "It is all right. It is the Lord's day; my wish is fulfilled. I have always desired to die on Sunday."

He spent the afternoon dozing on and off, his breathing thin and shallow. A little after three, he called out, "Order A. P. Hill to prepare for action! Pass the infantry to the front. . . . Tell Major Hawks—" He smiled and closed his eyes. "Let us cross over the river," he muttered, "and rest under the shade of the trees." Then he died.

Jefferson Davis declared a day of national mourning. "From the Rio Grande to the Potomac will go up one wild wail of lamentation over the great departed," said the Sandersville *Central Georgian.* "All Israel will mourn, for truly a great and good man has fallen."

VICKSBURG IS THE KEY

Winfield Scott. Irvin McDowell. George McClellan. John Pope. George McClellan again. Ambrose Burnside. Joseph Hooker.

Lincoln could not find the general he needed. He knew that the southern armies had to be crushed and he had the men to do the job, but he did not have a commander with the will to use them. "No general yet found," he said, "can face the arithmetic, but the end of the war will be at hand when he shall be discovered."

Nor could he find a way to take the town he believed central to a Union victory, Vicksburg, Mississippi, on a high bluff on the river's eastern side. "Vicksburg is the key," Lincoln said. "The war can never be brought to a close until the key is in our pocket." No one understood Vicksburg's importance better than Lincoln, who had twice followed the twisting Mississippi from Illinois to New Orleans and back as a youthful flatboatman. "We can take all the northern ports of the Confederacy, and they can still defy us from Vicksburg. It means hog and hominy without limit, fresh troops from the States of the far South, and a cotton country where they can raise the staple without interference."

Naval forces had already tried and failed to seize the town. "Mississippians," said the military governor, "don't know, and refuse to learn, how to surrender." In the autumn of 1862, Lincoln had assigned U. S. Grant and his Army of the Tennessee, at Memphis, the task of taking Vicksburg by land. A force under William Tecumseh Sherman led the way, only to be stopped cold at Chickasaw Bluffs by Lieutenant General John C. Pemberton.

On the last day of January, 1863, Grant and 45,000 men reached Young's Point, twenty miles above Vicksburg and on the other side of the river. For two and a half months, Grant doggedly attempted to dig or cut or float his army through the tangled bayous and seize the bluffs north and south of the city. Nothing worked. The press accused him of sloth and stupidity, hinted that he was drinking again, and began to call for his removal.

Finally, in late March, he decided on a daring plan: he would march down the river, cross below Vicksburg, and—without hope of resupply or reinforcement—come up from behind and take the town. Even Sherman advised against the gamble.

To confuse the Confederates, Sherman was ordered to feign an attack north of Vicksburg, while 1,700 cavalrymen were sent inland to tear up railroads. On April 30, Admiral David Porter's Union gunboats blasted their way past the town and began to ferry Grant's army across the Mississippi.

"When [the crossing] was effected," Grant wrote later, "I felt a degree of relief scarcely ever equalled since. . . . I was now in the enemy's country, with a river and the stronghold of Vicksburg between me and my base of supplies. But I was on dry ground on the same side of the river with the enemy."

In the next three weeks, cut off from all communication with the outside world, Grant's army marched 180 miles, fought and won five battles—Port Gibson, Raymond, Jackson, Champion's Hill, and Big Black River—befuddled the Confederate commander, Joseph E. Johnston, and finally surrounded Vicksburg itself, trapping 31,000 Confederates under General Pemberton.

Views of Vicksburg (opposite above): Market House and the heart of the business district, photographed shortly after Vicksburg's capture, probably by the proprietor of the Washington Photographic Gallery housed above Tillman's Saddlery.

Ulysses S. Grant fights his way to Vicksburg (opposite below): After crossing the Mississippi and leaving behind his supply lines, he struck at the rebels five times, captured Jackson, the state capital, and came up on the Confederate stronghold from behind.

WASHINGTON GALLERY
Wm. TILLMAN'S SADDLE & HARNESS MAN
STAPLE GOODS & GROC

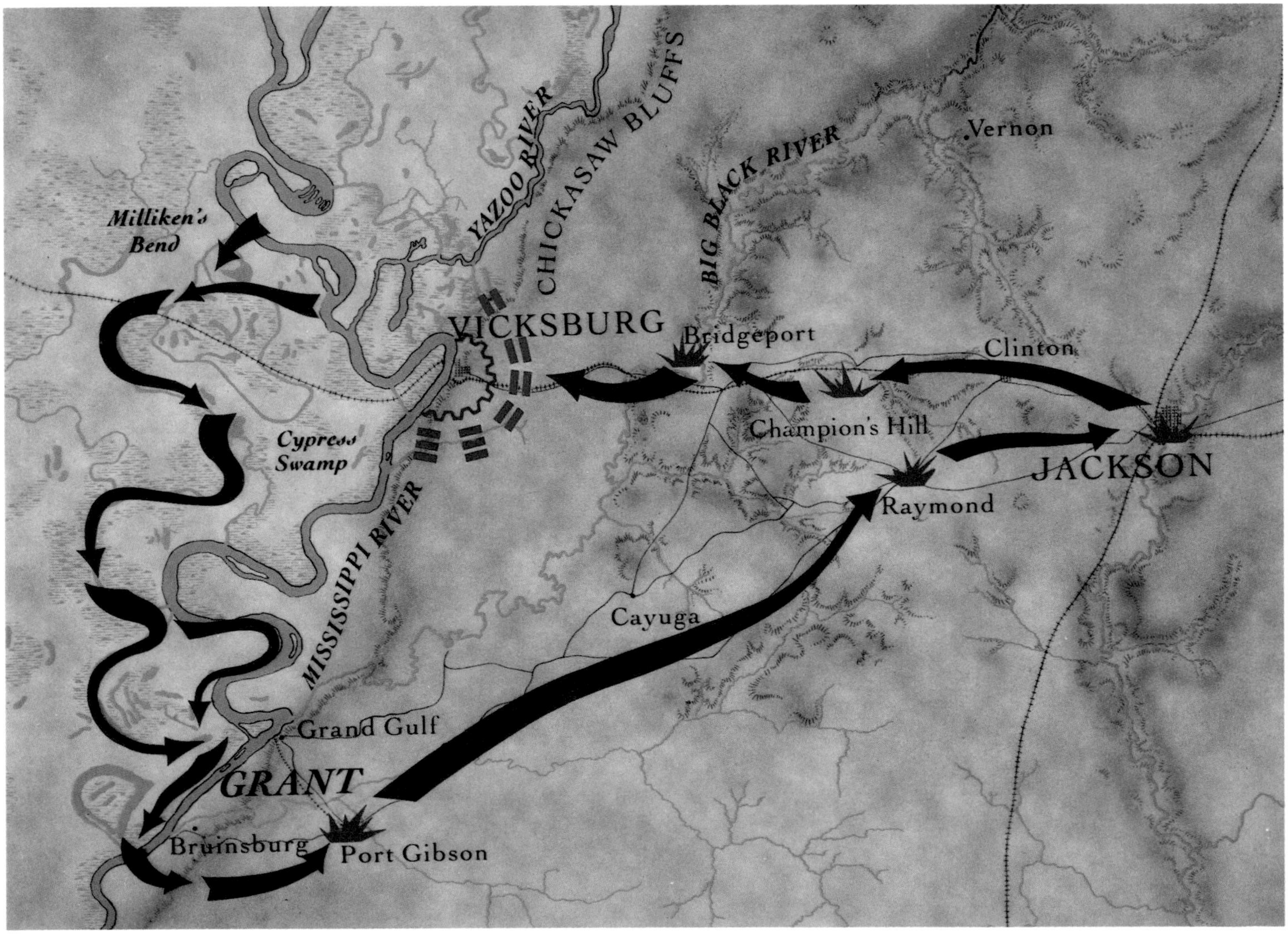

Milliken's Bend
YAZOO RIVER
CHICKASAW BLUFFS
BIG BLACK RIVER
Vernon
VICKSBURG
Bridgeport
Clinton
Cypress Swamp
Champion's Hill
JACKSON
Raymond
MISSISSIPPI RIVER
Cayuga
Grand Gulf
GRANT
Bruinsburg
Port Gibson

Grant then tried to seize the town by force and was beaten back. "Thanks be to the great Ruler of the Universe," a Mississippi chaplain wrote on May 19, "Vicksburg is still safe. The first great assault has been most successfully repelled—All my fears in reference to taking the place by storm now vanished."

Two more assaults failed before Grant settled in for a siege, resolved, he said, "to outcamp" the enemy. His soldiers were happy for the rest. "Now that we have tried to take the enemy's works by storm," an Illinois private said, "we suffering terrible and doing the enemy but little harm, we are all—generals *and* privates—content to lay a regular siege to the place."

Grant began a steady artillery barrage. Confederate civilians and soldiers alike vowed simply to ignore it. "It is *such* folly for them to waste their ammunition like that," one woman wrote. "How can they ever take a town that has such advantages for defense and protection as this? We'll just burrow into these hills and let them batter away as hard as they please."

On May 15, Jefferson Davis summoned Lee to Richmond. Something had to be done about Grant. The Confederate President wanted Lee to send James Longstreet west to relieve Vicksburg but Lee had a bolder scheme: his Army of Northern Virginia would again invade the North, striking this time into southern Pennsylvania, attacking Harrisburg and Philadelphia, and forcing Grant north to defend Washington. Davis and his war council agreed.

With luck, Washington itself might fall.

Everything now hung on Vicksburg in the west and Pennsylvania in the east. As Grant pressed his siege, Lee moved north.

James Ewell Brown Stuart, known as Jeb, whom Lee called "the eyes and ears of my army."

THE UNIVERSE OF BATTLE

"This army has never done such fighting as it will do now," a Virginia private promised. "We must conquer a peace. . . . We will show the Yankees this time how we can fight." As Lee's seventy thousand men moved toward Pennsylvania in late May, they were divided into three corps. The 1st was commanded by James Longstreet, the sturdy Georgian whose men called him "Old Pete" and whom Lee fondly called "my old warhorse."

The 2nd—Stonewall Jackson's old command—was under Richard S. Ewell, a veteran of Jackson's Shenandoah campaign who had lost a leg at Second Bull Run.

The 3rd was led by A. P. Hill, newly appointed corps commander, who, under Jackson, had helped gain southern victories at Cedar Mountain, Second Manassas, Fredericksburg, and Chancellorsville, and had staved off Confederate disaster at Sharpsburg.

Union cavalry under Alfred Pleasonton, sent to discover what Lee was up to, surprised Jeb Stuart and his Confederate raiders at Brandy Station on the Rappahannock. Twenty-one thousand mounted men clashed along the river for twelve hours, the biggest cavalry engagement in American history. It was a standoff, but the North now knew the Confederates were on the move.

Stuart, embarrassed at having been caught off guard, and determined to redeem himself, started out on still another showy ride around the Union army.

General George Gordon Meade (third from left) and members of his staff: Meade's sudden appointment to succeed Hooker in the face of Lee's advancing army came as a shock to him, but he did not turn it down, telegraphing Washington, "As a soldier, I obey it, and to the utmost of my ability will execute it."

Ewell's advancing column scattered the Union garrison at Winchester, took four thousand Union prisoners, and led the rest of Lee's army across the Potomac in mid-June.

For two weeks, the much larger Army of the Potomac, still commanded by Joseph Hooker, followed along, careful to keep between Lee and Washington in case he turned toward the capital.

Hooker wanted to attack Richmond now that Lee was moving north. Lincoln reminded him that Lee's *army,* not the Confederate capital, was the objective. Hooker complained that he needed more men, more time, more equipment. "I don't know whether I am standing on my head or feet," he said.

On June 28, Lincoln replaced him with a new Union commander, George Gordon Meade, a blunt, bookish veteran of Fredericksburg and Chancellorsville, fondly described by one subordinate as a "damned old goggle-eyed snapping turtle."

If the Union generals were not sure where Lee was going, Lee had no idea where the Union army even was: Stuart was riding too far ahead of the advancing forces to keep him informed. Still, Lee's army pushed north into Pennsylvania, seizing animals, food, wagons, and clothing from Pennsylvania civilians—and promising to pay for them all in Confederate money once they had won the war. Southern soldiers also seized free blacks and sent them south into slavery: a Chambersburg woman saw black women and children being "driven by just like we would drive cattle."

"My friends," a Confederate officer asked the frightened inhabitants of one town, "how do you like *this* way of coming back into the Union?" Union General Abner Doubleday recalled northern nervousness at the unopposed southern advance: "People began to feel that the boast of Senator Robert Toombs of Georgia, that he would [one day] call the roll of his slaves at the foot of Bunker Hill Monument, might soon be realized."

GETTYSBURG: THE FIRST DAY

JULY 1, 1863 The greatest battle ever fought on the North American continent began as a clash over shoes. There was rumored to be a large supply of shoes stored somewhere in the little crossroads town of Gettysburg, and at dawn on July 1 an infantry officer in Ewell's command led his men there to commandeer them for his footsore men.

The South came in from the north that day and the North came in from the south. About three miles from town, the Confederate advance guard ran headlong into General John Buford's Union cavalry. While both sides sent couriers pounding off for reinforcements, Buford tried desperately to hold his ground.

Every Confederate and Union division in the area now converged on Gettysburg. The Confederates were closest, and as the Union forces slowly gathered, the rebels pushed them back through the town until General Winfield Scott Hancock rallied the retreating troops into defensive positions on Culp's Hill and Cemetery Hill, where a sign near the arched gateway to the graveyard that gave the ridge its name read: "ALL PERSONS FOUND USING FIREARMS IN THESE GROUNDS WILL BE PROSECUTED WITH THE UTMOST RIGOR OF THE LAW."

"People were running here and there," a Gettysburg woman named Sallie Broadhead recalled, "screaming that the town would be shelled. No one knew where to go or what to do. My husband went to the garden and picked a mess of beans . . . for he declared the Rebels should not have *one.*"

Lee arrived in the middle of the afternoon and ordered Richard Ewell to renew the attack on the high ground before nightfall, "if practicable." Ewell chose to think it *im*practicable; his men needed rest.

James Longstreet argued that now was the time to swing around the Union left, take a stand somewhere between Meade's army and Washington, and wait for the Union to attack. Even though Lee still did not know his enemy's strength or whereabouts—Stuart had still not been heard from—he overruled Longstreet. "No," he said, "I am going to whip them [here], or they are going to whip me."

"I cannot sleep . . ." Sallie Broadhead wrote that night. "We know not what the morrow will bring forth. . . . I think little has been gained so far. Has our army been sufficiently reinforced?"

"Though the shells fell thick around us, shattering trees, knocking bricks out of the house, etc., Cousin Jennie stood on the cellar steps cutting bread, spreading it with apple butter and giving it to the poor men who had been marched double-quick for miles without any breakfast. The poor fellows were so grateful, and would say, 'Courage ladies; we'll drive the rebs!'"

ANNA MARY YOUNG, Gettysburg

GETTYSBURG: THE SECOND DAY

JULY 2, 1863 Through the night, the two armies continued to gather. By morning, 65,000 Confederates faced 85,000 Federal troops. The Union line along Cemetery Ridge was shaped like a fishhook. Hills overlooked the Federal positions at either end: Culp's and Cemetery Hills on the right, Big and Little Round Tops at the left.

Lee wanted the heights taken.

Meade, in command of the Army of the Potomac for just five days, was no less determined to hold his ground and issued stern instructions to his officers: "Corps and other commanders are authorized to order the instant death of any soldier who fails in his duty at this hour."

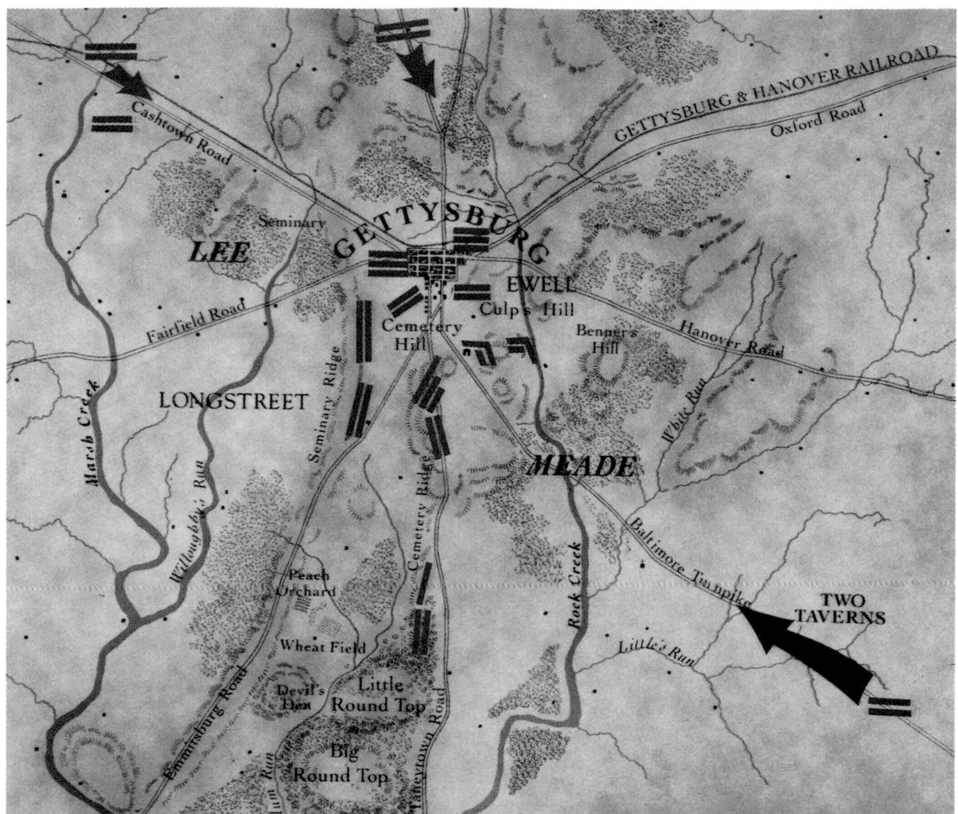

The Battle of Gettysburg begins: On the morning of July 1, 1863, Confederate cavalry ran into Union horsemen on the Cashtown Road, northwest of town. Each side sent for help. The rebels got there first, and by afternoon had driven the Federals south of town, where they rallied into defensive positions on Culp's Hill and Cemetery Hill.

The gatehouse of the Evergreen Cemetery, the graveyard that gave Cemetery Hill its name. During the fighting, Federal troops would take what cover they could behind its headstones.

Lee's plan called for Ewell to assault Culp's Hill, while Longstreet went after the Round Tops.

It took Longstreet all morning and most of the afternoon to shift two divisions into position for an assault on the Union left. As preparations were under way, Jeb Stuart rode up tired, dusty, and far ahead of his men. Lee's face darkened in anger when he saw his errant cavalry commander and, one officer remembered, he raised his hand as if to strike him.

"I have not heard from you for days, and you the eyes and ears of my army," he said.

"I have brought you 125 wagons and their teams, General," Stuart answered.

"Yes," said Lee, "and they are an impediment to me now." Then, seeing Stuart's anguish, his voice grew gentle: "Let me ask your help. . . . We will not discuss this matter further. Help me fight these people."

Assigned to hold the Union left against Longstreet was the 3rd Corps, under General Daniel Sickles, a turbulent ex–Tammany politician best known for having shot and killed his wife's lover before the war. (Secretary of War Stanton had been his attorney and got him off on a plea of "temporary insanity.") Sickles had used the quiet morning to disobey orders, shifting his corps from its position on lower Cemetery Ridge out into the Peach Orchard that stood on a flat-topped ridge, half a mile in front of the Union line—leaving the Round Tops and the Union's left flank entirely undefended. Meade angrily ordered him to fall back, but before he could do so, at about four o'clock, Longstreet finally began his attack.

As the Confederates swept forward, the 15th Alabama scrambled up Big Round Top. From its summit, three hundred feet above the fighting, their colonel, William C. Oates, saw his chance: if he could haul guns to the summit of *Little* Round Top, directly overlooking the Federal lines, he could blow them apart.

Meanwhile, Meade dispatched the Union army's chief engineer, General Gouverneur K. Warren, and a young lieutenant of engineers named Washington Roebling, to the summit of Little Round Top to see what was happening. Only a handful of signalmen held the hill. Longstreet's corps was moving down and around the Union left. Sickles was pinned down in the Peach Orchard below. "One glance sufficed to note the head of Hood's Texans coming up the rocky ravine which separates Little and Big Round Top," Roebling recalled. "I ran down, told General Warren, he came up with me and saw the necessity of immediate action."

Warren sent at once for reinforcements for Little Round Top. The last of four regiments to be ordered in was the 20th Maine. "It was a critical moment," Private Theodore Gerrish remembered. "If that line was permitted to turn the Federal flank, Little Round Top was untenable, and with this little mountain in the Confederate's possession, the whole *position* would be untenable. It was a most fortunate fact for the Union cause that in command of the Twentieth Maine was Colonel Joshua Lawrence Chamberlain."

As Chamberlain and his two brothers, Tom and John, rode abreast together toward the hill, a Confederate shell narrowly missed them. "Boys," the colonel said, "another such shot might make it hard for mother. Tom, go to the

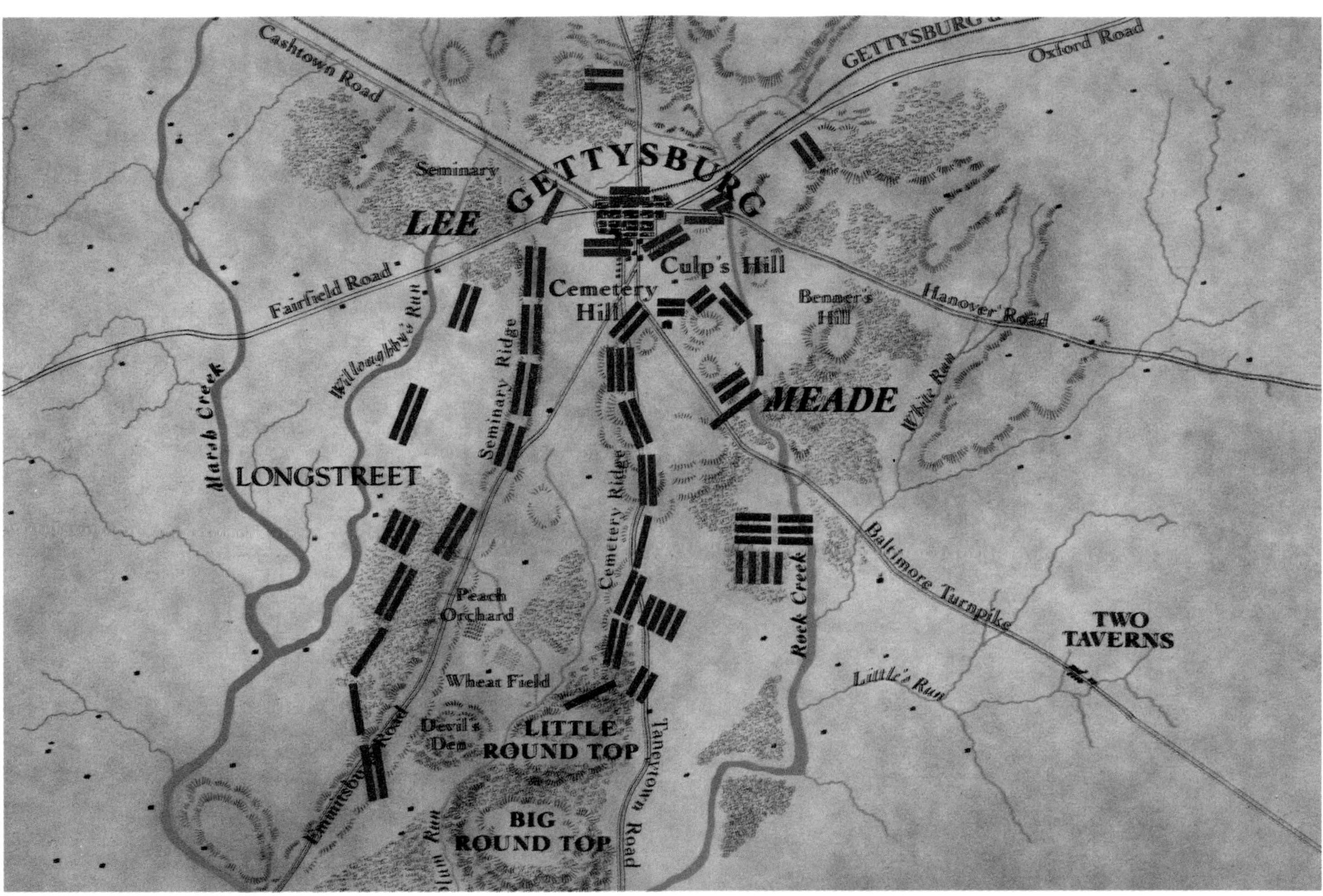

The Battle of Gettysburg, the second day: By the morning of July 2, 1863, 150,000 Union and Confederate troops had converged on the little Pennsylvania town. The southerners occupied a line west of the Emmittsburg Road, along Seminary Ridge. The northern men waited along Cemetery Ridge—a slightly more elevated crest that ran south toward two hills, Big and Little Round Top. Lee's plan called for an assault on the left, or southernmost, end of the Union line.

General James Longstreet (opposite above), whose differences with Robert E. Lee at Gettysburg never affected their fondness for one another; and General Daniel Sickles (opposite below), here recuperating from the loss of his leg on the battle's second day.

rear of the regiment and see that it is well closed up! John pass up ahead and look out a place for our wounded."

Chamberlain's orders were to hold Little Round Top "at all hazards." His 350 men clambered up the south slope and found what cover they could behind boulders. They had less than ten minutes to spare. At the last possible moment Chamberlain sent the men of Company B across the hollow between the hills to bolster his left flank. Before they were in place, Oates and his Confederates were upon them, the blue-white smoke of rifle fire blanketed the scene, and Chamberlain assumed they had been annihilated.

The Maine men fired into the Alabamians, who regrouped and came again, slowly gaining ground and now threatening to slip around the Union left. Chamberlain ordered that wing of his line to drop back, re-forming at right angles to the rest of the regiment, firing without a break all the while. "Imagine, if you can," Private Gerrish wrote later, "nine small companies of infantry, numbering perhaps three hundred men, in the form of a right angle, on the extreme flank of an army of eighty thousand men, put there to hold the key of the entire position against a force at least ten times their number. . . . Stand firm, ye boys from Maine."

Colonel Oates remembered the ferocity of the fighting:

> I again ordered the advance . . . waving my sword, shouting, "Forward men, to the ledge!," and was promptly followed by the command in splendid style. [The 20th Maine fell back to the next ridge, then] charged my line, coming right up in a hand-to-hand encounter. . . . A Maine man reached to grasp the staff of the colors when Ensign Archibald stepped back and Sergeant Pat O'Connor stove his bayonet through the head of the Yankee.

In less than an hour and a half, some forty thousand rounds were fired on that slope. Saplings halfway up the hill were gnawed in two by bullets.

The Alabamians drove the Maine men from their positions five times. Five times they fought their way back again. At some places, the muzzles of the opposing guns almost touched.

"The edge of the conflict swayed to and fro," Chamberlain said, "with wild whirlpools and eddies. At times I saw around me more of the enemy than of my own men; gaps opening, swallowing, closing again; squads of stalwart men who had cut their way through us, disappearing as if translated. All around, a strange, mingled roar."

A third of Chamberlain's men fell, 130 out of 386.

Then the sounds of battle behind the 20th Maine intensified. Chamberlain assumed Little Round Top was being surrounded. His men were running out of ammunition. "A critical moment has arrived, and we can remain as we are no longer," Private Gerrish remembered thinking, "we must advance or retreat. It must not be the latter; but how can it be the former?"

Chamberlain decided to advance, and ordered his men to fix bayonets.

After the battle was over, a photographer talked this Federal soldier into taking up a position atop one of the Round Tops overlooking the Devil's Den, as if he were still in combat. The dead Confederates below and right are real enough: the men at the left below lie in the patch of woods at the foot of Big Round Top that came to be called "the Slaughter Pen"; the lone man at the right sprawls in the rocks nearby.

"Within half an hour I could convert Little Round Top into a Gibraltar that I could hold against ten times the number of men that I had."

COLONEL WILLIAM C. OATES
15th Alabama

Then, while the right of his regiment held straight, he had his left plunge down the hillside, all the while wheeling to the right—"like a great gate upon a post," an eyewitness said.

The Confederates were taken by surprise. Some of those in front dropped their weapons. "An officer fired his pistol at my head with one hand," Chamberlain remembered, "while he handed me his sword with the other."

Others turned and ran. They had gone only a few paces when they received another horrifying surprise. Chamberlain's Company B, which had survived the earlier fighting by taking shelter with Union sharpshooters behind a stone wall, rose and fired into the retreating rebels. "While one man was shot in the face, his right-hand comrade was shot in the side or back," Oates remembered. "Some were struck simultaneously [by] two or three balls from different directions."

The Alabamians wavered, broke, fled for their lives. "We ran like a herd of wild cattle," Oates wrote. "As we ran, a man . . . to my right and rear had his throat cut by a bullet, and he ran past me breathing at his throat and the blood spattering. . . . My dead and wounded were then nearly as great in number as those still on duty. They literally covered the ground. . . . The blood stood in puddles in some places on the rocks; the ground was soaked with blood."

Fighting continued on other parts of the slope, but Little Round Top held. "The Regiment we fought and captured was the 15th Alabama," a Union corporal wrote. "They said they never were whipped before, and never wanted to meet the 20th Maine again." Joshua Lawrence Chamberlain received the Congressional Medal of Honor.

But far out in front of the Union lines, Sickles and his men were in desperate

4070

Mathew Brady, leaning against the tree at left, surveys the stony ground over which the 20th Maine and 15th Alabama struggled on the second day at Gettysburg. Little Round Top is on the left, Big Round Top on the right.

Enterprising photographers often did more than merely document Civil War battles: the dead Confederate below was dragged some forty yards to a snipers' nest in Devil's Den in order to provide Timothy O'Sullivan with an especially dramatic photograph.

Dead horses belonging to the 9th Massachusetts artillery fill the yard of a farmhouse near the Peach Orchard; some fifteen hundred artillery horses are estimated to have been killed at Gettysburg.

trouble. The Confederates blasted the Peach Orchard, their shells tearing the branches from the trees and bounding among the Union troops. "I was within a few feet of General Sickles when he received the wound by which he lost his leg," a Union captain wrote. "A terrific explosion seemed to shake the very earth . . . instantly followed by another. I . . . noticed that [his] pants and drawers at the knee were torn clear off to the leg, which was swinging loose. . . . He was carried from the field, coolly smoking a cigar."

"An artillerist's heaven," remembered General E. Porter Alexander, the commander of Longstreet's artillery, "is to follow the routed enemy after a tough resistance, and to throw shells and canister into his disorganized and fleeing masses. . . . There is no excitement on earth like it. Now we saw our heaven just in front and were . . . breathing the very air of victory. But we only had a moderately good time with Sickles' retreating corps after all. They fell back upon fresh troops."

Reinforced, Sickles's men counterattacked, fell back, held, and pushed the Confederates back, retreated again, through places still remembered for the ferocity of the fighting that took place there—the Wheat Field, Devil's Den, the Valley of Death.

"The balls were whizzing so thick," a Texan remembered, "that it looked like a man could hold out a hat and catch it full." Half a century later, a Massachusetts private could not forget the awful *sound* of the struggle:

"When the [second day's] battle was over, General Lee pronounced it a success . . . but we had accomplished little toward victorious results."

GENERAL JAMES LONGSTREET

Generals Winfield Scott Hancock (to the right of the tree) and David Bell Birney (to Hancock's left) pose with their staffs. For his extraordinary valor at Gettysburg and elsewhere, Hancock would win the nickname "Hancock the Superb."

> The hoarse and indistinguishable orders of commanding officers, the screaming and bursting of shells, cannister and shrapnel as they tore through the struggling masses of humanity, the death screams of wounded animals, the groans of their human companions, wounded and dying and trampled underfoot by hurrying batteries, riderless horses and the moving lines of battle . . . —a perfect hell on earth, never, perhaps to be equaled, certainly not to be surpassed, nor *ever* to be forgotten in a man's lifetime. It has never been effaced from my memory, day or night, for fifty years.

Union reinforcements, hurrying toward the Wheat Field, left a gap on Cemetery Ridge, and an Alabama brigade raced to drive through it. Winfield Scott Hancock spotted the trouble and ordered a single, small regiment, the 1st Minnesota, to countercharge and stop them. "Every man realized in an instant what that order meant," a survivor wrote, "—death or wounds to us all, the sacrifice of the regiment to gain a few minutes' time and save the position."

The tiny Minnesota force—just 262 men—raced down the slope at the oncoming 1,600 Confederates with fixed bayonets. The astonished southerners fell back and the gap in the Union line closed, but only 47 of the Minnesotans survived unhurt—82 percent of them fell in less than five minutes, the highest percentage of casualties taken by any Union regiment in the war.

As the sun set, the Union left and right still held; perhaps an all-out Confederate attack on the center would work the following day. "Who is victorious, or with whom the advantage rests," Sallie Broadhead wrote that evening, "no one here can tell. . . . Some think the rebels were defeated, as there has been no boasting as on yesterday, and they look uneasy and by no means exultant. . . . I fear we are too hopeful. We shall see tomorrow."

GETTYSBURG: THE THIRD DAY

JULY 3, 1863 The third day began badly for Lee. Ewell's men were driven back from Culp's Hill. Jeb Stuart was supposed to get behind the Federals and attack them from the rear, but Union cavalry stopped and held him, thanks in part to a series of headlong charges led by a twenty-three-year-old general, George Armstrong Custer.

So everything now depended on Longstreet's assault on the Union center on Cemetery Ridge. Longstreet still opposed attacking: he had commanded the rebel gunners at Fredericksburg and seen what well-protected men with rifled muskets could do to massed men advancing in the open. "General Lee,"

Pickett's Charge: At about three in the afternoon of July 3, 1863, Robert E. Lee ordered the most fateful assault of the war, against the center of the Union line.

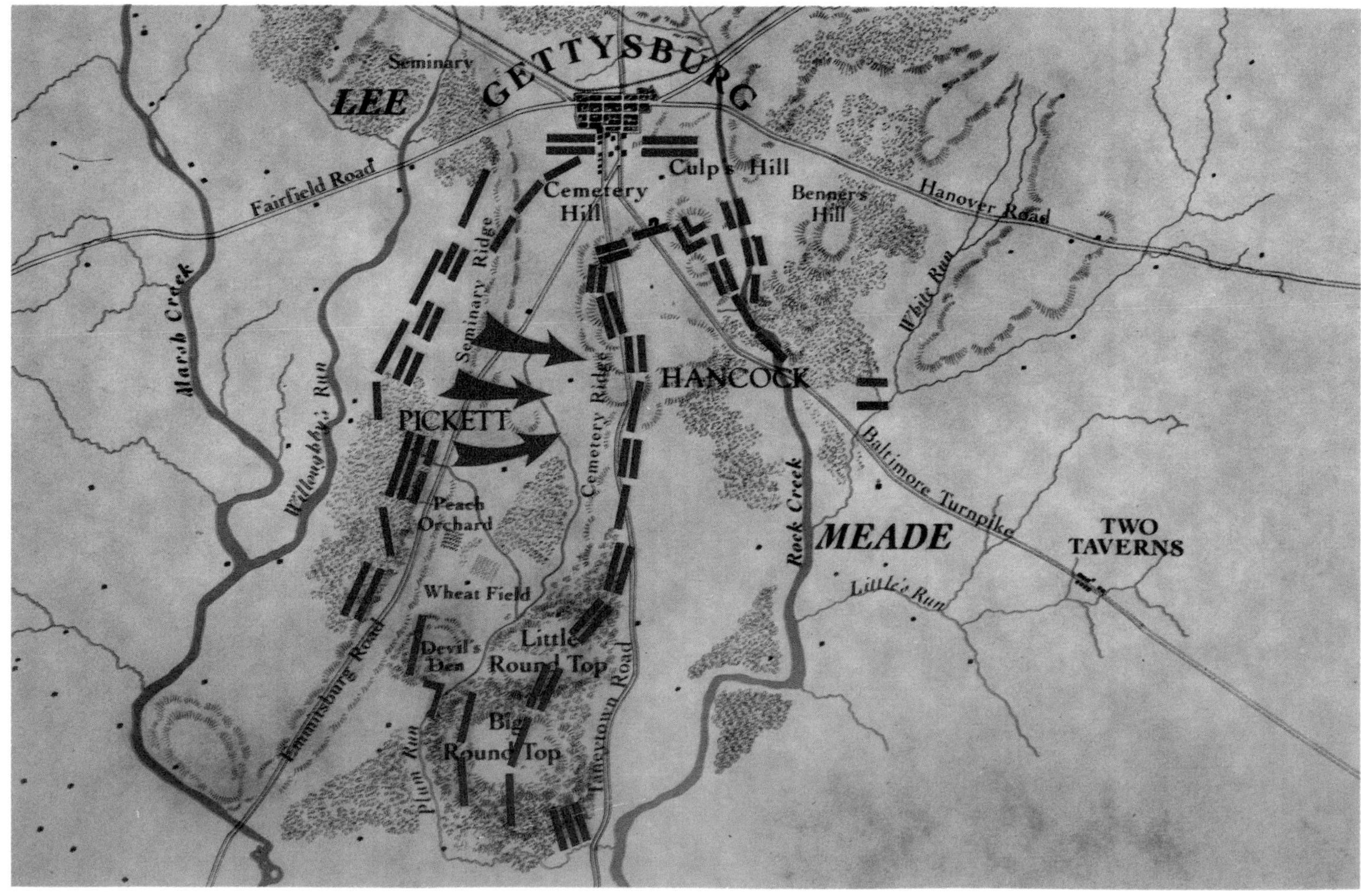

he recalled telling his commander, "there never was a body of fifteen thousand men who could make that attack successfully." Lee again overruled him: "The enemy is there, General Longstreet," he said, "and I am going to strike him."

Meade saw it coming. General John Gibbon, commander of the 2nd Corps at the center, was alerted to expect the day's major blow.

The man Lee chose to organize the assault was a fellow Virginian and special favorite of Longstreet's, General George E. Pickett. At thirty-eight, Pickett was about to marry a teen-age sweetheart and favored a beard and long ringlets, "all curling," according to a friend, "and giving off the scent of Araby."

"Fight for the Standard," by an unidentified artist, perfectly expresses the chivalric image of themselves cherished by cavalrymen in both armies. The infantry were less romantic about the horsemen who routinely dismissed them as "web feet." "I do wish that the Yankees would capture all the cavalry . . ." wrote one rebel foot soldier. "They never will fight So I think it is useless to have them in the Army Eating rations."

Pickett's men filed into the woods and waited, leaning on their rifles. They knew what was about to be required of them, and to relieve the tension some of the men pelted each other with green apples. When a rabbit jumped from the bushes and bounded back behind the lines, one of the men shouted after it, "Run, old hare. If I was an old hare, I'd run, too."

A massive artillery barrage began at one o'clock, intended to soften up the Union defenses.

The earth shook, and "the storm broke upon us so suddenly," a Union soldier recalled, "that numbers of soldiers and officers who leaped from their tents or lazy siestas on the grass were stricken in their rising with mortal wounds and died, some with cigars between their teeth, some with pieces of food in their fingers, and one at least—a pale young German from Pennsylvania, with a miniature of his sister in his hands."

General Meade had just left his commanders finishing their lunch when the barrage began; as an orderly served them butter, a shell tore him in two. To keep up his men's courage, General Hancock rode up and down the line without flinching at the screaming shells. A brigadier finally told him not to risk his life. "There are times," Hancock answered, "when a corps commander's life does not count."

"Cemetery Hill and Ridge were ploughed and furrowed . . ." a Union private huddled there recalled. "The flowers in bloom upon the graves at the Cemetery were shot away. Tombs and monuments were knocked to pieces, and ordinary gravestones shattered in rows."

"A shell burst over our heads," Elisha Rhodes remembered, "immediately followed by showers of iron. . . . Most of the shells that came over the hill struck in the road on which our Brigade was moving. Solid shot [split boulders] as if exploded by gunpowder. The flying iron and pieces of stone struck some men down in every direction. . . . About 30 men of our Brigade were killed or wounded."

Answering Union shells took a fierce toll of the Confederate infantry, still waiting in the woods for the signal to move forward. Two hundred and fifty guns were now firing at once. "We sat and heard in silence," a Union officer remembered. "What other expression had we that was not mean for such an awful universe of battle?"

But after about an hour, the Federal guns fell silent, to conserve ammunition for the attack Meade was sure was coming—and to lure the enemy out onto the open fields between the lines.

In this teeming canvas by James Walker, Union forces at the Angle struggle to hold on against the furious onslaught of the Confederates, commanded by Major General George Pickett (inset). At the center, General Lewis A. Armistead, mortally wounded, hands over his watch to be presented to his old friend Winfield Scott Hancock for safekeeping.

It worked. The Confederates believed they had destroyed the Union batteries.

Should his men now go forward? Pickett asked. Longstreet, unable to bring himself to speak, nodded. Pickett scribbled a final note to his fiancée—"If Old Peter's nod means death, then good-bye and God bless you, little one"—and handed it to Longstreet to mail.

At a little after three, Pickett gave the order: "Up men, and to your posts! Don't forget today that you are from old Virginia."

"[We] obeyed with alacrity and cheerfulness," a Confederate captain remembered, "for we believed the battle was practically over, and we had nothing to do but march unopposed to Cemetery [Hill] and occupy it."

Three divisions—thirteen thousand men—started out of the woods toward

the stone wall at a brisk, steady pace, covering about one hundred yards a minute. They were silent as they marched, forbidden this time to fire or to give the rebel yell until they were on top of the enemy.

A Union officer watched them come.

> More than half a mile their front extends . . . man touching man, rank pressing rank. . . . The red flags wave, their horsemen gallop up and down, the arms of [thirteen] thousand men, barrel and bayonet, gleam in the sun, a sloping forest of flashing steel. Right on they move, as with one soul, in perfect order without impediment of ditch, or wall, or stream, over ridge and slope, through orchard and meadow, and cornfield, magnificent, grim, irresistible.

"The next morning was the Fourth of July, but it seemed at the time to those who were at Gettysburg a somber and terrible national anniversary, with the indescribable horrors of the field, as yet hardly mitigated by the work of mercy, before the eye in every direction. The army did not know the extent of the victory; the nation did not realize as yet what had been done. The armies were still watching each other."

LIEUTENANT JESSE BOWMAN YOUNG
3rd Army Corps

Aftermath: Hospital tents crowd the Gettysburg countryside; the 2,400 inhabitants of Gettysburg now had ten times that many dead and wounded men to help care for. Inset at right, a Federal gun carriage and the horse that pulled it, smashed by a rebel shell; and inset below, some of the Union dead, their shoes pulled off by retreating Confederates whose desperate need for footwear had brought on the battle in the first place.

"It was," another northern officer remembered, "the most beautiful thing I ever saw."

Union guns on Cemetery Ridge and Little Round Top opened fire on the right of the advancing Confederate line. "We could not help hitting them at every shot," an officer recalled. As many as ten men at a time were destroyed by a single bursting shell. Watching the slaughter from behind their stone wall, the Union troops began chanting, "Fredericksburg! Fredericksburg!"

The Confederates still "came on in magnificent order," an admiring Union private wrote, "with the step of men who believed themselves invincible. . . . Solid shot ploughs huge lanes in their close columns [but] their shattered lines do not waver. With banners waving, with steady step, they sweep on like an irresistible wave of fate."

"Cheer after cheer rose from the triumphant boys in blue, echoing from Round Top . . . from Cemetery Hill, resounding in the vale below and making the very heavens throb."

LIEUTENANT JESSE BOWMAN YOUNG

When the first southerners came within two hundred yards, a Confederate lieutenant cried out to his men. "Home, boys, home! Remember, *home* is over beyond those hills!"

"All was orderly and still upon our crest," a Union soldier recalled; "no noise and no confusion. . . . General Gibbon rode down the lines, cool and calm, and in an unimpassioned voice he said . . . 'Do not hurry, men, and fire too fast, let them come up close before you fire and then aim slow.'"

Behind their stone wall, the Union men continued to hold their fire. Union General Alexander Hays told them they were about to "see some fun." Finally, he ordered them to fire: eleven cannon and seventeen hundred muskets went off at once. "[The rebel lines were] at once enveloped in a dense cloud of dust," a Federal officer said. "Arms, heads, blankets, guns and knapsacks were tossed into the clear air. A moan went up from the field."

The Confederates reached the Union line at just one place, a crook in the wall that became known as "the Angle." They were led by General Lewis A. Armistead of North Carolina, who jumped over the stone wall, waving his hat on his sword, and seized a Union battery before he was shot down. Hancock was in command at the Angle, and he and Armistead had known each other well before the war; now it was Armistead's dying wish that his old friend send his personal effects home to his family.

When it seemed possible that the Union line might break, officers rallied their men. "[The flat of my saber fell] on some patriotic backs, not lightly," one remembered, "and with a look at me as if I were the destroying angel, they again faced the enemy."

One Vermont regiment performed a dazzling drill-field maneuver, company after company firing as they wheeled in line to enfilade the Confederates, first on one side, then the other. The fighting was as furious as any seen during the war. "Seconds are centuries, minutes ages. Men fire into each other's faces," a survivor wrote, "not five feet apart. There are bayonet thrusts, sabre strokes, pistol shots . . . men going down on their hands and knees, spinning round like tops, throwing out their arms, gulping blood, falling; legless, armless, headless. There are ghastly heaps of dead men."

All the Confederates who breached the wall were killed or captured. The gap in the Union line closed. "The [southern] lines waver," a newspaper correspondent wrote. "The soldiers of the front rank look round for their supports. They are gone—fleeing over the field, broken, shattered, thrown

THE ARTISTS' WAR

The lenses of the big, cumbersome wet-plate cameras that Mathew Brady, Alexander Gardner, Timothy O'Sullivan, and their compatriots employed were far too slow to freeze battle action—and the art of engraving photographs for reproduction had yet to be invented in any case. So the readers of newspapers and magazines such as *Leslie's Weekly, Harper's Weekly,* the *New York Illustrated News,* and *London Illustrated News,* eager to see what the fighting actually looked like, had to rely on the work of "special artists."

Among those whose on-the-spot pen-and-ink sketches, often dashed off perilously close to danger, were hurried back to editorial offices and there turned into wood engravings by relays of more or less skilled artisans were Theodore R. Davis, Edwin Forbes, Winslow Homer, Henry Walke, and two British-born brothers, William and Alfred Waud.

"To be a spectator was nearly as dangerous as being a participant," Edwin Forbes remembered. And editors were not always as understanding as they might have been. Most people, Forbes's colleague Theodore Davis wrote, "seem to have an idea that all battlefields have some elevated spot upon which the general is located, and that from this spot the commander can see his troops and direct all their maneuvers and courteously furnish special artists an opportunity of sketching the scene."

Alfred Waud at Gettysburg, where he witnessed the fighting on Cemetery Hill (above right) and Seminary Ridge.

IT HAS PLEASED THE GOD OF BATTLES

Thomas Batchelor of Red River Landing in Point Coupee Parish, Louisiana, sent three sons, Albert, Charles, and James, off to the war, then struggled to keep track of them as best he could:

My dear son Albert:
. . . I received your affectionate letter yesterday and I assure you, my dear son, it gives me great relief of mind to hear that you and your dear brothers were still in the land of the living. I had not heard one word from you since Barlow Rogers returned home, hearing of so many battles in Virginia . . .

May God bless you, my dear Albert. Your devoted father,
Thomas A. G. Batchelor

Caring for the wounded: A nurse at Gettysburg whose patients were well enough to take the summer sun.

July 3, 1863. Gettysburg.

Dear Father:
. . . Finally I came to poor Albert lying on the ground wounded under the left eye, the ball passing through and under his nose, bulging out his right eye and coming out in the temple. He also had a ball shot through his left leg. I had no one to help me bear him from the field. I then called a captain of another company to assist me. He did so, and we bore Albert six hundred yards through a dense swamp all bleeding and sore with pain before we could find any of the Ambulance Corps to bear him off to the hospital. Finally, the Ambulance Corps came and, taking him by the arms, I assisted him in the stretcher. Dropping a tear of grief upon his bleeding face, I bade him goodbye.

Charles Batchelor

The field headquarters of the U.S. Sanitary Commission.

August 30, 1863. Hospital near Gettysburg.

My Dear Father:
It has pleased the God of Battles that *I* should number among the many wounded of the great and hotly contested battle fought near this place on the first, second and third of July. But through His infinite kindness and mercy I am once more permitted, after an almost miraculous escape and recovery, to inform you that I have so far recovered that I am able to go about, morning and evening. Brother Charles was in the fight and came out safe; he and the captain of the next company to ours bore me two to three hundred yards to the rear, there they met some Ambulance Corps and gave me to them, and went back to their commands. . . . I was wounded in two places: first through the hip, second, the ball entered the inner corner of my left eye and came out at the lower tip of my right ear, both are doing fine and healed up.

Write to me. I may get the letter.

Your devoted son,
Albert Batchelor

Albert Batchelor survived the war; so did both his brothers.

Confederate dead, about to be buried in a shallow grave.

into confusion by the remorseless fire.... Thousands of rebels throw down their arms and give themselves up as prisoners."

Thirty-eight Confederate battle flags had been left behind. Union officers tied them behind their horses and dragged them in the dust to taunt the fleeing southerners.

Lee rode out among his men, now staggering back to Seminary Ridge, urging them to regroup. "It was all my fault," he told them. "Get together and let us do the best we can toward saving that which is left us." But there was nothing more he or they could do that day.

Pickett had watched it all in horror: 6,500 men had fallen or been captured, half those who marched out of the woods. All fifteen regimental commanders had been hit; so had sixteen of seventeen field officers, three brigadier generals and eight colonels. Every single man of the University Greys, a

Mississippi company made up entirely of students from the University of Mississippi, had been killed or wounded.

When told to rally his division for a possible counterattack, Pickett answered, "General Lee, I *have* no division now." He never forgave Lee for what had happened to his men. "That old man," he said years later, "had my division slaughtered at Gettysburg."

Gettysburg was the bloodiest battle of the war. Almost a third of those engaged—51,000 men—were lost. The North suffered 23,000 casualties; the South, 28,000.

"[The dead lay] upon the open fields . . ." a New Jersey soldier said, "in crevices of the rocks, behind fences, trees and buildings; in thickets, where they had crept for safety only to die in agony; by stream or wall or hedge, wherever the battle had raged or their weakening steps could carry them."

A Union artilleryman remembered them, too:

> The dead bodies of men and horses had lain there, putrefying under the summer sun for three days. . . . Corpses swollen to twice their original size, some of them actually burst asunder with the pressure of foul gases and vapors. . . . Several human or inhuman corpses sat upright against a fence, with arms extended in the air and faces hideous with something very like a fixed leer, as if taking a fiendish pleasure in showing us what we essentially were and might at any moment become.

"Everything . . . points to the advantage to be derived from a new commander. . . . I know that he will have as gallant and brave an army as ever existed to second his efforts."

ROBERT E. LEE

The 2,400 inhabitants of Gettysburg were left with ten times that many dead and wounded to tend to. "Wounded men were brought into our houses and laid side-by-side in our halls and first-story rooms . . ." a woman remembered. "Carpets were so saturated with blood as to be unfit for further use. Walls were bloodstained, as well as books that were used as pillows."

The Confederacy could not afford such sacrifices. All hope of invading the North had been ended. The next afternoon, Lee began the long, limping retreat back to Virginia through a summer downpour that washed the blood from the grass and pelted the wounded Confederates riding in the wagon train that stretched for seventeen miles.

Despite urgings from Washington, Meade was still too wary of Lee to attack his retreating army. Another opportunity to destroy the Army of Northern Virginia was lost and Lincoln was again disappointed.

Lee wrote Jefferson Davis, offering to resign. He had been ill earlier in the year, still felt feeble, and feared he had lost the confidence of his men. "I cannot even accomplish what I myself desire; how can I fill the expectations of others?" he said. "I generally feel a begrowing failure of my bodily strength. . . . I . . . anxiously urge the matter upon Your Excellency from my belief that a younger and abler man than myself can readily be obtained."

The offer was not accepted. To find a better commander than Lee, President Davis said, was "an impossibility." "It only remains for me to hope," he told his general, "that you will take all possible care of yourself, that your health and strength may be entirely restored, and that the Lord will preserve you for the important duties devolved upon you in the struggle of our suffering country for the independence which we have engaged in war to maintain."

Confederates captured at Gettysburg.

THE FOURTH OF JULY

"July 4, 1863. Was *ever* the Nation's Birthday celebrated in such a way before?" Elisha Rhodes exulted in his diary. "I wonder what the South thinks of us Yankees now! I think Gettysburg will cure the Rebels of any desire to invade the North again."

Still more good news for the Union came the next day: "Glorious news!" Rhodes wrote. "We have news that Vicksburg has fallen! We have thousands of prisoners and they seem to be stupefied with the news."

Since May, Grant had slowly, inexorably tightened his noose around the besieged Mississippi town. "Every day," a Union private wrote, "the regiments, foot by foot, yard by yard, approached nearer the . . . rebel works. We got so we bored like gophers and beavers, with a spade in one hand and a gun in the other."

More than two hundred Union guns pounded the town every day from land, while Porter's gunboats battered it from the river. "We are utterly cut off from the world, surrounded by a circle of fire. Would it be wise, like the scorpion, to sting ourselves to death?" a woman wondered. "The fiery shower of shells goes on, day and night. . . . People do nothing but eat what they can get, sleep *when* they can, and dodge the shells."

Civilians dug some five hundred caves in the yellow clay hillsides, a few with several rooms fitted out with rugs, beds, and chairs, and staffed with slaves. "It was living like plant roots," one woman said. Union troops began calling Vicksburg "prairie dog village."

"We were in hourly dread of snakes," a cave dweller recalled. "The vines and thickets were full of them, and a large rattlesnake was found one morning under a mattress on which some of us had slept all night."

Another woman kept a journal:

> June 25. A horrible day. We were all in the cellar when a shell came tearing through the roof, burst up-stairs, tore up that room and the pieces coming through both floors down into the cellar, tore open the leg of [my husband's pants]. On the heels of this came Mr. J. to tell us that young Mrs. P. had her thighbone crushed. When Martha went for the milk, she came back horror-stricken to tell us that the black girl had her arm taken off by a shell. For the first time I quailed.

Fewer than a dozen civilians were killed in the shelling, but thirty were injured. The worst damage to the town was done by the townspeople themselves, who burned down the shops of alleged profiteers. But the danger was real enough, and exaggerated stories of the deaths of children spread throughout the South.

As the weeks dragged by, the suspense—and the boredom—affected men on both sides. "A favorite amusement . . ." a Union major remembered, "was to place a cap on the end of a ramrod and raise it just above the head-logs, betting on the number of bullets which would pass through it within a given time."

"Fighting by hand grenades was all that was possible at such close quarters," a southern veteran recalled. "As the Federals had the hand grenades

In order to move swiftly on Vicksburg that spring, Grant required help from David Porter's gunboats to get some of his men and supplies past the Confederate guns with which the town was surrounded. Porter attempted the passage by night with a dozen vessels, in the face of relentless rebel fire and burning barrels of pitch along the shore that brilliantly illuminated the targets. "It was as if hell itself were loose," an Iowan remembered, and the passage took two and a half hours, but Porter made it through.

and we had none, we obtained our supply by using such of theirs as failed to explode, or by catching them as they came over the parapet and hurling them back."

The boredom got to General Grant as well: two days running he gave in to the bottle, and had to be kept from appearing before his men too drunk to stand.

Food ran low among the city's defenders. They were reduced to eating mules, horses, dogs, and a ghastly bread made of equal parts corn and dried peas. "It had the properties of India rubber," one soldier recalled, "and was worse than leather to digest." When a soldier gave a small girl a jaybird for a pet, the child's mother made it into soup. Rats were sold in butcher shops; one boy remembered being surprised to find that fried rats had a flavor "fully equal to that of squirrels."

Vicksburg: Rebels and Yankees alike dug into hillsides during the siege; the bomb-proof shelters above were scratched out by the men of the 45th Illinois. On the opposite page, the Stars and Stripes flies from the Warren County courthouse.

By late June, almost half the Confederates were on the sick list or in the hospital.

"Houses dilapidated and in ruins," a weary Confederate sergeant wrote, "rent and torn by shot and shell . . . fences torn down and houses pulled to pieces for firewood. . . . Lice and filth covered the bodies of the soldiers. Delicate women and little children . . . peered at the passer-by with wistful eyes from the caves in the hillsides."

Still, the city held out. There was no more newsprint; the Vicksburg *Citizen* was now being printed on the back of flowered wallpaper. But the tone of its editorials remained defiant:

> July 2. The Great Ulysses—the Yankee Generalissimo surnamed Grant—has expressed his intention of dining in Vicksburg on the Fourth of July. . . . Ulysses must get into the city before he dines in it. The way to cook a rabbit is "first *catch* the rabbit."

"We have had the dark hour. The dawn has broken, and the collapsed confederacy has no place where it can hide its head. Bells are ringing wildly all over the city. Citizens grin at one another with fairly idiotic delight. One is on top of his house, frantically swinging a dinner bell, contributing thus his share of patriotic clamor to the general ding-dong. Bully for him!"

CAPTAIN WILLIAM THOMPSON LUSK
Wilmington, Delaware

By then, daily rations were down to one biscuit, a rebel soldier remembered, and "one *bit* of bacon." Some of the men finally sent their commander, John Pemberton, a polite note:

> The army is now ripe for mutiny, unless it can be fed. If you can't feed us, you'd better surrender us, horrible as the idea is, than suffer this noble army to disgrace themselves by desertion.
>
> Signed,
> Many soldiers

Pemberton acquiesced. "Proud as I was of my brave troops, honoring them as I did," he said later, "I felt that it would be an act of cruel inhumanity to subject them longer to the terrible ordeal. I saw no advantage to be gained by protracting a hopeless defense, which I knew must be attended with a useless waste of life and blood."

Thirty-one thousand Confederates surrendered on the forty-eighth day of the siege, July 4. The day was chosen by the Confederate commander, himself a Pennsylvanian: "I know my people," he told his staff. "I know their peculiar weaknesses and their national vanity; I know we can get better terms from them on the Fourth of July than on any other day of the year." The Union men did not jeer their captives. "They did not seem to exult much over our fall," a Confederate chaplain said, "for they knew that we surrendered to famine, not to them."

The Stars and Stripes was raised above the Vicksburg courthouse. Union officers celebrated their victory at Brierfield, Jefferson Davis's nearby plantation, and aboard Porter's flagship, where, the admiral remembered, "I opened all my wine lockers, which contained only catawba. It disappeared down the parched throats and exhilarated that crowd as weak wine never did before. . . .

General Grant was the only one in the assemblage who did not touch the simple wine offered him. He contented himself with a cigar."

Civilians filed out of their caves to see what was left of their homes. The Fourth of July would not be celebrated again in Vicksburg for eighty-one years.

The Confederacy had been cut in two. Five days later, a Confederate force at Port Hudson, above Baton Rouge, Louisiana, also surrendered after a six-week Union siege. The Mississippi had become a Union highway. "The Father of Waters," Lincoln said, "again goes unvexed to the sea."

In Richmond, Josiah Gorgas, the chief of Confederate ordnance, saw what the Union victories meant.

> Events have succeeded one another with disastrous rapidity. One brief month ago we were apparently at the point of success. Lee was in Pennsylvania, threatening Harrisburg, and even Philadelphia. Vicksburg seemed to laugh all Grant's efforts to scorn. . . . Now the picture is just as sombre as it was bright then. . . . It seems incredible that human power could effect such a change in so brief a space. Yesterday we rode on the pinnacle of success—today, absolute ruin seems to be our portion. The Confederacy totters to its destruction.

In far-off London, Henry Adams allowed himself a rare moment of exultation: "It is now conceded that all idea of [British] intervention is at an end. . . . I want to hug the army of the Potomac. I want to get the whole army of Vicksburg drunk at my own expense. I want to fight some *small* man and lick him."

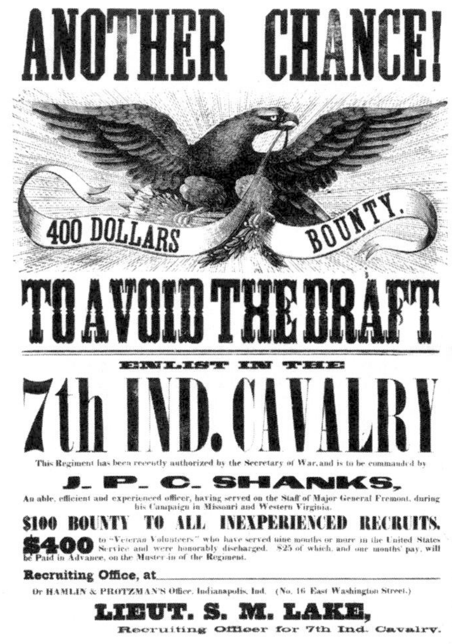

REVOLUTION, NORTH, SOUTH, EAST, AND WEST

But the war was not over, and Lincoln needed still more men to fight it. He issued the first Federal draft call that summer, eager to replenish his army with 300,000 fresh troops, then finish the job begun by Meade and Grant.

All men between twenty and forty-five were enrolled, and all men inducted were to serve three years. The law favored the well-to-do. Any man who could come up with $300 as a "commutation fee," or could find a substitute willing to serve in his place, was exempt. "[This law] is a rich man's bill," Congressman Thaddeus Stevens charged, "made for him who can raise his $300, and against him who cannot raise that sum."

The fathers of Theodore and Franklin Roosevelt paid substitutes. So did Andrew Carnegie and J. P. Morgan, and two future Presidents, Chester A. Arthur and Grover Cleveland.

George Templeton Strong found his substitute, "a big 'Dutch' boy of twenty or thereabouts, for the moderate consideration of $1,100. . . . My *alter ego* could make a good soldier, if he tried. Gave him my address and told him to write to me if he found himself in the hospital or in trouble, and that I would try to do what I properly could to help him." Abraham Lincoln himself, though technically overage, tried to set an example by paying for a substitute, an otherwise unremarkable young man from Stroudsburg, Pennsylvania, named John Summerfield Staples.

The promise of sizable bounties to those who enlisted before they were called up under the first Federal conscription act helped boost enlistments. But resentment at the favored treatment the new law provided for the wealthy, combined with the ever greater casualty lists telegraphed to newspaper offices such as that of the New York *Evening Post Bulletin* (opposite right), combined to spark riots and arson in several northern cities.

VOL. XII—NO. 3635.

ANOTHER DAY OF RIOTING.

CONTINUATION OF MOB RULE.

A PROCLAMATION FROM THE MAYOR.

A Morning and an Evening Fight--The Streets Raked with Canister.

A Large Number of Rioters Killed.

Several Soldiers Killed and Wounded.

THE EVENING MOB ARMED WITH RIFLES.

They Pick Off the Soldiers from the Housetops.

Citizen Volunteers Killed--Col. Jardine Wounded.

MORE NEGROES HUNG.

Opportunities for corruption were everywhere. Unscrupulous physicians granted unwarranted deferments for a fee. "The prospect of involuntary service," said the New York *Illustrated News,* "develops an amount of latent diseases and physical disabilities that are perfectly surprising." Other doctors colluded with substitute brokers, approving for service alcoholics scoured from city streets, invalids, retarded boys lured from their homes.

Professional bounty jumpers—men who signed up from one district, received a reward for enlisting, then deserted to do the same from another district—also made a good living: one managed to repeat the process thirty-two times before he was caught.

None were more resentful of the system's inequities than the immigrant Irish of the northern city slums, who feared the blacks with whom they competed for the lowest-paying jobs, and for whose freedom they did not wish to fight.

Democratic politicians fanned their anger. "*Remember this,*" said New York Governor Horatio Seymour, "that the bloody and treasonable and revolutionary doctrine of public necessity can be proclaimed by a mob as well as by a government."

On Saturday, July 11, the names of the first draftees were drawn in New York City. They appeared in the newspapers the next day, alongside long lists

"July 14th. Fire bells clanking as they have clanked at intervals throughout the evening. . . . Shops were cleaned out and a black man hanged in Carmine Street for no offense but that of negritude."

GEORGE TEMPLETON STRONG

Soldiers of the 7th New York Militia patrol the streets of Manhattan in the aftermath of the draft riots. "I wish they would send the 2nd Rhode Island to New York City," Elisha Rhodes wrote. "The riots in that city are a disgrace to the nation and ought to be suppressed at any cost of money or life."

of those who had fallen at Gettysburg. As more names were drawn on Monday morning, a mostly Irish mob attacked the draft office, destroyed the files, razed the building, then fanned out across the city, stoning Horace Greeley's offices at the New York *Tribune,* setting fires and looting stores.

"On Monday evening," *Harper's Weekly* reported, "a large number of marauders paid a visit to the extensive clothing store of Messrs Brooks Brothers [and] helped themselves to such articles as they wanted." A woman watched the mob race through the streets:

> Thousands of infuriated creatures, yelling, screaming and swearing. . . . The rush and roar grew every moment more terrific. Up came fresh hordes faster and more furious: bare-headed men, with red, swollen faces brandishing sticks and clubs . . . and boys, women and children hurrying on and joining with them in this mad chase up the avenue like a company of raging fiends.

For three days, the east side of Manhattan belonged to the mob. They broke into the homes of the wealthy and smashed store windows, killed two disabled veterans who tried to stop them, beat the chief of police unconscious, stoned to death an unarmed officer home on leave. But blacks were their special targets: they burned down black boardinghouses, a black church, a black orphanage, and lynched a crippled black coachman while chanting, "Hurrah for Jeff Davis," then set his corpse on fire.

Police and soldiers battled rioters back and forth through the streets, in and out of buildings, across rooftops, until, on the fourth day, sunburned troops fresh from Gettysburg helped impose order.

At least 105 people had been killed. Forty-three regiments were eventually encamped around the city to ensure that fighting did not break out again.

Smaller but bloody riots occurred in other northern cities, including Boston and Troy, New York. "The nation," wrote the editor of the Washington *Times,* "is at this time in a state of Revolution, North, South, East and West."

John Singleton Mosby and one of his most prized trophies—a Union general's dress coat.

On March 9, 1863, General John Singleton Mosby's Confederate Rangers raided Fairfax Court House, Virginia, capturing two captains, thirty privates, Brigadier General Edwin Stoughton—and fifty-eight horses. "For that I am sorry," Lincoln said, "for I can make brigadier generals but I can't make horses."

Mosby was a diminutive attorney who had learned his law while in jail for shooting a fellow student. After serving in the Virginia cavalry, he became a Partisan Ranger, a guerrilla paid for all the weapons and supplies he and his men could capture from the enemy.

He spent the rest of the war cheerfully tearing up rail lines, blowing up bridges, robbing trains—and eluding the Union hosts sent galloping after the man they called "the Grey Ghost." In 1864, General Philip Sheridan dispatched one hundred men equipped with Spencer repeating rifles to hunt him down. Mosby and his men killed or wounded all but two of them, then sold their weapons to the Confederacy.

Mosby survived the war despite seven wounds and was mentioned more often than any other Confederate officer in Robert E. Lee's dispatches.

Nowhere was that revolution more vicious and unrestrained than along the Missouri border, which had not seen lasting peace since 1854. Northern and southern guerrillas fought one another there and slaughtered civilians with a murderous abandon unmatched elsewhere in the war.

The leader of the Union guerrillas, or Jayhawkers, was James H. Lane, a cadaverous former United States Senator from Kansas, who considered Missourians "wolves, snakes, devils, and, damn their souls, I want to see them cast into a burning hell." He did his conscientious best to cast them there, following in the wake of an invading force of Confederate troops, first to ravage the homes of those settlers who had dared welcome the rebels, then to burn and plunder whole towns. His actions set the bloody pattern for the atrocities that followed: soon Confederate guerrillas, or Bushwhackers, in the Ozarks were shooting and hanging men "with no charge against them except that they had been feeding Union men."

The best-known Bushwhacker was William Clarke Quantrill, a transplanted Ohioan and one-time schoolteacher who began his wartime career as a Jayhawker, switched sides, and won a captaincy from the Confederacy for helping to capture Independence, Missouri, for the South in 1861. He then gathered together a band of wild young men, most of them more interested in excitement and plunder than States' Rights, and began to raid northern sympathizers wherever they could be found. Jim Lane, Quantrill vowed, would be burned at the stake.

On the morning of August 21, waving one of the four Colt revolvers he carried in his waistband, he led 450 men into the sleeping antislavery town of Lawrence, shouting, "Kill! Kill! Lawrence must be cleansed, and the only way to cleanse it is to kill! Kill!"

Kill they did. While Quantrill himself savored a big breakfast at a hotel, his men systematically butchered at least 150 men and boys, most of them unarmed, while their mothers, wives, and daughters were made to watch. (Jim Lane, Quantrill's main target, had managed to escape through a cornfield in his nightshirt.) Then they looted and burned all of the town except the saloon, whose inventory they carried away with them.

Unable to stop sympathetic settlers from supplying the guerrillas, the Union commander, General Thomas Ewing, Jr., brother-in-law of William Tecumseh Sherman, then issued Order No. 11, forcing from their homes every man, woman, and child living in three Missouri border counties and half of a fourth. Ten thousand people were driven onto the open prairie, while bands of Jayhawkers plundered and burned the empty houses they left behind, then slashed at their huddled refugee columns, looting wagons, stealing even wedding rings—the region would be known for years as the Burnt District. "It is heart sickening to see what I have seen here . . ." wrote a Union officer who tried to maintain some semblance of order during this forced exodus. "A desolated country and men & women and children, some of them almost naked. Some on foot and some in old wagons. Oh God."

Enraged Missouri civilians now seemed ready to seek revenge, and twelve thousand regular Confederate troops under General Sterling Price moved into the state the next autumn to encourage them, hoping with the help of Quantrill and other Bushwhackers to foment an uprising and hurl the Yankees out. The invaders failed. Federal troops under General Samuel Curtis beat them at Pilot's Knob, near Westport, Missouri, then chased them all the way into Arkansas.

"This year has brought about many changes that at the beginning would have been thought impossible. The close of the year finds me a soldier for the cause of my race. May God bless the cause, and enable me in the coming year to forward it on."

CHRISTIAN FLEETWOOD

Only seven thousand rebels made it. Quantrill fled into Texas and resumed his raiding from there. But his force was less an army than a loose assembly of killers, too undisciplined to remain together long. It split up into distinct bands, the most murderous led by William "Bloody Bill" Anderson, already fond of killing before his sister died in Federal custody, and afterward apparently psychotic, riding into battle with a necklace of Union scalps around his horse's neck, laughing as he helped gun down unarmed Yankee captives, then encouraging his men to scalp and mutilate their corpses. "If you proclaim to be in arms against the guerrillas, I will kill you," Anderson wrote to one newspaper. "I will hunt you down like wolves and murder you. You cannot escape."

A large force of Union militia finally cornered Anderson and seventy of his followers in northwestern Missouri. True to form, the guerrilla leader charged into them, a pistol in each hand, and even managed to make it through the Federal line before he was shot twice through the back of the head.

Organized Confederate resistance in Missouri ended, but the bitterness inspired by the bloody warfare that went on there survived intact long after the war. For years, two of Quantrill's veterans, Frank and Jesse James, were able to survive and prosper as outlaws in the Burnt District, fed and sheltered from government pursuers by families who never forgot being forced from their homes by blue-coated soldiers.

BOTTOM RAIL ON TOP

"Once let the black man get upon his person the brass letters, 'U.S.,'" said Frederick Douglass, "let him get an eagle on his buttons and a musket on his shoulder and bullets in his pocket, and there is no power on earth which can deny that he has earned the right to citizenship in the United States."

Abolitionists had been pressing to put blacks into battle since the first shots were fired. Congress authorized their recruitment in 1862, and Lincoln's Emancipation Proclamation had urged it, but it took a full year before the first black men put on blue coats to serve under white officers.

"*Resolved,*" said a convention of free blacks, assembled at Poughkeepsie, New York, that summer to urge greater participation of black troops in the struggle for the Union. "More effective remedies ought now to be *thoroughly*

Black troops guarding twelve-pounders on their way to the front (above), and demonstrating in camp the martial skills they would soon be permitted to display on the battlefield (right).

tried, in the shape of warm lead and cold steel, duly administered by two hundred thousand black doctors."

Yet even the top Union command still could not agree as to the wisdom of arming blacks. "I have had the question put to me often," said William Tecumseh Sherman. " 'Is not a negro as good as a white man to stop a bullet?' Yes: and a sand-bag is better; but can a negro do our skirmishing and picket duty? Can they improvise bridges, sorties, flank movements, etc., like the white man? *I* say no."

Sherman's friend Grant said yes: "I have given the subject of arming the Negro my hearty support. This, with the emancipation of the Negro, is the heaviest blow yet given the Confederacy. . . . By arming the Negro we have added a powerful ally. They will make good soldiers and taking them from the enemy weakens him in the same proportion they strengthen us."

Lincoln had come to agree with Grant, and when the opposition complained, he hit back hard:

> You say you will not fight to free Negroes. Some of them seem willing to fight for you. [When victory is won] there will be some black men who can remember that, with silent tongue and clenched teeth, and steady eye and well-poised bayonet, they have helped mankind on to this great consummation; while, I fear, there will be some white ones, unable to forget that with malignant heart and deceitful speech, they strove to hinder it.

On June 7, fifteen hundred Texans attacked a smaller force of black and white Union troops at Milliken's Bend, Louisiana; it was the first important engagement in which black troops took part. "After it was over," a Union officer wrote, "many men were found dead with bayonet stabs, and others with their skulls broken open by butts of muskets. . . . The bravery of the blacks at Milliken's Bend completely revolutionized the sentiment of the army with regard to the employment of Negro troops. I heard prominent officers, who formerly had sneered . . . at the idea of the Negroes fighting, express themselves after that, as heartily in favor of it."

"The arm of the slaves [is] the best defense against the arm of the slaveholder," Frederick Douglass told his fellow blacks. "Who would be free themselves must strike the blow. . . . I urge you to fly to arms and smite to

IT DID NOT FALTER

On July 18, just three days after the draft riots ended, six hundred men of the all-black 54th Massachusetts assaulted a Confederate position at Fort Wagner, South Carolina, part of a thwarted campaign to take Charleston. More than 40 percent of them did not return.

When the color bearer fell and the order to withdraw was given, Sergeant William Carney (right) seized the colors and made it back to his lines despite bullets in the head, chest, right arm, and leg. He was the first of twenty-three blacks to win the Congressional Medal of Honor during the war—although he had to wait thirty-seven years to receive it.

"It is not too much to say that if this Massachusetts 54th had faltered when its trial came," said the New York *Tribune*, "two hundred thousand troops for whom it was a pioneer would never have put into the field. . . . . But it did not falter. It made Fort Wagner such a name for the colored race as Bunker Hill has been for ninety years to the white Yankees."

Colonel Robert Gould Shaw, the Boston abolitionist's son who had commanded the 54th Massachusetts, was among the dead. Confederates stripped his body, then threw it into a ditch with those of his men. Shaw's grieving father spoke to the press.

The poor, benighted wretches thought they were heaping indignities upon his dead body, but the act recoils upon them. . . . They buried him with his brave, devoted followers who fell dead over him and around him. . . . We can imagine no holier place than that in which he is . . . nor wish him better company—what a bodyguard he has!

Provost Guard of the 107th Colored Infantry at Fort Corcoran, part of the defenses of Washington.

"Will the slave fight? If any man asks you, tell him No. But if anyone asks you will a Negro *fight, tell him Yes!"*

WENDELL PHILLIPS

Battery A of the 2nd United States Colored Artillery at gun drill (above).

The identities of the two men on this and the facing page are known—Sergeant Harry Stewart (right) and Private Abraham Brown (opposite page, bottom right), both of the 54th Massachusetts. The rest are remembered now only for the obvious pride they took in fighting for the freedom of their people.

"Folks talk about the fighting being nearly over," said Private Jerry Sullivan, "but I believe there is a heap yet to come. Let the colored men accept the offer of the President and cabinet, take arms, join the army, and then we will whip the rebels, even if Longstreet and all the Streets of the South concentrate at Chattanooga."

In some black regiments, officers and civilian volunteers added lessons in reading and writing to the new skills taught to their recruits: several of these men hold primers open in their laps.

death the power that would bury the Government and your liberty in the same hopeless grave. This is your golden opportunity."

They responded to such appeals in astonishing numbers. Constituting less than one percent of the North's population, blacks would make up nearly one-tenth of the northern army by the end of the war. Some 185,000 blacks wore Union blue—more than twice the size of Lee's army at Gettysburg.

The bulk of those who entered the army were slaves from the border states—where enlistment was the swiftest route to freedom—and from the Confederacy itself. Slaves seeking to reach the Union lines and enlist were pursued with dogs, beaten, shot. A Confederate captain reported his success at hunting down runaways:

> Crystal River, Florida. After chasing them about two miles through the saw grass we came up in gun shot of them. They returned the fire very cool but we soon got in close range . . . and killed them. One of these Negroes was recognized by some of my men as belonging to Mr. Everett. . . . I could not get any information from either of the four that was killed, as they were dead.

Black regiments were often restricted to the most menial military tasks. Their officers were almost all white. In 166 black regiments there were scarcely 100 black officers, and no black soldier was ever allowed to rise above captain.

From Fort Sumter onward, Frederick Douglass campaigned ceaselessly for black recruitment. "The Negro is the key to the situation," he said, "the pivot upon which the whole rebellion turns. . . . This war, disguise it as they may, is virtually nothing more or less than perpetual slavery against universal freedom." When the all-black 54th Massachusetts charged into the guns at Fort Wagner, Douglass's two sons were among them—and survived.

Nonetheless, they took great pride in their new status as soldiers fighting for the freedom of their race. One celebrated his newfound ability to "walk fearlessly and boldly through the streets [of New Orleans] . . . without being required to take off his cap at every step." Another found himself face to face with his former owner, now a prisoner of war. "Hello, Massa," he said, "bottom rail on top dis time."

Black privates were paid just ten dollars a month, three dollars less than whites. Several regiments served without pay for months rather than submit to that inequality. In mid-November 1863, the men of one black company stacked their arms before the tent of their regimental commander and refused to pick them up again until they received equal pay. Their sergeant, William Walker, was found guilty of mutiny and executed by firing squad in the presence of his brigade.

Blacks were also denied the clothing allowance granted whites, so that they were more susceptible to severe weather, and white doctors proved reluctant to serve with them, so that the death rate from disease among blacks was double that of the rest of the army.

Douglass discussed these and other black grievances with Lincoln, and noted the President's response. "The employment of colored troops at all was a great gain to the colored people, [he said] . . . their enlistment was a serious offense to popular prejudice. . . . That they were not to receive the same pay as white soldiers seemed a necessary concession to smooth the way to their employment as soldiers."

The Confederate army used blacks, too, as laborers—sometimes at gunpoint and under fire from Union troops. But after Gettysburg and Vicksburg, some Confederates began to argue that they should serve as soldiers, too. "The time has come for us to put into the army every able-bodied Negro man . . ." a Louisiana planter said. "He must play an important part in this war. He *caused* the fight and he will have his portion of the burden to bear." General Patrick R. Cleburne agreed: "[I recommend] that we immediately commence training a large reserve of the most courageous of our slaves and further that we guarantee freedom within a reasonable time to every slave in the South who shall remain true to the Confederacy in this war."

"I think that the proposition to make soldiers of the slaves is the most pernicious idea that has been suggested since the war began," General Howell Cobb of Georgia countered. "You cannot make soldiers of slaves, or slaves of soldiers. The day you make a soldier of them is the beginning of the end of the revolution. And if slaves seem good soldiers, *then our whole theory of slavery is wrong.*"

Faced with such opposition, President Davis shelved the idea, but he did not reject it outright.

ALL HELL CAN'T STOP THEM

In the autumn, Grant crowned his Vicksburg victory with another great triumph—Chattanooga.

Standing above a bend of the Tennessee River at the meeting point of two important railroads, Chattanooga guarded the gateway to the eastern Con-

The Tennessee River snakes past Chattanooga, in a view made from Lookout Mountain.

federacy and the rebel war industries in Georgia. From it, the Confederate army could mount expeditions into Tennessee and Kentucky. If the Union could seize it, they could move south into Georgia and further divide the Confederacy.

At the end of 1862, the Union Army of the Cumberland had tried to drive the Confederate Army of Tennessee out of the central part of the state. The northern commander was William Rosecrans, an Ohioan called "Old Rosy" by his admiring soldiers.

The Confederate commander was Braxton Bragg, a Louisiana sugar planter trained at West Point, an impatient, anxious soldier given to explosions of temper and migraine headaches. He was much admired by Jefferson Davis, but not by his own officers or men, as Sam Watkins made plain:

> None of General Bragg's soldiers ever loved him. They had no faith in his ability as a general. He was looked upon as a merciless tyrant. The soldiers were very scantily fed. Bragg was never a good feeder. . . . He

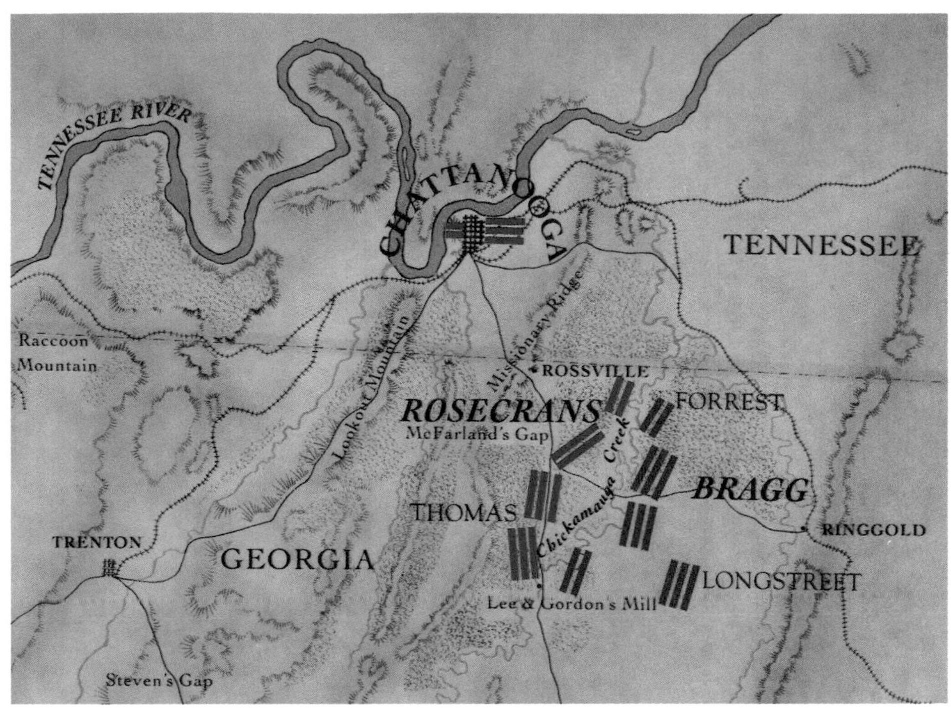

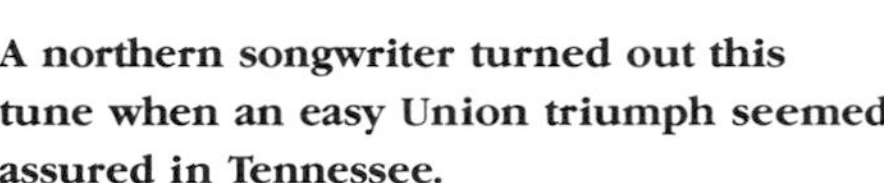
A northern songwriter turned out this tune when an easy Union triumph seemed assured in Tennessee.

The Battle of Chickamauga: The first day of the ferocious struggle fought along a little stream in North Georgia on September 19 and 20, 1863, may have been even more bloody than Antietam, but in the official tallying that followed, no one was ever able to separate those killed on the first day from those slaughtered on the second.

loved to crush the spirit of his men. The more of a hang-dog look they had about them, the better was General Bragg pleased. Not a single soldier in the whole army every loved or respected him.

On December 30, 1862, Union forces came upon Bragg's ragged army camped along Stone's River, a mile northwest of Murfreesboro. The two armies spent the night only a few hundred yards apart, their bands competing with one another, alternating northern and southern tunes. Then one band struck up "Home, Sweet Home," another joined in, and then another, until 78,000 men were singing it together in the icy darkness.

The next day, the Confederates attacked at dawn. The fighting was some of the fiercest of the war, the artillery so thunderous that men stopped fighting long enough to pick raw cotton from the fields and stuff it into their ears. The South seemed to be winning until Rosecrans rallied his men, riding up and down the lines apparently oblivious of the shelling that blew off the head of an aide riding at his side. Two days later, the rebels attacked again, only to be beaten back. It was a standoff. Each army lost roughly a third of its men; Bragg withdrew toward Tullahoma. "I see no prospects of peace for a long time," one Confederate wrote after Stone's River. "The Yankees can't whip us and we can never whip them."

For almost six months thereafter, the two armies feinted at one another while Confederate cavalry under John Hunt Morgan dashed northward into Ohio—where they were captured—and Union cavalry tried to cut the Chattanooga-Atlanta railroad, raiding into Alabama, where *they* were captured, by Bedford Forrest.

Lincoln demanded more decisive action. Rosecrans resisted, requesting more troops, horses, mules, time. Finally threatened with dismissal, Rose-

It was thanks in large part to the resolution of George "Pap" Thomas, the "Rock of Chickamauga" (above), that the Union forces managed to make it back into Chattanooga more or less intact. Surrounded there for two cold autumn months, Federal troops knocked down houses for firewood and built shelters for themselves with planks still covered with wallpaper (opposite, top). Not long after U. S. Grant established a supply line to Chattanooga, enterprising civilians had opened the "Sutlers' Row" (above left), to sell dry goods and delicacies to the Union forces. The Federal soldier's chronic enthusiasm for supplementing his diet is made understandable by photographs like the one at the bottom of the opposite page, showing men from the quartermaster's department doling out the standard ration of meat.

crans moved in June, launching a series of swift, almost bloodless flanking maneuvers despite a steady rain—"No *Presbyterian* rain, either," a soldier remembered, "but a genuine Baptist downpour."

He drove Bragg eighty miles, first to Tullahoma—whose name, one weary Confederate said, came from *tulla,* the Greek word for "mud," and *homa,* meaning "*more* mud"—then to Chattanooga.

Rosecrans forced him out of there, too, but then ran into trouble. Bragg, reinforced by 12,000 men under James Longstreet sent in by rail, lured part of the Union army out of the city and attacked it along Chickamauga Creek.

The furious two-day battle fought there cost 4,000 lives and 35,000 casualties in all. Bragg hit the Union army hard, and on the second day Rosecrans made a near-fatal mistake, ordering his troops to close a gap in the Union line—that wasn't there. In the process, he opened up a new one and Longstreet's troops stormed through it, routing two Union corps, and sending Rosecrans and most of his army staggering back to Chattanooga. Rosecrans, Lincoln said, was "confused and stunned, like a duck hit on the head."

Troops under George Henry Thomas, a Unionist from Virginia known to his men as "Pap," managed a stubborn, staged, last-minute withdrawal that kept Chickamauga from being worse for the Union than it was—and earned Thomas a new nickname, "the Rock of Chickamauga."

The Confederates occupied the field at day's end, but Bragg refused to follow up his advantage. His officers were livid. Longstreet formally demanded Bragg's removal. "I am convinced," he said, "that nothing but the hand of God can help as long as we have our present commander."

Lincoln's sorrow at the Union defeat was intensified by the death at Chickamauga of his wife's brother-in-law, Confederate Brigadier General Ben Hardin Helm. Mary Lincoln wept privately but remained stoical in public; she

"If there was little of beauty or elegance in the place when our troops retreated into it from Chickamauga, there was a great deal less subsequently. Like many other Southern towns, Chattanooga grew suddenly old."

W. F. G. SHANKS
Newspaper correspondent

hoped *all* her Confederate relatives would be killed, she told a friend: "They would kill my husband if they could, and destroy our Government—the dearest thing of all of us."

Bottled up in Chattanooga, the Union troops were cold, infested with vermin, cut off from all but a thin trickle of supplies. They demolished houses and hacked down every tree and fence in town for fuel. "The fall rains were beginning," an officer remembered. "Ten thousand dead mules walled the sides of the road from Bridgeport to Chattanooga. . . . The men were on less than half rations. Guards stood at the troughs of artillery horses to keep the soldiers from taking the scant supply of corn. . . . Men followed the wagons . . . picking up the grains of corn and bits of crackers that fell to the ground."

The Confederates besieging the city were in little better shape, according to Sam Watkins.

> Our rations were cooked up by a special detail train ten miles in the rear and were sent up to us every three days; . . . those three days' rations were generally eaten at one meal, and the soldiers had to starve the other two days and a half. The soldiers were . . . almost naked and covered all over with vermin and camp-itch and filth and dust. The men looked sick hollow-eyed and heart-broken.
>
> In the very acme of our privations and hunger, when the army was most dissatisfied and unhappy we were ordered into line . . . to be reviewed by Honorable Jefferson Davis. When he passed us with his great retinue of staff-officers at full gallop, cheers greeted him with the words, "Send us something to eat, Massa Jeff. I'm hungry! I'm hungry!"

General Philip Sheridan, whose influence on his own men's fighting spirit, one aide said, was "like an electric shock."

Davis had come to Bragg's headquarters to settle a dispute among his officers. Bragg had dismissed three members of his staff for failing to obey orders and angrily blamed others for his own decision not to follow up his victory at Chickamauga. Bedford Forrest was so enraged by Bragg's "meanness" that he refused to serve under him further, leaving to take up an independent command in Mississippi after calling Bragg "a damned scoundrel" and warning him not to interfere with him "at the peril of your life."

Davis finally asked each corps commander, in turn, if Bragg should be replaced. All said yes. But Davis, who personally disliked the two most likely alternative commanders—Beauregard and Joseph E. Johnston—paid no attention, and kept Bragg in charge.

In October, Lincoln named U. S. Grant to command all the Union armies between the Appalachians and the Mississippi.

Grant hurried to Chattanooga. He replaced Rosecrans with Thomas as head of the Army of the Cumberland. "When Grant arrived," an officer recalled, "we began to see things move. We felt that everything came from a plan." He punched a hole through the southern perimeter, laid a pontoon bridge across the Tennessee, and set up a sixty-mile "cracker line" to supply his troops with food.

Bragg's army occupied the six-mile crest of Missionary Ridge east of the city, and Confederate guns, massed on the two-thousand-foot summit of Lookout Mountain, commanded a field of fire on the south and west.

Civilians and soldiers roam the lower slope of Lookout Mountain shortly after the battle, looking for souvenirs.

U. S. Grant (at left, above) enjoys a cigar after Lookout Mountain is safely in Union hands. Following the fighting, an Ohio cameraman named Royan M. Linn (the bearded man at top, opposite) did a nice business making *carte de visite* photographs of sightseers posed on Point Lookout.

Grant resolved to drive them off.

The two-day battle of Chattanooga began on November 24. Sherman's attack on the left flank of Bragg's line stalled, but Joe Hooker's men stormed Lookout Mountain and planted the Stars and Stripes on the summit, fighting through such dense fog that it was remembered as the "Battle Above the Clouds."

The next day, George Thomas's veterans of Chickamauga were asked to make a limited attack on the first line of Confederate trenches below Missionary Ridge, while Hooker launched an all-out assault on the right. The southern positions looked impregnable: artillery lining the crest; rifle pits along the slope; trenches at the base of the hill.

Thomas's men moved toward the hill and overran the trenches at its bottom, then waited for orders.

With them was General Phil Sheridan, an Irish immigrant's son, whose 115

pounds were no measure of his courage or energy. He pulled a flask from his pocket and toasted the Confederate gunners on the slope above him. "Here's at you," he shouted. They opened fire, spattering him and his officers with dirt. Furious, Sheridan roared, "*That* was ungenerous! I'll take your guns for that!"

It was all his men needed. They started up the slope toward the rebel guns. Worried, Grant asked, "Who ordered those men up the hill?" An aide answered, "No one. They started up without orders. When those fellows get started, all hell can't stop them."

The men were determined to avenge themselves. Shouting, "Chickamauga! Chickamauga!" they fought their way past the rifle pits and on toward the summit. One of Grant's aides watched with him.

> At times their movements were in shape like the flight of migratory birds—sometimes in line, sometimes in mass, mostly in V-shaped groups, with the points toward the enemy. At these points regimental flags were flying, sometimes dropping as the bearers were shot, but never reaching the ground, for other brave hands were there to seize them. Sixty flags were advancing up the hill.

Eighteen-year-old Lieutenant Arthur MacArthur, Jr., of the 24th Wisconsin, bore his unit's colors to the top of Missionary Ridge, shouting, "On, Wisconsin," in the face of fire that had killed three color bearers before him. His heroism impressed Sheridan, who recommended him for the Medal of Honor; much later, it would inspire his son, Douglas MacArthur.

Some Confederates began to break and run. "A column of Yankees swept right over where I was standing," Sam Watkins recalled. "I was trying to stand aside to get out of their way, but the more I tried to get out of their way, the more in their way I got."

Sections of the slope were so steep that the Union troops had to crawl; some men used tree branches or bayonets to haul themselves up, but they kept coming. "Those defending the heights became more and more desperate as our men approached the top," one remembered. "*They* shouted 'Chickamauga' as though the word itself were a weapon; they thrust cartridges into guns by the handsful, they lighted the fuses of shells and rolled them down, but nothing could stop the force of the charge."

"I saw Day's brigade throw down their guns and break like quarter horses," Watkins remembered. "Bragg was trying to rally them. I heard him say, 'Here is your commander,' and the soldiers hallooed back, 'Here is your *mule*.'"

Four thousand Confederate prisoners were taken on Missionary Ridge and sent north to prison camps. Bragg characteristically blamed his own men: "No satisfactory excuse can possibly be given for the shameful conduct of our troops," he wrote. "The position was one which ought to have been held by a line of skirmishers."

The next day, General Thomas ordered a Union cemetery laid out on the slope of a hill called Orchard Knob that had seen especially savage fighting. The chaplain in charge asked if the burials should be by state. "No, no, mix 'em up," Thomas said. "I'm *tired* of States' Rights."

LITTLE NOTE, NOR LONG REMEMBER

On November 19, 1863, Abraham Lincoln came to Gettysburg to dedicate the new Union cemetery. The featured speaker was to be Edward Everett, the former governor of Massachusetts, diplomat, clergyman, politician, and now, at seventy, best known for his lush, patriotic oratory. The President had been asked only to offer a few "appropriate remarks."

A crowd of nearly six thousand gathered to hear the speeches, and local entrepreneurs set up tables on its outskirts to sell them cookies and lemonade and battle relics—minié balls, canteens, buttons, dried wildflowers, grown on the battlefield and preserved in daguerreotype cases.

Everett was introduced, and launched into a speech that lasted one hour and fifty-seven minutes. While he listened, the President fussed with the wording of his own remarks.

Finally, Lincoln rose to speak.

> Fourscore and seven years ago our fathers brought forth on this continent a new nation, conceived in liberty, and dedicated to the proposition that all men are created equal.
>
> Now we are engaged in a great civil war, testing whether that nation, or any nation so conceived and so dedicated, can long endure. We are met on a great battlefield of that war. We have come to dedicate a portion of that field as a final resting place for those who here gave their lives that that nation might live. It is altogether fitting and proper that we should do this.
>
> But, in a larger sense, we can not dedicate—we can not consecrate—we can not hallow—this ground. The brave men, living and dead, who struggled here, have consecrated it, far above our poor power to add or detract. The world will little note, nor long remember, what we say here, but it can never forget what they did here. It is for us the living, rather, to be dedicated here to the unfinished work which they who fought here have thus far so nobly advanced. It is rather for us to be here dedicated to the great task remaining before us—that from these honored dead we take increased devotion to that cause for which they gave the last full measure of devotion—that we here highly resolve that these dead shall not have died in vain—that this nation, under God, shall have a new birth of freedom—and that government of the people, by the people, for the people, shall not perish from the earth.

Lincoln was displeased with his performance. "That speech won't scour," his friend Ward Hill Lamon remembered his saying. "It's a flat failure." The correspondent for the London *Times* agreed: "The ceremony was rendered ludicrous by . . . the sallies of that poor President Lincoln. . . . Anyone more dull and commonplace it would not be easy to produce."

But Edward Everett felt different. "I should be glad," he wrote to the President, "if I could flatter myself that I came as near to the central idea of the occasion, in two hours, as you did in two minutes."

An unknown local photographer did his best to cover Lincoln's visit to Gettysburg. At the top right is his view of the procession to the cemetery in which the President (not visible here) rode a horse some onlookers thought altogether too small for him. He also took a photograph of the speaker's stand, a detail from which at bottom right reveals the high forehead of the seated President, just to the left of the tall man in top hat and sash. No photograph survives of Lincoln actually reading his speech, probably because, having spoken just 269 words, he was back in his seat before the photographer could get his shutter open.

Men at War

An Interview with Shelby Foote

SHELBY FOOTE WAS BORN IN 1916, IN GREENVILLE, Mississippi, attended the University of North Carolina, and served as a captain of field artillery in the Second World War. In 1953, he signed a contract to write a short history of the Civil War. He had scarcely begun when he realized, as he once said, that he would have "to go spread-eagle, whole hog on the thing." In the end, his classic three-volume narrative, *The Civil War,* took twenty years and three thousand pages to complete.

Ken Burns spoke with him on camera for more than two days. The interview that follows was culled from those conversations.

In addition to *The Civil War,* Foote has published five novels: *Tournament, Follow Me Down, Love in a Dry Season, Shiloh,* and *Jordan County.*

Why are we drawn to the Civil War?

Any understanding of this nation has to be based, and I mean really based, on an understanding of the Civil War. I believe that firmly. It defined us. The Revolution did what it did. Our involvement in European wars, beginning with the First World War, did what it did. But the Civil War defined us as what we are and it opened us to being what we became, good and bad things. And it is very necessary, if you're going to understand the American character in the twentieth century, to learn about this enormous catastrophe of the nineteenth century. It was the crossroads of our being, and it was a hell of a crossroads.

As a southerner I would say one of the main importances of the war is that southerners have a sense of defeat which none of the rest of the country has. You see in the movie *Patton* the actor who plays Patton saying, "We Americans have never lost a war." That's a rather amazing statement for him to make as Patton because George Patton's grandfather was in Lee's Army of Northern Virginia and he certainly lost a war.

We think we are a wholly superior people. If we'd been anything like as superior as we think we are, we would not have fought that war. But since we did fight it, we have to make it the greatest war of all times. And our generals were the greatest generals of all time. It's very American to do that.

Why did Americans kill each other in such great numbers?

Basically, it was a failure on our part to find a way not to fight that war. It was because we failed to do the thing we really have a genius for, which is compromise. Americans like to think of themselves as *un*compromising. But our true genius is for compromise. Our whole government's founded on it. And it failed.

Southerners saw the election of Lincoln as a sign that the Union was about to be radicalized and that they were about to be taken in directions they did not care to go. The abolitionist aspect of it was very strong and they figured they were about to lose what they called their property, and faced ruin. Southerners would have told you they were fighting for self-government. They believed that the gathering of power in Washington was against them. Another important thing historically is that when they entered into that federation they certainly would never have entered into it if they hadn't believed it would be possible to get out. And when the time came when they wanted to get out, they thought they had every right.

Of course, they say wars never settle anything—but that business about secession was settled by that war.

What was the country like when the war began?

It had a simplicity that we are not able to comprehend. Many people spent their entire lives not being over fifty or a hundred miles from home. But they gained things. They weren't torn on the bias the way we are. They weren't pulled at from so many different directions. Lincoln said human nature doesn't change, and human nature *hasn't* changed, but men's belief had a startling simplicity to it. For example, a soldier in line at Gettysburg was told, "You will advance a mile across that open valley and take that hill." I, for one, would say, "General, I don't think we should do this. I don't believe we can get there." But they took it as a matter of course, and you must remember they fought for four years, which is a long time, and the simplicity was severely tested, but they never lost it. Duty, bravery under adversity, very simple virtues, and they had them.

[When the war began, and] militia units and volunteers in large numbers assembled and went off to war, there

was a feeling that they were heading into a great experience—a feeling on both sides that they were going to save their country, meaning the two countries, and there was all that exuberance and a sense of a great adventure lying ahead. That aspect of it is very particular to that war. Civil wars are notorious for being cruel and bloody, [but] that side of it hadn't come to them [yet]. It was as if they were going to engage in a family argument, vociferously.

Did the soldiers on both sides really know what they were fighting for?

Early on in the war, a Union squad closed in on a single ragged Confederate. He didn't own any slaves and he obviously didn't have much interest in the Constitution or anything else. And they asked him, "What are you fighting for anyhow?" And he said, "I'm fighting because you're down here." Which was a pretty satisfactory answer. Lincoln had the much more difficult job of sending men out to shoot up somebody else's home. He had to unite them before he could do that, and his way of doing it was twofold. One was to say the Republic must be preserved, not split in two. That was one. And the other one he gave them as a cause: the freeing of the slaves.

But no one on either side thought it would last long. Those few individuals who said that it *would,* William Tecumseh Sherman for instance, were actually judged to be insane for making predictions about casualties which were actually low. There was even a congressman, I believe from Alabama, who said there would be no war, and offered to wipe up all the blood that would be shed with a pocket handkerchief. I've always said someone could get a Ph.D. by calculating how many pocket handkerchiefs it would take to wipe up all the blood that was shed. It would be a lot of handkerchiefs.

What made it such a bloodbath?

It was brutal stuff, and the reason for the high casualties is really quite simple: the weapons were way ahead of the tactics. Take the rifle itself. It threw a .58-caliber soft lead bullet at a low muzzle velocity, and when it hit, the reason there were so many amputations was that if you got hit in the upper arm, say, it didn't just clip the bone the way the modern steel-jacketed bullet does: you didn't have any bone left up there. They had no choice but to take the arm off. And you'll see pictures of the dead on the battlefield with their clothes in disarray, as if someone had been rifling their bodies. That was the men themselves tearing their clothes up to see where the wound was, and they knew perfectly well that if they were gut-shot, they'd die.

[Yet for much of the war] they still believed that to take a position you massed your men and moved up and gave them the bayonet. In fact there were practically no bayonet wounds in the Civil War. They never came in that kind of contact, or at least very seldom came in that kind of contact. But they still thought that to mass their fire they had to mass their men. So they lined up and marched up to an entrenched line and got blown away.

Someone once remarked that the Civil War occurred during the medical middle ages. What was it like?

When you see the instruments used in surgery, it's enough to make your hair stand on end—the bone saws and things. I'm sure they did the best they could. In many instances on the southern side they didn't have medicines to use. Lack of chloroform, for instance, during amputations was a horrible thing to contemplate.

They not only didn't subscribe to the germ theory: they didn't suspect that it existed. Blood poisoning, erysipelas, pneumonia, even measles was a big killer. They did not know how to treat them, let alone not having penicillin. It was just a question of a crisis and surviving or a crisis and dying. It's a wonder they did as well as they did.

In the early days of the war especially, a camp, whether northern or southern, was an uproarious thing with the coughing. There was a tremendous amount of coughing in the camps in the early days. They all shook down. You couldn't tell a city boy from a country boy after they'd been in the army a year or two.

The Civil War introduced great technological innovations.

There were many inventions, but perhaps the one thing that the Civil War contributed really to the art of warfare was field fortifications. That was primarily due to James Longstreet, whose men invented it, and Stonewall Jackson saw it and emulated it. Lee used it, too. Finally, that army got so they could flow into a position the way water seeks its own level. They could get into a position and have overlapping fields of fire that a master might have designed.

There were hand grenades, too. In fact, there was a great shortage of hand grenades in the South, while the North had plenty of them. They were not hand grenades the way we know them now: they were just steel cylinders filled with powder with a fuse attached. And the Confederates had two ways of improvising hand grenades. One was just to pick up those that didn't go off and re-fuse them and throw them back; the other was to throw them back before they went off. While it was lying there with the fuse sputtering, you'd pick it up and throw it back in the other direction. They improvised other things as well. They took large-caliber artillery shells that had been duds and re-fused them and rolled them down the hill into Federal entrenchments. That was quite effective.

There were many crazy ideas along with the good ones. There was one plan to use two cannon, each with a cannonball and the two cannonballs connected by a chain. You would fire the two cannons at the same time and the balls would go out an the chain between them would just cut a swath through everything in the way. The trouble was one cannon, of course, went off before the other one did, with the result that the ball went around in a circle from the other cannon.

What was it like for the enlisted man?

It was tough. There were little things. They made regular twenty-five-mile marches. I made two or three twenty-five-mile marches in the army and I was broken down for days after it. They made them frequently, and when you were issued a pair of shoes in the northern army, they weren't left foot and right foot, they were the same foot. You *wore* them into being a left-foot shoe or a right-foot. And when you imagine making twenty-five-mile marches with inferior footwear, let alone barefoot, the way many Confederates were, it's unbelievable the way they could function.

There was a lot of boredom, as there is in all armies. Combat is a very small part of army service if you're talking about the amount of time spent in it. Everything is boring. The food is bad. The time on your hands is bad. The lack of reading materials is bad. It's nearly all boredom. All armies have that saying, "Hurry up and wait." There was an awful lot of that. The boredom was especially oppressive when combined with the heat of summer, as at Vicksburg or Petersburg. Partly out of bravado but mainly out of boredom, the men would leap up on the parapets and make insulting gestures toward the other side while they shot at him—just from sheer boredom. Some of them got shot doing it, too.

A trip to the whorehouse, incidentally, was called "going down the line." There were many other terms for it, too. And there were a great many prostitutes on both sides, principally in the cities where the boys went on furlough, like Richmond and New York.

A historian once said the Civil War produced the first democratic armies.

In the Confederate army, all officers below the rank of brigadier were elected by the troops. You would think that would be a poor system, because men would select officers who would be easy on them rather than men who were skillful. You couldn't be wronger. They knew that they were electing men whom they were willing to trust with their lives, so you better believe they selected the best men.

There was no expiration of enlistments on the Confederate side. They were in for the war. There were expirations of enlistment on the Union side and plenty of them. For instance in the trenches at Cold Harbor there were men whose time was up in the middle of the battle and who left, crawling on all fours to keep from being killed while getting away.

There were no medals awarded in the Confederate army—not one in the whole course of the war. The Confederate reason for that was that they were all heroes and it would not do to single anyone out. They were not all heroes, of course. But when the suggestion was made to Lee that there be a roll of honor for the Army of Northern Virginia, Lee disallowed it. The highest honor you could get in the Confederate army was to be mentioned in dispatches. And that was considered absolutely enough.

The Confederates had a very particular battle cry, didn't they?

They both had a particular way of yelling. The Northern troops made a sort of Hurrah—it was called by one soldier "the deep generous manly shout of the Northern soldier." The Confederates of course had what was called the Rebel Yell. We don't really know what that sounded like. It was basically, I think, a sort of fox-hunt yip mixed up with a sort of banshee squall, and it was used on the attack. An old Confederate veteran after the war was asked at a United Veterans of the Confederacy meeting in Tennessee somewhere to give the Rebel Yell. The ladies had never heard it. And he said, "It can't be done, except at a run, and I couldn't do it anyhow with a mouthful of false teeth and a stomach full of food." So they never got to hear what it sounded like!

Why are there different names for the same battles? Go over some of those great struggles.

The tendency was for northern armies officially to call them after the nearest stream of water, Antietam Creek, for instance. And the Confederates tended to name them after towns: Sharpsburg in that case. Same way with Manassas and Bull Run or Murfreesboro and Stone's River. I've often thought that that's because towns were unusual to southerners, who lived rurally, so they named them after the nearest town.

It's my belief that the war in the West is at least as important as the one in the East. There's a general opinion, because of the amount of writing done about the eastern theater and the amount of tourist visits, that the war was fought in Virginia while we were just skirmishing out in this direction. I don't think the opposite is true but I think it's closer to the truth. The Union victory at Fort Donelson, for example, lost all of Kentucky for the Confederacy, and most of Tennessee. It saw the emergence of Ulysses S. Grant and Nathan Bedford Forrest. It was when the northern juggernaut began to roll, and the battle of Shiloh was an attempt to stop it, a desperate attempt to stop it that failed.

Shiloh was the first big battle—the first great bloody battle; First Manassas, or Bull Run as it's sometimes called, was nothing compared to Shiloh. It was fought in early April [of 1862]. The trees were leafed out and the roads were meandering cowpaths. Nobody knew north from south, east from west. They'd never been in combat before, most of them, especially on the southern side. So it was just a disorganized, murderous fistfight, a hundred thousand men slamming away at each other. The generals didn't know their jobs, the soldiers didn't know their jobs. It was just pure determination to stand and fight and not retreat.

The bloodiness of Shiloh was astounding to everyone. Out of 100,000 men, over 20,000 were killed, wounded, captured, or missing. Shiloh had the same number of casualties as Waterloo [which ended the Napoleonic wars]. And yet, when it was fought, there were another twenty Waterloos to follow. Grant, shortly before Shiloh, said he considered the war to be practically over, that the South was ready to give up. The day after Shiloh he said, "I saw it was going to have to be a war of conquest if we were to win." Shiloh also corrected a southern misconception which had said, "One good southern soldier is worth ten Yankee hirelings." They found out that wasn't true by a long shot. Shiloh did that. It sobered the nation up something awful to realize that they had a very bloody affair on their hands. And it called for a huge reassessment of what the war was going to be.

Antietam.

Sharpsburg is an unusual battle in that there was no need for fighting it at all. Lee didn't have to fight it, but he was determined not to be run out of Maryland and he stopped to fight. A lot of people think he was wrong to stop there and fight, but from then on, when Lee was on a retreat, anybody closing in on him was very, very cautious, probably because they remembered Sharpsburg.

It was a bloody one. It was unbelievable. It was three battles, one after another, left, center, and right. It's a highly dramatic action. If you wanted to see a battle that was highly dramatic, you'd probably take Sharpsburg or

Fredericksburg, where you could see practically the whole field.

After the bloody fighting at Sharpsburg, particularly in the cornfield and around the Dunker church, after his part of the fighting was over, Stonewall Jackson was sitting on his horse eating a peach and his medical director, Dr. McGuire, was there. Jackson was an eerie character: an Old Testament warrior who believed in smiting them hip and thigh. And he looked out over this field where there were dead of both sides littered all over the place. And as he was eating the peach he said, "God has been very kind to us this day."

The men in that war seem to have shown a special courage. Did those on one side fight more bravely than those on the other?

More credit for valor is given to Confederate soldiers: they're supposed to have had more élan and dash. Actually I know of no braver men in either army than the Union troops at Fredericksburg, which was a serious Union defeat. But to keep charging that wall at the foot of Marye's Heights after all the failures there'd been—and they were all failures—is a singular instance of valor. It was different from southern élan. It was a steadiness under fire, a continuing to press the point.

It was very unusual to see the northern lights that far south, but after the battle of Fredericksburg that night the whole heavens were lit up with streamers of fire and whatever the northern lights are. The Confederates took it as a sign that God Almighty himself was celebrating a Confederate victory.

Fredericksburg and Chancellorsville were really Lee and Jackson at their greatest, weren't they?

Chancellorsville in many ways is Lee's masterpiece. It's where the odds were longest. It's where he took the greatest risk in dividing his army in the presence of a superior enemy and kept the pressure on.

The only fault at Chancellorsville was that the attack was staged so late in the day that they were not able to push it to the extent that Stonewall Jackson had intended to and he was even attempting to make a night attack, a very rare thing in the Civil War, because he knew he hadn't finished up what he'd begun. And that's where he received the wound that eventually killed him.

What happened to Lee at Gettysburg?

Gettysburg was the price the South paid for having R. E. Lee.

The first day's fighting was so encouraging, and on the second day's fighting he came within an inch of doing it. And by that time Longstreet said Lee's blood was up, and Longstreet said when Lee's blood was up there was no stopping him. Longstreet tried to stop him and Lee said, "No, he's there"—meaning the enemy—"and I'm going to strike him." And that was the mistake he made, the mistake of all mistakes.

[Pickett's charge] was an incredible mistake, and there was scarcely a trained soldier who didn't know it was a mistake at the time, except possibly Pickett himself, who was very happy he had a chance for glory. But every man who looked out over that field, whether it was a sergeant or a lieutenant general, saw that it was a desperate endeavor and I'm sure knew that it should not have been made.

The casualties were almost exactly 50 percent of the men who took part in that charge, including the captured as well as the killed and wounded.

William Faulkner, in *Intruder in the Dust,* said that for every southern boy, it's always in his reach to imagine it being one o'clock on an early July day in 1863, the guns are laid, the troops are lined up, the flags are already out of their cases and ready to be unfurled, but it hasn't happened yet. And he can go back in his mind to the time before the war was going to be lost and he can always have that moment for himself.

The Confederate surrender at Vicksburg, coming only a day after Gettysburg, must have been terribly demoralizing to the South.

I had a great-uncle. His name was Walter Jolley. And he was nine years old at the time of the surrender [of Vicksburg]. And on the 4th of July [1863], when the Federal troops marched in, he was standing on the sidewalk by the street, and he had on a coat with large brass buttons down the front of it. And he was standing there watching these Federal soldiers who had been trying to kill him all these days, and out of the ranks stepped a very large black corporal and took out a knife, which my uncle thought he was going to use to cut his throat. Instead he cut the buttons off of his blouse and put them in his pocket and got back in ranks. Uncle Jolley told me about that when I was a little boy, and I could put myself in his position. It must have been terrifying.

Chickamauga isn't so well known as some of the battles in the East, but in some ways it was the worst.

Chickamauga, like all Indian words, is interpreted to mean "river of death." God knows what it really means. You can translate Indian words almost any way. But the second day at Chickamauga may have been the bloodiest day of the war. It was a horrendous battle. A lot of breakthroughs. A lot of hand-to-hand combat. A long ragged retreat. A glorious southern victory, which was unexploited. All the western heroes were there, from Nathan Bedford Forrest on down. It's a great battle.

Cold Harbor was another major southern victory.

At Cold Harbor the Confederates were well dug in. Those were men who knew how to take a position where you could do the most killing from. The whole army was lined up there, waiting and hoping and praying something would come at them. And Grant threw three corps at them, and in approximately seven minutes they shot about seven thousand men. It was a bloody mess. It's the only thing Grant ever admitted that he'd done wrong. He said after the war, "If I had it to do over again, I don't believe I'd make that charge at Cold Harbor."

But at Petersburg the character of the war seemed to change.

Petersburg is a magnificent salute to the durability of men on both sides. It was a rehearsal for World War I trench warfare. And they stood up very well to it, but the soldiers always did in that war. It's to us an almost incredible bravery, considering the casualties.

In some ways, the Battle of Franklin in late 1864 strikes me as one of the most terrible. Confederate Private Sam Watkins said it seemed as if the "Death Angel" was here to gather his last harvest.

Franklin was a horrendous battle. The charge at Franklin, Tennessee, was a more difficult charge than Lee's charge at Gettysburg, and the casualties were as high and the flower of the southern army fell. There's a strong suspicion that John Bell Hood was trying to discipline his army by staging that charge at Franklin and there's some truth in it. He was exasperated by what had happened at Spring Hill shortly before that and the idea was to put the iron to them. His army was wrecked, and the defeat at Nashville is in large part due to what had happened at Franklin a month before.

How could those men do what they did and make the charges they made? It seems incredible.

The main reason you did it was because the man next to you did it. It was unit pride. If you stop to think about it, it would have been much harder not to go than to go. It would have taken a great deal of courage to say, "Marse Robert, I ain't goin'." Nobody's got that much courage.

But it's hard to understand. Those men seem larger than life in what they could endure, especially if you know anything about the medical attention they got. It was so crude, the lack of anesthetics, all those things. It's almost unbelievable that men could perform over a period of four years. Anybody could go out and perform some afternoon. These men kept it up year after year.

You must remember that [the men in a regiment] were all from the same state. They had followed the same flag. The names of the battles they had fought in were stitched on that flag. And there was a great deal of unit pride. And I'm sure there was a great deal of sadness over the losses that they suffered. But there was closeness among those men that came from years of being exposed to the most horrendous warfare that I know of.

There was a big problem with units of men all from the same state or county or even town. If one of those regiments got into a very tight spot in a particular battle, like in the cornfield at Sharpsburg, the news might be that there were no more young men from that town. They were all dead. That happened to units from Clarksville, Tennessee. I once saw some figures on how many men they sent to war and how many men came back, and you wouldn't believe the low number that came back.

Let's talk about people.

Bedford Forrest's granddaughter lived here in Memphis. She recently died and I got to know her and she even let me swing the general's saber around my head once, which was a great treat. And I thought a long time and I called her and said, "I think the war produced two authentic geniuses. One of them was your grandfather. The other was Abraham Lincoln." And there was a silence at the other end of the phone. And she said, "Well, you know in our family we never thought much of Mr. Lincoln." She didn't like my coupling her grandfather with Abraham Lincoln all these years later. Southerners are very strange about that war.

Tell me about Lincoln.

A very mysterious man. He's got so many sides to him. The curious thing about Lincoln to me is that he could remove himself from himself, as if he were looking at himself. It's a very strange, very eerie thing and highly intelligent. Such a simple thing to say, but Lincoln's been so smothered with stories of his compassion that people forget what a highly intelligent man he was. And almost everything he did, almost everything he did was calculated for effect. He knew exactly how to do it.

My favorite story that Lincoln told was he described a Union general out in front of his troops on horseback. And they were having a review and the horse got to kicking and prancing and jerking around, and somehow or another, the horse got his rear foot hooked in the stirrup and the general looked down at this ridiculous situation and said to the horse, "If you're going to get on, I'll get off."

Lincoln's literary ability: he's knocking on the door of Mark Twain. He's a very great writer. When I was a child in Mississippi, I was required to memorize the Gettysburg Address. Now the Gettysburg Address says that if the South had won the war, government of, by, and for the people would have perished from the earth. What it said didn't have anything to do with whether or not I was required to memorize it. It was literary skill that made me memorize it. And he demonstrated it time after time again, even in incidental notes which he wrote that he thought no one would ever see. His literary skill is almost unbelievable.

It was the English who recognized him as a stylist first. Many Americans were ashamed of his style, which someone said "had the bark on." He wrote American and people thought American was a language all right. It could be used for vaudeville skits or jokes, but they didn't think it belonged in state papers. And what Lincoln wrote was American, same kind of American that Mark Twain was to write later.

What draws you so to Nathan Bedford Forrest?

Well, you're asking about the most man in the world in some ways. Forrest was a natural genius. Someone said he was born to be a soldier the way John Keats was born to be a poet. He had some basic principles that, when you translate them, fit right into the army manual. When he said, "Get there first with the most men," he's saying, "Take the interior lines and bring superior force to bear." He had some very simple things. He used to say, "Hit 'em on the eend," and he used to say, "Keep up the skeer." And these are all good military principles expressed in Forrest's own way. And he was able to look at a piece of ground and see how to use it. He had a marvelous sense of topography. He could see the key to a position and know where to hit.

He was only surprised in battle once. It was a place called Parker's Crossroads up in Tennessee. He was on a raid and he was closing in on an opponent and fixing to finish him off when he was attacked in the rear by a force that he did not suspect was there. And everybody was terribly upset and said, "General, what shall we do?" And he said, "Split in two and charge both ways." And they did, and got out.

He had thirty horses shot from under him during the

course of the war. And he killed thirty-one men in hand-to-hand combat. And he said, "I was a horse ahead at the end."

Why did Robert E. Lee go over to the Confederacy?

The North didn't leave Robert E. Lee any ground to stand on and you had a lot of occasion for regretting it. When Lee had to choose between the nation and Virginia, there was never any doubt about what his choice would be. He went with his state. And he said, "I can't draw my sword against my native state," or as he often said, "my country."

Lee is one of the most difficult people to talk about because he's been immortalized, or as they call him now, some people, he's the "marble man." He's been dehumanized by the glory and the worship. He was a warm, outgoing man, always had time for any private soldier's complaint. Once a northern soldier being marched to the rear as a prisoner complained to Lee in person that someone had taken his hat. And he said, "That man got it." And Lee made the man give him his hat back.

Once there was some man brought before him for an infraction of the rules. And can you imagine being brought before General Lee for having broken the rules? And the young man was trembling, and Lee said, "You need not be afraid. You'll get justice here." And the young man said, "I know it, General, that's what I'm scared of."

He is a very great general. And he's superb on both the offensive and the defensive. He took long chances but he took them because he had to. If Grant had not had superior numbers, he might have taken chances as long as Lee took. The only way to win for Lee was with long chances, and it made him brilliant.

He read northern papers assiduously. He questioned prisoners on occasion. He knew how to put himself in another man's mind. He knew what Grant was going to do because he could make himself Grant long enough to figure out what Grant would do in the situation. The Union fired five or six generals before they got to Grant. By the time they let McClellan go, Lee said, "I'm afraid they're going to keep making these changes until they get someone I don't understand." They never got anyone he didn't understand. But they finally got Grant, who knew how to whip him and did.

Grant seems always to be overshadowed by Lee, and yet he's one of the most compelling figures of the war.

Grant the general had many qualities but he had a thing that's very necessary for a great general. He had what they call "four-o'clock-in-the-morning courage." You could wake him up at four o'clock in the morning and tell him they had just turned his right flank and he would be as cool as a cucumber. He had an ability to concentrate. A good example of that is, he would be working at his desk, bent over writing, and he would need something across the room, a document or something. He would get up and never get out of that crouched position and go over there and pick up the document and he'd come back to his desk and sit down again without ever having straightened up. It's an example of how he could concentrate.

[During the Vicksburg campaign] the men knew they were cut loose from their base of supplies, but Grant himself gave them confidence. They believed Grant knew what he was doing, and one great encouragement for their believing that was that quite often on the march, whether at night or in the daytime, they'd be moving along a road or over a bridge and right beside the road would be Grant on his horse—a dust-covered man on a dust-covered horse—saying, "Move on, close up." So they felt very much that he personally was in charge of their movement and it gave them an added confidence.

Grant in the Wilderness, after that first night in the Wilderness, went to his tent, broke down, and cried very hard. Some of the staff members said they'd never seen a man so unstrung. Well, he didn't cry until the battle was over, and he wasn't crying when it began again the next day. It just shows you the tension that he lived with without letting it affect him.

Right in the middle of the Battle of the Wilderness, all the staff men who'd been fighting in the East all this time—Grant had just come from the West—kept talking "Bobby Lee, Bobby Lee, he'll do this, that, and the other." And Grant finally told them, "I'm tired of hearing about Bobby Lee. You'd think he was going to do a double somersault and land in our rear. Quit thinking about what he's going to do to you and think about what you're going to do to him. Bring some guns up here." Things like that. Grant, he's wonderful.

What kind of man was Jefferson Davis?

Lee said it best. He said, "I don't think anyone could name anyone who could have done a better job than Jefferson Davis did, and I personally don't know of anyone who could have done as good a job." That's from Robert E. Lee, which is pretty good authority.

He's often described as a bloodless pedant, a man who filled all his time with small-time paperwork and never anything else, an icy-cold man who had no friendliness in him. I found the opposite to be true in all those respects. Davis was an outgoing, friendly man, a great family man who loved his wife and children and had an infinite store of compassion. I forget the figures now about how many soldiers Lincoln had shot. Davis had a bare handful. These misconceptions about Davis are so strange that it's as if a gigantic conspiracy was launched. It was partly launched by southerners, who, having lost the war, did not want to blame it on the generals, so they blamed it on the politicians and, of course, Davis was the chief politician. So it was the southerners more than the northerners who vilified Jefferson Davis. The northerners wanted to hang him from a sour apple tree, but the southerners really tore him down after the war.

William Tecumseh Sherman—he's one of my favorites.

Sherman was not much on a field of fight, but he was a superb strategist. He would set things up so that he would win no matter what happened on the field.

Sherman was maybe the first truly modern general. He was the first one to understand that civilians were the backers-up of things and that if you went against civilians, you'd deprive the army of what kept it going. So he quite purposely made war against civilians. He had the real notion. He saw from the very beginning how hard a war it was going to be. And when he said how hard a war it was going to be, he was temporarily retired under suspicion of insanity and then brought back when they decided that maybe he wasn't so crazy after all.

The really strange one was Stonewall Jackson.

He had this strange combination of religious fanaticism and a glory in battle. He loved battle. His eyes would light up. They called him "Old Blue Light" because of the way his eyes would light up in battle. He was totally fearless, and had no thought whatsoever of danger at any time when the battle was on. And he could define what he wanted to do. He said, "Once you get them running, you stay right on top of them, and that way a small force can defeat a large one every time." He knew perfectly well that a reputation for victory would roll and build. It was just everything about him. He was not a strict disciplinarian. He would shoot men, but he didn't care how they were dressed, whether they saluted properly or any of that foolishness.

He had a strange quality of overlooking suffering. He had a young courier, and during one of the battles Jackson looked around for him and he wasn't there. And he said, "Where is Lieutenant So-and-so?" And they said, "He was killed, General." Jackson said, "Very commendable, very commendable," and put him out of his mind. He would send men stumbling into battle where fury was and have no concern about casualties at the moment. He would march men until they were spitting cotton and white-faced and fell by the wayside. He wouldn't even stop to glance at one of them, but kept going.

Did the South ever have a chance of winning?

I think that the North fought that war with one hand behind its back. At the same time the war was going on, the Homestead Act was being passed, all these marvelous inventions were going on. In the spring of 1864, the Harvard-Yale boat races were going on and not a man in either crew ever volunteered for the army or the navy. They didn't need them. I think that if there had been more southern victories, and a lot more, the North simply would have brought that other arm out from behind its back. I don't think the South ever had a chance to win that war.

And things began to close in on them more and more. There was scarcely a family that hadn't lost someone. There was disruption of society. The blockade was working. They couldn't get very simple things like needles to sew with, very simple things. And the discouragement began to settle in more and more with the realization that they were not going to win that war. The political leaders did everything they could, especially Jefferson Davis, to assure them that this was the second American revolution and that if they would stand fast the way their forefathers had, victory was unquestionably going to come. But the realization came more and more that it was not going to come. And especially that they were not going to get foreign recognition, without which we wouldn't have won the first revolution. And all those things closed in on them. [With it came] a realization that defeat was foreordained. Mary Chesnut, for instance, said, "It's like a Greek tragedy, where you know what the outcome is bound to be. We're living a Greek tragedy."

It sounds like the beginning of the Lost Cause. What is the Lost Cause?

The Lost Cause is the Confederacy. It is referred to as the Lost Cause. On the Confederate monument in my home-

town of Greenville, Mississippi, the Confederacy is referred to as the only nation that was ever born and died without a sin having been committed on its part. And a lot of people have that view of it. Lost things are always prized very highly.

But those people should command our sympathy. The South conducted itself bravely in an extremely difficult situation. Many of the things we're proudest of in the American character were exemplified in the southern soldier, for instance. We take a justifiable pride in the bravery of those men, North and South.

So who won the war?

I can tell you who lost it—the South lost the war. But I'm not sure anybody won that war. It's a tragedy. The Centennial was called a celebration that should have been a time of mourning. If anybody won the war, it's people like Jay Gould and Jim Fiske, the robber barons of late in the century. That war was defined once in an outrageous way by [the writer] Allen Tate as an attempt on the part of the North to put the South into Arrow collars. That was a joke, but there's some truth to it: the homogenization of our society, and the really cruel follow-through of Reconstruction.

Capitalism went spread-eagle and diversity went out of our life. I think that when the South was defeated to the extent that it was that the whole nation lost something when they lost that civilization, despite the enormous stain and sin of slavery.

I don't know of anything we gained that we couldn't have gained without a war—with certain exceptions. War always creates inventions. The fountain pen was invented during the Civil War. The machine for stitching uppers to the soles of shoes was invented. In the North, as an example of how prosperous they were, any number of institutions of higher education were established: MIT, Vassar, and so on.

On the face of it, the North won the war. But the bill for winning it was huge in human values, not to mention human lives.

How did the war change us? What did we become?

The Civil War was really one of those watershed things. There was a huge chasm between the beginning and the end of the war. The nation had come face-to-face with a dreadful tragedy and we reacted the way a family would do with a dreadful tragedy. It was almost inconceivable that anything that horrendous could happen. You must remember that casualties in Civil War battles were so far beyond anything we can imagine now. If we had 10 percent casualties in a battle today, it would be looked on as a bloodbath. They had 30 percent in several battles. And one after another, you see.

And yet that's what made us a nation. Before the war, people had a theoretical notion of having a country, but when the war was over, on both sides they knew they had a country. They'd been there. They had walked its hills and tramped its roads. They saw the country and they knew they had a country. And they knew the effort that they had expended and their dead friends had expended to preserve it. It did that. The war made their country an actuality.

Before the war, it was said, "The United States are . . ." Grammatically, it was spoken that way and thought of as a collection of independent states. After the war, it was always "The United States *is* . . ."—as we say today without being self-conscious at all. And that sums up what the war accomplished. It made us an "is."

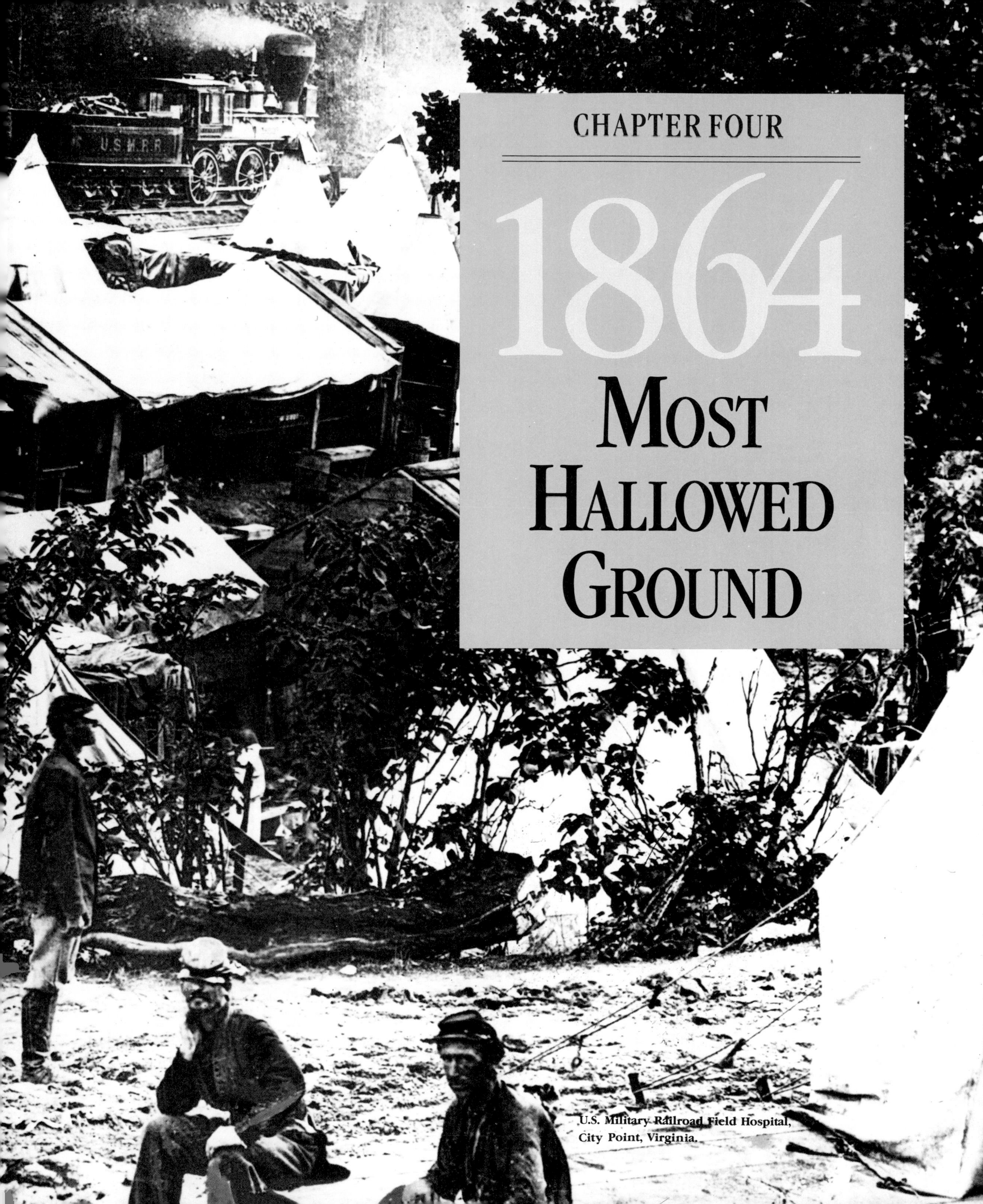

CHAPTER FOUR

1864

MOST HALLOWED GROUND

U.S. Military Railroad Field Hospital, City Point, Virginia.

SAM GRANT

"The Willard Hotel," Nathaniel Hawthorne wrote during the Civil War, "may be much more justly called the center of Washington and the Union than either the Capitol, the White House, or the State Department. *Everybody* may be seen there. . . . You may exchange nods with governors of sovereign states; you elbow illustrious men, and tread on the toes of generals; you hear statesmen and orators, speaking in their familiar tones. You are mixed up with office-seekers, wire-pullers, inventors, artists, poets, prosers . . . clerks, diplomats, until your own identity is lost among them."

On the afternoon of March 8, 1864, a stubby, rumpled man in a linen duster made his way across the Willard's crowded lobby to the front desk. A fourteen-year-old boy carrying a satchel followed in his wake. No one, including the desk clerk, paid much attention to him until he signed the guest register: "U.S. Grant and son, Galena, Illinois."

The clerk snapped to attention and personally carried the general's bag upstairs to a suite. Word spread fast that the man Lincoln had recently placed at the head of all the Union armies was in the hotel, and when Grant and his son entered the dining room, the other diners stood and gave him three cheers.

After dinner, he strolled two blocks up Pennsylvania Avenue to the White House, where President and Mrs. Lincoln were giving a reception. There, too, the guests applauded at the sight of him. Lincoln, eight inches taller than he, eagerly pumped his hand: "Why, here is General Grant. Well, this is a great pleasure, I assure you!" The crowd pressed so close that Grant stepped up onto a sofa to shake their hands. He stayed there almost an hour.

"For once at least, the President of the United States was not the chief figure in the picture," a congressman remembered. "The little, scared-looking man who stood on a crimson-covered sofa was the idol of the hour."

Less than three years earlier, Grant had been an unknown, unhappy midwestern civilian, notable only for the consistency of his failures. Now he was the conqueror of Donelson and Vicksburg and Chattanooga, come to Washington to receive the specially created rank of lieutenant general, last held by George Washington. He held command of all the armies of the United States, 533,000 armed men, and he had something in many ways more potent—the confidence of a President with a long history of dissatisfaction with his generals. "I wish to express my entire satisfaction with what you have done up to this time, so far as I can understand it," Lincoln told him. "The *particulars* of your plans I neither know nor seek to know."

Grant appreciated both the compliments and the confidence, but not the city in which they were given. Washington, he felt, was no place for an honest soldier. He was eager to get back to battle.

There was nothing in his ancestry and little in his early career to suggest he would ever amount to much. His grandfather had done time in a debtors' prison. His father, Jesse, had run a tannery in Point Pleasant, Ohio, when

"Grant don't care a snap if men fall like the leaves fall; he fights to win, that chap does. . . . He has the disagreeable habit of not retreating before irresistible veterans."

MARY CHESNUT

General Ulysses S. Grant, momentarily at rest to oblige a photographer.

Abraham and Mary Lincoln during the presidential years: "My wife is as handsome as when she was a girl and I a poor nobody," the President told a visitor; he had fallen in love with her then, he added, "and have never fallen out."

Hiram Ulysses Grant was born in 1822. Its stench was one of his first memories.

He was sensitive and withdrawn with people, wonderful with horses; at seven he drove his father's teams. But when he tried, at eight, to buy a horse, he proved overeager and paid more than he should have, something his harsh father and his own contemporaries never let him forget. "Boys enjoy the misery of their companions," he remembered, "at least, village boys of that day did."

Jesse Grant got his short, skinny, impractical son an appointment to West Point in 1839, hoping the army would guarantee him a living. A clerk wrote down his name as Ulysses Simpson Grant and, rather than complain, he lived with it. He was an undistinguished cadet, who showed real enthusiasm only for riding and watercolors. His friends called him "Sam."

"A military life had no charms for me," he said later. "I rarely read over a lesson the second time during my entire cadetship." He was graduated in the middle of his class, and failed to get the cavalry duty he wanted. The next year he got engaged to Julia Dent, the sister of his West Point roommate and the daughter of a Missouri slaveowner. "You can have but little idea of the influence you have over me, Julia," he wrote to her early on, "even while far away. If I feel tempted to do anything that I think is not right, I am sure to think, 'Well, now, if *Julia* saw me, would I do so?'"

In Francis B. Carpenter's ornate rendering of the reception Grant attended at the Executive Mansion on March 8, 1864, the general can be seen at the right of Lincoln, whom the artist unaccountably chose to portray with a mere wisp of beard. Other guests, not actually present but portrayed as if they had been, include Generals William Tecumseh Sherman, George McClellan, Winfield Scott, and George Gordon Meade.

Although he thought the Mexican War "wicked," he served in it anyway. "I considered my supreme duty," he wrote, "was to my flag." He fought bravely as a regimental quartermaster, riding alone through enemy fire to bring ammunition to his men.

He married Julia in 1848, and had three sons and a daughter. The army sent him to a Pacific outpost without them. He was miserable and lonely, unable to earn enough extra money to bring his family west. A grocery failed; so did a scheme to raise potatoes. His savings melted away. He began to drink. "You do not know how forsaken I feel here," he wrote Julia. "I sometimes get so anxious to see you and our little boys, that I am almost tempted to resign and trust to Providence, and my own exertions for a living. Whenever I get to thinking upon the subject, however, *poverty, poverty* begins to stare me in the face."

In 1854, he did resign his commission and went back east to rejoin Julia and work a piece of land his father-in-law gave him. He called it "hardscrabble farm" and could not make a go of it, either, even when he hired two slaves to help with the work.

He tried bill collecting, real estate, peddling firewood on the streets of St. Louis. Nothing worked. One Christmas, he pawned his watch to buy his

Grant as a young officer in 1843 (above), and in camp in 1864, with his son Jesse and wife, Julia—her head carefully turned away from the camera to hide the crossed eyes her husband refused to hear of trying to correct because, he is supposed to have said, he liked them just the way they were.

family Christmas presents. Finally, his father gave him a job clerking in his leather store in Galena, Illinois; his older brother was his boss. He was there, living quietly and sometimes talking politics with a neighbor, John A. Rawlins, when the war began.

Because he was the town's only graduate of West Point, Grant was elected to preside over a citizens' meeting to discuss raising troops; afterward, he reentered the army and did not look back. "I never went into our leather store after that meeting," he remembered, and his friend Rawlins saw the change in him: "In this season, I saw new energies in Grant. . . . He dropped a stoop-shouldered way of walking, and set his hat forward on his head in a careless fashion."

Washington failed to give him command of a regular regiment—George McClellan had been too busy even to see him—but the Governor of Illinois made him a colonel of volunteers. He was promoted to brigadier general, won a small battle at Belmont, Missouri, then the momentous one at Fort Donelson, at a time when other northern generals were suffering humiliating defeats, and became a northern hero.

He did not look heroic. He disliked uniforms, didn't much like marching bands, and said he could recognize only two tunes. "One was Yankee Doodle," he said; "the other wasn't." And he had his quirks: he insisted that his meat be cooked dry because even the suggestion of blood on his plate made him sick,

"His soldiers do not salute him, they only watch him, with a certain sort of familiar reverence. [They] observe him coming and, rising to their feet, gather on each side of the way to see him pass."
THE NEW YORK TIMES

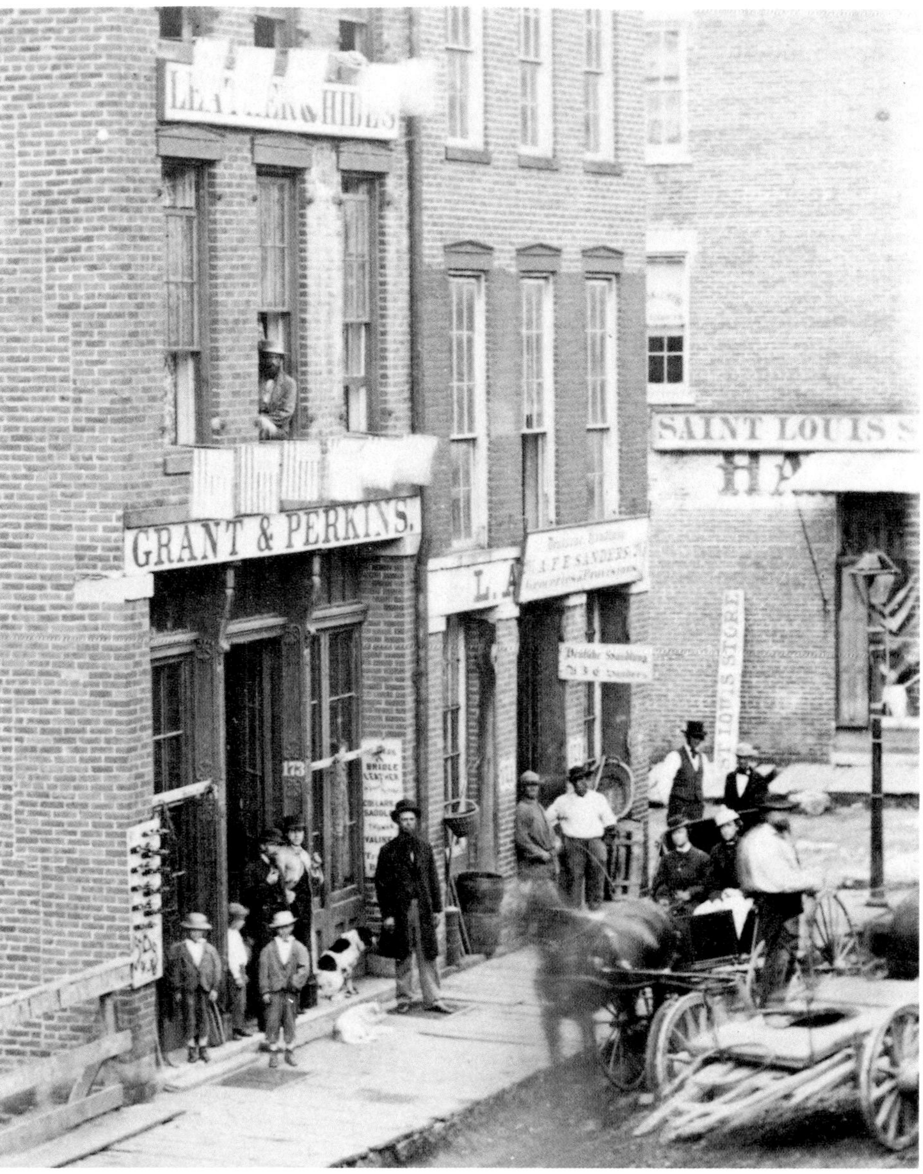

The family store at Galena, Illinois, in which Grant was working as a clerk when the war came. Once back in uniform, he remembered, "I never went into our leather store . . . to put up a package or do other business."

and once, on the eve of a battle in which thousands of men were to die, he had a teamster tied to a tree for six hours for daring to mistreat a horse.

John Rawlins, his Galena neighbor, was made his chief of staff and took it upon himself to keep Grant sober. "I don't know whether I am like other men or not," Grant once confessed, "but when I have nothing to do, I get blue and depressed." And when he got blue and depressed, bourbon whiskey provided momentary surcease. "Rawlins could argue, could expostulate, could condemn, could even upbraid," an aide remembered, "without interrupting for an hour the fraternal confidence and good will of Grant. . . . He became a living, speaking conscience for his general."

When Grant's army was caught by surprise at Shiloh with fearful losses, and newspapers called for his removal, Lincoln withstood them: "I can't spare this man," he said. "He *fights*."

He was also methodical, dogged, and clearheaded under fire, never losing sight of his objective or what it would take to get there. "There is one striking thing about Grant's orders," a Union general said, "no matter how hurriedly he may write them on the field, no one ever has the *slightest* doubt as to their meaning."

His purpose now was characteristically simple: "To get possession of Lee's army was the first object. With the capture of his army, Richmond would necessarily follow. It was better to fight him outside his stronghold than in it."

After receiving his new command, Grant traveled south to Meade's headquarters at Brandy Station, near Culpeper, Virginia, the largest and most elaborate Union encampment of the war. Elisha Rhodes was among the men who turned out to see him:

> April 19. Yesterday, the 6th Corps was reviewed by Lieutenant General U. S. Grant. [He] is a short, thick-set man and rode his horse like a bag of meal. I was a little disappointed in the appearance, but I like the look of his eye.

While Grant conferred with Meade, members of his staff described his triumphs in the West. Veterans of the Army of the Potomac were not impressed. "That may be," one said, "but you never met Bobbie Lee and his boys."

Lee as a lieutenant of engineers, painted in 1838 by William E. West.

THE MARBLE MODEL

The man Grant faced across the Rapidan came from a family as celebrated as his own was obscure. Robert E. Lee was related to most of the first families of Virginia—Lees, Carters, Randolphs, Fitzhughs, Harrisons. His father, Light Horse Harry Lee, had been a friend and favorite lieutenant of George Washington.

But Light Horse Harry was also a spendthrift, who squandered two wives' fortunes before leaving his family for the West Indies. (Later, his eldest son, Henry, misappropriated *his* wife's fortune, slept with her sister, and was known for his scandalous behavior as Black Harry.)

Robert E. Lee was born in 1807, and raised by his mother in straitened but genteel surroundings. She taught him to revere the memory of Washington, a neighbor remembered, "to practice self-denial and self-control" in all things, and to do all that he could to restore his family's tarnished honor.

From early boyhood, he felt responsible for his anxious invalid mother, leaving her side only to enter West Point at eighteen. "How can I *live* without Robert?" she said. "He is son, daughter, and everything to me."

Lee was an outstanding cadet. In four years he did not earn a single demerit—classmates called him "the Marble Model," but liked him in spite of his perfection—and he was graduated second in his class in 1829.

His military career was as distinguished as his lineage: appointed to the prestigious Corps of Engineers; three times brevetted for bravery in Mexico—where he was once said to have reprimanded young Captain Ulysses Grant for slovenly dress; Superintendent of West Point; Commander of the

Union soldiers lounge on the front steps of Lee's Arlington home: "[It is] the hereditary mansion of that fine old fellow [Robert E. Lee], now unhappily a traitor," George Templeton Strong wrote after he visited it early in the war, ". . . queer place, an odd mixture of magnificence and meanness, like the castle of some illustrious, shabby, insolvent old Irish family; for example, a grand costly portico with half-rotten wooden steps."

Marines who captured John Brown in 1859; widely considered the nation's most promising soldier at the outset of the war.

In 1861, Lee refused command of the northern army and followed his state out of the Union, not because he favored either slavery or secession, but because he believed his first duty was to Virginia. He may sometimes have regretted the consequences of that decision, but he never apologized for what his sense of honor had made him do: "I did only what my duty demanded. I could have taken no other course without dishonor. And if it were all to be done over again, I should act in precisely the same manner."

His wife, Mary, whom he married in 1831, was a Custis, the granddaughter of Martha Washington. The Lee mansion at Arlington, Virginia, with its sloping lawns and 250 slaves, was her home before it was his. Although often immobilized by arthritis, she bore him seven children, and endured his long, painful absences as best she could.

Women worshiped Lee; it became impossible for him to visit a barber because of their clamoring for locks of his gray hair. A Union girl, watching Lee ride past her Pennsylvania home toward Gettysburg in 1863, is said to have cried, "Oh! I wish he were *ours!*"

He delighted in such attentions, took pleasure in music, dancing, good

"I think that Lee should have been hanged. It was all the worse that he was a good man and a fine character and acted conscientiously. . . . It's always the good men who do the most harm in the world."

HENRY ADAMS

Lee on his gray war horse, Traveller: "He sat his horse very gracefully," Mary Chestnut wrote. "He was so distinguished. . . . All the same . . . [c]an *anybody* say they know [the General]? I doubt it, he looks so cold, so quiet, so grand."

food, harmless flirtation. After the war, a friend watched him chat with two blushing schoolgirls while his great gray warhorse, Traveller, pranced and pawed beneath him. The old general was secretly producing this spirited effect, the friend noticed, with "a dexterous and coquettish use of the spur."

But Lee was perpetually faithful to his wife, neither drank nor swore nor smoked, prayed long and often, never owned a slave himself, and, in the midst of the war, freed those who had belonged to his late father-in-law. "General Lee is . . . the handsomest man of his age I ever saw," a British visitor wrote. "His manners are most courteous and full of dignity. . . . He has none of the small vices . . . and his bitterest enemy never accused him of any of the greater ones."

He had been ridiculed as "Granny Lee" early in the war for having failed to hold western Virginia for the Confederacy, but after he replaced Joseph E. Johnston as commander of the forces defending Richmond in 1862, drove McClellan off the Peninsula, stopped Pope at Second Manassas, demolished Burnside at Fredericksburg, and destroyed Hooker at Chancellorsville—all against overwhelming odds—he won the unshakable confidence of Jefferson Davis and the unqualified love of his officers and men. Even Stonewall Jackson, who normally placed his trust only in his Old Testament God, trusted him. "So great is my confidence in General Lee," he said, "that I am willing to follow him blindfolded."

"Can *anybody* say they know the General?" Mary Chesnut asked. "I doubt it, he looks so cold, so quiet, so grand." His natural dignity turned away too much familiarity. No one ever called him "Bobby Lee" to his face; his men favored "Uncle Robert" or "Marse Robert." Like his hero, Washington, he had a terrible temper, which he worked hard all his life to control. When he was angered, his cold stare was unforgettable. But he always referred to the Union army as "those people" rather than the enemy. "His house on the Pamunky river was burnt to the ground and the slaves carried away . . ." a friend noted, "while his residence on the Arlington Heights was not only gutted of its furniture, but even the very relics of George Washington were stolen from it. . . . Notwithstanding all these personal losses . . . when speaking of the Yankees, he . . . evinced [no] bitterness of feeling . . . but alluded to many of his former friends and companions amongst them in the kindest terms."

Now the northern soldiers, whom Lee called "those people," had a new commander whom he had not yet tested.

INTO THE WILDERNESS

"The Union armies were now divided into nineteen departments," Grant wrote. "Before this time these various armies had acted separately and independently of each other. . . . I determined to stop this. . . . My general plan was now to concentrate all the force possible against the Confederate armies in the field."

The plan he now outlined for Meade and the general staff called for four coordinated, simultaneous blows against the Confederacy.

Benjamin Butler was to lead an army up from the James River.

Union troops waiting for the order to move out at Brandy Station in the early spring of 1864. The chimney of a burned house makes a handy oven (below), while officers (right) chat near the tent of the regimental sutler, A. Foulke, who dealt in everything from sweets to stationery.

Grant's army on the move in the spring of 1864.

"This advance by General Grant inaugurated the seventh act in the 'On to Richmond' drama played by the armies of the Union. The first advance, led by General McDowell, had been repelled by Beauregard and Johnston at Bull Run; the next five, under the leadership respectively of McClellan, Pope, Burnside, Hooker, and Meade, had been repelled by Lee."

GENERAL JOHN B. GORDON

"I want to push on as rapidly as possible to save hard fighting. These terrible battles are very good things to read about for persons who lose no friends, but I am decidedly in favor of having as little of it as possible. The way to avoid it is to push forward."

U. S. GRANT

Franz Sigel would advance up the Shenandoah Valley.

William Tecumseh Sherman had orders to strike out from Chattanooga for Atlanta.

Finally, George Gordon Meade was to lead the Army of the Potomac, 110,000 strong, south against Lee. "Wherever Lee goes, you will go also," Grant told Meade, and Grant himself would go there, too.

Lee's strategy was also straightforward: destroy the Union resolve to wage war. To offset Grant's superior numbers, he would force him to attack fortified positions and make the cost of trying to force the South back into the Union at gunpoint so high that the northern public would finally refuse to pay it and sue for peace. There was to be a presidential election in November and it was Lee's hope that by holding Grant to a bloody draw he could bring about the defeat of Abraham Lincoln. "Lee hoped—perhaps I may say was almost convinced—" wrote John B. Gordon, "that if we could keep the Confederate army between General Grant and Richmond, checking him for a few months longer ... some crisis in public affairs or change in public opinion at the North might induce the authorities at Washington to let the Southern states go."

In glades they meet skull after skull
Where pine cones lay—the rusted gun,
Green shoes full of bones, the
mouldering coat
And cuddled-up skeleton;
And scores of such. Some start as in
dreams,
And comrades lost bemoan:
By the edge of those wilds Stonewall
had charged—
But the year and the Man were gone.

HERMAN MELVILLE

"On the morning of May 4th," a Union chaplain noted, "we, with the entire Grand Army of the Potomac, were in motion toward the Rapidan. The dawn was clear, warm, and beautiful. As the almost countless encampments were broken up [with] bands in all directions playing lively airs, banners waving, regiments, brigades, and divisions falling into line ... the scene even to eyes long familiar with military displays, was one of unusual grandeur."

Lee's sixty thousand Confederates were waiting in the tangled thicket known as the Wilderness, in which they had trapped the same army under the unsteady Hooker a year earlier. They knew things would be different this time. "That man [Grant]," James Longstreet said, "will fight us every day and every hour till the end of the war."

Advance units of the Union army camped for the night on the old Chancellorsville battlefield, where winter rains had washed open the shallow Union and Confederate graves. "It grew dark and we built a fire," a green private remembered. "The dead were all around us; their eyeless skulls seemed to stare steadily at us.... The trees swayed and sighed gently in the soft wind. As we sat smoking ... an infantry soldier who had ... been prying [into the ground] with his bayonet suddenly rolled a skull on the ground before us and said in a deep, low voice: 'That is what you are all coming to, and some of you will start toward it tomorrow.'"

The fighting began in chaos around noon the next day—and would continue without a break for a full month thereafter. "No one could see the fight fifty feet from him," a Union private remembered. "The lines were very near each other, and from the dense underbrush and the tops of trees came puffs of smoke, the 'ping' of the bullets and the yell of the enemy. It was a blind and bloody hunt to the death, in bewildering thickets, rather than a battle."

Units got lost, fired on their own comrades. Officers tried to navigate by compass. There were no lines. The fighting went on all day. "During the night of the fifth, two men came back to the Lacey House, both slightly wounded. One was a Rebel ... the other, one of our men," a Union soldier wrote. "They

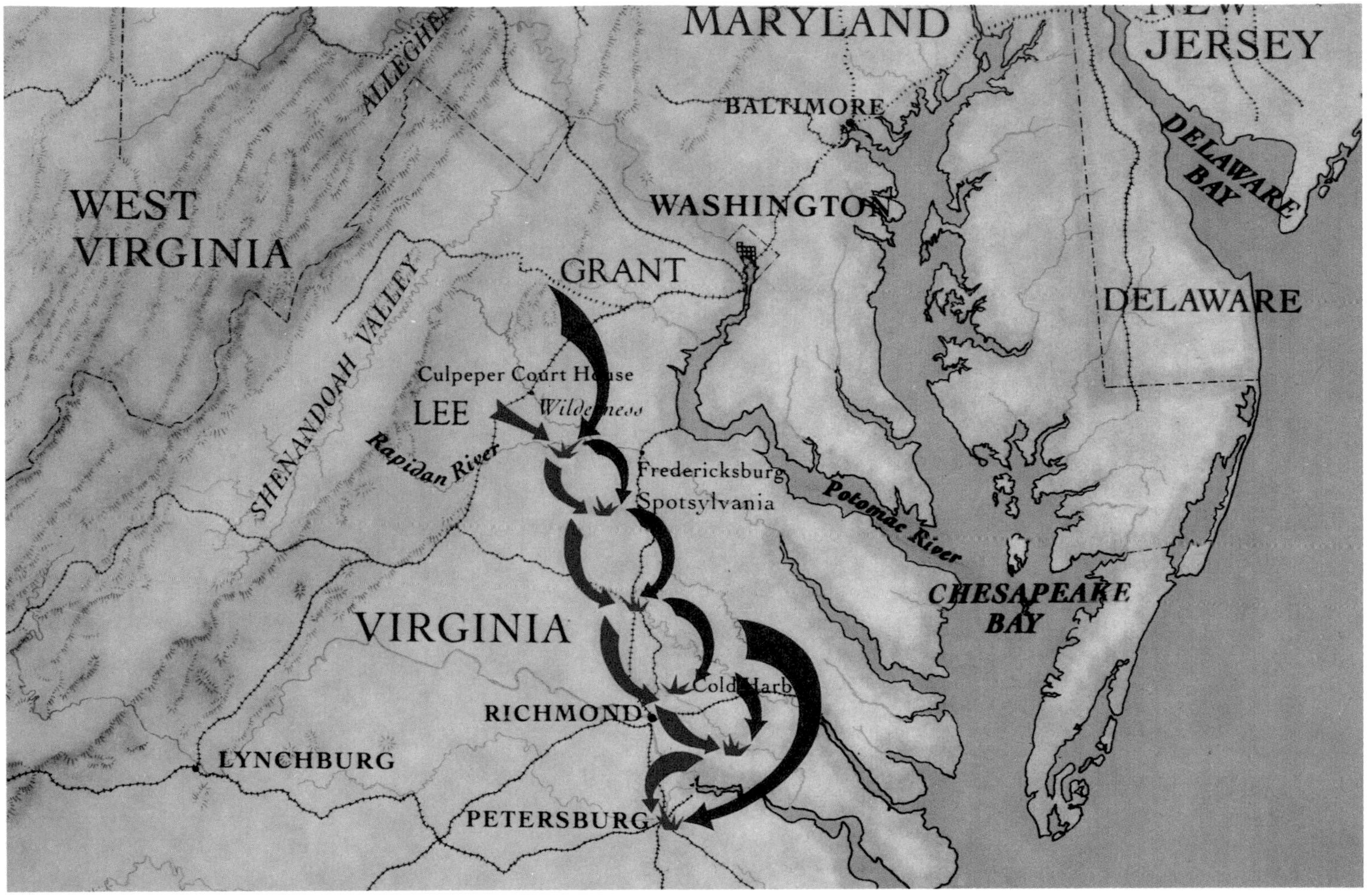

From the Wilderness to Petersburg: Beginning on the old Chancellorsville battlefield on May 5, 1864, and continuing without a break for the six bloodiest weeks of the war, Grant tried again and again to get around the right flank of Lee's army, destroy it, then move on Richmond and end the war. And again and again, Lee saw what he was trying to do and managed to thwart him. The struggle continued along a hundred-mile crescent before the two exhausted armies settled in for a siege at Petersburg, southeast of the Confederate capital.

When the Union soldiers settled down for the night in the Wilderness, the bones of some of those who had died there the previous year could still be seen, scattered among the leaves.

had got together, both had lost their muskets, and as the brush was getting afire they made the best of their way out of it together, taking their chances as to which of the two lines they might fall into."

On the second day, Union forces, led by General James Wadsworth, drove through the Confederate center. As a worried Lee watched, Longstreet's corps hurried up to plug the hole, led by General John Gregg's Texans. "Attention Texas Brigade," Gregg shouted to his men, "the eyes of General Lee are upon you, forward march." "Scarce had we moved a step," a Texan recalled, "when General Lee in front of the whole command, raised himself in his stirrups, uncovered his grey hairs, and with an earnest voice exclaimed . . . 'Texans *always* move them.' Never before in my lifetime did I ever see such a scene as was enacted when Lee pronounced these words. A yell rent the air that must have been heard for miles around. . . . A courier riding by my side, with tears coursing down his cheeks, exclaimed, 'I would charge hell itself for that old man.'"

"I am holding my breath in awe at the vastness of the shadow that floats like a pall over our heads. It has come that man has no longer an individual existence, but is counted in thousands and measured in miles."

CLARA BARTON

It was something like hell. The Texans faced the enemy at fifteen paces, desperately clinging to the position until the rest of Longstreet's men reached them. There were 673 Texans when the Federals attacked, 223 when they had beaten them back. One proud survivor asked, "*Did we or did we not* do all that men could?"

By day's end, the Confederates under John B. Gordon had smashed Grant's right, seized two generals and six hundred prisoners, and come close to cutting off the Union supply line. Grant received these reports without comment. "He keeps his own counsel, padlocks his mouth," an officer noted, "while his countenance . . . indicates nothing—that is, gives no expression of his feelings and no evidence of his intentions. He smokes almost constantly, and . . . has a habit of whittling with a small knife. He cuts a small stick into small chips, making nothing."

The first two days in the Wilderness had cost Grant seventeen thousand men. That night in his tent he wept, and as he cried, brushfires raged through the Wilderness, burning some two hundred wounded men alive.

With their screams echoing in his ears, an exhausted Elisha Rhodes jotted a note in his diary before trying to sleep: "We have entrenched ourselves the best we can with logs and earth and are waiting events. If we were under any other General except Grant I should expect a retreat, but Grant is not that kind of soldier, and we feel that we can trust him."

Rhodes had correctly judged his man. The next morning Grant ordered his men south once again. For the first time, the Army of the Potomac was moving forward after a defeat. "Whatever happens," Grant assured Lincoln, "we will not retreat." "Our spirits rose," one Union man remembered. "We marched free. The men began to sing."

That was what Lee thought his new opponent would do. "General Grant is not going to retreat," he told his staff. "He will move his army to Spotsylvania. I am so sure of his next move that I have already made arrangements . . . so that we may meet him there."

When Grant reached Spotsylvania, Lee was waiting for him. On May 11,

Confederate dead at Spotsylvania, May 20, 1864: Within weeks of the battle of Gaines' Mill, the only way to identify the armies to which the men at the right had once belonged was by the uniforms half buried with them.

Grant wired Washington: "We have now ended the sixth day of very heavy fighting [and] the result up to this time is much in our favor. I intend to fight it out on this line if it takes all summer."

At dawn the next day, Grant sent twenty thousand men under Winfield Scott Hancock against the Confederate center, along a curved salient the men first called "the Mule Shoe."

The Confederates fell back at first, and the Union men occupied their log breastworks. Lee himself resolved to lead a counterattack, but John B. Gordon stopped him. "In a voice which I hoped might reach the ears of my men," he remembered, "I called out, 'General Lee, you shall not lead my men in a charge. No man can do that, sir. *Another* is here for that purpose. These men behind you are Georgians, Virginians and Carolinians. They have never failed you on any field. They will not fail you here. Will you, boys?'"

The men shouted, "No, no, no; we'll not fail him," and then, seeing that Lee was still exposed to danger, they called out, "General Lee to the rear!" They gathered around him and turned Traveller away from the fighting. "I . . . believe that, had it been necessary," Gordon said, ". . . they would have carried on their shoulders both horse and rider to a place of safety."

Gordon's men reclaimed the works, but the battle went on, surging back and forth all day as attack followed counterattack. A Union veteran remembered it simply as "the most terrible day I have ever lived."

"Rank after rank was riddled by shot and shell and bayonet thrusts, and finally sank, a mass of torn and mutilated corpses," General Horace Porter wrote: "Trees over a foot and half in diameter were cut completely in two by the incessant musketry. . . . We had not only shot down an army, we had shot down a forest. . . . Even the darkness failed to stop the fierce contest, and the deadly strife did not cease till after midnight."

The Red River dam approaches completion.

A HARD AND ANXIOUS TIME

As Grant's army pushed relentlessly into Virginia in the spring of 1864, Federal forces beyond the Mississippi were engaged in the largest—and most disastrous—western campaign of the war. A thirty-thousand-man land-and-water force under General Nathaniel Banks and Admiral David Porter set out in March to blast its way up the twisting Red River with orders to take Shreveport, Louisiana, then occupy East Texas. They never got there. After the first few days, nothing much went right, and crippling delays and steady harassment by the Confederates combined to force the northerners back downriver in April.

But the Red River was falling fast by then, and the gunboats of Porter's Mississippi squadron required seven feet of water. When the Union forces reached Alexandria, Louisiana, the fleet was stranded. If something was not done, rebels on shore could blow it apart. It was, Porter wrote his mother, "a hard and anxious time."

An ingenious Wisconsin engineer, Colonel Joseph Bailey, saved him from what seemed certain disaster. Employing some three thousand troops as workers, he managed to build a dam across most of the river's 758-foot width in just ten days, using nothing but trees, rocks, and bags of dirt, then sank four barges filled with stone to fill the gap and raise the level of the river. The improvised structure held just long enough to allow the Union fleet to go roaring over it, to the cheers of thirty thousand grateful men.

"Before God," said a contraband watching from shore, "what won't the Yankees do next?"

Men wounded during the Wilderness campaign await treatment at a field hospital. "When the strife ceased . . ." a chaplain recalled, "I went back about two miles to *one* of the large depots for the wounded—of hospitals in this wilderness, there was none. Here about two thousand wounded had been collected. Such multiplied and accumulated suffering is not often seen."

The two armies had lost twelve thousand men. In the early hours of the morning, Lee ordered his army to fall back.

"At dawn," Porter noted, "we could see that the enemy's dead . . . were piled upon each other in some places four layers deep, exhibiting every ghastly phase of mutilation. Below the mass of fast-decaying corpses, the convulsive twitching of limbs . . . showed that there were wounded men still alive. . . . The place was well named the 'Bloody Angle.'"

The fighting flickered on around Spotsylvania for several days, and at one point a northern unit found itself back at the Angle. "It seems almost incredible what a change . . . a little less than a week had wrought," its chaplain noted. "The hair and skin had fallen from the head and the flesh from the bones—all alive with disgusting maggots. Many of the soldiers stuffed their nostrils with green leaves. Such a scene does seem too revolting to record. Yet, how else convey any just conception of what is done and suffered here?"

The armies began to move again, Lee seeking to elude or destroy his dogged pursuer, Grant skirting south and east to get around him, the two armies locked in a brutal, clumsy lockstep as the battle lines lurched toward Richmond. "We must destroy this army of Grant's before he gets to the James," Lee told an aide. "If he gets there, it will become a siege, and then it will be a mere question of time."

"I had seen the dreadful carnage in front of Marye's Hill at Fredericksburg. . . . But I had seen nothing to exceed this. It was not war; it was murder."

GENERAL EVANDER LAW, C.S.A.

They now raced for a crossroads called Cold Harbor, near the Chickahominy River. Lee got there first again, and ordered his men to entrench themselves and prepare for the all-out assault he was sure would follow.

As they settled down for the night on June 2, Union veterans sensed what was coming. "The men were calmly writing their names and home addresses on slips of paper and pinning them to the backs of their coats," General Porter noted, "so that their bodies might be recognized and their fate made known to their families at home."

The bugles blew for the attack at 4:30 a.m., and sixty thousand Union men started toward the unseen enemy.

The Confederates watched them come in the gray light. "Our officers had great difficulty in restraining the men from opening fire too soon," a private recalled. "But when close enough, the word 'fire' was given, and the men behind the works raised deliberately, resting their guns upon the works, and fired volley after volley."

In front of the Confederate guns the ground itself seemed to "seethe," a Massachusetts soldier said, like "a boiling cauldron from the incessant pattering of shot which raised the dirt in geysers and spitting sand." An Alabama colonel remembered seeing "dust fog out of a man's clothing in two or three places at once where as many balls would strike him at the same moment." A handful of men from one Union regiment, the Irish 164th Zouaves, actually managed to reach the southern works before they were riddled; their colonel's shattered body could be identified after the battle only by his brass officer's buttons.

"I had seen the dreadful carnage in front of Marye's Hill at Fredericksburg," a rebel general remembered, "but I had seen nothing to exceed this. It was not war; it was murder." The volume of sound seemed unprecedented, too, combining the "fury of the Wilderness musketry," a Union cannoneer thought, "with the thunders of the Gettysburg artillery superadded."

When it stopped, Colonel William Oates of the 15th Alabama remembered, ". . . not a man of them was standing. All who were not *shot* down had lain down for protection. One little fellow raised his head to look, and I ordered him to come in. He came on a run, the Yankees over in the woods firing at him every step of the way, and as he climbed over our works one shot took effect in one of his legs. They evidently took him to be a deserter."

Between 5,600 and 7,000 Union men fell at Cold Harbor, most of them in the first eight minutes. Grant himself later said he regretted ever giving the order; nothing had been gained to warrant such sacrifice.

When another assault was suggested, Union officers rejected the idea outright. "I will not take my regiment in another such charge," said a New Hampshire captain, "if Jesus Christ himself should order it!"

For three days and nights the two armies glared at one another, each

Grant (standing, fifth from right) and his staff at City Point, Virginia: "Grant is certainly a very extraordinary man," wrote Charles Francis Adams, [but] he does not look it and might well pass . . . for a dumpy and slouchy little subaltern, very fond of smoking. Neither do I know that he shows it in his conversation, [he] doesn't seem to be a very talkative man, anyhow."

commander unwilling to concede defeat by asking for a truce to collect the wounded or bury the dead. One wounded man was seen slitting his own throat. "The stench from the dead between our line and theirs was . . . so nauseating," Colonel Oates wrote, "that it was almost unendurable; but we had the advantage, as the wind carried it away from us to them. The dead covered more than five acres of ground about as thickly as they could be laid."

By the time the litter bearers were finally allowed onto the field, just two of the thousands of Union wounded remained alive. The rest had died or managed somehow to crawl to safety.

The fighting since the Wilderness had been a bad time for generals, too. Union General James Wadsworth was killed instantly by a bullet in the brain. John Sedgwick, who had survived Antietam and Chancellorsville and Gettysburg, reassured his men that Confederate snipers "couldn't hit an elephant at this distance," then fell dead with a bullet below the left eye; Grant said Sedgwick had been worth a division to the Union. James Longstreet was shot through the throat and shoulder by his own pickets not far from where Stonewall Jackson had been hit by his pickets, just one year and one day earlier, but lived to fight again.

NOW, FIX ME

Grant's Virginia campaign yielded an average of two thousand wounded men every day. Most of them made their way to Washington hospitals, where one of those who cared for them was the poet Walt Whitman.

He was forty-two when the war began, too old for the ranks, unqualified to be an officer, unenthusiastic "about firing a gun and drawing a sword on another man." Critics found his poetry obscene and blasphemous; the public merely found it baffling. He lived with his mother in Brooklyn.

But when his younger brother was wounded at Antietam, and Whitman went to find him in a hospital, he was so appalled by conditions there that he moved to the capital to see what he could do to help. He became a representative of the Christian Commission, giving out small gifts, changing dressings, playing "an amusing game called twenty questions," declaiming his poetry.

The men whom he tended had undergone appalling ordeals before they reached him. The war was fought, the Union Surgeon General remembered, "at the end of the medical middle ages." Physicians knew nothing of what caused the diseases that raced through their wards, did not understand the need for sanitation or good nutrition, or know how to halt infection.

The wounded man's first stop was often the surgeon's tent. "We operated in old, blood-stained and often pus-stained coats," a surgeon recalled. ". . .We used undisinfected instruments from undisinfected plush-lined cases. . . . If a sponge or instrument fell on the floor it was washed and squeezed in a basin of . . . water and used as if it were clean."

Union surgeons amputated limbs steadily for four days and two nights during the Battle of the Wilderness. "As a wounded man was lifted on the table, often shrieking with pain as the attendants handled him," General Carl Schurz remembered, "the surgeon quickly examined the wound and resolved upon cutting off the wounded limb. Some ether was administered. . . . The surgeon snatched his knife from between his teeth, where it had been while his hands were busy, wiped it rapidly once or twice across

"I believe the doctors kills more than they cure," an Alabama private said. "Doctors h'ain't got half sense." A heap of amputated feet awaits burial (above) after the surgeons have been at work. The amputation (below left) may have been staged for a photographer, but the crude conditions under which it is apparently being performed are authentic enough. The volunteer nurses from Michigan (below) are tending the wounded from Cold Harbor; the men on the opposite page were wounded at Savage's Station in 1862; some of those who died were buried within a few yards of their wounded comrades.

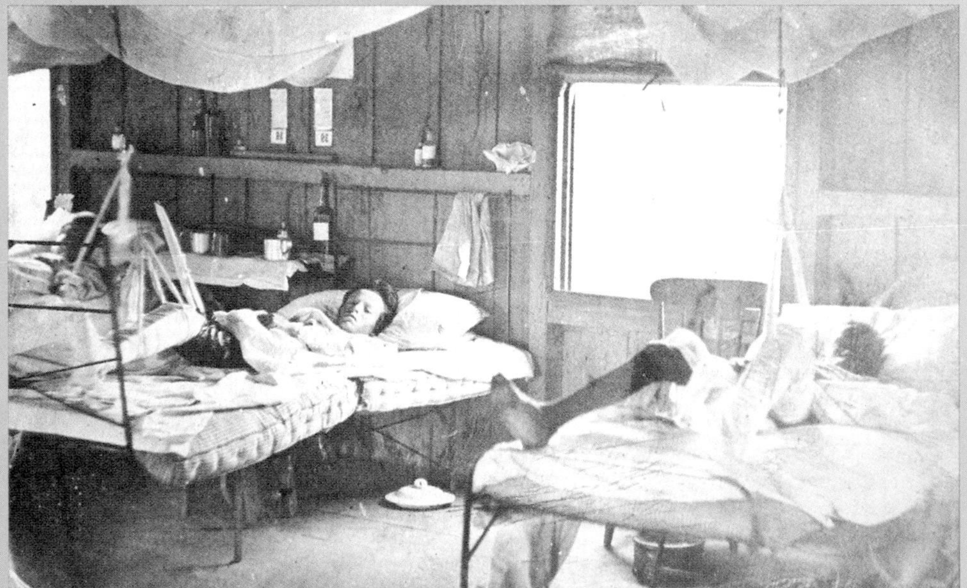

"If a fellow has [to go to the] Hospital," a Union soldier said, "you might as well say goodbye." The photographs above were made at Harewood Army Hospital in Washington. The more airy ward in the Armory Square Hospital (opposite above), appears to have been decorated either for the Fourth of July or perhaps for the end of the war. Despite the tidy look of Camp Convalescent in Alexandria (opposite below), its languishing inmates called it "Camp Misery."

his blood-stained apron, and the cutting began. The operation accomplished, the surgeon would look around with a deep sigh, and then—'Next!'"

Those who survived battlefield surgery were often left on the ground until they could be transferred to hospitals behind the lines. The lucky ones were sheltered in churches, houses, barns, shops.

Clara Barton was there.

I saw, crowded into one old sunken hotel, lying upon its bare, wet, bloody floors, 500 fainting men hold up their cold, bloodless, dingy hands as I passed, and beg me in Heaven's name for a cracker to keep them from starving (and I had none); or to give them a cup that they might have something to drink water from, if they could get it (and I had no cup and could get none). . . .

I saw 200 six-mule army wagons in a line, ranged down the street to headquarters, and reaching so far out on the Wilderness Road that I never found the end of it; every wagon crowded with wounded men, stopped, standing in the rain and mud, wrenched back and forth by the restless, hungry animals all night— The dark spot in the mud under many a wagon told all too plainly where some poor fellow's life had dripped out in those dreadful hours.

When the war began there were just 16 army hospitals in all of the North. By its end, the Union army was running more than 350 hospitals, the Confederacy 154.

The biggest and best, North or South, was Chimorazo at Richmond, with 8,000 beds, 5 soup houses, 5 ice houses, 200 dairy cattle, a herd of goats, a 400-keg brewery, and a bakery that turned out 10,000 loaves of bread a day. But even the most up-to-date institutions could do very

little. The patients "would see that the doctor gave them up," a Confederate steward recalled, "and would ask me about it. I would tell them the truth. I told one man that and he asked, 'How long?' I said, 'Not over twenty minutes.' He did not show any fear. They never do. He put his hand up so and closed his eyes with his own fingers and he stretched himself out and crossed his arms over his breast. 'Now, fix me,' he said. I pinned the toes of his stockings together. That was the way we lay corpses out, and he died in a few minutes. His face looked as pleasant as if he was asleep. And many is the time the boys have fixed themselves that way before they died."

There were sixteen Union hospitals in Washington alone, and when even these proved inadequate to handle the flow of wounded, men were cared for in the House and Senate chambers, the Georgetown jail, even the Patent Office, where Whitman visited them. "Two of the immense apartments," he wrote, "are fill'd with high and ponderous glass cases, crowded with models in miniature of every kind of utensil, machine or invention it ever enter'd into the mind of man to conceive. . . . Between these cases are lateral openings perhaps eight feet wide . . . and in these are placed the sick, beside a great double row of them, up and down through the middle of the hall."

President and Mrs. Lincoln came there, too, and the President gently chided one patient for laughing out loud at the

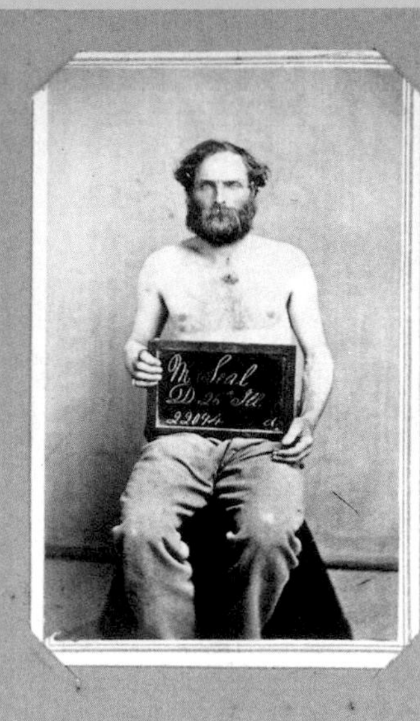
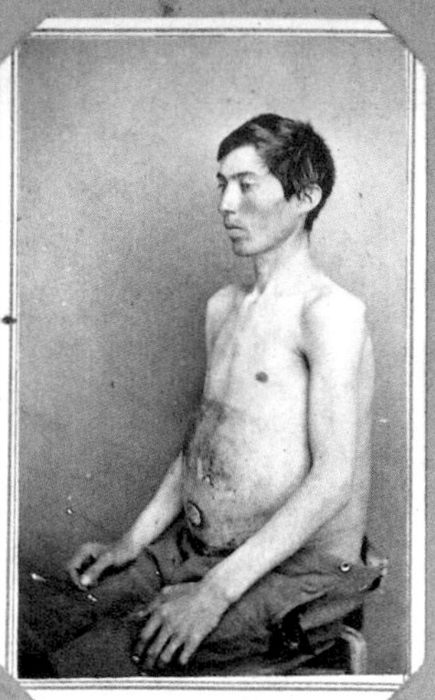

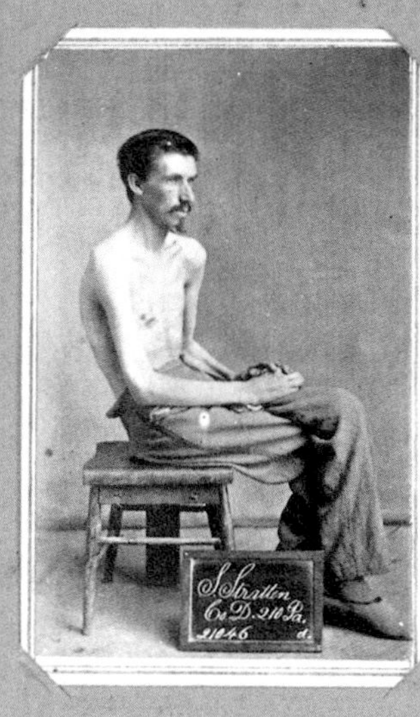
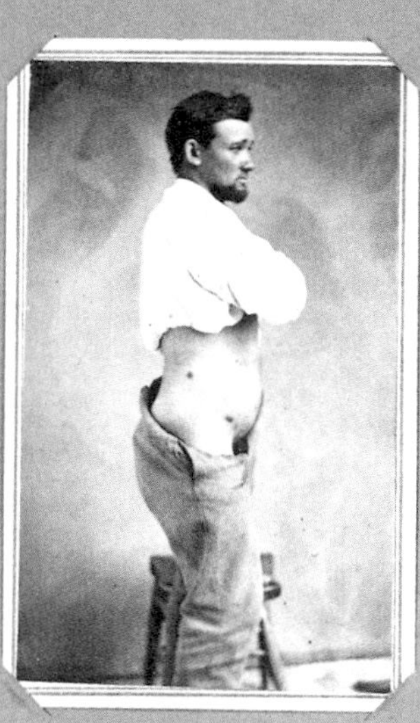
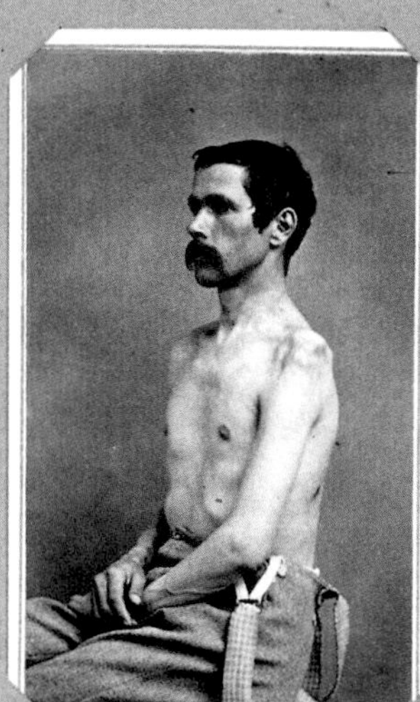

The *carte de visite* photographs of maimed men displaying their wounds on these and the following two pages are part of a catalogue of misery carefully assembled by Dr. Reed Brockway Bontecou, surgeon of the 2nd New York and director of the Harewood Army Hospital in Washington. All of these men were wounded in Virginia during the last two weeks of the war, and were photographed apparently to provide both a record of their treatment and instructional aids to young surgeons.

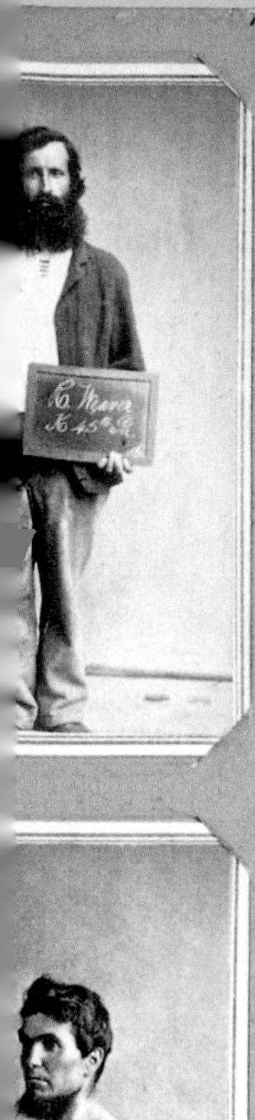

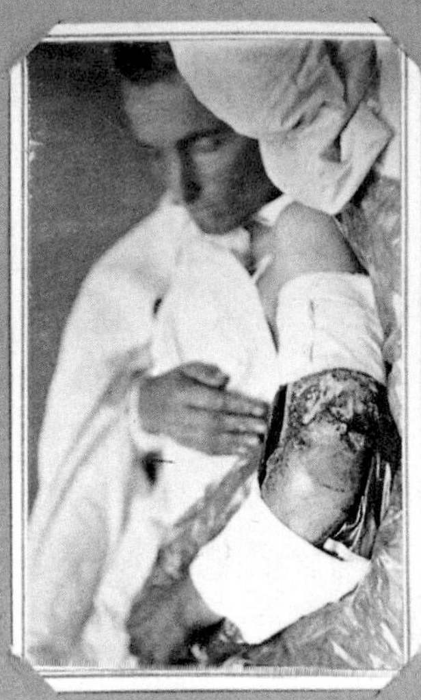

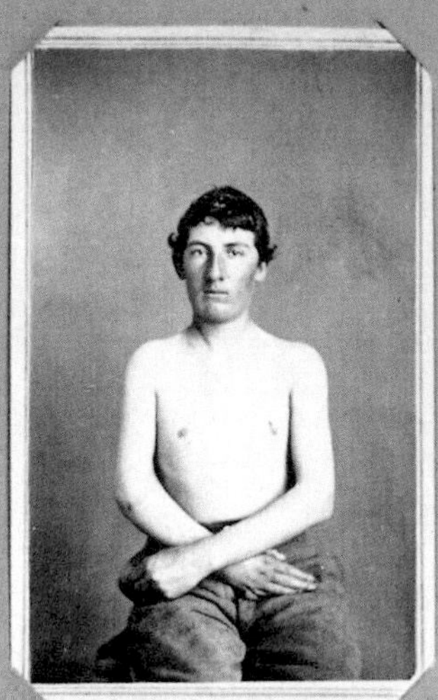

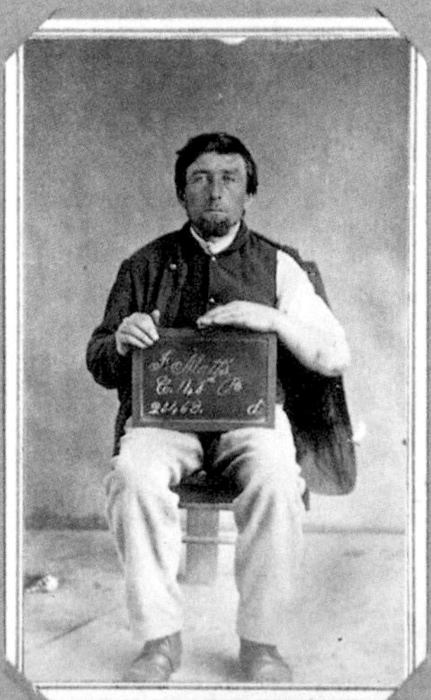

COURTESY STANLEY B. BURNS, M.D., AND THE BURNS ARCHIVE.

religious tract just handed him by an earnest visitor. The soldier apologized, but said he couldn't help it. "The pamphlet is on 'The Sin of Dancing,' and both my legs are shot off."

Nurses, male and female, did what they could to make the men comfortable. They worked long hours without complaint, but the feeling of helplessness was hardest to endure. "I am learning not to let myself feel as much as I did at first," wrote one woman after her first week at the Armory Square Hospital in Washington, "yet I can never get used to it. O, my men are dying so fast! . . . [T]his hospital . . . is always filled up with the very worst cases. . . . There comes a man to tell me, 'Captain Bell is bleeding,' a secondary hemorrhage, and I thought his amputated leg was doing nicely."

Whitman recorded a bedside vigil in the same hospital:

Lorenzo Strong. Company A. 9th United States cavalry, shot by a shell last Sunday; right leg amputated on the field . . . took a turn for the worse. I stayed and saw all . . . the convulsive spasms and workings of the muscles, mouth, and throat. . . . The doctor comes in and gives him a little chloroform. One of the nurses constantly fans him for it is fearfully hot. He asks to be raised up, and they put him in a half-sitting posture. He called for "Mark" repeatedly, half-deliriously, all day. Life ebbs, runs now with the speed of a mill race. . . . His eyes turn back. A crowd, including two or three doctors, several students and many soldiers has silently gathered. . . . The struggle goes on, and dwindles, a little more and a little more—and then welcome oblivion, painlessness, death. A pause, the crowd drops away.

Shortly afterward, Whitman wrote his mother that "this place seems to have got the better of me. I have bad nights and bad days, too. Some of the spells are pretty bad. . . . The doctors have told me for a fortnight I must leave. I think I shall come home for a short time."

This pontoon bridge at Deep Bottom, Virginia, a Federal crossing point on the James River north of Petersburg, was guarded by Benjamin Butler's Army of the James.

In the thirty days since Grant had first clashed with Lee in the Wilderness, his Army of the Potomac had lost fifty thousand men, half as many as it had lost in the three previous *years* of struggle. Critics began to complain that he was no better than his predecessors. "Grant is a butcher and not fit to be at the head of an army," Mary Lincoln said. "He loses two men to the enemy's one. He has no *management,* no regard for life . . . I could fight an army as well myself."

Grant kept going. Under cover of darkness, he slipped his army out of its trenches, crossed the Chickahominy, feinted toward Richmond, then shifted left again to the James River. His target was Petersburg, a communications center just south of the Confederate capital; if he could take it and choke off supplies, Richmond would be forced to surrender, just as Vicksburg had been a year before.

For the first time, Lee misjudged Grant's intentions, rushing much of his army to the outskirts of Richmond to repel an attack Grant did not plan to

"Here is the Potomac Army at a seemingly dead stand. No more flank movements practicable. Richmond not yet captured, nor soon likely to be ... General Grant finds it a far different matter pushing aside Western armies ... to conquering Lee and taking Richmond. This, nevertheless, a dogged perseverance may yet accomplish—though before Petersburg, which is but an outpost of Richmond, we may be compelled to burrow for six months to come."

CHAPLAIN A. M. STEWART

Petersburg, Virginia, all that stood between Grant and the capital of the Confederacy in the summer of 1864—besides Lee's army.

make, while Union engineers built a 2,100-foot pontoon bridge across the James in just eight hours. On June 12, the massive Army of the Potomac started to cross; it would take four days for the last man to reach the other side. Grant watched his men begin to move before boarding his steamer. "His cigar had been thrown aside," an aide remembered, "his hands were clasped behind him and he seemed lost in the contemplation of the spectacle.... A fleet of transports covered the surface of the water below the bridge, and gunboats floated lazily upon the stream, guarding the river above. Drums were beating the march, bands were playing stirring quicksteps...." In his pocket as he watched was a fresh telegram from Washington: "I begin to see it. You will succeed. A. Lincoln."

Sixteen thousand Union troops under General W. F. ("Baldy") Smith were the first to reach Petersburg, on June 15. The town was defended by a thin line of fewer than three thousand Confederates under Beauregard. Smith moved slowly to the attack; reinforcements intended to aid him got lost on the way. Still, his late-afternoon assault made progress and Petersburg seemed within the Union's grasp when night fell.

Winfield Scott Hancock urged a moonlight assault. Smith begged off and ordered a withdrawal, remembering Cold Harbor. "The rage of the enlisted men was devilish," a Union officer wrote. "The most bloodcurdling blasphemy I ever listened to I heard that night." While the Federal troops cursed and waited, Beauregard was reinforced—and the war prolonged by months.

Repeated Union assaults were beaten back.

Colonel Joshua Lawrence Chamberlain led his 20th Maine in one of them. As they raced toward the Confederate lines, he turned to rally his men and a bullet smashed through both hips and his pelvis, severed arteries, and nicked his bladder. He stayed on his feet, leaning on his sword with one hand and waving on his men with the other, until they had passed him by and he was no longer needed. Then he sank to the ground. Doctors did not expect him to live. In tribute to his courage, Grant made him a brigadier general. His obituary appeared in the newspapers.

Federal firepower: Below, safely out of range of Confederate guns for the moment, Pennsylvania artillerymen go through the motions of shelling the enemy for one of Mathew Brady's cameramen. The 13-inch, 8.5-ton mortar *Dictator* (inset right), largest of the siege guns at Petersburg, stood on a railroad flatcar and hurled missiles that weighed two hundred pounds. The damage to the home of a Petersburg civilian named Dunlop (inset left) was done by a Union shell. "The glorious fourth has come again," Elisha Rhodes wrote on July 4, 1864, "and we have had quite a celebration with guns firing shot and shell into Petersburg to remind *them* of the day. This day makes four 4th of Julys that I have passed in the army. The first at Camp Clark . . . the second at Harrison's Landing, the third at Gettysburg, and today at Petersburg."

Fort Sedgwick, designed by Major Washington Roebling, just one small section of the maze of Petersburg trenches in which Union men would spend ten miserable months. The sharpened stakes, or fraises, at the right were intended to discourage enemy assaults.

In six weeks of steady combat, Grant and Lee had all but crippled one another. Their armies now dug in for a siege. The burrowing would go on for ten months. The men lived in a labyrinth of trenches, plagued by flies, open to rain and to the fierce Virginia sun, and exposed to shell and mortar fire. "No one could say at any hour that he would be living the next," a Union veteran wrote. "Men were killed in their camps, at their meals, and . . . in their sleep. So many men were daily struck in the camp and trenches that men became utterly reckless, passing about where balls were striking as though it was their normal life and making a joke of a narrow escape or a noisy whistling ball."

Elisha Rhodes was in one of the trenches.

> June 20. Yesterday, Sergeant Major George F. Polley, 10th Massachusetts Volunteers, showed me a board on which he had carved his name, date of birth and had left a place of the date of his death. . . . I asked him if he expected to be killed and he said no, and that he had made his head board only for *fun.* Today he was killed by a shell fired by a rebel battery.

"Our matters here are at a deadlock; unless the Rebs commit some great error they will hold us in check until kingdom come. . . . Everyone knows that if Lee were to come out of his trenchments we could whip him, but Bob Lee is a little too smart for us."

MAJOR WASHINGTON ROEBLING

Federals take time out from the ceaseless digging that accompanied the siege; the presence of the armed sentry suggests that these men were performing punishment duty.

Colonel Washington Roebling was there, too.

June 23 . . . The demand down here for killing purposes is far ahead of the supply. Thank God, however, for the consolation that when the last man is killed, the war will be over. This war . . . differs from all previous wars in having no object to fight for; it can't be finished until all the men on either the one side or the other are killed; both sides are trying to do that as fast as they can because it would be a pity to spin this affair out for two or three years longer.

To the people of the North it seemed again that the war was going nowhere, and Lincoln's chances of reelection in the fall looked dim. "Our bleeding, bankrupt, almost dying country," wrote Horace Greeley, "longs for peace, shudders at the prospect of further wholesale devastation, of new rivers of human blood."

"The enemy throw a number of shells daily into Petersburg," a Confederate officer noted, "but they do little damage, the . . . women and children seem

Thirty-eight regiments of black troops took part in the Petersburg siege. These men lived on the advance line in shallow dugouts the men bravely called "bombproofs," and it was their task to warn the men in the trenches behind them of enemy movements.

not to mind them at all—on one street yesterday where such a number of shells burst that I would have considered it a warm place in the field, women were passing about with little concern, dodging around a corner when they heard a shell coming, or putting their heads out of their windows to see [what] damage they had done. . . . A lady yesterday sent Wardlaw and myself some ice cream and cakes."

Meanwhile, City Point, a sleepy river town on the James, suddenly found itself one of the world's great seaports, with Union bakeries, barracks, warehouses, a two-hundred-acre tent hospital, more than a mile of wharves, and a brand-new railroad to bring supplies and fresh troops right up to the Federal trenches. "Not merely profusion but extravagance," a visitor wrote, "wagons, tents, *ad libitum.* Soldiers provided with *everything.*"

To take some of the pressure off his own poorly supplied army, Lee sent ten thousand men under Jubal Early hurrying north to push Union troops out of the Shenandoah, exact tribute from Pennsylvania towns, and harass Washington itself.

Early burned the Maryland home of the Union Postmaster General, Montgomery Blair, in retaliation for a Union general's having razed the Virginia Military Institute. To avenge *that* fire, Ben Butler sent troops to

Life and death in the trenches: The Union soldiers at right guard the entrance to a powder magazine, carefully buried beneath six feet of packed earth supported by logs. The Confederate below was killed the day Petersburg finally fell to Federal troops in 1865, but more than twenty thousand of his fellow rebels had been killed or wounded or had deserted during the preceding ten months.

Fredericksburg to burn down the country home of James Seddon, the Confederate Secretary of War.

Blair asked that the cycle of vengeance be stopped: "I have a great horror of lawlessness, and it does not improve my repugnance to it that it is practiced upon the lawless."

Grant reluctantly dispatched some veterans of the Wilderness campaign to Washington to bolster the nervous local militia and drive off Jubal Early. Elisha Rhodes was one of those who marched through Washington. "Many citizens had guns in their hands," he noted that evening,

> and the Treasury clerks were drawn up in front of the Treasury Building. One young man had on a straw hat, linen duster, kid gloves, well polished boots and eyeglasses. . . . Wishing to be polite to me as he passed, he "presented arms" with the barrel of his musket to the front! Our boys cheered him in great style.

When Early's infantry attacked Fort Stevens in the Washington suburbs on July 11, the 2nd Rhode Island helped beat them back. Rhodes noticed a pair of interested spectators.

> On the parapet I saw President Lincoln . . . Mrs Lincoln and other ladies were sitting in a carriage behind the earthworks. For a short time it was warm work, but as the President and many ladies were looking on, every man tried to do his best. . . . I never saw the 2nd Rhode Island do better. The rebels, supposing us to be Pennsylvania militia, stood their ground, but prisoners later told me that when they saw our lines advance without a break they knew we were veterans. The Rebels broke and fled. . . . Early should have attacked early in the morning [before we got there]. Early was *late.*

Major General Jubal Early—"Old Jube" to his men—was so serious an irritant to the Union that Grant ordered sent after him "veterans, militiamen, and everything that can be got to follow."

THE CRATER

Meanwhile, at Petersburg, a regiment of Pennsylvania coal miners were doing their best to carry out a scheme hatched by General Ambrose Burnside—digging a five-hundred-foot tunnel beneath the Confederate lines and packing it with four tons of gunpowder. The object was to blow a hole in the Petersburg defenses, then rush through to take the town. "The mine which General Burnside is making," a Union soldier wrote home, "causes a good deal of talk and is generally laughed at. It is an affair of his own entirely, and has nothing to do with the regular siege."

At dawn on July 30, the fuse was lit. "Suddenly, the earth trembled beneath our feet," a Union general wrote.

> An enormous mass sprang into the air. A mass without form or shape, full of red flames, and carried on a bed of lightning flashes, mounted towards heaven with a detonation of thunder. It spread out like a sheaf, like an immense mushroom whose stem seemed to be of fire and its head of smoke. Then everything appeared to break up and fall in a rain of earth mixed with rocks, with beams, timbers, and mangled human bodies.

SPIES

By all odds, the most useful military intelligence either army gathered during the war was provided to Union officers by mostly anonymous slaves and contrabands, eager to help bring about the Confederacy's collapse. After all, one Union officer said, "they have been spies all their lives."

But there were more conventional agents at work as well. Even before Bull Run, secrets streamed between Washington and Richmond: Allan Pinkerton (below right) ran the Federal Secret Service; Confederate Major William Norris, officially head of the Confederate Signal Bureau, oversaw a clandestine spy network that extended as far north as Montreal; James Bulloch, the Georgia-born uncle of Theodore Roosevelt, was the Confederacy's agent in Britain.

"Women who come before the public now are in a bad box," Mary Chesnut wrote. "All manner of things, they say, come over the border under the huge hoops now worn. So they are ruthlessly torn off. Not legs but arms are looked for under hoops. And, sad to say, found."

In fact, women made good operatives: they were suspected less quickly than men and, if caught, punished less severely. Perhaps the most celebrated female agent was Belle Boyd (right), whose admirers called her "La Belle Rebelle." Six highly publicized arrests failed to stop her from soliciting secrets from Union officers in Washington; once she passed them on in code to a shady agent she knew only as "C.H.," inside rubber balls tossed through her cell window.

Perhaps the ablest female operative working for the Union was Elizabeth Van Lew, a Richmond unionist thought a harmless eccentric by her neighbors, who managed to plant a spy among Jefferson Davis's own servants.

For men, spying, desertion, and treating with the enemy were often rewarded with death by hanging or firing squad (below). In November 1863, a southern courier, Sam Davis, was sentenced to death for spying at Pulaski, Tennessee. His bravery on the scaffold proved so moving that the commanding general could not bring himself to order the trap sprung. Davis finally gave the order himself.

The Crater: "[T]he whole floor of the trench was strewn with the dead bodies of negroes," a Virginian who witnessed the fighting there recalled, "in some places in such numbers that it was difficult to make one's way along the trench without stepping on them."

When the smoke began to lift, the men could see that a great crater had been torn in the ground, 30 feet deep, 70 feet wide, 250 feet long. For 200 yards on either side of it, the southerners had fallen back in terror.

Then Burnside's plan began to fall apart. A precious hour went by before the Union assault force got started, and then three divisions in turn stormed down *into* the great hole, rather than around it. Their commander, General James H. Ledlie, did not even watch the battle, huddling instead inside a bomb-proof shelter with a bottle of rum.

A rebel private recorded what happened next: "When they reached our lines, instead of treating the opening as a mere passageway . . . they halted, peeped and gaped into the pit, and then, with the stupidity of sheep, followed their bell-wethers into the crater itself, where, huddled together, all semblance of organization vanished."

There was no way up the sheer, thirty-foot wall of the pit—and no one had thought to provide ladders. As the Union troops milled helplessly, the Confederates regrouped and began pouring fire down upon them. By afternoon, the survivors raised a white flag. "Out of [the pit] filed as prisoners eleven hundred and one Union troops," the same rebel private wrote, "and we captured 21 standards and several thousand of small arms. Over a thousand of the enemy's dead were in and about the breach, and his losses exceeded [4,500] effective troops, while *our* lines were reestablished just where they were when the battle began."

White troops were allowed to surrender unmolested. But scores, perhaps hundreds, of black troops were killed when they tried to surrender, bayoneted or clubbed to death by Confederates shouting, "Take the white man! Kill the nigger!"

Grant thought it "the saddest affair I have ever witnessed in the war. Such opportunity for carrying fortifications I have never seen and do not expect again to have." He dismissed General Ledlie from command. Burnside was granted extended leave and never recalled to duty.

The siege continued. "We should never have wars like this again," a Union soldier said.

"July 30th, 1864. The work and expectations of almost two months have been blasted. . . . The first temporary success had elevated everyone so much that we already imagined ourselves in Petersburg, but fifteen minutes changed it all and plunged everyone into a feeling of despair almost of ever accomplishing anything. Few officers can be found this evening who have not drowned their sorrows in the flowing bowl."

MAJOR WASHINGTON ROEBLING

The newspapers again called Grant a butcher. His losses had been fearful; his grand strategy seemed to have stalled. Franz Sigel's army had been routed in the Shenandoah. Benjamin Butler's army, which was supposed to have attacked Richmond and might have helped take Petersburg, was bottled up, instead, in a loop of the James River called the Bermuda Hundred. Grant himself was frozen in front of Petersburg.

Only Sherman remained on the move, in Georgia.

On July 30, the same day as the disaster in the Crater, Jubal Early's cavalry, still loose in the North, demanded $500,000 ransom from the citizens of Chambersburg, Pennsylvania, and when they refused to pay, burned the business district to the ground. (Early liked cities, he is supposed to have said, because they burned so nicely.)

The failure of yet another attempt at ending the war quickly had badly damaged Lincoln's chances for reelection.

Those chances had never seemed good. No other nation had ever held an

Classical columns mark the site of the Bank of Chambersburg, Pennsylvania, burned, along with the business district in which it stood, by Jubal Early's Confederate raiders.

MOST HALLOWED GROUND

Already, by the spring of 1864, the Union dead had completely filled the military cemeteries of Washington and Alexandria. Secretary of War Stanton ordered the Quartermaster General, Montgomery Meigs, to choose a new site. Meigs was a Georgian who had once served under Lee in the peacetime army, but he had developed an intense hatred for all southerners who fought against the Union he still served. Without hesitation, he picked Robert E. Lee's lawn at Arlington for the new army cemetery and ordered that the Union dead be laid to rest within a few feet of the front door of the man he blamed for their deaths, so that no one could ever again live in the house.

In August, Meigs personally inspected the site and was furious to find that he had been disobeyed: officers stationed there had buried the first bodies out of sight, in a distant corner of the estate once reserved for the burial of slaves. He immediately ordered that twenty-six Union coffins be brought to Arlington and then watched personally as they were lowered into the earth in a ring around Mrs. Lee's old rose garden. Later, he would order built at the center of that garden a Tomb of the Unknown Dead, filled with the anonymous bones of eleven hundred soldiers, gathered from unmarked graves on battlefields within twenty-five miles of Washington.

In October, Meigs's own son, Lieutenant John R. Meigs, killed by Confederate guerrillas in the Shenandoah Campaign, was buried in his father's old commander's lawn.

The men Grant was sending to fight Robert E. Lee were being buried in Robert E. Lee's own front yard. That yard became Arlington National Cemetery, the Union's most hallowed ground.

New cemeteries at Arlington (opposite), City Point (right), and elsewhere provided resting places for the fallen. But itinerant embalmers followed the armies (below), advertising their services to those who wished eventually to have their dead brought home for permanent burial: "Persons at a distance, desiring to have the bodies of their deceased friends . . . disintered, embalmed, disinfected, or prepared and sent home, can have it promptly attended to by application to the office of Simon Garland, 35 South 13th Street, Philadelphia. No zinc, arsenic or alcohol is used. Perfect satisfaction guaranteed."

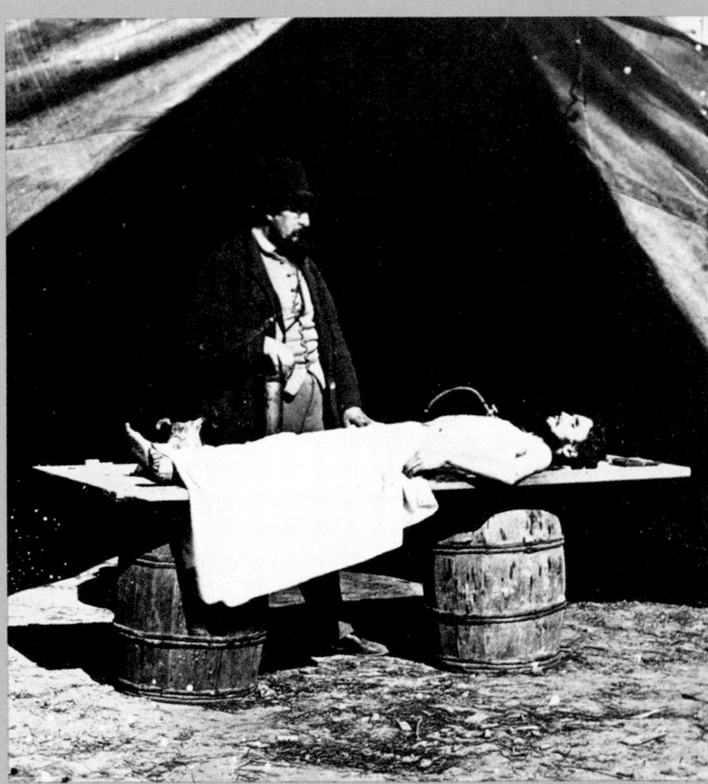

Cemetery at Stone's River, Tennessee.

"The immense slaughter of our brave men chills and sickens us all." GIDEON WELLES

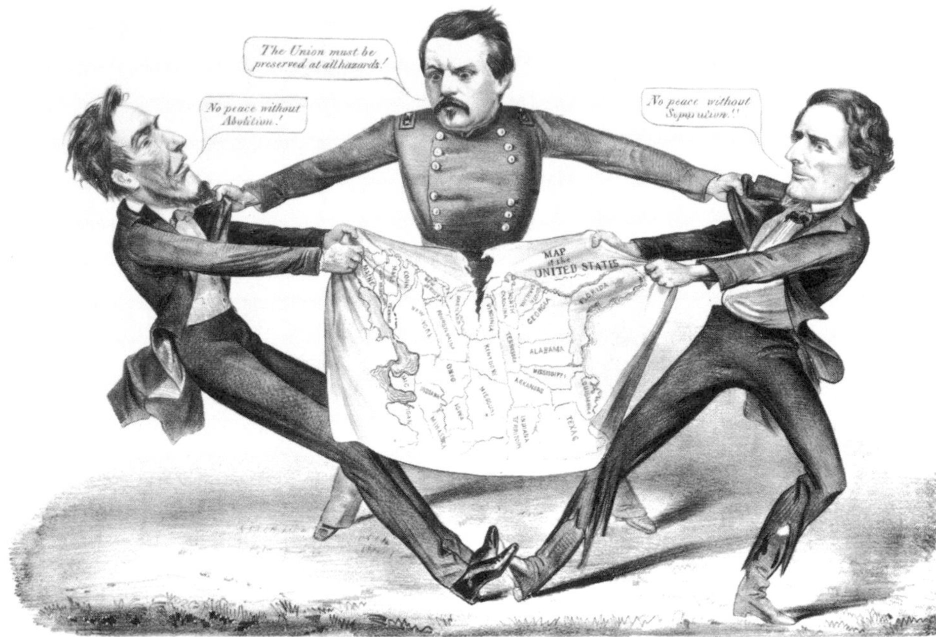

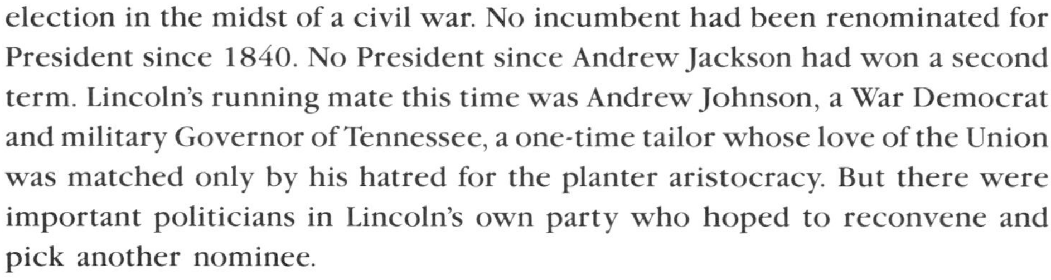

election in the midst of a civil war. No incumbent had been renominated for President since 1840. No President since Andrew Jackson had won a second term. Lincoln's running mate this time was Andrew Johnson, a War Democrat and military Governor of Tennessee, a one-time tailor whose love of the Union was matched only by his hatred for the planter aristocracy. But there were important politicians in Lincoln's own party who hoped to reconvene and pick another nominee.

In the election-year Democratic cartoon at left, George McClellan (above) is depicted playing the heroic part in which he liked to picture himself—savior of his country.

The Democratic nominee was General George B. McClellan. The chesty general's ego had not shrunk since the man he routinely dismissed as "the original gorilla" had removed him from command of the Grand Army of the Potomac. Nor had his resentment.

But Peace Democrats wrote the platform upon which McClellan agreed to run. It called for peace before Union and, for all his ambition, McClellan could not agree to that. He was a nationalist before he was a believer in States' Rights. The South, he said, would have to rejoin the Union before there could be peace. The result was a certain amount of confusion. "The truth is, a Republican editorialist wrote, "neither you, nor I, nor the Democrats themselves, can tell whether they have a peace platform or a war platform. . . . Upon the whole, it is *both* peace and war, that is peace with the rebels but war against their own government."

The campaign was ugly. Republican speakers charged the Democrats with treason, said McClellan was the captive of the Copperheads. Democrats countered that the real goal of "the negro-loving, negro-hugging worshippers of old Abe" was miscegenation, a new word for "the blending of the white and black."

Many in the South rejoiced at McClellan's nomination—"the first ray of real light," said Vice President Alexander Stephens, "since the war began."

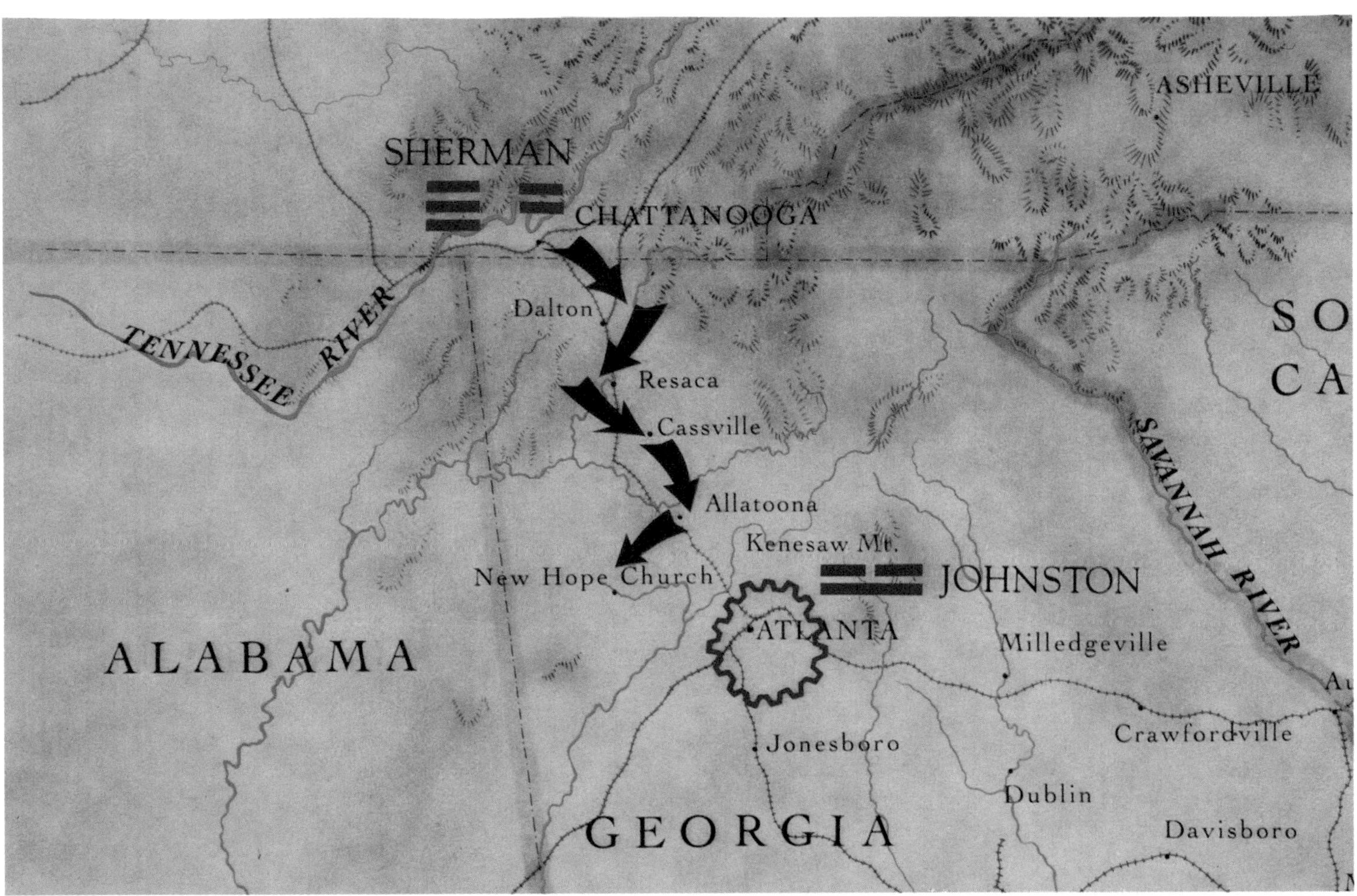

The March on Atlanta: Starting at Chattanooga, Tennessee, on May 6, 1864, William Tecumseh Sherman (opposite below) moved inexorably southeastward, forcing the Confederates under Joseph T. Johnston, sent to try to stop him, out of one position after another, until their backs were to Atlanta itself. Taking the heavily fortified city would present more of a challenge.

WAR IS THE REMEDY

"I am going to be beaten," Lincoln said in August, "and unless some great change takes place, *badly* beaten." His frail hopes for victory now lay with William Tecumseh Sherman, the only one of Grant's commanders still moving forward against the enemy. "War is the remedy our *enemies* have chosen," Sherman declared, "and I say let us give them all they want; not a word of argument, not a sign of let-up, no cave in till we are whipped—or *they* are."

Sherman was Grant's most trusted lieutenant. They had survived hard times together; back in Kentucky, early in the war, when Sherman had come close to a breakdown, persuaded that he had too few troops to hold off the enemy and that the war itself would never end, Grant had steadied him, and they had fought side by side ever since. "[Grant] stood by me when I was crazy," Sherman once explained, "and I stood by him when he was drunk; and now we stand by each other always."

Grant had entrusted his friend with the second most important part of his grand strategy—to seize Atlanta, the "Gate City of the South" and the second most important manufacturing center of the Confederacy, and to smash the combined Confederate armies of the Tennessee and Mississippi under Joseph E. Johnston that would try to stop him.

Sherman was nervous, rumpled, irritable. He wore shoes rather than military boots, slept little and talked a lot, "boiling over with ideas," a friend said, "while discussing every subject and pronouncing on all." "[He was always] too busy to eat much," an aide added.

> He ate hardtack, sweet potatoes, bacon, black coffee off a rough table, sitting on a cracker box, wearing a grey flannel suit, a faded old blue blouse and trousers that he had worn since long before Chattanooga. He talked and smoked cigars incessantly, giving orders, dictating telegrams, bright and chipper.

"We have devoured the land and our animals eat up the wheat and cornfields close. All the people retire before us and desolation is behind. To realize what war is one should follow our tracks."

WILLIAM TECUMSEH SHERMAN
June 26, 1864

He hated newspapermen and politicians of both parties. His family and friends called him "Cump"; his men called him "Uncle Billy." And he was implacable in war.

On May 6, two days after Grant stepped off into the Wilderness, Sherman's Grand Army of the West had moved south from Chattanooga into Georgia. The 98,000 men under his command were divided into three great columns: the Army of the Tennessee, under James McPherson, on the right; the Army of the Ohio, under John Schofield, on the left; and in the center, the Army of the Cumberland, commanded by "Pap" Thomas, "the Rock of Chickamauga."

Joseph E. Johnston, the Confederate commander who faced them, was disliked by Jefferson Davis, who blamed him for retreating before McClellan on the Peninsula in 1862, and for failing to rush to lift the siege of Vicksburg in 1863. But he was very nearly worshiped by the men of his tattered army, Sam Watkins among them. "I do not believe there was a soldier in his army but would gladly have died for him. With him, everything was his soldiers. . . . He would feed his soldiers if the country starved."

With Johnston was General Leonidas Polk, another of the Confederate army's best-loved generals. Polk was a West Pointer who had left soldiering for the clergy and become Episcopal Bishop of Louisiana, before putting on a new uniform at the onset of the war.

Outgunned, outsupplied, outnumbered almost two to one, Johnston and his lieutenants could only hope to slow Sherman's advance, and perhaps lure him into making the kind of doomed frontal attack that would help swing the election against Lincoln.

Sherman's march was a masterpiece of planning. In a matter of hours, its engineers replaced burned bridges and ripped up rail lines. "Our profoundest admiration," wrote an Indiana private, "goes to the way Sherman keeps up his railroad and our rations. On the 11th, High Tower bridge was completed and an engine crossed immediately . . . crying in its loudest whistle, 'How-do-you-doo-oo-General Sherman!' "

Even when Bedford Forrest's raiders collapsed a tunnel in Sherman's rear, a weary southern private was not impressed: Sherman, he said, probably carried a spare tunnel, too.

Sherman had surveyed parts of Georgia as a young lieutenant and seemed to remember every creek and valley and wooded hillside. "I knew Georgia better than the rebels did," he wrote, and he knew that whatever fighting was to be done there would be scattered, sporadic, informal—"a big Indian war," he called it.

The men of the western Union armies were leaner and less strictly disciplined than their eastern counterparts, but no less determined. These unidentified westerners, probably part of Pap Thomas's Army of the Cumberland, were photographed near Stevenson, Alabama, during the struggle for Tennessee.

The heat was terrible, the dust unrelenting, the woods filled with insects. "The men's bodies are alive with creeping things," an Illinois private complained. "They will crawl through any cloth and bite worse than fleas. . . . Salt-water bathing would cure them, but salt is too scarce to use on human flesh. Many of the boys anoint their bodies with bacon rinds, which chiggers can't go."

Rather than risk head-on assaults against Johnston's retreating rebels, Sherman preferred to send McPherson and the fast-moving Army of the Tennessee to flank them out of their positions. A surrendering Confederate told his captors, "Sherman'll never go to hell; he will flank the *devil* and make heaven in spite of the guards."

Sherman forced Johnston out of Dalton to Resaca, to Cassville, to Allatoona, to New Hope Church. He was making steady progress, but more slowly than he liked, and he grew frustrated. "A fresh furrow in a plowed field will stop the whole column!" he said. "We are [supposed to be] on the offensive and . . . must assail and not defend."

By mid-June, as Grant's army stalled before Petersburg, he was ready to change his tactics. Johnston's men were dug in across the face of Kennesaw Mountain, just twenty miles from Atlanta. Sherman decided to attack them there and destroy the southern army at one blow. "Uncle Billy," a soldier said, "is going to take Kennesaw or shoot it damn full of iron."

Moving up, he spotted a knot of Confederate officers conferring on a hillside eight hundred yards away. "How saucy, they are!" he told an artilleryman. "Make 'em take cover." The Union battery opened up. Joe Johnston and his staff scrambled for cover. Leonidas Polk did not make it, and was torn apart. Sherman was pleased, and wired Washington the news: "June 14. To the Secretary of War. We killed Bishop Polk yesterday, and made good progress today."

"I always shot at privates. It was they who did the shooting and killing, and if I could kill or wound a private, why, my chances were so much the better. I always looked upon officers as harmless personages."

SAM WATKINS

Union General John A. "Black Jack" Logan (the lead horseman at the left) orders his men to ignore the Confederate fire pouring down on them and charge up the slope during the Battle of Kenesaw Mountain.

On June 27 thirteen thousand Union men stormed the Confederates on Kennesaw Mountain—and failed. The Federals "seemed to walk up and take death," a Southerner remembered, "as coolly as if they were automatic or wooden men." The most savage slaughter took place on the right, at a salient that came to be called the Dead Angle. Sam Watkins was there, rifle in hand.

> I've heard men say that if they ever killed a Yankee during the war they were not aware of it. I am satisfied that on this memorable day, every man in our regiment killed from . . . twenty to a hundred each. All that was necessary was to load and shoot. Afterward, I heard a soldier say he thought "hell had broke loose in Georgia, sure enough."

Three days after the battle, an armistice was granted for burying the fallen—"Not for any respect either army had for the dead," a Confederate remembered, "but to get rid of the sickening stench." All day, Confederate and Yankee burial details moved over the battlefield. "I get sick now when I . . . think of it," Watkins recalled. "Long and deep trenches were dug, and hooks made from bayonets crooked for the purpose, and all the dead were dragged and thrown pell mell into these trenches. Nothing was allowed to be taken off the dead, and finely dressed officers, with gold watch chains dangling over their vests, were thrown into the ditches."

Sherman never admitted he had made a mistake at Kennesaw Mountain, but he never repeated it, either. And he returned to his flanking maneuvers, forcing Johnston back to within sight of Atlanta itself.

On July 17, Davis suddenly removed Joe Johnston from command, somehow persuaded that he lacked the will to win. "This act," a Confederate veteran remembered, "threw a damper over this army from which it never

While Fort Morgan fires on the Yankee fleet trying to pick its way among the floating mines that have already disabled the U.S.S. *Tecumseh,* three Confederate gunboats, led by the outsize *Tennessee,* steam out of Mobile Bay to engage the enemy.

recovered." No one was more stunned than Sam Watkins. "'General Joe Johnston is relieved,'" he wrote.

> [The news] came like a flash of lightning, staggering and blinding every one. Old Joe . . . had taken command of the Army of the Tennessee when it was crushed and broken . . . in rags and tatters, hungry and heart-broken. . . . He was more popular with his troops every day. . . . Farewell, old fellow! We privates loved you because you made us love ourselves.

The Union blockade of southern ports was tightening, but the port of Mobile was still open to Confederate shipping. To close it—and to divert attention from Sherman's advancing army—Admiral David Farragut, the captor of New Orleans, now led a Union flotilla of eighteen ships storming past three forts to engage a Confederate fleet.

Farragut was sixty-three years old, frail, and suffering from vertigo so intense that he ordered himself lashed to the rigging of his flagship, the *Hartford.* A torpedo (as mines were then called) sank the lead ship, and the captains of the other Union vessels quailed at the sight of more floating mines. Farragut shouted, "Damn the torpedoes, full speed ahead!" The water-logged mines bumped along the Union hulls but failed to go off, and Farragut steamed on to force the surrender of the defending fleet, including the *Tennessee,* the largest ironclad afloat.

Desperate Confederate attempts to break the blockade failed. At Charleston, Federal guns now pounded southern troops inside Fort Sumter. To relieve the pressure, the *Hunley,* a crude Confederate submarine, cranked by hand and with a mine lashed to a spar protruding from its bow, slipped out into the harbor intent on torpedoing the Union steam sloop *Housatonic.*

Thirteen men, including her inventor, had drowned in three earlier trials. The mine worked—the *Housatonic* sank in five minutes, the first vessel ever destroyed by a submarine—but the explosion demolished the *Hunley,* too, sending her and all nine men aboard to the bottom.

Farther out to sea, the war was going badly for the South, as well. The *Alabama,* commanded by Raphael Semmes, was the most successful of all the Confederate commerce raiders. In three years and 75,000 miles of steady prowling from Singapore to South America, she had seized and sunk sixty-five Union merchant vessels. In June, the U.S.S. *Kearsarge* caught up with her in the English Channel seven miles off Cherbourg, France, and opened fire. After a furious hour-long battle, the Confederate ship was sunk at last.

In front of Atlanta, Joseph Johnston's replacement as commander of the Confederate army was thirty-three-year-old John Bell Hood of Kentucky. His arm had been mangled at Gettysburg and he had lost a leg at Chickamauga, but his boyish impetuosity remained intact. "Hood is a bold fighter," Lee said. "I am doubtful as to other qualities necessary." His own men called him "Old Woodenhead."

Sherman was delighted at his appointment, sure he would be attacked at last, and began to close on Atlanta. To cut off the city's rail links with Richmond, he dispatched McPherson and his Army of the Tennessee to Decatur, ten miles to the east. Just thirty-five, McPherson was a special favorite of Sherman's, handsome, warmhearted, intelligent: "If he lives," Sherman predicted, "he'll outdistance Grant and myself."

The battles for Atlanta: Between July 20 and 28, 1864, the new Confederate commander, John Bell Hood, hit Sherman's advancing army three times—at Peachtree Creek to the north; again just west of Decatur, where Sherman's friend and fellow Ohioan James B. McPherson (opposite below) had been sent to sever rail lines in what is now remembered as the Battle of Atlanta; and once more at Ezra Church to the west. Hood lost all three battles but the city remained in Confederate hands.

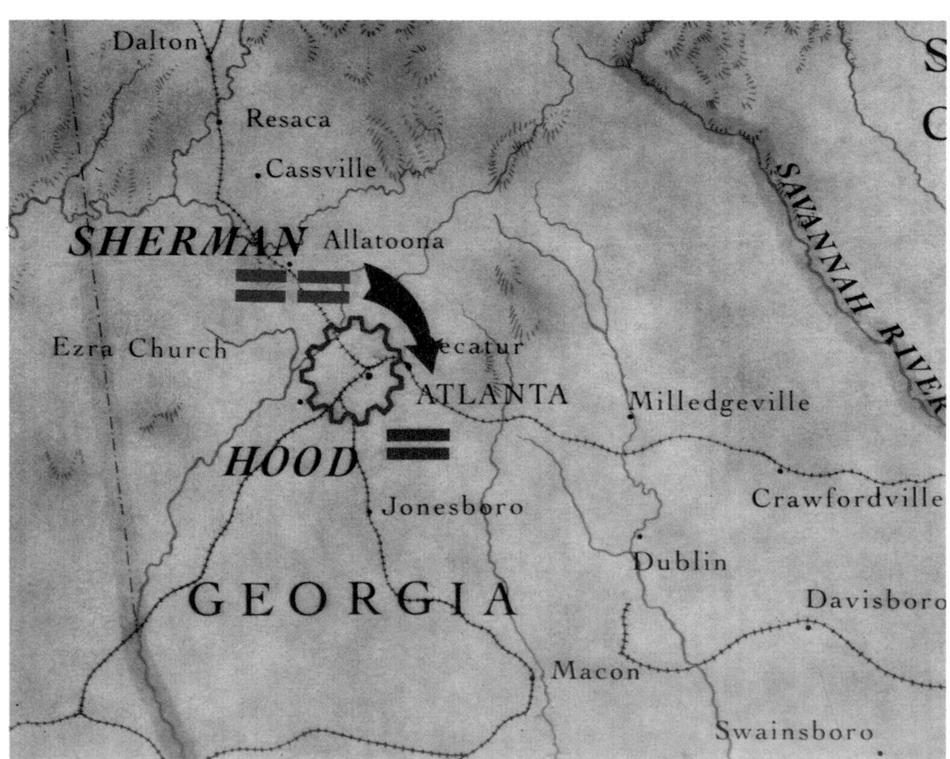

This panoramic view of Atlanta was made from a seminary steeple shortly after the city fell to Sherman's army. "Mine eyes have beheld the promised land," a Federal major wrote when he first saw the city. "The 'domes and spires' of Atlanta are glittering in the sunlight before us and only 8 miles distant."

On July 20, less than forty-eight hours after taking command, Hood hit Sherman hard at Peachtree Creek, north of the city. The attack, staged late in the day, was driven back, and as the Confederates withdrew, word came that McPherson was marching on Atlanta from the east.

Hood rushed to counter the new Union threat, and on July 22 what came to be called the Battle of Atlanta began. It raged all afternoon, the lines forming, falling back, re-forming, attacking again. At 2:00, McPherson himself went to inspect the imperiled Union position—and rode right into a band of rebel skirmishers. Ordered to surrender, McPherson raised his hat, turned his horse about, and raced for the Union lines. The rebels shot him in the back.

Sherman covered the body of his young friend with an American flag, and wept. But Sherman, General Jacob D. Cox remembered, "had the rare faculty of [remaining calm] under great responsibilities and scenes of great excitement. At such times his eccentricities disappeared. His mind seemed never so clear, his confidence never so strong, his spirit never so inspiring ... in the crisis of some fierce struggle like that of the day when McPherson fell in front of Atlanta."

Sherman replaced McPherson with General John "Black Jack" Logan, who re-formed his men and ordered a massive counterassault, riding up and down the lines crying, "McPherson and revenge, boys, McPherson and revenge." Hood was driven from the field in less than thirty minutes.

At Ezra Church, west of the city, Hood tried and failed again to drive off Sherman's army. In little more than a week, a third of his force—20,000 men—was gone, and he fell back into Atlanta.

Behind their ramparts, the Confederates waited for Sherman to attack. "The Yankee gents can't get their men to charge our works," a Texan said, but Sherman saw no need to be so rash. He sealed off the city's supplies and waited. Federal guns began shelling the heavily fortified Confederate trenches and the city beyond.

The siege went on for a month. "Another week of anxiety and suspense has

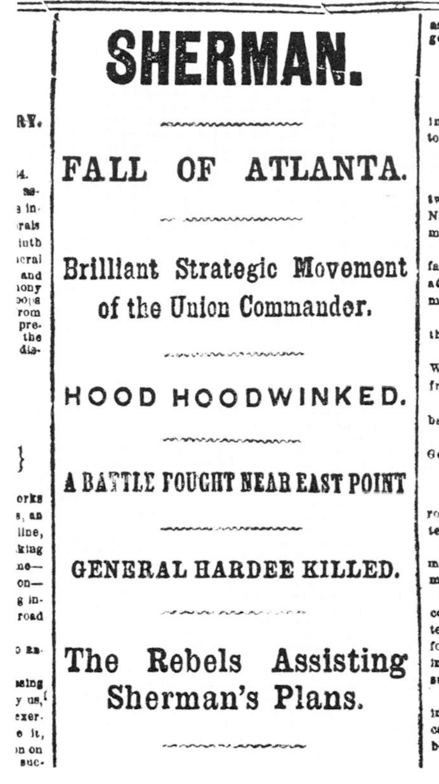

SHERMAN.

FALL OF ATLANTA.

Brilliant Strategic Movement of the Union Commander.

HOOD HOODWINKED.

A BATTLE FOUGHT NEAR EAST POINT

GENERAL HARDEE KILLED.

The Rebels Assisting Sherman's Plans.

The formidable Confederate works surrounding Atlanta (opposite) discouraged Sherman (right) from a direct attack: "The whole country is one vast fort," he wrote. But the hungry, exhausted men who manned the city's defenses could not hold out once he had cut off their supplies.

passed," a merchant wrote on Saturday, August 21, "and the fate of Atlanta is still undecided. It is said that about twenty lives have been destroyed by these terrible missiles since the enemy began to throw them into the city. It is like living in the midst of a pestilence. No one can tell but he may be the next victim."

Every evening during the siege a Georgia sharpshooter played ballads on his cornet—"Come Where My Love Lies Dreaming," "I Dreamt I Dwelt in Marble Halls"—while both armies stopped shooting long enough to listen.

Finally, on August 31, Sherman hurled most of his army against the Macon & Western Railroad south of the city, in one more attempt to break Hood's grip. It worked, and on September 1, the Confederates evacuated Atlanta. Sherman's veterans marched into the city the next day. "Atlanta is gone," Mary Chesnut wrote. "That agony is over. There is no hope but we will try to have no fear."

Grant ordered a one-hundred-gun salute in Sherman's honor fired into the Confederate works in front of Petersburg. "I feel you have accomplished the most gigantic undertaking given to any general in this war," he told his friend and chief lieutenant, "and with a skill and ability that will be acknowledged in history as not surpassed, if not unequalled. It gives me as much pleasure to record this in your favor as it would in favor of any living man, myself included."

"Atlanta is ours and fairly won."

WILLIAM TECUMSEH SHERMAN

Both sides helped destroy Atlanta. The wreckage here strewn across the Georgia Central tracks and the ruins of the factory beyond them are all that remained after Hood's retreating troops blew the factory up rather than have it fall to the Federals. Union troops tore down the roundhouse (right) and, as they moved on toward Savannah, burned the car sheds (below right) as well. "We have utterly destroyed Atlanta," wrote an Indiana private. "I don't think any people will want to try and live there now. It is pretty hard . . . but it is war."

VOL. XIII.—NO. 4080.

VICTORY!

Another Great Battle in the Valley.

Longstreet Whipped by Sheridan.

VICTORY WRESTED FROM DEFEAT.

The Rebel Attack at First Successful.

Timely Arrival of Gen. Sheridan.

THE REBELS THEN UTTERLY DEFEATED.

Forty-three Pieces of Artillery Captured.

More bad news was coming for the Confederacy. Phil Sheridan and 45,000 men stormed into the Shenandoah Valley with orders from Grant to follow Jubal Early "to the death" and to strip the valley itself so thoroughly that "crows flying over it for the balance of the season will have to carry their provender."

Grant had picked the right man for the job. No Union officer was fonder of fighting than Sheridan; none save Sherman was so relentless. Railroad lines were demolished. Crops and barns belonging to unionists as well as secessionists were burned, and their herds driven off. "The time had fully

General Philip Sheridan, as he really was (top) and as he liked best to be portrayed (bottom), spurring his men on to victory.

Long ABRAHAM LINCOLN a Little Longer.

come to *peel* this land," a Union chaplain wrote, "and put an end to the long strife for its possession." Sheridan himself cheerfully recorded that peeling:

> The whole country from the Blue Ridge to the North Mountains has been made untenable for a rebel army. I have destroyed over 2,000 barns filled with wheat, hay, and farming implements; [and] over 70 mills; . . . have driven in front of the army 4,000 head of stock and have killed . . . 3,000 sheep. . . . Lieutenant John R. Meigs, my engineer officer, was murdered beyond Harrisburg. . . . For this atrocious act all the houses within an area of five miles were burned. . . . Tomorrow I will continue the destruction. . . . When this is completed, the Valley . . . will have but little in it for man or beast.

On September 19, Early and Sheridan clashed at Winchester, and the Confederates were forced to withdraw. "We have just sent them whirling through Winchester," Sheridan reported to Washington, "and we are after them tomorrow. This army behaved splendidly."

Lincoln's reelection prospects were rapidly improving.

Before dawn on October 18, Early tried one last time to destroy Sheridan's army by attacking it at Cedar Creek while Sheridan himself was asleep at Winchester, twenty miles away. At first it seemed he had succeeded. The Union forces were driven from their camps.

Sheridan mounted his great black horse, Rienzi, and galloped toward the battlefield through his disorganized, retreating men, waving his cap and urging them to turn back. They stopped, and began to chant his name. "Cheers seemed to come from throats of brass," an officer said, "and caps were thrown to the tops of the scattering oaks. . . . No more doubt or *chance* for doubt existed; we were safe, perfectly and unconditionally safe, and every man knew it."

"God *damn* you!" Sheridan shouted. "Don't cheer *me*. Fight! We will lick them out of their boots!" A colonel told Sheridan how glad the men were to see him. "Well, by God," said Sheridan, "I'm glad to *be* here!"

The Union retreat stopped, the lines re-formed—and won back the field. Early fled, and the ravaged Shenandoah was closed forever to the Confederacy. At the victory, General George Armstrong Custer lifted his little commander off the ground and danced with joy. "General Sheridan," Lincoln said, "when this particular war began, I thought a cavalryman should be at least six feet four inches high, but I have changed my mind. Five feet four will do in a pinch."

In front of Petersburg, Grant fired a second jubilant hundred-gun volley into the enemy trenches.

On November 8, Lincoln awaited the election returns at the Washington telegraph office. Despite the last-minute flood of good news from the front, he was nervous. No one knew how the soldiers McClellan had commanded in the field would vote. "McClellan was our first commander," Private Theodore Gerrish of the 20th Maine wrote, "and, as such, he was almost worshipped by his soldiers. The political friends of General McClellan well understood that fact, and it was a very crafty thing for them to nominate him as their candidate for the Presidency." But in the end the Union army went solidly for Lincoln. The men may still have admired their old general, but they disliked the peace platform on which he had run so uneasily. "That grand old army performed many heroic acts . . ." Gerrish continued, "but never in its history did it do a more devoted service [than vote for Abraham Lincoln]."

Lincoln carried all but three northern states—Delaware, Kentucky, and New Jersey—and 54 percent of the popular vote. A large, happy crowd had gathered outside the telegraph office to cheer the reelected President. "I give thanks to the Almighty," he told them, "for this evidence of the people's resolution to stand by free government and the rights of humanity.

Humiliated a second time by the Illinois politician he loathed, General McClellan announced that "for my Country's sake, I deplore the result," then left for a long European vacation. The alternative, he believed, was exile—like that of his hero, Napoleon—in Utah or Nevada territory.

At Richmond, Jefferson Davis professed to be unmoved by the Union victories that helped make Lincoln's reelection possible. Addressing the Confederate Congress, he insisted that the importance of the fall of Atlanta had been exaggerated. The Confederacy could do without the Shenandoah, too.

> There are *no* vital points on the preservation of which the continued existence of the Confederacy depends. There is *no* military success of the enemy which can accomplish its destruction. Not the fall of Richmond, nor Wilmington, nor Charleston, nor Savannah, nor Mobile, *nor all combined,* can save the enemy from the constant and exhaustive drain of blood and treasure which must continue until he shall discover that no peace is attainable unless based on the recognition of our indefeasible rights.

As Davis spoke, congressmen could hear the thump of Grant's guns at Petersburg, just twenty miles away.

"I said, 'Don't shoot me.' One of them said, 'Go out and hold my horse.' I made a step or two and he said, 'Turn around: I will hold my horse and shoot you, too.' I no sooner turned around than he shot me in the face. I fell down as if I was dead. He shot me again and hit my arm, not my head. I laid there until I could hear him no more, and then I started back. I got back about sunup and wandered about until a gunboat came along, and I came up on that with about ten others."

PRIVATE GEORGE SHAW
Company B,
6th U.S. Heavy Artillery

Lincoln proclaimed the last Thursday in November a National Day of Thanksgiving. A company of Indiana soldiers of Sherman's army was camped near Milledgeville, Georgia, that evening, feasting on whatever delicacies foragers could scavenge from the surrounding countryside, when a band of gaunt Union escapees from the prison camp at Andersonville tottered into the firelight. The sight "sickened and infuriated" the troops, their colonel remembered: "An officer may instruct, command and threaten the men, but when foraging they think of the tens of thousands of their imprisoned comrades, slowly perishing with hunger, they sweep with the besom of destruction."

In the trenches at Petersburg, Union cooks served up 120,000 turkey and chicken dinners to the men of Grant's great army. Dug in only yards away, the Confederates had no feast, but held their fire all day out of respect for the Union holiday. "We lay in grim repose," a captain from South Carolina wrote, "and expected the renewal of the mortal conflict. The conviction everywhere prevailed that we could sustain but one more campaign."

CAN THOSE BE *MEN*?

THE MASSACRE AT FORT PILLOW

Official Confirmation of the Report.

Three Hundred Black Soldiers Murdered After Surrender.

Fifty-three White Soldiers Killed and One Hundred Wounded.

RETALIATION TO BE MADE

One of the cruelest charges made against Abraham Lincoln was that he was guilty of "shameful disregard" of the thousands of Union prisoners languishing in southern prisons.

The Confederates considered captured black troops who had once been slaves rebels and contraband rather than prisoners of war and refused to exchange them for their own prisoners. They were sometimes returned to their former masters instead, or sold to the highest bidder, or simply murdered. A Confederate officer recalled how he dealt with a squad of captured black soldiers who attempted to escape: "I . . . ordered every one shot, and with my Six Shooter I assisted in the execution of the order."

Back in April, Bedford Forrest's Tennesseans had surrounded Fort Pillow, held by 557 black troops and a unit of Tennessee unionists, and demanded its surrender. When the Federal forces refused, they stormed the fort, then butchered as many as three hundred of its disarmed defenders, black and white. "The poor, deluded Negroes would run up to our men," a rebel soldier recalled, "fall upon their knees and with uplifted hands, scream for mercy, but were ordered to their feet, and then shot down." Another reported, "I saw four white men and at least 25 negroes shot while begging for mercy, and I saw one Negro dragged from a hollow log . . . and as one rebel held him by the foot, another shot him."

Forrest was unrepentant. "The river was dyed with the blood of the slaughtered for 200 yards," he reported. "It is hoped that these facts will demonstrate to the northern people that negro soldiers cannot cope with Southerners."

Confederates captured at Cold Harbor wait at White House Landing for shipment to the Federal prison camp at Point Lookout, Maryland.

Five days later, Grant ordered an end to the prisoner exchange in effect since early in the war, until and unless the South formally agreed to recognize "no distinction whatever in the exchange between white and colored prisoners." In response, the southern exchange agent vowed the South "would die in the last ditch" before "giving up the right to send slaves back to slavery as property recaptured."

Grant's order further strained dwindling southern manpower; it also made the already inadequate prison camps still more nightmarish, North and South.

At Libby Prison, a converted ships' chandlery in Richmond, six dank rooms held thirteen hundred Union officers, while at Belle Isle in the James, 90 percent of the survivors weighed less than one hundred pounds. "Can those be *men*?" asked Walt Whitman when he saw several prisoners returned from Belle Isle: "Those

These men of the 11th New York Fire Zouaves, seized at First Bull Run, kept up their morale while locked up in Castle Pinckney in Charleston Harbor. Life was far grimmer in Richmond's Libby Prison (below).

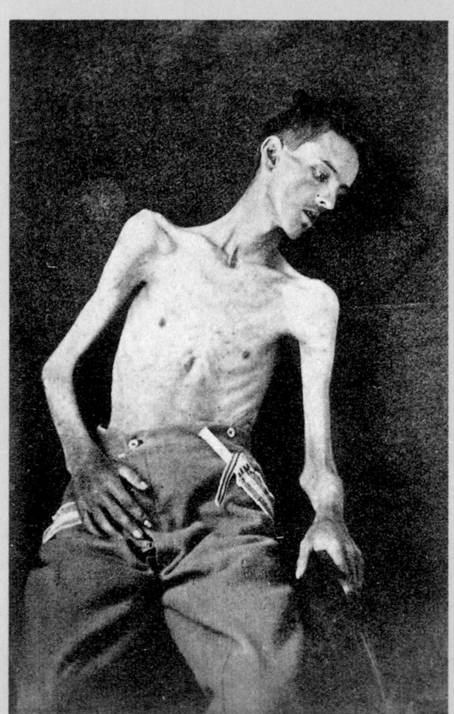
A survivor of the Confederate prison camp at Belle Isle in Richmond.

little livid brown, ash streaked, monkey-looking dwarfs?—are they not really mummied, dwindled corpses? They lay there, most of them, quite still, but with a horrible look in their eyes and skinny lips (often with not enough flesh to cover their teeth). . . . The dead there are not to be pitied as much as some of the living that have come from there—if they can be called living—many of them are mentally imbecile, and will never recuperate."

Smallpox killed eighteen hundred Confederates at Rock Island, Illinois, and there were never enough blankets for all the southerners at Elmira, New York, where, a survivor recalled, every morning "the men crawled out of their bunks shivering and half-frozen, when a scuffle,

Men of the 19th Iowa, imprisoned at Camp Ford, Tyler, Texas (above). Although Camp Morton near Indianapolis, Indiana (below), is thought to have been one of the best-run prison camps, North or South, more than seventeen hundred Confederates died there during the course of the war.

and frequently a fight, for a place by the fire occurred. God help the sick or the weak, as they were literally left out in the cold." Food was in short supply, too: "As there was very little currency . . . tobacco, rats, pickles, pork, and light bread were mediums of exchange. Five chews of tobacco would buy a rat, a rat would buy five chews of tobacco, a loaf of bread would buy a rat, a rat would buy a loaf of bread."

Even drinking water was foul. "The standing rain water," wrote a rebel locked up in Fort Delaware, "breeds a dense swarm of animalculae, [and when the] interior sediment is stirred up . . . the whole contents become a turgid, jellified mass of waggle tails, worms, dead leaves, dead fishes and other putrescent abominations. . . . The *smell* of it is enough to revolt the stomach . . . to say nothing of making one's throat a channel for such stuff."

Nearly fifty thousand men died in prison camps, ten times the number killed at Gettysburg.

The worst was Andersonville in Georgia. Opened in early 1864 and meant to hold a maximum of 10,000 Federal prisoners, it held 33,000 by August—and was the fifth largest city in the Confederacy. Its commandant, a temperish German-Swiss immigrant named Henry Wirz, forbade prisoners to build shelters; most lived in holes scratched in the ground, covered by a blanket. Any man caught closer than fifteen feet to the stockade was shot.

Each inmate's daily ration was a teaspoon of salt, three tablespoons of beans, and half a pint of unsifted cornmeal. A foul trickle called Sweet Water Branch served as both drinking water and sewer.

Thirteen thousand men died at Andersonville and were buried in mass graves; on one day they died at the rate of a man every eleven minutes. A southern woman was allowed to climb a guard tower and overlook Andersonville. She never forgot what she saw.

My heart aches for these poor wretches, Yankees though they are, and I am afraid God will suffer some terrible retribution to fall upon us for letting such things happen. If the Yankees should ever come to southwest Georgia and go to Anderson and see the graves there, God have mercy on the land!

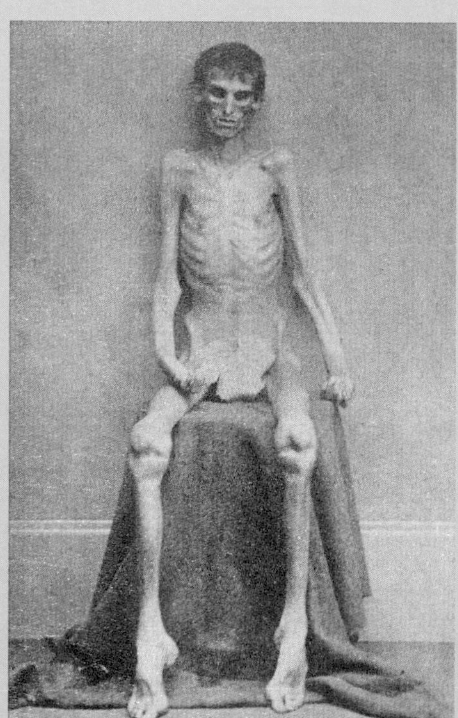

The barely living Union prisoner above emerged from Belle Isle. In 1864, Federal prisoners were moved from Richmond to Andersonville (above right). "I saw several men," a new arrival wrote, "who had been vaccinated . . . and into their arms the gangrene had eaten a hole large enough to lay a half an orange in. They will be dead men soon enough." At right, workers bury the day's dead; the cemetery at far right was laid out after the war, under the supervision of Clara Barton.

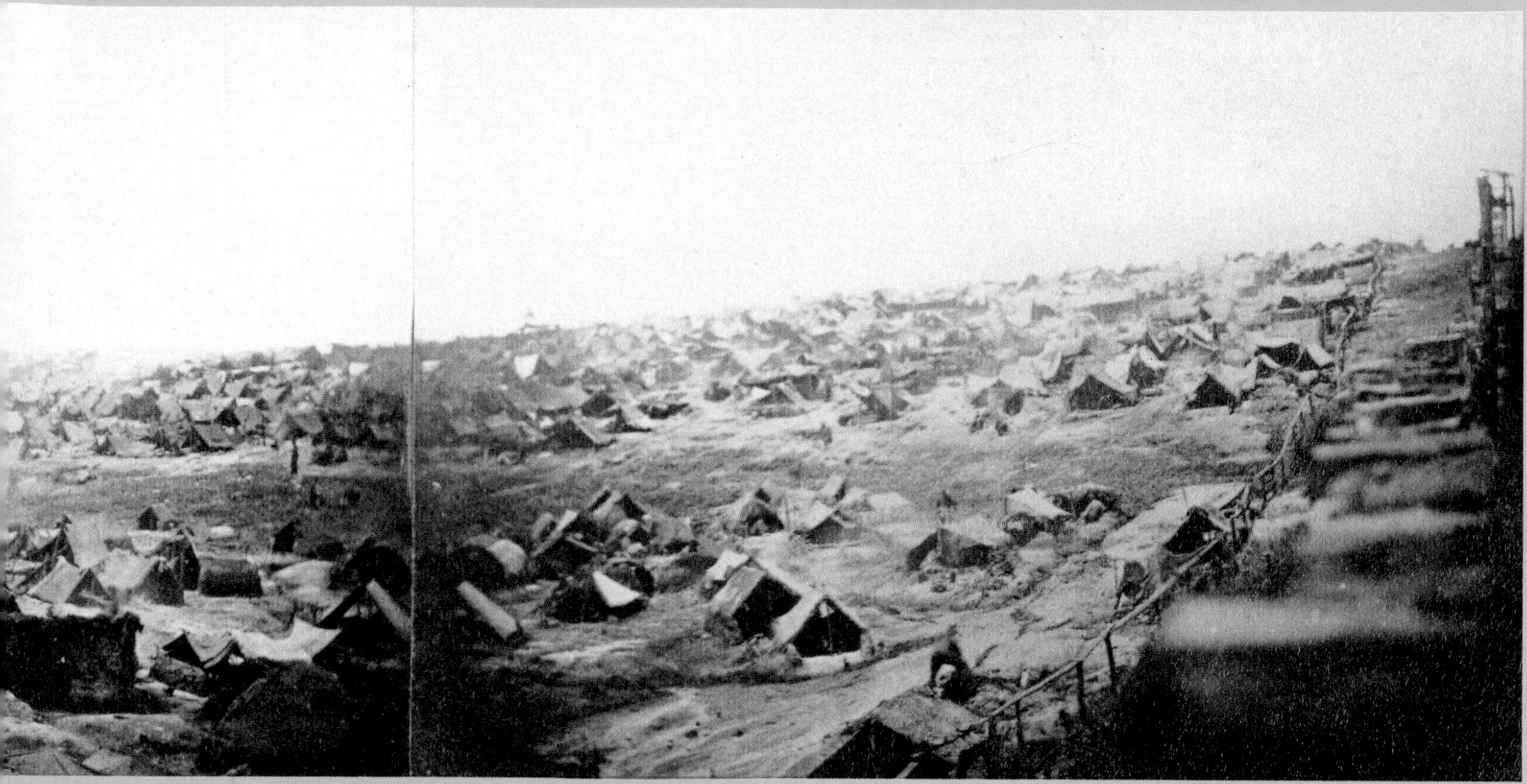

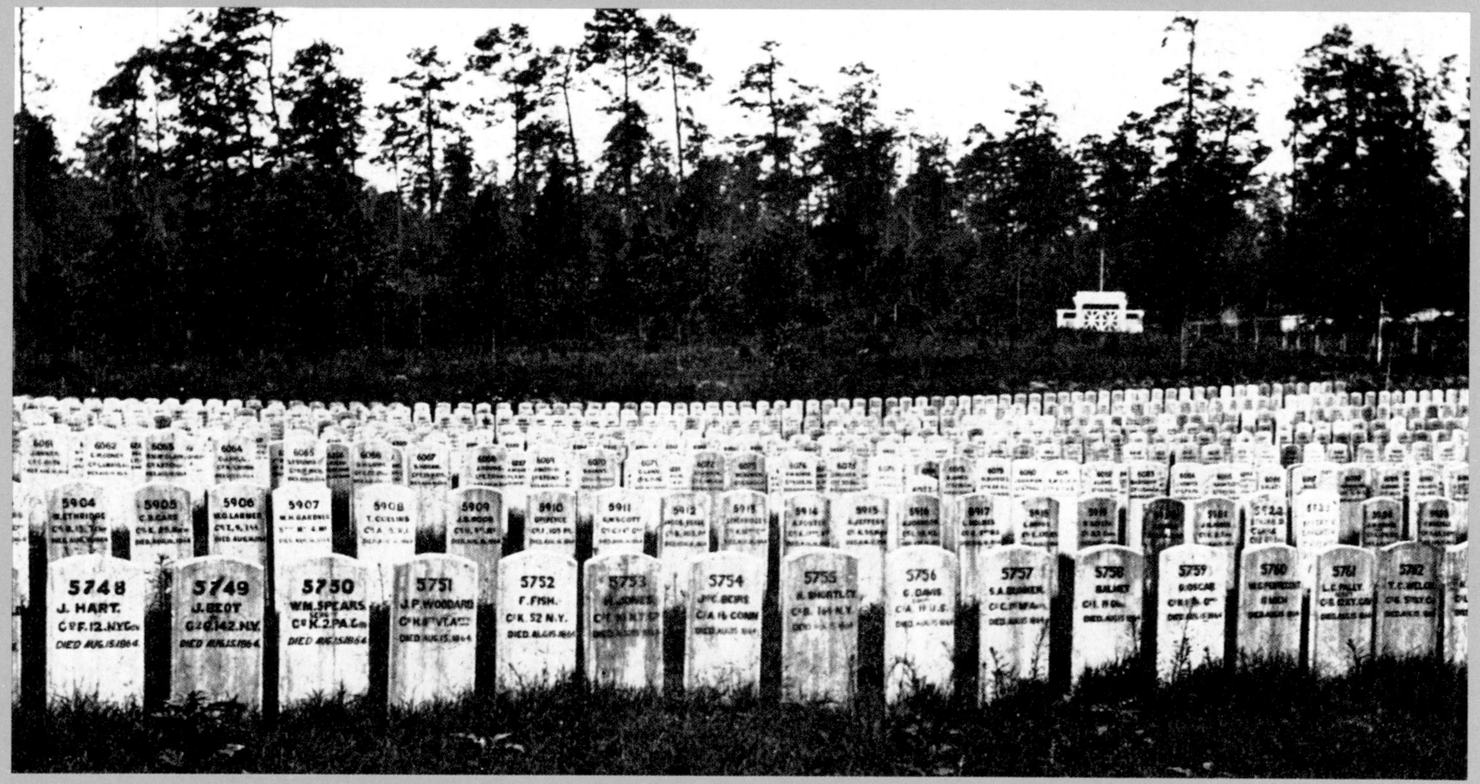

5904
5905
5906
5907
5908
5909
5911
5748
J. HART.
DIED AUG.15.1864.
5749
DIED AUG.15.1864.
5750
WM.SPEARS
DIED AUG.15.1864.
5751
J.P. WOODARD
DIED AUG.15.1864
5752
F. FISH.
Co K. 52 N.Y.
5753
5754
5755
5756
5757
5758
5759
5760
5761
5762

MARCHING TO THE SEA

With Atlanta in his grasp, Sherman now proposed to lead his army through the heart of Georgia all the way to the coastal city of Savannah. He would be unable to communicate with Washington while marching, and would be cut off from his base of supply. His army would live off the land, destroying everything in its path that could conceivably aid the faltering Confederacy—and a good deal that couldn't. He promised to "make Georgia howl." "If *you* can whip Lee and I can march to the Atlantic," Sherman told Grant, "I think Uncle Abe will give us twenty days' leave of absence to see the young folks."

Lincoln's advisors thought Sherman's plan foolhardy; the President approved it, although he worried, too. "I know the hole he went *in* at," he told a caller, "but I can't tell you what hole he'll come out of." Military experts outside government, too, thought the risk great. "The name of the captor of Atlanta, if he fails now, will become the scoff of mankind," wrote the London *Herald,* "and the humiliation of the United States for all time. If he succeeds it will be written on the tablet of fame."

Sherman himself had no doubts. When he ordered civilians out of the city, the mayor and two city councilmen sent him a formal protest. His reply was brief and to the point:

> Gentlemen: You cannot qualify war in harsher terms than I will. War is cruelty and you cannot refine it. . . . But you cannot have peace and a division of our country. You might as well appeal against the thunderstorm as against these terrible hardships of war.

Sixteen hundred whites—and an unknown number of blacks—packed what they could carry and fled Atlanta. Soon, Sam Watkins remembered, "the roads were filled with loaded wagons of old and decrepit people, who had been hunted and hounded from their homes with a relentless cruelty."

Sherman ordered a third of the empty city burned, then began his march on November 16, 1864.

As the Union columns moved out, poor whites and blacks slipped into the ruined neighborhoods to plunder what little was left. Sherman himself recalled his final glimpse of Atlanta:

> Reaching the hill just outside the old rebel works, we paused to look back. . . . Behind us lay Atlanta, smoldering and in ruins, the black smoke rising high in the air, and hanging like a pall. . . . Then we turned our horses' heads to the East; Atlanta was soon lost behind the screen of trees, and became a thing of the past.

Sixty-two thousand men in blue were on the move in two great columns—218 regiments, including 52 from Ohio alone, and a cavalry unit from Alabama, made up of poor, upcountry unionists with scores to settle with the well-to-do. Their supply train stretched twenty-five miles.

A menagerie of pets went with them—an owl, a bear, scores of dogs. Old Abe, the eagle mascot of the 8th Wisconsin, rode along, tethered to a cannon.

"There are rumors that we are to cut loose and march south to the ocean. We are in fine shape and I think could go anywhere Uncle Billy would lead."

PRIVATE THEODORE UPSON
100th Indiana

A column of Sherman's supply wagons threads its way through Atlanta.

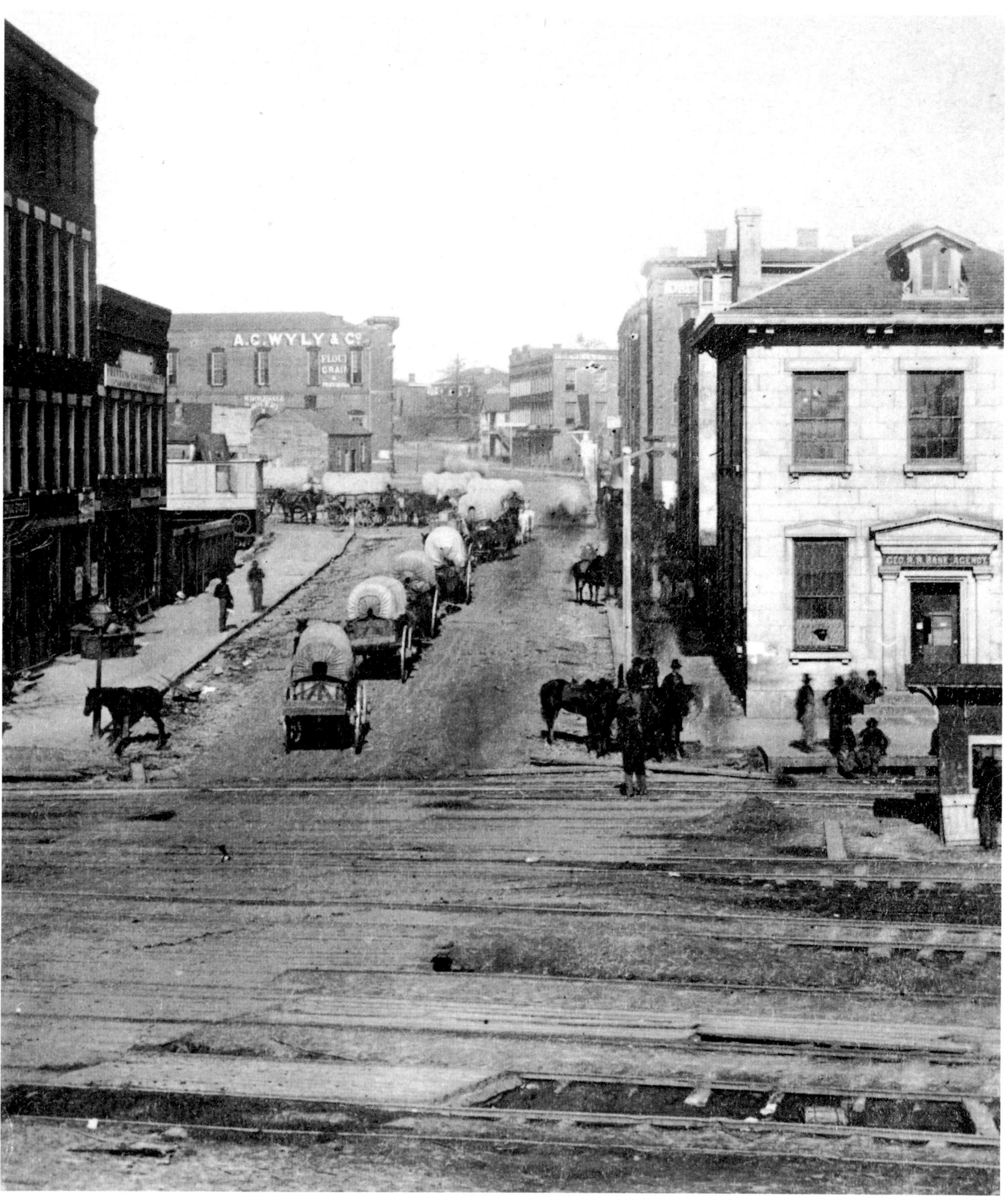
A.C.WYLY & Co.
GEO. R. R. BANK AGENCY

There were scores of fighting cocks, too; victorious birds were named Grant and Bill Sherman; losers were called Beauregard, Jeff Davis, and Bob Lee.

A slave watched part of this mighty host stream past and wondered aloud if anybody was *left* up north.

Sherman was something new in warfare, a soldier who believed that he could defeat the enemy's army only after he had crushed the will of the civilians who sustained it. "We cannot change the hearts of these people of the South," he said, "but we can make war so terrible . . . and make them so *sick* of war that generations [will] pass away before they again appeal to it."

"This is probably the greatest pleasure excursion ever planned," a Union soldier wrote. "It already beats everything I ever saw soldiering, and promises to prove much richer yet." Sherman expressly forbade his men to plunder the homes they passed, but neither he nor they took the order very seriously. "We had a gay old campaign," a private recalled. "Destroyed all we could not eat, stole their niggers, burned their cotton and gins, spilled their sorghum, burned and twisted their railroads and raised Hell, generally."

The mistress of a roadside plantation remembered how the Union men came:

Sherman marches to the sea: "My first object," William Tecumseh Sherman wrote before leaving Atlanta on his way to Savannah, "was, of course, to place my army in the very heart of Georgia." On November 16, 1864, he set out across the state at the head of two vast columns. Cut off from supplies or contact with the North, his men devoured or destroyed most of what stood in their way, and four days before Christmas, took Savannah, three hundred miles away.

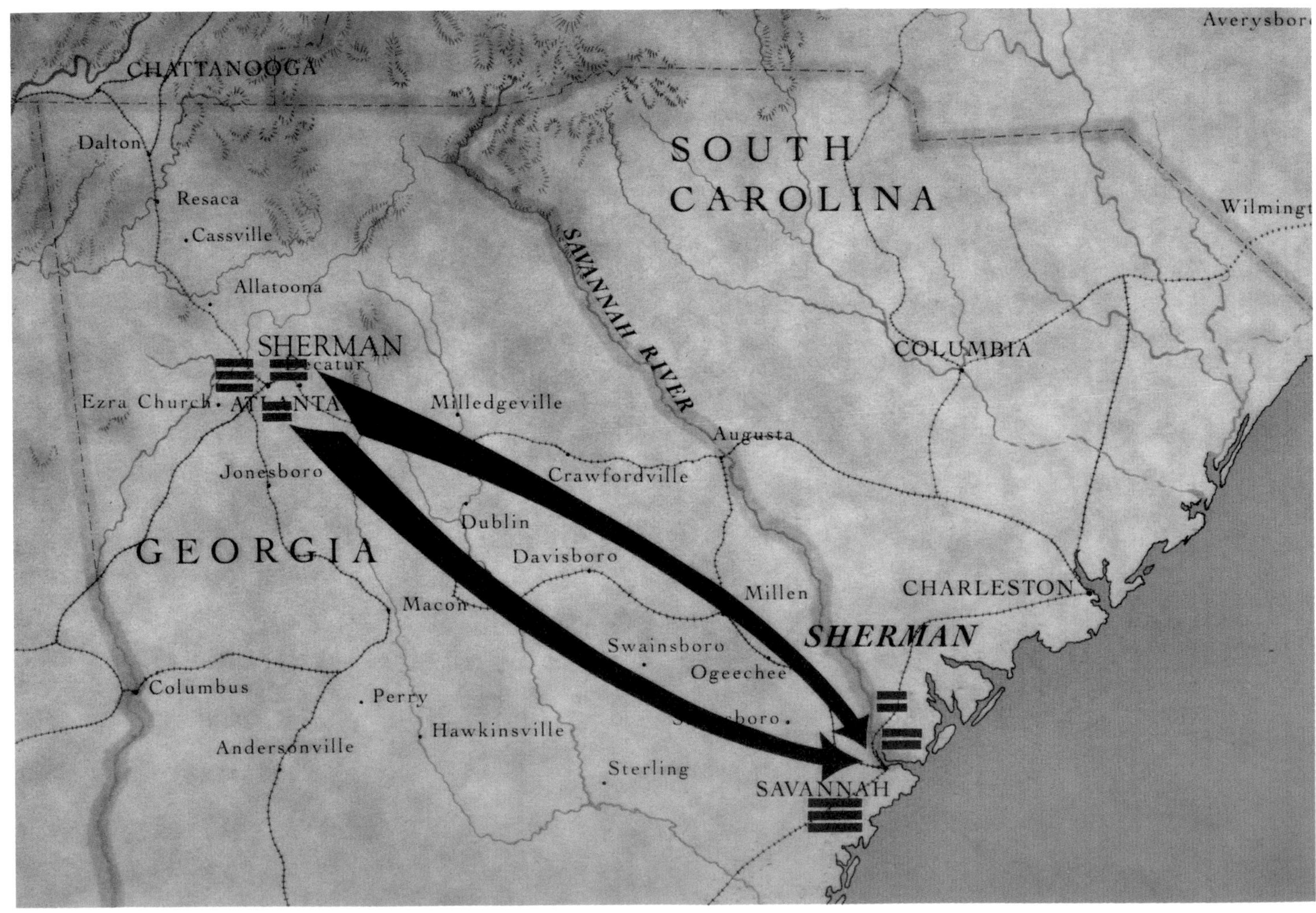

Civilians survey some of the damage done by the Union occupiers of Atlanta: "Now that war comes home to you . . ." Sherman told the city council, "you deprecate its horrors, but did not feel them when you sent car-loads of soldiers and ammunition, and moulded shells and shot, to carry war into Kentucky and Tennessee, to desolate the homes of hundreds and thousands of good people who only asked to live in peace . . . under the Government of their inheritance."

> Like Demons they rushed in! . . . To my Smoke House, my dairy, pantry, kitchen and cellar, like famished wolves they come, breaking locks and whatever is in their way. The thousand pounds of meat in my smoke house is gone . . . my flour, my meat, my lard, butter, eggs, pickles . . . wine, jars and jugs are all gone. My 18 fat turkeys, my hens, chickens, and fowl, my young pigs, are shot down in my yard . . . as if they were the rebels themselves.

White women were sometimes terrified by Sherman's men but rarely molested. Slave women were not so fortunate.

The troops looted slave cabins as well as mansions, poked their ramrods into farmyards in search of buried valuables. At one house, a freshly buried spaniel was dug up four times in one day because its grave seemed suspicious to passing Federal troops. "As far as the eye could reach," another woman remembered, "the lurid flames of burning [houses] lit up the heavens. . . . I could stand out on the verandah and for two or three miles watch [the Yankees] as they came on. I could mark when they reached the residence of each and every friend on the road." "The cruelties practiced on this campaign

Georgia railroad track transformed into one of "Sherman's hairpins." Pried up, heated until they were red-hot, then bent around trees by practiced veterans, they were sometimes further twisted into the shape of a doughnut to make doubly sure the enemy could never use them again.

toward the citizens," a Union corporal wrote, "have been enough to blast a more sacred cause than ours. We hardly deserve success."

"I doubt if history affords a parallel," Sherman himself admitted, "to the deep and bitter enmity of the women of the South. No one who sees them and hears them but must feel the intensity of their hate."

At Milledgeville, the Georgia capital, Sherman's men boiled their coffee over bonfires of Confederate currency, held a mock session of the legislature that passed a resolution rejoining the Union, then ransacked the state library—an act that horrified one New Englander: "I don't object to stealing horses, mules, niggers and all such *little things,*" he said, "but I will not engage in plundering and destroying public libraries!"

Before they were through, Sherman and his men would cross 425 miles of hostile territory and do $100 million worth of damage. "They say no living thing is found in Sherman's track," Mary Chesnut wrote, "only chimneys, like telegraph poles, to carry the news of [his] attack backwards."

John Bell Hood and his dwindling army tried to divert Sherman's attention by moving north to join forces with Bedford Forrest's cavalry and invade Tennessee.

"We will fight you to the death," General John Bell Hood (above) warned the Yankee invaders. "Better to die a thousand deaths than submit to live under you . . . and your negro allies." But he soon saw his army fall apart during the battle for Nashville (right).

Sherman was delighted. "If he will go to the Ohio River I'll give him rations," he said. "*My* business is down South."

Hood had to be strapped to his saddle each morning, but he fought as hard and as recklessly as ever. At Franklin, on November 30, 1864, he ordered a series of thirteen gallant, hopeless charges in which 6 Confederate generals died and more than 6,250 southern soldiers were killed or wounded or missing, a quarter of his army. Sam Watkins survived the fight. "We were willing to go anywhere, or to follow anyone who would lead us," he wrote. "We were anxious to flee, fight or fortify. I have never seen an army so confused and demoralized. The whole thing seemed to be tottering and trembling."

At Nashville, on December 5, Union forces under "Pap" Thomas splintered the rest of Hood's army. Watkins lived through that, too.

> The army was panic-stricken. The woods everywhere were full of running soldiers. Our officers were crying "Halt! Halt!"
>
> My boot was full of blood, and my clothing saturated with it. I [reached] General Hood's headquarters. He was much agitated and affected, pulling his hair with his one hand (he had but one), and crying like his heart would break.

Hood's army had disintegrated. "I beheld for the first and only time," he confessed, "a Confederate army abandon the field in confusion." He resigned his command in January. Only ragged militia and scattered cavalry units were left to pick at Sherman's columns. "In the morning we found 3 Yanks driving

THE WIZARD OF THE SADDLE

William Tecumseh Sherman once called Nathan Bedford Forrest "the most remarkable man our Civil War produced on either side." But that did not prevent him from demanding that Forrest be "hunted down and killed if it cost ten thousand lives and bankrupts the Federal treasury."

Born in Bedford County, Tennessee, the son of an illiterate blacksmith, Forrest had become a wealthy planter by the time the war began, in part because of a brisk early trade in slaves—a source of revenue about which he was unapologetic but which won him the contempt of some well-born southern officers who saw nothing wrong with profiting from slavery but thought the actual buying and selling of slaves unworthy of gentlemen.

In 1861, he enlisted as a private, then raised and equipped an entire cavalry battalion out of his own pocket. By the war's end he had become a lieutenant general, the only man in either army to rise so far. He was the most feared cavalry commander of the war—"the wizard of the saddle"—wounded four times in battle and famous for having horses shot out from under him.

When one of his own officers, outraged over a reprimand, shot him at point-blank range, Forrest held his struggling attacker with one hand, picked up a penknife with the other, unclasped it with his teeth and stabbed him. "No damned man kills me and lives," he said. The hapless man staggered across the street and died. Forrest was back in the saddle thirteen days later.

He was a master of the lightning raid and an expert at winning against long odds. He fought, he said, "by ear," and proved able to anticipate his enemy's movements with uncanny precision.

He is said to have been surprised only once, at Parker's Crossroad, Tennessee, on the last day of 1862. Attempting to get away after a daring raid on Grant's lines, he was fighting his way through the Union force in front of him when he was unexpectedly hit from behind. His flustered staff asked what they were to do. "Split in two," Forrest said, "and charge both ways." They did, and got out.

In June 1864, at Brices Cross Roads near Tupelo, Mississippi, Forrest outdid even himself. The eight-thousand-man Union force sent to stop his constant harassment of Sherman's advancing army outnumbered his almost two to one, but Forrest was unimpressed. Factoring in the mud-clogged roads and the hot Mississippi sun, he predicted the Federal cavalry would arrive well ahead of the infantry, and thus give him time to whip them on his own terms. When the northern foot soldiers finally came up, exhausted by the heat, he would be able to ride right over them, too.

It all happened exactly as he said it would: in the end, Forrest accounted for 2,400 of his pursuers—killed, captured, or missing—and took most of their artillery and 176 supply wagons, as well.

Forrest was one of the most prominent of the "Young Bloods of the South" Sherman had warned his superiors against: "They are the most dangerous set of men that this war has turned loose upon the world. . . . War suits them, and the rascals are brave, fine riders, [and] bold to rashness. . . . They hate Yankees, per se, and don't bother their brains about the past, present or future. . . . These men must all be killed or employed by us before we can hope for peace."

Bedford Forrest was in the backwoods of Alabama when peace did finally come. Other officers had already surrendered to the Yankees, but he toyed for a time with the notion of riding all the way to Mexico rather than give up. "Which way, General?" an adjutant asked him. "Either," he said. "If one road led to hell and the other to Mexico, I would be indifferent which to take." But after further thought he decided he could serve his region best by leading his former soldiers back into the restored Union: "I have never on the field of battle sent you where I was unwilling to go myself," he told them, "nor would I now advise you to a course which I felt myself unwilling to pursue. You have been good soldiers. You can be good citizens. Obey the laws, preserve your honor, and the government to which you have surrendered can afford to be and will be magnanimous."

"Miss Kitty Diggs

"I want you to understand that mary is my Child and she is a God give rite of my own and you may hold on to hear as long as you can but I want you to remembeor this one thing that the longor you keep my Child from me the longor you will have to burn in hell and the qwicer youll get ther. . . . I have no fears about getting mary out of your hands this whole Government gives chear to me and you cannot help yourself."

PRIVATE SPOTSWOOD RICE
67th U.S. Colored Infantry

When retreating Confederates burned to the ground this railroad bridge over the Cumberland River near Nashville, Federal engineers had it rebuilt within days, complete with sentry boxes and heavy wooden gates in case it was attacked again.

off a lady's cows," wrote one rebel trooper. "We soon scattered their brains and moved on."

Union cavalry swatted away attacks at East Point, Rough and Ready, Jonesboro, Bear Creek. At Griswoldville, a pickup force of boys and old men hurled themselves at an Indiana regiment and were annihilated. "It was a terrible sight," a Union private wrote afterward. "Someone was groaning. We moved a few bodies and there was a boy with a broken arm and leg—just a boy, 14 years old; and beside him, cold in death, lay his father, two brothers and an uncle."

"The whole army of the United States could not restore the institution of slavery in the South," Sherman wrote. "They can't get back their slaves, any more than they can get back their dead grandfathers. It is dead." Twenty-five thousand slaves flocked to his army, jubilant that he had come to liberate them, but also fearful that if they strayed too far from the safety of his columns they would be caught by Confederate guerrillas and killed or forced back into slavery. "Perfect anarchy reigned," one planter said; another thought it "the breath of emancipation."

A slave family newly arrived in the Federal lines.

"[The slaves followed the army] like a sable cloud in the sky before a thunderstorm," a Union officer wrote. "They thought it was freedom now or never." An Indiana officer was moved by their desperation.

> It was very touching to see the vast numbers of colored women following after us with babies in their arms, and little ones like our Anna clinging to their tattered skirts. One poor creature, while nobody was looking, hid two boys, five years old, in a wagon, intending, I suppose, that they should see the land of freedom if she couldn't.

After Sherman left one town, slaves took over several abandoned plantations and divided the property of their former owners up among themselves, hoping to start new lives as free citizens.

Sherman was more annoyed than amused by this civilian army that ate up his supplies and got in his way. "Damn the niggers," he said. "I wish they . . . could be kept at work."

Union General Jefferson C. Davis, a violent Indianan who had already shot a fellow officer to death for daring to criticize him and who favored both slavery and the Union, was still more irritated by the slaves in his wake, and when he reached Ebenezer Creek on December 3, he ran a pontoon bridge across the river, ordered his men across—then snatched up the bridge, leaving the slaves on the far shore. Confederate cavalry opened fire on them; several drowned, the rest were returned to slavery. "Praise the Lord we got away . . ." said one old man who managed to swim the river with his wife and struggle on behind the army. "We got troubles on our road but bless the Lord, it will be all right in the end."

On December 22, 1864, Sherman sent Lincoln a telegram: "I beg to present you, as a Christmas gift, the city of Savannah, with 150 heavy guns and plenty of ammunition; also, about 25,000 bales of cotton."

The President was delighted: "Grant has the bear by the hind leg," he said, "while Sherman takes off its hide."

VOL. XIV.---NO. 4136.

SAVANNAH OURS.

Sherman's Christmas Present.

Official Dispatches from Generals Sherman and Foster.

WHAT SHERMAN FOUND.

150 Cannon, 200 Cars and Locomotives, 3 Steamers, 800 Prisoners, and 30,000 Bales of Cotton.

Twenty Thousand People in the City Quiet and Well Disposed.

The waterfront at Union-occupied Savannah in December 1865.

Darkest of all Decembers
Ever my life has known,
Sitting here by the embers
Stunned, helpless, alone.

MARY CHESNUT

WAR AND POLITICS

JAMES M. McPHERSON

THE MOST FAMOUS MAXIM OF THE NINETEENTH-century military theorist Karl von Clausewitz defined war as the continuation of politics by other means. In 1864, in America, politics was the continuation of war by other means.

The occurrence of a presidential election in the midst of war has not been unique in American history. Six times the quadrennial date for balloting has arrived during a war. On four of these occasions (1812, 1864, 1944, and 1972) the war policies of an incumbent President seeking reelection have been important campaign issues; in each case the incumbent won. In the other two elections (1952 and 1968), voters overturned the party in power partly because of the unpopularity of its war policies—and, indeed, of the war itself. But despite the centrality of war issues during these elections, in only one of them did voters perceive the survival of the United States to be at stake: in 1864. That election was seen as a referendum on whether the Union should continue fighting the Civil War to unconditional victory. The result of this political campaign did as much to determine the outcome of the war as did events on the battlefield. But military campaigns, in turn, decisively influenced the election.

Optimism prevailed in the North in the spring of 1864. The victories at Gettysburg, Vicksburg, and Chattanooga the previous year had sent the Confederacy reeling. President Lincoln had brought the hero of Vicksburg and Chattanooga, Ulysses S. Grant, to Washington as general-in-chief of all Union armies. Grant planned coordinated campaigns to give rebellion its *coup de grâce.* Southern leaders vowed defiantly to "die in the last ditch" before surrendering to Yankees. But these same leaders were quarreling among themselves over responsibility for past defeats, the southern economy was in shambles, civilians were hungry and disaffected, Confederate armies lacked supplies, and peace movements had sprung up in North Carolina and elsewhere. Powerful Union forces in Virginia under Grant's overall command and in Georgia under Sherman stood poised for invasions that they confidently expected to crush Confederate resistance well before the presidential election in November.

Grant and Sherman intended by a series of flanking movements to threaten Confederate communications and force the southern commanders Lee and Johnston into open-field combat, where superior Union numbers and firepower could be used to greatest advantage. The southern strategy, by contrast, was to block the Union's flanking movements and force northern armies instead to assault defenses entrenched on high ground or behind rivers, where fortifications and natural obstacles would more than neutralize superior numbers.

In part the South's smaller population and resources dictated this strategy, but it resulted also from the contrasting war aims of the two sides. To win the war, Union armies had to conquer and occupy southern territory, overwhelm or break up Confederate armies, destroy the economic and political infrastructure that supported the war effort, and suppress the southern will to resist. But in order to "win" on their terms, the Confederates, like Americans in the Revolution or North Vietnam in the 1960s, needed only to hold out long enough and inflict sufficient punishment on the enemy to force him to give up his effort to annihilate resistance. This was a strategy of political and psychological attrition—of wearing down the other side's will to continue fighting. Many historians have mistakenly argued that Grant pursued a military strategy of attrition in 1864—of using the North's greater numbers and resources to grind down the South's ability to resist. It turned out that way, but not because Grant initially intended it. Rather, the near success of the southern strategy of psychological attrition forced the North into a campaign of military attrition. The crucial turning point of both strategies was the Union presidential election of 1864.

Confederate strategy sought to influence the outcome of that election. On previous occasions when the war had gone badly for the North, the Copperhead peace faction of the Democratic party had grown in strength with demands for an armistice and peace negotiations—which would have amounted to southern victory. Confederates had cultivated this antiwar faction in the North with some success. In 1864 they sought ways to promote a Democratic victory in the Union election. Southern military leaders planned their operations around the objective of holding out until November. "If we can only *subsist*" until the northern election, wrote a War Department official in Richmond, "giving an opportunity for the Democrats to elect a President . . . we may have peace." Because of "the importance of this [military] campaign to the administration of Mr. Lincoln," Robert E. Lee meant to "resist manfully" in the hope of weakening the northern war party. "If we can break up the enemy's arrangements early, and throw him back," explained General James Longstreet, "he will not be able to recover his position or his morale until the Presidential election is over, and then we shall have a new President to treat with."

The Confederate secret service mounted a simultaneous effort to sway northern opinion. Operating from Canada, southern agents plotted a variety of raids to harass the Union war effort and sabotage the northern economy—including an attempt to liberate Confederate prisoners of war from Camp Douglas near Chicago and Johnson's Island near Sandusky, Ohio; the burning of factories and warehouses; and the subsidization of antiwar Democratic candidates for office in northern states. A few of these schemes resulted in action—a bank robbery in St. Albans, Vermont, the burning of a half-dozen military steamboats at St. Louis, subsidies to several northern newspapers and to the Democratic candidate for governor in Illinois, and fires in several large New York hotels that were quickly extinguished with little damage.

Efforts to encourage peace sentiment in the North by the offer of an armistice and negotiations to end the war were more serious. Canadian-based Confederate commissioners met with Horace Greeley, the editor of the New York *Tribune,* and Lincoln's private secretary, John Hay, at Niagara Falls, Canada, in July 1864. This meeting elicited from Lincoln a declaration of willingness to negotiate on the basis of reunion and emancipation. Cleverly obfuscating the South's insistence on recognition of Confederate independence as a precondition of negotiations, the southern commissioners released a statement blaming Lincoln's inflexible terms for the failure of these peace feelers. Picking up on this theme, northern Democrats broadcast the notion that if Lincoln would just drop his insistence on emancipation the war would end. But since he would not, the only way to get peace was to repudiate Lincoln at the polls. At the end of August, when the Democrats held their convention in Chicago, their prospects for electoral victory in November appeared bright.

How had this happened? How had the northern optimism of spring turned into such deep despair by late summer that all observers, Lincoln included, expected the President and his platform of war to victory to be rejected by the voters? The answer lies in the success of the Confederate strategy of attrition. In six weeks of the war's bloodiest fighting, from the Wilderness to Petersburg, the Army of the Potomac and the Army of Northern Virginia had crippled each other so badly that static trench warfare would characterize this theater for the next nine months. Fighting mainly on the defensive, Lee's army imposed almost a two-to-one ratio of casualties on the attacking Union forces. By July, the Army of the Potomac alone had suffered 65,000 casualties; losses of other northern armies brought the Union casualty total since the first of the year to 100,000. Prisoners of war were crammed into inadequate camps in both North and South, where thousands died from disease and exposure. The prisoner exchange system had broken down, largely because of the South's refusal to exchange black soldiers.

What had the North to show for this staggering carnage? Stalemate at Petersburg; stalemate in the West; a small Confederate army under Jubal Early rampaging through Maryland to the very outskirts of Washington; even in Georgia, Sherman's war of maneuver seemed to have bogged down in the steamy trenches before Atlanta. "Who shall revive the withered hopes that bloomed at the opening of Grant's campaign?" asked the leading Democratic newspaper, the New York *World*. "STOP THE WAR!" shouted Democratic headlines. "All are tired of this damnable tragedy. . . . If nothing else would impress upon the people the absolute necessity of stopping this war, its utter failure to accomplish any results would be sufficient." Republicans joined this chorus of despair. "Our bleeding, bankrupt, almost dying country . . . longs for peace," Horace Greeley told Lincoln, "shudders at the prospect of . . . further wholesale devastations, of new rivers of human blood." The veteran Republican leader Thurlow Weed observed in August that "the people are wild for peace. . . . Lincoln's reelection is an impossibility."

As usual, the buck stopped at the President's desk. As commander in chief, Lincoln knew that he must bear the responsibility for failure. His hold on the leadership of his party was less than solid. Though the Republican convention in June had renominated him almost unanimously, Radical Republicans expressed reservations about the President. They had considered him slow in embracing emancipation as a war aim, and had quarreled with him over the policy of reconstructing the South. When Lincoln killed a congressional reconstruction act (the Wade-Davis Bill) with a pocket veto, in order to preserve his own more moderate executive approach, the Republican rift widened.

By August, though, the crucial question was not what policy to pursue toward the South once the war was won, but whether it could be won at all. Some desperate Republicans began muttering about dumping Lincoln in favor of some other candidate less identified with failure. The President came under enormous pressure to drop emancipation as a condition of peace negotiations. Lincoln bent but did not break under this pressure. His Emancipation Proclamation had promised freedom, "and the promise being made, must be kept." "I should be damned in time & in eternity," said Lincoln, if I were "to return to slavery the black warriors" who had fought for the Union. "The world shall know that I will keep my faith to friends & enemies, come what will."

Lincoln was well aware of his probable fate in November. "I am going to be beaten," he told a friend in August, "and unless some great change takes place, *badly* beaten." On August 23, the President wrote his famous "blind memorandum" and asked his cabinet members to endorse it sight unseen: "This morning, as for some days past, it seems exceedingly probable that this Administration will not be re-elected. Then it will be my duty to so co-operate with the President elect, as to save the Union between the election and the inauguration; as he will have secured his election on such ground that he can not possibly save it afterwards."

Meeting in Chicago at the end of August, the Democratic convention adopted a peace platform. "After four years of failure to restore the Union by the experiment of war," it declared, we "demand that immediate efforts be made for a cessation of hostilities, with a view to an ultimate convention of the states, or other peaceable means . . . [that] peace may be restored on the basis of the Federal Union." But with their presidential nomination the Democrats revealed their own party rift. The nominee was George B. McClellan, removed by Lincoln from command of the Army of the Potomac two years earlier and now seeking vindication via politics. But McClellan was a War Democrat. He recognized that an armistice and negotiations without prior conditions would constitute a Confederate victory, making restoration of the Union impossible. Thus in his letter accepting the nomination McClellan constructed his own platform specifying reunion (but not emancipation) "as the one condition of peace."

Though the Democrats seemed to be sending a muddled message—a war candidate on a peace platform—jubilant southerners celebrated McClellan's nomination. The Democratic nominee's election on this platform "must lead to peace and our independence," declared the Charleston *Mercury*, if "for the next two months *we hold our own and prevent military success by our foes.*"

It didn't go that way. Three days after the Democrats adjourned, telegraph wires brought news of Sherman's capture of Atlanta and electrified the North. "VICTORY!" blazoned Republican headlines. "IS THE WAR A FAILURE? OLD ABE'S REPLY TO THE CHICAGO CONVENTION." Hard on the heels of Atlanta's fall came Phil Sheridan's spectacular series of victories over Jubal Early in the Shenandoah Valley and minor successes of northern arms on the Richmond-Petersburg front. For Lincoln and the Republi-

cans, these military triumphs transformed electoral prospects from darkest midnight to bright noonday. A gray, ominous twilight settled over the South. The "disaster at Atlanta," lamented the Richmond *Examiner,* came "in the very nick of time" to "save the party of Lincoln from irretrievable ruin. . . . It will obscure the prospect of peace, late so bright. It will also diffuse gloom over the South."

By October, the political signs pointed to a Republican landslide. The most remarkable part of this phenomenon was the soldier vote. Having won the military victories that turned the war around, these citizens in uniform prepared to give "Old Abe," as they affectionately called their commander in chief, a thumping endorsement at the polls. Absentee voting by soldiers was a bold experiment in democracy, pioneered by both sides in the Civil War. By 1864, nineteen northern states allowed soldiers to vote in the field. Just three state legislatures had refused to do so—those of Illinois, Indiana, and New Jersey—all controlled by Democrats who knew which way most soldiers would vote. Although 40 to 45 percent of the soldiers had been Democrats when they joined the army, only 20 to 25 percent of them voted Democratic in 1864. In the twelve states that tabulated the army vote separately, 78 percent of the soldiers voted for Lincoln—despite the lingering admiration of some men in the Army of the Potomac for their old commander, McClellan. The civilian vote, by way of comparison, went 54 percent for Lincoln.

Why this large difference between the civilian and soldier vote? For most soldiers, their honor as fighting men was at stake. They had gone to war for flag and country, and they meant to bring home the flag of a united country with *all* of its thirty-five stars in place. To vote Democratic, to admit that the war was a failure and their sacrifices had been in vain, to march home with a flag shorn of eleven stars would plunge their country and its manhood to the depths of shame. "We want peace too," wrote an Ohio officer, a former Democrat turned Republican, "*honorable* peace, won in the full light of day at the bayonet's point, with our grand old flag flying over us as we negotiate it, instead of a cowardly peace purchased at the price of national dishonor." A New York private spoke for most Union soldiers; he intended, he wrote, to "give the rebellion another thump this fall by voting for Old Abe. I cannot afford to give three years of my life to maintaining this nation and then give the Rebels all they want."

These were the convictions that reelected Lincoln by a margin of 212 to 21 in the electoral college (the President lost only New Jersey and the border slave states of Kentucky and Delaware). Republicans increased their majority in both houses of Congress to more than three-fourths. It was a powerful endorsement of Lincoln's iron-willed determination to fight on to unconditional victory. The election demonstrated to a British war correspondent that the North was "silently, calmly, but desperately in earnest . . . in a way the like of which the world never saw before. . . . I am astonished the more I see and hear of the extent and depth of [this] determination . . . to fight to the last."

The ruins of Richmond in April 1865.

CHAPTER FIVE

1865

THE BETTER ANGELS OF OUR NATURE

THE MIGHTY SCOURGE

The winter of 1864–1865 was the coldest that had been known for many years," Sam Watkins remembered. "The ground was frozen and rough, and our soldiers were poorly clad, while many, yes, very many, were entirely barefooted. . . . Everything and nature, too, seemed to be working against us. Even the keen, cutting air that whistled through our tattered clothes . . . seemed to lash us."

"The deep waters are closing over us." MARY CHESNUT

William Tecumseh Sherman lashed them, too, turning his columns northward, into the Carolinas. "When I go through South Carolina," he promised, "it will be one of the most horrible things in the history of the world. The devil himself couldn't restrain my men in that state."

A steady winter rain was falling, and Confederate generals were confident no army could march through the mud, but Sherman and his men continued to make a steady ten miles a day, sometimes sleeping in trees to escape the spongy ground. "When I learned that Sherman's army was marching through the Salk[iehatchie] Swamps," Joseph Johnston remembered, "making its own . . . roads at the rate of a dozen miles a day . . . and bringing its artillery and wagons with it, I made up my mind that there had been no such army in existence since the days of Julius Caesar."

Nothing seemed to slow Sherman's soldiers. Battalions of axmen led the way, hacking down whole forests to construct corduroy roads. When mines buried beneath the road injured several of his men, Sherman ordered Confederate prisoners to march ahead of his column to search for more. They protested they had no more idea than he did where the mines were buried. "I don't care a damn if *you're* blown up," he shouted. "I'll not have my own men killed like this."

True to their commander's word, Sherman's men were still harsher in South Carolina than they had been in Georgia. "Here is where treason *began,*" a private said, "and, by God, here is where it shall end!" Few houses in their path were left standing.

In Washington, on January 31, 1865, Congress voted 119 to 56 to pass the Thirteenth Amendment, to abolish slavery, then sent it to the states for ratification.

The following day, Salmon P. Chase, once Lincoln's Secretary of the Treasury and now Chief Justice of the United States, admitted a Massachusetts lawyer named John Rock to practice before the Supreme Court. Six years earlier, in the Dred Scott decision, Chase's predecessor had ruled that blacks could never be citizens. John Rock was a dentist, physician, and orator as well as a Boston attorney, and he spoke both French and German. He was also black.

Five days later, on February 6, the Confederate Congress gave Robert E. Lee overall command of all that was left of the Confederate armies. Hundreds of his men were deserting every day, cold, hungry, barefoot, driven by desperate letters from their families back home. "We haven't got nothing in the house to

General Robert E. Lee, photographed by Mathew Brady on the back porch of his Richmond home, just one week after surrendering his army.

A southern refugee family loads what it can aboard a wagon before taking to the road.

eat but a little bit of meal," one woman wrote her soldier husband. "Try to get off and come home and fix us all up some and then you can go back. If you put off coming, t'wont be no use to come, for we'll all . . . be out there in the garden in the graveyard with your ma and mine."

The back roads of the South were filled with Confederate refugees. One woman wrote that the road from Baton Rouge was "a heart-rending scene. Women searching for their babies . . . others sitting in the dust and crying and wringing their hands. All the talk was of burning homes, houses knocked to pieces by balls, famine, murder, desolation."

Thousands fled all the way to Texas, in search of a new start. Thousands more flocked to Richmond, hoping that the Confederate government would care for them. There was little it could do; the government was falling apart.

States' Rights still came first. The Governor of Georgia was now threatening to secede from the Confederacy. The Governor of North Carolina refused to permit any but his own troops to wear the 92,000 uniforms he was hoarding. "If the Confederacy falls," Jefferson Davis said privately, "there should be written on its tombstone: *Died of a Theory.*"

On February 17, Columbia, South Carolina, fell to Sherman. "It is with a

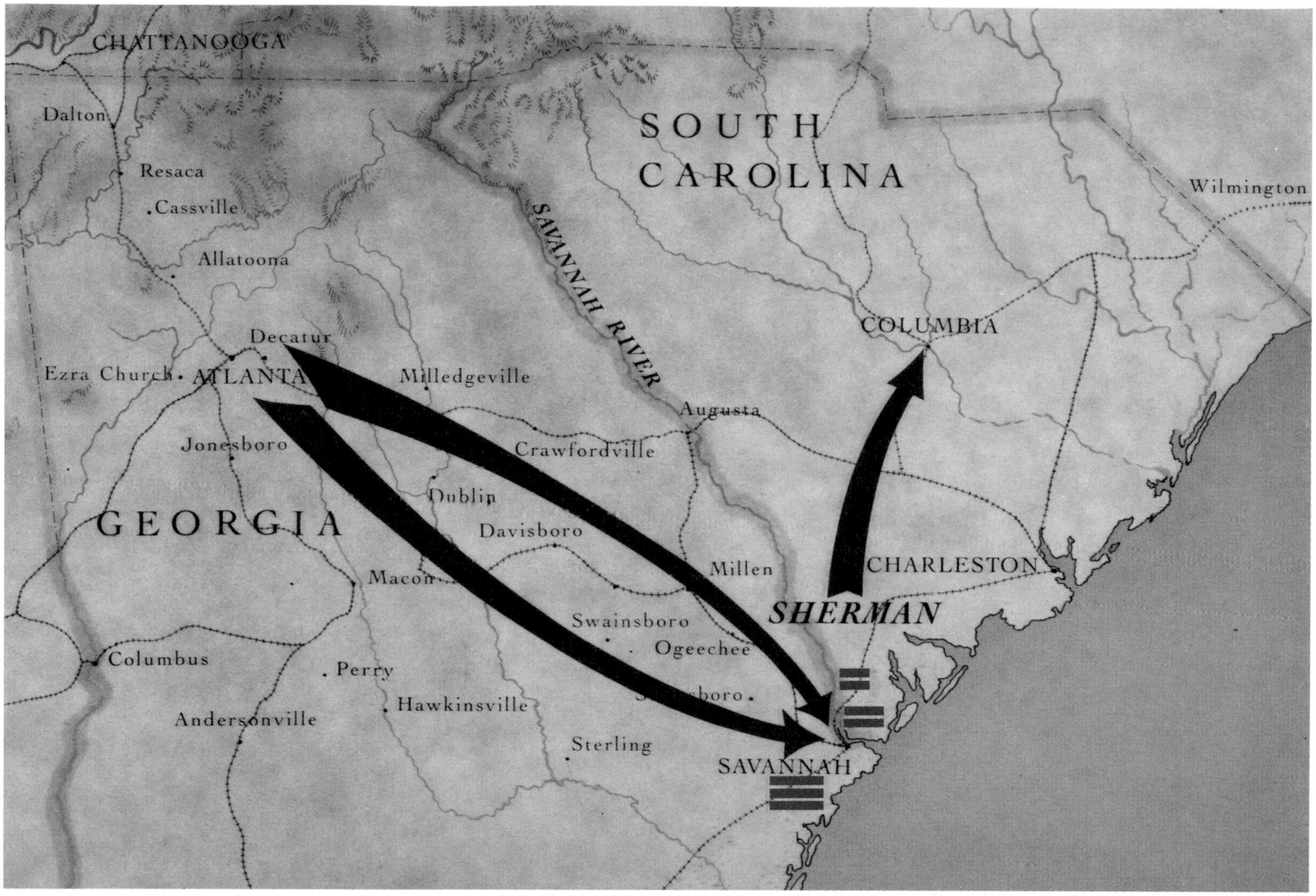

Sherman turns north: Having seized Savannah, and undeterred by relentless rain, rugged terrain, or sporadic resistance, Sherman ordered his Union armies to move into South Carolina on January 17. They laid waste to much of the state where the rebellion began and reached its capital, Columbia (right), in less than a month. Southerners blamed Sherman for setting Columbia ablaze, although the fire seems to have begun among cotton bales lit by retreating rebel cavalry before his army ever reached the city. In any case, Sherman said, "Though I never ordered it, and never wished it, I have never shed any tears over the event, because I believe that it hastened what we all fought for, the end of the war."

feeling of proud exultation that I write the date of Columbia," a Federal soldier wrote.

> We have conquered and occupy the capital of the haughty state that instigated ... the treason which has brought on this desolating war.... The beautiful capitol bears the marks of Yankee shot and shell, and the old flag which the Rebels insulted at Sumter now floats freely in the air from the housetops of the central city of South Carolina."

To a seventeen-year-old Confederate girl, that same old flag was "a horrid sight! What a degradation! After four long bitter years of bloodshed and hatred, now to float there at last... that hateful symbol of despotism."

Like Atlanta, Columbia was set ablaze: Sherman blamed retreating Confederates; southerners accused drunken Union men. "The wind moans among the bleak chimneys and whistles through the gaping windows..." a local woman noted. "The market is a ruined shell ... its spire fallen in,—the old bell, 'Secessia,' that had rung out every state as it seceded, lying half-buried in the earth."

That same day, Fort Sumter surrendered to the seaborne Union force that had besieged it for almost two years. "*This* disappointment," Jefferson Davis admitted, "to me is extremely bitter."

The U.S. Capitol, its dome at last completed, on the morning of Lincoln's second inauguration, March 4, 1865. "I like to stand aside," Walt Whitman wrote, "and look a long, long while up at the dome. It comforts me, somehow." The actor John Wilkes Booth (opposite below) was an interested spectator as Lincoln (opposite above) called for a "just and lasting peace."

Inauguration Day, March 4, was cold and windy in Washington, just as it had been four years earlier. But the U.S. Capitol was now complete, its soaring new iron dome at last in place, crowned by a great bronze Liberty.

Lincoln was again both gentle and unequivocal.

> Fondly do we hope—fervently do we pray—that this mighty scourge of war may speedily pass away. Yet if God wills that it continue until all the wealth piled by the bondman's two hundred and fifty years of unrequited toil shall be sunk, and until every drop of blood drawn with the lash shall be paid by another drawn with the sword, as was said three thousand years ago, so still must be said, "The judgments of the Lord are true and righteous altogether."
>
> With malice towards none; with charity for all; with firmness in the right as God gives us to see the right, let us strive on to finish the work we are in; to bind up the nation's wounds; to care for him who shall have borne the battle and for his widow, and his orphan—to do all which may achieve and cherish a just and lasting peace among ourselves, and with all nations.

"I am a tired man," Lincoln said afterward. "Sometimes I think I am the tiredest man on earth."

The President rode back to the White House from the ceremonies with ten-year-old Tad at his side, and without the clattering escort that had surrounded him in 1861. The war was nearly over; there was no longer much need to worry about his safety.

Among the invited guests at the Inauguration had been the young actor John Wilkes Booth. Later, it would occur to him that his vantage point

overlooking the oath-taking had offered him "an excellent chance . . . to kill the President, if I had wished."

Booth was a successful performer. Not as good as his father, Junius Brutus Booth, had been, or his older brother, Edwin, was. But impressive enough to earn $20,000 a year. Lincoln himself had gone to see him in *The Marble Heart* a week before he spoke at Gettysburg.

But Booth was persuaded he belonged at the center of a much larger stage. Born and raised in Maryland, he was a feverish believer in slavery and white supremacy. He told his sister he was a spy who smuggled quinine south, he was briefly detained once for saying the northern government should go to hell, and he may have at least been in touch with the Confederate Secret Service.

Yet, during four years of war, he had not been able to bring himself actually to *fight* for the southern cause. "I have begun to deem myself a coward," he confided to his diary, "and to despise my own existence."

His mind fixed on Lincoln as the tyrant responsible for all the country's troubles—and his own. "Lincoln will become *King* of America," he warned. "You'll see, you'll see, *re-election means succession.*"

"Assassination is not an American practice or habit, and one so vicious and so desperate cannot be engrafted into our political system. This conviction of mine has steadily gained strength since the civil war [began]. Every day's experience confirms it."

SECRETARY OF STATE WILLIAM H. SEWARD, 1864

Booth's circle (clockwise from top left): Lewis Powell, alias Lewis Paine; George A. Atzerodt; David E. Herold; Mary Surratt.

He hatched a scheme to kidnap the President and exchange him for Confederate prisoners of war, and gathered a worshipful band of malcontents willing to help him out—provided he paid for their room and board: Lewis Powell, a wounded Confederate veteran who had sworn allegiance to the Union; David E. Herold, a druggist's clerk, possibly retarded; George Atzerodt, a German-born wagon painter, barely able to make himself understood in English; John H. Surratt, a sometime Confederate spy, whose widowed mother, Mary, kept a Washington boardinghouse where Booth and his admirers sometimes met.

On the night of March 17, Booth and his accomplices, all wearing masks, rode out to the Soldiers Home on the outskirts of the city, where the Lincolns sometimes slept, to seize their prize. The President was not there. "So goes the world," Booth wrote in apparent resignation. "Might makes right."

One of Lee's first acts as overall commander was to reappoint Joseph E. Johnston as head of the Confederate forces in the Carolinas. At Bentonville, North Carolina, on March 19, Johnston tried to halt Sherman's relentless advance. The wily old Confederate was game, but his men numbered just

"I daily part with my raiment for food. We find no one who will exchange eatables for Confederate money. So we are devouring our clothes."

MARY CHESNUT

The rooftops of Richmond, looking across the James toward Manchester, where the riverfront flour mills stood empty and idle in the spring of 1865.

20,000, and the Union generals could muster 100,000 against him. Johnston limped from the field after three days of fighting, leaving 2,600 men behind.

Sherman's march continued.

Grant and Lee had faced one another in front of Petersburg for nine months now. Slowly, steadily, Grant had extended his trenches to the left; Lee's line had been forced to stretch, too, but his army was shrinking not growing. Sixty thousand soldiers had deserted.

He begged Davis and the Confederate Congress for more troops, more supplies, but there were none to give. "I have been up to see the Congress," Lee told his son, "and they do not seem able to do anything except eat peanuts and chew tobacco, while my army is starving. . . . [W]hen this war began I was opposed to it, and I told those people that unless every man should do his whole duty, they would repent it; . . . And now they will repent."

A single stick of firewood cost five dollars in Richmond. The price of a barrel of flour had risen to $425—when one could be found. "The surgeons and matrons," wrote a hospitalized Confederate soldier, "ate rats and said they were as good as squirrels, but, having seen the rats in the morgue running over the bodies of the dead soldiers, I had no relish for them."

Lee asked that slaves now be armed to defend the Confederacy. "We must decide," he said, "whether the Negroes shall fight for us, or against us." Those willing to fight, he added, should be freed after the war. There was a brisk debate, but on March 13, the Confederate Congress authorized black troops largely because, as the Richmond *Examiner* said, "The country will not deny General Lee *anything* he may ask for."

Six days later, spectators in Richmond saw an astonishing sight: a new Confederate battalion made up of three companies of white convalescents from Chimborazo Hospital and two companies of *black* hospital orderlies, all of them without uniforms, marching up Main Street to the strains of "Dixie" to begin drilling together on Capitol Square.

Those attending the March meeting aboard the *River Queen* (above) included (below, left to right) Sherman, Grant, Lincoln, and Porter.

ELEMENTS OF GREATNESS

At the end of March, Abraham Lincoln sailed down to City Point, Virginia, to confer with his commanders aboard U. S. Grant's floating headquarters, the *River Queen*. William Tecumseh Sherman, who interrupted his march through the Carolinas to attend, had met the President only once before, in 1861, and had not been impressed. Lincoln, he had said then, was a weak and partisan politician, unequal to his task.

The talks lasted two days. Grant, Sherman, and Admiral David Porter detailed plans for one final concerted campaign against the Confederacy. Satisfied that victory seemed within reach at last, Lincoln also mused about the peace to follow.

If the rebels would lay down their weapons and go home, Sherman recalled his saying, they should be welcomed back as citizens of the United States.

For Sherman, the meeting with the President was a revelation. "I never saw him again," he wrote later. "Of all the men I ever met, he seemed to possess more of the elements of greatness and goodness than any other."

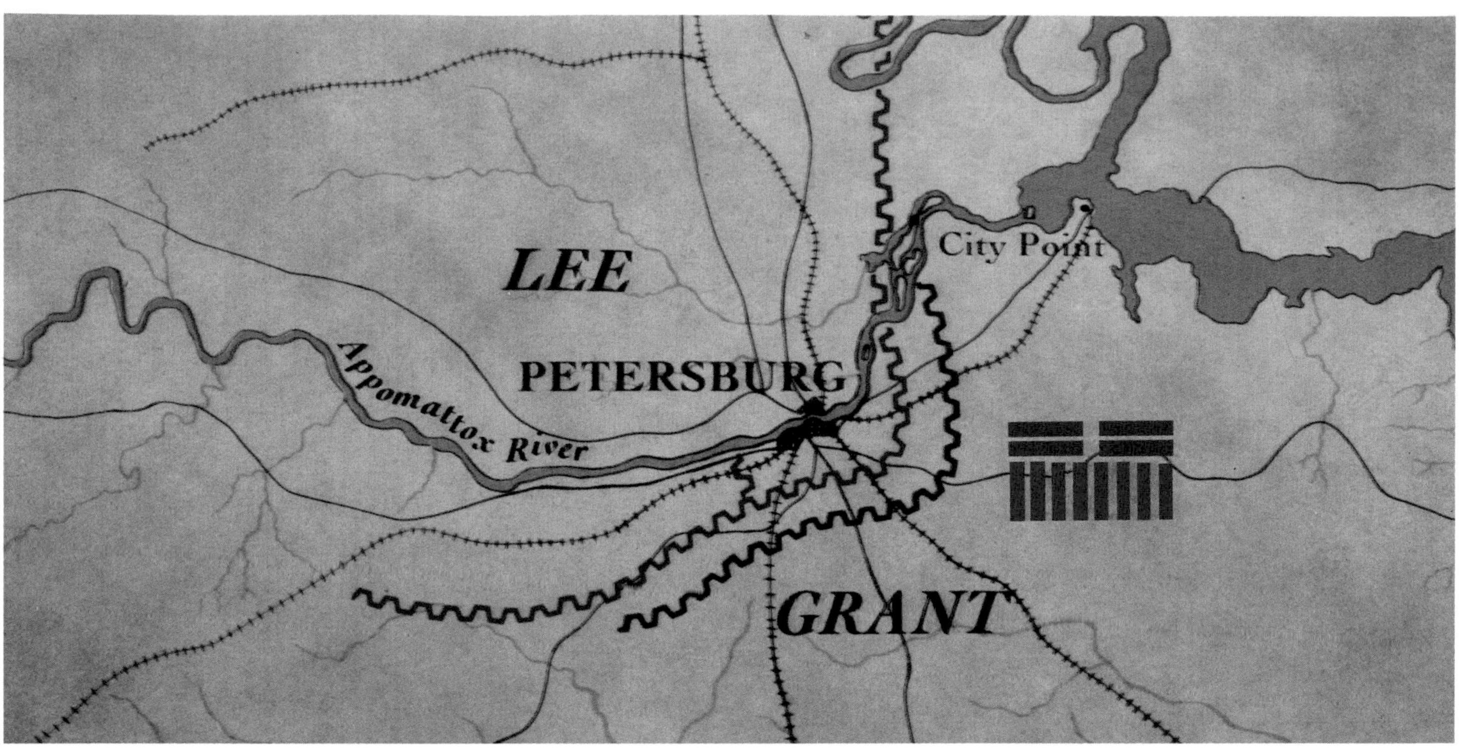

Trench warfare at Petersburg: By the spring of 1865, the lines at Petersburg—where, U. S. Grant said, "I mean to end the business"—ran for fifty-three miles. The efficient Union war machine kept its army fed, supplied, and reinforced from its constantly restocked depots at City Point, while the Confederate army—ill fed, ill clothed, and hopelessly outnumbered—steadily melted away.

THE ROAD TO APPOMATTOX

The thinning Confederate lines around Petersburg finally extended fifty-three miles. Grant's force had grown to 125,000. Lee's had dwindled to 35,000. "My own corps was stretched," John B. Gordon remembered, "until the men stood like a row of vedettes, fifteen feet apart. . . . It was not a line; it was the mere *skeleton* of a line." Soon the gaps between the men stretched to twenty feet.

Lee's only hope lay in moving his army safely out of the trenches and to the southwest, to link up with Johnston in the hills of North Carolina.

Grant wanted to ensure that he did not get away.

Lee moved first. On March 25, Confederates under Gordon mounted a sudden night assault that briefly won possession of an earthwork called Fort Stedman before superior Union firepower drove them off. It was merely "a little rumpus," Lincoln reported to his Secretary of War.

Grant counterattacked, sending Phil Sheridan, two infantry corps, and 12,000 cavalry racing around Lee's flank to block Lee's exit at a crossroads called Five Forks. There, on April 1, they routed a Confederate division under George Pickett, taking 4,500 prisoners. "They had no commanders," a northern newspaperman noted, "at least no orders, and looked for a guiding hand. A few more volleys, a new and irresistible charge . . . and with a sullen and tearful impulse, five thousand muskets are flung upon the ground."

When Grant got the news he simply said, "All right," and ordered an all-out Union attack all along the Petersburg line for 4:30 the next morning. Slowly, relentlessly, his men drove the Confederates out of their trenches. Among the southern dead left behind were old men and shoeless boys as young as fourteen.

The beginning of the end: Federal troops guard rebel prisoners (left) captured by Philip Sheridan at the Battle of Five Forks on April 1, 1865; this victory served as a signal for Grant to redouble his pressure on Petersburg. When the Union forces finally occupied the rebel trenches they found them still littered with Confederate dead (below): "[O]ld men with silver locks lay dead . . . side by side with mere boys of thirteen or fourteen," wrote Major Washington Roebling. "It almost makes one sorry to have to fight against people who show such devotion for their homes and their country." At the right, a Union supply train moves through Petersburg. "We sat all day in the front room," a local woman wrote, "watching the splendidly equipped host as it marched by . . . on its way to capture Lee."

A. P. Hill, whose death added to Lee's woes during his retreat from Petersburg.

A. P. Hill, who had served Lee faithfully in a dozen battles and had staved off disaster at Sharpsburg, could do nothing for him now. Two Union infantrymen shot him through the heart as he rode between the lines. "He is at rest . . ." Lee said, "and we who are left are the ones to suffer."

As the Union columns started into Petersburg, Lee's army slipped across the Appomattox. "This is a sad business," Lee told an aide. "It has happened as I told them in Richmond it would happen. The line has been stretched until it is broken."

Jefferson Davis was attending ten-o'clock services that Sunday morning at St. Paul's Episcopal Church in Richmond. His wife and children had already left the city for safety farther south. The sexton handed him a message from his commander. A woman seated near Davis watched him read it: "I plainly saw the sort of gray pallor that came upon his face as he read [the] scrap of paper thrust into his hand."

"My lines are broken in three places," the note said. "Richmond must be evacuated this evening."

Davis hurried from the church, and ordered that his government move to Danville, 140 miles to the south. He took only a few belongings with him, but entrusted a heroic marble bust of himself to a slave, instructing him to hide it from the Yankees so that he would not be ridiculed.

The President of the Confederacy and his cabinet boarded the last train—a series of freight cars, each bravely labeled "Treasury Department," "Quarter Masters Department," "War Department." It was "Government on Wheels," said one man who watched it pass.

A slave dealer named Lumpkin failed to get his coffle of fifty chained slaves

Occupied Richmond: Former slaves (opposite left) freed by the Federals wait aboard barges for the teams of mules that will tow them away from the city; at the far end of Main Street (above), a long line of Union wagons stretches into the distance. Local people never forgot the shock of seeing their first Yankees. "I saw a Confederate soldier on horseback pause . . . under my window," one woman recalled. "He wheeled and fired behind him, rode a short distance, wheeled and fired again. . . . Coming up the street rode a body of men in blue."

aboard the crowded train. A soldier with a bayonet barred him, until he unlocked his $50,000 worth of property in the street and let them go.

Chaos was all around them. Much of Richmond had been set afire by retreating Confederates. Mobs plundered shops, broke into abandoned houses. "Fierce crowds of skulking men and coarse . . . women gathered before the stores . . ." an eyewitness remembered. "Whiskey ran in the gutters ankle deep; and half-drunken women, and children even, fought to dip up the coveted fluid in tin pans, [and] buckets."

Rear Admiral Raphael Semmes blew up all that was left of the Confederate fleet anchored in the James, the shock shattering windows throughout the city. Then the fire on land spread to the Confederate arsenal, filled with gunpowder and artillery shells. A Confederate captain, on his way out of the city, described the bedlam left behind:

> Every now and then, as a magazine exploded, a column of white smoke rose . . . instantaneously followed by a deafening sound. The ground seemed to rock and tremble. . . . Hundreds of shells would explode in the air and send [down] their iron spray. . . . As the immense magazines of cartridges ignited, the rattle as of thousands of musketry would follow, and then all was still, for the moment, except the dull roar and crackle of the fast-spreading fires.

Union troops occupied the city the next day, cheered by ecstatic crowds of blacks, and did their best to restore order. "Our . . . servants were completely crazed," a Richmond matron noted. "They danced and shouted, men hugged

each other, and women kissed.... *Imagine* the streets crowded with these people!"

Two Union officers spurred their horses to the deserted Confederate Capitol. "I sprang from my horse," remembered Lieutenant Livingston de Peyster of New York, "first unbuckling the Stars and Stripes [from my saddle], [and] with Captain Loomis L. Langdon, Chief of Artillery, I rushed up to the roof. Together, we hoisted the first large flag over Richmond and on the peak of the roof drank to its success."

"Exactly at eight o'clock," a Richmond woman noted, "the Confederate flag that fluttered above the Capitol came down and the Stars and Stripes were run up.... We covered our faces and cried aloud. All through the house was the sound of sobbing. It was as the house of mourning." Nearby, another woman remembered, "We tried to comfort ourselves by saying in low tones (for we feared spies even in our servants) that the capital was only moved temporarily... that General Lee would make a stand and repulse the daring enemy, and that we would yet win the battle and the day. Alas, Alas, for our hopes."

Mrs. Robert E. Lee, too disabled by arthritis to travel, remained in Richmond. The Union commander posted a guard before her house to ensure no harm came to her—a black cavalryman. Mrs. Lee complained that the presence of a black soldier on her doorstep was "perhaps an insult," and was assigned a new guard, a white Vermonter—to whom she sent out meals on a little tray.

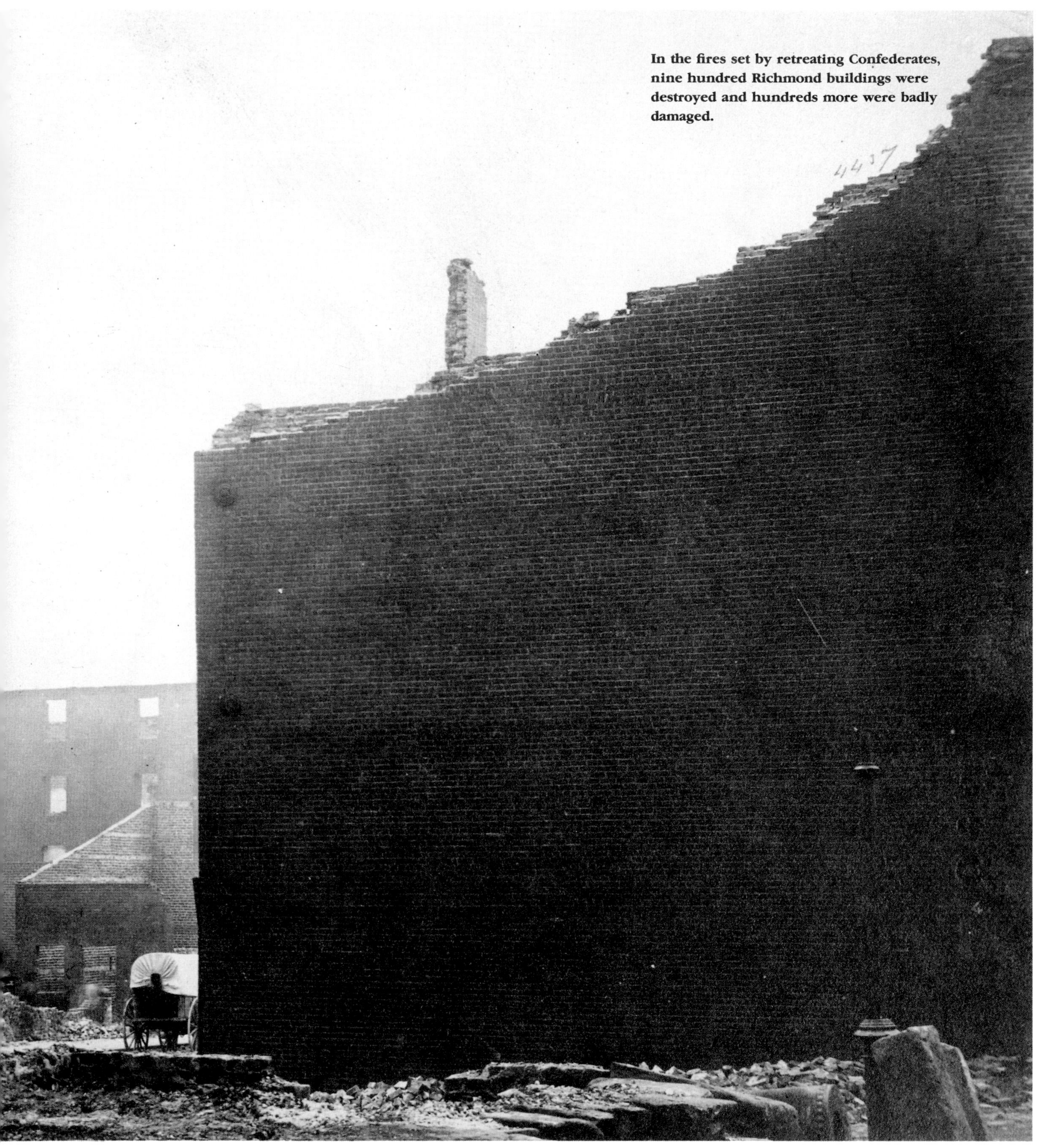

In the fires set by retreating Confederates, nine hundred Richmond buildings were destroyed and hundreds more were badly damaged.

The American flag, flying above the State House at Richmond (left), and draped over the door of the Confederate Executive Mansion (inset). "Ah, it is a bitter pill," wrote Judith Brockenbrough, a member of the family that had occupied the house before the war. "I would that dear old house, with all its associations, so sacred to Southerners . . . had shared in the general conflagration. Then its history would have been unsullied."

On April 3, Abraham Lincoln and his son Tad arrived at Rockett's Wharf aboard a small barge. "Thank God I have lived to see this," he said. "It seems to me that I have been dreaming a horrid nightmare for four years, and now the nightmare is over."

Blacks mobbed the President, laughing, singing, weeping for joy, kneeling before him, straining to touch his hand. "I know I am free," said one man, "for I have seen Father Abraham and felt him."

"Richmond has fallen—and I have no heart to write about it. . . . They are too many for us. Everything lost in Richmond, even our archives. Blue-black is our horizon."

MARY CHESNUT

Lincoln was taken aback. "Don't kneel to me," he said. "You must kneel to God only, and thank Him for your freedom."

The President walked about a mile through the smoking city, surrounded by a sea of joyous blacks, then loped up the steps of the Confederate White House, now Union headquarters. When he sat down at Jefferson Davis's desk, the troops outside burst into cheers.

A reporter for the New York *World* took a walk through the Confederate capital that evening.

> There is a stillness, in the midst of which Richmond, with her ruins, her spectral roofs . . . and her unchanging spires, rests beneath a ghastly, fitful glare. . . . We are under the shadow of ruins. From the pavements where we walk . . . stretches a vista of devastation. . . . The wreck, the loneliness, seem interminable. . . . There is no sound of life, but the stillness of the catacomb, only as our footsteps fall dull on the deserted sidewalk, and a funeral troop of echoes bump . . . against the dead walls and closed shutters in reply, and this is Richmond. Says a melancholy voice: "And this is Richmond."

Swathed in black, Richmond women drift through the streets of their ruined city.

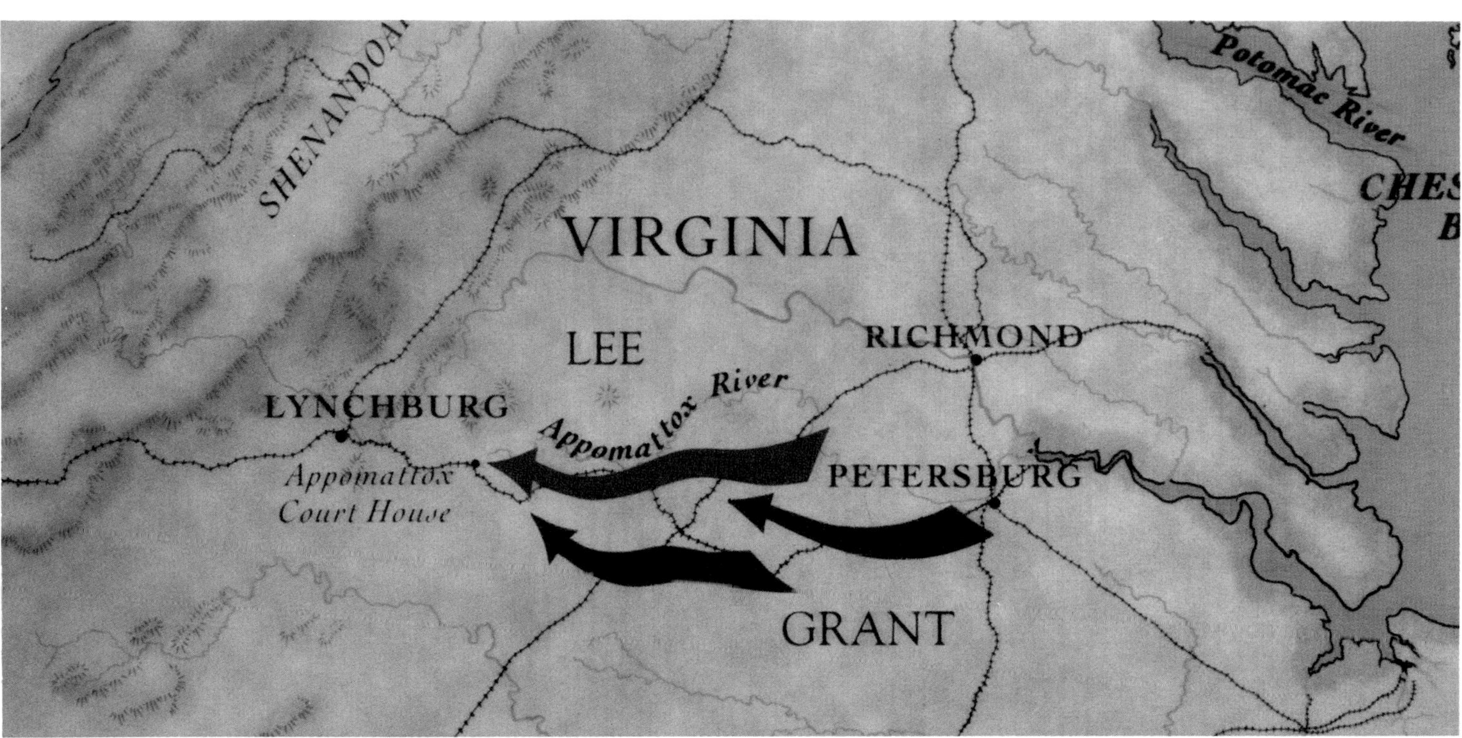

Lee's last campaign: Forced from his trenches at Petersburg on April 2, 1865, the Confederate commander led the remnant of his army westward in a desperate quest for food. Grant's huge force followed eagerly along behind.

Lee's army moved west, the Federals in constant pursuit. His first objective was Amelia Courthouse, where he had asked the Confederate Commissary Department to have ready for him the hundreds of thousands of rations his men would need if they were to fight on.

"On and on, hour after hour," wrote John B. Gordon, whose task it was to cover the retreat, "from hilltop to hilltop, the lines were alternately forming, fighting, and retreating, making one almost continuous battle. A boy soldier came running by at the top of his speed. When asked why he was running, he shouted back, '... I'm running 'cause I can't fly!'"

Their commander did his best to keep their spirits up. "General Lee was riding slowly along the line of ... tangled wagons ..." his physician noted. "He rode erect, as if *incapable* of fatigue.... From his manner no man would have discovered that which he so well knew, that his army was melting away, that his resources were exhausted."

But he was sorely discouraged when his hungry army finally reached Amelia on April 3, to find not a single ration stored there—somehow, Lee's request had never reached the commissary officials—and when foragers fanned out through the Virginia countryside to beg farmers for whatever food they could spare, they returned with almost nothing.

The next day, Jefferson Davis—now at Danville and about to flee farther south—issued a proclamation pledging that the army would fight on.

> Relieved from the necessity of guarding cities ... with our army free to move from point to point ... nothing is now needed to render our triumph certain but ... our own unquenchable resolve.... No peace [will ever] be made with the infamous invaders.

One hundred and twenty-five thousand Federal troops were closing in from three sides on Lee's 25,000 as they resumed their westward march, sustaining themselves now on handfuls of dried corn originally meant for the horses.

The pursuing Union soldiers were hungry, too: in their zeal to be in at the kill, they pushed far ahead of their supply wagons. The rebels staggered on, scattering weapons and bedrolls in their wake, their numbers steadily diminishing as some famished troops left the line of march in search of scraps to eat and others slipped away simply to surrender. A Union trooper, musket in hand, came upon a ragged southerner, cooling his feet in a stream. "I've got you this time!" he shouted. "Yes," said the rebel, too tired even to stand. "You've got me, and a hell of a git you got."

The Confederate commanders, as dazed by hunger and exhaustion as their men, allowed their lines to become fragmented as they approached a place called Sayler's Creek on April 6, and Federal forces gleefully took advantage of the opportunity to attack. Lee's haggard men fought with special desperation against overwhelming odds. "I saw numbers of men kill each other with bayonets and the butts of muskets and even bite each other's throats and ears and noses, rolling on the ground like wild beasts," a Confederate officer remembered. "I saw a young fellow of one of my companies join the muzzle of his musket against the back of the head of his most intimate friend, clad in a Yankee overcoat, and blow his brains out. I well remember the demoniacal triumph with which that simple country lad . . . clubbed his musket and whirled savagely upon another victim." But in the end, some eight thousand Confederates were lost or taken prisoner, a third of Lee's army.

Phil Sheridan wired Grant: "If the thing is pressed, I think that Lee will surrender." Lincoln answered, "Let the *thing* be pressed."

"Though not entertaining the opinion you express on the hopelessness of further resistance on the part of the Army of N. Va. I reciprocate your desire to avoid useless effusion of blood, and therefore, before Considering your proposition, ask the terms you will offer on condition of its surrender."

ROBERT E. LEE
to Ulysses S. Grant, April 7, 1865

High Bridge over the Appomattox near Farmville, Virginia, was twice contested during Lee's retreat from Petersburg: on April 6, Confederates drove off Federals sent to burn it and thereby cut off the rebel retreat; after crossing over it the next day, the rebels ordered it set on fire to thwart Federal pursuers, but failed to destroy it.

"[P]eace *being my great desire, there is but one condition I would insist upon, namely: that the men and officers surrendered shall be disqualified for taking up arms again, against the Government of the United States."*

ULYSSES S. GRANT
to Robert E. Lee, April 8, 1865

Grant sent Lee a message:

> 5 p.m. April 7, 1865.
> The result of last week must convince you of the hopelessness of further resistance. . . . I . . . regard it as my duty to shift from myself the responsibility of any further effusion of blood, by asking of you the surrender of that portion of the Confederate States Army known as the Army of Northern Virginia.

An officer urged Lee to surrender. The general asked angrily what the country would think of him if he failed to fight on. "Country be damned!" said the officer. "There *is* no country. There has been no country, for a year or more. You're the country to these men."

The Confederate army was moving roughly parallel to the Appomattox River, a willow-fringed run that, in places, any country boy could jump, into a jug-shaped peninsula between it and the James. "There was but one outlet," a Confederate general wrote, "the neck of the jug at Appomattox Court House, and to that General Grant had the shortest road."

On April 8, Lincoln and his wife took a drive past a country cemetery on the outskirts of Petersburg. "It was a retired place," Mary Lincoln recalled,

> shaded by trees, and early spring flowers were opening on nearly every grave. It was so quiet and attractive that we stopped the carriage and walked through it. Mr. Lincoln seemed thoughtful and impressed. He said, "Mary, you are younger than I; you will survive me. When I am gone, lay my remains in some quiet place like this."

Sheridan again flanked Lee's army and captured two precious trainloads of supplies at Appomattox Station. There was no more hope of food for the Confederates.

That night, Lee and his weary lieutenants gathered around a campfire in the woods near Appomattox Court House. "[We] met in the woods at his headquarters," Gordon remembered, "by a low-burning bivouac fire. There was no tent, no table, no chairs, no camp stools. On blankets spread upon the ground or on saddles at the roots of trees, we sat around the great commander."

They were almost entirely surrounded, outnumbered nearly four to one, without food or hope of resupply or reinforcement.

Still, Lee ordered Gordon to make one more attempt at breaking out. Just 250 men remained in one of his "divisions"; one "brigade" had only eight. "The few men who still carried their muskets had hardly the appearance of soldiers . . ." a Virginia cavalry colonel remembered, "their clothes all tattered and covered with mud, their eyes sunken and lusterless . . . [yet still they were] waiting for General Lee to say where they were to face about and fight."

His first instinct was to do just that. "I will strike that man a blow in the morning," he said Saturday evening, April 8.

The next day was Palm Sunday. At dawn, just outside Appomattox Court House, Gordon's men drove Federal cavalry from their positions and swept forward to the crest of a hill. Below them, a solid wall of blue was advancing—the entire Union Army of the James.

"Lee couldn't go forward," a private in that army said, "he couldn't go backward, and he couldn't go sideways."

Lee knew it was over. The North had nearly a million men under arms; the South fewer than 100,000. "There is nothing left for me to do," he told his aides, "but to go and see General Grant and I would rather die a thousand deaths." A tearful aide asked him what he thought history would say of his having surrendered his army in the field. Hard things, Lee answered. "But that is not the question, Colonel: the question is, is it right to surrender this army? If it is right, then I will take all the responsibility."

Shortly before noon, Lee dispatched a white flag—a white towel, in fact—along with a note, into the Union lines. Grant and his officers were resting in a field when a horseman galloped up behind them, "at full speed," a reporter noted, "waving his hat above his head, and shouting at every jump." The Union commander had been suffering from a pounding headache. He opened the envelope, looked at it, then asked his friend General John Rawlins to read it aloud: Lee would surrender. "No one looked his comrade in the face," a reporter noted. "Finally, Colonel Duff, chief of Artillery, sprang upon a log . . . and proposed three cheers. A feeble hurrah came from a few throats, when all broke down in tears."

The house in which Grant accepted Lee's surrender belonged to Wilmer McLean (above), whose fate it was, a southern officer wrote, to be "in at the beginning and in at the death" of the Civil War. In the rendering of the scene in the McLean parlor on the opposite page, painted by Louis Guillaume just two years after the surrender, the two commanders are shown sitting together at a single table; actually, they sat at separate tables, some distance apart.

Grant himself said nothing, betrayed no more emotion, a witness said, than "last year's bird nest." But his headache had disappeared.

Lee dispatched Colonel Charles Marshall to Appomattox Court House to find a suitable building in which he and Grant might meet. The streets were almost deserted. Marshall stopped the first civilian he happened to see—Wilmer McLean, who had moved to this quiet little place to escape the war after the first battle of Bull Run had been fought across his backyard. McLean reluctantly agreed to loan the army his front parlor.

The Confederate commander arrived at the McLean house first, magnificent in a crisp gray uniform, an engraved sword at his side. "I have probably to be General Grant's prisoner," he explained to an aide, "and thought I must make my best appearance."

He waited half an hour for Grant to arrive. When he did appear, the Union commander wore a private's dirty shirt; his boots and trousers were splattered with mud; he had no sword.

The two men shook hands. "What General Lee's feelings were, I do not know," Grant later wrote. "As he was a man of much dignity, with an impassible face . . . his feelings . . . were entirely concealed from my observation."

The Federal commander did his best to ease the tension, reminding Lee that they had met once before, during the Mexican War. Lee said he had not been able to remember what Grant looked like. "Our conversation grew so pleasant that I almost forgot the object of our meeting," Grant said. Finally, "General Lee called my attention to the object."

The terms Grant offered were simple and generous. Confederate officers

could keep their side arms and personal possessions; officers and men who claimed to own their horses could keep them, too; and "each officer and man will be allowed to return to his home, not to be disturbed by the United States authorities."

Grant asked how many men Lee had and if they needed food. Lee said he no longer knew the number, but he was sure all were hungry. Grant offered 25,000 rations. "This will have the best possible effect upon my men," Lee said. "It will be very gratifying and do much toward conciliating our people."

Colonel Eli Parker, a Seneca Indian on Grant's staff, inscribed the articles of surrender for the two commanders to sign. The two men shook hands again. Lee left the house first, mounted Traveller, and started back toward his army. Grant remembered feeling "sad . . . and depressed at the downfall of a foe who

"Sunday April 9, 1865. Near Appomattox Court House, Va. Glory to God in the highest. Peace on Earth, good will to men! Thank God Lee has surrendered, and the war will soon end.... Some time in the afternoon we heard loud cheering at the front, and soon Major General Meade commanding the Army of the Potomac rode like mad down the road with his hat off shouting: 'the war is over and we are going home!' Such a scene only happens once in centuries.... I cried and laughed by turns. I was never so happy in my life."

ELISHA RHODES

Celebrating the surrender: Gleeful Union troops array themselves in front of the McLean house (above). Major General John Gibbon (left, at center of tree), escorted by winners of the Medal of Honor, pauses on his way to the War Department to present seventy-one captured Confederate battle flags to Secretary Edwin Stanton.

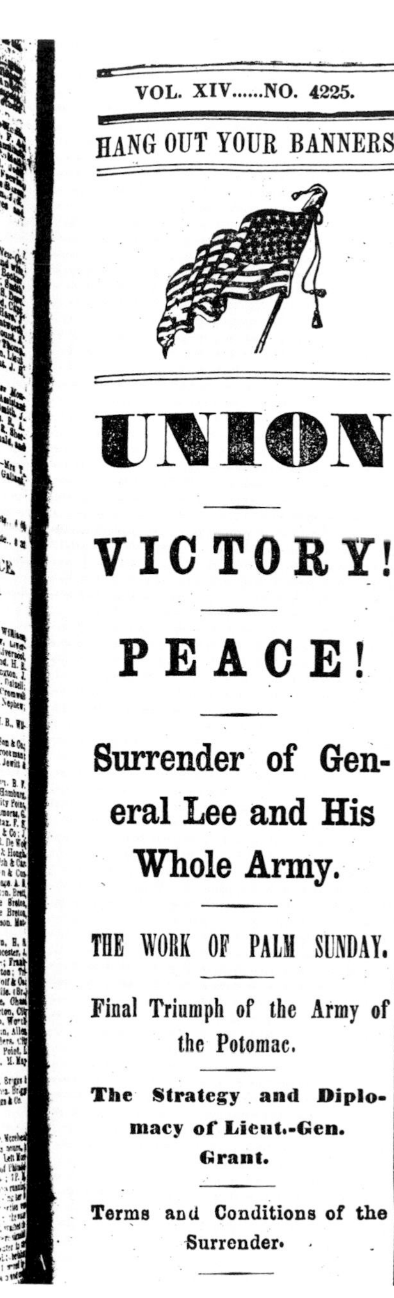
VOL. XIV......NO. 4225.

HANG OUT YOUR BANNERS

UNION

VICTORY!

PEACE!

Surrender of General Lee and His Whole Army.

THE WORK OF PALM SUNDAY.

Final Triumph of the Army of the Potomac.

The Strategy and Diplomacy of Lieut.-Gen. Grant.

Terms and Conditions of the Surrender.

had fought so long and valiantly and had suffered so much for a cause, though that cause was, I believe, one of the worst for which people ever fought."

Behind him, Union officers began to bargain over Wilmer McLean's parlor furniture. Sheridan paid twenty dollars for Grant's table; Custer rode off with another table over his head.

The Union soldiers began to cheer and Federal artillery started to fire salutes. Grant ordered them to stop: "The Confederates were now our prisoners and we did not want to exult over their downfall," he remembered. "The war [was] over. The Rebels [were] our countrymen again."

Lee's men lined the road to his camp. "As he approached," one remembered, "we could see the reins hanging loose . . . and his head was sunk low on his breast. As the men began to cheer, he raised his head and hat in hand he passed by, his face flushed, his eye ablaze." James Longstreet recalled that the men "looked upon him with swimming eyes. Those who could find voice said goodbye, those who could not speak . . . passed their hands gently over the sides of Traveller." Another officer recalled that each "group began in the same way with cheers and ended in the same way with sobs, all the way to his quarters. Grim, bearded men threw themselves on the ground, covered their faces with their hands, and wept like children. Officers sat on their horses and cried aloud." One old man called out, "I love you just as well as ever, General."

A crowd of weeping soldiers waited in front of Lee's tent. "Boys," he told them, "I have done the best I could for you. Go home now, and if you make as good citizens as you have soldiers, you will do well, and I shall always be proud of you. Goodbye, and God bless you all."

He turned and disappeared into his tent.

Three days later, the Army of Northern Virginia formally surrendered. General John B. Gordon, shot through the face and wounded four more times in the service of the Confederacy, led twenty thousand men toward the Union lines for the last time, not to do battle but to stack their arms and surrender their battle flags.

There to receive them was Major General Joshua Lawrence Chamberlain, himself wounded six times for the Union and still in pain from the bullet that had almost killed him before Petersburg. He watched this last Confederate advance with frank admiration:

> On they come, with the old swinging route step and swaying battle flags. In the van, the proud Confederate ensign. . . . Before us in proud humiliation stood the embodiment of manhood; men whom neither toils and sufferings, nor the fact of death . . . could bend from their resolve; standing before us now, thin, worn, and famished, but erect, and with eyes looking level into ours, waking memories that bound us together as no other bond; was not such manhood to be welcomed back into a Union so tested and assured? . . . On our part not a sound of trumpet more, nor roll of drum; not a cheer, nor word, nor whisper or vain-glorying, nor motion of man . . . but an awed stillness rather, and breath-holding, as if it were the passing of the dead!

"If one army drank the joy of victory, and the other the bitter draught of defeat, it was a joy moderated by the recollection of the cost at which it had been purchased, and a defeat mollified by the consciousness of many triumphs. If the victors could recall a Malvern Hill, an Antietam, a Gettysburg, a Five Forks, the vanquished could recall a Manassas, a Fredericksburg, a Chancellorsville, a Cold Harbor."

WILLIAM SWINTON
The New York Times

Gordon reined in his horse beside the Union commander. As he did so, he recalled, "[Chamberlain] called his men into line and as my men marched in front of them, the veterans in blue gave a soldierly salute to those vanquished heroes—a token of respect from Americans to Americans."

"At the sound of that machine-like snap of arms," Chamberlain remembered, "General Gordon started . . . [then] wheeled his horse, facing me, touching him gently with the spur so that the animal slightly reared, and, as he wheeled, horse and rider made one motion, the horse's head swung down with a graceful bow, and General Gordon dropped his sword-point to his toe in salutation."

The news spread fast across the country. A galloping rider shouted it to Sherman's 20th Corps in North Carolina, and one gleeful soldier bellowed back at him, "You're the sonofabitch we've been looking for all these four years!"

Rather than live in a restored Union with members of "the perfidious, malignant and vile Yankee race," Edmund Ruffin, the old Virginia secessionist who had fired one of the first shots at Fort Sumter, blew off the top of his head.

"We are scattered," Mary Chesnut wrote, "stunned; the remnant of heart left alive is filled with brotherly hate. . . . Whose fault? Everybody blamed somebody else. Only the dead heroes left stiff and stark on the battlefield escape."

In Washington, fireworks filled the sky, government buildings were illuminated, a great crowd gathered around the White House and called for Lincoln. He was too weary to make a formal speech. "I have always thought 'Dixie' one of the best tunes I ever heard," he told the crowd, "Our adversaries over the

In this painting by Richard Norris Brooke, weeping veterans of Lee's Army of Northern Virginia furl their banner for the last time.

Edmund Ruffin (above) could not bear to live for long in a reunited country in which the American flag had been restored to the fort he had helped to shell four years before (right).

way attempted to appropriate it, but I insisted . . . that we fairly captured it [yesterday]. I presented the question to the Attorney General and he gave it as his legal opinion that it is our lawful prize. I now request the band to favor me with its performance."

While the band played, a friend found John Wilkes Booth alone in his darkened room at the National Hotel just a few blocks away. Would he like to go out for a drink? "Yes," said Booth, who was now downing a quart of brandy at a sitting, "anything to drive away the blues."

ASSASSINATION

April 14, 1865, was Good Friday. It also marked the fourth anniversary of the surrender of Fort Sumter, and at noon, within the pulverized fortress, its old commander, Major Robert Anderson, stood at attention at the foot of the flagpole, ready to haul up the same ragged banner he had been forced to pull down in 1861.

An audience of northern dignitaries and some four thousand former slaves watched. When Anderson began to speak, a northern woman recalled:

> At first I could not hear him, for his voice came thickly. But in a moment he said clearly, "I thank God that I have lived to see this day," and after a few more words he began to hoist the flag. It went up slow and hung limp . . . a weather-beaten, frayed and shell-torn old flag, not fit for much more work, but when it had crept clear of the shelter of the walls, a sudden breath of wind caught it and it shook its folds and flew straight above us.

About the same time Major Anderson was raising his flag, John Wilkes Booth dropped by Ford's Theatre in Washington to pick up his mail. A stagehand told him the President and General Grant were both expected to attend the theater that night, to see Laura Keene in a British comedy, *Our American Cousin.*

It was Booth's cue. Kidnapping had not worked. Killing would. "Our country owed all our troubles to [Lincoln]," Booth wrote later. "God . . . made me the instrument of his punishment."

He assigned the other would-be kidnappers parts in his new plan. Lewis Powell was to kill Secretary of State William Seward, recovering from a carriage accident at home. George Atzerodt was to shoot Vice President Andrew Johnson.

That evening, General and Mrs. Grant begged off the theater party and left the city for Philadelphia. The Lincolns arrived and took their seats in the presidential box. With them were Major Henry Rathbone and his fiancée, Clara Harris.

The play stopped while the audience applauded and the orchestra played "Hail to the Chief."

The President seemed to be enjoying the play; his wife held his hand.

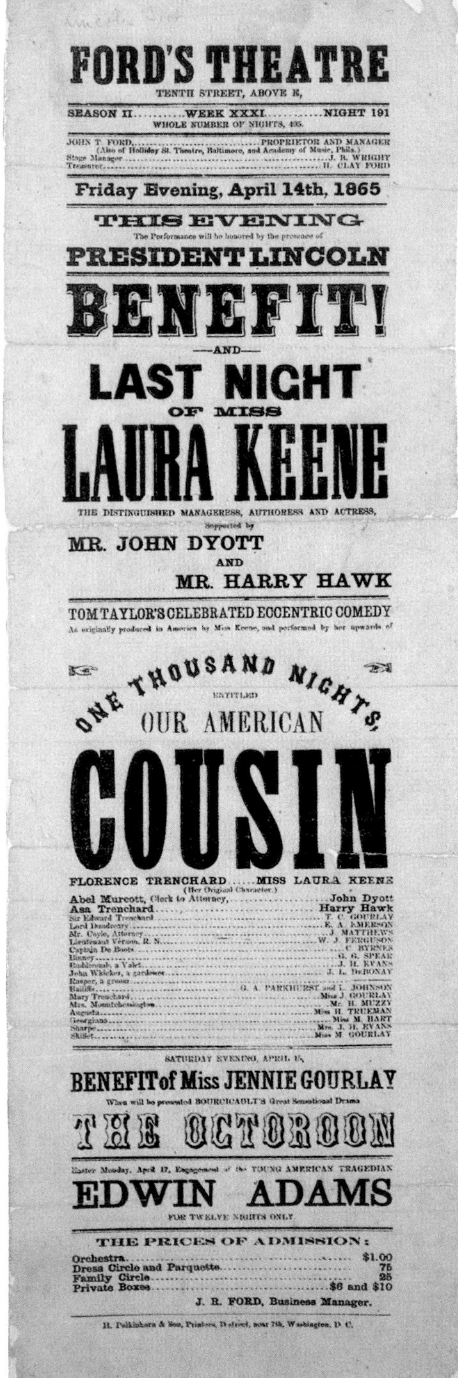

FORD'S THEATRE
TENTH STREET, ABOVE E,
SEASON II..........WEEK XXXI..........NIGHT 191
WHOLE NUMBER OF NIGHTS, 495.
JOHN T. FORD,..........PROPRIETOR AND MANAGER
(Also of Holliday St. Theatre, Baltimore, and Academy of Music, Phila.)
Stage Manager..........J. B. WRIGHT
Treasurer..........H. CLAY FORD

Friday Evening, April 14th, 1865

THIS EVENING
The Performance will be honored by the presence of
PRESIDENT LINCOLN

BENEFIT!
—AND—
LAST NIGHT
OF MISS
LAURA KEENE
THE DISTINGUISHED MANAGERESS, AUTHORESS AND ACTRESS,
Supported by
MR. JOHN DYOTT
AND
MR. HARRY HAWK

TOM TAYLOR'S CELEBRATED ECCENTRIC COMEDY
As originally produced in America by Miss Keene, and performed by her upwards of
ONE THOUSAND NIGHTS,
ENTITLED
OUR AMERICAN
COUSIN

FLORENCE TRENCHARD.....MISS LAURA KEENE
(Her Original Character.)
Abel Murcott, Clerk to Attorney,..........John Dyott
Asa Trenchard..........Harry Hawk
Sir Edward Trenchard..........T. C. GOURLAY
Lord Dundreary..........E. A. EMERSON
Mr. Coyle, Attorney..........J. MATTHEWS
Lieutenant Vernon, R. N...........W. J. FERGUSON
Captain De Boots..........C. BYRNES
Binney..........G. G. SPEAR
Buddicomb, a Valet..........J. H. EVANS
John Whicker, a gardener..........J. L. DeBONAY
Rasper, a groom..........
Bailiffs..........G. A. PARKHURST and L. JOHNSON
Mary Trenchard..........Miss J. GOURLAY
Mrs. Mountchessington..........Mr. H. MUZZY
Augusta..........Miss H. TRUEMAN
Georgiana..........Miss M. HART
Sharpe..........Mrs. J. H. EVANS
Skillet..........Miss M. GOURLAY

SATURDAY EVENING, APRIL 15,
BENEFIT of Miss JENNIE GOURLAY
When will be presented BOURCICAULT'S Great Sensational Drama
THE OCTOROON

Easter Monday, April 17, Engagement of the YOUNG AMERICAN TRAGEDIAN
EDWIN ADAMS
FOR TWELVE NIGHTS ONLY

THE PRICES OF ADMISSION:
Orchestra..........$1.00
Dress Circle and Parquette..........75
Family Circle..........25
Private Boxes..........$6 and $10
J. R. FORD, Business Manager.

H. Polkinhorn & Son, Printers, D street, near 7th, Washington, D. C.

Mrs. Montchessington: No heir to the fortune, Mr. Trenchard?
Asa Trenchard: Oh, no.
Augusta: What, no fortune?
Asa Trenchard: Nary red, it all comes to their barking up the wrong tree about the old man's property.

Booth downed two brandies at a nearby bar, then returned to the theater. He waited for the laughter to rise, then slipped silently into the President's box. He held a dagger in his left hand, a derringer pistol in his right.

Mrs. Montchessington: Augusta, dear, to your room.
Augusta: Yes, Ma. The nasty beast!
Mrs. Montchessington: I am aware, Mr. Trenchard, that you are not used to the manners of good society.
Asa Trenchard: Don't know the manners of good society, eh? Well, I guess I know enough to turn *you* inside out, you sockdoligizing old man-trap—

Booth fired his pistol, slashed at Major Rathbone with his dagger, vaulted over the front of the box, catching his right spur in the draped flag, and landed onstage, breaking his left leg.

He waved his dagger and shouted something to the stunned audience. Some thought it was "*Sic semper tyrannis!*"—"Thus be it ever to tyrants," Virginia's state motto. Others heard it as "The South is avenged!" Then he hobbled offstage and out into the alley, where a scene shifter had been holding his horse, and clattered away.

Booth's bullet had entered the back of Lincoln's head, torn through his brain, and lodged behind his right eye. A surgeon from the audience pronounced the wound mortal.

Soldiers bore the unconscious President from the theater. "I was down at his feet with one of the fellows," one of them remembered, "and two men at his head, and the middle of him was sagging until . . . two others took him in the middle and we six . . . carried him out of the theater. . . . We had him out on the street about five minutes, until we found a place to put him."

A civilian finally directed them into a boardinghouse across Tenth Street. "We put him in a room on the first floor," the soldier recalled, "and laid him on the bed. When we took him into the room we had to get out. . . . They wouldn't let anybody in without it was a doctor or something."

Doctors could do nothing. Mary Lincoln implored her husband to speak to her and wept so inconsolably that Secretary of War Edwin Stanton led her from the room.

Gideon Welles hurried to the boardinghouse as soon as word reached him of what had happened. "The giant sufferer lay extended diagonally across the bed, which was not long enough for him. He had been stripped of his clothes. His large arms, which were occasionally exposed, were of a size which one would scarce have expected from his spare appearance. His slow, full respiration lifted the clothes with each breath he took. His features were calm and striking."

Cabinet officers stood by helpless all night, doubly shocked to hear that Booth's accomplice, Lewis Powell, had stabbed and seriously wounded

Souvenirs of murder: The poster at the left announces the President's planned visit to Ford's Theatre. The photograph above, made by Alexander Gardner in the spring of 1865, is often said to be the last ever made of Lincoln; the plate cracked while being developed and was discarded soon after a single print was made; presumably, Gardner thought he would have plenty of other opportunities to photograph the President. Within hours of the assassination, a boarder in the house to which Lincoln was carried had photographed the bed on which he died, its pillow still stained with his blood.

Seward, then run out into the street, shrieking, "I'm mad! I'm mad!" George Atzerodt had proved too frightened to carry out Booth's order to kill the Vice President.

At about six the next morning, Secretary Welles stepped outside for some air and found the streets filled with silent, anxious people. "A little before seven I went back into the room . . ." he remembered. "The death struggle had begun. Robert, his son, stood at the head of the bed. He bore himself well, but on two occasions gave way . . . and sobbed aloud, . . . leaning on the shoulder of Senator Sumner."

Abraham Lincoln died at 7:22 a.m.

The telegraph carried the news across the country in minutes. No President had ever before been murdered. People would remember for the rest of their lives where they were and what they felt and what the weather was like when they heard it. Elisha Rhodes was in camp at Burkesville, Virginia.

> Saturday April 15. We are having a rainy day . . . but I have my tent pitched and so feel quite comfortable. Mr. Miller is reading to pass away the time.
>
> Bad news has just arrived. Corporal Thomas Parker has just told Mr. Miller that President Lincoln was dead, *murdered*. . . . It seems that a man by the name of Booth shot him with a pistol while at the theatre last night. We cannot realize that our President is dead.

Walt Whitman was back home in Brooklyn: "Mother prepared breakfast—and other meals—as usual; but not a mouthful was eaten all day by either of us. We each drank half a cup of coffee; that was all. Little was said. We got every newspaper, morning and evening . . . and passed them silently to each other."

In Manhattan, George Templeton Strong wrote that he had been "expecting this. I am stunned, as by a fearful personal calamity, though I can see that this thing, occurring just at this time, may be over-ruled to our great good. . . . We shall appreciate him at last."

Gideon Welles walked the wet streets of Washington:

> On the Avenue in front of the White House were several hundred colored people, mostly women and children, weeping and wailing their loss. This crowd did not diminish through the whole of that cold, wet day; they seemed not to know what was to be their fate since their great benefactor was dead, and though strong and brave men wept when I met them, [the] hopeless grief [of those poor colored people] affected me more than almost anything else.

Lincoln's casket lay in state, first in the East Room of the White House, then in the rotunda of the Capitol. He was to be buried in Springfield, his adopted home. The small coffin of his son Willie was disinterred to make the journey with him. Mary Lincoln was too overcome with grief to go.

The funeral train took fourteen days and traveled 1,662 miles through the soft spring landscape, retracing the route Lincoln had taken to Washington five years earlier.

In Philadelphia, Lincoln's coffin lay in Independence Hall, where he had declared he would "rather be assassinated" than surrender the principles embodied in the Declaration of Independence. The double line of mourners stretched three miles.

In Manhattan, scalpers sold choice window positions along the route for four dollars and up. The procession lasted four hours. Blacks had been barred from the New York ceremonies, but a last-minute change of heart by the mayor permitted them to take part—provided they marched at the rear.

At Cleveland, no public building was thought big enough to hold the expected crowds and an outdoor pavilion was set up through which ten

New York's City Hall, draped in mourning: 160,000 mourners accompanied the hearse down Broadway beneath a thicket of signs: "The assassin's stroke but makes the fraternal bond the stronger"; "A nation's heart was struck!,"; "In sorrowing tears the nation's grief is spent"; "Mankind has lost a friend and we a President."

Lincoln's hearse arrives at the Cook County Courthouse in Chicago.

Beneath umbrellas, a double line of mourners shuffles toward the special pavilion set up in Cleveland's Monument Square.

The train that bore Lincoln home, photographed at West Philadelphia with one of the specially decorated engines that pulled it; the funeral car in which the bodies of the President and his son Willie rode was the second from the rear. It was at Philadelphia, on his way to Washington in 1861, that Lincoln said he would "rather be assassinated on the spot" than give up the great promise embodied in the Declaration of Independence and Constitution "that in due time the weights should be lifted from the shoulders of all men and that all should have an equal chance."

Lincoln lies in state inside New York's City Hall.

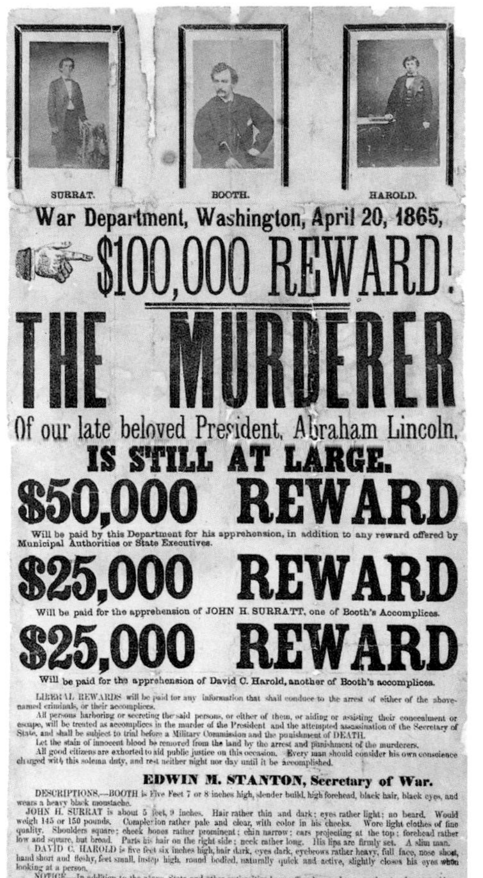

Journey's end: Five days after the poster above was issued, John Wilkes Booth was killed by Federal troops. At the right, the official Illinois delegation of mourners assembles in front of Lincoln's Springfield home before the start of the final funeral procession to Oak Ridge Cemetery (left), where townspeople and visitors watch as Lincoln's casket is placed in its temporary resting place. The massive monument beneath which he now lies was dedicated in 1874.

thousand mourners passed every hour, all day, despite a driving rain. There was a run on black drapery material in the city and many households had dyed their own. The rain caused scores of draped buildings to run with black.

In Chicago, the hearse was escorted by thirty-six maidens in white, one each for the states of the restored Union. A handful of members of the "Dramatic Profession of Chicago" bravely marched, too, to show that most actors were patriots.

It finally ended in Springfield on May 4. The coffin rode to the Illinois State House in a magnificent black-and-silver hearse borrowed from St. Louis, and lay open in the chamber of the House of Representatives, where Lincoln had warned that "a house divided against itself cannot stand." Among the thousands of people who shuffled past his bier were many who had known him in the old days—farmers from New Salem, law clients and rival attorneys, neighbors who had nodded to him each morning on his way to work.

General Joseph Hooker, in charge of the final leg of the long journey, led the slow march through a gentle rain to Oak Ridge Cemetery. Thousands of mourners watched as the coffins of Lincoln and his son were at last placed in a vault cut deep into the green hillside and filled with evergreens and sprays of spring flowers.

On April 26, Union cavalry trapped John Wilkes Booth in a Virginia tobacco barn. His accomplice David Herold surrendered, but Booth evidently preferred death. The soldiers had orders to take him alive, and the barn was set on fire to force him out, but an overeager sergeant, Boston Corbett, shot him in the back of the head. He was dragged to the porch of a nearby farmhouse.

MAY WE ALL MEET IN THE OTHER WORLD

Secretary of War Edwin Stanton and the new President, Andrew Johnson, were convinced Lincoln had been murdered under orders from the leaders of the defeated Confederacy.

Hundreds of southern sympathizers were detained without trial, and seven men and one woman were swiftly tried before a military commission. They were accused of having conspired not only with Booth but with a list of shadowy Confederate agents—and with Jefferson Davis himself, although no shred of credible evidence linking Booth and the Confederate President was ever produced.

All eight were found guilty.

The stagehand who held Booth's horse got eight years; three other men received life sentences. Four were sentenced to be hanged—Lewis Powell, George A. Atzerodt, David E. Herold, and Mary Surratt.

The executions took place before a sizable crowd in the Arsenal grounds at the Old Penitentiary Building on July 7.

The crowd fell quiet as the condemned climbed the thirteen steps and took their places on the scaffold. They sat in chairs while General J. F. Hartranft read out the charges. An umbrella was held over Mrs. Surratt, to shield her from the sun.

The nooses were adjusted. White hoods were slipped over their heads. Lewis Powell shouted, "Mrs. Surratt is innocent and doesn't deserve to die with us." George Atzerodt cried out, "Goodbye, gentlemen. May we all meet in the other world." General Winfield Scott Hancock clapped his hands, and soldiers knocked the front part of the platform out from under the conspirators (left). It took more than five minutes for the last of them to die.

"Tell my mother I died for my country . . ." he whispered. "I did what I thought was best." He asked to have his hands raised at the end, looked at them, and muttered, "Useless, useless."

The same day, Joseph Johnston surrendered what remained of his Army of Tennessee to Sherman. Elisha Rhodes got that news at Danville, Virginia.

> April 28. We have just received news that Johnston has at last surrendered and all our batteries are firing salutes. This is good news and the war is certainly over. . . . The roads were full of [Negroes] laughing and grinning. Of course we told them that they were free, but their masters would not believe it. At one place the overseers ordered the Negroes to go to work, and they refused. Some . . . came over to my camp for advice. When they returned they offered to work if paid for their labor. I do not know how the matter ended.

"Strange, (is it not?) that battles, martyrs, blood, even assassination should so condense—perhaps only really, lastingly condense—a Nationality."

WALT WHITMAN

Jefferson Davis, exhausted but still defiant, fled westward, hoping somehow to rally the Confederacy from a new base in Texas. On May 10, while in Kentucky, a Federal patrol mortally wounded the Confederate guerrilla leader William C. Quantrill. Union cavalry caught up with the former Confederate President and his dwindling entourage at Irwinville, Georgia. Davis was imprisoned in Fortress Monroe, kept in isolation in a cell kept perpetually lit, and made to wear chains, though he protested that "those are orders for a *slave,* and no man with a soul in him would obey such orders."

"Dear Varina," he wrote his wife, "this is not the fate to which I invited [you] when the future was rose-colored for us both; but I know you will bear it even better than myself, and that, of us two, I alone will ever look back reproachfully on my career."

Scattered fighting stuttered on in Louisiana, Alabama, and Mississippi—and in the far West, where on May 13, 1865, Private John J. Williams of the 34th Indiana became the last man to be killed in the Civil War, in a battle at Palmito Ranch, Texas. This final skirmish was a Confederate victory.

But still it was not quite over. Off the Pacific Coast, Captain James Iredell Waddell, commander of the Confederate raider *Shenandoah,* refused to believe his nation no longer existed. He would seize and burn twenty unarmed whaling ships in June, then sail all the way to Liverpool so that he could surrender to the British rather than the Yankees on November 6—seven months after Appomattox.

On the morning of May 23, 1865, the American flag flew at full staff above the White House for the first time since Lincoln's death. U. S. Grant and the new President, Andrew Johnson, stood side by side to watch the Grand Armies of the Republic pass in review down Pennsylvania Avenue from the Capitol.

The great procession of 150,000 men took two full days to pass, while thousands of schoolchildren lined the avenue, singing patriotic songs, waving flags, strewing the soldiers' path with flowers. The first day belonged to the Grand Army of the Potomac, Washington's own army, brilliantly uniformed, commanded by General George Gordon Meade, and marching one last time

"We have shared the incommunicable experience of war. We have felt, we still feel, the passion of life to its top.... In our youths, our hearts were touched by fire." OLIVER WENDELL HOLMES, JR.

"The pageant has passed. The day is over. But we linger, loath to think we shall see them no more together—these men, these horses, these colors afield."

JOSHUA LAWRENCE CHAMBERLAIN

The Grand Review: Triumphant Union troops march up Pennsylvania Avenue.

Among the dignitaries who sat beneath the flags emblazoned with the names of Union victories, enjoying the passing parade from the front row of the reviewing stand: General Grant, President Andrew Johnson, Secretary of the Navy Gideon Welles, and Generals Sherman and Meade.

with the effortless discipline mastered on a hundred marches from Bull Run to Appomattox. Only General George Armstrong Custer disturbed the formal majesty of the occasion, managing to pass the reviewing stand twice, once when he seemed uncharacteristically unable to control his horse and galloped past the dignitaries far ahead of his men, his long yellow hair whipping in the wind, and again after he had wheeled and returned to the head of his column.

That night, William Tecumseh Sherman fretted a little that his own lean, sunburned, shaggy troops, most of whom wore loose shirts and soft hats rather than crisp uniforms and képis, and who marched with a looser, longer stride than their eastern counterparts, might somehow seem less impressive when their turn came on the following day.

He needn't have worried. No one in Washington had ever heard such cheering as began at nine sharp the next morning, when, as bands began to blare "The Star-Spangled Banner," Sherman himself, battered slouch hat in hand, rode out onto Pennsylvania Avenue at the head of the great army he had led to the sea.

WHAT THE WAR MADE US

C. VANN WOODWARD

AFTER IT WAS ALL OVER AND THE FURY AND FEVER had died away, survivors of the Civil War were still haunted by the horror and madness of what had happened in the last few years. From John Brown at the beginning to John Wilkes Booth at the end of the killing, madness seemed to have taken over. Nothing appeared to go according to reason or as it was planned. Early in the war Nathaniel Hawthorne had taken a skeptical view of its course and its future. "No human effort, on a grand scale," he wrote, "has ever resulted according to the purpose of its projectors." He added ironically that "Man's accidents are God's purposes." Near the end of the war, in his second inaugural, Lincoln seemed to confirm Hawthorne's view. Whatever man's plans and purposes had been, "the Almighty has His own purposes," he said, with Calvinist resignation. "He gives to both North and South this terrible war."

Terrible it had been, terrible in its magnitude and its persistence, terrible in its ferocity, and its sickening cost in human life. There was nothing like it before or after in American history, and between the wars of Napoleon and those of the twentieth century, nothing comparable in European history. American lives lost in the Civil War exceed the total of those lost in all the other wars the country has fought added together. We think of Britain's losses in the First World War as bleeding her white, yet America's losses in the Civil War were proportionally greater. They were nearly twice as large in absolute terms as American losses in the Second World War, but to be proportionally as large, those of the late war would have had to be between six and seven times as large, some two and a half *million* deaths.

More terrible than the number of casualties was how they were inflicted—not by foreign enemies, but by fellow citizens. Despite the South's desire to call it a War Between the States, it *was* a civil war. Thousands of southerners fought for the Union, and thousands of northerners fought for the Confederacy—father against son, brother against brother, for the war divided families as well as states. To justify the mad things they were doing, both sides learned to live with paradox. Both armies sang a war song called "Battle Cry of Freedom" to the same music, but with different words. Southerners equated bondage for slaves with freedom for themselves and rebellion from the nation with loyalty to the Constitution. Northerners began the war as part of the world's largest slave republic, pledged to protect rights of slaveowners, but then in the midst of the war reversed themselves with the pledge to abolish slavery. Both sides waged relentless war as the only means of achieving peace. In the double-

Second Lieutenant J. Woods Price, 19th Virginia Cavalry, 1861.

J. Woods Price,
19th Virginia Cavalry Reunion, 1907.

think and truespeak of Civil War rhetoric lies a haunting anticipation of the Orwellian era.

Thinking back to the beginnings of the war at its end, the New York diarist George Templeton Strong wrote, "We have lived a century of common life since then." After Gettysburg, General George Meade wrote his wife that in ten days "I have lived as much as in the last thirty years." A junior official in diplomatic service during the war, Henry Adams wrote, "One does every day and without a second thought, what at another time would be the event of a year, perhaps of a life." The intensity of the wartime experience left on that generation marks that would remain with it long after the tension was released by the coming of peace.

The intensity of the ordeal and the tension underlying it sprang from the two coiled springs of doctrinaire absolutism that did so much to generate the conflict, one in the North, one in the South. Moralistic absolutism of the higher law versus legalistic absolutism of the Constitution: a head-on clash between "right" and "rights," morals and law. Presuming to act with divine guidance and to fulfill God's will, the higher-law abolitionists could tolerate no compromise, no legal obstruction, no due process, no majority consent. "One, on God's side, *is* a majority," declared Wendell Phillips. Total evil justified total war.

Equally sure of God's favor, the southern legalists could be as rigid and dogmatic about "rights" as their opponents were about "right," and no more given to peaceful compromise and halfway measures. Their appeal was to eternal principles, the iron rule of logic, and the sanctity of constitutional law. The southern absolutists contributed as much of the arrogance, the paranoidal suspicion, and the headlong recklessness that poisoned the wartime air as did their Yankee counterparts. Not that a small minority of extremists on both sides could have "caused" the war, but they did lend the fighting much of its apocalyptic righteousness ("As He died to make men holy . . .") and its hell-for-leather desperation (Jeb Stuart or Stonewall Jackson).

By the time the last casualty lists were posted and before the hospitals were cleared of the war's human wreckage, Americans had about had their fill of absolutism for a while. They were pretty sick of it. Four years of that kind of war had come near finishing off genuine antebellum radicalism up north. Emerson's anarchistic individualism and his assault on institutions had lost their appeal, and Emerson himself was marching to different drums, praising institutions and the blessings of civilization. Radicalism had become an anachronism. Just enough idealisms of the old abolitionist brand remained to write and pass the constitutional amendments protecting the rights of freedmen, but not enough to enforce them. Moral momentum of the war spirit was strong enough to demand of the South the moral fruits of a victory that had cost the lives of so many sons, but not strong enough to carry through with Reconstruction and assure those fruits.

The legalistic absolutism of the South took entirely new forms in the postbellum years. Legalists could still spare words for the defense of secession and States' Rights, but instead of dwelling on the eternal sanctity of the Constitution, they now sought ingenious means of evading it, as newly amended. Torturing the phrases of the new amendments with interpretations suitable to their own purposes, they succeeded in virtually nullifying the original intent. Talk of compromise and reconciliation between the sections filled the air. Whites of North and South contrived many reconciliations of differences, largely at the expense of blacks. The most important and durable of those was the Compromise of 1877, which in effect marked the abandonment of promises to the freedmen and forfeiting of some dearly won moral fruits of the Union victory.

The war had changed America profoundly. "The contest touches everything and leaves nothing as it found it," as a *New York Times* editorial saw it in October 1867. "Great rights, great interests, great systems of habit and of thought disappear during its progress. It leaves us a different people in everything." Two years later Professor George Ticknor of Harvard observed that the Civil War had opened a "great gulf between what happened before in our century and what has happened since, or what is likely to happen hereafter. It does not seem to me as if I were living in the country in which I was born."

The transformation took many shapes and forms, some more attractive than others. While quite aware of the less appealing forms that the war's heritage took, the late Robert Penn Warren pointed to a more benign legacy in the shaping of American pragmatism. William James gave the doctrine some of its more memorable expressions, and so did Oliver Wendell Holmes, Jr. With three serious wounds and many searing battle memories, the future justice left the war fed up with absolutes and ready to put his war experience into jurisprudence. Holmes placed experience above logic as "the life of the law," and preferred "the felt necessities of the time" to absolutes of the higher law. In this he echoed Lincoln, who felt that "it was better to make a rule for the practical matter in hand than to decide a general question."

Of course pragmatism could, and too often did, take the shape of expediency and opportunism to serve vulgar and selfish ends. "Compromise" in postwar usage came to mean abandonment of principle, and to be "pragmatic" came near meaning to be unprincipled. In that sense affairs of politics and government and transactions of business and market became increasingly "pragmatic." This was the slovenly, heedless generation to whose dubious ethics, spendthrift ways, and execrable taste Mark Twain gave a name that stuck, "the Gilded Age."

Former Private Charles A. Smith, Company C, 54th Massachusetts.

We have that period to thank for some of the most picturesque and unscrupulous politicians in the nation's chronicles. Not that their loot or their scandals rivaled recent records in size or number, but that they were so uninhibitedly flamboyant in their misconduct. Bewhiskered and obese, drooling tobacco juice and eating and drinking incredible amounts, they sometimes seemed devoid of shame. Into the hands of their likes were thrust the fabulous treasures and golden opportunities for statesmanship laid up by wartime idealists.

These included the Homestead Act of 1862, which placed in escrow half a continent, more than a billion acres of land for the landless, free for the taking—an opportunity unparalleled in world history. But the landless got precious little of the promised land, the great bulk of which slipped into possession of the favored and aggressive few who never thought of tilling it. While squandering those philanthropic opportunities, Gilded Age statesmen heedlessly squandered two more—long-due justice for two minorities, the black race in the South and the red race in the West. The legal foundations of a new order had been laid for both, built into the Constitution for the freedmen. The outcome, however, was much the same for both: racial subordination, white supremacy, and segregation for the red man as well as the black.

The new American economy of industries, cities, and railroads is sometimes attributed to the Civil War, since tremendous growth in all of these parts of the economy followed the war. Actually the war slowed down the growth of railroads, and historians still debate whether the war impeded more than it stimulated industrial progress. There can be no doubt, however, that the Civil War left its mark on the style, the speed, the bigness, and the recklessness of postwar economic development. "The close of the war," Senator John Sherman wrote his brother, General Sherman, had given "a scope to the ideas of leading capitalists," who now "talk of millions as confidently as formerly of thousands." Many of them, like Tom Scott and Andrew Carnegie, got their start in war supply operations. They proceeded with their conquest of an untamed West in much the same ruthless fashion with which Sherman had proceeded in Georgia. In manners and morals and in the ethics of gluttony the Gilded Age entrepreneurs were more than a match for the Gilded Age politicians, with whom they worked hand in glove.

The South proved to be more a field of operations and opportunity for the exploiters than a participant in the exploitation. Hers was the lot of the losers, the ruin and wreckage and bankruptcy of a lost war. It was the same war other Americans fought, but the South gained from it the "un-American" experience of defeat. Disarmed and occupied by the victors of the war, the South nevertheless won the peace, if the regime of white supremacy may be so called. But that did not spare the whites—and certainly not the blacks—the years of what would now be called "third-world" poverty, stagnation, failure, economic dependency, and exploitation.

From a longer perspective, however, all this should be viewed as the aftermath rather than the meaning of the war, the stench and debris left on the field of battle, not what took place there. These are not the images invoked by the mention of Shiloh and Antietam, Gettysburg and the Wilderness, Cold Harbor and Appomattox. Freeing the slaves and saving the Union were great historical results of the war, may have even explained and justified the war, but they could never subsume its full meaning in categories of right and wrong or in terms of national interest and political necessity. Important as were these moral and political consequences, we must probe deeper for profounder meaning, for truer understanding of the place the Civil War came to occupy in the American imagination, the fascination and wonder and awe it continues to inspire beyond anything else in our past.

Nothing in national experience approaches the poignancy of inner conflict, the anguish of self-inflicted wounds imposed by the Civil War—a war within, not only within the society or polity but often within the human heart. To be sure, the Revolution divided Americans and was in part a civil war. But an ocean separated the real seats of opposition, and the issues seem clearer—as did the mind and conscience and countenance of the great revolutionists. Great as they were, none of them faced the anguished decision of a Lee in 1861 or the anguish of many lesser captains and soldiers on both sides then and throughout the war. They may have been a generation of smaller moral stature than that of the Revolution, but theirs was a war that thrust figures of common clay into moments of true grandeur.

These years 1861–1865, not those of the Revolution, are clearly foremost in the national imagination, and it is they that constitute the enduring stuff of legend. It has been called our Homeric period. And that feeling would not seem to be merely an expression of civic piety or national vanity. Sir Denis Brogan, one of our keenest and most knowledgeable foreign critics, once observed that in "the world picture of America" the Civil War remained the most moving thing that ever happened here, "the great purging experience of the American people, their shame and their pride." Brogan goes further to say that "the United States is the only country since the Middle Ages that has created a legend to set beside the story of Achilles, Robin Hood, Roland, and Arthur." A Homer for our Civil War has yet to turn up, but if and when he ever does, a challenge worthy of the original bard of the name awaits him.

"Providence, R.I. July 28th 1865. Today the 2nd R.I. was paid off and discharged. . . . Thank God it is over and that the Union is restored. And so at last I am a simple citizen. Well, I am content, but should my country call again I am ready to respond."

ELISHA RHODES

"My shoes are gone; my clothes are almost gone. I'm weary, I'm sick, I'm hungry. My family have been killed or scattered. . . . And I have suffered all this for my country. I love my country. But if this war is ever over, I'll be damned if I ever love another country."

CONFEDERATE SOLDIER
to General James Longstreet,
during the retreat to Appomattox

Going home: Veterans of the 8th Pennsylvania Volunteers (opposite, top left) and the 35th and 36th Massachusetts Infantry (left) stand one last time with their torn battle flags before returning to their hometowns. Schoolboys turned out to cheer the 4th Vermont (right) when it got back to Brattleboro. The freed Federal prisoners of war who crowded the decks of the steamboat *Sultana* (above), eager to head north at last, never received the welcome they expected: nineteen hours after this photograph was made at Helena, Arkansas, on April 26, 1865, her boiler blew up midriver and seventeen hundred men drowned or burned to death still hundreds of miles from home.

THE UNITED STATES IS

Private Leander Stilwell of the 100th Indiana went home:

I arrived at the little village of Otterville about sundown . . . and I stalked up the middle of the one street, with my sword poised on my shoulder, musket fashion, feeling . . . proud [and] hoping to see some old friend. [A man in a store] leaned forward and looked at me, but said nothing. A . . . big dog sprang off the porch of a house and . . . standing on his hind legs with his forepaws on the palings, barked at me loudly and persistently—but I attracted no further attention. . . .

I was soon at my old boyhood home. My folks were expecting me. . . . There was no "scene" when we met . . . but we all had a feeling of profound contentment and satisfaction . . . too deep to be expressed by mere words.

I found that the farm work my father was then engaged in was cutting and shucking corn. So, the morning after my arrival, I doffed my uniform of first lieutenant, put on some of my father's old clothes and proceeded to wage war on the standing corn.

Photography had come of age just as the war began, and more than a million photographs of it are thought to have been made. While the fighting went on, the public appetite for the pictures was insatiable, but when it stopped no one seemed to want them anymore, as if their vivid reality too painfully perpetuated in the mind the calamity just ended. Thousands of glass plates were sold to gardeners, not for the precious images they held, but for the glass itself. In the years following Appomattox, the sun slowly burned away the war from thousands of greenhouse panes.

Memories, too, were softened and erased, so that the war's reality was lost in myth, and it soon became hard to tell just what was lost and what was gained.

Six hundred and twenty thousand men died in the Civil War, almost as many as in all the rest of America's wars combined. Millions were left with vivid memories of men who should still have been living.

During the war, half the men of military age in the state of Iowa served in the Union army, filling forty-six regiments. Twelve thousand five hundred and fifty-three of them died: 3,540 on the battlefield, 515 in prison camps, 8,498 from disease; 8,500 more went home with serious wounds. Those figures were fairly typical: in Mississippi, in 1866, one-fifth of the state's revenue was spent on artificial limbs.

The South was devastated: ten billion dollars in property had been laid waste; two-fifths of its livestock had been destroyed—it would take a quarter of a century just to replace the horses. In the end, for all the bravura of its leaders, for all the courage of the men who fought to establish and defend it, the Confederacy had been little more than that—an assortment of states unified only by their belief in the abstract right to secede.

Despite emancipation, blacks fared worst after the war. Four million Americans had been freed after four years of agony, but the full meaning of that freedom remained unresolved. The Thirteenth Amendment was followed by a fourteenth, and a fifteenth, which promised full citizenship and due process of the law for all American men, white and black. But those promises were soon overlooked in the scramble for a new prosperity, and white supremacy was brutally reimposed throughout the old Confederacy. The white South won that war of attrition, and it would take another century before blacks regained much of the ground for which so many men had given their lives.

"After our Rebellion," U. S. Grant wrote, "when so many young men were at liberty to return to their homes, they found they were not satisfied with the farm, the store, or the workshop of the villages, but wanted larger fields." Lincoln had wistfully voiced a desire to take the transcontinental railroad all the way out West "when this war is over." Now that railroad bound the coasts together and the Great Plains filled with farms while farmers' sons and immigrants flooded into the cities and the factories that grew up around them.

Before the war, people had tended to say "the United States are." After it was over, they said "the United States is." "America has no north, no south, no east, no west," Sam Watkins wrote after it was all over; "the sun rises over the hills and sets over the mountains, the compass just points up and down, and we can laugh now at the absurd notion of there being a north and a south. . . . *We are one and undivided.*"

When commissioning this memorial photograph, Anne Wallace, the widow of Union Brigadier General William H. L. Wallace, who was killed at Shiloh, asked that everything she had left of her husband be included—his portrait, his horse, and the flag for which he went to war—all carefully arranged in front of the Ottawa, Illinois, home to which he had not returned.

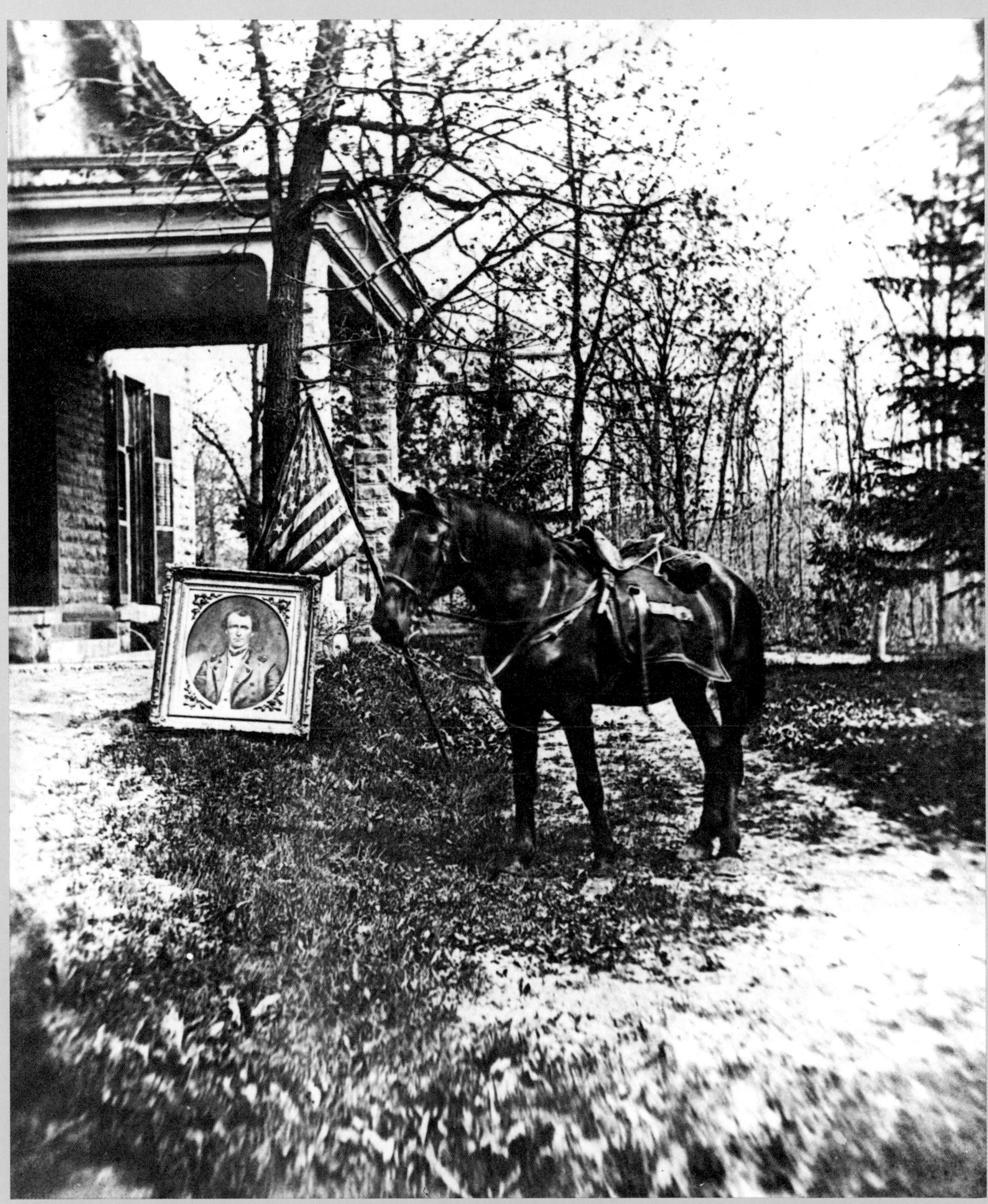

THE PICKLOCKS OF BIOGRAPHERS

The war made Elisha Rhodes. Having risen from private to colonel during the war, he was promoted to brigadier general after it, then went into the cotton and wool business in Providence. He devoted nearly every idle hour to veterans' affairs, and never missed a regimental reunion.

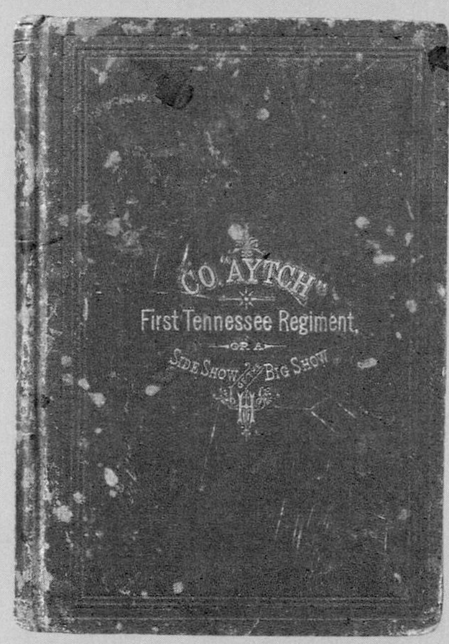

Sam Watkins returned to Columbia, Tennessee, ran the family farm, and in the evenings worked on his memoirs, *"Co. Aytch." A Side Show of the Big Show,* despite "a house full of young rebels clustering around my knees and bumping my elbows."

Joshua Lawrence Chamberlain (center) received the Medal of Honor for his courage on Little Round Top. After the war, despite almost constant pain from the unhealed internal damage done him by a Confederate minié ball at Petersburg, he served four terms as governor of Maine, then became president of Bowdoin College, where he managed to teach every subject in the curriculum except mathematics. He died of his ancient wound in 1914.

On November 10, 1865, Henry Wirz, commandant at Andersonville Prison in Georgia, was hanged in the yard of the Old Capitol Prison in Washington for war crimes. He pleaded he had only followed orders.

After having been driven to prison in a horse-drawn ambulance (left), Jefferson Davis (inset) served two years behind bars but was never tried for treason. Nor could he ever bring himself to ask for a pardon. He was finally released on bond and spent his last years living off the charity of a wealthy widow and working on a massive memoir, *The Rise and Fall of the Confederate Government.* He died, still persuaded of the justice of his cause, in 1889 at the age of eighty-one.

Vice President Alexander H. Stephens, too, was imprisoned briefly, then returned to politics, and was elected to his old congressional seat from Georgia as if there had never been a Confederacy.

When James and Mary Chesnut returned to Mulberry Plantation near Camden, South Carolina, they found the old house stripped by Union men, the cotton burned. Mary managed to make a little money selling butter and eggs in partnership with her faithful maid, and she continued to write—reminiscences, translations, novels—but she never completed the mammoth task of reworking her war diary.

Nathan Bedford Forrest promoted railroads for a time, without much success. In 1867, he became the very first Imperial Wizard of the Ku Klux Klan, but quit when its members grew too violent even for him.

John Bell Hood, who had survived some of the fiercest fighting of the war, died with his wife and a daughter in the New Orleans yellow fever epidemic of 1878, leaving ten orphaned children, who were adopted by well-to-do admirers all across the South.

Walt Whitman published *Drum Taps,* a book of Civil War poems he thought his finest, then turned largely to prose.

Frederick Douglass continued to fight as hard for civil rights as he had against slavery; he held several Federal posts after the war and became the most powerful black politician in America. A young visitor once asked him what he should do with his life. "Agitate!" the old man answered. "Agitate! Agitate!"

George McClellan stayed in Europe three years after losing the election to Lincoln. He heard no slander about himself there, he said. Then he came home and managed to get himself elected governor of New Jersey.

Clara Barton took her courage and nursing skill to Europe during the Franco-Prussian War, then came home to found the American Red Cross.

James Longstreet joined the Republican party, served as Grant's minister to Turkey, dared criticize Lee's tactics at Gettysburg in print—and for all these things was considered a traitor to the South by his former comrades-in-arms.

John B. Gordon went back to Georgia and the law, served one term as governor, three as senator, and then became the first commander in chief of the United Confederate Veterans.

George Pickett never overcame his bitterness over the destruction of his division at Gettysburg. Suffering from severe depression, he refused commands from the Khedive of Egypt and the President of the United States, and ended up in the insurance business.

Pierre Gustave Toutant Beauregard, the conqueror of Fort Sumter (above), promoted railroads, managed the Louisiana state lottery, and got rich.

Phil Sheridan (left) moved West to take on a new enemy, declaring the only good Indian a dead one. George Armstrong Custer (above) went West, too, carrying with him his belief in his own invincibility. In 1876, at the Battle of the Little Big Horn, the Sioux and Cheyenne proved him wrong.

Julia Ward Howe helped lead the American Woman Suffrage Association for fifty-five years. At her funeral in 1910, four thousand mourners joined in singing "The Battle Hymn of the Republic."

Mary Todd Lincoln never recovered from her husband's murder; her son Tad died in 1871; five years later, her eldest son, Robert, had her committed to a mental institution. She spent her last years in her sister's Springfield home, rarely leaving a room whose curtains were never raised.

Dan Sickles (center) escaped court-martial for his folly at Gettysburg. He had his leg mounted in a miniature casket and gave it to the Army Medical Museum at Washington, where he visited it regularly for fifty years.

William Tecumseh Sherman remained a soldier, pacifying western Indians and shunning politics until his retirement in 1884. "If nominated I will not run," he told a Republican delegation urging him to run for President. "If elected I will not serve." He died in New York City in the winter of 1891. Among the honorary pallbearers who stood bare-headed in the cold wind outside the church was eighty-two-year-old Joe Johnston, who had fought Sherman in Georgia and the Carolinas. When a friend warned him he might fall ill, Johnston told him, "If I were in [Sherman's] place and he were standing here in mine, he would not put on his hat."

Johnston died ten days later, of pneumonia.

On the campus of Washington College, students, townspeople, and cadets from the Virginia Military Institute mourn Lee's death.

I have fought against the people of the North because I believed they were seeking to wrest from the South its dearest rights. But I have never cherished toward them bitter or vindictive feelings, and I have never seen the day when I did not pray for them.

Robert E. Lee

Robert E. Lee swore renewed allegiance to the United States—and by so doing persuaded thousands of his former soldiers to do the same. He was weary, ailing, and without work in the summer of 1865, when an insurance firm offered him $50,000 just for the use of his name. He turned it down: "I cannot consent to receive pay for services I do not render."

Instead, he accepted the presidency of tiny Washington College at Lexington, Virginia, a small school so threadbare its trustees had to borrow fifty dollars from a tobacco farmer just to keep the doors open. There, for the rest of his life, he showed Americans that one can lose as well as win with grace. Taken to see a woman whose prized tree had had its branches shot away by Federal artillery, he urged her, "Cut it down, my dear Madam, and forget it."

Congress refused to pardon him or restore his citizenship, but he did not complain. Nor did he ever return to his old home in Arlington, though he did glimpse it through the window of a moving train, while on a visit to Washington to pay his respects to President Grant. Lee never forgot Grant's magnanimity at Appomattox and once, when a professor said something disparaging about the Union commander, he dressed him down. "Sir," he said, "if you ever again presume to speak disrespectfully of General Grant in my presence, either you or I will sever his connection with this university."

Henry Ward Beecher raised funds for Robert E. Lee's college. Horace Greeley proposed him for President in 1868.

"The greatest mistake of my life," he said, "was taking a military education," and whenever his students and those of the neighboring Virginia Military Institute marched together, Lee made a point of staying out of step.

He died peacefully after suffering a heart attack in 1870. In his last moments he went back to the war, ordering A. P. Hill to bring up his troops, just as Stonewall Jackson had on his deathbed after Chancellorsville. Then he called out, "Strike the tent."

For he will smile
And give you with unflinching courtesy,
Prayers, trappings, letters, uniforms and orders,
Photographs, kindness, valor and advice,
And do it with such grace and gentleness
That you will know you have the whole of him
Pinned down, mapped out, easy to understand
And so you have. All things except the heart.
The heart he kept . . . a secret to the end
From all the picklocks of biographers.

Stephen Vincent Benét,
John Brown's Body

The qualities that served U. S. Grant so well in war—resolution, independence, aversion to politics—deserted him in peacetime. He entered the White House pledged to peace, honesty, and civil rights. But corruption tainted his two terms—though it did not touch him personally—and the North was already weary of worrying about the status of southern blacks.

Grant left the presidency in 1877, took a triumphal trip around the world, then settled in Manhattan, where he lent his name to a Wall Street brokerage firm. Another partner in the firm, a chaplain's plausible son named Ferdinand Ward, stole millions from the shareholders in 1884—and bankrupted the Grant family. Once again, U. S. Grant was penniless.

At almost the same moment, he was found to be suffering from inoperable cancer of the throat.

Determined to provide for his family before he died, he set to work writing his memoirs. In the summer of 1885, he moved to a cottage at Mount McGregor in the Adirondacks. Unable now to eat or speak, he sat on the front porch in the afternoons, laboring over his book.

He finished his manuscript on July 16. "There is nothing more I should do to it now," he wrote to his doctor, "and therefore I am not likely to be more ready to go than at this moment."

He died exactly one week later.

Two and a half miles of armed and uniformed veterans marched up Broadway for Grant's funeral. Most were men from his old command, but four Confederate companies marched, too, and General Simon Bolivar Buckner, who had surrendered Fort Donelson to Grant in the first year of the war, was among the pallbearers.

Grant's memoirs, published by Mark Twain, sold half a million copies and restored his family's fortune. He dedicated them to "the American soldier and sailor," and toward the end of them he wrote, "I feel that we are on the eve of a new era, when there is to be a great harmony between the Federal and Confederate. I cannot stay to be a living witness to this prophecy, but I feel it within me that it is so."

Grant at work on his memoirs during the last few weeks of his life.

THE DAY THE WAR ENDED

By the turn of the century, monuments and memorials and statues stood in city parks and courthouse squares from Maine to Mississippi, and the boys who had gone off to the war had become old men, marching in steadily thinning ranks each Memorial Day—May 30 throughout the North; on three different days in the South because the states of the former Confederacy could never all agree on one.

North and South, the veterans continued to be honored, sometimes to their embarrassment. Asked to demonstrate the rebel yell after a dinner given by the United Daughters of the Confederacy, an old Tennessean declined as politely as he could: It was "impossible unless made at a dead run full charge against the enemy," he told the admiring ladies; but it was "worse than folly to try to imitate it with a stomach full of food and a mouth full of false teeth."

In 1913, the Federal Government held a fiftieth anniversary reunion at Gettysburg. It lasted three days. Thousands of survivors bivouacked on the old battlefield, swapping stories, looking up comrades. Joshua Chamberlain was there, still imposing at eighty-four. The reunion was a transcendental experience, he said, "a radiant fellowship of the fallen."

Thousands of ordinary tourists came, too, and so did a swarm of photographers, including an eighteen-year-old named Philip Myers, who many years later jotted down his memories of the celebration. He remembered the big moon over the great encampment and the sounds of the first musician blowing taps: "When the last plaintive notes of that somber call had faded, he was followed by another trumpeter farther off, then by another still more remote, and another, until it was impossible to tell if the notes we heard were real or imaginary."

He remembered, too, photographing a venerable Yankee, badly wounded in the face, who spent most of the reunion's second day at Devil's Den because, the old man explained, although he had fought on Little Round Top fifty years before, "I wanted to see where that so-and-so that shot me must've been standin'."

For the most part the old men got along well enough, but over dinner at a restaurant one evening harsh words were passed between a Yankee and a rebel and they went at one another with forks: "Unscathed in the melee of 1863," Myers wrote, "one of them—and I never learned which—was almost fatally wounded in 1913 with table hardware!"

The climax of the gathering was a reenactment of Pickett's Charge. Thousands of spectators gathered to watch as the Union veterans took their positions on Cemetery Ridge, and waited as their old adversaries emerged from the woods on Seminary Ridge and started forward toward them again, across the long, flat fields. "We could see," Myers wrote, "not rifles and bayonets but canes and crutches. We soon could distinguish the more agile ones aiding those less able to maintain their places in the ranks."

As they neared the northern line, they broke into one final, defiant rebel yell. At the sound, "after half a century of silence, a moan, a sigh, a gigantic gasp of unbelief" rose from the Union men on Cemetery Ridge. "It was then," wrote Myers, "that the Yankees, unable to restrain themselves longer, burst from behind the stone wall, and flung themselves upon their former enemies . . . not in mortal combat, but re-united in brotherly love and affection."

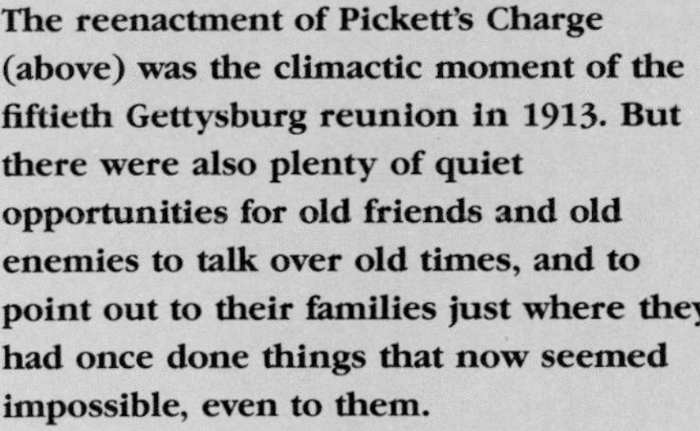

The reenactment of Pickett's Charge (above) was the climactic moment of the fiftieth Gettysburg reunion in 1913. But there were also plenty of quiet opportunities for old friends and old enemies to talk over old times, and to point out to their families just where they had once done things that now seemed impossible, even to them.

Yesterday's heroes: On Beacon Street in Boston on May 1, 1897 (top), veterans of the 54th Massachusetts halt in front of the newly unveiled memorial designed by Augustus Saint-Gaudens to commemorate the heroism displayed by them and their commander, Colonel Robert Gould Shaw, at Fort Wagner, thirty-four years before. The sturdy monument and the small stone-walled cemetery above honor Union Colonel William B. Hazen's brigade on the Stone's River Battlefield; they stand on the spot from which the brigade hurled back repeated rebel onslaughts and constitute the oldest intact Civil War monument, having been built in the summer of 1863.

These gentlemen, resting with their ladies in Devil's Den at an 1886 Gettysburg reunion, once belonged to the 2nd Rhode Island; their old colonel, Elisha Rhodes, stands eighth from the right.

MAURICE FOX
R.I. Exc. Devil's Den.
Oct 14th '86.

Remembering the war: General Joseph Hooker is memorialized by the city of Boston in 1903 (left); a black family in Richmond celebrates emancipation—and the Emancipator (below left); and on an unknown battlefield a new generation unveils its tribute to the past.

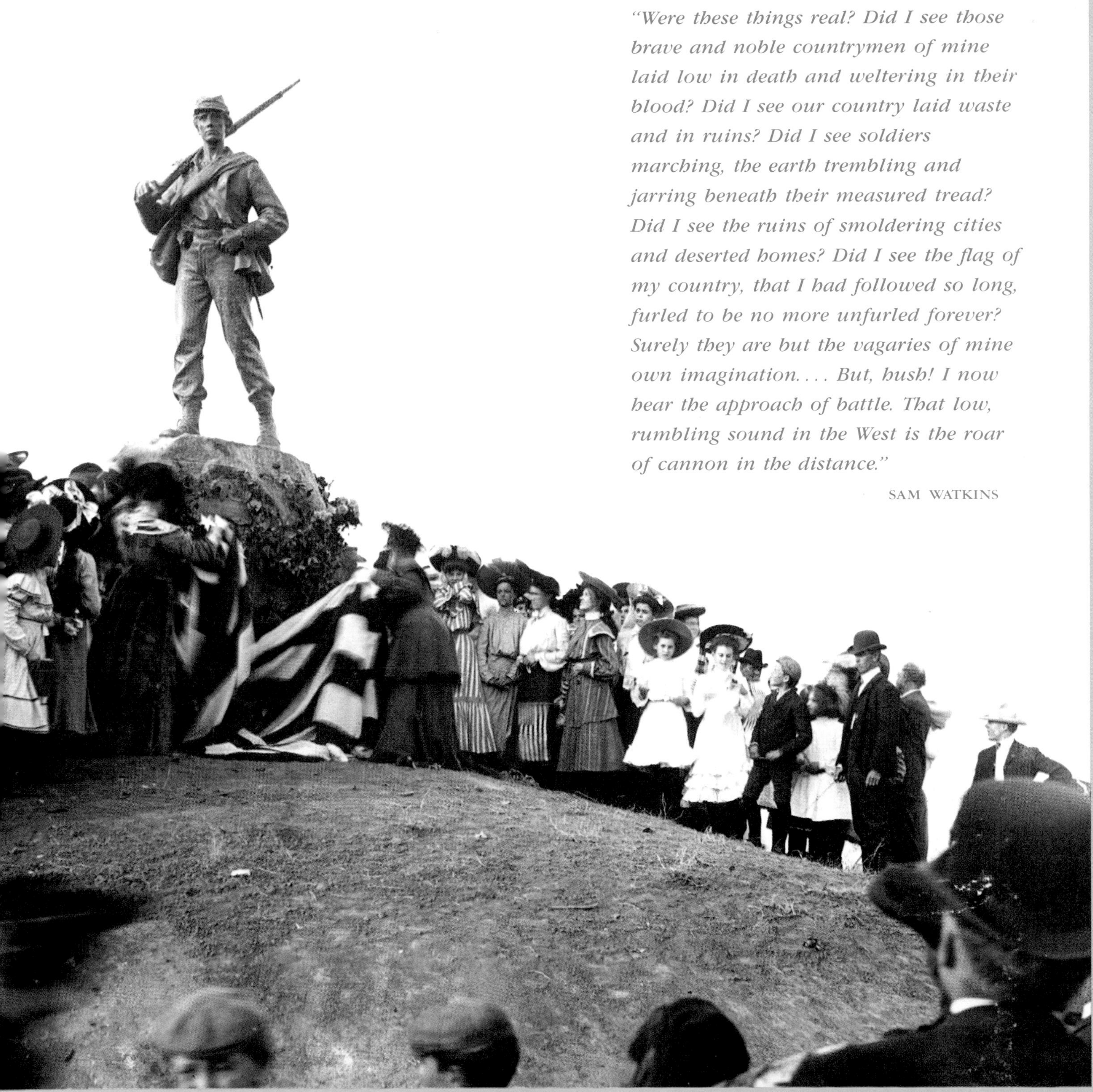

"Were these things real? Did I see those brave and noble countrymen of mine laid low in death and weltering in their blood? Did I see our country laid waste and in ruins? Did I see soldiers marching, the earth trembling and jarring beneath their measured tread? Did I see the ruins of smoldering cities and deserted homes? Did I see the flag of my country, that I had followed so long, furled to be no more unfurled forever? Surely they are but the vagaries of mine own imagination. . . . But, hush! I now hear the approach of battle. That low, rumbling sound in the West is the roar of cannon in the distance."

SAM WATKINS

ACKNOWLEDGMENTS

This book, like the film series it emerged from, was a collaborative enterprise—so much so that it is impossible to thank all those who have helped us with it. But we can mention a few of those who have helped most. The main narrative and picture captions for this book, which recounts the central military and political events of the war and which is based on our nine-part PBS film series, were written by Geoffrey C. Ward. It may seem unusual to be thanking the man who wrote this book, but we want to acknowledge again how crucial a role Geoff has played throughout the development of the film series and the book. We cannot imagine a better collaborator: he has a historian's eye for the telling detail and an acute ear for the language, sensibility, and humor of the time, along with a writer's vocation simply to tell a story.

We also owe an enormous debt to our consultants, above all to Don Fehrenbacher, Barbara Fields, C. Vann Woodward, James McPherson, and Shelby Foote, who, having helped us all along, helped us again by contributing original essays, or in the case of Shelby, an extraordinary interview. Each has had an enormous influence on the shape of our project and our understanding of the Civil War. In numerous ways, Shelby Foote has been the presiding spirit of our project. Combining the virtues of a scholar and a novelist, he seems to understand the war as no one else.

David McCullough, who in addition to narrating the film series served as its senior creative consultant, influenced the film, and thus this book, in more ways than we can possibly describe.

We would also like to thank our consultants, Daniel Aaron, Ira Berlin, Eric Foner, Charles Fuller, Robert Johannsen, William E. Leuchtenburg, Tom Lewis, Jerome Liebling, William McFeely, Michael Musick, Stephen W. Sears (who scrupulously checked our manuscript for accuracy; any inaccuracies that have crept in are ours alone), Gene Smith, Richard F. Snow, the late Robert Penn Warren, and Bernard Weisberger.

Paul Barnes, Bruce Shaw, Tricia Reidy, Phoebe Yantsios, Meredith Woods, Joshua Levin, and Ed Barteski physically put the film together with a tact, sensitivity, and cheerfulness that kept us all sane. Catherine Eisele, Stephen Ives, Mike Hill, Julie Dunfey, and Lynn Novick shared with us the enormous task of producing the film. Allen Moore's extraordinary cinematography helped us to see the war.

Special thanks go to Ashbel Green, our editor, along with Virginia Tan, Ellen McNeilly, Nancy Clements, and our designer, Wendy Byrne, who made the book look as good as it does. We also wish to thank Gerry McCauley for his steadfast support, and Randy Balsmeyer and Mimi Everett, who intelligently and painstakingly created the maps for both film and book. Tim Hallinan and Connie Stone, who developed the educational material that accompanied the series, were a delight to work with.

The film series could not have been made without the generous support of General Motors, and especially Jack McNulty and George Pruette; the National Endowment for the Humanities, especially Lynne Cheney and Jim Dougherty; the Corporation for Public Broadcasting, especially Don Marbury and Sonia Warriner; the Arthur Vining Davis Foundations, especially Dr. Max King Morris; and the John D. and Catherine T. MacArthur Foundation, especially Bill Kirby.

From the very start our good friends Ward Chamberlin and Tammy Robinson of WETA-TV stood by us and helped make all of this possible.

When the 10th Mississippi Cavalry surrendered in 1865, its flag bearer, Silas C. Buck, then only seventeen, hid his unit's battle flag rather than hand it over to the Yankees. Later he proudly unfurled it at reunions of the United Confederate Veterans.

SELECTED BIBLIOGRAPHY

According to the historian James M. McPherson, there are some 50,000 volumes on the Civil War, and more books about Abraham Lincoln alone than there are about any other historical figure, except for Jesus of Nazareth and William Shakespeare.

No one has ever consulted them all, of course, least of all the team that worked together to produce this book and the film on which it is based. But in the course of our work we did find certain volumes indispensable, and thought it worthwhile to list them here for those readers interested in pursuing further this richest and most rewarding of all American stories.

Angle, Paul M., and Miers, Earl Schenck. *Tragic Years: 1860–1865,* 2 vols. (New York, 1960).

Berlin, Ira, ed. *Freedom: A Documentary History of Emancipation 1861–1867,* 2 vols. (Cambridge, 1982).

Bowman, John S., ed. *The Civil War Almanac* (New York, 1983).

Catton, Bruce, *Glory Road* (Garden City, 1952).

———.*Grant Moves South* (Boston, 1960).

———.*Grant Takes Command* (Boston, 1968).

———.*Mr. Lincoln's Army* (Garden City, 1951).

———.*A Stillness at Appomattox* (Garden City, 1953).

———.*This Hallowed Ground* (Garden City, 1951).

Commager, Henry Steele, ed. *The Blue and the Gray: The Story of the Civil War as Told by Participants* (Indianapolis, 1950).

Davis, William C., ed. *The Image of War 1861–1865,* 6 vols. (Garden City, 1984).

Faust, Patricia L., ed. *Historical Times Illustrated Encyclopedia of the Civil War* (New York, 1987).

Fehrenbacher, Don E. *The Dred Scott Case: Its Significance in Law and Politics* (New York, 1978).

Foote, Shelby. *The Civil War: A Narrative,* 3 vols. (New York, 1958, 1963, 1974).

Frassanito, William A. *Antietam: The Photographic Legacy of America's Bloodiest Day* (New York, 1976).

———.*Gettysburg: A Journey in Time* (New York, 1975).

———.*Grant and Lee: The Virginia Campaigns 1864–1865* (New York, 1983).

Leech, Margaret. *Reveille in Washington* (New York, 1941).

Lewis, Lloyd. *Captain Sam Grant* (Boston, 1950).

———.*Myths After Lincoln* (New York, 1929).

———.*Sherman: Fighting Prophet* (New York, 1932).

Linderman, Gerald F. *Embattled Courage* (New York, 1987).

Long, E. B., ed. *The Civil War Day by Day* (New York, 1971).

McFeely, William S. *Grant: A Biography* (New York, 1981).

McPherson, James M. *Battle Cry of Freedom: The Civil War Era* (New York, 1988).

———.*Ordeal by Fire: The Civil War and Reconstruction* (New York, 1982).

Miller, Francis T., ed. *The Photographic History of the Civil War* (Secaucus, N.J., 1987).

Neeley, Mark E., Jr. *The Abraham Lincoln Encyclopedia* (New York, 1982).

Nevins, Allan. *The Emergence of Lincoln,* 2 vols. (New York, 1950).

———.*The Ordeal of the Union,* 2 vols. (New York, 1947).

———.*The War for the Union,* 4 vols. (New York, 1971).

Oates, Stephen B. *With Malice Toward None: The Life of Abraham Lincoln* (New York, 1977).

Potter, David M., and Fehrenbacher, Don E. *The Impending Crisis 1848–1861* (New York, 1976).

Pullen, John J. *The Twentieth Maine: A Volunteer Regiment in the Civil War* (Philadelphia, 1957).

Rhodes, Robert Hunt, ed. *All for the Union: A History of the 2nd Rhode Island Volunteer Infantry in the War of the Great Rebellion as Told by the Diaries and Letters of Elisha Hunt Rhodes Who Enlisted as a Private in '61 and Rose to the Command of His Regiment* (Lincoln, R.I., 1985).

Sears, Stephen W. *George B. McClellan: The Young Napoleon* (New York, 1988).

———.*Landscape Turned Red* (New Haven, 1983).

Thomas, Benjamin P. *Abraham Lincoln: A Biography* (New York, 1952).

Time-Life Books, eds. *The Civil War,* 28 vols. (Alexandria, Va., 1987).

Warren, Robert Penn. *Jefferson Davis Gets the Citizenship Back* (Lexington, 1980).

———.*The Legacy of the Civil War* (New York, 1961).

Watkins, Sam R. *"Co. Aytch": A Side Show of the Big Show* (New York, 1962).

Weisberger, Bernard A. *Reporters for the Union* (Boston, 1953).

Wheeler, Richard. *The Siege of Vicksburg* (New York, 1978).

———.*Voices of the Civil War* (New York, 1976).

———.*Witness to Gettysburg* (New York, 1987).

Whitman, Walt. *Specimen Days* (Boston, 1971).

Wiley, Bell Irvin. *The Life of Billy Yank: The Common Soldier of the Union* (Baton Rouge, 1984).

———.*The Life of Johnny Reb: The Common Soldier of the Confederacy* (Baton Rouge, 1984).

Woodward, C. Vann, ed. *Mary Chesnut's Civil War* (New Haven, 1981).

INDEX

ILLUSTRATION CREDITS

When there is more than one credit for a page, left to right is separated by a semicolon, top to bottom by a dash.

Abbreviations

CHS Chicago Historical Society
HHL Henry E. Huntington Library and Art Gallery
IMP International Museum of Photography at George Eastman House
ISHL Illinois State Historical Library, Springfield, IL
LC Library of Congress
NA National Archives
NPG National Portrait Gallery, Smithsonian Institution, Washington, DC
NYHS New-York Historical Society, New York
SB Stanley B. Burns, M.D., and the Burns Archive
USAMHI U.S. Army Military Historical Institute, Carlisle, PA

Endpapers: USAMHI.
ii: LC. v–vii: LC. viii: NPG. ix: NA. x: LC. xi: USAMHI. xii: LC. xiii: LC. xiv: LC. xviii: LC. xx: USAMHI—LC; USAMHI. xxi: LC; U.S. Military Academy Library, West Point.

1861

1: LC. 3: Boston Athenaeum. 4: NA. 5: CHS. 7: USAMHI. 8: NYHS. 9: NYHS—ISHL. 10: Collection of Jay P. Altmayer. 11: Peabody Museum, Harvard University. 13: LC. 14: Department of Special Collections, Wichita State University. 15: Ex–Arnold Crane Collection. 16: Beinecke Rare Book & Manuscript Library, Yale University. 17: IMP. 18: The Metropolitan Museum of Art, Gift of I. N. Phelps Stokes, Edward S. Hawes, Alice Mary Hawes, Marion Augusta Hawes, 1937 (37.14.15); CHS. 19: The Schlesinger Library, Radcliffe College—Boston Athenaeum. 20: Kansas State Historical Society. 22: LC. 23: LC. 24: NA. 25: LC; LC—NPG. 26: ISHL. 27: NYHS. 29: NA; CHS. 30: NPG. 31: Boston Athenaeum. 32: The Connecticut Historical Society. 35: LC. 36–7: LC. 38: USAMHI. 39: NA. 40–1: NA. 42–3: NYHS. 44–7: IMP. 48: Vermont Historical Society. 49: LC. 51: Inset: Robert Rhodes Collection; The Rhode Island Historical Society. 53: Cook Collection, Valentine Museum, Richmond, VA. 54: USAMHI. 55: Collection of Mr. & Mrs. Franklyn Fulton. 56: The Kunhardt Collection. 58: NYHS. 59: NA; LC. 60: LC. 62–3:

IMP. 65: LC. 68: Stonewall Jackson House, Historic Lexington Foundation. 66–7: National Park Service, photograph by Lon Mattoon, © 1983 Time/Life Books, Inc., from the "Civil War" series, *First Blood,* pp. 164–5. 70: United States Publishers Association, Inc.—CHS. 71: CHS. 72–3: LC. 74: USAMHI. 75: LC. 77: LC—USAMHI; NYHS. 78: Dale Snair Collection—USAMHI; LC. 79: Tom Farish Collection—Tom Farish Collection; Richard F. Carlile Collection. 80: Boston Athenaeum; ISHL. 82: William J. Prince; Larry B. Williford, Portsmouth, VA. 83: Dubose Collection; Larry B. Williford, Portsmouth, VA. 85: NYHS. 86: Eleanor S. Brockenbrough Library, The Museum of the Confederacy, Richmond, VA, copy photograph by Katherine Wetzel

1862

88–9: LC. 91: NA. 93: NA; LC—NPG. 94: CHS. 96–7: CHS. 98: CHS. 99: West Point Museum, U.S. Military Academy. 100: USAMHI. 101: LC; IMP. 102: NA. 103: USAMHI. 104: Boston Athenaeum. 105: NA. 106: Boston Athenaeum. 107: CHS—Boston Athenaeum; Dubose Collection; Boston Athenaeum. 108: Lightfoot Collection. 109: USAMHI—USAMHI; Stowe-Day Foundation. 111–12: LC. 114: LC. 115: NA. 116: LC. 117: Dubose Collection—CHS. 118–19: USAMHI. 121: ISHL. 122: IMP—USAMHI. 123: Herbert Wheary Collection—USAMHI; Lightfoot Collection. 124: NA. 125: Historic New Orleans Collection, Museum/Research Center, Acc. #1974.80. 126: NA—USAMHI. 129: North Carolina Division of Archives & History; LC. 130: LC. 131: LC—Association of American Railroads—NA; HHL. 132: USAMHI. 133: Robert Rhodes Collection. 134: USAMHI. 136: Fenton Historical Society, Jamestown, NY, photograph by Lon Mattoon, © 1984 Time/Life Books, Inc., from the "Civil War" series, *Decoying the Yanks,* pp. 118–19. 139: Cook Collection, Valentine Museum, Richmond, VA; LC. 140–1: USAMHI. 143: LC; Vermont Historical Society. 144–5: LC. 146: American Antiquarian Society. 147: USAMHI. 148: USAMHI—Museum of the City of New York. 149: USAMHI; Boston Public Library—NPG. 152–3: LC. 154: USAMHI. 155: NA; USAHMI—LC. 156–7: National Park Service, U.S. Dept. of the Interior, photograph by Larry Sherer. 158: LC. 159: USAMHI. 161: USAMHI—Massachusetts Historical Society. 162: USAMHI. 163–5: LC. 166: Architect of the Capitol, photograph by Larry Sherer, © 1985 Time/Life Books, Inc., from the "Civil War" series, *Twenty Million Yankees,* p. 148. 167: USAMHI; Lightfoot Collection—USAMHI. 169: John Henry Kurtz. 170: USAMHI; Pejepscot Historical Society. 171: HHL. 172–3: ISHL. 174–5: LC. 176: USAMHI. 179: CHS.

1863

182–3: LC. 185: NA. 186: *The Photographic History of the Civil War in Ten Volumes* (Patriot Publishing Co., Springfield, Mass., 1911); LC. 187–8: LC. 189: HHL. 190: LC. 191: Boston Public Library—USAMHI. 192–3: IMP. 194: LC. 196: Boston Athenaeum. 197: USAMHI. 199: Larry B. Williford, Portsmouth, VA. 200: LC. 203: NA. 205: USAMHI. 206: Robert M. Hicklin Jr., Inc., Spartanburg, SC. 207: Civil War Library and Museum, Philadelphia, PA, photograph by Larry Sherer, © 1985 Time/Life Books, Inc., from the "Civil War" series, *Rebels Resurgent,* p. 136. 208: Sotheby's, Inc. 209: NA—HHL. 210: LC. 211: Virginia Military Institute Archives. 213: USAMHI. 214: LC. 215: LC. 217: NA. 218: USAMHI—NA. 220: USAMHI—LC. 221: LC. 222–3: LC (inset: USAMHI). 224: USAMHI. 225: NA. 227: The Ella Gallup Sumner and Mary Catlin Sumner Collection, Wadsworth Atheneum. 228–9: Collection of Jay P. Altmayer (inset: LC). 230: LC. 231: USAMHI—LC. 233: LC. 234: USAMHI—Special Collections, New York Public Library, Astor, Lenox and Tilden Foundations. 235–7: LC. 238–9: *The Union Fleet Passing Vicksburg,* by Tom Lovell, © 1989 The Greenwich Workshop, Inc., Trumbull CT 06611. 240: LC. 241: Old Court House Museum, Vicksburg, MS. 242: CHS. 243: Lightfoot Collection. 244: Seventh Regiment Fund, Inc., photograph by Al Freni, © 1985 Time/Life Books, Inc., from the "Civil War" series, *Twenty Million Yankees,* p. 109. 245: USAMHI. 247: LC; USAMHI. 248: USAMHI. 249: LC. 250: CHS—CHS; Richard Carlile. 251: Massachusetts Historical Society; CHS—Massachusetts Historical Society; CHS. 252: LC. 253: NPG. 254–5: USAMHI. 256: LC. 257: USAMHI—Minnesota Historical Society. 258: NPG. 259: Dubose Collection. 260: NA. 261: T. Scott Sanders Collection—Wisconsin Historical Society. 262: LC. 263: USAMHI—LC. 265: Dubose Collection. 268: CHS. 273: Dubose Collection.

1864

274–5: Association of American Railroads. 277: IMP. 278: LC. 279: White House Historical Association, photograph by the National Geographic Society. 280: LC; NPG. 281: CHS. 282: Washington/Custis/Lee Collection, Washington & Lee University, Lexington, VA. 283–9: LC. 291: LC; NA. 292: USAMHI. 293: NA. 295: USAMHI. 296: SB—Edward G. Miner Library, University of Rochester School of Medicine and Dentistry; Lightfoot Collection. 297: LC. 298: LC; SB. 299: NA—HHL. 300–3: SB. 304: ISHL. 305: USAMHI. 306–8: LC. 309: NA. 310: LC. 311: USAMHI—LC. 312; LC. 313: CHS—ISHL; LC. 314: NA. 315: Minnesota Historical Society. 316: NA. 317: USAMHI—LC. 318: NA. 320: ISHL; USAMHI—NA. 323: Behringer-Crawford Museum, Covington, KY. 324–5: Dubose Collection. 327: LC—NA. 328–31: LC. 332: USAMHI—Dubose Collection. 333: ISHL. 335: USAMHI. 336: LC—USAMHI; LC. 337: USAMHI. 338: LC; USAMHI. 339: USAMHI—NA. 341: LC. 343: USAMHI. 344: NA. 345: LC. 346–7: USAMHI. 348–51: LC. 352: Larry B. Williford, Portsmouth, VA. 353: William J. Prince.

1865

354–5: USAMHI. 357–59: LC. 360: Louis A. Warren Lincoln Library and Museum, Fort Wayne, IN. 361: LC—CHS. 362: LC; LC—HHL; LC. 363: USAMHI. 364: USAMHI—The White House Historical Association, photograph by the National Geographic Society. 366–7: LC. 368: LC; USAMHI. 369: Eleanor S. Brockenbrough Library, Museum of the Confederacy, Richmond, VA. 370–1: LC. 372–3: NA (inset: Valentine Museum, Richmond, VA). 374–6: LC. 378: Appomattox Court House National Historical Park, National Park Service, U.S. Dept. of the Interior. 379: Appomattox Court House National Historical Park, photograph by Ronald Jennings, © 1987 Time/Life Books, Inc., from the "Civil War" series, *Pursuit to Appomattox,* p. 147. 380: LC—D. Mark Katz Collection. 382: West Point Museum, U.S. Military Academy. 383: NA; LC. 384: Harvard Theater Collection, photograph by Henry Groskinski, © 1987 Time/Life Books, Inc., from the "Civil War" series, *The Assassination,* p. 73. 385: LC—Lloyd Ostendorf, Dayton, OH. 387: IMP. 388–90: ISHL. 391: ISHL. 392: LC. 394–5: Massachusetts Historical Society. 396: NA. 397: LC. 398–9: Eleanor S. Brockenbrough Library, Museum of the Confederacy, Richmond, VA. 400: Massachusetts Historical Society.

EPILOGUE

402: USAMHI. 403: State Archives of Michigan—Vermont Historical Society. 405: CHS. 406: Robert Rhodes Collection; Mr. & Mrs. Franklyn Fulton—Pejepscot Historical Society; LC. 407: USAMHI; LC—USAMHI; NA. 408: CHS—USAMHI. 409: Boston Athenaeum; LC; USAMHI—LC. 410: Washington & Lee University. 411: LC. 412: RG25 Gettysburg Commission, Pennsylvania State Archives, Harrisburg, PA. 413: Brown Brothers. 414: Massachusetts Historical Society—NA. 415: Robert Rhodes Collection. 416: USAMHI—Valentine Museum, Richmond, VA. 417: USAMHI. 419: Kentucky Historical Society.

Endpapers: Robert Rhodes Collection.

A NOTE ABOUT THE AUTHORS

Geoffrey C. Ward is the author of *Before the Trumpet: The Young Franklin Roosevelt* and *A First Class Temperament: The Emergence of Franklin Roosevelt,* which won the National Book Critics Circle Award for biography. A former editor of *American Heritage,* Ward has also written a number of documentary films for public television, including *The Civil War, Huey Long,* and *Thomas Hart Benton* (all with Florentine Films). He is a frequent contributor to *Audubon, MHQ, Smithsonian,* and other magazines.

Ken Burns, founder of Florentine Films, is one of the most celebrated documentary filmmakers working today. He has produced and directed a number of award-winning films, including *Huey Long, Brooklyn Bridge, The Statue of Liberty, The Shakers, The Congress,* and *Thomas Hart Benton.* He was producer, director, cinematographer, and co-writer of the PBS series *The Civil War.*

Ric Burns is a producer and writer of *The Civil War* and was educated at Columbia and Cambridge universities. He is currently producing and directing a documentary history of Coney Island.

A NOTE ON THE TYPE

The text of this book was set in an adaptation of Garamond designed by Tony Stan in 1977 for the International Typeface Corporation.

The original, designed by Claude Garamond (1480–1561), first appeared in books printed in Paris around 1532. There have been many subsequent versions designed for both European and American type founders in the twentieth century, many of which were based on the Jean Jannon cut of the mid-seventeenth century.

ITC Garamond is distinguished by a greater x-height than most versions; the ascenders and descenders are proportionately shorter. The curved letters are very round.

Composed by the Sarabande Press, New York, New York. Film preparation by Capper, Inc., Knoxville, Tennessee. Printed and bound by R.R. Donnelley & Sons, Willard, Ohio.
Maps designed by Balsmeyer and Everett, Inc.
Book designed by Wendy Byrne.

FILM CREDITS

THE CIVIL WAR

A film by
Ken Burns

Produced by
Ken Burns and Ric Burns

Written by
Geoffrey C. Ward, Ric Burns, and Ken Burns

Edited by
Paul Barnes, Bruce Shaw, and Tricia Reidy

Narrated by
David McCullough

Voices
Sam Waterston, *Abraham Lincoln*
Julie Harris, *Mary Chesnut*
Jason Robards, *Ulysses S. Grant*
Morgan Freeman, *Frederick Douglass*
Paul Roebling, *Joshua L. Chamberlain, etc.*
Garrison Keillor, *Walt Whitman, etc.*
George Black, *Robert E. Lee*
Arthur Miller, *William T. Sherman*
Chris Murney, *Pvt. Elisha Hunt Rhodes*
Charley McDowell, *Pvt. Sam Watkins*
Horton Foote, *Jefferson Davis*
George Plimpton, *George Templeton Strong*
Philip Bosco, *Horace Greeley, etc.*
Terry Courier, *George McClellan*
Jody Powell, *Stonewall Jackson, etc.*
Studs Terkel, *Benjamin F. Butler*

With
Derek Jacobi, Jeremy Irons, Kurt Vonnegut, Gene Jones, Jerome Dempsey, Larry Fishburne, Shelby Foote, Betsy Apple, Carol Craven, Marissa Copeland, Halo Wines, David Marks, Pamela Reed, Ronnie Gilbert, M. Emmet Walsh, Hoyt Axton, John Hartford, Walt MacPherson, Colleen Dewhurst, Latanya Richardson, Bradford Washburn, Jesse Carr, Wendy Tilghman, Joe Matty, and Library of Congress ex-slave recordings

Cinematography
Ken Burns, Allen Moore, and Buddy Squires

Assistant Editors
Phoebe Yantsios and Meredith Woods

Apprentice Editors
Joshua Levin and Ed Barteski

Coordinating Producer
Catherine Eisele

Associate Producer/Post-Production
Lynn Novick

Co-Producers
Stephen Ives, Julie Dunfey, and Mike Hill

Consultants
Shelby Foote, C. Vann Woodward, Stephen W. Sears, James McPherson, Michael Musick, Eric Foner, Robert Johannsen, William E. Leuchtenburg, Charles Fuller, Ira Berlin, Robert Penn Warren, Dayton Duncan, Barbara J. Fields, Don Fehrenbacher, William McFeely, Bernard Weisberger, Richard F. Snow, Stephen B. Oates, Tom Lewis, Daniel Aaron, Charley McDowell, Gene Smith, Jerome Liebling, Amy Stechler Burns

Senior Creative Consultant
David McCullough